1228 PAGES   98,240 NAMES

1905 - 1906

THE
BUYERS'
GUIDE

THOMAS'
REGISTER
of American
Manufacturers
A N D
First Hands
in all Lines

LOANED ON SUBSCRIPTION CONTRACT

PRICE, $10.00

PER YEAR

I...

See exp...

THOM...

D1266399

Printed by The Thomas Press, 18-20 Rose St., New York

Concerning this Publication

(The result of ten years experience in Publishing Trades Reference Books.)

COMPACTNESS—

Type, paper, and arrangement have been adopted with this object in view. The book contains more information than anything ever issued heretofore, and without using any complicated index system, we have condensed into a 24-ounce desk pigeon-hole volume, a work of 1228 text pages—containing 98,240 names—2,500 divisions and 38,450 subdivisions.

COMPLETENESS—

More than $25,000 has been expended in the production of this work — every manufacturer (except those whose business area is strictly local) is entitled to full and complete representation absolutely free of charge or any obligation whatever. We earnestly solicit additions or corrections for next edition, and will be obliged to manufacturers and others who may favor us with any such.

ADVERTISING—

Only the highest class American Manufacturers are solicited for advertisements. To those who know, a casual glance over the representations in this edition will make comment on this point superfluous. Display advertisements constitute the only paid representation in the book. They are of two classes — the colored pages in the front, and descriptive reading matter as shown on page 597.

PRICES:—Colored pages, $100.00 per page. Descriptive reading matter, 10c. per word—not less than 50 words in one place

An advertisement in this book lasts for One Year, but costs for only one issue.

Thomas Publishing Co.
NEW YORK

EIGHTH YEAR 1905.

Thomas Wholesale

Grocery and Kindred

Trades Register. .·. .·.

CONTENTS

MORE ACCURATE,

MORE COMPLETE,

MORE INFORMATION THAN ANY OTHER PUBLICATION.

PRICE $10.00 PER YEAR.

Thomas Publishing Co.
New York.

THE BEST
COLLECTION
SYSTEM.

THE LIST OF BONDED ATTORNEYS

issued by the Association of Bonded Attorneys, Milwaukee, Wis., gives the name of the leading Commercial Attorney in every city and town of the United States and Canada. The list is corrected and published four times per year, a revised list being sent to subscribers quarterly.

COLLECTIONS

When dunning does not bring remittance, the account is sent direct to the attorney at the required point as given in the Bonded List.

GUARANTEE

Immediately upon advice that a claim has been placed in the hands of any Attorney in this list, the Association forwards the Subscriber a Fidelity Bond of the Fidelity & Deposit Co., of Baltimore, Maryland, guaranteeing the Subscriber against excessive fees, embezzlement or fraud of any kind on the part of the Attorney to whom the claim is sent.

SPECIAL REPORTS

When a special Credit Report is wanted on any firm or individual in the United States or Canada, the name of the Attorney in the city or town from which the report is wanted is found in the list of Attorneys; a request is sent to him with fee of 25 cents (except in very large cities where 50 cents is required) and he returns the desired report, written up to date from his personal knowledge and investigation.

The Attorneys will also look after Subscribers' interests in any case requiring it and will keep them posted by mail or telegraph in cases where prompt information is necessary to protect subscribers' interest. It gives subscribers a personal repesentative at every point in United States and Canada.

FREE LEGAL ADVICE

Our subscribers may consult the attorneys listed by us in their respective communities, on such points of law as require explanation, and post themselves generally without charge or expense, but the privilege intended to be accorded them does not include the investigation of matters requiring search of authorities or extended investigation.

SUBSCRIPTION PRICE, $5.00
one year.

Thomas Publishing Company,
NEW YORK, N. Y.

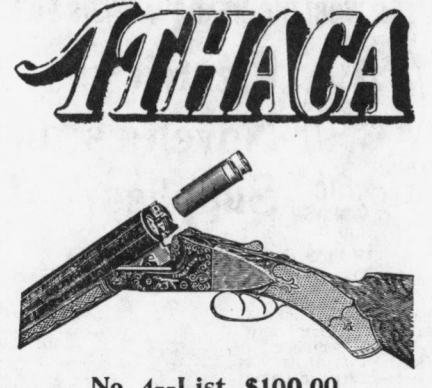

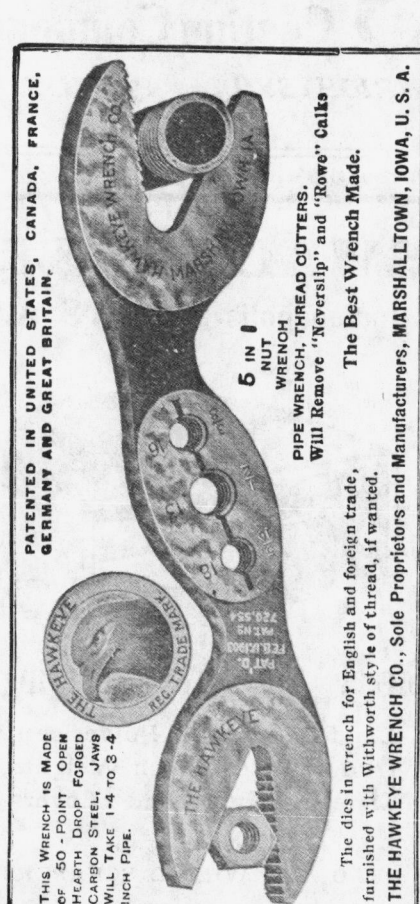

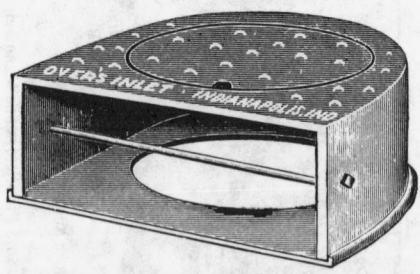

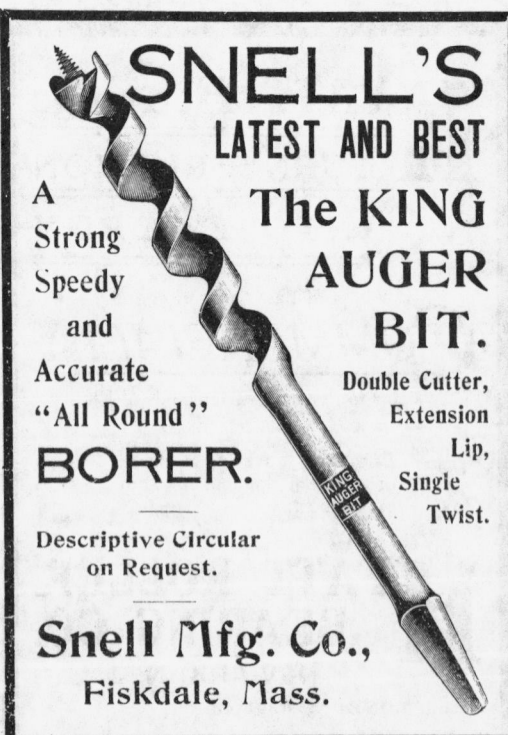

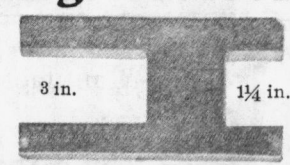

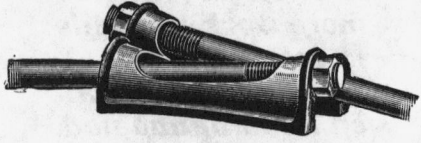
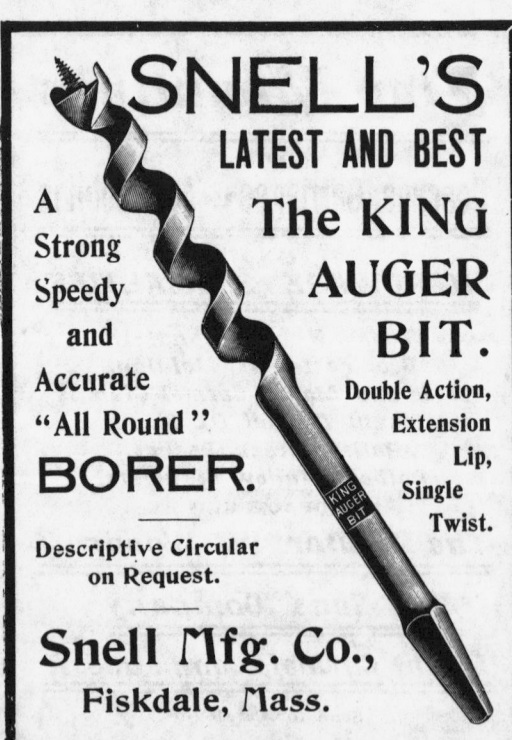

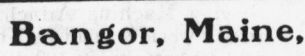

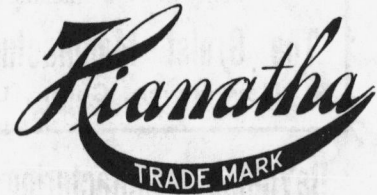

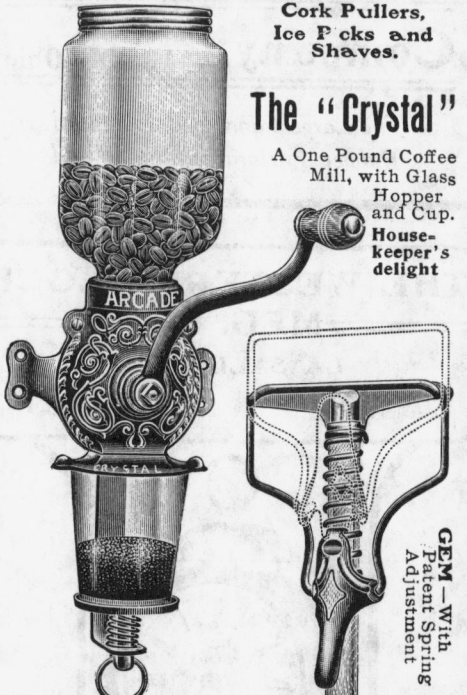

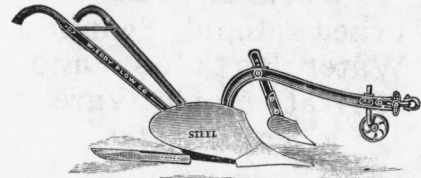

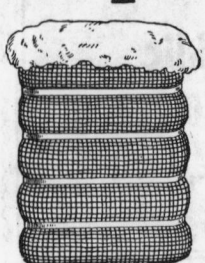

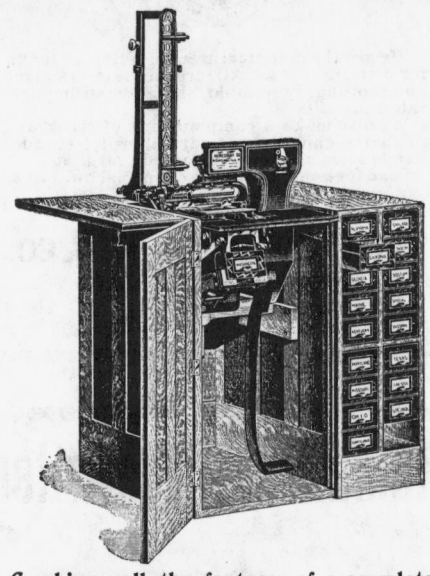

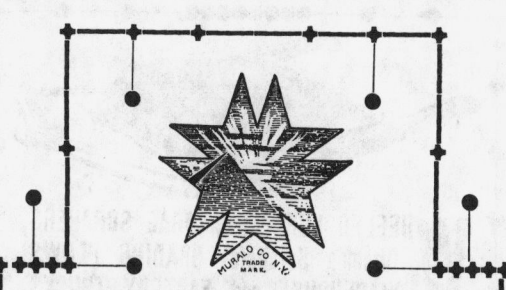

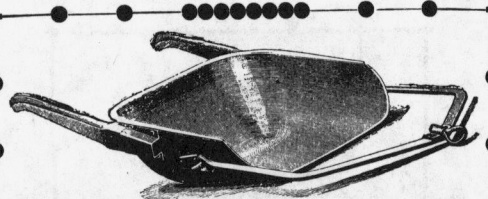

ABRASIVES
See Emery; Corundum, &c.

ABSINTHE
See Cordials

ACCORDEONS
See Musical Instruments

ACCUMULA-TORS

CONN.—Waterbury
Waterbury-Farrell Foundry & Machine Co. (Hydraulic) ....AA
ILL.—Chicago
Allis-Chalmers Co.; Home Ins. Bldg. (Steam) .AAAA
American Battery Co. (Electric) C
Elmes Engineering Works, C. F., Morgan & Fulton (Hydraulic) ....A
Helios Mfg. Co., 222 Fullerton Av. (Chloride) ...D
IOWA—Davenport
Davenport Foundry & Machine Co. (Hydraulic) ..D
MASS.—Worcester
Morgan Construction Co. (Hydraulic) ....A
N. J.—Newark
Burroughs Co., Charles (Hydraulic) C
N. Y.—Brooklyn
Robertson & Co., John, 129 Water (Hydraulic) ......A
New York City
C. & C. Electric Co. (Electric) ....AA
Niles-Bement-Pond Co., 136 Liberty (Hydraulic) AAAA
Watson-Stillman Co., 46 Dey St. (Hydraulic; Steam) ....AA
N. Y.—Schenectady
General Electric Co. (Electric) ....AAAA
N. Y.—Syracuse
Boomer & Boschert Press Co. (Hydraulic) ....A
OHIO—Alliance
Alliance Machine Co. (Hydraulic) ....B
Morgan Engineering (Hydraulic) ....AA
OHIO—Cleveland
Snider-Hughes Co., Coe & Hamilton (Hydraulic) ..B
OHIO—Youngstown
Tod Co., William (Hydraulic) ....AA
PA.—Chambersburg
Chambersburg Engineering Co. (Hydraulic) ....A
PA.—Chester
Vulcan Works (Hydraulic) E
PA.—Newcastle
Penn. Engineering Works (Hydraulic) ....AA
PA.—Philadelphia
Electric Storage Battery Co. (Electric) ......AAAA
Olsen & Co., Tinius, 500 No. 12th (Hydraulic) ......B
Philadelphia Roll & Machine Co., So. 23d & Washn' Av. (Hydraulic) ....A
Sellers & Co., Wm., 1600 Hamilton (Hydraulic) AAAA
Southwark Foundry & Machine Co. (Hydraulic) AAA
Wood & Co., R. D., 400 Chestnut (Hydraulic) ....AAAA
PA.—Pittsburg
Garrison Foundry Co., A. (Hydraulic) ....AAA
Lewis Foundry & Machine Co., 1001 Bingham (Hydraulic) ....A
Mesta Machine Co., Lewis Blk. (Hydraulic) ...AA
Schaife Foundry & Machine Co., 28th & Smallman (Hydraulic) ......B
United Engineering &

ACCUMULATORS '(Con.)
Foundry Co., 54th & A. Y. Ry. (Hydraulic) .....A
WIS.—Cudahy
Power & Mining Machine Co. (Chloride; Hydraulic) ....AAA

ACETANILED
MO.—St. Louis
Mallinckrodt Chemical Works ....AAAA
New York City
Bischoff & Co., C. ....B
Merck & Co...........AAA
N. Y. Quinine & Chemical Wks ....AA
Phair, R. W. ....F
Roessler & Hasslacher Chem. Co ....AA
PA.—Philadelphia
Powers - Weightman - Rosengarten Co. .....AAAA

ACETONE
MASS.—Boston
Billings, Clapp & Co.......A
N. Y.—Buffalo
Schoellkopf, Hartford & Hanna Co ....AAA
New York City
Erhenbrach, Geo. A.......D
Roessler & Hasslacher Chemical Co., 100 William ....AA
OHIO—Cleveland
Harshaw, Fuller & Goodwin ....AA
PA.—Brandt
Kessler & Co...........B
PA.—Philadelphia
Powers - Weightman - Rosengarten Co. ......AAAA

ACIDOMETERS
ILL.—Chicago
Lemo & Co..............E
OHIO—Cincinnati
Berghausen Chem. Co., The E................B

ACIDS
CAL.—National City
Cal. Citrus Products Co. (Citric) ....B
CAL.—San Francisco
Pacific Coast Borax Co. (Boracic) ....AAAA
San. Fran. Chemical Co. Marquette Bldg. (Sulphuric) ....B
COLO.—Denver
Western Chemical Co. (Muriatic; Nitric; Sulphuric) AA
GA.—Newnan
Coweta Fertilizer Co. (Sulphuric) ....AAAA
ILL.—Chicago
Fuller & Fuller (Acetic) ..AA
Hutchinson & Son, W. H. (Citric; Tartaric) ......A
Liquid Carbonic Acid Mfg. Co. (Liquid Carbonic) AAAA
Mineral Point Zinc Co., Marquette Bldg. (Sulphuric) ....AA
ILL.—East St. Louis
Carbon Di-oxide Corp. (Carbonic) ....B
Liquid Carbonic Co. (Carbonic) ....AAAA
ILL.—La Salle
Mathiessen & Hegeler Zinc Co. (Sulphuric) ....AAAA
ILL.—Peru
Illinois Zinc Co. (Sulphuric) AAA
LA.—New Orleans
National Acid Co. (Muriatic; Nitric; Sulphuric) A
Standard Guano & Chemical Co. (Sulphuric; Muriatic) AA
MD.—Baltimore
Davidson Chemical Co. (Sulphuric ....AA

I

ACIDS (Con.)

Hubbard Fertilizer Co. (Sulphuric) C

Thomson Chemical Co. (Acetic; Muriatic; Nitric; Sulphuric) ....B

MD.—Perryville

Eureka Fertilizer Co. (Sulphuric) ....B

MASS.—Boston

Avery Chemical Co. (Lactic) C

American Oxalic Acid Co., 185 Summer (Oxalic)...X

Billings-Clapp Co. (Acetic; Carbolic; Gallic; Hydrobromic; Hydrocyanic; Muriatic; Nitric; Oleic. Oxalic, Picric. Sulphuric)..A

Cochrane Chemical Co. (Nitric; Muriatic; Sulphuric; Acetic) ....AA

Merrimac Chemical Co. (Muriatic; Nitric; Sulphuric; Acetic) ...AAA

Swift & Co., Wm. H. (Mineral; Picric) ....AA

MICH.—Detroit

Michigan Carbon Works (Sulphuric; Phosphoric; Muriatic) ....AAA

MO.—St. Louis

Herf & Frerichs Chemical Co. (Salicylic) ....A

Larkin & Scheffer Chemical Co. (Acetic) ....A

Mallinckrodt Chemical Works (Acetic; Benzoic; Boracic; Butyric; Carbolic; Chromic; Gallic; Hydrobromic; Hydroflouric; Lactic; Muriatic; Nitric; Salicylic; Sulphuric; Valerianic) ......AAAA

N. J.—Belleville

Eastwood Chemical Co. (Acetic; Pyroligneous)..B

N. J.—Newark

American Oil & Supply Co. (Jewelers) ....B

Butterworth Judson Co. (Acetic; Hydroflouric; Muriatic; Nitric; Sulphuric) ....AAA

N. Y.—Albany

Albany Chemical Co. (Carbolic) ....A

N. Y.—Binghamton

Bayless & Berkalew (Wood) ....A

Corbett & Co., M. J. (Wood) ....A

Corbett & Stuart (Wood).B

Finch-Ross Chemical Co. (Wood) ....E

Hammond & Co., S. (Wood) ....A

N. Y.—Brooklyn

Amerigan Tartar Co. (Citric; Tartaric) X

Enequist, Erik. N. 8th & Roebling (Hydrofluoric) ....D

Squibb & Sons, E. R. (Acetic) ....A

Wiarda & Co., John C. (Arsenious; Gallic; Hydroflouic; Boracic) ....A

N. Y.—Buffalo

Schoelkopf, Hartford & Hanna Co. (Boracic; Crystal; Carbolic; Phosphoric; Benzoic; Cresylic) ..AAA

N. Y.—Corbettsville

South Branch Mfg. Co. (Wood) ....B

New York City

American Agricultural Chemical Co. 26 Broadway (Sulphuric) ..AAAA

American Carbonate Co. (Carbonic) ....A

Anatron Chem. Co. 31 Burling Slip (Chromic) ...X

Barrett Mfg. Co. (Carbolic; Hydroflouric) ....AAAA

Berlin Aniline Wks., 213 Water (Pyrogallic) ..B

Bischoff & Co., C. (Carbolic; Oxalic) ....B

Boehringer & Soehme (Pyrogallic; Salicylic)..A

ACIDS (Con.)

Calm & Bro., M. (Boracic) ....AA

Cooper & Co., Chas., 194 Worth (Chromic; Nitric; Muriatic; Liquid Carbonic; Hydrobromic; Hydroflouric; Phosphoric; Sulphuric) ....A

Feuchtwanger & Co. L. (Hydroflouric) ....A

Fuerst Bros. & Co. (Acetic; Carbolic) ....D

General Chemical Co., 25 Broad (Acetic; Nitric; Muriatic; Sulphuric).....AAAA

Heyden Chem. Wks., 135 So. William (Salicylic).A

Johnson & Johnson (Boracic; Salicylic) ....AAA

Kalbfleisch Co. Franklin H., 31 Burling Slip (Acetic) ....AA

Kuttroff, Pickhardt & Co. (Carbolic; Sulphuric)...A

Lehn & Fink (Carbolic)..AAA

McKesson & Robbins (Carbolic; Oleic) .....AAAA

Manhattan Oil Co., 51 Front St. (Stearic) ....D

Merck & Co. (Salicylic; Carbolic) ....AAAA

New Jersey Zinc Co. (Sulphuric) ....AAAA

New York Quinine & Chemical Works (Acetic)...AA

Pacific Coast Borax Co. (Boracic) ....AAAA

Pfizer & Co., Charles, 81 Maiden Lane (Boracic; Citric; Tannic; Tartaric) ....AAA

Roessler & Hasslacher Chem. Co. (Acetic; Boracic) ....AA

Schieffelin & Co., W. H. (Oxalic; Carbolic; Tartaric) ....AA

Selling Co., The (Acetic)AA

Sholes & Co., C. E. (Acetic; Muriatic; Nitric; Sulphuric) X

Tartar Chemical Co. (Tartaric) ....AAA

Warner Chem. Co., 141 Broadway (Butyric).AAA

Wegelin & Wilches (Carbolic) ....B

White Tar Co. (Carbolic; Picric) ....E

Zinsser & Co., Wm. (Salicylic) ....A

N. Y.—Niagara Falls

Roberts Chemical Co. (Muriatic) X

N. Y.—Syracuse

Will & Baumer Co. (Stearic) ....AA

N. C.—Wilmington

Spiritine Chemical Co. (Pyroligous) ....O

OHIO—Cincinnati

Emery Candle Co. (Stearic) ....AA

Gordon Wood Alcohol & Chemical Wks., N. J. M. (Acetic) ....B

Harkness & Cowing Co. (Stearic) ....A

Merrill Chem. Co., W. S. (Salicylic) C

Procter & Gamble Co. (Stearic) ....AAAA

OHIO—Cleveland

Grasselli Chemical Co. (Nitric; Muriatic; Sulphuric; Acetic) ....AAAA

Harshaw, Fuller & Goodwin Co. (Acetic).....AA

OHIO—Sandusky

Jarecki Chemical Co. (Sulphuric) ....AA

PA.—Bradford

Bradford Chemical Co. (Acetic) C

Smith Chemical Co., A. B. (Acetic) ....A

PA.—Canton

Beardsley Bros. & Rhodes (Wood) ....D

PA.—Easton

Baker & Adamson Chemical

2

ACIDS (Con.)

Co. (Nitric; Muriatic; Sulphuric; Tannic; Carbolic; Chromic; Citric; Hydrobromic; Oxalic; Acetic; Boracic; Hydroflouric; Phosphoric; Tartaric)..A

PA.—Philadelphia

Ammonia Co. of Phila., Gray's Ferry Rd. (Sulphuric) ....B

Barrett Mfg. Co. (Carbolic) ....AAAA

Harrison Bros. & Co. (Acetic; Muriatic; Nitric; Sulphuric) ....AAAA

Moro-Phillips Wks. (Acetic; Muriatic; Hydrofluoric; Nitric; Sulphuric).AAAA

Penna Salt Mfg. Co., 115 Chestnut (Nitric; Muriatic; Sulphuric)...AAAA

Powers - Weightman - Rosengarten Co. (Nitric; Acetic; Muriatic; Sulphuric; Tannic; Butyric; Chromic; Flouric; Hydrobromic; Hydrocyamic; Tartaric; Carbolic).AAAA

PA.—Susquehanna

Lackawanna Chemical Co. (Wood) C

Wright & Co., C. F. (Wood) ....B

PA.—York

York Chemical Co. (Hydroflouric; Sulphuric) ....A

R. I.—Providence

Shepard & Co., T. P. (Sulphuric) ....A

S. C.—Summerville

Summerville Fernoline Wks. (Pyrolignous) ....D

VA.—Norfolk

Royster Guano Co., F. S. (Sulphuric) ....A

VA.—Richmond

Va.-Carolina Chem. Co. (Nitric; Sulphuric) ...AAAA

ACTIONS

ILL.—Chicago

Piano & Organ Supply Co. (Piano) ....AA

IND.—New Castle

Krell Piano Co., French (Piano) ....AA

MASS.—Cambridgeport

Tower, Sylvester Co. (Piano) ....A

Seaverns Piano Action Co. Geo. W. (Piano) C

Standard Action Co. (Piano) C

N. J.—Fort Lee

Abbott Piano Action Co. (Piano) ....D

New York City

Strauch Bros., 30 10th Av. (Piano) ....A

Roth & Engelhart 2 E. 47th (Piano) ....B

VT.—Brattleboro

Carpenter Co., The E. P. (Organ) ....B

ADJUSTERS

CONN.—Bridgeport

Perkins Electric Switch Mfg. Co. (Cord) ....B

CONN.—New Britain

Russell & Erwin Mfg. Co. (Window Blind; Casement) ....AAAA

CONN.—New Haven

Ives Co. Hobart B. (Window Shade; Stop) ....B

DEL.—Wilmington

American Vulcanized Fibre Co. (Cord) ......AAAA

Delaware Hard Fibre Co. (Cord) C

ILL.—Chicago

Johnson, R. R., 167 Dearborn (Window Shade)...D

Lever Mfg. Co., C. H. (Cord) ....F

Read. & Co., H. P., 16 N. Canal (Window Shade).H

MASS.—Boston

Boston Electric Co., 29 Harrison Av. (Cord) ......B

ADJUSTERS (Con.)

Marshall Elec. Mfg. Co., 301 Congress (Cord) ...C

MASS.—Fitchburg

Novelty Turning Co. (Cord) ....D

MASS.—Millers Falls

Millers Falls Co. (Window Shade) ....AA

MASS.—Worcester

Wire Goods Co. (Blind)..A

N. J.—Newark

Hartshorn Co., Stewart (Window Stop) .....AAA

New York City

American Hard Rubber Co. (Cord) ....AAAA

Bogert & Hopper, 162 William St. (Cord) ......B

Bolles Revolving Sash Co. (Window Stop) ......H

McCreary & Co., A. A., 136 Liberty (Cord) ......F

Sargeant & Co., 151 Leonard (Casement; Window Stop) ....AAAA

Yale & Towne Mfg. Co., 9 Murray (Casement)AAAA

N. Y.—Rochester

Gay Mfg. Co., 177 W. Main (Cord) ....F

OHIO—Cleveland

Columbian Hardware Co.-(Window Blind) .....AA

Standard Tool Co. (Bicycle Chains) ....AAA

OHIO—Columbus

Universal Shade Adjuster Co. (Shades) ....F

OHIO—Mechanicsburg

Wilcox Mfg. Co., D. (Bicycle Chains) ....A

PA.—Philadelphia

Stewart Frank & Co. (Cord) C

PA.—Pittsburg

Westinghouse Air Brake Co. (Automatic Slack).AAAA

PA.—Reading

Reading Hdw. Co. (Casement) ....AAAA

WIS.—La Crosse

Vought-Berger Co. (Cord)B

WIS.—Milwaukee

League Cycle Wks. (Bicycle Chain) ....D

ADZES

CONN.—Collinsville

Collins Co. (House; Railroad; Ship) ....AAA

CONN.—Westport

Bradleys Sons, G. W. ....D

IND.—Evansville

Evansville Tool Wks. ...B

IND.—Terre Haute

Terre Haute Shovel & Tool Co. ....AAAA

N. J.—Newark

Sayre & Son, L. A. ......B

N. Y.—Buffalo

White Co., L. & I. J......A

N. Y.—Cattaraugus

U. S. Edge Tool Co.......D

N. Y.—Cohoes

Peck Edge Tool Co.......F

New York City

American Axe & Tool Co., 253 Broadway .....AAAA

N. Y.—Rochester

Mack & Co. ....AAAA

OHIO—Findlay

Findlay Axe & Tool Co...A

OHIO—West Park

Norton Tool Co. (R. R.)..C

PA.—Chester

Block & Co., N. B.......AA

PA.—Glassport

Am. Axe & Tool Co..AAAA

PA.—Philadelphia

Plumb, Fayette R.......AA

AERATORS

OHIO—Cincinnati

Deckebach Sons Co., F. C. (Beer) C

New York City

Schneible Co., Jos. (Beer)B

N. Y.—Cortland

Champion Milk Cooler Co. (Milk) ....E

3

AERATORS (Con.)

ILL.—Chicago
Sturges & Burns Mfg. Co.
  (Milk) ....A
VT.—Bellows Falls
Vermont Farm Mach. Co.
  (Milk) C

AGALITE

N. J.—Lincoln
Atlas Mineral & Machine
  Co. ....,.D
N. Y.—Gouverner
Ontario Talc. Co........D
New York City
International Pulp Co.
  AAAA
PA.—Easton
Williams & Co. C. K.....A

AGATES

See Jewelry

AGATEWARE

See Enamelled Iron Ware

AGITATORS

ILL.—Chicago
Allis-Chalmers Co. (Mining)
  AAAA
Perrin & Co., W. R. (Lard)
  A
MO.—St. Louis
Brecht Butchers' Sup. Co..
  G. V. (Lard) ......AAA
N. J.—Trenton
Crossley Mfg. Co. (Clay).B
New York City
Kreig Co., J. K. (Ink,
  Shoe Factory) ....B
OHIO—Cincinnati
Day & Co., J. H. (for
  Liquids) ....A
Triumph Ice Mach. Co.....A
OHIO—Youngstown
Pollock & Co., W. B.
  (Brewery) ....AA
OHIO—Zanesville
Griffith & Wedge Co.
  (Mining) ....A
PA.—East Downingtown.
Downingtown Mfg. Co.
  (Paper Makers) ....A
PA.—Pittsburg
Carroll-Porter Boiler &
  Tank Co. (Mining).....B
Riter-Conley Mfg. Co.
  (Mining) ....AAA
PA.—Washington
Petroleum Iron Wks. Co.
  (Oil) ....D

AGRICUL-TURAL IMPLE-MENTS

ALA.—Tuscumbia
Barton Agricultural Wks.
  (The Barton Cultivator)
  E
CAL.—Benecia
Benecia Agr'l Works (Cul-
  tivators; Harrows; Buck.
  Rakes; Seeders; Disk,
  Rotary, Gang, Steam,
  Sulky & Wheel Plows;
  Hay Presses) ......AAA
CAL.—Fresno
Parteous, James (Plows) B
CAL.—Los Angeles
Keystone Iron Works (Gang
  Plows) ....B
CAL.—Marysville
Empire Fdy. & Harvester
  Wks. (Corn Harvesters)E
CAL.—San Francisco
Jackson — Byron Machine
  Wks.. 411 Market (Hand
  & Sweep Hay Rakes)...A
CAL.—San Leandro
Best Mfg. Co. (Combined
  Harvesters, Binders, &c.)
  B
Morehouse, L. C. (Hay
  Rakes) ....B
CAL.—Stockton
Holt Mfg. Co. (Combined
  Harvesters ....AAA

AGR. IMPS. (Con.)

Houser & Haines Mfg. Co.
  (Combined Grain Drills;
  Harvesters) ......B
Shaw Co., H. C. (Gang
  Plows) ....B
Stockton Mfg. Co. (Bean
  Threshers) ....F
COLO.—Denver
Jackson Hay Press Mfg. Co.
  (Hay Presses) ....F
COLO—Pueblo
Mead Hay Press Co. (Har-
  rows; Cultivators) ....F
CONN.—Higganum
Cutaway Harrow Co. (Har-
  rows; Disc, Sulky Plows)
  F
Scoville, D. & H. (Hoes)
  AA
CONN.—Southport
Jelleff Mfg. Co., C. O.
  (Smoothing Harrows) ..C
GA.—Atlanta
Atlanta Plow Co. (Plows;
  Cultivators; Harrows;
  Corn Planters) C
Southern Agricultural Works
  Co. (Disc Plows) X
Walker-Sims Plow Co.
  (Plows) X
GA.—Columbus
Southern Plow Co. (Break-
  ing, Garden, Shovel Plows
  & Cotton Planters) ...AA
GA.—Dalton
Sanders Mfg. Co. (Pea &
  Bean Hullers; Cultiva-
  tors; Hay Presses X
GA.—Helena
Sikes Mfg. Co. (Hay
  Presses) C
GA.—Macon
Gault, J. T. (Cotton Plant-
  ers) ....,..B
GA.—Rome
Towers & Sullivan Mfg. Co.
  (Cotton Planters; Plows;
  Cultivators; Roman &
  Ace Side Harows; Fertil-
  izer Distributors) C
ILL.—Alton
Hapgood Plow Co. (Grain
  & Corn Drills; Grain Lis-
  ters; Breaking, Gang,
  Sulky, Riding & Wheel
  Plows) ....B
ILL.—Aurora
Phillips, T. L. (Feed Mills)
  D
Western Wheeled Scraper
  Co.) Plows; Road Scrap-
  ers) ....AA
ILL.—Batavia
Appleton Mfg. Co. (Fanning
  & Feed Mills; Stalk &
  Feed Cutters; Corn Shell-
  ers and Threshers).....B
Challenge Co. (Feed Mills;
  Corn Shellers; Feed Cut-
  ters) ....AAA
U. S. Wind. Engine & Pump
  Co. (Feed Mills; Corn
  Shellers) ....A
ILL.—Belleville
Gundlach, P. M. (Grain
  Drills) ....A
ILL.—Bradley
Bradley Mfg. Co. (Hay
  Presses; Breaking, Disc,
  Rotary, Gang, Shovel,
  Subsoil, Sulky & Wheel
  Plows; Bar Lever & Gas
  Pipe Frame Harrows; Cul-
  tivators; Rakes; Force
  Drop Corn & Cotton
  Planters; Corn Drills; Po-
  tato Diggers) ......AAA
ILL.—Canton
Parlin & Orendorff Co.
  (Planters, Listers, Rid-
  ing & Walking Cultiva-
  tors; Canton Pine Frame
  Lever & U Bar. Lever
  Scotch Smoothing Har-
  rows; Breaking, Disc,
  Ditching, Gang, Gang
  Steam, Gang Wheel, Gar-
  den, Potato, Shovel, Sub-
  soil, Sulky, Riding or
  Wheel Swivel Reversible
  & Hillside Plows; Corn
  Planting Drills; Corn &
  Cotton Planters; Potato

Diggers) ....AAAA

ILL.—Carpentersville
Star Manufacturing Co. (Feed Cutters; Walking Cultivators; Spike, Tooth & U Bar Harrows; Breaking Plows; Corn Threshers; Potato Diggers)...A

ILL.—Chicago
Bristol & Gale Co., 112 W. Wash. (Shovel Plows; Corn Shellers) ....B
International Harvester Co. (Mowers; Reapers; Binders; Rakes; Harvesters).. AAAA
Plano Mfg. Co., West Pullman (Mowers; Reapers; Binders; Rakes; Corn Harvesters) X
Whitman & Barnes Mfg. Co., 66 S. Canal ......AAAA

ILL.—Decatur
Chambers - Bering - Quinlan Co. (Hay Loaders; Rakes; Check Rowers; Corn & Potato Planters) ......B
Haworth & Sons Mfg. Co. (Grain Drills; Corn Planters) ....AA
Tait Mfg. Co. F. B. (Rakes; Corn Planters; Corn Shellers; Harrows) ....B
Union Iron Works (Power Corn Shellers) ....B

ILL.—De Kalb
Haish Wire & Implement Co. (Harrows; Corn Shellers) ....B

ILL.—Dixon
Grand Detour Plow Co. (Listers; Riding & Walking Cultivators; Pipe Beam, U Bar, Angle Bar, Wood & Steel Harrows; Breaking, Gang, Subsoil & Sulky Riding or Wheel Plows; Corn Planters).... AAA

ILL.—Dwight
Spencer, J. A. (Hay Presses) C

ILL.—Freeport
Schofield & Co. (Potato Planters) ....D
Stover Mfg. Co. (Feed Mills & Corn Shellers) .....AA

ILL.—Galesburg
Brown & Co., G. W. (Rakes; Corn Planters; Listers; Corn Shellers; Riding & Walking Cultivators; Lever Pipe, U Bar & Wood Harrows; Breaking, Shovel, Sulky Riding or Wheel Plows; Corn Planters) X

ILL.—Galva
Hayes Pump & Planter Co. (Riding & Walking Cultivators; Steel, U Bar, Angle Bar or Pipe with Spike Tooth Harrows; Corn Planters) ....A
Wiestrand Mfg. Co. (Corn Planters) ....D

ILL.—Havana
Ashurst Press. Drill Co. (Grain Drills) ....B

ILL.—Joliet
Adam, W. J. (Feed Mills; Corn Shellers & Seeders) B
Humphrey & Sons (Feed Mills) ....AAA
Joliet Mfg. Co. (Corn Shellers) ....A

ILL.—Kewanee
Peters Pump Co. (Pumps; Corn Planters) ....B

ILL.—Marseilles
Marseilles Mfg. Co. (Feed Mills; Hay Loaders; Corn Shellers; Fanning Mills & Feed Cutters) ....A

ILL.—Mendota
Tower & Sons, J. D. (Pulverizers; Clod Crushers; Walking & Riding Cultivators; & Weed Exterminators) ....A

ILL.—Moline
Deere & Co. (Listers; Rid-

ing & Walking Cultivators; Zig-zag, Deer Lever & Scotch Harrows; Breaking, Disc, Gang, Gang Steam, Gang Wheel, Garden Potato, Shovel, Subsoil, Sulky, Riding or Wheel & Swivel, Reversible & Hillside Plows; Potato Diggers) ....AAAA
Deere & Mansure Co. (Hay Loaders; Listers; Corn Shellers; Seeders; Sugar Cane Cultivators; Spading Harrows; Garden Plows; Corn & Cotton Planting Drills; Bean & Pea, Corn, Cotton & Potato Planters; Hand, Side Delivery & Sulky Hay Rakes)..AAA
Moline Plow Co. (Harrows; Listers; Riding & Walking Cultivators; Breaking, Disc, Gang, Gang Wheel, Shovel, Subsoil, Sulky Riding or Wheel & Swivel, Reversible & Hillside Plows; Plow Coulters; Corn Planting & Cotton Planting Drills; Pea & Bean, Corn & Cotton Planters; Potato Diggers) AAAA
Sechler Carriage Co., D. M. (Cultivators; Harrows; Pulverizers; Corn Planters) ....A

ILL.—Monmouth
Monmouth Plow Co. (Gang & Sulky Riding or Wheel Plows) ....B
Pattee Plow Co. (Cultivators; Plows) C

ILL.—Ottawa
King & Hamilton Co. (Cultivators; Corn Planters) AA
Porter Co.,J. E.(Rakes; Hay Carriers; Hay Presses; Stickers; Steel Corn Planters; Hay Loaders).A

ILL.—Pekin
Pekin Plow Co. (Cultivators; Listers; Rakes; Lever & Disc Harrows; Gang & Sulky Riding or Wheel Plows; Corn Planting Drills) ....A

ILL.—Peoria
Avery Mfg. Co. (Threshers; Riding & Walking Cultivators; Corn & Cotton Planters; Hay Stackers) A
Hart Grain Weigher Co. (Grain Weighers) ......B
Kingman & Co. (Harrows; Listers; Corn Shellers; Riding & Walking Cultivators; Spring Tooth Harrows) ....AAA
Kingman Plow Co. (Cultivators; Listers; U Bar Harrows; Breaking, Gang, Shovel & Sulky Riding or Wheel Plows; Plow Coulters; Corn Planters) AAA
Luthy & Co. (Corn Shellers; Sulky Riding or Wheel Plows; Corn Planters)..A
Peoria Drill & Seeder Co. (Harrows; Grain Drills; Seeders & Sowers) ....A

ILL.—Peru
Peru Plow & Wheel Co. (Harrows; Listers; Riding & Walking Cultivators; Breaking, Gang, Shovel, Subsoil & Sulky, Riding & Wheel Plows; Corn Planters; Potato Diggers)..AA

ILL.—Plano
Sears, Albert H. (Cultivators; Garden Plows; Potato Planters) ....A

ILL.—Quincy
Collins Plow Co. (Corn Drills; Hay Presses; Iowa Riding & Walking Combined Cultivators; Quincy Lever & Steel U Bar Harrows; Gang & Sulky Rid-

ing or Wheel Plows) ...A

Ertel Co., George (Hay Presses) C

Quincy Corn Planter Co. (Corn Planters) ....D

ILL.—Rockford

Emerson Mfg. Co. (Breaking, Disc, Gang, Shovel & Sulky Riding or Wheel Plows; Corn Planting Drills) ....AAA

Rockford Mfg. Co. (Plows; Cultivators; Steel & Wood Lever Harrows) ....B

ILL.—Rock Island

Rock Island Plow Co. (Cultivators; Hay Loaders; Listers; Seeders; Sowers; Steel & Wood Lever & Flexible Harrows; Breaking, Disc, Gang, Gang Wheel, Garden, Potato, Shovel, Subsoil & Sulky Riding or Wheel Plows; Corn Planting & Disc Grain Drills; Corn Planters; Potatoe Diggers) ....AAA

ILL.—Sandwich

Sandwich Mfg. Co. (Feed Mills; Hay Loaders; Corn Shellers; Hay Presses; Cotton Planters) .....AA

ILL.—Sparta

Sparta Plow Works (Cultivators; U. Bar Harrows; Breaking, Gang & Sulky Riding or Wheel Plows)B

ILL.—Springfield

Heinecke & Co. (Combination Wind & Raddle Stackers) C

Sattley Mfg. Co. (Cultivators; Rakes; Listers; Seeders; Sowers; Lever Harrows; Breaking, Disc, Gang, Sulky Riding or Wheel Plows; Corn Planters) X

ILL.—Sterling

Harrison Mfg. Co. (Hand Corn Planters) ....D

Keystone Co., The (Hay Loaders; Rakes; Planters; Corn Shellers; Seeders; Hay Presses; Corn Planting Drills) ....B

Sterling Mfg. Co. (Corn Planters; Potato Diggers) ....A

ILL.—Sycamore

Patten Co., F. C..........B

IND.—Bluffton

Bluffton Mfg. Co. (Corn Planters) C

IND.—Columbus

Reeves & Co. (Grain Weighers; Clover Hullers; Shovel Plows; Rice Threshers) ....AA

IND.—East Chicago

Famous Mfg. Co. (Sweep Rakes; Hay Presses; Swinging Hay Stackers)B

IND.—Evansville

Blount, Henry F. (Walking & Riding Cultivators; Shovel, Subsoil, Sulky Riding or Wheel Plows)..............................AAA

Hartig-Becker Plow Co. (Plow Cultivators).AAAA

Heilman Machine Works (Threshers & Engines)..B

Vulcan Plow Co. (Breaking, Shovel, Sulky Riding or Wheel & Swivel Reversible & Hillside Plows).A

IND.—Hammond

Champion Potato Mchy. Co. Self-Feeding Potato Planters; Potato Diggers)...D

IND.—Indianapolis

American Buncher Mfg. Co., 645 S. Penn. (Clover Machines) ....A

Indiana Mfg. Co., Stevenson Bldg. (Wind Stackers)..A

Nordyke & Marmon Co. (Feed, Corn, Cob & Fanning Mills; Corn Shellers) ....AAA

Pneumatic Elevator &

Weigher Co., 165 E. Morris (Grain Weighers) C

Saltley Stacker Co. (Stackers) ....AAA

Wagner Plow Co. (Breaking Plows) ....B

IND.—Kendallville

Flint & Walling Mfg. Co. (Feed & Wind Mills)...A

IND.—La Porte

Michael, Chas. H. (Fanning Mills) ....AAAA

Rumley Co., M. (Threshers; Hay Presses; Clover Stackers; Traction Engines; Hullers) .....AAA

IND.—Liberty

Rude Bros. Mfg. Co. (Rakes; Riding & Walking Cultivators; Corn Planting, Fertilizer & Grain Drills) ....A

IND.—Logansport

King Drill Co. (Corn Planting & Grain Drills) C

IND.—Mt. Vernon

Keck-Gonnermann Co. (Threshers) ....A

IND.—Peru

Spring Grain Drill Mfg. Co. (Grain Drills) ....D

IND.—Richmond

Gaar, Scott & Co. (Stackers; Clover Hullers; Traction Engines; Grain Weighers; Corn & Rice Threshers)..................AAA

Hoosier Drill Co. (Corn Planting & Disc Grain Drills; Corn Planters) ....AAAA

Richmond Plow Co. (Breaking, Garden & Shovel Plows) ....D

Robinson & Co. (Threshers; Stackers; Grain Weighers; Hay Presses)A

Wayne Works (Grain Drills; Corn Planters) ....A

IND.—Rising Sun

Ciore's Sons, W. (Plows).E

IND.—South Bend

Birdsell Mfg. Co. (Straw Stackers; Clover Hullers) ....AA

Bissell Chilled Plow Wks. (Disc, Gang, Garden, Subsoil, Sulky Riding or Wheel & Swivel, Reversible & Hillside Plows; Cultivators; Harrows; Planters) ....AAAA

Bowsher Co., N. C. (Feed Mills; Barley Crushers) B

Oliver Chilled Plow Wks. (Breaking, Gang. Shovel, Subsoil, Sulky, Riding or Wheel & Swivel, Reversible & Hill-side Plows) ....AAA

South Bend Chilled Plow Wks. (Smoothing & New Market 14 teeth Harrows; Breaking, Disc, Gang, Shovel, Subsoil, Sulky, Riding or Wheel & Swivel Reversible & Hillside Plows; Planters)...AA

IND.—Vincennes

Hartman Mfg. Co. (Riding & Walking Cultivators).C

IOWA—Council Bluffs

Children & Sons, E. (Cultivators) ....B

IOWA—Des Moines

Wood Bros. Steel Self-Feeder Co. (Cultivators) ...B

IOWA—Dubuque

Cooper Wagon & Buggy Co., A. A. (Plows; Cultivators; Feed Mills; Corn Planters) ....B

IOWA—Fort Madison

Morrison Mfg. Co. (Cultivators; Steel Leven Harrows; Breaking, Gang, Garden, Shovel, Subsoil & Sulky Riding or Wheel Plows; Plow Coulters; Beet, Corn & Cotton Planters) ....AAA

IOWA—Ottumwa

Dain Mfg. Co. (Feed Mills;

Hay Loaders; Haying Tools; Rakes; Hay Presses; Hay Stackers).A
Janney Mfg. Co. (Feed Mills & Corn Planters).A

IOWA—Prairie City
Dowden Mfg. Co., Ltd. (Potato Harvesters & Weed Harrows) C

IOWA—Sioux City
Sioux City Plow Co. (Cultivators; Breaking & Sulky Riding or Wheel Plows) C

IOWA—Waterloo
Kelly & Tannehill Co. (Feed Mills & Well Drilling Machinery) ....B
Litchfield Mfg. Co. (Feed Mills; End Gates; Forges)

IOWA—Webster City
Closz & Howard Mfg. Co. (Grain Separators) .....B
C

KANS.—Coffeyville
Coffeyville Impt. & Mfg. Co. (Gang & Sulky Riding or Wheel Plows) C

KANS.—Kansas City
Strait Mfg. Co., H. N. (Hay Presses; Scales) ......B

KANS.—Manhattan
Blue Valley Mfg. Co. (Corn Harvesters) ....F

KY.—Louisville
Avery & Sons, B. F. (Rakes; Riding & Walking Cultivators; Lever Spike Tooth Harrows; Breaking, Disc, Gang, Gang Wheel, Garden, Shovel, Subsoil, Sulky Riding or Wheel, Swivel, Plows; Plow Coulters; Corn & Cotton Planting Drills; Corn & Cotton Planters; Fertilizer Distributors; Potato Diggers) AAA
Brennan & Co. (Corn Shellers; Feed Cutters; Grain Reversible & Hillside & Disc Grain Drills)....A
Brinly-Hardy Co. (Breaking, Garden, Potato, Shovel, Subsoil & Swivel Reversible & Hillside Plows)...A

KY.—Maysville
Ball, Mitchell & Co. (Shovel & Swivel Reversible & Hillside Plows) ....D
Hall Plow Co., Jas. H. (Cultivators; Subsoil & Swivel Reversible & Hillside Plows) ....AA

MD.—Baltimore
Sinclair Scott Co. (Hay Presses) ....E

MASS.—Boston
Ames Plow Co. (Cultivators; Tedders; Fanning Mills; Feed Cutters; Disc Harrows; Ditching, Garden, Ice, Subsoil Reversible & Hillside Plows; One Horse, One Row Corn Planters) ....AA

MASS.—Chicopee Falls
Belcher & Taylor Agricultural Tool Co. (Fanning Mills; Tedders; Feed Cutters; Potato Diggers; Prouts Hoeing Machine; Eclipse Weed Harrow; Shares; Coulters; Harrow & Yankee Pulverizer; Shovel, Sulky; Riding or Wheel & Swivel Reversible & Hillside Plows; Corn & Potato Planters; Fertilizer Distributors).A

MASS.—Lowell
Dennis & Co., J. M. (Hay Presses) ....E

MASS.—Milford
Mann Co., F. W. (Corn Shellers) ....B

MASS.—Tyringham
Garfield & Son, D. M. (Hand Hay Rakes) ....F

MASS.—Worcester
Colvin, J. A., 52 Jackson (Hay Presses) ....A
Richardson Mfg. Co. (Mow-

ers; Rakes; Tedders)...A

MICH.—Albion
Gale Mfg. Co. (Rakes; Listers; Seeders; Sowers; Bean & Pea Harvesters; Riding & Walking Cultivators; Spring Tooth Steel. Lever, Spike Tooth & Steel U Bar Harrows; Breaking, Gang, Garden. Hop, Potato & Subsoil Plows; Corn Planting Drills; Bean & Pea, Beet, Corn & Cotton Planters)...AAA

MICH.—Alpena
Kline, L. T. (Hay Presses)D

MICH.—Battle Creek
Advance Thresher Co. (Threshers, Stackers & Grain Weighers) ....AAA
Nichols & Shephard Co. (Threshers, Stackers & Grain Weighers) ...AAA

MICH.—Buchanan
Black, Geo. H. ....E

MICH.—Cass City
Cass City Foundry Co. (Gang Plows) ....D

MICH.—Cassopolis
Cassopolis Mfg. Co. (Grain Drills) C

MICH.—Detroit
Amer Harrow Co., 1482 Hastings (Plows; Bean Harvesters; Spring Tooth & Disc Harrows; Riding & Walking Cultivators; Bean & Pea Corn & Potato Planters) ....AA
Mason-Campbell Co. (Fanning Mills) C

MICH.—Dowagiac
Dowagiac Mfg. Co. (Grain Drills) ....A

MICH.—Greenville
Greenville Planter Co. (Bean & Pea, Corn, Hand Corn & Potato Planters) ....D
Greenville Implement Co. (Plows; Feed Cutters; Star Shovel Cultivators; Gang Plows; Delmore & Bell Potato Planters)...B

MICH.—Ionia
Arnold's Son, G. W. (Bean & Pea Harvesters) ....E

MICH.—Jackson
Aspinwall Mfg. Co. (Potato Planters & Diggers)....A
Empire Drill Co. (Grain Drills) ....A.A

MICH.—Kalamazoo
Smith & Pomeroy Windmill Co. (Feed & Wind Mills)B
Kalamazoo Tank & Silo Co. (Harrows & Wind Mills) B

MICH.—Lansing
Bements Sons. E. (Planters; Riding & Walking Cultivators; Spike Tooth, U Bar & Lansing Coil Spring Harrows; Breaking, Disc, Gang, Shovel, Sulky Riding or Wheel Plows; Corn Planting Drills; Corn & Cotton Planters) X

MICH.—Lyons
Beach Mfg. Co. (Bean & Pea Harvesters ....F

MICH.—Mt. Clemens
Donaldson Bros. (Plows; Cultivators; Feed Cutters; Spike Tooth Harrows; Corn Planters) ....A

MICH.—Pontiac
Howland Mfg. Co. (Feed Cutters; Pea & Bean Harvesters; Little Giant Walking Cultivators; Spring Tooth Harvesters; Shovel Plows) C

MICH.—Port Huron
Port Huron Engine & Thresher Co. (Plows; Stackers; Feed Mills; Corn Shellers; Weighers; Corn & Straw Preserving & Rye Threshers) ...AAAA

MICH.—St. Johns
Mason & Co., F. H. (Hand Cultivators; Corn & Potato Planters) C

AGR. IMPS. (Con.)

MICH.—Saginaw
Ferrell Co., A. T. (Fanning Mills, &c.) ....B
MICH.—Three Rivers
Roberts, Throp & Co. (Potato Diggers) ....B
MICH.—Traverse City
Potato Implement Co. (Hand, Corn & Potato Planters) ....E
MICH.—Ypsilanti
Thompson & Sons, O. E...C
MINN.—Austin
Johnson & Smith Co. (Steel Harrows; Grub, Sod Breaking & Shovel Plows) B
MINN.—Minneapolis
Howell & Co., R. R. (Riding Cultivators) ....B
Kinnard Haines Co. (Hay Presses) C
Minneapolis Plow Co. (Scotch Steel Frame & Lever Harrows; Breaking Sulky, Riding or Wheel Plows) ....B
Minneapolis Threshing Machine Co. (Threshers; Stackers; Corn Shellers; Baggers) ....AAA
Monitor Drill Co. (Grain Drills; Seeders; Sowers; Riding Cultivators) .AAA
Owens Co., J. L. (Fanning Mills; Grain Cleaning Machinery) ....B
MINN.—Owatonna
Owatonna Mfg. Co. (Grain Drills; Seeders & Growers) B
MINN.—St. Paul
Amer. Grass Twine Co. (Mowers; Rakes; Bean Harvesters) .... AAA
Fosston Mfg. Co. (Wind Stackers) C
MINN.—Sauk Center
Keller Mfg. Co. (Harrows; Cultivators; Threshers; Fanning Mills) ....B
MINN.—Stillwater
North West Thresher Co. (Threshers; Stackers; Engines & Grain Weighers) AAA
MINN.—Winona
New Winona Mfg. Co. (Feed Mills; Shellers; Steam Power Hay Presses)...A
MISS.—Jackson
McDonnell & Son, J. (Plows, &c.) C
MISS.—Meridian
Hyde, Chas. (Hay Presses)E
MO.—Browning
Jenkins Hay Rake & Stacker Co. (Feed Mills; Haying Tools & Hay Stackers)C
MO.—Carrollton
Farm Tool Mfg. Co. (Listers; Disc, Knife & Riding & Walking Cultivators & Hay Presses)..C
MO.—Huntsville
Fleming & Son Mfg. Co. (Corn Harvesters & Hay Stackers) C
MO.—Kansas City
Eagle Mfg. Co. (Harrows; Cultivators; Listers; Breaking, Disc, Shovel & Sulky Riding or Wheel Plows; Cotton Planters; Hay Presses) ....A
Eclipse Hay Press Co. 8th & Mill (Hay Presses)..D
Kansas City Hay Press Co. (Feed Mills; Hay Presses; Haying Tools; Corn Harvesters & Hay Stackers) AA
Smith & Sons Mfg. Co. (Plows; Rakes & Hay Presses) ....B
Western Mfg. Co. (Cultivators & Grain Drills)...C
MO.—Linneus
Superior Hay Stacker Mfg. Co. (Hay Stackers).....D
MO.—St. Joseph
Cartmell Machine Co......C
St. Joseph Plow Co. (Riding

AGR. IMPS. (Con.)

& Walking Cultivators; Scotch, Channel & Pipe or Tap Bar, Steel Spike Tooth Harrows; Breaking, Ditching, Shovel & Sulky, Riding or Wheel Plows; Corn Planting Drills)...A
MO.—St. Louis
Kingsland Mfg. Co. (Threshers; Corn Shellers, etc.) ....B
McGowan & Finigan Fdy. & Machine Co., 204 N. 3d (U Bar Steel Harrows).A
Whitman Agricultural Co. (Harrows; Grain Drills; Feed Mills; Shellers; Seeders; Sowers; Feed Cutters; Steam & Hand Power Hay Presses & Corn Threshers) ......A
MO.—Sweet Springs
Fischer, Conrad (Harrows) C
NEBR.—Beatrice
Dempster Mfg. Co. (Cultivators; Grain Drills, etc.) A
NEBR.—Nebraska City
Dullenty Plow Co. (Cultivators) ....B
King Drill Mfg. Co. (Grain Drills) C
NEBR.—Omaha
Martin Anderson Co. (Hay Stackers) C
N. J.—Greenloch
Bateman Mfg. Co. (Riding, Walking & Horse Hoe Cultivators; Iron Age Harrows; Garden & Sulky Riding or Wheel Plows; Fertilizer Drills; Bean & Pea Planters) ......A
N. J.—Hightstown
Shangle, Jno. R. (Gang Plows & Potato Diggers)C
Peppler, Thos. (Gang Plows) ....D
N. J.—Millington
Nash, Duane H. (Pulverizers; Clod Crushers; Acme Pulverizer Harrows; Leveler & Hand Corn Planters) ....A
Nishwitz Mfg. Co. (Harrows, etc.) ....A
N. J.—Phillipsburg
Phillipsburg Mfg. Co. (Feed Mills, etc.) C
N. J.—Pittstown
Deats, Hiram, Jr. (Plows, Threshers & Corn Shellers) C
N. Y.—Albany
Dederick's Sons, P. K. (Hay Presses) ....AA
N. Y.—Auburn
Bowen & Quick (Threshers, etc.) C
New Birdsall Co. (Threshers & Engines) ......AAA
Osborne & Co., D. M. (Mowers; Reapers; Rakes; Tedders; Corn Harvesters; Horse, Hoe & Steel Cultivators; Columbia & Junior Peg & Spring Tooth Harrows) ....AAA
N. Y.—Avon
Champion Drill Co. (Cultivators & Grain Drills)...C
N. Y.—Batavia
Bidwell, Chas. H. (Bean Threshers; Bean & Pea Harvesters) C
Johnston Harvester Co. (Binders; Cultivators; Reapers; Rakes; Tedders; Seeders; Sowers; Corn & Rice Harvesters; Steel Harrows) ....AAA
Wiard Plow Co. (Bean & Pea Harvesters; Cotton, Corn & Spading Harrows; Gang Steam, Subsoil, Sulky Riding & Swivel, Reversible & Hillside Plows; Bean & Pea & Hand Corn Planters)..AA
N. Y.—Buffalo
Buffalo Pitts Co. (Rakes; Threshers; Stackers; Rid-

ing & Walking Cultivators; Spike Tooth Harrows) ....AA

N. Y.—Cambridge
Lovejoy & Son, H. H. (Cultivators; Tooth Harrows; Shovel Plows & Corn Planters) C

N. Y.—Canandaigua
Robinson Chilled Plow Co. (Hillside & Reversible Plows) X

N. Y.—Canastota
Patten & Stafford Co. (Harrows; Rakes, &c.) .....A

N. Y.—Cato
Dutton & ∪o., E. Q. (Garden Plows) ....E

N. Y.—Chapinville
Chapinville Wheel Co. (Harrows; Rakes & Seed Sowers) C

N. Y.—Cobleskill
Harder Mfg. Co. (Threshers; Farming Mills; Clover Hullers & Rye Thresher, Cleaner & Binder Combined) C

N. Y.—Cohoes
Excelsior Mach. Co. (Potato Diggers) ....E

N. Y.—Copake Iron Wks.
Columbia Plow Works Chilled Swivel, Reversible & Hillside Plows) ..AA

N. Y.—Corning
Allen Fdy. Co., E. R. (Potato Diggers) C

N. Y.—Dansville
Sweet Mfg. ∪o., George (Mowers & Reapers) ..C

N. Y.—East Aurora
Peck, S. H. (Potato Diggers) ....B

N. Y.—Elmira
Clipper Chilled Plow Co. (Harrows; Cultivators; Rakes & Sulky Reversible Plows) ....A

N. Y.—Gardenville
Scheopflin, Charles (Feed Cutters & Shovel Plows) C

N. Y.—Gowanda
Gowanda Agricultural Wks. (Plows; Walking Cultivators; Hop, Shovel & Swivel Reversible & Hillside Plows; Potato Diggers X

N. Y.—Greene
Lynn Iron Works (Feed Cutters) C

N. Y.—Greenwich
Eddy Plow Co., W (Straw Pressing & Rye Threshers) ....B

N. Y.—Hoosick Falls
Wood Mowing & Reaping Machine Co., Walter A. (Mowers; Reapers; Binders; Rakes; Tedders & Corn Harvesters) ...AAA

N. Y.—Ithaca
Williams Bros. (Rakes; Well Machinery; Fertilizer Distributors) ..AA

N. Y.—Kingston
Hendricks & Co., D. B. (Hay Pressers) ......D

N. Y.—Leonardville
Babcock Mfg. Co. (Cultivators) ....D

N. Y.—Leroy
Leroy Plow Co. (Bean & Pea Harvesters; Hillside & Flatland Plows) ....B

N. Y.—Lyons
Nagley Mfg. Co. (Hand Corn & Pumpkin Planters) C

N. Y.—Macedon
Bickford & Huffman (Fertilizer, Garden Seed & Grain Drills) ....A

N. Y.—Mt. Morris
Genesee Valley Mfg. Co. (Grain Drills; Corn Shellers; Fanning Mills; Fargo & V-Tooth Harrows) ...B

N. Y.—Munnsville
Munnsville Plow Co. (Bean & Pea Harvesters; Ditch-

ing; Shovel; Subsoil; Reversible & Hillside Plows) ....B

N. Y.—Newark Valley
Kemp Mfg. Co., J. S. (Manure Spreaders) ....B

New York City
Watson-Stillman Co., 46 Dey (Hay Presses) ....AA

N. Y.—Owego
Champion Wagon Co. (Grain Drills, &c.) ....B

N. Y.—Phelps
Crown Mfg. Co. (Grain Drills, &c.) ....B

N. Y.—Poughkeepsie
Adriance, Platt & Co. (Mowers; Reapers; Binders; Rakes & Peg & Spring Harrows) ....AAA

N. Y.—Riverhead
Hudson, S. T. (Four-in-One Harrows) ....D

N. Y.—Rome
Adams & Son, S. (Hop Plows) C

N. Y.—Schenectady
General Electric Co. (Snow Plows) ....AAAA
Westinghouse Co. (Threshers; Stackers; Combined Grain & Clover Threshers) ....AA

N. Y.—Seneca Falls
Gould Mfg. Co., The (Corn Shellers. &c.) .....AAA
Rumsey & Co. (Corn Shellers) ....AAAA

N. Y.—Shortsville
Empire Drill Co. (Corn Planting Drills) ......A

N. Y.—Spencerport
Wallace & Ireland (Potato Diggers) ....D

N. Y.—Stamford
Cowley & Son, W. A. (Swivel Reversible & Reversible Hillside Plows) X

N. Y.—Syracuse
Syracuse Chilled Plow Co. (Cultivators; Spring & Spike Tooth Harrows; Gang, Gang Wheel, Shovel, Sulky Reversible & Sulky Riding or Wheel Plows) ....AA
Whitman & Barnes Mfg. Co. (Harrows; Cultivators; Planters & Corn Shellers) ....AAAA

N. Y.—Utica
Childs & Co., Chas. H. (Cultivators) ....B
Davison Harrow Co. (Harrows) ....B
Eureka Mower Co. (Spike, Spring & Shovel Tooth Cultivators; Mowers; Corn, Hand Corn & Potato Planters) ....B
Standard Harrow Co. (Cultivators; Corn Shellers; Superior Spike Tooth Lever Harrows; Corn Harvesters) ....A

N. Y.—Warsaw
Warsaw Elevator Co. (Bean, Pea & Corn Planters) ..B

N. C.—Asheville
Drummond Plow Co. (Shovel Plows; Potato Diggers) .F

N. C.—Charlotte
Cole Mfg. Co. (Cotton Planters) ....E

OHIO—Akron
Akron Cultivator Co. (Pivot Axle Automatic Cultivators; Riding & Walking Shovel Plows) ....B
Aultman Miller Buckeye Co. (Mowers; Reapers; Rakes; Corn & Rice Harvesters) AAAA
Oyler Plow Co. (Cultivators) X
Whitman & Barnes Mfg. Co. (Riding & Walking Cultivators; Garden Plows; Garden Seed Drills & Corn Planters) ..AAAA

OHIO—Avery
Hoover, Prout & Co. (Po-

AGR. IMPS. (Con.)
tato Diggers) ....B
OHIO—Bellevue
Ohio Cultivator Co. (Sulky
& Walking Cultivators;
Steel Lever Harrows,
Bean & Pea Harvesters;
Listers; Corn & Ohio
Sulky Planters, Plows;
Pulverizers) ....AA
OHIO—Berea
Dunham & Son, J. W. (Har-
rows, Corn Shellers, &c.)
..................C
OHIO—Bryan
Bryan Plow Co. (Plows,
Harrows, &c.) ....B
OHIO—Bucyrus
Shunk Plow Co. (Cultiva-
tors, Combined Horse
Hoes; Breaking & Shovel
Plows) C
OHIO—Canton
Aultman Co. (Threshers,
&c.) ....A
Bucher & Gibbs Plow Co.
(Riding & Walking Cul-
tivators; Imperial Lever
Spike Tooth, Spring Tooth
& Wood Bar Harrows;
Breaking, Gang, Garden,
Subsoil, Sulky Riding or
Wheel & Swivel Reversi-
ble & Hillside Plows; Po-
tato Diggers ....AA
Dick Agricultural Works,
Jos. (Fodder Cutters, &c.)
..................B
Kohler & Co. F. E. (Hand
Corn Planters) C
Ney Mfg. Co. (Hay Forks)
..................B
U. S. Implement Co. (Cul-
tivators) X
OHIO—Cincinnati
Straub Machinery Co., 1940
W. 6th (Feed Mills, &c.)
..................C
OHIO—Cleveland
Bartlett & Snow Co. (Feed
Mills; Corn Shellers,
&c.) ....B
Empire Plow Co. (Harrows;
Cultivators & Shovel
Plows) ....A
OHIO—Columbiana
Enterprise Mfg. Co. (Feed
Mills, &c.) ....B
OHIO—Columbus
Brown, Hinman & Hunting-
ton Co. (Corn & Cotton
Planters) ....A
Kilbourne & Jacobs Mfg.
Co. ....AAA
OHIO—Crestline
Burch Plow Works Co.
(Breaking Plows) ....AA
OHIO—Dayton
Cast Steel Plow Co., 122 N.
Front (Sulky, Riding &
Wheel Plows) C
Ohio Rake Co. (Corn Plant-
ers & Shellers; Cultiva-
tors; Corn Planting Drills;
Hay Loaders; U-Bar,
Quail L-Bar & Spike
Tooth Harrows; Planters;
Seeders & Tedders; Rakes)
..................AA
Parrott Mfg. Co. (Breaking
Plows) ....B
Stoddard Mfg. Co. (Riding
& Walking Cultivators;
Corn Planting & Dix Press
Runner & Hoe Drills; Pea,
Bean, Corn & Cotton
Planters; Rakes; Tedders
& Seeders) ....AAA
OHIO—Defiance
Clipper Plow Co. (Cultiva-
tors; Grain Drills; Plant-
ers; Breaking & Shovel
Plows) C
OHIO—De Graff
De Graff Mfg. Co. (Grain
Separators, &c.) ......B
OHIO—Doylestown
Sieberling & Miller Co.
B i n d e r s; Harvesters;
Mowers & Reapers) ....A
OHIO—Fremont
Lehr Agricultural Co. (Rid-
ing & Walking Cultiva-
tors; Peg Tooth Harrows;

AGR. IMPS. (Con.)
Corn Harvesters; Corn &
Cotton Planters; Break-
ing & Shovel Plows) ...B
OHIO—Geneva
Geneva Tool Co. (Shovel
Plows & Hand Hay
Rakes) ....AA
OHIO—Hamilton
Deuscher Co., H. P. (Har-
rows; Cotton Planters,
&c.) ....A
Long & Allstatter Co. (Rid-
ing & Walking Cultiva-
tors; Feed Cutters; Disc
or Rotary & Sulky Rid-
ing or Wheel Plows) ..AA
OHIO—Harrison
Campbell Corn Drill Co.
(Corn Planters) ......E
OHIO—Hillsboro
Bell Co., C. S. (Cane Mills;
Feed Mills) ....A
OHIO—Ironton
Ironton Disc Plow Co. (Disc
Plows) C
OHIO—Kent
Peterson Mfg. Co. (Pulver-
izers) ....D
OHIO—Lancaster
Eagle Machine Co. (Corn
Shellers; Feed Cutters;
Feed Mills; Hand Plant-
ers) ....A
Hocking Valley Mfg. Co.
Feed Cutters; Grain
Drills; Hay Loaders &
Tedders) ....A
OHIO—Malta
Brown-Manly Plow Co.
Cultivators; Breaking &
Shovel Plows) ....A
OHIO—Mansfield
Aultman & Taylor Machin-
ery Co. (Clover Hullers,
Stackers & Threshers)
..................AAAA
Lean Roderick Mfg. Co.
(All Steel Lever & Spring
Tooth & Zigzag Harrows)
..................B
OHIO—Marietta
Marietta Mfg. Co. (Corn
Planters & Plows) ....B
OHIO—Marion
Huber Mfg. Co. (Threshers;
Stackers; Weighers, En-
gines, &c.) ....AAA
Implement Mfg. Co. (Plows)
..................C
Marion Mfg. Co. (Threshers;
Stackers, &c.) ....A
OHIO—Martinsville
West & Townsend (Cultiva-
tors) ....F
OHIO—Massillon
Harrison & Co., W. R. (Fod-
der Cutters, &c.) C
Massillon Engine & Thresher
Co. (Threshers; Stackers,
&c.) ....B
Russell & Co. (Threshers;
Stackers, &c.) ...AAAA
OHIO—Middletown
Fetzer & Co. (Corn Plant-
ing & Drain Drills; Corn
Planters; Disc Harrows;
Seeders; Potato Diggers)
..................AAAA
OHIO—Mt. Gilead
Hydraulic Press Mfg. Co.
(Grain Weighers, &c.)..A
OHIO—Napoleon
Morning Star Mfg. Co.
(Threshers, &c.) C
OHIO—Newark
Newark Machine Co. (Clover
Hullers; Fanning Mills;
Straw Stackers) ......B
OHIO—New Bremen
Lanferseick-Grothaus (
(Breaking Plows) C
OHIO—New Lexington
Star Mfg. Co. (Feed Mills
& Powers, &c.) C
OHIO—Orrville
Champion Thresher Co.
(Grain Seperators; Clover
Hullers, &c.) C
OHIO—Salem
Silver Mfg. Co. (Feed Mills
& Feed Cutters) ......A
OHIO—Sandusky
Klotz Machine Co. (Corn

Shellers, &c.) ....B

OHIO—Springfield

Am. Seeding Machine Co. (Harrows; Corn Planters, &c.) ....AAAA

Foos Mfg. Co. (Corn Harvesters & Planters) ....A

Mast & Co., P. P. (Riding & Walking Cultivators; Corn Planting, Fertilizing & Disc & Hoe & Shoe Grain Drills) .....AAAA

Rogers Iron Co. (Corn Shellers & Feed Mills)..C

Ross Co., E. W. (Feed Mills; Corn Shellers & Cane Mills Feed Cutters) ....A

Superior Drill Co. (Corn Planting with Fertilizer Attachment, Hoe, Shoe & Disc Drills; Harrows; Seeders; Hay Tools, &c.) ....AAA

Thomas Mfg. Co. (Grain Drills; Spike Tooth Harrows; Hay Loaders; Rakes; Tedders, &c.) ....AAA

Warder, Bushnell & Glessner Co. (Rice Harvesters) ....AAAA

OHIO—Tiffin

Tiffin Wagon Co. (Corn Shellers, &c.) ....A

OHIO—Toledo

Hickox, Mull Mfg. Co. (Seeding Machines; Grinding Mills) ....A

Toledo Plow Co. (Spike or Spring Tooth Harrows; Breaking, Gang, Shovel & Sulky Riding or Wheel Plows) ....U

U. S. Pump & Supply Co. (Plows, &c.) ....B

OHIO—Upper Sandusky

Berry Mfg. Co. (Hay Presses) ....D

OHIO—Westerville

Bennett & Co., H. L. (Corn Harvesters) ....D

OHIO—Zanesville

Brown Mfg. Co. (Riding & Walking Cultivators; Harrows & Shovel Plows).AA

OREGON—Portland

Russell & Co. (Plows).AAA

PA.—Carnegie

Carnegie Plow & Mfg. Co. (Plows, &c.) ....B

PA.—Easton

Wilson Bros. (Feed Mills & Feed Cutters) ....A

PA.—Elizabethtown

Buch's Son, A. (Corn Shellers; Fanning Mills; Feed Cutters) C

PA.—Kennett Square

American Road Machine Co. (Road Making Machinery; Breaking & Ditching Plows) ....AA

PA.—Lansdale

Heebner & Sons (Harrows; Feed Mills; Feed Cutters & Threshers) ....B

PA.—Lenover

Chalfant's Sons, Jno. M. (Threshers, &c.) C

PA.—Mechanicsburg

Comstock, Geo. S. (Feed Cutters & Rakes) C

PA.—Mifflinburg

Albright & Son, Jas. H. (Riding & Walking Cultivators) ....D

PA.—Mountville

Mountville Mfg. Co. (Corn Shellers; Planters & Plows) C

PA.—Muncy

Sprout, Waldron & Co. (Corn Shellers; Feed Mills. &c.) ....A

PA.—New Brighton

Logan & Strobridge Iron Co. (Corn Shellers; Feed Mills, &c.) ....B

PA.—Oakland Station

Sellers, Edw. (Corn Planters & Plows) ....E

PA.—Philadelphia

Allen & Co., S. L., 1107 Market (Cultivators; Fertilizer Drills; Harrows; Bean Harvesters; Bean, Pea & Beet Planters; Garden Plows; Pulverizers; White & Sweet Potato Diggers) ....AA

PA.—Pottstown

Ellis Keystone Agricultural Wks. (Feed Mills & Threshers) ....B

PA.—Tatamy

Messenger Mfg. Co. (Walking Cultivators; Grain with Grass Seeder Drills; Feed Cutters: Corn & Potato Planters; Breaking Plows; Tedders; Seperator & Cleaner Threshers; Potato Diggers) ......B

PA.—Waynesboro

Frick Co. (Stackers; Shellers; Threshers; Traction Engines) ....AAA

Geiser Mfg. Co. (Gang & Gang Steam Plows; Baggers; Clover Hullers; Threshers; Traction Engines & Weighers).AAAA

PA.—York

Farquhar Co., A. B. (Corn Shellers; Riding & Walking Cultivators; Force, Feed, Grain, Grass & Phosphate Drills; Engines; Feed Cutters; Spring Tooth Harrows; Corn & Cotton Planters; Gang Shovel & Subsoil Plows; Corn & Rice Threshers) ....AAA

Hallock Weeder Co. (Weeders, &c.) ....AA

Hench, Dromgold & Co. (Corn Shellers; Corn Planters; Riding & Walking Cultivators; Feed Cutters; Fertilizer & Grain Drills; Spike Tooth Steel & Wood Frame Harrows; Breaking, Shovel, Sulky Driving or Wheel & Swivel Reversible & Hillside Plows & Seeders)..A

Keystone Farm Machine Co. (Corn Shellers; Riding & Walking Cultivators; Feed Cutters; Spring & Spike Tooth Harrows; Corn, Cotton & Potato Planters; Gang Wheel & Shovel Plows; Fertilizer Distributors) ....B

Spangler Mfg. Co. (Corn Planters & Grain Drills; Fertilizer Distributors).D

S. C.—Bennettsville

Star Pea Thresher Co. (Pea Threshers) ....A

S. DAK.—Watertown

Lee Bros. (Breaking Plows) ....E

TENN.—Chattanooga

Chattanooga Implement Mfg. Co. (Hay Pressees) ....A

Chattanooga Plow Co. (Cane Mills Evaporators; Breaking, Disc & Shovel Plows) ....A

Sanders-Newell Plow Co. (Disc Plows) ....B

TENN.—Clarksville

Ground Hog Plow & Fdy. Co. (Plows) ....B

Patch, A. H. (Corn Shellers) ....B

TENN.—Harriman

Harriman Hoe & Tool Co..B

Harriman Plow & Handle Co. (Plows) ....B

TEXAS—Brenham

Schuerenberg, F. W. (Breaking Plows) ....A

TEXAS—Bryan

Chatham Machinery Co. (Feed Mills) ....B

TEXAS—Dallas

Texas Disc Plow Co. (Disc Plows) C

TEXAS—Longview

Kelly Plow Co., G. A.

(Plows) C

TEXAS—San Antonio
Alamo Iron Works (Hay
Presses) C
Collins Mfg. Co., F. F.
(Hay & Cotton Presses)
.................................C

VT.—Middletown Springs
Gray's Sons, A. W. (Threshers, &c.) ....AA

VT.—St. Albans
St Albans Fdy. & Implement
Co. ....B

VA.—Alexandria
May & Son, Wm. H.
(Plows) ....B

VA.—Charlottesville
Harris & Son. R. F. C

VA.—Fredericksburg
Hunter, Chas. E. (Plows).A
Southern Fdy. & Mach. Co.
(Corn Planters) ....A

VA.—Lynchburg
Lynchburg Plow & Fdy. Co.
(Plows) ....A

VA.—Norfolk
Billup's Son & Co., C....A
White & Bro., S. R. (Corn
S h e l l e r s; Cultivators;
Feed Cutters; Pea, Corn &
Cotton Planters; Breaking
& Shovel Plows) ....A
Whitehurst Co., R. W.
(Corn, Cotton & Potato
Planters; Garden, Potato
& Hop Plows & Hay
Presses) ....B

VA.—Petersburg
Ayers, J. R. (Cotton & Peanut Planters) ....D

VA.—Richmond
Cardwell Machine Co. (Feed
Cutters; Bean & Pea
Harvesters; Corn Plant-
ers; Horse Power & Hay
Presses; Rice Threshers)
.................................A
Starks Dixie Plow Wks.
(Plows, &c.) ....A

WASH.—Walla Walla
Hunt, Gilbert Co. (Threshers, &c.) ....B

WIS.—Beaver Dam
Rowell Mfg. Co., J. S.
(Cultivators; F a n n i n g
Mills; Grain Drills; Bean
& Pea Harvesters; Rakes
& Seeders) ....A

WIS.—Beloit
Thompson & Sons Mfg. Co.
(Cultivators; U-Bar, Steel
Lever & Champion Pipe-
Bar Harrows; Listers;
Corn Planters; Breaking,
Gang, Shovel & Sulky
Riding or Wheel Plows)
.................................AA

WIS.—Cudahy
Steitz, J. R. (Potato Planters) ....F

WIS.—Evansville
Baker Mfg. Co. (Feed Mills,
&c.) ....A

WIS.—Hartford
Hartford Plow Works (Feed
Cutters; Boss Lever,
Angle Bar & Scotch Har-
rows & Rowell Cultiva-
tors) C

WIS.—Horicon
Van Brunt Mfg. Co. (Cul-
tivators; Grain & Disc
Grain Drills & Seeders)
.................................AA

WIS.—Janesville
Janesville Machine Co. (Cul-
tivators; Grain Drills;
Tubular Lever Harrows;
Gang & Sulky Riding or
Wheel Plows; Listers &
Mowers) ....AA
Kent, A. C. (Hand Corn
Planters) C
Rock River Machine Co.
Hand Corn Planters) ...D

WIS.—La Crosse
Fountain City Drill Co.
(Riding Corn Cultivators;
Grain Drills; Steel Lever
Harrows & Seeders) ...B
La Crosse Plow Co. (Riding
& Walking Cultivators;
Tubular, Zigzag, Steel &

Wood, Flexible & Wood
Lever Harrows; Breaking,
Gang & Sulky Riding or
Wheel Plows) ....AA

WIS.—Madison
American Plow Co. (Plows;
Cultivators, &c.) C
Fuller & Johnson Mfg. Co.
(Cultivators; Grain Drills;
Boss, Bonanza Lever &
U Pipe-Bar Harrows; Lis-
ters; Corn Planters;
Breaking. Gang, Garden,
Shovel, Subsoil & Sulky
Riding or Wheel Plows)
.................................AA

WIS.—Manitowoc
Smalley Mfg. Co. (Corn
Shellers; Feed Cutters &
Plows) ....B

WIS.—Marinette
Stevens Co., A. W. (Corn
Shellers; Engines; Wind
Stackers & Threshers).A

WIS.—Menomonee Falls
Roweel Co., S. B. (Scotch
Harrows; Gang Plows) B
.................................B

WIS.—Milwaukee
Hirsch Bros., 267 Reed (Po-
tato Planters) ....D
Milwaukee Harvester Co.
(Corn Planters; Corn Har-
vesters; Mowers & Reap-
ers) ....AAAA
Milwaukee Hay Tool Co.
(Corn Huskers; Fodder
Threshers; Haying Tools)
.................................A

WIS.—Racine
Belle City Mfg. Co. (Feed
Mills; Feed Cutters, &c.)
.................................B
Case Plow Works, J. L.
(Cultivators; Harrows;
Listers; Planters; Plows;
Straw Preserving & Rye
Threshers) ....AA
Case Threshing Machine Co.,
J. I. (Riding & Walking
Cultivators; Critic & Case
Lever & Scotch Harrows;
Corn Planters; Breaking,
Gang, Garden, Shovel,
Subsoil, Sulky Riding or
Wheel Plows; Stackers;
Weighers & Threshers)
.................................AAAA
Dickey Mfg. Co. (Corn
Shellers; Fanning Mills,
&c.) ....F
Foster & Williams Mfg. Co.
(Fanning Mills; Feed Cut-
ters; Drag Rakes & Seed-
ers) ....B
Freeman & Sons Mfg. Co., S.
(Corn Shellers; Seeders;
Fanning Mills; Feed Cut-
ters, &c.) ....A

WIS.—Sheboygan
Meyer & Co., Philip (Feed
Cutters & Feed Mills)..C

WIS.—Stoughton
Stoughton Wagon Co.
(Plows; Wagons, &c.)
.................................AA

WIS.—Superior
Duplex Mfg. Co. (Feed
Mills, &c.) ....B

WIS.—Waupun
Althouse-Wheeler Co. (Feed
Mills, &c.) ....A

ALARMS

CONN.—Ansonia
Ansonia Electrical Co.
(Burglar) ....A

CONN.—New Haven
Reeves Mfg. Co. (Burglar)
.................................C

ILL.—Chicago
Crane Co., 10 N. Jefferson
(Low Water) .....AAAA
Hilk-McCanna Co., 50 N.
Wells (Low Water)....F
Illinois Malleable Iron Co.,
30 W. Monroe (Low
Water; Electric Burglar;
Fire Sprinkler) ....A
Monash-Younker Co., 203 S.
Canal (Low Water)....B
Railroad Supply Co. (High-

ALARMS (Con.)

way Crossings) ....A
Western Electric Co. (Burglar & Fire) .....AAAA

LA.—New Orleans
National Automatic Fire Alarm Co. of La. (Fire, Thermostatic & Aut. Systems) C

MD.—Baltimore
Viaduct Mfg. Co. (Fire, Thermostatic & Aut. Systems) ....B

MASS.—Boston
American Steam Gauge & Valve Mfg. Co., Jamaica Plain (Low Water).....C
Boston Automatic Fire Alarm Co. (Fire, Thermostatic & Aut. Systems).A
Boston Electric Co. (Burglar) ....B
Crossby Steam Gauge & Valve Co. (Low Water) ....AA
Electric Gas Lighting Co., 195 Devonshire (Burglar) ....A
National Fire Appliance Co., 161 Franklin (Fire, Thermostatic & Automatic Systems) ....E
Ziegler Apparatus Co. (Burglar & F~re) .....E

MASS.—Brookline
Holtzer-Cabot Electric Co. (Burglar) ....A

MICH.—Detroit
Detroit Lubricator Co., Hodges Building (Low Water) ....AA
Heath Electric Co. (Burglar) C
Michigan Lubricator Co. (Low Water) ....B

NEBR.—Omaha
Western Electrical Co. (Electric, Fire) ....D

N. J.—Jersey City
Griffing Iron Co., A. A. (Low Water) ....AA

N. J.—Newark
Wilcox, L. M., 219 Market (Burglar) ....H

N. Y.—Binghamton
Binghamton Machine Tool Works (Low Water)...F
Star Electric Co. (Fire, Manual & Aut. Systems) E
Schafer & Budenberg, 10 Division (Low Water).D

New York City
Ashcroft Mfg. Co., 85 Liberty (Low Water) ......A
Automatic Fire Alarm Co. (Fire, Ther. & Aut. Systems) ....AA
Benjamin, Geo. P., 81 Fulton C
Bunnell & Co., J. H., 20 Park Pl. (Burglar, Fire, Manual & Aut. Systems) A
Carleton-Chase Electric Co., 26 Cortlandt (Burglar)..B
Consolidated Fire Alarm Co., 30 Broad (Fire, Manual & Aut. Systems) ....A
Edwards & Co., 407 E. 144th (Burglar, Fire, Manual & Aut. Systems) C
Einbigler & Adler (Burglar) F
Foote, Pierson & Co., 82 Fulton (Fire, Manual & Aut. Systems) ....D
Gamewell Fire Alarm Tel. Co., 19 Barclay (Fire, Manual & Aut. Systems) A
Herzog Teleseme Co., 51 W. 24th (Burglar, Fire, Ther. & Aut. Systems).......D
Holmes Electric Protective Co., 26 Cortlandt (Burglar) ....B
Manhattan Electric Supply Co., 32 Cortlandt (Burglar) ....A
Manhattan Fire Alarm Co., 19 Barclay (Fire, Manual & Aut. Systems).......C
Natl. Aut. Fire Alarm Co.

ALARMS (Con.)

(Fire, Ther. & Aut. Systems) X
Ostrander & Co., W. R. 22 Dey (Burglar)......B
Pearce, Frederick (Burglar, Fire, Manual & Aut. Systems) ....B
Sargent & Co., 151 Leonard (Elec. Burglar)....AAAA
Special Fire Alarm Elect. Signal Co., 18 Rose (Fire, Manual & Aut. Systems).E
Stanley & Patterson, 93 Liberty (Burglar) ....A
United Pneumatic Fire Alarm Tel. Co., 37 E. 18th (Fire, Manual & Aut. Systems) ....D

N. Y.—Rochester
Standard Electric Signal Co. (Fire, Manual & Aut. Systems) ....E

N. Y.—Schenectady
General Electric Co. (Electric Fire) ....AAAA

N. Y.—Utica
Utica Fire Alarm & Tel. Co. (Fire, Manual, Police & Aut. Systems) C

N. Y.—Yonkers
Van Auken-Clevauc Co. (Low Water) ....H

OHIO—Cincinnati
Lunkenheimer Co., Beekman & Waverly (Low Water) AAA
Natl. Automatic Fire Alarm Co. (Fire, Ther. & Aut. Systems) ....D
Steigert, Leopold, Elder & Logan (High & Low Water) ....F
Thompson, Walter M. (Low Water) ....G

OHIO—Cleveland
Reliance Guage Column Co. (Low Water) ....D
Reliance Mach. & Tool Co. (Low Water) C

OHIO—Dayton
Buckeye Iron & Brass Wks. (Low Water) ....A
Dayton Supply Co. (Burglar) ....B

PA.—Erie
Erie Mfg. & Supply Co. (Low Water) ....B
Sims Co. (Low Water)...E

PA.—Philadelphia
Partrick, Carter & Wilkins, 1231 Callowhill (Burglar, Fire, Manual, Water & Aut. Systems) ....B

PA.—York
Burrows Mfg. Co. (Low Water) ....E

R. I.—Providence
General Fire Extinguisher Co. (Fire) ....AAAA
R. I. Elect. Protective Co. (Fire, Ther. & Aut. Systems) ....D

WIS.—Milwaukee
Signalphone Co. (Fire; Police) ....B

ALBERTYPES

MASS.—Boston
Forbes Lithograph Mfg. Co. AA

New York City
Federal Litho. Co........B

ALBOLINE

New York City
McKesson & Robbins AAAA

ALBUMEN

ILL.—Chicago
Kohnstamm & Co., H. (Egg) AA
Stein, Hirsh & Co. ....AAA

New York City
Kohnstamm & Co. H., 87 Park Pl. (Egg).......AA
Zinkeisen & Co., 26 Cliff (Egg) C

OHIO—Cincinnati
Berghausen Chem. Co. ...B

ALBUMS

ILL.—Chicago
Barker Mfg. Co., A. C..B
Chicago Binder & Felt Co.,
  43 Fulton (Photo)......E
MD.—Baltimore
Bergner & Co., Fred....A
New York City
Boorum & Pease Co. (Au-
  tograph; Photograph)
              AAA
Gennert, G. (Photograph).B
Horn, Bro. & Co., W. C.,
  541 Pearl (Auto.; Easel;
  Music; Photo.).......AA
Langsdorf & Co., S. (Photo-
  graph) ....AA
Perfection Sample Card Co.,
  410 Broadway (Sample).E
Schafuss & Co., F. L.
  (Photo.) C
N. Y.—Saugerties
Saugerties Mfg. Co. (Au-
  tograph) ....AA

ALCHOHOL

See also Spirits

CAL.—Vina
Vina Distillery Co...AAAA
CONN.—So. Norwalk
U. S. Alcohol Ref'g. Co...D
ILL.—Chicago
Rosenfield Bros. & Co.
              AAAA
Woodford Distilling Co...A
ILL.—Peoria
Corning & Co......AAAA
Standard Distillery & Dist.
  Co. ....AAAA
Woolner, S. & A......AAAA
KY.—Covington
Gold Leaf Distillery Co...B
Licking Valley Co........A
Mullins, A. R...........B
KY.—Cynthiana
Ashbrook Distillery Co.,
  F. S. ....A
KY.—Early Times
Beam, J. H.............B
LA.—New Orleans
Louisiana Distillery Co.
  (Ethyl) ....AA
Southern Re-Distillery &
  Rectifying Co. ....A
MD.—Baltimore
Webb & Sons, A. L. (Wood)
              B
MASS.—Boston
Graves & Sons, C. H...AA
Merrimac Chemical Co.
  75 Broad (Wood)...AAA
MICH.—Bay City
Mich. Chemical Co.....AAA
MICH.—Cadillac
Cummer, Diggins & Co.
  (Wood) ....A
MICH.—Detroit
Antrim Chemical Co.
  (Wood) ....B
Berry Bros. (Ltd.) (Wood)
            AAA
Burrell Chem. Co. (Wood)
            AA
Southern Chem. Co. (Wood)
            A
MICH.—Elk Rapids
Elk Rapids Iron Co. (Wood)
            AAA
MICH.—Manistique
Burrell Chem. Co. (Wood)
            AA
MICH.—Traverse City
Desmond Chem. Co. (Wood)
            X
MICH.—West Bay City
Young Chem. Co., W. D.
  (Wood) ....A
MO.—St. Louis
Larkin & Scheffer Chemi-
  cal Co. (Wood) ....A
Mallinckrodt Chemical Wks.
            AAAA
N. Y.—Binghamton
Bayless & Co., F. J.
  (Wood) ....AA
Binghamton Chem. Co.
  (Wood) ....H
Brandt Chem. Co. (Wood)

Colchester Chem. Co.
  (Wood) ....D

ALCOHOL (Con.)
Collier, H. C. (Wood)....B
Corbett & Co M. J.
  (Wood) ....A
Finch-Ross Chem. Co.
  (Wood) ....E
Inderlied Chem. Co. (Wood)
            F
N. Y.—Buffalo
Wood Products Co. (Wood)
            AAAA
N. Y.—Cooks Falls
Leighton & Co. (Wood)..B
Treys & Hart Chem. Co.
  (Wood) ....D
New York City
Cooper & Co., Chas. (Wood)
            A
Salomon & Bro., L. A., 216
  Pearl (Wood) ....A
N. Y.—Redbury
Tyler-Hall Chemical Co.
  (Wood) C
OHIO—Bradford
Lewis Run Mfg. Co.
  (Wood) C
Smith Chem. Co., A. B.
  (Wood) ....B
OHIO—Brandt
Kessler & Co. (Wood)....B
OHIO—Canton
Beardslee Bros. & Co.
  (Wood) ....D
Innes Bros. & Co. (Wood)
            D
OHIO—Cincinnati
Freiberg & Workum (Wood)
            AAAA
Clifton Springs Distillery
  Co. ....AA
OHIO—Hazlehurst
Hazlehurst Chemical Co.
  (Wood) C
OHIO—Kane
La Mount Chem. Co. (Wood)
            C
Forest Chem. Co. (Wood).B
OHIO—Mt. Alton
Bartley & Co., John (Wood)
            F
OHIO—Nansen
Nansen Chemical Co.
  (Wood) ....B
OHIO—Newark
Heinmann Chem. Co.
  (Wood) ....A
OHIO—Philadelphia
Davis, Paul A.. Jr. (Wood)
            A
Griffin, Nicholas J.......F
OHIO—Port Allegheny
Gray Chem. Co. (Wood)..F
Wyman Chem. Co. (Wood)
            C
OHIO—Susquehanna
Lackawanna Chem. Co.
  (Wood) C
Wright & Co., C. F.
  (Wood) C
OHIO—Wilcox
Wilcox Mfg. Co. (Wood)..C
OHIO—Williamsport
Hermance Chem. Co. (Wood)
            C
McKean Chem. Co. (Wood)
            C
Otto Chem. Co. (Wood)..C

ALE

CAL.—San Francisco
Eggers & Co. (Ginger)..F
CONN.—Seymour
Arethusa Spring Water Co.
  (Ginger) ....AA
MD.—Baltimore
Gosman Ginger Ale Co.
  (Ginger) ....B
MICH.—Grand Rapids
Rademaker & Sons, H.
  (India Pale) ....E
MONT.—Butte City
Centennial Brewing Co.
  (Ginger) ....A
N. J.—Jersey City
Lembeck & Betz......AAA
N. J.—Newark
Ballantine & Sons, P.
  (India Pale) ......AAAA
Feigenspan, Christian
            AAAA
N. Y.—Hudson
Evans & Sons, C. H.

ALE (Con.)

(India Pale) ....AA
N. Y.—Rochester
Bartholomay Brewing Co.
AAA
New York City
De Lisser & Co. (Ginger)..B
Ross & Bro., Wm. A.
(Belfast-Ginger) ......B
N. Y.—Syracuse
Greenway Brewing Co.
(India Pale) ....B
OHIO—Cleveland
Sachs, Kirkpatrick Co.
(Ginger) ....D
OHIO—Columbus
Hoster Brewing Co., S...AA
OHIO—Dayton
Sachs, Pruden Ginger Ale
Co. (Ginger—India Pale)
D
PA.—Philadelphia
Bergner & Engel Brew. Co.
(India Pale) ......AAAA
PA.—Pittsburg
Pittsburg Brewing Co.
AAAA
TEXAS—El Paso
Houck & Dieter (Ginger)..A
WIS.—Waukesha
Bethesda Mineral Spring Co.
(Ginger) ....A

ALFORJAS

New York City
Abercrombie & Fitch.....B

ALIZARINE

See Colors

ALKALI

KY.—Louisville
Kentucky Refining Co.
AAAA
MD.—Baltimore
Thomsen Chem. Co.......B
MASS.—Boston
Linder & Meyer...........A
New York City
Fuerst Bros. & Co.......D
Selling Co., The.........B
Wing & Evans...........AAA
N. Y.—Niagara Falls
Roberts Chem. Co.......X
N. Y.—Syracuse
Solway Process Co...AAAA
OHIO—Cincinnati
Am. Chemical Co.......C
Winkler & Bro., Isaac...AA
OHIO—Cleveland
Clark Co., F. G..........A
PA.—Philadelphia
Hollingworth & Peterson.B

ALKALOIDS

ILL.—Chicago
Baker & Co., Chas. S.....O
MICH.—Detroit
Parke, Davies & Co...AAAA
New York City
McKesson & Robbins
(Opium & Salts)..AAAA
New York Quinine & Chem-
ical Works, Ltd. (Cin-
chona; Opium & Salts).A
Schieffelin & Co., W. H.
(Cinchona & Salts)...AA
PA.—Philadelphia
Powers-Weightman-Rosen-
garten Co. (Cinchona &
Salts) ....AAAA
Shoemaker & Co.. Robert
(Opium & Salts)......AA

ALLEYS

CAL.—San Francisco
Am. Bowling Alley Co...X
MICH.—Detroit
Schulenburg Mfg. Co.
(Bowling) C
New York City
Brunswick-Balke-Collender
Co. (Bowling) ....AAAA
Grote & Co., F. (Bowling)
D
OHIO—Toledo
Stevens, B. A. (Bowling).A
R. I.—Providence
Narragansett Mach. Co.

ALLEYS (Con.)

(Bowling) ....A

ALLIGATOR

See Leather

ALLOYS

CONN.—Bridgeport
Bridgeport Deoxidized
Bronze & Metal Co.
(Aluminum) C
CONN.—New Haven
Hill, Albert M. (Nickel;
Copper) ....E
CONN.—Waterbury
Benedict & Burham Mfg.
Co. (Copper; Nickel)
AAAA
Scovill Mfg. Co. (Alumi-
num) ....AAAA
ILL.—Chicago
Frink & Young (Dental)..D
IND.—Indianapolis
Fox & Garhart Spec. Co.
(Dental) ....B
Garhart Dental Mfg. Co.
(Dental) ....D
MICH.—Detroit
Moore & Son, E. C. (Fu-
sible) ....F
MO.—St. Louis
Hisey Dental Mfg. Co.
(Gold, Dental) X
Varney Dental Co. (Dental)
E
N. J.—Jersey City
Williams & Son, E. A., 105
Plymouth (Aluminum)
AAA
N. J.—Riverside
Riverside Metal Co. (Gold)
A
N. Y.—Lockport
Cowles Elect. Smelting &
Aluminnm Co. (Alumi-
num; Manganese; Silicon;
Special; White Metal) B
New York City
Boker & Co., Hermann
(Nickel) ....AAA
Cons. Dental Mfg. Co.
(Dental) ....B
Kemp Co., W. H., 165
Spring (Aluminum).....B
Hungerford, U. T. (Metal)
AA
Lissberger & Son, Marks, 397
W. 12th (White Metal).B
Nassau Smelting & Refin-
ing Wks., 603 W. 29th
AAA
Orford Copper Co., 43
Exchange Pl. (Nickel)
AAA
Roessler & Hasslacher Chem.
Co., 100 William (Ferro)
AA
OHIO—Cleveland
Cleveland Dental Mfg. Co.
(Dental) ....B
PA.—Connellsville
Riverside Metal Refining
Co. ....D
PA.—Philadelphia
Janney, Steinmetz & Co.
(Aluminum) ....D
Phosphor Bronze Smelting
Co., 2200 Washn. Av.
(Phosphor Bronze) ....B
Sibley, Gideon (Dentists'
Gold; Dentists' Platinum)
AA
PA.—Pittsburg
Pittsburg Reduction Co.
Park Bldg. (Aluminum)
ALLOYS—(Con.)
Aluminum Hollow Ware)
AAA
R. I.—Providence
Wall & Co., A. T. (Gold;
Silver) C

ALMONDS

See Nuts

ALOIN

MO.—St. Louis
Larkin & Scheffer Chemical
Co. ....A

ALOIN (*Con.*)
Mallinckrodt Chemical Wks.
............................AAAA
New York City
New York Quinine & Chemical Works (Ltd.) ....A
PA.—Philadelphia
Powers-Weightman-Rosengarten Co. ....AAAA

ALPACA

See Silk Goods

ALPHABETS

See Stencils

ALTARS

ILL.—Chicago
Andrews Co., A. H......AA
Sherman & Flavin (Marble)
............................B
ILL.—Quincy
Schenk Altar Co..........G
IOWA—Dubuque
Dubuque Altar Mfg. Co..X
MASS.—Cambridge
Wall Co., Chas. E. (Marble)
............................A
MO.—St. Louis
Pickel Marble & Granite Co.
(Marble) ....A
New York City
Fisher & Co., Robert C.
(Marble) ....AA
Lamb, J. & R. (Church)..D
Stoltzenberg Co., 51 Barclay
(Church) ....B
OHIO—Cincinnati
Great Western Marble Wks.
(Marble) C
PA.—Glen Rock
Glen Mfg. Co...........B
PA.—Philadelphia
Gara, McGinley & Co.
(Church) ....A
VT.—Fair Haven
Fair Haven Marble & Marbleized Slate Co. (Church)
............................B

ALTERNATORS

See also Dynamos

MINN.—Minneapolis
Electric Machinery Co.
(Electric) ....A
New York City
Roche & Co., F. A., 656
Hudson (Electric) .....F
N. Y.—Schenectady
General Electric Co. (Electric) ....AAAA
PA.—Pittsburg
Westinghouse Electric &
Mfg. Co. (Electric).AAAA

ALUM

ILL.—Chicago
Fuller & Fuller (Ground)
............................AA
MD.—Baltimore
Thomsen Chemical Co., 310
Equit. Bldg. ....F
MASS.—Boston
Cochrane Chemical Co.
(Porous) ....AAA
Merrimac Chemical Co., 75
Broad ....AA
MICH.—Detroit
Detroit Chemical Works, 238
Junction Av. ....B
MO.—St. Louis
Hygenic Chemical Co., 710
N. 2d ....A
New York City
General Chemical Co., 25
Broad ....AAAA
Jones Chem. Co., Enos F.
51 Jay ....A
Kuttroff, Pickhardt & Co..A
Selling Co., The........B
Sholes Co., C. E........X
N. Y.—Syracuse
Solvay Process Co...AAAA
PA.—Easton
Baker & Adamson Chemical

ALUM (*Con.*)
Co. ....A
PA.—Philadelphia
Harrison Bros. & Co. (Inc.)
............................AAAA
Penn. Salt Mfg. Co., 115
Chestnut (Porous; Lump;
Ground) ....AAAA
Powers-Weightman-Rosengarten Co. ......AAAA

ALUMINA

MASS.—Boston
Cochrane Chemical Co....AA
Merrimac Chem. Co. (Sulphate; Chloride; Hydrate;
Acetate) ....AA
MO.—St. Louis
Mallinckrodt Chemical Wks.
(Sulphate) ....AAAA
N. Y.—Brooklyn
Wiarda & Co., John C.
(Fluoride) ....AA
New York City
General Chemical Co., 25
Broad (Sulphate) ..AAAA
Klipstein & Co., A.....AA
Kuttroff Pickhardt & Co. A
............................A
Roessler & Hasslacher
Chem. Co. ....AA
Sholes Co., C. E........X
Williamson & Co., D. D.
14 Dey (Flouride) .....B
PA.—Philadelphia
Penn. Salt. Mfg. Co. (Sulphate) ....AAAA
Harrison Bros. & Co..AAAA

ALUMINUM

See also Ingots

CONN.—Waterbury
Scovill Mfg. Co. (Sheet)
............................AAAA
ILL.—Chicago
Harrington & King Perforating Co., 224 No. Union
(Perforated) ....A
Turners Brass Works......A
MO.—St. Louis
Schwahn Reduction Co...X
N. J.—Jersey City
Williams & Son, E. A...AA
New York City
Kemp, W. H., Co., 105
Spring (Rolled) ......B
Mundt & Sons, Chas., 441
Pearl ....B
Wilson Aluminum Co., 99
Cedar ....AA
Zucker & Levett & Loeb
Co., 528 W. 25th......A
OHIO—Canton
Canton Brass & Aluminum
Co. ....D
OHIO—Cincinnati
Obermayer Co., S. (Ferrosilicon) ....AA
OHIO—Jackson
Star Furnace Co. (Ferrosilicon) ....A
PA.—Philadelphia
Janney, Steinmetz & Co.,
Drexel Building ....D
PA.—Pittsburg
Pittsburg Reduction Co.
(Sheet; Ingot, etc.) AAAA
U. S. Aluminum Co......B
R. I.—Providence
Wall & Co., A. T. (Tubing)
............................C

ALUMINUM WARE

Cooking, &c.

ILL.—Lemont
Ills. Pure Aluminum Co...B
MICH.—St. Joseph
Bradford Co. C
N. Y.—Buffalo
Shepard & Co., Sidney
............................AAAA
New York City
Abercrombie & Fitch
(Sportsmen's Goods)....B
Thurnauer & Bro., G. M.,
35 Park Pl. X

ALUMINUM (Con.)

OHIO—Sidney
Wagner Mfg. Co. ....A
PA.—Erie
Griswold Mfg. Co. ....A
PA.—Pittsburg
U. S. Aluminum Co. ....B

AMALGAMATORS

See also Machinery

N. Y.—Brooklyn
Ross & Son Co., Chas. ...D
OHIO—Zanesville
Griffith & Wedge Co. .....B

AMALGAMS

See also Fillings

MO.—St. Louis
Nolde Dental Mfg. Co., Jno.
T. (Dental) ....B
OHIO—Cleveland
Cleveland Dental Mfg. Co.
(Dental) ....B
New York City
Cons. Dental Mfg. Co.
(Dental) ....B
PA.—Philadelphia
Johnson & Lund.........AA

AMBER GOODS

ILL.—Chicago
Reiss Bros. & Co. .....AA
New York City
Kaldenburg Importing &
Trading Co. ....D
X
Reichert, H., 540 E. 145th
X
Zuern, G., 56 University Pl.
B

AMBULANCES

ILL.—Quincy
Miller & Co., E. M. .....A
IND.—Jeffersonville
Holzbog & Bro., Geo. H...A
IND.—So. Bend
Studebaker Bros. Mfg. Co.
AAAA
OHIO—Cincinnati
Crane & Breed Mfg. Co. ..AA

AMETHYSTS

See Jewelry; Prec. Stones

AMMETERS

See also Meters

CONN.—Waterbury
Bristol Co. (Electric) ....D
ILL.—Chicago
McIntosh Battery & Optical Co. ....D
MASS.—West Somerville
American Coil Co. ....D
MO.—St. Louis
Wagner Electric Mfg. Co.
AA
N. J.—Waverly Park
Weston Electric Instrument
Co. ....A
N. Y.—Schenectady
General Electric Co...AAAA
New York City
Western Electric Co., 57
Bethune ....AAAA
OHIO—Cincinnati
Craighead Engineering Co.
D
PA.—Pittsburg
Westinghouse Elec. & Mgf.
Co. (Electric) ....AAAA

AMMONIA

CAL.—San Francisco
Herrmann Co., Geo., 310
Sacramento ....B
Pacific Ammonia & Chemical Co., Fran. & Webster ....AAA
COLO.—Denver
Colorado Ammonia & Chemical Co. ....AAA
Western Chemical Mfg. Co.

AMMONIA (Con.)

(Aqua) ....AA
DEL.—Wilmington
Atlantic Dynamite Co.
· (Salts of) ....AAA
National Ammonia Co..AAA
ILL.—Chicago
Armour Ammonia Works
(Anhydrous) .....AAAA
Higbie Co., F. K., 35 So.
Water ....D
Delaware Chemical Co....C
Northwestern Fertilizing
Wks. (Aqua) ......AAAA
Wolf Co., Fred W. (Condensed) ....AAAA
KY.—Louisville
Clapp Ammonia Co........B
LA.—New Orleans
Barrett Mfg. Co. Hibernia
Bank Bldg. .....AAAA
MD.—Baltimore
Gilpin & Moore, 920 E.
Fort Av. C
McCormick & Co. (Aqua &
Anhydrous) ....D
Thomsen Chemical Co.
(Aqua; Phosphate) .....B
MD.—Hagerstown
Hagerstown Chemical Co..F
MASS.—Boston
Billings, Clapp & Co. (Aqua,
Salts of) ....,..B
Cochrane Chemical Co.
(Aqua) ....AA
Merrimac Chem. Co. (Aqua)
AA
N. E. Gas & Coke Co. (Sulphate) ....B
MASS.—Chelsea
Hecla Compressed Gas Co.
(Anhydrous Insolution) .E
MASS.—Easthampton
Bay State Chemical Co...F
MICH.—Detroit
Michigan Ammonia Works
(Carbonate) ....A
Michigan Carbon Works
(Salts of) ....AAA
MO.—St. Louis
Herf & Frerichs Chemical
Co. (Aqua; Anhydrous)
A
Larkin & Scheffer Chemical
Co. (Aqua) ....A
National Ammonia Co., 3600
N. Bway...........AAA
Mallinckrodt Chemical Co.
(Aqua; Spirits of; Salts
of) ....AAAA
N. J.—Camden
Consumers Ammonia Co...D
N. J.—Fieldsboro
Caven-Williamson Ammonia Co. ....D
Severn, W. B.,.........D
Standard Ammonia & Chemical Co. ....D
N. J.—Newark
Lesters Agricultural Chemical Wks. (Salts of).AAAA
N. Y.—Brooklyn
Columbia Chemical Wks.,
43 Sedgwick (C. C. Parson's Household) ......B
Kern, Geo. (For Domestic
Use) X
Wiarda & Co., John C.
(Salts of; Aqua)......AA
N. Y.—Buffalo
Schoellkopf, Hartford &
Hanna Co. (Carbonate)
AAA
Towns & Wright, 230 Washington ....D
New York City
Am. Coal Products Co.
(Sulphate) X
Clapp Ammonia Co., B. P.,
245 Bway.............B
Cooper & Co., Chas. (Aqua)
AA
Fuerst Bros. & Co., 2 Stone
(Carbonate) ....B
General Chemical Co., 25
Broad (Aqua) ....AAAA
Hirsh & Son, L., 368
Greenwich C
Erkenbach, Geo. A. (Aqua;
Nitrate) ....D
Heller, Hirsh & Co. (Aqua)
AA
Jordan & Co., Stanley (Carbonate) ....D

AMMONIA (*Con.*)

Listers Agricultural Wks.
(Sulphate) ....AAAA
Jones Chemical Wks., Enos
F. (Aqua) ....B
Kalbfleisch Co., F. H., 35
Burling Slip...........B
McKesson & Robbins (Salts
of) ....AAAA
National Ammonia Co., 90
William ....AAA
Schieffelin & Co., W. H.
(Aqua) ....AA
Sholes Co., C. E. (Aqua)..X
N. Y.—Pen Yan
Empire Chemical Co. ....B
N. Y.—Syracuse
Solvay Process Co. (Aqua)
AAAA
OHIO—Cincinnati
American Chemical Co., 642
Carr. ....D
OHIO—Cleveland
Grasselli Chemical Co.
(Aqua) ....AAAA
PA.—Easton
Baker & Adamson Chemical
Co. (Aqua) ....A
PA.—Erie
Watson Co., H. F. (Aqua)
AAA
PA.—Harrisburg
Carlisle & Roberts.........C
PA.—Philadelphia
Ammonia Co. of Phila.,
Grays Ferry Av. (Aqua;
Sulphate; Anhydrous)..X
Caven-Williamson Ammonia
Co., 109 No. Front......D
Consumers Ammonia Co., 143
N. Front ....D
Continental Mfg. Co. (Aqua)
D
Ferguson Bros. (Sulphate)
A
Goldschmid Co., Theo, J.
3346 Frankford Av......A
Harrison Bros. & Co. (Aqua)
AAAA
Moro-Phillips Wks. (Aqua)
AAAA
National Ammonia Co..AAA
Penna. Salt Mfg. Co. (Aqua)
AAAA
Powers-Weightman-Rosen-
garten Co. (Aqua; Spirits
of; Salts of)......AAAA
Warrington & Co., E. R.,
Step. Girard Bldg. .....A
VA.—Richmond
Armitage Mfg. Co........B
Va.-Carolina Chem. Co.
AAAA

AMMUNITION

See Powder; Shot; Car-
tridges; Shells, &c.

AMUSEMENTS

See Games; Toys, &c.

AMYL

N. Y.—Albany
Albany Chemical Co. (Ace-
tate) ....A
N. Y.—Buffalo
Schoellkopf, Hartford &
Hanna Co. (Acetate).AAA
New York City
Cooper & Co., Chas. (Ace-
tate) ....AA
Maas & Waldstein (Ace-
tate) ....A
Warner Chemical Co...AAA

ANCHORS

CONN.—Middletown
Wilcox, Crittenden & Co..A
CONN.—New Haven
National Steel Fdy. Co.
(Ship) ....A
ILL.—Chicago
Country Home Telephone
Mfg. Co. (Guy)........F
IND.—New Albany
Goetz Box Anchor Co.
(Joist) ....E
MASS.—Gloucester
Cape Ann Anchor Works
(Ship) ....A

ANCHORS (*Con.*)

MICH.—Detroit
Amos Co., Chas. ....F
MO.—St. Louis
Kupferle, John C. (Build-
ing) ....AA
Matthews & Bro., W. N.
(Ship) ....D
Plueger & Henger Mfg. Co.
(Building) ....A
N. J.—Boonton
Lincoln Iron Wks. (Build-
ing) ....B
N. J.—Camden
Dialogue & Sons, John H.
(Ship) ....AA
New York City
De Grauw, Aymar & Co.
(Ship) ....AA
Dimond, Thomas (Ship)..A
New Jersey Fdy. & Mach.
Co., 9 Murray (Screw;
Ship) ....D
Star Expansion Bolt Co., 149
Cedar (Screw) ....F
Tiebout, W. & J., 118
Chambers (Ship) ......B
OHIO—Cleveland
Van Dorn Iron Works Co.
(Steel Joist) ....AA
OHIO—Kenton
Champion Iron Co. (Joist)
AA
OHIO—Toledo
Donovan Wire & Iron Co.
(Building) C
PA.—Chester
Baldt Anchor Co. (Ship)..A
Seaboard Steel Casting Co.
(Ship) ....AA
Admiral Anchor Co. X
PA.—Philadelphia
Chester Steel Casting Co.
(Ship, Folding) ......AA
Uhler & English (Ship)..AA
PA.—Pittsburg
Lanz & Sons, M. (Building;
Rock) ....AA
PA.—South Bethlehem
Bethlehem Foundry & Ma-
chine Co. (Ship, Building)
C
R. I.—Pawtucket
Pawtucket Mfg. Co.......A
R. I.—Providence
Amer. Ship Windlass Co.
(Ship & Yacht)......AA
TENN.—So. Pittsburg
Blacklock Fdy. Co. (Build-
ing) C
WIS.—Milwaukee
Bayley & Sons Co., Wm.
(Building) X

ANCHOVIES

New York City
Ams, Max, 372 Greenwich
AA
Strohmeyer & Arpe Co.,
33 Water ....A
PA.—Philadelphia
Niemeyer, W., 2d & Ells-
worth ....F

ANDIRONS

COLO.—Denver
Richter Iron Wks........G
CONN.—Meriden
Bradley & Hubbard Mfg.
Co. (Brass) ....AAA
CONN.—New Haven
Elm City Brass Co., 80
Audubon ....H
Rostand Mfg. Co. ....D
CONN.—Southampton
Peck, Stow & Wilcox Co.
(Brass & Iron)....AAAA
ILL.—Chicago
Winslow Bros. Co., 368 Car-
roll Av. (Hand Forged)
AA
KY.—Louisville
Peerless Mfg. Co........AA
MASS.—Boston
Boston Brass Andiron Co..G
MO.—St. Louis
Pleuger & Henger Mfg. Co.
A
New York City
Graf, Frank H., 322 7th Av.
D
Jackson & Bro., E. A., 50

ANDIRONS (*Con.*)
Beekman C
Jackson Co., W. H., 29 E.
17th (Brass & Iron) ....A
Judd & Co., H. L. (Brass)
AA
Mott Iron Wks., J. L. (Iron)
AA
Sargent & Co., 151 Leonard
AAAA
N. C.—Charlotte
Mecklenberg Iron Wks....X
OHIO—Cincinnati
Haven Co., Jas. L. (Iron).B
PA.—Allegheny
Pittsburg Lamp, Brass &
Glass Co. (Brass)..AAAA
PA.—Philadelphia
Harrison's Sons, Wm. H.
(Brass & Iron) ....E
PA.—Pittsburg
Pittsburg Brass Co. (Brass)
D
TENN.—So. Pittsburg
Blacklock Foundry C

ANEMOME-
TERS

MD.—Baltimore
Friez, Julian P., 1230 E.
Balto. ....E
New York City
Keuffel & Esser Co., 127
Fulton ....AA
Tagliabue, G., 302 Pearl..B

ANGELICA

See Liquors

ANGLES

See Iron & Steel; Brass;
Copper

ANIMALS

See Toys

ANILINE

See Colors; Dyes

ANKLETS

Surgical

N. Y.—Lockport
Empire Mfg. Co. ....A
N. Y.—Richfield Springs
Waiontha Knitting Co....B
PA.—Philadelphia
Philadelphia Truss Co....X
VT.—Bennington
Cooper, Chas. ....B

ANNATONE

ILL.—Chicago
Fuller & Fuller.........AA

ANNEALERS

ILL.—Chicago
Chicago Pneumatic Tool Co.,
Fisher Bldg. (Armor
Plate) ....AAAA

ANNUNCI-
ATORS

CONN.—Ansonia
Ansonia Electrical Co.
(Elect.) ....A
GA.—Atlanta
Wotton Electric & Mfg. Co.
(Elevator) ....D
ILL.—Chicago
Moon Mfg. Co., 49 S. Canal
(Electric) ....E
Western Electric Co., 259
S. Clinton (Electric)
AAAA
MD.—Baltimore
Viaduct Mfg. Co., 10 So.
Howard (Electric).....B
MASS.—Boston
Boston Electric Co., 29 Har-
rison Av. (Electric)....B
Electric Gas Lighting Co.,

ANNUNCIATORS (*Con.*)
195 Devonshire (Electric)
B
MASS.—Brookline
Holtzer-Cabot Electric Co.
(Electric) ....A
N. Y.—Binghamton
Star Electric Co. (Electric)
D
N. Y.—Buffalo
Proctor-Raymond Mfg. Co.,
442 Niagara (Electric).D
New York City
Bunnell & Co., J. H., 20
Park Pl. (Electric).....B
Edwards & Co., 407 E. 144th
(Electric, Elevator)....C
Herzog Teleseme Co., 51 W.
24th (Elevator) ....D
Manhattan Elect. Supply Co.
32 Cortlandt (Electric).A
Ostrander & Co., W. R., 22
Dey (Electric) ....B
Stanley & Patterson, 93 Lib-
erty (Electric)..........A
N. Y.—Rochester
Bradley & Co., E. C.,
(Electric) ....H
N. Y.—Utica
Utica Electrical Mfg. &
Supply Co. (Electric)..X
OHIO—Akron
Garl Electric Co. (Electric)
F
OHIO—Cleveland
Ohio Electric Co. (Electric)
D
PA.—Philadelphia
Gifford & Henry, 17 S. 3d
(Electric) ....F
Novelty Electric Co., 52 No.
4th (Electric)..........C
Partrick, Carter & Wilkins,
1231 Callowhill (Electric,
Elevator) ....B

ANODES

CONN.—Hartford
Ney & Co., J. M. (Gold &
Silver) C
CONN.—Seymour
Seymour Mfg. Co. (Brass;
Bronze; Copper).....AAA
MASS.—New Bedford
Taunton-New Bedford Cop-
per Co. (Copper).....AAA
N. J.—Bloomfield
Hudson Rolling Mill Co.
(Copper) ....E
New York City
Zucker & Levett & Loeb Co.
(Brass; Copper; Nickel).A
R. I.—Providence
Remington & Son Co.,
Horace C

ANODYNE

MD.—Baltimore
Sharp & Dohme (Hoff-
man's) ....AAAA
MASS.—Boston
Billings, Clapp & Co.
(Hoffman's) ....B
MO.—St. Louis
Mallinckrodt Chemical Wks.
(Hoffman's) .....AAAA
New York City
New York Quinine & Chem.
Wks. (Ltd.) (Hoffman's)
A

ANTI-
CANDLES

CONN.—New Haven
English & Mersick Co....B

ANTIMONY

ILL.—Chicago
Blatchford & Co., E. W.
AAAA
Raymond Lead Co., 51 W.
Lake ....AAAA
Ryan & Co., J. J., 68 W.
Monroe C
MASS.—Boston
Waite, Ranlet & Co.......B
MO.—St. Louis
Hiertz & Son, Theo., 10th

19

ANTIMONY (Con.)

& Poepping ....D
Hoyt Metal Co. ......AAAA

N. J.—Jersey City
Williams & Son, E. A...AA

N. Y.—Brooklyn
Enequist, E., 9th & Roeb-
  ling (Oxide) ....D
Wiarda & Co., Jno. C.
  (Needle Ground)......AA

New York City
American Metal Co., 52
  Bway. ....AAA
Davol & Sons, John, 100
  John ....AA
Frankel, Jos., 81 Fulton..C
Hendricks Bros., 49 Cliff
  ....AAAA
Quincy & Co., Jno. W., 81
  Fulton ....B
Vogelstein, L., 90 Wall...H

PA.—Easton
Baker & Adamson Chem.
  Co. ....A

PA.—Philadelphia
Merchant & Co., 517 Arch)
  AA
Trotter & Co., Nathan, 36
  No. Front ....AA
U. S. Smelting Wks......B

PA.—Pittsburg
Hussey & Co., C. G...AAA

ANTIPYRENE

New York City
Fries Brothers, 92 Reade.A

ANTI-RATTLERS

**See Rattlers; also Hard-
ware; Carriage**

ANTISEPTICS

COLO.—Denver
Am. Antiseptic Co........H

MASS.—Boston
Willard Chemical Co.....B

New York City
Preservaline Mfg. Co.
  (Food) ....AA
Am. Antiformin Co. (Brew-
  ers) X
Farbenfabriken & Elber-
  feld Co. (Brewers).....B

WIS.—Milwaukee
Northwestern Chemical Co.
  (Brewers) C
Milwaukee Com. Importing
  Co. (Brewers) ....D

ANTI-TOXIN

MICH.—Detroit
Parke, Davis & Co...AAAA

New York City
Parke, Davis & Co...AAAA

PA.—Philadelphia
Mulford & Co., H. K..AAA

ANVILS

CONN.—Hartford
Billings & Spencer Co.
  (Jewelers) ....AA

ILL.—Carpentersville
Illinois Iron & Bolt Co...AA

ILL.—Chicago
Chicago Wheel & Mfg. Co.,
  39 W. Randolph (Farm-
  ers') C
Vaughan & Bushnell Mfg.
  Co. (Plow) ....A

ILL.—Ottawa
Porter Co., J. E. (& Vise
  Combined) ....A

ILL.—Rockford
Sovereign, C. E...........C

IND.—Evansville
Evansville Tool Works
  (Plow) ....A

IOWA—Cedar Rapids
Adams, A. L. (& Vise &
  Drill Combined)........E

IOWA—Dubuque
Schrieber & Conchar Mfg.
  Co. ....A

IOWA—Waterloo
Litchfield Mfg. Co. .....A

MASS.—Worcester
Richardson Mfg. Co. (& Vise

ANVILS (Con.)
  Combined) ....A

MICH.—Detroit
Fulton Iron Works (& Vise
  Combined) ....AA

MICH.—Saginaw
Wickes Bros. ....AAA

MO.—St. Louis
Cahill, Swift & Co........B
Kupferle, John C. (Farm-
  ers') ....AA

N. J.—Newark
Atha Tool Co. (Plow)....A

N. J.—Trenton
Fisher & Norris...........B

N. Y.—Brooklyn
American Wrought Anvil
  Co. 12 Richards.......H
Hay-Budden Mfg. Co., 250
  No. Henry ....B

New York City
Lewis Tool Co., 44 Barclay D
Millers Falls Co., 28 Warren
  (Farmers') ....AA
Wiebusch & Heilger, 9
  Murray (Blacksmiths')...A

N. Y.—Palmyra
Allen, Jos. (& Vise Com-
  bined) ....D

N. Y.—Phoenix
Phoenix Hdw. Mfg. Co...H

OHIO—Cleveland
Columbia Hdw. Co., Coe &
  Hamilton (Blacksmiths')
  AA
Russ Mfg. Co., A. E., 87
  Wade Park Av........D
Van Wagoner & Williams
  Hdw. Co.,............X

OHIO—Columbus
Columbus Forge & Iron Co.,
  D
Columbus Anvil & Forging
  Co..................D

OHIO—Springfield
Foos Mfg. Co. (& Vice Combined ....A

PA.—Erie
Hollands Mfg. Co. (Bench)
  C

PA.—Philadelphia
Disston & Sons, Hy., (Saw)
  AAAA
Plumb, Fayette R., (Plow)
  AA

PA.—Wrightsville
Wrightsville Hdw. Co.
  (Paper Weight) ......B

R. I.—Pawtucket
Jenks, Henry F., ...D

APIOL

MO.—St. Louis
Mallinckrodt Chemical Wks.
  AAAA

PA.—Philadelphia
Powers-Weightman-Rosen-
  garten Co. ....AAAA

APPARATUS

CAL.—Los Angeles
Braun & Co., F. W., (Chemical) ....AAA

CAL.—San Francisco
Caire Justenian Co. 521 Market (Chemical) ......AA

COLO.—Denver
Denver Fire Clay Co.
  (Chemical) ....AA

CONN.—Waterbury
Scovil Mfg. Co. (Photo)
  AAAA

ILL.—Chicago
Adams & Westlake Co.,
  Ontario & N. Franklin
  (Car Lighting) ....AAAA
Garden City Fan Co. (Hot
  Blast) ....B
Goetz & Flodin Mfg. Co.
  (Brewers') ....A
Kaestner & Co. (Brewing:
  Racking) ....A
Magnus Sons Co., A. (Brew-
  ing; Racking, &c.) ....B
Pyle National Electric Head-
  light Co., Monadnock Blk.
  (Acetyline Gas. Car) ..D
Sargent & Co., E. H., 143
  Lake (Chemical) ......B
Smith & Co., James H.,
  (Photographic) ....D
Stier Mfg. Co. (Brewers';

APPARATUS (Con.)
Cooling) ....D
Trenkhorst, Frank (Brewers'; Cooling) ....F
Western Electric Co. (Elec. Scenic Theatre) ..AAAA
Wilson & Co., F. C., 239 Lake (Car Lighting) ..B
Wolf Co., Fred. W., (Water Distilling, Thawing) AAA

KANS.—Fort Scott
Ft. Scott Fdg. & Mach. Co. C. Eller, Prop., (Vacuum) .....H

MASS.—Boston
Crosby Steam Gauge & Valve Co. (Gauge Testing) AA
Edson Mfg. Co. (Gymnasium) ....AA
Gleeson, Thos. W., (Physical) ....F
Knott Aparatus Co., L. E., 16 Ashburton Pl. (Chemical) C
Morse & Son, Andrew J., (Diving) ....B
Star Brass Mfg. Co. (Gauge Testing) ....H

MASS.—Lynn
Thompson Electric Welding Co. (Elec. Welding) ....B

MASS.—South Boston
Hersey Mfg. Co. (Drying) .....AA
Brecht Butchers' Supply Co., Gus. V., (Slaughter House) ....AAA

MICH.—Detroit
Huettemant & Cramer Co. (Brewers'; Cooling)....A

MO.—St. Louis
Aufrihtig,. Alois (Brewer's; Cooling) ....
Barry-Wehmiller Machinery Co. (Brewers'; Pasteurizing) ....B

N. H.—Exeter
Exeter Machine Wks. (Green House Heating) .....B

N. J.—Newark
Isbell-Porter Co. (Gas Works) ....D

N. Y.—Albany
Consolidated Car Heating Co. (Car Lighting) ....B

N. Y.—Brooklyn
Graham Chemical Pottery Wks., 1018 Met. Av. (Stone Acid Proof Chemical) ....D
Guild & Garrison (Vacuum) .....B

N. Y.—Buffalo
Buffalo Dental Mfg. Co. Blowpipe, Laboratory, Nitrous Oxide Gas) .....A

N. Y.—Irvington-on-Hudson
Lord & Burnham Co. (Green House, Heating) .....A

N. Y.—Newburg
Newburg Ice Mach. & Engine Co. (Water Distilling) ....A

New York City
Berge, J. & H., 95 John (Chemical, Laboratory).B
Boynton Furnace Co. (Hot Water & Green House, Heating) ....A
Bramhall-Deane Co. (Sterilizing) ....B
Davidson, M. F., (Water Distilling) ....A
Elmer & Amend, 211 3rd Av. Chemical, Laboratory) AA
Gennert, G., (Photo-Enlarging) ....A
Goodyear Rubber Co. (Diving) ....AAAA
Goodyear India Rubber Glove Mfg. Co. (Diving) AAAA
Greiner, Emil, 78 John (Chemical) ....AA
Griffing Iron Co., A. A., AA
Hitchings & Co. (Green House Heating) ....B
Mica Mfg. Co. (John A. O'Neill) (Special Meteorological) C
New York Calcium Light Co. ..(Calcium Light) B
Ramsperger & Co., H. G.,

APPARATUS (Con.)
(Magnesium Flash Light) .....B
Reichhelm & Co., E. P., (Blowpipe) ....A
Roche, Wm., 42 Vesey (Flashlight) ....D
Safety Car Heating & Lighting Co., 160 B'way (Car Lighting) ....AAA
Schneible Co., Jos. (Brewers'; Cooling) ....B
Schrader's Son, A., (Diving) .....B
Smith, Charles G., 350 Pearl (Car Lighting) ....B
Spaulding & Bros., A. G., (Inc.) (Gymnasium) ... AAAA
Torchiani, H. (Brewers'; Racking) ....D
Von Lengerke & Detmold (Magnesium Flash Light) .....A

N. Y.—Rochester
Yawman & Erbe Mfg. Co. (Brewers') ....AA

N. Y.—Troy
Fuller & Warren Co. (Green House Heating) ....AA

OHIO—Cincinnati
Deckebach Sons Co., F. C. (Brewers'; Cooling)....C

OHIO—Cleveland
Bartlett, C. O., & Snow (Drying) ....A

PA.—Philadelphia
Feidt & Co., Geo. D., 528 Arch (Chemical) C
Kensington Engine Wks. (Ltd) (Disinfecting) ..A
Pennsylvania Iron Wks. Co. (Gas Works) ......AAA
Queen & Co. 1010 Chestnut (Chemical) ....AA
Thomas Co., A. H., 12th & Walnut (Chemical) ....B
Whitall, Tatum & Co. (Laboratory) ......AAAA

PA.—Reading
Reading Elect. Mfg. Co. (Electrical Dental) ....B

R. I.—Providence
Narragansett Machine Co. (Gymnasium) ....A
Providence Gas Burner Co. (Blowpipe) ....A

WIS.—Milwaukee
Ross & Bros. Co., Chas. (Brewers'; Cooling; Racking) ....A
Smith-Medberg Mfg. Co. (Brewers'; Racking)...D
Vilter Mfg. Co. (Brewers'; Pasteurizing) ....AA

APPLES

See Canned Goods & Dried Fruit; also Pine Apples; also Produce, in Appendix

APPLIANCES

ILL.—Chicago
Haussmann & Dunn (Orthopaedical) C
Sharp & Smith (Deformity) .....A

IND.—Indianapolis
Armstrong & Co., Wm. H. (Deformity) ....B

LA.—New Orleans
McDermott Surgical Instrument Co. (Ltd.) (Orthopaedical) ....D

MD.—Baltimore
Chloride of Silver Dry Cell Battery Co. (Electro-Medical & Surgical) ....B

MICH.—Detroit
Simpson, Wm. T. (Deformity) ....F

MO.—St. Louis
Aloe & Co., A. S. (Deformity) ....A

New York City
Frees, C. A., 853 Broadway (Deformity) ....A
Hospital Supply Co. (Surgical Electric) ....A
Marks, A. A. (Deformity).. AA
Seabury & Johnson (Electro;

APPLIANCES (Con.)
  Medical; Surgical)....AA
Tiemann & Co., Geo. (De-
  formity) ....A
N. Y.—Rochester
Fuller Co., Geo. R. (De-
  formity) ....E
PA.—Philadelphia
Flemming & Co., Otto (Elec-
  tro; Medical; Surgical).X
Kolbe & Son, D. W.
  (Orthopaedical) X
White Dental Mfg. Co., S. S.
  (Electro; Medical; Surgi-
  cal) ....AAAA

APRICOTS
Canned Goods & Dried Fruit

APRONS
See also Clothing
CONN.—Fairfield
Fairfield Rubber Co. (Car-
  riage Dash) C
CONN.—New Haven
Goodrich & Co., J. F. (Car-
  riage) ....AA
ILL.—Chicago
Michael, John C.........D
Overdier Mfg. Co. (Butch-
  ers') ....E
Smith, David A. (Carriage)
                        D
ILL.—Mattoon
Buck Mfg. Co., Geo. N.
  (Carpenters') ....B
IND.—Anderson
Buckeye Mfg. Co. (Carriage)
                        AA
MAINE—Portland
Chenery Mfg. Co. ....B
MASS.—Beverly
Carter Co., F. F. (Butchers'
  & Tanners') ....D
MASS.—Boston
Boston Belting Co., 256
  Devonshire (Endless; Rub-
  ber; Flange & Paper Mill)
                        AAAA
Stoughton Rubber Co. (Car-
  riage & Ice) ....AA
MASS.—Clinton
Clinton Wire Cloth Co.
  (Cotton & Wool) ...AAA
MASS.—Lawrence
Barlow Co., John W. (End-
  less & Worsted Combing)
                        E
MASS.—Lowell
Gates & Sons, Josiah
  (Worsted Combing) X
Parr, Wm. (Worsted
  Combing) ....D
MASS.— No. Brookfield
Hall Overall Co. (Butchers';
  Carpenters'; Waiters') ..B
MASS.—South Attleboro
Coupe & Co., Wm. (Worsted
  Combing & Excelsior) ..X
MASS.—West Newton
Martin Mfg. Co. ....D
MASS.—Worcester
Rowell & Co., W. P.......D
Hildreth & Co., A. G.
  (Butchers'; Carpenters';
  Waiters') ....B
N. J.—Jersey City
N. J. Car Spring & Rubber
  Co. (Endless) ....AA
N. Y.—Albany
Munson, Samuel L. (Linen;
  Butchers'; Carpenters';
  Waiters' & Womens').AA
New York City
Goodyear Rubber Co. (Rub-
  ber; Carriage & Ladies'
  Rubber) ....AAAA
Goodyear's Ind. Rubber
  Glove Mfg. Co. (Carriage;
  Ice; Ladies' Rubber; Me-
  chanics'; Rubber; Nur-
  sery) ....AAAA
Gutta Percha & Rubber
  Mfg. Co., 126 Duane (End-
  less) ....AAAA
Hodgman Rubber Co., 806
  Broadway (Carriage; Ice
  & Rubber) ....AA
Rosenthal Bros. & Co.
  (Linen) ....A
OHIO—Akron
Goodrich Co., B. F. (Ice;

APRONS (Con.)
  Rubber & Tanners')AAAA
OHIO—Cincinnati
Monarch Carriage Goods Co.
  (Carriage) ....B
PA.—Lancaster
Helvetia Leather Co.
  (Leather) ....D
R. I.—Providence
American Multiple Fabric
  Co. (Worsted Combing).A
Davol Rubber Co. (Rubber)
                        AA
WIS.—Milwaukee
Am. Sign Co., 51 Erie
  (Advertising) ....A

AQUA FORTIS
OHIO—Cleveland
Grasselli Chemical Co.
                        AAAA

AQUARIA
ILL.—Chicago
Barbee Wire & Iron Works
                        B
MASS.—Boston
Jones & Co., Melville D..G
New York City
Fiske Iron Works, J. W...B
OHIO—Hamilton
Meyers Mfg. Co., Fred J..B
PA.—Beaver Falls
Co-operative Flint Glass Co.
  (Glass & Fish Globes)..A
PA.—Philadelphia
Gillinder & Sons (Glass &
  Fish Globes) ....A
Whitall, Tatum & Co.
  (Glass & Fish Globes)...
                        AAAA
PA.—Pittsburg
McKee & Co., S. (Glass &
  Fish Globes) ....D

ARABIC
See Gum

ARBORS
CONN.—Hartford
Cushman Chuck Co. (Reap-
  er; Drill Chuck) .....AA
Pratt & Whitney Co. (Shell
  Reamer; Reaper; Drill
  Chuck) ....AAAA
Whitney Mfg. Co. ....B
CONN.—New Britain
Skinner Chuck Co. (Drill
  Chuck) ....A
Union Mfg. Co. (Drill
  Chuck) ....AA
CONN.—New Haven
Brown & Co., R. H. (Drill
  Chuck) ....B
IND.—Indianapolis
Atkins & Co., E. C.
  (Saw) ....AAAA
MASS.—Boston
Woods Mach. Co., S. A., 445
  Dorchester (Circular Saw)
                        AA
MASS.—Fitchburg
Putnam Mach. Co. ....A
Simonds Mfg. Co. (Circular
  Saw) ....AAA
MASS.—Greenfield
Goodell-Pratt Co. (Circular
  Saw) ....B
Wiley & Russell Mfg. Co...
                        AA
MASS.—New Bedford
Morse Twist Drill & Ma-
  chine Co. (Drill Chuck;
  Shell Reamer) ...AAA
MICH.—Grand Rapids
Hayden & Co., J. M.
  (Emery Wheel) ....E
MICH.—Saginaw
Wickes Bros. (Circular Saw)
                        AAA
N. J.—Elizabeth
Braunsdorf-Mueller Co.
  (Lathe) ....D
N. J.—Gloucester
Rogers Boat, Gauge & Drill
  Works (Shell Reamers).A
N. J.—Newark
National Saw Co. (Circu-
  lar Saw) ....B
N. Y.—Lockport

ARBORS (Con.)

Trevor Mfg. Co. (Drill Chuck; Lumber) ......B
New York City
Etna Mfg. Co., 253 B'way (Shell Reamers') X
OHIO—Akron
Whitman & Barnes Mfg. Co. (Drill Chuck) .....AAAA
OHIO—Canton
Buckeye Mfg. Co. ......D
OHIO—Cincinnati
Cincinnati Screw & Tap Co. (Shell Reamers') ......A
Fay, J. A. & Egan Co. (Saw) ....AAAA
OHIO—Cleveland
Cleveland Twist Drill Co. (Shell Reamers') ......A
Standard Tool Co. (Drill Chuck & Shell Reamers') ....AA
PA.—Allentown
Grammes & Son, L. F.....A
PA.—Montrose
Beach, H. L. (Saw) .....D
PA.—Philadelphia
Disston & Sons, H. (Circular Saw) ....AAAA
Grammes & Son, L. F. (Saw) ....A
R. I.—Providence
Brown & Sharpe Mfg. Co... ....AAAA

ARCHERY

See Sporting Goods

ARCHES

WIS.—Milwaukee
Filer & Stowell Co. (Saw) ....AAA
DEL.—Wilmington
McCullough Iron Co. (Curved Corrugated) ....AA
ILL.—Chicago
Barbee Wire & Iron Wks. (Cemetery & Garden)..B
MO.—Kansas City
Kansas City Wire & Iron Wks. (Garden) ....A
New York City
Howard & Morse (Garden)D
Moseley Iron Bridge & Roof Co., '39 Cortland (Curved Corrugated) ....B
OHIO—Cleveland
Garry Iron & Steel Co. (Curved Corrugated)...A
OHIO—Dayton
Raymond & Co., Chas. W. (Brick Kiln) ....A
OHIO—Hamilton
Meyers Mfg. Co., Fred. J. (Garden) ....B
OHIO—Youngstown
Youngstown Iron & Steel Roofing Co. (Curved Corrugated) ....AA

ARCTICS

See also Boots & Shoes

CONN.—Naugatuck
Goodyear's M. R. Shoe Co. ....AAAA
MASS.—Boston
Hood Rubber Co. ....AAAA
New York City
Goodyear Rubber Co..AAAA
R. I.—Bristol
National Ind. Rubber Co... ....AAAA
R. I.—Woonsocket
Woonsocket Rubber Co. ....AAAA

ARGOLS

CONN.—Hartford
Beach & Co. (Ground).AAA
N. Y.—Brooklyn
Wiarda & Co., John C. (Ground) ....AA

ARMATURES

COLO.—Denver
Flint-Lomax Elect. & Mfg. Co., 1937 Curtis (Electric) C

ARMATURES (Con.)

ILL.—Chicago
Chicago Edison Co., 139 Adams (Electric)..AAAA
Gregory Electric Co., 58 S. Clinton (Electric) ....AA
IND.—South Bend
Knoblock - Heldeman Mfg. Co. (Electric; Rewinding) ....B
MD.—Baltimore
Southern Elect. Co., 203 E. Fayette (Electric) .....B
MASS.—Boston
Chase-Shawmut Co., 390 Atlantic Av. (Electric)...B
Ridlon Co., Frank, 200 Summer (Electric) .....A
MICH.—Detroit
Commercial Supply Co., 104 Wayne (Electric) .....G
N. J.—Newark
Heck, Louis, 35 N. J. R. R. Av. (Electric) C
N. J.—Paterson
Sipp Elect. & Machine Co. (Electric) C
N. Y.—Brooklyn
Columbia Mach. Wks. & Malleable Iron Co., 167 Chestnut (Electric) C
New York City
Bogue, Chas. J., 213 Centre (Electric) C
Jordan Bros., 74 Beekman (Electric) ....F
Martin Electric Co., 32 Vesey (Electric) ....E
Rossiter, MacGovern & Co., 141 B'way (Electric) ...A
N. Y.—Utica
Utica Elect. Mfg. & Supply Co. (Electric) X
OHIO—Cleveland
Cleveland Armature Wks., Coe & Hamilton (Electric) ....E
Elliott, S. K., Blackstone Bldg. (Electric) ....D
Elliott Bros. Elect. Co., 970 Hamilton (Electric) ....F
Van Dorn-Elliott Elect. Co., 1796 Madison (Electric).. ....AA
PA.—Philadelphia
Electric Railway Equipment Co., 31st & Chestnut (Electric) ....D
Electro-Dynamic Co. of Phila., 224 Ionic (Electric) ....AA
PA.—Pittsburg
Brown & Son, James, 207 Wood (Electric) ......B
Doubleday-Hill Elect. Co., 535 Wood (Electric)....A
PA.—Scranton
Elect. Supply & Mfg. Co (Electric) ....G
S. C.—Charleston
Electrical Supply Co. (Electric) ....A

ARMBANDS

See Suspenders

ARMLETS

ILL.—Chicago
Stein & Co., A., 316 Franklin ....A
MASS.—Chicopee Falls
Taylor, Bramley & Co...B
PA.—Philadelphia
Kendrick, Jas. R., 133 Harvey ....E

ARMOR

MASS.—Boston
Morse & Son, A. J., 140 Congress (Submarine) .....A
New York City
Ogden & Wallace (Plate).A
Schrader Son, A., 30 Rose (Submarine) ....B

ARMS

Artificial, see Limbs

ARMS
Cross, see Brackets

ARMS
Fire, see Fire Arms

ARMS
Miscellaneous

MASS.—Reading
Pierce Organ Pipe Co., Samuel (Organ) C
MICH.—Grand Rapids
Grand Rapids Brass Co. (Umbrella) ....A
OHIO—Columbus
Ohio Tool Co. (Panel Plow) ....AA
PA.—Philadelphia
Underwood & Co., H. B. (Portable Facing)......B
PA.—Pittsburg
McDowell Mfg. Co. (Steel Telephone) ....D

ARMURES
See Jewelry

ARRESTERS
ILL.—Chicago
Amer. Elect. Fuse Co., 50 W. Jackson Boul. (Lightning) C
Barbee Wire & Iron Wks., 44 Dearborn (Spark) ...B
Chicago Die & Elect. Co., 87 W. Lake (Lightning) ...F
Chicago Fuse Wire Mfg. Co., 358 Dearborn (Lightning) ....D
Electric Appliance Co., 92 W. Van Buren (Lightning) ....B
Eureka Electric Co., 143 So. Clinton (Lightning) ....B
Farr Telephone & Construction Sup. Co., 118 W. Jackson Boul. (Lightning) ....D
Harrington & King Perforating Co., 224 N. Union (Spark) ....A
Harvard Electric Co., 66 W. Van Buren (Lightning) .B
Western Electric Co., 259 So. Clinton (Lightning)..
.................AAAA
Western Telephone Construction Co., Fisher Bldg. (Lightning) ....B
IND.—Ft. Wayne
Ft. Wayne Electric Wks. (Lightning) ....AAA
IND.—Kokomo
Kokomo Telephone & Electric Mfg. Co. (Lightning) F
IND.—Lafayette
Sterling Electric Co. (Lightning) ....B
IND.—South Bend
South Bend Spark Arrester Co. (Spark & Lightning)E
IOWA—Keokuk
Garton & Daniels Co. (Lightning) ....D
MD.—Baltimore
Viaduct Mfg. Co., 10 So. Howard (Lightning)...B
MASS.—Boston
Anderson Mfg. Co., 287 A.. S. B. (Lightning) ......B
MASS.—Pittsfield
Stanley Electric Mfg. Co. (Lightning) ....AA
MASS.—Worcester
Wright Wire Co. (Spark)..
...AA
MICH.—Detroit
Byram & Co. (Spark).....C
Michigan Wire & Iron Wks. (Spark) ....AA
MINN.—Minneapolis
Howell & Co., R. R. (Spark) ....B
MO.—St. Louis
Central Union Brass Co., 832 N. 2nd (Lightning) ....E

ARRESTERS (Con.)
Commercial Elect. Supply Co., 1007 Market (Lightning) C
Western Electric Supply Co., 7th & Clark Av. (Lightning) ....B
N. J.—Newark
McIntire Co., C., 13 Franklin (Lightning) ....D
New York City
Bunnell & Co., J. H., 20 Park Pl. (Lightning) ..B
Foote, Pierson & Co., 84 Fulton (Lightning) ....D
Howard & Morse (Spark)..D
McLeod, Ward & Co., 27 Thames (Spark) ......E
Mundt & Sons, Chas., 441 Pearl (Spark) ....B
N. Y.—Schenectady
General Electric Co. (Lightning) ....AAAA
OHIO—Cleveland
North. Electric Co., 155 St. Clair (Lightning) ......A
Williams-Abbott Electric Co. (Lightning) ....B
OHIO—Elyria
Rawson Electric Co. (Lightning) ....F
OHIO—Hamilton
Meyers Mfg. Co., Fred. J. (Spark) ....A
OHIO—Mansfield
Ohio Brass Co. (Lightning)
AA
PA.—Carbondale
Hendrick Mfg. Co. (Ltd.) (Spark) ....AA
PA.—Philadelphia
Paxton & Co., J. W., 1021 N. Delw. Av. (Cupola Spark) ....AA
Pringle, Wm. F. (Lightning) ....D
PA.—Pittsburg
Keystone Elec. Telephone Co., 565 Diamond (Lightning) ....AAAA
Westinghouse Elect. Mfg. Co. (Lightning) ...AAAA

ARSENIC
MO.—St. Louis
Herf & Frerichs Chemical Co. (Purified) ....A
Mallinckrodt Chemical Wks. (Purified) ....AAAA
N. Y.—Brooklyn
Wiarda & Co., Jno. C....AA
N. Y.—Buffalo
Schoellkopf, Hartford & Hanna Co. ....AAA
New York City
Binney & Smith Co......AA
Bischoff & Co., C........B
Fuerst Bros. & Co........D
Hill's Sons Co., Edw. ..AA
Klipstein & Co., A.......AA
McKesson & Robbins.AAAA
Metz & Co., H. A........A
Roessler & Hasslacher Chem. Co. ....AA
OHIO—Cincinnati
Winkler & Bro., Isaac..AA
OHIO—Cleveland
Harshaw, Fuller & Goodwin Co. ....AA

ARTOTYPES
MASS.—Springfield
Taber-Prang Art Co. ...AA

ASBESTOS
DEL.—Wilmington
Wood & Co., James F....F
ILL.—Chicago
Chicago Fire Proof Covering Co., 18 N. Canal (Material; Cement; Felt & Roofing) ....B
Sall Mountain Asbestos Co., 123 Ontario (Material)..B
IND.—Terre Haute
American Asbestos Co. ...D
MD.—Baltimore
Noble & Co., 18 S. Gay (Material) ....H

ASBESTOS (*Con.*)

MASS.—Boston
Nightingale, S. C. & Childs Co. (Material) ....D
Trainer Mfg. Co., C. W., 89 Pearl (Material; Paper & Mill Board) ....F

MASS.—Sprinfield
Springfield Asbestos Co., 275 Main (Material) ..D

MINN.—Minneapolis
Nott Co., W. S., 200 S. 1st Av. (Material) ....A

MO.—Kansas City
Midland Asbestos Co. (Fibre; Material; Paper & Mill Board) ....D

N. J.—Camden
New Jersey Asbestos Co. (Felting & Material)..AA

New York City
Asbestos Felting Wks., 79 Maiden Lane (Material & Packing) ....D
Gilmour Mfg. Co., R. M., 105 John (Felting; Material; Paper; Mill Board & Furnace Cement) D
International Asbestoc Co., 309 B'way (Crude & Fibre) E
Johns-Manville Co., H. W., 100 William Cement; Paper; Furnace Cement; Mats; Baking Sheets; Iron Rests; Materials; Mittens & Gloves; Rubber Tapes; Tubes; Glass Workers'; Board; Cloth; Rubber Cloth; Cord; Covering; Dental Blocks; Felt; Gaskets; Hangings; Jewelers'; Packing; Metallic Packing; Roofing; Rope; Rugs; Sheathing; Stove Lining; Twine; Wicks & Yarn) ....AAAA
Martin, R. H., 220 B'way (Crude & Fibre) ......B
New Jersey Asbestos Co., 52 Dey ....AA
N. Y. Fire Proof Covering Co. (Cement & Covering) E
Pettit Chemical Co......B
Robertson & Sons, Jas. L. (Packing) ....D

N. Y.—Troy
Adams Laundry Machine Co. (Stove Linings) ....B

OHIO—Alliance
Alliance Asbestos Mfg. Co. (Felting; Fibres; Paper & Mill Board) ....B

OHIO—Cincinnati
Cincinnati Roofing Co. (Covering) ....H

OHIO—Cleveland
Standard Pipe Covering Co., 20 Michigan (Material).H

OHIO—Lockland
Carey Mfg. Co., Philip (Felting; Fibres; Material; Paper; Mill Board; Furnace Cement; Covering; Rope & Twine) ...A

PA.—Ambler
Keasbey & Mattison Co. (Material; Paper; Mill Board; Covering; Felt & Sheathing) ......AAAA

PA.—Easton
Baker & Adamson Chemical Co. (Glass Workers')...A

PA.—Erie
Watson Co., H. F. (Paper; Board; Covering; Felt; Mill Boards; Cement; Packing; Roof Coatings; Rope; Sheathing & Wicks) AAA

PA.—Franklin
Franklin Mfg. Co. (Felting; Material; Paper; Mill Boards; Furnace Cement & Stove Linings)..C

PA.—Philadelphia
Asbestos Mfg. Co., 426 Market (Felting; Fibres; Material; Paper; Mill Boards; Cloth & Yarn)..B

PA.—Pittsburg

ASBESTOS (*Con.*)

McConnell & Co., John A., 239 Water (Felting & Cement) ....D

PA.—York
York Chemical Co. (Cement) A

VA.—Richmond
Southern Asbestos Mfg. Co. (Material) C

ASH

COLO.—Denver
Denver Fire Clay Co. (Bone) AA

MICH.—Detroit
Michigan Carbon Wks. (Bone) ....AAA

MICH.—Wyandotte
Michigan Alkali Co. (Soda) AAAA

N. Y.—Brooklyn
Wiarda & Co., John C. (Pearl; Bone; Soda)..AA

New York City
Fuerst Bros. & Co. (Soda)D
Jones Chemical Wks., Enos F. (Pearl) ....B
Hills' Sons Co., Edw. (Soda) ....AA
Klipstein & Co., A. (Soda) AA
Wing & Evans (Pearl & Soda) ....AAA
Lee & Co., Jas. (Soda)...A

N. Y.—Syracuse
Solvay Process Co. (Soda).. AAAA

OHIO—Deshler
Cottingham, S. (Pearl)...E

OHIO—Cincinnati
Am. Chemical Co. (Soda).C
Winkler & Bro., A. (Soda) AA

OHIO—Cleveland
Clark Co., Fred. G. (Soda) A

PA.—Philadelphia
Pennsylvania Salt Mfg. Co. (Soda) ....AAAA

R. I.—Providence
Arnold, Hoffman & Co. (Soda) ....AA

ASHES

New York City
American Cotton Oil Co., 11 Broadway (Cotton Seed; Hull) ....AAAA

ASPARAGUS

See Canned Goods

ASPHALT

CAL.—Los Angeles
Densmore Stabler Refining Co. (Miners'; Refiners'; Liquid; Solid; Pipe Dip & Pitch) ....B

CAL.—San Francisco
Union Oil Co., Mills Bldg. (Miners'; Refiners'; Liquid; Solid; Pipe Dip & Pitch) ....A

ILL.—Chicago
Barrett Mfg. Co. (Miners'; Refiners' & Roofing).... AAAA
Powell Co., M. W., 204 Dearborn (Dealers) C

ILL.—Rock Island
Lewis Mfg. Co., F. J......C

MASS.—Boston
Warren Bros. Co., 93 Federal ....A

MO.—St. Louis
Asphalt Roofing Co., 808 Theresa Av. (Liquid; Solid; Mastic; Pitch; Mastic Floors & Insulating)E
Gilson Asphaltum Co., Wainwright Bldg. (Miners'; Refiners' & Importers')B

N. J.—Jersey City
Stowell Mfg. Co., 114 Culver Av. (Insulating) ....B

N. J.—Newark ....
Lister's Agricultural Chemical Wks. (Substitute)... AAAA

ASPHALT (Con.)

New York City
Asphalt Construction Co., Madison, cor. 137th (Dealers) C
Asphalt Ready Roofing Co., 136 Water (Dealers)....C
Eastern Granite Roofing Co., Irving Bldg. (Dealers) .B
Gabriel & Schall, 205 Pearl (Mastic) C
Hastings Pavement Co. (Paving Blocks) .....AA
Lamson & Bro., John S., 77 Maiden Lane (Dealers).A
Neuchatel Asphalt Co., 265 B'way (Dealers) ....B
Saacke, Chas. W., 76 William (Dealers) C
Sicilian Asphalt Paving, Times Bldg. (Miners' & Refiners') C
Warren Chem. & Mfg. Co. (Paving Blocks & Roofing) ....A
N. Y.—Syracuse
Warner-Quinlan Asphalt Co. (Miners' & Refiners')... AAAA

OHIO—Lockland
Carey Mfg. Co., Philip (Pavements & Roofing Pitch) ....AAA
OHIO—Toledo
Schillinger Bros., 412 City Park Av. (Dealers)....D
PA.—Erie
Watson Co., H. F. (Roofing) AAA
PA.—Philadelphia
Barber Asphalt Paving Co., Land Title Bldg. (Miners' Pitch & Pavements) AAAA
PA.—Pittsburg
Globe Asphalt Co., Bakewell Bldg. (Miners'; Refiners'; Liquid & Solid) C
TEXAS—Cline
Walde Asphalt Co. (Miners' & Refiners) ....A
VA.—Richmond
Armitage Mfg. Co. ......B

ASPHALTUM

ILL.—Chicago
Elliott Varnish Co. ......F
IND.—Asphaltum
Indian Asphalt Co. (Gum) C
N. J.—Jersey City
Woolsey Paint & Color Co., C. A. ....A
New York City
Lamson & Bro., Jno. S....A
Melchior, Armstrong & Dessau ....A
Warren Chemical & Mfg. Co. A
OHIO—Akron
Akron Varnish Co. X
PA.—Philadelphia
Felton, Sibley & Co...AAA
PA.—Pittsburg
Gulf Refining Co. ....AAA
Lawrence & Co., W. W..AA

ASPIRATORS

IND.—Indianapolis
Nordyke & Marmon Co.AAA
New York City
Mason & Co., Marcus, Prod. Ex. ....A
PA.—Philadelphia
Boekel & Co., Wm., 578 Vine (Laboratory) .....A

ASSAFOETIDA

New York City
Hopkins & Co., J. L....A

ASTRACHAN

N. Y.—Buffalo
American Buffalo Robe Co. B
N. Y.—Fonda
Fonda Glove Lining Co....C
N. Y.—Milton
Bells' Sons Co.. Hy. H....B
PA.—Philadelphia
Hanifen & Co., J. E......A

ATOMIZERS

See also Rubber Goods

CONN.—New Haven
Seamless Rubber Co.....AA
MASS.—Andover
Tyer Rubber Co.........AA
MASS.—Boston
Codman & Shurtleff C
Davidson Rubber Co....A
Leach & Greene (Ointment) F
MASS.—East Cambridge
McElroy, P. J............E
N. J.—Belleville
Hardman Rubber Co......A
N. Y.—East Syracuse
Benedict Mfg. Co., M. S. (Silver) ....AA
New York City
Am. Hard Rubber Co.AAAA
Ellis & Goetermann, 86 Leonard C
Goodyear Rubber Co..AAAA
Goodyear's Ind. Rub. Glove Mfg. Co., 503 B'way.... AAAA
Gorham Mfg. Co. (Fancy Silver) ....AAAA
Hodgman Rubber Co. ..AA
Kneuper, Geo. ....A
Mattson Rubber Co., 26 W. B'way ....A
Meineke & Co., 50 Pk. Pl..B
Parker, Stearns & Sutton, 228 South ....B
Weinhagen, Henry (Medical) ....B
Wetmore Co., S. H. (Medical) ....D
OHIO—Akron
Goodrich Co., B. F. (Medical) ....AAAA
Faultless Rubber Co...AAA
OHIO—Cleveland
Cleveland Rubber Co..AAAA
OHIO—Toledo
De Vilbiss Mfg. Co. (Surgical) C
PA.—Philadelphia
Boekel & Co., Wm. (Laboratory) ....A
Shaw & Co., J. Elliott, 632 Arch X
Whitall, Tatum & Co.... AAAA
R. I.—Providence
Davol Rubber Co. ......AA

ATTACHMENTS

CAL.—San Francisco
Jackson Machine Wks., Byron (Threshing Machine)A
CAL.—Stockton
Holt Mfg. Co. (Harvesting Drapers) ....AA
CONN.—Bridgeport
Curtis & Curtis Co. (Lathe Pipe Threading) .....AA
CONN.—Guilford
Spencer's Sons, I. S. (Electric Gas) ....A
CONN.—Hartford
Dwight Slate Machine Co. (Lathe Centering) .....B
Pratt & Whitney Co. (Milling) ....AAAA
CONN.—Meriden
Miller & Co., Edw. (Converble Gas) ....AAAA
CONN.—Middletown
Palmer, I. E. (Bedstead; Canopy & Hammock) AAA
CONN.—New Haven
Toof, Edwin J. (Sewing Machine) ....D
CONN.—Norwich
Rogers & Co., C. B. (Planer Knife Grinder) ....AAAA
CONN.—Stonington
Atwood-Morrison Co. (Loom) ....AA
CONN.—Torrington
Hendy Machine Co. (Shaper) ....AA
CONN.—Westville
Greist Mfg. Co. (Sewing Machine) ....B

ILL.—Aurora
American Well Wks.
(Power Wind Mill)....AA
ILL.—Bradley
Bradley Mfg. Co., David
(Cultivator) ....AAA
ILL.—Chicago
Barbee Wire & Iron Wks.
(Wire Guard) ....B
Fairbanks, Morse & Co.
(Power Wind Mill).AAAA
ILL.—Elgin
Moseley Lathe Co. (Jewelers' & Watchmakers'
Lathe) ....D
ILL.—Freeport
Stover Mfg. Co. (Power
Wind Mill) ....AA
ILL.—Mendota
Tower & Bro., J. D. (Cultivator) ....A
ILL.—Ottawa
King & Hamilton Co. (Cultivator) ....AA
ILL.—Sandwich
Sandwich Mfg. Co. (Cultivator) ....AA
IND.—Kendallville
Flint & Walling Mfg. Co.
(Power Wind Mill)...AA
IND.—Muncie
Adamson Typewriter Press
Co. (Two-Colored Printing) ....H
IND.—Richmond
Gaar, Scott & Co. (Threshing Mach.).......AAAA
IOWA—Dubuque
Adams Co. (Milling) ....A
KY.—Louisville
Avery & Sons, B. F. (Culti-
& Sulky Plow) .....AAA
MAINE—No. Berwick
Hussey, Timothy B. (Celery
Earther) ....E
MAINE—Waterville
Webber & Philbrick (Wood
Barker) ....B
MASS.—Athol
Starrett Co., L. S.
(Wrench) ....A
MASS.—Boston
Ames Plow Co., Quincy Hall
(Mule & Fertilizer).AAAA
Faneuil Watch Tool Co.,
"Brighton" (Lathe)...B
Harwood & Son, Geo. S., 53
State (Feeder Clutch)..A
Reece Button Hole Machine
Co. (Boot & Shoe Sewing
Machine) ....AAA
Woods Machine Co., S. A.
(Planer; Knife Grinding)
AA
MASS.—Fitchburg
Fitchburg Machine Wks.
(Shaft Turning & Shaper)
B
Putnam Machine Co. (Lathe;
Pit & Shaft Turning)...A
MASS.—Hyde Park
Becker-Brainerd Milling
Machine Co. (Milling).AA
MASS.—Lowell
Bagshaw, W. H. (Est. of)
(Mule) ....B
Lahne & Co., M. M. (Loom)
E
Stott, S. E. & T. (Mule,
Spinning) X
MASS.—Readville
Stafford Co., Geo. W.
(Loom) ....A
MASS.—Waltham
Am. Watch Tool Co.
(Bench Lathe) ....D
MASS.—Worcester
Crompton & Knowles Loom
Wks. (Loom) .....AAAA
Norton Emery Wheel Co.
(Grinding) ....AA
Steele & Bro., A. H.
(Loom) ....D
MICH.—Dowagiac
Dowagiac Mfg. Co. (Grain
Drill) ....A
MICH.—Kalamazoo
Phelps & Bigelow Wind
Mill Co. (Power Wind
Mill) ....B
MICH.—Lansing
Lansing Wheelbarrow Co.

(Sled & Sleigh Runner)..
AAA
MINN.—Minneapolis
Minneapolis Threshing Machine Co. (Threshing Machine) ....AAAA
N. J.—Highstown
Peppler, Thomas (Furrowing) ....D
N. J.—Newark
Gould & Eberhardt (Key
Seating; Rock Cutting;
Shaft Turning & Shaper)
A
Peters Harness & Saddlery
Co. (Hame Strap) C
N. J.—Paterson
Eastwood Co., Benjamin
(Loom) C
N. Y.—Batavia
Johnston Harvester Co.
(Cultivator) ......AAAA
N. Y.—Buffalo
Holmes Machinery Co., E.
& B. (Planer; Knife
Grinding) ....B
Pratt & Letchworth Co.
(Trace) ....AAA
Rogers & Co., S. C. (Planer;
Knife Grinding) C
N. Y.—Cohoes
Sweet & Doyle (Knitting
Machine) C
New York City
Garvin Machine Co., Varick
& Spring (Milling) ..AA
Hayden Mfg. Co. (Bidet).D
Kruse & Murphy Mfg. Co.
(Sewing Machine) ....D
Niles, Bement, Pond Co.,
136 Liberty (Milling)....
AAAA
Prentiss Disc Co., 44 Barclay (Wrench) C
Singer Mfg. Co. (Sewing
Machine) ....AAAA
N. Y.—Mount Morris
Genesee Valley Mfg. Co.
(Fertilizer) ....B
N. Y.—Phelps
Crown Mfg. Co. (Fertilizer)
A
N. Y.—Seneca Falls
Seneca Falls Mfg. Co. (Drilling & Tapping) ....B
N. Y.—Yonkers
Saunder's Sons, D. (Bolt
Threading & Nut Tapping) ....A
OHIO—Akron
Whitman & Barnes Mfg. Co.
(Reaper & Mower).AAAA
OHIO—Cincinnati
Cincinnati Milling Machine
Co. (Milling) ....AA
Fay, J. A. & Egan Co.
(Planer; Knife Grinding)
AAAA
Lodge & Shipley Mach. Tool
Co. (Shaft Turning) .AA
OHIO—Dayton
Dayton Malleable Iron Co.
(Malleable Drawbar).AAA
OHIO—Hamilton
Niles Tool Wks. Co. (Shaft
Turning) ....AAAA
OHIO—Massillon
Russell & Co. (Threshing
Machine) ....AAA
PA.—Elizabethtown
Buch's Sons Co., A. (Horse
Hoe Marking) ....A
PA.—Philadelphia
Allen & Co., S. L. (Celery
Earther; Furrowing;
Marking; Cultivator;
Wheel Hoe & Seed Drill)
AA
Branson Machine Co., 504
N. American (Knitting
Machine) ....A
Diamond Textile Machine
Wks., 2nd & Diamond
(Mule) ....E
McCambridge & Co. (Ltd.)
(Bidet) ....B
Power & Co., L. (Planer;
Knife Grinding) ....A
Seifert, C. H., 306 Master
(Mule) ....H
PA.—Pittsburg
Standard Scale & Supply Co.

R. I.—Providence
Beaman & Smith (Loom)..A
Brown Bros. Co. (Loom)..B
Brown & Sharpe Mfg. Co.
(Milling) ....AAAA
VT.—Bennington
Cooper, Chas. (Knitting
Machine) ....B
VA.—Richmond
Cardwell Machine Co.
(Fertilizer) ....A

ATTEMPER-ATORS

ILL.—Chicago
Wolf Co., Fred. W.
(Brewers') ....AAA
New York City
Jochum, Andrew (Brewers')
E

AUGERS & BITS

CONN.—Bridgeport
Adams, A. L., (Expansion
Auger Bits) ....E
Bridgeport Gun Implement
Co., 219 Elm (Auger Bits)
A
CONN.—Centerbrook
Connecticut Valley Mfg. Co.
(Auger, Dowel, Car, Bor-
ing Machine, Screw Dri-
ver) C
CONN.—Chester
Chester Mfg. Co. (Boring
Machine, Etc) ....G
Deuse, J. S., (German,
Double Club, Electricians'
& Bell Hangers' Augers &
Gimlets) ....E
Ferguson & Co., J. R.,
(Auger Bits) ....F
CONN.—Deep River
Russell Jennings Mfg. Co.
(Boring Machine, Mill-
wright) ....AA
CONN.—Forestville
American Auger Bit Co.
(Auger Bits) ....H
CONN.—Hamden
Hamden Mfg. Co. (Car &
Expansion Bits, Hollow,
Rafting & Ring Augers) D
CONN.—New Britain
Russell & Erwin Mfg. Co.
(Auger Bits) .....AAAA
CONN.—New Haven
Brown & Co., R. H., 169
Ashman (Expansion Bits)
C
Kilborn & Bishop Co. (Auger
Bits) C
CONN.—Norwich
Rogers & Co., C. E., (Boring
Machine Augers) ..AAAA
CONN.—Plantsville
Acme Mfg. Co. (Screw Dri-
ver Bits) ....F
CONN.—Seymour
Garrett & Beach (Auger
Bits & Gimlets) ......E
Humphreyville Mfg. Co.
(Augers, Auger Bits &
Gimlets) ....E
New Haven Copper Co.
(Auger & Boring Machine
Bits) ....AA
Swan Co., Jas., (Auger,
Expansion & Screw Driver
Bits, Gimlets & Hollow
Augers) ....A
CONN.—Southington
Peck, Stow & Wilcox Co.
(Auger Bits) .....AAAA
GA.—Atlanta
Wood & Sons Co., A. A.,
(Fore & Hollow Augers) E
ILL.—Aurora
American Well Wks. (Earth
Augers) ....AA
ILL.—Chicago
Austin Mfg. Co. Manhattan
Bldg. (Earth & Well
Augers) ....AAA
Klein & Son, Matthias, 89
W. Van Buren (Post Hole
Augers) ....A
Mark Mfg. Co., Evanston

Pratt Mfg. Co., Wm. E., 91
Lake (Post Hole Augers)
B
Redlich Mfg. Co., 6 Oak
(Bung Augers) ....B
Solid Steel Tool & Forge
Co., Monod. Blk. (Rail
Drill Augers) ....F
Vaughan & Bushnell Mfg.
Co., 875 Carroll Av. (Post
Hole Augers; Screw Dri-
ver Bits) ....B
ILL.—Downers Grove
Dicke Tool Co. (Post Hole
Augers) ....D
ILL.—Ottawa
Porter Co., J. E., (Post Hole
Augers) ....A
ILL.—Rockford
Forest City Bit & Tool Co.
(Brace & Boring) C
ILL.—Streator
Iwan Bros. (Post Hole &
Well Augers) ....D
IND.—Anderson
Buckeye Mfg. Co. (Boring
Machine & Post Hole Au-
gers) ....A
IND.—Indianapolis
Tucker & Dorsey Mfg. Co.
State Av. & Bates (Post
Hole Augers) ....B
IND.—Kokomo
Rockford Bit Co. (Auger
Bits) ....B
IND.—Montpelier
Jackson Shovel & Tool Co.
(Post Hole Augers) ....F
IND.—Richmond
Eureka Fence Mfg. Co.
(Earth Augers) ....E
IOWA—Des Moines
Monarch Mfg. Co. (Post
Hole Augers) ....E
IOWA—Ft. Madison
Morrison Mfg. Co. (Earth
Augers) ....A
MAINE—Portland
Laughlin Co., Thos., (Ship
Augers) ....A
MASS.—Brockton
Tuck Mfg. Co. (Screw
Driver Bits) ....E
MASS.—Fiskdale
Snell Mfg. Co. (Auger &
Screw Driver Bits, Boring,
Ring, Pump, Rafting, Ma-
chine, Ship & Post Augers
& Gimlets) ....B
MASS.—Fitchburg
Sawyer Tool Mfg. Co.
(Screw Driver Bits) ...C
MASS.—Holyoke
Ford Auger Bit Co. (Ship,
Boring, Machine, Carpen-
ters' & Nut Augers) ...B
MASS.—Millbury
Buck Bros. (Screw Driver
Bits) ....B
Buck, Chas., (Screw Driver
Bits) ....F
MASS.—Millers Falls
Millers Falls Co. (Screw
Driver Bits & Hollow
Augers) ....AA
MASS.—Shelburne Falls
Mayhew Co., H. H., (Auger,
Gimlet & Screw Driver
Bits, Gimlets) C
MICH.—Detroit
Anderson & Sons, W. H.,
(Earth Augers) C
MINN.—Minneapolis
Howell & Co., R. R., 30th
Av. & S. E. 5th (Earth
Augers) ....F
MO. St. Louis
Cook Well Co. 15 S. 4th
(Earth Augers) C
N. J.—Newark
Kreuter & Co. 577 18th Av.
(Earth Augers) ....E
N. Y.—Brooklyn
U. S. Bung Mfg. Co. 50 S.
2nd (Bung Augers) ....H
N. Y.—Ithaca
Williams Bros. (Earth
Augers) ....AA
New York City
Jennings Co., C. E. 42 Mur-
ray (Auger, Expansive,

AUGERS & BITS (Con.)

Gimlet & Screw Driver Bits; Boring Mach., Ship, Hollow Expansive, Millwrights' & Treenail Augers) ....B

Millers Falls Co. 28 Warren (Hollow Augers) ....AA

Peck, Stow & Wilcox Co. 27 Murray (Auger).AAAA

Russell & Erwin Mfg. Co. 43 Chambers (Brace & Boring Machine) ..AAAA

Tower & Lyons Co. 95 Chambers (Auger & Expansive Bits) ....B

N. Y.—Seneca Falls

Rumsey & Co. (Earth Augers) ....H

N. Y.—Syracuse

Stearns & Co., E. C. 100 Oneida (Hollow & Taper Augers) ....AA

Syracuse Twist Drill Co. (Screw Driver Bits) ...B

OHIO—Akron

Star Drilling Machine Co. (Earth & Well Augers) A

Whitman & Barnes Mfg. Co. 66 S. Canal (Screw Driver Bits) ....AAAA

OHIO—Cincinnati

Cincinnati Tool Co. Norwood. (Electricians' & Bell Hangers' Bits; Hollow & Spoke Augers) ..C

Fay, J. A. & Egan Co. (Hollow Augers) ..AAAA

Tatum Co., Samuel C., 414 W. Water (Auger Bits) B

OHIO—Cleveland

Standard Tool Co. 1260 Central Av. (Screw Driver Bits) ....AAA

OHIO—Columbus

Ohio Tool Co. 63 N. Scioto (Auger & Screw Driver Bits; Boring Mach. Augers & Gimlets) ....A

OHIO—Fremont

Lehr. Agricultural Co. (Post Hole Augers) ....B

OHIO—Salem

Silver Mfg. Co. (Hollow Augers) ....A

OHIO—Sandusky

Sandusky Tool Co. (Machine Bits) ....A

OHIO—Wilmington

Irwin Auger Bit Co. (Auger, Car, Dowel, Hollow Chisel, Mach. & Screw Driver Bits; Boring Mach., Rafting, Ring, Ship Millwrights' ....B

PA.—Allegheny

Hardsocg Mfg. Co. (Auger Bits) ....E

PA.—Meadville

Meadville Vise Co. (Expansion Bits) C

PA.—Oxford

Slack, Timothy, (Auger Bits) ....E

These are the old fashioned double twist, double cut augers. We claim that rightly made from good steel, they are the best.

We make augers and bits of all sizes and lengths, as follows: Carpenter, Millwright, Post and Gas augers; Brace, Car, Machine (right or left hand) countersink, Plug bits, etc. These are made of Black Diamond crucible cast steel, and especially adapted to workers in hard wood.

We cannot appeal to you on the score of low prices, but a trial will prove that in the end they are cheap.

PA.—Philadelphia

Bonney Vise & Tool Wks. 3015 Chestnut (Hollow Augers) ....B

Enterprise Mfg. Co. N. 3d &

AUGERS & BITS (Con.)

Dauphin (Dried Fruit & Sugar Augers) ....AAAA

Keystone Drop Forge Wks. (Drop Forged Screw Driver Bits) ....B

Pugh, Job. T., 3101 Ludlow (Auger & Machine Bits) C

Stortz & Son, John, 210 Vine (Electricians' & Bell Hangers; Gimlets) ....D

Gills' Sons, John D., (Mine Augers) ....D

PA.—Pittsburg

Hubbard & Co. Murtland Bldg. (Boring Machine Augers) ....A

Pittsburg Tool & Drop Forge Co. Arrott Bldg. (Miners') E

TENN.—Memphis

Chickasaw Iron Wks. (Earth Augers) ....A

WIS.—Racine

Racine Malleable & Wrought Iron Co. (Post Hole Augers) ....B

AUTOCOPYISTS

New York City

Ten Eyke, H. B., ...G

AUTOMOBILES

CAL.—Los Angeles

Auto Vehicle Co. (Gasoline) 942 Main ....D

Sturgis & Bros., S. D.,....E

CAL.—San José

Letchter Automobile Co...D

CAL.—San Leandro

Best Mfg. Co. ....B

CONN.—Bridgeport

Locomobile Co. of America, The (Steam & Gasoline) AAA

CONN.—Hartford

Electric Vehicle Co. (Electric & Gasoline) ..AAAA

CONN.—Middletown

Baker Mfg. Co. (Gasoline) D

CONN.—New Britain

Corbin Motor Vehicle Corp. The (Gasoline) ....B

ILL.—Aurora

Aurora Automatic Mchy. Co. B

ILL.—Belvidere

National Sewing Machine Co. (Gasoline) ......AAA

ILL.—Chicago

Coey & Co., C. A., 5311 Cottage Grove Av. (Electric & Gasoline) .....A

Fanning Mfg. Co., Pratt & Morgan (Electric) C

National Sewing Machine Co. 463 Madison (Gasoline) AAA

Woods Motor Vehicle Co., 110 E. 20 (Electric) ..AA

ILL.—Oak Park

Kenilworth Machine Co...D

ILL.—Peoria

739 1:6 '05 543 Register 22

IND.—Auburn

Auburn Automobile Co. (Gasoline) ....B

Eckhart Carriage Co......B

Model Gas Engine Co., (Steam) ....B

IND.—Evansville

Single Center Buggy Co. (Gasoline) ....D

IND.—Indianapolis

National Motor Vehicle Co. (Electric & Gasoline) ..A

Premier Motor Mfg. Co., 222 W. Maryland (Gasoline) D

IND.—Kokomo

Haynes & Apperson Co. (Gasoline) ....A

White Steam Wagon Co., 365 W. 15 (Steam freight wagons) ....D

IND.—Logansport

Western Motor Co., The AA

IND.—Muncie

Muncie Wheel & Jobbing Co. A

IND.—South Bend
Studebaker Bros. Mfg. Co.
                AAAA

IND.—Terre Haute
Standard Wheel Co.,
  (Gasoline) ....AAA

IND.—Union City
Union Automobile Co.
  (Gasoline) ....B

IND.—Waterloo
Waterloo Motor Wks.
  (Gasoline) ....A
Waterloo Wagon Buggy &
  Omnibus Co C

MASS.—Boston
Lyman & Burnham, 43 Columbus Av. (Gasoline) B
Phelps Motor Co. C
Stanley Mfg. Co. (Steam) C

MASS.—Cambridge
Crest Mfg. Co. (Gasoline) D

MASS.—Chicopee Falls
Stevens Arms & Tool Co., J.,
  (Gasoline) ....AA

MASS.—Dedham
Thatswell & Co., H. K., D

MASS.—Hyde Park
Pope-Robinson Co. (Gasoline) C

MASS.—Lawrence
O'Neil, John E., (Gasoline)
                  B
Stanley Mfg. Co. (Steam) C

MASS.—Newton
Stanley Bros. ....A

MASS.—Orange
Grout Bros. Automobile Co.
  (Steam & Gasoline) ....A

MASS.—Springfield
Knox Automobile Co.
  (Gasoline) ....A
Warwick Cycle & Automobile Co. (Gasoline) .....D

MASS.—Waltham
Waltham Mfg. Co. (Gasoline) ....B

MICH.—Charlotte
Dolson & Sons, John L.,
  (Gasoline) ....D

MICH.—Chelsea
Chelsea Mfg. Co. (Ltd) ..D

MICH.—Detroit
Cadillac .Automobile Co.,
  1347 Cass Av. (Gasoline)
                  A
Ford Motor Co., 688 Mack
  Av. (Gasoline) ....B
Nothern Mfg. Co., Champlain & Canton (Gasoline) C
Olds Motor Wks., Concord
  cor Jefferson Av. (Gasoline) ....A
Packard Motor Car Co.,
  (Gasoline) ....B
Reid Mfg. Co. (Gasoline)
                AA

MICH.—Grand Rapids
Austin Automobile Co.
  (Gasoline) ....B
Matheson Motor Car Co.
  (Ltd) (Gasoline) C

MICH.—Houghton
Hodge Iron Co. ....A

MICH.—Jackson
Jackson Automobile Co.
  (Gasoline & Steam) ....D

MICH.—Kalamazoo
Michigan Automobile Co. B
Michigan Buggy Co.
  (Gasoline) ....B

MICH.—Lansing
Clark Mobile Co. (Gasoline)
                 A

MICH.—Mancelona
Eclipse Motor Wks. ......D

MICH.—Owatonna
Virtue & Pond Mfg. Co...C

MO.—Joplin
Freeman Foundry & Machine
  Wks. ....A
Reynolds, Graves & Co...D

MO.—St. Louis
Brecht Butchers Supply Co.,
  G. V., (Electric & Steam)
                AAA
St. Louis Motor Carriage Co.
  1211 N. Vandewater
  (Gasoline) C

NEBR.—Doniphan
Wilson, Harry, ...C

N. J.—Burlington
Birch, Jas. H., (Gasoline)
                AA

N. J.—Hoboken
Fischer Motor Vehicle Co.
  (Gasoline) ....B

N. J.—Jersey City
Commercial Motor Co.
  (Gasoline) ....B

N. Y.—Brooklyn
Mack Bros. Co., The, 540
  Atlantic Av. ....D
Vehicle Equipment Co.,
  (Inc.) Borden & Review
  Aves. (Electric) ....A
Wood Vapor Vehicle Co.,
  811 Union Av. (Vapor) C

N. Y.—Bronxville
Ward-Leonard Electric Co.
  (Gasoline) ....A

N. Y.—Buffalo
Buffalo Electric Carriage
  Co., Military Rd. (Electric & Steam) C
Centaur Motor Vehicle Co.
  (Electric) C
Pierce Co., Geo. N.,
  (Gasoline) ....A
Thomas Motor Co., E. R.,
  1190 Niagara (Gasoline) B

N. Y.—Green Island
Grant, Ferris & Co. .....D

N. Y.—Long Island City
Daimler Mfg. Co., 939 Steinway Av. (Gasoline) ....D

New York City
Electric Vehicle Co., 100
  Bway. (Electric & Gasoline) ....AAAA
Empire State Engineering
  Co., 553 E. 116 (Steam) D
Gas Engine & Power Co.,
  & Chas. Seabury & Co.
  (Con.) Morris Heights
  (Gasoline) ....AA
International Power Co., 74
  Bway. (Steam & Electric
  trucks) ....AAAA
Knox Automobile Co.
  (Gasoline) ....A
Lozier Motor Co., 1 Bway.
  (Gasoline) ....D
Locomobile Co. of Amer.,
  The (Steam & Gasoline)
                AAA
Mobile Co. of Amer., The
  (Steam) ....A
Prescott Automobile Mfg.
  Co. (Steam) ....B
Stevens Arms & Tool Co., J.
  (Gasoline) ....AA

N. Y.—No. Tonawanda
Herschell Spillman & Co.,
  (to order) ....D

N. Y.—Poughkeepsie
Lane Motor Vehicle Co.,
  (Steam) ....B

N. Y.—Schnectady
General Electric Co.
  (Electric) ....AAAA

N. Y.—Syracuse
Century Motor Vehicle Co.
  (Elec; Gas; Steam) X
Franklin Mfg. Co., H. H.,
  400 S. Geddes (Gasoline) A

N. Y.—Troy
Grant-Ferris Co., (Hydrocarbon ....D

N. Y. Utica
Remington Motor Vehicle
  Co., Broad cor Niagara
  (Gasoline) ....D
Smith and Co., D. B., 69
  Genesee (Gasoline) C

N. Y.—Yonkers
Howard Auto. Co. 67 Dock
                 D

OHIO—Chillicothe
Motor Storage & Mfg. Co.,
  The ....D

OHIO—Cleveland
Ajax Motor Vehicle Co.,
  (Electric) ....A
Amer. Motor Carriage Co.
  (Gasoline) C
Baker Motor Vehicle Co.,
  The 116 Jessie (Elec.) A
Berg Automobile Co., 131
  2nd Av. (Gasoline) ....B
Konigslow, Otto (Gasoline)
                 C
Peerless Motor Carr. Co.,
  The (Gasoline) ....A

AWNINGS, ETC. (Con.)
gated Steel) ....B
ILL.—Decatur
Decatur Tent & Awning Co.
C
IND.—Evansville
Mesker & Co., Geo. L. (Corrugated Steel) ....A
IOWA—Mason City
Mason City Bedding Co.
(Tents & Flags) C
Mason City Fur Co. C
IOWA—Sioux City
McNeil & Son, H. C.......C
KANS.—Topeka
Schick, Wm.............C
MD.—Baltimore
Hooper & Co. ....B
Nicholson & Son, Jas. A..C
Sisco Bros. C
MASS.—Boston
Wheeler & Co., H. A......C
MASS.—Lawrence
Pemberton Mfg. Co. (Awnings) ....AA
MICH.—Detroit
Bolles Iron & Wire Wks., J.
E. (Metal) X
Goss Co., John C........C
Lewis, Hy. B., 45 Jos. Campau av. (Corrugated Steel) ....D
MO.—Kansas City
Baker & Lockwood Mfg. Co.
A
Kansas City Roofing & Corrugating Co. (Corrugated Steel) ....D
Swearingen Shutter & Iron Works Co., 1st & Gillis (Corrugated Steel).....F
MO.—St. Joseph
Klos Mfg. Co.............C
MO.—St. Louis
Globe Iron & Foundry Co.,
9th & Victor (Corrugated Steel) ....B
Mesker & Bro., 421 S. 6th (Corrugated Steel) ...AA
Missouri Tent & Awning Co.
B
Morrison Tent & Awning Co. C
Union Iron & Foundry Co.,
1458 S. 2d (Corrugated Steel) ....B
Wenzel, Herman C
Zittlosen Mfg. Co. C
New York City
Abercrombie & Fitch (Outfits; Camping) C
Boyle & Co., John (Tents only) ....AA
De Graw, Aymar & Co.
(Flags only) ....A
Hopkins & Co., John C.....C
Magee & Son, M., 147 Fulton C
Meehan & Co., Jno., 135 Cedar ....D
McHugh, John F.........C
Rehm & Co., 141 Fulton (Awnings; Flags) ....D
Sawyers & Sons, John M..C
Wilson Mfg. Co., 3 W. 29th (Venetian) ....A
N. Y.—Rochester
Bickford Bros. C
Field Co., James ....B
OHIO—Canton
Berger Mfg. Co. (Corrugated Steel) ....AA
Eller & Co., J. H. (Corrugated Steel) ....A
OHIO—Cincinnati
National Flag Co. (Printed Flags only) ....A
Patton Co., R. J........B
Pettibone Bros. Mfg. Co.
(Flags) ....A
Ryling & Son, John.......C
OHIO—Cleveland
Wagner Mfg. Co., 15205 Euclid av. C
OHIO—Middletown
American Steel Roofing Co.
(Corrugated Steel) ...AA
OHIO—Salem
Mullins, W. H. (Metal)..A
OHIO—Toledo
Hettrick Bros. Co. (Awnings & Flags) ....B
Wilcox Co., M. I........A

AWNINGS, ETC. (Con.)
OREGON—Portland
Noon Bag Co. W. C.....B
PA.—Easton
American Flag Co. (Bunting; Silk; Muslin Flags)
C
PA.—Meadville
Shryock, John J.........C
PA.—Philadelphia
Gara, McGinley & Co., 23
S. 17th (Corrugated Steel)
B
Merritt & Co., 1024 Ridge av. (Corrugated Steel)..E
PA.—Pittsburg
Scaife Sons & Co., Wm. B.,
221 1st Av. (Corrugated Steel) ....AAA
TENN.—Chattanooga
Ornamental Iron & Wire Co.
(Corrugated Steel) ....B
WIS.—Fond du Lac
Fond Du Lac Awning & Tent Co. ....B
WIS.—Milwaukee
Joys Bros. & Co. ....B

AXES

CONN.—Collinsville
Collins Co. (Chopping)AAAA
CONN.—Southington
Peck, Stowe & Wilcox Co.
(Ice) ....AAAA
CONN.—Westport
Bradley's Sons, G. W. (Ice)
D
CONN.—Winsted
Winsted Edge Tool Works (Chopping) ....B
ILL.—Chicago
Born Packers Supply Co., H.
A. (Butchers') ....D
IND.—Alexandria
Kelly Axe Mfg. Co........C
IND.—Evansville
Evansville Tool Works (Broad; Ice; Stone Workers') ....A
IND.—Gas City
Indiana Edge Tool Co.
(Chopping) ....B
MAINE—Bangor
Bangor Edge Tool Co. (Chopping) ....D
MAINE—Belfast
Kelly & Co., B. (Chopping)
D
MAINE—Caratunk
Witham, G. T...........G
MAINE—Hallowell
North Wayne Tool Co.
(Chopping) C
MAINE—Oakland
Emerson & Stevens Mfg. Co.
(Chopping) ....D
MASS.—Arlington
Wood & Co., Wm. T. (Ice)
A
MASS.—Boston
Harvey, H. H., 608 Atlantic (Stone Workers).D
MICH.—Detroit
Anderson & Sons, W. H.
(Ice; Stone Workers)..C
MICH.—Eaton Rapids
Holcomb & Woodruff.....G
MICH.—Gladstone
Marble Safety Axe Co.
(Pocket Safety) ....B
MICH.—Grand Rapids
Munson Co., E. A........E
MO.—Kansas City
Hauck, W. J. (Stone Workers) ....F
MO.—St. Louis
Brecht Butchers Supply Co.,
G. V., 1201 Cass Av.
(Butchers') ....AAA
N. H.—East Lebanon
Emerson Edge Tool Co....X
N. J.—Newark
Atha Tool Co. (Stone)....A
Harding Edge Tool Works.F
N. J.—Rockaway
McKinnon, Wm. (Chopping)
F
N. Y.—Athens
Dernell & Co., H. F......E
N. Y.—Buffalo
White Co., L. & I. J.
(Chopping; Ice) ......A
N. Y.—Cattaraugus

AXES (Con.)

United States Edge Tool Co.
(Ice) ....D

N. Y.—Clayville
Babbitt-Harris Co. (Broad)
D

N. Y.—Cohoes
Peck Edge Tool Co. (Broad;
Chopping; Firemans; Ice)
X

N. Y.—Dunkirk
Romer Axe Co. (Boys; Half;
Three-quarter; Handled)
B

N. Y.—Napanoch
Pillsbury, M. M. (Chopping)
C

New York City
American Axe & Tool Co.,
253 B'way (All Kinds)
AAAA
Collins & Co., 212 Water
(Boys; Cast Steel; Broad;
Chopping; De Tumba;
Double Bitted; Spanish)
AAAA
Safety Fire Extinguisher
Co., 29 W. 42d (Fire)..X
Sargent & Co., 151 Leonard
(Ice) ....AAAA
Weed, Riley & Co., 11 Gold
(Chopping) ....D

N. Y.—Staatsburgh
Bodenstein & Co., J. G.
(Ice) ....D

N. Y.—Troy
Palmer Hdw. Mfg. Co.,
Green Island P. O. (Ice)
D

OHIO—Cleveland
Gerlach & Co., Peter, 27
Columbus (Ice) ....A

OHIO—Findlay
Findlay Axe & Tool Co.
(Chopping) ....A

OHIO—West Park
Norton Tool Co. (Broad;
Half; Ice; Quarter;
Bench; Boys'; Three-
quarter) C

PA.—Chester
Black & Co., H. B. (Butchers') ....AA

PA.—El Dorado
Colclesser Bros. (Chopping)
D

PA.—Eldred
Prouty & Co., C.........B

PA.—Glassport
American Axe & Tool Co.
(Inc.) Double; Bitted;
Firemans'; Ice; Bench;
Boys'; Broad; Hunters';
Side; Single Bitted;
Handled; Unhandled)
AAAA

PA.—Honesdale
White Axe Co., G. (Chop-
ping) ....D

PA.—Lewistown
Mann, Jas. H. (Chopping)
A
Mann Edge Tool Co. (Chop-
ping) ....AA

PA.—Ogontz
Hammond & Son, C. (Chop-
ping; Stone Workers')..A

PA.—Philadelphia
Germantown Tool Wks., 518
Commerce (Boys'; Hun-
ters') ....A
Plum, Fayette R., cor.
Tucker & P. R. R.
(Broad; Butchers'; Fire-
mens'; Stone) ....AA
Stortz & Son, John, 210
Vine (Ice) ....E

PA.—Pittsburg
Hubbard & Co., Murtland
Bldg. (Ice) ....AA
Klein-Logan Co., S. 13th &
Breed (Stone Workers')..A

PA.—Ridgway
Standard Axe & Tool Wks.
(Chopping) ....D

PA.—Warren
Warren Axe & Tool Co.
(Chopping; Firemans';
Ice; Turpentine) ......B

VT.—East Highgate
Rixford Mfg. Co. ....B

AXLE GREASE
See Grease

AXLES
See also Hardware; Carriage & Wagon

ALA.—Selma
Peacock's Iron Wks. (Mine
Car. &c.) C

CONN.—Hartford
Billings & Spencer (Auto-
mobile) ....AA

CONN.—Mildale
Clark Bros. & Co. (Bicycle)
A

DEL.—Wilmington
Johnson Forge Co. (Car; Locomotive) ....B

ILL.—Chicago
Chicago Screw Co., 2 N.
Canal (Bicycle) ...AAA
Griffin Wheel Co., 138 Jack-
son Boul. (Car & Locomo-
tive) ....AAA
Reading Iron & Steel Co.,
Stock Exch. Bldg. (Car &
Locomotive) ....AA
Republic Iron & Steel Co.,
108 La Salle (Car).AAAA

IND.—Fort Wayne
Bass Foundry & Machine
Co. (Iron & Steel Car;
Driving, &c.) ....AA

IND.—Logansport
Dorner Truck & Fdy. Co.
(Street Car) ....D

KY.—Louisville
Louisville Steam Forge Co.,
308 5th (Locomotive &
Car) ....B

MAINE—Portland
Portland Co. (Car & Loco-
motive) ....A

MD.—Baltimore
Baltimore Car Wheel Co.,
Patterson Av. & Payston
(Car) ....B

MASS.—Boston
American Roller Bearing
Co., 40 Binford (Ball &
Roller) ....B
Boston Forge Co., 340 Mav-
erick, E. B. (Car; Tender;
Truck; Driving) ....A
Eastern Forge Co., 70 Kilby
(Car, &c.) ....B
Jones & Co., B. M., 141
Milk (Car & Locomotive)
A

MICH.—Three Rivers
Sheffield Car Co. (Light
Car) ....A

MO.—St. Louis
American Car & Foundry
Co., 706 Chestnut (Car;
Locomotive; Mine Car)
AAAA
Helmbacher Forge & Roll-
ing Mill Co., 706 Chestnut
(Locomotive; Car, &c.)
AA
St. Louis Car Co., 8000 N.
B'way (Street Car)AAAA
St. Louis Steam Forge &
Iron Wks., Main & Miller
(Locomotive; Car, &c.).A

N. H.—Lakeport
Cole Mfg. Co. (Locomotive;
Street Car) ....A

N. J.—Carteret
Canda Mfg. Co. (Street Car)
C

N. J.—High Bridge
Taylor Iron & Steel Co. (Car
& Locomotive) ....AAAA

N. Y.—Buffalo
New York Car Wheel Wks.
(Cold Rolled) ....AA
Sizer, W. S., foot Jefferson
(Locomotive Car) ......A

New York City
Gould Coupler Co., 20 W.
34th (Car & Locomotive)
AA
New Jersey Foundry & Ma-
chine Co., 9 Murray (Car)
D

OHIO—Akron
Akron Foundry Co. (Steel)
C

33

AXLES (Con.)

OHIO—Carthage
Block-Pollak Iron Co. (Car;
Locomotive; Driving)..AA
OHIO—Cincinnati
Mowry Car Wheel Wks.
(Car) ....B
OHIO—Cleveland
Atlas Bolt & Screw Co.,
Marquette opp. Hamilton
(Mine, &c.) ....A
AA
Atlas Car & Mfg. Co. (Car)
AA
Cleveland City Forge &
Iron Co., 67 Case Av. (Lo-
comotive & Car) ......AA
Federal Mfg. Co. (Automo-
bile) ....AAA
Fulton Fdy. Co. (Car)....C
Otis Steel Co. (Ltd.) Lake
& Lawrence (Steel; Loco-
motive; Car) ....AAAA
Van Dorn & Dutton Co.. 1796
E. Madison Av. (Elect.
Car) ....B
OHIO—Columbus
Kilbourne & Jacobs Mfg. Co.
AAAA
OHIO—Lima
Lima Locomotive & Machine
Co. (Car) ....AAA
PA.—Allegheny
Carlins' Sons, Thos. (Car).A
PA.—Beaver Falls
Union Drawn Steel Co.
(Steel Car) ....AA
PA.—Eddystone
Tindel-Morris Co. (Car).AA
PA.—Fullerton
Lehigh Car Wheel & Axle
Works (Car) ....AAAA
PA.—McKees Rocks
Lockhart Iron & Steel Co.
(Car; Driving, &c.)...AA
PA.—Nazareth
Nazareth Fdy. & Machine
Co. ....B
PA.—Philadelphia
Brill Co., J. G., Woodland
Av. & 62d (Street Car)
AAAA
Cambria Steel Co., Arcade
Bldg. (Steel; Car; Loco-
motive) ....AAAA
Midvale Steel Co., Nice-
town (Nickel Steel; Loco-
motive; Tender; Truck;
Car) ....AAAA
Pennsylvania Steel Co., Gi-
rard Bldg. (Hammered;
Steel; Car; Locomotive)
AAAA
Pressed Steel Mfg. Co.,
Ridge Av. & Willow (Ball
Bearing; Steel; Carriage)
D
Roberts Co., A. & P. (Car)
AAAA
Standard Steel Wks., Har-
rison Bldg. (Car & Loco-
motive) ....AA
PA.—Pittsburg
Carbon Steel Co., 32d &
Smallman (Nickel Steel;
Car; Locomotive) ....A
Carnegie Steel Co., Carnegie
Bldg. S(teel; Car; Loco-
motive) ....AAAA
Jones & Laughlins (Ltd.)
(Car) ....AAAA
Pittsburg Forge & Iron Co.,
10th & Peni Av. (Ham-
mered; Locomotive; Car)
A
PA.—Reading
Reading Iron Co. (Driving,
&c.) ....AAAA
PA.—South Bethlehem
Bethlehem Steel Co. (Nickel
Steel; Car; Locomotive,
&c.) ....AAAA
PA.—Titusville
Titusville Forge Co. (Car
& Locomotive) ....B
PA.—Wilkesbarre
Vulcan Iron Wks. (Car &
Locomotive) ......AAAA
VA.—Richmond
Johnson & Co., J. R. (Loco-
motive; Car, &c.) ....D
Tredegar Co. (Car) ..AAA

BACK-GROUNDS

IND.—La Porte
Carter & Lay (Photo)....X

BACKING

CONN.—New Haven
Kissinger & Geiger (Picture
Frame) C
ILL.—Chicago
Story Furnishing Co., 209
So. Chuton (Cloth) .....D
ME.—Foxcroft
Ranger & Ayer Mfg. Co.
(Picture) ....D
MO.—St. Louis
Webber Moulding Co. J. R.,
Cass Av. & 21st (Picture
Fibre) ....B
N. Y.—Brooklyn
Allmann W., 71 Leonard
(Shoe Goods) C
OHIO—Cincinnati
Knerr Paper Co. Lewis
(Minor) ....A
WIS.—Two Rivers
Hamilton Mfg. Co. (Wood-
en, Electrotype) .....AA

BACKS

CONN.—Waterbury
Matthews & Willard Co.
(Stamped Metal; Metallic;
Comb) ....AAAA
White Co., Luther C. (But-
ton) C
ILL.—Chicago
Smith, David A. (Buggy).G
IND.—New Castle
Krell French Piano Co. (Pia-
no) ....AA
IOWA—Dubuque
Adams Co. (Iron Chimney
Stove) ....A
N. Y.—Brooklyn
Perfection Book Back Co.,
427 Hamilton Av. (Book)
D
N. Y.—Cortland
Davis Mfg. Co., J. E. (Pia-
no) ....B
New York City
Lalance & Grosjean Mfg.
Co., 19 Cliff (Sink) AAAA
Froelich, A. (Est of) (Fire)
B
Jackson Co., Wm. H., 29 E.
17 (Fire) ....A
Mott Iron Wks., J. L. (Iron
Chimney) ....AA
N. Y.—Olean
Tanner's Shoe Stock Co.
(Brush) ....B
OHIO—Piqua
Piqua Handle & Mfg. Co.
(Brush) ....A
PA.—Philadelphia
Harrison's Sons, W. H.
(Fire) ....E
R. I.—Providence
Van Stone Mfg. Co. (Brush)
X
WIS.—Milwaukee
Rundle Mfg. Co. (Enameled
Iron Sink) ....A

BADGES

See also Jewelry

COLO.—Denver ..
Denver Novelty Wks. &
Mfg. Co. ....D
CONN.—Bridgeport
Schwerdtte Stamp Co. ....F
MD.—Baltimore
Torsch & Franz Badge Co.,
332 N. Howard (Silk)..F
MASS.—Attleborro
Robbins, Chas. M. (Police)
C
Robbins Mfg. Co., Jno. (Me-
tal) ....E
MASS.—Boston
Woodman Mfg. & Supply
Co. (& Medals) ......F
N. J.—Newark
Durand & Co. (Inc.) (Gold
& Silver) ....AA
International Badge & Nov-
elty Co. (Society etc.).D

BADGES (Con.)

Whitehead & Hoag Co. (Metal; Advertising; Firemen's) ....AAA
New York City
American Railway Supply Co., 24 Park Pl. (Embroidered; Police) X
Braxmer & Co., C. G., 10 Maiden Lane (Metal) (Gold; Silver) ....B
Cairns & Bro. (Firemen's) D
Cooke, Robt. F. ....F
French, S. A. ....B
Koster Co., C. H. (Embroidered; Silk) ....D
Lamb, J. & R. (Gold; Silver) D

New York Stencil Wks. (Firemen's) ....D
New York Woven Label Mfg. Co., 262 Canal (Woven) ....D
Stafford Co., Nelson, 66 Fulton (Metal) ....F
OHIO—Cincinnati
Pettibone Bros. Mfg. Co. (Metal) ....A
OHIO—Columbus
Lilly & Co., The M. C. AAAA
PA.—Philadelphia
Quint & Son, S. H. (Metal) C
R. I.—Providence
Irons & Russell (Gold)....A
WIS.—Milwaukee
Schwaab Stamp & Seal Co. C

BAGGERS

See also Agr. Implts.

IND.—Richmond
Gaar Scott Co. (Grain) AAAA
MICH.—Port Huron
Port Huron Engine & Thresher Co. (Threshing Machine) ....AAA
MINN.—Minneapolis
Minneapolis Threshing Machine Co. (Grain) ....AAAA
OHIO—Napoleon
Morning Star Mfg. Co. (Threshing Machine) ..B
PA.—Waynesboro
Geiser Mfg. Co. (Threshing Machine) ....AAAA
WIS.—Racine
Case Threshing Mach. Co., J. I. (Threshing Machine) AAAA

BAGGING

CAL.—Oakland
California Cotton Mills Co. (Cotton) ....AA
CAL.—San Francisco
Neville & Co. (Inc.) ....A
GA.—Atlanta
Fulton Bag & Cotton Mills (Jute; etc.) ....A
GA.—Augusta
Riverside Mills (Cotton AA
GA.—Columbus
Friedlander & Co., Julius (Cotton) ....E
ILL.—Chicago
Neahr & Co., M. J., 89 S. Clinton ....A
IND.—Peru
Peru Bagging Mfg. Co. (Jute) ....B
MD.—Baltimore
U. S. Cotton Duck Corporation ....AAAA
MASS.—Boston
Ludlow Mfg. Co. (Gunny & Jute) ....AAAA
MASS.—Springfield
Iroquois Mfg. Co., 275 Main F
MINN.—Minneapolis
Hardwood Mfg. Co., 101 S. 3d Av. ....A
MISS.—Columbus
Tombigbee Cotton Mills (Cotton) C
MO.—St. Louis
American Mfg. Co., 220 N. 4th (Jute) ......AAAA
Bemis Bros. Bag Co., 601 S. 4th (Jute; etc.) ...AAAA

BAGGING (Con.)

Home Cotton Mills (Cotton) AAAA
N. H.—Manchester
Stark Mills (Cotton) AAAA
N. Y.—Brooklyn
Empire State Bag Co., 742 Wythe Av. (Flax ; Jute) Cotton) C
N. Y.—Cohoes
Harmony Mills ......AAAA
New York City
American Mfg. Co., 65 Wall (Gunny; Jute) ....AAAA
Collins, J. Ross, 197 West (Jute; Cotton) ....D
Halstead & Co., E. S., 75 Pearl ....B
Hoffman-Corr Mfg. Co., 107 Duane ....AA
Kurtz & Co., 2 Stone ....G
Waterbury Rope Co. (Cotton) ....AAAA
N. C.—Concord
Odell Mfg. Co. C
N. C.—Franklinville
Franklinville Mfg. Co. (Cotton) ....B
N.C.—Wilmington
Willard Bag & Mfg. Co. (Cotton & Burlap Bags) D
OHIO—Cincinnati
King Mfg. Co., Front & Main (Cotton; Burlap; etc.) ....D
Raymond Bag Co., 317 John (Cotton) ....D
OREGON—Portland
Ames & Harris (Inc.) (Jute; etc.) C
PA.—Philadelphia
Bailey & Co., John T., S. Water & Morris (Jute; Burlap) ....AAAA
S. C.—Charleston
Charleston Bagging Mfg. Co. (Cotton; Jute) ....AAAA
S. C.—Cherokee Falls
Cherokee Falls Mfg. Co..AA
TENN.—Jackson
Jackson Fibre Co. (Cotton Cloth) ....AAAA
TENN.—Nashville
Morgan & Hamilton Co. ..A
Tennessee Mfg. Co. .....D
TEXAS—Galveston
Galveston Bagging & Cordage Co. (Jute) ....AA

BAGS

Miscellaneous
See also Leather Goods

ARK.—Little Rock
Little Rock Tent & Awning Co. (Cotton Picking)....C
CAL.—Oakland
California Cotton Mills (Cotton) ....AA
CAL.—San Francisco
California Jute Mill Co., S California (Grain; Sugar; Coffee; Wool) ....B
Neville & Co. (Inc.), 31 California (Grain, &c.)..A
COLO.—Denver
Denver Tent & Awning Co. (Ore) C
CONN.—Middletown
Palmer, I. L. (School) .AAA
CONN.—Naugatuck
Goodyear's India Rubber Glove Mfg. Co. (Grain; Rubber; Gas; Navy; Sponge; Game; Toilet; Brush; Saddle) ..AAAA
CONN.—New Haven
Seamless Rubber Co. (Rubber; Ice) ....AA
GA.—Atlanta
Atlanta Paper Co. (Hardware; Paper; Flour)...A
Fulton Bag & Cotton Mills (Cotton, &c.) ....AA
GA.—Dalton
Smith, M. D. & H. L. (Corn) ....D
ILL.—Chicago
Beckley-Ralston Co. (Tool) C
Charmon Co., H., Market & Rand (Coal) ....AA
Chicago Rubber Brokerage

35

BAGS (Con.)

Co. (Rubber Hat) .....E
Chicago Sporting Goods Mfg.
Co., 126 Jefferson (Base
Ball Bat; Punching) ..B
Cook & Bro., E. C. (Cart-
ridge ; Office Mail)...A
Haskell Bros. (Tourists';
Traveling) ....A
Lanz, Owen & Co. (Gulf;
Leather) ....A
Morgan & Wright, 333 W.
Lake (Gas Engine) ....A
Neahr & Co., M. J., 89 S.
Clinton (Grain; Cotton;
Jute; Burlap) ....A
Wilt, Chas. T. (Traveling;
Railroad Mail; Toilet)..B

IND.—Indianapolis
Armstrong & Co., Wm. H.
(Surgical Emergency) ..B

IND.—Madison
Eagle Cotton Mills Co.
(Brown Cotton; Muslin)
AA

KY.—Grahamton
Grahamton Mfg. Co. (Seam-
less Grain) ....B

LA.—New Orleans
Delta Bag Co. (Safety Ship-
ping) C
Gulf Bag Co. (Burlap;
Sugar Filter) C

MAINE—Lewiston
Androscoggin Mills (Grain,
&c.) ....AAA
Bates Mfg. Co. (Grain)
AAAA

MAINE—Kennebunk
Leatheroid Mfg. Co. (Imi-
tation Leather Traveling)
A

MAINE—Westbrook
Dana Warp Mills (Grain,
&c.) ....B

MD.—Baltimore
U. S. Cotton Duck Corpora-
tion (Seamless Grain, &c.)
AAAA

MASS.—Andover
Tyer Rubber Co. (Rubber
Gas; Ice; Sponge) ....AA

MASS.—Athol
Bates Bros. Co. (Chatelaine)
B

MASS.—Boston
Bacon, Chas. A. (Felt)..E
Boston Belting Co. (Rubber
Hat) ....AAAA
Clifton Mfg. Co. (Rubber
Gas) ....A
Davidson Rubber Co. (Rub-
ber; Ice; Gas; Sponge).A
Dennison Mfg. Co. (Opera
Glass) ....AAA
Ludlow Mfg. Co. (Jute; Bur-
lap; Linen) ......AAAA

MASS.—Springfield
Iroquois Mfg. Co., 275 Main
(Feed) ....F

MASS.—Westboro
Hunt Mfg. Co. (Tool; Bi-
cycle Tool) ....B

MASS.—Worcester
Hanson & Sons, Chas. F.
(Musical Instrument) ..E
Warren Leather Goods Co.
(Leather) ....A

MICH.—Belding
Ballow Basket & Bag Co.
(Coal; Coke) ....D

MICH.—Detroit
Detroit Bag & Mfg. Co....A

MICH.—Grand Rapids
Coye, Chas. A. (Coal; Coke)
D

MINN.—Minneapolis
Hardwood Mfg. Co., 101 S.
3d Av. (Burlap; Cotton;
Jute; Grain) ....A

MO.—St. Louis
Bemis Bros. Bag Co., 601
S. 4th (Jute, &c.)..AAAA
Chase Bag Co., H. & L., 18
N. Main (Grain; Cotton;
Jute; Burlap; Feed; Bal-
last) ....AA
Meyer, Bannermann & Co.
(Saddle) ....AAA
Strauss Saddlery Co., Jacob
(Saddle) ....A
Zittlosen Mfg. Co. (Ore;

BAGS (Con.)

Feed) ....B

N. H.—Manchester
Stark Mills (Grain, &c.)
AAAA

N. H.—Plymouth
Draper & Maynard Co.
(Bowling Ball; Carryall)
A

N. J.—Jersey City
Mehl & Co., John (Hand;
Tourists'; School).....AA

N. J.—Mt. Holly
Standard Hicks Hammock
Co. (School) C

N. J.—Newark
Osborne & Co., C. S. (Tool;
Saddle) ....B
Peddie & Co., T. B. (Inc.),
(School; Golf; Hand;
Traveling; Tool; Office;
Railroad Mail) ......AA
Peters Harness & Saddlery
Co. (Saddle; Feed) C

N. Y.—Albany
Huyck & Sons, F. C. (Sleeping) ....AA

N. Y.—Brooklyn
Brantigan, Robt., N. 10th
& Roebling (Filter) C
Empire State Bag Co., 742
Wythe Av. (Flax; Jute).C
Gair Co., Robt. (Water)
AAA

N. Y.—Buffalo
American Buffalo Robe Co.
(Sleeping) ....A

N. Y.—Cohoes
Harmony Mills (Cotton;
Grain) ....AAAA

N. Y.—Fulton
Victoria Paper Mills Co.
(Flour; Cement; Nail
Sacks; Sugar Bags)....B

N. Y.—Johnstown
Ricketts Chamois Novelty
Co. (Chamois Watch)...B

N. Y.—Matteawan
New York Rubber Co. (Rub-
ber Hat) ....AA

New York City
Abercrombie & Fitch, 314
B'way (Sleeping) C
American Railway Supply
Co. (Office Mail) X
Boyle & Co., John, 112
Duane (Office Mail; Feed;
Traveling) ....AA
Chelsea Jute Mills (Seam-
less) ....A
Collins, J. Ross, 197 West
(Jute; Cotton) ....D
Galewski, A., 90 Chambers
(Leather Mail) ....D
Crouch & Fitzgerald (Hand;
Tourists'; Traveling)...A
Goodyear Rubber Co. (Rub-
ber; Sleeping; Gas; Ice;
Navy) ....AAAA
Gutta Percha & Rubber
Mfg. Co. (Rubber Hat;
Gas) ....AAAA
Hahn & Co., A. (Hand;
Traveling) ....B
Halstead & Co. E. S., 75
Pearl (Ballast; Burlap;
Cotton; Coffee; Flour;
Grain; Gunny; Hemp;
Jute) ....B

We manufacture Bur-
lap and Cotton Bags of
every description, includ-
ing Grain, Flour, Cement,
Sugar, Fertilizer and
Coffee. Also Wool Sacks,
Ham, Bacon, Pork and
Shoulder Bags.

We make a specialty
of the manufacture of
Burlap and Cotton Beef
Bags; also Burlap and
Cotton Sheep Bags.

We deal also in second
hand Bags of every de-
scription, and can furnish
any bag that may be in-
quired for, either new or
second hand. We also
deal in Twine and Tar-
red Sisal.

BAGS (Con.)

Hodgman Rubber Co. (Rubber; Confectioners'; Face; Gas; Ice; Navy; Sponge; Throat; Cartridge) ...AA

Hoffman-Corr Mfg. Co., 107 Duane ....AA

Ingersoll & Bro., R. H., 51 Maiden Lane (Punching) A

Johnson, F. Coit (Office Mail; Filter) ....A

Kent, Percy (Jute) ......A

Kurtz & Co., 2 Stone (Grain; Burlap) ....G

Lissa & Co., Henry (Hand; Tourists'; Traveling)...B

Livingston & Co., L. (Chatelaine) ....B

McHugh, John F. (Ballast; Feed) C

Matthews & Co. (Traveling) D

Mattson Rubber Co. (Rubber; Ice; Sponge) .....B

Mechanical Rubber Co. (Rubber Gas) ....AAAA

Meinecke & Co., 50 Park Pl. (Rubber) C

Peerless Rubber Mfg. Co. (Rubber Gas) ......AA

Plath & Son, Chas. (Live Fish) ....F

Rehm & Co., 141 Fulton (Feed) ....D

Smith, Worthington & Co. (Saddle) ....AA

Spalding & Bros., A. G. (Inc.) (Cartridge; Game; Punching) ......AAAA

Spencer Optical Co. (Opera Glass) C

Tingue, Brown & Co. (Sugar; Filter) ....D

Tonk & Bro., Wm., 452 10th Av. (Musical Inst.)....C

Von Lengerke & Detmold (Cartridge; Game) .....A

Walbridge & Co., J. H., 337 B'way (School) ....B

N. Y.—Portchester

Lane & Bro., W. T. (Coal; Coke) ....F

N. Y.—Rochester

Likly & Co., Henry (Traveling) ....A

N. Y.—Watertown

Taggart Bros. Co. (Flour; Cement Sacks) ....A

N. Y.—Yonkers

Van O'Linda Mfg. Co. (Coal) ....H

N. C.—Concord

Odell Mfg. Co. (Grain, &c.) C

N. C.—Durham

Golden Belt Mfg. Co. (Tobacco, &c.).........AAA

N. C.—Franklinville

Franklinville Mfg. Co. (Seamless) ....B

N. C.—Randleman

Naomi Falls Mfg. Co. (Seamless Grain; Salt, &c.) ....D

N. C.—Wilmington

Willard Bag & Mfg. Co. (Burlap; Cotton) .....D

N. C.—Worthville

Worth Mfg. Co. (Seamless) X

OHIO—Akron

Akron Rubber Wks. (B. T. Goodrich Co.) (Rubber; Gas; Ice; Confectioners' Iceing) ....AAAA

Rubber Specialty Co. (Rubber) X

OHIO—Canton

Gilliam Mfg. Co. (Tool)...A

OHIO—Cincinnati

Cincinnati Bag Co., 2d & Walnut (Cotton Seamless) C

King Mfg. Co., Front & Main (Cotton; Burlap, &c.) ....D

Raymond Bag Co., 317 John (Cotton) ....D

Seinsheimer Paper Co. (Hardware; Shaft Covering; Sugar; Bicycle Tool) B

BAGS (Con.)

OHIO—Cleveland

Adams Bag Co. (Burlap; Paper) ....A

Federal Mfg. Co. (Bicycle; Automobile Tool)..AAAA

Likly & Rockett (Traveling) B

OHIO—Toledo

Hettrick Bros. Co. (Cotton) B

OREGON—Portland

Ames & Harris (Inc.) (Grain, &c.) C

Noon Bag Co., W. C. (Grain, &c.) ....B

PA.—Philadelphia

Bailey & Co., John T., S. Water & Morris (Jute; Burlap) ....AAAA

Belber Trunk & Bag Co. (Traveling) ....B

Patterson, Holibfield Mfg. Co. (Knit School) C

Paxson Co., J. W. (Dusting) AA

Reach Co., A. J. (Punching) AA

Rumpp & Sons, C. F. (Opera Glass) ....AAA

Shipley, Malcolm A. (Live Fish) ....D

Weston & Wells Mfg. Co. (Knit School) ....B

PA.—Pittsburg

Tarentum Paper Mills (Cement; Flour; Paper).AAA

R. I.—Providence

American Supply Co. (Bleeding) ....AA

Davol Rubber Co. (Rubber Gas; Ice; Throat) .,..AA

R. I.—Woonsocket

Ray Cotton Co. (Seamless) AA

S. C.—Charleston

Royal Bag & Yarn Mfg. Co. (Seamless; Flour) ....A

TENN.—Columbia

Columbia Cotton Mill Co. (Grain; Seamless; Paper) A

TENN.—Jackson

Jackson Fibre Co. (Cotton Cloth) ....AAAA

TENN.—Nashville

Morgan & Hamilton Co. (Grain, &c.) ....A

Tennessee Mfg. Co. (Seamless; Grain; Cloth) ...D

TEXAS—Sherman

Sherman Cotton Mills (Seamless; Grain) .....B

VA.—Petersburg

Seward Trunk & Bag Co. (Hand) ....AA

VA.—Richmond

Millhiser & Co., M. (Tobacco) ....B

WIS.—Milwaukee

Abel & Bach Co. (Traveling; Club) ....AA

Carpeles Co. (Traveling)..A

Milwaukee Bag Co., 206 So. Water (Printed or Plain Cotton; Paper; Burlap; Fur; Flour; Grain; Sugar; Coffee; Seeds; Cement; Wool; Seamless Cotton Grain & 2nd hand) A

Western Bag Mfg. Co.....F

WIS.—Oshkosh

Schmit Bros. Trunk Co. (Tourist; Traveling) ...A

WIS.—Racine

Secor Trunk Co., M. M. (Hand; School; Traveling; Tool) ....A

WIS.—West Superior

Lake Superior Bag Co. (Grain, &c.) ......AAAA

BAGS (PAPER)

CAL.—San Francisco

Crown Paper Co., 707 Front A

CONN.—Kensington

American Paper Goods Co..B

GA.—Atlanta

Atlanta Paper Co., 73 S Pryor ....A

BAGS: PAPER *(Con.)*

National Paper Co., 257-263
Decatur C
ILL.—Chicago
Hollis & Duncan, 10 Market ....A
Tarentum Paper Mills, 451
5th Av. ....AAA
Union Bag & Paper Co.
AAAA
Wheeler, Fisher & Co.,
Fisher Bldg. C
IND.—Elkhart
Consolidated Paper & Bag
Co. C
IND.—Ft. Wayne
Fisher Bros. ....A
IND.—Indianapolis ..
Capital Paper Co. ......A
Indiana Paper & Bag Co...C
IOWA—Rumford Falls
Continental Paper Bag Co.
AAA
MD.—Baltimore
Columbia Paper Bag Co...B
Smith-Dixon Co. ....A
Stevens' Bros., C. E......C
MD.—Frederick
Great Southern Printing &
Mfg. Co., The..........C
MASS.—Boston
Continental Paper Bag Co.,
406 Atlantic Av. .....AA
Hollingsworth & Whitney
Co., 60 India ......AAAA
MO.—St. Louis
Cupples Woodenware Co.,
S. ....AAAA
NEBR.—Omaha
Marshall Paper Co. C
N. J.—Jersey City
Riegel Sack Co., 333 Washington ....B
N. Y.—Ballston Spa
Union Bag & Paper Co.
AAAA
N. Y.—Canajoharie
Arkell & Smith ....A
N. Y.—Fulton
Victoria Paper Mills Co...B
N. Y.—Brooklyn
Gair Co., Robt......AAAA
Phoenix Paper Co. (Ltd.), 89
John C
New York City
Bailey, Christopher, 320
Broadway ....A
Belden, M. B., 320 B'way.A
Clochessy, John, 150 Worth
C
Columbia Paper Bag Co., 329
Greenwich ....B
Continental Paper Bag Co.,
10 Battery Pl. ......AAA
Consolidated Bag Co. ....B
Hefferman Paper Co., 142
Worth C
Hollingsworth & Whitney
Co., 309 B'way ....AAAA
Union Bag & Paper Co., 1
B'way ....AAAA
Walton & Co., D. S., 132
Franklin ....AAAA
N. Y.—Sandy Hill
Union Bag & Paper Co.
AAAA
N. Y.—Watertown
Taggart Bros. Co. ....A
N. Y.—Westfield
Kent, Hermon L. C
OHIO—Akron
Cleveland-Akron Paper Co.,
The ....AAAA
OHIO—Chagrin Falls
Adams Bag Co. ....A
OHIO—Cincinnati
Bowen, E., 120 E. 6th...B
Chatfield & Woods Co., Central Av. & 4th.......A
Cincinnati Cordage & Paper
Co., 641 Main.........B
Curry Woodenware Co., 22
E. 2d ....B
Dirm & Wing Paper Co.,
318 Elm ....AA
Seinsheimer Paper Co., 1118-
1122 Bank ....B
OHIO—Cleveland
Adams Bag Co., Caxton
Bldg. ....
Cleveland Bag Factory, 86-
100 Bank ....AAA
Cleveland-Akron Paper Co.,

BAGS: PAPER *(Con.)*

652 B'way ....A
Standard Bag & Paper Co.,
540 Forest ....B
OHIO—Dayton
Aull Bros. Paper Co., 136
W. 5th ....B
Dayton Paper Novelty Co.,
1st & Foundry C
Kinnard Mfg. Co., Clinton
& Bacon ....B
Nixon & Costello Co.....E
Weston Paper & Mfg. Co..C
OHIO—Lockland
Fox Paper Co...........A
OHIO—Middletown
Advance Bag Co., The....B
Gardner-Colin Co........A
Wardlow-Thomas Paper Co.
AA
OREGON—Oregon City
Crown Paper Co. ....A
OREGON—Portland
Pacific Paper Co.........B
PA.—Philadelphia
Boyer, Evans & Co., 502
Commerce C
Griswold, Wm. A., 7 N.
Front C
Haverstick & Son, A. ....D
McDowell Paper Mills....B
Royal & Co., Thos. M., 3d
& Locust ....B
Silvers, Frank, 1712 N.
Camac ....A
Spangler & Co., E. J., 507
Ludlow C
Wilson's Sons Co., Henry L.,
43 N. 3d C
PA.—Pittsburg
Tarentum Paper Mills, 1019
Liberty Av. ....AAA
PA.—Reading
Hercules Paper Bag Co.,
The C
PA.—Tarentum
Tarentum Paper Mills.AAA
TENN.—Memphis
Memphis Paper Co. C
TENN.—Nashville
Morgan & Hamilton Co....A
VA.—Richmond
Eagle Paper Co. C
Wortendyke Mfg. Co. ....B
W. VA.—Wellsburg
George Co., S. ....A
WIS.—Superior
Lake Superior Bag Co.
AAAA

BAIT
See Fishing Tackle

BAKERS
CRACKERS, ETC
ALA.—Birmingham
Birmingham Baking Co.
(National Biscuit Co.)
AAAA
ALA.—Montgomery
Dreyfus Bros. Cracker Co.
B
CAL.—Los Angeles
Bishop & Co. ....AA
Pacific Coast Biscuit Co.
AA
Southern California Cracker
Co. ....B
CAL.—Oakland
Standard Biscuit Co.....B
CAL.—Sacramento
American Biscuit Co....AA
Pacific Coast Biscuit Co.
AA
Sacramento Cracker Co....C
CAL.—San Francisco
American Biscuit Co., Battery & B'way .....AAA
Eagle Cracker & Biscuit Co.,
Mission & 11th C
Mutual Biscuit Co., 610 Battery ....B
Pacific Coast Biscuit Co.,
2d & Folsom ....AA
Standard Biscuit Co., 701
Front ....B
COLO.—Denver
Continental Biscuit Co....B
Crocker Bakery (Natl. Biscuit Co.) ....AAAA
COLO.—Pueblo

BAKERS (Con.)
Natl. Biscuit Co. (Branch Chicago, Ill.) .....AAAA
CONN.—Bridgeport
Wallace & Son, A. W.....A
CONN.—Hartford
Parks-Savage Bakery (Natl. Biscuit Co.) .....AAAA
CONN.—Manchester
Eastern Biscuit Co......A
CONN.—New Haven
New Haven Bakery (Natl. Biscuit Co.) .....AAAA
CONN.—New London
Boss & Son, C. D. ......AA
CONN.—Waterbury
Natl. Biscuit Co. (Branch Chicago, Ill.) .....AAAA
Trott Baking Co. C
D. C.—Washington
Havenner Baking Co., 472 C., N. W............AA
National Biscuit Co. (Br. Chicago, Ill.), 616 E., N. W. .....AAAA
GA.—Atlanta
Block Co., F. E.........AA
Lewis, T. S.............B
GA.—Augusta
Claussen, H. H..........C
GA.—Macon
Winn-Johnson Co. C
GA.—Savannah
Solomon & Son, H......AA
ILL.—Aurora
Mason Factory (Natl. Biscuit Co.) ....AAAA
ILL.—Chicago
Brenner, D. F. (Natl. Biscuit Co.), 76 O'Brien AAAA
Bryce Baking Co., 22 N. Lincoln ....A
Durand & Kasper Co., 153 W. Lake ....AAA
Kennedy Bakery (Natl. Biscuit Co.) .....AAAA
McMahon Cracker & Biscuit Co., 46 S. Green........B
Moody & Waters Co., 283 W. Congress (Whol. Pies)..B
Natl. Biscuit Co., 205 La Salle ....AAAA
Schmidt Baking Co., 75 Clybourn Av. ....A
ILL.—Decatur
Decatur Bakery (Natl. Biscuit Co.) ....AAAA
ILL.—Peoria
Natl. Biscuit Co. (Br. Chicago, Ill.) .....AAAA
Thomas & Clarke ....A
IND.—Evansville
Marsh-Scantelin Bakery (Natl. Biscuit Co.).AAAA
IND.—Fort Wayne
Fox Bakery (Natl. Biscuit Co.) ....AAAA
Perfection Biscuit Co....B
IND.—Indianapolis
Bryce Baking Co.........B
Century Biscuit Co.......B
Hitz Bakery (Natl. Biscuit Co.), 150 Virginia..AAAA
Natl. Biscuit Co. (Br. Chicago, Ill.) .....AAAA
Parrott-Taggert Bakery (Natl. Biscuit Co.), 131 S. Penn........AAAA
Home Cracker Co. ......B
Lafayette Cracker & Confect. Co., Inc......B
IND.—Richmond
Natl. Biscuit Co. (Br. Chicago, Ill.) .....AAAA
IND.—Terre Haute
Miller Bakery (Natl. Biscuit Co.) ....AAAA
IOWA—Burlington
Natl. Biscuit Co. (Br. Chicago, Ill.) .....AAAA
IOWA—Cedar Rapids
Continental Biscuit Co....B
IOWA—Clinton
Item & Sons, L. (Inc.)...C
IOWA—Davenport
Crescent Macaroni & Cracker Co. C
IOWA—Des Moines
Continental Biscuit Co...A
DesMoines Baking Co.....B
National Biscuit Co. (Br.

BAKERS (Con.)
Chicago, Ill.) .....AAAA
IOWA—Dubuque
Albee Bakery (Natl. Biscuit Co.) ....AAAA
IOWA—Sioux City
National Biscuit Co. (Br. Chicago, Ill.)....AAAA
KY.—Louisville
U. S. Bakery (Natl. Biscuit Co.) ....AAAA
LA.—New Orleans
Continental Biscuit Co., 516 S. Peters ....A
Langles Factry (Amer. Biscuit Co.) ....AA
Reiss Co., J. J., 423 Decatur ....B
MAINE—Auburn
Huston & Co., T. A.......B
MAINE—Bangor
Bangor Biscuit Co. ......B
National Biscuit Co. (Br. Chicago, Ill.)....AAAA
MAINE—Portland
Shaw & Co., G. C.........B
MD.—Baltimore
Baltimore Biscuit Co., 412 W. German ....B
Maryland Biscuit Co., 516 S. Charles ....A
Mason Bakery (Natl. Biscuit Co.), 17 E. Pratt AAAA
Stiltman Bakery (Natl. Biscuit Co.) ....AAAA
MASS.—Boston
Austin, Young & Co., 116 Commercial ....AA
Potter & Wrightington, 60 Commercial ....AA
U. S. Bakery (Natl. Biscuit Co.) ....AAAA
MASS.—Brockton
National Biscuit Co. (Br. Chicago, Ill.) .....AAAA
Washburn & Co., F. B...A
MASS.—Cambridge
National Biscuit Co. (Br. Chicago, Ill.) .....AAAA
MASS.—Chelsea
Austin, Young & Co.....AA
MASS.—Lawrence
Bruce Bakery (Natl. Biscuit Co.) ....AAAA
MASS.—Milton
Bent & Co. (Natl. Biscuit Co.) ....AAAA
MASS.—New Bedford
Snell Bakery (Natl. Biscuit Co.) ....AAAA
MASS.—Newburyport
Pearson & Son (Natl. Biscuit Co.) ....AAAA
MASS.—North Adams
Clark & Co., H. W.......AA
MASS.—Pittsfield
Teeling Bakery (Natl. Biscuit Co.) ....AAAA
MASS.—Springfield
Carr Bakery (Natl. Biscuit Co.) ....AAAA
Natl. Biscuit Co. (Br. Chicago, Ill.) .....AAAA
MASS.—Worcester
Natl. Biscuit Co. (Br. Chicago, Ill.) .....AAAA
Natural Food Co. (Br. Niagara Falls, N. Y.)..AAAA
MICH.—Bay City
Whitney-Plum Bakery (Natl Biscuit Co.).AAAA
MICH.—Detroit
Haste-Harris Bakery (Natl. Biscuit Co.), 9 Orchard AAAA
Kruce & Co., E. J., 243 Lafayette C
Vail-Crane Bakery (Natl. Biscuit Co.), 40 Woodbridge E ....AAAA
MICH.—Grand Rapids
Sears Bakery (Natl. Biscuit Co.) ....AAAA
MICH.—Jackson
National Biscuit Co. (Br. Chicago, Ill.) .....AAAA
MICH.—Lansing
Hammell Cracker Co.....B
MICH.—Saginaw
National Biscuit Co. (Br. Chicago, Ill.) .....AAAA
MINN.—Duluth

BAKERS (Con.)

Duluth Cracker Bakery

Stolzenbach Bakery (Br. (Natl. Biscuit Co.).AAAA

MINN.—Minneapolis

Biscuit Co.'s Works, 17 S. 3d ....,.A

Kennedy Agency (Nat. Biscuit Co.)......AAAA

Lillibridge Bremner Factory (Natl. Biscuit Co.), 15 S. 3d. ....AAAA

National Biscuit Co. (Br. Chicago, Ill.) .....AAAA

MINN.—St. Paul

Griggs, Cooper & Co., 242 E. 3d ....AAA

National Biscuit Co. (Br. Chicago, Ill.) .....AAAA

MINN.—St. Peter

St. Peter Biscuit Co......C

MINN.—Wadena

Wadena Cracker Co. C

MO.—Kansas City

Loose-Wiles Cracker & Candy Co., 8th & Santa Fe ....AAA

Loose Bros. Factory (Natl. Biscuit Co.), 200 Main AAAA

MO.—St. Louis

Bayle, Geo. A., 113 S. 2d.B

Columbia Biscuit Co., Papin & 14th.........AA

Columbia Pretzel & Bakery Co., 1721 De Kalb......C

Dozier Bakery (Natl. Biscuit Co.), Morgan & 16th AAAA

Manewal-Lange Biscuit Co., Clark Av. & 15th.......A

Pfenniger Pretzel & Bakery Co., 1409 S. 8th........C

St. Louis Cracker Co., 1815 Chouteau Av. C

Union Biscuit Co., 1106 No. 6th ....B

MONT.—Helena

National Biscuit Co. (Br. Chicago, Ill.) .....AAAA

NEBR.—Lincoln

Jones-Douglas Bakery (Natl. Biscuit Co.) ...,.AAAA

NEBR.—Omaha

National Biscuit Co. (Br. Chicago, Ill.) .....AAAA

N. H.—Concord

Norris & Co., J. C.......A

N. J.—Cape May

Cape May Baking Co.....C

N. J.—Newark

Longstreet, Morton & Mitchell, 81 Mt. Prospect Av. AA

Manhattan Biscuit Co., 84 Brunswick ....A

Medlar Co., A. J., Ltd....B

Mulford & Althen Bakery (Natl. Biscuit Co.) 265 Mt. Pleasant Av. ..AAAA

Newark Bakery (Natl. Biscuit Co.), 30 Lombardy AAAA

N. J.—Trenton

Exton & Co., A.........AA

Original Trenton Cracker Co. C

N. Y.—Albany

Larrabee Bakery (Natl. Biscuit Co.) ....AAAA

N. Y.—Binghamton

National Biscuit Co. (Br. Chicago, Ill.) .....AAAA

N. Y.—Brooklyn

National Biscuit Co. (Br. Chicago, Ill.), 42 Fulton AAAA

N. Y.—Buffalo

Faxon, Williams & Faxon.A

Niagara Bakery (Natl. Biscuit Co.) ....AAAA

Ovens Bakery (Natl. Biscuit Co.) ....AAAA

N. Y.—Canandaigua

Continental Baking Co..AA

Greives, Alex. ....B

N. Y.—Jamestown

Jamestown Bakery (Natl. Biscuit Co.) .....AAAA

N. Y.—Lansingburgh

Fox Cracker Bakery (Natl. Buiscuit Co.) ....AAAA

New York City

BAKERS (Con.)

Bowery ....B

Boss & Son, C. D. (Br. New London, Conn.), 59 Gansvoort ....AA

Clark, S. B., 496 Grand..A

Consumers Biscuit & Mfg. Co., 517 W. 19th......C

Continental Biscuit Co., 300 South ....B

Goodman & Son, 638 E. 17th C

Manhattan Biscuit Co., 394 Greenwich ....A

National Biscuit Co. (Br. Chicago, Ill.), 469 West AAAA

Plasmon Co. of America, 116 Broad ....AAA

N. Y.—Niagara Falls

Natural Food Co.....AAAA

N. Y.—Ogdensburg

Ogdensburg Bakery (Natl. Biscuit Co.) ....AAAA

N. Y.—Poughkeepsie

Poughkeepsie Cracker Co., (Natl. Biscuit Co.).AAAA

N. Y.—Rochester

Anthony Bakery (Natl. Biscuit Co.) ....AAAA

Deininger Bros. ....B

National Biscuit Co. (Br. Chicago, Ill.) .....AAAA

N. Y.—Syracuse

Grassman Bros. Bakery (Natl. Biscuit Co.).AAAA

N. Y.—Utica

Holmes Coutts Larrabee Agency (Natl. Biscuit Co.) ....AAAA

Young, Geo., Bakery......B

N. Y.—Watertown

Nill & Jess ....A

OHIO—Akron

Akron Bakery (Natl. Biscuit Co.) ....AAAA

OHIO—Cincinnati

Achor Bakery (Nat. Biscuit Co.), 456 E. 6th...AAAA

Banner Baking Co. (Simon & Well)................C

Kroger Grocery & Baking Co., 43 Vine.........AA

Langdon Bakery (Natl. Biscuit Co.), 323 Lock AAAA

Muth Bakery (Natl. Biscuit Co.), 411 Richmond.AAAA

National Biscuit Co. (Br. Chicago, Ill.) .....AAAA

Strictman's Sons Co., 12th & Plum ....B

OHIO—Cleveland

Cleveland Bakery (Natl. Biscuit Co.) ......AAAA

Ohio Bakery Co., 768 Superior ....AA

R. B. Biscuit Co., 117 Bridge ....A

Robinson Bakery (Nat. Biscuit Co.), 117 Bridge AAAA

OHIO—Columbus

Coleman & Co. C

Columbus Baking Co.....B

Felber Co. C

National Biscuit Co..AAAA

OHIO—Kenton

Kenton Cracker Co.......B

OHIO—Mansfield

Crawford-Taylor Bakery (Natl. Biscuit Co.) AAAA

OHIO—Marysville

Marysville Candy Co.......C

OHIO—Newark

Welant Bakery (Br. Natl. Biscuit Co.) ....AAAA

OHIO—Springfield

Springfield Bakery (Br. Natl. Biscuit Co.).AAAA

OHIO—Toledo

Maumee Valley Baking Co.

National Biscuit Co. (Br. Chicago, Ill.) .....AAAA

Toledo Biscuit Co., George & Locust Sts. ....A

United Baking Co........B

OHIO—Youngstown

Peyton Cracker Co., A. A..B

OHIO—Zanesville

40

BAKERS (Con.)

Anger Baking Co., 79 Natl. Biscuit Co.)..AAAA

OREGON—Portland

Bishop & Co. (Br. Los Angeles, Cal.) ....AA

Pacific Coast Biscuit Co. ....AA

PA.—Allegheny

Herd Bakery (Natl. Biscuit Co.) ....AAAA

Maginn & Co., E.......AA

National Biscuit Co. (Br. Chicago, Ill.) .....AAAA

PA.—Chester

Keebler-Weyl Baking Co..A

PA.—Erie

Sands Bakery (Natl. Biscuit Co.) ....AAAA

PA.—Philadelphia

Colonial Biscuit Co., 209 N. 19th ....,..A

Ivins Son, J. S., 625 No. Broad ....AA

Keebler-Weyl Baking Co., 258 N. 22d..........A

Medlar Co., A. J., 1434 Fairmount Av. ....B

National Biscuit Co. (Br. Chicago, Ill.) .....AAAA

Phila. Steam Bakery (F. Burns, Prop.), 118 N. 22d ....A

U. S. Biscuit Co., 1029 Ridge Av. C

PA.—Pittsburg

Hardie Bakery (Natl. Biscuit Co.), 16th & Liberty Av. ....AAAA

Marvin Bakery (Natl. Biscuit Co.), 421 Liberty Av. ....AAAA

National Biscuit Co. (Br. Chicago, Ill.), 1004 Penn. Av. ....AAAA

Pittsburg Baking Co.....B

Ward, Mackay Co., 3212 Liberty Av. ....A

PA.—Pittston

Hitchner's Bakery (Natl. Biscuit Co.) ......AAAA

PA.—Reading

National Biscuit Co. (Br. Chicago, Ill.) .....AAAA

PA.—Scranton

Kelly, M. J...............C

National Biscuit Co. (Br. Chicago, Ill.) .....AAAA

Niagara Baking Co. (Natl. Biscuit Co.) ......AAAA

Pennsylvania Baking Co...C

PA.—Wilkesbarre

Carr, J. B. C

PA.—Williamsport

Williamsport Bakery (Natl. Biscuit Co.) ......AAAA

PA.—York

Stauffer, D. F...........A

York Cracker Bakery (Natl. Biscuit Co.) .....AAAA

R. I.—Providence

Rice & Hayward ....A

S. C.—Charleston

Claussen & Co., J. C. H., 34 Market ....B

Margenhoff, O. G........C

TENN.—Chattanooga

Mountain City Milling Co.

TENN.—Memphis

National Biscuit Co. (Br. Chicago, Ill.) .....AAAA

TENN.—Nashville

Kemker Woolwine Candy & Cracker Co. ....B

National Biscuit Co. (Br. Chicago, Ill.) .....AAAA

TEXAS—Fort Worth

Ft. Worth Candy & Cracker Co. (Natl. Biscuit Co. ....AAAA

TEXAS—Galveston

National Biscuit Co. (Br. Chicago, Ill.) .....AAAA

UTAH—Salt Lake City

National Biscuit Co. (Br. Chicago, Ill.) .....AAAA

VT.—Burlington

Arbuckle Co. ....B

Burlington Bakery (Natl. Biscuit Co.) ......AAAA

VT.—Montpelier

BAKERS (Con.)

Cross & Co., C. H........B

VT.—Rutland

Hoag Bakery (Natl. Biscuit Co. ....AAAA

VT.—White River Junction

Smith & Son..............B

VA.—Alexandria

Gill Bakery (Natl. Biscuit Co.) ....

VA.—Richmond

Harrelson & Co., T. A...B

National Biscuit Co. (Br. Chicago, Ill.) .....AAAA

Southern Biscuit Works...B

WASH.—Seattle

American Biscuit Co. (Br. San Fran., Cal.).....AAA

Pacific Coast Biscuit Co. ....AA

Portland Cracker Co......AA

Seattle Candy & Cracker Co. C

Superior Cracker & Candy Co. C

WASH.—Spokane

Inland Cracker Co........C

Washington Cracker Co...B

WASH.—Tacoma

Pacific Coast Biscuit Co..AA

W. VA.—Wheeling

Wheeling Bakery (Natl. Biscuit Co.) ......AAAA

WIS.—Green Bay

Annen Candy & Biscuit Co. C

WIS.—La Crosse

La Crosse Cracker & Candy Co. ....:.B

WIS.—Milwaukee

Carpenter Underwood Factory, (Natl. Biscuit Co.), 518 Grand Av. ....AAAA

Johnston Bros. Factory (Natl. Biscuit Co.).AAAA

Johnston & Co., Robt.,Florida & Clinton ....AA

WIS.—Watertown

Woodward & Stone Co....A

BALANCES

COLO.—Denver

Ainsworth & Sons, Wm. (Assay; Chemical) .....B

Smith & Thompson (Assaying) ....D

CONN.—Bridgeport

Bridgeport Brass Co. (Spring) ....AAA

CONN.—New Britain

Landers, Frary & Clark (Spring) ....AAA

CONN.—Southington

Peck, Stow & Wilcox Co. (Assay; Spring) ...AAAA

ILL.—Chicago

American Cutlery Co. (Spring) ....AA

Coleman Hardware Co., 59 Dearborn (Sash) ....A

Fairbanks, Morse & Co. (Butchers' & Jewelers') ....AAAA

Gardner Sash Balance Co. 166 Dearborn (Sash) ..C

Pelouze Scale & Mfg. Co. (Spring) C

MASS.—Boston

Star Brass Mfg. Co. (Locomotive Spring) ....A

N. J.—Newark

National Lock Washer Co. (Sash) ....B

N. Y.—Buffalo

Buffalo Scale Co. (Butchers') ....AA

N. Y.—New Rochelle

Becker Bros. (Assaying; Jewelers') ....D

New York City

Ashcroft Mfg. Co., 85 Liberty (Locomotive Spring).A

Becker, Christian, 5 Maiden Lane (Assaying) ......D

Chatillon & Sons, John, 85 Cliff (Butchers'; Spring)..............A

Eimer & Amend, 205 3rd Av. (Assaying) ....AA

Fairbanks Co., 416 Broome (Assaying) ....AAAA

Forschner & Sons, Chas. (Butchers'; Spring) X

Kohlbusch, Herman, 194

BALANCES (Con.)
B'way (Bullion; Assaying; Jewelers') C
Sargent & Co., 151 Leonard (Spring) ....AAAA

N. Y.—Rochester
Caldwell Sash Balance Co. (Ship; Sash) C
Pullman Sash Balance Co. (Bicycle; Car & Spring Sash; Show & Wall Case) B

Streeter & Co., N. R. (Spring Sash) ....A

N. Y.—Syracuse
Stearns & Co., E. C. (Sash) AA

OHIO—Cicinnati
Schriver & Co., O. P. (Sash) B

PA.—Jersey Shore
American Balance Slide Valve Co. (Slide Valve) D

PA.—Philadelphia
North Bros. Mfg. Co. (Spring) ....AA
Queen & Co., 1010 Chestnut (Assaying) ....A
Troemmer, Henry, 710 Market (Assaying) .....AAA
Thomas Co., A. H., 12th & Walnut (Assaying) ....B

PA.—Pittsburg
Scientific Materials Co. ..C

BALCONIES

ILL.—Chicago
Braumveller & Son, Henry (Iron) ....B

MICH.—Detroit
Bolles Iron & Wire Wks., J. E. (Arch'l Iron) ....D

New York City
Fiske Iron Works, J. W. (Iron) ....B

OHIO—Akron
Burger Iron Co. (Iron) ..C

OHIO—Cleveland
Van Dorn Iron Wks. Co. (Iron) ....AA

OHIO—Wapakoneta
Wapakoneta Machine Co. (Telephone) C

BALLAST

CONN.—New Haven
Connecticut Trap Rock Quarries (Railroad) ..B

N. J.—Jersey City
Williams & Son, E. A. (Lead) ....AA

New York City
U. S. Foundry Co. (Lead) F

OHIO—Columbus
Franklin Stone Co. (Railroad) C

PA.—Harrisburg
Walton Quarries (Blue Limestone) ....E

PA.—So. Bethlehem
General Crushed Stone Co. (Railroad) ....E

PA.—Tyrone
American Lime & Stone Co. (Railroad) ....AAAA

TEXAS—El Paso
El Paso Ice & Refrigerator Co. (Railroad) ....A

WIS.—Kenosha
Davy Burnt Clay Ballast Co. (Railroad) ....A

BALLERS

ILL.—Quincy
Ertel, George, Co. (Steel) A

MASS.—Lowell
Entwistle Co., T. C. ....B

OHIO—Miamisburg
Hoover & Gamble Co. ....B

BALLOONS

New York City
American Flag Co., 45 Elizabeth (Toy; Paper) ....A
Behrend & Rothschild, 355 Broadway (Rubber) ..B
Detwiller & Street Fireworks Mfg. Co. (Toy; Paper) .A

OHIO—Akron
Faultless Rubber Co. (Rubber Air) ....AA

BALLOONS (Con.)
OHIO—Cincinnati
Due Fireworks Co., A. L. (Paper) C

BALLOTS

MICH.—Port Huron
Tunnel City Regalia Co. ..D

BALLS

CONN.—Bridgeport
Baumann Rubber Co. (Rubber) C
Canfield, H. O. (Fuller Rubber) ....B
Cornwall & Patterson Mfg. Co. (Base) ....AA
Ives & Williams Co. (Base) C

CONN.—Meriden
Meridan Britania Co. (Tea) AAAA

CONN.—Mount Carmel
Woodruff & Sons Co., Walter W. (Ox) ....A

CONN.—New Britain
Corbin, P. & F. (Ox) AAAA

CONN.—Southington
Peck, Stow & Wilcox Co. (Ox) ....AAAA

CONN.—Wallingford
Wallace & Sons Mfg. Co. (Tea) ....AAAA

ILL.—Chicago
Ball & Bro. A. (Billiard; Pool) ....AA
Chicago Sporting Goods Mfg. Co., 126 Jefferson (Foot; Base) ....B
Excelsior Supply Co. (Steel) A
Steel Ball Co., 840 Austin Av. (Steel) ....A

IND.—Indianopolis
Federal Mfg. Co. (Tool Steel) ....D

MAINE—Bangor
Hathorn Mfg. Co. (Steel) .E

MASS.—Boston
Boston Gear Works, 152 Purchase (Steel, for bearings) ....B
Boston & Lockport Block Co. (Ten Pin) ....A
Davidson Rubber Co. (Golf) A
Harvey, Henry H. (Granite Work Sets) ....D
Wright & Ditson (Inc.) (Foot) ....AA

MASS.—Fitchburg
Simonds Rolling Machine Co. (Steel for Bearings) ..A

MASS.—Lowell
Woode, Sherwood & Co. (Tea) ....E

MASS.—Natick
Harwood & Son, H. (Base) A

MASS.—Worcester
National Mfg. Co. (Tea) ..A
Wyman & Gordon (Steel; Unfinished) ....D

MICH.—Detroit
Schulenberg Mfg. Co. (Billiard; Pool; Tenpin ..C

MICH.—Port Huron
Draper Mfg. Co. (Brass; Hollow Brass; Steel) ..D

MINN.—St. Paul
Union Brass & Metal Mfg. Co. (Float) ....A

N. J.—Newark
Sommer's Sons, John (Tenpin) ....A
Strieby & Foote Co. (Grinding Machine) ....B

N. J.—Trenton
Stokes Rubber Co., Jos. (Float Pump) ....A

N. Y.—Albany
Albany Billiard Ball Co. (Billiard; Pool) C

N. Y.—Binghamton
Sportsmen's Supply Co. (Foot) C

N. Y.— Buffalo
Excelsior Machine Co. (Steel; for Bearings; Aluminium; Brass) C

New York City
Blanchard & Co. (Earring) D

42

BALLS (*Con.*)

Bogert & Hopper, 162 William (Ten Pin) ......**B**
Brecher Co., E. A., 95 Reade (Steel) ....**E**
Brunswick Balke-Collender Co. (Billiard; Pool; Ten-pin) ....**AAAA**
Dayton & Co., G. S. 76 Nassau (Base; Foot) .**D**
Dillingham, Wm. G. (Ten Pin) ....**C**
Estes & Son, E. B., 45 John (Wood; Ten Pin) ......**A**
Goodyear Rubber Co. (Foot; Rubber) ....**AAAA**
Goodyear's India Rubber Glove Mfg. Co., 503 B'way (Foot; Rubber) ....**AAAA**
Grote & Co., F. (Billiard; Pool; Ten Pin) ....**D**
Hartley Co., M. (Base) ..**AAAA**
Hoe & Co., R. (Inking) ....**AA**
Hodgman Rubber Co., 806 Broadway (Foot; Rubber) ....**AA**
Horsman, E. J. (Base) ...**C**
Ingersoll & Bro., R. H., 51 Maiden Lane (Foot) ..**A**
Kaldenberg Importing & Trading Co. (Billiard; Pool) ....**D**
New York Rubber Co., 84 Reade (Rubber; Valve) ....**AA**
N. Y. Sporting Goods Co., 61 Nassau (Foot; Base) **C**
Russel & Erwin Mfg. Co., 43 Chamber (Ox) ..**AAAA**
Sargent & Co., 151 Leonard (Ox) ....**AAAA**
Shardlow, Joseph, 116 Fulton (Ten Pin; Billiard; Pool) ....**D**
Spalding & Bros., A. G. (Inc.) 126 Nassau (Base; Foot) ....**AAAA**

OHIO—Akron
Faultless Rubber Co. (Rubber) ....**AA**
Goodrich Co., B. F. (Foot; Golf; Rubber) .....**AAAA**
Whitman & Barnes Mfg. Co. (Fuller Rubber; Ox; Golf; Valve) ....**AAAA**

OHIO—Cincinnati
Edwards Mfg. Co. (Half; Copper; Zinc) ....**C**
Goldsmith's Sons, P. (Base; Basket; Foot) ....**D**

OHIO—Cleveland
Cleveland Ball & Screw Co. "The Arcade" (Tool Steel) ....**E**
Reseck Machine Tool Co., 227 St. Clair (Steel) ..**H**

OHIO—Dayton
Crawford, McGregor & Canby Co. (Ten Pin) ..**AA**

PA.—Aliquippa
Vulcan Crucible Steel Co. (Steel) ....**B**

PA.—Philadelphia
Reach Co., A. J. Tulip & Palmer (Base; Foot) **AA**
Shite & Co., J. D. (Base) **D**

PA.—Pittsburg
Armstrong Cork Co. (Cork) ....**AAAA**
Wormser Glass Co. (Glass) ....**X**

PA.—Reading
Reading Hartware Co. (Ox) ....**AAAA**

PA.—Williamsport
Darling Pump & Mfg. Co. (Ltd.) (Brass) ....**B**

R. I.—Pawtucket
Fuller & Son, Geo. H. (Earring) ....**A**

R. I.—Providence
American Ball Co. (Steel) **D**
American Enamel Co. (Plain & Enameled Wooden) ....**C**
Davol Rubber Co. (Rubber) ....**AA**
Narragansett Machine Co. (Ten Pin) ....**A**
Wall & Co., A. T. (Seamless; Hollow) ....**C**

BALSAM

ILL.—Chicago
Hamlins Wizard Oil Co. .**B**
MASS.—Boston
Fowle & Sons, Seth W. ..**B**
MASS.—New Bedford
Ashley, A. Davis (Honey).**C**
OHIO—Newark
Styron—Beggs Co. (Cough) ....**A**

BALUSTERS
AND
BALUSTRADES

CAL.—San Francisco
Wilson & Bros. (Inc.) ..**AA**
GA.—Savannah
Southern Pine Co. of Georgia ....**AAA**
KY.—Covington
Ohio Scroll & Lumber Co. (Twisted Stair) ......**D**
MO.—St Louis
Huttig Sash & Door Co. .**A**
N. Y.—Binghamton
Roberson & Son, A. ...**AA**
N. Y.—Buffalo
Elias & Bro., G. ....**AA**
New York City
Fischer & Bro. Co. ......**B**
OHIO—Salem
Mullins H. H. (Copper; Zinc) ....**A**
PA.—Pittsburg
Murphy Mill & Lumber Co. ....**A**
PA.—Union City
Novelty Wood Wks. .....**B**
S. C.—Spartanburg
Morgan Iron Works .....**D**
WIS.—Milwaukee
Willer Mfg. Co. ....**A**

BAMBOO GOODS

See Furniture

BANDAGES

CONN.—New Haven
Seamless Rubber Co. (Surgical) ....**AA**
ILL.—Chicago
Bauer & Black (Suspensory) ....**A**
Common Sense Truss Co. (Suspensory) ....**D**
Sharp & Smith (Cotton and Silk Elastic) ....**B**
MASS.—Andover
Tyer Rubber Co. (Elastic) ....**AA**
MASS.—Boston
Davidson Rubber Co., 19 Milk (Elastic) ....**A**
Hub Gore Makers (Elastic) ....**A**
N. Y.—Lockport
Empire Mfg. Co. (Surgical; Elastic) ....**A**
New York City
Goodyear Rubber Co. (Surgical) ....**AAAA**
Goodyears India Rubber Glove Mfg. Co. (Surgical) ....**AAAA**
Hodgman Rubber Co., 806 Broadway (Surgical; Rubber) ....**AA**
Kny-Scheerer Co., 225 4th Av. (Abdominal) ......**C**
Mattson Rubber Co. (Elastic) ....**B**
Parker, Stearns & Sutton (Gum) ....**B**
Seabury & Johnson (Surgical) ....**AA**
Traun Rubber Co. (Elastic) ....**E**
Wetmore Co., S. H., 240 Pearl St. (Suspensory).**D**
N. Y.—Syracuse
Wells Mfg. Co., A. J. (Surgical) ....**D**
OHIO—Akron
Akron Rubber Wks. (B. E. Goodrich Co.,) (Surgical; Gum) ....**AAAA**
PA.—Philadelphia
Flavell & Bro., G. W. (Sur-

43

BANDAGES (*Con.*)
gical; Elastic; Suspensory)
...............................A

Horn & Bro., Wm. H. (Elastic; Suspensory) ......B
Kendrick James R. "Germantown" (Suspensory).E
Perry, Fergus (Suspensory)
...............................D
Philadelphia Truss Co.
(Elastic & Suspensory).X
Seeley, Isaac. B. (Suspensory) ....F
PA.—Pittsburg
Feick Bros. (Suspensory).D
R. I.—Providence
Davol Rubber Co. (Elastic)
...............................AA

BANDANAS

See Handkerchiefs

BANDINGS

CONN.—Middletown
Russell Mfg. Co. (Cotton; Spindle) ....AAAA
CONN.—Moodus
Undine Twine Mills (A. E. Purple, Prop.) (Sail) ..A
CONN.—Norwich
Ossawan Mills Co. (Braided)
...............................B
CONN.—Westport
Lees Mfg. Co. (Cotton) ..A
MD.—Baltimore
Hopper & Sons, Wm. E. (Cotton) ....AAAA
MASS.—Fall River
Covel & Osborn Co., 139 Pleasant (Braided; Cotton) ....B
Holden, James H. (Braided)
...............................F
Small Bros. (Braided; Cotton) ....D
Toohey & Co., M J. (Braided; Twisted; Drum)
...............................E
N. J.—Paterson
Frost & Sons, Geo. T. (Braided; Cotton) ......H
N. Y.—Buffalo
Buffalo Weaving & Belting Co. (Braided) ....A
New York City
Hoffman-Corr Mfg. Co., 107 Duane (Braided; Cotton)
...............................AA
PA.—Philadelphia
Elder, James "Germantown" (Cotton) ....F
Hodson, John M. (Cotton).C
Kensington Machine Wks., 2423 Mascher (Braided)
...............................X
Moore & Co., C., 14 S. 5th (Braided) ....A
R. I.—Pawtucket
Briggs & Co., H. A. (Cotton) ....B
Jencke's Mfg. Co., E. (Cotton) ....A
R. I.—Providence
American Supply Co. (Cotton) ....AA
Chase & Co., F. A. (Cotton)
...............................B

BANDOLINE

New York City
Colgate & Co ....AAA

BANDS

See Surgical Goods

BANDS, ARM

See Suspenders

BANDS

Dust; Mud; Hub, etc., see
Hardware; Carriage

BANDS

IRON & STEEL

See Iron & Steel

BANDS

Miscellaneous

CONN.—Bridgeport
Knapp, Geo. S. (Horse Tail)
...............................E
CONN.—Naugatuk
Goodyear's India Rubber Glove Mfg. Co. (Rubber)
...............................AAAA
CONN.—Mount Carmel
Woodruff & Sons Co., W. W. (Vehicle; Hub; Sand; Mud) ....A
CONN.—New Haven
Cowles & Co., C. (Silver) .A
CONN.—Tolland
Somner Belting Co., Wm. (Sewing Machine) ....D
ILL.—Chicago
Curtis & Co. Mfg. Co., 42 S. Canal (Black; Galvanized Box) C
Illinois Malleable Iron Co., W. Monroe (Hose).AAAA
Pratt Electro-Med. Appliance Co. (Magnetic) ...F
IOWA—Des Moines
Des Moines Novelty Co. (Horse Tail) ....F
MASS.—Andover
Tyer Rubber Co. (Rubber)
...............................AA
MASS.—Boston
Boston Belting Co. (Rubber)
...............................AAAA
Cutter-Tower Co. (Metal Filing) ....B
Davidson Rubber Co. (Rubber) ....A
Ladd & Co., Geo H. (Surgical Elastic) ....F
Lothrop & Co., H. O. (Brush) ....E
MASS.—Chicopee Falls
Taylor-Bramley Co. (Abdominal) ....B
MASS.—Highlandville
Moseley & Co. (Infants) ..C
MASS.—Leominster
Hudson Parer Co. (Hose).E
MASS.—Springfield
Smith Mfg. Co., R. H. (Rubber) C
MO.—St. Louis
Kupferle, John C., 2nd & Mound (Hose) ....AA
Pleuger & Henger Mfg. Co., 1015 Herbert (Hose) ...A
Zelincker Supply Co., Walter A., 408 N. 4th (Cold Rolled; Iron Shingle Box)
...............................C
N. J.—Hoboken
Beck Bros. (Silk Cigar) ..C
N. J.—Paterson
Columbia Ribbon Co. (Hat)
...............................B
Frost & Sons, Geo T. (Spindle Hook; Auto Motor Vehicle) ....H
Graef National Band Mfg. Co. (Silk Hat) ....D
N. Y.—Brooklyn
De Haven Mfg. Co. (Shingle; Box) C
N. Y.—Farmer
Covert's Saddlery Wks. (Horse Tail) C
N. Y.—Fort Plain
Yerdon, Wm. (Hose) C
N. Y.—Homer
Phoenix Hardware Mfg. Co. (Hose) ....D
New York City
Faber, Eberhard (Rubber)
...............................AAA
Graham & Co., John H., 113 Chambers (Hose) ......B
Judd & Co., H. L. (Curtain)
...............................AA
Leschen & Sons Rope Co., A. (Shingle; Box) ......AA
McNab & Harlin Mfg. Co., 56 John (Hose) ......AA
Mattson Rubber Co. (Rubber) ....B
Parker, Stearns & Sutton (Rubber) ....B
Tiebout, W. & J., 118 Chambers (Gaff; Boom; Mast) ....B
Wintjin, John G. (Leather)
...............................E

BANDS (Con.)

N. Y.—Richford
Hilts, Wrench & Mfg. Co.
(Spring Apron) ....F
N. Y.—Troy
Goodman, Saperstein & Co.
(Neck; Wrist) ....F
N. Y.—Unadilla
Tie Company (Horse Tail)
D
OHIO—Akron
Akron Rubber Wks. (B. F.
Goodrich Co.,) (Rubber)
AAAA
Whitman & Barnes Mfg. Co.
(Rubber) ....AAAA
OHIO—Canton
Kohler & Co. ,F. E. (Hose)
C
OHIO—Cleveland
Standard Welding Co. (Ve-
hicle; Hub; Sand; Mud)
AA
OHIO—Niles
Ohio Galvanizing & Mfg. Co.
(Shingle) C
OHIO—Springfield
Springfield Brass Co. (Hose)
E

PA.—Burnham
Logan Iron & Steel Co. (Ve-
hicle; Hub; Sand; Mud)
AA
PA.—Philadelphia
Bins Patent Band Co. 5th &
Berks (Spindle Hook) .X
Hoffstetter Bros. (Dry
Goods; Hosiery) C
Horstmann Co., Wm. H.
(Book Head) ......AAAA
Loeb, Lipper & Co. (Book
Head) ....A
PA.—Pittsburg
Budke Mfg. Co. (Box)....B
Canonsburg Iron & Steel Co.
Steel Box) ....B
R. I.—Providence
Davol Rubber Co. (Rubber)
AA

BANGLES

See Jewelry

BANJOS

See Musical Instruments

BANKS

ILL.—Chicago
Keyless Bank Co., 36 La-
salle (Individual Savings)
E
New York City
Piaget Novelty Co. 265
Broadway (Registering
Savings) ....D
N. Y.—Buffalo
Crosby Co., 179 Pratt (Sav-
ings) ....A
OHIO—Zanesville
Owens Pottery Co. ,J. B.
(Money. Pottery) .....A
PA.—Freemansburg
Shimer Son & Co., Wm.
(Iron Toy) ....B
PA.—Marietta
Reinhold J. J. (Individual
Savings) ....G
PA.—Philadelphia
American Home Savings
Bank Co., North Am.
Bldg. (Savings) ......D

BANNERS

MD.—Baltimore
Sisco Bros. ....E
MICH.—Kalamazoo
Henderson-Ames Co. (Pa-
rade) ....A
MO.—St Louis
Zittlosen Mfg. Co. X
New York City
American Flag Co. (Silk) A
Boyle & Co., John ......AA
Cairns & Bro. (Firemens') F
Koster, C. H. ....D
Lamb, J. & R. (Church) ..C
Mc Hugh, John F. C
Rehm & Co. ....D
OHIO—Cincinnati
Beck & Sons Co.. Wm. ...C
Pettibone Bros. Mfg. Co. .A

BANNERS (Con.)

OHIO—Columbus
Lilly & Co.. M. C. ...AAAA
OHIO—Toledo
Hettrick Bros. ....B
PA.—Easton
American Flag Co. (Silk) A
PA.—Philadelphia
Horstmann & Co., Wm. H.
AΣAA

BARGES & HULLS

CAL.—Port Richmond
Burlee Dry Dock Co.......X
CAL.—San Francisco
Union Iron Works ...AAAA
PA.—Philadelphia
Cramp & Sons Ship & Engine
Bldg. Co. (Steel) .AAAA
Kensington Engine Works
(Disinfecting) ....A
VA.—Newport News
Newport News Ship Building
& Dry Dock Co. (Steel)
AAAA

BARIUM

MO.—St Louis
Nulsen, Klein & Krausse
Mfg. Co. (Buoyant) .AAA
N. Y.—Brooklyn
Wiarda & Co., John C.
(Carbonate) ....AA

BARKS

See also Drugs; Crude

CAL.—San Francisco
Frank & Co., S. H. (Tan-
ners) ....AAA
CONN.—Stamford
Stamford Mfg. Co....AAAA
KY.—Clay City
Eastern Kentucky Stave Co.
(Tan) ....B
KY.—Somerset,
Thurman. J. H. (Tanners) X
MD.—Baltimore
Sharp & Dohme (Pressed)
AAA
MASS.—Boston
Cutting, F. A. (Tanners) .B
MASS.—Alpena
Northern Extract Co. (Tan-
ners) ....B
MICH.—Detroit
Parke, Davis & Co.
(Pressed) ....AAA
MICH.—Northport
Koehl Bros. (Tanners) ...D
MICH.—Onekama
Burmeister Byron (Tan-
ners) ....F
MICH.—Pierport
Perry & Co., C. H. (Tan-
ners) ....E
MICH.—Saginaw
Briggs, Cooper & Co. (Hem-
lock) C
MINN.—Minneapolis
Mc Millian Fur & Wool Co.
(Pressed) X
N. Y. Brooklyn
Wiarda & Co., John C.
(Birch. Ground) .....AA
New York City
Adams & Co., Walter
(Pressed) ....H
PA.—Colegrove
Heineman, H. N. (Tanners)
B
PA.—Lancaster
Eureka Bark Mills Co. (Tan-
ners) X
TENN.—Rockwood
Staples. H. C. (Tanners) .F
VT.—Burlington
Wells & Richardson Co.
(Pressed) ....AA
VA.—Fredericksburg
Hurkamp Co., John G. (Tan-
ners) ....B
VA.—Petersburg
Jones, Vaughan & Co.
(Tanners) ....B
WASH.—Chehalis
Northwest Chittem Co.
(Cascara) X
WIS.—Fond Du Lac
Huber & Fuhrman Drug
Mills (Pressed) ....B
WIS.—Marinette
Davis & Stitt Co. ....B

BARLEY

CAL.—San Francisco
Del Monte Miling Co. . . . .A
Stockton Milling Co. . . .AAA
ILL.—Chicago
American Cereal Co. AAAA
MO.—St. Louis
Stobie Cereal Mills . . . . . .B
New York City
Hecker-Jones-Jewell Milling
Co. (Crushed) . . . .AAAA
WASH.—Seattle
Seattle Cereal Co. (Pearl) A

BAROMETERS

ILL.—Chicago
Bieder Co., J. L., 53 Lake
(Color) . . . . .D
Martin Co., Edw. P., ...C
Weiskopf, A., (Aneroid) .E
N. H.—Petersboro
Wilder, Chas., (Est. of)..C
New York City
Goldbacher, Ernest (Cottage) C
Keuffel & Esser Co., 127
Fulton . . . . .AA
Tagliabue, G., ...B
Tagliabue, Chas. J., ...A
N. Y.—Rochester
Taylor Bros. Co., 29 Elizabeth . . . . .AA
N. Y.—Watertown
Watertown Thermometer
Co. C
PA.—Philadelphia
Queen & Co. (Aneroid) AA

BARRELS

See also Cooperage

CAL.—San Francisco
Hendy Mach. Wks., Joshua
38 Fremont (Amalgamating) . . . . .AA
Krogh Mfg. Co., 9 Stevenson (Amalgamating) . .C
Marshuty & Lantrell, Main
& Howard (Amalgamating) . . . . .A
Union Iron Wks., 222 Market (Amalgamating, Chlorinating, Cyanide Etc.)
. . . . AAAA
COLO.—Denver
Mine & Smelter Supply Co.
(Amalgamating, Chlorinating Etc.) . . . . .AAA
CONN.—Oakville
Baird Machine Co. (Tumbling) . . . . .E

CONN.—Waterbury
Henderson Bros. (Tumbling
& Rumbling) . . . . .D
Waterbury Mach. Co.
(Tumbling & Rumbling) B
ILL.—Chicago
Acorn Brass Mfg. Co. (Steel,
& Half) . . . . .D
Allis-Chalmers Co., Home
Ins. Bldg. (Amalgamating; Chlorinating; Cyanide Etc.) . . . . . . .AAAA
ILL.—Freeport
Stover Mfg. Co. (Tumbling
& Rumbling) . . . . .AA
ILL.—Harvey
Whiting Foundry Equipment Co. (Tumbling &
Rumbling) . . . . .A
IND.—Mishawaka
Dodge Mfg. Co. (Tumbling
& Rumbling) . . . . . .AAA
MASS.—Boston
Burton Elect. Smelting Co.,
183 Summer (Amalgamating) . . . . .AAA
MASS.—Bridgewater
Millers' Sons, H. J.,
(Tumbling) . . . . .D
Perkins Co., Henry, (Tumbling) . . . . .B
MASS.—Chicopee Falls
Stevens Arms & Tool Co., J.,
(Rifle) . . . . .AAA
MASS.—Orange
Leavitt Machine Co. (Swing)
. . . . .D
MASS.—Salem
Locke Regulator Co. (Tumbling & Rumbling) C

BARRELS *(Con.)*
MICH.—Detroit
Byram & Co. (Tumbling &
Rumbling) . . . . .D
Northern Engineering Wks.,
Chene & Atwater (Tumbling & Rumbling) . . . .A
MICH.—Saginaw
Wickes Bros (Tumbling &
Rumbling) . . . . .AA
MICH.—Three Rivers
Sheffield Car Co. (Tumbling) . . . . .AA
New York City
Estes & Sons, E. B., 45
John (Tack) . . . . .AA
Iron Clad Mfg. Co., 4 Cliff
(Sheet; Steel) . . . . . .AAA
N. Y.—Saratoga Springs
Lawrence, C. W. (Tin
Lined) . . . . .B
OHIO—Cincinnati
Obermayer Co., S., 647
Evans (Tumbling; Rumbling) . . . . .A
Tudor Boiler Mfg. Co.
(Tumbling) . . . . .B
OHIO—Cleveland
Bowler Foundry Co. (Tumbling; Rumbling) . . . . . .A
Cleveland Twist Drill Co.
(Metal) . . . . .A
Cleveland Wire Spring Co.,
(Sheet Steel) C
Globe Machine & Stamping
Co., 970 Hamilton (Tumbling; Rumbling) . . . . . .F
Shelby Steel Tube Co. (Tumbling; Metal Wks.) AAA
OHIO—Columbus
Kilbourne & Jacobs Mfg. Co.
(& Half; Steel) . .AAAA
OHIO—Mansfield
Barnes Mfg. Co. (Brass;
Working; Oil Well; Seamless Steel) . . . . .A
OHIO—New Philadelphia
Spicer Mfg. Co. (Wire Nail
Cleaning) C
OHIO—Salem
Clark Co., W. J., (Sheet
Steel) . . . . .B
PA.—Philadelphia
Paxon Co., J. W., 1021 N.
Del. Av. (Tumbling; Rumbling) . . . . .AA
PA.—Pittsburg
Phillips & McLaren, 24th
& Smallman (Tumbling;
Rumbling) . . . . .B
McCormack Co., J. S.,
(Tumbling; Rumbling) B
Scaife & Sons Co., Wm. B.,
221 1st Av. (Amalgamating; Cyanide) . . . . .A
PA.—Royersford
Royersford Fdy. & Mach.
Co. (Tumbling; Rumbling) C
PA.—Williamsport
Darling Pump & Mfg. Co.
(Tumbling) . . . . .B
VT.—Burlington
Vermont Shade Roller Co.
(Bobbin) . . . . .A
WIS.—Milwaukee
Allis-Chalmers Co. (Cyanide)
. . . . AAAA

BARRETTES
See Jewelry

BARROWS

CAL.—San Francisco
Western Iron Wks., 123
Beale (Steel) . . . . .B
CONN.—Windsor Locks
Clark Co., Geo. P. (Baggage & Express) C
GA.—Atlanta
White Hickory Wagon Mfg.
Co. . . . . .A
ILL.—Aurora
Western Wheeled Scraper
Co. . . . . .AA
ILL.—Chicago
Archer Iron Wks., 34th Pl.
& S. Western Av. (Coke,
Foundry. Furnace Charging, Steel, Steel Tubular
& Stone) . . . . .D
Chicago Scale Co., 292 Jack.

BARROWS (Con.)

Boul. (Wheel; Baggage) A
  A

Fairbanks, Morse & Co.,
  Franklin & Monroe (Baggage, Express, Coke,
  Foundry, Furnace Charging, Steel & Steel Tubular) ....AAAA

Railroad Supply Co., Old
  Colony Bldg. (Track)...A

IND.—Anderson

Anderson Fdy. & Mach.
  Wks. (Brick & Mould)..B

IND.—Indianapolis

Potts & Co., C. & A. (Brick
  & Canal) ....B

IOWA—Fort Madison

Iowa Farming Tool Co.,
  (Garden) ....A

IOWA—Keokuk

Scott Mfg. Co. (Brick)....D

KY.—Louisville

Broderick, John C

MAINE—So. Paris

Paris Mfg. Co.............A

MASS.—Boston

Boston & Lockport Block
  Co., 160 Commercial (Baggage & Express) ......B

MASS.—Chicopee Falls

Belcher & Taylor Agrc. Tool
  Co. (Garden) ....A

MASS.—Worcester

Ames Plow Co. (Canal, Coal
  & Garden) ....AA

MICH.—Adrian

Kells Fdy. & Mach. Co.
  (Brick) ....D

MICH.—Jackson

Withington & Cooley Mfg.
  Co. (Stone, Coal, Coke,
  etc.) ....AA

MICH.—Kalamazoo

Kalamazoo Railway Supply
  Co. (Baggage & Express)
  B

MICH.—Lansing

Lansing Wheelbarrow Co.
  (Baggage, Express, Brick,
  Coke, Foundry, Wheel,
  Wooden, Furnace Charging, Steel, Steel Tubular
  & Stone) ....AA

MICH.—Morence

Michigan Brick & Tile Mach.
  Co. (Brick) C

MINN.—Minneapolis

Puffer-Hubbard Mfg. Co.
  (Brick, Coke, Garden,
  Mortar, Ore, Steel &
  Stone) C

MO.—Farmington

Lang & Bro. ....A

MO.—St. Louis

Fernholtz Brick Machy. Co.,
  Boyle Av. (Brick).....E

Western Electric & Supply
  Co. (Track) ....B

Whitman Agricultural Co.,
  6900 S. B'way (Baggage,
  Express, Brick, Coal &
  Garden) ....A

N. J.—Hoboken

Union Iron Wks. (Foundry)
  D

N. Y.—Albany

Dederick's Sons, P. K.
  (Brick & Coal) ......AA

N. Y.—Brooklyn

Phillips Doup & Co., 56
  Pearl (Brick; Coal;
  Foundry) ....E

N. Y.—Buffalo

Buffalo Scale Co. (Baggage
  & Express) ....AA

N. Y.—Long Island City

Stuebner, G. L., Iron Wks.,
  170 3d (Coke; Iron;
  Foundry) ....A

New York City

Fairbanks Co. 186 Elm
  (Baggage, Express, Brick,
  Coke, Foundry, Furnace
  Charging Steel, Steel Tubular & Stone) ....AAAA

Howard & Morse, 45 Fulton (Foundry) ....B

Pollock, Alex., 203 West
  (Foundry, Furnace Charging & Steam Tubular)..A

Pugsley & Chapman......D

BARROWS (Con.)

N. Y.—Poughkeepsie

McWinnie Wheelbarrow
  Wks., Thos. (Brick, Steel,
  Tubular, Stone, Canal &
  Garden) ....D

N. Y.—Syracuse

Syracuse Chilled Plow Co.
  (Baggage, Express, Brick,
  Foundry, Furnace Charging, Garden, Mortar, Ore,
  Pig Iron, Steel, Steel Tubular & Stone) ......AA

N. Y.—West New Brighton

Hunt Co., C. W. (Coal;
  Coke; etc) ....AA

OHIO—Akron

Akron Cultivator Co. (Steel
  Tray Brick, Coke, Furnace
  Charging, Pig Iron, Steel
  & Steel Tubular)......B

McNeil Boiler Co. (Steel).F

OHIO—Bryan

Bryan Mfg. Co. (Brick,
  Coke, Folding Steel Frame,
  Foundry, Furnace Charging, Mining, Garden, Mortar, Steel, Steel Tubular
  & Stone) ....B

OHIO—Bucyrus

American Clay Working
  Mach. Co. (Brick &
  Canal) X

OHIO—Cincinnati

Haven Co., James L......B

Obermayer Co. S., 647
  Evans (Foundry) ....AA

OHIO—Cleveland

American Fork & Hoe Co.
  (Wheel & Brick) ..AAAA

Atlas Bolt & Screw Co.,
  Marquette, opp. Hamilton
  (Coke, Coal, etc) ....A

Atlas Car & Mfg. Co.
  (Wheel, Ash, Coal, Coke
  & Charcoal) ....AA

Cleveland Wire Spring Co.
  (Hand Wheel) ....A

Niles Mine & Mill Supply
  Co. (Coke) C

Osborn Mfg. Co. (Coal,
  Coke, etc.) ....B

Smith Fdy. Supply Co., J.
  D., 40 S. Water (Foundry)
  D

OHIO—Columbus

Kilbourne & Jacobs Mfg. Co.
  (Baggage, Express, Brick.
  Coke, Foundry, Furnace
  Charging, Steel, Steel Tubular & Stone) ......AA

OHIO—Dayton

Raymond Co., C. W. (Brick)
  A

OHIO—Galion

Freese & Co., E. M. (Brick)
  C

OHIO—Girard

Girard Boiler & Mfg. Co.
  (Ore) ....B

OHIO—Lowellville

Meehan Boiler & Construction Co. (Coal, Coke, etc.)
  B

OHIO—New London

Arnold, Creager Co. (Brick;
  Ash; Coal; Tile) ......B

OHIO—Painsville

Horton Mfg. Co. (Brick).C

OHIO—Salem

Clark & Co., W. J. (Baggage; Furnace; Steel;
  Hand) ....A

OHIO—Sidney

American Steel Scraper Co.
  (Steel Tubular) ......B

Sidney Steel Scraper Co.,
  (Foundry Steel Tubular.
  Charging & Garden) C

OHIO—Steubenville

Means Fdy. & Machine Co.
  (Brick) ....D

OHIO—Toledo

Toledo Metal Wheel Co.
  (Garden) ....AA

Toledo Wheelbarrow Wks.
  (Geo. W. Thomas & Co.)
  (Garden, Stone, Brick &
  Steel) ....A

OHIO—Wellington

Wellington Machine Co.
  (Brick) ....B

BARROWS (Con.)

PA.—Connellsville
Boyle, Porter & Co. (Coal) B
Connellsville Machine & Car Co. (Coke & Steel).....A
PA.—Elizabethtown
Buch's Sons Co., A. (Wheel & Garden) ....A
PA.—Harrisburg
Jackson Mfg. Co. (Brick, Coke, Foundry, Furnace Charging & Steel).....B
PA.—Lancaster
Martin Brick Mach. Co., Henry (Brick) ....B
PA.—Lebanon
Union Boiler & Mfg. Co. (Furnace Charging).....D
Weimer Machine Wks. (Foundry Charging)....A
PA.—Philadelphia
Paxson Co., J. W., 1012 N. Del. Av. (Foundry)...AA
PA.—Pittsburg
Pittsburg Wheel Scraper Co. 66 S. Main (Stone)....F
PA.—York
Farquhar & Co., A. B. (Baggage & Garden).AAA
Keystone Farm Mach. Co. (Garden) ....B
TENN.—Chattanooga
Chattanooga Wheelbarrow Mfg. Co. (Brewers).....D
VT.—Bellows Falls
Derby & Ball ....B
VT.—Rutland
Howe Scale Co. (Baggage & Express) ....AA
W. VA.—New Cumberland
Davis & Price Fdy. & Mach. Co. (Brick) ....D
WIS.—Sheboygan
Ortenberg & Sonneman (Steel) ....F

BARS

See also Fixtures; also Iron & Steel

ALA.—Selma
Peacock's Iron Wks. (Grate Draw) C
CAL.—San Francisco
Doble Co., Abner (Crow, Lining & Tamping).....B
CONN.—Ansonia
Ansonia Electrical Co. (Commutator) ....A
CONN.—Bridgeport
Bridgeport Brass Co. (Copper, Brass, Commutator) AA
Bridgeport Chain Co. (Chain) ....A
CONN.—Collinsville
Collins Co. (Pinch & Crow) AAAA
CONN.—Hartford
Billings & Spencer Co. (Commutator) ....AA
Pope Tube Co. (Bicycle Handles) ....AAAA
CONN.—Middletown
Palmer, I. E. (Mosquito, Hammock) ....AAA
CONN.—New Britain
Russell & Erwin Mfg. Co. (Shutter) ....AAAA
Stanley Works (Shutter) AAA
CONN.—New Haven
Dann Bros. & Co. (Bicycle Handles) ....B
Ives Co., Robert B. (Shutter) C
Kibborn & Bishop Co. (Commutator) C
Mallory, Wheeler Co. (Shutter) ....AA
CONN.—Southington
Peck, Stow & Wilcox Co. (Shutter) ....AAAA
CONN.—South Norwalk
Norwalk Lock Co. (Shutter) H
CONN.—Stamford
Yale & Towne Mfg. Co. (Shutter) ....AAAA

BARS (Con.)

CONN.—Torrington
Coe Brass Mfg. Co. (Copper, Commutator) ......AAAA
DEL.—Wilmington
Edge Moor Iron Co. (Draw) AAA
ILL.—Chicago
Branmoeller & Son, Henry (Shutter) ....B
Chicago Metallic Sash Wks., 21 Mohawk (Metallic Sash) ....D
Mohr & Sons, John (Grate) AAA
Morden Frog & Crossing Wks., The Rookery (Tie) A
Republic Iron & Steel Co., 108 La Salle (Iron, Muck) AAAA
Sellers Mfg. Co. (Splice).B
Schomer, Henry (Clothes).D
Solid Steel Tool Co., 11 S. Jefferson (Lining, Coupling, Driving, Pinch & Shackle) ....P
Sterion Copper, Brass & Bronze Co., 63 N. Ashland Av. (Commutator).....D
Sullivan Machinery Co., 135 Adams (Quarry).AAA
Thornburgh-Creel Co. (Pinch) X
Union Drop Forge Co., 66 E. Ohio (Claw, Lining, Tamping & Crow) ....A
Webster Mfg. Co. (Pinch) AA
ILL.—Downers Grove
Dicke Tool Co. (Lining & Tamping) ....D
IND.—Bluffton
Bluffton Mfg. Co. (Clothes) C
IND.—Columbus
Columbus Handle & Tool Co. (Lining; Tamping) .....B
IND.—Evansville
Evansville Tool Wks. (Railroad, Claw, Tamping, Crow, Pince, Wedge, Lining, Point) ....A
IND.—Fort Wayne
Olds Wagon Wks. (Bicycle Handle) X
IND.—Indianapolis
Lanter, H. (Bicycle Handle) A
Udell Wks. (Clothes).....A
IND.—South Bend
Miller-Knoblock Electric Mfg. Co. (Commutator).B
KY.—Louisville
Louisville Seam Forge Co. (Draw) ....D
MAINE—Portland
Laughlin & Sons, Thos. (Claw) ....B
MASS.—Arlington
Wood & Co., W. T. (Ice).A
MASS.—Boston
Harvey, H. H., 608 Atlantic Av. (Claw & Crow).....B
Ideal Plating Co. (Bicycle Handle) ....B
Pearson Jack Co. (Claw) H
Walworth Mfg. Co. (Grate) AAAA
MASS.—Chicopee
Ames Sword Co. (Bicycle Handle) ....B
MASS.—Everett
Faxon Co., Geo. H. (Piano Pressure) ....D
MASS.—Holyoke
Holyoke Bar Co. (Roll)..E
Holyoke Machine Co. (Grates) ....AA
MASS.—Lawrence
Horne & Sons Co., J. H. (Barbed Jordan & Roll).A
MASS.—Lowell
Lowell Machine Shop (Roll) AAAA
MASS.—North Attleboro
Barrows & Co., H. T. (Chain) ....A
MASS.—Springfield
Springfield Drop Forge Co. (Pure Unalloyed Copper

48

BARS (Con.)
Commutator) ....B
MICH.—Detroit
Amos & Co., Charles, 94 W.
  Larned (Mettalic Sash).F
Anderson & Sons, W. H.
  (Claw, Draw, Lining,
  Tamping, Pinch, Quarry
  & Crow) C
Barnum Wire & Iron Wks.,
  E. T., 99 Shelby (Metallic
  Sash) ....B
Detroit Copper & Brass Roll-
  ing Mills (Wire, Copper)
  ....AAAA
Detroit Steel & Spring Co.
  (Claw) ....B
Phillips Co., John (Ltd.), 51
  Fort (Metallic Sash &
  Clothes) C
Vulcan Co. (Metallic Sash)
  ....F
MICH.—Kalamazoo
Harrow Spring Co. (Soft
  Merchant, Spring Steel).B
Kalamazoo Ry. Supply Co.
  (Claw, Lining, Tamping &
  Crow) ....A
MINN.—Albert Lea
Edwards, C. D. (Equalizing)
  ....D
MINN.—Minneapolis
Commutator Co., 121 N. 1st
  Av. (Commutator) .....D
Howell & Co., R. R. (Grate)
  ....B
MO.—St. Louis
Crescent Novelty Mfg. Co.,
  703 S. Bway. (Pinch)...D
Handlan-Buck Mfg. Co., 212
  N. 3d (Lining & Tamping)
  ....AA
N. J.—High Bridge
Taylor Iron & Steel Co.
  (Draw, Grate) ....AAAA
N. J.—Jersey City
Williams & Son, E. A.
  (Commutator) ....AA
N. J.—Newark
Atha Tool Co., ft. Chapel
  (Claw, Lining, Tamping,
  Shackle & Crow) ......A
Marson, Arthur (Jewelers)
  ....F
N. J.—Paterson
Dempwolf, Chas., Jr.
  (Glass) X
Passaic Rolling Mill Co.
  (Eye & Tie) ....AAAA
Passaic Steel Co. (Eye &
  Merchant) ....A
N. J.—Perth Amboy
Pardee Wks., C. (Steel)
  ....AAA
N. J.—Riegelsville
Taylor, Stiles & Co. (En-
  gine Fly; Roll) ....A
N. J.—Trenton
Stahl, Harry E. (Bicycle
  Handle) ....F
N. Y.—Brooklyn
Columbia Mach. Wks. &
  Malleable Iron Co., 167
  Chestnut (Droped Forged
  Commutators) C
Hecla Iron Wks. (Metallic
  Sash) ....AA
Pollard, Jos. G. (Crow) .F
N. Y.—Buffalo
Abel, George L., 18 Elk
  (Commutator) ....F
Pratt & Letchworth Co.
  (Draw) ....AA
White Co., L. & I. J.
  (Ice) ....A
N. Y.—Gowanda
Gowanda Agricultural Wks.
  Co. (Post Steel Handle &
  Point) ....B
N. Y.—Hillburn
Ramapo Iron Wks. (Switch)
  ....AAA
N. Y.—Irvington-on-Hudson
Lord & Burnham Co. (Green-
  House Sash) ....A
N. Y.—Jamestown
American Mfg. Concern
  (Drying) ....A
Empire Walker Co. (Folding
  Dry) ....A
N. Y.—Munnsville
Munnsville Plow Co. (Hop)
  ....B

BARS (Con.)
New York City
Anderton, Ralph L., 210
  Grand (Metallic Sash)..B
Ansonia Brass & Copper Co.,
  99 John (Commutators)
  ....AAAA
Bemis Car Truck Co., 130
  Liberty (Draw).........C
Brass Goods Mfg. Co. (Shut-
  ter) ....B
Ingersoll-Sergeant Drill Co.,
  26 Cortlandt (Quarry)
  ....AAAA
Jessop & Sons, Wm. (Ltd.)
  91 John (Steel).....AAA
Jones & Co., Trevor F., 374
  W. Bway. (Metallic Sash)
 X
Larter, Elcox & Co. (Chain)
  ....A
N. Y. Boat Oar Co. (Cap-
  stan) ....A
Railway Steel Spring Co., 71
  Bway. (Draw) ....AAAA
Rand Drill Co., 128 B'way
  (Quarry) ....A
Richards & Co., E. Ira
  (Chain) ....AAA
Rutzler, E. (Grate) ......A
Salamander Grate Bar Co.
  126 Liberty (Grate) ....D
Sargent & Co., 151 Leonard
  (Shutter) ....AAA
Tupper & Co., Wm. W., 39
  Cortlandt (Grate) ......D
N. Y.—Rochester
Rochester Snow Case Wks.
  (Metal Sash) ....D
Sheldon, Smith (Metallic
  Sash) ....D
N. Y.—Syracuse
Sweets Steel Co., 332 S.
  West (Claw, Driving,
  Lining, Tamping, Crow &
  Pinch) ....A
N. Y.—Troy
Burden Iron Co. (Iron)
  ....AAAA
OHIO—Akron
Whitman & Barnes Mfg. Co.
  (Equalizing) ......AAAA
OHIO—Cambridge
Cambridge Rolling Mill Co.
  (Harrow & Cultivator).B
OHIO—Canton
Buckeye Mfg. Co. (Digging;
  Tamping) ....D
Cleveland Axle Mfg. Co.
  (Pinch & Wedge).......A
OHIO—Cincinnati
Weir Frog Co. (Switch)..A
OHIO—Cleveland
Federal Mfg. Co. (Bicycle
  Handle) ....AAAA
Forest City Electric Co., 111
  Windsor Av. (Commuta-
  tor) ....A
Homer Commutator Co.
  (Standard & Special Com-
  mutators) ....D
Van Dorn-Elliott Electric
  Co. (Commutator & Jail)
  ....B
OHIO—Columbus
Coulsen & Co., J. W. (Tran-
  som; Metallic Sash) ...X
OHIO—Dayton
Simonds & Son, A. A. (En-
  gine) ....B
OHIO—Hicksville
Kerr Bros. & Co. (Bicycle
  Handle) ....A
OHIO—Mansfield
Mansfield Tempered Copper
  Co. (Commutator) ....A
Ohio Brass Co. (Commuta-
  tor) ....B
OHIO—Steubenville
La Belle Iron Wks. (Steel)
  ....AAAA
OHIO—Toledo
American Woodenware Mfg.
  Co. (Clothes) ....B
Snell Cycle Fittings Co.
  (Bicycle Handle) ......F
OHIO—Youngstown
Youngstown Iron Sheet &
  Tube Co. (Sheet Bars;
  Muck) ....AAAA
PA.—Aliquippa
Vulcan Crucible Steel Co.
  (Steel) ....B

BARS *(Con.)*

PA.—Beaver Falls
Standard Gauge Steel Co. (Steel Finished Rounds; Flats; Squares & Finished Shapes) ....A
PA.—Braeburn
Braeburn Steel Co. (Steel)A
PA.—Burnham
Logan Iron & Steel Co. (Iron; Crown) ....AA
PA.—Chester
Keystone Drop Forge Wks. (Commutators) ....B
PA.—Downingtown
Downingtown Mfg. Co. (Fly) ....A
PA.—Ellwood City
Glen Mfg. Co. (Sash; Metal Covered) C
PA.—Girard
Ely Mfg. Co., Thos. J. (Clothes) ....B
PA.—Harrisburg
Harrisburg Pipe & Pipe Bending Co. (Flat; Iron; Square) ....AAA
PA.—Lancaster
Chalfant Mfg. Co. (Shutter) ....D
PA.—Lebanon
American Iron & Steel Mfg. Co. (Arch) ....AAAA
PA.—McKees Rocks
Kidd Bros. & Burgher Steel Wire Co. (Steel & Arch)B
PA.—Mechanicsburg
Wilcox Mfg. Co., D. (Bicycle Handle) ....A
PA.—Milton
Milton Mfg. Co. (Iron & Muck) ....AA
PA.—New Castle
New Castle Forge & Bolt Co. (Lining; Tamping & Crow) ....B
PA.—North East
Eureka Tempered Copper Wks. (Digging; Commutator) ....
PA.—Oil City
Oil City Boiler Wks. (Grate) ....AA
PA.—Philadelphia
American Bridge Co. (Eye) ....AAAA
Bement, Miles & Co. (Boring) ....AAAA
Cambria Iron Co. (Splice) .A
Disston & Sons, Henry (Steel) ....AA
Hoeg & Co., R. C., 11th & Catherine (Shutter) ....H
Keystone Drop Forge Wks., 20th & Clearfield (Commutators) ....B
Logan Iron & Steel Co., Harrison. Bldg. (Crow) ..AA
Phoenix Iron Co., 410 Walnut (Upset Eye) ......D
Plumb, Fayette R., "Frankford" (Claw; Lining; Tamping & Crow).....AA
Samuel, Frank, 1502 Market (Low Phosphorus Melting & Muck) ....A
PA.—Pittsburg
Carnegie Steel Co. (Arch; Eye & Draw) ....AAAA
Colonial Steel Co. (Jail) ....AAA
Crucible Steel Co. of America, Frick Bldg. (Commutator; Copper) ....AAAA
Hubbard & Co., Murtland Bldg. (Claw; Lining; Tamping & Pinch) ...A
Iron City Tool Wks. (Ltd.) 23rd & Smallman (Claw; Lining; Tamping; Punch & Crow) ....B
Jones & Laughlins Steel Co. (Claw; Steel; Bicycle Chain) ....AAAA
Klein & Logan Co., 265 S. 13th (Claw; lining; Tamping & Crow) ....A
Munroe & Son, R. (Grate)..AAA
Oliver Iron & Steel Co., S. 10th & Muriel (Claw; Lining & Tamping).AAAA
Pittsburg Forge & Iron Co..

BARS *(Con.)*

10th & Penn Av. (Draw & Splice) ....A
Pittsburg Reduction Co. (Aluminum) ....AAAA
Pittsburg Tool & Drop Forge Co., Arrott Bldg. (Mine; Claw; Lining & Tamping) ....E
Verona Tool Wks., Murtland Bldg. (Claw; Lining; Tamping; Pinch & Shackle) ....A
Zug & Co. (Ltd.) (Iron; Horseshoe) ....AAA
PA.—Reading
Pennsylvania Hardware Co. (Shutter) ....AA
Reading Hardware Co. (Shutter) ....AAAA
Reading Standard Cycle Mfg. Co. (Bicycle Handles) ....B
PA.—Scranton
McClave, Brooks & Co. (Grate) ....A
PA.—So. Bethlehem
Bethlehem Steel Co. (Iron) ....AAAA
PA.—Steelton
Pennsylvania Steel Co.(Eye; Steel Splice; Swivel; Switch; Tie) ...AAAA
PA.—Wilkesbarre
Vulcan Iron Wks. (Grate)..AAAA
R. I.—Pawtucket
Fuller & Son, Geo. H. (Chain) ....A
Narragansett Machine Co. (Gymnasium) ....A
R. I.—Providence
Wall & Co., A. T. (Chain) .C
S. C.—Spartanburg
Morgan Iron Wks. (Grate)D
VA.—Bristol
Va. Iron, Coal & Coke Co. (Iron) ....A
W. VA.—Huntington
Union Rail Co. (Iron)...X
WIS.—Beloit
Beloit Iron Wks. (Roll)...A
WIS.—Milwaukee
Bremer Cycle Mfg. Co. (Bicycle Handle) ......F
League Cycle Works (Bicycle Handle) ....D
WIS.—Oshkosh
Oshkosh Logging Tool Co. (Digging; Lining; Tamping) ....B
WIS.—Racine
Racine Malleable & Wrought Iron Co. (Bicycle Handle) A

BARYTES

MO.—Mineral Point
Point Mining & Mineral Co. ....A
MO.—St. Louis
Nulsen, Klein & Krausse Mfg. Co. (Floated) ....A
New York City
Bartels, E. C. ....B
Berg Mining Co., 123 Front ....D
Franklin & Ferguson, Cotton Exchange ....F
Gabriel & Schall, 305 Pearl C
Osborn, Clarence J., 140 Maiden Lane ....D
Waddell & Co., R. J....AA
OHIO—Cleveland
Harshaw, Fuller & Goodwin Co. ....AA
TENN.—Knoxville
Commercial Mining & Milling Co. ....A

BASALT

MD.—Baltimore
Thomson Chemical Co. ..AA

BASE BALL SUITS

See Clothing, Men's

BASES

See also Woodwork

CONN.—Bridgeport
Bridgeport Brass Co.
(Lamp) ....AAAA
CONN.—Torrington
Turner & Seymour Mfg. Co.
(Incandescent Lamp) ..A
Union Hardware Co. (Battery Cut-Out) ....A
CONN.—Waterbury
Scovill Mfg. Co. (Incandescent Lamp) ....AAAA
Steele & Johnson Mfg. Co.
(Incandescent Lamp)...A
ILL.—Chicago
Illinois Malleable Iron Co.,
30 W. Monroe (Branch
Central Fdy. Co.) (Vertical Boiler) ....AA
Inland Steel Co. 204 Dearborn (Steel Plow).AAAA
MINN.—St. Paul
Raucher, John (Battery Cut-Out) ... .B
N. J.—Newark
Hay Foundry & Iron Works
(Cast Iron Building).AAA
Sterling-Meaker Co., 420 Ogden Av. (Trolley) ......E
N. J.—New Brunswick
New Jersey Lamp & Bronze
Works (Incandescent
Lamp) ....AA
New York City
Bogert & Hopper, 162 William (Battery Cut-Out).B
Estes & Son, E. B., 45 John
(Switch; Battery Cut-Out)
...............A
Klumpp's Sons, J. G., 13
Baxter (Battery Cut-Out)
...............D
OHIO—Cleveland
Homer Commutator Co., 110
Mason (Trolley) ....D
Homer & Co., F. E. (Trolley) ....D
Van Dorn Iron Works Co.,
1793 E. Madison Av.
(Post) ....AA
OHIO—Salem
Clark Co., W. J. (Post).B
PA.—Philadelphia
Conroy, P. J., Island Road
(Vertical Boiler) X
PA.—Reading
National Brass & Iron Wks.
(Lamp) ....A
R. I.—Providence
American Enamel Co. (Battery Cut-Out) C
VT.—Fair Haven
Vermont Slate Syndicate
(Ltd.) (Lamp) X
WIS.—So. Milwaukee
Stowell Mfg. & Foundry Co.
(Garment Stand) ......A

BASINS

See also Tinware; Enamelled Ware, etc.

CONN.—Meriden
Manning, Bowman & Co.
(Enamelled; Wash) ..AA
CONN.—Waterbury
Randolph Clowes Co. (&
Bath Supplies) ......AAA
Waterbury Brass Co.
(Brass; Wash) ....AAAA
ILL.—Clyde
Coonley Mfg. Co. (Wash).B
ILL.—Chicago
Illinois Malleable Iron Co.,
30 W. Monroe (Catch)..
...............AAAA
MINN.—Minneapolis
Decarie Mfg. Co., 200 1st
Av. (Catch) ....B
MO.—St. Louis
St. Louis Stamping Co.
(Enamelled; Wash)AAAA
N. J.—Trenton
Maddock & Sons, Thos.
(Wash) ....AA
Trenton Potteries Co.
(Plumbers') ....AAA
N. Y.—Buffalo
Aldrich Mfg. Co. (Copper;
Wash) ....B

BASINS (Con.)
New York City
Ansonia Brass & Copper Co.
(Brass; Copper Wash)...
...............AAAA
Central Stamping Co. (Tin
Wash) ....AA
Cordley & Hayes (Wash).A
Haydensville Co. (Plumbers') ....A
Lalance & Grosjean Mfg.
Co. (Enamelled; Wash)
...............AAAA
Meyer-Sniffen Co. (Ltd.)
(Plumbers') ....A
Stoutenborough, X. (Tin)..D
Trageser Steam Copper
Wks., John (Copper Plug)
...............B
N. Y.—Rochester
Rochester Stamping Co.
(Wash) ....AAA
N. Y.—Rome
Rome Mfg. Co. (Wash)...B
N. Y.—Troy
Troy Stamping Wks. (Tin;
Wash) ....AAAA
PA.—Pittsburg
Standard Mfg. Co. (Enamelled Iron Wash) ....AA
WIS.—Milwaukee
Bayley & Sons Co.,W.
(Catch) X
Rundle Mfg. Co. (Enamelled
Iron) C

BASKETS

ALA.—Bridgeport
Bridgeport Woodenware
Mfg. Co. (Fruit; Vegetables) ....B
CONN.—Elmwood
Goodwin Bros. Pottery Co.
(Hanging) ....B
CONN.—Georgetown
Gilbert & Bennett Mfg. Co.
(Hanging; Wire; Moss.)..
...............AAA
DEL.—Elsmere
Diamond State Fibre Co.
(Mill) ....B
DEL.—Farmington
Simmons Mfg. Co. (Fruit)
...............E
DEL.—Laurel
Marvill, J. D. (Fruit).....A
Ward & Co., N. (Fruit)..AA
DEL.—Wilmington
American Vulcanized Fibre
Co. (Mill) ....AAAA
Delaware Hard Fibre Co.
(Fibre) ....A
FLA.—Jacksonville
Bean, E. (Fruit) ....D
GA.—Atlanta
Atlanta Woodenware Co...B
GA.—Fort Valley
Georgia Fruit Package Co.
(Fruit) C
ILL.—Chicago
Barbee Wire & Iron Wks.
(Desk; Farm; Fruit;
Hanging; Waste Paper;
Wire; Frying; Wire
Moss; Wire Sponge; Fruit
Canning) ....B
Chicago Willow & Rattan
Works (Automobile)....C
ILL.—Metropolis
Roberts, J. N. (Fruit) ....A
IND.—Indianapolis
Indianapolis Basket Co....C
IND.—New Albany
New Albany Box & Basket
Co. (Fruit) ....D
IND.—Peru
Peru Basket Co. (Bamboo
Baskets) C
IOWA—Burlington
Burlington Basket Co.
(Laundry; Bakers) ....D
IOWA—Cedar Rapids
Adams Mfg. Co., A. L.
(Galvanized Steel) ....E
KY.—Henderson
Anderson Box & Basket Co.
(Clothes) ....E
KY.—Louisville
Caummesar, T. C. C
Dow Wire Wks. Co. (Wire)
...............D

BASKETS (Con.)

LA.—Roseland
Roseland Veneer & Package Co. (Bushel) ......E

MAINE—Kennebunk
Leatheroid Mfg. Co. (Mill) A

MD.—Baltimore
Md. Veneer & Basket Co. (Fruit; Market) ....E

MASS.—Becket
Ballou & Son, M. E. (Mill) C

MASS.—Gardner
Heywood Bros. & Wakefield Co. (Rattan; Waste Paper; Work) ......AAAA

MASS.—Lawrence
Barlow Co., John W. (Mill; Rawhide) ....E

MASS.—Leominster
Whiting Reed Chair Co. (Rattan) ....AAAA

MASS.—Lowell
Woods, Sherwood & Co. (Wire; Hanging; Wire Moss; Wire Sponge)....E

MASS.—Northampton
Williams Mfg. Co. (Clothes) ....A

MASS.—Westfield
Crane Bros. (Mill; Laundry; Linenoid Powder; Waste Paper) ....AAA

MASS.—Worcester
National Mfg. Co. (Hanging; Wire Moss; Frying) A
Parker Wire Goods Co. (Letter) ....D
Wire Goods Co. (Counter Display; Letter) ....A

MICH.—Belding
Ballou Basket Wks. (Mill; Clothes; Coal; Cotton; Lunch; Market; Farm; Waste Paper) C

MICH.—Benton Harbor
Colby-Hinkley Co. (Bushel) ....A
Anderson-Tully Co. (Fruit; Splint) ....AAA
Thayer & Co., G. B. (Fruit) ....B

MICH.—Detroit
Stenius, P. ....D

MICH.—Grand Rapids
Michigan Barrel Co. (Fruit) C

MICH.—Lansing
Lansing Wheelbarrow Co. (Fire) ....AAA

MICH.—Rockwood
Baumeister, Sr., Fred.....A

MICH.—Saginaw
Saginaw Basket Co. (Fruit; Market; Satchel) C

MICH.—St. Joseph
Wells, Higman Co. .....A

MINN.—St. Paul
Twin City Reed & Rattan Co. (Automobile) ......D

MO.—St. Joseph
St. Joseph Basket & Box Factory ....D

MO.—St. Louis
Huke Rattan & Willowware Mfg. Co. (Butchers)....D
St. Louis Basket & Box Co. (Market) ....A

N. H.—Centre Sandwich
Marston & Son, J. A......F

N. H.—Peterboro
Needham, H. B. ....D

N. J.—Atlantic City
Behm, H. ....H

N. J.—Beattystown
Le Bar & Johnson (Peach; Vegetable) C

N. J.—Califon
Hoffman, I. H. ....F

N. J.—Camden
Becker, F. ....G
Leconey, G. W. ....F

N. J.—Changewater
Castner, J. P. (Peach)...E

N. J.—Clymer
Denink Bros. ....E

N. J.—Cookstown
Hartshorn, W. D.........H

N. J.—Crosby
Finton, G. W. ....D

N. J.—Dividing Creek
Dilks, M. J. ....F

N. J.—Edinburg
Hart, A. ....H

BASKETS (Con.)

Saltie, M. ....H
N. J.—Ewan
Dilkes, T. C. ....H
N. J.—Ferrell
Lafferty. J. M...........H
N. J.—Frenchtown
Campbell, W. ....D
N. J.—Hardingville
Morgan, W. ....H
N. J.—Lebanon
McPherson, G. T.........E
N. J.—Medford
Warnock, C. ....G
N. J.—New Egypt
Moore, G. F. ....H
Stidfole, A. H............H
N. J.—Paulsboro
Parker, J. W. ....D
N. J.—Port Murray
Beaty Arthur (Peach)....E
N. J.—Saddle River
Smith, M. M. ....F
N. J.—Yardville
Morris & Co. (Mill; Cotton Duck) ....A
N. Y.—Altay
Lamb, D. A. (Grape) ....H
N. Y.—Arkwright
Snow Bros. (Grape) ......F
N. Y.—Bombay
Shields Bros. ....B
N. Y.—Brockton
Crandall, J. E. (Grape)...D
N. Y.—Brooklyn
New York Stamping Co. (Silver; Nickel-Plated).A
N. Y.—Buffalo
Buffalo Wire Wks. Co. (Fish; Sponge) ....A
Western Wire Goods Co. (Letter) ....D
N. Y.—Bushnell's Basin
Collins, A. ....H
Stockham, J. ....H
N. Y.—Canisteo
Canisteo Woodenware Co. (Laundry) ....E
N. Y.—Cassadaga
Bebee & Co., C. V.......E
N. Y.—Charlotte
West Webster Basket Co..F
N. Y.—Clarence
Humbert & Kibler ......F
Schurr, J. G. ....H
N. Y.—Crosby
Bullock, H. ....E
Guile & Windnagle ......F
N. Y.—Dansville
Wagner, J. A. ....G
N. Y.—Dundee
Rapalee. J. C. ....F
N. Y.—Farmer
Ryno & Longstreet ......D
Stout, M. E.............F
N. Y.—Forestville
Forestville Veneer & Mfg. Co. (Grape) ....B
N. Y.—Forsythe
Folvay Bros. & Co. (Fruit) F
N. Y.—Fredonia
Crocker. L. L. (Grape)...D
Turk, E. J. (Grape) .....F
N. Y.—French Creek
Sullivan, Mrs. C.........G
N. Y.—Frewsburg
Frewsburg Basket Co.....C
N. Y.—Gasport
Booth & Ensign C
N. Y.—Gates
Fess. J. ....E
N. Y.—Gorham
Rapalee. J. C............F
N. Y.—Hammondsport
Younglove, O. H. (Grape).C
N. Y.—Harrisville
Universal Wooden Ware Co. (Berry) ....D
N. Y.—Highland
Westcott, J. ....F
N. Y.—Hogansburg
Daly, J.. Jr. ....D
N. Y.—Holland
Tanner, D. F. (Retort for Canners') ....E
N. Y.—Lansing
Allport & Son ....D
N. Y.—Ledyard
Rafferty, J. ....G
N. Y.—Lockport
Graham & Turner (Fruit).F
N. Y.—Lodi Center
Auble, F. ....F

BASKETS (Con.)

Bailey, W. ....F
N. Y.—Loyd
Relyea, A. D. (Agent)...F
N. Y.—Marlboro
Clark, F. ....F
Wygant, E. E. ....D
N. Y.—Middleburg
Griffin, C. S. (Fruit)... F
N. Y.—Middleport
Royalton Basket Co. .....F
N. Y.—Mill Grove
Ryan, M. ....H
N. Y.—Mountainville
Barton & Smith (Fruit)..F
N. Y.—Newark
Arcadia Basket Co. .....D
N. Y.—Newfane
Newfane Basket Mfg. Co..D
New York City
Estey Wire Goods Co.,
  59 Fulton (Waste Paper;
  Wire Sponge ....D
Howard & Morse, 45 Fulton
                         D
International Silver Co., 9
  Maiden Lane (Silver;
  Nickel-Plate) .....AAAA
Jackson & Co., W. H. (Fire)
                         A
Jansen, Edward (Fancy;
  Fruit; Perfumery) ...A
Leipzig, Abraham (Clothes;
  Lunch) ....A
Mott Iron Wks., J. L.
  (Fire) ....AA
Ollesheimer & Bros., 139
  Duane ....AA
Zinn & Co. Chas. (Oak
  Stave; Willow; Work)..B
N. Y.—North Collins
Sherman, W. P. (Grape;
  Bushel) ....E
N. Y.—North Germantown
Lown, J. B. ....F
N. Y.—North Hector
Smith, A. ....G
Westcott, F. ....H
Witham & Thayer ....F
N. Y.—Oxford
Munyon & Yates ....F
N. Y.—Pen Yan
Pratt, S. L. (Grape) ....B
Robinson Basket Co......AA
Thayer & Son, J. W......H
Townsend, W. B. ....F
N. Y.—Perrysburg
Waite, I. M. (Grape).....G
N. Y.—Phelps
Whitney. H. B..........E
N. Y.—Potsdam
Thatcher Mfg. Co. (Milk
  Bottle) ....F
N. Y.—Poughkeepsie
Lane & Bro., W. T. (Mill) C
N. Y.—Pulteney
Retan, N. ....F
N. Y.—Ransomville
Ransomville Basket & Mfg.
  Co. ....G
N. Y.—Ripley
Rickenbrode, W. B. ......D
N. Y.—Sherman
Cobb. C. E. (Grape)......D
N. Y.—South Butler
Hibbard Basket Works....E
N. Y.—Stockton
Cutling, L. E. ....F
Hall, C. A. ....F
N. Y.—Utica
Clark, Horrock Co. (Fish-
  ing) ....A
N. Y.—Wayne
Wixson, S. R. (Grape)...F
N. Y.—Webster
Hart, S. M. ....F
Kittleberger Bros. ....F
N. Y.—Westfield
Burns, A. (Fruit).......E
Crandall, S. C. (Grape) .D
N. Y.—West Webster
West Webster Basket Co..F
N. Y.—Winfield Junction
Dippolt, H. ....E
N. C.—Highpoint
Snow, W. H.............F
N. C.—Warsaw
Pierce, T. B. (Vegetable).F
OHIO—Chardon
Lyman Mfg. Co. ....E
OHIO—Cincinnati
Bromwell Brush & Wire
  Goods Co. (Wire Moss;

BASKETS (Con.)

Wire Sponge) ....AA
OHIO—Cleveland
Oviatt Mfg. Co. C
OHIO—Columbus
Columbus Wire & Iron
  Works (Fire Truck).....D
OHIO—Coshocton
Diamond Basket Co. .....D
OHIO—Edgerton
Edgerton Basket Mfg. Co.
                         E
OHIO—Geneva
Castle, Cyrus R. ....H
OHIO—Hamilton
Kahn & Bro., F. & L.
  (Fire) ....A
Meyers Mfg. Co., Fred. J.
  (Wire; Wire Moss;
  Sponge) ....B
OHIO—Hillhouse
Harrison Bros. ....F
OHIO—Newton Falls
Newton Falls Basket Co..F
OHIO—North Dover
Oviatt Mfg. Co., C. M.....C
OHIO—Oak Harbor
Oak Harbor Basket Co.
  (Oak Stave) ....E
OHIO—Painesville
Robinson Basket Co......AA
OHIO—Sandusky
Germania Basket Co. ...E
OHIO—Sidney
Bryant, John F. ....E
OHIO—South Euclid
Reker, F. ....F
OHIO—Springfield
Reash, Andrew ....E
OHIO—Unionville
Truax. L. E.............H
PA.—Beaver Falls
Knott, Harker & Co. (Fire-
  place; Frames) ......AA
PA.—Coudersport
Coudersport Mfg. Co. C
PA.—Greenfield
Sweet, E. A. ....G
PA.—Lebanon
Shepp, N. A.............H
PA.—New Brighton
Pittsburg Clay Mfg. Co.
  (Hanging) ....AAAA
PA.—Philadelphia
Darby & Sons, Edw., 233
  Arch (Sponge) ....A
PA.—Reading
Cook & Son, John ......:.F
Wunder, W. L. ....F
PA.—York
Schum, J. H. ....F
R. I.—Providence
Brown Bros. & Co. (Mill).B
Holbrook, A. & C. W. (Mill)
                         B
S. C.—Charleston
Charleston Basket & Veneer
  Mfy. ....D
TENN.—Greenfield
Ward-Kent Co. (Fruit)....A
TENN.—Humboldt
Jarrell & Co., B. C. (Fruit)
                         B
VT.—Bellows Falls
Gage & Co., Sidney C
VT.—Woodstock
Reed Bros. ....E
VA.—Churchland
Southern Fruit Package
  Wks. (Fruit) ....E
VA.—Petersburg
South Side Mfg. Co.
  (Fruit) ....B
VA.—Suffolk
Virginia Mfg. Co. (Fruit).B
WIS.—Ellsworth
Ellsworth Mfg. Co. ......E
WIS.—Milwaukee
Meinecke & Son, A.
  (Clothes; Laundry;
  Waste Paper) ....AA
WIS.—Racine
Belle City Basket Co. ....F
WIS.—South Milwaukee
Moore Whitman Co. .....D

BARS

See Iron & Steel

BARS: GRATE

See Grates

BASSOONS
See Mus. Insts.

BASSWOOD
See also Lumber

MICH.—Grand Rapids
Grand Rapids Veneer Wks.
....AA
MICH.—Hermansville
Wisconsin Land & Lumber
Co. ....AAAA
MINN.—Winona
Doud, Sons & Co..........C
N. Y.—Buffalo
Elias & Bro., G. ....AA

BATES
PA.—Philadelphia
Harkinson & Co., Robert
(Fanners' Safety) .....D

BATHS
See also Tubs

ILL.—Chicago
Cameron, Amberg & Co.
(Copying Sheet) .....AA
Eureka Blotter Bath Co.,
6500 State (Copying
Sheet) ....E
Sturges & Burn Mfg. Co.
(Plunge; Sitz) ....A
MASS.—Boston
Dalton-Ingersoll Co.
(Shower) X
MO.—St. Louis
Nelson Mfg. Co., N. O.
(Shower) ....AAA
St. Louis Stamping Co.
(Foot) ....AAAA
N. Y.—Brooklyn
Sweeney Mfg. Co., W. H.
(Sponge) ....A
N. Y.—Buffalo
Jewett Mfg. Co., Jno. C.
(Sponge; Foot) ......AA
Shepard & Co., Sidney
(Foot; Plunge; Sitz)....
........................AAAA
New York City
Cordley & Hayes (Foot;
Infants') ....A
Lalance & Grosjean Mfg.
Co. (Foot; Infants')....
........................AAAA
Mayor, Lane & Co. (Needle;
Shower) ....A
Meyer—Sniffen Co.
(Needle; Shower) ....A
Mott Iron Wks., J. L.
(Swimming; Needle; Russian; Turkish) ......AA
Stoutenborough, X.
(Sponge) ....D
Trageser Steam Copper
Wks.. Jno., 447 W. 26th
(Hospital; Galvanized
Steel) ....B
OHIO—Cincinnati
Cincinnati Tool Co. (Copying Sheet; Blotter) .....B
Globe-Wernicke Co. (Copy
Sheet) ....AAAA
Tatum Co., Saml. C.
(Copying Sheet) ......B
OHIO—Cleveland
Cleveland Copying Bath Co.
(for Copy Books) ......H
OHIO—Mansfield
Humphreys Mfg. Co. ....B
OHIO—Toledo
Meilink Mfg. Co. (Shower)
........................C
PA.—Beaver Falls
Co-op. Flint Glass Co.
(Bird) ....A
PA.—Philadelphia
Blessing, C. A. (Shower)AA
Boekel & Co., Wm. (Shower)
........................A
Gillinder & Sons (Bird) ..A
Cooper Brass Wks., W. S.
(Shower) C
Hill Mfg. Co., B. B. (Copying Sheet) ....B
McCambridge & Co. (Ltd.)
(Hip; Shower) ....B
Owen & Salter (Portable)..A

BATHS (Con.)
PA.—Pittsburg
McKee & Co., S. (Bird)...D
Standard Mfg. Co. (Portable; Foot; Sitz; Hip;
Enamelled Hip; Hospital;
Shower) ....AA
W. VA.—Wheeling
Hazel-Atlas Glass Co.
(Bird) ....AAAA

BATONS
N. Y.—Brooklyn
Cloos, Geo. (Conductors';
Drum Majors') ....E

BATS
ILL.—Chicago
Chicago Sporting Goods
Mfg. Co., 126 So. Jefferson (Base Ball) C
IND.—South Bend
South Bend Toy Mfg. Co.
(Base Ball) ....A
MICH.—Grand Rapids
Rademaker & Sons, H.
(Base Ball) ....E
MICH.—Pontiac
Pontiac Turning Co. (Base
Ball) ....D
New York City
Estes & Sons, E. B., 45
John (Base Ball) ....AA
Horstman, E. I. (Base Ball)
........................C
Spalding & Bros., A. G.
(Inc.) (Base Ball).AAAA
N. Y.—Sidney
Sidney Novelty Co. (Ball)B
OHIO—Cincinnati
Goldsmith's Sons, P. (Base
Ball) ....D
PA.—Monroeton
Booth & Rockwell (Base
Ball) ....F

BATTERIES
CAL.—San Francisco
Union Iron Wks. (Stamp)..
........................AAAA
CONN.—Ansonia
Ansonia Electrical Co.
(Closed; Open Circuits;
Electric) ....A
DEL.—Wilmington
Pusey & Jones Co. (Diffusion) ....AAA
ILL.—Chicago
Allis-Chalmers Co., Home
Ins. Bldg. (Stamp).AAAA
Birtman & Co., C. F. (Medical) ....D
Harvard Electric Co., 224
So. Clinton (Dry) ......D
La Salle Elect. Co., 47 W.
Lake (Electric; Open
Circuit) ....E
McIntosh Battery & Optical Co. (Galvanic; Position; Office; Medical;
Tartaric) ....B
Porter Battery Co.. Monadnock Bldg. (Electric;
Storage) ....E
Western Electric Co., 259
So. Clinton (Closed & Open
Circuits; Blasting; Carbon Cylinder; Dry; Chloride of Silver) ....AAAA
IND.—Indianapolis
McOuat. Robert L., 125 So.
Meridian (Dry) ....F
IND.—Peru
Peru Electric Mfg. Co. (Sal
Ammoniac) ....A
KANS.—Burlington
Electric Appliance Co. (Inc.)
(Dry; Medical) ....D
KANS.—Fort Scott
Fort Scott Fdy. & Machine
Co. (Diffusion) ....F
MD.—Baltimore
Chloride of Silver Dry Cell
Battery Co.. 409 N. Paca
(Dry; Chloride of Silver;
Closed Circuit; Electric;
Medical) ....B
McRae, Hector C., 316 St.
Paul (Storage) ....F
Viaduct Mfg. Co., 10 So.

BATTERIES (Con.)

Howard (Closed Circuit)B

MASS.—Boston

Boston Electric Co., 29 Harrison Av. (Closed Circuit; Open Circuit) ....B

Clark & Mills, 543 Boyleston (Circuit; Storage)...D

Dow Portable Electric Co., 218 Tremont (Dry; Medical) ....D

Electric Gas Lighting Co., 195 Devonshire (Electric; Closed Circuit; Dry)....B

Electric Storage Supply Co., 185 Franklin (Closed Circuits) ....A

Swett & Lewis Co., 18 Boyleston (Galvanic; Medical) E

MASS.—Brookline

Holtzer-Cabot Electric Co. (Open Circuit) ....A

MASS.—Peabody

Helios-Upton Co. (Electric) X

MINN.—Minneapolis

Minneapolis Elect. & Cons. Co., 17 S. 4th (Open Circuit) ....H

MO.—St. Louis

Aloe Co., A. S. (Medical)..A

N. J.—Jersey City

Otto & Sons, F. G. (Medical) X

N. Y.—Buffalo

American Battery Co., 172 S. Clinton (Storage) ....D

National Battery Co., 368 Mass Av. (Automobile; Gas; Gasoline; Motor; Storage) ....A

New York City

American Elect. Novelty & Mfg. Co., 308 Hudson (Dry) C

Bunnell & Co., J. H., 20 Park Place (Closed Circuit; Dry; Blasting; Open Circuit; Blasting; Carbon Cylinder; Chloride of Silver; Gravity; Medical; Pocket) ....

Cornell Co., J. B. & J. M., 26th & 11th Av. (Diffusion) ....AA

Deely & Co., Robert, 507 W. 32d (Diffusion) ..AA

Edison Mfg. Co., 83 Chambers (Closed Circuit) .AA

Edison Phonograph Agency (Medical) ....D

Empire Storage Battery Mfg. Co., 154 E. 57th (Storage) ....F

Gordon Battery Co., 439 E. 144th (Electric; Closed or Open Circuits) ....B

Gordon-Burnham Battery Co. (Electric; Carbon Cylinder; Le Clanché; Primary Electric) ....D

Gould Storage Battery Co., 25 W. 3rd (Electric; Storage) ....D

Green & Co., W., 6 Maiden Lane (Jewelers' Plating) B

Hydra Double Battery Co., 32 B'way (Dry) ....B

Jones & Son, J., 64 Cortlandt (Dry; Electric; Medical) ....D

Krajewski-Pesant Co., 32 B'way (Diffusion) ...AA

Laflin & Rand Powder Co., 99 Cedar (Blasting) ...B

Le Clanché Battery Co. (Electric; Le Clanché)..D

Macbeth & Co., James (Blasting) ....D

Manhattan Electrical Supply Co., 32 Cortlandt (Closed & Open Circuits; Dry).AA

Metallic Cap Mfg. Co.,271 B'way (Blasting) ....A

Ostrander & Co., W. R. (Electric; Medical) .....D

Pearce, Frederick, 18 Rose (Closed Circuits; Electric) B

Prentiss Clock Improvement Co., 49 Dey (Dry) .....A

Rendrock Powder Co.

BATTERIES (Con.)

(Blasting) ....B

Stanley & Patterson, 93 Liberty (Dry; Open Circuit)C

Storage Battery Supply Co., 239 E. 27th (Automobile; Carriage; Storage; Sparkling) ....D

Swan Electric Mfg. Co., 59 William (Dry) ....B

Van Houten & Ten Broeck, 300 4th Av. (Open Circuit; Medical) C

Williams, P. G., 6 Barclay (Faradic; Plating; Medical) C

N. Y.—Schnectady

General Electric Co. (Gravity) ....AAAA

N. Y.—Troy

Bernard Co., E. C. (Carbon Cylinder; Le Clanché)...D

N. Y.—Utica

Utica Elec. Mfg. & Supply Co. (Electric) X

OHIO—Cincinnati

Electrical Appliance Co., 136 Longworth (Closed Circuits; Dry; Open Circuit; Storage) ....D

King Powder Co. (Electric) AAAA

OHIO—Cleveland

Dyer & Co., E. H., Newe England Bldg. (Diffusion) A

Elwell-Parker Electric Co. (Storage) ....A

Kilby Mfg. Co. (Diffusion) A

National Carbon Co., Madison & Highland Av. (Closed & Open Circuits; Automobile; Gas & Gasoline Motor; Carbon Cylinder) ....AAAA

Nungeeser Elect. Battery Co., The, 27 King (Closed & Open Circuit; Dry; Automobile; Telephone ...E

Ohio Electric Wks., 76 Ellen (Dry; Electric; Medical) F

Willard Storage Battery Co. (Storage) ....A

OHIO—Dayton

Dayton Elect. Mfg. Co. (Storage) C

Dayton Mfg. Co. (Storage) A

OHIO—Miamisburg

Allen & Co., D. H. (Dry)..D

Miamisburg Electric Co. Electric; Dry) C

PA.—Philadelphia

Electric Storage Battery Co., 19th & Allegheny Av. (Storage; Electric; Gravity) ....AAAA

Electro-Dynamic Co. (Gravity) ....A

Harrison Bros. & Co., 35th & Grays Ferry Rd. (Open Circuit) ....AAAA

Helios-Upton Co., 1231 Callowhill (Storage) ....A

Morris, Henry G., Phila. Bourse (Diffusion) ....F

Novelty Electric Co., 50 N. 4th (Closed & Open Circuits) C

Partrick, Carter & Wilkins, 1231 Callowhill (Closed & Open Circuits; Dry; Carbon Cylinder) ....B

Vallee Bros. Electrical Co., 625 Arch (Dry) ....B

White Dental Mfg. Co. S. S. 1130 Chestnut (Closed Circuit) ....AA

PA.—Pittsburg

Keystone Elec. Telephone Co., 565 Diamond (Dry; Electric) ....AAAA

Kirk & Son, Arthur (Blasting) X

R. I.—Providence

R. I. Telephone & Electric Co. (Open Circuit) ....E

BATTING

CONN.—Montville
Palmer Bros. Co. (Cotton
.... AAAA

CONN.—Unionville
Broadbent & Son, J. (Cotton) ....B

GA.—Atlanta
Fulton Bag & Cotton Mills
(Cotton) ....AAAA

MASS.—Walpole
Lewis Batting Co. (Cotton)
.... C

MASS.—Westport
Westport Mfg. Co. (Carpet;
Cotton) ....A

MICH.—Detroit
Detroit Cotton Batting Co.
(Cotton) ....F

N. Y.—Cohoes
Walker & Harp Mfg. Co.
(Medicated Cotton) C

N. Y.—Hudson
Hudson Fibre Co. (Fibre) .B

N. Y.—Lockport
Rogers & Son, E. W. (Cotton) ....B

OHIO—Cincinnati
Maish & Co., Chas. A. (Cotton) ....B

OHIO—Lockland
Stearns & Foster Co. (Cotton) ....AAA

R. I.—Pawtucket
Union Wadding Co. (Cotton)
.... AAAA

BAUXITE

DEL.—Wilmington
General Bauxite Co. ....AA

BAYONETS

CONN.—Hartford
Colts' Patent Fire Arms
Mfg. Co. ....AAAA

CONN.—New Haven
Winchester Repeating Arms
Co. ....AAAA

MASS.—Chicopee
Ames Sword Co. ....B

MASS.—Chicopee Falls
Stevens Arms & Tool Co., J.
A

BAYRUM

See Rum

BEADERS

CONN.—New Britain
Stanley Rule & Level Co.
(Hand) ....AAA

ILL.—Chicago
Allis-Chalmers Co., Home
Ins. Bldg. (Sheet Metal)
.... AAAA

N. Y.—Buffalo
Niagara Mach. & Tool Wks.
(Hand; Sheet Metal).AAA

New York City
Peck, Stow & Wilcox Co.,
27 Murray (Hand; Sheet
Metal) ....AAAA

BEADS

See also Jewelry

New York City
Goodman & Byck (Coral) .F

OHIO—Niles
Bostwick Steel Lath Co.
(Corner) C

OHIO—Youngstown
Youngstown Iron & Steel
Roofing Co. (Corner).AA

R. I.—Providence
Lewis & Co., S. M. (Coral)
X

Lorsch & Co., Albert (Coral)
AAA

Wall & Co., A. T. (Gold &
Silver; Seamless) C

BEAMERS

See also Machinery

MASS.—Lowell
Entwistle Co., T. C.......B

BEAMERS (Con.)

MASS.—Worcester
American Card Clothing, Co.
AAA

N. J.—Paterson
Paterson Machine Works..F

PA.—Philadelphia
Butterworth & Sons Co., H.
W. ....E
Fairmount Machine Co....A
Furbush & Son Mach. Co.,
M. A. ....A
Hughes & Russum ......E
Smith Woolen Mchry. Co.,
Jas., 411 Race ....AA

BEAMS

See also Iron & Steel; Lumber

ALA.—Birmingham
Birmingham Rolling Mill
Co. (Iron) ....AAAA

CONN.—Southington
Peck, Stow & Wilcox Co.
(Scale) ....AAAA

DEL.—Wilmington
Davis Pressed Steel Co.
(Brake) ....B

ILL.—Bradley
Bradley Mfg. Co., David
(Cultivator) ....AAA

ILL.—Chicago
Chicago Railway Equipment
Co., 40th & Princeton Av.
(Brake) ....AA

Chicago Scale Co. (Cotton;
Hopper; Scale) ....A
Fairbanks, Morse & Co.
(Cotton; Scale) ....AAAA
Goodrow Moulding Co., 719
W. Lake (Ceiling) X
Republic Iron & Steel Co.,
Stock Exch. Bldg. (Channels) ....AAAA

ILL.—Rock Island
Rock Island Plow Co. (Cultivator) ....AAA

IND.—Terre Haute
United States Scale Co.
(Hopper) ....A

IOWA—Burlington
Murray Iron Works Co.
(Steel) ....A

IOWA—Davenport
Bettendorf Axle Co. (Brake)
AA

MD.—Baltimore
Poole & Son Co., Robert
(Duck Loom) ....A

MASS.—Lowell
Lowell Machine Shop (Warper) ....AAAA

MO.—St. Louis
Damascus Brake Beam Co.,
2d & Washn. (Brake) ..B

NEBR.—Omaha
Paxton & Vierling Iron Wks.
(Iron; Steel) ....A

N. J.—Paterson
Passaic Steel Co. (& Channels) ....A

N. J.—Trenton
Trenton Iron Co. (Br. N. Y.
City) (Iron) ....AA

N. Y.—Binghamton
Jones of Binghamton (Cotton) ....A

N. Y.—Buffalo
Buffalo Scale Co. (Cotton;
Hopper; Scale) .....AA

New York City
Chatillon & Sons, Jno., 85
Cliff (Cotton; Scale) ..A
Cornell Co., J. B. & J. M.
(Iron; Steel) ....AA
Dimond, Thos. (Iron; Iron
Tank) ....A
Fairbanks Co., 416 Broome
(Cotton; Scale) ...AAAA
Forschner & Sons, Chas., 206
E. 19th (Meat) X
Page, Dennis & Co. (Cotton)
B

OHIO—Bucyrus
Shunk Plow Co. (Plow)...C

OHIO—Cleveland
Forest City Steel & Iron
Co. (& Channels) ......A

OHIO—Hudson
Shields, E. B. (Plow) ....F

BEAMS (Con.)

OHIO—Kenton
Champion Iron Co. (Iron)
    AA
OHIO—Toledo
Donovan Wire & Iron Co.
  (& Channels) C
OHIO—Youngstown
Pollock & Co., Wm. B.
  (Iron) ....B
PA.—Harrisburg
Harrisburg Pipe & Pipe
  Bending Co. (& Channels)
    AA
PA.—Lebanon
American Iron & Steel Mfg.
  Co. (Brake) ......AAAA
PA.—Philadelphia
Allison Mfg. Co., 32d &
  Walnut (Brake) ....AAA
Phoenix Bridge Co. (Iron;
  Channel; Iron Desk;
  Steel) ....A
Phoenix Iron Co. (& Chan-
  nels) ....D
Roberts Co., A. & P. (Steel;
  Steel Desk) ....AA
Sterlingworth Railway Sup-
  ply Co., North American
  Bldg. (Brake) ....B
PA.—Pittsburg
American Iron & Steel Co.
  (Steel) ....D
American Steel Hoop Co. (&
  Channels) ....AAAA
Carnegie Steel Co., Ltd.
  (Iron) ....AAAA
Jones & Laughlin Steel Co.
  (& Channels) .....AAAA
Lanz & Sons, Matthew (&
  Channels) ....B
Pressed Steel Car Co.
  (Brake) ....AAAA
Scaife & Sons Co., W. B.
  (& Channels) ....A
Standard Scale & Supply
  Co., Ltd. (Cotton; Hop-
  per) ....B
Standard Steel Car Co.,
  Frick Bldg. (Brake) ..B
PA.—Pottsville
Pottsville Iron & Steel Co.
  (Iron) X
PA.—Steelton
Pennsylvania Steel Co.
  (Steel) ....AAAA
PA.—York
Variety Iron Works (Iron).A

BEANS: BAKED

ILL.—Bloomington
Bloomington Canning Co...B
ILL.—Chicago
Armour & Co., 205 La Salle
    AAAA
ILL.—Elgin
Elgin Packing Co. (Canned
  Lima) ....B
ILL.—Eureka
Dickinson & Co. C
IND.—Indianapolis
Columbia Conserve Co.....A
Huffman Packing Co., W.
  D., 24 Dunlap C
Van Camp Packing Co.
  (Canned) ....AA
IOWA—Glenwood
New Glenwood Canning Co.C
MAINE—Portland
Burnham & Merrill Co...AA
MASS.—Boston
Pickert Fish Co., L. C
Potter & Wrightington
  (Canned) ....AA
MICH.—Adrian
Acme Preserving Co......D
MICH.—Ludington
Pere Marquette Canning Co.
    E
N. Y.—Buffalo
E r i e P r e s e r v i n g Co.
  (Canned) ....AAA
N. Y.—Rochester
Curtice Bros. Co. (Canned)
    AAA
OHIO—Barnesville
Barnesville Canning & Pack-
  ing Co. (The)....,...D
OHIO—Canton
Jackson Canning Co......D
OHIO—Cincinnati
Loudon, Chas. F., Court &
  Sycamore C

BEANS, BAKED (Con.)

National Pure Food Co., 920
  Sycamore C
Weller Co., J., Spring Grove
  & Ala. Avs. ....A
OHIO—Cleveland
Haserot Canneries Co.
  (Canned) ....B
PA.—Allegheny
Lutz & Schramm Co.....AA
PA.—Pittsburg
Heinz Co., H. J.....AAAA
WIS.—Fort Atkinson
Fort Atkinson Canning Co.
    D
WIS.—Waukesha
Waukesha Canning Co. ...B

BEANS: CANNED

See Canned Goods

BEANS: DRIED

CAL.—Hueneme
Levy, A. ....A
CAL.—Los Angeles
Backer & Co., F. W.....D
Germain Fruit Co. ......A

Simpson & Hack Fruit Co.
    C
CAL.—Sacramento
Henderson & Longton C
CAL.—San Francisco
Barnard & Co., W., 202 Sac-
  ramento ....B
California Commission Co.,
  124 California ....B
Denison & Co., W. E., 117
  Sacramento ....B
Johnson-Locke Mercantile
  Co., 123 California ....A
Scatena & Co., L., 104
  Washington ....B
Schultz-Hansen Co., 308
  Davis ....D
CAL.—Santa Ana
Santa Ana Produce Co.....C
ILL.—Chicago
Dickinson & Co., Albert,
  West Taylor & The River
    AA
MICH.—Allegan
Sutphin & Co., B. B. (Ship-
  per) C
MICH.—Ann Arbor
Michigan Milling Co. ..AA
MICH.—Bangor
Smith Edgar (Buyer & Ship-
  per) ....E
MICH.—Battle Creek
McLane, Swift & Co......C
Michigan Canning & Pre-
  serving Co. ....A
Rupert & Morgan ....D
MICH.—Bay City
Buck, H. E., (Shipper)...D
MICH.—Bayport
Wallace & Orr Co. ......B
MICH.—Belding
Chapple, E. ....F
MICH.—Benton Harbor
Morrow & Stone (Shippers)
    D
MICH.—Birch Run
Wolohan, Charles (Whole-
  sale Shipper) ....D
MICH.—Bravo
Nash, W. A. ....D
MICH.—Caro
Kelsey & Co., F. E. (Ship-
  per) ....D
MICH.—Carson City
Rockafellow Grain Co. ..D
MICH.—Charlotte
Packard, O. E. (Shipper)
    C
Sheppard Grain & Bean Co.,
  L. H. ....D
MICH.—Chesaning
Ainsworth, H. N. ....D
MICH.—Clyde
Baker, W. W. (Shipper)..E
MICH.—Davisburg
Walls, W. S. (Shipper)..D
MICH.—Detroit
Caughey & Curran, Chamber
  of Commerce ....A
Horning, J. T., Chamber of

Commerce ....B

MICH.—Elk Rapids
Lang, M. B. (Shipper)....C

MICH.—Fennville
Whitbeck & Orr (Shippers)

MICH.—Flint
Flint Produce & Coal Co..B
Putnam & Co., R. (Shippers) ....B
Switzer Bros. (Shippers)..D

MICH.—Flushing
Ottaway & Co., J. E....D

MICH.—Grand Blanc
Crapser & Walker ....D

MICH.—Grand Ledge
Doty & Doty ....D

MICH.—Grand Rapids
Metzger, C. B. (Shipper)..C
Moseley Bros. ....A

MICH.—Grass Lake
Parsons & Hobart (Shippers)
                D

MICH.—Greenville
Gibson & Co., C. H. (Shippers) C
Miller & Miller ....D

MICH.—Hamburg
Watkins, J. J. ....D

MICH.—Haslett
Babbitt, E. M. ....D

MICH.—Highland Station
Seaver & Co. X

MICH.—Howard City
Lovely, W. H. (Shipper).A

MICH.—Howell
Keary, A. J. (Shipper)...C

MICH.—Jackson
Helling & Co. ....D
Isbell & Co., S. M. C
McQuillan & Sons, M. (Shippers) ....D
Stockbridge Elevator Co...D

MICH.—Leslie
Prescott & Co., W. F....B

MICH.—Marlette
Mathews, Wm. L. (Estate of) ....D
Wilson & Co., H. W. (Shippers) ....D

MICH.—Mason
Coy & Co., R. G. (Shippers)
                D

MICH.—Midland
Baker, W. L. (Shipper)..D
Reardon Bros. Mercantile Co. (Shippers) ....D

MICH.—Milford
Weaver & Watkins C

MICH.—Morrice
Towner Co., F. M........D

MICH.—Napoleon
Griffin, E. L. ....D

MICH.—Nashville
Townsend, R. (Shipper)..D

MICH.—Onsted
Onsted & Kerr ....D

MICH.—Orion
Swayzee, George C

MICH.—Pigeon
Leipprandt Bros. (Shippers)
                C

MICH.—Plainwell
Harwood & Co., F. A. ...D

MICH.—Plymouth
McLaren & Co., J. D....B

MICH.—Pontiac
Richmond Produce Co. ..D

MICH.—Port Huron
McMorran Milling Co. ...A

MICH.—Reese
Donaldson & Co. (Shippers)
                D

MICH.—Richmond
Richmond Elevator Co. ..B

MICH.—St. Louis
Bernard & Son, J. W.....D

MICH.—Sebewaing
Liken & Co., John A.....A

MICH.—Sparta
Johnson & Co., A. A. (Shippers) ....B

MICH.—Stanton
Devine, Patrick J. ......D

MICH.—Stockbridge
De Puy Co., C. E. (Pea).B

MICH.—Sturgis
Jacobs & Co., A..........D

MICH.—Traverse City
Keeney & Son, N. B. (Shippers) ....A
Morgan & Son, J. C.....D

MICH.—Unionville
Kemp, J. H. (Shipper)....D

MICH.—Waterford
Cross & Wager Co. ......D

MICH.—Williamston
Corwin, O. D. ....D

MICH.—Zeeland
Lahuis & Co., Albert ....B

N. Y.—Albion
Skinner, H. W. C
Tilden, M. W. C

N. Y.—Brockport
Dailey Bean Co. ....B
Harrison Co., Hy. ......B
Raymond Co. ....E

N. Y.—Castile
Coleman, L. S. ....D

N. Y.—Cato
Hapeman & Goodfellow ,..C

N. Y.—Cohoes
Rogers & Son, A. ....D

N. Y.—Geneseo
Belden & Co. C

N. Y.—Geneva
Dilman Bros. C

N. Y.—Groveland Station
Ewart & Lake ....D

N. Y.—Holley
Partridge & Son, D. H...D

N. Y.—Le Roy
Gleason, P. ....B

N. Y.—Livonia Station
Belden & Co. C

N. Y.—Lockport
Shaeffer, W. E. C

N. Y.—Marion
Malcolm & Co., J. B.....D

N. Y.—Middleport
Prisch, D. L. ....D

N. Y.—Moscow
Belden & Co. C

New York City
Crooks & Co., Robt., 136 Front ....AA
Hartwig & Bennett, 61 N. Moore ....A
Starace, Achille, 76 Pearl (Importer) ....B
Wakeman & Co., John, 65 Broad ....AA

N. Y.—North Rose
Hill, John ....D

N. Y.—Palmyra
Bennett & Mason .. ....D

N. Y.—Penn Yan
Birkett Mills ....A
Fenner, B. F. (Shipper)..D

N. Y.—Pierrepont Manor
Grenell, W. H. ....D

N. Y.—Rochester
Doyle & Co., M..........A
Ferrin Bros. Co. ....B
Upton & Co., E. M.....AA

N. Y.—Spencerport
Goff, H. H. C

N. Y.—Springwater
Willis & Withington ....D

N. Y.—Tuscarora
Creveling. W. M. ....D

N. Y.—Waterport
Harris, R. W. ....D

N. Y.—Wyoming
Howard, S. C

N. Y.—York
Stewart, C. N. ....B

WIS.—Berlin
Safford, M. ....D

WIS.—Cambria
Stedman & Sons, H. C

WIS.—Colona Station
Roberts. E. O. C

WIS.—De Pere
Follett, Vilas (Shipper)..D

WIS.—Fall Creek
Dousman Milling Co., John P. ....B

WIS.—Green Bay
Niebuhr, Wm. ....D
Smith Bros. ....D

WIS.—Milwaukee
Courteen. S. G., 54 2d....C
Pierce Co., A. J. W., 305 Broadway ....B

BEANS: VANILLA

CAL.—San Francisco
California Commission Co., 124 California ....B
Erlenbach, M., 320 Battery
                F

BEANS: VAN (Con.)
Lueders & Co.. Geo., 124
  Market ....A
Thayer, I. E., 28 California
                      A
Thamhauser & Co., 311 Cal-
  ifornia ....A
Wightman, J. Jr., 309 Cal-
  ifornia ....B
ILL.—Chicago
Omo & Co.. H. V. C
MASS.—Boston
Goodwin & Co., H. W., 76
  Broad ....B
New York City
Bush & Co., W. J., 5 Jones
  La. (Br. London, Eng.)AA
Dodge & Olcott .....AAA
Fuerst Bros. & Co., 2 Stone
                      B
Green & Co., D. E., 1 Platt
                      A
Lueders & Co., Geo., 218
  Pearl ....B
Manheimer & Eben, 28 Gold
                      C
Magnus & Lauer ....B
Thurston & Braidich, 130
  William ....AA
Tyler & Finch Co., 13 Gold
                      A
PA.—Philadelphia
Fleer & Co., Frank H., Ham-
  ilton & 24th ....AA
Hires Co., C. E., 17 S.
  Front ....A
Ingersoll & Co., 163 N.
  Front ....D

BEARERS

OHIO—Cleveland
Chandler & Price Co. (Printers' Roller) ....A

BEARINGS

CONN.—Bantam
Bantam Mfg. Co. (Ball;
  Roller Thrust) ....F
CONN.—Bridgeport
Armstrong Mfg. Co. (Anti-
  Friction) ....A
Bridgeport   Deoxidized
  Bronze & Metal Co. (Anti-
  Friction; Journal; Lead-
  lined; Car Journal) ...C
Sanford, D. C., (Car Jour-
  nal) ....F
CONN.—New Britain
New Britain Hdw. Mfg. Co.
  (Ball) ....B
CONN.—New Haven
Graham & Co.. Jas., (Anti-
  Friction; Journal) ....A
DEL.—Wilmington
Diamond State Car Spring
  Co. (Journal; Car Jour-
  nal) ....D
Wilmington Malleable Iron
  Co. (Malleable Iron Anti-
  Friction) ....A
ILL.—Aurora
Wilcox Mfg. Co. (Ball) ..B
ILL.—Chicago
Besly & Co., Chas. H., (Anti-
  Friction; Journal) ..AA
Caldwell & Son Co., H. W.,
  (Ring Oiling) ....A
Chicago Railway Equipt.
  Co. (Slide for Cars) ..AA
Hewitt Mfg. Co. 21 Ontario
  (Anti-Friction; Journal) B
Jones Fdry. & Machine Co.,
  W. A., 143 W. North Av.
  (Anti-Friction) C
Link Belt Mchry. Co.
  (Shaft) ....A
McCord & Co. 84 Van Buren
  (Torrey Anti-Friction) B
McGuire-Cummings Mfg. Co.
  122 N. Sagamon (Journal;
  Car Journal) ....A
Nat'l. Railway Specialty Co.
  (Journal) ....B
Railroad Supply Co. Old
  Colony Bldg. (Anti-Fric-
  tion; Journal) ....A
Raymond Lead Co. 51 W.
  Lake ..(Anti - Friction)
                    AAAA
Sellers Mfg. Co. (Anti-Fric-
  tion) ....B
Webster Mfg. Co. 1075 W.
  15th (Self Oiling) ..AA

BEARINGS (Con.)
IND.—Hammond
Simplex Railway Appliance
  Co. (Journal; Roller) ..A
IOWA—Ottumwa
Johnston & Sharp Mfg. Co.
  (Ball) ....D
KANS.—Leavenworth
Great Western Mfg. Co.
  (Anti-Friction; Journal)
                      AA
MAINE—Bath
Watson, Frye & Co. (Jour-
  nal) ....D
MAINE—Portland
Portland Co. (Anti-Friction)
                      AA
MD.—Baltimore
Aumen Machinery & Supply
  (Anti-Friction) ....D
Baltimore Ball Bearing Co.
  Calvert Bldg. (Ball) ..A
Poole & Son Co., Robt.,
  (Step; Thrust; Angle) A
Shultz & Co.. A., 1016 E.
  Balto. ("Eureka" Anti-
  Friction) ....A
MASS.—Boston
American Roller Bearing Co.
  40 Binford (Roller) ..B
Boston & Lockport Block
  Co. (Self-Oiling) ......B
Merrill & Co.. W. B., 74
  India (Anti-Friction) ..E
Phillips Co., The 197 High
  (Anti-Friction; Fountain)
                      D
MASS.—Fitchburg
Hardy, Wm. A., (Anti-Fric-
  tion; Journal) ....B
MASS.—Pittsfield
Jones & Sons Co., E. D.,
  (Anti-Friction; Journal) B
MASS.—Springfield
Bemis Car Box Co. (Car
  Journal) ....B
MICH.—Detroit
Fulton Iron & Engine Wks.
  28 Brush (Anti-Friction;
  Journal) ....AA
Muzzy-Lyon Co. 58 Wood-
  ward Av. (Anti-Friction;
  Electrical; Journal; Mo-
  tor) ....F
Nat'l. Fulton Brass Mfg. Co.
  28 Brush (Brass; Bronze;
  Anti-Friction; Journal) AA
                      AA
Wing & Co. J. T., (Granite)
  19 Woodward Av. (Anti-
  Friction; Electrical; Gra-
  phite Motor) ....D
MICH.—Grand Rapids
Hayden & Co., J. M., (Anti-
  Friction) ....D
MICH.—Jackson
Schieffler Roller Bearing Co.
                      D
MICH.—Saginaw
Moffett Vehicle Bearing Co.
  (Roller; Vehicle) .....B
MINN.—Minneapolis
Minn. Steel & Machy. Tool
  Co. (Ring Oiling) ......A
MO.—St. Louis
Garratt Brass Fdry. Co., J.
  W., 2028 Walnut (Jour-
  nal; Anti-Friction).....B
Hiertz Roller Bearing Co.
  10th & Poepping (Anti-
  Friction) ....D
Medart Patent Pulley Co.
  3500 DeKalb (Shaft; Anti-
  Friction; Self Oiling;
  Self Oiling Journal) ..AA
More-Jones Brass & Metal
  Co., 3138 N. Bway. (Anti-
  Friction; Journal; Slide)
                      A
St. Louis Car Co., 8000 N.
  Bway. (Electrical; Jour-
  nal; Spiral) ....AA
Spiral Journal Bearing Co.
  (Journal; Spiral) ......A
Standard Railway Equipt.
  Co., Union Trust Bldg.
  (Pneumatic Roller) ....D
Western Electrical Supply
  Co. (Car Journal) ......A
N. J.—Belleville
Eastwood Wire Mfg. Co.
  (Anti-Friction) ....A
N. J.—Bound Brook
Graphite Lubricating Co.

BEARINGS (Con.)
(Anti-Friction; Electrical;
Graphite Motor; Trolley
Wheel; Clutch Pulley;
Journal; Loose Pulley;
Step; Woodworking Mach-
ine; Car Journal) ......A

N. J.—Harrison
Hyatt Roller Bearing Co.
(Anti-Friction; Journal;
Shaft; Roller; Self Oil-
ing) ....B

N. J.—Jersey City
Brady Brass Co., 204 10th
(Anti-Friction; Journal;
Motor) ....B
Williams & Son, E. A.,
(Anti-Friction; Journal;
Car Journal) ....AA

N. Y.—Auburn
Auburn Ball Bearing Co.
(Ball) ....B

N. Y.—Brooklyn
Columbia Mach. Wks. &
Malleable Iron Co., 167
Chestnut (Anti-Friction;
Journal; Motor) C

N. Y.—Buffalo
Magnus Metal Co., 820 Elli-
cott Sq. (Anti-Friction;
Magnus Metal; Tanite
Bronze; Lead Lined; Jour-
nal; Electrical; Shaft;
Side) ....AAAA

N. Y.—Long Island City
North American Metaline
Co. (Oilless; Shaft; Jour-
nal; Anti-Friction) X

New York City
Brown Co., A. & F., 26
Cortlandt (Anti-Friction;
Journal; Step) ....A
Koppel, Arthur, 66 Broad
(Roller) ....AA
Lassberger, Marks & Son
397 W. 12th (Anti-Fric-
tion) ....B
McKenna & Bro. J. J., 424
E. 23d (Journal; Car Jour-
nal) ....F
Magnolia Metal Co., 511 W.
13th (Metal; Anti-Fric-
tion; Journal; Car Jour-
nal) ....A
Nat'l. Lead Co., 100 William
(Anti-Friction; Journal;
Motor) ....AAAA
Wendell & McDuffie (Car
Journal) ....B

N. Y.—Syracuse
Empire Metal Co., 118 Grape
(Anti-Friction) ....A

N. Y.—Troy
Taylor Elec. Truck Co.
(Journal) ....B

N. Y.—Watervliet
Meneely & Son, Geo. R.,
(Anti-Friction; Journal;
Car Journal) ....A

OHIO—Canton
Timken Roller Bearing Axle
Co. (Roller; Vehicle; Auto-
matic) ....B

OHIO—Cincinnati
Edna Smelting & Refining
Co., 525 Reading Rd.
(Metal; Graphite; Jour-
nal) ....B

OHIO—Cleveland
Atlas Car & Mfg. Co.
(Roller) ....A
Federal Mfg. Co. (Wringer)
................AAAA
U. S. Bronze Co., 145 Col-
umbus, (Anti-Friction;
Journal) ....B
Van Dorn & Dutton & Co.
(Anti-Friction; Journal;
Car Journal) ....B

OHIO—Columbus
Case Mfg. Co. (Oilless
Shaft; Ring Oiling) ..A

OHIO—Dayton
Buckeye Iron & Brass Wks.
3d & Wyandot (Anti-
Friction) ....A

OHIO—Mansfield
Mansfield Tempered Copper
Co. (Anti-Friction; Jour-
nal; Motor; Car Journal;
Electrical) ....A
Ohio Brass Co. (Anti-Fric-
tion; Electrical; Journal;
Car Journal) ....B

OHIO—Piqua

BEARINGS (Con.)
Piqua Handle & Mfg. Co.
(Wood) ....A

OHIO—Youngstown
Falcon Bronze Co. (Anti-
Friction) ....D

PA.—Allegheny
Damascus Bronze Co., 928
South Av. (Journal) ..A

PA.—Bradford
Stilson Mfg. Co. (Roller;
Ball) ....AAA

PA.—Chester
Chester Steel Casting Co.
(Journal) ....AAA
Crown Smelting Co. (Anti-
Friction; Journal; Loco-
motive) ....A
Vulcan Wks. (Anti-Fric-
tion) ....B

PA.—Fullerton
Lehigh Car Wheel & Axle
Wks. (Anti-Friction)
................AAAA

PA.—Nazareth
Nazareth Fdry. & Machine
Co. (Ring Oiling) .....B

PA.—Philadelphia
Ajax Metal Co. 46 Richmond
(Anti-Friction; Journal)
....................AA
Allison Mfg. Co., 32d &
Walnut (Journal; Self-Oil-
ing; Car Journal) .AAAA
Ball Bearing Co. 2322 Mar-
ket (Ball; Roller; Thrust)
....................X
Brill Co., J. G., 62d & Wood-
land Av. (Journal; Self-
Oiling; Car Journal)
..................AAAA
Cresson Co., Geo. V., (Step;
Angle; Ring Oiling) AA
Fairmont Machine Co., 22d
& Wood (Self-Oiling; Jour-
nal; Step) ....A
Holmes Fibre Graphite Mfg.
Co., 5155 Wakefield (Elec-
trical; Graphite) .....D
Klein, Chas. C., 2850 N.
Marshall (Self-Oiling;
Step for Vertical Shafts;
Self Oiling Journal) ..D
McHatton Smelting Co. 1500
Wash. Av. (Anti-Friction)
.....................E
Mayer & Englund 1024 Fil-
bert (Journal Car Journal)
......................A
Merchant & Co., 517 Arch
(Anti-Friction; Motor) AA
Phillips & Sons Co., F. R.,
Harrison Bldg. (Anti-
Friction; Journal) ....D
Phosphor Bronze & Smelting
Co., 2200 Wash. Av. (Ati-
Friction; Journal) ....B
Pressed Steel Mfg. Co.,
The Bourse (Ball) C
Reeves & Son, Paul S., 1413
Catherine (Anti-Friction;
Journal; Electric; Motor;
Car Journal) ....B
Standard Roller Bearing
Co., 48th & Girard Av.
(Roller) ....B

PA.—Pittsburg
Hyde Bros. & Co., Lewis
Bldg. (Anti-Friction) ..B
Jones & Laughlins Steel Co.
(Self-Oiling) ......AAAA
Kinzer & Jones Mfg. Co.
(Anti-Friction) X
Lawrenceville Bronze Co.,
3046 Penna. Av. (Bronze;
Metal; Anti-Friction) ..D
Nuttall Co., R. D., Fayette
& Garrison (Motor; Axle;
Car Journal) ....A
Pittsburg White Metal Co.,
1739 Liberty Av. (Anti-
Friction; Bronze Metal;
Electrical; Motor) ....B

PA.—Wilkesbarre
Vulcan Iron Wks. (Step)
................AAAA

R. I.—Providence
Amer. Ball Co. (Ball;
Roller; Thrust) ....D
Mossberg, Granville Mfg.
Co. (Roller; Thrust) ..A
Standard Mchry. Co. (Ball;
Roller; Thrust) ....A

R. I.—Woonsocket

BEARINGS (Con.)

Woonsocket Mach. & Press Co. (Anti-Friction; Self-Oiling; Self-Oiling Journal) ....AA

TENN.—Chattanooga
Frictionless Metal Co. (Anti-Friction; Electrical; Journal Motor; Machinery)..C

TENN.—Knoxville
Knoxville Iron Co. (Angle) ....AA

WIS.—Milwaukee
Filer & Stowell Co. (Ltd.) (Journal) ....AAA
Milwaukee Brass & Copper Wks. (Car Journal) C

BEATERS

CONN.—Freeport
Arcade Mfg. Co. (Carpet) A

CONN.—Meriden
Manning, Bowman & Co. (Culinary) ....AA

CONN.—New Britain
Landers, Frary & Clark (Culinary) ....AAA
Taplin Mfg. Co. (Egg) ..D

CONN.—Torrington
Turner & Seymour Mfg. Co. (Culinary) ....A

CONN.—Unionville
Humphrey, H. W., (Culinary) ....D

MD.—Baltimore
Sinclair-Scott Co. (Culinary) E

MASS.—Cambridge
Dover Stamping & Mfg. Co. (Egg) C

MASS.—Lowell
Woods, Sherwood & Co. (Culinary) ....E

MASS.—Worcester
National Mfg. Co. (Culinary; Egg) ....A
Parks Wire Goods Co. (Egg) D
Wire Goods Co. (Culinary; Egg) ....A

MINN.—Minneapolis
Lloyd Mfg. Co. (Carpet; Clothes) ....A

N. Y.—Auburn
Cady Mfg. Co. (Carpet; Rug) ....G

N. Y.—Buffalo
Western Wire Goods Co. (Clothes; Carpet; Etc.) D

N. Y.—Kingston
Browne Mfg. Co., W. G., (Egg) ....E

New York City
Lalance & Grosjean Mfg. Co. (Culinary) ....AAAA
Silver & Co. (Inc.) (Culinary) ....E
Stoutenborough, X., (Culinary) ....D
Thurnauer & Bro., G. M., 35 Park Pl. (Egg) X

N. Y.—Tarrytown
Holt & Lyon Co. (Clothes; Carpet; Egg) ....F

N. Y.—Troy
Parks & Parks (Culinary; Rug) ....D

N. Y.—Windsor
Carpet Beater Co. (Carpet) C

OHIO—Cincinnati
Day & Co., J. H., (Culinary; Egg) ....A
Randall & Co. (Hair) ....B

OHIO—Hamilton
Meyers Mfg. Co., F. J., (Egg) ....B

PA.—Corry
Raymond Mfg. Co. (Clothes; Carpet) ....B

PA.—Philadelphia
Darby & Sons, Edw. (Egg) A
Fries Sons, Geo., 900 Filbert (Egg; Cream) ....D
Weston & Wells Mfg. Co. (Braided Wire Egg) ..B

PA.—Pittsburg
National Mfg. & Supply Co., 301 Smithfield (Egg; Cream) ....E

BEAVERS

See Woolen Goods

BECKS

N. J.—Paterson
Watson Machine Co. (Dye) A

PA.—Philadelphia
Butterworth & Sons Co., H. W., (Dye) ....A

R. I.—Woonsocket
Woonsocket Machine & Press Co. (Dye) .....AA

BEDDING

ALA.—Birmingham
Birmingham Mattress Co. (Mattresses; Springs; Cots; Pillows) ....E
Perfection Mattress Co. ...C

ARK.—Centre Point
Centre Point Woolen Mills (Blankets) C

ARK.—Fort Smith
Perfection Bedding Co. (Mattresses; Pillows) C

ARK.—Little Rock
Oates Mattress Co. (Mattresses) ....D

ARK.—Pine Bluff
Pine Bluff Bedding Co. (Mattresses) ....D

CAL.—San Francisco
Bernard Mattress Co. (Mattresses; Pillows) .....A
Crescent Feather Co. (Mattresses; Feathers; Pillows) ....D
Frank, H. W., (Mattresses) B
Golden Gate Woolen Mfg. C.o, Bryant & 19th (Woolen Blankets) ....A
Schrock, W. A., (Mattresses) B

CAL.—Santa Rosa
Santa Rosa Woolen Mills (Woolen Blankets) C

CAL.—Stockton
Stockton Woolen Mills (Blankets) C

COLO.—Denver
Kent & Stuchfeld (Mattresses; Pillows) .....A
Kindel, Geo. J., (Mattreses; Comforters) ....B

COLO.—Pueblo
Colorado Bedding Co. (Mattresses) ....D

CONN.—Hartford
Hartford Woven Wire Mattress Co. (Wire Mattresses) ....B

CONN.—Montville
Palmer Bros. Co. (Cotton Comfortables) .....AAAA

CONN.—New Haven
Savage & Co., R. B., (Mattresses) C

CONN.—Saugatuck
Wakeman, Rufus (Mattresses) C

D. C.—Washington
Loewenthal, Wm., (Mattresses) ....D
Stumph & Lyford (Mattresses; Pillows) ......A

GA.—Atlanta
Southern Spring Bed Co. (Mattresses; Pillows) C

GA.—Columbus
Hamburger Cotton Co. (Bedspreads; Ticking) A
Muscogee Mfg. Co. (Cotton Ticking) ....A
Swift Mfg. Co. (Bedspreads; Ticking) ....A

GA.—Griffin
Griffin Mfg. Co. (Ticking) AA
Kincaid Mfg. Co. (Cotton Ticking) ....AA

ILL.—Chicago
Burton Co., J., (Mattresses) B
Chase & Co., L. C., (Com.; Blankets) ....AA
Cold Blast Feather Co. (P. Woll & Sons, Phila. Pa., Props.) (Mattresses; Pillows) ....AAA
Columbia Feather Co. (Feathers;. Pillows; Down; Floss; Hair Mattresses) D
Emmerich & Co., Chas., (Feathers; Pillows) ...A
Empire Mattress Co. (Mat-

61

BEDDING (Con.)

tresses) ....E
Ernst Bros. Co. (Mattresses)
............D
Faulkner, Page & Co. (Com.
Blankets) ....AAA
Fowler, John P., (Mat-
tresses) C
Loeser & Co., John, (Mat-
tresses; Pillows) ......H
Shultz & Hirsch Co. (Fea-
ther Mattresses; Pillows;
Down) ....B
Washington, Lloyd, (Com.
Blankets) ....AA

ILL.—Joliet
Wilcox Bros. (Mattresses) B

ILL.—Lincoln
Fisher & Co., Chas. A., (Cotton; Felt; Mattresses) D

ILL.—Peoria
Peoria Lounge & Mattress
Co. (Mattresses) ......D

ILL.—Springfield
Springfield Mattress Co.
(Mattresses) ....D

IND.—Evansville
Hasse, Conrad, (Mattresses)
............D

IND.—Indianapolis
Clune, M., & Sons (Mat-
tresses; Pillows) ......AA
Hirschman, J. C., Co.
(Mattresses; Pillows) D

IND.—Madison
Schofield & Son, Jno.,
(Blankets) C

IND.—New Albany
New Albany Woolen Mill
Co. (Blankets) ....B

IND.—Seymour
Seymour Woolen Fcty. Co.
(Blankets) ....B

IND.—South Bend
Russell & Ober (Mattresses;
Pillows) ....D

IOWA—Bonaparte
Meek Bros. Co. (Blankets;
Wool) ....B

IOWA—Davenport
Davenport Woolen Mills Co.
(Woolen Blankets) ....B

IOWA—Des Moines
Capital City Woolen Mills
(Wool Blankets) ......A
Schmidt & Henry Mfg. Co.
(Mattresses) ....A

IOWA—Dubuque
Dubuque Mattress Factory
(Mattresses) ....E

IOWA—Farmington
Stirling Woolen Mills Co.
(Wool Blankets) C

IOWA—Fort Dodge
Fort Dodge Mattress Co.
(Mattresses; Feather Pil-
lows) ....E

IOWA—Mason City
Mason City Bedding Co.
(Mattresses) C

IOWA—Sioux City
Hopper, Chas. T., (Mat-
tresses) C

KANS.—Ft. Scott
Bearman, J. M., (Mat-
tresses) ....F

KANS.—Topeka
Schick, Wm., (Mattresses)
............C

KANS.—Wichita
Wetterhold, Geo., (Mat-
tresses) .... .E

KY.—Louisville
Beargrass Woolen Mills
(Wool Blankets) C
Louisville Pillow Co. (Mat-
tresses; Pillows; Com-
forts) C
Schupp & Smidt Mfg. Co.
(Mattresses; Pillows) D

LA.—New Orleans
Crescent Mattress Co. (Felt;
Moss; Hair; Excelsior
Mattresses) ....A
Gulf City Spring Bed &
Mattress Mfg. Co. (Mat-
tresses) ....A
Magee, F. P., (Mattresses) C
Nevins, P. J., (Mattresses)
............C
Tebault, W. G., (Mattresses)
............A

LA.—Shreveport
Shreveport Mfg. Co. (Ltd.)
(Mattresses) ....D

BEDDING (Con.)

MAINE—Lewiston
Avon Mfg. Co. (Quilts) B
Bates Mfg. Co. (Quilts)
............AAAA

MAINE—Monmouth
Annabessacook Mills (Wool
Blankets) ....A

MAINE—Sanford
Emery & Co., S. B., (Mat-
tresses) ....A

MAINE—So. Berwick
Newichanick Co. (Wool
Blankets) ....A

MAINE—Winthrop
Winthrop Mills Co. (Wool
Blankets) ....A

MD.—Baltimore
Joyce Mfg. Co. (Wire Mat-
tresses) ....A
Lears, Clement H., (Mat-
tresses; Pillows) ......D
Perfection Mattress Co.
(Mattresses) C
Pollock, Uriah A., (Mat-
tresses) ....B
Seldner & Co., Geo. L.,
(Mattresses) C
Spindler, Geo., (Couches) D
Walpert & Co., F., (Mat-
tresses) C
South Baltimore Upholstery
& Mattress Mfg. Co. (Mat-
tresses; Feather Pillows)
............C

MD.—Gowanstown
Everding & Co. (Mattresses)
............D

MD.—Hagerstown
Hagerstown Mattress Co.
(Mattresses; Pillows; Bol-
sters; Cushions) ......D
Hagerstown Woven Wire
Mattress Co. (Hair; Husk;
Cotton; Fibre; Straw; Ex-
celsior; Woven Wire and
Spring Matresses; Pillows;
Bolsters) ....D

MASS.—Boston
Chase & Co., L. C. (Com.
Blankets) ....AA
Faulkner, Page & Co. (Com.
Blankets) ....AAA
Kelly & Co., Thomas (Com.
Blankets) ....A
Bent, G. W. & Co. (Mat-
tresses) ....B
Decatur, A. L., Co. (Mat-
tresses) ....D
Holman, John & Co. (Mat-
tresses) ....D
Kenny & Co., A. E. (Mat-
tresses; Pillows) ......A
Merrimac Mattress Mfg. Co.
(Mattresses) C
Olmstead & Tuttle Co. (Felt
Mattresses) ....D
Paine Furniture Co. (Mat-
tresses; Pillow-) ......A
Sammet, G. W. & Son (Mat-
tresses; Pillows) ......D
Standard Wire Mattress Co.
(Mattresses; Pillows) ..D
Wheeler & Co., A. W. (Mat-
tresses; Pillows) C
Willcomb, Geo. & Co. (Mat-
tresses; Pillows) ....AA

MASS.—Canton
Knitted Mattress Co. (Mattresses) C

MASS.—Chicopee
Olmstead & Tuttle Co. (Comfortables) ....A

MASS.—Fall River
Stevens Mfg. Co. (Marseil-
& Crochet Quilts) ...AAA

MASS.—Great Barrington
Monument Mills (Marseilles
& Crochet Quilts)....AAA
Riverdale Mills (Marseilles
& Crochet Quilts) C

MASS.—Holyoke
Springfield Blanket Co.
(Wool Blankets) ......B
Wagner Spring Bed Mfg.
Co. (Cotton; Felt; Hair)
............E

MASS.—Lawrence
Pemberton Mfg. Co. (Ticks)
............AA

MASS.—Lowell
Tremont & Suffolk Mills
(Cotton Blankets) ...AAA

MASS.—Palmer
Boston Duck Co. (Cotton

BEDDING (Con.)

Blankets) ....AA

MASS.—Pittsfield
Pontoosue Woolen Mfg. Co. (Wool Blankets) ......A

MASS.—Southboro
Cordaville Woolen Co. (Wool Blankets) C

MASS.—Taunton
Pool Mills, Elizabeth (Cotton Blankets) ....B
Whittenton Mfg. Co. (Cotton Blankets) ......AAA

MASS.—Worcester
Griffin, John J. (Est. of) (Mattresses; Down, Feather & Floss Pillows) C

MICH.—Alpena
Alpena Mattress Works (Excelsior, Cotton & Hair Mattresses) ....F

MICH.—Detroit
Detroit Mattress & Spring Bed Co. (Mattresses) ..D
Jenks & Muir Mfg. Co. (Mattresses) ....A

MICH.—Grand Rapids
Feather Co., H. B. (Mattresses ....D

MICH.—Jackson
Gallup & Lewis (Mattresses)

MINN.—Faribault
Klemer & Sons, C. H. (Wool Blankets) C

MINN.—Minneapolis
Gangelhoff Bros. (Mattresses; Pillows) ......B
Minneapolis Bedding Co. (Mattresses) ....B
North Star Woolen Mills Co. (Wool Blakets) ......AA
Salisbury & Satterlee (Mattresses; Pillows) ......A

MINN.—Rushford
Webster & Co., Jonathan (Wool Blankets) C

MINN.—St. Paul
Northwestern Bedding Co. (Mattresses; Pillows) .C
Union Mattress Co. (Mattresses; Pillows) C
United States Bedding Co. (Mattresses; Pillows) ..D

MO.—California
California Woolen Mills Co. (Woolen Blankets) C

MO.—Kansas City
Lloyd, J. H. (Mattresses; Pillows) ....A
Sammons, A. H. (Mattresses) ....B
Sammons, V. K. (Mattresses) ....B

MO.—St. Joseph
Buell Mfg. Co. (Wool Blankets) ....A

MO.—St. Louis
American Bed Co. (Felt Mattresses) ....A
Brazill, E. (Mattresses) ..D
Evans-Smith Bedding & Upholstery Co. (Mattresses)D
Kaiser & Co., Jacob (Mattresses) ....B
Liflander, M. (Mattresses) D
Mellon Mfg. Co., Peter H. (Mattresses) ....B
Nichols Folding Felt Mattress Co. (Mattresses) D
Perfection Mattress Co. (Mattresses) C
Prufrock, Wm. (Mattresses) A
Smith & Davis Mfg. Co. (Mattresses) ....A
Stewart Mattress Co. (Mattresses) C

MONT.—Butte
Chapman Mattress Co. (Mattresses) C

NEBR.—Fremont
Parlor Furniture & Mattress Co. (Mattresses) ..D

NEBR.—Lincoln
Western Mattress Co. (Mattresses) ....D

NEBR.—Omaha
Doup, L. G. (Mattresses) C

N. H.—Claremont
Monodnock Mills (Marseilles & Satin Quilts) ....A

N. H.—Milton
Townsend, Hy. H. (Wool

BEDDING (Con.)

Blankets) ....A

N. H.—Nashua
Nashua Mfg. Co. (Blankets) AAAA

N. J.—Jersey City
Runyon, J. D. Mfg. Co. (Mattresses; Pillows) ..D

N. J.—Newark
Roeders, August (Feather; Down) ....A

N. J.—Rutherford
Blate, Simon (Mattresses) D

N. J.—Passaic
Brighton Mills (Crochet; Marseilles Quilts) ......A

N. J.—Trenton
Bloom & Godley (Mattresses; Bed Springs; Cots; Cushions; Pillows; Quilts) A
Trenton Spring Mattress Co. (Mattresses) ....D

N. Y.—Albany
Hasselbarth, C. O. (Mattresses; Pillows) C

N. Y.—Auburn
Auburn Blanket Co. (Wool Blankets) ....A
Brooks & Sons, Jas. (Wool Blankets) ....D

N. Y.—Brooklyn
Farley, Thomas M. (Mattresses) ....D
Flegenheimer, Marcus (Mattresses) C
Glassgold & Prigohzy (Mattresses) ....D
Robinson, W. H. (Feathers; Down Pillows; Sterilized Hair Mattresses) ......D

N. Y.—Buffalo
Buffalo Mattress Co. (Mattresses) ....D
Buffalo Lounge Co. (Lounges; Couches) C
Hard, Chas. H. (Woven Wire Mattresses) ......D
Hard Mfg. Co. (Mattresses) C
McGrath & Bisgood (Mattresses ....D

N. Y.—Elmira
Blystone, F. M. (Mattresses; Pillows) C

N. Y.—Jamestown
Blystone, W. I. (Mattresses; Pillows) C
Jamestown Lounge Co. (Lounges; Couches) ....A
Sherman Bros. Co. (Lounges; Couches) ....D

New York City
Acme Bedding Co. (Mattresses) ....B
Amory Browne & Co. (Com. Blankets) ....AAA
Bloomfield, Daniel C. (Felt Mattresses; Pillows) ..D
Brown Sons & Co., M. (Com. Blankets) ....B
Converse, Stanton & Co. (Blankets; Com.) ...AAA
Englander, Max (Mattresses) ....D
Fitch & Co., B. (Mattresses) D
Fogg, M. W. (Mattresses) C
Golding, J. (Mattresses) D
Greer & Hutton (Mfrs. Agts Quilts) ....D
Hall, Frank A. (Mattresses) B
Hayes & Co., O. H. (Com. Blankets) ....AA
Kelly & Co., Thos (Com. Blankets; Quilts) ......A
Lein, Irvine, & Co. (Mattresses) ....D
Libby & Co., H. J. (Com. Blankets) ....A
Marcus & Bro., M. H. (Mattresses) ....A
New York Couch Bed Co. (Mattresses) ....B
Ostermoor & Co. (Felt Mattresses) ....B
Parker, Wilder & Co. (Com. Blankets; Quilts) .AAAA
Pneumatic Mattress & Cushion Co. (Mattresses; Pillows) ....D
Pomroy & Gamble Co. (Mattresses; Pillows) ......B
Rogers & Co., Chas. P.

BEDDING (Con.)

(Quilts) ....A
Sperry & Beale (Felt Mattresses; Pillows) C
Weisglass, S. (Felt Mattresses; Pillows) ......D
Whitehead & Asiel (Pillow Shams) ....D
Whiteside, Jos. S. (Com. Cotton & Wool Blankets) ....B
Whitman & Co., Clarence (Com. Quilts) ....AA
Wilson & Bradbury (Wool Blankets; Com.) ....AAA
Ziegel, Sigmund (Felt Mattresses; Pillows) ......D

N. Y.—Rochester

Wegman ,Wm. J. (Mattresses; Pillows) .....D

N. Y.—Utica

Utica Couch & Mattress Co. (Mattresses) C

N. Y.—Waverly

Merriam, Frank W. (Mattresses) C

N. Y.—Westbrookville

Ashworth & Sons, J. E. (Wool Blankets) .....D

N. C.—Concord

Gibson Mfg. Co. (Cotton Blankets) ....A

N. C.—Elkin

Chatham Mfg. Co. (Wool Blankets) ....B

N. C.—Goldsboro

Royall & Borden (Mattresses) ....D

N. C.—Patterson

Gwyn-Harper Mfg. Co. (Wool Blankets) ......B

N. C.—Spray

Leakesville Woolen Mills (Wool Blankets) ....A

N. C.—Stovall

Stovall Mattress Co. (Felt Mattresses) X

OHIO—Bellefontaine

Bellefontaine Mattress & Upholstering Co. (Mattresses) ....D

OHIO—Cincinnati

Bohnert Co., A. A. (Mattresses) ....D
Cincinnati Mattress & Spring Co. (Mattresses) .....D
Maish & Co., Chas. A. (Cotton Comfortables) .....B
Stearns & Foster Co. (Cotton Felt Mattresses) AAA
Wells & Co., Samuel (Feathers) C
Wessel, Herman (Mattresses) ....E
Wuest, Joseph (Mattresses) B

OHIO—Cleveland

Beckman Co., The (Blankets) ....A
Cleveland Mattress Co. (Mattresses; Pillows) ..E
Randall Mattress Co. (Mattresses; Pillows; Feathers) C

OHIO—Columbus

Billow & Lupfer Co. (Mattresses; Pillows; Feathers) ....D
Columbus Woolen Mill Co. (Wool Blankets) .....B

OHIO—Dayton

Buckeye Bedding Co. (Felt Mattresses) ....E
Dayton Felting Co. (Felt Mattresses) ....D

OHIO—Delphos

Hinde & Dauche Paper Co. (Bolster Rolls) ....A

OHIO—Hamilton

Schantz, Frank (Mattresses; Feather Pillows) C
Shuler & Benninghofen (Wool Blankets) ....AA

OHIO—Lockland

Stearns & Foster Co. (Cotton Felt Mattresses) AAA

OHIO—New Bremen

Bakhaus & Kneuzel Co. (Wool Blankets) .....B

OHIO—St. Mary's

St. Mary's Woolen Mfg. Co. (Wool Blankets) .....B

OHIO—Toledo

Toledo Spring & Mattress Co. (Mattresses) .....E

BEDDING (Con.)

OREGON—Baker

Queen City Furniture Co. (Mattresses; Pillows) ..D

OREGON—Eugene

Willamette Valley Woolen Mfg. Co. (Wool Blankets) C

OREGON—Oregon City

Oregon City Mfg. Co. (Wool Blankets) ....A

OREGON—Portland

Portland Woolen Mills (Wool Blankets) .....B

PA.—Allegheny

Allegheny Mattress & Spring Bed Co. (Mattresses) .D

PA.—Clifton Heights

Kent Mfg. Co., Thos. (Wool Blankets) ....AA

PA.—Eden

Rumpf's Sons, Fred'k (Mitchilene & Fancy Colored Quilts) ....B

PA.—Everett

Mann, L. C. (Mattresses) D

PA.—Harrisburg

Ball Bros. Mfg. Co. (Mattresses) ....A

PA.—Honesdale

Birdsall Bros. (Wool Blankets) ....B

PA.—Muncy

Muncy Woolen Mills Co. (All Wool White & colored Blankets) ....B

PA.—New Cumberland

Susquehanna Woolen Co. (Wool Blankets) .....B

PA.—Philadelphia

Blankenburg & Co., R. (Cotton, Wool & Down Comfortables) ....A
Bunting, John R. (Mattresses) ....B
Dobson, Jno. (Wool Blankets) ....B
Dougherty & Co., H. L. (Mattresses; Pillows) ..C
Hale & Kilbourn Mfg. Co. (Mattresses) ....AAAA
Hey & Son, Rich. (Woolen Blankets) ....AA
Imperial Woolen Co. (Wool Blankets) ....AA
Mc Mahen, W. H. (Feather Pillows; Bolsters) ....B
Milligan, B. T. (Mattresses) D
Schadewald & Sons, Hy. (Marseilles, Crochet, Jacquard & Mitcheline Quilts) B
Smith & Sons Co., Oscar (Felt, Hair, Fibre & Cotton Mattresses) C
Western & Wells Mfg. Co. (Braided Wire Spring Pillows) ....B
Wilson & Bradbury (Com. Blankets) ....AAA
Witty & Co., Cas. H. (Crochet Quilts) ....A
Woll & Sons Mfg. Co., Peter (Feathers; Down; Pillows) A

PA.—Scranton

Farr, John R. (Mattresses) B
Scranton Bedding Co. (Mattresses; Pillows) C

PA.—Woolrich

Rich & Bros., Jno. (Wool Blankets) ....A

PA.—Worthington

Graff & Co., Peter (Wool Blankets) ....A

R. I.—Providence

Allendale Co. (Quilts) ...C
Brady, James W. (Mattresses) ....D
Mechanical Rubber Co. (Rubber Mattresses) ..A
Sweeny Co., Wm. (Mattresses; Pillows) .....D

S. C.—Anderson

Anderson Mattress & Spring Bed Co. (Mattresses) ..D

S. C.—Charleston

Charleston Excelsior Mattress & Broom Works (Mattresses) C

TENN.—Chattanooga

Alexander Mfg. Co. (Mattresses; Pillows) ......E

BEDDING (Con.)

Parkham, J. H. (Mattresses; Pillows) ....E
TENN.—Jefferson City
Jefferson City Woolen Mills (Woolen Blankets) ...B
TENN.—Memphis
Memphis Mattress Co. (Mattresses) ....F
Ross & Co., J. (Mattresses; Pillows) ....B
TENN.—Nashville ..
Crutcher Mfg. Co. (Mattresses) ....D
TEXAS—Dallas
Olive & Meyers Mfg. Co. (Mattresses) ....B
TEXAS—Houston
Davis, H. P. & N. F. (Cotton Felt Mattresses) ...D
TEXAS—Waco
Dennis Mfg. Co. (Mattresses; Pillows) ......D
UTAH—Manti
Hoggan, James E. (Cotton Spreads) C
UTAH—Ogden
Ogden Woolen Mills Co. (Woolen Blankets) ...B
VA.—Bonsack's
Bonsack Bros. (Woolen Blankets) ....B
VA.—Manchester
James River Furniture & Mattress Co. (Straw, Hush, Fibre, Moss, Cotton, Felt & Hair Mattresses) B
VA.—Mouth of Wilson
Fields & Hash Mfg. Co. (Woolen Blankets) ....B
VA.—Portsmouth
Lindsay, Frank (Mattresses) D
VA.—Richmond .
James River Furniture & Mattress Co. (Mattresses) B
WASH.—Seattle
Carman Mfg. Co. (Mattresses) ....A
Seattle Mattress & Upholstery Co. (Mattresses) .D
Washington Mattress & Furniture Co. (Mattresses; Pillows) ....D
WASH.—Tacoma
Carman Mfg. Co. (Mattresses) ....A
W. VA.—Huntington
Ashworth, L. J. (Mattresses; Pillows; Pads) ....D
W. VA.—Wheeling
Wheeling Mattress Co. (Mattresses; Feathers; Feather Pillows) C
WIS.—Cedarburg
Cedarburg Woolen Mills (Woolen Blankets) ....B
WIS.—Janesville
Howe Bros. (Mattresses & Pillows) ....B
Rock River Cotton Co. (Mattresses; Pillows; Feathers) ....A
WIS.—Kenosha
Simmons Mfg. Co. (Woven Wire Mattresses) ...AAA
WIS.—Marshfield
Marshfield Bedding Co. (Mattresses) ....D
WIS.—Milwaukee
Berger Bedding Co. (Mattresses; Pillows) ......A
Milwaukee Bedding Co. (Mattresses; Pillows) ..D
Preusse Co. R. J. (Mattresses; Pillows) C
Standard Bedding Co. (Mattresses; Pillows) C
Weigell, A. (Feather Pillows) ....A
WIS.—Oshkosh
Edwards-Ihrig Co. (Mattresses) ....D
Oshkosh Bedding Co. (Mattresses) ....D

BEDS

See also Furniture; also Woodwork; Carriage and Wagon.
ILL.—Chicago
Adams & Westlake Co. (Metal for R. R.) ..AAA

BEDS (Con.)

Barbee Wire & Iron Works (Jail) ....B
IND.—Indiana
Potts & Co., C. A. (Dumping) ....B
IOWA—Marshalltown
Atlas Slate Co. (Slate Billiard Table) ....D
MASS.—Andover
Tyer Rubber Co. (Water) AA
New York City
Brunswick Balke-Callender Co. (Billiard Table) AAAA
Hodgman Rubber Co. (Air Water) ....AAAA
Goodyear India Rubber Glove Mfg. Co. (Air; Canoe; Water) ....AAAA
Hodgman Rubber Co. (Air Water) ....A
Palmer Galvanic Bed. Co. (Galvanic) X
N. Y.—Oxford
Clark Blue Stone Co., F. G. (Engine) ....A
OHIO—Akron
Goodrich Co., B. F. (Air) AAAA
OHIO—Dayton
Raymond & Co., Chas. W. (Dumping) ....A
OHIO—Westerville
Bennett & Co., H. L. (Dumping) ....F
PA.—East Bangor
East Bangor Cons. Slate Co. (Billiard Table) ......AA
PA.—Easton
Penna Structural Slate Co. (Billiard Table) ......F
PA.—Erie
Walker Fdry. Co. (Engine; Machine) ....B
PA.—Slatington
Slatington Slate Co. (Billiard Table) C
R. I.—Providence
Davol Rubber Co. (Air; Water) ....AA
VT.—Bennington
Scott. Olin (Rubbing) ...A
VT.—Fairhaven
Allen's Sons. S. (Slate Billiard Table) ....D
Coulman & Westcott (Slate Billiard Table) ....D
Eureka Slate Quarry (Billiard Table) ....B
VT.—Rutland
Lincoln Works (Rubbing) A
WIS.—Racine
Chicago Rubber Clothing Co. (Air) ....A
Gold Medal Camp. Furn. Co. (Camp) ....B

BEADSTEADS

See Furniture

BEECH

See Lumber

BEEF

See Meat Packers

BEER

ALA.—Birmingham
Alabama Brewing Co. (Lager) ....B
ALA.—Montgomery
Montgomery Brewery (Lager) X
CAL.—San Francisco
Nat'l Brewing Co. (Lager) AA
DEL.—Wilmington
Hartman & Fehrenbach Brewing Co. (Lager; Export) ....AA
GA.—Augusta
Portner Brewing Co. (Lager) ....AAA
ILL.—Chicago
Cooke Brewing Co. (Lager) AAA
Funk, Ernst (Weiss) ....D
Schoenhoefen Brewing Co.,

BEER (Con.)

Peter (Lager) .....AAAA

Wacker & Birk Brewing & Malting Co. (Lager) AAA

ILL.—Decatur

Decatur Brewing Co. (Lager) ....A

IND.—Evansville

Cook Brewing Co., F. W. (Lager; Pilsener; Export) AA

ILL.—Fort Wayne

Berghoff Brewing Co., Herman (Lager) ....AA

IND.—Indianapolis

Indianapolis Brewing Co. (Lager) ....AA

IND.—Madison

Madison Brewing Co. (Lager) ....A

IND.—New Albany

Reising Brewing Co., Paul (Lager) ....B

IND.—Terre Haute

Terre Haute Brewing Co. (Lager) ....AAA

KY.—Louisville

Schaefer-Meyer Brewing Co. (Lager) ....AAAA

Stang, Geo. (Root) ......G

LA.—New Orleans

New Orleans Brewing Co. (Lager) ....AAA

MD.—Baltimore

Bauernschmidt Brewing Co. Fred (Lager) ....B

Weissner & Bros., J. F. (Lager) ....AA

MASS.—Boston

Burkhardt Brewing Co. (Lager) X

Houghton Co., A. J. (Lager) AAAA

Jones Brewing Co., Frank (Lager) ....AAAA

Suffolk Brewing Co. (Lager) A

MICH.—Detroit

Stroh Brewing Co., B. (Lager) ....AA

MICH.—Houghton

Haas Brewing Co., A. (Lager) ....A

MICH.—Muskegon

Muskegon Brewing Co. (Lager) ....AA

MINN.—Duluth

Fitger & Co., A. (Lager) AA

MINN.—Mankato

Bierbauer, Wm. (Est. of) (Lager) ....B

MINN.—New Ulm

Schell, August (Lager) ..A

MINN.—St. Paul

Hamm Brewing Co. (The) (Lager) ....AAAA

Yeorg Brewing Co. (Lager) B

MO.—Kansas City

Heim Brewing Co., Fred. (Lager) ....AAAA

MO.—St. Louis

Anheuser-Busch Brewing Ass'n (Lager; Export) AAAA

Lemp Brewig Co., Wm. J. (Lager) ....AAAA

St. Louis Brewing Ass'n (Lager) ....AAAA

MONT.—Butte City

Centennial Brewing Co. (Lager) ....A

NEBR.—Omaha

Metz Bros. Brewing Co. (Lager) ....AA

N. J.—Newark

Ballantine & Sons, P. (Lager; Export) ......AAAA

Feigenspan, Christian (Lager) ....AAAA

Krueger Brewing Co., Gottfried (Lager) X

Lyon & Sons' Brewing Co. (Lager) X

N. Y.—Albany

Weber, A. C. & G. F. (Weiss) ....D

N. Y.—Brooklyn

Liebmann's Sons Brewing Co., S. (Lager ....A

Munch Brewery, Fred (Inc.) (Lager) ....D

N. Y. & Brooklyn Brewing Co. (Lager) ....A

BEER. (Con.)

Obermeyer & Liebmann Brew. Co. (Lager) ....A

N. Y.—Canandaigua

McKechnie Brewing Co., J. & A. (Lager) ....B

N. Y.—Clifton

Bachmann Brewing Co. (Lager) ....A

N. Y.—Hudson

Evans & Sons, C. H. (Export) ....AA

New York City

Beadleston & Woertz (Inc.) (Lager; Export) ......A

Ehret, Geo. (Lager) AAAA

Everard's Breweries (Inc.), James (Lager) ....A

Finck & Son, August (Lager) ....A

Hughes, J. F. (Weiss) ...E

Koch's Son, A. (Weiss) ..D

Ringler & Co. (Inc.), Geo. (Lager) ....AAA

Ruppert, Jacob (Lager; Export) ....AAAA

Seely's Son, G. B. (Root; Weiss) ....B

Stevenson Brewing Co., David (Lager) ....B

N. Y.—Niagara Falls ......

Niagara Falls Brewing Co. (Lager) ....A

N. Y.—Rochester

Amer. Brewing Co. (Lager) AA

Bartholomay Brewing Co. (Lager) ....AAAA

Genesee Brewing Co. (Lager) ....A

N. Y.—Stapleton

Bechtel Brewing Co., Geo. (Lager; Export) X

Rubsam & Horrmann Brewing Co. (Lager) ......AA

N. Y.—Syracuse

Greenway Brewing Co. (Lager) ....B

N.Y.—Utica

Eagle Brewing Co. (Lager) A

OHIO—Cincinnati

Foss-Schneider Brewing Co. (Lager) X

Gambrinus Stock Co. (Lager) ....AA

Gerke Brewing Co. (Lager) AAA

Hauck Brewing Co., Jno. (Lager) ....AAAA

Jung Brewing Co. (Lager). B

Kauffman Brewing Co., Jno. (Lager) X

Moerlein Brewing Co., C. (Lager) ....AAAA

Sohn & Co., Wm. S. (Lager) ....AA

Walker Brewing Co., J. (Lager) ....A

Windish-Muhlhauser Brew. Co. (Lager) ......AAAA

OHIO—Columbus

Born & Co., C. (Lager) .AA

Hoster Brewing Co., L. (Lager) ....AA

OHIO—Defiance

Diehl Brewing Co., Christian (Lager) ....B

OHIO—Toledo

Grasser & Brand Brewing Co. (Lager) ....AA

PA.—Philadelphia

Bergner & Engle Brew. Co. (Lager; Export) ...AAAA

Clements Bottling Co. (Ltd.) Thos. (Weiss) X

Hires, Chas. A. (Root) AA

Roth & Sons, F. A. (Lager) A

TENN.—Memphis

Tennessee Brewing Co. (Lager) ....AA

TEXAS—Dallas

Dallas Brewery (Lager) B

TEXAS—Houston

Houston Ice & Brewing Co. (Lager) ....AA

TEXAS—San Antonio

Lone Star Brewing Co. (Lager) ....A

UTAH—Salt Lake City

Salt Lake City Brewing Co. (Lager) ....AA

W. VA.—Wheeling

BEER (*Con.*)

Reymann Brewing Co. (Lager) ....AAA
Schmulbach Brewing Co. (Lager) ....AAA

WIS.—La Crosse
Gund Brewing Co., Jno. (Lager; Export) ..AAAA
Michel Brewing Co., C & J. (Lager) ....AA

WIS.—Milwaukee
Blatz Brewing Co., Valentine (Lager) ......AAAA
Cream City Brewing Co. (Lager) ....AA
Jung Brewing Co. (Pilsener) ....AA
Pabst Brewing Co. (Lager; Export) ....AAAA
Schlitz Brewing Co., Joseph (Lager; Export) ..AAAA

WIS.—Racine
Weber Bros. (Weiss) ....F

BELLADONA

New York City
Hopkins & Co., J. L., 100 William ....A

BELLOWS

CAL.—San Francisco
California Bellows Mfg. Co., 79 Federal (Blacksmiths'; Molders', &c.) ....E

ILL.—Chicago
Brand & Co., S. H., 99 W. Monroe (Blacksmiths'; Molders', &c.) ....E
Scott, Geo. M. 436 Johnson (Blacksmiths'; Molders', &c.) ....A
White Mfg. Co. (Foot Power) ....E

ILL.—Paxton
Paxton Hdw. Mfg. Co. (Insect Powder) X

MASS.—Athol
Athol Machine Co. (Square) ....B

MICH.—Grand Rapids
Grand Rapids Veneer Wks. (Organ) ....AA

MO.—St. Louis
Christen & Sons, F., Dock & Main (Blacksmiths'; Molders', &c.) C

N. J.—Harrison
Hahn & Stumpf (Leather) ....AA

N. J.—Newark
Smith, C. L. & R. E. (Leather) ....A

N. Y.—Buffalo
Buffalo Dental Mfg. Co. (Foot) C
Churchyard, Joseph J. (Blacksmiths'; Insect Powder; Molders) X

N. Y.—Canastota
Dobson, Wm. (Blacksmiths'; Molders'; Foundry).....F

New York City
Goodyear Rubber Co. (Air) ....AAAA
Houchin Co., Thos. W. (Insect Powders) ....D
Jackson Co., Wm. H., 29 E. 17th (Union Sq.) (Brass & Wood) ....A
Keese, Chas. H., 4 Gold (Blacksmiths'; Molders', &c.) ....H
Neumann & Co., R. (Leather) ....A
Reichhelm & Co., E. P. (Foot) ....A
United States Leather Co. (Leather) ....AAAA
Vought & Williams, 365 Greenwich (Blacksmiths'; Molders', &c.) ......B

N. Y.—Peekskill
MacKellars' Sons Co., R. (Molders) ....D

N. Y.—Troy
Parks & Parks (Insect Powder) ....D

OHIO—Cincinnati
Cincinnati Plow & Bellows Wks., 2025 Reading Rd. (Blacksmiths'; Molders', &c.) ....F

BELLOWS (*Con.*)

Obermayer Co., S., **647**
Evans (Blacksmiths'; Molders'; Hand) ......E

OHIO—Cleveland
Bullock Bellows Co., T. H. (Blacksmith; Miners'; Molders'; Hand) .....E
Osborn Mfg. Co., 16 S. Water (Blacksmiths'; Molders) ....D
Smith Fdy. Supply Co., J. D. (Blacksmiths'; Molders', &c.) ....D

PA.—Corry
Howard & Co., J. W. & A. P. (Leather) ....AA

PA.—Philadelphia
Bickerton, T. B. (Blacksmiths') X
Paxton Co., J. W., 1021 N. Del. Av. (Blacksmiths'; Molders'; Foundry) ..AA
Woodason, Thos., 2900 D (Blacksmiths'; Molders'; Insect Powder; Portable Force; Painters'; Spraying; Casing; Fire; Fog Horn) ....F

R. I.—Pawtucket
Bliss Mfg. Co., R. (Piano) ....AAAA

WIS.—Two Rivers
Hamilton Mfg. Co. (Hand; Printers') ....AA

BELLS

CAL.—San Francisco
Garratt & Co., W. T., 142 Fremont (Church; Fire Alarm) ....AA
Globe Brass & Bell Fdy., 128 Main (Foundry) ......E
Kingwell, Vincent, 228 Fremont (Foundry) C

CONN.—Ansonia
Ansonia Electrical Co. (Electric) ....B

CONN.—Bridgeport
American Tube & Stamping Co. (Car; Gong) ...AAA
Bridgeport Brass Co. (Unmounted; Telephone; Gongs; Bicycle; Electric; Clock) ....AA
Ives & Williams Co. (Dumb) C

CONN.—Bristol
Ladd, W. C. (Telephone) ..F
Liberty Bell Co. (Automobile; Bicycle) ....B
New Departure Bell Co. (Unmounted; Foundry; Gong; Bicycle; Call; Car; Chime; Door; Alarm; Fire Alarm; House; Peal; Tea) ....A

CONN.—East Hampton
Bevin Bros. Mfg. Co. (Church; Cow; Door; Engine; Sleigh; Car; Telephone; Unmounted; Altar; Bicycle; Call; Alarm; Farm; Fire Alarm; Gong; Hand; House; Jingle; Lodge; School; Sheep; Ship; Signal; Tea; Team; Sleigh Chimes; Saddle Chimes; Electric) ......B
East Hampton Bell Co. (Unmounted; Cow; Gong)...B
Forbes, Jas. A. (Unmounted; Gong) C
Gong Bell Mfg. Co. (Automobile; Bicycle; Electric; Engine; Unmounted; Gong; Call; Door; Alarm; Lever; Hand; Signal; Steamboat; Tea) C
Hill Brass Co., N. N. (Car; Unmounted; Telephone; Gong; Alarm; Altar; Bicycle; Call; Cat; Church; Door; Electrical; Fog; Sheep; School; Team; Toy) ....A
Starr Bros. Bell Co. (Electric; Sleigh; Car; Gong; Alarm; Altar; Automobile; Call; Church; Door; Engine; Fog; Locomotive; Sheep) ....B

BELLS (Con.)

CONN.—Meriden
Bradley & Hubbard Mfg. Co. (Foundry; Call; Hotel; Brass Smoke) ....AAAA
Connecticut Telephone & Electric Co. (Telephone) C
Meriden Britannia Co. (Call) AAAA

CONN.—Middletown
Chapman & Co., W. H. (Sheep; Body; Strap; Shaft; Saddle Chimes) Staff ....B

CONN.—New Britain
Landers, Frary & Clark (Call; Hand) ....AAA
Russell & Erwin Mfg. Co. (Car; Gong; Door).AAAA

CONN.—New Haven
Hehn & Co., A. S. (Tea)..F
New Haven Clock Co. (Electric) ....AAA
Sargent & Co. (Alarm; Lever; House; Cow)AAAA

CONN.—Southington
Peck, Stow & Wilcox Co. (Car; Gong; Call; Door; Alarm; Bicycle) ..AAAA

CONN.—Wallingford
Wallace Sons' Mfg. Co., R. (Tea) ....AAAA

CONN.—Waterbury
American Ring Co. (Sheep; Sleigh; Body; Strap; Shaft; Sleigh; Chime)..A
Scovill Mfg. Co. (Bicycle) AAAA
Plume & Atwood Mfg. Co. (Telephone; Unmounted; Gong; Sleigh; Clock).AAA
Waterbury Mfg. Co. (Unmounted; Gong) ....AAAA

GA.—Atlanta
Wotton Elec. & Mfg. Co., 52 Greenwood Av. (Extension Ringing) ......D

GA.—Augusta
Lombard Iron Wks. & Supply Co. (Dumb) ....A

ILL.—Chicago
Acme Electric Co., 231 S. Canal (Telephone) .....D
Adams & Westlake Co., Ontario (Car; Gong)..AAAA
American Elec. Telephone Co., 36 W. Jackson Boul. (T e l e p h o n e; Magneto Call ....AAAA
Farr Telephone & Construction Supply Co., 118 W. Chicago Boul. (Telephone) D
Internatl. Telephone Mfg. Co., Harrison & Clinton (Telephone) ....D
Spies & Co., 87 W. Van Buren (The Burglar Proof Electric) ....E
Western Electric Co., 259 S. Clinton (Electric; Magnet; Call) ....AAAA
Western Telephone Construction Co., Fisher Bldg. (Telephone) ....B

ILL.—Freeport
Arcade Mfg. Co. (Door)...A

IND.—Elkhart
Chicago Telephone Supply Co. (Telephone) ....D

IND.—Hartford City
Sneath Glass Co. (Glass Smoke) ....B

IND.—Indianapolis
Over. Ewald (Farm) C
Wilson Mfg. Co., O. B., Barth Av. & Sanders (Foundry) C

IOWA—Burlington
Swedish Sleigh Bell Mfg. Co. (Sleigh) ....D

IOWA—Keokuk
Garton-Daniels Co. (Extension Ringing) ....D

MD.—Baltimore
McShane Mfg. Co., Henry, 441 North (Chime; Fire; Church) ....A
Regester & Sons, J. (Engine) ....A
Viaduct Mfg. Co., 10 S. Howard (Telephone; Fire

BELLS (Con.)
Alarm; Electric; Magneto Call) ....B

MASS.—Attleboro
Mossberg Co., Frank (Carriage; Automobile; Bicycle) ....B

MASS.—Boston
Bay State Brass Foundry (Foundry) ....D
Boston Electric Co., 29 Harrison Av. (Electric) ...B
Edson Mfg. Co., 255 Atlantic Av. (Ship) ....B
Electric Gas Lighting Co. (Electric) ....A

MASS.—Brookline
Holtzer-Cabot Electric Co. (Electric & Telephone).A

MASS.—Chelsea
Low Tile Co. (Call) ....F

MASS.—Springfield
Springfield Foundry Co. (Dumb) ....A

MASS.—Worcester
Wheeler Fdy. Co. (Engine; Dumb) ....D

MICH.—Menominee
Menominee Electric Mfg. Co. (Telephone) C

MICH.—Northville
American Bell & Fdy. Co. (Church) ....A

MICH.—Three Rivers
Three Rivers Railway Supply Co. (Highway Crossing) ....B

MO.—St. Louis
Pleuger & Henger Mfg. Co., 11th & Herbert (Car; Unmounted; Gong) ....A
Stuckstede Bell Fdy. Co., Henry, 1312 2d (Church) C
Western Electric Supply Co. (Car) X

NEBR.—Beatrice
Beatrice Mfg. Co. (Door).D

N. H.—Manchester
Campbell, Jno. (Dumb)...H

N. J.—Jersey City
Williams & Son, E. A. (Engine; Car; Gong; Amalgam; Factory; Farm; Ferry; Fire Alarm; Fog; Hand; Peal; P r i s o n; School; Ship) ......AAA

N. J.—Newark
Hardware Specialty Co. (Door) ....D
Sommer's Sons, Jno. (Dumb) A

N. Y.—Buffalo
Proctor-Raymond Mfg. Co., 442 Niagara (Electric).D
Wilhelm Telephone Mfg. Co., 41 N Division (Telephone) ....B

New York City
Ashcroft Mfg. Co. (Gong).A
Bunnell & Co., J. H., 20 Park Pl. (Electric; Magneto Call) ....A
Cory & Son, Charles, 279 Division (Electric; Engine) E
Edwards & Co., 407 E. 144th (Automobile; B i c y c l e; Electric; Car; Buzzers).C
Gould-Mersereau Co. (Brass Smoke) ....B
Graham & Co., J. H., 113 Chambers (Bicycle; Car; Fire) ....AA
Judd & Co., H. L. (Brass Smoke) ....AA
Keil & Son, Francis, 667 E. 163d (Electric) ....A
Manhattan Brass Co. (Brass Smoke) ....A
Manhattan Electric Supply Co., 32 Cortlandt (Electric; Telephone) ......A
Meneely Bell Co., 177 B'way (Chime; Church; Factory; Farm; Ferry) ....E
Ostrander & Co., W. R., 22 Dey (Electric; Mechanical; Lever; Pneumatic Call) ....B
Pearce, Fredk., 18 Rose (Electric) ....B
Stanley & Patterson, 93 Liberty (Faraday Iron Box

68

BELLS (Con.)
Electric) ....A
United States Fdy. Co.
(Dumb) ....F
N. Y.—Rochester
Bradley & Co., E. C. (Electric; Magneto Call)....H
Clark Novelty Co. (Bicycle)
D

N. Y.—Seneca Falls
Goulds Mfg. Co. (Factory;
School) ....AAA
Rumsey & Co., Ltd. (Engine; Church; Factory;
Farm; Fire Alarm)....AA
N. Y.—Troy
Bernard Co., E. G. (Electric) ....D
N. Y.—Utica
Utica Fire Alarm Telegraph
Co. (Telephone; Fire
Alarm) C
N. Y.—Watervliet
Meneely & Co. (Chime;
Church; Factory) ....A
OHIO—Cincinnati
Blymyer Iron Works Co.
(Church; Factory; Fire
Alarm; School) ....D
Buckeye Bell Fdy. Co., 428
E. 2d (Chime; Church;
Engine) C
Cincinnati Bell Fdy. Co.
(Church; Car; Fire Alarm;
Organ; School; Steamboat) ....D
Knecht Co., Victor (Dumb)
B
Tatum & Co., Saml. C.
(Dumb) ....B
Vanduzen Co. E. W. (Car;
Gong; Chime; Church;
Engine; Alarm; Fire
Alarm; Mule; School;
Ship; Steamboat; Tower
Clock) C
OHIO—Cleveland
North Electric Co., 157 St.
Clair (Telephone) ...B
Williams Electric Co., 78
Seneca (Electric; Telephone; Electric Exchange;
Extension Electric; Multiple Toll Line; Magneto
Call) ....B
Williams - Abbott Electric
Co., 12 Columbus (Telephone; Magneto) ......B
OHIO—Dayton
Dayton Mfg. Co. (Car;
Gong) ....A
OHIO—Fremont
Lehr Agricul. Co. (Farm;
School) ....B
OHIO—Hillsboro
Bell & Co., C. S. (Church;
Farm; Hand; School)..A
OHIO—Mansfield
Ohio Brass Co. (Car; Gong)
B
OHIO—Piqua
Piqua Handle & Mfg. Co.
(Dumb) ....A
OHIO—Springfield
Downey & Co., Wm. C.
(Farm) C
PA.—Allegheny
Wall Mfg. Supply Co., P.
(Car; Gong) ....G
PA.—Atglen
Chalfant Mfg. Co. (Dumb)
X
PA.—Cheswick
Cheswick Mfg. Co. (Car;
Gong) ....D
PA.—Philadelphia
Brill Co., J. G., 62d &
Woodland Av. (Car; Gong)
AAA
Gill & Co. (Glass Smoke).A
Gillinder & Sons (Glass
Smoke) ....A
Mayer & Englund, 1024 Filbert (Car; Gong) .....A
Mousley, Chas., 7241 Howard (Foundry) ....D
Novelty Electric Co. (Electric) C
Partrick, Carter & Wilkins,
1231 Callowhill (Electric;
Telephone) ....B
Phosphor Bronze Smelting

BELLS (Con.)
Co., Ltd. (Car) ....A
U. S. Metallic Packing Co.
B

PA.—Pittsburg
Chaplin Fulton Mfg. Co.
(Church) ....B
PA.—Reading
Penn Hdw. Co. (Door)..AA
Reading Hdw. Co. (Electric
Ring; Rotary & House;
Alarm) ....AAAA
PA.—Tatamy
Messinger Mfg. Co. (Farm)
B
PA.—Wrightsville
Wrightsville Hardware Co.
(Dumb) ....B
R. I.—Central Falls
Mossberg Wrench Co. (Automobile; Bicycle) C
R. I.—Providence
Durfee & Co., Walter H.,
151 Pond (Tubular
Chime) ....D
Fuller Iron Works, 40 Tockwolton (Church) .....A
Rhode Island Telephone &
Elec. Co. (Telephone)...F
S. C.—Sumpter
Sumpter Telephone Mfg. Co.
(Telephone) ....B
Telephone Co. (Telephone)
E
TENN.—Chattanooga
Ross-Meehan Foundry Co.
(Chime & Church; Unmounted; Gong) ....A
TENN.—South Pittsburg
Blacklock Foundry (Dumb)
C
WIS.—Milwaukee
Campbell, Gardiner Co., 238
Oregon (Chime; Church)
D
Meinecke & Sons, A.
(Dumb) ....AA
Northwestern Telephone &
Electric Co., 77 Wisconsin (Telephone) ....H

BELTING
See also Rubber Goods

CAL.—San Francisco
Boston Woven Hose & Rubber Co., 14 Fremont (Cotton Stitched) ......AAA
Bowers Rubber Co., 42 Sacramento (Rubber) C
California Belting Co., 523
Mission (Leather) .....D
Cook Belting Co., 124 Fremont (Leather) ......A
Degen Belting Co., 107 Mission C
Gutta Percha & Rubber Mfg.
Co., 32 Fremont (Concentrator) ....AAAA
Neville & Co., 530 Davis
(Cotton) ....A
Revere Rubber Co., 527
Market (Oak Leather;
Rubber) ....AAAA
CONN.—Bridgeport
Palmer & Co., N. (Charter
Oak; Short Lap Leather)
D
CONN.—Hartford
Hartford Rubber Works
(Rubber) ....A
Jewell Belting Co., 15
Trumbull (Leather &
Round or Twist ....AAA
CONN.—Middleton
Russell Mfg. Co. (Solid Cotton) ....AAA
CONN.—New Haven
Coe & Brown, 204 George
(Leather) ....B
CONN.—Norwich
Norwich Belt Mfg. Co.
(Leather) ....AAAA
Ulmer Leather Co.
(Leather) ....A
CONN.—Tolland
Sumner Belting Co., Wm.
(Patent Cotton; Leather;
Watch Twist; Angular or
V.; Round Solid; Plain
Cotton; Round Twist; Con-

BELTING (Con.)
    veyor) ....E
DEL.—Wilmington
McComb, Thomas, 9 S.
    Broad ....E
Rhoads & Sons, J. E., 3d
    & Orange (Leather; Oak;
    Round) ....B
Standard Tool & Machine
    Co., 114 Orange (Chain
    or Link) ....F
GA.—Atlanta
Cotton States Belting &
    Supply Co., 9 S. Broad
    (Leather) ....B
Southern Belting Co., 40 S.
    Forsyth (Leather) C
GA.—La Grange
Unity Cotton Mills (Cotton)
    ....AA
ILL.—Chicago
Allen Mfg. Co., W. D., 151
    Lake (Leather; Rubber,
    &c.) ....B
Borden & Selleck Co., 48
    Lake (Chain or Link)...B
Boston Woven Hose & Rub-
    ber Co., 185 Lake (Cotton
    Stitched) ....AAA
Carpenter & Co., Geo. B.,
    202 S. Water........AAA
Chicago Belting Co., 67 S.
    Canal (Leather) ......B
Chicago Rawhide Mfg. Co.,
    75 E. Ohio (Rawhide)..A
Chicago Rubber & Belting
    Co., 312 Dearborn (Rub-
    ber) ....E
Ewart Mfg. Co., Monadnock
    Bldg. (Chain & Link)..A
Hoisting & Conveying Ma-
    chinery Co., 44 Elizabeth
    (Chain & Link) ......H
Link Belt Machinery Co.,
    39th & Stewart Av.
    (Chain or Link; Detach-
    able Link) ....A
Lyon & Son, Samuel, 8 S.
    Canal (Oak Tanned)....C
Munson Belting Co., Chas.,
    38 S. Canal (Leather;
    Oak; Round) ....A
Rossendale-Reddaway Belt-
    ing & Hose Co., 16 N.
    Canal (Stitched Cotton;
    Camels' Hair Brand &
    Thresher) ....N
Skillin-Richards Mfg. Co.,
    241 S. Jefferson (Detach-
    able Link) C
Thomas Belting Co., 46 S.
    Clinton (Leather) .....D
Webster Mfg. Co., 1075 W.
    15th (Chain or Link)..AA
Weller Mfg. Co., 118 E.
    North Av. (Chain or Link)
   C
Whitman & Barnes Mfg. Co.,
    66 Canal (Broncho Hontas
    Rubber; Chain or Link;
    Cotton Stitched; Detach-
    able Link) ....AAAA
ILL.—Franklin Park
Forster, Waterbury & Co.
    (Detachable Link)......B
ILL.—Peoria
Herschel Mfg. Co., R.
    (Chain or Link) ......A
IND.—Columbus
Mooney & Sons, W. W.
    (Leather) ....AA
IND.—Evansville
Evansville Leather Belting
    Co. (Leather) C
IND.—Indianapolis
Diamond Chain & Mfg. Co.
    (Diamond Chain).......A
Hide Leather & Belting Co.
    227 S. Meridan (Leather..A
Indianapolis Belting & Sup-
    ply Co., Stevenson Bldg..C
IND.—Mishawaka
Dodge Mfg. Co. (Chain or
    Link) ....AAA
KY.—Louisville
Conrad Tanning Co.
    (Leather) ....AA
LA.—New Orleans
Rice & Co., Louis P., 516
    Common ....B
Whitney & Sloo Co., 108
    N. Peters (Leather) ....B

BELTING (Con.)
MD.—Baltimore
Baltimore Belting Co., 6 E.
    Lombard (Leather).....D
Baltimore Rubber Co., 41 S.
    Liberty (Rubber).......C
Carey Machy. & Supply Co.,
    26 Light ....A
Chesapeake Belting Co., 823
    McKim (Cotton Stitched &
    Stitched Canvas) C
Gandy Belting Co. (Cotton
    Stitched & Sewed Cotton
    Duck) C
Whitehurst Belting Co. (Cot-
    ton Duck Sewed & Thresh-
    er & Cotton Stitched) ..C
MASS.—Boston
Barnes, H. K., 104 Franklin
    (Leather) C
Bay State Belting Co.
    (Leather; Oak Leather).A
Boston Belting Co., 256 Dev-
    onshire (Rubber; Stitched;
    Gutta Balata Forsyth
    Patent; Conveyor; Eleva-
    tor; Endless; Red Fric-
    tioned & Polishing;
    Round; Emory) .....AAAA
Boston Woven Hose & Rub-
    ber Co. (Cotton; Rubber)
    ....AAAA
Carton Belting Co., 52 Ev-
    erett Alls. (Canvas & Cot-
    ton Stitched) C
Choate & Brown, 134 Con-
    gress (Leather) ....E
Globe Leather Belting Co.,
    132 Pearl (Leather) ....D
Ireson, C. L., 148 High
    (Leather) C
Sewing Machine Supply Co.
    (Round) ....B
Stevens Co., E. E., 134 Con-
    gress (Leather) C
Union Belt Co., 139 Congress
    (Oak Tanned) C
MASS.—Cambridge
Boston Woven Hose & Rub-
    ber Co. (Agricultural;
    Canvas; Rubber) ..AAAA
Sawyer Belting Co. (Canvas;
    Cotton Stitched) C
MASS.—Chicopee
Ames Sword Co. (Canvas &
    Duck) ....B
MASS.—Clinton
Clinton Wire Cloth Co.
    (Conveyor; Wire) ...AAA
MASS.—Fall River
Union Belt Co. (Leather) ..B
MASS.—Holyoke
Holyoke Belting Co. (Oak
    Leather) C
MASS.—Lowell
Gates & Sons, Josiah (Leath-
    er) X
Whiting, Henry F. (Leath-
    er) ....D
MASS.—Salem
Kelton-Bruce Mfg. Co. (In-
    dian Tan & Raw Hide).C
MASS.—South Attleboro
Coune & Co., Wm. (Raw
    Hide) X
MASS.—South Fitchburg
Fitchburg Duck Mills
    (Duck) ....AA
MASS.—Worcester
Graton & Knight Mfg. Co.
    (Ash Tanned Leather;
    Waterproof) ......AAAA
Hudson Belting Co., 3
    Eaton Pl. (Leather).....B
Warren Co., J. F. & W. H.
    44 Vine (Oak Tanned)..C
MICH.—Detroit
Buhl Malleable Co. (Chain
    or Link) ....A
Detroit Oak Belting Co., 262
    Wight (Oak Tanned;
    Short Lap) ....B
Wing & Co., J. T., 19 Wood-
    ward Av. (Leather)....D
MICH.—Grand Rapids
Rainville Co., F. R. (Leath-
    er) ....B
Studley & Barclay (Oak
    Tanned; Short Lap)....C
MICH.—Niles
Natl. Rawhide & Belting
    Co. (Rawhide) ....E
MICH.—Port Huron
Port Huron Engine &

70

BELTING (Con.)
Thresher Co. (Chain or Link) ....AAAA
MINN.—Minneapolis
Nott Co., W. S., 200 S. 1st Av. (Oak Tanned Leather) ....A
Plant Rubber Co., 322 1st Av. (Leather, &c.) C
Sikes Co., S. R., 915 Washn. (Leather) ....B
MO.—St. Louis
Byrnes Belting & Hose Co., Jas. W., 310 Washn. Av. ....A
Hartmann Hide & Leather Co., E., 1905 Shenandoah Av. (Leather) ....A
Leschen & Sons Rope Co., A., 920 N St. (Rope) ....AAA
Missouri Belting Co., 120 S. Coml. (Rawhide & Oak Tanned) ....A
Shultz Belting Co., 402 Barton (Rawhide & Woven Leather Link) .....AAA
Spring Belting Co., 715 N. Second (Leather) ....E
N. H.—Concord
Page Belting Co. (Flat; V. Round; Braided; Folded; Solid Link) ....AA
N. H.—Dover
Williams & Sons, J. B. (Leather) ....AAA
N. H.—Manchester
Hobbs, Alfred (Short Lap Oak Tanned) ....D
N. J.—Bloomfield
Comb Rubber & Belting Co., (Rubber) ....A
N. J.—High Bridge
Taylor Iron & Steel Co. (Chain or Link) ....AAAA
N. J.—Jersey City
Eureka Fire Hose Co. (Cotton) ....AA
N. J. Car Spring & Rubber Co. (Quilt Stitched; Cotton Stitched; Rubber).AA
Rubber Celluloid & Harness Trimming Co. (Cotton Stitched) ....A
Voorhees Rubber Mfg. Co., 18 Bostwick (Nubian Rubber) ....B
N. J.—Newark
Rossendale-Reddaway Belting & Hose Co. (Camel's Hair; Cotton) ....A
N. J. Paterson
Van Houten & Co., C. C..D
Van Riper Mfg. Co. (Leather) ....B
N. J.—Trenton
Consolidated Rubber Co. (Rubber) C
Crescent Belting & Packing Co. (Rubber) C
Empire Rubber Mfg. Co. (Rubber; Stitched; Cotton; Duck) ....A
Hamilton Rubber Mfg. Co. (Rubber) ....B
Home Rubber Co. (Rubber) C
Mercer Rubber Co. (Rubber) ....AA
Trenton Rubber Mfg. Co. (Rubber & Cotton Stitched) C
United Rubber Co. (Rubber) ....AAA
United & Globe Rubber Mfg. Co. (Rubber) ....A
Whitehead Bros. Rubber Co. (Rubber) ....A
N. Y.—Albany
Albany Belting & Supply Co., 372 Bway., (Leather) ....D
N. Y.—Brooklyn
Brooklyn Leather Belting Co., 42 S. 6th C
N. Y.—Buffalo
Bickford & Francis Belting Co., 55 Exchange (Leather) ....B
Buffalo Belting Works, 122 Washington (Leather)..A
Buffalo Weaving Co., 234 Chandler (Cotton) .....A
Mey Chain Belting Engin-

BELTING (Con.)
eering Wks., 14 Perry (Chain or Link) ....F
Peerless Belting Co., 59 Terrace ....D
N. Y.—Lockport
Empire Mfg. Co. (Solid Cotton; Waterproof)....A
New York City
Ballard Rubber Co., Stephen 90 W. Bway. (Rubber).C
Brand, Randolph, 38 Cortlandt (Round) ....E
Diamond Rubber Co., 15 Warren (Rubber) ....AA
Eureka Fire Hose Co., 13 Barclay (Eureka Cotton) ....AA
Fairbanks Co., 416 Broome (All Kinds) ......AAAA
Fay Belting Co., 3 Jacob (Indian Tanned Leather) ....E
Ladew, F. R., 91 Liberty ("Hoyt" Oak Tanned).AA
Goodyear Rubber Co., 787 Bway. (Rubber) ..AAAA
Goodyear's India Rubber Glove Mfg. Co., 503 Bway. (Rubber) ....AAAA
Gutta Percha & Rubber Mfg. Co., 35 Warren (Rubber) ....AAAA
Imperial Rubber Co., 132 Liberty C
Manhattan Rubber Mfg. Co., 18 Vesey (Rubber)...A
Marine Mfg. & Supply Co., 157 South C
Mechanical Rubber Co., 22 Murray (Rubber)..AAAA
Mineralized Rubber Co. (Rubber) ....A
National Leather Belting Co., 7 Ferry (Leather)..D
New York Belting & Packing Co., 25 Park Pl. (Rubber) ....D
New York Leather Belting Co., 8 Ferry (Oak Tanned; Round or Twist; Rawhide Centre) ....A
New York Rubber Co., 84 Reade ....AAA
Penna. Rubber Co., 1665 B'way (Rubber) ....A
Rahmann & Co., Geo., 6 Ferry (Leather; Angular) ....D
Rees Sons, Hans, 17 Ferry (Leather) ....A
Robins Conveying Belt Co., 17 Park Row (Rubber).A
Schieren & Co., Chas. A., 47 Ferry (Oak Tanned Leather & Perforated) ....AAAA
Southwick Co., Geo. W., 149 Centre (Reinforced Double) ....D
Stine & Co., J. R. (Leather; Oak Leather; Round)...A
United States Leather Co., 28 Ferry (Leather) AAAA
Waterbury Rubber Mfg. Co., 49 Warren (Rubber)....D
Western Raw Hide & Belting Co., 131 Worth (Raw Hide & Round or Twist) ....B
N. Y.—Rochester
Cross Bros. & Co., 114 Mill (Leather) ....B
Estes Mfg. Co., 301 State (Oak Leather) C
N. Y.—Syracuse
Syracuse Supply Co., 314 W. Fayette (Oak Tanned Leather) C
N. Y.—Troy
Barnum Bros. Co., 179 River (Oak Tanned) C
Pine & Co., 745 Third Av. (Leather) ....A
Troy Belting & Supply Co., 6 Grand (Leather; Oak Leather) ....D
N. C.—Charlotte
Charlotte Belting Co. (Short Oak Lap) C
Charlotte Supply Co. (Leather) C
OHIO—Akron
Akron Belting Co. (Oak

BELTING (*Con.*)
Leather; Rubber) .....B
Goodrich Co., B. F. (Titanic
Rubber & Gutta Percha)
AAAA

OHIO—Canton
Aultman Co. (Chain or Link)
A

OHIO—Cincinnati
American Oak Leather Co.,
Lincoln Park (Oak Leath-
er) ....AAAA
Bradford Belting Co., 2d &
Walnut (Leather) .....A
McGowan Co., Jno. H.
(Leather) ....A

OHIO—Cleveland
Bartlett & Snow Co. (Chain
or Link; Roller Chain) .B
Bodifield Belting Co., 24 S.
Water (Leather) C
Consumers Rubber Co., 190
Bank (Rubber) ....D

OHIO—Columbus
Case Mfg. Co. (Canvas &
Duck) C
Jeffrey Mfg. Co. (Chain or
Link; Cotton) ....AA

OHIO—Toledo
Hettrick Bros. Co. (Canvas)
D

OHIO—Youngstown
Amer. Belting Co. (Canvas;
Cotton Stitched & Thresh-
er) C
Republic Rubber Co. (Rub-
ber) ....AAAA

OREGON—Portland
Simonds Mfg. Co.....AAAA

PA.—Allegheney
Lappe & Co., N. A.
(Leather) ....A

PA.—Easton
World Refg. Co. (Oil) ....D

PA.—Erie
Lake Shore Rubber Co.
(Rubber) C

PA.—Lancaster
Helvetia Leather Co.
(Leather) ....D

PA.—Muncy
Strout-Waldron & Co.
(Leather) ....A

PA.—Philadelphia
Alexander Bros., 410 N.
3d (Oak Tanned) .....A
Arny & Son. Chas. W., 228
N. 3d (Oak Tanned).....D
Canos Mfg. Co., 146 N. 2d
(Leather & Canvas; Round
or Twist) ....D
Etsweiler, Wm., 230 N. 3d
(Indian Tanned) C
Levick & Co., R., 720 Chest-
nut (Rubber) ....A
Link Belt Engineering Co.,
Nicetown (Chain or Link
& Detachable Link).....A
Main Belting Co.. 1219 Car-
penter (Leviathan; Can-
vas) C
Paulus & Co.. Jac. C., 415
Commerce (Leather) ...C
Pechin, T. E.. 19th, cor.
Allegheny Av. (Oak
Tanned) C
Restein & Co., Clement, 139
N. 2d ....B
Rhoads & Son. J. E., 241
Market (Oak Leather;
Flat & Round) ....A
Richie, Crawford & Co., 420
N 3d. (Leather) C
Smith & Co. (Inc.), James
(Leather) ....B
Wise & Bailey. Front, cor.
Race (Leather) ....D

PA.—Pittsburg
Hartley-Rose Belting Co.,
634 Smithfield (Leather)
A
Pittsburg Rubber & Leather
Co.. 10 Wood (Rubber &
Leather) ....AA
Scaife Fdry. & Machine Co.
(Chain or Link) ....A

PA.—Pittston
Exeter Machine Wks.
(Chain or Link).......B

PA.—South Bethlehem
Bethlehem Fdry. & Machine
Co. C

BELTING (*Con.*)
PA.—Williamsport
Slate's Sons, Geo. (Leather)
C

R. I.—Central Falls
Weatherhead, Thompson &
Co. (Leather) ....A

R. I.—Pawtucket
Weatherhead, Thompson &
Co. (Leather; Oak Leath-
er; Raw Hide; Round;
Waterproof) ....A

R. I.—Providence
American Supply Co., 13
Eddy (Leather; Oak
Leather) ....A
Brown Bros. Co. (Oak
Leather) ....B
Burgess & Son, A., (Leath-
er) X
Providence Belting Co.
(Leather; Oak Leather;
Round) ....B

TENN.—Memphis
Southern Belting Co., 328
Front ....B

VT.—Montpelier
Lane Mfg. Co. (Leather)..A

VA.—Alexandria
Smoot & Sons Co., C. C.
(Leather) ....AA

VA.—Richmonu
Richmond Leather Mfg. Co..
2201 E. Cary (Leather)..D

WIS.—Milwaukee
Chain Belt Co., 766 Park
(Chain or Link) ....B
Filer & Stowell Co. (Link)
AAA
Western Raw Hide & Belt-
ing Co. (Leather & Raw
Hide & Superior Surface
Tanned; Twist).........A

BELTS

See also Leather Goods

CAL.—San Francisco
Heineman, H. W. (Leather)
B

CONN.—Waterbury
Waterbury Brass Co. (Shot)
AAAA

CONN.—Windsor
Windsor Collar & Cuff Co.
(Rubber Dress) X

ILL.—Chicago
Bunker Saddle Co., 208 Lake
(Ladies') ....D
Cook & Bro.. E. C., 40 Dear-
born (Cartridge) ......A
Horne's Elec. Belt & Truss
Co.. Dr., 985 N. Clark
(Electric) X
Kittleman & Little........E
Riordan Mfg. Co., T. G...C

ILL.—Downers Grove
Dicke Tool Co. (Linemen's)
D

IND.—Indianapolis
Union Mfg. Co. ....D

IOWA—Des Moines
Des Moines Skirt & Corset
Mfg. Co. (Ladies')......E

KANS.—Burlington
Electric Appliance Co. (Inc.)
(Electric) ....D

LA.—New Orleans
Weydig & Son. Martin
(Fire) X

MASS.—Andover
Tyer Rubber Co. (Electric)
AA

MASS.—Athol
Bates Bros. Co. (Ladies')
B

MASS.—Boston
Hewes & Potter (Leather)
A
Hub Gore Makers. 91 Bed-
ford (Elastic) ....A
Trafton, H. O. (Womens')
E

MASS.—Chicopee
Ames Sword Co. (Sword)..B

MASS.—Worcester
Warren Leather Goods Co.,
8 Washn. Sq. (Cartridge;
Sword) ....B

MO.—St. Louis
Brauer Bros.. Mfg. Co.
(Cartridge) ....E
Straus Saddlery Co., Jacob

72

BELTS (Con.)
D., 410 N. 6th (Cartridge)
...................................A
N. J.—Hoboken
Lehman & Co. (Leather)..A
N. J.—Jersey City
Mehl & Co., Jno. (Inc.)
(Ladies'; Leather)...AA
N. J.—Newark
Peters Harness & Saddlery
Co. (Leather; Cartridge).C
N. Y.—Lockport
Empire Mfg. Co. (Abdo-
minal) ....A
New York City
Cairns & Bro., 143 Grand
(Fire) ....D
Ferris Bros. Co., 341 Bway.
(Ladies' Sanitary) ....A
Galewski, Adolph, 30 Cham-
bers (Linemen's) ......F
Goodyear Rubber Co., 787
Bway. (Elastic) ..AAAA
Hahn & Co., A., 296 Bway.
(Ladies') ....B
Knothe Bros...............C
Livingston & Co., L., 537
Bway. (Ladies') ......B
Maas, Blum & Co., 370
Bway. (Ladies'; Leather)
..........................AA
Medford Fancy Goods Co.,
75 Duane (Dog Collars).E
New York Woven Label
Mfg. Co., 262 Canal
(Dress) ....B
Pall-Mall Elec. Assn., 870
Bway. (Electric).......F
Pomeroy Co., 17 Union Sq.
(Abdominal) ....B
Rice's Sons, Bernard, 518
Bway. (Ladies') ......A
Samstag & Hilder Bros...A
Scheuer & Bro., 329 Canal
(Ladies'; Leather).....X
Tower & Lyon Co., 95
Chambers (Police) ....B
Spaulding & Bros., A. G.
Inc.), 126 Nassau (Cart-
ridge, Athlete's; Shot)
........................AAAA
Von Lenzerke & Detmold,
318 Bway. (Cartridge;
Shot) ....A
Wade Corset Co. (Abdo-
minal) ....AAAA
N. Y.—Rochester
Schaefer & Klein (Silk)..C
OHIO—Cleveland
Cleveland Elec. Wks. (Elec-
tric) X
OHIO—Toledo
Hettrick Bros. Co. (Emery
Polishing) ....B
PA.—Philadelphia
Horn & Bros., Wm. H., 453
N. 3d (Abdominal; Elas-
tic) ....E
Horstmann Co., Wm. H.,
Cherry & N. 5th (Leath-
er; Sword) ....AAAA
Kendrick, James R., Ger-
mantown (Abdominal &
Sanitary) ....E
Kolbe Co., D. W., 1339 Arch
(Abdominal) X
Loeb, Lipper & Co., 319 N.
Darien (Dress; Ladies').A
Oppenheimer's Sons, Lewis
...........................C
Perry, Fergus. 5013 Wake-
field (Abdominal) .....D
Philadelphia Truss Co., 610
Locust (Abdominal)...X
Rosenblatt & Co., H. M.,
1025 Vine (Leather; Cloth-
ing) ....A
Seeley, Isaac B., 1027 Wal-
nut (Elastic) ....B
R. I.—Providence
Brown Bros. & Co. (Leath-
er) ....B
TENN.—Nashville
Carlsbad Suspender Co.
(A. Bennie & Co., Props.)
...........................D

BENCHES

See Furniture & Tables
CONN.—Bridgeport
American Tube & Stamping
Co. (Draw) ....AAA
Armstrong Mfg. Co. (Wire
Drawing) ....A
Spencer, J. E. (Wire Draw-

BENCHES (Con.)
ing) 123 Railroad ......H
CONN.—Derby
Birmingham Iron F'dry
(Wire Drawing) ....B
CONN.—Norwich
Rogers & Co., C. B. (Saw)
.........................AAAA
CONN.—Waterbury
Waterbury Machine Co.
(Wire Drawing) ....B
Waterbury Farrell F'dry &
Machine Co. (Draw &
Hydraulic Draw) ....AA
ILL.—Batavia
Challenge Wind Mill & Feed
Mill Co. (Saw) ......AAA
U. S. Wind Engine & Pump
Co. (Saw) ....AA
ILL.—Chicago
Covel Mfg. Co. (Saw) 8 S.
Canal C
Greenlee Bros. & Co (Saw)
..........................AA
Illinois Malleable Iron Co.
(Tub & Wringer) ..AAAA
Schomer, Henry, 301 Canal
(Folding Wash) ....D
ILL.—Joliet
Bates Machine Co. (Draw;
Wire Drawing) ....A
Bliss Co., E. W., 19 Adams
(Draw) ....AAAA
IND.—Goshen
I. X. L. & Goshen Pump Co.
(Folding Wash) ....B
IND.—Indianapolis
Chandler & Taylor Co. (Cord
Wood Saw) ....AA
Udell Wks. (Folding Wash;
Piano; Wringer) ......A
IND.—Marion
Nat'l Sweeper Co. (Tub &
Wringer) ....AAAA
MASS.—Boston
Woods Machine Co., S. A.
(Saw) ....AA
MASS.—Brocton
Kimball Bros. & Sprague
153 Centre (Circular Saw)
...........................B
MASS.—Harvard
Hildreth Bros. (Saw) ....B
MASS.—Orange
Chase Turbine Mfg. Co.
(Saw; Power Feed Saw).A
MASS.—Springfield
Bullock & Co., O. W.
(Jewelers Draw) ......A
MASS.—Worcester
Morgan Construction Co.
(Draw; Wire Drawing) B
Reed & Co., F. E. (Scrapers)
...........................A
MICH.—Fenton
Philipps Co., A. J. (Tub &
Wringer) ....A
MICH.—Grand Rapids
American Machinery Co.
(Circular Saw) ....A
Grand Rapids Hand Screw
Co. (Cabinet Makers') .B
MO.—St. Louis
Parker Russell Mining &
Mfg. Co. (Gas Retort)
..........................AAA
N. H.—Nashua
Nashua Novelty Works
(Wash) ....B
N. J.—Newark
Gould & Eberhardt, 95 N. J.
R. R. Av. (Wire Draw-
ing; Draw) ....A
Ohl & Co., Geo A. (Draw)
...........................B
N. J.—Paterson
Royle & Sons, Jno. (Saw) A
N. J.—Smithville
Smith Machine Co., H. B.
(Saw) ....A
N. J.—Trenton
Mac Kenzie, Duncan (Wire
Drawing) ....A
Trenton Iron Co. (Draw) AA
N. Y.—Brooklyn
Cooper & Mc Kee, 119
Gwinett (Wash) ....A
N. Y.—Buffalo
Frank M'ch'ry Co. (Saw) .C
Holmes M'ch'ry Co., E. &
B. (Saw) ....B
Oliver Mfg. Co., 1483
Niagara (Draw; Jewelers;
etc.) C
N. Y.—Jamestown
Empire Washer Co. (Folding

BENCHES (Con.)

Wash) ....A
New York City
American Tool Chest Co.,
200 W. Houston (Work) C
American Wood Working
Mach. Co., 141 Broadway
(Saw) ....AAAA
American Wringer Co., 99
Chambers (Folding Wash)
AAAA
Fairbanks Co., 416 Broome
(Machinists Work) AAAA
Mace & Co., L. H., 111 E.
Houston (Wash) .....B
New Jersey Foundry & Machine Co. (Draw) .....B
Watson-Stillman Co., 210 E.
43rd (Draw & Hydraulic
Draw) ....AA
N. Y.—Troy
Parks & Parks (Folding
Wash) ....B
OHIO—Cuyahoga Falls
Turner, Vaughan & Taylor
Co. (Draw; Wire) .....B
OHIO—Toledo
Baker Bros. (Circular Saw;
Pattern Maker's) .....A
Toledo Machine & Tool Co.
(Wire Drawing) ....A
PA.—Allentown
Grammes & Sons, L. F.
(Saw) ....A
PA.—Bloomsburg
Richards Mfg. Co. (Draw)
C
PA.—Erie
American Mfg. & Novelty
Co (Wash) C
Lovell Mfg. Co (Ltd) (Folding Wash) ....AA
Standard Sawmill M'ch'ry
Co., 911 E. 12th (Saw) .B
PA.—Harrisburg
Hickok Mfg. Co., W. O.
(Sewing) ....AA
PA.—New Castle .
Vulcan F'dry & Machine Co.
(Draw) ....B
PA.—Philadelphia
Colladay, Jos. O., 626 Race
(Saw) ....B
Cresson Co., Geo. V. 18th &
Allegheny Av. (Draw) AA
Hammond & Son, J. T. 4534
Hedge (Folding Wash) .B
Power & Co., L., 20 S. 23rd
(Saw) ....A
PA.—South Bethlehem
Bethlehem F'dry & Machine
Co. (Folding) C
R. I.—Pawtucket
Bliss Mfg. Co., R. (Sewing)
AAAA
Mossberg & Granville Mfg.
Co. (Draw; Jewelers'
Draw) ....A
R. I.—Providence
Standard Machinery Co.
(Draw) ....A

BENDERS

See also Hardware; Carriages.

DEL.—Wilmington
Hilles & Jones Co. (Rail) AA
ILL.—Carpentersville .
Ill. Iron & Bolt Co. (Roller
Blaring Tire) ....A
ILL.—Chicago
Gibson Co., W. D., 23 N.
Clinton (Pipe; Wire) ...B
Railway Appliance Co., Old
Colony Bldg. (Rail) ...A
Wallace Supply Co., 169
Jackson Boul. (Angle &
Eye; Hand Power) ....D
ILL.—Evanstown
Mark Mfg. Co. (Lead Pipe)
B
ILL.—Moline
Williams, White & Co.
(Tire) ....A
ILL.—Rockford
Weyburn Co. (Tire) .....D
ILL.—Sandwich
Espen & Dolan (Angle &
Eye; Ring & Hinge; Hand
Power) ....G
IOWA—Ottumwa
Hardsocg Mfg. Co. (Coal
Miners' Rail) ....B

BENDERS (Con.)

MASS.—Boston
Butts & Ordway Co., 190
High (Tire) ....D
MASS.—Canton .
Kinsley Iron & Machine Co.
(Tire) ....AA
MASS.—Greenfield
Wiley & Russell Mfg. Co.
(Tire) ....AA
MASS.—Worcester
Boynton & Plummer (Tire)
B
MICH.—Detroit
Fulton Iron & Engine W'ks.
(Tire) X
National Fulton Brass Mfg.
Co.(Tire) ....A
MICH.—Kalamazoo
Kalamazoo Railway Supply
Co. (Rail) ....B
MO.—St. Louis
Pleuger & Henger Mfg. Co.,
11th & Hebert (Tire) ..B
Western Glass Bending
Works, 1520 Gratiot
(Glass) ....D
N. H.—Penacook
Concord Axle Co. (Tire) ..B
N. J.—Newark
Bernz, Otto, S. 13th & S.
Orange Av. (Lead Pipe)
B
N. Y.—Buffalo
Buffalo Forge Co. (Tire)
AA
New York City
Billings Pipe Bender Mfg.
Co., 38 Park Pl. (Brass;
Copper; Lead Pipe) ..D
Watson-Stillman Co. (Hydraulic; Rail) ....AA
N. Y.—Syracuse
Kane & Roach (Tire) ....D
OHIO—Cincinnati
Haven Malleable Casting
Co. (Tire) ....B
OHIO—Cleveland
Cleveland Wire & Spring Co.
(Lead Pipe; Wire) C
OHIO—Hamilton
Long & Allstatter Co. (Rail)
A
OHIO—Youngstown
Sennett Co., G. B. (Rail) **A**
PA.—Corry
Raymond Mfg. Co. (Lead
Pipe; Wire) C
PA.—Lancaster
Champion Blower & Forge
Co. (Tire) ....B
Potts, David H. (Tire) ...D
PA.—Nazareth
Nazareth F'dry & Machine
Co. (Rail) ....B
PA.—Philadelphia
Espen-Lucas Machine W'ks,
Broad & Noble (Rail) ..D
Morris, P. H., 1501 S.
Front; (Rail) C
PA.—Pittsburg
Best Mfg. Co. (Iron, Steel,
Brass; Copper; Extension)
A
PA.—Scottdale
Kenney & Co. (Tire) ....A
PA.—South Bethlehem
Bethlehem F'dry & Machine
Co. (Rail; Tire) C

BENDS

CONN.—Bridgeport
Belknap Mfg. Co. (Brass;
Copper; Iron; Steel) ...C
CONN.—Hartford
Whitlock Coil Pipe Co.
(Pipe; Wrought Iron for
Steam Plants) ....A
CONN.—New Haven
National Pipe Bending Co.
(Pipe; Brass; Copper;
Iron; Steel) ....B
ILL.—Chicago
Blatchford & Co., E. W.
(Lead) ....AA
Crane Co. (Wrought Iron for
Steam Plants) ....AAAA
Ill. Malleable Iron Co.
(Iron) ....AA
MD.—Baltimore
Robertson Mfg. Co., Jas.
(Lead) ....A
MASS.—Boston
Walworth Mfg. Co., 100
Pearl (Pipe; Brass; Cop-

BENDS (Con.)
per) ....AAAA
New York City
Nat'l Lead Co. (Pipe;
Lead) ....AAAA
OHIO—Canton
Mc Lain Co, Jas. H. (Brass)
AA
PA.—Allentown
Albrights' Son & Co. (Pipe)
A
PA.—Harrisburg
Harrisburg Pipe & Pipe
Bending Co. (Ltd) (Pipe;
Brass; Copper; Iron;
Steel) ....AA
PA.—Philadelphia
Philadelphia Pipe Bending
W'ks., 4129 No. 5th (Pipe;
Iron) ....F
R. I.—Providence
Phillips Co., Thos (Copper)
C

BENEDICTINE
See Liquors; Cordials

BENZINE
ILL.—Chicago
Indian Asphalt Co. (Railway Exch. Bldg.) ....B
PA.—Bradford
Emery Mfg. Co. ....AAAA
PA.—Petrolia
Petrolia Refining Co. C
PA.—Philadelphia
Crew, Levick & Co. ...AAA

BENZOIN
New York City
Hopkins & Co., J. L., 100
William ....A
Mc Kesson & Robbins (Gum)
AAAA

BENZOLE
CAL.—San Francisco
Pacific Refining & Roofing
Co., 113 New Montgomery
D
N. Y.—Buffalo
Schoellkopf, Hartford &
Hanna ....AAA
N. Y.—Syracuse
Solvay Process Co. ..AAAA
New York City
White Tar Co. ....E
PA.—Philadelphia
Barrett Mfg. Co. ...AAAA
PA.—Pittsburg
McClintock & Irvine Co.
(Crude) ....B

BERRIES
See Canned Goods & Dried
Fruit.

BEVELERS
CAL.—Los Angeles
Raphael & Co., H., 509 So.
Main (Glass) ....AA
CAL.—San Francisco
Ingerson & Glaser Co.
(Glass) ....D
ILL.—Chicago
Schuler & Mueller Co., Cor.
Madison & Canal (Glass)
D
MICH.—Detroit
Friedricks & Wolfrum, 107
Gratiot Av. (Glass) ....E
MO.—St. Louis
Hadley-Dean Glass Co., 11th
Cor. Lucas Av. (Glass) A
Oriel Glass Co. (Glass) ...B
N. J.—Newark
Smith, M. A., 65 Chambers
(Glass) ....D
N. J.—Paterson
Royle & Sons, John ......A
N. Y.—Brooklyn
Jones Decorative Glass Co.,
Thos., Concord Cor. Hudson
Av. (Glass) C
New York City
Popper & Sons., Leo., 7 Sullivan (Glass) ....A
OHIO—Cincinnati
Cincinnati's Bevelling & Sil-

BEVELERS (Con.)
vering Co., 430 Oliver
(Glass) ....B
Western Mirror Plate Co.,
824 Wade (Glass) ......B
OHIO—Cleveland
Crane Glass & Mfg. Co., 286
St. Clair (Glass) C
PA.—Pittsburg
Pittsburg Plate Glass Co.,
Frick Bldg. (Glass) AAAA

BEVELS
CONN.—New Britain
Stanley Rule & Level Co.
AAA
CONN.—Pine Meadow
Chapin-Stephens Co. .....B
CONN.—Unionville
Upson Nut Co. ....AAA
MASS.—Athol
Athol Machine Co. C
Standard Tool Co. X
Starret Co., L. S. (Combination Universal, etc.) ....B
MASS.—Chicopee
Stevens Arms & Tool Co., J.
AAA
MASS.—Fitchburg
Sawyer Tool Mfg. Co.
Combination) ....E
MASS.—Springfield
Bemis & Call Hdw. Co. ..B
PA.—Philadelphia
Disston & Sons, Henry,
75 W. Wash'n. Tacomy E
R. I.—Providence
Brown & Sharpe Mfg. Co.
AAA

BIBBS
See Cocks & Bibbs

BIBLES
See Books

BICYCLES
CONN.—Bridgeport
Liberty Cycle Co., 166 John
(Sundries) ....E
CONN.—Hartford
Pope Mfg. Co. (Motor)
AAAA
CONN.—Torrington
Eagle Bicycle Mfg. Co...A
ILL.—Belvidere
Natl. Sewing Machine Co.
AAA
ILL.—Chicago
Amer. Cycle Co., 501 Wells
(Mfrs) ....AAAA
Chicago Scale Co., 292 W.
Jackson Boul. ....A
Featherstone & Co., A., 1614
Armour Av. ....A
Fowler Cycle Wks. ......E
Haussman & Dunn, 107 S.
Clark C
Sturges & Burn Mfg. Co..A
Temple Cycle Co., Ralph..C
ILL.—Harvard
Hunt, Helm & Ferris....B
IND.—Butler
Butler Co. ....B
IND.—Indianapolis
Sensitive Governor Co....B
IND.—La Porte
Lonn & Sons Co., J.......A
IND.—Richmond
Henly Bicycle Wks......A
MASS.—Fitchburg
Johnson, Iver Arm & Cycle
Wks., ...A
MASS.—Springfield
Hendee Mfg. Co. (Motor) .X
Warwick Cycle Mfg. Co...B
MASS.—Waltham
Waltham Mfg. Co. ......AA
MICH.—Battle Creek
Bown Machine Wks. .....G
MICH.—Bay City
Natl. Cycle Mfg. Co......C
MICH.—Hudson
Bean Chamberlain Mfg. Co.
(Mfrs.) ....B
N. J.—Smithville
Smith Machine Co., H. B..A
N. J.—Trenton
Stahl, Harry E. ....D
N. Y.—Buffalo
Pierce & Co., Geo. N...AA
Thomas Motor Co., E. R.
(Motor) ....A

BICYCLES (Con.)
N. Y.—Ilion
Remington Arms Co. (Br.
  N. Y. City) ....AA
N. Y.—Jamestown
Fenton Metallic Mfg. Co..A
New York City
Ingersoll & Bro., Robt. H.,
  163 Washn. ....A
Mace & Co., L. H.
  (Children's) ....B
N. Y.—Syracuse
Stearns & Co., E. C.....AA
OHIO—Cincinnati
Norwood Machine & Mfg.
  Co. (Mfrs.) 2d & Plum..B
OHIO—Cleveland
White Sewing Machine Co.
                     AAA
OHIO—Clyde
Elmore Mfg. Co. ....A
OHIO—Dayton
Davis Sewing Machine Co.
                      AA
OHIO—Elyria
Fay. Mfg. Co. (Children's)
                       D
OHIO—Hamilton
Meyers Mfg. Co., Fred J..B
OHIO—Middletown
Miami Cycle & Mfg. Co...B
OHIO—Springfield
Thomas Mfg. Co.......AAA
OHIO—Toledo
Gendron Wheel Co. (Chil-
  dren's) ....AA
Kirk Mfg. Co. ....D
Toledo Metal Wheel Co. AA
U. S. Pump & Supply Co..C
PA.—Philadelphia
Wall Mfg. Co., R. C., 725
  Arch ....F
PA.—Pottstown
Light Cycle Co. ....B
PA.—Reading
Packer Cycle Co.........F
Reading Standard Cycle Co.
                       B
PA.—Williamsport
Demarest Mfg. Co.........A
WIS.—Milwaukee
Bremer Cycle Mfg. Co...F
Durant, W. N. (Bamboo)..E
League Cycle Wks. ....D
WIS.—Two Rivers
Aluminum Mfg. Co. (Alu-
  minum) ....A

BICYCLE CLOTHING

See Clothing; Mens'

BIDETS

CONN.—New Haven
Peck Bros. Co. ....A
MASS.—Boston
Dalton-Ingersoll Co.......A
New York City
Hale Co. X
Mason & Co., J. W.......D
Mott Iron Wks., J. L., 88
  Beekman ....AA
OHIO—Cincinnati
Alms Mfg. Co., F. W.....X

BIGGINS

CONN.—Meriden
Manning, Bowman & Co.
  (Coffee) ....AAAA
MO.—St. Louis
St. Louis Stamping Co.
  (Coffee) ....AAAA
N. Y.—Brooklyn
Sweeney Mfg. Co., W. H.
  (Coffee) ....B
New York City
Lalance & Grosjean Mfg.
  Co. (Coffee) ......AAAA

BILLETS

See Iron & Steel

BILLIES

CAL.—Los Angeles
Western Whip Co., 816 San
  Pedro (Policemen's)....F
ILL.—Chicago
Brown, H., 759 Elston Av.

BILLIES (Con.)
  (Policemen's) ....D
New York City
Estes & Sons, E. B., 45
  John (Policemen's) ...AA

BINDER TWINE

See Cordage

BINDERS

See Agr. Implements

BINDINGS

See also Silk Goods

CONN.—Middletown
Russell Mfg. Co. (Blanket;
  Cotton Back; Worsted)
                    AAAA
MASS.—Boston
White & Son, W. B. (Metal
  Pattern) ....D
MASS.—Clinton
Clinton Spec. Mfg. Co.
  (Dress) ....D
MASS.—Lawrence
Wright Mfg. Co. (Worsted
  Dress) ....B
MASS.—Lexington
Merriam, M. H. (Leather
  Shoe) ....B
  S.—Lynn
Parker Bros. (Leather;
  Shoe) ....E
MASS.—Worcester
Thayer Mfg. Co., L. D.
  (Dress, &c.) C
Witer & Co., H. M. (Dress;
  Blanket) ....D
MICH.—Belding
Belding Bros. & Co. (Silk)
                    AAAA
Richardson Silk Co. (Silk)
                      AA
N. J.—Hoboken
Beck Bros. (Silk Dress)...C
N. J.—Newark
Goulds' Sons, M. (Metallic;
  Carpet) ....A
New York City
Conover Co., C. E. (Com-
  mission—Dress) ....D
Dresser & Olmstead (Com-
  mission) C
Dunlap & Co. (Silk; Hat)
                      AA
Freydberg Bros. (Silk
  Skirt) C
Gould Mersereau Co. (Corner
  & Metallic; Carpet) ...B
Judd & Co., H. L. (Metallic;
  Carpet; Oilcloth) ....AA
Knapp Rubber Binding Co.
  (Carpet; Oilcloth; Rub-
  ber) ....B
Loth & Co., Joseph (Silk)
                      AA
Schloss Bros. (Silk)......D
Strouse, Adler & Co. (Cor-
  set) ....AAAA
Warner Bros. Co. (Corset)
                    AAAA
N. Y.—Rochester
Rochester Textile Wks.
  (Dress; Silk) ....E
PA.—Philadelphia
Adamson & Co., Joseph
  (Oilcloth; Stay) ....A
Kroute & File Mfg. Co.
  (Dress) ....B
Horstmann Co., Wm. H.
  (Carpet; Silk) ....AAAA
Murphy & Son, Matthew
  (Tapestry) ....A
Sullivan & Sons Mfg. Co.,
  J. (Dress Stay) ......D
Weimer Bros. (Dress) ....D
Wilson & Sons, James (Car-
  pet) ....A
R. I.—Pawtucket
Kenyon Mfg. Co., Jno. J.
  (Corset; Stay) ....B
R. I.—Providence
Fletcher Mfg. Co. (Oil-
  cloth) ....AAA
Hope Webbing Co. (Blanket;
  Carpet; Corset; Stay;
  Mattress) ....AAA

BINNACLES

MASS.—Boston
Thaxter & Son, S., 125 State
                     C

New York City
Bliss & Co., John, 28 Front
  (Ship) ....D
Keuffel & Esser Co., 127
  Fulton ....AA
Merrills' Sons, Robt......B
PA.—Philadelphia
Riggs & Bro., 310 Market.B

BINS

ALA.—Mobile
Union Iron Works (Coal).B
CONN.—Derby
Birmingham Iron Fdy. (Ore)
                  AA
ILL.—Chicago
Warren Mfg. Co., J. D., 502
  Masonic Temple (Nail)..B
IND.—Muncie
Glasscock Bros. Mfg. Co.
  (Flour) ....B
KANS.—Fort Scott
Ft. Scott Fdy. & Machine
  Co. (Ore) ....H
MICH.—Homer
Seeder Mfg. Co. (Flour)..F
N. Y.—Jamestown
Fenton Metallic Mfg. Co.
  (Postal) ....A
New York City
Morgan & Connell, 211
  Duane (Grocers; Tea; Cof-
  fee) X
OHIO—Salem
Clark Co., W. J. (Portable
  Steel Hdw.; Nail)......A
OHIO—Warren
Peerless Sifter Co. (Flour)
                 E
PA.—Pittsburg
Riter-Conley Mfg. Co. (Coal
  Storage) ....AAA
Scaife Machy. Co., 221 First
  Av. (Steel) ....A
PA.—Wilkesbarre
Vulcan Iron Wks. (Ore)
               AAAA
WIS.—Cudahy
Power & Mining Machinery
  Co. (Steel) ....AAA
WIS.—Milwaukee
Wisconsin Bridge & Iron..
  Co. (Coal) ....AA

BIRDS

CONN.—Meriden
Bradley & Hubbard Mfg.
  Co. (Sewing) ....AAA
CONN.—New Britain
Landers, Frary & Clark
  (Sewing) ....AAA
MASS.—Boston
New England Novelty Mfg.
  Co. (Sewing) ....H

BISCUIT

See Bakers

N. J.—Newark
Spratt's Patent (America)
  Ltd. (Dog) ....B

BISMUTH

MO.—St. Louis
Mallinckrodt Chemical Wks.
               AAAA
Herf & Frerichs Chemical
  Co. (Subnitrate) ....A
N. Y.—Brooklyn
Enequist, Erik N., No. 9th
  & Roebling ....D
New York City
New York Quinine & Chem-
  ical Works, 114 William A

BITS

See Augers

BITTERS

See also Liquors

New York City

BITTERS (Con.)

Funke, Jr., L., 72 Beekman
  (Bakers) ....B

BLACK

LA.—New Orleans
Standard Guano & Chemical
  Mfg. Co. (Bone)......AA
MASS.—Boston
Cabot, Godfrey L. (Lamp;
  Carbon; Bone; Ivory;
  Drop) ....A
Cabot, Saml. (Lamp)....A
Seaver & Co. (Carbon;
  Ivory; Drop; Bone; Lamp)
                 E
MICH.—Detroit
Michigan Carbon Works
  (Bone) ....AAA
N. Y.—Evergreen
Lyons, Jas. (Lamp) X
New York City
American Agricultural
  Chem. Co. (Bone).AAAA
Bartels, Ernest C. (Lamp;
  Carbon; Drop; Ivory;
  Bone) ....B
Binney & Smith Co., 81
  Fulton (Carbon; Ivory;
  Bone; Lamp) ....AA
Taylor Co., Geo. F. (Bone)
                 F
Wegelin & Wilckes Black
  Mfg. Co. (Carbon; Lamp;
  Ivory; Drop; Bone)....B
PA.—Philadelphia
Bihn & Wolff (Carbon;
  Drop; Ivory; Lamp; Bone)
                 B

BLACK-BOARDS

CONN.—East River
Munger & Son (Cloth;
  Coated) C
CONN.—Winsted
Gilbert Clock Mfg. Co.
  (Slate) ....AA
MASS.—Leominster
Whitney Reed Chair Co.
  (Folding; Coated)..AAAA
N. H.—Nashua
Maine Mfg. Co. (Childrens';
  Coated) ....A
New York City
New York Silicate Book
  Slate Co. (Roll; Silicate)
                 D
OHIO—Cleveland
Auld & Conger, 262 Prospect
  Av. (Slate) ....A
PA.—Bangor
Bangor Peerless Slate Co.
  (Slate) C
Dernberger. Isaac D. (Slate)
                 D
PA.—Danielsonville
Hower Slate Co. (Slate)..B
PA.—East Bangor
Bangor Consolidated Slate
  Slate Co. (Bangor Slate)
               AA
PA.—Easton
Bangor Excelsior Slate Co.
  (Bangor Slate) ....A
PA.—Pen Argyl
Crown Slate Co. (Slate)...C
Lobb's Sons, William (Slate)
                 C
PA.—Pittsburg
Lawrence & Co., W. W.
  (Slate) ....AA
PA.—Slatington
Slatington-Bangor Slate
  Syndicate (Slate).......D
Eureka Slate Mfg. Co.
  (Slate) ....E
VT.—Fair Haven
Fair Haven Marble & Mar-
  bleized Slate Co. (Bangor
  Slate) ....B
WIS.—Milwaukee
Meinecke & Son, A. (Chil-
  dren's; Folding)......AA

BLACKING

See also Paste; Polish

ILL.—Chicago
Martell Co., 303 Dearborn

BLACKING (Con.)
(Harness; Shoe; Paste) E
Martin & Martin, 1398 Carroll (Shoe) ....D
MASS.—Boston
Baker & Co., Chas. F. (Shoe
& Paste) ....A
Brown & Co., B. F. (Shoe
& Paste) ....H
Burbank Mfg. Co., 62 Alvord (Shoe) C
Congo Blacking Mfg. Co.,
63 Oliver (Shoe) ......F
Hauthaway & Sons, C. L.,
346 Cong. (Shoe).....AA
Morse Blacking Co., 34
Binford (Shoe; Finish).D
Wood Co., Geo. H. (Shoe &
Paste) C
MASS.—Canton Junction
Crow Blacking Co. (Leather)
E
MASS.—Worcester
Albertson, W. R. (Shoe)..D
Pike Mfg. Co. (Shoe)....D
MICH.—Grand Rapids
West & Co., S. H. (Shoe &
Polish) ....F
MINN.—Winona
Roesner Mfg. Co. (The)
(Shoe; Polish) ....F
N. J.—Camden
Hollingshead & Co., R. M.
(Shoe) ....B
N. Y.—Buffalo
Favorite Mfg. Co., 1067
Niagara (Shoe Dressing)
D
Stinson & Co., B. F., 418
Niagara. (Shoe) ....D
New York City
Bixby & Co., S. M., 194
Hester (Shoe; Paste)....C
Griffin Mfg. Co., 82 Cortlandt (Shoe) C
Loewenstein, M., 71 Washington Sq. So. (Shoe)..D
Miller Co., Frank, 349 W.
26th (Shoe; Paste: Leather; Boot Edge; Harness)
A
Moss, Geo. A., 167 Reade
(Shoe; Paste) ....B
Prescott & Co., J. L. (Shoe
& Paste) ....A
Raven Gloss Mfg. Co., 81
White (Shoe) ....D
Restorff & Bettmann, 35
Bond (Shoe) ....B
Rothschild Bros. & Co.,
(Shoe) ....AA
N. Y.—Rochester
American Chemical Mfg. &
Mining Co. (Shoe) .....B
Rochester Chemical Co.
(Shoe) ....B
OHIO—Cincinnati
Ampt & Co., Chas. F. (Shoe)
D
PA.—Philadelphia
Boyer & Co., 135 No. 2d
(Shoe) ....B
Colburn Co., A. (The)
(Shoe) ....AA
Diamond & Onyx (Shoe)..B
Diamond, McDonnell & Co.
(Shoe; Paste) C
Eclipse Cement & Blacking
Co. (Shoe) C
Mason Co., James S. (Shoe
& Paste) ....A
Paxson Co., J. W.
(Foundry) ....AA
WIS.—Milwaukee
Diamond Ink Co. (Shoe)..D

BLADDERS

ILL.—Chicago
Morgan & Wright, 333 W.
Lake (Rubber) ....AA
MASS.—Andover
Tyer Rubber Co. (Football)
AA
OHIO—Akron
Faultless Rubber Co. (Rubber Ball) ....AA
Goodrich Co., B. F. (Football; Punching)....AAAA

BLADES

CAL.—San Francisco
Pacific Saw Mfg. Co. (Cur-

BLADES (Con.)
riers; Band Saw) X
CONN.—Bridgeport
Bridgeport Brass Co. (Metal
Fan) ....AA
CONN.—Lakeville
Holley Mfg. Co. (Plush Cutting) ....B
CONN.—New Haven
West Haven Mfg. Co. (Hack
Saw) ....B
CONN.—Waterbury
Holmes Booth & Haydens Co
(Metal Fan) ....AAA
DEL.—Wilmington
Hiller & Ives Co. (Meat
Shear) ....AAAA
GA.—Atlanta
Southern Saw Wks. (Saw)
B
ILL.—Chicago
Republic Iron & Steel Co.,
Stock Exch. Bldg. (Steel
Stone; Screw) ....AAAA
ILL.—Rockford
Barnes Co., W. F. & John
(Scroll Saw) ....AA
IND.—Indianapolis
Atkins & Co., E. C. (Band
Saw; Hack Saw; Wood
Saw; Scroll) ......AAAA
Barry Saw & Supply Co., W.
B. (Hand Saw; Saw)...C
IND.—Lawrenceburg
Bishop & Co., Geo. H. (Saw;
Butchers' & Woods Saw)
A
MASS.—Athol
Athol Machine Co. (Hack
Saw) ....B
MASS.—Fitchburg
Fitchburg File Wks. (Hack
Saw; Butchers' Saw) .D
Simonds Mfg. Co. (Band
Saw; Metal Shears; Wood
Saw; Butchers Saw;
Scroll) ....AAA
MASS.—Greenfield
Goodell-Pratt Co. (Butchers
Saw; Hack Saw) .....B
Nichols Bros. (Butchers'
Saw) C
MASS.—Southbridge
Harrington. T. J. (Cuban
Cigar; Extension) .....D
Richard Stephan Co. (Cloth)
E
N. J.—Newark
National Saw Co. (Curriers';
Band Saw; Butchers'
Saw; Doctors'; Hack Saw;
Scroll Saw; Wood Saw) B
Ohl & Co., G. A. (Metal
Shear) ....B
N. Y.—Amsterdam
Breedons' Son, Wm. (Burr)
B
N. Y.—Brooklyn
Mack & Winkle, 172 Skillman Av. (Butchers' Saw)
F
Oldham & Sons Inc. Joshua (Steel Stone Saw) .D
N. Y.—Buffalo
Diamond Saw & Stamp'g
Wks. (Butchers' Saw; Hack
Saw) ....D
Niagara Machine-Tool Wks.
(Metal Shear) ....A
White Co., L. & I. J.
(Shear) ....A
New York City
American Wood Working
Mach. Co. (Band Saw)
AAAA
Chatillon & Sons, J., 85
Cliff (Butchers' Saw) ..B
Jennings & Co., C. E., 101
Reade (Scroll Saw; Hack
Saw; Wood Saw) .....B
Loyd & Co., Chas., 558
Water (Metal Shear)...B
OHIO—Cincinnati
Cincinnati Punch & Shear
Co. (Metal Shear) .....D
Fay & Eagan Co., J. A.
(Band Saw) ......AAAA
OHIO—Leetonia
Crescent Machine Co. (Band
Saw) ....D
OHIO—Youngstown
Sennet Co., G. B. (Metal
Shear) ....B
PA.—Beaver Falls
Emerson, Smith Co. (Ltd.)

BLADES (Con.)
(Band Saw; Scroll Saw; Saw) ....A
PA.—Philadelphia
Disston & Sons, Hy. (Band Saw; Curriers' Saw; Doctor's; Hack Saw; Gin Roller; Metal Shear; Scroll Saw; Wood Saw) ....AAAA
Horn & Bro., Wm. H. (Curriers') ....B
PA.—Pittsburg
American Steel Hoop Co. Steel Stone; Plain; Corrd Saw) ....D
Jones & Laughlin Steel Co. (Steel Stone Saw).AAAA
Heppenstall Forge & Knife Co. (Gin Roller) ......B
Pittsburg Steel Co. (Steel Stone Saw) ....AAAA
VT.—Bennington
Cooper, Charles (Burr)...B
WIS.—Racine
Freeman & Sons Mfg. Co., S. (Saw) ....A

BLANKETS
See Bedding

BLANKETS
HORSE

COL.—Denver
Denver Tent & Awning Co.C
ILL.—Chicago
Johnson Co., J. W. ......B
KY.—Louisville
Louisville Girth & Blanket Mills (Saddle) ....D
MASS.—Hampden
Kenworthy, Jno. X
MASS.—Holyoke
MO.—St. Louis
Zittlosen Mfg. Co. (Horse) ....B
Springfield Blanket Co..B
N. H.—Troy
Troy Blanket Mills ....B
N. J.—Burlington
Birch, Jas. H. ....AA
N. J.—Newark
Peters Harness & Saddlery Co. C
N. Y.—Candor
Candor Blanket Co. C
N. Y.—Cossayuna
Alexander Blanket Co. ...D
New York City
Chase & Co., L. C. (Com.). ....AA
Smith, Worthington Co., 40 Warren ....AA
N. Y.—Oriskany
Waterbury & Sons Co., H. ....A

OHIO—Cincinnati
Columbia Mfg. & Supply Co. X
Engelke Saddlery Co. ...C
OHIO—Tiffin
Tiffin Woolen Mills ...B
PA.—Philadelphia
Ayres & Sons, Wm. .....AA
Erskine, Alexander ......B
Stafford & Co. C
WIS.—Burlington
Burlington Blanket Co. (Lined, Duck Stable; Cattle; Saddle) ....A
WIS.—Fond du Lac
Fond du Lac Awning & Tent Co. (Stable) ....B

BLANKS

CONN.—Hartford
Billings & Spencer Co. (Thumb Nut; Screw; Snap Gauge) ....B
CONN.—Terryville
Eagle Lock Co. (Key)..AAA
CONN.—Torrington
Coe Brass Mfg. (Cartridge) ....AAAA
CONN.—Waterbury
Rogers & Hamilton (Spoon & Fork) ....AAAA
ILL.—Chicago
Baker & Vawter Co. (Mani-

BLANKS (Con.)
fold Shipping; Order).AA
Whitman & Barnes Mfg. Co., West Pullman (Thumb; Nut;; Screw).. ....AAAA
IND.—Alexandria
Lippincott Glass Co. (Lead Glass) ....A
IND.—Madison
Ohio Valley Shell & Pearl Co. (Button) ....E
IOWA—Fort Madison
Fort Madison Button Co. (Button) ....B
MASS.—Boston
Little, Brown & Co. (Law) ....AA
MASS.—Holyoke
Franklin Paper Co. (Lithograph) ....A
Hampden Glazed Paper & Card Co. (Lithograph; Railroad) ....A
Whitmore Mfg. Co. (Lithograph; Railroad) ......A
MASS.—Springfield
Holyoke Card & Paper Co. (Lithograph; Railroad).A
N. E. Card & Paper Co. (Lithograph) ....A
MICH.—Grand Rapids
Barlow Bros. (Manifold Shipping) ....B
N. Y.—Brooklyn
Bohannan, Wilson (Key)..C
New York City
Baker, Voorhis & Co. (Law) ....A
Williams & Co., J. H., 9 Richards (Thumb; Nut; Screw) ....AAA
N. Y.—Rochester
Sargent & Greenleaf Co. (Key) ....AA
OHIO—Bellaire
Rodefer, T. A. (Decorators' Opal Glass) ....A
OHIO—Cincinnati
Clark Co., Robt. (Law)...B
OHIO—Columbus
Case Mfg. Co. (Gear)...A
OHIO—Hamilton
Hamilton Autographic Register Co. (Manifold Shipping; Manifold Order)..B
PA.—Eddystone
Tindell Morris Co. (Gear).. ....AA
PA.—Lancaster
Penna. Iron Co. (Thumb; Nut; Screw) ....A
PA.—Nazareth
Nazareth Fdry. & Mach. Co. (Gear) ....B
PA.—Philadelphia
Keystone Drop Forge Wks., 19th & Clearfield (Thumb; Nut; Screw) ....B
R. I.—Pawtucket
Rhode Island Cardboard Co. (Lithograph; Railroad).A
R. I.—Providence
New England Butt. Co. (Key) ....AA
Wall & Co., A. T. (Jewelers' Round; Square) C

BLEACH

MASS.—Lynn
Hadley Cement Co. (Sole).B
N. Y.—Albany
Albany Chemical Co. (Laundry) ....A

BLEACHERS
See Machinery

MASS.—Holyoke
Holyoke Machine Co. (Rotary) ....AA
MASS.—Lawrence
Horne & Sons Co., J. H. (Rotary) ....A
MASS.—Lowell
Lowell Machine Shop (Rotary) ....AAAA
New York City
United States Finishing Co., 320 Broadway (Cotton Fabric) ....AAAA

BLEACHERS (Con.)
PA.—Schuylkill Haven
Rowland, Saml. (Knit
  Goods) ....D

BLEACHES
See Powder; Bleaching

BLENDERS
New York City
Bradley & Smith (Paint)
  ....AA
Hanlon & Goodman (Paint)
  ....A

BLENOL
OHIO—Cincinnati
Merrill Chemical Co., Wm.
  S. ....AAA

BLINDS
See Saddlery & Harness; also
  Woodwork.

BLOATERS
See Fish

BLOCK
BRAKE
See Hardware; Carriage

BLOCKERS
See also Machinery

OHIO—Akron
Talpin, Rice & Co. (Clay).B
Webster, Camp & Lane
  Mach. Co. (Clay) ..AAAA

BLOCKING
CONN.—South Norwalk
Le Count, Wm. G. (Adjustable) ....D
New York City
Sheridan, T. W. & C. B.
  (Bookbinders' Presses).A
PA.—Harrisburg
Hickok Mfg. Co., W. O.
  (Bookbinders' Presses)AA

BLOCKS
See Brick; Asbestos, etc.

CAL.—San Francisco
Jackson Machine Works,
  Byron (Wooden Hoisting)
  ....A
Union Iron Wks., 222 Market (Differential Chain)
  ....AAAA
CONN.—Derby
Shelton Co. (Bronze Hoisting) ....A
CONN.—Hartford
Pratt & Whitney Co.
  (Die) ....AAAA
CONN.—Meriden
Runge Mfg. Co. (Joiners'
  Bench) X
CONN.—Middletown
Wilcox, Crittenden & Co.
  (Yacht; Chain Hoisting;
  Deck; Snatch; Pulley).A
CONN.—New Britain
Brady, T. H. (Pulley for
  Electric Light Poles)...C
CONN.—New Haven
Dann Bros. & Co. (Carriage;
  Wagon Head) ....B
CONN.—Plainville
Hills, Edwin (I. & S. Pulley) ....A
CONN.—Stamford
Yale & Towne Mfg. Co.
  (Iron Hoisting)....AAAA
CONN.—Torrington
Union Hardware Co.
  (Tackle; Wooden Hoisting) ....A
D. C.—Washington
Washington Asphalt Block
  & Tile Co., S. Capital &
  R., S. E. (Asphalt)....A

BLOCKS (Con.)
ILL.—Chicago
Allis-Chalmers Co., N. Y.
  Life Bldg. (Pillow)AAAA
Barrett Mfg. Co., Merchants Loan & Trust
  Bldg. (Asphalt) ..AAAA
Borden & Selleck Co., 48
  Lake (Pillow) ....B
Born Packers Supply Co.,
  309 W. Van Buren (Meat
  Chopping) ....F
Caldwell & Son Co., H. W.,
  Western Av. & 17th (Pillow) ....AA
Chicago Wheel & Mfg. Co.
  (Leveling) C
Channon Co., H., Market &
  Rand (Pulley) ......AA
Hoisting & Conveying Machinery Co. (Pillow)...H
Jones Foundry & Machine
  Co., 143 W. North Av.
  (Pillow) C
Klein & Son, Mathias, 87
  W. Van Buren (Steel
  Tackle; Pulley for Electric Light Poles) ......A
Link Belt Machy. Co. (Pillow) ....AAA
Macomber & Whyte Rope
  Co., 19 S. Canal (Wire
  Rope; Steel) ....E
Pioneer Fire Proofing Co.,
  204 Dearborn (Hollow
  Building) ....A
Plamondon Mfg. Co., 57 S.
  Clinton (Pillow) ....A
Webster Mfg. Co. (Pillow)
  ....AA
Wolff, Sayer & Heller (Meat
  Chopping) ....AA
ILL.—Downer's Grove
Dicke Tool Co. (Chain Hoisting; Pulley; Steel Hoisting) ....D
ILL.—Effingham
Boos & Co., John (Artificial
  Flower; Meat) ....D
ILL.—Joliet
Bates Machine Co. (Pillow)
  ....A
ILL.—Sycamore
Patton Co., F. C. (Swage).A
IND.—Brazil
Indiana Paving Brick &
  Block Co. (Hollow Building) ....F
IND.—Mishawaka
Dodge Mfg. Co. (Pillow)
  ....AAA
IND.—Terre Haute
Terre Haute Brick & Pipe
  Co. (Vitrified Paving)..A
IND.—Wabash
Underwood Mfg. Co., H. C.
  (Alphabet) ....E
IOWA—Mason City
Mason City Brick & Tile Co.
  (Hollow Building) C
KANS.—Leavenworth
Great Western Mfg. Co.
  (Pillow) ....A
MAINE—Danforth
Butterfield, Jas. K. (Last)
  ....D
MAINE—Houlton
Gilpatrick, Ora (Last)....
  ....AAAA
MAINE—Orland
Valentine & Soper (Last) .E
MAINE—Portland
Laughlin & Son, Thos.
  (Chain; Iron; Wooden
  Hoisting) ....B
MD.—Baltimore
Donohue & Co., Jno. T.
  (Iron; Steel; Pulley)...C
Poole Engineering & Machy.
  Co. (Pillow)..........AA
MD.—Cumberland
Gardner Bros. (Furnace)..B
MASS.—Boston
Boston & Lockport Block
  Co., 100 Commercial
  (Chain Hoisting; Cutting;
  Deck; Snatch; Wood;
  Differential Chain; Pulley; Tackle; Steel; Iron
  Hoisting; Old Derrick)..B
Boston Belting Co. (Rubber;
  Rubber Hat) ......AAAA
Clapp Rubber Co., E. H.

BLOCKS (Con.)

(Rubber) ....A
Golding & Co., 177 Fort
  Hill Sq. (Stereotype)...B
Harvey, H. H., 608 Atlan-
  tic Av. (Differential
  Chain; Iron Hoisting)..B
Merriman Bros., 162 Com-
  mercial (Chain Hoisting;
  Deck; Snatch; Tackle;
  Wire Rope)............D
Seelye Mfg. Co. (Die)....C
MASS.—Fitchburg
Putnam Machine Co. (Man-
  drel) ....A
MASS.—Greenfield
Wells Bros. & Co. (Swage)
  ....A
Wiley & Russell Mfg. Co.
  (Swage; Leveling) ...AA
MASS.—Leominster
Whitney-Reed Chair Co.
  (Toy; Building) ..AAAA
MASS.—Lowell
Cragin & Co., F. W. (Shoe
  Mfrs.'; Butchers').....F
MASS.—Pittsfield
Jones & Sons Co., E. D.
  (Pillow) ....A
MASS.—Somerset
Somerset Enamel Brick Co.
  (Cupola) ....D
MASS.—Springfield
Bradley Co., Milton (Toy;
  Alphabet) ....A
Bullock & Co., O. W. (Jew-
  elers') ....A
MASS.—Taunton
Union Stove Lining Co.
  (Jewelers') C
MASS.—Worcester
Kidder, R. E., 2 Hermon
  (Cutting) ....E
MICH.—Bay City
Michigan Pipe Co. (Creo-
  soted Wood Paving) ..AA
MICH.—Detroit
Buhl Malleable Co., Wright
  & Adair (Tackle) .....A
Edwards & Co., H. D. (Iron
  and Steel Pulley) ....AA
Nat'l Fulton Brass Mfg. Co.,
  28 Brush (Sure Grip Steel;
  Tackle) ....A
Rousseau Mfg. Co., F. X.,
  564 Porter (Tackle) ...F
MICH.—Northville
Dubuar Mfg. Co., J. B.
  (Wooden Hoisting).....X
MICH.—Saginaw
Morley Bros. (Log Loading)
  ....AA
Wickes Bros. (Pillow).AAA
MO.—St. Louis
Brecht Butchers' Sup. Co.,
  G. V. (Meat Chopping)..
  ....AAA
Leschen & Sons Rope Co.,
  A. (Steel; Chain Hoist-
  ing; Deck; Snatch; Desk;
  Steel Hoisting; Tackle;
  Wire Rope) ....AAA
Medart Patent Pulley Co.
  (Pillow) ....AAA
Pleuger & Henger Mfg. Co.
  (Swage) ....A
N. J.—Jersey City
Williams & Son, E. A.
  (Sheet Metal Soldering).
  ....AA
N. J.—Harrison
Hyatt Roller Bearing Co.
  (Pillow)..............D
N. J.—Newark
Newark Hat Block & Ma-
  chine Co. (Hat) ....E
N. J.—Peapack
Ludlow Bros. (Wheel Hub)
  ....E
N. J.—Trenton
Trenton Rubber Mfg. Co.
  (Rubber; Prop.)........A
N. J.—Woodbridge
Valentine & Bro., M. D.
  (Blast Furnace) .....AA
N. Y.—Albany
Dederick's Sons, P. K.
  (Chain Hoisting; Iron
  Hoisting) ....AA
Embossing Co. (Alphabet)B
N. Y.—Auburn
Eccles, Richard (Carriage;
  Wagon Head) ....A

BLOCKS (Con.)

N. Y.—Buffalo
Buffalo Dental Mfg. Co.
  (Sheet Metal Soldering).B
Buffalo Last Wks. (Boot;
  Shoe Pasting) ....B
Contractors' Plant Mfg. Co.,
  129 Erie (Sheave; Chain
  Hoisting; Iron Hoisting;
  Wood; Pulley) ....B
Howard Iron Wks. (Book-
  binders' Iron Bench) ...A
Noye Mfg. Co., 50 Lake-
  wood Av. (Pillow) .....F
N. Y.—Cobleskill
Harder Mfg. Co. (Meat
  Chopping) C
N. Y.—Cohoes
Cohoes Iron Foundry & Ma-
  chine Co. (Differential
  Chain) ....A
N. Y.—Jamestown
Am. Mfg. Concern (Toy A.
  B. C.) ....A
N. Y.—Kreischerville
Kreischer Brick Mfg. Co.
  (Fire Clay) ....B
N. Y.—Lockport
Western Brock Co. (Deck;
  Snatch; Dock; Pulley;
  Wire Rope) ....B
N. Y.—Long Island City
North American Metaline
  Co. (Tackle) ....D
Steubner, G. L. (Chain
  Hoisting; Wire Rope; Iron
  Hoisting) C
New York City
American News Co. (Build-
  ing) ....AAAA
American Type Founders'
  Co. (Stereotype) ...AAAA
American Wood Working
  Mach. Co. ....AAAA
Ashwell, Henry A., 536 W.
  B'way (Hat) ....F
Bacon, Earle C. (Wire
  Rope) ....D
Braddock Machine & Mfg.
  Co., 26 Cortlandt (Pillow)
  ....D
Brown, A. & T., 26 Cort-
  landt (Pillow) ....A
Cuming & Co., Mari A., 49
  Bleecker (Hat) ....D
Donegan & Swift, 6 Mur-
  ray (Chain) C
Drummond & Co., M. J., 192
  B'way (Derrick Foot)..A
Eckstein, Chas. G., 249 Cen-
  tre (Deck; Snatch; Chain;
  Hoisting) ....D
Empire Rubber Mfg. Co.
  (Prop) ....AA
Fairbanks Co., 416 Broome
  (Differential Chain).....
  ....AAAA
Farmer & Son Type Foun-
  dry Co., A. D. (Stereo-
  type) ....B
Goodyear Rubber Co.
  (Prop) ....AAAA
Gutta Percha & Rubber
  Mfg. Co. (Rubber)AAAA
Hastings Pavement Co. (As-
  phalt Paving) ....AA
Hoe & Co., R. (Stereotype)
  ....AAAA
Horsman, E. D. (Building)
 C
Hunt Co., C. W. (Iron Hoist-
  ing; Wooden Hoisting)AA
Lindsay Type Foundry
  (Stereotype) ....B
McCoy Co., Jos. F., 157
  Chambers (Differential
  Pulley; Leveling; Tackle)
 C
McLaughlin Bros. (Toy; Al-
  phabet) ....AAA
McMullen's Sons, W. A., 153
  South (Tackle; Wooden
  Hoisting) ....B
Mace & Co., L. H. (Toy;
  Building) ....B
Macomber - Whyte - Moon
  Co., 131 Worth (Wire
  Rope) ....E
Metal Stamping Co. (Prop)
  ....A
**N. J. Foundry & Machine
  Co. (Differential Pulley)**
  ....D
Tiebout, W. & J., 118

81

Chambers (Deck; Snatch)
Warren Chemical & Mfg. Co. (Asphalt Paving)..A
Yale & Towne Mfg. Co., 9 Murray (I. & S. Pulley; Chain Hoisting)..AAAA

N. Y.—Niagara Falls
Dobbie Foundry & Machine Co. ,(Chain Hoisting; Deck; Snatch; Derrick; Foot; Sheave; Differential Chain; Tackle; Wire Rope) ....D

N. Y.—Poughkeepsie
Lane Bros. Co. (Wooden Hoisting) ....A

N. Y.—Seneca Falls
Westcott-Jewell Co. (Kalido; Toy; Alphabet; Building) ....D

N. Y.—Syracuse
Zimmermann, Chas. E. (Furniture Corner; Head)
E

N. Y.—Troy
Adams Laundry Mach. Co. (Cupola) ....B
McMurray Co., C. F., Centre Island (Pillow) C
Ostrander Fire Brick Co. (Locomotive) ....A

OHIO—Akron
Akron Vitrified Clay Co. (Building) ....B

OHIO—Canton
Aultman Co. (Pillow) ...A

OHIO—Cincinnati
Creagbead Engineering Co. 313 Walnut (Pillow; Pulley) ....D
Randall & Co. (Saddlers' Collar; Saddlers' Cutting)
B
Tatum Co., Samuel C. (Pillow) ....B

OHIO—Cleveland
Bartlett & Snow Co., French near Columbus (Tackle) B
Burr Mfg. Co. (Steel Tackle; Pulley for Electric Light Poles) ....D
Central Builders Supply Co., The (Self-Locking Tackle; Concrete Hollow Building)
C
Chisholm & Moore Mfg. Co., cor. Lake & Kirkland (Chain Hoisting; Differential Chain; Pulley; Iron Hoisting) ....AA
Cleveland Block Co., 163 River (Malleable Iron; Steel; Tackle; Wooden Hoisting; Iron) ....B
Dunn. Jas. P. (Wooden Hoisting) ....H
Dyson & Sons, Jos. (Die)..A
Hartz & Co., Henry V. (Tackle) C
Van Dorn Iron Wks. Co. (Horse) ....AA

OHIO—Columbus
Case Mfg. Co. (Iron Hoisting) ....A
Jeffrey Mfg. Co. (Pillow)
AAAA

OHIO—Cuyahoga Falls
Falls Rivet & Machine Co. (Pillow) C

OHIO—Dayton
Fletcher Mfg. Co. (Pulley for Electric Light Poles)
F

OHIO—Defiance
Defiance Machine Wks. (Pillow) ....AAA

OHIO—Haydenville
Haydenville Co. (Paving).A

OHIO—Logan
Hocking Clay Mfg. C. (Hollow Building) ....B

OHIO—Magnolia
Greer Beatty Clay Co. (Hollow Building) C

OHIO—Mineral City
Markley, Geo. J. (Hollow Building) ....F

OHIO—Piqua
Piqua Handle & Mfg. Co. (Radiator Brush; Brush; Floor Broom) ....A

OHIO—Ravenna
Byers, John F. (Wood Hoisting) ....B

OHIO—Waynesburg
Whiteacre Fire Proofing Co. (Hollow Building) C

OHIO—West Lafayette
West Lafayette Mfg. Co. (Alphabet) ....E

OHIO—Youngstown
Sennett Co.. Geo. B. (Die)A

PA.—Aliquippa
Vulcan Crucible Steel Co. (Die) ....B

PA.—Allegheny
Pittsburg Clay Pot Co. (Glass-melting Tank)..AA

PA.—Chambersburg
Wolf Co. (Pillow) ....A
Woods' Sons, T. B. (Pillow)
B

PA.—Corry
Mahle Boring Machine Co. (Broom; Brush) ....B

PA.—Eddystone
Tindel-Morris Co. (Die)..A

PA.—Erie
Standard Saw Mill Machinery Co. (Carriage: Wagon Head) C

PA.—Harrisburg
Hickok Mfg. Co. (Bench; Iron Bench; Bookbinders')
AA

PA.—KANE
Holgate Bros. Co. (Whitewash; Broom; Brush) ...C

PA.—Mechanicsburg
Wilcox Mfg. Co., D. (Carriage; Wagon Head) ...A

PA.—Nazareth
Nazareth Foundry & Machine Co. (Pillow) ....B

PA.—New Bethlehem
Canton Hollow Brick Co. (The) (Plain; Rock-Faced Hollow Building) C

PA.—Philadelpnia
Abrasive Material Co. (Emery Grinding) ......A
Borgner, Cyrus (Furnace).B
Cresson Co.. Geo. V.. 18th & Allegheny Av. (Pillow)
AA
Harrington Son & Co.. Edwin 17th & Callowhill (Chain Hoisting; Iron Hoisting) ....AA
Nittinger. Aug.. Sr., 826 4th (Meat Chopping) ....A
Olsen & Co., Tinius (Iron Hoisting) ....A
Philadelphia Roll & Machine Co. (Die) ....A
Sellers & Co., Wm., 1600 Hamilton (Pillow).AAAA

PA.—Pittsburg
American Clay Mfg. Co., Keystone Bldg. (Hollow Building) ....AAAA
American Sewer Pipe Co., 2nd Nat'l Bank Bldg. (Hollow Building).AAAA
Columbia Bridge Co., Park Bldg. (Pillow) ....B
Dagus Brick Co. (The), Smith Blk (Hollow Building) ....AAAA
Jones & Laughlin's Steel Co. (Pillow) ....AAAA
National Fire Proofing Co., Frick Bldg. (Hollow Building) ....AAAA
Pittsburg Pulley Co., Frick Bldg. (Pillow) ....B
Pittsburg & Buffalo Co., Frick Bldg. (Hollow Building) ....AAA
U. S. Fire Proofing Corp'n, 326 Tenth Av. (Hollow Building) ....A

PA.—Reading
Reading Chain Block Wks. (Differential) X
Reading Crane & Hoist Wks. (Differential Pulley; Chain Hoisting; Iron Hoisting) C
Penna. Fire Proofing Co. (Hollow Building) ....B

PA.—Tamaqua
Tamaqua Mfg. Co. (Pillow)
B

BLOCKS (Con.)

PA.—Waynesboro
Frick Co. (Pillow) ..AAAA
PA.—Wilkesbarre
Vulcan Iron Wks. (Pillow;
Iron; Steel Pulley).AAAA
PA.—Williamsport
Valley Iron Wks. (Pillow) A

R. I.—Pawtucket
Bliss Mfg. Co., R. (Toy;
Building) ....AAAA
R. I.—Providence
Coleman & Sons, Walter
(Yacht; Steel Hoisting;
Wooden Hoisting) C
Franklin Mach. Co. (Pillow)
A
Rhode Island Tool Co.
(Chain & Eye)....AAAA
R. I.—Westerly
Calder & Carnle (Paving).F
R. I.—Woonsocket
Woonsocket Mach. & Press
Co. (Pillow) ....A
TENN.—Memphis
Chickasaw Iron Wks.
(Pillow) ....A
VT.—Barre
Trow & Holden (Granite
Cutters' Working)......B
W. VA.—Parkersburg
Parkersburg Mill Co.
(Broom; Brush) ....A
WIS.—Milwaukee
Filer & Stowell Co. (Pillow)
AAA
Winship Mfg. Co. (Butch-
ers') ....E
WIS.—So. Milwaukee
Stowell Mfg. & Fdry. Co.
(Bucket; Deck; Lead;
Pulley for Electric Light
Poles; Log Loading;
Snatch) ....A

BLOOMS

See Iron & Steel

BLOTTERS

See Pads; Blotting, also Paper.

BLOWERS

CONN.—Danbury
Peck Mfg. Co. (Fur).....D
CONN.—Hartford
Sterling Blower & Pipe Co.
A
ILL.—Chicago
Chicago Flexible Shaft Co.
(Pressure) ....B
Garden City Fan Co. (Pres-
sure; Positive) ....B
IND.—Connersville
Connersville Blower Co. (Ro-
tary; Pressure) ....A
Roots Co. P. H. & F. M.
(Blacksmiths'; Blast;
Brazing; Cupola; Exhaust;
Forge; Hand; Positive;
Pressure; Rotary) ..AA
MASS.—Boston
Bailey & Co., C. P. (Toy
Rubber; Bubble) ......B
Sturtevant Co., B. F.
(Blast; Cupola; Fan;
Forge; Hand; Mining;
Pressure; Electric; Rub-
ber) ....AAA
MASS.—Hyde Park
Boston Blower Co. (Forge;
Gas; Hand; Church Or-
gan; Electric) ....B
MASS.—Springfield
Hannan & Finton ....B
MICH.—Detroit
Amer. Blower Co., 1400 Rus-
sell (Volume; Cupola;
Fan; Forge; Laundry;
Pressure) ....AA
N. H.—Exeter
Exeter Machine Wks. (Elec-
tric; Furnace) ....B
N. J.—Newark
Backus Water Motor Co.
(Church Organ) ....B
N. J.—Trenton
De Laval Steam Turbine Co.
X

BLOWERS (Con.)

N. Y.—Brooklyn
Guild & Garrison, Kent Av.
& S. 10th (Piston; Acid)B
N. Y.—Buffalo
Buffalo Dental Mfg. Co.
(Foot; Jewelers') .....B
Buffalo Forge Co. (Blast;
Chain Pulley; Cupola;
Electric; Fan; Forge;
Hand; Mining; Pressure)
AAA
N. Y.—Lansingburg
Empire Forge Co. (Fan;
Hand) ....F
New York City
American Gas Furnace Co.
(Blast; Forge; Positive;
Pressure) ....A
Donegan & Swift, 6 Murray
(Cupola) C
Fairbanks Co., 416 Broome
(Hand; Power) ...AAAA
Niles - Bement - Pond Co.,
136 Liberty ......AAAA
Parson Mfg. Co., 320
B'way C
Slotkin & Praglin, 216 Canal
B
Sprague Electric Co. (Elec-
tric) ....AAAA
N. Y.—Schenectady
General Electric Co.
(Electric) ....AAAA
OHIO—Springfield
Foos Mfg. Co. (Fan; Hand;
Power) ....A
OHIO—Toledo
De Vilbiss Mfg. Co.
(Powder) C
PA.—Lancaster
Champion Blower & Forge
Co. (Forge; Crank; Fan;
Hand; Pressure) .....AA
Potts, David H. (Crank;
Fan) ....D
PA.—Mechanicsburg
Comstock, Geo. S. (Fan)..C
PA.—Philadelphia
Box & Co., Alfred (Chain
Pulley) ....B
Paxton Co., J. W., 1021 N.
Delaware Av. ....AA
Wilbraham - Green Blower
Co., 2526 Frankfort Av.
(Pressure; Rotary) ...B
PA.—Scranton
McClave, Brooks & Co.
(Organ; Steam; Powder)
A
PA.—South Bethlehem
Bethlehem Foundry & Ma-
chine Co. (Pressure) ..C
PA.—Wilkesbarre
Vulcan Iron Wks. (Hand;
Jet) ....AAAA
R. I.—Providence
Davol Rubber Co. (Powder)
AA
WIS.—Madison
Northern Electric Mfg. Co.
(Pressure) ....AAAA
WIS.—Milwaukee
Bailey & Sons Co., W. (Elec-
tric) X
National Blower Wks. (Pul-
ley; Forge; Volume;
Blast; Cupola; Fan;
Forge; Pressure) .....A

BLOWPIPES

ILL.—Chicago
Turner Brass Wks. (Gaso-
line) ....A
White Mfg. Co., 158 Ind ..X
N. Y.—Buffalo
Buffalo Dental Mfg. Co.
(Brazing; Jewelers')..AA
OHIO—Canton
Sun Vapor Street Light Co.
A
PA.—Philadelphia
Bockel & Co., Wm. (Lab-
oratory) ....A
R. I.—Providence
Providence Gas Burner Co.
(Jewelers') ....A

BLUESTONE

See Copper; Sulphate

N. J.—Chrome

BLUESTONE (Con.)
De Lamar's Copper Refining
Co. ....AAAA
New York City
Van Houten & Ten Broeck
Co. ....D
N. Y.—Oxford
Clarke Bluestone Co., F. G.
...........................A
PA.—Philadelphia
Maxwell's Sons, Jno. .....A

BLUING

ARK.—Fort Smith
Boos Mfg. Co. ....G
CONN.—New Haven
Doyle Co., Jno. T. (The)..D
ILL.—Chicago
Landell, Jno. E., 153 Walnut
...........................D
Puhl-Webb Co., 119 W.
Randolph C
Thomas Co., L. H., 220 S.
Peoria (Liquid; Solid)..C
IND.—South Bend
Russ Co. C
IOWA—Cedar Rapids
Shaver, Blake & Co. (Ball)
...........................D
KY.—Louisville
Mammoth Sky Blue Co., 144
E. Main ....F
MD.—Baltimore
Brady, Robinson Co., 126
South ....D
Crawford Co., W. H., 112
S. Gay (Indigo) ....E
Heller, E. W., 34 Hopkins
Pl. (Ball) ....D
MASS.—Boston
Carter's Ink Co. (Dry;
Liquid; Sheet; Laundry)A
Hubbard Blue Co., 72
Brighton Av. ....D
Palmer Premium Blue Co.,
200 Milk ....D
Sawyer Crystal Blue Co., 67
Broad (Laundry; Liquid;
Solid) C
Spear's Sons Co., Alden
(Laundry) ....AA
MASS.—Concord Junction
Bluine Mfg. Co. ....B
MICH.—Detroit
Michigan Paste & Mfg. Co.,
310 Grand River Av....F
MINN.—Minneapolis
Bertrand Mfg. Co., H., 137
N. 10th ....D
MO.—St. Louis
Donnell Mfg. Co., 612 S.
6th (Laundry) ....B
N. J.—Bayville
American Bluing Co. .....D
N. J.—Newark
Amer. Ultramarine & Globe
Aniline Wks., (Heller &
Merz Co.) Hamburg Pl..A
N. J.—Rahway
Harrison Mfg. Co. (Sheet)F
N. Y.—Brooklyn
Fischer Co., G. & L. W.,
127 Harrison Av. (Ball).E
Robinson Bros., Montrose &
Seneca Av. ....D
Voss, H. F., Park Av. ...D
Wiarda & Co., John C.
(Dry) ....AA
N. Y.—Buffalo
Abwender, E. E., 300 Ce-
dar (Bottle) ....D
American Bluing Co., 56
Mulberry ....D
Favorite Mfg. Co. (The)
1067 Niagara ....D
N. Y.—Clyde
Finch, Frank (Laundry)...C
N. Y.—Cropseyville
Davis, Aaron (Est. of)
(Laundry) ....D
N. Y.—Massena
Handy Package Dye Co.
(Laundry) ....F
New York City
Adler Color & Chemical Co.
(Dry; Laundry) ....A
Androvette, E. E., 250
Front (Indigo) ....D
Fischer & Co., C. H., 45
Harrison ....B
Heller & Merz Co., 22 Cliff
Liquid; Solid; Ball;
Laundry) ....A

BLUING (Con.)
Hirsh & Son, L., 368 Green-
wich (Ball) C
James & Bro., D. R., 123
Maiden Lane ....AA
Longman & Martinez
(Sheet) ....AAA
Miller Co., F., 349 W. 26th
(Laundry) ....B
Reckitt & Sons (Ltd.), 90
W. Broadway C
Royal Ball Blue Co., 167
Reade (Ball) ....F
Tiemann & Co., D. F., 46
Duane (Enameled Leath-
er; Indigo Wash; Dry in
Bulk; Laundry; Varnish)
......................AAA
OHIO—Cincinnati
E. Pearl (Laundry) ...D
OHIO—Cleveland
Zipp Mfg. Co., 111 Woodland
Av. C
Woodmansee, F. A., 133
......................C
OHIO—Newark
Styron, Beggs & Co.
(Liquid) ....A
PA.—Allegheny
Chamberlin & Johnson
(Laundry; Liquid) ....D
PA.—Easton
World Refining Co. X
PA.—Philadelphia
Clawson Co. (The), 45 S.
2nd C
Colburn & Co., A., 110 N.
2nd C
Continental Mfg. Co.
(Laundry) ....D
Diamond & Onyx, 317 De
Lancey (Stick) ....B
Diamond, McDonnell & Co.,
409 N. 4th (Indigo Stick;
Laundry) C
Dorn Wash Blue Mfg. Co.,
1038 N. 3rd ....E
Favorite Mfg. Co., 201 N.
Front C
Thayer & Bro., P. W., 23 S.
Front ....B
PA.—Pittsburg
Swearingen Ink Co., J. C.,
222 Wick ....D
TENN.—Bristol
Andrews Mfg. Co. C
Webb Mfg. Co. C
VA.—Richmond
Diamond Blue Mfg. Co.
(The) ....E
WIS.—Milwaukee
Gallasch Co., 298 Milwau-
kee ....E

BOARDS

For Binders'; Box; Bristol;
Card; Egg Case; Elec.;
Insulation; Fibre; Leath-
er; Manilla; Mill; Oiled;
Pulp; Straw; Trunk;
Press; See Paper List
For Wooden, See Lumber;
For Guide, See Guide-
Board.
For Wash, See Washboards
& Woodenware.
CONN.—Meriden
Manning, Bowman & Co.
(Ironing; Shirt) ......AA
CONN.—South Norwalk
Hoyt, Jas. L. (Cribbage) E
CONN.—Waterbury
Amer. Pin Co. (Cribbage;
Whist) ....AA
ILL.—Chicago
Abbott & Co., A. H., (Art-
ists' Mill) ....B
Belding-Hall Mfg. Co. (Iron-
ing) ....AA
Adams & Westlake Co.
(Stove) ....A
Carman, John A., 274 W.
Randolph (Shirt) .....D
Dietzgen Co., Eugene. (Art-
ists' Academy; Artists'
Mill; Drawing) ....A
Nicol & Co. (Bulletin; Gro-
cers') ....D
Kendtorff & Co., H.,
(Stove) ....D
Schomer, Henry (Skirt) .D
ILL.—Decatur
Chambers, Bering, Quinlan
Co. (Shoveling) ......A
Haworth & Sons Mfg. Co.

BOARDS (*Con.*)

(Shoveling) ....AA
Tait Mfg. Co., F. B.,
ILL.—De Kalb
De Kalb Fence Co (Steelwire
Fence) ....AA
ILL.—Galva
Hayes Pump & Planter Co.
(Shoveling) ....A
ILL.—La Salle
Matthiessen & Hegeler Zinc
Co. (Stove) ......AAAA
ILL.—Peru
Peru Elec. Mfg. Co.
(Tablet) ....A
IND.—Bluffton
Bluffton Mfg. Co. (Ironing)
.................C
IND.—Butler
Butler Co. (Shoveling) ...B
IND.—Fort Wayne
Fort Wayne Electric Cor-
pation (Electric Hanger)
.................AAA
Wayne Mfg. Co., Anthony,
(Ironing; Tapestry) X
IND.—Indianapolis
Udell Wks. (Ironing; Fold-
ing Lap) ....A
IND.—Muncie
Glasscock Bros. Mfg. Co.
(Metal Bread) ....B
IOWA—Davenport
Brammer Mfg. Co., H. F.,
(Ironing) ....A
IOWA—Prairie City
Dowden Mfg. Co. (Ltd.)
(Shoveling) ....A
IOWA—Webster City
Litchfield Mfg. Co. (Shovel-
ing) ....A
MAINE—South Paris
Paris Mfg. Co. (Ironing;
Lap) ....A
MASS.—Boston
Carrecabe & Co., J. M.,
(Leather) C
Collins & Co., Geo. Z.,
(Leather) C
Crosby Steam Gage & Valve
Co. (Gauge) ....AA
Hill & Cutler (Leather) ..B
Nat. Fibre Board Co.
(Fibre) ....A
Sewing Machine Supply Co.
(Plaiting) ....B
Whitcher & Co., Frank W.,
(Shoe Cutting) ....A
MASS.—Lowell
Lowell Machine Shop
(Paper Machine) ..AAAA
MASS.—Springfield
Bradley Co., Milton, (Back-
gammon; Checker; Chess)
.................A
MASS.—Worcester
Crompton & Knowles Loom
Wks. (Compass) ..AAAA
Hill Dryer Co. (Bread;
Pastry) ....D
MASS.—Winchendon
Clarke & Co., Wilder P.,
(Wash) ....A
MICH.—Bay City
Vance Box Co., E. J.,
(Bread Cloth Folding;
Advertising Sign) .....B
MICH.—Belding
Belding-Hall Mfg. Co.
(Stove) ....AA
MICH.—Detroit
Dwight Lumber Co. (Black)
.................A
MICH.—Kalkaska
Freeman Mfg. Co. (Wooden
Meat) ....B
MICH.—Saginaw
Lufkin Rule Co. (Glass Cut-
ting) ....AA
Saginaw Mfg. Co. (Wash)
.................AA
MINN.—Minneapolis
Northwestern Compo Board
Co. (Compo) ....A
N. H.—Ashland
Ashland Leather Board Co.
(Leather) ....D
N. H.—Grasmere
Excelsior Fibre Co. (Lea-
ther) X
N. H.—Lisbon
Parker & Young Co. (Sound-
ing) ....AA
N. H.—Meredith
Clarke & Co., Geo. H.,
(Hosiery) ....D

BOARDS (*Con.*)

N. H.—Milton
Milton Leather Board Co.
(Leather) ....D
N. H.—Nashua
Maine Mfg. Co. (Lap) ....A
Fletcher & Webster Furni-
ture Co. (Skirt) C
N. H.—North Rochester
Spaulding & Sons Co., J. C.,
(Leather) ....AA
N. J.—Bloomfield
Davay & Co., E. H., (Fric-
tion) ....D
N. J.—Paterson
Jackson & Sons, Jas.,
(Compass) X
Royle & Sons, Jno., (Com-
pass) ....A
N. Y.—Binghamton
Wilkinson Mfg. Co. (Folding
Lap) ....A
N. Y.—Brockport
Gleason, B. F., (Under-
takers' Cooling) ....E
N. Y.—Brooklyn
Cooper & McKee (Knife;
Meat; Pastry; Ironing;
Bosom; Shirt; Stove; Lap)
.................A
Sweeney Mfg. Co., W. H.,
(Stove) ....A
N. Y.—Buffalo
Shepard & Co., Sidney
(Stove) ....AAAA
N. Y.—Castleton
Ingalls & Co. (Trunk; Dress;
Suit Case) ....B
N. Y.—Cattaraugus
Oakes & Burger (Cheese
Scale) ....B
N. Y.—Gouveneur
Van Duzen Mfg. Co. (Lap) C
New York City
American Stove Board Co.
(Stove) ....A
Devoe, F. T. & C. J. Ray-
nolds Co., (Artists' Aca-
demy; Artists' Mill)
.................AAAA
Friedrichs, E. H., (Artists'
Academy; Mill; Drawing)
.................A
Grote & Co., F., (Cribbage)
.................D
Homan & Co., Andrew,
(Checkers; Chess) .....D
Mace & Co., L. H., (Bread;
Knife; Meat; Pastry;
Bosom; Ironing; Shirt;
Wash; Lap) ....B
McLoughlin Bros. (Back-
gammon; Checker; Chess)
.................AAA
Reilley Bros. (Paper-
hangers') ....E
Soltmann, E. G., 125 E. 42d
(Compo) ....B
N. Y.—Rochester
American Drafting Furn. Co.
(Drawing; also Parallel
Rule Attachment) ....E
National Casket Co. (Under-
takers' Cooling) ..AAAA
N. Y.—Syracuse
Onondaga Nov. Co. (Bread;
Ironing; Lap) ....E
N. Y.—Utica
Utica Electrical Mfg. &
Supply Co. (Distributing;
Electrical) X
OHIO—Cincinnati
Ault Woodenware Co.
(Bread; Ironing; Wash)
.................AA
Globe-Wernicke Co. (Paper
Clip) ....AAAA
OHIO—Cleveland
American Washboard Co.
(Wash) ....A
Cleveland Faucet Co.
(Dairy Drain) ......AAA
Lapham, Owen T., (Wash)
.................AA
OHIO—Hamilton
Black-Clawson Co. (Paper
Machine) ....A
OHIO—Salem
Clarke Co., W. J., (Wash)
.................A
OHIO—Toledo
Stevens, B. A., (Shuffle) A
Toledo Steam Cooker Co.
(Bread) C
PA.—Erie
American Mfg. & Novelty

BOARDS (Con.)
  Co. (Bosom) C
PA.—Harrisburg
Hickok Mfg. Co., W. O.,
  (Bookbinders' Cutting;
  Planished Tin; Pressing)
                      AA
PA.—Philadelphia
Dairyman's Supply Co.
  (Cheese Scale) ....B
Pearson, Jos. T., 1815 Tay-
  lor (Hosiery) ....AA
Schaum & Uhlinger (Com-
  pass) ....AAA
Weber & Co., F., (Artists'
  Academy) ....A
PA.—Pittsburg
Armstrong Cork Co. (Cork)
                      AAAA
PA.—Union City
Novelty Woodworks (Draw-
  ing) ....B
R. I.—Providence
Van Stone Mfg. Co. (Iron-
  ing; Shirt) X
VT.—Burlington
Crane. W. & D. G., (Cloth
  Folding) ....A
VA.—Richmond
Richmond Cedar Wks.
  (Wash) ....AAAA
W. VA.—Ravenswood
Moore, C. P., (Drawing) C
WIS.—Two Rivers
Hamilton Mfg. Co. (Press-
  ing) ....AA

BOATS

See also Ships; Vessels; Ca-
  noes; Launches; Yachts,
  etc.

CAL.—San Francisco
Union Iron Wks. (Steam)
                    AAAA
DEL.—Wilmington
Drein & Son, Thos., (Life;
  Wooden; Metallic; Row;
  Sail; Yacht) ....B
Harlan & Hollingsworth Co.
  (Steam; Ferry; Tow or
  Tug; Torpedo) X
Pusey & Jones Co. (Tow or
  Tug; Steam) .....AAA
ILL.—Chicago
Willard & Co., Chas. P.,
  (Tow or Tug) ....D
MAINE—Bath
Bath Iron Wks. (Ltd.)
  (Torpedo; Steam) ....D
New England Co. (Steam;
  Ferry; Tow or Tug) ....D
MD.—Baltimore
Nilson Yacht Building Co.
  (Yacht) ....D
MASS.—Boston
Atlantic Wks. (Steam;
  Ferry; Tow or Tug) AA
Lawley & Son, Geo., (Sail;
  Row) ....A
Sheldon Co., Orin, (Row;
  Sail; Yacht) ....D
MASS.—Gloucester
Higgins & Gifford Boat Mfg.
  Co. (Life; Sail; Row;
  Seine) X
MASS.—Osterville
Crosby, D., & Son (Cat) ..F
Crosby, Herbert F., (Cat) H
Crosby, Wilton, (Cat) F
MASS.—Westfield
Crane Bros. (Folding; Linen-
  old; Row) ....AAA
MICH.—Detroit
Michigan Steel Boat Co.
  (Folding) C
MICH.—Grand Rapids
Wolverine Motor Wks.
  (Steam; Stern Wheel) B
MICH.—Kalamazoo
King Folding Canvas Boat
  Co. (Folding Canvas) ..C
MICH.—Muskegon
Racine Boat Mfg. Co.
  (Automobile) ....A
MICH.—St. Joseph
Truscott Boat Mfg. Co.
  (Row; Sail) ....A
MINN.—Duluth
Pearson's Boat Construction
  Co. (Row; Sail, etc.) .B
MINN.—Wayzata
Moore, R. C., (Row) ....E
MO.—St. Louis
American Boat Wks.

BOATS (Con.)
  (Knocked Down) .....F
N. J.—Camden
Dialoque & Son, Jno. H.,
  (Tug; Steam) ....AA
N. J.—Gloucester City
Rogers Boat, Gauge &
  Drill Wks. (Sail) ....A
N. J.—Bayonne
Elec. Launch Co. (Electric;
  Motor) ....A
N. Y.—Brooklyn
Continental Iron Wks.
  (Steam; Ferry) ......A
Kahnweilers Sons, David,
  (Life; Row; Sail; Sheet
  Metal) ....B
N. Y.—Canton
Rushton, J. H., (Adiron-
  dack; Hunting; Row;
  Sail) ....F
N. Y.—Long Island City
Lane & DeGroot Co. (Collap-
  sible Life) ....D
New York City
Gas Engine & Power Co.
  (Row; Sail; Torpedo; Mo-
  tor) ....AAA
Smith, John T., (Life; Row;
  Metallic; Sail; Ships') E
Lozier Motor Co., 1 Bway.
  (Motor) ....D
N. Y.—Ogdensburg
Spalding St. Lawrence Boat
  Co. (Sail; Dingeys) C
N. Y.—Port Richmond
Burlee Dry Dock Co. (Tug;
  Ferry; Etc.) ....A
N. Y.—Roslyn
Clapham, Thos., (Sail) D
OHIO—Miamisburg
Acme Folding Boat Co.
  (Folding; Canvas; Pneu-
  matic) ....B
OHIO—Salem
Mullins. W. H., (Sheet
  Metal; Row; Steel; Duck-
  ing) ....A
OHIO—Toledo
Hepburn, J. W., (Row;
  Sail) X
PA.—Allegheny
Carlin's Sons, Thos.,
  (Derrick) ....A
PA.—Chester
Delaware River I. S. B.
  Engine Co. (Steam) AAA
PA.—Pittsburg
Armstrong Cork Co. (Life)
                    AAAA
Reese & Son, James, (Tow
  or Tug; Iron; Wooden;
  Steel) ....AA
R. I.—Bristol
Herreshoff Mfg. Co. (Tor-
  pedo; Steam) ....A

BOBBINS

CONN.—Bridgeport
Wheeler & Wilson Mfg.
  Co. (Sewing Machine)
                    AAAA
CONN.—Danielsonville
Jacobs Mfg. Co.. E. H., ..B
CONN.—Dayville
Arnold. O. S. ....F
CONN.—Hartford
Billings & Spencer Co. (Sew-
  ing Machine) ....AA
Hartford Machie Screw Co.
  (Sewing Machine) AAAA
CONN.—Windham
Hartson Co., L. M., (Iron;
  Fibre Head) X
GA.—Athens
Lyndon Mfg. Co. C
GA.—Macon
Georgia Spool & Bobbin Mfg.
  Co. (Spinning; Twister;
  Slobber; Speeder; Filling;
  Intermediate) C
ILL.—Chicago
American Electric Telephone
  Co. ....B
KY.—Maysville
Ohio Valley Pulley Wks. B
MASS.—Adams
Adams Bobbin & Spool Co. D
MASS.—Chicopee
Courtney. D. S. ....B
MASS.—Fall River
Fall River Bobbin & Shuttle
  Co. ....AAAA
Fall River Foundry &
  Machine Co. ....F

BOBBINS (Con.)

MASS.—Hopedale
Draper & Co. ....AAAA
MASS.—Lawrence
Sprague Co., L., ...AAAA
Weld Bobbin & Spool Co. D
MASS.—Lowell
New England Shuttle Co. X
MASS.—New Bedford
Greene & Wood ....B
MASS.—Winchester
Winchester Spool & Bobbin
Co. ....A
N. H.—Claremont
McGuire, Jno. A., ...C
N. H.—Colebrook
Woodward, Russell M., X
N. H.—Lisbon
Parker & Young Co. (& in
the rough) ....AA
N. H.—Littleton
Eaton, Henry A., ...C
N. H.—Manchester
Baldwin Co., Jas., ..AAAA
N.H.—Nashua
Eaton Co., Isaac, ...E
Murray, Chas. O., ...X
N. J.—Paterson
Atkinson & Co., J. (Silk) E
Daggers, Jno. R., ...B
Hall & Co. I. A., ...A
Van Riper Mfg. Co. ....B
N. Y.—Johnsonville
Baker & Sons, Michael, ..D
New York City
Household Sewing Machine
Co. (Sewing Machine) B
Kruse & Murphy Mfg. Co.
(Sewing Machine) ....D
New Home Sewing Machine
Co. (Sewing Machine)
AAAA
Singer Mfg. Co., Bway. &
Dey (Sewing Machine)
AAAA
N. Y.—Utica
Williams Co., J. H. ....A
N. C.—Greensboro
Sherwood Bobbin & Mfg.
Co. ....D
Southern Bobbin Co. .....D
N. C.—Lincolnton
Griggs Mfg. Co. ....E
OHIO—Cleveland
Standard Sewing Machine
Co. (Sewing Machine)
AAA
White Sewing Machine Co.
(Sewing Machine) AAAA
PA.—Allentown
Allentown Bobbin Wks.
(Silk; Steel) ....D
PA.—Carbondale ..
Clover Leaf Mfg. Co. ...D
PA.—Philadelphia
Billington Co., Jos. H., 113
Chestnut ....F
Bradford Woodworking Co.,
2154 N. 3d ....F
PA.—Pittsburg
Armstrong Cork Co.
(Fishing Line) ....AAAA
PA.—Weatherly
Mack Woodworking Co., H.
A., (Silk) X
R. I.—Providence
American Supply Co. ...AA
Brown Bros. Co. ....B
Fletcher Mfg. Co. ..AAAA
Providence Enamel Co....F
U. S. Bobbin & Shuttle Co.
AAAA
R. I.—South Scituate
Potter Bros. ....E
Wilburg Benjamin ....E
R. I.—Woonsocket
Colburn, Rred. S. X
S. C.—Westminster
Southern Shuttle & Bobbin
Co. ....B
VT.—Essex Junction
Vermont Spool & Bobbin Co.
C

BOBS

CONN.—New Britain
Russell & Erwin Mfg. Co.
(Plumb) ....AAAA
Stanley Rule & Level Co.
(Plumb) ....AAA
CONN.—New Haven
Sargent & Co. (Plumb)....
AAAA

BOBS (Con.)

CONN.—Southington
Peck, Stow & Wilcox Co.
(Plumb) ....AAAA
MASS.—Athol
Starrett Co., L. S. (Plumb)
A
MASS.—Boston
Welch & Co., T. F.
(Plumb) ....D
MASS.—Chicopee Falls
Stevens Arms & Tool Co., J.
(Plumb) ....AAA
MO.—St. Louis
Crescent Novelty Mfg. Co.
(Plumb) ....E
Kupferle, Jno. C. (Plumb)
AA
N. J.—Elizabeth
Braunsdorf-Mueller Co.
(Plumb) ....D
N. J.—Newark
Bernz, Otto (Plumb) .....B
Osborne & Co., C. S.
(Plumb) ....B
N. Y.—Homer
Phoenix Hardware Mfg. Co.
(Plumb) ....D
New York City
Jennings & Co., C. E., 79
Reade (Plumb) ....B
Keuffel & Esser Co., 127
Fulton (Plumb) .....AA
Seltmann, E. G., 125 E.
42nd (Plumb for Engineers
& Architects) ....B
Tower & Lyon Co., 95 Cham-
bers (Plumb; Trammel
Points) ....B
OHIO—Cincinnati
Haven Co., Jas. L. (Plumb)
B
PA.—Philadelphia
Disston & Sons, Henry
(Plumb) ....AAA
PA.—Reading
Reading Hardware Co.
(Plumb) ....AAAA
PA.—Wrightsville
Wrightsville Hardware Co.
(Plumb) ....B
R. I.—Providence
Brown & Sharpe Mfg. Co.
(Mercury; Plumb) .AAAA

BODIES

See also Woodwork; Car-
riage & Wagon

CONN.—Bridgeport
Braitling, F.K. (Doll) ...F
CONN.—Danbury
Mallory & Sons, A. E. (Hat)
AA
CONN.—New Haven
Dann Bros. & Co. (Carriage;
Hearse; Wagon) ....B
ILL.—Chicago
Illinois Malleable Iron Co.
(Water Column) .....AA
IND.—La Porte
La Porte Carriage Co. (Car-
riage) ....A
MASS.—Amesbury
Currier & Cameron Co.
(Carriage) C
MASS.—Boston
Wood Co., A. M. (Carriage)
C
MICH.—Detroit
Wilson Carriage Co., C. R.
(Carriage) ....D
MO.—St. Louis
Powitzki & Collins Carriage
Woodwork Co. (Carriage)
A
N. H.—Concord
Holt Bros. Mfg. Co.
(Wagon) ....B
OHIO—Cincinnati
Cincinnati Panel Co. (Car-
riage) ....B
Mill Creek Wagon Co. (Car-
riage; Wagon) C
PA.—Philadelphia
Knell, Francis B. (Doll) ..H
PA.—Pittsburg
U. S. Aluminum Co.
(Aluminum) ....B

BODKINS

New York City

BODKINS (Con.)
Hoe & Co., R. ......AAAA

BOILERS, STEAM

See also Heaters
See also Miscellaneous
Next Heading

ALA—Birmingham
Hardie-Tynes Foundry & Machine Co. (Steam) ..A
ALA—Montgomery
Hartley Boiler Wks. (Steam) C
CAL.—Los Angeles
Baker Iron Wks., 950 Buena Vista (Steam) ....A
Fulton Engine Wks., Chevez cor. Oneviolo (Steam)..B
Llewellyn Iron Wks.. E. R. R., cor. N. Main (Steam) ..A
Thomson & Boyle, 310 Requena (Steam) C
CAL.—Oakland
Oakland Iron Wks. (Steam) ..B
CAL.—Sacramento
Root, Neilson & Co. (Steam) ..A
CAL.—San Francisco
California Boiler Wks., 125 Fremont (Steam) C
Dundon, P. F., 223 Folsom (Steam) ....B
Eureka Boiler Wks., 113 Mission (Steam) C
Fulton Engineering & Ship Bldg. Wks., 15 1st (Steam) ....AA
Moynihan, Tim. J., 311 Mission (Steam) ....B
Risdon Iron & Locomotive Wks., Stewart & Folsom (Water Tube) .....AAA
San Francisco Iron Wks., 223 Folsom (Steam) ......B
Union Iron Wks., 224 Market (Portable on Wheels; Steam; Water Tube) .... AAAA
CAL.—Stockton
Stockton Iron Wks. (Steam) ..A
COL.—Denver
Davis Iron Wks., F. M., 8th & Larimer (Steam) ....A
Denver Boiler & Sheet Iron Wks., 35th & Wazee (Steam) C
Denver Engineering Wks., 30th & Blake (Steam)..A
Stearns-Rogers Mfg. Co. (Steam) ....A
Young, John, 2445 Blake (Steam) ....B
CONN.—Bridgeport
Skidmore & Sons, P. H., E. Wash. Av. & Hosatonic (Steam) ....A
CONN.—New Haven
Bigelow Co., 92 River (Steam) ....B
CONN.—Putnam
Putnam Foundry & Machine Corp. (Steam) ....B
DEL.—Edgemore
Edgemore Iron Co. (Water Tube; also Galloway; Internally Fired)....AAAA
DEL.—Wilmington
Pusey & Jones Co. (Marine; Stationary) ....AAA
Remington Machine Co. (Water Tube) ....A
D. C.—Washington
Gray & Co.. E. N., 316 Main Av. S. W. (Steam).....C
FLA.—Jacksonville
Merrill-Stevens Engineering Co. (Steam) ....B
GA.—Atlanta
Atlanta Mach. Wks., King & Ga. R. R. Steam) .B
Harrison Safety Boiler Wks., Prud. Bldg. (Steam) C
GA.—Augusta
Georgia Iron Wks. (Steam)C
Lombard-Forston Boiler Co. (Iron; Steam) ....A

BOILERS, ST'M (Con.)
GA.—Columbus
Columbus Iron Wks. Co. (Steam) ....AA
Golden Foundry & Machine Co. (Steam) ....A
GA.—Newman
Cole Mfg. Co., R. D. (Steam) ....A
GA.—Savannah
Kehoe & Sons, Wm. (Steam) ..A
McDonough & Ballantyne (Steam) ....B
Rourke & Sons, John (Steam) ....B
GA.—Valdosta
Valdosta Fdry. & Mach. Co. (Steam) C
ILL.—Chicago
Allis-Chalmers Co., Home Ins. Bldg. (Water Tube) AAAA
McGregor, Geo. L., 246 S. Clinton (Steam) C
Marine Iron Wks., Sta. A. (Steam) ....B
Mohr & Sons, John, 32 Ill. (Steam) ....A
National Boiler Wks., 56 Fulton (Steam) ....B
Pfeiffer Boiler Co., Chris., 70 Mich. (Steam) .....B
Standard Safety Boiler Co., Marquette Bldg. (Water Tube) C
Sullivan Mach. Co., 135 Adams (Steam) ....AAA
Willard & Co.. Chas. P., 15 N. Canal (Water Tube) .C
ILL.—Galesburg
Frost Mfg. Co. (Steam) ..A
ILL.—Kewanee
Kewanee Boiler Co. (Locomotive; Fire Box)..AAA
ILL.—Quincy
Michelman Boiler Co. (Steam) C
ILL.—Springfield
Drake, Wm. (Steam) C
Springfield Boiler & Mfg. Co. (Steam) ....A
IND.—Anderson
Anderson Fdy. & Mach. Wks. (Steam) ....B
Wooley Fdry. & Mach Wks. (Steam) ....B
IND.—Evansville
Heilman Machine Wks., 1st & Pine (Steam)........B
IND.—Ft. Wayne
Ft. Wayne Fdry. & Mach. Co. (Steam) C
IND.—Indianapolis
Atlas Engine Wks., 19th & Martindale Av. (Flue; Internally Fired; Water Tube) ....AAAA
Chandler & Taylor Co., 740 W. Wash. Av. (Tubular; Upright; Firebox; Portable on Wheels) ....A
IND.—Jeffersonville
Tweeny Shipyard & Fdry. Co. (Steam) C
IND.—La Porte
Rumley Co., M. (Steam)... AAAA
IND.—New Albany
Hegewald Co., Chas. (Steam) ....B
IND.—Richmond
Gaar, Scott & Co. (Steam.. AAA
Richmond Mach. Wks. (Steam) ....A
Robinson & Co. ((Steam)..A
IOWA—Burlington
Murray Iron Wks. Co. (Steam) ....A
IOWA—Des Moines
Beckman Bros. (Steam) ..C
Des Moines Mfg. & Supply Co. (Steam) ....A
IOWA—Dubuque
Iowa Iron Wks. (Ltd.), 9th & Wash. (Steam) ......B
Morrison Bros. (Steam) ..B
IOWA—Marshalltown
Lennox Machine Co. (Steam) C
Thorthill Co., A. E. (Steam) C

88

IOWA—Ottumwa
Fair-Williams Bridge &
Mfg. Co. (Steam) .....B
IOWA—Sioux City
Sioux City Boiler & Sheet
Iron Wks. (Tubular;
Steam) ....A
KANS.—Enterprise
Ehrsam & Sons, J. B.
(Steam) C
KY.—Louisville
Caldwell Co., W. E., 200
E. Branders (Steam)....A
Geiger, Fiske & Koop Co.,
725 E. Main (Steam) ..C
Grainger & Co., 131 10th
(Steam) C
Vogt-Mach. Co., Hy., 10th &
Ormsby Av. (Steam)..AA
LA.—New Orleans
Payne & Joubert, 423 Ca-
rondelet (Steam) C
MAINE—Bangor
Union Iron Wks. (Steam).A
MAINE—Bath
Bath Iron Wks. (Steam).AA
MAINE—Hallowell
Fullers' Sons, Geo. (Steam)
                          C
MAINE—Portland
Portland Co., 58 Fore (Ma-
rine & Stationery) ....AA
MD.—Baltimore
Baltimore Marine Railway
Mach. & Boiler Wks.,
Philips & Point (Steam)
                          A
Baltimore Ship Building &
Dry Dock Co., Locust
Point (Marine) ......B
Basshor & Co., Thos. C., 28
Light (Steam) ....A
Codd & Co., E. J., 700 S.
Caroline (Steam Engine)
                          A
Spedden Ship Bldg. Co., 915
S. B'way (Marine) C
MD.—Cumberland
McKay, Merwin (Steam)..A
MASS.—Boston
Atlantic Works, 70 Border,
E. Boston (Steam)....AA
Cunningham Iron Co., B. &
Fargo (Steam) C
Hodge Boiler Works, Sum-
ner & North Ferry, E.
Boston (Steam) ......B
MASS.—Cambridge
Kendall & Sons, Edw., 168
Main (Steam) ....A
Riverside Boiler Wks. 50
Howard (Steam) C
Roberts Iron Wks. Co., 180
Main (Steam) ....A
MASS.—Fitchburg
Fitchburg Steam Engine Co.
(Steam) ....B
MASS.—Florence
Norwood Engineering Co.
(Steam) C
MASS.—Lowell
Scannell & Wholey 26 Tan-
ner (Steam) C
MASS.—New Bedford
New Bedford Boiler &
Mach. Co. (Steam) ...C
MASS.—Quincy
Fore River Ship & Eng. Co.
(Marine; Water; Tube
&c.) ....AAAA
MASS.—Taunton
Taunton Locomotive Mfg.
Co. (Steam) ....AA
MASS.—Worcester
Allen & Sons Co., Wm., 65
Green (Steam) C
Stewart Boiler Wks. Albany
& Muskeego (Steam) ..B
MICH.—Battle Creek
Brennan & Co., John
(Steam) ....A
MICH.—Bay City
Bay City Boiler Co. (Steam)
                          C
Industrial Wks. (Steam) AA
McKimmon Mfg. Co.
(Steam) C
Marine Iron Co. (Steam)..C
MICH.—Cadillac
Hayes, Wm. (Steam) C
MICH.—Detroit
Brennan & Co., John, 24th
& M. C. R. R. (Steam)..A
Detroit Screw Wks. 346

Franklin (Water Tube)..A
Pratt, Stephen, Beecher, Av.
& M. C. R. R. (Steam) A
MICH.—Grand Rapids
Brobst, Hey. Canal & Cold-
brook (Steam) ....B
MICH.—Hancock
Portage Lake Boiler Wks.
(Steam) ....B
MICH.—Kalamazoo
Clark Engine & Boiler Co.,
Geo., 505 N. Church
(Steam) C
Dutton Co., C. H. (Steam) B
MICH.—Lansing
Lansing Boiler & Engine Co.
(Steam) ....B
MICH.—Manistee
Manistee Iron Wks. Co.
(Steam) ....B
MICH.—Port Huron
Jenks Ship Bldg. Co.
(Marine & Stationary)..A
MICH.—Saginaw
Bartlett & Co., A. F.
(Steam) ....A
Jackson & Church Co.
(Water Tube) ....A
Wickers Bros. (Water Tube)
                          AA
MINN.—Minneapolis
Bros Boiler & Mfg. Co.
Wm., Nicollet Island
(Steam) ....B
MISS.—Corinth
Adams Mach. Co., W. T.,
(Steam) ....AA
MISS.—Meridian
Martin Mach. Wks.
(Steam) C
MO.—St. Joseph
Augustine, T. C., 611 Patee
(Steam) ....AA
MO.—St. Louis
O'Brien Boiler Wks. Co.,
John, 11th c Mullanply
(Water Tube) ....AA
Stewart Boiler Co., 23d &
Papin (Steam) ....A
Wangler Boiler & Sheet Iron
Wks. Co., Jos. F., 1547 N.
9th (Steam) ....A
MO.—Springfield
Crescent Iron Wks.
(Steam) ....A
MONT.—Anaconda
Anaconda Copper Mining Co.
(Steam) ....AAAA
MONT.—Butte
Western Iron Wks. (Inc.
(Steam) ....B
N. H.—Exeter
Exeter Mach. Wks.
(Steam) ....B
N. J.—Burlington
Stuart & Peterson Co.,
(Steam Jacketed; Plain or
Porcelain) ....A
N. J.—Elizabeth
Moore & Sons Co., Sam'l L.,
(Steam) ....AA
N. J.—Gloucester City
Rogers Boat, Gauge &
Drill Wks., John M.
(Steam) C
N. J.—Hoboken
Fletcher Co., W. & A., 12th
& Hudson (Marine &c.).A
N. J.—Jersey City
Brown & Miller ft. Morris
(Steam) ....A
Smith & Sons Co., Theo.,
(Steam) ....A
N. J.—Newark
Hewes & Phillips Iron Wks.
Orange & Ogden (Steam)
                          A
Lambert Hoisting Eng. Co.,
117 Poinier (Steam)....C
N. J.—Paterson
Haes Mfg. Co. (Range;
Copper) ....B
Smith & Son, Sam'l., 130
R. R. Av. (Steam; Loco-
motive; Tubular) .....A
N. J.—Phillipsburg
Tippett & Wood (Steam) A
N. J.—Red Bank
Roberts Safety Water Tube
Boiler Co. (Water Tube)
                          B
N. J.—Ridgefield Park
Riverside Boiler Wks.
(Steam) ....A

700 Water (The McNaull;
Water Tube) ....B
OHIO—Warren
Warren City Boiler Works
(Steam) ....B
OHIO—Youngstown
E n t e r p r i s e Boiler Co.
(Steam) C
P o l l o c k Co., Wm. B.
(Steam) ....B
OHIO—Zanesville
U n i o n M a c h i n e Wks.
(Steam) ....A
OREGON—Astoria
Astoria Iron Works (inc.)
(Steam) ....B
OREGON—Portland
Willimette Boiler Works.
Front & Everett (Steam)
B
PA.—Allegheny
Porter Fdy. & Mach. Co.
(Steam) ....A
PA.—Allentown
Allentown Boiler Wks. (Col-
lum & Knonce) (Steam).C
H e i l m a n Boiler Wks.
(Steam) ....B
PA.—Bangor
Flory Mfg. Co., S. (Steam)
B
PA.—Beaver Falls
Keystone Driller Co. (Up-
right; Portable) ......B
PA.—Bradford
Bovaird & Seyfang Mfg. Co.
(Steam) ....A
PA.—Chester
Wetherill Machine Co., Jas.
P. (Steam; Berry Water
Tubs) ....AAAA
PA.—Coatsville
Coatsville Boiler Works
(Steam) ....A
PA.—Conshohocken
Bate & Son, Wm. T.
(Steam) ....A
PA.—Corry
Ajax Iron Works (Station-
ary; Portable) ....B
PA.—Dubois
Dubois Iron Wks. (Tubular)
AAAA
PA.—East Stroudsburg
International Boiler Works
Co. (Steam) C
PA.—Erie
Erie City Iron Wks. (Sta-
tionary; Portable; Verti-
cal) ....AAAA
Erie Engine Wks. (Water
Tube) ....A
Nagle Engine & Boiler Wks.
(Steam) ....AAA
Pennsylvania Boiler Works
(Steam) ....AA
Stearns Mfg. Co. (Water
Tube) ....AA
Union Iron Wks. (Steam).A
PA.—Harrisburg
Harrisburg Fdy. & Mach.
Wks. (Steam) ....A
Harrisburg Mfg. & Boiler
Co. (Water Tube) ....B
PA.—Kennett Square
American Road Mach. Co.
(Portable; Stationary).AA
PA.—Kutztown
Kutztown Foundry & Ma-
chine Co. (Steam) ....B
PA.—Lancaster
B e s t John (Est. of)
(Steam) ....B
PA.—Lebanon
Lebanon Boiler Works
(Steam) C
PA.—Meadville
Phoenix Iron Works Co.
(Steam; Portable on
Wheels) ....A
PA.—New Castle
Pennsylvania Engineering
Works (Steam) ....A
PA.—Norristown
Newbold & Son Co., R. S.
(Steam) ....A
PA.—Oil City
Oil City Boiler Wks. (inc.)
(Water Tube; Portable on
Wheels) ....AAAA
PA.—Philadelphia
Baizley Iron Wks., Jno., 510

S. Delaware Av. (Steam)
AA
Cramp & Sons Ship & Eng.
Bldg. Co., Wm., Beach &
Ball (Marine) ....AAAA
Ervien & Co., C. W., 420
Memphis (Steam) .....B
General Engineering Co., 764
Swanson (Steam) .....B
Goldner & Son, Hy., Tasker
St. Wharf, Del. River
(Steam) C
Harrison Safety Boiler
Works, 17th (Steam) ..A
Howard Foundry & Machine
Wks., 2123 Mkt. (Steam)
C
Kensington Engine Works
(Ltd.), 245 N. Broad (Re-
turn Tubular) ....A
Moore Water Tube Boiler
Co., E. J., 2227 Wood
(Steam) C
Naylor, John S., Front &
Girard (Steam) ....A
Nittinger, August, Sr., 826
N. 4th (Steam) ....A
Nuttall, John, 1723 N. 5th
(Steam) C
Phoenix Iron Works, Odd
Fellows Temple Bldg.
(Steam) ....A
Rich, J. & G., 120 N. 6th
(Steam) ....B
PA.—Pittsburg
Hyde Bros. & Co., Lewis
Blk. (Water Tube) ....B
McNeil & Bros. Co., Jas.,
29th & A. V. Ry. (Steam)
AA
Munroe & Son. R., 23d &
Smallman (Water Tube;
Portable on Wheels)....A
Oil Well Supply Co., 21st &
A. V. Ry. (Steam; Water
Tube) ....AAAA
Rhean & Co., S. B., 43d &
A. V. Ry. (Steam).....A
Riter-Conley Mfg. Co., 56
Water (Steam) ....AAA
PA.—Pittston
E x e t e r M a c h. W k s.
(Steam) ....B
PA.—Pottstown
Sotler Bros. (inc.) (Steam)
B
PA.—Pottsville
Sparks & Parker (Steam).C
PA.—Ridgway
Ridgway Mfg. Co. (Steam)
C
PA.—Scottdale
Kenney & Co. (Steam; Tu-
bular) ....A
PA.—Scranton
Finch Mfg. Co., N. 8th, c.
W. Linden (Steam) ..AA
PA.—Shamokin
Mullen & Son, Jno. (Water
Tube) ....A
PA.—Sharon
Sharon Boiler Wks. (Ltd.)
(Wheeler Water Tube)..C
PA.—Tatamy
Messinger Mfg. Co. (Low
Pressure) ....B
PA.—Titusville
Young & Sons, E. R.
(Steam) ....B
PA.—Troy
Troy Engine & Machine Co.
(Steam) ....B
PA.—Warren
Struthers-Wells Co. (Steam;
Portable on Wheels) ..AA
PA.—Washington
Petroleum Iron Works Co.
(Steam) ....B
PA.—Waynesboro
Frick Co. (Portable on
Wheels) ....AAA
Geiser Mfg. Co. (Steam)
AAA
PA.—Wilkesbarre
Vulcan Iron Wks. (Portable
on Wheels; Steam)...AA
PA.—Williamsport
Keeler Co., E. (Internat
Furnace; Water Tube).A
Larzeleye Mach. Co. (Steam)
B
PA.—York
Broomell, Schmidt & Steacy

BOILERS, ST'M (*Con.*)

Co. (American Combination Water Tube).....B

Farquhar & Co., A. B. (Steam; Locomotive).AAA

Motter & Sons, Geo. F. (Steam) ....B

York Mfg. Co. (Ltd.) (Return Tubular) ......AA

R. I.—Bristol

Herreshoff Mfg. Co. (Water Tube) ....A

R. I.—Hope Valley

Nichols & Langworthy Mach. Co. (Steam) ....AA

R. I.—Providence

Almy Water Tube Boiler Co., 178 Allens Av. (Water Tube) ....B

Harris Steam Engine Co., W. A., Park c. Promenade (Steam) ....B

S. C.—Spartansburg

Morgan Iron Wks. (Steam) C

TENN.—Chattanooga

Casey & Hedges Mfg. Co. (Steam) ....A

Sherman-Morris Mfg. Co. (Steam) ....B

Walsh & Weidner Boiler Co. Water Tube) ....A

TENN.—Jackson

Southern Eng. & Boiler Wks. (Steam; Portable on Wheels) ....A

TENN.—Memphis

Chickasaw Iron Wks., 2d c. Winchester (Steam)...A

TENN.—Nashville

Culbert & Sons, Wm., 127 S. Market (Steam) C

TEXAS—Galveston

Astall Iron Works. 2615 Strand (Steam) C

TEXAS—San Antonio

Alamo Iron Wks. (Steam).C

Collins Mfg. Co., F. F. (Steam) ....A

VT.—Rutland

Holmes & Co., J. H. (Steam) B

VT.—Winooski

Stevens Mach. Co. (Steam) B

VA.—Newport News

Newport News Shipbuilding & Dry Dock Co. (Steam) ▲▲▲

VA.—Norfolk

Duvall & Co., Geo. W. (Steam) C

WASH.—Everett

Sumner Iron Wks. (Water Tube) ....A

WASH.—Seattle

Moran Bros. Co. (Marine; Stationary) ....A

Washington Iron Wks. Co., Grant St. Bridge (Steam) B

WASH.—Spokane

Union Iron Wks. (inc.) (Steam) ....A

WASH.—Tacoma

Puget Sound Dry Dock & Machine Co., 1701 Dock (Steam) ....B

W. VA.—Charleston

South Side Fdy. & Machine Wks. (Steam) ....A

WIS.—Milwaukee

Davis Brothers Mfg. Co. (Steam) ....B

Milwaukee Boiler Co., 220 Oregon (Steam) ....A

WIS.—Racine

Freeman & Sons Mfg. Co., S. (Portable on Wheels; Steam) ....A

WIS.—Watertown

Kunert Mfg. Co., E. (Steam) C

BOILERS, MISCELLANE-OUS

CONN.—Waterbury.

Randolph-Clowes Co. (Copper Range) ....AAA

BOILERS, MISC. (*Con.*)

ILL.—Aurora

Phillips, T. L. (Hot Water) D

ILL.—Chicago

Clow & Sons, J. B., 344 Franklin (Galvanized Iron Range) ....AAA

Wolff Mfg. Co., L., 117 W. Lake (Copper Range) AAAA

ILL.—Clyde

Coonley Mfg. Co. (Rice; Coffee; Milk) ....A

IND.—Evansville

Grote Mfg. Co. (Hot Water) D

IND.—Kokomo

Globe Stove & Range Co. (Charcoal) ....A

MD.—Baltimore

McShane Mfg. Co., Hy., 441 North (Galvanized Iron Range; Copper) ...AAAA

Sadtler & Co., J. B., 813 S. Howard (Galvanized Iron Range) C

MASS.—Boston

Badger & Sons' Co. 65 Pitts (Copper Range; Wash).A

Reardon, John, 111 Albany (Copper Range) ....E

Walker & Pratt Mfg. Co., 31 Union (Hot Water).AA

MASS.—Worcester

Hamblin & Russell Mfg. Co. (Wire Egg) ....B

National Mfg. Co. (Egg).A

Wire Goods Co. (Vegetable) A

MICH.—Detroit

Detroit Range Boiler Co., 619 24th (Galvanized Iron Range) ....B

United States Heater Co., 251 Campbell (Hot Water) A

MICH.—Mt. Clemens

Donaldson Bros. (Farm)...A

MINN.—St. Paul

South Park Fdy. & Machine Co. (Heating) ....B

N. J.—Bartley

Bartley & Sons, Wm. (Heating) ....D

N. J.—Jersey City

Griffing Iron Co., A. A. (Cast Iron Hot Water) AA

N. J.—Trenton

Throop, Wm. R. (Rubber) A

N. Y.—Brooklyn

Brooklyn Range Boiler Co., Eagle (Galvanized Iron Range) ....B

Ronalds & Johnson Co.. 51 Boerum Pl. (Galvanized Iron Range; Copper) ..AA

N. Y.—Cortland

Wickwire Bros. (Vegetable) AAAA

New York City

Avery, Hy. W., 364 Front (Copper)..............D

Iron Clad Mfg. Co., 4 Cliff (Galvanized Iron Range) AAA

Jochum, Andrew, 148 E. 50th (Copper Range) ...D

Koven & Bro., L. O., 50 Cliff (Galvanized Iron Range) ....A

Lalance & Grosjean Mfg. Co., 19 Cliff (Galvanized Iron Range) .....AAAA

Steeger, Hy., 143 E. 31st (Copper Range) ....A

Trageser Steam Copper Works, 447 W. 26th (Coal Range) ....A

N. Y.—Oswego

Steam Carriage Boiler Co. (Automobile) ....D

N. Y.—Rochester

Rochester Stamping Co. (Coffee) ....AAA

OHIO—Cincinnati

Francis & Bro., Chas. E. (Glue) ....B

OHIO—Cleveland

Cleveland Stamping & Tool Co. (Vegetable) ....A

OHIO—Hamilton

BOILERS, MISC. (Con.)

Meyers Mfg. Co., Fred J. (Vegetable) ....B

OHIO—Lima
Star Iron Works (Shop)...D

OHIO—Toledo
Advance Machinery Co. (Glue) C

PA.—Conshohocken
Wood Mfg Co., John (Galvanized Iron Range)....B

PA.—Philadelphia
Blessing, C. A., 516 Montgomery Av. (Copper Range) ....AA
Carroll, Patrick, 1335 Mt. Vernon (Galvanized Iron Range) C
Darby & Son, Edw., 233 Arch (Vegetable) .... A
Harney, Wm., 1011 Master (Bath; Galvanized Iron Range) ....F
Hibbs, E. A., 209 Quarry (Galvanized Iron Range) D
Hill, Thos. D., 2314 N. 8th (Bath; Galvanized Iron Range) ....B
Janney, Steinmetz & Co., Drexel Bldg. (Automobile) D
Penna. Range Boiler Co., 2010 N. 10th (Galvanized Iron Range) ....B
Thompson Iron Wks., 1825 Callowhill (Galvanized Iron Range) ....D

PA.—Pittsburg
Scaife & Sons, Wm. B. (Galvanized Iron & Copper Range) ....AAA

WIS.—Milwaukee
Pressed Steel Tank Co. (Automobile) ....AAAA
Seamless Structural Co. (Automobile) ....D

BOLSTERS

See also Bedding

IND.—Hammond
Simplex Railway Appliance Co. (Car Truck; Body) AA

IOWA—Davenport
Bettendorf Axle Co. (Car Truck; Body) ....AA

MASS.—Boston
Bent & Co., Geo. W. ....B

MASS.—Hopedale
Westcott, A. W. (Spindle) F

MO.—St. Louis
American Car & Foundry Co. (Car Truck; Body AAAA

N. J.—Trenton
Bloom & Godley (Spindle) A

New York City
American Steel Foundries, 74 B'way (Car Truck; Body) ....AAAA

OHIO—Piqua
Piqua Handle & Mfg. Co. (Spindle) ....A

PA.—Chester
American Steel Foundries (Car Truck; Body).AAAA

PA.—Lebanon
American Iron & Steel Mfg. Co. (Car Truck; Body) AAAA

PA.—Philadelphia
Sterlingworth Railway Supply Co. (Car Truck; Body) B

PA.—Pittsburg
Pressed Steel Car Co. (Car Truck; Body) .....AAAA
Standard Steel Car Co., Frick Bldg. (Car Truck; Body) ....B

R. I.—Bridgeton
Hopkins Machine Works (Spindle) C

R. I.—Pawtucket
Payne & Co., Geo. W. (Spindle) ....A

BOLTERS

See also Machinery

MAINE—Bangor
Bangor Foundry & Machine Co. (Lath) ....F

MICH.—Bay City
Garland Co., M. (Gang)...C

MICH.—East Saginaw
Mitts & Merrill (Lath)...B

MICH.—Kalamazoo
Hill & Co., W. E. (Shingle; Lath) ....D

N. Y.—Buffalo
Holmes Machinery Co., E. & B. (Gang) ....B

N. Y.—Lockport
Trevor Mfg. Co. (Shingle) B

VT.—Montpelier
Lane Mfg. Co. (Shingle; Lath) ....A

WIS.—Eau Claire
Phoenix Mfg. Co. (Shingle) A

WIS.—Milwaukee
Allis-Chalmers Co. (Lath) AAAA
Filer & Stowell Co. (Ltd.) (Shingle; Gang) ....AAA

BOLTS

See Hardware; Carriage

ALA.—Birmingham
Southern Bolt & Nut Wks. (Bridge; Structural Machine) ....B

CAL.—San Francisco
Judson Mfg. Co., Howard & Beale (Track) .....AA
Payne's Bolt Wks. 121 Howard (Carriage) ....A

COLO.—Denver
Colorado Fuel & Iron Co., Boston Bldg. (Bridge; Structural; Machine; & Track) ....AAAA

CONN.—Bridgeport
Bridgeport Brass Co. (Brass; Copper) ....AA

CONN.—Derby
Birmingham Brass Co. (Brass) ....A

CONN.—Hartford
Billings & Spencer Co. (Hook & Eye) ....A
Hartford Machine Screw Co. (Stud Machine) ....AAAA

CONN.—Marion
Frost L. D., (Est.) (Carriage) C

CONN.—Middletown
Wilcox, Crittendon & Co. (Hook & Eye)..........A

CONN.—Milldale
Clark Bros. & Co. (Bicycle; Carriage; Hanger; Hook & Eye; Machine; Plow; Stove Special all Kinds..A

CONN.—Mt. Carmel
Mt. Carmel Bolt Co. (Stove) B

CONN.—New Britain
New Britain Hdw. Mfg. Co. (Machine; Planer Head) B
Stanley Works. (Barrel; Wroght Steel; Door; Window; Shutter) ..AAA

CONN.—New Haven
Cowles & Co., C. (Carriage) A
Reynolds & Co. (Belt or Elevator; Bridge; Structual; Coupling; Machine; Link; Stove; Stud; Tap) .....B
Sargent & Co. (Barn Door; Barrel; Door; Window; Hook & Eye for Shutters) AAAA

CONN.—Plantsville
Atwater Mfg. Co. (Whiffle-tree) ....A

CONN.—Seymour
New Haven Copper Co. (Copper) ....AA

CONN.—Shelton
Bassett, D. M. (Carriage).C
Shelton Co. (Carriage; Sink; Stove) ....A

CONN.—Southington
Peck, Stow & Wilcox Co. (Barn Door; Brass; Cop-

BOLTS (*Con.*)

per; Carriage; Copper Soldering; Door; Window; Stove; Tire) ......AAAA

Southington Cutlery Co.
Sleigh; Link; Shoe; Tire)
...... AA

CONN.—Torrington
Coe Brass Mfg. Co. (Brass)
...... AAAA
Progressive Mfg. Co.
(Bicycle) ....A

CONN.—Unionville
Union Nut & Bolt Co.
(Belt or Elevator; Bridge; Structural; Machine) ...A
Upson Nut Co. (Bridge; Structural; Carriage; Coupling; Hook & Eye; Loom; Machine; Plow; Sink; Stove; Stud; Tire; Track; Wiffletree) AAA

CONN.—Waterbury
Benedict & Burnham Mfg.
Co. (Brass) ......AAAA
Holmes, Booth & Hayden
Co. (Brass; Copper)AAAA
Plume & Atwood Mfg. Co.
(Brass; Copper) ...AAA
Scovill Mfg. Co. (Brass)
...... AAAA
Steele & Johnson Mfg. Co.
(Brass) ....A
Waterbury Brass Co.
(Brass) ....AAAA

CONN.—Winsted
Moore-Franklin Co. (Carriage; Countersunk; Shoe; Sleigh; Tire) ......A
Richards Hardware Co.
(Tire) C

DEL.—Wilmington
Diamond State Steel Co.
(Bridge; Structural; Carriage; Machine; Stud; Track) ....AAA

ILL.—Aurora
Wilcox Mfg. Co. (Expansion) ....B

ILL.—Chicago
Columbia Screw Co. (Belt; Elevator; Brass; Copper; Sink; Stove) ....
Continental Bolt & Iron Works, 22d & Union (Bridge; Structural; Car; Foundations; Key; Machine; Track) ....B
Illinois Screw Co., 19 Lake (Boiler; Patch; Planer head) ....
Republic Iron & Steel Co., Stock Exch. Bldg. (Boiler; Stay; Bridge; Structural; Carriage; Countersunk; Drift; Foundation; Hook & Eye; Plow; Sleigh; Shoe; Stud; Tap; Tire; Sink; Track) ......AAAA
Standard Screw Co., 2 N. Canal (Coupling; Planer Head; Stud; Machine Screw Coupling) ....AAA

ILL.—Freeport
Arcade Mfg. Co. (Door; Window) ....B

IND.—Indianapolis
Parkhurst Bros. & Co., 218 Kentucky Av. (Bridge; Structural; Carriage & Hanger) C

MD.—Baltimore
Clendenin Bros. 111 S. Gay. (Copper Soldering) ...A
Dietrich Bros. 344 North (Machine) ....A
National Supply Co. 7 W. Lombard ....B

MASS.—Boston
Boston Bolt Co., 33 Purchase (Belt; Elevator; Bridge; Structural; Expansion; Hook & Eye; Machine; Sink; Bolt; Track) ....B
New England Bolt & Nut Co., 253 Atlantic Av. (Barrel; Belt; Elevator; Bridge; Structural; Carriage; Expansion; Hook & Eye; Machine; Sink; Stud; Tap; Tire) C
Sylvester Co., 70 Kilby (Bridge Structural) ....B

MASS.—Lowell
American Bolt Co. (Belt; Elevator; Bridge; Struc-

BOLTS (*Con.*)

tural; Carriage; Hook & Eye; Machine; Stud; Track) ....B

MASS.—New Bedford .
Taunton-New Bedford Copper Co. (Brass; Copper; Yellow Metal only)..AAA

MASS.—Springfield
Transue & Williams Co.
Hook & Eye; Drop Forged)
A

MASS.—Worcester
Wire Goods Co., 20 Union (Hook & Eye) ....B

MICH.—Detroit
Anderson & Sons, W. H. (Drift; Foundation; Hook & Eye; Expansion; Wall; Anchor) C
Detroit Copper & Brass Rolling Mills (Copper; Brass) ....AAAA
Diamond Stamped Ware Co. Summit nr. River (Copper Soldering) ....A
Michigan Bolt & Nut Wks. Meldrun Av. (Boiler Stay; Bridge; Structural; Car; Carriage; Collar; Counter-Foundation; Hanger; Hook Head; Hook & Eye; Machine; Plow; Sleigh Shoe; Stove; Stud; Tap; Tire; Track) ....A

MO.—Kansas City
Kansas City Bolt & Nut Co.
Inde Av. & Bristol (Bridge; Structural; Carriage; Coupling; Drift; Foundation; Hanger; Hook & Eye; Key; Mach.; Stud; Tap; Track) ....A

MO.—St. Louis
Moran Bolt & Nut Mfg. Co. Florida & Maine, (Belt; Elevator; Boiler Patch; Boiler Stay; Bridge; Structural; Car; Carriage; Countersink; Drift; Foundation; Hanger; Hook & Eye; Key; Mach.; Plow; Stove; Stud; Track) ...A
St. Louis Screw Co. 3017 N. 13th (Bicycle; Boiler Patch; Coupling; Stove; Stud; Thumb) ....B

N. J.—Dover
Dover Iron Co., of N. J. ..A

N. J.—Jersey City
Ames & Co., W. (Track)..A

N. Y.—Brooklyn
Evans, F. H., 596 Kent Av. (Expansion; Expansion Eye; Expansion Switchboard; Hook & Eye; Toggle) C
Williams & Co., J. H., 9 Richards (Hook & Eye Drop Forge) ....AAA

N. Y.—Buffalo
Buffalo Bolt Co. (Door; Window) ....A

New York City
American Steel & Wire Co. 71 B'way (Machine) ....AAAA
Ansonia Brass & Copper Co. 99 John (Copper Soldering) ....
Gaskell & Son, Wm. 433 E. 25th (Bridge; Structural; Mach.) ....B
Greenlic, Wyatt & Co. 499 Water (Mach.; Tap) ..B
Hall's Sons, Sam'l. 229 W. 10th (Machine) ....A
Hendricks Bros. 49 Cliff. (Copper) ....AAAA
Hungerford Brass & Copper Co., U. T., 497 Pearl (Brass & Copper) ....A
McCabe Hanger Mfg. Co., 425 W. 25th (Expansion; Expansion Eye; Expansion Switchboard) C
Trenton Iron Co., 17 Burling Slip ....AA
Union Nut & Bolt Co., 107 Chambers (Machine) ...B

N. Y.—Port Chester
Russell, Burdsall & Ward Bolt & Nut Co. (Bicycles; Coupling Mach.; Sink; Sleigh Shoe; Stove; Tap; Tire; Whiffletree)....AA

BOLTS (Con.)

N. Y.—Rochester
Sargent-Greenleaf Co. (Door & Window) ....AA

N. Y.—Syracuse
Central City Bolt Co. Bell; Elevator; Bridge; Structural; Carriage; Hook; Eye; Machine; Stove; Tap; Tire) C

OHIO—Canton
Ney Mfg. Co. (Door; Window) ....B

OHIO—Cincinnati
Cincinnati Screw & Tap Co., 2442 Beekman (Boiler Patch; Coupling; Mach.; Planer Head; Steel)....B

OHIO—Cleveland
Atlas Bolt & Screw Co., Marquette opp. Hamilton (Barn Door; Carriage; Mach.; Sink; Sleigh Shoe; Stove; Tap; Tire)......A
Cleveland Bolt & Mfg. Co., Stanton & C. & P. R. R. (Carriage) C
Cleveland Cap & Screw Co., 66 Clarkwood Av. (Coupling; Stud) ....B
Cleveland City Forge & Iron Co., Case Av. c. Lake.AA
Eberhard Mfg. Co., Pennyson & C. & P. R. R. (Carriage) ....AA
Kirk-Latty Mfg. Co., Malcolm Av., Nickle Plate R. R. (Carriage; Sink; Tire) B
Lamson & Sessions Co., 412 Scranton Av. (Carriage; Countersink; H a n g e r; Hook; Eye; Key; Mach.; Plow Sink; Sleigh Shoe; Stove; Stud; Tap; Tire; Track) ....AA
National Screw & Tack Co., Stanton & C. & P. R. R. (Bicycle; Stove; Thumb; Tire) ....AA
Taylor & Boggis Co., 521 Seneca (Door; Window) AA

OHIO—Columbus
Berry Bros. (Carriage; Tire) B
C o l u m b u s Bolt Wks. (Bridge; Structural; Carriage; Hook; Eye; Mach.; Plow; Sink; Stove; Stud; Tap; Tire; Whiffletree) A
Weinman Machine Wks., 23 N. Sciott C

OHIO—Elyria
Western Automatic Machine & Screw Co. (Collar Coupling; Planer; Head; Stud; Bicycle; Brass; Copper; Case Hardened; Check; Jam; Semi-Furn.; Tapped) AA

OHIO—Mansfield
Ohio Brass Co. (Insulated) B

OHIO—Salem
Clark Co., W. J. (Belt; Elevator) ....B

OHIO—Toledo
Church, Isaac (Anchor; Awning Hinge; Expansion; Expansion Eye; Expansion Switchboard; Foundation; Shutter; Toggle) ....F

OHIO—Youngstown
Youngstown Car Mfg. Co. (Car) ....A
Youngstown Mfg. Co. (Bridge; Structural; Car) AA

PA.—Allegheny
Graham Nut Co., 755 Rebecca (Foundation) C

PA.—Erie
Griffin Mfg. Co. (Barrel; Door; Window) ....A

PA.—Lancaster
Penn Iron Co. (Anchor; Belt; Elevator; Car; Foundation; Machine; Track) A

PA.—McKees Rocks
Lockhart Iron & Steel Co.

BOLTS (Con.)
(Boiler Stay) ....AA

PA.—Mechanicsburg
Wilcox Mfg. Co., D. (Hook; Eye; Drop Forged Eye).B

PA.—Milton
Milton Mfg. Co. (Carriage; Machine; Stud; Tap)...A

PA.—New Castle
New Castle Forge & Bolt Co. (Carriage; Drift; Foundation; Hook; Eye; Mach.; Stone; Track)...B

PA.—Philadelphia
Brohard Co., 1624 N. 9th (Expansion) X
Cambria Steel Co., Arcade Bldg. (All Kinds).AAAA
Enterprise Mfg. Co., N. 3d & Dauphin (Barn Door) AAAA
Hoopes & Townsend Co., 1330 Buttonwood (Belt; Elevator; Boiler; Patch; Bridge; Stone; Car; Carriage; Cross Arm; Drift; Foundation; H a n g e r; Hook; Eye; Key; Mach.; Plow; Stud; Tap; Tire; Track) ....AAA
Keystone Drop Forge Co., Harrison Bldg. (Hook; Eye) ....B
McGooken, O., H., 1630 9th (Bridge; Structural)....C
Phosphor Bronze Smelting Co., 220 Washington Av. (Brass; Copper; Phosphor Bronze; Machine) .....B
Seaman & Co., D. C., 1638 N. Hutchinson (Expansion; Expansion Eye; Stud; Hook; Eye)......D
Steward & Romaine Mfg. Co., 124 N. 6th (Double Expansion; Hitching Ring; Expansion; Expansion Eye; Toggle; Hook & Eye) ....D

PA.—Pittsburg
Fort Pitt Forge Co. (Iron; Steel) ....B
Hubbard & Co., Murtland Bldg. (Carriage; Hook; Eye; Machine; Track)..A
Lanz & Sons, M., 101 S. 29th (Boiler Patch; Bridge; Structural; Carriage; Countersink; Foundation; Hook; E-e; Key; Loom; Machine; Track; Anchor) ....B
Oliver Iron & Steel Co., S. 10th & Muriel (Belt; Elevator; Boiler; Bridge; Stone; Car; Carriage; Collar; Coupling; Countersink; Drift; Foundation; Key; Machine; Stud; Track) ....AAAA
Pittsburg Screw & Bolt Co., 25th & Liberty (Boiler Patch; Coupling; Foundation H a n g e r; Hook Head; Mach.; Planer Head; Stud) ....B
Pittsburg Mfg. Co., 28th & A. V. Ry. (Bridge; Structural; Machine) ....B
Scaife & Sons' Co., Wm. B., 221 1st Av. (Bridge; Structural) ....B

PA.—Reading
Penn. Hdw. Co. (Barrel; Mortise; Door; Window) AA
Reading Hdw. Co. (Barrel; Brass; Copper; Door; Window) ....AAA

PA.—Scranton
Scranton Bolt & Nut Co. (Boiler Patch; Bridge; Structural; Car; Carriage; C o l l a r; Countersink; Coupling; Drift; Foundation; Hanger; Hook Head; Hook; Eye; Key; Mach.; Stud; Track; Whiffletree) A

R. I.—Pawtucket
Haskell Mfg. Co., Wm. H. (Belt; Elevator; Boiler Patch; Boiler Stay; Brass; Copper; Bridge; Struc-

BOLTS (Con.)

tural; Coupling; Hanger
Hook; Head Hook; Eye;
Mach.; Plow; Sink; Stud;
Tap) ....A

Pawtucket Mfg. Co. (Belt;
Elevator; Boiler Patch;
Brass; Copper; Bridge;
Structural; C o u p l i n g;
Hook; Eye; Mach.; Plow;
Tap) ....A

R. I.—Providence
American Screw Co., 21
Stevens (Bell; Elevator;
Stove; Tire) ......AAAA

Rhode Island Tool Co.
(Boiler Patch; Counter-
sink; Coupling; Founda-
tion; Hanger; Hook; Eye;
Key; Loom; Machine;
Planer; Head; Stud; Tap;
Thumb) ....AAA

VA.—Richmond
Old Dominion Iron & Nail
Works Co. (Bridge; Struc-
tural; Car; Countersink;
Drift; Foundation; Hang-
er; Key; Machine) ..AAA

Tredeger Co. (Track) ..AAA

W. VA.—Wheeling
Wheeling Hinge Co. (Car-
riage; Stove) ....AA

WIS.—Milwaukee
Milwaukee Tack Co., Wahl
& 27th Av. C
National Elastic Nut Co.,
Russell Av. c. Superior
(Machine; Track)......A

BONBON-NIERS

**See also Silverware &
Jewelry**

CONN.—Wallingford
Wallace & Sons Mfg. Co., R.
AAAA

New York City
Jansen, Edward ....A

BONDS

ILL.—Chicago
Adams & Westlake Co.,
Ontario & N. Franklin
(Rail) ....AAA
American Steel & Wire Co.,
The Rookery (Rail).AAAA
Atkinson & Co., J. M., 204
Dearborn (Rail).......F
Electric Appliance Co., 94
W. Van Buren (Rail)...B
Porter & Berg, 309 Dear-
born (Rail) ....D

MASS.—Boston
Anderson Mfg. Co., Albert
& J. M. (Rail).........B
Chase-Shawmut Co., 390 At-
lantic Av. (Rail).......B
Thomas, Edw. G., 4 State
(Rail) X

MASS.—Worcester
Morgan Spring Co. (Rail)..B

N. J.—Trenton
Roebling's Sons Co., John A.
(Rail) ....AAAA

N. Y.—Brooklyn
Columbia Machine Works &
Malleable Iron Co., 167
Chestnut (Rail) ....A

New York City
Harrington, S. H., 120 Lib-
erty (Rail; Diagonal Rail;
Protected Rail) ....E
Johns-Manville Co., H. W.,
100 William (Rail).AAAA

N. Y.—Schenectady
General Electric Co. (Rail)
AAAA

OHIO—Cleveland
Cleveland Brass & Bronze
Works, 1138 Hamilton
(Rail) ....D

OHIO—Mansfield
Ohio Brass Co. (Rail).....B

PA.—North East
Eureka Tempered Copper
Works (Rail) •.........B

PA.—Pittsburg
Westinghouse Electric &
Mfg. Co. (Rail) ...AAAA

BONDS (Con.)

R. I.—Providence
American Electrical Works
(Rail) ....AAAA

WIS.—Milwaukee
Falk Co., ft. 30th (Rail)..A

BONE

See also Rawbone

CONN.—Middletown
Rogers & Hubbard Co.
G r a n u l a t e d; Raw;
Ground) ....A

MICH.—Three Oaks
Warren Featherbone Co.
(Corset) ....AA

N. J.—Newark
Lister Agricultural Chem.
Co. (Leg; Fat) ...AAAA

N. Y.—Brooklyn
Wiarda & Co., John C.,
(Ground) ....AA

OHIO—Cincinnati
Obermayer Co., S. (Case
Hardening) ....AA

PA.—Philadelphia
Paxton Co., J. W. (Case
Hardening) ....AA

PA.—York
York Chemical Wks. (Gran-
ulated; Raw) ....A

VT.—Hyde Park
Page, Carroll S. (Fertilizing; Ground) ....A

BONNETS

See Millinery; Hats

New York City
Howard & Morse (Smoke
Stack) ....D
Sjoberg & Co., J. P., 533
W. 32d (Car) ....D

OHIO—Hamilton
Meyers Mfg. Co., Fred J.
(Smoke Stack) ....B

BOOKCASES

See Furniture

BOOKS

For Pocket Books, see Leather Goods. See Ledgers.

CAL.—San Francisco
Althof & Bahls (Account)
D
Hicks, Judd & Co. (Account)
B

CONN.—Derby
How Mfg. Co. (Pin)......A

CONN.—Hartford
Bailey Mfg. Co. (Letter
Copying) C
Burr & Co., J. B. (Account)
F
Burr Index Co. (Account;
Physicians; S c r a t c h;
Blank) ....B
Plimpton Mfg. Co. (Br. U.
S. Envelope Co., Spring-
field, O.) (Account).AAA

CONN.—Waterbury
Waterbury Blank Book Mfg.
Co. (Account; Contrac-
tors'; Index; Membership;
Quartermasters') C

CONN—Windsor Locks
Whittlesey, Frank H. (Letter Copying) ....B

ILL.—Chicago
Amberg File & Index Co.
(Letter Copying) .....A
Baker-Vawter Co. (Account;
Letter Copying) .....AA
Cameron, Amberg & Co.
(Account) ....AA
Conkey Co., W. B. (Juve-
nile) ....AAA
Ideal Specialty Co., 143 S.
Clinton (Scrap) ....G
Jones Stationery & Printing
Co., J. M. (Check; Draft)
D
McDonald & Co., J. S. (Ac-
count) ....A
Safeguard Account Co. (Ac-

BOOKS (Con.)

count) ....B
Shepard Co., Henry O. (Account) ....B
Western Bank Note & Engraving Co. (Check; Draft) ....AA
Wood & Co., Chas. H. (Letter Copying) ....F

IND.—Indianapolis
Allison Coupon Co. (Telegraph; Railroad; Coupon) ....B

IND.—South Bend
Pershing, H. Albert (Advertising; Copying; Coupon; Duplicate; Memorandum; Remittance) ....D

IOWA—Davenport
Egbert, Fidlar & Chambers (Account; Invoice; Memorandum) ....B

KANS.—Topeka
Adams Bros. (Duplicating Sales) ....D

MASS.—Boston
Forbes Lithograph Mfg. Co. (Check; Draft) ......AA
Gay & Co., Aaron R. (Account) ....F
Groom & Co., Thos. (Account; Hotel Register; Letter Copying; Note; Record) ....B
Webster Co., F. S. (Letter Copying) ....AA

MASS.—Holyoke
Griffith, Axtel & Cady Co. (Check; Draft) ......D
National Blank Book Co. (Account; Cash; Drawing; Memorandum; Pass)..AA

MASS.—Lowell
Dumas & Co. (Blank; Memorandum) C

MASS.—Springfield
Bradley Co., Milton (Kindergarten) ....A

MASS.—Worcester
Maynard-Gough Co. (Account; Hotel Register; Livery) ....E

MICH.—Detroit
Winn & Hammond (Account) ....D

MINN.—Minneapolis
Swinburne & Co. (Account) ....E

MINN.—St. Paul
Cosby & Co., Chas. E. (Manifold; Sales; Shipping) ....E

MO.—St. Louis
Barnard & Co., Geo. D. (Account; Memorandum; Pass) ....AA

N. Y.—Buffalo
Gies & Co. (Check; Draft) ....AAA

N. Y.—Castleton
Fort Orange Pad Co. (Composition; Note) X

N. Y.—Elmira
American Sales Book Co. (Sales; Grocers' Order).B

New York City
American Bank Note Co. (Cash; Check; Draft) ....AAAA
American Book Co. (Educational; Text; School; Writing) ....AAAA
Boorum & Pease Co. (Account; Business College; Cash; Drawing; Invoice; Letter Copying; Manifold; Memorandum; Note; Record; Sales; School; Writing; Scrap; Scratch; Blank) ....AAA
Brabant Needle Co., 47 Great Jones (Needle)...D
Corliss, Macy & Co. (Account; Check; Draft)...B
Faber, Eberhard (Memorandum; Blank) ....AAA
International Bank Note Co. Check; Draft) ....B
Johnson & Co., Milton C. (Check; Draft) ....E
Keuffel & Esser Co.. 127 Fulton (Engineers' Field) ....AA
Kiggins & Tooker Co. (Ac-

BOOKS (Con.)

count) ....B
Kissam, B. A. (Account) D
Koch, Sons & Co. (Account; Invoice; Music; Scrap).X
Liebenroth, Von Auw & Co. (Account) ....B
Lusk & Son, Richard E. (Account) ....B
McLaughlin Bros. (Toy) ....AAA
New York Bank Note Co. (Check; Draft) ....A
New York Blank Book Co. (Account; Composition; Invoice; Letter Copying; Memorandum; Order; Pass) ....AAAA
New York Cash Sales Book Co., 534 Pearl (Cash Sales) ....D
Ottman Lithographing Co. (Check; Draft) ....A
Shaw Blank Book Co., J. G. (Account; Letter Copying; Memorandum) ....B
Shipman, Asa L. (Invoice; Scrap) ....B
Slote & Co., Daniel (Account) ....B
Tower Mfg. & Novelty Co. (Account) ....A

N. Y.—Saugerties
Saugerties Mfg. Co. (Account) ....AA

N. Y.—Syracuse
Hall & McChesney (Index; Trial Balance) ....B
Wells Mfg. Co., A. J. (Account) X

OHIO—Cleveland
Brooks Co. (Account) ....A
Forman-Bassett-Hatch Co. (Account) ....A
McKim Co., C. S. (Letter Copying) ....D

OHIO—Coshocton
Forbes, J. B. (Coupon)....A

OHIO—Dayton
Reynolds & Reynolds Co. (Account; Order; Repeating) ....A

PA.—Philadelphia
Christy's Sons Co., Wm. M. (Account) X
Globe Bible Publishing Co. (Bibles; Toy) ......AA
Hofstetter Bros. (Account) C
Lippincott Co., J. B. (Account) ....AAA
Mann Co., Wm. (Account; Cash; Engineers' Field; Invoice; Letter Copying; Memorandum; Pass; Receipt; Sales; Scrap; Check; Draft) ......AA
Murphy & Sons' Co., W. F. (Account) ....AA

PA.—Roaring Spring
Roaring Spring Blank Book Co. (Account) ....A

R. I.—Providence
Hall Co., J. C. (Manifold; Order; Repeating; Check; Draft) ....B

TENN.—Nashville
Marshall & Bruce Co. (Account) ....A

VT.—Post Mills
Chubb Rod Co., T. H. (Fly; Tackle) ....A

VA.—Glenallen
Cussons, May & Co. (Advertising; Memorandum) ....B

WIS.—Milwaukee
Razall Mfg. Co., H. G. (Account; Letter Copying)..B
Sentinel Co. (Account) .AA

BOOSTERS

N. J.—Ampere
Crocker-Wheeler Co. (Electric) ....A

N. Y.—Watertown
Eager Electric Co. (Electric) ....D

PA.—Pittsburg
Westinghouse Elec. Mfg. Co. (Elec. R. R.) ...AAAA

BOOTHS

IND.—Peru
Brownell, Chas. H. (Telephone) ....A
MO.—St. Louis
Wabash Woodworking Co. (Exhibit) C
N. Y.—Jamestown
Fenton Metallic Mfg. Co. (Booths; Voting) ......A
New York City
American Steel House Co., 796 11th Av. (Steel; Wood; Election) ......D
Glaser, Rohrer & Co., 727 1st Av. (Exhibition)....D
OHIO—Cleveland
Forest City Steel & Iron Co. (Steel; Wood; Election).A
Van Dorn Iron Works Co. (Wood; Steel; Election) AA
OHIO—Columbus
Columbus Bar Fixture Co. (Telephone) C
OHIO—Toledo
Yesbera Mfg. Co. (Telephone) ....B
PA.—Marietta
Penna. Construction Co. (Wood; Steel; Election).A
Penna. Electric Co. (Wood; Steel; Election) ....B

BOOTS

See also Boots & Shoes

CONN.—Hartford
Stalker Mfg. Co. (Horse Interfering) ....E
ILL.—Chicago
Allis-Chalmers Co., Home Ins. Bldg. (Elevator) AAAA
Borden & Selleck Co., 48 Lake (Elevator) .....B
Caldwell & Son Co., 17th & Western Av. (Elevator).A
Skillin & Richards Mfg. Co., 147 Fulton (Elevator)...C
Weller Mfg. Co., 118 E. North Av. (Elevator)...A
ILL.—Marseilles
Marseilles Mfg. Co. (Elevator) ....A
IND.—Indianapolis
Nordyke & Marmon Co., 1101 W. Norris (Elevator) AAA
IND.—Mishawaka
Dodge Mfg. Co. (Elevator) AAA
IND.—Seymour
Hide & Leather Co. (John F. Shiel) (Horse Interfering) E
KY.—Newport
Higgins Mfg. Co. (Vehicle) A
MD.—Baltimore
Poole & Son Co., Robert, 233 E. German (Elevator)...A
MASS.—Beverly
Carter Co., J. F. (Oiled; Wagon) ....D
MICH.—Detroit
Buhl Malleable Co., Wight & Adair (Elevator) ...A
MINN.—Minneapolis
Minn. Steel & Machinery Co. (Elevator) ....A
N. Y.—Watervliet
Covert Mfg. Co. (Interfering Horse) ....A
OHIO—Canton
Aultman Co. (Elevator)..A
OHIO—Cincinnati
Monarch Carriage Goods Co. (Vehicle) ....B
OHIO—Cleveland
Bartlett & Snow Co., C. O., French (Elevator) ...B
OHIO—Columbus
Case Mfg. Co. (Elevator) AA
Jeffrey Mfg. Co. (Elevator) AA
OHIO—Springfield
Rogers Iron Co. (Vehicle).C
OHIO—Toledo
Kroh Co., C. Z. (Vehicle).E

BOOTS (Con.)
PA.—Pittsburg
Nease, McLean & McGinness (Vehicle) ....A
PA.—South Bethelehem
Bethlehem Foundry & Machine Co. (Elevator)....C
WIS.—Cudahy
Power & Mining Machinery Co. (Elevator) .....AAA
WIS.—Milwaukee
Chain Belt Co., 766 Park (Elevator) ....B
Grotenrath, Fred, 111 W. Water (Elevator) ......E

BOOTS & SHOES

CAL.—San Francisco
Buckingham & Hecht (Men's; Women's; Boys') AA
Cahn, Nickelsburg & Co..A
Nolan, Hewes, George Co. (Men's; Boys'; Women's; Childrens')...B
Rosethal, Feder & Co.....A
COLO.—Denver
Dunn Shoe & Leather Mfg. Co. ....B
CONN.—Beacon Falls
Beacon Falls Rubber Shoe Co. (Rubber) ....A
CONN.—Naugatuck
Goodyear's Metallic Rubber Shoe Co. ....AAAA
CONN.—South Norwalk
Lounsbury, Matthewson & Co. ....AA
Lounsbury & Soule (Women's; Misses; Childrens') B
GA.—Gainesville
Everett, Ridley, Ragan & Co. (Men's; Women's; Boys') ....AAAA
Smith Mfg. Co., J. A.....B
ILL.—Chicago
Columbia Overgarters & Leggins Co..........C
Edwards, Stanwood Shoe Co. A
Florsheim & Co. (Men's)..A
Mullin, John & Son......B
Phelps, Dodge & Palmer (Brogans) ....A
Seltz, Schwab & Co. (Brogans) ....AAAA
Smith & Sons Co., R. R. (Brogans) ....AA
Smith Shoe Co., J. P.....A
Smith-Wallace Shoe Co. (Felt) ....A
Tilt Shoe Co., J. E........A
Wells & Co., M. D. (Brogans) ....AAA
Wells Co., M. D.....AAAA
ILL.—De Kalb
ILL.—Dixon
Watson-Plummer Shoe Co. (Men's; Women's; Childrens' Welts) ....A
ILL.—Elgin
Selz, Schwab & Co....AAAA
ILL.—Gibson
Gibson Shoe Mfg. Co. (Men's; Boys') ....B
ILL.—Pontiac
Pontiac Shoe Mfg. Co. (Women's; Misses'; Childrens') ....A
IND.—Mishawaka
Beatty Felting Co. (Felt Boots; Shoes; Slippers).C
Mishawaka Woolen Mfg. Co. (Wool; Rubber) ...AA
IOWA—Ft. Dodge
Green-Wheeler Shoe Co. (Women's) ....B
IOWA—Grinnell
Morrison, McIntosh & Co. (Sheepskin Footwear)...B
IOWA—Keokuk
Huiskamp Bros. Co. (Men's; Women's; Misses; Childrens') ....AA
IOWA—Webster
Northwestern Felt Shoe Co. (Felt) ....B
KY.—Louisville
Conrad Rawls Shoe Co. (Women's; Misses'; Chil-

BOOTS & SHOES (Con.)
drens') ....B
LA.—New Orleans
Keiffer Bros. (Men's; Boys';
Women's) ....A
Montelone, A. ....AA
Rosenberg, B. & Son (Men's)
A
MAINE—Auburn
Cushman Co., Ara (Men's)
AA
Dingley-Foss S h o e C o.
(Men's) ....A
Foss, Packard & Co. (&
Brogans) ....AA
Parker & Peakes Co. (Men's;
Boys') ....A
MAINE—Bangor
Buck & Co., E. A. (Explor-
ers'; Prospectors'; Mocca-
sins) ....F
Sawyer Boot & Shoe Co.
Lumbermens' Boot & Shoe
Moccasins) ....B
MAINE—Calais
St. Croix Shoe Co. .. ...B
MAINE—Eastport
Holmes, E. A. F. A......B
MAINE—Freeport
Cumberland County Shoe Co.
(Men's; Boys') ....A
Shaw & Co., A. W. (Men's)
B
MAINE—Gardiner
Commonwealth S h o e &
Leather Co. ....A
MAINE—Hallowell
Johnson Bros. Shoe Mfg. Co.
A
MAINE—New Sharon
Harding & Jordan Shoe Co.
(Men's; Boys') ....B
MAINE—Norway
Spinney & Co., B. F.
(Women's) ....AAA
MAINE—Portland
Berry Shoe Co., A. H.
(Women's) ....A
Cox & Son, A. F. (Women's
Misses' Dongola) ......A
MAINE—Springvale
Usher & Son Shoe Co., W. R.
(Boys'; Youths') .....B
MD.—Baltimore
Baltimore Boot & Shoe Mfg.
Co. ....A
Carroll Shoe Co., John A.
(Women's) ....B
Colmary & Co., A. H.
(Women's; Misses') ...A
Dixon-Bartlett Co. ....B
Heiser, Vanneman Mfg. Co.
B
Hess & Bro., N. (Men's).B
MASS.—Avon
Littlefield, L. G. (Men's;
Boys') ....B
MASS.—Beverly
Millett, Woodbury & Co.
(Men's; Women's; Misses'
Childrens'; Warm) .....B
MASS.—Boston
American Rubber Co. (Rub-
ber) ....AAAA
Boston Rubber Shoe Co.
(Rubber) ....AAAA
Burt & Co., Geo. H. (Bro-
gans) C
Coffin & Co., C. A...AAAA
Davis Boot & Shoe Co.
(Felt) ....AA
AAA
Herman & Co., Jos. M.
(Brogans) ....A
Hood Rubber Co. (Rubber)
Mawhinney Co., H. H....B
Moulton & Co., Chas. H.
(Brogans) ....AA
Norman & Bennett ......B
O'Connell & Sons, John
(Brogans) ....AA
Plant Co., Thos. G. (Wom-
en's) ....AAAA
Rice & Hutchins (Men's;
Boys'; Childrens') .AAAA
MASS.—Bridgewater
McElwain & Co., W. H.
(Men's; Boys') ....A
MASS.—Brockton
Barry & Co., T. D. (Men's
Welts) ....A
Churchill & Alden Co. ...B
Douglas Shoe Co., W. L.
(& Brogans) ......AAAA

BOOTS & SHOES (Con.)
Eaton & Co., Chas. A.
(Men's) ....B
Field Co., D. W. ....B
Grover & Co., R. B.....A
Howard & Foster (Mens'
Welts) ....B
Kingman & Co., F. C.
(Men's; Boys') ....B
Packard & Field (Men's) .A
Parker & Lewis ....B
Reynolds & Co., L. M.
(Men's; Boys') ....B
Slater & Morrill Co. .....B
Snow, Geo. G. (Men's) ..AA
Stacy, Adams & Co. (Men's)
A
Taylor & Co., E. E. .....B
White & Co., Frank E..AA
MASS.—Brookfield
Moulton & Co., Chas. H. ..A
MASS.—Campello
Churchill & Alden Co......B
Grover & Co., R. B. .....A
Keith, E. & L. C. (& Bro-
gans) ....AAAA
Keith & Co., Geo. E.
(Men's; Women's; Boys')
AA
Keith Shoe Co., Preston B.
(Men's) ....A
MASS.—Chelsea
Bartels, Thelan & Co. (Wom-
en's; Misses'; Childrens')
A
Wright & Co., A. E. ....B
MASS.—East Weymouth
Clapp & Co., Edwin ......A
Dizer & Co., M. C.......A
Strong & Garfield Co.
(Men's) ....A
MASS.—Everett
Andrews & Co. (Women's;
Misses'; Childrens')....B
MASS.—Fitchburg
Dickinson & Co., E. M.
(M i s s e s'; Childrens';
Boys') ....A
MASS.—Gloucester
Fuller & Co., Chas. S.
(Cape Ann Shoe Co.)
(Women's; Misses'; Chil-
drens') ....A
MASS.—Haverhill
Bennett & Co. ....B
Chesley & Rugg (Women's;
Men's) ....B
Chick Bros. (Women's;
Misses'; Men's; Boys';
Youths' & Childrens') ..A
Durgin & Son, J. H. .....A
Fox, Chas. K. (Low Cut).B
Gale Shoe Mfg. Co. (Wo-
men's; Misses'; Chil-
dren's) ....B
Kimball, W. & V. O.....B
Lynch, J. A............B
Porter, Howard L. (Wo-
men's; Slippers; Sandals
& Ties) ....B
Russ Co., John W. (Men's)
Spaulding & Co., W. W.
(Boots; Shoes & Slippers)
A
Thayer, Maguire & Field
(Women's Slippers) ....A
Webster, Ira J. (Women's;
Boots; Shoes & Slippers)
B
Winchell & Co., J. H. ....A
MASS.—Hudson
Apsley Rubber Co. (Rubber)
AA
Brett Co., C. M. ....B
Brigham, F. & Gregory Co.
(Women's; Men's; Boys',
&c.) ....A
Jefts Co., L. T. ....B
MASS.—Lowell
Stover & Bean (Men's; Satin
& Kangaroo; Women's;
Glove Grain & Kangaroo)
B
MASS.—Lynn
Aborn & Co., C. H. (Wo-
men's; Boots & Oxfords)
B
Burt & Co., E. W. (Men's
& Women's) ....B
Burt & Co., Geo. H. .....B
Creighton & Son, G. A....B
Donovan & Co., D. A. ....A
Faunce & Spinney (Wo-

BOOTS & SHOES (Con.)

men's; Misses' & Children's) ....AAA
Grover's Sons, J. J. (Women's Hand Sewed)...B
Hennessey & Thompson..B
Herrick & Co., G. W. (Women's Shoes & Oxfords)..B
Hoag & Walden (Women's) ....B

Johnson & Co., Luther S. (Slippers) ....AA
Leonard Shoe Co..........B
Little & Co., A. E. ....B
Luddy & Currier (Women's & Children's)..........B
Phelan & Sons, James ...AA
Porter & Son, William...A
Seymour & Jackson......A
Smith Co., A. F..........B
Thomas, J. B., & Tarr (Misses' & Children's) ..AA
Walton & Logan Co. (Boys') ....B
Welch & Landregan......A
Williams, Clark & Co....A
Worthly, M. J............A

MASS.—Marlboro
Frye Shoe Co., John A...A
Howe Shoe Co., S. H. (Men's & Women's, &c.) ..AA
O'Connell & Sons, John..AA

MASS.—Middleboro
Leonard & Barrows.....AA

MASS.—Milford
Huckins, Temple & Wood.A
Milford Shoe Co. (Men's).B

MASS.—Millis
Herman & Co., Joseph M..B

MASS.—Natick
Walcott & Co., J. W.....A

MASS.—Newburyport
Burley & Stevens........A
Cole & Co., B. E.........AA
Dodge Bros. (Women's; Slippers; Shoes & Boots) ....AA

MASS.—North Abington
Arnold & Co., M. N. (Men's) ....AA
Crossett, Lewis A. (Men's) ....A

MASS.—North Adams
Fairfield, Millard & Co. ..A
Millard & Co., N. L......B
Brown & Co., H. H......B

MASS.—North Brookfield
Brown & Co., H. H......B

MASS.—North Grafton
Nelson & Son Shoe Co..J. S. (Men's; Youths'; Boys') ....B

MASS.—Oxford
Joslin Co., A. L. ......AA

MASS.—Rockland
Simmons & Hall Shoe Co. (Men's) ....B

MASS.—Salem
Brown & Sons, J. (Misses' & Children's) ....A
Dane & Co., Joseph A. (Misses' & Children's).A
Field Shoe Co., P. O. (Women's) ....B
Fuller & Co., C. S. (Boys') ....B
Lefavor & Co., D. D. (Misses' & Children's).A
Straw & Co., L. G........B
Woodbury & Co., E. S. (Misses' & Children's).A

MASS.—South Natick
Pfeiffer & Co., Wm. F..B

MASS.—Spencer
Jones & Co., E.........AAA
Prouty & Co., Isaac (Men's; Boys') ....A

MASS.—Ward Hill
Knipe Bros. (Men's Shoes & Slippers) ....B

MASS.—Webster
Corbin & Sons Co., B. A. (Men's; Boys'; Youths'; Little Men's; Women's).B

MASS.—Westboro
Brigham & Sons, Geo. B. (Men's & Youths')....B

MASS.—Whitman
Commonwealth Shoe & Leather Co. (Men's)..AA

MASS.—Worcester
Bay State Shoe & Leather

BOOTS & SHOES (Con.)

Co. (Men's Brogans)..AA
Heywood Boot & Shoe Co. (Men's & Boys' Welts).B
Worcester Supply Co. (Women's, Misses' & Children's Felt Slippers; Felt & Leather Soles) ......B

MICH.—Cairo
Lacy Shoe Co............B

MICH.—Detroit
Snedicor & Hathaway Co. (Men's & Boys')......AA

MICH.—Grand Rapids
Grand Rapids Felt Boot Co. (Wool; Felt; Knit & Rubber) ....B
Herold-Bertsch Shoe Co. (Men's; Boys'; Misses' & Children's) ....A
Rindge, Kalmbach, Logie & Co. (Men's; Boys'; Women's; Misses' & Children's) ....A

MASS.—Northville
Rodgers Shoe Co. (Succ. to Fisk & Thomas) ....A

MINN.—Anoka
North Star Shoe Co. (Men's; Boys') ....AA

MINN.—Duluth
Duluth Shoe Co. (Men's; Boys' & Lumbermen's Gds.) ....A

MINN.—Minneapolis
Grimsrud Shoe Co. ......B
North Star Shoe Co.....AA

MINN.—Red Wing
Foot & Co., S. B.........A

MINN.—St. Paul
Foot, Schulze & Co. (General line) ....AAA
Gotzian & Co., C. (Minnesota Shoe Co.) ......AA
Sharood Shoe Co. (Men's; Boys'; Women's; Misses' & Children's Shoes & Slippers) ....A

MINN.—Stillwater
Jordan Co., W. B. & W. G. ....A

MINN.—Winona
Williams, E. W. (General Line) ....B

MO.—Kansas City
Barton Bros. (Men's) ....A

MO.—St. Joseph
Noyes, Norman & Co. (Men's) ....A

MO.—St. Louis
Brown Shoe Co. (Men's; Women's; Boys'; Misses & Children's) ....AAAA
Courtney Shoe Co. ......AA
Dittman Boot & Shoe Co., Geo. F. (Women's; Misses & Children's) ....AAA
Friedman Bros. Shoe Co. (Men's; Women's; Boys' & Children's) ....AAA
Giesecke-D'Oench-Hayes Shoe Co. (Men's; Women's; Boys'; Misses' & Children's) ....AAA
Goodfellow Shoe Co. (Women's; Misses' & Children's) ....A
Hamilton Brown Shoe Co. (Men's; Boys'; Women's; Misses'; Children's)AAAA
Johansen Bros. Shoe Co. (Women's) ....A
La Prelle Shoe Co. ....AAA
Meier Shoe Co., John ...B
Mound City Boot & Shoe Co. ....A
Peters Shoe Co. (Men's & Women's) ....AA
Roberts, Johnson & Rand Shoe Co. (Men's; Women's; Misses' & Children's) ....AAAA
Tennent Shoe Co. ......AA
Ver Steeg Shoe Co. (Women's; Misses'; Boys' & Children's) ....AA
Wertheimer-Swarts Shoe Co. (Men's & Women's).AAA

NEB.—Omaha
Kirkendall & Co., F. P. (Men's) ....AA

N. H.—Dover
Hurd & Son. John H......B

N. H.—Exeter

BOOTS & SHOES (Con.)

Gale Bros. ....A

N. H.—Farmington

Aldrich & Co., C. E......B
Cloutman & Co., J. F. (Women's; Misses' & Children's) ....B
Farmington Shoe Co. (Men's) ....B

N. H.—Keene

Lancaster Shoe Co., C. B. (Women's; Misses'; Children's) ....A

N. H.—Littleton

Littleton Shoe Co. (Men's; Boys') ....B

N. H.—Manchester

Crafts, G. P. (Men's; Boys'; Little Men's) ....A
Eureka Shoe Co. (Men's; Boys') ....B
Green & Co., C. E. (Women's; Misses' & Children's; McKay sewed) .A
Holt Shoe Co., F. M. (Men's; Boys') ....A
Kimball Bros. Shoe Co. (Men's & Children's)....A
Reed & Co., H. B..........A

N. H.—Nashua

Brackett & Co., W. D..AAA
Estabrook-Anderson Shoe Co. AAA

N. H.—Portsmouth

Portsmouth Shoe Co....AA

N. H.—Rochester

Perkins, Linscott & Co. (Men's; Boys') ....A
Wallace, E. G. & E. AAAA

N. H.—Somersworth

Houghton, Hebard & Warren A

N. H.—West Derby

Perkins, Hardy & Co. (Women's; Misses' & Children's) ....B
Pillsbury, W. S. & R. W. (Women's; Misses' & Children's) ....A

N. J.—Burlington

Budd Shoe Co., J. F. (Misses'; Children's; Infants') ....A
Wood & Co., R. T. (Women's; Misses'; Infants' & Children's) ....A

N. J.—Lambertville

Lambertville Rubber Co. (Rubber) ....B

N. J.—Newark

Banister & Co., James A. (Men's; Boys'; Boots; Shoes & Slippers)......B
Dorsch & Sons Shoe Mfg. Co., Wm. ....B
Hogan Shoe Mfg. Co., E. E. (Women's) ....B
Johnston & Murphy......B
Peters Harness & Saddlery Co. (Horse) C

N. J.—Newton

Merriam Shoe Co., H. W. (Women's; Misses'; Infants'; Children's; Boys' & Youths') ....A

N. J.—Vineland

Chandler, D. Harry (Women's; Misses'; Children's) ....B
Keighley & Sons, Chas....A

N. Y.—Brockport

Moore-Shafer Shoe Mfg. Co. (Women's) ....B

N. Y.—Buffalo

Strootman, John (Women's; Misses' & Children's)...A

N. Y.—Dolgeville

Green Felt Shoe Co., Daniel (Shoes & Slippers)......B

N. Y.—Elmira

Richardson & Co.........B

N. Y.—Endicott

Endicott-Johnson Co. (Men's Goodyear Welts) .....B

New York City

Baker & Sons, Geo. (Women's; Misses' & Children's) ....B
Blynn & Sons, I..........B
Burt Co., Edwin C. (Women's) ....B
Cohen & Sons, B. (Oxfords; Slippers) ....B
Cousins, J. & T. (Women's;

BOOTS & SHOES (Con.)

Boots; Low Cuts; Slippers) ....A
Dix Shoe Mfg. Co., Robert (Spring Heel Co.)......A
Garside & Sons, A........A
Green & Co., Daniel (Felt) A
Hanan & Son ....AAA
Latteman Shoe Mfg. Co. John J. ....B
Parsons & Co., James (Men's & Women's) ....B
Ryan & Sons, Maurice....B
Strohbeck, Chas. W. (Women's; Misses'; Children's Welts & Turns)..B
Thomas & Co. ....A

N. Y.—Poughkeepsie

Hine & Lynch (Men's)....B

N. Y.—Rochester

Armstrong & Co., D. (Women's) ....B
Dugan & Hudson Co. (Boys' & Girls') ....B
Ford & Co., C. P. (Women's; Misses'; Children's)....B
Jenkins Co., J. W. (Women's) ....B
Kelly, John (Women's)..B
Moloney Bros. Co. (Women's; Misses'; Children's Shoes & Slippers) B
Newcomb, S. K..........B
Reed & Co., E. P. (Women's) ....A
Utz & Dunn (Women's; Misses'; Children's)....A
Williams, Hoyt & Co. (Misses'; Children's; Infants') ....B
Wright, Peters & Co. ....A

N. Y.—Syracuse

Fink's Sons, A. (Infants'; Children's; Misses) ....B
Gray's Son, H. H. (Women's) ....B
Nettleton, A. E. (Men's)..A
Syracuse Shoe Mfg. Co. (Women's Shoes & Oxfords).B

N. C.,—Elkin

Elkin Shoe Co.............B

OHIO—Canton

Gilliam Mfg. Co. (Horse).A

OHIO—Cincinnati

Bering & Co. (Women's Shoes & Oxfords)......A
Duttenhofer Sons Co., Val. (Women's) ....A
Gerstle & Co., G.........A
Helmers, Beltman & Co...B
Julian & Kokenge Co. (Women's ....A
Krippendorf & Dittman Co. AAAA
Krohn, Fechheimer & Co. (Women's) ....AAA
Manss Shoe Mfg. Co. (Men's) ....A
Plaut & Marks Shoe Mfg. Co. (Women's; Misses' Children's) ....B
Sachs Shoe Mfg. Co. (Women's) ....A
Stern, Auer & Co.........B
Sullivan & Co., P. (Women's) ....B
Wolf Bros. & Co. (Women's) B

OHIO—Cleveland

Pierce & Co., S. L........A

OHIO—Columbus

C. & E. Shoe Co. (Women's; Misses'; Children's; Boys) ....A
Godman Co., H. C. (Men's; Boys'; Women's; Misses'; Children's) ......AAA
Wolfe Bros. Shoe Mfg. Co. AA

OHIO—Lancaster

Fairfield Shoe Co. (Men's; Boys') ....AAA
Getz Shoe Mfg. Co., A. AAA

OHIO—Portsmouth

Drew Co., Irving (Women's; Misses'; Children's)....B
Drew Co., Shelby (Women's) AAA
Excelsior Shoe Co. (Men's; Boys'; Youths')........A
Heer Shoe Co. (Women's &

BOOTS & SHOES (Con.)
Misses) ....A
PA.—Allentown
Allentown Shoe Mfg. Co.
(Boys'; Old Ladies' Slippers, &c.) ....B
Leh & Co., H. (Men's;
Boys'; Women's; Misses';
Children's) ....AAA
Lehigh Valley Shoe Co.
(Boys') ....A
Roney & Berger (Youths';
Misses'; Children's & Infants') ....B
PA.—Carlisle
Carlisle Shoe Co. ....A
PA.—Chambersburg
Chambersburg Shoe Mfg. Co.
(Women's) ....B
PA.—Hanover
Sheppard & Myers Co.
(Men's) ....B
PA.—Harrisburg
Bay Shore Co. ....B
Harrisburg Boot & Shoe
Mfg. Co. (Women's;
Misses'; Children's).AA
PA.—Honesdale
Durand-Thompson Shoe Co.
(Men's; Boys'; also Brogan's) ....AA
PA.—Millersburg
Johnson, Bailie Shoe Co..B
PA.—Orwigsburg
Albright & Co., H. S. (Little
Men's; Misses'; Children's) ....A
PA.—Palmyra
Kreiders' Sons, W. L. (Infants'; Misses'; Children's) ....B
PA.—Philadelphia
Croxton, Wood & Co. (Women's; also Brogans)..AA
Elkins & Co., M. (Brogans)
.....................D
Hallahan & Sons (Women's)
.....................B
Laird, Schober & Co......A
McBrearty, John ....B
Smaltz Goodwin Co. .....B
Ziegler Bros. (Women's;
Misses'; Children's).AA
PA.—Reading
Curtis-Jones Co. (Children's
Turned) ....AA
PA.—Towanda
Tracy, Chas. L. (Men's;
Boys'; also Brogans)....B
PA.—Watsontown
Watsontown Boot & Shoe
Co. (Lumbermen's).....C
PA.—Williamsport
Lycoming Rubber Co. (Rubber) ....AAA
R. I.—Providence
Banigan Rubber Co., Jos.
(Rubber) ....AAA
Bourn Rubber Co. (Rubber)
.....................B
R. I.—Woonsocket
Woonsocket Rubber Co.
(Rubber) ....AAAA
TENN.—Memphis
Carruthers Jones Shoe Co..A
TENN.—Nashville
Carter & Co., J. W......A
TEXAS—Dallas
Padgitt Bros. Co. (Boot &
Shoe Uppers) ....A
UTAH—Salt Lake
Zions Co-operative Merc. Institution (Men's; Boys';
Youths'; Women's; Misses
& Children's) .....AAAA
VA.—Lynchburg
Witt Shoe Co., Geo. D....A
WIS.—Beloit
Foster Co., John (Women's)
.....................B
WIS.—Eau Claire
Cutter, A. A. (Lumbermen's
& Miners') ....B
WIS.—Milwaukee
Beals & Torrey Shoe Co...A
Bradley & Metcalf Co.
(Men's, Boys', Women's;
Misses') ....AA
Mayer Boot & Shoe Co., F.
.....................AA
Rich Shoe Co. (Women's).B
Schoenecker Boot & Shoe
Co., V. (General Line)..A
WIS.—Racine
Miller Co., J...........AA

BORAX

CAL.—San Francisco
Lillienthal & Co., Mission &
Beale (Crystal Powdered)
.....................AAA
Pacific Coast Borax Co., 101
Sansome (Refined).AAAA
COLO.—Denver
Denver Fire Clay Co.
(Glass) ....AA
ILL.—Chicago
Pacific Coast Borax Co. (Br.
San Francisco, Cal)AAAA
Thorkildsen & Co., T., Union
Stock Yards ....E
NEV.—Boyer
Anglo-American Borax Co.
.....................E
NEV.—Reno
Rose Valley Borax Co......F
N. Y.—Brooklyn
Wiarda & Co., John C. (Calcined Glass) ....AA
New York City
Archibald & Lewis, 193
Front C
Baker & Bro. H. J., 100
William (Refined) ....AA
Calm & Bro., M., 41 Warren
.....................AA
Croton Chemical Co., 20
Cedar (Refined) ....A
Feuchtwanger, & Co., L...B
Fuerst Bros. & Co., 2 Stone
.....................B
Jones Chem. Co., E. F., 51
Jay C
Pacific Coast Borax Co., 100
William (Refined) (Br.
San Fran., Cal.) AAAA
Pfizer & Co., Chas., 81
Maiden Lane .....AAAA
PA.—Easton
Baker & Adamson Chemical
Co. ....A

BORDERS

ILL.—Chicago
Barnhart Bros. & Spindler
(Printers') ....AA
MO.—Kansas City
Kansas City Wire & Iron
Wks. (Wire; Garden)...B
N. H.—Nashua
Highton & Sons, Wm.
(Brass; Bronze) ....D
New York City
Fiske Iron Works, J. W.
(Wire; Garden; Grave).D
Howard & Morse (Wire;
Garden) ....D
OHIO—Hamilton
Meyers Mfg. Co., Fred. J.
(Wire; Garden) ....B

BORERS

See also Drills; Machinery

CONN.—Hamden
Hamden Mfg. Co. (Tap;
Bunghole) C
ILL.—Chicago
Elmes Engineering Wks.,
Chas. F. (Bunghole)....A
IND.—Anderson
Buckeye Mfg. Co. (Carpenters') ....A
Lambert Gas & Gasoline
Engine Co. (Carpenters'
Hand) ....A
MASS.—Fiskdale
Snell Mfg. Co. (Carpenters')
.....................B
MASS.—Greenfield
Reece Co., E. F. (Counter)
.....................E
MASS.—Millers Falls
Millers Falls Co. (Carpenters') ....AA
MO.—St. Louis
Heynson Tool & Supply Co.
(Bung) ....D
N. H.—Lebanon
Hendrick & Davis (Counter)
.....................A
N. J.—Newark
Bernz, Otto, S. 13th c. S.
Orange Av. (Tap)......B
Osborne & Co., C. S. (Tap;
Bunghole) ....B
N. Y.—Buffalo
Holmes Machinery Co., E. &

BORERS (Con.)

B. (Bunghole) ....B
White Co., L. & I. J.
  (Bunghole) ....A
New York City
Jennings & Co., C. E. (Car-
  penters'; Tap; Bunghole)
  ....D
Russell & Erwin Mfg. Co.,
  47 Chambers (Bunghole)
  ....AAAA
N. Y.—Troy
Kellogg, W. P. (Carpent-
  ers') X
OHIO—Cincinnati
Fay & Egan Co., J. A.
  (Wood Pipe; Post &
  Pump) ....AAAA
OHIO—Cleveland
Cleveland Twist Drill Co.
  (Counter) ....A
OHIO—Toledo
Baker Bros. (Car Wheel)..A
PA.—Philadelphia
Enterprise Mfg. Co., 3rd &
  Dauphin (Bunghole)
  ....AAAA
Stortz & Son, John, 210
  Vine (Tap) ....F

BORTS

New York City
American Diamond Rock
  Drill Co. ....D
Dessau, S., 180 Bdway. ..C

BOSSES

PA.—Philadelphia
Chester Steel Castings Co.
  ....AAA

BOTTLES

CAL.—San Francisco
San Francisco & Pacific
  Glass Wks. (Green; Pre-
  scription & Druggists').X
ILL.—Alton
Illinois Glass Co. (Green;
  Prescription & Druggists')
  ....AAAA
ILL.—Belleville
Port Glass Works........B
ILL.—Chicago
Burley & Co., 118 Wabash
  Av. (Lettered Bar)....AA
Buttler Bros. (Prescription
  & Druggists') X
Foster & Co., A. M., 120
  Lake ....E
Horwich, B., 373 So. Canal
  (Secondhand) ....E
Horwich Bros., 480 S. Canal
  (Second Hand) ....E
Ward & Co., Montgomery
  (Prescription & Drug-
  gists') ....AAAA
Western Bottle Mfg. Co.,
  208 Randolph ....B
ILL.—Litchfield
Litchfield Bottle Glass Co.
  ....D
ILL.—Streator
Streator Bottle & Glass Co.
  (Green) C
IND.—Albany
Model Fruit Glass Co. ....A
North Baltimore Bottle
  Glass Co. ....A
IND.—Anderson
Anderson Flint Bottle Co..C
Anderson Glass Co. ......A
Pennsylvania Glass Co. (Pre-
  scription & Druggists')..A
IND.—Arcadia
Baker Bros. Glass Co....B
IND.—Cicero
Modes Turner Glass Co...A
IND.—Dunkirk
Maring, Hart & Co. (Flint;
  Milk; Brandy; Packing)
  ....A
IND.—Eaton
Western Flint Glass Co.
  (Brandy; Catsup) C
IND.—Gas City
Thompson Bottle Co. (Green
  & Amber) ....B
IND.—Greenfield
Greenfield Fruit Jar &
  Bottle Co. ....AAA
IND.—Hartford City
Diamond Flint-Glass Co...E
Hartford City Flint-Glass

BOTTLES (Con.)

Co. ....D
Sans Pariel Bottle Co.....D
IND.—Lapel
Lapel Bottle Co...........D
Lapel Flint Glass Co.....C
Wilcox Glass Co.........D
IND.—Loogootee
Lythgow Bottle Co.......D
IND.—Marion
Marion Flint Glass Co....A
Marion Fruit Jar & Bottle
  Co. ....AAA
IND.—Muncie
Ball Bros. Mfg. Co. (Green)
  ....AAAA
Boldt Glass Co., Chas. (Br.
  Cincinnati, O.)........A
Hemingray Glass Co.....A
IND.—Parker
Woodbury Glass Co.......A
IND.—Shirley
Baker Bros. Glass Co....B
Banner Glass Co.........D
Indiana Bottle Co........B
IND.—Sims
Sims Glass Co. ....D
Swoveland, A. F. ....F
IND.—Summitville
American Flint Bottle Co. D
Model Glass Wks.........D
IND.—Terre Haute
Modes Turner Glass Co.
  (Whiskey) ....A
North Baltimore Bottle
  Glass Co. ....AA
Root Glass Co............B
Terre Haute Glass Mfg.
  Co. ....B
IND.—Upland
Grant County Glass Co....D
Upland Co-operative Glass
  Co. C
IND.—Whealing
Continental Bottle Co.....E
IND.—Wilkinson
Snow Flint Glass Co.....E
IND.—Yorktown
Skillin-Goodin Glass Co.
  (Catsup; Condiment; Pre-
  scription; Extract &
  Pickles) ....E
KY.—Covington
Hemingway Glass Co.
  (Green; Flint) ....A
KY.—Louisville
Louisville Bottle Mfg. Co.,
  37th & Bank..........E
MD.—Baltimore
Baker Bros. & Co. (Green;
  Flint) ....A
Bonnert-Vogler Co. (Bar;
  Barbers') ....H
Swindell Bros. (Green;
  Flint; Prescription &
  Druggists') ....A
MASS.—Boston
Dean, Foster & Co., 14
  Blackstone ....B
Grossman & Co., E., 127
  Broad ....D
MO.—Brunswick
Oslerman & Co., Wm....D
MO.—St. Louis
Busch Glass Mfg. Co., A.
  Main & Dorcus.......AA
Hill & Bro., E. B. 1541 No.
  7th ....E
Obear-Nestor Glass Co., 402
  No. 3d ....B
St. Louis Glass & Queens-
  ware Co. (Flint; Prescrip-
  tion & Druggists')......A
Thompson Bottle Co., Se-
  curity Bldg. (Green)....B
N. J.—Bridgeton
Cumberland Glass Mfg. Co.
  (Green) ....B
More-Jonas Glass Co.
  (Green) X
N. J.—Clayton
Moore Bros. Glass Co.
  (Green; Prescription &
  Druggists') ....AA
N. J.—Glassboro
Whitney Glass Wks. (Green;
  Flint; Prescription &
  Druggists') ....AAA
N. J.—Millville
Whitall-Tatum & Co. (Drug-
  gists'; Exact Measure)
  ....AAAA
Wheaton Co., T. C. (Per-
  fumery) ....B

BOTTLES (Con.)

N. J.—Salem
Gaynor Glass Wks. (Green; Water) C
N. J.—Vineland
Capitol Glass Mfg. Co....B
Vineland Flint Glass Mfg. Co. ....D
N. J.—Woodbury
Woodbury Glass Wks. (Green) ....D
N. Y.—Brooklyn
Williamsburg Flint Glass Co., 260 Boerum.......E
N. Y.—Buffalo
Wright & Co., R. G. (Prescription & Druggists') AA
N. Y.—Clyde
Clyde Glass Wks. (Green) C
N. Y.—Corning
Hawkes & Co., T. G. (Flint; Cologne) ....A
N. Y.—Lancaster
Lancaster Co-operative Glass Wks. C
N. Y.—Lockport
Lockport Glass Wks. (Green) ....B
New York City
Biesecker, John S., 59 Murray (Milk) C
Boley Mfg. Co., 52 Cannon (Beer) ....D
Brooke, John B., 86 Fulton (Milk) C
Brookfield Glass Co. (Green) ....B
Dorflinger & Sons, C. (Prescription & Druggists').D
Gotham Co. (Green)......D
Hagerty Bros. & Co., 10 Platt (Green; Prescription & Druggists')..A
Mattson Rubber Co. (Green) B
N. Y.—Olean
Acme Glass Co............C
Olean Glass Co...........B
N. Y.—Port Jervis
Orange County Flint Glass Works (Caster).......A
N. Y.—Potsdam
Thatcher Mfg. Co. (Green; Milk) ....A
N. Y.—Poughkeepsie
Poughkeepsie Glass Wks. (Green; Flint).........A
N. Y.—Rochester
Reed & Co., F. E. (Rochester Glass Works)......C
OHIO—Bellaire
Bellaire Bottle Co. (Flint; Prescription & Druggists') A
OHIO—Bridgeport
Crystal Glass Co. (Inc.) (Green) ....A
OHIO—Cincinnati
Tatum Co., Saml. C. (Green) ....B
OHIO—Clinton
Warwick Glass Co. ....D
OHIO—Fostoria
Fostoria Bulb & Bottle Co. D
OHIO—Lancaster
Ohio Flint Glass Wks.....X
OHIO—Massillon
Massillon Bottle & Glass Co. ....B
Massillon Glass Wks. (Reed & Co., Props.).......A
Rhodes Glass & Bottle Co. (Green; Beer) C
Warwick Glass Co.......D
OHIO—Newark
Heisey & Co., A. H. (Inc.) (Prescription & Druggists') ....A
OHIO—Toledo
Libbey Glass Co. (Prescription & Druggists')....AA
OHIO—Zanesville
Kearns-Gorsuch Bottle Co. Mineral Water; Extract; Flint; Liquor; Prescription; Green; Beer; Patent Medicine; Pickle) .....B
PA.—Allentown
Allentown Flint Bottle Co. (Flint) C
PA.—Beaver Falls
Co-op. Flint Glass Co...A
Merriman & Co., J. (Prescription; Druggists')..A

BOTTLES (Con.)

PA.—Bendersville
Allen Flint Glass Wks., Jno. AAA
PA.—Blainsville
Whitney Glass Co........X
PA.—Bradford
Berney Glass Co. ....D
Bradford Flint Glass Bottle Co. (Flint) C
PA.—Condersport
Ladonia Glass Co........X
PA.—East Downingtown
Cohansey Glass Mfg. Co. AA
PA.—East Stroudsberg
Thomas Bros. (Flasks & Demijohns, Glass)......F
PA.—Everett
Everett Glass Co. ......E
PA.—Everson
Pittsburgh Seamless Bottle Co. ....D
PA.—Jeannette
Jennette Glass Co. ......D
PA.—Kane
Kane Flint Bottle Co.....C
McKee Bros. (Prescription; Druggists') ....B
PA.—McDonald
Warner Glass Co. (Citrate Magnesia; Panel; Prescription; Perfumery; Vaseline; Essential Oil; Morphine; Sterilizing; Nursing; Packing; Quinine; Tooth Powder; Sample Liquor & Oil; Soda Syrup; Tablet) ....D
PA.—Parkers Landing
Wightman Glass Co., Thos. F
PA.—Philadelphia
Burgin & Sons (Green; Flint) ....A
Flaccus Glass Co., C. L., 224 No. 3d........A
Fox & Sons, H. C. (Green; Prescription & Druggists') AA
Hero Fruit Jar Co. (Green) AA
Mason Fruit Jar Co. (Green) X
Standard Flint Glass Wks. (Flint) X
Whitall, Tatum & Co. (Green; Prescription & Druggists') ......AAAA
Whitney Glass Works, 227 So. Front X
PA.—Pittsburg
American Glass Co. (Green) X
Cunningham Glass Co., D. O. (Green) ....AA
Cunningham & Co. (Ltd.) (Green) ....B
Flaccus Glass Co., C. L. (Flint; Prescription & Druggists') ....A
Hamilton, J. T. & A. (Green; Flint) ....A
Hamilton Co., W. H. (Prescription & Druggists').A
McCully & Co., Wm. (Green; Prescription & Druggists') AAA
McKee & Bros. ......A
National Glass Co., Heeren Bldg. ....AAAA
Pittsburg Seamless Bottle Co. ....D
U. S. Glass Co. (Prescription & Druggists') AAAA
Wightman Glass Co., Thos. (Green; Flint; Prescription & Druggists')....AA
Wormser Glass Co. (Prescription & Druggists').X
Olean Glass Co..........B
PA.—Redman Mills
American Glass Wks. (Ltd.) B
PA.—Rochester
Point Bottle Wks. (Ltd.) (Flint; Prescription & Druggists') ....D
PA.—Royersford
Diamond Glass Co. (Soda Water; Wine; Bitters; Druggists'; Beer; Medicine) ....B
Newborn & Co.. W. H. ..B
PA.—Sharpsburg
Tibby Bros. Glass Co. ....A

BOTTLES (Con.)

PA.—Smithport
Hains Flint Bottle Co.
(Flint) ....E
PA.—Spring City
Spring City Glass Wks.
(Ltd.) C
PA.—Uniontown
Uniontown Flint Glass Co.
F
PA.—Washington
Hazel Glass Co. (Flint;
Prescription; Druggists)
AAA
R. I.—Providence
Aetna Bottle & Stopper Co.,
54 Peck ....D
S. C.—Columbia
Carolina Glass Co. X
TENN.—Chattanooga
Chattanooga Bottle & Glass
Mfg. Co. C
VA.—Richmond
Southern Glass Co. C
W. VA.—Lazearville
Scott & Hektein (Flasks;
Jars; Glass Fruit) ....D
W. VA.—Wheeling
Central Glass Wks. (Prescription; Druggists') ...A
Hazel-Atlas Glass Co.
(Snuff; Catsup; Ink; Oil;
Olives; Vaseline) .AAAA
North-Wheeling Glass Co.
(Flint) ....A
WIS.—Milwaukee
Franzen & Son, W., Lincoln
Av. & Chase ....A

BOTTLES MISCELLANEOUS

CONN.—New Haven
Seamless Rubber Co. (Rubber Water) ....AA
ILL.—Chicago
Ritchie & Co., H. C.
(Paper) ....
MASS.—Andover
Tyer Rubber Co. (Rubber
Water) ....B
MASS.—Boston
Davidson Rubber Co. (Rubber Water) ....A
N. J.—Belleville
Hardman Rubber Co. (Hot
Water Rubber) ....A
New York City
American Hard Rubber Co.,
9 Mercer St. (Rubber
Water) ....AAAA
Bishop Gutta Percha Co. 420
E. 25th (Gutta Percha) B
Cushman & Dennison, 240 W
23rd (Mucilage) C
Eggers & Carlsen (Rubber
Water) X
Goodyear Rubber Co. (Rubber Water) ....AAAA
Goodyear India Rubber
Glove Mfg. Co. (Rubber
Water) ....AAAA
Hodgman Rubber Co., 806
Bway (Rubber Water) AA
India Rubber Comb Co.
(Rubber Water) X
Mechanical Rubber Co.
(Rubber Water) .AAAA
Parker, Stearns & Sutton
(Rubber Water) ......B
OHIO—Akron
Akron Rubber Works (B. F.
Goodrich Co.) (Rubber
Water) ....AAAA
Faultless Rubber Co. (Rubber Nursing) ....AA
OHIO—Cleveland
Avery Stamping Co. (Steel)
B
PA.—Pittsburg
National Tube Co. (Steel)
AAAA
R. I.—Providence
Davol Rubber Co. (Rubber
Water) ....AA
WIS.—Racine
Chicago Rubber Clothing Co.
(Rubber Water) ....A

BOTTOMS

CONN.—Ansonia
Ansonia Brass & Copper Co.

BOTTOMS (Con.)
(Copper) ....AAAA
CONN.—Bridgeport
Bridgeport Brass Co. (Copper) ....AA
CONN.—Torrington
Coe Brass Mnfg. Co. (Copper) ....AAAA
CONN.—Waterbury
Randolph-Clowes Co. (Copper) ....AAA
IND.—Indianapolis
Nordyke & Marmon Co.
(Bin) ....AAA
MASS.—Taunton
Taunton Copper Mfg. Co.
(Copper) X
MASS.—Worcester
Hamblin & Russell Mfg. Co.
(Wire Kettle) ....B
MO.—St. Louis
Kay-Pim Mfg. Co. (Bin) ..B
WIS.—Kenosha
Chicago Brass Co. (Copper)
AA
WIS.—Menasha
Walbrun, A. (Chair) ....G

BOUGIES

New York City
Fougera & Co., E., 30 No.
William ....A

BOWLING

See Alleys

BOWLS

See Glassware; Tinware;
Silverware; Woodenware;
Pottery; Chinaware;
Enamelled Ware, etc.

CONN.—Meriden
Manning, Bowman & Co.,
(Soup; Enamelled Sugar)
AA
MO.—St. Louis
St. Louis Stamping Co.
(Soup) ....AAAA
N. J.—Burlington
Stewart & Peterson Co. (Icing; Chemists) ....A
N. Y.—Brooklyn
Cooper & McKee (Wooden)
A
New York City
Cordley & Hayes (Bread) .A
International Silver Co. (Silver Plated; Ices; Sugar;
Berry; Fruit, &c.).AAAA
Lalance & Grosjean Mfg.
Co. (Enamelled; Sugar)
AAAA
Mace & Co., L. H. (Wooden)
B
Stoutenborough, X. (Tin).D
N. Y.—Rome
Rome Mfg. Co. (Sugar,
Nickel Plated) ....B
OHIO—Cleveland
Avery Stamping Co. (Scotch;
Forged Separator) .....B
VA.—Richmond
Richmond Cedar Wks.
(Wooden) ....AAAA

BOWS

For Carriage, see Woodwork;
Carriage; For Neck, see
Neckwear

IND.—Fort Wayne
Yergens & Son, Wm.
(Buggy) ....D
IOWA—Ft. Madison
Iowa Farming Tool Co. (Ox)
A
MD.—Baltimore
Sinclair-Scott Co. (Ox.)...E
MASS.—Northampton
Hyde, Andrew (Violin)...D
MO.—St. Louis
Harris Mfg. Co., Loyd G.
(Express) ....A
OHIO—Cleveland
American Fork & Hoe Co.
(Ox) ....AAAA
PA.—York
Farquhar & Co., A. B. (Ox.)
AAA

BOXES: WAGON, ETC.

See Hardware; Carriage

BOXES MISCELLANEOUS

See also Ivory Goods; Leather Goods; Silverware, Cases; Jewelry.

BOXES

Paper; Music; Wooden, etc., in Succeeding Lists...Ice Boxes, see Refrigerator; Clothing Boxes, see Furniture.

CAL.—San Francisco
San Francisco Tool Wks. (Grindstone) ....F
Union Iron Wks. (Shaft) ....AAAA

COLO.—Denver
Zimmerhackel, Geo. (Cigar) ....D

CONN.—Ansonia
Gaylord Co., F. L. (Sand Street Car) ....F

CONN.—Bethel
Gilbert Bros. (Hat) ......D

CONN.—Hartford
Hart & Hegeman Mfg. Co. (Switch) C
Hart Mfg. Co. (Switch)...C
Hoadley, E. J. (Twine)...X
Sterling Blower & Pipe Mfg. Co. (Galvanized & Steel Storage) ....A

CONN.—Meriden
Meriden Britannia Co. (Postage Stamp) ......AAAA

CONN.—New Britain
Brady, Thos. H. (Fuse & Junction; Arc Cut-Out)..C
Corbin Cabinet Lock Co. (Letter) ....AA
Landers, Frary & Clark (Twine) ....AAA
Stanley Rule & Level Co. (Mitre) ....AAA

CONN.—New Haven
Munson Co. (Bottle; Candle; Candy; Cigarette; Clothing; Flower; Ice Cream; Ointment; Paper Folding; Pin) ....B
Natl. Folding Box & Paper Co. (Candy; Cigarette; Druggist; Ice Cream; Paper Folding; Pin; Hardware Telescope) ....AAAA
New Haven Clock Co. Watchmen's Station ....AAA

CONN.—Southington
Peck, Stow & Wilcox Co. (Twine) ....AAAA

CONN.—Stamford
Yale & Towne Mfg. Co. (Mail; Hallway Letter; Post Office) ......AAAA

CONN.—Torrington
Turner & Seymour Mfg. Co. (Twine) ....A
Union Hdw. Co. (Electric Bell; Magneto) ....AA

CONN.—Wallingford
Wallace & Sons, R. (Powder; Match; Postage Stamp) ....AAAA

CONN.—Waterbury
Novelty Mfg. Co. (Salt & Pepper) ....A
Scovill Mfg. Co. (Aluminum Tobacco & Match).AAAA

DEL.—Elsmere
Diamond State Fibre Co. (Mill) ....A

DEL.—Wilmington
American Vulcanized Fibre Co. (Mill)........AAAA
Davis Pressed Steel Co. (Journal) ....B
Garrett, Miller & Co. (Junction) ....E

BOXES (Con.)

ILL.—Aurora
Vindex Electric Co. (Fuse) ....H

ILL.—Chicago
American Radiator Co., Lake & Dearborn (Valve or Service) ....AAAA
Barbee Wire & Iron Wks. (Feed; Twine; Wire; Handkerchief) ....B
Besly & Co., C. (Tool)..AA
Central Electric Co., 266 5th Av. (District Call & Junction) ....A
Clow & Sons, Jas. B., 344 Franklin (Valve or Service) ....A
Crane Co., 10 N. Jeff. (Valve or Service) AAAA
Creamery Package Mfg. Co. (Butter; Cheese) ..AAAA
Cutler Hammer Mfg. Co. (Motor Starting) X
Dick Co., A. B. (Document) ....AA
Electric Appliance Co., 92 W. Van Buren (District Call) ....B
Harvard Electric Co., 224 So. Clinton (Fuse) ....E
Hewitt Mfg. Co., Monadnock Block (Journal).......B
Illinois Car & Equipment Co., Old Colony Bldg. (Journal) X
Illinois Malleable Iron Co., 32 W. Monroe (Valve or Service; Roadway; Stop Cock) ....AAAA
McCord & Co. (Journal)...D
Nicol & Co., 57 W. Washn. (Mail; Letter; Twine)..D
Payne Tapping Machine Co., 5991 Erie (Valve or Service) X
Purcell & Co., N. F., 232 So. Clinton (Mail) ....G
Railway Appliances Co., Old Colony Bldg. (Journal)..A
Tablet & Ticket Co. (Druggists') ....B
Western Electric Co., 259 S. Clinton (Electric Call; Fuse; Mail; Resistance; AAAA
Wilson & Co., F. Cortez (Fishing Tackle).......B

ILL.—Decatur
Mueller Mfg. Co., H. (Valve or Service) ....A

ILL.—Elgin
Elgin Butter Tub Co., (Cheese) ....A

ILL.—Freeport
Arcade Mfg. Co. (Salt; Spice; Knife) ....A

ILL.—Joliet
Signal Mail Box Co. (Mail) ....A

ILL.—Quincy
Modern Iron Wks. (Valve or Service) ....B

ILL.—Rockford
Mechanics Machine Co. (Adjustable Shaft) ....D

ILL.—Sterling
Novelty Iron Wks. (Feed).E

IND.—Anderson
Anderson Fdry. & Machine Wks. (Annealing)......B
Natl. Wrought Iron Annealing Box Co. (Annealing) ....B

IND.—Elkhart
Lakon Co. (Fuse & Junction) ....D

IND.—Fort Wayne
Ft. Wayne Electric Corp'n (Cut-Out; Fuse; Resistance) ....AAA

IND.—Goshen
Kelly Fdry. & Machine Co. (Rural Mail) ....A

IND.—Indianapolis
Keyless Lock Co. (Document) ....AAA
Sinker-Davis Co., 230 So. Missouri (Journal).....B
Tucker & Dorsey Mfg. Co. (Salt) ....A

IND—Logansport
Dorner Truck & Fdry. Co. (Journal; Electric Car).D

BOXES (Con.)

IND.—Mishawaka
Dodge Mfg. Co. (Shaft) ...... AAA

IND.—Wabash
Underwood Mfg. Co., H. C. (Dove-Tailed; Drill Bit; Family Medicine; Fancy; Medical Battery; Seed; Syringe; Electric Bell; Storage Battery; Transmitter, Rubber Stamp).X

IOWA—Burlington
Murray Iron Works Co. (Hanger) ....A

IOWA—Clinton
Smith & Son, F. (Beer)..C

IOWA—Fairfield
Louden Machy. Co. (Grain Dump) C

IOWA—Ottumwa
Nicholls Mfg. Co. (Mitre).D
Great Western Mfg. Co. (Journal) ....AA

LA.—New Orleans
Pelican Box Factory (Fruit; Packing) ....D

MD.—Baltimore
Poole & Son Co., Robt., 233 E. German (Journal & Shaft; Clamp; Grindstone; Hanger; Wall) ....A
Syminton & Co., T. R. (Journal) ....D
Viaduct Mfg. Co., 10 So. Howard (Fire Alarm; District Call)..........B

MASS.—Athol
Bates Bros. Co. (Mail; Letter) ....B

MASS.—Boston
Anchor Electric Co. (Conduit; Elec. Switch) X
Chase, Shawmut Co., 390 Atlantic Av. (Junction)..B
Dennison Mfg. Co. (Druggists'; Wedding Cake; Jewelry) ....AAAA
Electric Gas Lighting Co., 195 Devonshire (Mail) .A
Howard Watch & Clock Co. E. (Watchmen's Station) .....A
Johnson & Co., H. A. (Bread) ....B
Marshall Sanders Co., 303 Congress (Switch) C
Renim Specialty Co, 176 Federal (Junction & Switch) C
Ridlon Co., Frank, 200 Summer (Sand) ....A
Riley & Co., C. E., 65 Franklin (Drawing & Roving) ....A
Ziegler Appliance Co., 200 Summer (District Call)..E

MASS.—Brockton
Packard & Son, Sidney E. (Candy; Polish; Shoe).B
Bird & Son, F. W. (Lunch) ....AA

MASS.—Gloucester
Merchant Box & Cooperage Co. (Fish) ....B

MASS.—Greenfield
Goodell Mfg. Co. (Mitre; Bessemer Steel) ......B
Wells Bros. Co. (Farrier Tool) ....A

MASS.—Millers Falls
Millers Falls Co. (Mitre) ....AA

MASS.—Neponset
Coffin Valve Co. (Gas & Water; Service; Gate)..D

MASS.—New Bedford
Coffin Bros. (Cigar) .....D

MASS.—Norton
Sweet, A. H. (Chisel; Lager Beer Bottle; Mineral Water; Jewelry; Packing; Silver Ware; Auger)..B

MASS.—Orange
Chase Turbine Mfg. Co. (Hanger) ....A
Rodney Hunt Machine Co. (Shaft) ....B

MASS.—Pittsfield
Jones & Sons Co., E. D. (Journal) ....B

MASS.—Springfield
West Box Co. (Fancy; Wood for Poker Chips;

BOXES (Con.)

Cutlery; Tools)........C

MASS.—Westfield
Crane Bros. (Linenoid; Laundry, &c.) .....AAA
Ensign Cigar Box Co., A. E. (Cigar) ....D
Hampden Toy Co. (Folding Lunch) ....D

MASS.—Whitman
Atwood Bros. (Beer) .....B

MASS.—Worcester
Wire Goods Co. (Twine)..A
Worcester Steam Boiler Wks. (Steam) X

MICH.—Bay City
Vance Box Co., E. J. (Bottle; Canned Goods; Candy; Cleated; Packing; Partition; Salt; Shoe; Siphon; Starch; Tin; Tobacco; Wine; Candle; Celery; Glass; Lawn Mower; Powder) ....B

MICH.—Detroit
Briscoe Mfg. Co. (Rural Mail) ....B
Buhl Stamping Co. (Feed) ....AA
Co-operative Fdry. (Journal) ....E
Cross & Co., Milton O., 12 W. Atwater (Junction).F
Fulton Iron Wks., 28 Brush (Journal) X
Victor Jar Co. (Glass)....E

MICH.—Fenton
Phillips Co., A. J. (Family Nail; Shelf Hardware)..A

MICH.—Grand Rapids
Michigan Barrel Co. (Axle Grease; Bail; Butter; Salt) ....B

MICH.—Jackson
Hutchinson Mfg. Co., Jno. (Roller Bearing; Drop Hanger; Post Box Shaft) C

MICH.—Saginaw
Mershon & Co., Wm. B. (Beer; Bottle; Fish; Packing; Shoe; Tobacco; Wine) ....A
Saginaw Specialty Co. (Turned Wood) ....E
Wickes Bros. (Shaft Bearing) ....AAA

MICH.—Tecumseh
Century Box Co. (Mail)..D

MINN.—Minneapolis
Northwestern Casket Co. (Telephone) ....A

MINN.—St. Paul
South Park Fdry. & Machine Co. (Valve; Service) ....B

MO.—St. Louis
Amer. Car & Fdry. Co., 706 Chestnut (Journal).AAAA
Amer. Roll Paper Co. (Twine) ....B
Brownell Car Co., 2300 N. B'way (Fare) ....D
Central Union Brass Co., 811 N. 2nd (Journal) ..E
Fehlig Bros. Box Mfg. Co., 1909 Washn. (Beer) ....A
Medart Patent Pulley Co. (Shaft; Hanger; Wall)..A
Moser Cigar & Paper Box Co. (Cigar) ....A
Plenger & Henger Mfg. Co., 11th & Hebert (Valve; Service) ....A
St. Louis Car Co. 800 N. B'way (Fare; Sand)AAAA

NEV.—Verdi
Verdi Lumber Co. (Packing) ....AA

N. J.—Hasbrouck Heights
Olmsted, L. H. (Mitre)...B

N. J.—Jersey City
Dodge & Bliss Co. (Packing; Starch) ....AA
Mehl & Co., Jno. (Cuff; Collar) ....AA
Williams & Son, E. A. (Coal Car; Wagon) ....AA

N. J.—Montclair
Heller & Co., W. C. (Tote; Sheet Steel; Shelf Steel; Mail) ....F

N. J.—Newark
Celluloid Co. (Ointment;

BOXES (*Con.*)

Powder) ....B
Headley & Farmer Co.
 (Gent's Hat) ....A
Phelph & Sons, 110 Pen-
 nington (Mail) C
Sachs Iron Fdry., Louis
 (Shoe Blacking) ....A
Sterling-Meaker Co., 420
 Ogden (Sand) ....A
Toler Sons & Co., Jno., 108
 Adams (Junction; Switch)
 ....B

N. J.—Paterson
Smith & Son, Samuel
 (Steam) ....A
Watson Machine Co.
 (Steam) ....A

N. J.—Smithville
Smith Machine Co., H. B.
 (Grindstone) ....A

N. J.—Sussex
Little, O. J. (Feed)......D

N. Y.—Albany
Draper, Henry W. (Beer;
 Siphon) C

N. Y.—Binghamton
Star Electric Co. (Fire
 Alarm Signal) ....D

N. Y.—Bronxville
Leonard-Ward Electric Co.
 655 Hudson (Junction;
 Lined Electric Switch;
 Porcelain Lined; Outlet;
 Cut-Out) ....B

N. Y.—Brooklyn
American Stamping Co.
 (Bread & Cake; Cheese;
 Lunch; Salt; Pepper;
 Spice; Sugar; Cash) ..X
Columbia Machine Wks.,
 169 Chestnut (Fuse; Sand)
C
Cooper & McKee (Salt)....A
Hauck & Son, Chas. J.
 (Postage Stamp; Tobacco)
 ....B
Krantz Mfg. Co., 160 7th
 (Junction) ....D

N. Y.—Buffalo
Apel Mfg. Co. (Mailing)..F
Binghamton & Taylor
 (Valve; Service) .....AA
Buffalo Box Factory
 (Packing) ....A
McCarthy Bros. & Ford, 45
 N. Division (Junction) ..E
Noye Mfg. Co., Jno. F.
 (Wall) X
Shepard & Co., Sidney
 (Blacking; Bread; Cake;
 Lunch; Spice; Cash; Post-
 Office) ....AAAA
Ward, J. A. (Druggists').X

N. Y.—Coxsackie
Amer. Valve Co. (Valve;
 Service) ....D

N. Y.—Homer
Phoenix Hardware Mfg. Co.
 (Mail) ....D

N. Y.—Jamestown
Fenton Metallic Mfg. Co.
 (Ballot; Document) ....A

N. Y.—Knox
Cheesbro, Wm. J. (Drug-
 gists') ....A

N. Y.—Little Falls
Burrell & Co., D. H. (Butter; Cheese) ......AAAA

New York City
Alling & Co. (Match)....AA
American Steel House Co.,
 798 11th Av. (Patrol)..D
American Wood Working
 Mach. Co. (Journal)AAAA
Baldwin, L. H. (Axle
 Grease; Band; Blacking;
 Bluing; Bottle; Candle;
 Druggists'; Fancy; Fruit;
 Hat; Ice Cream; Jewelry;
 Ointment; Packing; Pow-
 der; Shelf; Wooden; Shoe;
 Siphon; Starch; Tobacco;
 Wedding Cake; Wine;
 Window) X
Bemis Car Truck Co., 120
 Liberty (Journal) ......E
Bogert & Hopper, 162 Wil-
 liam (Turned Wood) ..B
Brooke, John B., 86 Fulton
 (Milk) C
Brown Co., A. & F., 26 Cort-
 ladt (Journal; Shaft)..C
Bunnell & Co., 20 Park Pl.

BOXES (*Con.*)

(Fire Alarm Signal; Elec-
 tric Call; Resistance)..A
Central Stamping Co.
 (Bread; Cake) ......AA
Chatillon & Sons, J., 85
 Cliff (Twine) ....A
Diemer, Jno. F. (Shelf;
 Cloth for Flat Papers).D
Drummond & Co., M. J., 192
 B'way (Valve; Service).A
Edwards & Co., 407 E. 144th
 (Fire Alarm Signal; Mail)
C
Erichs & Co., H. W. (Cigar)
 ....A
Estes & Sons, E. B. (Axle
 Grease; Butter; Candy;
 Dove Tailed; Druggists';
 Fancy; Fruit; Jewelry;
 Ointment; Pill; Salt;
 Turned; Wine; Packing;
 Sugar; Powder; Ballot).A
Ettlinger & Sons, Louis
 (Jewelry) ....D
Fagan, James (Ice Cream)C
Fiske Iron Wks., J. W.
 (Plant) ....B
Folmer & Schwing Mfg. Co.
 (Plate Changing) ......B
Fountain, Jno. J. (Junction,
 Switch) ....F
General Electric Co., 44
 Broad (Fuse; Junction;
 Resistance) ....AAAA
General Incandescent Arc
 Light Co., 572 First Av.
 (Coupling for Feeder Ca-
 bles; Junction) ....A
Goodyear's India Rubber
 Glove Mfg. Co. (Match)..
 ....AAAA
Gould Coupler Co., 20 W.
 34th (Journal) ....A
Green, A. H., 22 Park Pl.
 (Shelf Hardware) .....D
Grote & Co., F. (Match;
 Powder) ....D
Herring - Hall - Marvin Co.
 (Iron; Cash; Bond Safe
 Deposit) ....B
Herzog Teleseme Co., 51
 W. 24th (District Call)..D
Hoe & Co., R. (Printers'
 Mitre) ....AAAA
Ingersoll-Sargeant Drill Co.,
 26 Cortlandt (Ticket Can-
 celling) ....AAAA
Jennings Co., C. E.
 (Mitre) ....B
Judd & Co., H. L. (Twine)
 ....AA
Kaufmann, Max (Cuff; Col-
 lar) ....F
Koch Sons & Co. (Cuff;
 Collar; Glove; Handker-
 chiefs; Wooden) X
Kraft, Geo. J. (Fancy)...B
Lalance & Grosjean Mfg. Co.
 (Lunch; Salt; Pepper;
 Cash) ....AAAA
La Roche Co., F. A., 656
 Hudson (Junction) ....E
Mace & Co., L. H., 111 E.
 Houston (Salt) ....B
Manhattan Brass Co.
 (Window) ....A
Manhattan Electrical Supp.
 Co., 32 Cortlandt (Mail)
 ....A
Matthews, Jno. (Firm of)
 (Siphon) ....AA
Mayer, Leopold (Pill; Pow-
 der) ....E
Meinat & Sons, C., 441
 Pearl (Tin) X
Meyer, Bernard (Candy;
 Druggists') ....D
Mosler Safe Co., 373 B'way
 (Safe Deposit; Iron; Cash;
 Bond) ....AAAA
Ostrander & Co., W. R., 22
 Dey (Switch; Mail; Let-
 ter) ....B
Pearce, Fred'k, 18 Rose
 (District Call; Fire
 Alarm) ....B
Peckham Mfg. Co., 26 Cort-
 landt (Sand) ....A
Prentiss Vise Co. (Vise;
 Screws) C
Russell & Erwin Mfg. Co.,
 43 Chambers (Twine) ...
 ....AAAA

BOXES (Con.)

Schier & Walter, 502 E. 74th (Cigar) C
Smith & Hemenway Co., 296 B'way (Mitre) ......B
Sprague Electric Co., 529 W. 34th (Junction) ...AAAA
Stoutenborough, X. (Bread; Cake; Safe Deposit)....D
Tower & Lyon Co., 95 Chambers (Auger Bit) ......B
Walsh, Owen, 117 Walker (Mail) ....D
Wicke Co., Wm. (Cigar).A
Wittemann Bros., 188 William (Bottlers'; Sipnon; Wine) ....A
Yale & Towne Mfg. Co., 9 Murray (Post Office)....
................AAAA
Zindars & Hunt, 127 5th Av. (Junction) ....D

N. Y.—North Tonawanda
Butts & Co., Chas. G. (Candle; Cleated; Dove-Tailed; Fish; Packing; Shoe; Tobacco; Wine; Fruit)..D

N. Y.—Poughkeepsie
Poughkeepsie Art Pulp Co. (Shelf) ....F

N. Y.—Pulaski
Tollner's Sons Co., Chas. (Pencil) ....B

N. Y.—Rochester
Stevens & Son, J. B. (Candle; Dove-Tailed; Druggists'; Packing; Shoe; Siphon; Tobacco) X

N. Y.—Schenectady
General Electric Co. (Fuse; Junction; Resistance) ..
................AAAA

N. Y.—Syracuse
Crouse-Hinds Electric Co. (Junction; Fuse) ......D
Gowing, D. H. (Butter)..C
Merriam Mfg. Co. (Cigar).A
Pass & Seymour (Junction) ....B
Stearns & Co., E. C. (Feed) ....AA
Wells Mfg. Co., A. J. (Document) X

N. Y.—Troy
Rensselaer Mfg. Co.. Van Schaick Island (Valve; Service) C
Taylor Electric Truck Co. (Journal) ....B
Troyan Button Fastener Co. (Inc.) (Sand; Street Car) C
Troy Stamping Wks. (Blacking; Tin) ....AAAA

N. Y.—Utica
Bossert Elec. Construction Co. (Junction) .....
Clark, Horrocks Co. (Bait; Fishing Tackle) ......A
Johnson & Morton, 44 Whitesboro (Junction)..E
Utica Elec'l Mfg. & Supply Co. (Electric Fuse; Junction) X
Utica Fire Alarm Telegraph Co. (Police Signal) .....B

OHIO—Ashtabula
Barber Mfg. Co. (Mail)..C

OHIO—Berlin Heights
Berlin Fruit Box Co. (Fruit; Honey) ....D

OHIO—Cambridge
Cambridge Foundry Co. (Annealing) ....F

OHIO—Canton
Diebold Safe & Lock Co. (Iron; Cash; Bond; Safe Deposit) ....AAA

OHIO—Cincinnati
Bourbon Copper & Brass Wks., 618 E. Front (Valve; Service) ....A
Globe-Wernecke Co. (Document) ....AAAA
Hall & Wood Ballot Box Co. (Steel & Wood Ballot)..X
Hall's Safe Co., Spring Grove Av. (Safe Deposit)A
Hall's Safe & Lock Wks. (Iron; Cash; Bond; Safe Deposit) ....A
Kiechler Mfg. Co. (Safe Deposit) C
Knecht. Victor, 819 Wade

BOXES (Con.)
(Sand; Street Car)......B
McFarlan & Spiker Mfg. Co. (Mitre) ....D
Randall & Co. (Loop)....B
Tatum Co., Saml. C., 414 W. Water (Mail; Journal; Letter; Twine) ....B
Trost. Saml. W. (Cigar)..A
Victor Safe & Lock Co. (Iron; Cash; Bond) .....A

OHIO—Cleveland
Avery Stamping Co., Lake & Coe (Tote; Sheet Steel)
................A
Bartlett & Snow Co., C. O. (Journal) ....B
Cleveland Faucet Co. (Coil) ....AAA
Cleveland Wire Spring Co., Wason & Hamilton (Tote; Sheet Steel) ....
Forest City Fdry. & Mfg. Co. (Mail) ....
Fulton Foundry Co., Marquette at L. S. & M. S. Ry. (Journal) C
Globe Machine & Stamping Co. (Mail) C
Nat'l Safe & Lock Co., Craw Av. & C. & P. R. R. (Safe Deposit) ....A
Osborn Mfg. Co. (Oil; Stoves) ....B
Ray Automatic Machine Co. (Annealing) ....D
Smith Fdry. Supply Co., J. D., 40 S. Water (Core).D
Taylor & Boggis Fdry. Co., 521 Seneca (Mail) .....AA
Van Dorn & Dutton Co., 1796 E. Madison Av. (Journal)
................AA

OHIO—Columbus
Buckeye Stamping Co. (Seamless Tin; Tin Insect Powder, &c.) ....D
Case Mfg. Co. (Shaft Bearing) ....A
Jeffrey Mfg. Co. (Adjusting; Journal) ....AAAA
Kilbourne & Jacobs Mfg. Co. (Tote; Sheet Steel; Seamless Steel) ....AA

OHIO—Cuyahoga Falls
Falls Rivet & Machine Co. (Journal; Shaft) ......A

OHIO—Dayton
Dayton Globe Iron Wks. (Hanger) ....B
Dayton Folding Box Co. (Folding Egg) ....B
Dayton Paper Novelty Co. (Band; Candy; Hat)....A

OHIO—Hamilton
Macneale & Uban Co. (Iron; Cash; Bond) X

OHIO—Lowellville
Meehan Boiler & Construction Co. (Annealing) ...C

OHIO—Mansfield
Ohio Brass Co. (Journal)..B

OHIO—Medina
Root Co., A. I. (Section; Honey) ....AA

OHIO—Niles
Niles Boiler Co. (Annealing) ....B

OHIO—Ravenna
Williams, A. G. (Twine).E

OHIO—Salem
Clark Co., W. J. (Coal; Tote; Sheet Steel; Seamless Steel; Rolling for Coating Wheels with Emery; Iron; Waste) .....B

OHIO—Sandusky
Knight, H. H. (Linenoid).D
Schwehr Box Co. (Cigar).C

OHIO—Springfield
Leffel & Co., Jas. (Journal)
................AA

OHIO—Toledo
Ohio Steam Cooker Co. (Bread) ....E
Sutton & Co., C. E. (Mitre) ....D
Toledo Display Horse Co. (Feed) ....A

OHIO—Warren
Warren City Boiler Wks. (Annealing) ....B

OREGON—Portland
Portland Lumbering Mfg. Co. (Packing) ....A

BOXES (Con.)

PA.—Allegheny

Carlins' Sons, Thomas (Concrete; Tubs; Street Car Sand) ....A

PA.—Chambersburg

Woods Sons, T. B. (Shaft) A

PA.—Erie

Griswold Mfg. Co. (Wagon) A

Hays Mfg. Co. (Valve; Service) ....B

PA.—Lebanon

Lebanon Electric Co. (Sand) ....F

PA.—Marietta

Penna. Construction Co. (Wood Ballot) ....A

PA.—Mohns Store

Warner, Franklin R. (Hat) C

PA.—New Brighton

Pittsburg Clay Mfg. Co. (Window) ....AAAA

PA.—New Castle

Vogan Bros. Mfg. Co. (Sand; Valve; Service) ....H

PA.—Philadelphia

Brill Co., J. G., 62d & Woodland Av. (Fare; Journal; Sand) ....AAAA

Cassel, Jacob C. (Window) D

Chester Steel Castings Co. (Cleated; Journal) ...AA

Cresson Co., Geo. V., 18th & Allegheny Av. (Journal; Shaft; Clamp; Iron Waste; Wall) ....AA

Fairmount Machine Co., 2108 Wood (Shaft; Clamp; Hanger; Wall) ....A

France Packing Co., 6512 State Rd. (Fuse) C

Haines, Wm. A. (Cuff & Collar) ....D

Heston & Sons, David (Pill) C

Holmes Fibre & Graphite Mfg. Co. (Hanger) .....D

Jones Paper Box Co., Jesse, 615 Commercial (Candy; Druggists'; Shelf; Wooden) ....B

Keystone Electrical Instr. Co. (Resistance) ......B

Miller, Walter P., 448 York Av. (Display for Counter Goods) ....F

Miller Lock Co., 4523 Tacony (Cash; Keyless Cash; Post Office) ....B

Patrick, Carter & Wilkins, 1231 Callowhill (Mail; District Call; Electric; Resistance) ....B

Pearson, Jos. T. (Packing) AA

Plumby, G. W. (Druggists') ....A

Pressed Steel Mfg. Co., Ridge Av. & Willow (Ball Bearing; Shafting) .....D

Rumpp, C. F. (Jewel; Leather) ....AAA

Sellers & Co., Wm. H., 1600 Hamilton (Shaft; Grindstone) ....AAAA

Sheip Mfg. Co., Henry H. (Cigar; Fancy; Locked Corner Wooden; Shelf Wooden; Syringe) ...AA

Wilfong Bros., 52nd & P. W. & B. R. R. (Annealing) C

PA.—Pittsburg

Barnes Safe & Lock Co. (Iron; Cash; Bond; Safe Deposit) ....D

Goff Mfg. Co., 345 4th Av. (Annealing) ....D

Iron City Tool Wks. (Vise; Screw) ....A

Jones & Laughlins' Steel Co. (Shaft) ....AAAA

McKenna Bros. Brass Co., 1st Av. & Ross (Fuse) ..A

McNeil & Bro., Jas., 29th & A. V. Ry. (Annealing) AA

Riter-Conley Mfg. Co., 56 Water (Annealing) ..AA

Scaife & Sons Co., Wm. B., 221 First Av. (Core; Sheet Steel; Tote; Annealing) .A

Standard Underground Cable Co., Westinghouse

BOXES (Con.)

Bldg. (Electrical; Junction) ....AAA

Westinghouse Electric & Mfg. Co. (Junction) .... AAAA

PA.—Reading

Reading Hdw. Co. (Letter) AAAA

Thalheimer & Son, Albert (Cigar) ....B

Weber, Sr., Julius (Hat) .D

PA.—South Bethlehem

Bethlehem Fdry & Machine Co. (Cast Iron Waste; Annealing) C

PA.—Towanda

Frost Mfg. Co., J. O. (Valve; Service) ......B

PA.—Waynesboro

Frick Co. (Clamp) ..AAAA

PA.—Williamsport

Darling Pump & Mfg. Co. (Valve; Service; Stuffing) B

PA.—York

Kauffman & Bro., A. (Cigar) ....B

York Safe & Lock Co. (Iron; Cash; Bond; Safe Deposit) A

R. I.—Providence

Brown & Sharpe Mfg. Co. (Cast Iron; Core for Foundry Use) ....AAAA

D. & W Fuse Co., 53 Aborn (Fuse; Junction; Subway; Coupling for Feeder Cables) C

Luther & Son, Wm. H. (Jewelry) ....B

Textile Finishing Mchry. Co. (Steam) ....AAA

Young Bros., 670 Eddy (Jewelry) ....B

R. I.—Woonsocket

Woonsocket Machine & Press Co. (Journal; Clamp; Hanger) ......AA

TENN.—Memphis

Chickasaw Iron Wks. (Journal) ....A

VT.—Burlington

Champlain Mfg. Co. (Packing) ....B

Crane, W. & D. G. (Packing) ....A

VT.—North Bennington

White Co., H. C. (Wooden) B

VA.—Lynchburg

Glamorgan Pipe & Foundry Co. (Gas; Water; Service; Valve) ....AA

VA.—Norfolk

Wrenn & Sons, A. (Wagon) AA

VA.—Richmond

Allegheny Box Co. (Tobacco) ....B

Randolph Paper Box Co., 1312 E. Franklin (Druggists'; Pill; Powder)....A

W. VA.—Ravenswood

Moore, C. P. (Shelf) C

WIS.—Fort Atkinson

Cornish, Curtis & Greene Mfg. Co. (Butter) .....A

WIS.—Milwaukee

Filer & Stowell Co., Becher, cor. Ziemer (Journal; Shaft) ....AAA

Signalphone Mfg. Co., 128 Sycamore (District Call) C

WIS.—Watertown

Henry Co., Ira L. (Druggists' Paper) C

BOXES, MUSIC

New York City

Jacot Music Box Co., 39 Union Sq. (Music) .....D

Regina Music Box Co., 11 E. 22d (Music) ....AA

PA.—Philadelphia

Gantschi & Sons, Hy., 1030 Chestnut (Music) ......D

BOXES, PAPER

CAL.—San Francisco

Crocker Co., H. S., 215 Bush AA

Fleischhacker & Co., A., 520

160

BOXES, PAPER (Con.)

Market ....A
Mutual Label & Lithograph
  Co., 2nd & Bryant ....AA
Pacific Fold'g Paper Box
  Fcty.; 14 Fremont C
CONN.—Bridgeport
Bridgeport Paper Box Co...A
Compressed Paper Box Co.
 C
Taylor, Thomas P. ......A
Warner Bros. Co., The ...
  ....AAAA
CONN.—Danbury
Clark Box Co., The C
CONN.—Meriden
Doolittle, E. J. ....B
CONN.—New Britain
Corbin & Son, H. H......C
CONN.—New Haven
Benton, Armstrong Fold'g
  Box Co., 89-97 Orange...B
Cronan Paper Box Co., P.
  J. C
Munson & Co., 385 Clinton
  Av. C
National Fold'g Box &
  Paper Co., 325 Congress
  Av. ....AAAA
Strouse, Adler & Co., 60
  Court (Corset) ......AAA
CONN.—New London
Bingham Paper Box Co...C
CONN.—Sandy Hook
Curtis & Son, S. ....A
CONN.—Shelton
National Fold'g Box &
  Paper Co. ....AAAA
CONN.—So. Coventry
Kingsbury Box & Print'g
  Co., The ....B
CONN.—Unionville
Humphrey, H. W.........D
CONN.—Waterbury
White & Wells Co. ....A
CONN.—Winsted
New England Pin Co. ....A
GA.—Atlanta
Empire Print'g & Box Co.,
  71 S. Pryor C
Montag Bros. C
Hirschberg Paper Co. C
ILL.—Bloomington
Bloomington Caramel Fac-
  tory C
ILL.—Chicago
Chicago Fold'g Box Co., 142
  W. Washington C
Chicago Label & Box Co.,
  226 Lake ....B
Clark & Pfister, 51-53 S.
  May C
Gair Co., Robt., 138 Wash-
  ington ....AAAA
Howe & Davidson, Taylor &
  Rockwell ....B
Randolph Box & Label Co.,
  27 S. Clinton C
Ritchie & Co., W. C., 488
  Carroll Av. C
Schroeter Mfg. Co., 71 W.
  Jackson Boul. C
Schultz & Co., 117-123 Mar-
  ket C
Sefton Mfg. Co., J. W., 241
  S. Jefferson ....AAA
Wolff & Son, C. F., 185
  E. Kinzie C
ILL.—Morris
Morris Paper Co. C
IND.—Anderson
Sefton Co., J. W........AAA
IND.—Indianapolis
Bee Hive Paper Box Co.,
  78½ W. Washington
  (Candy; Desk File) C
IOWA—Burlington
Burlington Paper Box Co.C
IOWA—Dubuque
Dubuque Paper Box Fac-
  tory C
KY.—Louisville
Bradley & Gilbert Co. ...B
LA.—New Orleans
Ringel & Levy ....B
MAINE—Auburn
Auburn Paper Box Co.....B
MAINE—Springvale
Goodwin Bros. C
MD.—Baltimore
Euler & Son, C. A., 408 Con-
  way C
Franke, Geo., 112 S. Eu-
  taw ....B
Friedenwald Co., Balt. &

BOXES, PAPER (Con.)

Eutaw ....B
Taylor & Co., C. J., 203
  W. Camden ....B
MASS.—Beverly
Allen, Geo. H. ....B
Copp Co., A. W..........C
MASS.—Boston
Busch Mfg. Co., H. C., 135
  Oliver C
Dennison Mfg. Co. ..AAAA
Dickerman & Co., Geo. H.,
  32 Green ....B
Forbes Lithograph Mfg. Co.,
  185 Summer ....AA
Gair Co., Robt., 101 Tremont
  ....AAAA
Stone & Forsyth, 268 Devon-
  shire ....B
MASS.—Brockton
Packard & Son, S. E.....C
MASS.—Campello
Packard & Son, S. E.....C
MASS.—East Walpole
Bird & Son, F. W.....AAA
MASS.—Haverhill
Currier, O. S. C
Hayes, C. H. ....B
Owens, John C
MASS.—Holyoke
Powers Paper Co. ......AA
MASS.—Lynn
Allen, Geo. H., 340 Broad.B
Littlefield & Plummer, 47
  Arch C
MASS.—New Bedford
Pairpont Corporation ....A
MASS.—Norton
Sweet, A. H. (Knit Goods) B
MASS.—Pittsfield
Collins & Co., D. M......AA
MASS.—So. Framingham
Framingham Box Co. C
MASS.—Spencer
Spencer Paper Box Co....A
MASS.—Springfield
National Papeterie Co...D
Taylor & Co., C. C.......D
MASS.—Worcester
Hill Env. Co., W. H. (Div.
  U. S. Env. Co.) ....AAAA
Logan, Swift & Brigham
  Env. Co. (Div. U. S.
  Env. Co.) ....AAAA
Sherman Envelope Co. ....B
Whitcomb Env. Co. (Div. U.
  S. Env. Co.) ....AAAA
Whitney Co., Geo. C. ....B
MICH.—Battle Creek
Ellis Publishing Co. (Ltd.)
  ....B
MICH.—Belding
Grand Rapids Paper Box
  Co., cor. Clay & St. Al-
  bins Av. (Yeast; Butter;
  Gas Mantel; Tea; Jelly;
  Jam; Butter; Lard; Sau-
  sage; Paint; Tobacco; Pre-
  serves; Honey; Baking
  Powder; Soda; Salt;
  Chemicals; Date; Dried
  Fruit; Coffee; Spices;
  Confectionery) C
MICH.—Detroit
Gem Fibre Package Co...C
Holliday, W. P., Fort &
  Brush ....A
MICH.—Fenton
Phillips Co., A. J. ....A
MICH.—Grand Rapids
Grand Rapids Paper Box Co.
 C
MICH.—Kalamazoo
American Playing Card Co.
  ....A
MICH.—Port Huron
Riverside Printing Co. ...C
MICH.—Ypsilanti
Sharf Tag, Label & Box Co.
 C
MINN.—St. Paul
Weinhagen & Co., Chas., 21
  8th C
MO.—Kansas City
Lechtman Print'g Co. C
National Paper Box Co...C
MO.—St. Joseph
Combe Print'g Co. ....B
MO.—St. Louis
Holman Paper Box Co., 8th
  & Chaton ....B
Moses Cigar & Paper Box
  Co., 208 Elm ....B
Mound City Print'g Co., 11
  S. 2nd (Candy; Druggist

112

BOXES, PAPER (*Con.*)

Rex & Co., D. J., 7th Av.
  & Grant ....A
Walker's Sons, A., 435-437
  2nd Av. C
PA.—Plymouth
West, Ambrose ....B
R. I.—Providence
Young Bros., 670 Eddy
  (Mailing) C
TENN.—Nashville
American Paper Co. C
Union Box & Paper Co....C
TEXAS—Dallas
Texas Paper Co. ....B
TEXAS—San Antonio
Duerer Mfg. Co., G. A...B
VT.—Bennington
Union Paper Box Co. C
VA.—Richmond
Randolph Paper Box Co.,
  1312 E. Franklin ......A
W. VA.—Wheeling
Stimmetz, C. ....A

BOXES, WOODEN PACKING

ALA.—Bridgeport
Bridgeport Woodenware
  Mfg. Co. (Fruit).......B
ALA.—Jackson
Speer Box & Lumber Co...A
ARK.—Fayetteville
Massengale & McIlroy....D
ARK.—Helena
Helena Box Co. ....B
ARK.—Judsonia
Hoag & Sons, C. F......E
CAL.—Beckwith
Horton Bros. ....D
CAL.—Los Angeles
Los Angeles Box Co. ....E
CAL.—Maderia
Packinpah Lumber Co,...E
CAL.—San Francisco
Hobbs, Wall & Co., 488
  Beale (Packing)......AA
CONN.—Derby
Eastern Lumber & Box Co.
  ....B
CONN.—South Norwalk
Norwalk Box Co. ....E
CONN.—Stafford Springs
Orcutt, C. ....E
GA.—Dawson
Dawson Crate & Box Co...D
ILL.—Aurora
Spear, Warren & Co. ...B
ILL.—Barrington
Plagger & Naeher C
ILL.—Cairo
Carey-Halloday Lumber Co.
  (Hardwood; Cottonwood;
  Sweet Gum) ....A
Three States Lumber Co.
  (Shooks) ....A
Weis-Peterson Box Co....D
ILL.—Chicago
Acme Box Co., 308 S. Clinton (Cereal; Canning)..E
Chicago Packing Box Co...
  ....AA
Consumers' Box Mfg. Co.,
  35 E. Ohio C
Goodwillie Bros., 171 La
  Salle (Br. Wausau, Wis.)
  ....A
Goodwillie Co., D. M., W.
  22nd & Centre Av......A
King & Co., C. L., 13 La
  Salle ....A
Maxwell Bros., Loomis &
  21st ....AA
Paepcke-Leicht Lumber Co.,
  Tribune Bldg. (Shooks)..
  ....AAA
Ransford & Co., T. F., 219
  S. Water (For Canners)
Tegtmeyer, C. W., Lumber
  & Canal (Shooks) .....B
Western Box Co., 42 River
  (Lock; Cornered; Fruit;
  Trimmed) ....E
Wintemeyers, J. C., 750
  Throop C
ILL.—Cobden
Mesler & Co., W. P.....A
ILL.—Dixon
Squires, Geo. H. ....B
ILL.—Hoopeston
Moore & McFerren (Cottonwood Shooks) ....AAAA

BOXES, WOOD (*Con.*)

ILL.—Metropolis
Roberts. J. N. (Fruit)....A
ILL.—Rockford
Rockford Screen & Box Co.
 C
IND.—Anderson
Indiana Box Co. ....B
IND.—Bremen
Wright, J. J. (Light)....B
IND.—Evansville
McFerson & Foster (Poplar;
  Cottonwood Shooks) ....B
IND.—Ft. Wayne
Fort Wayne Box Co. .....E
Peters Box & Lumber Co..B
IND.—Nappanee
Coppes Bros. & Zook ....AA
IND.—New Albany
New Albany Box & Basket
  Co. ....D
IND.—Rockport
Rockport Box Mfg. Co....D
IOWA—Clinton
Peterson-Bell Co. (Shooks)
 C
Smith & Sons, F. (Poultry)
  ....D
IOWA—Council Bluffs
Council Bluffs Box & Basket Co. ....D
IOWA—Muscatine
South Muscatine Lumber
  Co. (Shooks) ....AA
KANS.—Leavenworth
Voegel Box Co. ....D
KY.—Bardwell
Bodkins, D. W. C
KY.—Columbus
Standard Box Co. (Shooks)D
KY.—Henderson
Anderson Box & Basket Co.
  ....D
KY.—Louisville
McKown, W. M., 544 W.
  Main ....D
Mengel, Jr., & Bros. Co.,
  C. C. ....AA
KY.—Paducah
Riglesberger & Son, F.....B
MAINE—Auburn
Hutchins Co., H. W. (For
  Confectionery & Crackers)
 C
MAINE—Berry's Mills
Goodwin Bros. ....D
MAINE—Biddeford
Biddeford & Natick Mfg. Co.
  ....D
MAINE—Brunswick
Brunswick Box Co. (Lock
  Cornered) ....D
MAINE—Dry Mills
Liffy, Chas. E. (Shooks)..D
MAINE—Gardiner
Oakland Mfg. Co. ....B
Walker, James C
MAINE—Kingfield
Jenkins & Bogert Mfg. Co..C
MD.—Baltimore
American Lumber Co.,
  Merch. Nat. Bk. Bldg...C
Canton Box Co. ....B
Duker Box Co., J. H. ....E
Heise & Co., H. ....E
Thiemeyer & Co., J. H., 821
  S. Car. C
MD.—Cambridge
Cambridge Mfg. Co. ......A
MD.—Salisbury
Berry Bros. (Shooks) ...D
MD.—Wellington
Scott Bros. ....E
MD.—Whaleysville
Peter Mfg. Co. ....D
MASS.—Boston
Mt. Washington Box Co.. 70
  Kilby (Turned Wood)..A
N. E. Box Co., 221 Columbus Av. ....A
MASS.—Cambridge
Page Box Co., G. G.......A
MASS.—Chelsea
Bay State Improved Box Co.
  ....D
MASS.—Chicopee Falls
Griggs & Sons, D. B.
  (Shooks) ....D
MASS.—Dalton
Flansburgh, J. W. ....B
MASS.—Enfield
Woods & Ward ....D
MASS.—Gloucester
Merchants' Box & Cooperage
  Co. (For Fish) ....B

113

40 Watts (Drums) .....D
N. Y.—North Tonawanda
Butts & Co., C. G. ......B
Dodge & Bliss Co. ....D
N. Y.—Pulaski
Tollners Sons Co., C.......C
N. Y.—Rochester
Rochester Box & Lumber
Co. C
N. Y.—Romulus
Yerkes, J. ....E
N. Y.—Rouses Point
Millard Lumber Co.
(Shooks) ....A
N. Y.—Watervlict
Harrington Box Co. ......D
N. Y.—Williamson
Williamson Mfg. Co. (Fruit)
                    C
N. C.—Bethania
Knapp, T. F. (Tobacco)...D
N. C.—Walkertown
Leight Bros. (Tobacco)....C
OHIO—Auburn
Stafford & Co.. G. W.....E
OHIO—Barnesville
Hutchinson, E. J. ....D
OHIO—Cheviot
Kenker, Fred.............E
OHIO—Columbus
Devon Lumber Co. (Poplar
Shooks) X
OHIO—Cincinnati
Conkling, E. A., 908 Bway.A
OHIO—Cleveland
Cleveland Box Co. (&
Shooks) C
Ohio Cooperage Co. (&
Shooks) ....B
OHIO—Defiance
Defiance Box Co.........C
Tenzer Box Co., H. B......C
OHIO—Greenfield
Waddell Wooden Ware Co.B
OHIO—Marietta
Marietta Fruit Package &
Box Co................D
OHIO—Martins Ferry
Martins Ferry Keg & Bar-
rel Works ....B
OHIO—New Springfield
Reash, Andrew (Berry)...E
OHIO—Sandusky
Sandusky Lumber & Box
Co. (& Shooks) ....A
OHIO—Sidney
Bryant, J. F.............E
OHIO—Zanesville
Abel Box Co.............E
OREGON—Astoria
Astoria Box Co..........C
Clatsop Mill Co.........B
OREGON—Hobsonville
Truckee Lumber Co.....AA
PA.—Millmont
Smith & Co., W. E.......C
PA.—Reading
Deysher, A. S............C
R. I.—Providence
Van Stone Mfg. Co........X
S. C.—Charleston
Atlantic Woodenware Co..D
TENN.—Dyer
Dyer Fruit Box Mfg. Co.
(Fruit) ....D
TENN.—Greenfield
Greenfield Box & Package
Co. (Fruit) ....A
TENN.—Humboldt
Jarrell & Co., B. C. (Fruit)
                    B
TENN.—Memphis
Anderson-Tully Co. (Cotton-
wood; Gum Shooks).....A
TENN.—Trenton
Wade & Sons. R. H.......D
TEXAS—Velasco
Velasco Box Factory.....E
UTAH—Ogden
Griffen Co.. H. L. (Fruit;
Vegetable)............D
VT.—Barton
Drew, G. A..............C
VT.—Bristol
Drake. Smith & Co.......C
VT.—Burlington
Hickok Co., H...........B
Pope & Co., E. A........B
VT.—East Calais
Levison & Lamb Mfg. Co.
(Fancy) ....D
VT.—Johnson
Stearns & Son. O. W......C
VT.—Marshfield
Mears & Pitkin..........D

VT.—Richford
Manuel & Sons, C. C.....E
VA.—Roanoke
Good & Co., D. W., (Shooks)
                    D
WASH.—Puyallup
Morse Mfg. Co.. F. W.....E
WASH.—Seattle
Queen City Mfg. Co.......E
W. VA.—Keyser
Keyser Door & Box Co....C
WIS.—Eau Claire
Linderman Box & Veneer
Co. ....AAAA
WIS.—Green Bay
Murphy Box Co......AAAA
WIS.—Hazlehurst
Yawkey Lumber Co.
(Shooks) ....AAA
WIS.—Hustisford
Dehnse & Dehnse Mfg. Co.
(Cheese) ....D
WIS.—La Crosse
La Crosse Box Co.........D
WIS.—Manitowoc
Schnoor Bros.............E
WIS.—Marinette
Marinette & Menominee Box
Co. ....A
WIS.—Stevens Point
Stevens Point Box Co. (&
Shooks) C
WIS.—Watertown
Lewis Co., G. B..........A
WIS.—Wausau
Goodwillie Bros. (Shooks) A
Wausau Box & Lumber Co.
(Pine; Basswood) C
Wisconsin Box Co. (Pine;
Basswood Shooks) C

BOXWOOD

MICH.—Grand Rapids
Grand Rapids Boxwood Mfg.
Co. ....F
New York City
Walker, Geo. H., 174 Cen-
tre X
WIS.—Two Rivers
Hamilton Mfg. Co. (Engra-
vers') ....AA

BRACELETS

See Jewelry

BRACES

CONN.—Bridgeport
Fray & Co., Jno. S. (Stof-
ford Bit; Angle Bit; Cor-
ner Bit; Drill; Extension
Bit; Ratchet; Sleeve;
Plain Bit) C
Smith & Egge Mfg. Co.
(Bit) ....A
CONN.—Bristol
Bartholomew, H. S. (Bit) B
Turner & Deegan (Bit;
Gripe; Rachet) ....E
CONN.—Hamden
Hamden Mfg. Co. (Bit) ...C
CONN.—Mount Carmel
Woodruff & Son, Walter W.
(Vehicle Top) ....A
CONN.—New Haven
Brown & Co., R. H. 169
Ashman (Bit) ....B
Cowles & Co. C., (Inc.)
(Vehicle Top) ....A
English & Mersick Co.
(Vehicle Top) C
Seward & Son Co., M.
(King Bolt) ....A
CONN.—Plantsville
Blakeslee Forging Co......B
Smith & Co., H. D. (Sleigh)
                    AA
CONN.—Southington
Peck, Stow & Wilcox Co.
(Bit; Carpenters; Rachet)
                AAAA
DEL.—Wilmington
Diamond State Steel Co.
(Cross Arm) ....AAA
ILL.—Chicago
Ajax Forge Co. (Rail) ..AA
Common Sense Truss Co.
(Shoulder) ....D
Haussman & Dunn
(Shoulder) C
Republic Iron & Steel Co.
Stock Exch. Bldg. (Cross;

BRACES (Con.)

Pole) ....AAAA
Ryerson & Son. Jos. T., 18
  Milwaukee Av. (Boiler)
  ....AAAA
Scully Steel & Iron Co., 140
  Fulton (Boiler) ....AAA
ILL.—Downers' Grove
Dicke Tool Co. (Bit for Elec-
  tricians, Plumbers, &c.;
  Telegraph Cross Arm)...D
ILL.—East St. Louis
Elliott Frog & Switch Co.
  (Rail) ....A
ILL.—South Chicago
Morden Frog & Crossing
  Wks. (Rail) ....+....A
IOWA—Des Moines
Northwestern Suspender Co.
  (Shoulder) C
IOWA—Ft. Madison
Iowa Farming Tool Co.
  (Scythe) ....A
KANS.—Salina
Natural Body Brace Co.
  (Body) C
Perfect Body Brace Co.
  (Body) ....D
MAINE—Portland
Laughlin Co.. Thomas
  (Rudder) ....A
MASS.—Easthampton
Dibble & Warner (Shoulder)
  ....B
Nashawannuck Mfg. Co.
  (Shoulder) ....AA
MASS.—Greenfield
Goodell Pratt Co. (Bit)...B
Wells Bros. & Co. (Bit)...A
MASS.—Millers Falls
Millers Falls Co. (Bit) ..C
MASS.—Shelburn Falls
Mayhew Co.. H. H. (Bit)..C
MASS.—Winchendon
Mason & Parker (Bit) ..D
MASS.—Worcester
Winslow Skate Mfg. Co., S.
  (Skate: Ankle) ....B
MICH.—Detroit
Anderson & Sons. W. H.
  (Cross Arm; Pole Arm).C
Brownlee & Co. (Cross Arm)
  ....AA
Michigan Bolt & Nut Wks.
  ft. Meldrum Av. (Cross
  Arm; Pole Arm) .....A
MINN.—Minneapolis
Therien Tool Wks. (Cross
  Arm) ....E
MO.—Kansas City .
Kansas City Bolt & Nut Co.
  (Cross Arm: Pole Arm).A
NEBR.—Lincoln
Shinn. W. C. (Lightning
  Rod) ....D
N. J.—Dover
Ulster Iron Wks. (Boiler)
  ....AA
N. J.—Jersey City
Williams & Son, E. A.
  (Rudder) ....AAA
N. Y.—Auburn
Clapp Mfg. Co., E. D. (King
  Bolt; Vehicle Top)......A
N. Y.—Binghamton
Crandal. Stone & Co.
  (Vehicle Top) ....A
N. Y.—Buffalo
Du Mont Tool Co. (Bit;
  Corner) X
Pratt & Letchworth Co.
  (Wagon Box) ......AAA
N. Y.—Lancaster
Lancaster Machine & Knife
  Wks. (Ratchet; Straight
  Bit) ....D
New York City
Ferris Bros. Co. (Shoulder)A
Graham & Co.. J. H., 113
  Chambers (Bit) ....F
Jennings Co.. C. E. (Bit)..D
N. J. Fdry. & Machine Co.
  13 Murray; (Cross Arm) D
Ogden Co.. J. Edw., 147
  Cedar (Cross Arm)....B
Sargent & Co.. 151 Leonard
  (Corner Water Closet Par-
  tition) ....AAA
Tiebout. W. J. 118 Cham-
  bers (Rudder) ....B
N. Y.—Rochester
Fuller Co.. Geo. R.
  (Spinal) ....E
N. Y.—Schnectady
General Electric Co. (Cross
  Arm) ....AAAA

BRACES (Con.)

N. Y.—Victor
Locke, Fred M. (Telegraph
  Cross Arm) ....A
N. C.—Winston-Salem
Salem Iron Wks. (Cross
  Arm) ....A
OHIO—Bucyrus
Blair Husking Glove Co.
  (Contractors' Corner) ...D
Campbell Frog Wks. (Rail)
  ....A
OHIO—Cincinnati
Creaghead Engineering Co..
  802 Plum (Cross Arm)..D
Weir Frog Co. (Rail).....A
OHIO—Cleveland
Avery Stamping Co. (Cross
  Arm) ....A
Eberhard Mfg. Co. (Sleigh)
  ....AA
Forest City Steel & Iron Co.
  (Telephone; Cross Arm)A
Standard Tool Co. (Bit)AAA
OHIO—Columbus
Ohio Tool Co. (Bit) ......A
OHIO—Dayton
Dayton Malleable Iron Co.
  (Rail) ....AA
OHIO—Mansfield
Ohio Brass Co. (Cross Arm)
  ....B
OHIO—Niles
Ohio Galvanizing & Mfg. Co.
  (Cross Arm) ....B
PA.—Easton
Knickerbocker Brace Co.
  (Boys Shoulder) C
Natural Switch & Signal Co.
  (Rail) X
PA.—Lebanon
Amer. Iron & Steel Mfg. Co.
  (Cross Arm; Pole Arm)
  ....AAAA
PA.—Philadelphia
Hastings & McIntosh Truss
  Co. (Shoulder) ....B
Heinemann & Co.. Geo. M.,
  737 Girard Av. (Cross
  Arm) ....F
Hoopes & Townsend Co. 1330
  Buttonwood (Cross Arm)
  ....AAA
Horn & Bro.. W. H.
  (Shoulder) ....B
Penna. Steel Co. (Rail)
  ....AAAA
Philadelphia Truss Co.
  (Shoulder) X
Seeley, Isaac B. (Shoulder)
  ....F
Smith Co.. J. Barton, How-
  ard & Norris. (Bit)....AA
Stortz & Son, Jno., 210 Vine
  (Bit) ....F
PA.—Pittsburg
Hubbard & Co.. Murtland
  Bldg. (Cross Arm) .....A
Lanz Sons. Matthew. S. 29th
  & Carson (Cross Arm; Pole
  Arm; Side Arm Alley;
  Double Arming Angle:
  Flat) ....B
Oliver Iron & Steam Co.
  (Cross Arm; Pole Arm)
  ....AAAA
PA.—New Castle
Vogan Bros. (Cross Arm).H
PA.—Reading
Chantrell Tool Co. (Bit)...B
VT.—Derby Line
Butterfield & Co. (Bit)...B
VT.—Montpelier
Sabin Machine Co. (Music
  Rack) ....E
VA.—Richmond
Old Dominion Iron & Nail
  Wks. Co. (Cross; Pole
  Arm) ....A
W. VA.—Wheeling
Mountain State Electrical
  Co. (Cross; Pole) .....D
Wheeling Hinge Co. (Cross
  Arm; Box Corner) ...AA
WIS.—La Crosse
Alberts, Max (Bow Leg) .H

BRACKETS

ALA.—Birmingham
Brewer, W. P. (Wooden).A
CONN.—Branford
New York Lock Co. (Hand
  Rail) ....B
CONN.—Bridgeport
Bridgeport Gun Implement

BRACKETS (Con.)

Co. (Lamp) ....A
Bryant Electric Co. (Electric House) ....B
CONN.—Chester
Brooks & Sons, M. S. (Extension Wire; Brass Plated) ....B
CONN.—East Hampton
Bevin Bros. Mfg. Co. (Lamp) ....B
Climax Mfg. Co. (Lamp).F
Watrous Mfg. Co. (Bicycle Lamp) ....AAAA
CONN.—Guilford
Spencer's Sons, I. S. (Electric House; Window) ..B
CONN.—Hartford
Ideal Machine Co. ....D
CONN.—Ivoryton
Comstock, Cheney & Co. (Action) ....AA
CONN.—Meriden
Bradley & Hubbard Mfg. Co. (Flower Pot; Lamp; Druggists; Window Display) ....AAAA
Foster, Merriam & Co. (Candle; Lamp) ....A
CONN.—Middletown
Wilcox-Crittenden & Co. (Flag Pole) ....A
CONN.—New Britain
Brady, T. H., (Electric House; Shelf) C
Landers, Frary & Clark (Flower Pot) ....AAA
Russell & Erwin Mfg. Co. (Flower Pot; Hand Rail; Trolley Pole; Shelf; Lamp) D
Stanley Wks. (Wrought Steel Shelf) ....AAA
Stanley Rule & Level Co. (Roofing) ....AA
Union Mfg. Co. (Pew Rack; Stair Rail) ....AA
CONN.—New Haven
Atlas Mfg. Co. (Stamped Shelf) ....B
Hendryx, Andrew B. (Bird Cage) ....A
Ives & Co., Hobart B. (Stair Rail) C
CONN.—Norwich
Norwich Nickel & Brass Co. (Brass; Nickel; Window Display) ....B
CONN.—Southington
Peck, Stow & Wilcox Co. (Lamp; Rafter; Roofing; Shelf; Bird Cage; Flower Pot) ....AAAA
CONN.—Waterbury
American Pin Co. (Brass; Lavatory; Tank; &c.)..A
Holmes, Booth & Haydens Co. (Inc.) (Lamp).AAAA
New England Engineering Co. (Electric House)....A
CONN.—Winsted
Strong Mfg. Co. (Casket).A
ILL.—Aurora
Wilcox Mfg. Co. (Hand Rail) ....B
ILL.—Capron
Leavitt, R. H. (Trolley Pole) ....D
ILL.—Chicago
Allen-Hussey Co., 211 Randolph (Desk Telephone)F
Barbee Wire & Iron Wks. (Iron Balcony; Foot Rail; Ole; Blanket; Saddle) AA
Central Electric Co. 266 5th Av. (Wood Cross Arms; Pins) ....A
Clark & Co., A. C. (Dentists Wall) ....A
Illinois Malleable Iron Co. (Plumbers) ....AAAA
Lidell & Williams 597 Austin Av. (Wood) ....D
Nicol & Co. (Wagon Lamp) ....B
Noblitt Co., E. J., 898 35th (Wood Cross Arms; Trolley; Pins) ....B
Peirce ,Jr., C. L., 14 S. Jeff. (Electric House) F
Sherman & Flavin (Wooden) B
Western Electric Co., 259 S. Clinton (Trolley Pole) AAAA

BRACKETS (Con.)

ILL.—Decatur
Faries Mfg. Co. (Window Display) ....A
ILL.—Edwardsville
Edwardsville Brass Co. (Iron; Steel; Brass)....B
ILL.—Freeport
Arcade Mfg. Co. (Hand Rail; Shelf; Lamp; Flower Pot) ....A
Stover Mfg. Co. (Plumbers Shelf; Bird Cage; Flower Pot; Lamp; Shade Roller) AA
ILL.—Quincy
Modern Iron Wks. (Cast Iron Sink) ....B
ILL.—St. Charles
Glenn Mfg. Co. (Hand Rail; Plumbers' Sink) ....D
IND.—Elkhart
Buescher Mf Co. (Bicycle) A
IND.—Indianapolis
Enterprise Foundry & Fence Co. (Counter) ....B
McOuat, Robt. L., 125 S. Meridian (Trolley Pole).C
IND.—Muncie
Warner Electric Co. (Oxidized Finished Desk Telephone) C
IOWA—Fairfield
Louden Machinery Co. (Rafter) ....B
LA.—Patterson
Cypress Tank & Mfg. Co. (Wood) ....B
LA.—Whitecastle
Whitecastle Lumber & Shingle Co. (Wood Cross Arms; Pins) ....AAA
MD.—Baltimore
Baltimore Hinge Co. 1309 Bank (Shelf) ....D
Hoskins Lumber Co., J. S. Marine B'k. Bldg. (Wood Cross Arms; Pins) C
McShane Mfg. Co., H. 441 North (All Kinds) AAAA
Poole & Son Co., Robt. (Wall; Bicycle) .....A
MD.—Princess Anne
Cohn & Bock (Insulator; Trolley Pole; Cross Arms; Pins) ....B
MASS.—Boston
Bibber & Co., Thos. H. 37 Arch (Trolley Pole) ...X
Boston Bolt Co., 33 Purchase (Staging) ....B
Burnham & Duggan Ry. Appliance Co., 89 State (Trolley Pole) X
Jones & Co., M. D., 71 Portland ....F
Stearns Lumber Co., A. T. (Wood) ....AA
Sturtevant Co., B. F. (Shelf) ....AAA
Walworth Mfg. Co., 132 Federal (Trolley Pole).. AAAA
Young, Jos. H., 224 Franklin (Plumbers'; Galvanized Iron Tray; Sink) ....E
MASS.—Clinton
Clinton Wire Cloth Co. (Counter) ....AAA
MASS.—Monson
Danforth, A. H. (Folding) D
MASS.—Peabody
Clark, A. F., (Est. of) (Wood Cross Arms; Pins) C
MASS.—Westfield
Smith Co., H. B. (Step) AA
MASS.—Worcester
Bay State Stamping Co. (Adjustible Curtain)....E
National Mfg. Co. (Counter) A
Wright Wire Co. (Counter) AA
MICH.—Detroit
Buckley-Hart Mfg. Co., 527 Franklin (All kinds) ...D
Ireland & Matthews Mfg. Co. (for Plumbers' Tanks) A
Northwestern Fdry. & Supply Co. (Sink) ....D
Park & McKay ....D
Smith Co., Jos N. 29 W. Larned (Automobile

BRACKETS (*Con.*)
Lamp) C
MICH.—Grand Rapids
Grand Rapids Brass Co.
(Shelf) ....A
MICH.—Monroe
Sterling & Son, W. C.
(Wood Cross Arms; Pins)
A
MICH.—Saginaw
Morse Cedar Co. (Wood
Cross Arms; Pins) C
MISS.—Meridian
Brownlee & Co. (Wood Cross
Arms; Pins) C
MO.—Macon
Patton, J. W. (Shelf).....B
MO.—St. Louis
Berthold & Jennings (Wood
Cross Arms; Pins) ....A
Kupferle, Jno. C. (Sink;
Tank; &c.) ....A
Nelson Mfg. Co., N. O., 424
N. 8th (All kinds) .AAA
Pleuger & Henger Mfg. Co.
(Plumbing; Hand Rail;
Shelf; Flower Pot)....A
N. H.—Manchester
Campbell, Jno. (Harness).X
N. H.—Milford
Pierce & Co., Wm. E.
(Wood) ....F
N. J.—Montclair
Heller & Co. W. C. (Fork;
Hoe; Rake; Shovel)....D
N. J.—Newark
Redman & Co., C. H.
(Dental) ....E
Sommers' Son, Jno.
(Insulator) ....B
N. J.—Salem
Salem Brass & Iron Mfg. Co.
(Brass Lavatory) .....B
N. Y.—Brooklyn
Hecla Iron Wks. (Iron
Lamp) ....AA
N. Y.—Buffalo
Buffalo Dental Mfg. Co.
(Dental) ....B
Forsyth Mfg. Co. (Bicycle
Lamp) ....B
Noye Mfg. Co., Jno. T.
(Wall) ....B
N. Y.—Homer
Phoenix Hdw. Mfg. Co.
(Shelf) ....D
New York City
Aimone Mfg. Co. (Bamboo
Wall) ....B
Amer. Bridge Co., 100 Bway.
(Steel Trolley Pole)AAAA
Brass Goods Mfg. Co., 7
Warren (Shelf) ....B
Brown Co., A. & F. (Wall)A
Davenport & Treacy Co.
(Action) ....B
De Veau Telephone Mfg. Co.
27 Rose (Desk Telephone)
D
Dimond, Thomas (Iron
Balcony) ....A
Eccleston Lumber Co., 29
Bway. (Wood; Trolley
Pole; Cross Arms; Pins)D
Fiske Iron Wks., J. W.
(Iron Balcony; Street
Lamp) ....A
Gould Mersereau Co. (Brass
Wall) ....B
Judd & Co. H. C. (Brass;
Nickel; Picture Rod; Ole;
Lamp; Brass Wall)...AA
Krieg & Co., J. K. (Window
Display) ....
Lalance & Grosjean Mfg. Co.
19 Cliff (Plumbers')....
AAAA
Lamb, J. & R. (Brass;
Nickel; Candle; Lamp;
Iron Lamp) ....D
McCreary & Co. A. A. 136
Liberty (Flexible) ....F
Manhattan Brass Co.
(Lamp) ....
Maxwell, Jno. (Bird Cage)D
Mott Iron Wks. 88 Beekman
(All Kinds) ....AA
Mullaney's Son, Jas., 25th
& Lex. Av. (Brass Basin;
Cistern) ....D
Nason Mfg. Co. (Foot
Rail) ....A
Phelan, D. W., 277 Bway.
(Wood Cross Arms; Brackets; Pins) ....F
Railway & Electric Supply

BRACKETS (*Con.*)
Co., 115 Bway. (Trolley
Pole) ....H
Sargent & Co., 151 Leonard
(Shelf; Hand Rail; Window Screen; Corner)AAAA
Strauch Bros. (Action)...A
Tiebout, W. J. (Axe)...B
N. Y.—Schenectady
General Electric Co. (Trolley
Pole) ....AAAA
N. Y.—Syracuse
Stearns & Co., E. C.
(Plumbers') ....AA
Zimmerman, Chas. E., 204
Burnet Av. (Wood) ....H
N. Y.—Victor
Locke Insulator Mfg. Co.
(Wood Cross Arms; Trolley) ....A
N. C.—Aberdeen
Frost, Geo. A. (Wood Cross
Arms; Brackets; Pins) .E
N. C.—Asheville
Blue Ridge Locust Pin Co.
(Trolley Pole) ....H
N. C.—Elkin
Baily Mfg. Co. (Wood Cross
Arms; Brackets; Pins) X
N. C.—Rural Hall
Knapp & Miller Co. (Wood
Cross Arms; Wood Insulator) ....E
OHIO—Ashland
Myers & Bro., F. E.
(Rafter) ....AA
OHIO—Ashtabula
Barber Mfg. Co. (Adjustable
Nickled, &c.) C
OHIO—Canton
Ney Mfg. Co. (Rafter)...B
OHIO—Cincinnati
Creaghead Eng. Co., 313
Walnut (Flexible Trolley
Pole) ....D
Tatum Co., Saml. C.
(Shelf) ....B
OHIO—Cleveland
Sanitary Co., 335 Huron
(Plumbers' Brass) C
Taylor & Boggis Fdry. Co.
(Shelf) ....AA
Van Dorn & Dutton Co.,
1796 E. Mad. (Trolley
Pole) ....AA
OHIO—Columbus
Kilbourne & Jacobs Mfg. Co.
(Steel Sink; Truck)AAAA
OHIO—Dayton
Dayton Malleable Iron Co.
(Shelf) ....AA
Dayton Mfg. Co., 2240 E.
3d (Trolley Pole) ......A
Fletcher Mfg. Co. (Insulated; Electric House;
Cross Arms; Pins) ....D
OHIO—Hamilton
Meyers Mfg. Co., Fred J.
(Office; Flower Pot;
Counter) ....B
OHIO—Kenton
Champion Iron Co. (Iron
Balcony) ....AA
OHIO—Mansfield
Barnes Mfg. Co. (Plumbers';
&c.) ....B
Ohio Brass Co. (Trolley
Pole; All Kinds) ......B
OHIO—Piqua
Piqua Bracket Co. (Shelf).E
OHIO—Springfield
Elect. Construction Supply
Co. (Electric House)...E
OHIO—Toledo
Meilink Mfg. Co. (Desk
Telephone) C
PA.—Allegheny
McKinney Mfg. Co. (Shelf)
AA
Pittsburg Lamp & Brass Co.
(Brass; Nickel; Iron
Lamp) ....AAAA
PA.—Columbia
Columbia Grey Iron Casting
Co. (Flower Pot) ......A
PA.—Erie
Griffin Mfg. Co. (Shelf;
Lavatory; Steel Folding;
Sink; Flush; Tank;
Plumbing) ....A
PA.—Philadelphia
Berger Bros. Co., 231 Arch
(Roofing) ....A
Cresson Co., Geo. V. (Wall)
AA
Fairmount Machine Co.

BRACKETS *(Con.)*
(Wall) ....A
Haines, Jones & Cadbury Co.
1136 Ridge Av. (Plumbers') ....AA
Heinemann & Co., G. M.,
737 Girard Av. (Electric
House; Trolley Pole) ..E
Johnson & Lund (Dental)AA
K. & B. Co. (Wood Cross
Arms; Brackets; Pins).E
McCambridge & Co., 527
Cherry (Plumbers'; Brass;
Nickel) ....B
Newell-Booth Co., Broad &
Buttonwood (Plumbers';
Nickel Plated) ....E
Philadelphia Novelty Mfg.
Co. (Shelf) ....B
Sibley, Gideon (Dental) .AA
Union Railway Supply Co.
Real Estate Trust Bldg.
(Wood Cross Arms; Pins)
B
Wiler, Wm. (Ole; Umbrella;
Window Display) ......B
PA.—Pittsburg
Hubbard & Co. Murtland
Bldg. (Trolley Pole) ..A
Oliver Iron & Steel Co.
(Steel Trolley Pole)AAAA
Pittsburg Brass Co. (Brass;
Nickel; Nickeled Steel).X
Standard Mfg. Co. (Brass;
Nickel) ....AA
PA.—Reading
Penna. Hdw. Co. (Shelf;
Plumbers'; Cast; Wrought
Steel) ....A
Reading Hdw. Co. (Iron;
Brass Shelf; Hand Rail;
Lamp; Flower Pot; Window Screen Corner) AAA
PA.—Somerfield
Endsley, J. W. (Wood Cross
Arms; Pins) ....E
PA.—Wilkesbarre
Vulcan Iron Wks. (Iron
Balcony) ....AAAA
PA.—Wrightsville
Wrightsville Hdw. Co.
(Plain; Sink; Japanned;
Nickel Plated; &c.; Shelf;
Trolley Pole; Flag Pole)C
R. I.—Providence
New England Butt Co.
(Shelf) ....A
TENN.—Chattanooga
Central Mfg. Co. (Wood
Cross Arms; Insulator;
Trolley) ....B
TENN.—Johnson City
Harris, Wm. P. (Wood
Cross Arms; Pins)......E
TEXAS—Beaumont
Texas Arm & Pin Co. (Wood
Cross Arms; Pins; Pine
Insulator) ....D
VT.—Putney.
Stowell Mfg. Co. (Folding
Scaffold) ....D
VA.—Norfolk
Walworth & Nevill Mfg. Co.
(Wood Cross Arms; Pins)
AA
VA.—Round Hill
Moatz & Carnes (Wood Cross
Arms; Pins) ....H
W. VA.—Terra Alta
Rinard Lumber Co. (Wood
Cross Arms; Trolley)..E
W. VA.—Wheeling
Mountain State Electrical
Co. (Wood Cross Arms;
Trolley) ....D
WIS.——Milwaukee
Bayley & Sons Co., W.
(Shelf; Office; Counter)A
Meincke & Son, A. (Bamboo Wall) ....AA
Wisconsin Bridge & Iron Co.
Pabst Bldg. (Office; Trolley Pole) ....AA
WIS.—Oshkosh
Gould Mfg. Co. (Wooden) A
McMillen Co., R. (Wooden)
A
Oshkosh Logging Tool Co.
(Trolley Pole) C
WIS.—Racine
Racine Malleable & Wrought
Iron Co. (Rafter) .....AA
WIS.—So.. Milwaukee
Stowell Mfg. & Fdry. Co.
(Plain; Japanned; Nickel
Plated; Sink; Shelf;

BRACKETS *(Con.)*
Plumbing) ....A

BRADS

CONN.—New Britain
Stanley Works ......AAAA
ILL.—Grand Crossing
Chicago Tack Co. ....B
Grand Crossing Tack Co...A
IND.—Madison
Tower Mfg. Co. ....A
MASS.—Plymouth
Cobb & Drew ....AA
MASS.—Worcester
Wire Goods Co. (Wire; Wire
Steel) ....B
New York City
Russell & Erwin Mfg. Co.
(Wire) ....AAAA
PA.—Philadelphia
Duncannon Iron Co. .....AA
R. I.—Providence
American Screw Co. (Wire)
AAAA
WIS.—Milwaukee
Milwaukee Tack Co. (Wire)
C

BRAID

CONN.—Bridgeport
Connecticut Web. Co.
(Cotton) ....A
CONN.—Hamden
New Haven Webb Co. (Cotton) ....A
CONN.—New Haven
Globe Silk Works (Marvin
& Pardee) (Silk) ......B
CONN.—Putnam
Hammond, Knowlton & Co.
(Silk) ....B
CONN.—Westport
Lees Mfg. Co.............A
ILL.—Chicago
Chicago Braiding & Embroidery Co., 254 Franklin (Silk) ....B
MASS.—Becket
Becket Silk Mills (Silk;
Mohair; Cotton) ......F
MASS.—Boston
Schoenfuss, F. J. (Silk)..F
MASS.—E. Braintree
Jenkins Mfg. Co. (Cotton)B
MASS.—Easthampton
Glendale Elastic Fabrics Co.
A
MASS.—Fall River
Hanscom Bros. (Cotton) ..F
Heywood Narrow Fabric Co.
(Cotton) ....D
MASS.—Holyoke
Skinner Mfg. Co., Wm.
(Silk) ....AA
MASS.—Lawrence
Wright Mfg. Co. (Worsted)
B
MASS.—No. Grafton
Paton, Wm. (Cotton) ..AA
MASS.—Pittsfield
Rice & Co., A. H. (Silk;
Mohair) ....A
MASS.—Sandwich
Armstrong Braiding Co.
(Silk; Mohair) ....D
MASS.—Springfield
Union Braiding Co. (Silk).C
MICH.—Belding
Belding Bros. & Co. (Silk;
Mohair) ....AAAA
Richardson Silk Co. (Silk;
Mohair) ....A
N. J.—Paterson
American Braid Co. (Silk).D
Gregory, Wm. (Silk) ....F
N. J.—W. Hoboken
Mandel, Geo. (Silk; Mohair;
Cotton) C
N. Y.—Brooklyn
Barthels Mfg. Co. ....A
Castle Braid Co. (Silk; Mohair) ....AA
Levi, Joseph (Silk) C
Moll Mfg. Co., Aug. (Silk;
Cotton; Mohair) ......B
N. Y.—Harrison
Moosehead Silk Co. (Silk)X
New York City
Bedell, E. W. (Com.).....C
Hammond, Knowlton & Co.
(Silk) ....B
Hertlein, Chr. E. (Silk)..A
Hofman & Ellrodt (Silk)..C
Jonas & Co., Wm. (Silk)..C

BRAID (Con.)

Kresse, F. C. (Silk; Worsted; Mohair; Tinsel) ..F
Kursheedt Mfg. Co. (Silk) .. AA
Moll Mfg. Co., Aug. (Silk) .. B
New York Braid Co. (Silk; Mohair) ....B
Poncet & Neeses (Silk) ...B
Richardson Silk Co. (Silk) A
Salmon, Wm. (Silk; Mohair; Cotton) C
Schmitzler, B. (Silk) C
Snedeker & Co. (Com.) C
Sutro Bros. Braid Co. (Silk; Mohair) ....A
Van Nostitz & Trube (Silk; Mohair) C
Wright & Graham (Com.) B
N. Y.—Rochester
Rochester Textile Wks. (Dress) ....E
Vogt Mfg. & Coach Lace Co. (Silk Skirt) ....A
OHIO—Cincinnati
Hoffmeister Co., Alb. F...C
PA.—Philadelphia
Friedberger Mfg. Co. (Cotton; Silk) ....A
Keystone Braid Co. (Mohair; Silk; Worsted) ......A
Loeb, Lipper & Co. (Silk) A
Rosenau & Co., S. (Silk; Cotton; Mohair) ....A
PA.—Pittston
Franklin Mill (Cotton) ...D
R. I.—Pawtucket
Goff & Sons, D. (Mohair) .. AAA
Kenyon Mfg. Co., Jno. J. (Cotton) ....B
R. I.—Providence
Fletcher Mfg. Co. (Cotton) .. AAA

BRAKES

See also Hardware; Carriage & Wagon.

CONN.—Bristol
New Departure Bell Co. (Bicycle; Coaster) .....A
CONN.—East Hampton
Bevin Bros. Mfg. Co. (Bicycle) ....B
CONN.—New Haven
Goodrich & Co., J. F. (Carriage) ....AA
ILL.—Chicago
Dreis Andrews & Krump, 3216 S. Halsted (Cornice) .. E
Eames Vacuum Brake Co., 279 Dearborn (Air) X
McGuire Cummings Mfg. Co. 122 N. Sangamon (Car) AA
Turner Brass Wks. (Bicycle) .. D
IOWA—Muscatine
Giesler & Co. (Wagon) ....D
MD.—Baltimore
Ives Mfg. Co., 203 Hanover (Bicycle) ....E
MASS.—Boston
United States Steel Co., 145 Oliver (Electric Car) ..D
MICH.—Battle Creek
Knell Air Brake Co. (Air; Electric Car; Electric Crane; Car) ....D
MICH.—Detroit
Magann Air Brake Co., G. P., 4th & Porter (Air; Electric Car; Automobile Air; Car) ....D
MO.—St. Louis
American Brake Co. (Locomotive) ....A
N. J.—Newark
Ohl & Co., G. A. (Cornice) B
Sterling-Meaker Co., 420 Ogden (Car; Electric Car; Momentive; Safety Brake) .. A
N. Y.—Buffalo
Double Truss Cornice Brake Co., 37 Chandler (Cornice) .. D
Forsyth Mfg. Co. (Bicycle) .. C
Niagara Machine & Tool Wks. (Cornice) .....AAA

BRAKES (Con.)

New York City
Bemis Car Truck Co., 120 Liberty (Car) ....E
Graham & Co., J. H., 113 Chambers (Coaster; Bicycle) ....AA
New York Air Brake Co., 66 Bway. (Air; Vacuum; Automatic Air; Car; Locomotive) ....AAA
Peckham Mfg. Co., 26 Cortlandt (Car; Friction; &c.) .. A
Peck, Stow & Wilcox Co., 27 Murray (Cornice) AAAA
Standard Air Brake Co., 26 Cortlandt (Automatic Air) .. AAA
Stephenson Co. Jno. (Ltd.) 16 Exchange Pl. (Car) ..A
N. Y.—Schenectady
General Electric Co. (Electric Car; Car) .....AAAA
N. Y.—Syracuse
Western Co., I. A. (Bicycle) .. C
N. Y.—Troy
Taylor Electric Truck Co. (Car) ....B
OHIO—Cincinnati
Robinson Mfg. Co., J. M., 62 Central Av. (Cornice; Hand; Heavy Bending) ..C
OHIO—Cleveland
Cleveland Hdw. Co. (Wagon) ....A
Electric Controller & Supply Co., Central & Giddings Av. (Electric Crane) ...C
Van Dorn & Dutton Co., 1796 E. Madison Av. (Car) .. A
OHIO—Piqua
Poorman Mfg. Co. (Cornice) .. E
PA.—Philadelphia
Brill Co., J. G., 62nd & Woodland Av. (Car).AAA
PA.—Pittsburg
Westinghouse Air Brake Co. (Air; Locomotive; Automatic Air; Car; Steam; Vacuum) ....AAAA
PA.—Wilkesbarre
Vulcan Iron Wks. (Steam; Vacuum) ....AAA
PA.—Wilmerding
Standard Traction Brake Co. (Electric Car) ....AAAA
WIS.—Milwaukee
Christensen Eng. Co. (Air; Electric Car; Automatic Air) ....A
Nat. Elec. Co. (Auto. Air) .. AA
WIS.—Racine
Belle City Mfg. Co. (Wagon) .. B
Freeman & Co., Geo. B. (Wagon) ....E
Racine Malleable & Wrought Iron Co. (Wagon) .....B

BRAN

ALA.—Florence
Florence Milling Co. .....D
CAL.—Los Angeles
Capitol Milling Co. ....AA
ILL.—Chicago
Elkhart & Swan Milling Co. .. AAA
Norton & Co. ....AA
ILL.—Quincy
Dick Bros. Milling Co.....A
I. T.—Muskogee
Muskogee Roller Milling Co. (Patterson Merc. Co.).AA
KANS.—Forsha
Forsha, A. L. ....B
KANS.—Fort Scott
Goodlander Milling Co.....B
KANS.—Independence
Eagle Roller Mills .. ...F
KANS.—Lawrence
Bowersock Milling Co. (J. D. Bowersock) ....AA
KANS.—McPherson
Pearl Milling Co ....D
KANS.—Sterling
International Roller Mills.F
MICH.—Grand Rapids
Voight Milling Co. ......AA

BRAN (Con.)

MINN.—New Ulm
Eagle Roller Mill Co...AAA
MO.—Marionville
Marionville Roller Mill Co.
B
MO.—Oakgrove
Oakgrove Mill Co. ....E
MO.—St. Louis
Eggers Milling Co., H. B..A
MO.—Springfield
Meyer & Sons, Jno. F....AA
MO.—Webb City
Veatch Milling Co., S. H..F
NEBR.—Broken Bow
Broken Bow Roller Mill...F
N. Y.—Rochester
Whitney & Wilson X
OHIO—Toledo
Harter Milling Co., Isaac
AAA
OREGON—Corvallis
Benton County Flouring
Mills Co. C
PA.—Fertility
Groff, I. B. ....F
PA.—Irwin
Irwin Flour Mills........B
UTAH—Salt Lake City
Inter-Mountain Milling Co.
D

BRANDS

CONN.—Bridgeport
Schwerdtle Stamp Co.
(Burning) ....G
CONN.—Hartford
Parker, T. M. (Burning)..G
CONN.—New Haven
Hoggson & Pettis Mfg. Co.
(Burning) ....A
ILL.—Chicago
Bartlett & Sons, M. J., 196
S. Clark (Stock Marking)
H
MASS.—Boston
Woodman Mfg. & Supply Co.
(Burning) ....F
MASS.—Springfield
Smith Mfg. Co., R. H.
(Burning) C
MO.—St. Louis
Brecht Butchers' Supply Co.,
G. V. (Bacon) ......AAA
Illig & Hartman, 211 Pine
(Burning) ....E
New York City
Butler, A. G., 284 Pearl
(Burning) ....F
Ness, Jr., Geo. M., 61 Fulton (Burning) ....G
New York Stencil Works
(Burning) ....D
Stafford Co., N. (Burning)
F
OHIO—Cincinnati
Murdoch, Jr. Jas., 116 Longworth (Burning) ......B
OHIO—Cleveland
Sackman, F. A. (Burning).F
WIS.—Milwaukee
Pawling & Harnischfeger
(Brewers' Bung) ...AAA

BRANDY

See Liquors

BRASS

See also Ingots

CONN.—Bridgeport
Bridgeport Brass Co. (Bar;
Angles; Figured; Rod;
White; Roll; Sheet; Strip;
Embossed; Hoop; Printers'
Rule; Sign; Spring; Brazing) ....AA
B r i d g e p o r t Deoxidized
Bronze & Metal Co.
(Aluminum; Cartridge;
Sheet; White) ....B
CONN.—Seymour
Seymour Mfg. Co. (Sheet)
AA
CONN.—South Windham
Smith & Winchester Co.
(Roll) ....A
CONN.—Torrington
Coe Brass Mfg. Co. (Cartridge; Roll; Sheet Angles)
AAAA

BRASS (Con.)

CONN.—Waterbury
Benedict & Burnham Mfg.
Co. (Angles) ......AAAA
Holmes, Booth & Hayden
Co. (inc.) (Cartridge;
Roll; Sheet) ......AAAA
Plume & Atwood Mfg. Co.
(R o l l; S h e e t; Hoop;
Printers' Rule; Spring;
Brazing) ....AAA
Randolph-Clowes Co. (Sheet;
Roll; Sign; Engravers')
AAA
Scoville Mfg. Co. (Aluminum; Bar; Cartridge;
Roll; Sheet; Stick; Strip;
Brazing) ....AAAA
Waterbury Brass Co. (Roll;
Sheet; Embossed; Angles)
AAAA
ILL.—Chicago
Chicago Brass Co. (Printers'
Rule; Roll; Sheet) .....D
Harrington & King Perforating Co., 224 N. Union
(Perforated Sheet) .....A
ILL.—Evanston
Mark Mfg. Co. (Perforated)
AA
ILL.—Peru
American Nickeloid & Mfg.
Co. (Coated Sheet Zinc;
Polished) ....F
MICH.—Detroit
Detroit Copper & Brass Rolling Mills (Bar; Roll;
Sheet; Angles) ....AAAA
MICH.—Grand Rapids
Grand Rapids Brass Co.
(Sheet) ....A
N. J.—Jersey City
Williams & Son, E. A.
(Stick) ....AAA
N. Y.—Lockport
Cowles Electric Smelting &
Aluminum Co. (Aluminum) ....B
New York City
Ansonia Brass & Copper Co.,
99 John (Bar; Roll; Sheet;
Strip; Embossed; Sign;
Figured) ....AAAA
Manhattan Brass Co. (Roll;
Sheet; Angles) ......AA
Mundt & Sons, Chas., 441
Pearl (Perforated Sheet)
B
N. Y.—Rome
Rome Brass & Copper Co.
(Sheet; Angles) ...AAAA
PA.—Philadelphia
Merchant & Co. (Angles).AA
PA.—Pittsburg
Hussey & Co., C. G. (Roll;
Sheet) ....AAA
McKenna Bros. Brass Co.
(Roll; Sheet; Sign; Engravers') ....A
Pittsburg Reduction Co.
(Aluminum) ......AAAA
R. I.—Providence
Wall & Co., A. T. (Sheet)
C
WIS.—Milwaukee
Toepfer & Sons, W. (Perforated) ....B

BRAYERS

New York City
Hoe & Co., R. (Printers')
AAAA
N. Y.—Brooklyn
Wesel Mfg. Co., F. (Printers') ....AA
OHIO—Cleveland
Chandler & Price Co., 82
E. Prospect (Printers')..A

BRAZIERS

ILL.—Chicago
Arnstein, Eugene (Hot
Blast) ....A
Turner Brass Works (Hot
Blast) ....A
MICH.—Detroit
Union Heater Supply Co.
(Hot Blast) ....G
N. Y.—Buffalo
Buffalo Dental Mfg. Co.
(Bicycle) ....B
OHIO—Toledo
National Cement & Rubber

BRAZIERS (Con.)
Mfg. Co. C

BRAZING

PA.—Reading
Reading Machine & Tool Co.
........B
Reading Standard Cycle
Mfg. Co. ....B

BREAKERS

CONN.—Ansonia
Farrell Foundry & Machine
Co. (Stone) ......AAAA
GA.—Augusta
Lombard Iron Works & Sup-
ply Co. (Oil Cake)....A
ILL.—Chicago
Atkinson Co., J. M., 2427
Calumet Av. (Circuit)..F
Porter & Berg, 309 Dear-
born (Circuit) ....F
Scully Steel & Iron Co.
(Staybolt) ....AAA
ILL.—Harvey
Whiting Fdy. & Equipment
Co. (Casting; Scrap) .AA
IND.—Mishawaka
Dodge Mfg. Co. (Casting;
Scrap) ....AAA
MASS.—Boston
Boston Electric Co., 29 Har-
rison Av. (Circuit) ....B
Bradley Fertilizer Co. (Phos-
phate) X
Condit, Jr. & Co., S. B., 63
Oliver (Circuit) ....F
Firth Co., Wm., 150 Dev-
onshire (Bale) ....D
Sturtevant Mill Co. (Phos-
phate) ....B
MICH.—Detroit
Fisher Electrical Wks., 183
Larned (Circuit) ......D
N. Y.—Bronxville
Leonard Electric Co., W.
(Circuit) ....B
N. Y.—Brooklyn
Ross & Son, Chas., 16 Steu-
ben (Glue) ....D
N. Y.—Buffalo
McCarthy Bros. & Ford, 43
N. Division (Circuit)...E
Noye Mfg. Co., Jno. T,
(Coal; Phosphate) ......D
New York City
Carpenter Enclosed Resist-
ance Co., 78 E. 131st (Cir-
cuit) ....B
General Incandescent Arc
Light Co., 572 1st Av.
(Circuit) ....A
Hunt Co., C. W. (Coal) .AA
Jennings Co., C. E., 42 Mur-
ray (Ice) ....D
La Roche Co., F. A., 656
Hudson (Circuit) ......E
N. Y.—Schenectady
General Electric Co. (Cir-
cuit) ....AAAA
OHIO—Cleveland
Brown Hoisting Mchy. Co.
(Pig Iron) ....AAAA
OHIO—Columbus
Jeffrey Mfg. Co. (Coal) .AA
OHIO—Mansfield
Hartman Circuit Breaker Co.
(Circuit) ....F
Ohio Brass Co. (Circuit; Au-
tomatic) ....B
OHIO—Springfield
Foos Mfg. Co. (Oil Cake) .A
PA.—Allegheny
Carlins' Sons, Thos. (Skull)
......A
PA.—Carbondale
Hendrick Mfg. Co. (Coal)
......AA
PA.—Easton
Wilson Bros. (Phosphate) .A
PA.—Philadelphia
Cutter Electrical & Mfg.
Co., 19th & Hamilton (Cir-
cuit) ....A
Harrison Safety Boiler
Works, 3194 N. 17th (Ice)
......A
North Bros. Mfg. Co., Le-
high Av. & American (Cir-
cuit; Ice) ....A
Westinghouse Electric &
Mfg. Co., Westinghouse
Bldg. (Circuit) ....AAAA

BREAKERS (Con.)
PA.—Scottdale
Kenney & Co. (Coal) .....A
PA.—Scranton
Dickson Mfg. Co. (Coal;
Phosphate) ....D
PA.—Wilkesbarre
Vulcan Iron Works (Coal;
Phosphate) ....AAAA
PA.—York
Motter & Sons, Geo. F.
(Phosphate) ....B
R. I.—Pawtucket
Howard & Bullough, Am.
Machine Co., Ltd. (Bale)
AAA
WIS.—Milwaukee
Cutler-Hammer Mfg. Co.
(Circuit) ....B

BREAKS

IND.—Indianapolis
Over. Ewald (Hemp) C
IND.—South Bend
Studebaker Bros. Mfg. Co.
(Wagon) ....AAAA
N. J.—Newark
Sacks Iron Foundry, Louis
(Peg) ....A

BREASTS

PA.—Philadelphia
Philadelphia Textile Ma-
chine Co., Hancock &
Somerset (Metallic) ....B
Smith Woolen Mchy. Co.,
James (Metallic) ......A

BREECHINGS

ILL.—Chicago
Wallace & Sons, Wm., 88
Wells (Boiler) ....D
MD.—Baltimore
O'Connor, T. J. (Buggy;
Cart; Slip; Team; Wagon)
B
MO.—St. Louis
Heine Safety Boiler Co.
(Iron) ....AAA
Wangler Boiler & Sheet
Iron Works Co., J. T.
(Boiler) ....A
PA.—Allentown
Midvale Foundry Co., Ltd.
(Boiler) ....AAAA

BREWERS

See Beer, Ale etc.

BRICK

CONN.—Bridgeport
Springfield Mfg. Co. .....B
D. C.—Washington
Anacostia Brick Co. (Build-
ing) ....B
ILL.—Grant Park
Curtis Brick Co., Alonzo
(Building) C
IND.—New Castle
New Castle Brick & Tile Co.
(Building) ....B
KY.—Louisville
Hydraulic Brick Co., 12th
& St. Louis Av. (Building)
AA
MD.—Baltimore
Baltimore Retort & Fire
Brick Co. (Fire; Retort)
B
MO.—St. Louis
Laclede Fire Brick Mfg. Co.
(Fire) ....AAA
Evans & Howard Fire Brick
Co. (Building; Terra Cot-
ta) ....AAAA
Illinois Supply & Construc-
tion Co. (Building)...,E
Missouri Fire Brick Co.
(Fire) ....B
Parker, Russell Mining &
Mfg. Co. (Fire) ....AAA
N. Y.—Kingston
Terry Bros. (Building)...A
New York City
Hunnekes & Co., H. (Sand;
Lime) ....D
Kreischer Brick Mfg. Co.,
119 E. 23d (Fire; Terra
Cotta) ....B
Maurer & Son, Hy., 420 E.

BRICK (*Con.*)
23d (Fire; Terra Cotta:
  Porous; Roof) ......AA
Reconstructed Granite Co.,
  14 Dey (Rheostat) .....D
OHIO—Findlay
Findlay Hyd. Pressed Brick
  Co. ....A
OHIO—Zanesville
Mosaic Tile Co. (Terra Cot-
  ta) ....A
PA.—Keystone Junction
Savage Fire Brick Co.
  (Terra Cotta) ....AA
PA.—Philadelphia
Borgner, Cyrus (Fire) ...B
PA.—Pittsburg
Gardner, Jr. Co., Jas. (Fire)
                        B
Harbison-Walker Refracto-
  ries Co. (Terra Cotta)
                       AAAA
Welch, Gloninger & Maxwell
  (Building; Coke Oven).B
R. I.—Providence
American Emery Wheel
  Works (Emery) ....B

BRIDGES

For Elec., see Galvonome-
  ters.

CAL.—San Francisco
California Bridge Co. (Iron:
  Steel) X
CONN.—East Berlin
Berlin Construction Co.
  (Iron: Steel) ....A
DEL.—Wilmington
Edgemoor Iron Co. (Iron:
  Steel) ....AAA
GA.—Augusta
Lombard Iron Works & Sup-
  ply Co. (Iron; Steel;
  Small Highway) ......A
ILL.—Chicago
Austin Mfg. Co. (Iron;
  Steel) ....AAA
Chicago Bridge & Iron Co.
  (Iron; Steel) .....AAA
MAINE—Portland
Portland Co. (Iron; Steel;
  Wooden) ....AA
MASS.—Boston
Boston Bridge Works (Iron;
  Steel) ....AA
MICH.—Detroit
Detroit Bridge & Iron Wks.
  (Iron; Steel) .....AAAA
MINN.—Minneapolis
Gillette-Herzog Mfg. Co.
  (Iron; Steel) X
MO.—Kansas City
Kansas City Bridge Co.
  (Iron; Steel) ....E
MO.—St. Louis
Leschen & Sons' Rope Co.,
  A. (Suspension) ....AAA
N. J.—Trenton
New Jersey Steel & Iron Co.
  (Iron; Steel) ....D
N. Y.—Marathon
Climax Road Machine Co.
  (Steel Girder) ....B
New York City
American Bridge Co., 42
  B'way (Iron; Steel)....A
Roebling's Sons, Jno. A.
  (Suspension) ....B
OHIO—Bellefontaine
Bellefontaine Bridge & Iron
  Co. (Iron; Steel) .....B
OHIO—Cleveland
King Bridge Co. (Iron;
  Steel ....AAA
OHIO—Columbus
Rarig Engineering Co.
  (Draw; Railroad; Turn-
  pike) ....A
OHIO—Middleport
Ohio Machine Co. (Rail-
  road) C
OHIO—Springfield
Rogers Iron Co. (Iron:
  Steel) C
PA.—Beaver Falls
Penna. Bridge Co. (Iron:
  Steel) ....,.B
PA.—Philadelphia
Phoenix Bridge Co. (Iron:
  Steel) ....A
Stow Flexible Shaft Co.
  (Iron; Steel) ....B

BRIDGES (*Con.*)
PA.—Pittsburg
Bollinger Construction Co.,
  G. L., 2817 Liberty (Over-
  head Railroad) ....B
Carnegie Steel Co., Ltd.
  (Iron; Steel) .....AAAA
Carroll-Porter Boiler & Tank
  Co. (Iron; Steel) .....B
Riter-Conley Mfg. Co. (Iron;
  Steel) ....AAA
PA.—Steelton
Pennsylvania Steel Co. (Br.
  Phila., PA., (Iron; Steel)
                       AAAA

BRILLIAN-TINE

New York City
Caswell, Massey & Co.....X

BRIMSTONE
See Sulphur

BRISTLES

ILL.—Chicago
Armour Curled Hair Works
                      AAAA
MD.—Baltimore
Wilkens-Williams Co., Fred-
  erick Av. ....AA
MASS.—Boston
Bowditch, J. F., 6 India Sq.
  (Black; Chisel; Sash;
  White) ....D
New York City
Wilkens Bros., 440 Pearl..A
OHIO—Cincinnati
Brogle, Fred. ....D
PA.—Philadelphia
Woll & Sons, Peter, Mascher
  & Berks ....AAAA

BROADCLOTH
See Woolen Goods

BROGANS
See Boots & Shoes

BROILERS

ILL.—Chicago
Barbee Wire & Iron Works
  (Br. Lafayette, Ind.)
  (Oyster) ....B
ILL.—Paxton
Paxton Hdw. Mfg. Co.
  (Meat; Sheet; Steel)....X
MASS.—Boston
Simplex Electrical Co., Cam-
  bridgeport Sta. (Electric)
                        A
MASS.—Lowell
Woods, Sherwood & Co...C
MASS.—Worcester
National Mfg. Co. (Wire).B
Parker Wire Goods Co....A
Wire Goods Co. (Wire)....A
MICH.—Detroit
American Electrical Heater
  Co., 195 River (Electric)
                        E
MICH.—Jackson
Novelty Mfg. Co. (Sheet
  Steel) ....A
N. Y.—Buffalo
Shepard & Co., Sidney
                      AAAA
Western Wire Goods Co...D
New York City
Bramhall-Deane Co. .....B
Stoutenborough, X. ......D
OHIO—Cincinnati
Miller Range & Furnace Co.
  (Sheet Steel; Charcoal;
  Coke) ....A
OHIO—Cleveland
Dangler Stove & Mfg. Div.
  (Amer. Stove Co.) (Br.
  St. Louis, Mo.) .....AAAA
Schneider & Trenkamp (Br.
  Am. Stove Co.)......AAAA
OHIO—Hamilton
Meyers Mfg. Co., J. F....B
PA.—Philadelphia
Hall & Carpenter (Sheet
  Steel) ....AA
Darby & Sons, Ed., 233 Arch
                        A

BROMA

MASS.—Dorchester
Baker & Co., Walter..AAAA
New York City
Wilbur & Sons, H. O..AAA
PA.—Ambler
Keasbey & Mattison Co.
...................AAAA

BROMIDES

OHIO—Cleveland
Midland Chemical Co.
(Liquid Form) X

BROMINE

MO.—St. Louis
Mallinckrodt Chemical Wks.
...................AAAA
OHIO—Cleveland
Midland Chemical Co. ..,X
PA.—Allegheny
Beck Salt Co. ....A
PA.—McKeesport
Bissell Chemical Co......X

BROMOFORM

MO.—St. Louis
Herf & Frerichs Chemical
Co. ....A
Mallinckrodt Chemical Wks.
...................AAAA

BRONZE

See also Ingots

CAL.—San Francisco
Union Iron Works (Manganese) ....AAAA
CONN.—Bridgeport
Bridgeport Brass Co. (Aluminum) ....AA
Bridgeport Deoxidized
Bronze & Metal Co.
(Sheet; Aluminum; Phosphate; Manganese) ...B
CONN.—Waterbury
Benedict & Burnham Mfg.
Co. (Sheet) ......AAAA
Holmes, Booth & Haydens
Co. (Inc.) (Spinners)
...................AAAA
Plume & Atwood Mfg. Co.
(Metal) ....AAA
Randolph-Cowles Co. (Roll;
Sheet) ....AAA
Scovill Mfg. Co. (Metal)
...................AAAA
Waterbury Brass Co. (Roll;
Sheet) ....AAAA
CONN.—Winsted
Goodwin & Kintz Co. (Ornamental) ....D
ILL.—Chicago
Besly & Co., Chas. H. (Roll;
Sheet; Metal) ....AA
MAINE—Bath
Bath Iron Works (Manganese) ....D
MASS.—Boston
Hauthaway & Sons, Chas. S.
(Shoe) ....A
Whittemore Mfg. Co. (Shoe)
MICH.—Detroit
Detroit Copper & Brass Rolling Mills (Sheet) ..AAAA
.....................E
N. J.—Jersey City
Williams & Son, E. A. (Carbon; Manganese; Phosphor; Aluminum; Velvet)
...................AAA
N. Y.—Lockport
Cowles Electric Smelting &
Aluminum Co. (Manganese; Silicon; Aluminum)
.....................B
New York City
Ansonia Brass & Copper Co.,
99 John (Sheet; Tobin
Metal; Roll) ......AAAA
Manhattan Brass Company
(Angles) ....AA
OHIO—Springfield
Nolte Brass Co. (Phosphor)
.....................D
PA.—Allegheny
Damascus Bronze Co. (Phosphor) ....A

BRONZE (Con.)
PA.—Chester
Crown Smelting Co. (Manganese; Phosphor) .....A
PA.—Philadelphia
Cramp & Sons Ship & Eng.
Bldg. Co. (Manganese)
...................AAAA
Crescent Phosphorized Metal
Co., 2111 Indiana (Manganese; Phosphor) C
Janney, Steinmetz & Co.
(Aluminum) ....D
Phosphor Bronze Smelting
Co., Ltd. (Phosphor;
Manganese; Metal; Roll;
Sheet) ....A
Reeves & Son, P. S., 1415
Catherine (Manganese;
Metal; Phosphor; Roll;
Sheet) ....B
PA.—Pittsburg
Maloney Bronze Mfg. Co.,
3172 2d Av. (Ingot) ...D
Pittsburg Reduction Co.
(Aluminum) ......AAAA

BRONZES

See also Statuary

CONN.—Meriden
Bradley & Hubbard Mfg. Co.
(Art) ....AAAA
MD.—Baltimore
Limerick, J. Arthur, 12 S.
Calvert (Art) ....D
New York City
Bawo & Dotter, 26 Barclay
(Art) ....AA
Bing & Co., Ferd. 10 Washington Pl. (Art).......A
Borgfeldt & Co., Geo., 48
W. 4th (Art) .....AAAA
Harris & Harrington, 32
Vesey (Art) ....B
Lazarus, Rosenfeld & Lehmann, 62 Murray (Art).B
Levy & Co., L. W., 194
B'way (Art) ....B
Schwarz Bros. & Co., 29
Union Sq. (Art) .....B
Straus & Sons, L., 42 Warren (Art) ....AAAA
Vantine & Co., A. A., 20
E. 18th (Art) .....AAA

BROOCHES

See Jewelry

BROODERS

See Incubators

BROOM

See Corn; Broom

BROOMS

ALA.—Citronville
Cornell, H. P. & G. A...X
ALA.—Mobile
Partin, M. ....D
ARK.—Ft. Smith
Southern Broom Co. X
CAL.—San Francisco
California Broom Mfg. Co.,
218 Front ....B
Feldman & Co., L., 220
Front ....A
Van Laak Mfg. Co., 3175
17th ....E
Zan Bros. & Co., 316 Davis
.....................B
CAL.—Stockton
Hemingway, A. ....D
CONN.—New Hartford
Bancroft, Geo. W. C
CONN.—Thompsonville
Noble, Sr., G. L. ....D
DEL.—Newark
Curtis & Bro. (Brush) ..A
GA.—Savannah
Antiseptic Broom Co. ...C
Schwarz & Son. Geo. X
ILL.—Aurora
Roesch, John ....D
ILL.—Bement
Burgess, G. L. ....E
ILL.—Chicago
Chicago Broom Mfg. Co., 105
La Salle Av. ....AA
Dearborn Duster Co., 124 S.

BROOMS *(Con.)*

Green (Feather) ......D
Haisler Bros. Co., 3 S.
  Franklin (Stable) ....E
Illinois Broom Co., 248 Ran-
  dolph ....D
Pirrung Mfg. Co. ....B
U. S. Broom Co., 204 Dear-
  born ....A
Vehmeyer, W. F., 208 Mich-
  igan ....A

ILL.—Edwardsville
Berry, Wm. ....E
ILL.—Galesburg
Boyer Broom Co. ....A
ILL.—Mattoon
Roseboom & Co., J. A...A
ILL.—Odin
Sebastian Bros. ....E
ILL.—Paris
Merkle-Wiley Broom Co...C
ILL.—Wyoming
Poil, G. W. ....E
IND.—Evansville
Evansville Broom Wks.....C
Southwestern Broom Mfg.
  Co. ....B
IND.—Indianapolis
Indianapolis Brush & Broom
  Mfg. Co., 26 Brush (Rat-
  tan) C
IND.—Palmyra
Reising, Adam ....D
IND.—Ridgeville
Lay & Co., Joseph (Textile;
  Rattan Mixed; Steel
  Wire) ....B
IND.—South Bend
Jacobson, Peterson & Co...E
IOWA—Davenport
Lee Broom & Duster Co....B
IOWA—Des Moines
Des Moines Broom Co.....X
Harrah & Stewart Mfg. Co.
  (Whisk) C
IOWA—Dubuque
Miller Co., F. A. ....D
KANS.—Leavenworth
Kelly, M. A. ....D
KY.—Frankfort
Mason & Ford Co. .....AAA
KY.—Louisville
Caummisar, T. C., 133 3d
  Av. C
Gould & Co., L., 145 E.
  Jefferson ....D
Louisville Broom Works, 210
  10th ....B
LA.—New Orleans
Lesher, Mrs. B., 858 Tchoup
                   E
McGraw Woodenware Co.
  Ltd. 401 Tchoup ......A
Morris Co., J. C., Ltd., 324
  Tchoup ....B
MAINE—Portland
Twitchell-Champlin Co..AA
MD.—Baltimore
Engelhardt, E., 1018 Hillen
                   D
Maryland Broom Co. ....E
Ripple & Bros., 1231 Bur-
  gundy Av. ....F
Tottle & Co., W. A., 122
  Hanover ....B
MASS.—Fitchburg
Fitchburg Broom & Brush
  Co. ....B
MASS.—Somerville
Conrad Broom Co. ....E
MASS.—Worcester
Dean, O. M. ....E
MICH.—Detroit
Crabb & Son, L., 30 Ash..D
Hatch & Son, E. W......D
Manzelman, Chas. ....B
Wetherbee & Co., G. C., 49
  Jefferson Av. ....B
MICH.—West Bay City
Balwinski Bros. X
Sovereign, H. O. ....E
MINN.—St. Cloud
Blood & Smith ....G
MINN.—St. Paul
American Broom Co., 11 W.
  3d ....D
Fortmeyer Bros., 199 Penn
  Av. ....G
Poirier, Adolph ....H
Stewart, A. F. ....G
MO.—Jefferson City
Central Broom Co. .....D
MO.—Kansas City
Thompson, H. E., 1412 Lib-
  erty C

BROOMS *(Con.)*

MO.—St. Louis
American Broom Mfg. Co.,
  214 S. 17th ....E
Thompson Broom Co., H...D
Western Broom Co., 400 S.
  Commercial ....D
NEBR.—Deshler
Deshler Broom Factory....B
NEBR.—Lincoln
Flint, E. C. X
Gallagher & Cunningham..F
Lee Broom & Duster Co....B
N. H.—Concord
Thompson, H. ....E
N. J.—Newark
Jedel & Co., A. ....E
N. J.—Trenton
United States Broom Co...D
N. Y.—Albany
Frazier & Son, W. H.....D
N. Y.—Amsterdam
American Broom & Brush
  Co. ....A
Amsterdam Broom Co. (&
  Whisk) ....A
Aspelmeyer & Sons, F....X
Gardner Broom Co. ....E
Pioneer Broom Co. ....B
N. Y.—Brant
Erie Preserving Co. ....AA
N. Y.—Brooklyn
Adams & Co., J. J., 122
  Greenpoint Av. (Stable)
                   A
N. Y.—Buffalo
Buffalo Broom Works, 298
  Putnam Av. ....F
Young, Ernst B., 39 Cherry
  (Barn) ....D
N. Y.—Farnham
Erie Preserving Co. ....AA
N. Y.—Fonda
Mohawk Valley Broom Co.
                   D
N. Y.—Fort Hunter
American Broom & Brush
  Co. ....D
Aspelmeyer, F. ....F
Devendorf, D. A. C
N. Y.—Fultonville
American Broom & Brush
  Co. ....D
N. Y.—Lockport
Evans & Liddle ....B
N. Y.—Malone
Benmare Broom Co. ......D
N. Y.—Middleburg
Mattice, E. ....D
N. Y.—Mount Morris
Simerson & Co. ....E
New York City
Bookhop, F. H., 115 War-
  ren (Brass Sink) ......D
Escoba Mfg. & Supply Co.,
  147 Cedar ....F
Gerhardt, C., 591 Hudson
  (Brewers) ....D
Genesee Fruit Co., 501 West
                 AA
International Broom Co.,
  309 B'way X
Star Expansion Bolt Co.,
  147 Cedar (Steel Wire;
  Fibre) ....F
N. Y.—North Collins
Erie Preserving Co. ....AA
N. Y.—Ogdensburg
Keely & Leonard C
N. Y.—Orchard Park
Erie Preserving Co. ....AA
N. Y.—Rochester
Dobberton, A. C. ....F
N. Y.—Schenectady
Horstman & Co., D......D
Whitmyer, H. ....E
N. Y.—Syracuse
Onondaga Whisk Broom
  Works C
Syracuse Broom Co. ...AA
N. Y.—Tribes Hill
Whittemeyer & Sons, F...D
N. Y.—Waterloo
Post Broom Co., J. H.....H
OHIO—Cincinnati
Cremering Bros., 224 Main
                 E
De Roy, P., 105 E. Canal..D
Meyer, Sr., B., 19 E. Canal
                 D
OHIO—Cleveland
Osborn Mfg. Co. (Steel;
  Wire; Fibre; Track)...B
Smith Foundry Supply Co.,

BROOMS (Con.)

J. D. (Steel; Wire; Fibre)........D

OHIO—Columbus
Howard Broom Co., 220
Spruce ....E

OHIO—Columbus Grove
Smith & Basinger ....E

OHIO—New Bremen
New Bremen Broom Co...B

OHIO—New Philadelphia
Congleton, J. ....D

OHIO—Sidney
Donaldson & Boal Broom Co.
B

OHIO—Toledo
Ohio Broom & Supply Co...B

OHIO—Urbana
Urbana Broom Co. (&
Whisk) ....D
White Co., Val. (& Whisk)
B

OREGON—Portland
Zan Bros. ....B

PA.—Academy Corners
Taft & Son. A. D.........E

PA.—Allegheny
Lang Union Broom Co.....A

PA.—Campelltown
Fasnacht, D. S. ....G

PA.—Catawissa
Swank & Brandt ....F

PA.—Grove City
Montgomery & Co. ......E

PA.—Hamburg
Hamburg Broom Co. ....F

PA.—Philadelphia
Eastburn & Co., 110 Vine..D
Sellers Bros., 421 N. 3d...E

PA.—Pittsburg
McElroy & Co., 214 3d Av.
A
Smith Woodenware Co., L.
H. ....A
Standard Broom Co. .....F

PA.—Reading
Nies & Co., S. E.........D
Shanaman, W. B. ....E
Shanaman Bros. ..·.....C

PA.—Union City
Hatch & Son. E. W.......D

S. C.—Charleston
Charleston Excelsior Mat-
tress & Broom Wks.....C

S. C.—Spartanburg
Muckenfuss Mfg. Co. ....D

S. DAK.—Sioux Falls
Kuh Bros. ....B

TENN.—Memphis
Humphrey, T. N. C
Merchants Broom & Mop Co.
F

TENN.—Nashville
Kanel Broom Works......E

TEXAS—Round Rock
Round Rock Broom Co....B

TEXAS—Waco
Thompson. J. S. ....B

UTAH—Ogden
Scovill. M. G. (Barn)....E

VT.—Lyndonville
Eaton & Co., J. C........D

VA.—Alexandria
King & Son. Chas........A

VA.—Norfolk
Norfolk Broom Works.....B
Taylor & Co.. G. F.......C

VA.—Richmond
West Co.. W. B. C

WASH.—Seattle
Washington Broom Wks...G

WASH.—Spokane
Meese & Co., G. ....D
Neitzel Bros. & Theilmann
G

WIS.—Ft. Atkinson
Pounder. G. H. ....D

WIS.—La Crosse
Miller, A. C

WIS.—Milwaukee
Koch & Loeber Co., 121 Cly-
bourn ....B
Lemke. A. F.. 419 State...C
Milwaukee Dustless Brush
Co., 124 Sycamore .....F

WIS.—Racine
Kranz, W. H. ....E

BROUGHAMS

See Carriages & Wagons

BRUISERS

N. Y.—Auburn

BRUISERS (Con.)
Osborne & Co., D. M.
(Straw) ....AAAA

BRUSHES

See Silverware; Ebony
Goods, etc.

ALA.—Mobile
Partin, M. ....D

CAL.—San Francisco
Buchanan Bros., 609 Sacramento ....E

CONN.—Deep River
Rogers Brush Works (Coun-
ter; Glass Cleaning; Gun;
Lamp; Chimney; Water
Closet; Bath; Flesh; Nail)
F

CONN.—Meriden
Meriden Brittannia Co.
(Hat) ....AAAA

CONN.—New Hartford
Standard Brush Co. (Horse;
Machine; Printers'; Floor
Waxing & Polishing;
Scrub; Shoe & Daubers;
Stove; Special Bath;
Hair; Nail) ....D

CONN.—Wallingford
Wallace & Sons' Mfg. Co.,
R. (Crumb; Hat; Velvet;
Cloth; Hair; Nail; Shav-
ing; Sterling Silver Hair;
Tooth) ....AAAA

ILL.—Chicago
Chicago Flexible Shaft Co.,
121 La Salle (Steel Wire;
Wire; Casting; Gearing;
Flue) ....B
Chicago Wood Finishing Co.,
261 Elston Av. (Floor Pol-
ishing) ....B
Dietzgen Co., Eugene (Air)
A
Dilley. Wm., 172 Clark
(Paint; Varnish, &c.)...D
Elevator Supply & Repair
Co.. 34 W. Monroe (Woven
Wire) C
Gerts. Lumbard & Co., 210
Randolph (Paint; Var-
nish) ....AA
Kaefer. M. (Beer Bottle).D
Perrung Mfg. Co. ....B
Remitz, A. W., 22 Cornelia
F
Remitz, W. F., 406 Noble
G

ILL.—Rockford
Air Brush Mfg. Co. (Air).X

IND.—Evansville
Southwestern Broom Mfg.
Co. ....B

IND.—Ft. Wayne
Ft. Wayne Electric Corporation (Dynamo) .....AAA

IND.—Indianapolis
Indianapolis Brush & Broom
Mfg. Co. C
Interior Hdw. Co. (Weighted
Floor) ....A

IND.—Ridgeville
Lav & Co.. Jos. (Foundry;
Machine; Factory)......C

IND.—Sullivan
Holcomb Mfg. Co., J. I.
(Horse) C

IOWA—Davenport
Lee Broom & Duster Co.
(Floor; Hearth; Scrub).A

LA—New Orleans
Morris Co.. J. C., 324
Tchoupitoulas ....B

MAINE—Portland
True Bros. (Paint) ......D

MD.—Baltimore
Guider & Co., G. Chas.
(Whitewash; Dust; Flat
Paint) X
Rennous. Kleinle & Co., 848
Fkd. Av. (Bill Poster).A

MASS.—Attleboro
Blake & Co.. Jas. E. (Silver
Mounted) ....A
Marble, Forrister & Co. (Sil-
ver Mounted) C

MASS.—Boston
Bailey & Co.. C. J. (Shoe &
Daubers; Rubber Bath;
Rubber Hand; Rubber
Shampoo; Rubber Tooth)
B
Burton & Co.. A. & E. (Ar-
tists'; Painters'; Crumb;

126

BRUSHES (*Con.*)

Paste) .... B
Murphy, Leavens & Co., 28
    Exchange (Foundry; Machine; Factory) .... D
New England Novelty Mfg.
    Co. (Pocket; Hat) ...H
Pushee & Sons, Jno. C.,
    Randolph & Harrison
    (Paint; Varnish, &c.)..B
Whiting & Son Co., Jno. L.
    (Paint; Whitewash) ..AA
MASS.—Cambridge
Boston Woven Hose & Rubber Co. (Rubber Bath)
    AAAA
MASS.—Fall River
Wild, Joseph (Mill) .....F
MASS.—Fitchburg
Fitchburg Broom & Brush
    Co. .... B
MASS.—Florence
Florence Mfg. Co. (Hat;
    Pocket Hat; Cloth; Hair;
    Nail; Tooth; Wire Hair)
    A
MASS.—Lawrence
Columbia Napper Clothing
    Co. (Mill) ....H
MASS.—Lowell
Edwards & Co.. Henry, 146
    Fletcher (Mill) ....H
    E
Lahne & Co., M. M. (Mill)
Nebes. David, 256 Lawrence
    (Mill) ....H
MASS.—Worcester
Cleveland Machine Works
    (J. H. Whittic) (Steam)
    A
Curtis & Marble Machine Co.
    (Mill) ....A
Mason Brush Works (Mill)
    F
Wright Wire Co. (Whitewash; Horse; Shoe; Wire;
    Casting; Gearing; Flue)
    AA
MICH.—Detroit
American Brush Co. (Horse;
    Bakers'; Painters'; Whitewash; Bottle; Counter;
    Crumb; Floor; Lamp
    Chimney; Scrub; Shoe &
    Daubers'; Stove; Tumbler;
    Window; Bath; Nail)..E
MICH.—Grand Rapids
Grand Rapids Brush Co.
    (Horse; Moulders'; Plating; Printers'; Farmers';
    Curriers'; Billiard Table;
    Bottle; Counter; Crumb;
    Dust; Dish Washers';
    Floor; Glass Cleaning;
    Hat; Hearth; Kitchen;
    Scrub; Shoe & Daubers;
    Stove; Tumbler; Velvet;
    Window; Wood Filler;
    Bath Cloth; Complexion;
    Cosmetic; Flesh; Hair;
    Nail; Lamp Chimney)...A
MO.—St. Louis
Ludlow-Saylor Wire Co.. 4th
    & Elm (Foundry; Mach.
    Factory) ....AA
Pilley Packing Co.. 606 S.
    3d (Foundry; Machine;
    Factory) ....D
N. H.—Manchester
Felton & Son Co., S. A.
    (Foundry; Mach.; Paint;
    Varnish; Mill; Wheel;
    Factory) C
N. J.—Hoboken
Schimper & Co., Wm.
    (Cloth) ....AA
N. J.—Jersey City
Eastern Carbon Wks. (Carbon) ....A
Foot Mfg. Co.. Germania Av.
    (Foundry; Machine; Factory) C
N. J.—Newark
Hanson & Van Winkle Co.
    (Electro Plating) ....AA
Peters Harness & Saddlery
    Co. (Horse) C
N. J.—Verona
Jacobus. A. G. (Mill)...F
N. Y.—Binghamton
Stow Mfg. Co. (Portable
    Power Horse) ....A
N. Y.—Brooklyn
Adams & Co.. J. J.. 132
    Greenpoint Av. (Brewers';

BRUSHES (*Con.*)

Gilders'; Tar & Roofing;
    Billiard Table; Dust;
    Floor; Floor & Furniture
    Waxing & Polishing; Hat;
    Hearth; Kitchen; Scrub;
    Shoe; Silver Cleaning;
    Velvet; Window; Artists';
    Camels' Hair; Flat;
    Paint; Fresco Painters';
    Graining; Lettering; Ship
    Seam; Stencil; Stippling;
    Varnish; Bath; Clothes;
    Flesh; Hair; Nail; Shaving; Pastry; Composition;
    Tooth) ....A
N. Y.—Buffalo
Jewett Mfg. Co., Jno.
    (Crumb) ....AA
N. Y.—East Syracuse
Benedict Mfg. Co., M. S.
    (Nail) ....AA
N. Y.—Kingston
Herbert Brush Mfg. Co.
    (Bath) C
N. Y.—Lansingburg
Dennison & Sons. Owen
    (Moulders'; Steel Boiler
    Flue; Tar & Roofing;
    Whitewash; Billiard
    Table; Crumb; Hat;
    Hearth; Kitchen; Scrub;
    Shoe & Daubers'; Velvet;
    Window; Flat Paint;
    Fresco Painters'; Varnish;
    Bath; Cloth; Flesh; Hair;
    Nail) ....B
Flynn Bros. (Horse; Glue;
    Dust; Fresco Painters';
    Bath; Cloth; Dandruff;
    Flesh; Shaving) ....A
Van Kleeck, Wm. H. (Billiard Table; Crumb; Hat;
    Special; Dandruff; Bath;
    Cloth; Hair; Nail; Flesh)
    D
Wood Co.. E. & C. (Hat;
    Bath; Cloth; Flesh; Hair;
    Nail) ....D
New York City
American Hard Rubber Co.,
    9 Mercer (Rubber) .AAAA
Bogue, Chas. J., 213 Center
    (Sheet Metal) ....D
Bradley & Smith (Horse;
    Glue; Kalsomine; Moulders'; Tanners' & Curriers';
    Tar & Roofing; Whitewash; Billiard Table; Bottle; Chimney; Crumb;
    Dust; Floor; Floor Waxing & Polishing; Glass
    Cleaning; Hearth;
    Kitchen; Lamp Chimney;
    Scrub; Shoe & Daubers';
    Silver Cleaning; Stove;
    Window; Blind; Bordering; Camel Hair; Flat
    Hair; Fresco Painters';
    Graining; Lettering;
    Marking; Mottling; Ship
    Seam; Skimming; Spoke;
    Stencil; Stippling; Varnish; Wood Fillers; Lacquering; Bath; Cloth;
    Flesh; Shaving) ......AA
Chatillon & Son. J.. 85
    Cliff (Butchers'; Packers') ....A
Devoe. F. W. & C. T. Raynolds Co. (Gilders'; Scrub;
    Flat Paint; Fresco Painters'; Graining; Lacquering; Marking; Ship Seam;
    Artists'; Photographers')
    AAAA
Estey Wire Works Co., 59
    Fulton (Steel Wire; Casting; Gearing; Flue)....D
Gennert, G. (Photographers') ....B
Gesswein Co.. F. W. (Platers'; Polishers'. &c.)....B
Gilbert & Bennett Mfg. Co.
    (Steel Casting; Steel
    Wire) ....AAAA
Green & Co.. W.. 6 Maiden
    Lane (Jewelers') .....B
Hanlon & Goodman (Glue;
    Kalsomine; Machine; Tar
    & Roofing; Whitewash;
    Billiard Table; Bottle;
    Chimney; Crumb; Furniture Waxing; Hearth;

BRUSHES (Con.)

Kitchen; Lamp Chimney; Scrub; Silver Cleaning; Artists'; Blind Bordering; Camels' Hair; Flat Paint; Fresco Painters'; Lacquering; Lettering; Marking; Mottling; Ship Seam; Skimming; Spoke; Stencil; Strippling; Varnish; Wood Fillers; Flesh; Shaving; Chamois; Cosmetic) .... A

Hollingsworth & Kip, 447 Greenwich .... A
International Silver Co., 9 Maiden Lane (S i l v e r Plated) ....AAAA
Irwin, R. M. C., 103 Chambers (Fountain Brush)...X
Leiner, Moritz (Bath; Flesh) C
Martins' Sons, J. M. C. (Horse; Glue; Printers'; Steel Boiler Flue; Tar & Roofing; Whitewash; Billiard Table; Dust; Floor; Floor Waxing & Polishing; Scrub; Shoe & Daubers'; Silver Cleaning; Window; Artists'; Blind; Camels' Hair; Carriage & Coach; Flat Paint; Marking; Stencil; Strippling; Varnish; Bath; Cloth; Flesh; Shaving) .... A
Medford Fancy Goods Co. (Dog) .... E
Miles Bros. & Co. (Paint; Varnish, &c.) .... D
Mitchell, E. (Billiard Table; Crumb; Scrub; Silver Cleaning; Flat Paint; Stencil; Metal Mounting; Flesh; Shaving; Marking) .... E
Mulholland, J. H., 80 Elm (Foundry; Machine; Factory; Hot Water Heater) .... D
Myles Bros. & Co. (Artists') .... B
Pierce Co., F. O., 170 Fulton (Varnish; Whitewash) .... A
Reichhelm & Co., E. P. (Plating; Steel Wire; Satin Finished; Brass Wire; Scratch; Jewelers' Scratch) .... A
Rosenthal & Bro., H., 418 W. B'way (Horse; Glue; Camels' Hair; Flat Paint; Marking; Varnish; Household; Whitewash) .....A
Smith & Sons, A., 146 William .... D
Smith & Son, J. Finley (Glue; Tar & Roofing; Horse; Billiard Table; Bottle; Crumb; Scrub; Shoe & Daubers'; Silver Cleaning; Stove; Lacquering; Marking; Ship Seam; Skimming; Stencil; Strippling) .... B
Spinal Brush Co., 1133 B'way (Spinal) X
United Brush Mfrs., 21 Park Pl. (Paint; Varnish, &c.) .... D
Zucker & Levett & Loeb Co., 526 W. 25th (Electro Plating) .... A

N. Y.—Rochester
Rochester Brush Mfg. Co., 419 St. Paul (Foundry; Machine; Factory) .....D
Wood Mosaic Co. (Floor Waxing & Polishing) ..AA

N. Y.—Schenectady
General Electric Co. (Carbon Commutator) ..AAAA

N. Y.—Troy
Bernard Co., E. G. (Carbon Dynamo) .... D
Dennins' Sons 6th Av. & 20th (Foundry; Factory; Machine) C
Parks & Parks (Shoe & Daubers'; Stove) ......D

OHIO—Barberton
Pure Gum Specialty Co. (Rubber) C

BRUSHES (Con.)

OHIO—Cincinnati
Barron, Boyle Co., 424 Main (Floor Polishing) ......B
Bromwell Brush & Wire Goods Co. (Horse; Moulders'; Steel Casting; Whitewash; Tar & Roofing; Scrub; Shoe & Daubers'; Stove; Window; Spoke; Varnish; Cloth; Shaving) .... AA
Cincinnati Mfg. Co. (Steel Foundry; Machine; Factory; Paint; Varnish; Mill) C
Claasen, F. H., 1421 Main (Paint) .... B
Obermayer Co., S. (Machinists' Bench; Plating; Steel Boiler Flue; Steel Casting; Moulders'; Steel Wire) .... AA
Smith Foundry Supply Co., J. D. (Moulders'; Foundry; Casting; Gearing; Flue) X
Washburn & Co., Ira (Paint; Varnish, &c.) C

OHIO—Cleveland
Claason, F. H. (Varnish; Paint; &c.) .... B
Cleveland Facing Mill Co. (Wire; Casting; Gearing & Flue) X
National Carbon Co. (Carbon Dynamo) ....AAAA
Osborn Mfg. Co. (Billiard Table; Butchers'; Packers'; Electro Plating; Foundry; Furnace; Heaters; Machine; Pipe; Scrub; Steel Wire; Tumbler; Whitewash; Horse; Shoe; Wire; Casting; Gearing; Flue; Wire; Horse; Hair; Cattle; Wire Wheel)...B

OHIO—Hamilton
Meyers Mfg. Co., Fred J. (Steel Boiler Flue; Steel Casting) .... B

OHIO—Mansfield
Ohio Brass Co. (Woven Wire) .... B

OHIO—Miamisburg
Miamisburg Electric Co. (Dynamo) .... B

OHIO—Toledo
Allen Mfg. Co. (Fountain; Bath) X
Ames-Bonner Co. (Hair)..A

OHIO—Troy
Ohio Electric Specialty Mfg. Co. (Leaf Copper Dynamo; Woven Wire Dynamo)...G

OHIO—Wooster
Wooster Brush Wks. (Horse; Bakers'; Kalsomine; Paper Hangers'; Whitewash; Counter; Dust; Brewers'; Floor; Floor, Waxing & Polishing; Dusting; Varnish; Artists' & Painters'; Scrub; Paste) ....B

PA.—Columbia
East Columbia Brush Co. (Paint; Varnish; &c.)..C

PA.—Easton
Pollock Brush Co. (Horse; Cylinder; Moulders'; Dust; Jewelers' Wheel; Floor; Mill Sweeping; Pipe Cleaning Fibre; Shoe & Daubers; Water Closet; Window) .... D

PA.—Erie
Continental Rubber Works (Rubber) .... A

PA.—Northeast
Eureka Tempered Copper Wks. (Finger Copper; Sheet Metal & Woven Wire) .... B

PA.—Philadelphia
Ames-Bonner Co., Phila. Bourse .... A
Clinton & Co., E., 1008 Market .... A
Colescott & Co., W. A., 133 Market C
Darby & Sons, Edward, 232 Arch (Wire) .... A
Elder & Jenks, 127 No. 5th .... D

128

BRUSHES (Con.)

French & Co., Saml. H., 4th & Callowhill (Paint; Varnish, &c.) ....AAA
Galati, J. H., 4355 Main Myk. ....D
Holmes Fibre & Graphite Mfg. Co. (Commutator).D
Horn & Co., Wm. H. (Tanners'; Curriers') ....B
Keller, Robert (Beer Bottle) D
Lucas & Co., John (Gilders'; Scrub; Flat Point; Varnish) ....AAA
McKim & Co., J., 131 No. 10th ....B
Nelms & Co., 30 No. 4th..D
Paxson & Co., J. W. (Foundry; Plating; Steel Boiler Flue; Steel Wire) ....AA
Philadelphia Elec. & Mfg. Co. (Commutator) ...,.E
Stow Flexible Shaft Co. (Portable; Power; Horse) B
Thum, Chas. D. (Jewelers' Wheel; Machine; Silversmith' Wheel; Varnish).D
White Dental Mfg. Co. S. S. (Tooth) ....AAAA
Wirt Electric Co., 4523 Tacony (Sheet Metal)..D
PA.—Pittsburg
Wolfe, Walker & Co., 510 Wood (Paint; Varnish, &c.) ....B
R. I.—Pawtucket
Thayers' Son, Ellis (Kalsomine; Machine; Moulders'; Paper Hangers'; Printers'; Steel Wire; Satin Finished; Brass Wire; Scratch; Tanners'; Curriers'; Whitewash; Hat; Kitchen; Lamp Chimney; Scrub; Shoe & Daubers; Silver-Cleaning; Stove; Window; Blind; Flat Paint; Fresco Painters'; Power). X
R. I.—Providence
Bens, Wm. (Silver Mounted) C
Coe Mfg. Co., Wm. H. (Gilders') ....B
Foster & Bros. Co., Theo W. (Sterling Silver Hair) AA
Nicholson File Co. (File) AAAA
Rhode Island Brush Co. (Mill) ....A
Voelker, Philip L. (Mill)..F
VT.—Springfield
Parks & Woolson Machine Co. (Mill) ....B
WIS.—Milwaukee
Milwaukee Dustless Brush Co. (Dustless Floor)....D

BUCHU

New York City
Hopkins & Co., J. L., 100 William ....A

BUCKETS

See also Woodenware; Tinware, etc.

CAL.—Los Angeles
Thomson & Boyle Co. (Coal; Ore)...............C
CAL.—San Francisco
Hendy Machine Wks., Joshua (Coal; Ore)....AA
COLO.—Denver
Colo. Iron Wks. Co. (Coal; Mining) ....AA
Davis Iron Wks. Co., F. M. (Coal; Ore) ....A
Denver Engineering Wks. (Coal; Ore) ....A
Mine & Smelter Supply Co. (Coal; Ore) ....AAA
Montgomery Mchry. Co., J. H. (Ore) C
CONN.—Bridgeport
Canfield Co.,. H. O. (Rubber; Chain; Pump) ....D
CONN.—Meriden
Bradley & Hubbard Mfg. Co.

BUCKETS (Con.)

(Fireplace) ......AAAA
CONN.—New Britain
North & Judd Mfg. Co. (Dredge) ....AA
ILL.—Chicago
Allis-Chalmers Co., Home Ins. Bldg. (Elevator; Ore; Coal; Gold Dredging) AAAA
Borden & Selleck Co., 45 Lake (Coal; Ore) ......B
Bullock Mfg. Co., (Steel; Coal; Ore).......X
Caldwell & Son Co., H. W., 17th & Western Av. (Seamless; Steel; Elevator; Ore) ....A
Hoisting & Conveying Mchry. Co., 44 N. Elizabeth (Coal; Ore) ....D
Illinois Malleable Iron Co., 20 W. Monroe (Elevator; Ore) ....AAAA
Link Belt Machinery Co. (Elevator) ....AAA
Olmsted & Co., 100 N. Clinton (Chain Pump) C
Skillin & Richards Mfg. Co. 147 Fulton (Elevator)...C
Temple Pump Co. (Chain Pump) ....A
Thornburgh-Creel Mfg. Co. (Elevator) X
Webster Mfg. Co., 1075 15th (Elevator) ....AA
Weller Mfg. Co., 118 E. North Av. (Elevator)...C
ILL.—Evanston
Mark Mfg. Co. (Chain Pump) ....AA
ILL.—Marseilles
Marseilles Mfg. Co. (Elevator) ....A
IND.—Indianapolis
Cooney, Seiner & Co. (Elevator) ....B
Nordyke & Marmon Co., 1101 W. Morris (Elevator) ....AAA
IND.—Mishawaka
Dodge Mfg. Co. (Elevator) AAA
KANS.—Leavenworth
Great Western Mfg. Co. (Elevator) ....AA
LA.—New Orleans
New Orleans Roofing & Metal Wks. ....A
MD.—Baltimore
Ryan-McDonald Mfg. Co. (Hoisting; Coal; Steel; Ore) ....A
MICH.—Detroit
Buhl Malleable Co., Wight & Adair (Elevator).....A
Detroit Sprocket Chain Co. (Ltd.) (Coal) X
MICH.—Lansing
Lansing Wheelbarrow Co. (Coal) ....AA
MINN.—Minneapolis
Minneapolis Steel & Mchry. Co. (Elevator; Ore) ....A
MO.—Kansas City
Weber Gas & Gasoline Engine Co. (Ore) ....B
MO.—St. Joseph
St. Joseph Pump & Mfg. Co. (Elevator) ....B
MO.—St. Louis
Leschen & Sons Rope Co. (Hoisting; Ore; Self Dumping) ....AAA
Nat'l Enameling & Stamping Co. (Sewer) ......AAAA
St. Louis Stamping Co. (Factory) ....AAAA
N. H.—Keene
Impervious Package Co. (Sugar) ....B
N. H.—Sandown
Lovering, J. W. (Well)...C
N. J.—High Bridge
Taylor Iron & Steel Co. (Elevator) ....AAAA
N. J.—Jersey City
Smith & Sons Co., Theo. (Clam Shell) ....A
N. J.—Hoboken
Union Iron Wks. (Coal; Ore; Dredging; Excavating; Elevator) ....D
N. J.—Newark
Mundy, J. S. (Coal; Elevator) ....A

BUCKETS (Con.)

N. Y.—Albany
Dederick's Sons, P. K.
(Coal) ....A
N. Y.—Brooklyn
American Stamping Co.
(Fire; Galvanized) X
Phillips, Doup & Co., 56
Pearl (Clam Shell; Coal)
...............................D
N. Y.—Buffalo
Noye Mfg. Co., Jno. T.
(Elevator) ....D
Shepard & Co., Sidney (Fire;
Galvanized) ......AAAA
N. Y.—Cuba
Crosby Co. (Rubber for
Chain Pumps) C
N. Y.—Elmira
Cronk & Carrier Mfg. Co.
(Chain Pump) ....B
N. Y.—Long Island City
Stuebner, G. L. (Coal; Coal
Steel; Ore) C
New York City
Cordley & Hayes, 172 Duane
(Fire; Paper) ....A
Fairbanks Co., 416 Broome
(Elevator; Hoisting; Ore;
Self Dumping) ...AAAA
Goodyear's India Rubber
Glove Mfg. Co. (Deck;
Yacht; Fire; Rubber) ..
AAAA
Gutta Percha & Rubber Mfg.
Co., 35 Warren (Fire;
Rubber) ....AAAA
Haiss Mfg. Co., Geo., 141st
& Rider Av. (Coal; Ore)
...............................D
Hayward Co., 97 Cedar
(Clam Shell; Dredging;
Excavating) ....B
Hodgman Rubber Co., 595
Bway. (Fire; Rubber) AA
Howard & Morse, 45 Fulton
(Fire) ....D
Iron Clad Mfg. Co. (Eleva-
tor; Deck; Yacht; Fire;
Galvanized; Well) ..AAA
Lalance & Grojean Mfg. Co.
(Factory) ....AAAA
Link-Belt Engineering Co.
(Elevator) ....AA
Mineralized Rubber Co., 18
Cliff (Fire) ....AA
N. J. Foundry & Machine
Co. (Hoisting; Self Dump-
ing) ....D
Ransome Concrete Machy.
Co. (Elevator) C
Stoutenborough, X (Sewer)
.......................D
N. Y.—Niagara Falls
Dobbie Fdry. & Machine Co.
(Clam Shell; Coal; Ore;
Orange Peel) ....B
N. Y.—Syracuse
Syracuse Chilled Plow Co.
(Steel; Sewer) ....AA
N. Y.—Utica
Clark, Horrocks Co. (Min-
now) ....A
Miller & Son, Chas. (Sap)
AA
N. Y.—Warsaw
Warsaw Elevator Co. (Salt)
.......................B
N. Y.—West New Brighton
Hunt Co., C. W. (Hoisting)
.......................A

OHIO—Akron
Akron Rubber Works
(Rubber) ....AAAA
Webster Camp & Lane Co.
(Clam Shell) ....A
OHIO—Canton
Aultman Co. (Elevator)..A
OHIO—Cincinnati
American Copper & Brass
Wks. (Copper) ....A
Greenwald Co., I. & E.
(Elevator) ....A
Obermayer Co., S., 647
Evans (Foundry) .....A
OHIO—Cleveland
Avery Stamping Co. (Eleva-
tor; Steel, Seamless Eleva-
tor) ....A
Bartlett, C. O. & Snow Co.
(Coal; Ore; Elevator;
Hoisting) ....B
Brown Hoisting Mchry. Co.
(Elevator; Self Dumping)
AAAA
Cleveland Elevator Bucket

BUCKETS (Con.)
Co., 223 St. Clair .....D
Cleveland Galvanizing Wks.
(Factory; Pump; Eleva-
tor) ....B
Garry Iron & Steel Co. (Ore;
Hoisting; Self Dumping)
.......................A
Hunt & Dorman Mfg. Co.,
18 High (Fire) ...AAAA
McMyler Mfg. Co. (Coal;
Ore) ....A
Osborne Mfg. Co. (Factory)
.......................A
Schriver & Co., O. P.
(Rubber; Chain Pump).C
Smith Fdry. Co., J. D. 40
S. Water (Foundry; Fac-
tory) ....D
Wellman-Seaver-Morgan Co.
(Hoisting; Ore; Self
Dumping) ....AAAA
OHIO—Columbus
Case Mfg. Co. (Elevator) AA
Jeffery Mfg. Co. (Coal; Ore;
Dredging; Excavating;
Elevator; Crab) ......AA
OHIO—Salem
Clark Co., W. J. (Ore;
Dredge; Elevator; Eleva-
tor Steel, Seamless; Fac-
tory; Hoisting; Fire; Self
Dumping; Steel; Ore) ..A
OHIO—Sandusky
Kilbourn & Co. (Sugar) ...C
OHIO—Toledo
Union Mfg. Co. (Deck;
Yacht; Chain Pump; Rub-
ber) X
OHIO—Youngstown
Pollock Co., W. B. (Hoist-
ing; Ore; Pipe) ....B
OHIO—Zanesville
Griffiths & Wedge Co. (Ore)
.......................A

PA.—Allegheny
Carlin's Sons, Thos. (Hoist-
ing) ....A
PA.—Ashland
Laubenstein, A. L. (Eleva-
tor) ....D
PA.—New Castle
Penna. Engineering Wks.
(Elevator) ....A
PA.—Philadelphia
Paxon Co., J. W., 1021 Del.
Av. (Foundry) ....AA
Pfeiffer & Co., Jno., 224
Race (Coal; Galvanized
Iron; Asphalt) ....A
PA.—Pittsburg
Scaife & Sons Co., Wm. B.,
221 First Av. (Dredging;
Excavating; Elevator; Au-
to. Steam Coal) ......B
PA.—Pittston
Exeter Machine Wks.
(Clam Shell) ....B
PA.—South Bethlehem
Bethlehem Fdry. & Mach-
ine Co. (Elevator) C
PA.—Wilkesbarre
Vulcan Iron Wks. (Coal;
Ore; Hoisting; Elevator)
AA
R. I.—Providence
Hill Mfg. Co., Jas. (Galv.
Iron) ....B
VA.—Richmond
Richmond Cedar Wks.
(Well) ....AAAA
WIS.—Cudahy
Power & Mining Machinery
Co. (Coal; Ore; Dredging;
Excavating; Elevator)...
AAA
WIS.—Milwaukee
Chain Belt Co. (Hoisting;
Coal; Steel; Ore Steel;
Elevator) ....B

BUCKLES

See also Silverware, etc.

CONN.—Bridgeport
Armstrong Mfg. Co. (Ven-
tilator) ....A
Connecticut Web Co.
(Garter) ....A
CONN.—Middletown
Chapman & Co.. W. H.
(Harness) ....B
CONN.—Mt. Carmel
Woodruff & Sons. Walter
W. (Harness) ....A

BUCKETS (Con.)
CONN.—New Britain
North & Judd Mfg. Co.
  (Belt; Hat; Overshoe; Sus-
  pender; Trouser; Wire;
  Garter; Harness).....AA
Stanley Wks. (Back Band)
  AAA
Traut & Hine Mfg. Co.
  (Suspender) ....A
CONN.—New Haven
Cowles & Co., C. (Harness)
Fitch Co., W. & E. T. (Belt;
  Harness; Steel) .....AA
North & Co., O. B. (Steel;
  Harness; Arctic) .....AA
CONN.—Shelton
Mosher, Geo. D. (Harness)
  D
CONN.—Waterbury
Lane Mfg. Co. (Belt; Gar-
  ter) X
Scoville Mfg. Co. (Brass)
  AAAA
Waterbury Buckle Co.
  (Shoe; Belt) ....AA
CONN.—West Haven
American Buckle Co. (Gar-
  ter; Hat; Overshoe; Sus-
  pender; Trouser; Deformi-
  ty Appliance; Truss)..D
West Haven Buckle Co.
  (Suspender; Trouser)...C
ILL.—Chicago
Illinois Malleable Iron Co.
  (Pine) ....AAAA
MASS.—Boston
Boston Bolt Co., 33 Purchase
  (Pipe) ....B
MASS.—Springfield
Newell Bros. (Lock Prong)
  X
MASS.—Waltham
Thompson Mfg. Co., Judson
  C. (Overshoe) ....A
MASS.—Worcester
Spencer Wire Co. (Wire) .A
N. J.—Newark
Grossner, F. W. (Harness)
  H
Jenkinson & Co., R. C.
  (Belt; Trunk; Bag) AA
Newark Saddlery Co. (Arc-
  tic; Ladies' Belt) ....H
Sargeant Mfg. Co. (Harness)
  A
Weiner & Co. (Steel; Har-
  ness) C
N. Y.—Binghamton
Crandal, Stone & Co. (Har-
  ness) ....A
N. Y.—Brooklyn
Goodyear Buckle Co. (Arc-
  tic; Legging; Skate Strap;
  Overshoe) ....B
N. Y.—Fulton
Dilts Mach. Co. (Steel) ..C
New York City
Halls' Sons. S., 229 W. 10th
  (Pine; Pipe) ....A
Marks. A. A. (Deformity
  Appliance) ....AA
Metal Stamping Co. (Har-
  ness) ....B
Stimpson & Son, Edwin B.
  (Shoe) ....A
N. Y.—Syracuse
Frazer & Jones Co. (Arctic)
  AA
OHIO—Canton
Elbel Co. (Steel; Cinch; Fly;
  Girth; Harness; Skate;
  Spur Strap) ....A
OHIO—Cleveland
Eberhard Mfg. Co. (Har-
  ness; Brass) ....AA
OHIO—Mansfield
Ohio Brass Co. (Tongueless)
  AA
PA.—Lebanon
American Iron & Steel Mfg.
  Co. (Pipe) ....AAAA
PA.—Phila.
Develin Mfg. Co., Thos.
  (Steel) ....AA

BUCKRAM

MASS.—Medfield
Ray & Wilson C
MASS.—Taunton
Chandler Oilcloth & Buck-
  ram Co. ....A
N. J.—Bloomfield
Wiggins Sons Co., H. B...A

BUCKRAM (Con.)
N. J.—Passaic
McLean Co., Andrew ....AA
N. J.—Tenafly
Richter Mfg. Co..........C
New York City
Adams Mfg. Co., 106 Grand
  A
N. Y.—Valley Falls
Thompson & Co., Jas....AA

BUCKS

IND.—Goshen
I. X. L. & Goshen Pump
  Co. (Saw) ....B
IND.—Indianapolis
Atkins & Co., E. C. (Saw)
  AAA
Tucker & Dorsey Mfg. Co.
  (Saw) ....A
IOWA—Fort Madison
Iowa Farming Tool Co.
  (Saw) ....A
OHIO—Columbus
Ohio Tool Co. (Saw) .....A
OHIO—Toledo
Union Mfg. Co. (Saw)....X
PA.—Philadelphia
Disston & Sons, Henry
  (Saw) ....AAAA

BUCKSKINS

See Leather

BUCKWHEAT

See Cereals

BUFFERS

ILL.—Chicago
National Car Coupler Co.
  Monadnock Blk. ....A
MASS.—Boston
Edson Mfg. Co. (Broom)..B
N. J.—Newark
Heller Bros. Co. (Black-
  smith) ....AA

BUFFETS

See also Furniture

IND.—Cornersville
Indiana Furniture Co......A
MICH.—Grand Rapids
Grand Rapids Chair Co..AA
OHIO—Cincinnati
Mitchell Furniture Co., R.
  AAAA

BUFFS

See Wheels; Buffing

BUGGIES

See Carriages & Wagons

BUGLES

See Musical Instruments

BULBS

For Flowers, see Seeds

CONN.—New Haven
Seamless Rubber Co. (Rub-
  ber) ....AA
IND.—Alexandria
Lippencott Glass Co. (In-
  candescent Lamp) .....A
MASS.—Andover
Tyer Rubber. Co. (Rubber)
  AA
MASS.—Boston
Bailey & Co., C. J. (Rub-
  ber) ....B
Davidson Rubber Co. Rub-
  ber; Breast Pump).....A
MASS.—New Bedford
Pairpont Mfg. Co. (Incan-
  descent Lamp) ....AA
N. Y.—Corning
Corning Glass Co. (Incan-
  descent Lamp) ....A
N. Y.—New Brighton
Muralo Co. (Relief Paint-
  ing) ....A
New York City
Goodyear's India Rubber
  Glove Mfg. Co. (Rubber)
  AAAA
Mattson Rubber Co. (Rub-

BULBS (Con.)
ber) ....B
Parker, Stearns & Sutton
  (Rubber) ....B
Van Houten, E. J. S. (In-
  candescent Light) .....B
Wagner Glass Wks. 213 E.
  19th (Incandescent Lamp)
                         D
OHIO—Akron
Akron Rubber Wks., (B. F.
  Goodrich Co.) (Rubber)
                      AAAA
OHIO—Fostoria
Fostoria Bulb & Bottle Co.
  (Incandescent Lamp)...A
OHIO—Steubenville
Gill Bros. & Co. (Electric)
                        AA
OHIO—Toledo
Libbey Glass Co. (Incan-
  descent Lamp) ....AA
PA.—Pittsburg
Phoenix Glass Co. (Incan-
  descent Lamp) ....A
R. I.—Providence
Davol Rubber Co. (Rubber)
                       AA

BUMPERS
CONN.—Bridgeport
Canfield Co., H. O. (Screw;
  Rubber) ....B
Knapp & Cowles Mfg. Co.
  (Rubber; Car)........C
ILL.—Chicago
Morgan & Wright, 333 W.
  Lake (Elevator) .....AA
Railway Appliance Co. (R.
  R. Car) ....A
N. J.—Jersey City
N. J. Car Spring & Rubber
  Co. (Rubber; Car)....AA
N. J.—Trenton
Home Rubber Co. (Wagon)
                       AA
New York City
Gutta Percha & Rubber Mfg.
  Co. (Rubber; Car)..AAAA
Rubber Goods Mfg. Co. (R.
  R. Car) ....AAAA

BUNCHERS
See also Agr. Implements

IND.—Indianapolis
American Buncher Mfg. Co.
                        B
LA.—Shreveport
Henderson Iron Works &
  Supply Co., W. K.
  (Shingle) ....AA
N. J.—Hightstown
Shangle, John R. (Aspara-
  gus) C
N. Y.—Greene
Lyon Iron Works (Shingle)
                        B
PA.—Philadelphia
Dreer, Henry A. (Aspara-
  gus) ....A

BUNDLERS
MICH.—Kalamazoo
Hill & Co., W. E. (Lath)..B
New York City
Reilley Bros. (Wall Paper)
                        D
VT.—Montpelier
Lane Mfg. Co. (Lath)....A
WIS.—Eau Clair
Phoenix Mfg. Co. (Lath)..A

BUNGS
ILL.—Chicago
Economical Beer Pump Co.
                        D
Liquid Carbonic Acid Mfg.
  Co. ....AAAA
Redlich Mfg. Co. (Wood;
  Cork Lined)...........B
MAINE—Portland
Portland Cooperage Co.
  (Cut; Lager Beer).....C
MASS.—Cambridgeport
Standard Turning Wks. ...C
MASS.—Lowell
Bachelder & Co. (Beer Kegs)
                        C
N. J.—Newark
Sommers' Son, J. (Wooden)

BUNGS (Con.)
                         A
N. Y.—Albany
Kampf, Stephen ....E
N. Y.—Brooklyn
U. S. Bung Mfg. Co. .....A
New York City
Cahn & Co., Hugo ....A
OHIO—Cincinnati
U. S. Bung Mfg. Co.
  (Brewers) ....A
OHIO—Cleveland
Taylor & Boggis Fdry. Co.
  (Oil Can) ....AA
PA.—Philadelphia
Keller, Robert (Brewers').D
PA.—Pittsburg
Armstrong Cork Co...AAAA

BUNKS
See Beds

BUNTING
See also Cotton Goods

MASS.—Boston
Boston Regalia Co., 7
  Temple Pl. (Silk)......F
MASS.—Fitchburg
Fitchburg Worsted Co.....X
MASS.—Lowell
New England Bunting Co.
                      AAAA
U. S. Bunting Co.....AAAA
N. Y.—New Hartford
New Hartford Cotton Mfg.
  Co. ....A
PA.—Philadelphia
Horstmann Co., Wm. H.
                      AAAA
Prince, S. L., 2553 Jasper
  (Wool Flag) ....F
R. I.—Pawtucket
Slater Cotton Co........AA

BUOYS
DEL.—Wilmington
Drein & Son. Thos. ......B
N. Y.—Brooklyn
Kahnweilers' Sons, David
  (Marine) C
N. Y.—Long Island City
Lane & De Groot Co......D
PA.—Pittsburg
Armstrong Cork Co. (Cork;
  Cork Life; Marine), AAAA

BUREAUS
See Furniture

BURGEES
MINN.—Minneapolis
American Tent & Awning
  Co. ....F
New York City
American Flag Co. ....A
Boyle & Co., Jno........AA
Koster Co., C. H........D
McHugh, Jno. F.........C

BURLAPS
CAL.—San Francisco
California Jute Mill Co....A
GA.—Atlanta
Fulton Bag & Cotton Mills
                       AA
N. J.—Bloomfield
Wiggins Sons Co., H. B.
  (Decorative) ....A
N. J.—Tenafly
Richter Mfg. Co. (Decora-
  tive) C
New York City
Beck & Co., Fr. 7th Av. &
  29th (Decorative) ....A
Roberts, Edw. Craig. 13 E.
  30th (Japanese Decora-
  tive) X
Scott & Sons, Jas. (Com.)
                      AAA
Turner & Co., J. Spencer,
  88 Worth (Decorative)..A
White & Co., Jas. F. (Com.)
                      AAAA
PA.—Philadelphia
Bailey & Co., Jno. T.
                      AAAA
S. C.—Charleston
Charleston Bagging Mfg.
  Co. ....AAAA

BURLAPS (Con.)
TENN.—Jackson
Jackson Fibre Co.....AAAA

BURNERS

CAL.—San Francisco
Pacific Acetylene Gas Co.
(Acetylene Gas).......G
CONN.—Bridgeport
Bridgeport Brass Co. (Argand; Gasoline; Lamp; Lantern; Kerosene)..AAA
CONN.—Bristol
Bristol Brass & Clock Co.
(Lamp) ....F
CONN.—Meriden
Bradley & Hubbard Mfg. Co.
(Argand; Lamp)..AAAA
Miller & Co., Edw. (Incandescent Gas; Argand; Lamp; Lantern)....AAAA
CONN.—Stamford
Stamford Gas Stove Co. (Incandescent; Natural Gas)
                              C
CONN.—Waterbury
Benedict & Burnham Mfg.
Co. (Incandescent Gas; Lamp) ....AAAA
Electrical Appliance Mfg.
Co. (Electric Gas Lighting) ....G
Holmes, Booth & Haydens
Co. (Inc.) (Argand; Lamp) ....AAAA
Plume & Atwood Mfg. Co.
(Kerosene; Incandescent Gas; Argand; Lamp)
                            AAA
Scovill Mfg. Co. (Lamp; Kerosene) ....AAAA
ILL.—Chicago
Abner Acetylene Gas Co., La
Salle (Acetylene Gas)...E
Adams & Westlake Co.
(Oil Fuel) ....AAAA
Bystrom Gas Lamp Co., 91
Kinzee (Gasoline Gas).F
Carroll, J. B., 36 La Salle
(Acetylene Gas) ....E
Chicago Pneumatic Tool Co.,
Fisher Bldg. (Paint)
                           AAAA
Flory, Louis, 218 Washn.
(Gasoline; Gas) ....F
Illinois Malleable Iron Co.,
30 W. Monroe (Natural Gas) ....AAAA
International Gas & Fuel
Co., 183 Dearborn (Fuel Oil) X
Turner Brass Wks., 69 N.
Franklin (Gasoline Gas; Paint; Brazing) ....D
Union Drop Forge Co. (Oil Fuel) ....A
Williamson & Co., R., 52
E. Lake (Acetylene; Natural Gas) ....A
KY.—Louisville
Daylight Acetylene Gas Co.
(Acetylene Gas) ....E
MAINE—Portland
Conant Co., R. O. (Brazing)
                              F
MASS.—Boston
Boston Electric Co., 29
Harrison (Electric Gas Lighting) ....B
Electric Gas Lighting Co.,
195 Devonshire (Electric Gas Lighting) ....A
McKenney & Waterbury
(Natural Gas) ....D
Walworth Mfg. Co. (Gas Heating; Gasoline).AAAA
MASS.—Brookline
Holtzer-Cabot Electric Co.
(Electric Gas Lighting).A
MASS.—Somerville
Borg, Peter (Automobile Gasoline) C
MICH.—Detroit
Clayton & Lambert Mfg. Co.
(Acetylene Gas; Paint).B
Detroit Brass Wks., 7th &
M. C. R. R. (Natural Gas)
                              B
Economy Stove & Mfg. Co.
(Natural Gas) ....E
Union Heater Supply Co., 15
Macomb (Paint) ......G
MICH.—Muskegon
Muskegon Boiler Wks.
(Refuse) ....B

BURNERS (Con.)
MICH.—Saginaw
Jackson & Church Co.
(Refuse) ....A
MINN.—Minneapolis
Central Gas Fixture Co.
(Natural Gas) ....E
MO.—St. Louis
American Stove Co. (Natural Gas) ....AAAA
Eagle Generator Co., 16th &
Pine (Acetylene Gas)...D
Kraushaar Lamp & Reflector
Co., 510 Elm (Natural Gas) ....D
Merkel, Herman, 511 Elm
(Gasoline Gas) X
Planet Mfg. Co., 203 Pine
(Gasoline Gas) ....E
N. J.—Elizabeth
American Gas Furnace Co.
(Jewelers') ....A
N. J.—Gloucester City
Rogers Boat Wks. J. M.
(Fuel Oil; Kerosene)...B
Welsbach Light Co. (Incandescent Gas) ......AAA
N. J.—Jersey City
Wiederhold Light Co. (Incandescent Gas) ......D
N. Y.—Auburn
Standard Oil Fuel Burner
Co. (Hydro-Carbon) AAAA
N. Y.—Brooklyn
Incandescent Burner Co., 633
Fulton (Incandescent; Acetylene Gas) ....E
Northern Light Co., 1242
Fulton (Acetylene; Natural Gas) ....E
N. Y.—Buffalo
Buffalo Dental Mfg. Co.
(Gas Heating; Jewelers'; Bunsen) ....B
Niagara Machine & Tool
Wks. (Gasoline Stove)..A
O'Reilly, Michael J. (Natural Gas) ....D
Tallmage, M. F. (Natural Gas) ....B
Taylor, J. B. (Natural Gas)
                              F
Vim Cycle Hdw. Co., 224
Bway. (Natural Gas)..E
N. Y.—Hoosick Falls
American Acetylene Burner
Co. (Acetylene Gas)....B
New York City
Acetylene Gas Illuminating
Co., 105 Walker (Acetylene Gas) ....E
American Brass & Copper
Co. (Acetylene Gas)....E
American Incandescent
Lamp Co. (Incandescent Gas) ....E
Bogart Co., A. L., 123 Liberty (Electric Gas Lighting; Argand; Automatic)
                              B
Bramhall-Deane Co. (Jewelers') ....B
Colt Co., J. B., 21 Barclay
(Acetylene Gas) ......D
Crane Co., W. M., 1133
Bway. (Acetylene & Natural Gas; Self Lighting Gas) ....A
Cremo Incandescent Light
Co. 110 E. 129th (Incandescent Gas) ....F
Criterion Gas Stove Mfg.
Co., 445 Greenwich (Natural Gas) ....B
Deeley & Co., Robt. (Bagasse) ....AA
De Lery Light Co., 256 W.
23d (Natural Gas).....D
Dietz Co., R. E. (Lantern)
                              A
Edwards & Co., 407 E. 144th
(Electric Gas Lighting).C
Folmer & Schwing Mfg. Co.
(Gas) ....B
Gas Tin & Self Lighter Co.,
25 W. Bdway. (Acetylene Gas) ....B
Gilbert & Barker Mfg. Co.,
82 John (Fuel Oil; Incandescent Gas; Gas Heating) C
Gleason Mfg. Co., E. A.,
20 W. Houston (Acetylene; Natural Gas; Gas Heater) ....A
Gleason-Peters Air Pump Co.

BURNERS (*Con.*)

20 W. Houston (Hydro-Carbon) ....D

OHIO—Toledo

Hancock Inspirator Co., 85 Liberty (Fuel Oil) ......A

Iden & Co., 40 University Pl. (Acetylene Gas) ......AA

Imperial Gas Machine Co., 32 Park Pl. (Acetylene; Natural Gas) ....F

Kern Incandescent **Gas** Light Co., 18 Murray...C

Kirchberger & Co., M., 50 Warren (Acetylene Gas) B

Manhattan Brass Co., 338 E. 28th (Incandescent Gas) AA

Manhattan Electrical Supply Co., 32 Cortlandt (Electric Gas Lighting).....A

Manning, Maxwell & Moore, 85 Liberty (Hydro-Carbon) AA

Matchless Mfg. Co. (Gas Incandescent) ....D

Mitchell-Vance Co. (Gas) AA

Monmand, Sherman S., 672 Columbus Av. (Incandescent Gas) ....F

Nichols, Wm. S., 253 Bway. (Acetylene Gas) X

Orchard Mfg. Co., 51 Frankfort (Natural Gas).....F

Parsons Mfg. Co., 320 Bway. (Fuel Oil) C

Reilley Bros. (Painters'; Charcoal) ....D

Rochester Lamp Co., 38 Park Pl. (Natural Gas; Lamp) X

Rockwell Engineering Co., 26 Cortlandt (Fuel Oil).B

Rousseau's Electrical Wks., 329 4th Av. (Electric Gas Lighting) ....E

Seabury & Johnson (Cautery) ....AA

Tirrill Gas Machine Lighting Co., 441 Bway. (Gasoline Gas) ....A

United Metal Mfg. Co., 525 Broome (Acetylene Gas) D

Van Houten, E. J., 74 Park Pl. (Natural Gas).....B

Wellington Mfg. Co. (Gasoline) X

N. Y.—Oswego

Tonkin Boiler Co. (Automobile Kerosene) X

N. Y.—Rochester

Clark Nov. Co. (Kerosene Oil) ....D

OHIO—Canton

Best Street Light Co. (Paint) ....B

Sun Vapor Street Light Co. (Gasoline Gas) ....A

OHIO—Cincinnati

Incandescent Light & Stove Co., 420 Pearl (Gasoline Gas) ....D

Macleod & Co., Walter, 463 E. Front (Paint) ......B

Vanduzen Co., E. W. (Gas Engine) ....B

OHIO—Cleveland

Dangler Stove & Mfg. Div. Am. Stove Co. (Auto.) AAAA

Drake Acetylene Apparatus Co., 37 Hathaway (Acetyline Gas) ....F

Forest City Brass Works (Gasoline) ....B

Hull, M. L. (Paint; Street Lamp) ....H

Natural Stove & Illuminating Co., New England Bldg. (Acetylene Gas)..D

Schneider & Trenkamp Co. (Paint) ....AAAA

OHIO—Columbus

Elk Heater Mfg. Co. (Natural Gas) ....D

Ohio Pump Brass Co. (Natural Gas) ....D

Victor Lighting Co. (Gasoline Gas) ....F

OHIO—Dayton

Dayton Pipe & Cable Coupling Co. (Natural Gas)..B

OHIO—Massillon

Hess, Snyder Co. (Natural

BURNERS (*Con.*)

Gas) ....AA

OHIO—Toledo

National Cement & Rubber Mfg. Co. (Brazing) C

Toledo Gas & Oil Burner Co. (Natural Gas)......E

PA.—Allegheny

Enterprise Fdry. Co. (Natural Gas) ....E

Pittsburg Lamp Brass & Glass Co. (Incandescent Gas; Argand; Lamp) AAAA

Superior Mfg. Co. (Natural Gas) C

PA.—Claysville

Jamison & Co., T. H. (Natural Gas) ....F

PA.—Corry

Love Mfg. Co. (Natural Gas) F

PA.—Easton

William & Co., C. K. (Paint) ....A

PA.—Erie

Hollands Mfg. Co. (Natural Gas) C

Odin Stove Mfg. Co. (Natural Gas) ....B

PA.—Homestead

Lawson Mfg. Co., L. S. (Natural Gas) ....D

PA.—Meadville

Lord Co., L. I. (Natural Gas) ....D

PA.—New Brighton

Pittsburg Clay Mfg. Co. (Natural Gas).....AAAA

PA.—Philadelphia

Boekel & Co., Wm., 578 Vine (Bunsen; Glass Blower) ....A

Brown & Co., F. P., 45 N. 6th (Acetylene; Natural Gas) ....E

Cleverly Electric Wks., 1018 Chestnut (Electric Gas Lighting ....F

Cox & Sons Co., 215 Race (Fuel Oil) ....B

Gefrorer, C. A. (Gasoline) F

Janney, Steinmetz & Co. (Auto.) ....B

Morris, Henry G. (Bagasse) B

Parke & Co., Jno. G., 728 Cherry (Electric Gas Lighting) ....D

Vallco Bros. Electric Co., 625 Arch (Electric Gas Lighting) ....B

PA.—Pittsburg

Adler Co., H. (Natural Gas) B

Oil Well Supply Co. (Natural Gas) ....AAAA

Pittsburg Stove & Range Co. (Natural Gas) AAAA

Pittsburg Supply Co. (Natural Gas) ....B

Reineke Wilson Co. (Natural Gas) ....B

Simpson Stove & Mfg. Co., 26 Liberty Av. (Natural Gas) ....D

Standard Heating & Radiator Co., 108 Market (Furnace Gas) C

Tate, Jones & Co., Empire Bldg. (Fuel Oil) ......E

PA.—Reading

National Brass & Iron Wks. (Lamp) ....A

PA.—Titusville

Young & Sons, E. R. (Natural Gas) ....B

PA.—Uniontown

Johnson Machine Co. (Natural Gas) ....D

PA.—Washington

Petroleum Iron Wks. Co. (Fuel Oil) ....B

R. I.—Providence

Providence Gas Burner Co. (Gasoline Gas; Jewelers') C

S. C.—Charleston

Valk & Murdock Iron Wks. (Pyrites) ....B

TENN.—Chattanooga

American Lava Co. (Gas).D

Casey & Hedges Mfg. Co. (Bagasse) ....A

Crescent Novelty Co. (Acety-

BURNERS (Con.)

lene Gas) ....E
Starr Acetyline Gas Burner
Co. (Acetylene; Natural
Gas) ....B
State Line Mfg. Co. (Acety-
lene; Natural Gas) ......D
Steward Mfg. Co., D. M.
(Acetyline; Natural Gas)
..................B
Sunlight Acetylene Gas
Burner Co. (Natural Gas)
..................F
TENN.—Memphis
Irby & Gilliland (Natural
Gas) ....A
TEXAS—Fort Worth
Lewis Gas Machine Mfg.
Co. (Acetylene Gas)....F
W. VA.—Wheeling
Hibbard & Son, Geo. (Na-
tural Gas) ....E
Wheeling Gas Stove &
Range Co. (Natural Gas)
..................C
Wheeling Stamping Co.
(Lamp) ....A
WIS.—Milwaukee
Milwaukee Gas Stove Co.
(Natural Gas) C

BURNISHERS

See also Machinery

ILL.—Chicago
Latham Machy. Co. (Book-
binders) C
MAINE—Bangor
Bangor Edge Tool Co.
(Photograph) ....D
MASS.—Boston
United Shoe Machy. Co.
(Heel) ....AAAA
MASS.—Brockton
Miller, O. A. (Heel) ......B
Tuck Mfg. Co. ....E
SS.—Lynn
Elles & Co., Geo. W. (Heel)
..................C
MASS.—Millburg
Buck, Chas. ....B
Buck Bros. ....A
MASS.—Springfield
Bullock & Co., O. W. (Jew-
elers') ....A
MICH.—Kalamazoo
Humphrey Mfg. & Plating
Co. (Photograph) ......D
N. Y.—Brooklyn
Ross & Son Co., Chas. 16
Steuben (Can) ....D
N. Y.—Fulton
Acme Burnisher Co. (Photo-
graph) ....A
PA.—Harrisburg
Hickok Mfg. Co., W. O.
(Bookbinders) ....AA
PA.—Philadelphia
Entrekin. Mrs. Sarah,
Mayunk (Photograph)..E

BURRS

See also Washers

CONN.—Bridgeport
Bridgeport Brass Co. (Cop-
per) ....AA
CONN.—Bristol
Sessions & Son, J. H.
(Capitol) ....AAA
CONN.—New Britain
Stanley Wks. (Steel)..AAA
CONN.—Unionville
Upson Nut Co. (Iron)..AAA
CONN.—Waterbury
Benedict & Burnham Mfg.
Co. (Copper) ......AAAA
Holmes, Booth & Haydens
Co. (Inc.) (Copper)
..................AAAA
Plume & Atwood Mfg. Co.
(Copper) ....AAA
Waterbury Brass Co. (Cop-
per) ....AAAA
ILL.—Chicago
Grand Crossing Tack Co.
(Steel) ....AAA
MASS.—Plymouth
Cobb & Drew (Iron; Steel)
..................AA
Plymouth Mills (Steel)...B
MASS.—Worcester
Reed & Prince Mfg. Co.
(Iron) ....A

BURRS (Con.)

N. J.—Newark
Jenkinson & Co., R. C.
(Steel) ....A
New York City
Ansonia Brass & Copper Co.
(Copper) ....AAAA
Hall's Sons, Samuel (Steel)
..................A
Hungerford Brass & Copper
Co., U. T. (Copper)....A
OHIO—Canton
Elbel Co. (Iron) ....AA
R. I.—Providence
American Screw Co. (Iron;
Steel) ....AAAA
WIS.—Milwaukee
Wrought Washer Mfg. Co.
(Steel) ....A

BUSHINGS

See also Bearings

CONN.—Bridgeport
Belknap Mfg. Co. (Brass)
..................C
ILL.—Chicago
Economical Beer Bung Co.
(Brewers') ....D
Union Elevator & Machine
Co., 144 Ontario (Self
Lubricating) C
Western Tube Co., 204 Dear-
born (For Pipe Fittings)
..................X
IND.—Mishawaka
Dodge Mfg. Co. (Pulley)
..................AAA
IND.—Peru
Peru Electric Mfg. Co.
(Battery) ....A
MAINE—Bath
Torry Roller Bushing Wks.
(Roller Bearing & Trolley
Wheel) ....B
MASS.—Boston
Boston & Lockport Block Co.
(Pulley; Metalene) ....B
Hamlin & Emery Brass Co.,
26 Island (Brass Flush;
Hexagon) ....D
MICH.—Detroit
American Tap Bush Co.
(Brewers') C
N. J.—Bound Brook
Graphite Lubricating Co.
(Graphite; Bronze; Trol-
ley Wheel) ....A
N. J.—Harrison
Hyatt Roller Bearing Co.
(Roller Bearing)......D
N. J.—Trenton
Electric Porcelain & Mfg.
Co. (Porcelain) ....D
N. Y.—Brooklyn
Bliss Co., E. W., 17
Adams ....AAAA
N. Y.—Long Island City
North American Metalene
Co. (R. W. Thomas & Co.)
(Loose Pulley; Oilers;
Tackle Block Sheaves)..D
New York City
Heyman & Fischer (Brew-
ers') ....B
Schwenker, W. M. (Brew-
ers') ....B
N. Y.—Schenectady
General Electric Co..AAAA
N. Y.—Syracuse
New Process Raw Hide Co.
(Raw Hide) ....B
OHIO—Cincinnati
Powell Co., Wm., 2525
Spring Grove Av.....AAA
United States Bung Mfg. Co.
(Brewers') ....A
OHIO—Columbus
Case Mfg. Co. (Pulley).AA
OHIO—Toledo
Toledo Bushing Co. (Brew-
ers'; Chip Casks)......F
PA.—Philadelphia
American Pulley Co., 29th
& Bristol (of all kinds) A
Brill Co., J. G., 62d & Wood-
land Av. (Trolley Wheel)
..................AAAA
Holmes Fibre Graphite Mfg.
Co., 5155 Wakefield
(Electrical) ....D
Keller, Robert (Brewers';
Journal Bearing) ......D
Pressed Steel Mfg. Co.,
Ridge Av. & Willow

135

BUSHINGS (Con.)
(Ball Bearings; Pulley).C
PA.—Pittsburg
Fullman Co., Third (Conduit) ....E
Pittsburg Pulley Co. (Pulley) ....B
PA.—Scranton
Scranton Button Co. (Incandescent Lamp) ....A
PA.—Williamsport
Darling Pump & Mfg. Co. (Brass) ....B
WIS.—Milwaukee
Smith-Medberry Mfg. Co. (Brewers') ....D

BUSKINS
CONN.—Hartford
Wiley & Son, Wm. H.....A
ILL.—Chicago
Phelps, Dodge & Palmer Co. X
Wells & Co., M. D...AAA
MASS.—Boston
Daniels & Co., Geo. F.....A
MASS.—Lynn
Grovers' Sons. J. J.......A

BUSTLES
MD.—Baltimore
Brinkman & Co., A. H....C
Pohl & Co., E..........C
MICH.—Ann Arbor
Goodspeed Mfg. Co.......E
N. Y.—Syracuse
Wood & Co., J. E........C
PA.—Philadelphia
Weston & Wells Mfg. Co. (Braided Wire).......B

BUTTER
See Appendix

BUTTER
See Jams; Jellies & Marmalade.

BUTTERINE
See also Oleomargarine

ILL.—Chicago
Armour & Co. ......AAAA
Braun & Fitts. 187 No. Union ....AA
Friedman Mfg. Co., Union Stock Yards ....A
Hammond Co., G. H., Union Stock Yards.AAAA
Moxley. W. J., Rand & Clinton ....A
Swift & Co. ....AAAA
MO.—Kansas City
Dold Butterine Co., 1500 No. 9th ....F
N. J.—Jersey City
Ammon & Person, 138 9th B
New York City
Armour Packing Co...AAAA
Oakdale Mfg. Co., 16 Exchange Pl. ....AA
Schwarzschild & Sulzberger Co. ....AAAA
OHIO—Columbus
Capital City Dairy Co. (The) ....A
PA.—Pittsburg
Holland Butterine Co., 518 1st Av. ....D

BUTTERISES
CONN.—Southington
Peck, Stow & Wilcox Co. AAAA
MASS.—Greenfield
Wells Bros. & Co.........A
New York City
Sargent & Co., 151 Leonard AAAA
PA.—Philadelphia
Plumb. Fayette R. (Blacksmiths') ....AA

BUTTONS
See also Jewelry

CONN.—Ansonia

BUTTONS (Con.)
Ansonia Electric Co. (Push) A
?.—Derby
Griffin Button Co. (Horn) B
CONN.—Deep River
Pratt, Read & Co. (Ivory) AA
CONN.—East Hampton
Starr Bros. Bell Co. (Push) B
CONN.—Greystone
Greystone Mfg. Co. (Glove) F
CONN.—Guilford
Spencers' Sons, I. S. (Electric Push) ....A
CONN.—Meriden
International Silver Co. (Glove) ....AAAA
CONN.—Middletown
Rogers & Hubbard Co. (Bone) ....A
CONN.—New Britain
Corbin, P. & S. (Push) AAAA
CONN.—New Haven
Cowles & Co., C. (Inc.) Carriage; Tufting)....A
Mallory. Wheeler Co. (Electric Push) ....AA
Sargent & Co. (Push).AAAA
CONN.—Plainville
Clark & Son, A. N. (Advertising; Glove) ....B
CONN.—Torrington
Union Hdw. Co. (Push).AA
CONN.—Wallingford
Wallace & Sons Mfg. Co., R. (Glove) ....AAAA
CONN.—Waterbury
Lane Mfg. Co. (Brass; Cloth Covered; Dress; Cloak; Engraved; Metal; Military; Silver; Tin Faced; Patent Trousers; Trousers; Collar; Cuff).....X
Patent Button Co. (Rubber; Trousers) ....A
Platt Bros. Co. (Inc.) Brass; Metal; Trousers; Patent Trousers) ....B
Scovill Mfg. Co. (Brass; Cloth; Dress; Cloak; Engraved; Metal; Military; Composition; Rubber; Silk; Silver; Tin Faced; Trousers; Patent Trousers) ....AAAA
Steele & Johnson Mfg. Co. (Engraved; Metal; Military; Silver) ....A
Waterbury Button Co. (Composition; Covered; Dress; Cloak; Lasting; Metal; Military) ....A
Waterbury Mfg. Co. (Metal) AAAA
White Co. L. C. (Automatic; Cloth; Carriage).C
ILL.—Chicago
Parisian Novelty Co., 10 So. Canal (Advertising) ...C
ILL.—Freeport
Arcade Mfg. Co. (Door)..A
Stover Mfg. Co. (Door)..AA
IOWA—Davenport
Davenport Pearl Button Co. (Pearl) ....B
MASS.—Attleboro
Wilmarth & Co., W. H. (Aluminum) ....B
MASS.—Boston
Boston Button Co. (Brass; Cloth; Covered; Crochet; Dress; Cloak; Metal)....X
Mosley Button Mfg. Co. (Milonite Clothing & Shoe) ....A
New England Novelty Mfg. Co. (Patent Trouser; Glove) ....H
MASS.—Chelsea
Low Tile Co. (Push).....F
MASS.—Leominster
Earl & Co., W. D. (Horn) C
MASS.—New Bedford
Hedge-Lewis Mfg. Co. (Leather & Cloth Covered; Shoe) ....B
MASS.—North Attleboro
Cheever-Tweedy Co. (Glove) AAA

BUTTONS (Con.)

MASS.—Plainville
Plainville Stock Co. (Glove)
...............................A

MASS.—Springfield
Dickinson Hard Rubber Co.
(Rubber) C
Newell Bros. Mfg. Co. (Covered; Pearl; Vegetable Ivory) X
Rhodes & Sons Co., M. M. (Shoe) C

MASS.—Williamsburg
Hill Bros. & Co. (Tin Faced; Patent Trouser) C

MICH.—Grand Rapids
Hardware Supply Co. (Door)
...............................X

NEBR.—Omaha
Western Electrical Co. (Push) ....D

N. J.—Newark
Blakeman, Chas. (Pearl).B
Celluloid Co. (Glove; Celluloid Cuff, Collar) ......B
Conlan & Co., B. (Metal).B
Feddersen & Feldmeyer (Pearl) ....D
Howell & Co., T. P. (Leather) ....A
Huebner & Sons, E. (Pearl) C
International Badge & Novelty Co. (Society, &c.).D
Reynolds & Zahn (Metal).B
Sommers' Son, Jno. (Ivory; Wooden; Shoe) ....A
Whitehead & Hoag Co. (Advertising; Ivory; Wooden; Shoe; Decorative Flag)
...............................AAA
Williamson Wire Novelty Co., C. T. (Stair)......B

N. Y.—Binghamton
Crandal, Stone & Co. (Tufting) ....A
Noyes & Co., J. P. (Patent Trouser; Hand Snap)..B

New York City
Castle Braid Co. (Braid).AA
City Button Wks. (Covered; Metal; Crochet) ......A
Deknatel, Jno. A. (Jet)...B
Edwards & Co. (Push)....D
Ellison & Co., A. S. (Dress; Cloak) ....B
Empire Ivory Button Wks. (Ivory) ....B
Frank & Co. (Covered; Ivory) ....F
French, S. A. (Military)..B
Gorham Mfg. Co. (Glove)
...............................AAAA
Gould Son & Co., M. (Stair)
...............................A
Grote & Co., F. (Glove)..D
Howards Son & Co., S. E., 21 Mercer (Pat. Trousers)
...............................AA
Johnson & Co., E. S. (Glove) X
Judd & Co., H. L. (Stair).X
John Kroder & Henry Reubel Co. (Stair) ....B
Manhattan Elec. Supply Co. (Elec. Push) ....AA
Mechanical Rubber Co. (Rubber) ....AAAA
New York Button Wks. (Brass; Cloth; Covered; Engraved; Military)...B
Ostrander & Co., W. R. (Push) ....A
Peck, Stow & Wilcox Co., 27 Murray (Door).AAAA
Porter Bros. & Co., 114 Worth (Trousers; Horn; Metal) ....AA
Pratt & Farmer Co., 353 Bdway. (Jet; Pearl; Ivory) ....B
Rosenblatt, Geo. H., 229 Bdway. (Decorative Flag)
...............................D
Russell & Erwin Mfg. Co. (Door) ....AAAA
Schott Bros. (Patent) ....D
Tiebout, W. & J. (Door)..B
Tower & Lyon Co., 95 Chambers (Police) ....B
Union Pearl Wks. (S. L. & J. H. Lawles) (Pearl)..D
Western Elec. Co. (Elec. Sash) ....AAAA
Yale & Towne Mfg. Co. (Push) ....AAAA

BUTTONS (Con.)

N. Y.—Rochester
Bradley & Co., E. C. (Push)
...............................H

OHIO—Canton
Ney Mfg. Co. (Door)......B

OHIO—Cincinnati
Pettibone Bros. Mfg. Co. (Metal) ....A

OHIO—Piqua
Piqua Handle & Mfg. Co. (Electric Push) ....A

PA.—Erie
Keystone Pearl Button Co. (Pearl) ....D

PA.—Philadelphia
Novelty Electric Co. (Push)
...............................C
Patrick, Carter & Wilkins (Electric Push) ....B
Pearce & Feraille, 1030 18th (Dec. Flag) ......B

PA.—Reading
Penn Hdw. Co. (Push)..AA
Reading Hdw. Co. (Door)
...............................AAAA

PA.—Scranton
Scranton Button Co. (Ltd.) (Covered; Ivory; Push)
...............................A

R. I.—Providence
Tockwotton Co. (Leather Covered Carriage) .....F

BUTTS

See also Hinges; also Leather

CONN.—Beacon Falls
Bronson Co., Homer D. (Brass) C

CONN.—Bradford
New York Lock Co. (Bronze; Iron) ....B

CONN.—Bridgeport
Smith & Egge Mfg. Co. (Spring; Double Acting Spring) ....A

CONN.—New Britain
Corbin, P. & F. (Brass; Bronze) ....AAAA
Stanley Wks. (Ball Bearing; Bronze; Door; Loose Joint; Loose Pin; Steel; Japanned, Steel; Nickel Plated, Steel) ......AAA
Union Mfg. Co. (Brass; Bronze; Cast; Door)...AA

CONN.—New Haven
Sargent & Co. (Brass; Bronze; Door; Iron; Spring; Wrought Steel)
...............................AAAA

CONN.—Southington
Peck, Stow & Wilcox Co. (Bronze; Cast; Door; Spring) ....AAAA

CONN.—Stamford
Yale & Towne Mfg. Co. (Door; Shutter; Bronze)
...............................AAAA

CONN.—Terryville
Eagle Lock Co. (Brass)
...............................AAA

CONN.—Waterbury
American Ring Co. (Brass)
...............................A
Benedict & Burnham Mfg. Co. (Brass) ....AAAA
Plum & Atwood Mfg. Co. (Brass; Bronze).....AAA
Scoville Mfg. Co. (Brass)
...............................AAAA

ILL.—Chicago
Chicago Spring Butt Co. (Spring) ....B

ILL.—Freeport
Stover Mfg. Co. (Spring; Bronze) ....A

ILL.—Sterling
Lawrence Bros. (Brass; Bronze) ....AA
Natl. Mfg. Co. (Wrought Steel) ....D

MD.—Baltimore
Deford Co. (Oak Leather)
...............................AAA

N. H.—Concord
Page Belting Co. (Mill)
...............................AA

N. J.—Trenton
Williams, A. T. (Oak Leather) ....B

N. Y.—Brooklyn
Bommer Bros. (Spring;

BUTTS (Con.)
Double Acting Spring)..B
New York City
Brass Goods Mfg. Co. (Door)
.....................B
Hungerford Brass & Copper
Co., U. T. (Door) ....A
Ladew, Edw. R. (Oak Leath-
er) ....AA
Neumann & Co., R. (Oak
Leather) ....A
Rees' Sons, Hans (Oak
Leather) ....AA
Russell & Erwin Mfg. Co.
(Brass; Door; Bronze;
Cast Iron) ....AAAA
Tiebout, W. & J., 118
Chambers ....B
U. S. Leather Co. (Oak
Leather) ....AAAA
N. Y.—Syracuse
Stearns & Co., E. C.
(Spring) ....AA
OHIO—Cleveland
Taylor & Boggis Foundry Co.
(Cast Iron) ....AA
PA.—Allegheny
McKinney Mfg. Co. (Bronze;
Door; Spring) ....AA
PA.—Erie
Griffin Mfg. Co. (Wrought
Steel) ....A
PA.—Pittsburg
Lapps & Sons, M. Oak
Leather Co. (Oak Leather)
......................A

PA.—Reading
Reading Hdw. Co. (Brass;
Bronze; Cast Iron;
Wrought Steel) ..AAAA
R. I.—Providence
New England Butt Co.
(Brass; Door; Cast; Loose
Joint; Loose Pin) ......A
VA.—Alexandria
Smoot & Sons Co., C. C.
(Oak Leather) ....AA
W. VA.—Wheeling
Wheeling Hinge Co.
(Bronze; Door; Shutter;
Reversible; Table)....AA

BUZZERS

See Bells

BY-PASSES

New York City
Matchless Mfg. Co. (Incandescent Gas-Light).....D

CABANESE

MO.—St. Louis
Midvale Mining & Mfg. Co.
......................X

CABINETS

See also Furniture

ILL.—Chicago
Amberg File & Index Co.
(Filing) ....A
Barnhart Bros. & Spindlar
(Printers) ....AA
Brown & Besley (Inc.)
(Filing) C
Clark & Co., A. A. (Den-
tists; Physicians) ......A
Lyon Metallic Mfg. Co.
(Steel Letter Filing)...G
Martin Co., Edw. P. (Chem-
ical; Physical) C
Dick Co., A. B. (Filing) AA
Hygenic Bath Appliance Co.
(Bath) ....D
Kaufman & Spencer (Medi-
cine) ....F
Mekkelson & Co., Edw., 23
N. Jefferson (Towel Sup-
ply) ....
Salter Mfg. Co., 102 N. Oak-
ley Av. (Towel Supply) D
Warren Mfg. Co., J. D.(Fil-
ing; Stationery; Bicycle
Extras; Hardware Store)
......................B
ILL.—Freeport
Arcade Mfg. Co. (Medicine)
......................A
ILL.—Kankakee
Sheldon Novelty Co. (Medi-
cine) ....A

CABINETS (Con.)
ILL.—Rockford
Central Furniture Co.
(Ladies'; Music) ....A
Forest City Furniture Co.
(Music) ....A
IND.—Ft. Wayne
Browser & Co., S. F. (Oil;
Self Measuring Oil; Var-
nish) ....A
IND.—Indianapolis
Allison Co., W. D. (Physi-
cians' Display) ....B
Armstrong & Co., W. H.
(Physicians') ....B
Clark & Roberts (Physi-
cians') ....B
Perfection Chair Co.
(Physicians') ....D
Tucker-Dorsey Mfg. Co.
(Spice) ....A
Udell Wks. (Shoe Blacking;
Spice; Music; Parlor; Phy-
sicians') ....A
IND.—Tell City
Tell City Desk Co. (Mantel)
......................B
MD.—Baltimore
Berger & Co., Fred.
(Smokers) X
MASS.—Boston
Davenport, Albert H.
(Needle) ....AA
Golding & Co. (Printers)..B
Paine Furniture Co. (Music)
......................A
MASS.—Millers Falls
Millers Falls Co. (Tool).AA
MASS.—Springfield
Bradley, Milton (Micro-
scopical Slide) ....A
Springfield Moulding Wks.
(Hunters') ....E
MICH.—Detroit
Farrand & Votey Organ Co.
(Music) ....AA
Shaw-Walker Co. (Card In-
dex) ....A
MICH.—Grand Rapids
Chocolate Cooler Co. (Ice
Cream) C
Couffield Co., H. L. (Letter
Filing) X
G. R. Chair Co. (Music;
Parlor) ....AA
Leonard Mfg. Co. (Cata-
logue) ....A
Mills & Lacey Mfg. Co.
(Embalmers') ....D
Oriel Cabinet Co. (Music;
Standing; Wall)......AA
MICH.—Ludington
Tubbs Mfg. Co. (Type)....B
MINN.—Minneapolis
Minn. Furniture Co.
(Kitchen) ....A
MO.—St. Louis
Scarritt-Comstock Furniture
Co. (Music; Parlor).....A
N. H.—Manchester
Brown & Burpee (Ophthal-
mic) ....E
N. J.—Montclair
Heller & Co., W. C. (Hard-
ware Store) ....F
N. Y.—Brooklyn
Wesel Mfg. Co., F.
(Printers') C
N. Y.—Herkimer
Horrocks Desk Co. (Type-
writer; Filing) ....B
N. Y.—Middletown
Morgan & Wilcox Mfg. Co.
(Printers') C
New York City
American Tool Chest Co.,
200 W. Houston (Tool)..C
American Type Founders' Co.
(Printers') ....AAAA
Butler, A. G., 101 Beekman
(Filing; Stationery) ..F
Diemer, J. F. (Filing)....D
Deuze & Phillips, 24 Dey
(Vapor Bath) C
Gordon Battery Co. (Physi-
cians') C
Gutta Percha & Rubber
Mfg. Co. (Printers')AAAA
Hoe & Co., R. (Printers')
...................AAAA
Homan Co., Andrew (Music;
Parlor) ....D
Hospital Supply Co. (Physi-
cians'; Instrument).....AA
Houchin Co., Thos. W., 48
Warren ....D
Household Sewing Machine

CABINETS (Con.)

Co. (Sewing Machine)..B
Janusch, F. G. (Bath)....C
Mace & Co., L. H., 111
Houston (Shoe Blacking)
B
New York Oil Cabinet Co.
180 Cherry (Oil) ....A
Schloss & Co., E. (China;
Music; Parlor) ....A
Singer Mfg. Co. (Sewing
Machine) ....AAAA
Stokes & Co., Wm. A., 30
Warren (Hanging).....D
Tonk & Bro., Wm.
(Musical) ....D
Vogel & Co., F. (Parlor) .X

N. Y.—Rochester
American Drafting Furni-
ture Co. (Drawing Room)
E
National Casket Co.
(Casket) ....AAAA
Yawman & Erbe Mfg. Co.
(Filing) ....AA

N. Y.—Syracuse
Brown Furniture Co., C. G.
(Music) ....B
Onondaga Novelty Co. (Tool;
Medical) ....E
Wells Mfg. Co., A. J.
(Filing) X

N. C.—Statesville
Piedmont Furniture Co.
(Typewriter) ....H

OHIO—Akron
Akron Woodworking Co.
(Shoe Blacking) ......A

OHIO—Canton
Danner Mfg. Co., John
(Medicine) ....D
Berger Mfg. Co. (Steel
Filing) ....AA
Harvard Co. (Dentists';
Physicians') ....AA

OHIO—Cincinnati
Ballman Cabinet Co.. 530
Livingston (Mantel; Wall;
China; Music; Parlor)..C
Globe-Wernecke Co. (Filing)
AAAA
Kelsall Co., Thomas
(Physicians') ....B
Mitchell Furniture Co.,
Robt. (Ladies'; Parlor;
Wall) ....AAAA
World Mfg. Co., 505 Elm
(Bath) ....A

OHIO—Columbus
Columbus Asceptic Furniture
Co. (Physicians') X
Holtzman & Sons, Henry
(Music) ....A
Ohio Furn. Co. (Metal) ..B

OHIO—Dayton
Ohmer's Sons Co.. M. (Catalogue: Legal Blank) ..A

OHIO—Toledo
Cooking Cabinet Co.
(Cooking) X
Ransom & Randolph Co.
(Dentists') ....A
Robinson Thermal Bath Co.
(Vapor Bath) C
Toledo Cooker Co. (Bath) C

PA.—Allegheny
Pittsburg Lamp Brass &
Glass Co. (Onyx) .AAAA

PA.—Harrisburg
Hickok Mfg. Co., W. O.
(Type) ....AA

PA.—Philadelphia
American Specialty Mfg. Co.
521 N. 23d (Cheese)...E
Rumpp & Sons, C. F.
(Filing) ....AAA
White Dental Mfg. Co., S. S.
(Dentists') ....AAAA

PA.—Reading
Natl. Brass & Iron Wks.
(Metal) ....A

R. I.—Pawtucket
Bliss Mfg. Co., R. (Spool;
Smokers') ....AAAA

WIS.—Green Bay
Automatic File & Index Co.
(Letter Filing) ....E

WIS.—Sheboygan
Winter Lumber Co., M.
(Music) ....B

WIS.—Two Rivers
Hamilton Mfg. Co.
(Printers') ....AA

CABLES

CONN.—Ansonia
Ansonia Brass & Copper Co.
(Electric) ....AAAA

CONN.—Southport
Jelliff Mfg. Co., C. O. (Electric Light; Power) C

CONN.—Waterbury
Holmes, Booth & Haydens
Co. (Electric) .....AAAA

ILL.—Chicago
American Steel & Wire Co.,
The Rookery (Lead Cov-
ered; Submarine; Suspen-
sion Bridge) .....AAAA
Western Electric Co. (Submarine; Electric; Hoist-
ing) ....AAAA

IND.—Jonesboro
Indiana Rubber & Insulated
Wire Co. (Lead Covered;
Rubber Covered; Subma-
rine) ....AA

MASS.—Boston
Durable Wire Rope Co.
(Elevator; Wire) ......B
Eastern Electric Cable Co.,
61 Hampshire (Subma-
rine) ....A
Simplex Electrical Co., 110
State (Lead Covered; Sub-
marine; Weatherproof;
Underground; Electric) A

CONN.—New Bedford
New Bedford Cordage Co.
(Oil Well) X

MO.—St. Louis
Broderick & Bascom Rope
Co. (Wire) ....AA
Leschen & Sons Rope Co., A
(Steel Wire; Hoisting)..
AAA

N. J.—Passaic
Okonite Co. (Insulating
Electric) ....A

N. J.—Trenton
Crescent Insulated Wire &
Cable Co. (Lead Covered;
Submarine; Weatherproof)
A
Roeblings' Sons Co., Jno.
A. (Lead Covered, Subma-
rine; Suspension Bridge;
Weatherproof; Insulated,
Steel Wire; Steel Rail-
way) ....AAAA
Trenton Iron Co. (Steel
Wire) ....AA

New York City
Bishop Gutta Percha Co.,
422 E. 25th (Lead Cov-
ered; Rubber Covered;
Submarine; Electric)..B
Brixey, Wm. R., 203 Bway.
(Lead Covered; Subma-
rine) ....B
Bunnell & Co., J. H., 20
Park Pl. (Electric) ....B
Dewitt Wire Cloth Co.
(Wire) ....A
India Rubber & Gutta Per-
cha Insulating Co., 15
Cortlandt (Lead Covered;
Rubber Covered; Subma-
rine) ....B
Natl. Conduit & Cable Co.
41 Park Row (Lead Cov-
ered; Submarine)..AAAA
New York Insulated Wire
Co., 114 Liberty (Lead
Covered; Insulated; Elec-
tric) ....A
Okonite Co.. 253 Bway.
(Lead Covered; Subma-
rine; Underground; Wea-
therproof) ....A
Safety Insulated Wire &
Cable Co.. 114 Liberty
(Lead Covered; Subma-
rine; Electric) ....AA

OHIO—Columbus
International Fence & Fire-
proofing Co. (Concrete
Reinforcing) ....A

OHIO—Marion
Marion Steam Shovel Co.
(Hoisting) ....AAA

OHIO—Xenia
Kelly Co., R. A. (Oil Well)
A

PA.—Philadelphia
Moore, Alfred F.. 202 N.
3rd (Lead Covered; Rub-
ber Covered; Submarine;

CABLES (Con.)
Weatherproof; Electric)
AAAA
Tatham & Bros., 223 S.
5th (Lead Covered) .AAA
PA.—Pittsburg
Pittsburg Electrical & Machine Wks. (Electric)..E
Standard Underground Cable
Co., Westinghouse Bldg.
(Lead Covered; Rubber
Covered; Submarine; Weatherproof; Electric).AAA
PA.—Reading
Jackson & Son, Thos. (Oil
Well) ....AA
PA.—Wilkesbarre
Hazard Mfg. Co. (Lead Covered; Steel Wire; Wire;
Electric; Street Railway)
AAA
R. I.—Providence
American Electrical Wks.
(Lead Covered; Submarine; Rubber Covered;
Weatherproof; Electric;
Telephone; Wire)..AAAA
National India Rubber Co.
(Rubber) ....AAAA

CABLEWAYS

ILL.—Chicago
Allis-Chalmers Co., Home
Insurance Bldg. (Suspension) ....AAAA
MO.—St. Louis
Broderick & Bascom Rope
Co. (Suspension) .....AA
N. J.—Newark
Lambert Hoisting Engine
Co. (Logging) ....A
New York City
Lidgerwood Mfg. Co., 96
Liberty (Mining) ..AAA
Trenton Iron Wks. 17 Burling Slip ....AAA
PA.—Bangor
Flory Mfg. Co., S. (Logging;
Sewer) ....A

CABS

See Carriages & Wagons

CABS, ELEVATOR

MICH.—Detroit
Bolles Iron & Wire Wks.,
J. E., 4th & Porter.....X
Ingles Wire & Iron Wks.,
Wm., 61 E. Woodbridge.C
N. Y.—Buffalo
Nagel & Co., G. 656 Mich..E
N. Y.—Syracuse
Syracuse Wire Works
(Heise & Son) ....D
OHIO—Columbus
Columbus Wire & Iron Wks.
D
OREGON—Portland
Portland Wire & Iron Wks.
(C. W. Post) ....D

CACHETS

New York City
Fougera & Co., E. 30 N.
William ....A

CACHOUS

ILL.—Chicago
Searle & Hereth Co.
(Breath) ....A
MASS.—Cambridge
Thayer & Co., Henry .....A

CADDIES

ILL.—Chicago
Norton Bros. (Inc.) (Tin)
AAA
MO.—St. Louis
Pepmuller, H. (Tea) .....D
N. Y.—Buffalo
Shepard & Co., Sidney (Tin)
AAAA
New York City
New York Stamping Co.
(Tin; Tea; Coffee) ..A

CADGERS

PA.—Pittsburg

CADGERS (Con.)
Gem Mfg. Co. (Miners'
Steel) ....D

CADMIUM

N. Y.—Brooklyn
Wiarda & Co., Jno. C.
(Sulphide) ....AA

CAFFEINE

MO.—St. Louis
Mallinckrodt Chemical Wks.
AAAA
Monsanto Chemical Wks. .D
New York City
Boehringer & Sons, C. F..A
New York Quinine & Chem.
Wks. ....A
Roessler & Hasslacher
Chem. Co. 100 William AA
PA.—Ambler
Keasby & Matteson Co.
AAAA

CAGES

CAL.—San Francisco
Union Iron Wks. (Mining)
AAAA
COLO.—Denver
Davis Iron Wks., F. M.
(Mining) ....A
Hendrie & Bolthoff Mfg. &
Supply Co. (Mining) AAA
Mine & Smelter Supply Co,
(Mining) ....AAA
CONN.—New Haven
Hendryx Co., Andrew B.
(Bird; Squirrel; Parrot)
A
ILL.—Chicago
Allis-Chalmers Co., Home
Ins. Bldg. (Mining)AAAA
Barbee Wire & Iron Wks.
(Jail) ....B
Doolan Mfg. Co., 16 Larrabee (Bird) ....D
ILL.—Litchfield
Litchfield Fdry. & Machine
Co. (Mining; Safety) ..A
ILL.—Peoria
Lucas & Sons, A. (Mining) C
IND.—Terre Haute
Eagle Iron Wks. (Mining)
B
IOWA—Ottumwa
Ottumwa Iron Wks. (Mining; Safety) ....AA
MICH.—Adrian
Page Woven Wire Fence Co.
(Bear; Monkey; Bird) AA
MICH.—Bay City
Marine Iron Co. (Mining)..C
MICH.—Detroit
Buhl Stamping Co. (Bird).A
MICH.—Saginaw
Bartlett & Co., A. F.
(Mining) ....A
MO.—St. Louis
Ellison & Sons Mfg. Co.,
Wm., 1018 N, 6th (Mining) ....B
N. J.—Garwood
Beckley Co., A. J. (Jail) .D
N. Y.—Buffalo
Heinz & Munschauer (Bird)
A
Jewet Mfg. Co., Jno. C.
(Parrot; Squirrel) ...AA
Pierce Co., Geo. N. (Parrot; Squirrel) ....AA
N. Y.—Fultonville
Empire Cooping Co. (Cat;
Pigeon; Poultry) ......F
New York City
Cabble Excelsior Mfg. Co.,
A. M., 43 Fulton ....B
Lidgerwood Mfg. Co.
(Safety) ....AAA
Lindemann & Co., O. 35
Wooster (Bird; Squirrel)
B
Maxwell, Jno. (Bird; Parrot; Squirrel) ....D
OHIO—Akron
Webster Camp & Lane
Machine Co. (Mining)..A
OHIO—Cleveland
Van Dorn Iron Wks. Co.
(Station House) .....AA
OHIO—Hamilton
Meyers Mfg. Co., Fred. J.
(Bird; Squirrel; Wooden)
AA
OHIO—Nelsonville
Nelsonville Fdry. & Mach-

CAGES (Con.)
ine Co. (Mining) ....B
OHIO—Zanesville
Griffith & Wedge Co.,
(Mining; Safety) .....A
PA.—Connellsville
Connellsville Machine &
Car Co. (Mining) ......A
PA.—Ellwood City
Glen Mfg. Co. (Tellers;
Bird; Animal) ....D
PA.—Monongahela
Monongahela Mfg. Co. (Mining; Self Dumping; Steel
Hoisting) ....A
PA.—Osceola Mills
Stein & Sons, S. B. (Mining)
..........................B
PA.—Philadelphia
Darby & Sons. Edw. (Bird)
PA.—Scottdale
Kenney & Co. (Mining;
Safety) ....A
PA.—Wilkesbarre
Vulcan Iron Wks. (Mining;
Safety) ....AAAA
WASH.—Spokane
Union Iron Wks. (Mining) A

CAISSONS

MD.—Baltimore
Ellicott Machine Co., Canton
(Sheet Iron) C
N. J.—Paterson
East Jersey Pipe Co. (Sheet
Iron) ....B
OHIO—Youngstown
Pollock Co., Wm. B. (Sheet
Iron) ....B
PA.—Pittsburg
Carroll-Porter Boiler &
Tank Co. (Bridge; Sheet
Iron) ....B
Ritter-Conley Mfg. Co., 56
Water (Bridge; Mine;
Steel) ....AA
Scaife & Sons Co., Wm. B.,
221 First Av. (Bridge). A

CAKE

CONN.—Unionville
Broadbent & Son, J. (Cotton
Seed) ....B
GA.—Elberton
Elberton Oil Mills (Cotton
Seed) ....A
ILL.—Chicago
Fairbank & Co., N. K. (Cotton Seed) ....AAAA
MISS.—Port Gibson
Port Gibson Oil Works
(Cotton Seed) ....A
N. Y.—Buffalo
Mann Bros. & Co. (Linseed) ....A
New York City
American Cotton Oil Co., 27
Beaver (Cotton Seed)
.......................AAAA
R. I.—Providence
Union Oil Co. (Cotton Seed)
.......................AAA
TENN.—Memphis
Southern Cotton Oil Co.
(Cotton Seed) ....AAAA
Valley Oil Mills (Cotton
Seed) ....A
TEXAS—Belton
Belton Oil Co. (Cotton Seed)
.......................D
TEXAS—Taylor
Taylor Cotton Oil Wks.
(Cotton Seed) ....B

CAKES

See also Bakers

N. J.—Newark
Spratts Patent (American)
Ltd. (Dog) ....B

CALCITE

PA.—York
York Chemical Works. ..A

CALCIUM

ILL.—Chicago
Rhodes & Co., Jas. H., 117
Kinzie (Chloride) ....B
Stevenson & Co., Robt.
(Chloride) ....B

CALCIUM (Con.)
MD.—Baltimore
Thomsen Chemical Co., Race
& Winder (Acid Phosphate) ....B
MO.—St. Louis
Provident Chemical Wks.
(Acid Phosphate) ....AA
New York City
Calcium Carbide Export Co.
35 Nassau (Carbide) ...X
Roessler & Hasslacher Chemical Co. (Chloride) ....AA
Sholes Co., C. E. (Chloride)
.......................X
Union Carbide Co., 45 Bway.
(Carbide) ....A
Wing & Evans (Chloride)
.......................AAA
OHIO—Pomeroy
Acme Calcium Works
(Chloride) X
Eureka Calcium Wks.
(Chloride) X
Koehlers Excelsior Salt Wks.
(Chlorate) ....B
PA.—Carbondale
Carbondale Chemical Co.
(Chloride) ....E
W. VA.—Malden
Dickinson & Co., Jno. Q.
(Chloride) ....AA

CALCULA-TORS

R. I.—Providence
Brown & Sharpe Mfg. Co.
(Gear) ....AAAA

CALDRONS

See also Kettles

ILL.—Batavia
Sperry & Co., D. R.
(Farmers') ....B
ILL.—Chicago
Kaestner & Co. ....A
MASS.—Worcester
Wheeler Foundry Co.
(Farmers') ....D
N. J.—Burlington
Stewart & Peterson Co.
(Farmers') ....A
N. J.—Jersey City
Gibson Iron Wks. Co.
(Plain; Steam Jacketed)
.......................X
N. Y.—Buffalo
Doop Co., H. W............D
N. Y.—Munnsville
Munnsville Plow Co.
(Farmers') ....B
New York City
Mott Iron Wks., J. L.
(Butchers') ....AA
N. Y.—Utica
International Heater Co.
(Farmers') ....AAA
PA.—Reading
Mt. Penn. Stove Wks.
(Farmers') ....A

CALENDERS

CONN.—Ansonia
Farrel Foundry & Machine
Co. (Linoleum) ...AAAA
CONN.—Derby
Birmingham Iron Foundry
(Friction; Platers')....A
CONN.—So. Windham
Smith & Winchester Co.
(Breaker; Platers') ...A
DEL.—Wilmington
Lobdell Car Wheel Co. ...
.......................AAAA
ILL.—Chicago
Sewell-Clapp Mfg. Co. ...C
MASS.—Boston
Carter's Ink Co. ....A
Lowell & Co., John A. ..D
MASS.—Florence
Norwood Engineering Co.
(Breaker; Friction; Platers' Sheet; Web) ......B
MASS.—Holyoke
Holyoke Machine Co.
(Breaker; Friction; Platers' Sheet; Web) ....AA
N. Y.—Buffalo
Gies & Co. ....AAA
N. Y.—Fulton
Dilts Machine Works

CALENDERS (Con.)
(Doctors') ....B
New York City
Judd & Co. ....AA
Witteman Bros. ....A
PA.—Philadelphia
Butterworth & Son Co., H.
W. (Embossing) ....A
Fairmount Machinery Co.
(Embossing; Friction)..A
Moore & White Co., 15th &
Lehigh Av. ....AA
VA.—Glen Allen
Cussons, May & Co. .....B

CALFSKIN
See Leather

CALICOS
See Cotton Goods

CALIPERS
CONN.—Hartford
Billings & Spencer Co.
(Beam) ....A
Pratt & Whitney Co. .AAAA
CONN.—Southington
Peck, Stow & Wilcox Co.
AAAA
MASS.—Athol
Athol Machine Co. (Microm-
eter; Spring) ....B
Standard Tool Co. (Firm
Point; Micrometer;
Spring) X
Starrett Co., L. S. (Mi-
crometer) ....A
MASS.—Boston
Dame, Stoddard & Co. ...A
MASS.—Chicopee Falls
Stevens Arm & Tool Co., J.
AAA
MASS.—Fitchburg
Sawyer Tool Mfg. Co.
(Beam) ....A
MASS.—No. Easton
New England Specialty Co.
D
MASS.—Springfield
Bemis & Call Hardware &
Tool Co. ....A
Springfield Machine Screw
Co. ....B
MICH.—Saginaw
Lufkin Rule Co. (Log)..AA
N. H.—Keene
Humphrey Machine Co.
(Log) C
N. J.—Newark
Johnson, Wm. ....B
Kraeuter Co. (Micrometer;
Register) ....E
N. J.—Smithville
Smith Machine Co., H. B..A
New York City
Keuffel & Esser Co., 127
Fulton (Log) ....AA
Tower & Lyon ....B
OHIO—Cleveland
Warner & Swasey (Microm-
eter) ....A
R. I.—Providence
Brown & Sharpe Mfg. Co.
(Micrometer; Precision;
Gear Tooth; Vernier)....
AAAA
Slocomb & Co., J. T.
(Micrometer) ....E

CALKS
CONN.—Hartford
Rowe Patent Square Shoul-
der Shoe Calk Co. (Horse
Shoe) ....F
MAINE—Cornville
Palmer, Jas. S. (Toe) ...F
MASS.—Boston
Burke, P. F. Heel; Toe)..C
Franklin Steel Wks. (Toe)
C
Neverslip Horseshoe Co.
(Removable Horseshoe).D
MICH.—Saginaw
Lufkin Rule Co. (Lumber-
men's Boot) ....AA
N. J.—Newark
Sacks Iron Foundry, Louis
(Boot) ....A
New York City
Livingston Nail Co. (Heel;
Toe) ....B

CALKS (Con.)
OHIO—Elyria
Western Automatic Mach.
Screw Co. (Removable
Horseshoe) ....AA
PA.—Scranton
Williams Drop Forging Co.
(Horseshoe) ....D
R. I.—Providence
Rhode Island Perkins Horse-
shoe Co. (Heel; Toe)...
AAAA
WIS.—Eau Claire
Cutler, A. A. (Boot).....A

CALLS & CALLERS
N.—Waterbury
Waterbury Brass Co. (Dog)
AAAA
ILL.—Monmouth
Allen, F. A. (Duck).....F
New York City
Amer. Watchman's Time
Detector Co., 234 B'way
(Electric) X

CALOMEL
MO.—St. Louis
Mallinckrodt Chemical Co.
AAAA
New York City
Pfizer & Co., Chas. ..AAAA
PA.—Philadelphia
Powers - Weightman - Ros-
engarten Co. ......AAAA

CALORI-METERS
New York City
Eimer & Amend, 211 Third
Av. ....AA
PA.—Pittsburg
Scientific Materials Co...D

CAMBRICS
See Cotton Goods

CAMEOS
See Jewelry

CAMERAS
CONN.—Waterbury
Scovill Mfg. Co. .....AAAA
ILL.—Chicago
Adams & Westlake Co...
AAAA
Anderson, Jonas A. .....D
Anthony & Scovill Co., 122
5th Av. ....D
Folmer & Schwing Mfg. Co.
B
Gennert, G. (Detective)..B
Ingersoll & Bro., Robt. H.,
51 Maiden Lane ....A
N. Y.—Rochester
Eastman Kodak Co. (Detec-
tive; Photo) ......AAAA
Gundlach Optical Co.
(Photo) ....A
Rochester Optical Co.....A
PA.—Philadelphia
Buchanan, W. P., 1226 Arch
C
WIS.—Burlington
Mutiscope & Film Co.
(Panoramic) ....D

CAMPHOR
CONN.—Glenbrook
Phillips Chemical Co., Chas.
H. (Refined) ....B
MASS.—Boston
American Camphor Co.
(Refined) ....D
MO.—St. Louis
Mallinckrodt Chemical Wks.
(Refined) ....A
N. Y.—Brooklyn
Cresol Chemical Co., 377 5th
Av. (Chemical; Lavender;
Oriental Rice; Refined;
etc.) ....D
New York City
Baker & Bros., H. J., 100
William (Refined) ..AA

CAMPHOR (Con.)

Johnson & Johnson (Refined) ....AAAA
Jones Chemical Wks., E. F. (Refined) ....B
Pfizer & Co., Chas. (Refined) ....AAAA
Schieffelin & Co., W. H. (Refined) ....A
PA.—Philadelphia
Barrett Mfg. Co. .....AAAA
Powers - Weightman - Rosengarten Co. (Refined)... AAAA
Simes & Son, W. F. (Refined) ....A

CAMS

IND.—Montpelier
National Steel Castings Co. B
MASS.—Boston
Boston Gear Wks., Pearl & Purchase (Machinery)...B
N. Y.—Brooklyn
Chrome Steel Wks., Kent Av. & Keap ....AAA
OHIO—Cleveland
Dryson & Sons, Jos. ......A
PA.—Chester
Chester Steel Castings Co... AAA
PA.—Pittsburg
Reliance Steel Casting Co..X

CANDELABRA

CONN.—Meriden
Bradley & Hubbard Mfg. Co. (Brass; Bronze) ...AAAA
Foster, Merriam & Co. (Brass) ....A
Meriden Britannia Co. (Brass) ....AAAA
CONN.—Winsted
Goodwin & Kintz Co.....D
ILL.—Chicago
Royal Metal Mfg. Co., W. Washing'n (Undertakers') C
MASS.—Boston
Goodnow & Jenks, Stanhope St. C
N. Y.—Brooklyn
Goodnow & Jenks Stanhope St. C
N. Y.—East Syracuse
Benedict Mfg. Co., M. S... AA
New York City
Cassidy & Son Mfg. Co. (Bronze) ....A
Gleason Mfg. Co. (Iron)..A
Gotham Mfg. Co., Broadway & 19th ....AAAA
International Silver Co..... AAAA
Judd & Co., H. L. (Brass).. AA
Lamb, J. & R. (Brass; Bronze; Iron) ....D
Westervelt, A. B. & W. T. (Iron) ....B
Nesbet Co., D. M., 116 Nassau ....A
N. Y.—Schenectady
General Electric Co. (Bronze; Iron) ....AAAA
PA.—Lancaster
Hubley Mfg. Co. ....A
PA.—Philadelphia
North Bros. Mfg. Co.....AA
W. VA.—Moundsville
Fostoria Glass Co. (Glass) AAA

CANDLES

CAL.—San Francisco
Mission Soap & Candle Wks., 16 1st ....B
San Francisco Candle Co., 402 Front (Stearic; Adamantine) ....A
Standard Soap Co., 113 Sacramento ....AA
ILL.—Chicago
Schneider & Co., E., 19 Wabash Av. ....AA
Swain Lubricator, 250 Lake (Lubricating) ....B
MD.—Baltimore
Hoeffner & Sons, A. (Br. Buffalo, N. Y.) ......AA
MASS.—Boston

CANDLES (Con.)

Coburn & Co., H. B., 69 Broad C
Gregory & Co., F. W., 162 High C
Macomber & Co., H. S., 150 Milk ....D
Wood & Co., W. A., 371 Atlantic Av. ....B
MASS.—Braintree
Dow Portable Electric Co. (Electric) C
MASS.—New Bedford
Robinson & Co., W. A. (Spermaceti) ....B
MO.—St. Louis
Goodwin Mfg. Co., 3332 Chouteau Av. (Glycerine) AA
Merkle Wax & Candle Co., 10 N. 4th ....A
Schaeffer Bros. & Powell Mfg. Co., 325 N. 2nd...B
N. J.—Camden
Baxter's Sons, J. C
N. J.—Jersey City
Gross & Co., A., Provost & 1st ....AA
N. Y.—Buffalo
Gowans & Sons, 213 Chicago AA
Hoeffner Sons, A., 170 Van Rensselaer ....AA
New York City
Boyd, James (Tallow) ...B
Century Stearic Acid Candle Wks., 380 South .....E
Electric Contract Co., 202 Centre (Electric) ......E
Gross & Co., A., 75 Murray ....AA
Hammerschlag Mfg. Co., 234 Greenwich ....A
Howard Electric Novelty Co., 227 Canal (Electric) E
Mitchell, R. G., 141 Water ....AA
Reichend & Sons, Geo., 539 W. 43rd C
Seabury & Johnson (Sulphur) ....AA
Smith & Nichols, 143 Front B
Standard Oil Co., 26 B'way ....AAAA
Tardie, Emile J., 221 6th Av. (Electric) ....G
Will & Baumer Co., 18 Murray ....AAA
N. Y.—Syracuse
Cathedral Candle Co. (Paraffin; Stearic; Wax)...D
Finn's Sons, H. ....B
Mack, Miller Candle Co. (Wax) C
Marty & Co., F. (Wax; Paraffine) ....F
Syracuse Candle Co. ......E
Will & Baumer Co. (Beeswax; Christmas; Church; Paraffine; Stearic; Wax) AAA
OHIO—Cincinnati
Emery Candle Co., 111 E. 4th (Adamantine; Stearic; Wax) ....AAA
Harkness & Cowing Co., 513 Eggleston Av. (Wax)...A
Proctor & Gamble Co., United Bk. Bldg. (Stearic) ....AAAA
Themann, Anton, 113 W. Canal ....B
Werk Co., M., 411 Poplar (Adamantine; Stearic Acid) ....AA
OHIO—Columbus
Janitor & Sons, Geo. .....B
Ross, Thos. C
PA.—Allegheny City
Walker, W. & H. ....AAAA
PA.—Pittsburg
Walker, W. & H. (Church) AAAA

CANDLE-STICKS

CAL.—San Francisco
Doble Co., Abner (Miners') A
COLO.—Denver
Hendrie & Bolthoff Mfg. &

CANDLESTICKS (Con.)
Supply Co. (Miners').AA
CONN.—Bridgeport
Bridgeport Brass Co. (Brass;
Spring) ....AA
Jennings Bros. Mfg. Co. .AA
CONN.—Meriden
Bradley & Hubbard Mfg.
Co. (Brass; Bronze)AAAA
Manning, Bowman & Co.
(Brass; Bronze) .....AA
Meriden Britannia Co.
(Plated) ....AAAA
Miller & Co., Edward
(Brass) ....AAAA
CONN.—New Britain
Landers, Frary & Clark
(Brass) ....AAA
CONN.—New Haven
Elm City Brass Co., 80 Au-
dubon (Colonial) ......E
Rostand Mfg. Co. ....D
MASS.—Chelsea
Low Tile Co. (Enamelled)F
MASS.—Gardner
Smith, Frank W. X
MO.—St. Louis
Ludlow-Saylor Wire Co.
(Miners') ....A
St. Louis Stamping Co.
(Enamelled; Safety) ....
                    AAAA
N. J.—Newark
Sommer's Son, John (Brew-
ers') ....A
N. J.—New Brunswick
N. J. Lamp & Bronze Wks.
(Bronze) ....AA
N. Y.—Brooklyn
Hecla Iron Wks. (Iron).AA
N. Y. Stamping Co. .....A
N. Y.—Buffalo
Shepard & Co., Sidney
(Tin) ....AAA
N. Y.—East Syracuse
Benedict Mfg. Co., M: S.AA
New York City
Gorham Mfg. Co. of N. Y.,
B'way & 19th ....AAAA
Jackson Co., Wm. H., 29 E.
17th (Colonial) ....A
Lalance & Grosjean Mfg. Co.
(Enamelled) ......AAAA
Lamb, J. & R. (Brass;
Bronze) ....D
Manhattan Brass Co.
(Brass) ....AA
Peck, Stow & Wilcox Co.,
27 Murray ....AAAA
Russell & Erwin Mfg. Co.,
43 Chambers ......AAAA
Tower & Lyon Co., 95 Cham-
bers (Miners') ....B
N. Y.—Troy
Troy Stamping Co. (Tin)..
                    AAAA
OHIO—Cleveland
Cleveland Lock Co., Wason
& Hamilton (Miners')..D
PA.—Philadelphia
Gillinder & Son (Glass)..A
Hall & Carpenter, 518 Race
                    AA
North Bros. Mfg. Co. (Tin)
                    A
PA.—Pittsburg
McKee & Co., S. (Glass)..D
Pittsburg Lamp & Brass Co.
(Brass) ....AAA
PA.—Reading
National Brass & Iron
Wks. (Brass) ....A
W. VA.—Wellsburg
Riverside Glass Wks.
(Glass) C

CANDY

See Confectionery

CANE

MASS.—Gardner
Heywood Bros. & Wake-
field Co. (Chair) ..AAAA
MASS.—West Gardner
Conant, Ball & Co. (Chair)B
N. Y.—Brooklyn
Amer. Rattan & Reed Mfg.
Co., 18 Guernsey (Chair)
                    A
New York City
Gordau, Otto (Chair) ....B

CANES

ILL.—Chicago
Hirsh & Bro. ....A
MICH.—Detroit
Lingerman & Co., Casper..G
New York City
Demuth & Co., Wm. ..AAA
Fradley & Co., J. F......E
Friedman & Co., M......D
Kaldenberg Importing &
Trading Co. ....D
Locklin & Sons, P. H....G
Rest-Fenner-Smith Co., 37
Downing (Walking).....C
Winckley & Son, L. C
OHIO—Cincinnati
Kuhn, E. C. ....A
PA.—Lancaster
Lancaster Silver Plate Co.C
Rose Bros. & Co. ....A
PA.—Philadelphia
Harvey & Watts Co.
(Walking) ....A
Moxey, Howlett & Co., 915
Filbert (Walking) C

CANISTERS

CONN.—Meriden
Meriden Britannia Co. (Tea;
Coffee) ....AAAA
N. Y.—Brooklyn
New York Stamping Co...A
N. Y.—Buffalo
Shepard & Co., Sidney (Tea;
Coffee) ....AAAA
New York City
Morgan & Cornell, 211 Duane
(Tea; Coffee; Grocers').X
PA.—Easton
Canister Mfg. Co. (For Dry
Food Products) ....B
PA.— North East
Fernald Mfg. Co. (Tea;
Coffee) ....D

CANNED GOODS

**EXPLANATION OF NUM-
BERS FOLLOWING NAMES
OF CANNED GOODS
PACKERS**

(1)	Apples
(2)	Tomatoes
(3)	Beans
(4)	Vegetables
(5)	Corn
(6)	Fruit
(7)	Peaches
(8)	Pumpkin
(9)	Peas
(10)	Lobsters
(11)	Oysters
(12)	Salmon
(13)	Shrimp
(14)	Shell Fish
(15)	Sardines
(16)	Squash
(17)	Asparagus
(18)	Berries
(19)	Crabs
(20)	Fish
(21)	Pears
(22)	Plum Pudding
(23)	Meats
(24)	Figs
(25)	Succotash
(26)	Sauerkraut

ALA.—Bayou La Batre
Bayou La Batre Pack. Co.
(11-20-13-4) C
CAL.—Anaheim
Orange County Preserving
Co. ....B
CAL.—Benicia
Carquinez Pack. Co. (6-12)A
CAL.—Black Diamond
Sacramento River Packers'
Assn. (12) C
CAL.—Bouldin Island
Hickmott Asparagus Can-
ning Co. (Br. San Fran.)A
CAL.—Campbell
Ainsley Pack'g Co., J. C.
(2-7) ....B
CAL.—Fresno
Guggenhime & Co. (Br. San
(Fran.) ....A

CAL.—Geyersville
Walden & Co. ....A
CAL.—Gridley
Bendel, Nelson Co. (4-6)..B
CAL.—Haywards
Hunt Bros. & Co. (Br. San Fran.) C
CAL.—Los Angeles
Armsby Co., J. K. (Bkrs.) ....A
California Fruit Canners' Ass'n ....AAAA
Maier Packing Co. .....AA
Pioneer Green Chili Pack'g Co., 348 S. Alameda (Peppers) C
CAL.—Los Gatos
Los Gatos Canneries (G. H. Hooke, Prop.) (6) ....B
CAL.—Marysville
Marysville Cannery C
CAL.—Napa
California Canned Gds. Co. (6) C
Fisher Co., M. W. (6)..C
Napa Valley Packg. Co. (4-6) ....B
CAL.—Oakland
Central California Canneries (Br. San Fran.) ...AAAA
CAL.—Parlier
Guggenhime & Co. (Br. San Fran.) ....A
CAL.—Petaluma
Rose Canning Co. C
CAL.—Requa
Klamath Pack. & Trading Co. C
CAL.—San Diego
San Diego Fish Co. (Can. Smo.) ....B
San Diego Pack'g Co. ...C
CAL.—San Francisco
Alaska Packers' Assn., 308 Market (12) .....AAAA
Alaska Salmon Assn. (12).A
Alaska Salmon Co., 54 Steuart ....A
Armsby & Co., J. K., 138 Market (Br. Chicago, Ill.) Balfour, Guthrie & Co., 316 Cal. ....AAAA
Bristol Pack'g Co., 5 Market (12) ....A
California Commission Co. 124 California ....B
California Fruit Canners' Assn., 201 California (4-6) AAAA
Carquinez Pack. Co., 203 California (6-12) ......A
Catton, Bell & Co., 406 California (Agents) ......A
Cudahy Pack. Co., Luning Bldg. (Meats) ....AAAA
Getz Bros. & Co., 111 California (6-12-17) ..AAAA
Golden State Asparagus Co., 22 California (17) C
Gray, Lang & Stroh, Luning Bldg. (Brokers) C
Griffin & Skelley Co., 132 Market ....A
Griffith-Durney Co.,.200 California (Wh. Bkrs.).....A
Guggenhime & Co., 118 Davis ....A
Hicknott Asparagus Canning Co., 3 California ..A
Hume & Co., G. W., 203 California (6-12) .AAAA
Hume & Co., R. D., 421 Market (12) ....AA
Hunt Bros. Co., 3 California (6) C
Johnson-Locke Merc. Co., 123 California ....A
Klamath Pack. & Trading Co., 421 Market (12) ..A
Landsberger, A. H., 3 California (Broker) C
Los Gatos Canneries, 220 Market ....B
Naknek Pack. Co., 5 Market (12) ....A
North Alaska Salmon Co., Davis (12) ....AA
North Pacific Pack. & Trad. Co., 21 Main ...A
Overland Pack. Co., 9 Harrison (4-6) ....AAA
Pacific Pack'g & Navigation Co. (12) ....AAAA
Pike & Co., ~. W., 124 Cal-

ifornia (Brokers) C
Red Salmon Canning Co. 32 California (12) ...\..A
Sacramento River Pack. Assn., 122 Davis (12)..A
Wieland Bros., 121 Clay (20) ....A
CAL.—San José
California Fruit Canners' Assn. ....AAAA
Costa Orchard Canning Co., L. D. (1-2-3-4-7-8-9-17-21) ....A
Flickinger Co., J. H.....AA
Frank & Co., Geo. C
Golden Gate Pack. Co. (6) AA
Griffin & Skelley Co. (Br. San Fran.) ....A
Orchard Canning Co. (L. D. Costa) ....A
CAL.—Santa Ana
Guggenhime & Co. (Br. San Fran.) ....A
CAL.—Woodland
Guggenhime & Co. (Br. San Fran.) ....A
CAL.—Yuba City
Suttel Preserving Co. (2-3-6-7-9-21) ....B
COLO.—Delta
Delta Packing Co. ....E
COLO.—Denver
Eversman & Co., J. G., 1620 Market (20) ....B
Kuner Pickle Co., 22d & Blake (2-26) ....B
COLO.—Fort Lupton
Empson Package Co. (2-3-8-9-18) ....A
COLO.—Hotchkiss
Hotchkiss Fruit Growers' Assn.
COLO.—Longmont
Empson Packing Co. (Br. Ft. Lupton) (2-3-8-9-18-)....A
CONN.—Hartford
Bentley Co., Geo. Wm., 53 High (Bkrs.) ....B
CONN.—New Britain
Steele Bros. X
CONN.—Windsor
Windsor Cannery (1-2-6-4-19-16) ....B
DEL.—Bowers
Reese & Wilson C
DEL.—Bridgeville
Cannon, H. P. (1-2-4-5-6-7-8-9-16-17-18-21) ....B
DEL.—Camden
Stetson & Ellison Co. C
DEL.—Clayton
Clayton Canning Co. (C. W. Baker, Prop., Aberdeen, Md.) ....A
DEL.—Delmar
Seneca, S. J. (Br. Havre de Grace, Md.) ....A
DEL.—Dover
Richardson & Robbins .AAA
DEL.—Harrington
Flaming & Co. (2-5-7-8-9-21) B
DEL.—Laurel
Stradley & Co., G. W. ...A
DEL.—Leipsic
Levins' Sons, S. H.......AA
DEL.—Milford
North Milford Canning Co. (Geo. S. Grier & Son, Props.) (2) ....B
Draper & Hirsch (2) .....B
DEL.—Odessa
Watkins Packing Co. C
DEL.—Rising Sun
Farmers' Preserving Co. ..C
DEL.—Seaford
Greenabaum Bros. (2-7-9-21-22) ....A
Emery & Dutton (11).....C
Ross, E. C. (2-7-9-21) ...B
Stevens & Co., W. H. (11) C
DEL.—Smyrna
Hoffecker Canning Co., J. H. C
DEL.—Wyoming
Baker, C. W. (Br. Aberdeen, Md.) (2) ....A
FLA.—Apalachicola
Green Point Oyster Co. (Ruge Bros., Props.)....B
FLA.—Ft. Meyers
Seminole Canning Co. (2)..C

CANNED GOODS (Con.)

FLA.—Jacksonville
Dallam, W. M. (Broker)..B

FLA.—Key West
Granday & Co., A. (Green Turtle Soup) C

FLA.—St. Augustine
Goffin Bros. (4-11) ....AA

GA.—Albany
Eclipse Canning Co. ......A

GA.—Atlanta
Shewmake & Murphy C

GA.—Brunswick
Aiken Canning Co. (11)..C
Downing Co. (2) ......AA

GA.—Ft. Valley
Gray Bros. (2-7-9) .....B

GA.—Savannah
Herman & Bro., M. S. (11)
....
Lowden. G. W. (6-11)...B

GA.—Thunderbolt
Lowden, Geo. W. (6-11)..B

ILL.—Belvidere
Holden, C. N. (Packers) (2-3-4) ....A

ILL.—Bloomington
Bloomington Canning Co. (2-3-5-8) ....B
Welch & Co., W. J. (Com. Importers & Jobbers) (1-3-5-6-10-11-17-18) .....B

ILL.—Carrollton
Carrollton Canning Co. (Roberts, Ross & Co.) (2-5-9)
...........................C

ILL.—Chenoa
Bloomington Canning Co. (2-5-9) ....B

ILL.—Chicago
Armour & Co., 205 La Salle
...........................AAAA
Armsby Co., J. K., 46 River (Brokers) ....A
Batavia Preserving Co., Randolph & Mich. .....A
Boak & Co., R. B., 33 S. Water (Brokers) C
Booth & Co., A., 2 La Salle
...........................AAAA
Fairbanks Canning Co., Union Stock Yards ...AAAA
Fish & Co., S. T., 189 S. Water (Brokers) ......A
German-American Provision Co., Union Stock Yards (23) ....A
Hammond Co., G. H., Union Stock Yards (23)
...........................AAAA
Knight & Co., W. S., 2 Wabash Av. (Bkrs.)..B
Leslie & Co., John H., 29 Michigan Av. (Brokers).A
Libby, McNeill & Libby (Soups & Meat) ....AAAA
Morris, Nelson & Co. (Soups & Meats) ....AAAA
Mullen-Blackledge Co., 53 S. Water (Br. Indianapolis. Ind.) X
Pickert Fish Co., L., 8 Market (20) ....B
Polk & Co., J. T., 46 River (Br. Greenwood, Ind.) (2-3-4-5-9) ....AA
Reber Preserving Co., 12 River ....B
Reid, Murdoch & Co., Lake & Market ....AAAA
Smith Co., Herbert W., 189 S. Water (Brokers)....A
Wing & Co., L. R., 2 Wabash Av. (Brokers).....B

ILL.—Doltons Station
Illinois Canning Co. .....B

ILL.—Elgin
Elgin Packing Co. (3-5-9).B

ILL.—Eureka
Dickinson & Co. (2-3-5-8).C

ILL.—Gibson City
Gibson Canning Co. (5)....A

ILL.—Hampshire
Hampshire Canning Co. (5)
...........................C

ILL.—Hoopeston
Hoopeston Canning Co. (5)
...........................AAA
Illinois Canning Co. (3-5)
...........................AA

ILL.—Kansas
Kansas Canning Co. .....B

ILL.—Onarga
Iroquois Canning Co. (5).A

CANNED GOODS (Con.)

ILL.—Paxton
Paxton Canning Co. (2-5-9)
...........................A

ILL.—Peoria
Warrensburg Canning Co. (C. J. Off & Co., Props.)
...........................AA

ILL.—Springfield
Springfield Canning Co. (2-5) ....B

ILL.—Sycamore
Sycamore Preserving Wks. (5-9) ....B

IND.—Arcadia
Arcadia Canning Wks. (Martz Bros., Props)....C

IND.—Bloomingdale
Bloomingdale Canning Co. (2-5-7) C

IND.—Columbus
Rider, Preston C

IND.—Crothersville
Crothersville Canning Co. (P. Rider, Prop.) (2-3-5-8) C

IND.—Delphi
Great Western Canning Co. (2-3-5-8-9-16-26) C

IND.—Eaton
Indiana Packing Co. C

IND.—Evansville
Indiana Canning Co. (4-6).C

IND.—Franklin
Franklin Canning Co. (2-5)
...........................C

IND.—Greenwood
Johnson, Grafton ....A
Polk Co., J. T. (2-3-4-5-9)
...........................AA

IND.—Hammond
Hammond Co., G. H. (23)
...........................AAAA

IND.—Indianapolis
Columbia Conserve Co. (Soups) ....A
Huffman Packing Co., W. D. (2-5-9) C
Kingan & Co. (23) ..AAAA
Van Camp Packing Co. (1-2-3-8-9-16-22-23-26) .....AA

IND.—Kokomo
Johnson, Grafton (2-3-9-18)
...........................A

IND.—Ladoga
Ladoga Canning Co. (2)...C

IND.—Lexington
Lexington Canning Co. (2-7-8-18) C

IND.—Marion
Spener-Hogan Co. (2-5-9).A

IND.—Muncie
Tuhey Canning Co. ....B

IND.—Portland
Hood Co., W. H. (2-8-9).B

IND.—Scottsburg
Scottsburg Canning Co. (P. & J. W. Rider, Props.) (2) C

IND.—Sharpsville
Sharpsville Canning Co. (2-5-9) ....B

IND.—Tipton
Johnson, Grafton (Tipton Canning Co.) ....A

IND.—Wabash
Great Western Canning Co.
...........................C

IND.—Walton
Walton Canning Co......B

IND.—Whiteland
Johnson, Grafton ....A
Whiteland Canning Co. ...C

IND.—Windfall
Bailey, W. R. (2-8) .....B

IOWA—Atlantic
Atlantic Canning Co. (5)..A

IOWA—Cedar Falls
Cedar Falls Canning Co. (2-5) C

IOWA—Cedar Rapids
Cedar Rapids Canning Co. (5) C

IOWA—Garrison
Iowa Canning Co. ....B

IOWA—Gilman
Gilman Canning Co. C

IOWA—Glenwood
New Glenwood Canning Co. (2-4-5-6-25) C

IOWA—Independence
Independence Canning Co. (5) C

IOWA—Keokuk
Keokuk Canning Co. (2-9).A

CANNED GOODS (Con.)

Keokuk Pickle Co. (2-3-8-18)
..........................B

IOWA—La Porte City
Iowa Canning Co. (Br. Vinton) ....B
IOWA—Sac City
Sac City Canning Co. C
IOWA—Vinton
Iowa Canning Co. (2-5)....B
IOWA—Waterloo
Waterloo Canning Corporation (5) ....B
IOWA—Waverly
Kelley Canning Co. C
KANS.—Leavenworth
Globe Canning Co. (J. S. Edwards, Prop.) (2-5-8).C
KY.—McKinney
McKinney Canning Co. (H. L. Tanner & Son, Props.) (2) ....B
KY.—Owensboro
Blue Grass Canning Co. (1-2-3-5-7-8-9-26) ....B
KY.—South Union
Society of Shakers (6)....B
LA.—Morgan City
Coquenhem, M. (11) C
Dalton, Jno. (11-13) .....B
LA.—Neptune
Lopez & Dukate (11-13)...A
LA.—New Orleans
Barataria Canning Co., 512 Mazan (3-4-6-7-9-11) ..A
Dunbar Sons', G. W., 3400 Chartres (2-6-11-14) ...A
Graham-Boswell Co., P. O. Box 916 (11-13) C
LA.—Shreveport
Taylor Co., W. F., Ltd..AA
MAINE—Anson
Portland Packing Co. (Packers) ....AA
MAINE—Auburn
Burnham & Morrill Co. (5) ....AA
MAINE—Bethel
Webb Co., H. F. ....B
Wyman & Son, J. ....B
MAINE—Boothbay Harbor
Maddocks Packing Co. (15) C
MAINE—Bridgeton
Bridgeton Canning Co. (5) ....A
Burnham & Morrill Co. (5) ....AAA
MAINE—Brunswick
Baxter & Bro., H. C. (1-3-5-10-18-25) ....A
Snowflake Canning Co. (5) C
MAINE—Bryant Pond
Fernald, Keene & True Co. (5) ....AA
MAINE—Buckfield
Portland Packing Co. (Br.) ....AA
MAINE—Canton
Portland Packing Co. (Br.) ....AA
MAINE—Cherryfield
Wyman & Son, J. ....B
MAINE—Columbia Falls
Loggie, A. & R. ....B
MAINE—Cumberland Centre
Merrill Bros. (5) C
MAINE—Cutler
Wilder, F. H. (14-15)....C
MAINE—Denmark
Denmark Packing Co. ..AA
MAINE—Dufield
Burnham & Morrill Co. ..AA
MAINE—East Corinth
Wyman & Son, J. ....B
MAINE—East Fryeburg
Snowflake Canning Co. ..C
MAINE—Eastport
Holmes, E. A. (14-15) ...B
Sea Coast Canning Co. (15) ....AAAA
MAINE—East Sumner
Minot Packing Co. (3-5)..C
MAINE—Fairfield
Portland Packing Co. ...AA
MAINE—Farmington
Farmington Packing Co. (Burnham & Morrell Co., Prop.) Portland ....AAA
MAINE—Foxcroft
Portland Packing Co. (Br.) ....AA
MAINE—Friendship
Burnham & Morrell Co.

CANNED GOODS (Con.)

(Br.) ....AAA
MAINE—Fryeburg
Baxter & Bro., H. C. ....A
MAINE—Harrington
Burnham & Morrill Co. AAA
MAINE—Harrison
Harrison Packing Co. ...AA
MAINE—Hiram
Twitchell-Champlin Co. (Br, Portland) ....AA
MAINE—Hollis Centre
Saco Valley Canning Co. (1-3-5) C
MAINE—Kezar Falls
Baxter & Bro., H. C. (4-10) ....A
MAINE—Leeds
Webb Co., H. F. (5)....B
MAINE—Lisbon
Fernald, Keene & True Co. (5) ....AA
MAINE—Lovell
Snowflake Canning Co. (5) C
MAINE—Lubec
Lawrence Lumber & Packing Co. ....B
Seacoast Canning Co. (15) ....AAAA
MAINE—McKinley
Underwood & Co. (Br. Boston) (20) ....A
MAINE—Machias
Coffin, J. A. (5-18) ......B
MAINE—Machiasport
Machiasport Packing Co. (15) C
MAINE—Mechanics Falls
Minot Packing Co. (3-5-25) C
MAINE—Millbridge
Wyman & Son, J. (14-15-18) ....B
MAINE—Minot
Burnham & Morrill Co. (5) ....AAA
MAINE—Naples
Portland Packing Co. ..AA
MAINE—Newport
Portland Packing Co. (Br.) ....AA
MAINE—Norridgewock
Somerset Packing Co. ...AA
MAINE—No. Fryeburg
Snowflake Canning Co. (5) C
MAINE—Norway
Webb Co., H. F. (5) .....B
MAINE—Oakland
Portland Packing Co. ..AA
MAINE—Oxford
Fernald, Keene & True Co. (5) ....AA
MAINE—Poland
Fernald, Keene & True Co. (5) ....AA
MAINE—Port Clyde
Burnham & Morrill Co..AAA
MAINE—Portland
Armsby Co., J. K. (Br. Chicago) (5) ....A
Burnham & Morrill Co. (3-4-5-10-14-18-20-23-25) AAA
Conant, Patrick & Co. ....A
Fernald, Keene & True Co. (5) ....AA
Payson & Co., R. C......C
Portland Packing Co. (3-5-10-14-18-20-23; Soups) A
Saco Valley Canning Co...C
Thompson-Hall Co. (1-5-16) C
Twitchell-Champlin Co. (Importers) ....AA
Webb Co., H. F.........AA
Winslow Packing Co. ...C
MAINE—Redfield
Webb Co., H. F. ....B
MAINE—Rockland
Thorndike & Hix (1-3-5-8-14-16-18-20-25) C
MAINE—Saint Albans
Snowflake Canning Co. ...C
MAINE—Skowhegan
Portland Packing Co. ..AA
MAINE—South Paris
South Paris Packing Co..AA
MAINE—Southwest Harbor
Sea Coast Packing Co. (15) ....AAAA
MAINE—Turner
Fernald, Keene & True Co. (1-3-5-8-16-25) ....AA

MAINE—Unity
Portland Packing Co.....AA
 N E—Vanceboro
Loggie, A. & R. ......A
MAINE—Waldoboro
Twitchell-Champlin Co. (Br.
 Portland) ....AA
MAINE—Weld
Drummer, G. G. C
MAINE—West Jonesport
Underwood Co., Wm. (20).A
MAINE—West Minot
Minot Packing Co. (3-5)..C
MAINE—West Paris
West Paris Packing Co..AA
MAINE—West Poland
Fernald, Keene & True Co.
 (1-2-3-4-5-6-8-16-25) ...AA
MAINE—Winthrop
Portland Packing Co. ...AA
MD.—Aberdeen
Baker, C. W. (2).......A
Baker, J. B. (2).......B
Baker, W. B. (2).......B
Baker & Morgan (Brokers)
 (2) ....A
Michael, Jno. M. (5)...B
Mitchell, M. (2) C
Mitchell & Bro., J. S. (2).C
Strasbaugh, Steckel, Hewitt
 Co. (Brokers) C
MD.—Baltimore
Anginbaugh Canning Co.
 (1-2-3-4-6-7-8-9-11-18-21-25-
 26) ....B
Baugh & Sons' Co., 36 South
 (4-6) ....AAAA
Booth & Co., A., 727 S.
 Wolfe (4-6-11) ....AAAA
Boyer & Co., W. W., 600 W.
 Fall Av. (6-11) ....A
Continental Commercial Co.,
 1630 Bank (Brokers)...B
Fait, Jr. & Co., Wm., Boston
 & Patuxent (6-11) ....A
Gibbs Preserving Co., 2305
 Boston ....AA
Grebb, Louis, 2353 Boston
 (2-7-9-11) ....B
Grecht Co., Wm., 1316 S.
 Sharp (4-6-11) C
Heminway & Co., H. F.,
 2323 Orleans (4-6-11)...C
Hittle & Co., F., 114 Hol-
 lingsworth (11).........C
Jackson & Co., R. S., 113
 S. Charles (6) ....B
Kidwell Bros. & Co., 1407
 Philpott (6-11).........C
Langrall & Bro., J., 2111
 Aliceanna (6-11) C
McGaw, Davis & Co., Gay
 & Water (4-6) C
McGee & Co., W. H., 1138
 Block (11)............C
McGrath & Co., H. J., At-
 lantic Wharf (6-11) ...A
McWilliams & Co., H., 110
 E. York (11) ....B
Meehan & Co., Thos. J., 524
 S. B'way (Brokers)...B
Michael & Co., W. G., 520
 Union Dock (Packers'
 Agt.) C
Miller Bros. & Co., 913 S.
 Wolfe (4-6-11) ....AA
Moore & Brady, ft. E. Mont-
 gomery (11-20) ......AA
Morris, Nelson & Co., 233
 W. Pratt (Br. Chicago)
 (Meats) ....AAAA
Myer & Co., T. J., 514 W.
 Falls Av. (6-11) ......A
Orem & Co., O. C., 215 Mc-
 Elderrys Whf. (11)....C
Platt & Co., ft. Clement
 (11) ....A
Roberts Bros., 2337 Boston
 (4-6) ....A
Storey, Bunnell Packing Co.,
 ft. West (11) C
Sticker Bros., Enos & East
 B
Summers & Co., Chas. G.,
 415 W. Camden (4-6)..C
Torsch Packing Co., P. O.
 Box 73 (1-2-3-4-5-6-7-8-9-
 11-13-16-18-21-25-26) ...A
Underhill, J. J., Bowly's
 Wharf (4-6-11) ....B
Wagner, Martin Co., Pratt
 & Gay (4-6-11) ....A
MD.—Belair
Finney & Robinson (Bkrs.)
 C
MD.—Belcamp
Dietrich, E. A. C
MD.—Bethlehem
Messick, R. M. (2) C
MD.—Bivalve
Insley & Sons, G. D. (2-19)
 C
MD.—Bradshaw
Crossmore, A. C
MD.—Bruceville
Sharretts & Bro., O. H...C
MD.—Cambridge
Leonard & Co., J. L. (2-7-9)
 A
Mace, Woolford & Co. (11)
 C
Phillips Packing Co. (2-7-11)
 C
Wallace Packing Co., Jas.
 (2-7-9) ....B
Winterbottom, W. G. (11)
 B
MD.—Chestertown
Canning & Mercantile Co. of
 Kent C
MD.—Cordova
Saulsberry Bros. ....B
MD.—Crisfield
Crockett & Riggan (11)..C
Gibson & Bros., W. E. (14-
 17) C
Long, Coulbourn & Co. (11)
 C
Riggan & Co., J. H. (11)..C
Tangier Packing Co. (Dev-
 illed Crabs) ....B
MD.—East Brooklyn
Wagner, Martin Co. (4-6-11)
 A
MD.—E. Newmarket
Webster & Co., Chas. (26).D
MD.—Easton
Hubbard & Bro. (4-6)....C
Wrightson Packing Co. (11)
 C
MD.—Edgemont
Nicodemus, J. ....B
MD.—Eldorado
Brinsfield & Son, Z. H. (2-
 8-9) ....B
MD.—Elkton
Baker, C. W. (11) ....A
MD.—Fallston
Robinson, W. E. (2-5).....B
MD.—Fowling Creek
Dean, W. H. C
MD.—Gittings
Foard, J. B. C
MD.—Girdletree
Robinson, W. E. (2-5)....B
MD.—Golding Ring
Volz & Son, H. C
MD.—Goldsboro
Jarrell, R. (2-3-7-8-9) ...C
MD.—Havre de Grace
Seneca, S. J. (Broker, Pack-
 er & Com. Mer.) ......A
MD.—Hickory
Finney & Robinson (2-5)..C
MD.—Inverness
Clark, Wands & Bennett Co.
 (11) C
MD.—Jessups
Summers & Co., C. G. (4-6)
 C
MD.—Marion Station
Tull, Miles & Co. (11)....B
Tull & Co., A. E. (11)....B
MD.—Medford
Robinson & Engler (2)....C
MD.—Minefield
Robinson, W. E. (2-5).....B
MD.—Mitchellville
McGaw, Davis & Co. .....A
MD.—Oxford
Bayside Packing Co. (11).C
Wrightston Packing Co. (11)
 C
MD.—Perryman
Stockham, E. V. (2-5)....C
MD.—Preston
Preston Canning Co. .....B
MD.—Ridgely
Alliance Preserving Co. (2-
 6) ....B
Day, Swing & Co., T. L. (2)
 B
Saulsberry Bros. (2) ....B
MD.—Singerly
Robinson, W. E. (2-5) ....B
MD.—Snow Hill
Ayars & Co., R. F. (6)
 AAA

CANNED GOODS (Con.)
N. J.—Burlington
Birkmire, W. H. (2-6) ...B
Conwell & Co., L. A. (Br. Phila., Pa.) ....B
N. J.—Camden
Campbell Preserving Co., Jos. ....AA
N. J.—Canton
Carll & Harris (2-6) C
N. J.—Cape May
Stevens & Bro., W. L.....C
N. J.—Cedarville
Diamond & Son, J. E. (2) .B
Stevens & Bro., W. L. (2-4-9).............C
N. J.—Daretown
Ayers, Harry (2-5-9) C
N. J.—Elizabeth
Earl, E. B. & W. A. C. (2-5-6-9) ....B
N. J.—Elmer
Smith, Luke T. (2).......C
N. J.—Englishtown
Reid & Co., J. B.........C
N. J.—Fairton
Statham, Cosier & Camm (2-18) ....B
N. J.—Greenwich
Watson Bros. & Co. (2-6) .C
N. J.—Hancocks Bridge
Fogg & Hires Co. (2) ....B
N. J.—Jersey City
Franco-Amer Food Co. ...A
N. J.—Leesburg
Leesburg Packing Co. (2) .B
N. J.—Moorestown
Collins & Son, J. S. (4-6) .B
N. J.—Mt. Holly
Jones & Co., E. B........C
N. J.—Newport
Strathem, Cosier & Co. (6) B
N. J.—Norma
Allivine Co. ....B
N. J.—Penn Grove
Hughes, R. D. ....B
N. J.—Port Norris
Port Norris Canning Co....B
N. J.—Quinton
Kelty, S. L. (2).........C
N. J.—Red Bank
Stout, J. W. (Br.) .....A
N. J.—Salem
Bilderback, Albert C
Fogg & Hires Co. ......B
Grier, R. C
Hiles & Hillard (2) .....B
Jones, O. L. (6) ....A
Watson Bros. & Co. (2-6) ..C
N. J.—Shiloh
Davis, Rainear & Davis (2-8-21) ....B
N. J.—Shrewsbury
Hazard & Co., E. C. (Br. N. Y. C.) ....AA
N. J.—Tuckahoe
Diament & Son, J. E. (2-6) B
N. J.—Williamstown
Souder & Clark C
N. J.—Woodstown
Davis & Lippincott ......A
Farmers' Co-operative Canning Co. C
N. J.—Yorktown
Ewell, J. S. C
N. Y.—Akron
Hamburgh Canning Co. (Br. Hamburgh) ....A
N. Y.—Auburn
Hemingway & Co., H. C. 1-2-3-4-5-6-8-9-16-18) ...A
N. Y.—Batavia
Batavia Pressing Co. (Br. Chicago) ....A
N. Y.—Blossvale
White, F. & I. J. ....B
N. Y.—Brant
Erie Preserving Co. (2-5) .A
N. Y.—Brockport
Batavia Preserving Co. (1-2-3-4-6-7-17-18-21-26) ..A
N. Y.—Buffalo
Buffalo Preserving Co., P. O. Station O (1-2-3-4-5-6-7-8-9-16-17-18-21-22-25-26) A
Erie Preserving Co., 941 Perry (1-2-3-5-6-7-8-9-16-18) ....AA
Heinz Co., H. J., 106 Main (Br. Allegheny, Pa.) AAAA
United States Canning Co.,

CANNED GOODS (Con.)
425 Ellicott Sq. ......AA
N. Y.—Canastota
Canastota Canning Co. (3-5-9) C
Hubbard, F. F. (3-4-5-8-9-16-26) C
N. Y.—Clinton
Clinton Canning Co. (6) .AA
N. Y.—Clyde
Hemingway & Co., H. C. (Br. Syracuse, N. Y.) .A
N. Y.—Delta
Olney & Floyd (Br. Westernville, N. Y.).......A
N. Y.—Eden
Hamburg Canning Co. (Br. Hamburg, N. Y.) ...A
N. Y.—Fairport
Viele, P. B. (1-2-8-26)....A
N. Y.—Farnham
Erie Preserving Co. (5-6) AA
N. Y.—Fayetteville
Fayetteville Canning Co..AA
N. Y.—Fenton
Erie Preserving Co. (Br.) AA
N. Y.—Forrestville
Forrestville Canning Co. (Haserot Canneries Co., Cleveland, Ohio, Props.) (1-3-5-8-9)..............X
N. Y.—Franklinville
Franklinville Canning Co. (1-5-8-9) ....A
N. Y.—Fredonia
United States Canning Co. (4-6) ....A
N. Y.—Geneseo
Winters & Prophet (5)....B
N. Y.—Geneva
Geneva Preserving Co. ...B
N. Y.—Gowanda
Gowanda Canning Co. (Haserot Canneries Co., Props. Cleveland, Ohio) (1-3-5-8-9-25) X
N. Y.—Hamburg
Hamburg Canning Co. (2-5-6-9) ....A
N. Y.—Holley
Hudson & Co. (1-2-3-9-16-17) B
N. Y.—Islip
Doxsee & Sons, J. H.....C
N. Y.—Kenwood
Oneida Community (Ltd.) (2-5-17) .... AAA
N. Y.—Kirksville
Woerner Preserving & Packing Co. ....AA
N. Y.—Lenox
McKinley Canning Co., Wm. C
N. Y.—Le Roy
Le Roy Canning Co. (3-4-5-8-9-25) C
N. Y.—Liverpool
Woerner Preserving & Packing Co. ....AA
N. Y.—Lowville
Conover, W. G. (3-5-9-16-18) C
N. Y.—McConnellsville
Tuttle & Co. (5).........C
N. Y.—Mattituck
Hudson & Co. (4-17)......B
N. Y.—Mexico
Wilson, Geo. H. (Br. Taberg, N. Y.) ....A
N. Y.—Middleport
Batavia Preserving Co. (Br. Chicago) ....A
N. Y.—Minoa
Woerner Preserving & Packing Co. ....AA
N. Y.—Model City
Erie Preserving Co. (5) .AA
N. Y.—Mt. Morris
White, J. F. (Agt.) ......B
Winters & Prophet (1-2-3-4-5--8-9-16-25) ....B
N. Y.—Newark
Perkins Co., C. H. (1-2-3-4-5-6-8-9-16-18-21-25) ...AA
N. Y.—New Dorp
Tyson, D. J. ....AA
N. Y.—New Hartford
New Hartford Canning Co., Ltd. (2-3-5-7-8) ....A
N. Y.—Newport
Newport Canning Co. (5) .B

150

CANNED GOODS (Con.)

New York City

Arms, Max, 372 G'wich.AA
Anthony Co., H. M., 48
  W. B'way ....B
Armour & Co., 173 Duane
  (Br.) ....AAAA
Armsby Co., J. K., 87 Hudson (Br.) ....A
Bogle & Scott, 105 Hudson
  (Brokers) ....A
Booth & Co., A., 105 Hudson (20) ....AAAA
Bowers & Co., B. O., 6 Harrison (10-11-15) .....B
Burnham Co., E. S., 61
  Gansevoort ....D
Campbell Preserving Co., J.,
  182 Franklin (Br.) ...A
Chapman Co., J. M., Wool
  Exch. (Com. & Bkrs.)..C
Cohen & Co., W. H., 229
  Washington C
Cudahy Packing Co., 74
  Hudson (Br.) .....AAAA
Dudley & Co., U. H., 165
  Duane (Brokers) .....A
Erie Preserving Co., 107
  Hudson (Br.) ....A
Fairbank Canning Co., 46
  10th Av. ....AAAA
Gordon & Dilworth, 563
  Greenwich ....
Haaker Co., W., 99 North
  Moore ....B
Hartwig & Bennett, 61 N.
  Moore ....B
Hazard & Co., E. C., 117
  Hudson ....AA
Heinz Co., H. J., 206 Spring
  (Br.) ....AAAA
Howe & Co., C. T., 51 Hudson (Brokers) C
Hunt & Co., D., 105 Hudson (Brokers) ....A
Hurley & Co., J. B., 90 W.
  B'way (Brokers) .....B
Israel & Bro., C., 490 Canal
  ....B
Johnson Co., J. S., 219
  Washn. (Pineapples)...A
Johnstone, North & Co., 21
  Harrison (Brokers) ...C
Kemp, Day & Co., 73 Hudson (Brokers) ......AA
Kress & Co., A., 64 Dey..B
La Manna, Azema & Farnan,
  397 Washn. (9) ......B
Oettinger Bros. 336 G'wich.
  (Brokers) C
Oneida Community (Ltd.),
  395 Broadway ......AAA
Portland Packing Co., 105
  Hudson (Br.) ....A
Rafferty & Hosier, 67 Front
  ....B
Reiss & Brady, 340 Greenwich ....B
Ritter Conserve Co., P. J.,
  448 Washn. (Br. Phila.,
  Pa.) ....A
Rosenstein Bros. (Inc.), 96
  N. Moore ....AA
Royal Specialty Co., 92
  Reade (Clam Bouillon)..C
Schaefer, Jno. W., 6 Harrison ....B
Seeman Bros., 121 Hudson.A
Seggerman Bros., 91 Hudson
  ....B
Smith & Co., J. P., 94 Hudson ....AAA
Snider Preserve Co., T. A.,
  105 Hudson (Br.) ...AA
Strohmeyer & Arpe Co., 33
  Water ....A
Thompson, G. H., 107 Hudson ....A
Turle & Skidmore, 105 Hudson(rBokers) ....B
Waeber & Lea, 129 Hudson
  ....B
Walden & Co., 6 Harrison.B

N. Y.—North Collins

Erie Preserving Co. (5-6)
  ....AA

N. Y.—Oneida

Burt, Olney Canning Co....A

N. Y.—Orchard Park

Erie Preserving Co. .....AA

N. Y.—Oswego

Oswego Preserving Co. (1-2-
  3-5-6-9-18-21) C

CANNED GOODS (Con.)

N. Y.—Parish

Windholz, L. (5) C

N. Y.—Pulaski

Richland Canning Co. (4-5-6)
 C

N. Y.—Riverhead

Hudson & Co. (17) C

N. Y.—Rochester

Curtice Bros. Co. ....AA

N. Y.—Rome

Clinton Canning Co. (1-3-5-8-
  9-25) ....AA
Fort Stanwix Canning Co.
  (2-3-4-5-6-8-9-18-25) ....A

N. Y.—Sauquoit

Sauquoit Canning Co. (1-2-
  5-8-9) ....B

N. Y.—Sinclairville

Fredonia Preserving Co. (1-
  2-3-5-8-9-16-25) ......A

N. Y.—Springville

Springville Canning Co. (1-
  3-5-8-9-25) C

N. Y.—Syracuse

Hemingway & Co., H. C. (1-
  2-3-4-5-6-8-9-16-18) ...A
Merrell-Soule Co. (3-5-8-9-
  25) ....AA
Windholz, L. (6) ....B

N. Y.—Taberg

Wilson, G. H. (5) ....A

N. Y.—Utica

Sauquoit Canning Co. ....B
Utica Canning Co. (1-2-3-4-
  5-8-9-25) C

N. Y.—Vernon

Curtice Bros. Co. (Br. Rochester, N. Y.) ....AA

N. Y.—Webster

Webster Preserving Co. (1-
  2-3-18-26) ....B

N. Y.—Westernville

Olney & Floyd (5) ....A

N. C.—Elizabeth City

Robinson Packing Co. (11)
  ....A

N. C.—Oxford

White Canning Co. ......B

N. C.—Washington

Farren & Co., J. S. (Br.
  Balto., Md.) (6-11)....A

OHIO—Chillicothe

Sears & Nichols Co. (1-2-3-
  4-5-6-7-8-9-18-21-25-26) .A

OHIO—Cincinnati

Armour & Co., 17 E. 2d
  ....AAAA
Cincinnati Abattoir Co. (23)
  ....AA
Loudon, Chas. F., Court &
  Sycamore (22-23) C
National Pure Food Co., 920
  Sycamore C
Peebles' Sons Co., J. R.,
  Government Sq. ......A
Shaw & Co., Geo. A., 42
  Vine (Brokers) C
Snider Preserving Co., 209
  Sycamore ....A
Threlkeld & Son, H. C., 59
  Walnut (Brokers) C
Weller Co., J., Spring Grove
  & Ala. Avs. (2-3-7-8-18-26)
  ....A

OHIO—Circleville

Esmeralda Canning Co. ...C
Scioto Canning Co. (2-5)..A
Sears & Co., C. E. (2-5)..AA
Winorr Canning Co. (3-5-9)
 C

OHIO—Cleveland

Buckeye Fish Co., Line &
  C. T. & V. R. R. (20)..C
Haserot Canneries Co., 39
  Woodland Av. (1-3-5-8-9-
  25) ....B
Housum Co., B. W., The
  Arcade (Brokers) C
Wenham's Sons, A. J., 138
  Sheriff (4-6-20-23) ....AA

OHIO—Conneaut

Cummins Co., D. (2-8)...B

OHIO—Cortland

Cortland Canning Co. C

OHIO—Deshler

Johnson Canning Co., O. J.
 C

OHIO—East Palestine

Buckeye Canning Co. (2-5-9)
  ....B

OHIO—Hillsboro

Hillsboro Canning Co. (McKeehan-Heistand Grocery

CANNED GOODS (Con.)

Co., Props.) (2) ......A
OHIO—Jeffersonville
Jeffersonville Canning Co.
  (4-6) ....B
OHIO—Lebanon
Hayner & Co., J. M. (5)..B
OHIO—Salem
McNabob, J. B. (4-6)....B
OHIO—Smithville
Weller Co., J. (4-6) ......A
OHIO—Stoutsville
Sears & Co., C. E. (Br. Cir-
  cleville) (5) ....AA
OHIO—Toledo
East Toledo Canning Co...C
International Canning Co.
  (1-2-16) ....B
OHIO—Urbana
McCoy Canning Co. ......A
OHIO—Wooster
Wooster Preserving Co. (4-
  6) ....B
OHIO—Xenia
Xenia Canning Co. ......B
OREGON—Astoria
Alaska Fisherman's Packing
  Co. ....B
Booth Packing Co., A. (3-12)
  ....AAAA
Columbia River Packers'
  Assn. ....AA
Columbia River Packing Co.
  ....B
Elmore Packing Co. (12) B
Elmore & Co., Saml. (12)
  ....AA
Kinney, M. J. (12) ......A
Schmidt & Co., S. (2)...A
Tallant-Grant Packing Co.
  (12) ....A
OREGON—Florence
Kyle & Sons, W. (12)....A
OREGON—Gardiner
Umpqua Packing Co. (S. El-
  more & Co., Props.) (12)
  ....AA
OREGON—Garibaldi
Elmore Packing Co. (12)..B
OREGON—Lutjens
Elmore & Co., S. (12) ..AA
OREGON—Nehalem
Nehalem Packing Co. (12).A
OREGON—Portland
Barnes, F. C. (12) ......B
Cook Packing Co., J. W. &
  V. (12) ....AA
Kelley-Clarke Co. (Brokers)
  ....A
Warren Packing Co. (20).A
OREGON—The Dalles
Senfert Bros. Co. (12)....A
The Dalles Packing Co. (6)
 C
OREGON—Warrendale
McGowan & Sons, P. J. (12)
  ....A
Warren, F. M. (12) .....A
OREGON—Wedderbum
Hume, R. D. (12) ......AA

OREGON—Yaquina
Barnes, F. C. (12) ......B
PA.—Bryanville
McCourtney & Fulton (4-6)
  ....B
PA.—Lawrenceville
Perkins & Burnham (6) ..A
PA.—Littletown
Schriver & Co., B. F......A
PA.—North East
North East Preserving Wks.
  (Fink & McLaughlin,
  Props.) ....A
United States Canning Co.
  (Br. Buffalo, N. Y.) ..AA
PA.—Philadelphia
Armsby Co., J. K., 23 S.
  Front (Brokers) ....A
Comly, Flaningen & Co., 118
  S. Del. Av. ....AA
Githens, Rexamer & Co., 40
  S. Front ....AA
Levins' Sons, S. H., 238 N.
  Del. Av. ....AA
Miller & Co., Chas. C., 125
  S. Water (Brokers).....C
Neff & Co., R. K., 106 S.
  Del. Av. (2) ....B
Ritter Conserve Co., Philip
  J., 2156 E. Dauphin ...A
Roberts & Co., Thos., 116
  S. Front ....AAA
Yost & Co., J. C., 223 N.

CANNED GOODS (Con.)

Water (6) ....A
PA.—Pittsburg
Pressing & Orr, Mononga-
  hela Bk. Bldg. (Bkrs.).A
Voskamp Sons', B. H., 1011
  Liberty Av. ....AA
Woodruff Co., W. W., 1147
  Penn. Av. (Brokers)....B
PA.—Scranton
Porter Co., J. T. ....A
PA.—Venango
Venango Valley Canning Co.
  ....B
S. C.—Bluffton
Lowden, Geo. W. (6-11)...B
S. C.—Waverly Mills
Breslauer, Lachicotte & Co.
  (4-11-13-14-20) C
TENN.—Memphis
Bacigalupo & Sawtelle ...B
Baldwin, Knowlton & Lake
TENN.—Oak Grove
Oak Grove Canning Co. (1-
  2-3-7-8-16-18) ....B
TEXAS—Jacksonville
Jacksonville Fruit & Can-
  ning Co. (2-3-7-9-18-21).C
TEXAS—Lindale
Lindale Canning Co. C
UTAH—Brigham City
Brigham City Canning Co.
  (2) C
UTAH—Ogden
Wasatch Orchard Co. (1-2-3-
  6-8-9-17-18) ....A
VT.—Brattleboro
Snowflake Canning Co. (5)
 C
VT.—Essex Junction
Baxter & Bro., H. C.....A
VT.—Island Pond
Loggie, A. & R..........A
VT.—Northfield
Payson & Co., R. C. (5)..C
VT.—St. Albans
Payson & Co., R. C. (5)..C
VT.—Westminster
Baxter & Bro., H. C. (4-10)
  ....A
VT.—Windsor
Baxter & Bro., H. C. (4-10)
  ....A
VA.—Alexandria
King & Son, Chas. (2) ...A
VA.—Atlantic
Atlantic Oyster Co. ..:...C
VA.—Boons Mill
Taylor & Noell C
VA.—Buena Vista
Dickinson & Nininger (2-3-
  5-18) ....B
VA.—Chatham
Cherry Stone Canning Co...A
VA.—Chincoteaque Island
Bunting, J. W. (14) .....B
Whealton & Bro., J. D. (11)
  ....A
VA.—Daleville
Mininger, B. F. (6) C
VA.—Fleet
Huff Bros. ....B
VA.—Hampton
Armstrong Bros. (11) ....B
McMenamin & Co. (Devilled
  Crabs) ....B
VA.—Houston
Halifax Canning Co. ....B
VA.—Kilmarnock
Eubank & Noblett C
VA.—Marsh Market
Accomack Canning House.A
VA.—Mundy Point
Courtney, L. W. ....B
VA.—Norfolk
Atwood & Co., D. (Br.)....C
Barnes, J. E. (11) ....B
Crosby & Co., W. J. (11).B
Fenerstein & Co. (11)....C
Hemingway Packing Co. (4-
  6) C
Higgins & Co., R. R. (11).C
White & Co., J. T. (11)..B
VA.—Portsmouth
Fleming, J. H. (11) C
Wainwright & Son, J. C.
  (11) C
VA.—Roanoke
Nalls, C. M. (2-4-6) C
VA.—Springwood
Penna. Canning Co. C
VA.—Suffolk
McAnge & Co., W. N. (4-

CANNED GOODS (Con.)

14-19) C

VA.—Urbana

Hurley, J. W. (Rappahannock Packing Co.) (2-11-20) C

Nelson & Davis Co. (2-8).C

VA.—Whealton

Coulbourn Bros. (11) C

VA.—White Stone

Saunders, R. M. C

WASH.—Aberdeen

Gray's Harbor Packing Co. (12) ....B

WASH.—Anacortes

Alaska Packers' Assn. (12) ....AAAA

Fidelgo Island Canning Co. (12) ....A

WASH.—Bellingham

Carlisle Packing Co. ....B

WASH.—Blaine

Alaska Packers' Assn. (Br.) (12) ....AAAA

Cook Packing Co., J. W. V. (12) ....AA

Pacific Packing & Navigation Co. (12) ....AAAA

WASH.—Brookfield

Megler & Co., J. G. (12)..B

Pillar Rock Packing Co. (12)

WASH.—Cathlamet

Warren, F. M. (12) ......A

WASH.—Chinook

McGowan & Sons, P. J. (12) ....A

WASH.—Eagle Cliff

Hume, Wm. ....AA

WASH.—Friday Harbor

Pacific American Fisheries Co. (12) ....AA

WASH.—Ilwaco

Aberdeen Packing Co. (12) ....A

WASH.—McGowan

McGowan & Sons, P. J. (12) ....A

WASH.—Port Angeles

Manhattan Packing Co. (12) C

WASH.—Port Townsend

Port Townsend Packing Co. (12) ....B

WASH.—Seattle

Balfour, Guthrie & Co. (Exporters) ....AAAA

Chlopeck Fish Co. C

Kelley-Clarke Co. (Bkrs.).A

San Juan Fish & Packing Co. (12) ....B

WASH.—Semiahmoo

Alaska Packers' Association ....AAAA

WASH.—South Bend

Barnes, F. C. (12) ......B

McGowan & Seoborg (12).A

WASH.—Spokane

Kelley-Clarke Co. (Bkrs.).A

WASH.—Tacoma

Alaska Fish & Packing Co. ....B

Balfour, Guthrie & Co. ....AAAA

Kelley-Clarke Co. (Bkrs.).A

Union Packing Co. (Fish).A

W. VA.—Martinsburg

Rothwell-Lovett Co. (2)..B

W. VA.—Sir Johns Run

Mendenhall, M. J. (2-3-7-18) C

W. VA.—Wheeling

Baer Grocer Co. (2) ......A

Flaccus Bros. ....A

Flaccus Co., E. C. ....A

McMechen & Sons' Co., G. K. ....A

WIS.—Algoma

Algoma Packing Co. (9).A

WIS.—Appleton

McMurray Packing Co., L. (3-5-9-25-26) ....B

WIS.—Cassville

Klindt-Geiger Canning Co. (4) ....A

WIS.—Eau Claire

Lange Canning Co. (5-8-9-16) C

WIS.—Green Bay

Larsen & Co., Wm. ......A

WIS.—Janesville

Hohenadel & Co., P., Jr...A

WIS.—Kewaunee

Seyk & Co., W. (9) ......B

CANNED GOODS (Con.)

WIS.—Manitowoc

Landreth Co., A. (9) ......B

Manitowoc Pea Packing Co. (9) ....B

WIS.—Markesan

Markesan Canning Co. (2-5) ....B

WIS.—Medford

Medford Pea Canning Co. (9) C

WIS.—Oconto

Oconto Canning Co. (9)...C

WIS.—Ripon

Ripon Packing Co. (2-6)..C

WIS.—Sauk City

Sauk City Canning & Packing Co. (4-6-9) C

WIS.—Sturgeon Bay

Reynolds Preserving Co. (9) ....B

WIS.—Two Rivers

Vaudreuill Canning Co., E. J. (3-9) ....B

WIS.—Waukesha

Waukesha Canning Co. (1-2-3-5-8-9-16-25) ....B

CANNON

CONN.—Cromwell

Stevens Co., I. & E. (Yacht) ....A

CONN.—Middletown

Wilcox, Crittenden & Co. (Yacht) ....A

CONN.—New Haven

Brown & Co., R. H. (Yacht) ....B

Snow, L. T. (Yacht)....D

MASS.—Springfield

Barney & Berry (Yacht).AA

New York City

Naval Electric Co., 93 Liberty (Cadet Corps).....D

PA.—Freemansburg

Shimer Son & Co., Wm. (Brass; Iron; Paper Cap) ....B

PA.—Lancaster

Hubley Mfg. Co. (Yacht).A

PA.—Philadelphia

Schoenhut & Co., A. (Wooden Toy) ....A

CANOES

See also Boats

DEL.—Wilmington

Drein & Son, Thos. Sailing; Paddling; Metallic) ...B

MAINE—Old Town

Carleton Boat & Canoe Co. (Birch Bark; Cancas Covered) ....E

MASS.—Boston

Sheldon Co., Orin (Sailing; Paddling) ....D

MASS.—Rowley

Mather & Co., C. B. (Sailing; Paddling) ....E

MASS.—Westfield

Crane Bros. (Linenoid Seamless) ....AAA

N. Y.—Canton

Rushton, J. H. (Sailing; Paddling) ....F

N. Y.—Skaneateles

Skaneateles Boat & Canoe Co. (Sailing; Paddling).F

CANOPIES

See also Awnings

CONN.—Middleton

Palmer, I. E. (Mosquito) ....AAA

ILL.—Chicago

Eastern Metal Wks., 57 N. Clark (Theatre) ....F

MISS.—Meridian

Acme Canopy Co. (Mosquito Bar) ....E

New York City

Gage, John S., 510 Bway. (Mosquito) ....E

OHIO—Springfield

Springfield Tent & Awning Co. (Boat; Hammock)..D

OHIO—Troy

Troy Carriage Sun Shade Co. (Carriage) ....B

CANS

CAL.—San Francisco
American Can Co., 214 Missoin (Tin; Fruit, &c.) ...... AAAA
Bartlett Paper Can & Box Co. (Paper) .... E
Tay Co., G. H., 49 1st (Tin; Fruit, &c.) .... AA
Union Can Co. of San Francisco, 1107 Front (Tin; Fruit, &c.) .... A
CONN.—Bridgeport
American Tube & Stamping Co. (Oil; Paint; Varnish) .. AAA
CONN.—Hartford
Stirling Blower & Pipe Mfg. Co. (Ash; Garbage; Galvanized Iron; Ice; Waste) ... B
CONN.—Waterbury
Noera Mfg. Co. (Oil) .... B
DEL.—Elsmere
Diamond State Fibre Co. (Roving) .... B
DEL.—Wilmington
American Vulcanized Fibre Co. (Roving) ...... AAAA
ILL.—Arlington Heights
Bray & Kates (Tin; Fruit, &c.) C
ILL.—Chicago
Adams & Westlake Co., Ontario & No. Franklin (Oil) ... AAAA
American Can Co., 135 Adams (Tin; Fruit, &c.) ... AAAA
American Key Can Co., Marquette Bldg. (Tin; Fruit, &c.) C
Chicago Paper Tube & Can Co., 20 No. May (Paper) ... G
Norton Bros., Masonic Temple (Tin; Fruit; Oil; Baking Powder; Grease; Oyster; Paint; Varnish; Syrup; Tea; Coffee; Spice) ... AAAA
Ritchie & Co., W. C. (Paper) .... A
Sturgis & Burn Mfg. Co. (Milk; Sprinkling) ..... A
French & Co., D. G., 42 River (Tin; Fruit, &c.) .. C
Union Stock Yards Can Co., 225 N. Franklin (Meat) . A
Wilson Co., F. Cortez (Oil; Water; Benzine; Jacket) .. A
ILL.—Chicago Heights
Parish & Co., Chas. P. (Oil) ... B
ILL.—Evanston
Mark Mfg. Co. (Oil) ...... A
ILL.—Gibson City
Gibson Novelty Wks. (Oil) ... E
ILL.—Hoopeston
American Can Co. (Tin; Fruit. &c.) ...... AAAA
ILL.—Litchfield
Bumann Mfg. Co. (Oil) ... D
ILL.—Quincy
Quincy Stamping Co. (Powder) C
ILL.—Rockford
Palmer Co., H. H. Creamery) .... D
Rockford Can Co. (Tin; Fruit; Oil; Galvd. Iron; Wooden Jacket Tin) C
IND.—Indianapolis
American Can Co. (Tin; Fruit. &c.) ...... AAAA
Duckwall, J. S. (Tin; Fruit, &c.) .... D
IND.—Marion
Marion Fruit Jar & Bottle Co. (Glass; Oil) ..... AAA
IND.—Upland
Upland Co-operative Glass Co. (Oil) C
IND.—Wabash
Wabash Baking Powder Co. (Tin; Fruit. &c.) ...... B
IOWA—Des Moines
Iowa Can Co. (Tin; Tea; Coffee; Spice) .... D
IOWA—Glenwood
New Glenwood Can Co. (Tin;

CANS (Con.)
Fruit, &c.) C
IOWA—Keokuk
Tri-State Can Co. (Tin; Fruit, &c) .... B
KY.—Louisville
Hammock Oil Can Co. (Oil) ... F
Vogt Machine Co., Hy. (Artificial Ice) ...... AA
LA.—New Orleans
Gulf Mfg. Co. (Tin; Sample Sugar) .... B
New Orleans Roofing & Metal Wks. (Galvd. Ice) ... B
MD.—Baltimore
Amer. Can Co., Oak & 26th (Tin; Fruit; Oil) . AAAA
Baltimore Can Mfg. Co. (Tin; Fruit, &c.) C
Columbia Specialty Co., 1508 E. Fayette (Baking Powder; Cement; Confect.; Metal Polish; Snuff; Spice; White Lead) ..... E
Consumers Can Co., 1015 Fawn (Tin; Fruit. &c.) . D
Fait & Co., Wm., Jr., Boston & Patuxent (Tin; Fruit, &c.) .... A
Grecht & Co., W., 1316 So. Sharp (Tin; Fruit, &c.) ... C
Kirwan & Riggs (Tin; Fruit. &c.) C
McGinnis, Jas. Co., 702 Canton Av. Ext. (Tin; Fruit, &c.) .... D
Norton Tin Plate & Can Co. (Fruit; Oyster; Vegetable) ... AAAA
Smith Can Co., R. Tynes (The) (Tin; Fruit, &c.) ... A
Southern Can Co., 2121 Boston (Tin; Fruit; Vegetable; Coffee; Baking Powder) C
Summers Co., Chas. G. 415 W. Camden (Tin; Fruit. &c.) C
Shirkel Can Co. (Paint & Putty) C
MD.—Federalburg
Messenger, H. B. (Tin; Fruit, &c.) .... D
MD.—Havre de Grace
Seneca, Jessup (Tin; Fruit, &c.) .... A
MASS.—Boston
American Can Co., 9 Binford (Tin; Fruit, &c.) ... AAAA
Gray. Peter, 12 Marshall (Oil) .... D
New Can Co., 43 Purchase (Paper) .... D
MICH.—Detroit
American Can Co., Russell & Twombly Av. (Tin; Fruit, &c.) ...... AAAA
Briscoe Mfg. Co. (Oil) ..... A
Buhl Stamping Co. (Milk; Creamery) .... A
Buhl Sons & Co., 103 Woodbridge W. (Tin; Fruit, &c.) .... AAAA
Buhl Stamping Co. (Ice Cream) .... E
Detroit Paper Tube & Can Co., 26 Griswold (Paper) ... E
Gem Fibre Package Co. .Clay & St. Aubin (Paper, for Butter, Lard, Coffee, Spice. &c.) C
National Can Co. (Baking Powder) .... A
MICH.—Jackson
Jackson Paper Tube Co. (Paper) .... H
MO.—Kansas City
Ritzler Cornice & Ornamental Co. (Ice) ...... D
MO.—St. Louis
American Can Co., Branch & Hall (Tin; Fruit, &c.) ... AAAA
Blanke Can & Mfg. Co., W. F., 116 Pine (Tin; Fruit) etc) C
Columbia Can Co., Madison & 1st (Tin; Fruit, &c.) . C

CANS (*Con.*)

Handlan-Buck Mfg. Co., 212 No. 3d (Oil)..........AA

Ruemmell-Dawley Mfg. Co. (Ice) ....A

St. Louis Paper Can & Tube Co. (Paper) ....A

Schlueter Mfg. Co., 3116 No. 9th (Tin; Fruit, &c.)..D

N. H.—Keene

Impervious Package Co. (Tin; Fruit, &c.; Oil; Wooden Oil) ....B

N. H.—Nashua

White Mountain Freezer Co. (Ice Cream)........A

N. J.—Bridgeton

Ayars & Sons Co., Benj. B. (Tin; Fruit, &c.) C

N. J.—Burlington

Stewart & Peterson Co. (Faucet; Ice Cream)...A

N. J.—Newark

Garrison Mfg. Co., W. C. (Tin; Fruit, &c.).....B

Pimley, J. E. (Oil)......F

N. J.—New Brunswick

Consolidated Fruit Jar Co. (Oil) ....AAA

N. Y.—Albany

Hoy & Co., 25 Green (Oil).A

N. Y.—Belfast

Tanner Bros. Mfg. Co. (Tin; Fruit. &c.) ....D

N. Y.—Brooklyn

Deverall Perfection Mfg. Co., 38 Bridge (Oil)....D

Lecomte Mfg. Co. J., 92 3d (Tin; Fruit, &c.)....C

Mersereau Mfg. Co., 3d Av. & 3d (Tin; Fruit, &c.)..A

Somers Bros. (Decorated Tin) ....AAAA

Vogel Bros., Wm., 47 S. 9th (Oil; Aniline)....AA

N. Y.—Buffalo

Buffalo Tin Can Co., 1430 Niagara (Tin; Fruit, &c.) B

Fedders Mfg. Co. (Oil; Ice Cream; Packing) ......F

Niagara Machine & Tool Superior & Randell (Tin; Fruit, &c.) ....A

Shepard Co., Sidney, 191 Clinton (Tin; Fruit; Ash; Oil; Milk; Water; Creamery) Jacket; Storage Oil; Garbage; Dredge; Spice) AAAA

Wright & Co., R. G., 52 Terrace (Tin; Fruit, &c.; Glass Oil) ....AA

N. Y.—Cattaraugus

Oakes & Burger (Milk).AA

N. Y.—Cuba

Bates Mfg. Co., W. A. (Oil) C

N. Y.—Elmira

Elliott & Peake (Oil) ....G

N. Y.—Fort Plain

Yerdon, W. (Tin; Fruit; Oil) C

New York City

American Can Co., 11 Broadway (Every Description) AAAA

Central Stamping Co. (Creamery) ....AA

Clowes & Co., T. H., 70 Maiden Lane (Varnish).D

Crandall & Godley Co., 157 Franklin (Ice Cream; Tin) ....A

Empire Paper Tube & Box Co. (Paper) ....E

Fibre Mfg. Co., 303 Canal (Roving) ....D

Ginna & Co. (Tin; Fruit, &c.) ....AA

Hall Mfg. Co., 40 Cortlandt (Oil) ....F

Hoe & Co., R. (Benzine) AAAA

Howard & Morse, 45 Fulton (Ash; Garbage; Waste).D

Iron Clad Mfg. Co. (Ash; Mill; Ice Cream; Milk; Oil; Garbage; Creamery; Storage Oil) ......AAAA

Knapp Mfg. Co. (Oil).....E

Koven & Bro., L. O., 50 Cliff (Oil; Garbage)...A

Lalance & Grosjean Mfg.

CANS (*Con.*)

Co. (Milk; Creamery) AAAA

Manhattan Brass Co., 1st Av. & E. 28th (Engineers' Oil; Machinists' Oil).AA

Novelty Iron Bridge & Roof Co., 39 Cortlandt (Ash; Garbage) ....A

Nason Mfg. Co. (Engineers' Oil; Machinists' Oil)....A

North Star Ash Can Co., 140 Chrystie (Steel Ash)....H

Reilley Bros. (Oil; Paint; Varnish; Tin)..........D

Shepard Co., Sidney, 21 Cliff (Tin; Fruit; Oil) AAAA

Standard Mfg. Co. (Ash).X

Stoutenborough, X. (Galvanized Ash) ....D

N. Y.—Rochester

Rochester Automatic Oiler & Supply Co. (Oil).....E

N. Y.—Troy

Hart Specialty Co., C. W. (Oil) ....A

Parks & Parks (Oil)......D

Troy Stamping Wks. (Oil) AAAA

N. Y.—Utica

Jones, Frank L. (Creamery) C

Millar & Son Co., C. (Milk) AA

N. Y.—Whitestone

Norton Can Co. (Tin; Fruit, &c.) ....A

OHIO—Akron

Akron Mfg. Co. (Oil).....E

OHIO—Canton

Berger Mfg. Co. (Oil)...AA

OHIO—Cincinnati

American Can Co., Union Trust Bldg. (Tin; Fruit, &c) ....AAAA

Davenport Paper Box Co. (Paper) ....D

Heekin Can Co., 3d & Lock (Tin; Fruit, &c.) ......A

Kiechler Mfg. Co., Linn & Everett (Artificial Ice).C

Triumph Ice Machine Co., 610 Baymiller (Artificial Ice ....A

OHIO—Cleveland

Hunt Stamping Wks., H. B. (Gasoline; Oil) ....D

Hunt & Dorman Mfg. Co. (Oil) ....AAAA

OHIO—Columbus

American Can Co. (Tin; Fruit, &c.) ....AAAA

OHIO—Dayton

American Can Co. (Tin; Fruit, &c.) ....AAAA

New Century Mfg. Co. (Tin; Self Measuring Oil)....C

OHIO—Delphos

Delphos Can Co. (Oil)....C

OHIO—Greenfield

Harps Mfg. Co., J. A. (Alcohol; Benzine; Gasoline; Turpentine; Witch Hazel) C

OHIO—Kings Mills

Wilson, McClelland & Co. (Tin; Powder) ....D

OHIO—Niles

Ohio Galvanizing & Mfg. Co. (Artificial Ice; Street Cleaning) ....B

OHIO—Salem

Clark Co., W. J. (Mill; Rotary Oil; Oily Waste; Ash; Garbage; Waste)..B

OHIO—Tiffin

Ohio Lantern Co. (Oil; Wire-Cushioned) ....B

OHIO—Toledo

Brown Oil Can Co. (Oil).D

Snell Cycle Fittings Co. (Oil) ....B

Standard Oil Can Co. (Oil) E

OHIO—Urbana

Johnson Mfg. Co. (Engine Oil) ....D

OHIO—Warren

Winfield Mfg. Co. (Oil; Gasoline) ....A

OREGON—Astoria

American Can Co. (Tin) AAAA

PA.—Allegheny
Sands Mfg. Co. (Oil)......G
Wall Mfg. Supply Co., P.
(Oil)....................G
PA.—Easton
Canister Mfg. Co. (Tin Canisters for Coffee, Spices &
Cereals) ....A
PA.—Harrisburg
Harrisburg Pipe & Pipe
Bending Co. (Ltd.) (Galvanized Iron Ice).....AA
PA.—Meadville
Beman Automatic Oil Can
Co. (Ltd.) (Oil)........E
PA.—Morrell
Union Furnace Mfg. Co.
(Oil)....................D
PA.—Philadelphia
American Can Co., 251 No.
Front (Tin; Fruit, &c.)
AAAA
Clad & Sons, Valentine
(Ice Cream) ....B
Hero Fruit Jar Co., Gaul &
Adams (Oil) ....AA
Hocker Co., G. H., 1844 So.
Comac (Paint; Putty)..A
Pfeifer & So. (Ltd.), Jno.
(Ash) ....A
Reid, A. H. (Milk.......A
PA.—Pittsburg
Dunlap Co., Jno. (Tin;
Fruit; Paint; Varnish)..A
Gem Mfg. Co. (Oil)......D
McClintoch & Irvine (Oil).B
National Glass Co. (Glass)
X
Scaife & Sons Co., Wm. B.,
221 First Av. (Ash; Garbage; Galvanized Iron Ice)
A
PA.—Royersford
Diamond Glass Co. (Glass)
A
PA.—Sharpville
Jackson, J. W. (Oil)......F
PA.—York
Eureka Oil Can Co. (Oil).B
R. I.—Providence
Hill Mfg. Co., Jas. (Tin for
Lard. &c.; Dye House;
Roving; Galvanized Ash;
Garbage) ....B
New England Ventilating &
Heating Co., Manhattan
Av. (Mill; Roving).....D
TENN.—McKenzie
Walpole Can Co. (Tin; Oil)
H
VT.—Bellows Falls
Vermont Farm Machine Co.
(Milk) C
VT.—Rutland
Steward, L. & J. A. (Tin
for Food Products).....D
VA.—Richmond
American Can Co. (Tin;
Fruit, &c.) ....AAAA
Richmond Cedar Wks.
(Ltd.) (Wooden Water)
AAAA
VA.—Roanoke
Good & Co., D. Wm.
(Bkrs. Tin; Fruit, &c.).D
Nalls, C. M. (Tin; Fruit,
&c.) C
W. VA.—Wheeling
Wheeling Can Co. (Tin for
Packers) ....B
Wheeling Stamping Co.
(Oil) ....A
WIS.—Fort Atkinson
Cornish, Curtis & Greene
(Refrigerator) ....A
WIS.—Milwaukee
Cream City Can Wks. (Tin;
Fruit, &c.) ....D
Wallman Mfg. Co. (Shipping; Square Varnish)..E
Walsh & Co., F. A. (Tin;
Fruit. &c.) ....A
WIS.—Racine
Racine General Mfg. Co.
(Oil) C
Racine Malleable & Wrought
Iron Co. (Oil) ....B
WIS.—Two Rivers
Aluminum Mfg. Co. (Oil).B

CANTEENS

IND.—Indianapolis
Seiner, Chas. F., 122 E. 32d

CANTEENS (Con.)

(Miners') ....E
IOWA—Ottumwa
Hardsocg Mfg. Co. (Gold
Miners') ....B
MO.—St. Louis
Hemp & Co. (Galvanized). A
N. Y.—Troy
Troy Stamping Wks. (Army)
AAAA
WIS.—Racine
Gold Medal Camp Furn. Mfg.
Co. (Water Cooling)....B

CANTHA-RIDES

New York City
Hopkins & Co., J. L., 100
William................A
McKesson & Robbins AAAA
Schieffelin & Co. ....AA

CANTHOOKS

ILL.—Chicago
Klein & Son, M., 87 W. Van
Buren ....A
ILL.—Downers Grove
Dickle Tool Co. C
IND.—Columbus
Columbus Handle & Tool Co.
B
IND.— Indianapolis
Atkins & Co., E. C.....AAA
LA.—New Orleans
Simonds Mfg. Co. ....B
MAINE—Bangor
Bangor Edge Tool Co. ....D
MASS.—Boston
Boston & Lockport Block
Co., 160 Com'l ....A
MICH.—Detroit
Anderson & Sons, W. H....C
MICH.—Evart
Champion Tool & Handle
Works ....A
MO.—St. Louis
Zelnicker, W. A., 408 N. 4th
C
OHIO—Canton
Canton Saw Co. ....D
Knight Mfg. Co. ....E
OHIO—Cleveland
Gerlach & Co., Peter .....B
OHIO—Columbus
Buckeye Saw Mfg. Co., 285
Water ....D
PA.—Eldred
Prouty & Co., C ....A
PA.—Erie
Standard Saw Mill Machinery Co. C
PA.—Philadelphia
Keystone Drop Forge Co., 20
20th and Clearfield .....B
PA.—Pittsburg
Roberts, George, 1st and
Liberty ....F
WIS.—Oshkosh
Oshkosh Logging Tool Co.
C
Sanford Logging Tool Co.
..D

CANTILEVERS

New York City
Lancaster Co., Jas. H., 26
Cortlandt (Dredging) X

CANVAS

See also Duck

ILL.—Chicago
Dietzgen Co., Eugene (Artists') ....A
N. J.—Bloomfield
Wiggins Sons Co., H. B.
(Ceiling; Wall) ....A
N. J.—Tenafly
Richter Mfg. Co. (Decorative Burlap) C
New York City
Boyle & Co., John, 112 Duane
A
Chelsea Jute Mills ....A
F. W. Devoe & C. T. Raynolds Co. (Artists) .....A
Rehm & Co., 141 Fulton..D
PA.—Philadelphia
Weber & Co., F. (Artists';
Pastel, also Paper and
Boards) ....A

CANVAS (Con.)
W. VA.—Wheeling
Wheeling Tent & Awning Co.
(Show; Steamboat) ....F

CAPERS

ILL.—Chicago
Carr & Carr, 211 E. 57th..E
Wolff & Sons, M., 218 W.
Lake C
New York City
Alart & McGuire, 70 Madison ....A
Falcon Packing Co., 158
Franklin C
Gordon & Dilworth, 563
Greenwich ....A
Greenwich Packing Co., 462
Greenwich ....E
Gulden, Chas., 46 Elizabeth
AA
LaManna, Azema & Farnam
397 Wash. ....B
Moos & Co., 171 Duane ..A
Strohmeyer & Arpe Co., 33
Water ....A
PA.—Philadelphia
Alart & McGuire, 126 Cuthbert ....A
Chance's Sons, R. C., 433
Spruce C
W. VA.—Wheeling
McMechan & Son Co......B

CAPES

See Clothing; Ladies'

CAPITALS

See also Woodwork

ILL.—Chicago
Hartmann, Jno., 13 N. Jeff.
(Composition) ....E
Plastic Relief Mfg. Co. 298
N. Halsted (Composition)
C
MASS.—Boston
Emmel, Chas., 383 Albany
(Composition) ....B
Stearns Lumber Co., A. T.
Neponset & Devonshire
(Papier Mache) ......AA
N. Y.—Brooklyn
Heilman, R., 207 State
(Composition) ....E
N. Y.—Syracuse
Harnisch, Ad. (Composition)
E
OHIO—Madisonville
Florentine-Wilhelm Co.
(Porch) ....B
Spangler. Frank, 323 Lafayette (Composition) ....D

CAPPERS

ILL.—Chicago
Redlich Mfg. Co., 2 Oak
(Bottle) ....B
ILL.—Downers Grove
Dicke Tool Co. (Bottle) ..A

CAPS

For Percussion Caps, see also Primers; See also Hats & Caps.

CAL.—San Francisco
California Cap Co. (Blasting) ....A
Landsberger Co., J. A., 108
Market (Fruit Jar) C
CONN.—Bridgeport
Bridgeport Brass Co. (Varnish Can) ....AAA
Drouve Co., G. (Door; Window Metal) ....A
Union Metallic Cartridge Co.
(Percussion) ....AAA
CONN.—Meriden
Manning, Bowman & Co.
(Bottle) ....AAAA
CONN.—NewBritain
Union Mfg. Co. (Hitching
Post) ....AA
CONN.—New Haven
New Haven Button Co.
(Whisk Broom) ....E
CONN.—Waterbury
Waterbury Brass Co. (Per-

CAPS (Con.)
cussion) ....AAAA
ILL.—Chicago
Illinois Malleable Iron Co.,
30 W. Monroe (Hitching
Post; Hose) ......AAAA
ILL.—Warren
Warren Steel Co. (Door)..D
IND.—Evansville
Bernardin Bottle Cap Co.
(Bottle) ....B
IND.—Indianapolis
Bayior Mfg. Co. (Bottle;
Jar) ....D
IND.—New Albany
Goetz Box Anchor Co. (Joist,
Anchor; Timber)......E
KANS.—Emporia
Emporia Foundry & Mach.
Wks. (Iron Window) ...D
MD.—Baltimore
Ammidon & Co. (Tin Roofing) ....A
MASS.—Andover
Tyer Rubber Co. (Rubber)
AA
MASS.—Boston
Van Noorden & Co., E. (Iron
Window) C
MASS.—Cambridge
Hall & Co.. Chas. E. (Marble
Chimney) ....A
Hews & Co., A. H. (Carboy)
A
MO.—St. Louis
Kupferle John C., 2d and
Mound (Hose)........AA
Mesker & Bros. (Iron Window) ....AA
Pleuger & Henger Mfg. Co.,
1015 Herbert (Hose) ..A
N. H.—Manchester
Campbell, Jno. (Hitching
Post) ....H
N. J.—Camden
Sayford Paper Specialties
Co. (Paper Bottle) ...F
N. J.—Rahway
Cox & Spencer (Paper Bottle) X
N. Y.—Brooklyn
Brass Goods Mfg. Co. (Mucilage) ....B
Brooklyn Wire Forming Co.,
302 Pearl (Incandescent
Light) ....G
Duvinage & Co., P., 498
Leonard (Joist, Anchor;
Timber) ....F
N. Y.—Canastota
Smith-Lee Co. (Bottle; Jar)
A
N. Y.—Lockport
Empire Mfg. Co. (Knee) ..A
New York City
Biddle & Westermann (Metallic Bottle) ....A
Consolidated Fruit Jar Co.,
290 B'way (Metallic Bottle) ....A
Crooke Co., John J. (Bottle)
A
Cahn & Co., Hugo (Ginger
Ale) ....A
Detwiller & Street Mfg. Co.,
(Percussion) ....A
Goodyear's India Rubber
Glove Mfg. Co. (Rubber)
AAAA
Graham & Co.. John H., 113
Chambers (Hose) ....AA
Jackson Co., Wm. H., 29 E.
7th (Bronze) ....A
Lehmaier, Schwartz & Co.
(Bottle) ....AA
McNab & Harlan Mfg. Co.,
56 John (Hose) ......AA
Mattson Rubber Co. (Rubber, Bathing) ....B
Mechanical Rubber Co.
(Rubber) ....AAAA
Metallic Cap Mfg. Co. (Percussion; Blasting) ......A
Phoenix Cap Co., 108 Warren (Metal) ....E
Rendock Powder Co. (Blasting) ....B
Witteman Bros. (Bottle)..A
N. Y.—Potsdam
Thatcher Mfg. Co. (Paper
Milk Bottle) ....A
N. Y.—Poughkeepsie
Lane Bros. Co. (Stone Sliding Door) ....A
N. Y.—Syracuse
Stearns & Co., E. C. (Hitch-

CAPS (Con.)
ing Post) ....AA
OHIO—Canton
Berger Mfg. Co. (Door; Window; Metal) ....AA
Kohler & Co., F. E.(Hose) .C
OHIO—Cincinnati
King Powder Co. (Blasting)
AAA
Robertson Steel & Iron Co.,
W. F. (Tin Roofing) ...A
OHIO—Cleveland
Gary Iron & Steel Co. (Door)
A
Van Dorn Iron Wks. Co.,
1793 E. Madison Av.
(Joint; Anchor; Timber;
Post; Fence Post) ....AA
OHIO—Kenton
Champion Iron Co. (Joist;
Anchor; Timber) .....AA
OHIO—Salem
Clark Co., W. J. (Post) ...B
Mullins, W. H. (Iron Window) ....A
OHIO—Tiffin
Ohio Lantern Co. (Tin
Screw) ....B
PA.—Philadelphia
Pancoast Ventilator Co.
(Inc.) (Chimney) ....B
Philadelphia Truss Co. (Surgical Knee) X
Schoenhut & Co., A (Toy)..A
PA.—Scranton
Scranton Button Co. (Ltd.)
(Bicycle Handle).......A
VT.—Bennington
Cooper, Chas. (Surgical
Knee) ....B
W. VA.—Wheeling
Wheeling Hinge Co. (Bottle;
Milk Bottle) ....AA
Hazel-Atlas Glass Co. (Vacuum Jar) ....AAAA
WIS.—Two Rivers
Aluminum Mfg. Co. (Aluminum) ....B

CAPSICUM

See Tea, Coffee & Spice List

CAPSTANS

CAL.—San Francisco
Risdon Iron & Locomotive
Wks. ....AAA
MAINE—Bath
Hyde Windlass Co. (Power)
B
MASS.—Boston
Edson Mfg. Co. (Steam;
Bar) ....B.
MASS.—Newburyport
Russell & Sons, Albert C
MICH.—Northville
Dubuar Mfg. Co., J. A.(Bar)
X
MINN.—Redwing
Densmore Bros. (Cavel) ...D
New York City
Starke, Adolph (Est.) 441 E.
10th ....B
OHIO—Cleveland
Chase Machine Co., 111 Elm
(Steam) ....B
Rees & Son Co., James
(Steam) ....AA
Rogers, Charles ....E
R. I.—Providence
Amer. Ship Windlass Co.
(Electric; Horse Power;
Yacht; Bar; Crank; Dock;
Steam) ....A
Providence Steam Engine Co.
F

CAPSULES

IND.—Indianapolis
Lilly & Co., Eli (Filled) .AA
MD.—Baltimore
Sharpe & Dohme (Gelatine)
AAA
MASS.—Boston
Billings, Clapp & Co. (Gelatine) ....B
MICH.—Detroit
Parke, Davis & Co. (Gelatine; Filled) ....AAAA
N. Y.—Brooklyn
Planten & Son, Hy., 93 Henry ....A
New York City
Planten & Son, H., 224 William (Gelatine; Filled) ..A

CAPSULES (Con.)
Schieffelin & Co., W. H.
(Gelatine) ....AA
OHIO—Cincinnati
Hall Capsule Co. (Gelatine;
Filled) ....D
PA.—Allentown
Grape Capsule Co. C

CARAMELS

See Confectionery

CARBINES

See Fire Arms

CARBON & CARBONS

IND.—Peru
Peru Electric Mfg. Co. (Battery ....A
MASS.—Boston
Billings, Clapp & Co. (Bisulphide) ....B
MASS.—Canton
Morse Bros. (Battery & Arc
Light) ....AA
MO.—St. Louis
American Carbon & Battery
Co., 2134 DeKalb (Battery ....B
Mallinckrodt Chem. Wks.
(Bisulphide) ....AAAA
N. J.—Jersey City
Eastern Carbon Wks. (Battery Carbons) ....A
N. Y.—Brooklyn
Wheeler & Co., J. H., 577
Smith (Bisulphite) .....D
Wiarda & Co., Jno. C. (Prepared) ....A
New York City
Cooper & Co., Chas. (Bisulphide) ....AA
Erkenbrach, Geo. A. (Bisulbride) ....D
Machado & Roller, 234 Barclay (Arc Light Carbon)
D
Reisinger, Hugo, 11 B'way
(Arc Light; Battery ..AA
Yawger-Lexow Co., 12 John
(Diamond Drill) ....A
N. Y.—Niagara Falls
Acker Process Co. (Tetrachloide) ....D
N. Y.—Penn Yan
Taylor, E. R. (Bisulphide) .C
OHIO—Cleveland
Nat'l Carbon Co. (Arc Light;
Battery; Enclosed Arc
Light; Search Light; Electric Light; Flour; Granulated) ....AAAA
U. S. Carbon Co. (Searchlight) X
OHIO—Fostoria
Crouse-Tremaine Carbon Co.
(Arc Light) ....A
OHIO—Lancaster
Consumers Carbon Co. (Arc-Light) ....AA
Dickey Sutton Carbon Co.
(Battery) ....B
PA.—Jeannette
Faraday Carbon Co. (Arc
Light) ....A
PA.—Philadelphia
Powers - Weightman - Rosengarten Co. (Bisulphide)
AAAA
PA.—Pittsburg
Pittsburg Electrical & Machine Co. (Battery) ....E
PA.—St. Mary's
Speer Carbon Co. (Arc Light;
Battery) ....A
PA.—Washington
Washington Carbon Co. (Arc
Light; Searchlight; Electric Light; Special) ....A

CARBONIZERS

See also Machinery

MASS.—North Adams
Hunter Machine Co., Jas...A
MASS.—Westford
Sargents' Sons, C. G......A
N. Y.—Hudson
Hudson Fibre Co. ....B

CARBONIZERS (Con.)
PA.—Philadelphia
Am. Drying Machy. Co., ..Westmoreland ....D
Philadelphia Drying Machy. Co., 6721 Gtn. Av .....D
Philadelphia Textile Machy. Co., Hancock and Somerset ....AA
R. I.—Providence ..
Blanding Mfg. Co., C. L...X
Textile Finishing Mach. Co. ....AAA

CARBORUNDUM
N. Y.—Niagara Falls
Carborundum Co.........A

CARBOYS
New York City
Brookfield Glass Co., 220 Broadway ....B
PA.—Philadelphia
Burgin & Sons ....A
Whitall, Tatum & Co.AAAA
PA.—Reading
Reading Glass Works C

CARBURETTERS
ILL.—Chicago
Turner Brass Wks., Franklin & Mich. ....A
IND.—Kokomo
Byrne, Kingston & Co.....F
MASS.—Braintree
Dow Portable Electric Co. C
OHIO—Cleveland
Brew & Hatcher Co., 32 Columbus C
PA.—Bradford
Holly Motor Co. ....H
WIS.—Milwaukee
Clemick-Hirsch Co. ......D

CARDBOARD
See Paper

CARDIGANS
See Jackets

CARDS
CAL.—San Francisco
Stuparich Mfg. Co., 147 Fremont (Photographer) ..B
CONN.—Clintonville
Vibbert & Co., Geo. S. (Advertising; Bevel Edge; Chromo Cut; Dance Order; Holiday; Merit; Ragged Edge) ....D
CONN.—Highland Park
Case Bros. (Jacquard) ....A
CONN.—New Haven
Best Mfg. Co., E. P. (Show) F
Sargent & Co. (Woolen; Curry) ....AAAA
CONN.—South Manchester
Rogers Paper Mfg. Co. Inc.) (Jacquard) ....B
CONN.—Stafford Springs
Beckwith Card Co.(Hand).B
ILL.—Chicago
American Label Mfg. Co., 34 Washington Av. (Show; Adv.) ....A
Ball & Bros., A (Playing)AA
Chicago Card Co. (Playing) ..X
Gunning System (The) 15 Plymouth Ct. (Adv. Sign) AAA
Lazenby Color Card Co., J. (Paint Color) ....E
Rand, McNally & Co. (Show) AAAA
Regent Mfg. Co., 152 5th Av. (Show; Adv.) ....D
Shonk Co., Chas. W., 222 W. Van Buren (Iron Show).B
Standard Playing Card Mfg. Co., 31 E. Indiana (Playing) ....B
Western Glass Adv. Co. Show; Adv.) ....E

CARDS (Con.)
IND.—Connellsville
Root & Heineman (Show; Adv.) ....A
MASS.—Boston
Bufford's Sons Engraving & Lithographing Co. (Advertising) X
Dennison Mfg. Co. (Direction; Jewelers') ..AAAA
Firth Co., Wm., 150 Devonshire (Revolving Flat)..D
Housch Co., 156 Concord (Photograph) ....E
Lowe, Stephen C., 186 Devonshire (Revolving Flat) B
McKerrow & Co., H. G., 31 State (Revolving Flat)..X
Riley & Co., C. E., 65 Franklin (Revolving Flat; Woolen; Worsted) ....A
Stoddard, Haserick, Richards & Co., 152 Congress (Simplex Worsted; Woolen) ....B
Wheelright Paper Co., Geo. W., 95 Milk (Cut) ..AA
MASS.—Fall River
Fall River Foundry & Machine Co. (Cotton; Foss; Pevey) ....F
MASS.—Lawrence
Columbia Napper Clothing Co. (Hand) ....H
MASS.—Leicester
Watson Mfg.Co., L. S. (Steel Wire Strippers; Woolen; Hand Cotton; Curry)....B
MASS.—Lowell
Lowell Machine Shop (Cotton; Floss; Pevey; Revolving Flat) ....AAAA
Pevey Bros. (Cotton; Foss; Pevey) C
MASS.—Newton Upper Falls
Crocker & Sons, Chas. F. (Jacquard) ....A
Saco & Pettee Machine Shops (Cotton; Foss; Pevey; Revolving Flat) ...... AAA
MASS.—Springfield
Colby Mfg. Co. (Photograph) E
MASS.—Taunton
Mason Machine Wks. (Cotton) ....AA
MASS.—Whitinsville
Whitin Mach. Wks. (Cotton; Revolving Flat) ..AAAA
MASS.—Worcester
American Card Clothing Co. (Woolen) ....AAA
Cleveland Machine Wks. (Felt; Woolen; Shoddy; Worsted) ....A
Howard Bros. Mfg. Co., 42 Vine (Hand) ....A
Whiting Co., Geo. C. (Holiday) ....A
MICH.—Kalamazoo
American Playing Card Co. (Playing) ....A
MO.—St. Louis
Igelstroem Sign & Label Co., Jno., 19 S. Broadway (Show; Adv.) ....D
Nixon-Jones Printing Co. (Show) ....D
N. H.—Manchester
Campbell, Jno. (Curry) ..H
N. H.—Nashua
Nashua Card & Glazed Paper Co. (Cut; Sample) ...AA
N. J.—Newark
Whitehead & Hoag Co. (Show; Adv.) ....AA
N. Y.—Brooklyn
Bainbridge's Sons, Chas. T. 2 Cumberland (Cut) ....A
N. Y.—Buffalo
Dunstan, G. H. (Show; Adv.) ....A
New York City
American Bank Note Co. (Show) .... AAAA
American Sample Co., 292 Church (Sample) ......F
Barnum & Co. (Bevel Edge; Cut) ....D
Bloom & Mandell, 81 Walker (Sample) ....D
Brett Lithographing Co. (Show) ....B
Dougherty, Andrew, 78 Cen-

ILL.—Chicago
Olsen Rug Co. (Rugs)....C

MASS.—Boston
Roxbury Carpet Co. (Tapestry; Velvet Carpets).AAA

MASS.—Dedham
Cochrane Mfg. Co. (Tapestry; Velvet Carpets)....A

MASS.—Lowell
Bigelow Carpet Co. (Carpet)
AAAA

MASS.—Palmer
Palmer Carpet Mill (Body Brussels Carpets)..AAAA

MASS.—Somerville
Hodges Fibre Carpet Co. (Fibre Carpet; Rugs)...B

MASS.—Worcester
Whittall, Mathew J. (Wilton; Plush Carpets)
AAAA

MICH.—Wyandotte
Bishop Co.; J. H. (Fur)...A

N. J.—Camden
Fries-Breslin Co. (Smyrna Carpets; Rugs)........B

N. J.—Gloucester
Fries-Harley Co...........A

N. J.—Hightstown
Hightstown Smyrna Rug Co. (Smyrna) ....D

N. J.—Little Falls
Beattie Mfg. Co. (Velvet Carpets) ....A

N. J.—Paterson
Lamond & Robertson Co. (Smyrna; Jute Rugs; Hemp Carpets) C

N. J.—Yardville
Morris & Co. (Cotton Carpets) ....A

N. Y.—Amsterdam
Sanford & Sons, Stephen (Axminster; Brussels; Velvet Carpets) ...AAAA
Shuttleworth Bros. Co. (Brussels Carpets; Wilton Rugs) ....B

N. Y.—Auburn
American Axminster Industry (Axminster Carpets)
AA
Nye & Wait Carpet Co. (Ingrain Carpets) .....A

N. Y.—Brooklyn
Chelsea Jute Mills (Hemp; Jute) ....AAAA
Planet Mills Mfg. Co. (Hemp; Ingrain) ...AAA

New York City
Persian Rug Manufactory (Persian Chenille & Axminster Rugs) ....B
Sloane's Sons, Jas. (Mats; Rugs) ....A

N. Y.—Yonkers
Smith & Sons Carpet Co., Alex. (Axminster; Moquette; Tapestry; Brussels; Velvet) .....AAAA

PA.—Bloomsburg
Magee Carpet Co. (Ingrain Tapestry; Velvet Carpets)
A

PA.—Bristol
Leedom Co., Thos. L. (Worsted; Union Carpets; Smyrna Rugs; Art Squares)
AA

PA.—Centre
Letort Carpet Co. (Rag; Jute; Ingrain Carpets).A

PA.—Cheltenham
Pike, E. V. (Smyrna Rugs)
D

PA.—Conshohocken
Hall, Jas. (Venetian; Ingrain; Damask Carpets).B

PA.—Philadelphia
Artman, Treichler Carpet Co., E. R. (Worsted & Cotton Ingrain Carpets)...A
Binz, F. (Granite Ingrain Carpets) C
Boggs' Sons, Jno. (Ingrain Carpet) C
Boggs & Son, Thomas (Ingrain Carpet) ....A
Bromley Bros. Carpet Co. (Ingrain Carpets; Ingrain; Smyrna Rugs) ....A
Bromley, Jas. & Geo. D. (Squares; Velvet; Ingrain) ....A

Bromley & Sons, Jno. (Smyrna Rugs) ......AAAA
Carson, Geo. (Ingrain; Art Squares) ....D
Carson & Son, Robt. (Extra Super Ingrain) ....B
Caves & Sons, Thomas (Ingrain) ....B
Cleeland & Sons, Robt. (Rag; Yarn; Metting; Granite Carpets) ....A
Cochrane, Chas. P. (Damask & Venetian Stair Carpets)
B
Currie, Daniel (Carpets)..B
Danby & Fetterolf (Carpets)
B
Develon's Sons, Thos. (Wool Ingrain Carpets) .....A
Dickel & Son, Hy. (Ingrain Carpets) C
Dickey & McMaster (Damask; Venetian; Art Squares) ....A
Dobson, J. & J. (Wilton; Velvet; Brussels Carpets)
AAAA
Doerr & Sons, Phillip (Ingrain Carpet) ....A
Dorman Bros. (Ingrain Carpets) ....AAA
Dunlap & Son, Jno. (Ingrain Carpets) ....A
Ford, W. & R. (Ingrain Carpets) ....B
Gay's Sons, Jno. (Ingrain Carpets) ....A
Getty & Spratt (Ingrain Carpets) C
Hamilton, Jno. (Ingrain Carpet) ....AA
Hirst & Roger (Tapestry; Velvet Carpets) ....B
Holmes & Sons. Hy. (Fine Ingrain Carpets; Art Squares) ....A
Huston & Co., Thomas (Wool, Cotton Chain & Union Ingrain Carpets).A
Ivins, Dietz & Metzger Co. (Bundar & French Wilton Rugs & Carpets; Body Brussels; Ingrain & Columbian Carpets; Art Squares) ....AAAA
Jackson & Son, David (Ingrain Carpet) ....A
Jamieson's Sons. D. (Ingrain Carpets) ....D
Keefer, Wm. B. (All Wool, Cotton Chain, Ingrain Ingrain Carpets)........D
Lansdowne Mfg. Co. (Smyrna Rugs) ....D
McDowell & Co. David (Ingrain Carpets) ....B
Masland & Sons, C. H. (Ingrain; Velvet Tapestry Carpets; Rugs; Art Squares) ....A
Miller, Nathan (Ingrain Carpets) ....D
Moore & Bro. (Ingrain Carpets) ....B
Nelson, Hugh (Ingrain Carpets) C
Newbold & Co. ....D
Petzoldt & Son. Herman (Rag Carpet) ....D
Pollock & Son, Jas. (Damask; Venetian; Ingrain; Granites) ....A
Ricker & Logan (Ingrain Carpets) C
Schofield, Mason & Co. (Wilton; Body Brussels Carpets) ....A
Scholes & Co., Wm. (Ingrain Carpets; Art Squares) ....A
Smith. Jno. (Ingrain Carpets) ....D
Smith & Son, W. T. (Smyrna Rugs, Carpets & Mats)
AA
Stead Miller & Co. (Smyrna Rugs) ....AA
Stinson Bros. (Tapestry; Velvet Carpets) .....AAAA
Swire & Scott (Ingrain Carpets; Art Squares).....B
Watt & Bro. (Ingrain Carpet) ....B

KY.—Louisville
Avery Sons, B. F. (Road
Carts) ....AAA
Kentucky Wagon Mfg. Co.
(Farm; Freight Wagon;
Drays) ....AAAA
KY.—Owensboro
Ames & Co., F. A. (Light) A
Owensboro Wagon Co. (Farm
Wagons; Carts; Drays) AA
LA.—Shreveport
Henderson Iron Wks., A. K.
(Saw Mill Carriages).AA
MAINE—Bangor
Union Iron Wks. (Saw Mill
Carriages) ....A
MAINE—Portland
Bailey Carriage Co., F. O.
Light; Heavy; Wagons) B
MD.—Baltimore
Jackson, Wm. L. (Chil-
drens Carriages) ......D
MASS.—Amesbury
Biddle & Swart Co. (Dog;
Village Carts) ....B
Bailey & Co., S. R. (Light)
A
Briggs Carriage Co. (Light;
Heavy Carriages; Carts)
C
Currier-Cameron Co. (Light;
Heavy in the White)....C
Feltch & Co., E. S. (Spring;
Road Carts) C
Hassett & Hodge (Light;
Heavy; Carts) ....A
Hume Carriage Co. (Light;
Heavy) C
Morrill Co., Osgood (Light)
C
Judkins & Sons Co., J. B.
(Heavy) C
MASS.—Boston
French & Co. Fred. F. (Vis-
a-Vis Carriages; T. Carts)
D
Kimball Bros. Co. (T.; Dog;
Village Carts) ....B
Thomas & Co., Chauncey
(Pony; Dog Carts) C
MASS.—Gardner
Heywood Bros. & Wakefield
Co., (Childrens'; Chil-
drens' Rattan Body)
AAAA
MASS.—Greenfield
Field Mfg. Co., Chas. R.
(Childrens'; Childrens'
Rattan Body) ....D
MASS.—Leominster
Whitney Carriage Co., F. A.
(Childrens') ....A
Whitney Reed Chair Co.
(Doll) ....AAAA
MASS.—Merrimac
Lancaster & Co., J. A.
(Light; Pony) ....A
MASS.—Woodville
Cooldridge Co., L. E. (Es-
tate of) (Light; Wagon)
B
MICH.—Bay City
Garland Co., M. (Saw Mill
Carriages) C
MICH.—Detroit
Anderson Carriage Co.
(Light; Wagons) ......A
Chope & Sons, Edward
(Wagon; Truck) C
Detroit Carriage Co.
(Light) C
Detroit Folding Cart Co.
(Dog Carts) ....D
MICH.—Flint
Durant-Dort Co.
(Carriages; Road Carts)
AAAA
Flint Wagon Works (Light;
Farm; Road Carts) ..A
Paterson Co., W. A.
(Light) ....E
Flint Buggy Co. (Light;
Road Carts) ....E
MICH.—Grand Rapids
Belknap Wagon Co. (Heavy
Wagons) C
Harrison Wagon Co. (Farm
Wagons) ....AA
Pettit & Co., Wm. H. (Chil-
drens' Carriages) ......F
MICH.—Ionia
Ionia Wagon Co. (Farm;
Coal Wagons) ....B
MICH.—Jackson
Ames-Dean Carriage Co.

(Light Carriages; Carts) C
Fuller Buggy Co. (Light).B
Granger & Hayden Carriage
Co. (Light) ....B
Jackson Sleigh Co. (Light;
Wagons) ....B
Jackson Vehicle Co. (Light;
Wagon) ....B
MICH.—Jonesville
Deal & Son, J. J. (Light;
Heavy; T. Carts) .....B
MICH.—Kalamazoo
American Carriage Co.
(Light Carriages; Carts) B
Kalamazoo Wagon Co.
(Light; Carts) ....B
Lull Carriage Co. (Light;
Pony; Wagons) ....B
Michigan Buggy Co. (Light;
Wagons; Carts) ....B
MICH.—Lansing
Bement's Sons, E. (Light;
Wagon) ....A
Clark & Co. (Light; Wagon)
C
Lansing Wagon Works
(Farm; Freight; Spring;
Light) ....A
MICH.—Marshall
Page Bros. Buggy Co.
MICH.—Menominee
Prescott, D. Clint Co. (Saw
Mill Carriages) ....B
MICH.—Ovid
Ovid Carriage Works
(Light) C
MICH.—Owosso
Owosso Carriage Co. (Light;
Wagon; Carts) ....B
MICH.—Pontiac
Dunlap Vehicle Co. (Light;
Wagon) ....B
Imperial Buggy Co. (Light)
C
Pontiac Buggy Co. (Light;
Spring Wagon; Drays) .A
Pontiac Spring & Wagon
Works (Light; Wagon).B
Scott & Co., R. D. (Light;
Wagon; Carts) ....B
Taylor, C. V. (Light;
Wagon) ....A
MICH.—Saginaw
Farmers Handy Wagon Co.
(Farm Wagons) C
Wickes Bros. (Saw Mill
Carriages) ....AAA
MICH.—Wayne
Prouty & Glass Carriage Co.
(Light) ....B
MINN.—Minneapolis
Diamond Iron Wks. (Saw
Mill Carriages) ....B
MINN.—Winona
Winona Carriage Co.
(Farm & Mountain Wag-
ons; Trucks) ....AA
Winona Wagon Co. (Drays;
Farm Wagons; Carts).AA
MO.—Macon
Blees Carriage Co., The
(Light; Heavy) ....A
MO.—St. Louis
Banner Buggy Co., 914 S.
B'way (Light) ....A
Cook Bros. Carriage Co., 2nd
cor. Branch (Light;
Wagon) C
Deere Plow Co., John. Clin-
ton & N. Bway. (Light)
AAAA
Embree-McLean Carriage
Co., 1823 Olive (Light;
Trap) ....B
Gestring Wagon Co., 1718
Bway. (Farm; Log Wag-
on) ....B
Kaiser & Co., Jacob (Chil-
drens' Doll Carriages).A
Luedinghans - Espenscheid
Wagon Co., 1717 N. Bway.
A
Luking, John F., 1615 N. 7th
(Farm Wagons) C
McCabe, Bierman Wagon
Co., 1213 N. Bway.
(Spring Wagons) C
Moon Bros. Carriage Co.,
Gano. Av. (Light) .....A
Moon Buggy Co., Joseph W.,
Main (Light) ....A
Scaritt-Comstock Furniture
Co. (Childrens' Carriages)
Union Carriage Co., Hall

cor. Branch (Light)....B
Weber & Damme Wagon Co.,
1613 N. Bway. (Farm
Wagons) ....B

N. H.—Concord
Abbott-Downing Co. (Hose
Carriages) X

N. H.—Newton
Hayford & Son., Edward
(Light; Wagons) C

N. J.—Burlington
Birch, James (Light) ....B

N. J.—Newark
Quimby & Co., J. M.
(Carriages; Carts) .....A
Hedden & Co., C. M.
(Pneumatic) ....A

N. J.—Trenton
Trenton Iron Co. (Trolley
Carriages) ....A

N. Y.—Albany
Goold Co., James, The
(Light; Heavy; Hearses;
Carts) C

N. Y.—Belmont
Clark Bros. (Saw Mill Carriages) ....A

N. Y.—Binghamton
Sturtevant - Larrabee Co.
(Light) ....A

N. Y.—Buffalo
King Spring Co., 1400 Niag-
ara (Light in the White;
Finished) C

N. Y.—Cortland
Cortland Wagon Co. (Light;
Heavy Wagons; Carts)..A
Keator & Wells (Light
Wagons; Carts; Drays).B

N. Y.—Dunkirk
Milholland Spring Gear Co.
(Road Carts in the White)
B

N. Y.—Geneva
Geneva Wagon Co. (Light;
Wagon) C

N. Y.—Glens Falls
Glens Falls Buckboard Co.
(Light; Buckboards) ...C
Joubert & White (Buck-
board) ....B

N. Y.—Groton
Groton Wagon Works
(Light; Business Wagons)
B

N. Y.—Homer
Brockway, W. N. (Light).A
Homer Wagon Co. (Light;
Wagon; Drays) C

N. Y.—Ilion
Coleman Carriage & Harness
Co., Fred. (Light) C

New York City
Brewster & Co., J. B. (Vis-
a-Vis; Carriages; Carts
&c.) ....B
Crandall Carriage Co. (Chil-
drens' Rattan Body Car-
riages) ....D
Demarest & Co., A. T. (Vis-
a-Vis Carriages; Carts).A
Hayward & Co., S. F., 20
Warren (Hose Carriages)
B
Mace & Co., L. H. (Chil-
drens' Carriages) ......B
N. J. Foundry & Machine
Co., 9 Murray (Trolley
Carriages) ....B

N. Y.—Olean
New Conklin Wagon Co.
(Farm Wagons) ....B

N. Y.—Owego
Champion Wagon Co. (Farm;
Business) ....B

N. Y.—Rochester
Hughes, Francis L. (Chil-
drens' Carriages) ......A
Sullivan Bros. (Light;
Carriages; Wagons) C

N. Y.—Seneca Falls
American-La France Fire
Engine Co. (Hose Car-
riages) ....AA
Rumsey & Co., (Ltd.)
(Hose Carriages) ......A

N. Y.—Syracuse
Moyer, Harvey A. (Light;
Wagons) ....A

N. Y.—Troy
Payne, Martin (Estate of)
(Sulky) ....A
Troy Carriage Works (Vis-
a-Vis Carriages; Road
Carts) ....B

N. Y.—Utica
Childs & Co., C. H. (Light)
B

N. Y.—Waterloo
Waterloo Wagon Co. (Ltd.)
(Light; Wagons) ......A

N. Y.—Watertown
Babcock Co., H. H. (Light;
Heavy Carriages; Carts)
AA
Excelsior Carriage Co.
(Light; Wagons) ......A
Union Carriage & Gear Co.
(Light; Wagons) C
Watertown Carriage Co.
(Light; Wagons) ......A

N. C.—Carthage
Tyson & Jones Buggy Co.
(Light; Heavy) ....B

N. C.—Henderson
Corbitt Buggy Co. (Light).C

N. C.—Hickory
Piedmont Wagon Co. (Farm
Wagons) ....A

N. C.—Oxford
Taylor-Cannady Buggy Co.
(Light) C

N. C.—Thomasville
Ryder Cramer Wagon Works
(Farm Wagons) C

N. C.—Wilson
Hackney Bros. (Light;
Wagons) ....B

N. C.—Winston-Salem
Nissen, C. F. C
Salem Iron Works (Saw
Mill Carriages) ....A

OHIO—Alliance
Morgan Engineering Co.
(Gun Carriages) ......AA

OHIO—Bucyrus
Shunk Plow Co. (Steel Farm
Wagons) C

OHIO—Canton
Knight Mfg. Co. (Saw Mill
Carriages) ....B

OHIO—Carthage
Jewell Carriage Co., The
(Light) ....B

OHIO—Cincinnati
Acorn Buggy Co., The, 212
E. Cort (Buggies)......C
American Carriage Co., The,
1275 Budd (Light; Wag-
ons) ....A
Anchor Buggy Co., South
cor. Summer (Light;
Wagons; Traps) ......AAA
Armleder Co., O., The, 324-
330 Longworth (Delivery
Wagons) C
Auel Carriage Co., John,
1669 Central Av. (Light;
Surrey; Wagons) ......B
Barnett Carriage Co. cor.
Richmond & Carr (Light)
A
Behlen's Sons Co., Charles
1434 Vine (Light; Heavy)
C
Brown Carriage Co., 1602
Gest. (Light; Surreys)..B
Continental Carriage Co.,
The, Central Av. & York
(Light; Surreys) ......B
Eagle Carriage Co. (Pony) E
Emerson & Fisher Co. (Jump
Seat Carriages) X
Enger, Frank J., 2100 Gest
(Light; Traps) ....AAA
Fisher Carriage Co., 910
Evans (Light) C
Hickory Carriage Co., 2109
South (Light; Surreys)..C
Lion Buggy Co., The, 2100
W. 8th (Light; Surreys;
Springs) ....B
Marquarat Carriage & Toy
Co. (Childrens' Doll Car-
riages) ....E
Mill Creek Wagon Co., The,
Richmond & Carr (Light
in the White) C
Phoenix Carriage Co., The
901 Evans (Light) C
Rattermann & Luth. 1911
W. 8th (Light) ....B
Royal Carriage Co., E.
Court cor. Spring (Light)
A
Schacht Mfg. Co., The, 2727-
2731 Spring Grove Av.
(Wire wheel vehicles ex-
clusively) C
Sechler & Co., 538 E. 5th

CARRIAGES & WAGONS

(Light) ....A

OHIO—Columbus

Buckeye Buggy Co., 482 N. High (Light; Heavy) .AA

Case Mfg. Co. (Trolley Carriages) ....A

Columbus Buggy Co., Chestnut cor. Front (Light) AA

New Climax Buggy Co., Spring (Light) ....A

Poste Bros. Buggy Co., Jefferson Av. (Light) ....B

Scioto Buggy Co., The, 504 Buttles Av. (Light) ..C

OHIO—Crestline

Holcker Bros. Buggy Co. (Light) C

OHIO—Dayton

Woodhull Carriage Works (Light) ....B

OHIO—Defiance

Turnbull Wagon Co. (Farm Wagons) ....AA

OHIO—Elmwood Place

Highland Buggy Co., The (Buggies; Phaetons; Surries) ....B

OHIO—Findlay

Adams Bros. Co. (Saw Mill Carriages) ....AA

Findlay Carriage Co. The (Light; Wagon) C

OHIO—Fostoria

Peabody Buggy Co. (Light) C

OHIO—Hamilton

Columbia Carriage Co., The (Light) ....A

OHIO—Hillsboro

Carroll & Sons, M. F. (Light) ....B

OHIO—Marietta

Ohio Valley Wagon Co. (Spring; Farm Wagons) B

OHIO—Miamisburg

Enterprise Carriage Co., The (Light) ....A

Kauffman Buggy Co. The (Light; Carts; &c.)....B

OHIO—Middletown

Decatur Buggy Co. (Light) C

OHIO—New Waterford

Koch Bros. (Light) C

OHIO—Sidney

Bimel Carriage Co., The (Light) C

OHIO—Tiffin

Tiffin Wagon Co., The (Wagons; Farm Wagons)

OHIO—Toledo

Gendron Wheel Co. (Childrens' Carriages) .....AA

Milburn Wagon Co. The (Carts; Drays; Light; Farm; Business Wagons) AAA

OHIO—Troy

Troy Buggy Works Co., The (Light Carts; &c.)....B

Troy Wagon Works Co., The (Wagons; Farm Wagons) ....B

OHIO—Youngstown

Youngstown Carriage & Wagon Co., The (Light; Carts) ....B

OHIO—Zanesville

Brown Mfg. Co., The (Farm Wagons) ....AA

PA.—Brookville

Brookville Mfg. Co. (Farm Wagons) C

PA.—Columbia

Columbia Carriage Co. (Farm Wagons; Dump Carts).B

PA.—Du Bois

Du Bois Iron Works (Saw Mill Carriages) ..AAAA

PA.—Emigsville

Acme Wagon Co. (Farm; Business; Contractors'; Carts) ....B

PA.—Erie

Standard Saw Mill Mchy. Co. (Saw Mill Carriages) C

Thaer & Co., H. N. (Childrens' Carriages) .....A

PA.—Lancaster

Bailey & Co., L. C. (Light) A

Hoover, Joseph F. Jr. (Light; Wagons) C

CARRIAGES & WAGONS

Safety Buggy Co. (B. G. Dodge, Prop.) (Light)..B

PA.—Mifflinburg

Mifflinburg Carriage Co. (Light) C

PA.—Philadelphia

Anderson Matthew M. (Childrens' Carriages)..D

Fulton & Walker Co. (Carriages; Carts) ...AA

Philadelphia Roll & Machine Co., So. 23d & Wash. Av. (Gun Carriages) .AA

Sowney Bros., 1204 Frankfort Av. (Heavy; Hearses) C

PA.—Reading

Keystone Wagon Works, The (Light; Coal Wagons; Light in the White) ....B

PA.—Waynesboro

Frick Co. (Saw Mill Carriages) ....AAAA

PA.—Wilkesbarre

Vulcan Iron Works (Hoisting Carriages) ...AAAA

PA.—Williamsport

Williamsport Wagon Co. (Light; Wagons) ......B

PA.—York

Hoover Wagon Co. (Wagons) C

Martin Carriage Works (Light; Wagons; Road Carts) ....A

York Carriage Co. (Light; Wagons) ....A

S. C.—Rock Hill

Rock Hill Buggy Co. (Light) A

TENN.—Chattanooga

Chattanooga Wagon Co., The (Farm Wagons)...A

Wheland Machine Works (Saw Mill Carriages) ...A

TENN.—Jackson

Southern Engine & Boiler Works (Saw Mill Carriages) ....A

TENN.—Memphis

Bodley Wagon Co. (Farm Wagons) ....B

James & Graham Wagon Co., The (Farm; Lumber Wagons) ....B

Lilly Carriage Co. (Light).B

TENN.—Nashville

De Ford Carriage Mfg. Co., J. M. (Light) C

VT.—Brattleboro

Smith & Co., S. A. (Childrens' Carriages) ...AAA

VT.—Montpelier

Lane Mfg. Co. (Saw Mill Carriages) ....A

VA.—Danville

Horner & Co., W. P. & Drays) X

VA.—Lynchburg

Taylor Wagon Works (Farm Wagons) C

VA.—Norfolk

Wrenn & Sons, A. (Light; Wagons; Carts).......A

WIS.—Eau Claire

McDonough Mfg. Co. (Saw Mill Carriages) ....A

WIS.—Fond-du-lac

Sweet, B. F. & I. H. (Farm Carts) ....A

WIS.—Fort Atkinson

Northwestern Mfg. Co. (Light; Wagons) ......A

WIS.—Janesville

Wisconsin Carriage Co. (Light) C

WIS.—Kenosha

Bain Wagon Co. (Wagons; Dump Carts) ....AA

WIS.—La Crosse

La Crosse Carriage Co. (Light) C

Smith Mfg. Co. (Farm Wagons) ....B

WIS.—Madison

Fuller & Johnson Mfg. Co. (Light; Wagons) ....AAA

WIS.—Marinette

Prescott Supply Co. (Saw Mill Carriages) X

WIS.—Milwaukee

Filer & Stowell Co. (Ltd.) (Saw Mill Carriages) AAA

Eckhefer Elevator Co., **A.**

CARRIAGES & WAGONS

(Hoisting Carriages)...C
Meinecke &. Son, A. (Childrens' Carriages) .....AA
Suelflohn & Seefeld (Milk Wagons) ....A

WIS.—Oshkosh
Clark, J. L. (Light) ....B
Streich Co. & Bro., A. (Wagons; Dump Carts: Trucks) ....B
Streich, Gabriel (Wagons; Dump Carts; Trucks)...B
Thompson Carriage Co. (Ltd.) (Spring Wagons) C

WIS.—Racine
Fish Bros. Wagon Co. (Farm Wagons; Carts).A
Mitchell & Lewis Co. (Farm Wagons: Road Carts; Drays) ....AA
(Barb Wire) ....AA
Racine-Sattley Co. (Light; Wagons) ....AAAA

WIS.—Sheboygan
Garton Toy Co. (Doll Carriages) ....B

WIS.—Stoughton
Stoughton Wagon Co. (Light; Wagons) ....AA

WIS.—Wausau
Murray Mfg. Co., D. J. (Saw Mill Carriages) ....B

CARRIERS

CONN.—Meriden
Manning, Bowman & Co. (Dinner) ....AA

CONN.—New Britain
North & Judd Mfg. Co. (Trace) ....AA

CONN.—New Haven
Acme Cash Railway Co. (Cash) X
Burgess, E. A. (Estate of) (Bundle; Cash) ......E

CONN.—New London
Starr, Joseph (Bundle; Cash) X

FLA.—Nocatee
Weller, W. G. (Basket)...A

ILL.—Aurora
Wilcox Mfg. Co. (Elevated Feed) ....B

ILL.—Batavia
U. S. Wind Engine & Pump Co. (Ensilage; Hay) ...A

ILL.—Chicago
Air Line Carriers Co., 903 Monroe (Cash) ....B
Baldwin & Co., Jas. L. 171 Wash. (Cash) ....D
Barbee Wire & Iron Wks. (Package) ....B
Borden & Selleck Co., 48 Lake (Endless Apron; Trunk) ....B
Bostedo Pneumatic Tube Co. 154 Lake (Cash) C
Caldwell & Son Co., H. W. (Endless Apron) ......AA
Creamery Package Mfg. Co. (Butter) ....AAAA
International Harvester Co. (Hay) ....AAAA

ILL.—Decatur
Chambers - -Bering - Quinlan Co. (Hay) ....A

ILL.—Harvard
Hunt, Helm & Ferris (Hay) ....B

ILL.—Ottawa
Porter Co., J. E. (Steel Track Hay) ....A

ILL.—Sandwich
Sandwich Mfg. Co. (Hay)...AA

ILL.—Sterling
Keystone Mfg. Co. (Hay)..AA

IND.—Indianapolis
Taisey Pneumatic Service Co. (Cash) ....B
Tucker & Dorsey Mfg. Co. (Bundle; Cash) ....A

IOWA—Fairfield
Louden Mchry. Co. (Hay).D

KY.—Louisville
Dow Wire Works Co. (Bicycle Luggage) .....D

MASS.—Boston
Consolidated Store Service Co., 115 Chancy (Cash).X

CARRIERS (Con.)

MASS.—Lowell
Lamson Consolidated Store Service Co. (Cash; Bundle) ....A

MASS.—Worcester
Parker Wire Goods Co. ..D
Warren Leather Goods Co. (Bicycle Luggage) .....B
Wire Goods Co. (Bicycle Luggage.. Milk Bottle).A

MICH.—Detroit
Buhl Malleable Co. (Endless Apron; Sawdust) ......A

MICH.—Jackson
Cement Machry. Co. (Adjustable Block) ....B

MICH.—St. Johns
Mason & Co., F. C. (Steel Track or Cable Hay) ..C

MINN.—Minneapolis
Biltrite Mfg. Co. (Cash; Package) ....E

MO.—St. Louis
Ludlow-Saylor Wire Co.
St. Louis Stamping Co. (Water; Dinner) ..AAAA

N. Y.—Buffalo
Jewett Mfg. Co., Jno. C. (Water) ....AA
Squirer Mfg. Co., Geo. L. (Cane; Bagesse) ....A
Western Wire Goods Co. (Milk Bottle) ....D

N. Y.—Frankfort
Acme Road Mchry. Co. (Street Sweeping Bag)..C

New York City
Central Stamping Co. (Dinner) ....AA
Estey Wire Wks., 59 Fulton (Milk Bottle) ....E
Lalance & Grosjean Mfg. Co. (Dinner; Fire) ....AAAA
Motley, Green Co., 12 John (Street Sweeping Bag)..X
N. J. Foundry & Mach. Co., 9 Murray (Endless Apron; Hand Hoist) ....D
Niles-Bement-Pond Co., 136 Liberty (Hand Hoist)....
...........................AAAA
Pearsall Pneumatic Tube & Power Co., 154 W. 27th (Cash) ....D
Robins Conveying Belt Co., 17 Park Row (Endless Apron) C
Stoutenborough, X. (Dinner)
...........................D
Westcott-Jewell Co. (Package) ....D

N. Y.—Rochester
Star Egg Carrier & Tray Mfg. Co. (Egg) ....D

N. Y.—Syracuse
Frazer & Jones Co. (Trace)
...........................AA
Syracuse Chilled Plow Co. (Hay) ....AA

N. Y.—Utica
Eureka Mower Co. (Hay).B

N. Y.—Warsaw
Warsaw Elevator Co. (Hay)
...........................B

OHIO—Akron
Whitman & Barnes Mfg. Co. (Steel; Hard Wood Track Hay) ......AAAA

OHIO—Ashland
Myers & Bro., F. E. (Hay)..
...........................AA

OHIO—Canton
Elbel & Co. (Trace) .....B
Ney Mfg. Co. (Hay; Hand Hoist; Trunk) ....B
Ney Co.. V. L. (Hay) ....B

OHIO—Cleveland
Gerlach Co.. Peter, 28 Columbus (Timber) .....A
Hahn Co.. J. N. (Arc Light Globe; Beer) ....B

OHIO—Columbus
Case Mfg. Co. (Hand Hoist) ....A
Kilbourne & Jacobs Mfg. Co. (Stone; Trunk) ......AA

OHIO—Mansfield
Barr Cash & Package Carrier Co. (Cash) ....A
Mansfield Cash & Package Carrier Co. (Cash) C

PA.—Philadelphia
Johnson & Lund (Needle

CARRIERS (Con.)

Foil) ....AA
Link-Belt Engineering Co.,
  Nicetown (Endless Apron)
                     A
Reid, A. H. (Butter) ....A
Sibley, Gideon (Needle
  Foil) ....AA
Wall Mfg. Co., R. C. (Lug-
  gage) ....F

VT.—Bellows Falls
Vermont Farm Machine Co.
  (Butter) C
VT.—Rutland
Stoddard Mfg. Co. (Butter)
                     F
WIS.—Ft. Atkinson
Cornish, Curtis & Greene
  Mfg. Co. (Butter) ......A
WIS.—Manitowoc
Smalley Mfg. Co. (Ensilage)
                     B
WIS.—Racine
Belle City Mfg. Co.
  (Ensilage) ....B
WIS.—South Milwaukee
Stowell Mfg. Co. & Fdry.
  Co. (Hand Hoist) ......A

CARS

ALA.—Anniston
Kilby Locomotive & Ma-
  chine Wks. (Mine; Log-
  ging; Plantation) ......D
ALA.—Birmingham
Southern Car & Fdry. Co.
  (Freight; Steel) ....AAA
ALA.—New Decatur
North Alabama Engineering
  Co. (Dryer; Logging; Ore;
  Tram; Pole Road) ....F
ALA.—Selma
Peacock Iron Wks. (Mining;
  Construction; Track Lay-
  ers'; Dump; Freight;
  Lever Hand; Logging;
  Iron Coal; Plantation;
  Pit; Steel Mining; Push)
                     C
ARK.—Brinkley
Brinkley Car Wks. & Mfg.
  Co. (Freight) ....A
ARK.—Pine Bluff
Dilley Fdry. Co. (Logging)
                     B
CAL.—San Francisco
Carter Bros., 220 Market
  (Freight; Passenger;
  Street; Electric) ....AA
Hammond & Co., J., 2nd &
  Townsend (Freight; Pas-
  senger; Street; Electric)
                     B
CAL.—San José
San José Agricultural Wks.
  (Fruit Dryers' Tray)...X
CAL.—Stockton
Holt Mfg. Co. (Freight;
  Passenger; Baggage;
  Mail) ....AA
COLO.—Denver
Davis Iron Wks. (The), F.
  M. (Dumping Mine; Ore)
                     A
Denver Engineering Wks.
  (Dumping; Mine; Ore) .A
Hendrie & Bolthoff Mfg.
  Co., 1625 17th (Mine)...
                   AAA
Mine & Smelter Supply Co.
  (Dumping; Mine; Ore)...
                   AAA
Montgomery Machine Co.,
  J. H., 1220 Curtis (Mine)
                     C
Truax Mfg. Co., 1725 Wazee
  (Dumping Steel; Mine;
  Ore; Steel Mining; Dump;
  Tram) ....E
CONN.—Middletown
Middletown Car Wks. (Flat;
  Freight) X
CONN.—Windsor Locks
Clark & Co., Geo. P.
  (Hand Dump) C
DEL.—Wilmington
Delaware Hand Fibre Co.
  (Warehouse Fibre) .....A
Harlan & Hollingsworth
  (Passenger; Mail; Bag-
  gage; Freight; Cable) ..A

CARS (Con.)

GA.—Atlanta
American Equipment Co.
  (Flat; Gondola) X
Georgia Car & Mfg. Co.
  (Freight) ....E
May & Spalding (Coal;
  Mine; Pit; Railroad) ..B
GA.—Waycross
South Atlantic Car Mfg. Co.
  (Caboose) ....A
ILL.—Aurora
Western Wheeled Scraper
  Co. (Ballast; Dump) AA
ILL.—Belleville
Belleville Pump & Skein
  Wks. (Mine) ....A
Herzler & Henninger
  (Mine) ....F
ILL.—Chicago
Allis-Chalmers Co., Home
  Ins. Bldg. (Drop Botton;
  Hot Metal; Slag Indus-
  trial Railway; Mine; Ore;
  Pit) ....AAAA
American Engineering Wks.
  (Mining) ....F
Archer Iron Wks., 34th Pl.
  (Mine) ....F
Austin Mfg. Co., Manhattan
  Bldg. (Drop Bottom;
  Dumping; Mine) ....AAA
Contractors' Supply & Equip-
  ment Co., 232 5th Av.
  (Dumping; Mine) ......B
Fairbanks, Morse & Co.,
  Franklin & Monroe
  (Bridge; Gang; Dumping;
  Flat; Hand; Push; In-
  spection; Logging; Mine;
  Ore; Track Laying; Ve-
  locipede; Velocipede Gaso-
  line Motor) ....AAAA
Gates Iron Wks. (Br. Allis-
  Chalmers Co.) (Mine)....
                 AAAA
Hicks, F. M., 227 Dearborn
  (Mfrs.' Agent; Clay;
  Dumping; Freight; Log-
  ging; Passenger; Refrig-
  erator; Tank) C
Illinois Car & Equipment
  Co., Old Colony Bldg.
  (Derrick; Crane; Freight;
  Logging; Plantation) ..C
McGuire-Cummings Mfg.
  Co., 122 Sangamon
  (Sprinkling Street Rail-
  way; Street Railway)..A
Pease, F. M., 355 Dearborn
  (Dumping; Flat; Logging;
  Passenger; Tank) .....B
Pullman Co., Pullman Bldg.
  (Freight; Passenger;
  Street; Electric; Dining;
  Drawing; Sleeping; Cable;
  Steam Motor) .....AAAA
Rodgers Ballast Car Co.,
  Fisher Bldg. (Ballast)..B
Shaw, Willis, N. Y. Life
  Bldg. (Dumping) ......D
Wells & French Co. (Street;
  Electric; Freight) X
Western Steel Car & Fdry.
  Co., Old Colony Bldg.
  (Freight; Steel) ......AA
ILL.—Danville
Danville Fdry. & Machine
  Co. (Mine) C
ILL.—Decatur
Lender Mfg. Co. (Clay)...A
ILL.—Harvey
Buda Fdry. & Mfg. Co.
  (Dumping; Hand; Push;
  Inspection; Mine; Planta-
  tation; Track Laying;
  Velocipede; Wood Wheel
  Hand; Push) ....A
Whitney Fdry. Equipment
  Co. (Billet; Core; Oven;
  Foundry) ....A
ILL.—Litchfield
Litchfield Car Wks. (Dump;
  Freight; Pit; Passenger)X
Litchfield Fdry. & Machine
  Co. (Mine) ....B
ILL.—Mattoon
Starbuck's Sons Co.
  (Velocipede) ....G
ILL.—Mt. Vernon
Mt. Vernon Car Mfg. Co.
  (Flat; Ore; Refrigerator;

CARS (Con.)

Mining; Construction;
Pile Driver; Wrecking;
Dump; Coal; Ore Dump;
Drop Bottom; Freight;
Gondola; Logging C

ILL.—Peoria

Peoria Car Co. (Street; Electric) ....AAAA

ILL.—Sterling

ILL.—Springfield

Aetna Fdry. & Machine Co.
(Mine) C

Rock Falls Mfg. Co.
(Passenger) ....A

IND.—Aurora

Steadman's Foundry &
Mach. Wks. (Dumping).C

IND.—Hagerstown

Light Inspection Car Co.
(Inspection; Motor Inspection; Velocipede) ...E

IND.—Indianapolis

Potts & Co. (Inc.), C. &
A. (Dump) ....B

IND.—Jeffersonville

Ohio Falls Car Co. (Passenger) ....AAAA

IND.—Michigan City

Haskell & Barker Mfg. Co.
(Drop Bottom; Dumping;
Flat; Freight; Mine; Ore;
Construction; Oil Tank;
Refrigerator; Gondola;
Passenger; Mail) ..AAAA

IND.—Mishawaka

Dodge Mfg. Co. (Industrial
Railway) ....AAA

IND.—Terre Haute

Eagle Iron Wks. (Mine)..B

Prox & Brinkman Mfg. Co.
(Mine) ....A

IOWA—Mason City

Hathorn Fdry. & Machine
Co. (Brick; Transfer)..E

IOWA—Ottumwa

Ottumwa Iron Wks. (Mine;
Freight) ....AA

KANS.—Abilene

Parker, Chas. (Ballast)..B

LA.—New Orleans

Coleman, H. Dudley
(Freight; Passenger;
Plantation) X

MAINE—Portland

Portland Co. (Freight)..AA

MD.—Baltimore

Ryan-McDonald Mfg. Co., 44
South (Clay; Derrick;
Crane; Drop Bottom;
Dumping; Freight; Hand
Dump; Mine; Hand; Push;
Ore; Plantation; Pole
Road; Steam Shovel;
Track Laying) ....A

South Baltimore Car Wks.
(Freight) ....A

MD.—Hagerstown

Railway Cycle Mfg. Co.
(Hand; Push) X

MASS.—Amesbury

Briggs Carriage Co. (Street
Railway; Cable; Electric)
D

Ellis Car Co. (Street Railway; Cable; Electric;
Steam Motor) ....H

MASS.—Boston

Laconia Car Co., 50 State
(Passenger; Freight;
Steam; Electric; Refrigerator) ....AAA

Sturtevant Co., B. F.
(Dump; Foundry) ..AAA

Thomson-Houston Electric
Co. (Electric) ....H

MASS.—Brightwood

Wason Mfg. Co. (Freight;
Passenger; Street Electric; Drawing Room)..A

MASS.—Newburyport

Newburyport Car. Mfg. Co.
(Cable; Electric; Steam;
Motor) X

MASS.—Sagamore

Keith Mfg. Co. (Freight)..D

MASS.—Woburn

Smith & Wallace (Sprinkling Street Railway)...D

MASS.—Worcester

Bradley, Osgood & Sons
(Freight; Passenger;
Street; Electric) ......A

Wright Wire Co. (Ele-

CARS (Con.)

vator) ....AA

MICH.—Bay City

Industrial Wks. (Derrick;
Crane; Wrecking) ...AA

MICH.—Detroit

American Blower Co.
(Brick Transfer) .....AA

Byram & Co., 435 Guoin
(Billet; Core Oven; Foundry; Hot Metal; Slag;
Freight) ....D

Mitshkun Co., W., Chamb.
of Commerce (Dumping;
Flat; Logging; Passenger)
C

Northern Engineering Co.,
Chene & Atwater (Billet;
Core Oven) ....A

Russel Wheel & Fdry. Co.
(Dumping; Logging;
Plantation; Hand; Mine;
Mill Yard) ....A

MICH.—Grand Rapids

Butterworth & Lowe (Hand;
Push; Broad Gauge; Narrow Gauge; Logging; Velocipede) ....B

MICH.—Kalamazoo

Kalamazoo Railway Supply
Co. (Dumping; Hand;
Push; Inspection; Mine;
Motor Inspection; Plantation; Steel; Track Laying;
Velocipede; Velocipede
Gasoline Motor) ....B

MICH.—Lansing

Lansing Wheelbarrow Co.
(Hand; Push; Mine; Steel
Mining; Dump; Freight)
AA

MICH.—Port Huron

Port Huron Engine &
Thresher Co. (Dumping).
AAAA

MICH.—Saginaw

Bartlett & Co., A. F.
(Mine) ....A

MICH.—Three Rivers

Roberts Car & Wheel Co.
(Hand; Push; Inspection;
Track Laying; Velocipede) ....B

Sheffield Car Co. (Billet;
Bridge; Gang; Canopy;
Clay; Core Oven; Deep
Bottom; Dumping; Flat;
Foundry; Hand Dump;
Hand; Push; Hot Metal;
Slag; Ingot; Inspection;
Mine; Motor Inspection;
Ore; Plantation; Plate;
Sheet Mill; Sail Wood;
Steel Mining; Dump;
Track Laying; Tram;
Transfer; Velocipede; Velocipede Gasoline Motor;
Weed Cutting; Construction; Wrecking; Road
Masters'; Steam Hand;
Wood Wheel Hand; Logging; Passenger; Dining;
Observation; Sleeping;
Mill Pond; Electric;
Steam Motor; Gas Motor)
AA

MINN.—Minneapolis

Gillette-Herzog Mfg. Co.
(Steel Mining) X

Peteler Portable Railway
Mfg. Co. (Dumping)....C

MO.—Kansas City

Weber Gas & Gasoline Engine Co., 11th & 12th
(Ore; Coal Dump).....B

MO.—St. Charles

St. Charles Car Co. (Construction; Dump; Coal;
Ore Dump; Drop Bottom;
Freight; Oil Tank; Gondola; Refrigerator; Hand;
Logging; Mine; Passenger; Baggage; Drawing
Room; Excursion; Dining;
Mail; Push; Street Railway; Cable; Electric;
Steam Motor; Crane)....
AAAA

MO.—St. Louis

American Car & Fdry. Co.,
706 Chestnut (Billet;
Clay; Derrick; Crane;
Drop Bottom; Dumping;
Flat; Freight; Hand

CARS (Con.)

Dump; Hand; Push; Hot Metal; Slag; Inspection; Refrigerator; Baggage; Mail; Observation; Street; Electric; Logging; Mine; Ore; Passenger; Plantation; Steel; Steel Mining; Dump) ....AAAA

American Steel Fdry. Co., 509 Olive (Steel) ....AAA

Brownell Car Co., 2300 N. B'way (Street; Electric; Freight; Cable; Steam Motor) ....D

Ellisons' Sons Mfg. Co., Wm. M., 1018 N. 6th (Mine; Amalgam) .....B

Ingoldsby Automatic Car. Co., Chemical Bldg. (Drop Bottom; Dumping) ....AAA

Laclede Car Co., 4500 N. 2nd (Street; Electric; Freight; Baggage; Cable; Steam Motor) ....A

Ludlow-Saylor Wire Co. (Elevator) ....AA

Missouri Car & Fdry. Co. Circus; Freight; Refrigerator; Logging) X

St. Louis Car Co. (Freight; Passenger; Street Railway; Cable; Electric; Steam Motor) ....AAAA

Whitman Agr'l Co. 6900 S. B'way (Coal; Wood; Drop Bottom; Dumping; Hand Dump; Hand; Push; Hot Metal; Slag) ....A

Zelnicker Supply Co., Walter A. (Logging) X

NEBR.—Omaha

Western Electrical Co. (Electric) ....F

N. J.—Elizabeth

Stephenson, Jno. C. (Flat; Passenger; Street; Electric; Cable) ....AA

N. Y.—Albany

Dederick's Sons, P. K. (Dump) ....A

Osgood Dredge Co. (Derrick) ....A

N. Y.—Brooklyn

Evans, F. H. (Iron; Coal) .C

Hecla Iron Wks. (Passenger; Elevator) ......AA

Philips, Doup & Co., 56 Pearl (Clay; Dumping).E

Pioneer Iron Wks., 15 William (Plantation; Transfer) ....A

N. Y.—Buffalo

Buffalo Car Mfg. Co. (Br. Amer. Car & Fdry. Co., St. Louis, Mo.) (Freight) ....AAAA

Buffalo Wire Wks Co. (Elevator) ....A

N. Y.—Hillburn

Ramapo Iron Wks. (Canopy; Dumping (all kinds) Flat; Freight; Gas Coke; Hand Dump; Hand; Push; Hot Metal; Slag; Industrial Railway; Logging; Mine; Ore; Plantation; Steel; Steel Mining; Dump; Track Laying; Tram).AA

N. Y.—Lockport

Norman & Evans (Ballast) ....B

N. Y.—Long Island City

Daimler Mfg. Co. (Inspection; Street Railway).AA

Stuebner Iron Wks.. G. L. Mining; Iron Coal; Ore; Dumping; Push) C

New York City

American Locomotive Co., 25 Broad (Logging) AAAA

Apex Equipment Co. (Dumping; Flat; Freight) ....E

Bacon, Earle Co., 26 Cortlandt (Drop Bottom; Dumping; Mine; Steel Mining; Dump) ....D

Connelly, Jno. E. (Gas Motor) X

Davis. Frank, 68 Broad (Mfrs.' Agt.—all kinds of) X

Fairbanks Co. (Dump; Rail-

CARS (Con.)

road Hand; Sugar Cane). ....AAAA

Goodwin Car Co., 96 5th Av. (Dumping; Ore; Steel; Dumping Railroad).AAAA

Hamlin Car & Wheel Mfg. Co., 66 Broad (Dumping; Mine) X

Hopkins & Co. (Passenger Elevator) ....D

Hunt Co., C. W., 45 B'way (Billet; Charging; Core Oven; Derrick; Crane; Dumping; Flat; Foundry; Freight; Gas Coke; Hand; Push; Ingot; Industrial Railway; Plate; Sheet Mill; Shop) ....A

Koppel, Arthur, 68 Broad (Mfrs.' Agt.—all kinds of) ....AA

Koven & Bro., L. O., 50 Cliff (Dump) ....A

Leavitt & Co., C. W., 15 Cortlandt (Mfrs.' Agt.—all kinds of) ....D

Mead & Co., Jno. A. (Dumping) ....AA

N. J. Fdry. & Machine Co., 15 Murray (Dumping; Flat; Freight; Mine) ...D

Standard Mfg. Co. (Steel Mining) X

Stephenson Co., Jno. (Freight; Passenger)...A

Turls' Sons, Jno., 534 W. 28th (Plantation) .....A

Wagner Palace Car Co. (Passenger; Dining; Drawing Room; Private; Sleeping) C

Wendell & McDuffee, 26 Cortlandt (Sprinkling Street Railway) ....B

N. Y.—Niagara Falls

Dobbie Fdry. & Machine Co. (Derrick; Crane; Damping) ....B

N. Y.—Schenectady

General Electric Co. (Electric) ....AAAA

N. Y.—Watervliet

Jones' Sons, J. M. (Street; Electric; Freight; Passenger; Baggage) ....A

N. C.—Statesville

Steele & Son, J. C. (Clay)C

OHIO—Akron

Webster, Camp & Lane Mach. Co. (Mine; Ore)..A

OHIO—Barnesville

Watt Mining Car Wheel Co. (Mine; Freight) C

OHIO—Bucyrus

American Clay Working Machine Co. (Brick Transfer; Construction; Dump) ...B

OHIO—Cambridge

Cambridge Mine Car Co. (Mine) X

OHIO—Canton

Bonnot Co. (Clay Dredge; Dumping; Transfer) ...B

Canton Fdry. & Machine Co. (Coal; Mine; Pit) ......B

Structural Steel Car Co. (Clay; Flat; Freight; Gondola; Mine; Ore; Steel; Steel Mining; Dump; Tank) X

OHIO—Cincinnati

Queen City Carouselle Co., South & Evans (Ballast) ....H

Sayers & Scovill, 2247 Colerain Av. (Funeral) ..AA

Stacey Mfg. Co., 239 Mill (Coal Elevator) ......A

Stewart Iron Wks. (Elevator) ....B

Tudor Boiler Mfg. Co. (Tank) ....B

OHIO—Cleveland

Atlas Bolt & Screw Co. (Billet; Brick; Charging; Clay; Core Oven; Drop Bottom; Dryer; Dumping; Foundry; Hand; Push; Hot Metal; Slag; Ingot; Logging; Mine; Ore; Plantation; Plate; Sheet Mill; Steel Mining; Dump; Freight) ....A

CARS (Con.)

Atlas Car & Mfg. Co. (Brick; Core Oven; Foundry; Railroad; Rolling Mill; Steel Sugar Cane; Tank) ....A

Bowler & Co. (Freight)...A

Brown Hoisting Machinery Co. (Ltd.) (Damp; Ship) ....AAAA

Cleveland Car Co. (Billet; Brick; Clay; Core Oven; Drop Bottom; Dumping; Logging; Mine; Ore; Plantation; Plate; Sheet Mill; Steam Shovel; Steel) ....E

Gary Iron & Steel Co. (Steel) ....A

McMyler Mfg. Co. (Dump) ....A

Niles Mine & Mill Supply Co. (Mine) C

Ohio Ceramic Engineering Co., 50 Fall (Brick)....D

Osborn Mfg. Co. (Core Oven; Foundry) ....A

Tyler Co., W. S. (Elevator) ....AA

Wellman - Seaver - Morgan Co. (Coal; Mine; Pit; Ship; Steel) ......AAAA

OHIO—Collinwood

Kuhlman Car Co., G. C. (Street; Electric; Freight; Passenger; Mail) ......A

OHIO—Columbus

Jeffrey Mfg. Co. (Dumping) ....AA

Kilbourne & Jacobs Mfg. Co. (Brick; Core Oven; Dumping; Hand; Push; Mine; Steel; Construction; Street Railway) ......AA

OHIO—Dayton

Barney & Smith Car Co. (Freight; Passenger; Street; Electric; Baggage; Mail) ....A

Raymond & Co., W. C. (Dumping) ....A

OHIO—Galion

Freese & Co., E. M. (Brick Transfer) C

OHIO—Hamilton

Meyers Mfg. Co., F. J. (Elevator) ....B

OHIO—Lima

Lima Locomotive & Machine Co. (Steel Dumping; Logging; Mine; Steel; Steel Mine Dumping; Freight). ....AA

OHIO—Marion

Marrion Steam Shovel Co. (Steam Shovel; Wrecking) ....AA

OHIO—Massillon

Heinmann & Bro., A. (Mine) C

OHIO—Nelsonville

Nelsonville Fdry. & Machine Co. (Mine) ....B

OHIO—Newark

Jewett Car Co. (Passenger; Street; Electric) ......B

OHIO—New Lexington

Star Mfg. Co. (Mine) C

OHIO—New Philadelphia

Spicer Mfg. Co. (Mine)...D

OHIO—Niles

Niles Boiler Co. (Core Oven) ....B

Niles Car & Mfg. Co. (Passenger; Street; Electric)B

OHIO—Painesville

Horton Mfg. Co. (Brick; Clay; Dumping) C

OHIO—Ravenna

Byers, Jno. F. (Derrick; Crane) ....B

OHIO—Salem

Clark Co., W. J. (Dump).B

OHIO—Steubenville

Means Fdry. & Machine Co. (Dryer) ....D

OHIO—Toledo

Donovan Wire & Iron Co. (Elevator) C

OHIO—Wellington

Wellington Machine Co. (Brick) ....B

OHIO—Youngstown

Pollock Co., W. B.

CARS (Con.)

(Foundry) ....B

Youngstown Car Mfg. Co. (Freight) ....A

OHIO—Zanesville

Griffith & Wedge Co. (Mining) ....A

PA.—Allegheny

Carlins' Sons, Thomas (Dump; Freight; Mill Yard) ....A

PA.—Bangor

Flory Mfg. Co., S. (Dumping) ....B

PA.—Bloomsburg

Bloomsburg Car Mfg. Co. (Dumping; Flat; Freight; Mine) ....A

Harmon-Cogger Co. (Coal; Mine; Pit) ....A

PA.—Brownsville

Herbertsons' Sons, J. (Mine) ....D

PA.—Catasauqua

Lehigh Car Wheel & Axle Wks. (Clay; Flat; Mine; Ore) ....AAAA

PA.—Catawissa

Catawissa Car & Fdry. Co. (Dumping; Flat; Mine).D

PA.—Connellsville

Connellsville Machine & Car Co. (Mine) ....A

PA.—Corry

Climax Mfg. Co. (Logging) ....AA

PA.—Easton

Sterlingworth Ry. Supply Co. (Flat; Freight; Steel) ....A

PA.—Ellwood City

Glen Mfg. Co. (Elevator).D

PA.—Erie

Erie Car Wks. (Hamilton & Knoll) (Caboose; Clay; Flat; Freight; Gondola; Mine; Ore; Steel; Steel Mining; Dump; Tank; Refrigerator) ....B

PA.—Greensburg

Hempfield Fdry. Co. (Mine) ....F

PA.—Harrisburg

Jackson Mfg. Co. (Billet; Core Oven; Foundry; Hot Metal; Slag; Mine; Plate; Sheet Mill; Steel Mining; Dump) ....B

PA.—Irwin

Hockensmith Wheel & Mine Car Co. (Mine) ....A

PA.—Lancaster

Martin Brick Machine Mfg. Co., Henry (Dryer; Dump) ....B

PA.—Lebanon

Lebanon Mfg. Co. (Foundry; Coal; Ore Dump; Freight; Refrigerator; Mine; Passenger; Observation) ..X

Weimer Machine Wks. Co. (Hot Metal; Slag; Freight) ....A

PA.—Monongahela

Monongahela Mfg. Co. (Mine) C

PA.—New Castle

Penn Engineering Wks. (Hot Metal; Slag) ....A

PA.—Osceola Mills

Stine & Son, S. B. (Mine).D

PA.—Philadelphia

Allison Mfg. Co., 708 Chestnut (Derrick; Crane; Drop Bottom; Dumping; Freight; Hand; Push; Logging; Mine; Ore; Plantation; Track Laying; Oil Tank; Refrigerator; Road masters'; Steam Hand; Passenger; Mail; Steam Motor) ....AAAA

American Car Sprinkler Co., 62nd & Woodland Av. (Sprinkling Street Railway) X

Brill Co., J. G., 62 Woodland Av. (Freight; Hand; Push; Passenger; Plantation; Sprinkling Street Ry.; Street; Electric; Refrigerator; Tramway; Sleeping; Cable) ..AAAA

Darby & Sons, Edward

CARS (Con.)
(Passenger Elevator)...A
Link-Belt Engineering Co.,
Nicetown (Coal; Mine;
Pit) ....A
McFadden Co. (Construction) X
PA.—Pittsburg
Carlin Co., W. J., 25th &
A. V. Ry. (Billet;
Foundry; Hot Metal;
Slag; Mine; Ore) ....A
Carroll-Porter Boiler &
Tank Co. (Oil Tank)..B
Phillips Mine & Mill Supply
Co. (Mine; Steel; Wood)
AA
Porter Co., H. K. (Street
Railway) ....AA
Pressed Steel Car Co.,
Trademen Bldg. (Freight;
Steel) ....AAA
Riter-Conley Mfg. Co.
(Tank) ....AA
Schoen Pressed Steel Co.
(Freight; Steel Mining).B
Standard Steel Car Co.,
Frick Bldg. (Freight;
Steel; Wood; Composite;
Steel Mining; Dump)..
AAAA
Union Fdry. & Machine Co.
(Hot Metal; Slag) C
PA.—Pittston
Exeter Machine Wks.
(Mine) ....B
PA.—Scottdale
Kenny & Co. (Mine)......A
PA.—Shamokin
Muller & Son, Jno. (Drift)
A
PA.—Tamaqua
Tamaqua Mfg. Co. (Mine).B
PA.—Warren
Struthers, Wells & Co.
(Oil Tank) ....AA
PA.—Wilkesbarre
Vulcan Iron Wks. (Dumping; Hot Metal; Slag).AA
PA.—Williamsport
Moltz, Jacob J. (Logging)
D
PA.—York
Billmeyer & Small Co.
(Dumping; Freight; Hand;
Push; Logging; Mine;
Passenger; Construction)
AA
Dempwolf & Co., C. H.
(Dump) ....B
TENN.—Chattanooga
Chattanooga Car & Fdry. Co.
(Drop Bottom; Dumping;
Freight; Hand; Push;
Logging; Mine; Plantation Oil Tank) ....A
TENN.—Knoxville
Scotts' Patent Brick Car
Co. (Brick) C
TENN.—Memphis
Bodley Wagon Co. (Drop
Bottom; Plantation;
Tram; Dump) ....B
TEXAS—Marshall
Marshall Car Wheel & Fdry.
Co. (Logging) ....B
TEXAS—Pine Bluff
Dilley & Son, Geo. M.
(Logging) ....D
VT.—Rutland
Lincoln Iron Wks. (Freight)
B
VA.—Richmond
Tredegear Co. (Freight; Oil
Tank; Refrigerator; Logging; Mine; Passenger)..
AAA
WASH.—Spokane
Union Iron Wks. (Ore)...A
W. VA.—Fairmount
Helmick Fdry. Machine Co.
(Mine) ....D
WIS.—Cudahy
Power & Mining Machinery
Co. (Charging; Hot Metal;
Slag; Mine; Ore; Steel
Mining; Dump) ......AA
WIS.—Milwaukee
Allis-Chalmers Co. (Mining)
AAAA
Filer & Stowell Co. (Ltd.)
(Coal Elevators) ....AAA
WIS.—Racine
Mitchell & Lewis Co.
(Dumping) ....AA

CARTONS

See Boxes; Paper

CARTRIDGES

See also Shells

CAL.—San Francisco
Selby Smelting & Lead Co..
AAA
CONN.—Bridgeport
Union Metallic Cartridge
(Co. (Rifle, etc.).AAAA
CONN.—New Haven
Winchester Metallic Cartridge Co. (Rifle, etc.)..
AAAA
ILL.—Alton
Western Cartridge Co.
(Rifle; Revolver, etc..)A
MASS.—Chicopee
Ames-Leonard Co. ....B
MASS.—Lowell
U. S. Cartridge Co. (Rifle,
etc.) ....AA
New York City
Von Lengerke & Detmold
(Shotgun) ....A
N. Y.—Utica
Savage Arms Co. (Rifle)..A
OHIO—Cincinnati
Peters Cartridge Co. (The)
(Rifle. etc.) ....AAA
OHIO—Cleveland
Chamberlain Cartridge &
Target Co. (Shotgun) ...B

CARTS

See also Carriages & Wagons

ALA.—Mobile
Southern Log Cart & Supply
Co. (Dog.) ....A
CONN.—Danielson
Jacobs Mfg. Co., E. H.
(Hose) ....B
ILL.—Bradley
Bradley Mfg. Co., David
(Hand) ....AAA
ILL.—Canton
Parlin & Orendorff Co.
(Hand) ....AAAA
ILL.—Chicago
Borden & Sellick Co., 48
Lake (Push) ....B
Chicago Scale Co. (Push)..A
Fairbanks, Morse & Co.
(Barrel) ....AAAA
ILL.—Downers Grove
Dicke Tool Co. (Linemen's)
C
ILL.—Galva
Hayes Pump & Planter Co.
(Hand; Barrel) ....A
ILL.—Harvey
Austin Mfg. Co. (Street
Sprinkling; Garbage)..AA
ILL.—Havana
Havana Metal Wks. Co.
(Barrel) ....A
ILL.—Oregon
Entyre & Co., E. L. (Street
Sprinkling) ....D
ILL.—Sandwich
Sandwich Mfg. Co.
(Hand; Barrel) ......AA
ILL.—Sterling
Novelty Iron Wks. (Barrel)
E
ILL.—Sycamore
Patton Co., Frank C.
(Hand; Barrel) ....B
IND.—Anderson
Anderson Bridge & Scraper
Co. (Street Sprinkling).D
IND.—Goshen
Kelly Fdry. & Mach. Co.
(Barrel) ....A
Walker-Lewis Carriage Co.
(Hand) ....B
IND.—South Bend
Studebaker Bros.' Mfg. Co.
(Hose; Street Sprinkling;
Hand; Barrel) ......AAAA
Winkler Bros. (Street
Sprinkling) ....B
LA.—New Iberia
Bernard, A. M. (Cane)....D
MAINE—South Paris
Paris Mfg. Co. (Pony)...A

CARTS (Con.)

MASS.—Boston
Ames Plow Co. (Farm; Ox;
Railroad; Hand) ..AAAA

MICH.—Lansing
Lansing Wheelbarrow Co.
(Street Sprinkling; Hand;
Barrel; Coal; Dump;
Laundry; Log; Water;
Push; Water) .....AAA

MICH.—Port Huron
Port Huron Engine &
Thresher Co. (Road
Spreading; Sprinkling)...
AAA

MICH.—Three Rivers
Sheffield Car Co. (Coal;
Drop Bottom; Crushed
Ice) ....AA

MINN.—Minneapolis
Howell & Co., R. R. (Bar-
rel) ....B
Nott Fire Engine Co.
(Hose) ....B
Puffer Hubbard Mfg. Co.
(Hand; Barrel) ....B
MacLeod & Smith (Black-
ing) ....B

MO.—St. Louis
Cooney Mfg. Co., P. J.
(Hose) C
Luedinghaus - Espenscheid
Wagon Co. (Railroad) AA
Whitman Agricultural Co.
(Hand) ....AA
Zelnicker Supply Co., Wal-
ter A. (Log) X

N. H.—Concord
Abbott-Downing Co. (Hose;
Street Sprinkling) X

N. J.—Grenloch
Bateman Mfg. Co. (Barrel;
Push) ....A

N. Y.—Frankford
Acme Road Machinery Co.
(Hand; Street Sweeping;
Sprinkling) ....B

New York City
Am. Fire Engine Co., 85
Liberty (Hose) X
Fairbanks Co. 416 Broome
(Hose; Hand; Barrel; De-
livery; Dump); Lumber;
Push; Steel) ......AAAA
Farquhart & Co., A. B., 21
Cotton Exch. (Hand).AA
Hayward & Co., S. F., 20
Warren (Hose) ....AA
International Fire Engine
Co. (Hose) ....AAAA
Woodhouse, J. S. (Street
Sprinkling) C

N. Y.—Oneida
Aubeuf, Frank J. (Hand).C
Schubert Bros. Gear Co.
(Hand) C

N. Y.—Rochester
Stewart, A. F. & S. C.
(Hose) ....E

N. Y.—Seneca Falls
American La France Fire
Engine Co. (Hose) .....B
Goulds Mfg. Co. (Hose)..
AAA
Rumsey & Co. (Ltd.)
(Hose) ....A

N. Y.—Syracuse
Syracuse Chilled Plow Co.
(Hand; Barrel; Push).AA

OHIO—Canton
Aultman Co. (Street Sprinkling) ....AAAA

OHIO—Cincinnati
Kisinger-Ison Co., 466
Pioneer (Street Sprink-
ling) ....D

OHIO—Columbus
Buckeye Buggy Co. (Break-
ing) ....AAA
Kilbourne & Jacobs Mfg. Co.
(Hand; Barrel; Dump;
Ox; Railroad; Push; Lum-
ber) ....AAAA

OHIO—Mansfield
Lean Roderick Mfg. Co.
(Hand; Barrel) ......AA

OHIO—South Paris
Walborn & Riker (Hose)..X

OHIO—Springfield
Mast & Co., P. P. (Hand)..
AAAA

OHIO—Toledo
Gendron Wheel Co. (Toy)AA

CARTS (Con.)

Milburn Wagon Co. (Barrel)
AAA

PA.—Kennett Square
American Road Machine Co.
(Road Spreading) ....AA
Good Roads Machinery Co.
(Road Spreading) ......D

PA.—Mechanicsburg
Comstock, Geo. L. (Barrel)
C

PA.—Philadelphia
Wirt & Knox Mfg. Co., 219
N. 3d (Hose) ....D

PA.—Pittsburg
Watson Wooden Tank Co.,
418 3d Av. (Sprinkling).E

TENN.—Memphis
Bodley Wagon Co. (Cane) A

VT.—Battleboro
Battleboro Mfg. Co. (Hose)
D

VA.—Norfolk
Whitehurst Co., R. W.
(Hand; Barrel; Push)...B

WIS.—Kenosha
Bain Wagon Co. (Railroad)
AAA

WIS.—Milwaukee
Meineck & Son, A (Push).
AA

WIS.—Racine
Belle City Mfg. Co. (Barrel;
Hand) ....B
Winship Mfg. Co. (Street
Sprinkling) ....E

CARVINGS
See also Woodwork

MAINE—Portland
Berlin Mills Co. (Wood)
AAAA

MD.—Baltimore
Meislahn & Co., C. F., 19
Clay (Hand) ....D

MASS.—Boston
Stearns Lumber Co., A. T.
(Classic Wood) ....A

MICH.—Grand Rapids
Grand Rapids Wood Carving
Co. (Wood) ....D
Waddell Mfg. Co. (Wood).B

New York City
Herts Bros. (Wood) X
Hess & Co., D. S. (Wood).A
Kimbel & Sons, A (Wood).A
Lamb, J. & R. (Wood) ...D

CASCARA

MICH.—Detroit
Parke, Davis & Co. ..AAAA

N. Y.—Buffalo
Schoellkopf Hartford &
Hanna Co ....AAA

New York City
Hopkins Co., J. L. ....A
Lehn & Fink ....AAA
McKesson & Robbins.AAAA
Parke, Davis & Co. ..AAAA

OREGON—Portland
Heitscher & Co., S ....D

CASES
See also Boxes; Furniture;
Leather Goods

CAL.—San Francisco
Herring, Richard (Cabinet
Book) ....F

CONN.—Meridan
Meridan Britannia Co. (Sil-
ver Card; Playing Card)
AAAA
Parker Co., Chas. (Specta-
cle; Eye Glass) .....AAA
Wilcox Silver Plate Co.
(Jewelry) ....AAA

CONN.—New Haven
English & Mersick Co. (Toilet) ....B
Mallory-Wheeler Co. (Spectacles) ....AA
New Haven Clock Co. (Railroad Ticket) ....AAA

CONN.—Wallingford
Wallace Sons Mfg. Co., R.
(Leather; Silver Card;
Cigar; Cigarette; Specta-
cle; Eye Glass) ..AAAA

CONN.—Waterbury
Scovil Mfg. Co. (Cigar; Cig-

arette) ....AAAA
DEL.—Wilmington
Delaware Hard Fibre Co.
(Fibre) ....A
GA.—Atlanta
Hall & Co., L. H. (Burial) B
ILL.—Altamont
Altamont Mfg. Co. (Egg) .D
ILL.—Chicago
Acme Box Co., 306 S. Clinton
.(Egg) ....D
Amberg File & Index Co.
Filing) ....A
Andrews Co., A. H. (Map)
..............AA
Ball & Bro., A (Playing
Card) ....AA
Bodach, Chas. (Show) ....B
Boekel & Co., Wm. (Needle)
..............X
Central Mfg. Co. (Book) ..A
Chicago Case Mfg. Co., 75
W. Monroe (Eye Glass) E
Chicago Plush & Leather
Case Co., 126 Dearborn
(Plush; Leather; Jewelry)
..............X
Creamery Package Mfg. Co.,
182 Kinzie (Egg) AAAA
Dick Co., A. B. (Legal
Blank) ....AA
Fitzgerald Trunk Co. (Sample) ....AA
Gilgen, Peter, Mrs. (Musical
Instrument) ....F
Haskell Bros. (Liquor; Sample) ....A
Hausmann & Dunn (Clinical
Thermometer; Urine Test)
..............C
Lyon & Healy (Musical Instrument) ....AAAA
Redlich Mfg. Co., 2 Oak
(Wooden Mailing) C
Union Show Case Co. (Jewelers Show) ....B
Warren Mfg. Co., Masonic
Temple (Catalogue; Cutlery; Display; Screw;
Bolt) ....A
Western Box Co. (Mailing)
..............E
Western Jewelry Case Co.,
208 State (Jewelry) ...F
Western Leather Mfg. Co.
(Medicine; Vial; Blacking; Leather Card; Cigar;
Toilet Traveling) ......A
Wilt, Chas. T. (Coupon;
Dressing; Hat; Sample;
Suit; Telescope; Trunk;
Toilet) ....B
ILL.—Elgin
Illinois Watch Case Co.
(Gold; Silver; Nickle
Watch) ....AA
ILL.—Quincy
Knittel Show Case Co., Joseph (Show) ....A
Quincy Show Case Wks.,
(Jewelers; Show) .....A
Stahl, Geo. H. (Show) ..D
ILL.—Rockford
Central Furniture Co.(Book)
..............A
Forest City Furniture Co.
(Book) ....A
Rockford Burial Case Co.
(Burial) ....B
ILL.—Sterling
Rock Falls Mfg. Co. (Burial) ....A
IND.—Decatur
Decatur Egg Case Co., W. H.
(Physicians') ....B
Udell Works (Blacking) .A
IND.—New Castle
Krell French Piano Co. (Piano) ....AA
IND.—Richmond
Hutton & Co., J. M. (Burial)
..............A
IOWA—Burlington
Embalming Burial Case Co.
(Burial) ....B
IOWA—Cedar Rapids
Cherry, J. G., Co. (Egg) ..C
IOWA—Clinton
Smith & Son, F. (Egg) ...C
IOWA—Dubuque
Iowa Coffin Co. (Burial)AA
IOWA—Sioux City
Curtis Sash & Door Co.
(Show) ....AA

IOWA—Waterloo
Weis Henry (Egg) ....A
MAINE—Kennebunk
Leatheroid Mfg. Co. (Hat;
Spy Glass) ....A
MASS.—Athol
Bates Bros. Co. (Card) ...B
MASS.—Attleboro
Bates & Bacon (Gold; Filled
Watch) ....AAA
Blake Co., Jas. E. (Cigar;
Cigarette; Pencil) ....A
Inman & Co., J. T. (Cigar;
Cigarette) ....D
MASS.—Boston
Cummings' Son & Co., Josiah
(Sample) C
Davenport, Albert H.(Dressing) ....AA
Dennison Mfg. Co. (Morocco;
Plush; Jewelry; Mailing;
Playing) ....AAAA
Golding & Co. (Printers) .B
Margot, Eugene F. (Gold
Watch) ....E
Monson Maine State Co., 113
Devonshire (Slate Burial;
Vaults) X
New England Novelty Mfg.
Co. (Needle) ....H
Orient Mfg. Co. (Eye Glass)
..............X
Paine Furniture Co. (Book)
..............A
Rand-Avery Supply Co.
(Coupon; R. R. Ticket)
..............AA
U. S. Mailing Case Co., 40
Water (Mailing) ....F
White & Son. W. B. (Leather Card; Spectacle; Eye
Glass) ....D
Sturdy Mfg. Co., W. A.
(Cigar; Cigarette) ....B
MASS.—Florence
Florence Furniture Co. (Burial) C
MASS.—Leominster
(Piano) C
Richardson Piano Case Co.
(Piano) ....B
MASS.—Southbridge
American Optical Co. (Trial;
Spectacle; Eye Glass; also
Frames) ....AAA
MASS.—So. Deerfield
Arms Mfg. Co. (Card) ....B
MASS.—Westfield
Crane Bros. (Bicycle Tourists'; Gun; Musical Instrument) ....AAA
MASS.—Worcester
Maynard-Gough Co. (Mailing) ....E
Torrey & Co., J. R (Cutlery;
Shaving; Toilet) ......A
Warren Leather Goods Co.
(Medicine;Blacking; Card;
Dressing; Drinking Cup;
Fishing Rod; Gun; Lence;
Musical Instrument; Regalia; Sample; Sporting
Goods; Sword; Telescope;
Trunk Toilet; Spectacle;
Eye Glass) ....B
MICH.—Bay City
Vance Box Co., E. J. (Ltd.)
(Egg) ....B
MICH.—Benton Harbor
Spencer & Barnes Co.
(Dressing) ....A
MICH.—Detroit
Detroit Casket Co., 179 W.
Congress (Burial) ......B
Detroit Show Case Co. (Jewelers Show) C
Hargraves Mfg. Co. (Toilet) ....A
Johnston Optical Co. (Spectacles; Eye Glass) ......A
Mancha Show Case Co.
(Show) C
Parke, Davis & Co. (Veterinary ....AAAA
Phillips & Co., John (Ltd.)
(Show) C
Widman & Co., C. D. (Show)
..............A
Wolverine Burial Case Co.
(Burial) ....F
MICH.—Grand Rapids
Berkey & Gay Furniture Co.
(Book; Cabinet Book) .AA
Grand Rapids Chair Co.

CASES (Con.)

Filled; Nickle Watch)
AAAA

Kimes & Co., J. B., 1822 Filbert (Slate Burial; Vaults)
C

Langfield Bros. & Co. (Writing) ....AA

McIntire Magee & Brown (Spy Glass) ....A

Muhr's Watch Case Co. (Gold; Filled; Nickle) ..D

Rosenblatt & Co., H. M., 22d & Oxford (Musical Instrument) ....A

Rumpp & Sons, C. F. (Cigar, Photograph; Sample; Toilet; Dressing; Card; Medicine; Writing) ....AAA

Sheip Mfg. Co., H. H. (Jewelry; Toilet) ....AA

Simons Bros. & Co. (Manicure) ....A

Sommer & Co., H. B., 628 Arch (Jewelry) C

Varwig & Bro., H., 900 Chestnut (Jewelry) ...C

Weaver Mailing Env. & Box Co. (Mailing)..........D

PA.—Pittsburg

Budke Mfg. Co. (Cartridge)
B

Lorsch Bros. (Burial) ...D

Pittsburg Show Case Co. (Ltd.) (Show) ....D

PA.—Walnutport

Hahn Granville (Slate Burial; Vaults) ....E

R. I.—Providence

Barstow & Williams (Cigar; Cigarette) C

Clark Mfg. Co. (Burial) ..B

Cross, A. F. (Pen; Pencil) C

Household Sewing Machine Co. (Barbers' Cup) ....D

Providence Stock Co. (Manicure) ....D

TENN.—Chattanooga

Loomis & Hart Mfg. Co. (Knocked Down Burial)
AA

TENN.—Memphis

Anderson-Tully Co. (Egg)
AAA

UTAH—Salt Lake City

Culmer & Bros., G. F. (Show) ....A

VT.—Bristol

Drake, Smith & Co. (Mailing) ....B

VT.—Fair Haven

Dalrymple Iron Wks. (Wheel) ....E

Pelkey, W. H. (Slate Burial; Vaults) ....E

VT.—Lunenburg

Lunenburg Mfg. Co. (Burial)
F

VT.—Poultney

Fleming Slate Co. (Slate Burial; Vaults) C

VA.—Arvonia

Williams Slate Co. (Slate Burial; Vault) ....B

VA.—Grottoes

American Hardwood Mfg. Co. (Annunciator) C

WIS.—Hazlehurst

Yawkey Lumber Co. (Egg)
AAA

WIS.—Milwaukee

Abel & Bach Co. (Traveling)
AA

Kipp Co., B. A. (Blacking) ....B

WIS.—Oshkosh

Buckstaff-Edwards Co. (Burial) ....AA

Schmidt Bros. Trunk Co. (Blacking; Dressing; Sample; Traveling) ....A

WIS.—Racine

Secor Trunk Co., M. M. (Sample; Toilet; Traveling) ....A

WIS.—Sheboygan

Winter Lumber Co., M. (Knocked Down, Show) .B

WIS.—Two Rivers

Hamilton Mfg. Co. (Printers'; R. R. Ticket; Type)
AA

CASINGS

See also Woodwork

CASINGS (Con.)

ILL.—Chicago

Bechstein & Co. (Sausage)
AA

Born Butchers' Supply Co. Inc., H. A. (Sausages)..D

IOWA—Cedar Rapids

Sinclair & Co., T. M. (Inc.) (Sausage) ....AAA

LA.—Ramos

Ramos Lumber & Mfg. Co. (Cypress) ....AA

MICH.—Bay City

Michigan Pipe Co. (Steam Pipe) ....B

MICH.—Hermansville

Wisconsin Land & Lumber Co. (Ceiling) ......AAAA

MO.—St. Louis

Brecht Butchers' Supply Co., G. V. (Sausage) ....AAA

NEBR.—South Omaha

Cudahy Packing Co. (Sausage) ....AAAA

N. Y.—Elmira

Wyckoff & Son, A. (Steam Pipe) ....AAA

N. Y.—Lockport

American District Steam Co. (Steam Pipe) ......AAA

New York City

Oppenheimer & Co., S. (Sausage) ....AAA

OHIO—Cleveland

Garry Iron & Steel Co. (Steel; Elevator) .....A

OHIO—Salem

Clark Co., W. J. (Steel; Elevator) ....A

OHIO—Steubenville

La Belle Iron Works (Oil Well) ....AAAA

PA.—McKeesport

National Tube Wks. (Steam Pipe) ....AAAA

CASKETS

See cases; Burial

CASKS

See Cooperage

CASSIA

Teas, Coffees & Spices

CASSIMERES

Woolen Goods

CASTERS

See also Silverware; Glassware

CONN.—Meriden

Foster, Merriam & Co. (Furniture) ....A

Schenck Co., M. B. (Furniture; Ball; Roller Bearing; Truck; Bed Plate)..A

CONN.—Southington

Peck, Stow & Wilcox Co. (Furniture; Bed Plate; Truck) ....AAAA

CONN.—Windsor Locke

Clark, Geo. P. (Furniture; Rubber Wheel Truck)...C

IND.—Indianapolis

Phoenix Caster Co. (Furniture) ....B

Tucker & Dorsey Mfg. Co. (Furniture; Truck; Bed Plate) ....A

IOWA—Dubuque

Adams Co. (Truck) ......B

KANS.—Coffeyville

Pioneer Flint Glass Co. (Glass) C

MD.—Baltimore

Duer & Sons, John (Furniture) ....A

MASS.—Boston

Elastic Tip Co. (Rubber Wheel) ....B

MASS.—Everett

Faxon Co., Geo. H. (Piano)
D

MASS.—Lowell

Woods, Sherwood & Co. (Wire) C

MICH.—Grand Rapids

CASTERS (Con.)

Michigan Stove & Caster Co. (Furniture) ....A

MICH.—Lansing

Lansing Wheelbarrow Co. (Anti-Friction) .....AAA

MO.—St. Louis

Pleuger & Henger Mfg. Co. (Truck) ....A

NEBR.—Nebraska City

Faultless Caster Co. (Bed) C

N. J.—Newark

Sommers' Son, John (Furniture) ....A

Toler, Sons & Co., John (Furniture) ....B

N. Y.—Chappaqua

Acme Ball-Bearing Co. (Ball Bearing) ....A

New York City

International Silver Co., 9 Maiden Lane (Silver Plated) ....AAAA

Peck, Stow & Wilcox Co., 27 Murray (Bed Plate) AAAA

Sargent & Co., 151 Leonard (Bed Plate; Truck) .AAA

Smith & Hemenway Co., 226 B'way (Ball; Roller Bearing; Bed Plate) ......D

Universal Caster & Foundry Co., 316 E. 23d (Ball; Roller Bearing; Bed Plate) ....A

N. Y.—Syracuse

Stearns Co., E. C. (Furniture; Truck) ....AA

N. Y.—Troy

Palmer Hdw. Mfg. Co. (Bed Plate) ....D

OHIO—Bellaire

Bellaire Bottle Co. (Inc.) (Glass) ....A

National Glass Wks. (T. A. Rodefer, Prop.) (Glass) A

OHIO—Cincinnati

Haven Co., James L. (Furniture) ....B

Tatum Co., Samuel C. (Furniture; Truck) ....B

OHIO—Columbus

Kilbourne & Jacobs Mfg. Co. (Truck) ....AA

PA.—Erie

Continental Rubber Works (Rubber) ....A

PA.—Philadelphia

Fox & Sons, H. C. (Glass) AA

PA.—Pittsburg

McKee & Co., S. (Glass).D

PA.—Reading

Reading Hardware Co. (Bed Plate; Truck) .....AAAA

PA.—Wrightsville

Wrightsville Hardware Co. (Furniture; Bed Plate) ..C

W. VA.—Wellsburg

Riverside Glass Wks. (Inc.) (Glass) C

W. VA.—Wheeling

Central Glass Co. (Glass) .A

CASTINGS

ALA.—Birmingham

Dimmick Pipe Co. (Cupola; Air Furnace; Railroad) A

Gibb & Son, V. (Brass; Bronze; Copper) ......D

Tennessee Coal, Iron & R. R. Co. (Steel) ....AAAA

ALA.—Cullman

Ehrensperger, H. (Brass) D

ALA.—Huntsville

Huntsville Fdy. & Machine Works (Brass) ....B

ALA.—Mobile

Alabama Iron Works (Brass) B

ALA.—Selma

Peacock's Iron Works (Railroad) C

ARK.—Little Rock

Thomas Mfg. Co. (Brass).B

CAL.—Los Angeles

Axelson Machine Co. (Brass) B

Graham & Noble (Brass)..A

Hutchison Co., W. G. (Brass) ....B

CASTINGS (Con.)

Llewellyn Iron Wks. (Brass) AA

Los Angeles Gas & Electric Fixture Mfg. Co. (Brass) F

CAL.—San Francisco

Garratt & Co., W. T. (Brass; Bronze) ...AA

Greenberg's Sons, M., 223 Beale (Brass) ....D

Hendey Machine Works (Heavy; Light Iron)...A

Kingwell, Vincent, 228 Fremont (Brass) C

Richmond Fdy. & Mfg. Co., 516 Market (Grey Iron).A

Roylance Brass Wks., 112 Main (Brass) ....B

Tay Co., Geo. H., 49 First (Brass) ....A

Union Iron Works, 222 Market (Manganese; Bronze; Steel) ....AAAA

Western Tube Co., Mills Bldg. (Brass) ......AAA

CAL.—Stockton

Holt Mfg. Co. (Iron)..AA

COLO.—Denver

Creswell Mfg. Co., 1624 Blake (Brass) ....A

Denver Brass Works Co., 1303 Lawrence (Brass).D

Flint, Lomas Elec. & Mfg. Co., 1937 Curtis (Brass) C

CONN.—Ansonia

Farrell Foundry & Machine Co. (Semi-Steel; Heavy) AAAA

Phelps & Bartholomew Co. (Brass) C

CONN.—Branford

Hammer & Co. (Malleable Iron for Hdw. Spec.)...X

Malleable Iron Fittings Co. (Semi-Steel; Homogeneous Metal; Steel; Malleable Iron Air Furnace Refined) A

New York Lock Co. (Bronze) ....B

CONN.—Bridgeport

Bridgeport Brass Co. (Brass) ....AAA

Bridgeport Deoxidized Bronze & Metal Co. Aluminum; Brass; Bronze; Copper) ......B

Bridgeport Malleable Iron Co. (Refined Malleable Iron) ....AA

Eaton, Cole & Burnham Co. (Brass; Grey Iron).AAAA

Pacific Iron Wks. (Iron)..A

Rowell & Co., W. G. (Aluminum; Brass; Bronze; Copper; Gun Metal; Phosphor Bronze) ....D

CONN.—Bristol

Sessions Foundry Co. (Grey Iron) ....AAA

CONN.—Derby

Birmingham Iron Foundry (Semi - Steel; Heavy; Steel; Iron) ....A

CONN.—Guilford

Spencer's Sons, I. S. (Brass; Bronze; Grey Iron)....B

CONN.—Hartford

Blake & Son, J. T. (Manganese; Bronze; Phosphor Bronze) ....E

Hartford Foundry Co. (Grey Iron) ....B

Howard Co., Jas. L. (Brass) A

Laragy, P. (Grey Iron)...C

Phoenix Brass Foundry (Brass) ....D

Pratt & Cady Co. (Brass; Bronze; Grey Iron)...AA

Veeder Mfg. Co. (White Metal) ....B

CONN.—Lime Rock

Barnum-Richardson Co. (Railroad) ....AAA

CONN.—Middletown

Wilcox, Crittenden & Co. (Brass; Grey Iron) ...A

CONN.—Mt. Carmel

Woodruff & Sons' Co., W. W. (Brass; Malleable Iron Carriage) ....A

CASTINGS (Con.)

CONN.—Naugatuck
Naugatuck Malleable Iron Co. (Malleable Iron)..A

CONN.—New Britain
Malleable Iron Wks. (Grey; Malleable Iron) ......B
North & Co., O. B. (Sad; Light) ....A
North & Judd Mfg. Co. (Brass; White Metal).AA
Vulcan Iron Works (Grey; Malleable Iron) ....A

CONN.—New Haven
Barnum, S. H. (Grey Iron) ....B
Fitch Co., W. & E. T. (Small to order) ....AA
Graham & Co., Jas. (Brass) ....A
Hendryx & Co., A. B. (Aluminum; Brass; ronze; Copper) ....A
Ives Co., Hobart B. (Brass; Bronze) C
National Steel Foundry Co. (Chemical Works; Locomotive; Car) ....A
New Haven Malleable Casting Co. (Malleable Iron) X
Peck Bros. & Co. (Brass)..A
Stannard & Son (Grey Iron) ....D
Warner Mfg. Co., G. F. (Grey Iron) C

CONN.—New London
Hopson & Chapin Mfg. Co. (Automobile; Grey Iron) ....B

CONN.—Norwalk
Arnold & Co. (Iron) .....B
Norwalk Brass Co. (Brass) ....D

CONN.—Norwich
Vaughn & Sons, A. S. (Grey Iron) C

CONN.—South Norwalk
United States Foundry & Scales Co. (Bench Leg; Dynamo Motor; Pulley).D

CONN.—Stonington
Miller, A. B. (Brass; Iron) ....D

CONN.—Terryville
Terry Co., Andrew (Malleable Iron Small)......B

CONN.—Torrington
Turner & Seymour Mfg. Co. (Brass; Grey Iron)....A

CONN.—Waterbury
American Pin Co. (Brass; Bronze) ....A
Holmes, Booth & Haydens Co. (Brass) ....AAA
Scovill Mfg. Co. (Aluminum; Brass) ....AAAA
Steel & Johnson Mfg. Co. (Brass) ....B

DEL.—Wilmington
Diamond State Steel Co. (Railroad) ....AAA
Lobdell Car Wheel Co. (Heavy Brass Car; Locomotive; Machinery; Railway) ....AAAA
Remington Machine Co. (Brass) ....A
Speakman Supply & Pipe Co. (Brass) ....B
Wilmington Malleable Iron Co. (Semi-Steel; Steel; Malleable Iron) ....A

D. C.—Washington
Somerville & Sons, Thos. (Brass) ....A

GA.—Atlanta
Withers Foundry & Machine Works (Brass; Iron)...D

GA.—Augusta
Lombard Iron Works & Supply Co. (Iron; Bridge; Building) ....A

GA.—Savannah
Kehoe & Sons, Wm. (Brass; Grey Iron) ....A

GA.—West Point
West Point Iron Works (Brass; Iron) ....H

ILL.—Carpentersville
Illinois Iron & Bolt Co. (Wagon; Carriage) ..AA
Star Mfg. Co. (Steel Plow Shapes; Specialties) ...A

CASTINGS (Con.)

ILL.—Chicago
Acorn Brass Works, 193 Fulton (Brass) ....B
Adams & Westlake Co., Ontario & Franklin (Brass) ....AAA
Allen Mfg. Co., W. D., 151 Lake (Brass) ....B
Allis-Chalmers Co., Home Ins. Bldg. (Brass; Iron) ....AAAA
American Brake Shoe & Fdry. Co., Wesern Union Bldg. (Steel small 30 lbs. & under) ....A
American Bronze Fdry. Co., 73d & Woodlawn Av. (Brass; Bronze) ....D
American Steel Casting Co., 279 Dearborn (Steel, open hearth) ....AAAA
Anderson, A. H., 52 N. Ann (Aluminum; Brass; Bronze) ....F
Barbee Wire & Iron Works (Iron; German Silver; Phosphor Bronze; Zinc).B
Barnum & Richardson Mfg. Co., 64 S. Jefferson (Grey Iron) ....A
Bastian Mfg. Co., Chas. L., 76 Illinois (Brass) ......D
Burdett, Rowntree Co., 85 W. Jackson Boul. (Brass) C
Chicago Brass & Copper Works, Monadnock Bldg. (Brass; Copper) ....D
Chicago Hdw. Fdy. Co., 45 W. Washn. (Brass; Grey Iron) ....B
Chicago Malleable Castings Co., 120th & Centre Av. (Malleable Iron) X
Commonwealth Co. (Steel) ....AAA
Eddy Fdy. Co., R. M., 59 Ind. (Grey Iron; Boiler; Machinery; Grate, &c.) A
Edna Smelting & Refining Co., 60 Monadnock Blk. (Brass) ....B
Featherstone Fdy. & Machine Co., 348 Halsted (Grey Iron for Railroad use) ....AAA
Graham, John I., 104 S. Clinton (Brass) ....A
Griffin Wheel Co., Western Union Bldg. (Railroad) ....AAA
Harris & Bro., Geo. P., 64 Lake (Brass) ....B
Hewitt Mfg. Co., Monadnock Blk. (Brass) ....B
Hills, Robert E., 57 N. Wells (Brass) ....D
Illinois Malleable Iron Co., 30 W. Monroe (Brass; Grey Iron; Pipe Fittings) ....AAAA
Jones Fdy. & Machine Co., W. A., 143 W. North Av. (Electrical) ....A
King & Andrews Co., Chicago Heights (Steel, Light) ....A
Link Belt Machy. Co. (Machinery) ....A
McMaster-Davis Supply Co., 160 E. Lake (Brass) ...B
Massillon Iron & Steel Co., The Rookery (Roller Mill; Furnace; also Steel) ..A
National Car Coupler Co., Monadnock Blk. (Steel, open hearth) ....A
National Malleable Castings Co., 26th & Blue Island Av. (Railroad; Malleable Iron) ....AAAA
Pennsylvania Steel Co., 215 Dearborn (Steel) ..AAAA
Ryan & Co., J. J., 68 W. Monroe (Aluminum; Brass; Bronze; Copper; Manganese Bronze) C
Sargent Co. (Steel) ......D
Smeeth's Copper & Bronze Co., 20 N. Desplaines (Brass; Bronze; Copper) ....B
Smith Steel Casting Co.,

CASTINGS (*Con.*)

Geo. H., 40 Dearborn (Steel) C

Smith Wire & Iron Works, 100 Lake (Brass; Bronze) ....B

Sterion Copper & Bronze Co., 65 N. Ashland Av. (Brass; Bronze; Copper) ....D

Street & Kent, 43 Fulton (Brass) ....D

Tarrant Foundry Co., 46 Ind. (Grey Iron, Light & Heavy) C

Thomas Bros. Mfg. Co., Fillmore Av. (Brass).......D

Turner Brass Works, Franklin & Michigan (Aluminum; Brass; Bronze; Copper) ....D

U. S. Cast Iron Pipe & Fdy. Co., The Rookery (for Music Boxes; Graphophones, &c.) ....AAAA

Western Foundry, 3654 S. Albany Av. (Grey Iron).A

Western Iron & Steel Co., 40th & Union Av. (Grey Iron) ....B

Western Steel Car & Foundry Co., Old Colony Bldg. Railroad; Steel) .....AA

ILL.—East St. Louis

Missouri Malleable Iron Co. Malleable Carriage; Railroad; Street Car)....AA

ILL.—Edwardsville

Edwardsville Brass Co. (Brass; Copper) ......B

ILL.—Franklin Park

Forster, Waterbury & Co., (Grey; Malleable Iron).B

ILL.—Freeport

Arcade Mfg. Co. (Grey Iron, Light) ....A

Stover Mfg. Co. (Aluminum; Brass; Bronze; Grey Iron) ....AA

ILL.—Harvey

Buda Foundry Co. (Railroad) ....B

ILL.—Kewanee

Western Tube Co. (Gas; Steam; Water Ftgs.).AAA

ILL.—Litchfield

Litchfield Foundry & Machine Co. (Brass; Grey Iron) ....A

ILL.—Moline

Schmidt. Henry (Brass)...D

ILL.—Mt. Vernon

Mt. Vernon Car Mfg. Co. (Railroad Car) .....AAA

ILL.—Morris

Nickle Mfg. Co. (Grey Iron) C

ILL.—Peoria

Kinsley & Mohler Co. (Brass) ....B

ILL.—Quincy

Central Iron Wks. (Brass).B

Ellington Mfg. Co. (Grey; Refined; Malleable Iron) A

Van Doorn Co. (Brass)....D

ILL.—Rockford

Rockford Brass Works (Brass) ....D

Rockford Malleable Iron Wks. (Railroad; Machinery; Malleable) ....A

Weyburn & Briggs Co. (Agricultural Machinery) ..B

ILL.—St. Charles

Moline Malleable Iron Co. (Malleable Iron) X

ILL.—Sterling

Novelty Iron Wks. (Horse Stall Division) X

IND.—Anderson

Anderson Malleable Iron & Mfg. Works (Malleable Iron) C

IND.—Elkhart

Buescher Mfg. Co. (Aluminum) C

IND.—Ft. Wayne

Ft. Wayne Fdy. & Machine Co. (Railroad) C

IND.—Indianapolis

Dean Bros. Steam Pump Works (Brass) ....AA

Enterprise Fdy. & Fence Co., 366 S. Senate Av. (Grey Iron) C

CASTINGS (*Con.*)

Langsenkamp Bros. Brass Works (Brass) ....B

National Malleable Castings Co. (Malleable Iron) AAAA

Over, Ewald (Grey Iron; Sewer) ....D

IND.—Kokomo

Kokomo Brass & Iron Wks. (Brass; Iron) C

IND.—Logansport

Dorner Truck & Fdy. Co. (Brass; Iron) ....D

IND.—Marion

Marion Grey Iron Fdy. Co. (Grey Iron) ....D

Marion Malleable Iron Wks. (Malleable Iron) ......B

IND.—Montpelier

National Steel Castings Co. (Steel) ....B

IND.—Muncie

Whiteley Malleable Castings Co. (Agricultural; Railroad; Malleable) ....A

IND.—South Bend

South Bend Malleable Iron Co. (Malleable Iron) ..B

IND.—Terre Haute

Prox & Brinkman Mfg. Co. (Railroad) ....A

IOWA—Burlington

Murray Iron Works Co. (Iron) ....A

IOWA—Davenport

Davenport Fdy. & Machine Co. (Brass; Grey Iron)..B

IOWA—Des Moines

Des Moines Mfg. & Supply Co. (Brass) ....A

IOWA—Dubuque

Adams Co. (Stove; Grey Iron) ....A

Novelty Iron Wks. (Bridge; Bridge Pier; Building; Grey Iron; Engine) ...H

IOWA—Fort Madison

Ft. Madison Iron Works Co. (Railway) ....F

IOWA—Ottumwa

Ottumwa Iron Works (Engine) ....AA

KANS.—Fort Scott

Fort Scott Fdy. & Machine Co. (Chas. Eller, Prop.) (Grey Iron) ....H

KY.—Louisville

Ahrens & Ott Mfg. Co., 325 W. Main (Brass) ....AAA

Drummond Mfg. Co. (Iron) A

Howe Mfg. Co., 1107 W. Main (Brass) ....A

Vogt Machine Co., Henry, 327 E. Main (Brass).AAA

LA.—Monroe

Sanders, Jno. G. (Brass; Iron) ....D

LA.—New Orleans

Haubtman & Loeb Co., 317 Gravier (Brass) ....A

Moore's Brass Foundry, 835 Tchoup (Brass) ....A

Swoop, Julian A., 913 Girod (Gun Metal) ....A

MAINE—Bangor

Union Iron Works (Brass).A

MAINE—Bath

Bath Iron Wks. (Brass).AA

Torrey Roller Bushing Wks. (Brass) ....B

MAINE—Biddeford

Watson, Frye & Co. (Brass; Bronze; Railroad; Marine; Mill) ....D

MAINE—Camden

Knowlton Bros. (Brass)...B

MAINE—Dexter

Fay & Scott (Brass; Iron) C

MAINE—Mechanics Falls

Penney & Sons' Co., J. W. (Brass) ....B

MAINE—Portland

Megguier & Jones Co., 29 Pearl (Brass) ....B

Portland Co. (Brass; Bronze) ....AA

MD.—Baltimore

Baltimore Malleable Iron & Steel Casting Co. (Charles & Wells) (Grey Iron, Soft; Steel; Iron; Railroad; Machinery) .....A

CASTINGS (Con.)

Baltimore Shipbuilding & Dry Dock Co., Locust Point (Brass) ....B
Bartlett, Haywood & Co. (Gas Works; Bench)..B
Bates' Sons, James, Pratt & President (Architectural; Ornamental) ....A
Coale Bros. Mfg. Co., 1325 Guilford Av. (Brass)..D
Ellicott Machine Co., Bush & Severn (Grey Iron)....C
Gibson & Kirk, 45 Cheapside (Brass) ....D
Gisriel & Son, Wm., 1527 Guilford (Brass; Bronze) D
McShane Mfg. Co., H., 417 North (Brass) .....AAAA
Poole & Son, Robert, 233 E. German (Grey Iron; Gun Metal) ....B
Regester & Sons, J. (Brass; Rolling Mill; Furnace) AAAA
Ryan & McDonald Mfg. Co., 44 South (Brass) .....AA
Sinclair-Scott Co. (Light Grey Iron) ....E

MD.—Cumberland

Maryland Sheet & Steel Co. (Steel) C

MASS.—Boston

American Tool & Machine Co., 109 Beach (Brass; Lead) ....AA
Ashton Valve Co., 271 Franklin (Brass) .....A
Bay State Brass Fdy. Co., 155 A (Aluminum; Brass; Bronze; Phosphor Bronze) D
Boston Brass Co., 36 Oliver (Brass) ....D
D'Este, Julian Co. (Bronze; Brass) ....D
G. & P. Engraving Co., 185 Franklin (Brass; Copper) D
Granular Metal Co., Farnham & Gerard (Brass)..D
Gurney & Co., Jas. (Brass; Marine) ....D
Hall & Co., Wm., 82 Sudbury (Brass) C
Hamlin & Emery Brass Co., 26 Island (Brass) ....D
Laconia Car Co., 50 State (R a i l r o a d; Malleable; Electrical) ....AA

MASS.—Boston

Livermore, H. F., 85 Pearl (A l u m i n u m; Brass; Bronze; Steam Fitters'; Malleable Iron) C
McCafferty & Co., J. H., 434 Harrison Av. (Brass; Bronze) ....D
McGann, Thos. F., 104 Portland (Bronze) ....E
Magee Furnace Co. (Art) AA
Mechanics Iron Foundry Co. (Iron) C
Iron Corrosive Metal Co., 39 Pitts (Aluminum)......D
Murdock Corp. (Bronze).X
Star Brass Mfg. Co., 108 E. Dedham (Brass) ....A
Strater & Sons, Herman, 74 Sudbury (Brass) ....A
Sturtevant Co., B. F. (Bench Leg) ....AAA
Walworth Co., 128 Federal (Brass) C
Walworth Mfg. Co. (Brass; Iron) ....AAAA
Whittier Mach. Co. (Brass; Iron) ....A

MASS.—Bridgewater

Perkins Co., Hy. (Composition) ....E

MASS.—Chicopee

Ames Foundries (Bronze).F
Ames Sword Co. (Brass; Bridge Pier) ....B
Mosman, M. H. (Bronze).C

MASS.—Clinton

Clinton Foundry Co. (Brass; Iron) ....B

MASS.—Easton

Belcher Malleable Iron Co. (Malleable; Machinery;

CASTINGS (Con.)

Agricultural) C

MASS.—Fall River

Kilburn, Lincoln & Co.....A
Mechanics Fdy. & Machine Co., Davol (Brass) .....D

MASS.—Fitchburg

Goodnow Foundry Co., L. H. (Grey Iron) C
Hardy, Wm. A. (Brass; Bronze) ....B

MASS.—Haydenville

Haydenville Co. (Brass)...A

MASS.—Holyoke

Holyoke Machine Co. (Iron; Machinery) ....AA

MASS.—Lowell

Pevey Bros. (Brass; Bronze) C

MASS.—Newburyport

Russell & Sons, Albert (Ship) C

MASS.—Orange

Hunt Machine Co., Rodney (Brass) ....A

MASS.—Pittsfield

Jones & Sons, E. D. (Iron) B

MASS.—Quincy

Bay State Aluminum Co. (Aluminum; Brass) X

MASS.—Springfield

Bausch Machine Tool Co. (Iron) ....B
Emery Mfg. Co. (Brass)..C
Hawkins Iron Works, R. F. (Railway) C
Knox Automobile Co. (Brass Automobile) ....A
Stebbins Mfg. Co., E. (Brass) ....B
Springfield Fdy. Co. (Brass) A
Wason Mfg. Co. (Railroad) AA

MASS.—Taunton

Taunton Locomotive Mfg. Co. (Railroad) ....AA

MASS.—Webster

Prescott & Son, J. B. (Brass) C

MASS.—Westfield

Smith Co., H. B. (Iron).AA

MASS.—Worcester

Arcade Malleable Iron Co. (Iron; Steel, all kinds)..A
Worcester Malleable Iron Works (Malleable Iron; Steel) ....B

MICH.—Albion

Albion Malleable Iron Co. (Malleable; Agricultural; Carriage, &c.) ....B

MICH.—Battle Creek

Sherman Mfg. Co., H. B. (Brass) ....B

MICH.—Bay City

Smalley Bros. & Co. (Brass; Iron) ....B

MICH.—Detroit

Buckley-Hart Mfg. Co., 527 Franklin (Brass; Plumbers'; Bronze) ....D
Buhl Malleable Co., Wight & Adair (Grey; Malleable Iron) ....AAAA
Capitol Brass Works, 284 Rivard (Brass) ....D
Co-operative Foundry, Junction Av. & Wabash (Chemical Work) ....D
Detroit Brass Works, 1300 Brooklyn Av. (Brass)..B
Detroit Copper & Brass Rolling Mills. McKinstry Av. (Brass; Copper) .AAAA
Detroit Steel Castings Co., 124 Mich. Av. (Steel; Steel Dredge) ....B
Eagle Brass Works, 218 Elizabeth, E. (Brass) ..D
Essex Brass Co., G. B., 480 Franklin (Brass) C
Frontier Iron Works (Brass) X
Great Lakes Engineering Works, Rivard (Brass; Marine) ....A
Griffin Car Wheel Co. (Railroad) ....AAA
Ireland & Matthews (Aluminum; Brass; Bronze; Copper; Zinc) ....A
Leland & Faulconer Mfg. Co.

181

CASTINGS (Con.)

(Grey Iron) ....B
McRae & Roberts Co., 227
  Campbell (Brass) ......A
Michigan Malleable Iron Co.
  (Car; Carriage; Agricultural) ....AA
National Fulton Brass Mfg.
  Co. (Brass; Car; Locomotive; Bronze) ....AA
Olds Motor Works, Jefferson
  & Concord Avs. (Brass)
  ....AA
Russell Wheel & Fdy. Co.,
  Chene (Builders') .....A
Stephens, Roe Mfg. Co., McKinley Av. & G. T. Ry.
  (Brass) ....A
Sterling & Skinner Mfg. Co.,
  Russell c. E. Grand Boul.
  (Brass) C

MICH.—Grand Rapids

Grand Rapids Brass Co.
  (Brass; Bronze) ....A
Grand Rapids Malleable Co.
  (R. R., &c.) ....A
Rempes & Gallmeyer Fdy.
  Co. (Aluminum; Brass).B
Wolverine Brass Works
  (Brass) ....B

MICH.—Hancock

Portage Lake Fdy. & Machinery Co. (Brass)....B

MICH.—Jackson

Holton & Weatherwax
  (Aluminum; Brass) ....B

MICH.—Kalamazoo

Star Brass Wks. (Street
  Car) ....F

MICH.—Lansing

Lansing Boiler & Engine
  Works (Brass; Iron)....B

MICH.—Manistee

Manistee Iron Works (Railroad; Iron, &c.)........B

MICH.—Menominee

Prescott Co., D. Clint.
  (Grey Iron) ....B

MICH.—Muskegon

Standard Malleable Iron Co.
  (Malleable Agricultural)
  ....B

MICH.—Port Huron

Port Huron Malleable Iron
  Co. (Malleable Iron)....X

MICH.—Saginaw

Bartlett Co., A. F. (Brass)
  ....A

MICH.—Three Rivers

Sheffield Car Co. (Car; Railroad) ....AA

MICH.—West Detroit

Michigan Brass & Iron Wks.
  (Brass; Iron) ....A

MICH.—Ypsilanti

Michigan Mfg. Co. (Brass)
  ....AA

MINN.—Minneapolis

National Brass & Metal Co.,
  116 First Av. (Aluminum;
  Brass) C
Northwestern Foundry Co.
  (Railroad) ....A

MINN.—St. Paul

Helwig Mfg. Co. (Aluminum; Brass) ....F
Northwestern Copper &
  Brass Works (Brass; Copper) ....D
South Park Fdy. & Machine
  Co. (Brass) ....B
Valley Iron Works, Water
  & Livingstone Av. (for
  Musical Boxes; Graphophones, &c.) ....D

MO.—Kansas City

Crampton- Farley Brass Co.
  (Brass; Plumbers' Specialties) C
Kansas City Wire & Iron
  Works, 1428 Oak (Brass)
  ....B

MO.—St. Charles

St. Charles Car Co. (Car;
  Malleable Iron) X

MO.—St. Louis

American Brass Mfg. Co.,
  409 S. 2d (Aluminum;
  Brass; Bronze) ....D
American Car & Fdy. Co.
  (Railroad) ....AAAA
American Steel Foundries,
  318 N. 8th (Steel; Railroad. Heavy; Bastic, Open
  hearth) ....AAA

CASTINGS (Con.)

Garratt Brass Fdy. Co., J.
  W., 2028 Walnut (Brass)
  ....B
Green's Car Wheel Mfg. Co.,
  3018 N. B'way (Railroad;
  Locomotive; Rock Crusher) ....B
Keepferle Bros. Mfg. Co.,
  602 N. 2d (Brass)......A
Messmer Mfg. Co., Ferd.10
  S. B'way (Aluminum;
  Brass; Phosphor Bronze)
 C
More-Jones Brass & Metal
  Co., 3138 N. B'way.
  (Brass) ....A
Pleuger & Henger Mfg. Co.,
  11th & Herbert (Brass;
  Bronze; Copper; Grey
  Iron) ....A
St. Louis Car Wheel Co.,
  421 Olive (Railroad).AAA
St. Louis Iron & Machine
  Co. (Heavy Iron) ......A
St. Louis Iron & Steel Fdy.
  Co., 8th & Hickory (Steel)
  ....A
St. Louis Malleable Casting
  Co. (Malleable Iron)....A
Scullin-Gallagher Iron &
  Steel Co., Kraft (Steel,
  open hearth) ....AAA
Union Iron Fdy. Co., 1458 S.
  2d (Bronze) ....B

NEBR.—Lincoln

Smith, R. T. (Brass; Iron)
  ....D

NEBR.—Omaha

Paxton & Vierling Iron Wks.
  (Brass; Bridge; Iron;
  Water Works) ....A

N. H.—Concord

Ford & Kimball (Brass)..B

N. H.—Exeter

Exeter Brass Works (Brass)
  ....D

N. H.—Lakeport

Cole Mfg. Co. (Brass; Railroad) ....A

N. H.—Manchester

Varney, David B. (Est.)
  (Brass) C

N. H.—Penacook

Concord Axle Co. (Brass).B

N. J.—Belleville

Eastwood Wire Mfg. Co.
  (Brass; Bronze; Copper)
  ....A

N. J.—Burlington

McNeal Pipe & Fdy. Co.
  (Heavy Iron) ....AAA

N. J.—Camden

Fullmer & Co., A. J. (Brass)
  ....A
Voigt Metal Co. (Brass)..B

N. J.—Glen Ridge

Benson, H. K. & F. S.
  (Brass) C

N. J.—High Bridge

Taylor Iron & Steel Co.
  (Chrome Steel; Rock
  Crusher; Steel) ....AAAA

N. J.—Hoboken

New York Switch & Crossing
  Co. (Railroad) ....A
Union Iron Works (Brass)..C

N. J.—Jersey City

Atlantic Brass Wks. (Brass)
 C
Brady Brass Wks., 204 10th
  (Brass; Bronze) ....B
Columbia Iron Fdy., 42
  Morris (Marine) ......D
Krouse, George, 150 Morgan
  (Brass) C
Magnus Metal Co., 364 9th
  (Brass; Bronze) ....AAAA
Steele & Condit, Pearl &
  Steuben (Rock Crusher).C
Williams & Son, E. A., 105
  Plymouth (Aluminum;
  Brass; Bronze; Copper;
  Gun Metal; Manganese
  Bronze; Phosphor Bronze;
  Gong; Ship; Tin; Engine;
  Mchry.; Railroad) .AAA

N. J.—Mahwah

American Brake Shoe & Fdy.
  Co. (Grey Iron) .....AA

N. J.—Newark

Atha Steel Co. (Steel, machine moulded) ....A
Barlow, Arthur E. (Malle-

182

CASTINGS (Con.)
able Iron) ....D
Barrett & Co., Oscar E.
(Light & Medium Malle-
able Iron) C
Hewes & Phillips Iron Wks.
(Brass) ....A
Hodges & Bro., 10 R. R. Pl.
(Brass) C
Meeker, Stephen J. (Grey
Iron; Malleable Iron)...A
Sacks, Louis, Hamburg Pl.
& Av. L. (Grey Iron)..A
Watts-Campbell Co. (En-
gine) ....AA
N. J.—New Brunswick
New Jersey Lamp & Bronze
Works (Brass; Bronze)
AA
N. J.—Paterson
Eastwood Co., Benj. (Build-
ers' Iron) ....A
McNab & Harlin Mfg. Co.
(Brass) ....AA
Paterson Machine Works
(Light Iron) ....F
N. J.—Perth Amboy
Schantz & Eckert (Brass;
Iron) ....D
N. J.—Trenton
Crossley Mfg. Co. (Brass).B
Trenton Iron Co. (Br. N. Y.
City) (Wrought Iron).AA
N. Y.—Albany
Albany Foundry Co. (Grey
Iron) ....A
Albany Malleable Iron Wks.
(Railroad) ....AA
Angus, C. H. (Aluminum;
Brass; Bronze) ....D
Clark, John W. (Iron;
Brass; Bronze) C
Cox Brass Mfg. Co. (Brass)
C
Page's Sons, Isaiah (Rail-
road) ....A
Townsend Furnace Machine
Shop Co. (Grey Iron)...B
N. Y.—Auburn
Osborne & Co., D. M. (Malle-
able Iron) ....AAAA
N. Y.—Brooklyn
Chrome Steel Works, Kent
Av. & Keap (Chrome
Steel) ....AAA
Columbia Machine Wks. &
Malleable Iron Co., 169
Chestnut (Malleable Iron)
C
Hay-Budden Mfg. Co., 205
N. Henry (Steel) .....B
Hecla Iron Works, 11th &
Wythe Av. (Aluminum;
Bronze) ....AA
Taylor & Co., 415 Driggs
Av. (Brass) ....D
N. Y.—Buffalo
Abel, Geo. L., 18 Elk
(Aluminum; Brass;
Bronze; Copper) ....F
Bingham & Taylor, 575
Howard (Brass) .....AA
Buffalo Foundry Co. (Cupo-
la or Air Furnace; Grey
Iron) ....AA
Deck Bros., 20 Ind. (Brass)
C
Farrar & Trefts (Railway)
AAA
Lumen Bearing Co.. 1155
Sycamore (Brass; Bronze;
Aluminum; Copper; Man-
ganese; Phosphor Bronze)
D
New York Car Wheel Wks.
(Car; Locomotive) ...AA
Pratt & Letchworth Co.
(Railroad; Malleable;
Car; Locomotive; also
Steel) ....AAA
Sherwood Mfg. Co., 34
Washn. (Brass) ......B
Trout & Co., H. G. (Engine)
B
Zero Valve & Brass Mfg.
Co., 296 Seneca (Alumi-
num; Bronze) ....D
N. Y.—Cambridge
Lovejoy & Son, H. H. (Grey
Iron) C
N. Y.—Cohoes
Cohoes Iron Fdy. & Machine
Co. (Brass; Bronze; Grey
Iron; Iron) ....A

CASTINGS (Con.)
N. Y.—Copake Iron Works
Columbia Plow Wks.
(Chilled) ....AA
N. Y.—Corning
Allen Foundry Co., E. R.
(Architectural; Bench
Leg; Chair; School Desk;
Dynamo Motor; Furnace;
Iron; Grey Iron) C
N. Y.—Coxsackie
Newbury, J. G. (Grey Iron)
D
N. Y.—Depew
Gould Coupler Co. (Railroad;
Malleable) ....AA
N. Y.—Fishkill on Hudson
Fishkill Landing Machine
Co. (Brass; Iron) ......A
N. Y.—Glens Falls
Dix Foundry Co., J. L.
(Brass; Iron) ....D
N. Y.—Grassy Point
Wiles Co., A. M. & W. H.
(Brass; Iron) ....B
N. Y.—Hillburn
Ramapo Iron Works (Rail-
road) ....AAA
N. Y.—Hoosick Falls
Wood Mowing & Reaping
Machine Co., Walter A.
(Malleable Iron) ....AAA
N. Y.—Horseheads
Weller Hardware & Foundry
Co. (Grey Iron) ....D
N. Y.—Lancaster
Lancaster Malleable Iron
Wks. (Railroad; Malle-
able) ....A
N. Y.—Lockport
Holly Mfg. Co. (Brass; Iron)
D
N. Y.—Manlius
Cheney & Son, S. (Grey
Iron) ....A
N. Y.—Newburgh
Coldwell-Wilcox Co. (Brass)
B
Marvel & Co., T. S. (Brass)
B
Newburgh Ice Machine &
Engine Co. (Brass)....A
New York City
Allen & Co., Edgar, 51 John
(Manganese Steel; Steel)
B
Atlantic Brass Co., 192
B'way (Brass; Car, &c.)
B
Claudat & Son, Frank, 446
W. 16th (Bronze) .....D
Cornell Co., J. B. & J. M.,
26 11th Av. (Brass;
Bronze; Chemical Work)
AA
Crane Co., W. H., 1133
B'way (Grey Iron) ....A
Deeley & Co., Robt. (Heavy
Iron) ....AA
Drummond & Co., M. J., 182
B'way (Electrical) ....A
Eynon-Evans Mfg. Co., 120
Liberty (Brass; Bronze;
Copper; Manganese; Phos-
phor Bronze; Bronze)...B
Flagg & Co., Stanley G., 220
B'way (Steel) ....AAA
Floyds, James R. (Gas
Works) ....A
Gorham Mfg. Co., 19th &
B'way (Bronze) ....AAAA
Gould Steel Co., 25 W. 33d
(Steel) ....A
Henry-Bonnard Bronze Co.,
430 W. 16th (Bronze)..C
Jackson Co., Wm. H., 29 E.
17th (Bronze) ....A
Johnson & Co., Isaac G..
Spuyten Duyvil (Steel;
Malleable Iron) ......AA
Lehigh Foundry Co., 28
Broad (Grey Iron, light &
heavy) ....B
Manhattan Brass Co., 334
E. 28th (Brass; Bronze)
AA
Marine Engine & Machine
Co., 80 B'way (Marine).A
Mott Iron Works, J. L.
(Iron) ....AA
N. J. Foundry & Machine
Co., 15 Murray (Builders'
D

CASTINGS (Con.)

Sargent Co., 170 B'way (Steel) ....AAAA
Sheridan Co., T. W. & C. B. (Machinery) ....B
Shriver & Co., T., 333 E. 56th (Aluminum; Brass; Bronze; Copper; Gas Engine; Grey Iron; Gun Metal; Semi-Steel) ....A
Tiebout, W. J., 118 Chambers (Brass) ....B
Union Equipment & Bronze Co., 514 W. 36th (Bronze) ....E
Westervelt, A. B. & W. T. (Iron) ....B
Williams, John, 558 W. 27th (Bronze) ....B

N. Y.—Niagara Falls
Dobbie Fdy. & Machine Co. (Aluminum; Copper) ...B

N. Y.—North Tonawanda
Armitage-Herschell Co. (Canal Boat; Steam Barge; Planing; Saw Mill) ....A

N. Y.—Oriskany
Oriskany Malleable Iron Co. (Railroad; Malleable, light & heavy) ....B

N. Y.—Rochester
Enterprise Foundry Co., 48 Olean, (Bronze; Aluminum) ....B
Wray & Son, Henry, 195 Mill (Brass) ....B

N. Y.—Sandy Hill
Sandy Hill Iron & Brass Works (Brass; Iron)....A

N. Y.—Seneca Falls
Climax Specialty Co. (Brass) ....B

N. Y.—Syracuse
Central City Brass & Mfg. Co. 120 Burnet Av. (Brass) ....B
Economy Fdy. & Machine Co. (Grey Iron) ....B
Engelberg Huller Co., 121 W. Fayette (Brass; Grey Iron) X
Franklin Mfg. Co., H. H. (Aluminum; Franklin Metal) C
Frazer & Jones (Malleable Iron Sad; Agricultural; General) ....AA
Syracuse Malleable Iron Wks. (Malleable; Car, &c.) ....A

N. Y.—Troy
Gurley, W. & Lee (Brass) AA
Kemp & Son, Wm. (Brass; Bronze) ....AAA
Torrance Iron Co. (Malleable; Railroad; Stove)..C
Troy Malleable Iron Co. Malleable Track; Railroad; Electrical) ....A
West Side Foundry Co. (Brass; Copper; Railroad; Grey Iron) ....A

N. Y.—Utica
Blasier & Co., M. E. (Brass) D

N. Y.—Westmoreland
Westmoreland Malleable Iron Co. (Agricultural; Carriage; Sad, &c.)....C

N. Y.—West Troy
Empire Forge Co. (Light Grey Iron) ....F

OHIO—Akron
Adamson, Alex. (Brass)..C

OHIO—Canton
Best Street Light Co. (Brass; Bronze) ....B
Canton Malleable Iron Co. (Brass; Iron; Malleable; Saddlery) ....B
Canton Roll & Machine Co. (Rolling Mill; Furnace).B
Canton Saw Co. (Brass; Copper; Grey Iron; Steel)..D
Elbel Co. (Malleable; Saddlery; Hardware) ....B
McLain Co., Jas. H. (Brass) AA

OHIO—Cincinnati
American Copper & Brass Works, 614 E. Front (Brass; Copper) ....B
American Valve & Meter Co.

CASTINGS (Con.)

(Brass; Gun Metal; Phosphor Bronze) C
Bourbon, Copper & Brass Works, 618 E. Front (Brass; Copper) ......A
Deckebach's Sons Co., F. C., 123 W. Court (Brass)...B
Edna Smelting & Refining Co., 527 Hunt (Brass, light & heavy; Phosphor Bronze) ....B
Electric Railway Equipment Co., 431 E. Front (Brass) A
Enterprise Brass & Plating Works, Clark & Harriet (Brass) ....B
Eureka Foundry Co. (Grey Iron) ....A
Hauck Mfg. Co. (Bronze; Brass) ....D
Haven Malleable Castings Co., 68 Plum (Malleable; Carriage; Hardware)...B
Hesterburg & Co., R., Spg. Grove & Gerard Avs. (Brass) C
Hoefinghoff & Lane Fdy. Co. (Iron) ....A
Kinsley, J. R., 115 E. 6th (Brass) ....A
Kirkup & Co., 616 Lodge (Bronze; Brass) C
Knecht, Victor (Iron) ....B
Lunkenheimer Co., Beekman (Brass; Bronze; Phosphor Bronze; Gun Metal) .AA
McGowan Co., Jno. H., 54 Central Av. (Brass)....A
Messmer Co., Andrew, Patterson & Bank (Brass)..B
Mowry Car Wheel Works (Bridge; Car; Engine)..B
National Brass Mfg. Co., 216 W. Pearl (Brass; Copper) B
Newman-Kuhn Mfg. Co., 8th & McLean Av. (Brass)...B
Powell Co., Wm., 2525 Spg. Grove Av. (Brass)...AAA
Riegler-Hauck Co., 322 W. Pearl (Zinc) X
Schreiber & Sons Co., L., 8th & Eggleston Av. (Bronze) ....A
Tatum Co., Saml. C., 414 W. Water (Grey Iron Fine Castings) ....B
U. S. Aluminum Casting Co., 1623 Blue Rock (Aluminum; Automobile) C
Van Duzen Co., E. W., 428 E. 2d (Brass; Bronze; Gun Metal) C

OHIO—Cleveland
Acme Foundry Co. (Iron; Grey Iron) ....B
American Shipbuilding Co., 120 Viaduct (Aluminum) AAAA
Bowler Foundry Co., 14 Winter (Blast Furnace).A
Central Brass Foundry Co., 735 Cedar Av. (Brass)..C
Chisholm & Moore Mfg. Co., Lake & Kirtland (Automobile; Light Malleable; Smooth; Annealed) ...AA
Cleveland Steel Casting Co. Steel Heavy Open Hearth) A
Columbian Hdw. Co., Coe & Hamilton (Aluminum; Brass; Bronze; Copper; Tempered Copper for Commutation Bars) ....AA
Eberhard Mfg. Co. (Malleable Iron) ....AA
Farnan Brass Works, 25 Center (Brass) ....A
Forest City Brass Works, 90 Merwin (Brass) ....B
Forest City Electric Co., 111 Windsor Av. (Copper)...A
Forest City Hinge & Foundry Co. (Grey Iron, Small) A
Fulton Foundry Co. (Iron; Railway; Track) ......F
Glauber Brass Mfg. Co., 89 River (Brass) ....A
Hoffman Hinge & Foundry Co. (Grey Iron, Light)..B

Interstate Foundry Co.
(Grey Iron) ....B
Macbeth Iron Co., 57 W.
Center (Brass) C
Maher Wheel & Fdy. Co., 20
Carter (Railroad) ......B
Natl. Malleable Castings
Co. (Mal. Iron) ....AAAA
Ohio Foundry Co., Giddings
Av. (Brass & Grey Iron).A
Otis Steel Co., Lake & Law-
rence (Steel, 100 to 75,000
lbs.) ....AAAA
Palmers & De Mooy Found-
ry Co. (Iron) ....A
Riverside Fdy. Co., 26 Car-
ter (Railroad; Rolling
Mills; Furnace) ....A
Standard Brass Fdy Co.,
1155 Giddings Av. (Brass)
　　　　　　　　　　　B
Standard Fdy. & Mfg. Co.
(Grey Iron, Light; Hdw.
Specialties) ....A
Taylor & Boggis Fdy. Co.
(Grey & Light Iron)...AA
U. S. Bronze Co., 149 Col-
umbus (Brass; Bronze;
Phosphor Bronze) ......B
OHIO—Columbus
Buckeye Mal. Iron & Coup-
ler Co. (Mal. Car, &c.).A
Case Mfg. Co. (Bench Leg;
Pulley) ....A
Columbus Brass Co., 94 N.
6th (Brass)............B
Columbus Malleable & Grey
Iron Casting Co. ......B
OHIO—Dayton
Barney & Smith Car Co.
(Railroad) ....AAAA
Buckeye Iron & Brass Wks.
(Aluminum; Brass) ....A
Dayton Malleable Iron Co.
(Railroad; Malleable Car-
riage, &c.) ....A
Dayton Mfg. Co. (Brass)..A
OHIO—Defiance
Defiance Machine Works
(Iron) ....A
OHIO—Kenton
Champion Iron Co. (Grey
Iron) ....AA
OHIO—Lima
Lima Locomotive & Machine
Co. (Brass) ....AA
OHIO—Lorain
Lorain Foundry Co. (Alu-
minum; Brass; Bronze;
Copper Cupola or Air Fur-
nace; Rolling Mill; Fur-
nace) ....A
OHIO—Mansfield
Mansfield Tempered Copper
Co. (Aluminum; Brass;
Bronze; Copper; Phosphor
Bronze; Tempered Copper
for Commutation Bars).A
Ohio Brass Co. (Aluminum;
Brass; Bronze; Copper
Phosphor Bronze) ......B
OHIO—Marietta
Patton Bros. Co. (Brass;
Grey Iron) ....B
OHIO—Marion
Marion Malleable Iron Co.
(General) ....B
OHIO—Massillon
Massillon Iron & Steel Co.
(Blast Furnace) ....A
OHIO—Middleport
Ohio Machine Co. (Cupola or
Air Furnace; Rolling Mill;
Furnace) C
OHIO—Mt. Vernon
Cooper Co., C. & G. (Rolling
Mill; Furnace) ....AA
OHIO—Portsmouth
Portsmouth Steel Co. (Steel)
　　　　　　　　　　AA
OHIO—Sandusky
Klotz Machine Co. (Brass)
　　　　　　　　　　　B
Warren Electric Co. (Brass;
Bronze; Grey Iron)......A
OHIO—Springfield
Leffel & Co., Jas. (Phosphor
Bronze) ....AA
Nolte Brass Co. (Brass,
rough finished) ....D
Robbins & Myers Co. (Grey
Iron, light & medium)..B
Rogers Iron Co. (Grey Iron)
　　　　　　　　　　　C

Springfield Brass Co. (Alu-
minum; Brass; Bronze).D
Springfield Malleable Iron
Co. (General) ....A
Whiteley Machine Co. (Mal.
Agric.; Carriage; Car,
&c.) ....F
OHIO—Steubenville
Means Fdy. & Machine Co.
(Brass) ....B
OHIO—Toledo
Baker Bros. (Locomotive
Car) ....A
Natl. Malleable Castings Co.
　　　　　　　　　　AAAA
Vulcan Iron Works (Brass)
　　　　　　　　　　　A
Welks Foundry Co. (Grey
Iron, Heavy) C
OHIO—Warren
Trumbull Mfg. Co. (Auto-
mobile) C
OHIO—Youngstown
Falcon Bronze Co. (Brass;
Bronze) C
Mahoning Fdy. & Machine
Co. (Rolling Mill; Fur-
nace) C
Sennett Co., Geo. B. (Roll-
ing Mill; Furnace) .....A
Union Iron & Steel Co.
(Agricultural Machy.)..X
Youngstown Bronze Co.
(Brass; Bronze) ....D
Youngstown Engineering Co.
(Grey Iron) ....A
Youngstown Fdy. & Machine
Co. (Rolling Mill; Fur-
nace) C
Youngstown Steel Castings
Co. (Steel Open Hearth,
1 to 100,000 lbs. rough
machined) ....A
OHIO—Zanesville
Zanesville Malleable Iron
Co. C
OREGON—Albany
Albany Iron Works (Brass;
Iron) ....D
OREGON—Astoria
Astoria Iron Works (Brass;
Iron) ....A
OREGON—Portland
Columbia Engineering Wks.
(Brass) ....B
Honeyman & Co., J. (Brass;
Iron) ....D
Portland Iron Works (Brass;
Iron) C
Williamette Iron & Steel
Wks. (Brass; Iron; Steel)
　　　　　　　　　　　B
PA.—Allegheny
Carlins Sons, Thos. (Iron;
Sewer Manhole) ....A
Damascus Bronze Co., 928
South Av. (Brass; Bronze;
Phosphate) ....A
Natl. Gear Wheel & Fdy.
Co., South Av. (Rolling
Mill; Furnace) C
Pittsburg Lamp, Brass &
Glass Co., 3 River Av.
(Brass) ....AAAA
Rosendale Fdy. & Machine
Co., Washn. & Preble
(Railroad; Rolling Mill;
Furnace) ....B
PA.—Allentown
Allentown Fdy. & Mach.
Works Co. (Vacuum Pan)
　　　　　　　　　　　A
Allentown Rolling Mills
(Railroad) ....AAA
Weaver-Hirsch Co. (Grey
Iron) ....A
PA.—Avonmore
West Penn. Fdy. & Machine
Co. (Rolling Mill; Fur-
nace) ....B
PA.—Beaver Falls
Knott-Harken & Co. (Ma-
chinery) ....AA
PA.—Bellwood
Bellwood Mfg. Co. (Rail-
road Car) C
PA.—Birdsboro
Diamond Drill & Machine
Co. (Cupola; Air Furnace;
Steel; Steel Open Hearth)
　　　　　　　　　　　B

CASTINGS (Con.)

PA.—Bloomsburg
Bloomburg Car Co. (Railroad General) ....A

Harman & Hassert (Brass) A

PA.—Braddock
Braddock Machine & Mfg. Co. (Mill; Furnace)....B

PA.—Bradford
Caldwell & Co., E. R. (Railroad, up to 10,000 lbs.).B

PA.—Catasauqua
Davis & Thomas Co. (Railroad; Elect. Railroad).AA

PA.—Chester
American Steel Castings Co. (Nickel Steel; Steel Open Hearth, 1 to 40,000 lbs.) AAA

Chester Steel Casting Co. (Elect. Railroad; Rock Crusher; Steel) ...AAA

Crown Smelting Co. (Aluminum; Brass; Bronze; Copper; Gun Metal; Manganese Bronze; Marine; Phosphor Bronze) ....A

Johnston Railroad Frog & Switch Co. (Railroad)...B

Penn. Steel Casting & Machine Co. (Railroad; Steel) ....A

Seaboard Steel Casting Co. (Steel, up to 80,000 lbs.) AAA

Solid Steel Casting Co. (Steel; R. R.; Machine) AA

Wetherell & Co., R. (Steel) AAAA

PA.—Columbia
Columbia Grey Iron Co. (Grey Iron) C

PA.—Connellsville
Bovts. Porter & Co. (Brass; Iron) ....A

Connellsville Machine & Car Co. (Brass; Iron) ......B

PA.—Conshohocken
Bate & Son, Wm. S. (Brass) A

Wood, John, Jr. (Bronze; Brass) ....B

PA.—Corry
Ajax Iron Works (Brass; Iron) ....B

McInnes Steel Co. (Steel Tool) C

PA.—Danville
Curry & Vannan (Brass)..A

PA.—Du Bois
Du Bois Iron Works (Grey Iron) ....AAAA

PA.—Easton
Sterlingworth Railroad Supply Co. (Ref. Air Furnace) A

PA.—Eddystone
Eddystone Fdy. & Machine Co. (Cupola; Air Furnace; Rolling Mill; Furnace).A

PA.—Erie
Erie Malleable Iron Co....A

Griswold Mfg. Co. (Steam; Gas; Water) ......AAAA

Natl. Foundry Co. (Grey Iron) ....A

Walker Foundry Co. (Grey Iron) ....B

PA.—Franklin
Franklin Rolling Mill & Fdy. Co. (Steel) ......B

PA.—Freemansburg
Jones & Biscler Mfg. Co. (Aluminum; Brass; Bronze; Grey Iron).....D

PA.—Fullerton
Lehigh Car Wheel & Axle Wks. (Railroad).AAAA

Lehigh Foundry Co. (Culola; Air Furnace; Grey Iron; Railroad) ....A

PA.—Hanover
American Foundry & Machine Co. (Brass & Iron) C

PA.—Harrisburg
Hickok Mfg. Co., W. O. (Brass) ....AA

PA.—Hyde Park
Hyde Park Fdy. & Machine Co. (Rolling Mill; Furnace; Steel) ....B

CASTINGS (Con.)

PA.—Johnstown
Cambria Iron Works (Steel) B

PA.—Kutztown
Kutztown Foundry & Mach. Co. (Iron) ....A

PA.—Lancaster
Barry & Zecker (Brass; Iron) ....D

Hubley Mfg. Co. (Grey Iron Light) ....A

Martin Brick Machine Mfg. Co., Hy. (Iron) ....B

PA.—Lanesboro
Barnes Mfg. Co. (Iron)...B

PA.—Lansdale
Bancroft & Co. (Mal. Iron) X

PA.—Lebanon
Lebanon Boiler, Foundry & Machine Co. (Mill Machy.) C

Weimer Machine Wks. (Rolling Mill; Furnace) AA

PA.—McKees Rocks
Fort Pitt Mall. & Grey Iron Co. ....B

Penna. Malleable Co. (Mal. R. R. Castings) ....A

PA.—Meadville
Meadville Malleable Iron Co. (Railroad Mal. Iron)...B

PA.—Middletown
Middletown Car Works (Railroad) ....A

PA.—Mt. Joy
Grey Iron Casting Co. (Grey Iron) ....AA

PA.—Nazareth
Nazareth Fdy. & Machine Co. (Brass; Bronze; Grey Iron) ....B

PA.—New Castle
American Car & Ship Hdw. Mfg. Co. ((Brass; Bronze) B

Penn. Engineering Wks. (Rolling Mill; Furnace; Steel) ....A

Vulcan Fdy. & Machine Co. (Rolling Mill & Furnace) B

PA.—Norristown
Newbold & Son Co., R. R. (Rolling Mill; Furnace).A

PA.—Northeast
Eureka Tempered Copper Wks. (Brass; Bronze; Copper) ....B

PA.—Philadelphia
Ajax Metal Co., 46 Richmond (Brass) ....AA

Bancroft & Co., Drexel Bldg. (Brass; Bronze; Copper; Iron) X

Belfield & Co., 435 N. Broad (Brass; Bronze; Copper; Phosphor Bronze) AA

Bureau Bros. 21st & Allegheny Av. (Bronze) ....D

Chester Steel Castings Co., 407 Sansom (Electrical; Railroad; Rock Crusher; Steel; Steel Dredge; Sugar Mill) ....AAA

Cramp & Sons, Wm., Beach & Ball (Brass; Manganese Bronze; Marine;)..AAAA

Creswell Iron Works, S. J. (Iron) ....B

Devlin Mfg. Co., Thos., 3d & Lehigh Av. (Agric.; Brass; Carriage; Saddlery; Pipe, &c.) ....AAA

Evans & Son, S. W., 4623 Paul Fkd. (Brass)......A

Eynon-Evans Mfg. Co., 15 Clearfield (Aluminum; Brass) ....B

Flagg & Co., S. G., 424 N. 19th (R. R.: Machine; Hdw.; Pipe, &c.)...AAA

Gaumer & Co., Jno. L., 19th & Hamilton (Brass) C

Halstead & Co., 1129 Cherry (Aluminum; Brass; Bronze) ....D

Hill Mfg. Co., B. B., 1020 New Market (Brass)....B

Hooks Smelting Co. (Brass) A

CASTINGS (Con.)

Janney, Steinmetz & Co. (Aluminum) ....D
Keystone Brass Fdy. Co. (Brass) ....D
Latrobe Steel Co., Girard Bldg. (Steel) .....AAAA
Lonergan & Co., J. E., 211 Race (Brass) ....A
Merchant & Co., 517 Arch (Manganese Bronze; Phosphor Bronze) ....AA
Midvale Steel Co., Blabon & P. & R. R. R. (Ordnance; Railroad; Steel for Gun Carriage Mounts, &c.; Armor Piercing Shot & Shell) ....AAAA
Moore Machine & Fdy. Co., 2227 Wood (Aluminum; Grey; White; Semi-Steel; Alloy) C
Mousley & Sons, Charles, 457 N. 12th (Aluminum; Brass; Bronze) ....D
North American Smelting Co., 9th & Thompson (Brass) ....AA
North Bros. Mfg. Co. (Brass Light & Specialty).....A
Philadelphia Fdy. & Machine Co., 30th & Gray |Grey Iron, Daily Capacity, 40 Tons) ....B
Philadelphia Hdw. & Mal. Iron Wks. (Hdw.; Small) ....B
Philadelphia Roll & Machine Co., 23d & Wash. Av. (Cupola; Air Furnace; Gun Metal; Rolling Mill; Furnace) ....A
Philadelphia Steel & Iron Co., Frankford (Atlas Steel; Cupola; Air Furnace; Steel) ....B
Philadelphia Stove & Iron Fdy., 1625 N. 5th (Grey (Iron) ....B
Phoenix Bridge Co. (Bridge; Grey Iron) ....A
Phosphor Bronze Smelting Co., 220 Washn. Av. (Brass; Bronze; Phosphor Bronze) ....A
Reeves & Son, Paul S., 1415 Catherine (Aluminum; Bronze; Copper; Gun Metal; Manganese Bronze; Manganese Steel; Marine) ....B
Savill; Thos., 11th & Wood (Brass) C
Sharpless & Watts (Heavy Brass) ....B
Sheeler-Hemsher Co., 811 Fairmount Av. (Aluminum; Brass; Bronze; Copper) ....D
Southwark Foundry & Mach. Co. (Heavy Iron)....AAA
Standard Steel Wks., Harrison Bldg. (Steel Locomotive) ....AA
Sterlingworth Railway Supply Co., N. Amer. Bldg. Copper; Cupola; Air; Furnace) ....A
Swoyer Co., A. P., 17 N. 7th (Brass) ....A
Tacony Iron Co. (Grey Iron) ....A
Thompson & Co., J. (Special) ....B
Wharton & Co., Wm., Jr., 25th & Wash. Av. (Railroad & Steel) ......AAA
Wood & Co., R. D. (Gas Works) ....AAAA
Yocum & Son, James, 145 N. 2d (Brass) ....B
PA.—Phœnixville
Logan Mfg. Co. (Dynamo; Motor; Furnace; Lath).B
PA.—Pittsburg
American Fdy. & Construction Co. (Cupola; Air Furnace; Rolling Mill)....B
Bailey-Farrell Mfg. Co. (Aluminum; Brass; Bronze; Copper; Phosphor Bronze) ....AA
Best Mfg. Co., 25th & A. V. Ry. (Brass; Bronze; Copper; Climax Bronze; Gun Metal; Phosphor Bronze; Semi-Steel) ....A
Cadman Mfg. Co., Smallman (Aluminum, Brass; Bronze) ....D
Carnegie Steel Co., Ltd. (Iron) ....AAAA
Chaplin-Fulton Mfg. Co., 28 Penn. Av. (Brass)......A
Epping-Carpenter Co., 41st & A. V. Ry. (Brass; Bronze) ....A
Ft. Pitt Malleable & Grey Iron Co. ....B
Garrison Fdy. Co., A., So. 9th & Bingham (Rolling Mill; Furnace) .....AAA
Hogg Iron & Steel Fdy. Co., Geo. A., 24th & R. R. (Rolling Mill; Furnace Steel) ....A
Keystone Bronze Co., 20th & A. V. Ry. (Bronze)...C
Lewis Fdy. & Machine Co., 1001 Bingham (Rolling Mill; Furnace) ....A
McConway & Torley Co., 48th & A. V. R. R. (Steel Open Hearth; Mal. R. R.) ....AA
McKenna Bros. Brass Co., 1st Av. & Ross (Brass).A
Mackintosh, Hemphill & Co., ft. 12th (Rolling Mill; Furnace; also Steel).AAA
Mansfield Mfg. Co., 50 First Av. (Brass) ....B
Marshall Foundry, 28th & R. R. (Rolling Mill; Furnace) ....AA
Mesta Machine Co., Lewis Blk. (Rolling Mill; Furnace; also Steel)...AAA
Penna. Malleable Co. (Mal. R. R.) ....A
Pittsburg Brass Mfg. Co., 107 Wood (Aluminum; Brass; Copper) ....D
Pittsburg Malleable Iron Co. (Motor; R. R., &c.).B
Pittsburg Mfg. Co. (Iron).A
Pittsburg Steel Fdy., 541 Wood (Railroad; Steel) ....AA
Pittsburg Piping & Equipment Co., 35th (Brass; Bronze) ....B
Pittsburg Reduction Co. (Aluminum) ......AAAA
Pittsburg Valve Fdy. & Construction Co. Duquesne Way (Brass; Bronze; Grey Iron; Phosphor Bronze) ....AA
Sterritt Foundry Co., Thos., 32d & Smallman (Rolling Mill; Furnace) ....A
Union Fdy. & Machine Co. W. Carson (Railroad)...B
Union Steel Casting Co., 61st & A. V. R. R. (Steel)..B
Union Engineering & Fdy. Co., 5th & A. V. R. R. (Brass; Bronze; Steel) ....AAAA
U. S. Aluminum Co. (Aluminum) ....B
Velte Fdy. & Machine Co., Home & A. V. R. R. (Rolling Mill; Furnace).C
Yagle & Co., Wm., 400 32d (Rolling Mill; Furnace Runners; Fountains; Sprue Plates. &c.) C
PA.—Reading
Connard, Henry (Brass)..C
Johnston Fdy. & Machine Co. (Rolling Mill; Furnace) ....B
(Brass; Iron) ....A
Natl. Brass & Iron Wks. (Brass; Iron) ....A
Reading Foundry Co. (Special) ....B
Reading Iron Co. (Rolling Mill; Furnace) .....AAA
PA.—Scottdale
Kenny & Co. (Iron) .....A
PA.—Scranton
Everhart Brass Works (Aluminum; Brass) ....A
McClave-Brooks Co. (Brass)

187

A

Scranton Steam Pump Co.
(Brass) ....B
PA.—Sharon
Natl Malleable Casting Co.
(Steel Open Hearth; R.
R. Castings; Motor Gear
Blks.) ....AAAA
Sharon Foundry Co. (Rolling
Mill; Furnace) ....AA
PA.—South Bethlehem
Bethlehem Fdy. & Machine
Co. (Chemical Work; Ma-
rine) C
Bethlehem Steel Co. (Rail-
road; Iron; Steel)..AAAA
PA.—Steelton
Pennsylvania Steel Co.
(Street Railway Tracks)
AAAA
PA.—Tamaqua
Tamaqua Mfg. Co. (Iron;
Stove) ....B
PA.—Tatamy
Messinger Mfg. Co. (Grey
Iron) ....B
Burley Heater Co. (Grey
Iron) ....D
PA.—Tyrone
Tyrone Fdy. & Machine Co.
(Railroad; Rolling Mill;
Furnace) C
PA.—Warren
Allegheny Foundry Co.
(Semi-Steel) ....E
Jacobson Machine Mfg. Co.
(Brass & Iron).........B
PA.—Wilkesbarre
Vulcan Iron Wks. (Brass;
Bridge; Bridge Pier;
Building; Copper; Heavy
Grey; Malleable Iron; Gun
Metal; Heavy Iron; Mill;
Saw Mill; Store Front;
Bronze; Car; Engine; Lo-
comotive; Machinery;
Railway) ....AAAA
PA.—Williamsport
Darling Pump & Mfg. Co.
(Brass; Bronze; Phosphor
Bronze) .... B
Valley Iron Works (Brass;
Bronze; Castings for Musi-
cal Boxes, &c.) ....A
PA.—Wrightsville
Susquehanna Casting Co.
(Grey Iron, light).....AA
PA.—York
Norway Iron & Steel Co.
(Iron; Steel; up to 500
lbs; Light Malleable Iron)
A
York Mfg. Co. (Grey Iron;
Gun Metal) ....AA
R. I.—Hills Grove
Rhode Island Malleable Iron
Wks. (Mal. Iron).......B
R. I.—Providence
Brown & Sharpe Mfg. Co.
(Iron; Bench Leg).AAAA
Builders Iron Foundry
(Brass; Iron) ......AAA
Carpenter & Sons Fdy. Co.,
A. (Grey Iron) ....B
Franklin Machine Co. (Mill)
A
Fuller, Frederick (Brass;
Bronze) ....A
Harris Steam Engine Co.,
Wm. A. (Brass; Iron)..B
Providence Aluminum Co..F
White, Stillman (Brass)..B
S. C.—Spartanburg
Morgan Iron Works (Iron)
C
TENN.—Chattanooga
Chattanooga Car & Fdy. Co.
(Bronze; Brass) ....A
Ornamental Iron & Wire Co.
(Brass; Iron) ....D
Southern Malleable Iron Co.
(Railroad; Machy., &c.)
A
TENN.—Jackson
Southern Engine & Boiler
Co. (Brass; Iron;
Bronze) ....B
TENN.—Memphis
Chickasaw Iron Works
(Brass; Bridge; Railway)
C
Livermore Fdy. & Mach. Co.
(Brass; Iron) ....A

TEXAS—Dallas
Moser Mfg. Co. (Brass)..C
TEXAS—El Paso
El Paso Foundry & Mach.
Co. (Iron) ....A
TEXAS—Fort Worth
Midland Brass Works (Alu-
minum; Brass; Bronze;
Copper) ....D
TEXAS—Houston
Dixon Car Wheel Co. (Rail-
road Car; Engines, &c.).A
VT.—Bellows Falls
Bellows Falls Machine Co.
(Brass) ....B
VT.—Burlington
Lang & Goodhue Mfg. Co.
(Brass) ....B
VA.—Lynchburg
Glamorgan Pipe & Foundry
Co. (Special) ....A
VA.—Norfolk
Edmunds, Walker (Brass).D
Whitehurst Co., R. W.
(Agricultural Machy.)..B
VA.—Petersburg
Petersburg Iron Works Co.
(Marine) ....D
VA.—Pulaski
Doe Fdy., Car Wheel & Mo-
chine Co. (Brass) ..AAAA
WASH.—Spokane
National Iron Works (Brass;
Railroad) C
WASH.—Whatcom
Puget Sound Iron & Steel
Wks. (Brass; Iron; Steel)
B
W. VA.—New Cumberland
Davis-Price Fdy. & Machine
Co. (Brass) C
W. VA.—Wheeling
Portsmouth Steel Co. (Steel)
AA
Wheeling Mold & Fdy. Co.
(Railroad; Rolling Mill;
Furnace) ....A
WIS.—Beaver Dam
Beaver Dam Mal. Iron Co.
(Iron) ....B
WIS.—Corliss
Brown-Corliss Engine Co.
(Rolling Mill; Furnace)
AA
WIS.—Cudahy
Power & Mining Machy. Co.
(Grey Iron; Phosphor
Bronze; Rock Crusher;
Semi-Steel; Steel)....AA
WIS.—Kenosha
Badger Brass Mfg. Co.
(Brass) ....B
WIS.—Milwaukee
Bayley & Sons Co., Wm.
(Iron) ....A
Christensen Engineering Co.
Park Pl. (Brass; Bronze)
A
Dutcher & Co., J. A. & P.
E., (Steel) ....B
Falk Co. (Railroad)......A
Filer & Stowell Co. (Iron)
AAA
Hewitt Mfg. Co., 241 Green-
field Av. (Brass) ......A
Hoffman & Billings Co., 96
2d (Brass) ....AA
Milwaukee Mal. & Grey
Iron Wks. ....D
North Western Mal. Iron
Co. (Agric.; Car, &c.).AA
Shaw Gerlinger Steel Cast-
ing Co. (Steel Crucible).C
Shaw Steel Casting Co.,, 128
S. Bay (Steel) ....B
Sheriffs Mfg. Co. (Brass;
Iron) ....B
Western Mal. & Grey Iron
Co., 139 Burrell C
Wisconsin Malleable Iron
Co. (Railroad)..........A
WIS.—Racine
Belle City Malleable Iron
Co. (Carriage, &c)....B
Dickey Mfg. Co., A. P.
(Grey Iron) ....E
Lakeside Malleable Iron Co.
B
Racine Malleable Wrought
Iron Co. (Wagon, &c.)..A
Rowland, John T. (Brass;
Copper) ....D
WIS.—South Milwaukee
Stowell Mfg. & Fdy. Co.

CASTINGS (Con.)
(Light Iron for all purposes) ....A
WIS.—Waukesha
Waukesha Mal. Iron Co.
(Implements, &c.)......B

CASTS
ILL.—Chicago
Dietzgen Co., Eugene (Artists') ....A
MICH.—St. Johns
St. Johns Iron Wks. (Expansion) ....E
New York City
Bergers' Sons (Plaster; Composition) ....E
Castelvecchi & Co., L., 225 4th Av. (Bronze; Plaster; Artists') ....D
OHIO—Cleveland
Francis Statuary Co. (Plaster) ....D

CATALOGUES
New York City
Thomas Press, 18-20 Rose (Trade, &c.) ....A

CATAPULTS
CONN.—New Haven
Seamless Rubber Co. ....AA

CATCHERS
CONN.—New Haven
New Haven Car Register Co. (Trolley Pole).....X
ILL.—Decatur
Chambers-Bering-Quinlan Co. (Hog.) ....A
MINN.—Minneapolis
Minn. Beekeeper's Supply Mfg. Co. (Swarm) X
N. Y.—Brooklyn
Wilson & Co., 313 Fulton (Trolley Pole) X
N. Y.—Syracuse
Stearns & Co., E. C. (Trolley Pole) ....AA
OHIO—Akron
Whitman & Barnes Mfg. Co. (Grass) ....AAAA
OHIO—Canton
Ney Mfg. Co. (Grass) ....B
OHIO—Cleveland
Taylor & Bogges Fdy. Co. (Mail) ....AA
PA.—Philadelphia
Enterprise Mfg. Co. (Grass) ....AAAA
Philadelphia Lawn Mower Co., 3100 Chestnut (Grass) ....B
Supplee Hdware. Co. (Grass) ....AA

CATCHES
CONN.—Bridgeport
Gaynor & Mitchell Mfg. Co. (Screen Door) ....D
CONN.—Bristol
Sessions & Son. J. H. (Trunk) ....AAA
CONN.—New Haven
Mallory, Wheeler Co. (Cupboard) ....AA
Sargent & Co. (Cupboard; Screen Door; Refrigerator; Elbow; Showcase; Transom; Window) ....AAAA
CONN.—Stamford
Yale & Towne Mfg. Co. (Cupboard; Screen Door; Transom; Elbow) ..AAAA
ILL.—Freeport
Arcade Mfg. Co. (Refrigerator) ....B
ILL.—Rockford
Sovereign, C. E. (End Gate) C
MICH.—Grand Rapids
Grand Rapids Brass Co. (Door) ....A
Hardware Supply Co. (Door) ....F
N. Y.—Manlins
Cheney & Son. S. (Barn Door) ....A
New York City
Ludwig. A., 75 Spring (Box) ....B
Peck, Stow & Wilcox Co..

CATCHES (Con.)
27 Murray (Cupboard; Screen Door; Transom) ....AAAA
Russell & Erwin Mfg. Co., 43 Chambers (Cupboard; Elbow; Screen Door; Transom; Window) ....AAAA
N. Y.—Rochester
Caldwell Mfg. Co. (Window) ....E
OHIO—Canton
Ney Mfg. Co. (Door; Elbow) ....B
OHIO—Cincinnati
Gebhardt Bros., Lion Bldg. (Safety for Lapel Buttons) C
OHIO—Cleveland
Universal Fastener Co. (Cupboard; Door; Window) .F
OHIO—Ravenna
Williams, A. C. (Barn Door) ....A
PA.—Lancaster
National Mfg. Co. (Cupboard; Screen Door) ..D
PA.—Philadelphia
Schoenhut & Co., A. (Cigar; Plush Box) X
PA.—Reading
Chantrell Tool Co. (Cupboard) ....B
Reading Hardware Co. (Cupboard; Elbow; Screen Door; Showcase; Transom; Window) .....AAA
R. I.—Providence
Wall & Co., A. F. (Jewelry) C

CATGUT
N. J.—Paterson
Dempwolf, Chas. Jr.......X

CATHETERS
IND.—Indianapolis
Armstrong & Co., Wm. H. (Rubber) ....B
MASS.—Andover
Tyer Rubber Co. (Rubber) AA
New York City
Johnson & Johnson, 100 William (Rubber) .....B
Parker, Stearns & Sutton (Rubber) ....B
OHIO—Akron
Akron Rubber Wks. (B. F. Goodrich Co., Prop.) (Rubber) ....AAAA
Faultless Rubber Co. (Rubber) ....AA
Miller Rubber Mfg. Co. (Rubber) ....B

CATSUP
See Condiments

CAUSTIC
N. Y.—Syracuse
Solvay Process Co. (Alkali) ....AAAA

CAVIAR
See Fish

CEDAR
See Lumber

CEILINGS
DEL.—Wilmington
McCullough Iron Co. (Iron; Steel) ....AA
GA.—Savannah
Southern Pine Co. (Yellow Pine) ....AAA
ILL.—Chicago
Friedley & Voshardt. 196 Mather (Sheet Steel) .C
Illinois Malleable Iron Co. (Plate) ....AA
Moore & Co., E. B. (Parquet) ....D
Wallace Supply Co., 169 Jackson Boul. (Car)...D
LA.—Lake Charles
Bradley-Ramsey Lumber Co. (Yellow Pine) ...AAAA
MINN.—St. Paul
St. Paul Roofing Cornice &

CEILINGS (Con.)

Ornament Co. (Sheet Steel) ....B
MINN.—Winona
Doud Sons & Co. (Bead) .C
MO.—St. Louis
Harry Steel Wks., O. K. (Steel) ....B
Meska & Bro. (Metal) .AA
Souther Iron Co., E. E., 2206 N. 2nd (Sheet Steel) ..B
N. J.—Harrison
Bowers Mfg. Co. (Car) ...X
N. J.—New Orange
American Veneer Co. (Car) ....D
N. Y.—Binghamton
Roberson & Son, A. (Wood) ....AA
N. Y.—Brooklyn
American Metal Ceilings Co., 215 Montague (Sheet Steel) ....F
Brooklyn Metal Ceiling Co., 283 Greene Av. (Sheet Steel) ....E
New York City
Coburn & Dodge, 244 Water (Mfrs. Agt. Sheet Steel) .F
Denzi & Phillips, 24 Dey (Marbleized Glass) ...C
Frost Veneer Seating Co., 206 Canal (Car) ......AA
Lyle & Mills Metal Ceiling Co., 231 William (Sheet Steel) ....F
Manhattan Glass Tile Co., 157 10th Av. (Marbleized Glass) ....D
Mansfield & Co., 158 Chambers (Marbleized Glass) .F
Moseley Iron Bridge & Roof Co., 39 Cortlandt (Iron; Steel) ....B
N. Y. Metal Ceiling Co., 537 W. 24th (Sheet Steel) ..A
Northrop, H. S., 40 Cherry (Sheet Steel) ....B
OHIO—Cambridge
Cambridge Roofing Co. (Sheet Steel) ....B
OHIO—Canton
Berger Mfg. Co. (Sheet Steel; Metal; Iron) ..AA
Canton Steel Roofing Co. (Sheet Steel; Metal; Iron; Steel) ....A
Eller & Co., J. H. (Sheet Steel) ....A
Kanneberg Roofing & Ceiling Co. (Sheet Steel) ..C
OHIO—Cincinnati
Hyndmann Steel Roofing Co. (Corrugated) C
OHIO—Cleveland
Garry Iron & Steel Co. (Metal; Iron; Steel) ..A
OHIO—Columbus
Kinnear & Gayer Co. (Sheet Iron; Steel) ....A
OHIO—Forest
Dickelman Mfg. Co. (Sheet Steel) ....B
OHIO—Martins' Ferry
Acme Sheet Metal Co. (Sheet Steel) ....D
OHIO—Middletown
American Steel Roofing Co. (Sheet Steel) ....AA
OHIO—Niles
Sheet Metal Mfg. Co. (Sheet Steel) ....B
OHIO—Salem
Millins, W. H. (Steel; Zinc) ....A
OHIO—Youngstown
Youngstown Iron Sheet & Tube Co. (Iron; Steel) ....AAAA
Youngstown Iron & Steel Roofing Co. (Iron; Steel) ....AA
PA.—McKeesport
Encaustique Metal Interior Co. (Sheet Steel) X
PA.—Philadelphia
Cortright Metal Roofing Co. (Metal) ....B
Gara, McGinley & Co. (Metal; Steel) ....A
Penn. Metal Ceiling & Roofing Co. (Sheet Steel) ....D
Wood Alan Iron & Steel Co. 519 Arch (Iron; Steel) ....AAAA

CEILINGS (Con.)

PA.—Pittsburg
Goff, Horner & Co. (Iron; Steel) ....A
Iron City Metal Ceiling Co., Schmidt Bldg. (Sheet Steel) ....E
Keigley Metal Ceiling & Mfg. Co., S. Locust & Chestnut (Sheet Steel; Iron) ....D
Scaife & Sons Co., Wm. B. 221 1st Av. (Sheet Steel; Iron; Steel; Metal) ....AAA
PA.—Reading
Reading Terra-Cotta & Stove Lining Wks. (Terra-Cotta) C
PA.—Rochester
Miller & Sons Co., Wm. (Wood) ....A
W. VA.—Wheeling
Laughlin Nail Co. (Sheet Steel) ....AA
West Virginia Steel Co. (Sheet Steel) ....A
Wheeling Corrugating Co. (Sheet Steel; Corrugated; Embossed Steel; Metal) ....AAAA
WIS.—Milwaukee
Milwaukee Corrugating Co. (Sheet Steel) ....A
WIS.—Sheboygan
Frosts' Veneer Seating Co. (Car) ....B

CELLARETTES
See Furniture

CELLS

ILL.—Chicago
Smith Wire & Iron Works (Jail) ....AA
MASS.—Boston
New England Pottery Co. (Battery; Filter) C
MICH.—Detroit
Barnum, E. T. (Jail) ....B
Bolles Iron & Wire Wks., J. E. (Jail) ....D
N. J.—Jersey City
Eastern Carbon Wks. (Cylinder) ....A
N. J.—Salem
Salem Glass Wks. (Battery) ....B
New York City
Edison Phnograph Agency (Battery) ....D
Gordon Battery Co. (Battery) ....D
OHIO—Akron
Goodrich Co., B. F. (Battery) ....AAAA
OHIO—Bellaire
Rodefer Bros. (Battery) .A
OHIO—Canton
Diebold Safe & Lock Co. (Jail) ....AAA
OHIO—Cincinnati
Stewart Iron Works (Jail) ....A
OHIO—Cleveland
National Carbon Co. (Battery) ....AAAA
Van Dorn Iron Wks. Co. (Jail) ....AA
OHIO—Springfield
Rogers Iron Co. (Jail) ..B
TENN.—Chattanooga
Ornamental Iron Wks. Co. (Jail) X

CELLULOID GOODS

MASS.—Athol
Wilcox, Joseph...........D
MASS.—Leominster
Blodgett & Co., B. F. .....B
Columbia Comb Co. (Combs) X
Damon Co. ....B
Earl & Co., W. D. (Combs) C
Goodale Comb Co. (Combs) X
Howe Comb Co. (Combs) D
Kingman & Co., E. B. ....B
Leominster Button Co. (Buttons) ....D

CELLULOID GOODS

Leominster Comb Co.
(Combs) ....D
Newton & Merriman
(Combs) ....D
Paton Mfg. Co. (Combs)..B
Pickering-Metcalf Co.
(Combs) C
Tenney & Porter (Combs) C
Tillon & Cook ....E
Union Mfg. Co. ....E
Williams & Winn Co......D
MASS.—Newburyport .
Richardson Co., G. W.
(Combs) ....D
N. J.—Newark
Celluloid Co. ....B
Newark Tortoiseshell Nov-
elty Co. ....D
Whitehead & Hoag Co. AAA
N. Y.—Rochester
Pulver Co., F. F. (Adver-
tising Novelties) ......B

CEMENT

ALA.—Birmingham
Southern Cement Co.
(Portland; Hydraulic)..A
ALA.—Demopolis
Alabama Portland Cement
Co. (Ltd.) (Portland).A
ARK.—White Cliffs
Southwestern Portland Ce-
ment Co. (Portland)....A
CAL.—Los Angeles
Balfour-Guthrie & Co. (Bel-
gian; English) ....AAAA
California Portland Cement
Co. (Portland) ....A
CAL.—San Francisco
California Anti-Caloric Co.
(Furnace; Stove)......E
Cowell & Co., Henry
(Hydraulic) ....AAA
Pacific Portland Cement Co.
(Portland) ....A
Spreckles Bros. Co., J. D.
(Importers English)AAAA
COLO.—Portland
Portland Cement Co. (Port)
A
CONN.—Bethel
Shepard & Co., Geo. A.
(Rubber) ....F
CONN.—Derby
Clark Cast Steel Cement Co.
(Iron; Steel Castings) ..G
CONN.—Hartford
Hartford Rubber Wks. Co.
(Rubber) ....AAAA
Jewell Belting Co. (Belt)
AAA
CONN.—Shelton
Clark & Co., D. N. (Cast
Steel) C
GA.—Atlanta
Southern Roofing Mfg. Co.
(Fibrous Asbestos)......D
Southern States Portland
Cement Co. (Portland)..A
GA.—Savannah
Hanley Co., Andrew (Im-
porters Belgian; English)
A
ILL.—Chicago
Chicago Asbestos Mfg. Co.,
96 W. Lake (Asbestos) E
Chicago Fire Proof Covering
Co., 18 N. Canal (Asbes-
tos; Furnace; Stove; Roof-
ing) ....A
Chicago Portland Cement Co.
(Portland) ....A
Crane Co. (Pipe Joint;
Steamfitters') ....AAAA
Excelsior Steel Furnace Co.,
40 W. Monroe (Asbestos)
A
German American Portland
Cement Works ....A
Gumbo Cement Co., 86 N.
Clark (Pipe Joint)....F
Illinois Steel Co. (Cement
Dept.) (Puzzolan)..AAAA
Martell Co. (Leather; Rub-
ber) ....E
Morgan & Wright (Inc.) 333
W. Lake (Brush; Shoe;
Steel; Rubber) ......AA
Munson Belting Co., Chas.
(Belt) ....B
Rosenthal Mfg. Co. (Jewel-
ers) X
Sall Mountain Asbestos Co.,
123 Ontario (Asbestos).F

CEMENT (Con.)

Spinks & Co., Wm. A. 3 N.
Clark (Billiard Cue Tip) A
ILL.—Rockland
Lewis Roofing Co. (Asphalt)
B
ILL.—Utica
Utica Cement Mfg. Co.
(Nat. Hyd.) ...'....A
Utica Hydraulic Cement Co.
(Nat. Hyd.) ....A
IND.—Evansville
Ellert. C. H. (Leather;
(Rubber) X
IND.—Jeffersonville
Kentucky & Indiana Cement
Co. (Hyd.) ....A
IND.—Lafayette
Boyle Mfg. Co. (Roofing).D
KANS.—Iola
Iola Portland Cement Co.
(Port.) ....AAAA
Kansas Portland Cement Co.
(Port.) ....A
KY.—Louisville
Louisville Cement Co. (Nat.
Hyd.) ....A
Union Cement & Lime Co.
(Nat. Hyd.) ....A
MD.—Baltimore
Baltimore Roofing & Coal
Tar Co., 1211 Leaderhall
(Roofing) ....F
Baltimore Terra-Cotta Wks.
(Fire) ....B
Clarke, Wirt & Son (Im-
porters English) ......F
McCormick & Co. (Glass;
Crockery) ....D
Maryland Cement Co.
(Port.; Hyd.) ....A
Maryland Lime & Cement
Co., 217 Borolys Whf.
(Imp. Belgian; English)
A
National Building Supply
Co., Lex. & North (Imp.
Belgian; English; Ger-
man) ....B
MD.—Cumberland
Cumberland Hyd. Cement &
Mfg. Co. (Hyd.) ....A
MD.—Hancock
Round Top Hyd. Cement Co.
(Hyd.) ....A
MASS.—Boston
Boston Belting Co., 256 Dev-
onshire (Rubber) .AAAA
Golding & Co. (Binders';
Printers') ....B
Hauthaway, C. L. (Rubber)
A
Trainer Mfg. Co., C. W., 89
Pearl (Furnace; Stove).E
Waldo Bros. (Importers Bel-
gian; English; German)
AAA
Warren Bros. Co., 93 Fed-
eral (Asphalt; Roofing)
AA
Wheeler, Asabel, 53 High
(Pipe Joint) C
MASS.—Cambridgeport
Pursell, Hycent, 441 Main
(Original Elastic; Original
Roofing) ....D
Webster, W. F. (Elastic;
Roofing) C
MASS.—Gloucester
Russia Cement Co. (Belt).A
MASS.—Newburyport
Victor Mfg. Co. (Elastic;
Roofing) ....E
MASS.—Swampscott
Para Rubber Cement Co.
(Rubber) ....B
MASS.—Taunton
Presbrey Fire Brick Wks.
(Fire) ....F
Union Stove Lining Co.
(Fire) C
Williams Stove Lining Co.
(Furnace; Stove).......B
MASS.—Worcester
Algonquin Red State Co., 10
E. Worcester (Elastic;
Roofing) ....B
Desper. Henry A. (Pipe
Joint) ....F
MICH.—Alpena
Alpena Portland Cement Co.
(Port.) ....A
MICH.—Bronson
Bronson Port. Cement Co.
(Port) ....A

CEMENT (*Con.*)

MICH.—Coldwater
Wolverine Port. Cement Co.
(Port.) ....AAA
MICH.—Detroit
Detroit White Lead Works
(Rubber) ....AAA
Great Northern Cement Co.
(Port.) ....A
Wabash Portland Cement Co.
(Port.) ....A
MICH.—Elk Rapids
Elk Rapids Port. Cement Co.
(Port.) ....AAA
MICH.—Jackson
Peninsular Portland Cement
Co. (Port.) ....A
MICH.—Jonesville
Omega Portland Cement Co.
(Port.) ....A
MICH.—Newaygo
Newaygo Portland Cement
Co. (Portland) ....A
MICH.—Saginaw
United States Graphite Co.
(Pipe Joint).........AAA
Wickes Bros. (Machinery)
AAA
MICH.—Union City
Peerless Portland Cement
Co. (Port.) ....A
Silexoid Portland Cement
Co. (Portland) ....A
MINN.—Minneapolis
Maire Paint Co., 241 1st
Av. (Elastic Roofing; all
minerals) ....F
Nott Co., W. S. (Asbestos)
AA
MINN.—Winona
Union Fibre Co. (Asbestos)
B
MO.—Kansas City
Midland Asbestos Mfg. Co.
Asbestos; Stove; Fur-
nace) ....E
MO.—St. Louis
Amer. Insulating Material
Mfg. Co., 213 N. 3d (Gran-
ite Rock; Asphalt Roof-
ing) ....B
Asphalt Roofing Co. (As-
phalt Roofing) X
Nolde Dental Mfg. Co., J.
T. (Dental) C
St. Louis Portland Cement
Co. (Portland) ....AAAA
Shultz Belting Co. (Belting)
AA
Trinadad Asphalt Mfg. Co.
(Asphalt; Asphalt Roof-
ing) ....A
N. H.—Concord
Page Belting Co. (Leather)
AA
N. J.—Alpha
Alpha Portland Cement Co.
(Portland) ....AAAA
N. J.—Bound Brook
Graphite Lubricating Co.
(Pipe Joint) ....B
N. J.—Camden
New Jersey Asbestos Co.
(Asbestos; Pipe Joint) AA
N. J.—Elizabeth
Rankin Co., W. H. (Roof-
ing) ....AA
N. J.—Jersey City
Baker, W. T. (Pipe Joint)
D
Dixon Crucible Co., Jos.
(Pipe Joint Furnace;
Stove) ....AAA
Smooth-On Mfg. Co. (Pipe
Joint; Iron) ....B
Stowell Mfg. Co.. 114-134
Culver Av. (Asphalt Roof-
ing) ....A
Woolsey Paint & Color Co.
(Roofing) ....A
N. J.—Newark
Cleaver, Wm. P. (Glass;
Crockery) X
Eureka Cement Co.. Emmet
cor. Av. A (Rubber) ...D
Hetzel, J. G. (Est. of) 67
Maine (Roofing) ......B
N. Y.—Akron
Akron Cement Wks. (Hy-
draulic) ....A
N. Y.—Albany
Helderberg Cement Co.
(Hyd.; Port.) ....A
N. Y.—Alseni
Alseni Am. Port. Cement
Wks. (Port.) ......AAAA

CEMENT (*Con.*)

N. Y.—Brooklyn
Wilson, Geo. W., 612 Myrtle
Av. (Furnace Stove) ..A
N. Y.—Buffalo
Buffalo Cement Co., Ltd.
(Port.) ....AAAA
Hall & Sons (Fire) ......A
McLennan Paint Co.
(Brine Pipe)..........AA
Union Akron Cement Co. ..A
N. Y.—Clinton
Clinton Metallic Paint Co.
(Roofing) C
N. Y.—Fayetteville
Bangs & Gaynor (Nat. Hyd.)
A
N. Y.—Glens Falls
Glens Falls Port. Cement Co.
(Port.) ....A
N. Y.—Hudson
Hudson Port. Cement Co.
(Port.) ....A
N. Y.—Ithaca
Cayuga Lake Cement Co.
(Port.) ....A
N. Y.—Jamesville
Alvord & Co., E. B. (Nat.
Hyd.) ....A
Spencer & McCarthy (Nat.
Hyd.) ....A
N. Y.—Kingston
Lawrence Cement Co. ....A
N. Y.—Manlius
Alvord, A. E. (Nat. Hyd.)
A
New York City
Atlas Portland Cement Co.,
30 Broad (Portland) AAAA
Behrend, F.. 54 Front (Im-
porters'; Fire) ....B
Callahan & Co.. Geo.. 218
Front (Pipe Joint; Roof-
ing) ....F
Cookston. Wm. H.. 185
Wooster (Pipe Joint)...E
Coplay Cement Mfg. Co.,
949 Broadway (Nat. Hy-
draulic) ....AAAA
Fairbanks Co., 416 Broome
(Machinery) ....AAAA
Gabriel & Schall, 205 Pearl
(Importers German Port-
land) ....B
Gast, Frank J., 26 Cortlandt
(Asbestos) ....E
Goodyears India Rubber
Glove Mfg. Co., 503 Bway.
(Rubber) ....AAAA
Goodyear Rubber Co., 787
Broadway (Rubber) AAAA
Hammill & Gillespie, 240
Front (Importers German
Portland) ....A
Johns-Manville Co., H. W.,
100 William (Asbestos;
Pipe Joint; Roofing; Fire
Proof; Furnace; Retort)
AAAA
Major Cement Co.. 461 Pearl
(China; Leather; Rubber)
X
Manhattan Rubber Mfg. Co.,
18 Vesey (Rubber) ..AA
Marquardt & Co., 135 So.
William (Importers' Ger-
man Portland) ....A
Maurer & Son, Henry, 420 E.
23d (Fire).............AA
Newark Lime & Cement Co.
(Nat. Hydraulic) .AAAA
New York Asbestos Mfg. Co.
123 Liberty (Asbestos) C
New York Belting & Pack-
ing Co., 23 Park Pl. (Rub-
ber) ....AAAA
New York Cement Co., 17
Battery Pl. (Hydraulic) A
Northampton Portland Ce-
ment Co., 26 Broadway
AAAA
Stewart Mfg. Co., Wm. H.,
81 Franklin (Furnace;
Stove) C
Thiele. E.. 99 John (Im-
porter Belgian; English;
German Portland) .....B
Virginia Portland Cement
Co. 68 William ....A
Warren Chemical Mfg. Co.,
170 Bway. (Roofing) ...A
Wheeling Corrugating Co.,
47 Cliff (Roofing) .AAAA
Whitehead Bros. Co.. 537
W. 27th (Foundry) .AA
Zinsser & Co., W., 197 Will-

CEMENT (Con.)

iam (Adhesive) ....A

N. Y.—Rochester

Wayland Portland Cement
Co. ....A

N. Y.—Smiths Landing

Catskill Cement Co. (Port.)
A

N. Y.—Syracuse

Colebrook Sons & Co., W. H.
1419 Orange (Furnace;
Stove) ....B

N. Y.—Troy

Cheney & Claxton (Wall) C

Connors Paint Mfg. Co.,
Wm. (Asbestos; Elastic;
Roofing; Furnace; Stove)
A

Thompson Sons & Co.,
John L. (Furnace) ....A

N. Y.—Warners

Empire Portland Cement Co.
(Port.) ....A

N. Y.—Wayland

Millen Co., Thomas (Port.)
A

OHIO—Bellefontaine

Buckeye Portland Cement
Co. (Port.) ....A

OHIO—Cincinnati

Bradford Belting Co. (Belt)
A

Obermayer Co., S. (Hydraulic; Stove; Foundry; Iron)
AA

OHIO—Cleveland

Bartlett, C. O. & Snow Co.
(Machinery) ....A

Diamond Portland Cement
Co. ....A

Garry Iron & Steel Roofing
Co. (Roofing) ....A

Gorsuch, T. M., 55 James
(Roofing) ....A

Kelly Island Lime & Trans-
port Co. (Importers Ger-
manPortland) .....AAAA

U. S. Dental Mfg. Co.
(Dental) ....D

Wellman-Seaver-Morgan Co.
(Machinery) ....AAAA

OHIO—Columbus

Case Mfg. Co. (Belting) .A

Union Brick Supply Co.
Ruggery Bldg. (Roofing)
E

OHIO—Cuyahoga Falls

Turner, Vaughn & Taylor
Co. (Machinery) ....B

OHIO—Ironton

Ironton Portland Cement
Co. ....A

OHIO—Lockland

Carey Mfg. Co., Philip (Asbestos; Furnace; Stove;
Roofing; Retort) ..AAA

OHIO—Sandusky

Sandusky Portland Cement
Co. ....AAA

OHIO—Struthers

Struthers Furnace Co.
(Puzzolan) ....A

OHIO—Toledo

National Cement & Rubber
Mfg. Co. (Rubber; Bicy-
cle; Fire) C

OHIO—Youngstown

Brier Hill Coal & Iron Co. A

Republic Rubber Co. (Rub-
ber) ....AA

PA.—Allegheny

Chamberlin & Johnson
(Marble Cutters'; Rubber;
Gas Fitters') ....D

Eagle Paint & Varnish Co.
(Pipe Joint) ....B

PA.—Allentown

Lehigh Portland Cement Co.
AAAA

Penn-Allen Portland Cement
Co. ....A

PA.—Ambler

Keasbey & Mattison Co. (Asbestos; Pipe Joint).AAAA

PA.—Egypt

American Cement Co. (Portland) ....AA

PA.—Erie

Watson Co. H. F. (Asbestos;
Asphalt; Furnace; Stove;
Pipe Joint; Roofing)
AAA

PA.—Franklin

Franklin Mfg. Co. (Asbes-
tos; Furnace; Pipe Joint)
AA

CEMENT (Con.)

PA.—Nazareth

Dexter Portland Cement Co.
A

Nazareth Foundry & Mach.
Co. (Machinery) ......B

Phoenix Cement Co. (Port-
land; Hydraulic) ....A

PA.—Norristown

Norristown Covering Co.
(Asbestos; Pipe Joint) ..C

PA.—Philadelphia

Alexander Bros., 410 N. 3rd
(Belting) ....A

American Cement Co. of N.
J. (Port.) ....AAAA

Bonneville Portland Cement
Co., (Port.; Nat.; Hyd.)
AAA

Bowen's Sons, S., 4th &
Sedgley Av. (Roofing;
Furnace; Stove) ....E

Buckhorn Port. Cement Co.
(Port.) ....A

Eclipse Cement & Blacking
Co. (Leather; Rubber; Bi-
cycle) C

Edison Port. Cement Co.
(Port.) ....AAAA

French & Co., Sam'l H.,
York Av. (Importers Eng-
lish; French; German)..A

Lawrence Cement Co. of Pa.
Nat.; Hyd) ....AAAA

Lucas & Co., John, 4th &
Race (Roofing) ....AAA

Meng & Co., Anthony, 190
S. Front (Importers Bel-
gian) ....F

Sibley, Gideon (Dental)..AA

Vulcanville Port. Cement
Co. (Port.) ....AAAA

Van Stan's Stratena Co.
(Ltd.) (Adhesive)......E

Whitehall Port. Cement Co.
(Port.) ....A

PA.—Pittsburg

Atlas Paint Co. (Ltd.), 2638
Liberty Av. (Roofing)..X

Castalia Portland Cement
Co. (Portland) ......AA

Hommel Co., O., 110 Mar-
ket (Pipe Joint) ....D

McConnell Asbestos & Cov-
ering Co. (Asbestos; Hot
Blast) ....B

PA.—Reading

Reading Cement Co. (Nat-
ural Hydraulic) ....A

Wilhelm Co., A. (Aluminum;
Para Roofing) ....AA

PA.—Sharon

Stewart Iron Co. (Cement
Dept.) (Puzzolan) .AAAA

PA.—So. Bethlehem

Bethlehem Foundry & Mach.
Co. (Machinery) C

PA.—Wampum

Crescent Portland Cement
Co. ....A

PA.—York

York Chemical Co. (Asbes-
tos) ....A

R. I.—Providence

Holbrook, A. & C. W.
(Belt) ....B

U. S. Gutta Percha Paint
Co. (Roofing; Elastic)..A

S. C.—Charleston

South Eastern Lime & Ce-
ment Co. (Importers Bel-
gian; English; German).B

TENN.—Chattanooga

Chicamauga Cement Co....A

TEXAS—Galveston

Parr & Co., William (Bel-
gian; English; German)B

UTAH—Salt Lake City

Portland Cement Co. of
Utah (Port.) ....A

VT.—Rutland

Rutland Fire Clay Co. (Furnace; Stove; Cupola;
Foundry) ....B

VA.—Richmond

Selp. Jno. A. (Asbestos)..F

WIS.—Milwaukee

Milwaukee Cement Co. (Natural Hydraulic) ....A

CENTERERS

MASS.—Boston

United Shoe Machinery Co.

CENTERERS (Con.)
(Vamp) ....AAAA

CENTERS

CONN.—Branford
New York Lock Co. (Sash;
Transom) ....B
CONN.—Hartford
Pratt & Whitney Co.
(Bench; Index; Planer;
Shaper) ....AAAA
CONN.—New Britain
Russell & Erwin Mfg. Co.
(Sash Fastener) ..AAAA
CONN.—New Haven
New Haven Mfg. Co.
(Planer) ....AA
CONN.—Southington
Peck, Stow & Wilcox Co.
(Sash Fastener) ..AAAA
CONN.—South Norwalk
Norwalk Lock Co. (Sash
Fastener) X
CONN.—Torrington
Hendey Machine Co.
(Planer; Shaper) ......A
DEL.—Wilmington
Betts Machine Co. (Planer)
A
ILL.—Rockford
Sovereign, C. E. (Swivel) .C
IOWA—Dubuque
Adams Co. (Iron Clothes
Reel) ....B
MAINE—Dexter
Fay & Scott (Planer) .,..C
MASS.—Fitchburg
Fitchburg Machine Wks.
(Planer) ....A
Putnam Machine Co.
(Bench; Planer) ......AA
MASS.—Hyde Park
Becker-Brainard Milling
Mach. Co. (Indexing).AA
MASS.—Springfield
Waltham Watch Tool Co.
(Index) ....B
MASS.—Worcester
Reed Co., Francis (Planer)
D
Whitcomb Mfg. Co. (Planer)
A
MO.—St. Louis
Kupferle, John C., 2nd &
Mound (Sash Fastener) .A
Pleuger & Henger Mfg. Co.,
11th & Hebert (Sash
Fastener) ....A
N. J.—High Bridge
Taylor Iron & Steel Co.
(Car Wheel) ......AAAA
N. J.—Newark
Gould & Eberhardt, 95 N. J.
R. R. Av. (Index) .....A
N. Y.—Farmer
Coverts Saddlery Wks.
(Neck Yoke) C
New York City
Garvin Machine Co., 137
Varick (Index; Planer)..
AAA
Manning, Maxwell & Moore,
85 Liberty (Index)..AAA
Niles-Bement-Pond Co., 136
Liberty (Index; Planer).
AAA
Sargent & Co., 151 Leonard
(Sash; Transom) ..AAAA
Yale & Towne Mfg. Co., 9
Murray (Sash; Transom).
AAAA
OHIO—Cincinnati
Cincinnati Milling Machine
Co. (Index) ....A
PA.—Philadelphia
Newton Machine Tool Wks.,
2343 Vine (Index) .....A
Standard Tool Wks., Harri-
son Bldg. (Car Wheel)..
AA
PA.—Pittsburg
Pittsburg Steel Fdry. (Car
Wheel) ....AA
Reli   Steel Castings Co.
(Car wheel) X
PA.—Reading
Penn. Hdw. Co. (Sash
Fastener) ....AA
Heading Hdw. Co. (Sash
Fastener) ....AAA
PA.—Wrightsville
Wrightsville Hdw. Co. (Sash
Fastener) C

CENTERS (Con.)
R. I.—Providence
Brown & Sharpe Mfg. Co.
(Bench; Index) ...AAAA
WIS.—Milwaukee
Kempsmith Mfg. Co., Lewis,
cor. Woodward (Index).A

CENTRI-FUGALS

See also Machinery

MASS.—Boston
American Tool Machine Co.,
109 Beach (Belt Water;
Electrical Driven; for
Laboratory; Experimental
Use) ....AAA
N. C.—Winston Salem
Salem Iron Wks. (Coffee) .A

CERAMICS

See Mosaics

CERATE

N. Y.—Elmira
Rice Darby Co. (Rose) ..D

CERESINE

New York City
De Bruenn Chem. & Dye-
stuff Co., 6 Cedar ..D
PA.—Easton
Baker & Adamson Chemical
Co. ....A

CERTIFI-CATES

ILL.—Chicago
Cory & Co., C. W., 41 S.
Jefferson (Marriage) ..F
MASS.—Boston
Brooks, Lyman B. (Stock)D
MASS.—Springfield
Taber-Prang Art Co. (Mar-
riage) ....AA
WIS.—Milwaukee
Gugler Lithographic Co..A

CESSPOOLS

CONN.—New Haven
Peck Bros. & Co. ....A
ILL.—Chicago
Barbee Wire & Iron Wks.
(Gutter) ....B
Illinois Malleable Iron Co...
AAAA
Wolff Mfg. Co., 177 W.
Lake ....AAAA
ILL.—Quincy
Modern Iron Wks. (Ball
Trap; etc.) ....B
ILL.—St. Charles
Glenn Mfg. Co. (Ball
Trap, etc.) ....D
MASS.—Springfield
Peck Bros. & Co. ..:....B
Springfield Brass Co. ....B
MICH.—Detroit
Northwestern Fdry & Sup-
ply Co. ....D
MO.—St. Louis
Kupferle, John C., 2nd &
Mound ....AA
Pleuger & Henger Mfg. Co.
A
N. J.—Trenton
Trenton Brass & Machine
Co. ....B
New York City
Central Fdry. Co., 116 Nas-
sau ....AAAA
Morrison Co., David ......E
N. Y.—Seneca Falls
Goulds Mfg. Co. ......AAA
N. Y.—Syracuse
Stearns & Co., E. C.
(Gutter) ....AA
N. Y.—West Coxsackie
West Coxsackie Iron Fdry.
Co. ....F
OHIO—Ashtabula
Barber Mfg. Co. C
OHIO—Cleveland
Madison Av. Foundry Co..D

CESSPOOLS (Con.)

OHIO—Columbus
McDonald Bros. C
OHIO—Mansfield
Barnes Mfg. Co. (Hydrant)
...........................B
Humphreys Mfg. Co. ....A
PA.—Philadelphia
Haines, Jones & Cadbury,
1136 Ridge Av. ......AA
PA.—Pittsburg
Standard Mfg. Co. (Hydrant) ....AA

CHAINS

**See also Jewelry; Hardware;
Furnace**

CAL.—Stockton
Holt Mfg. Co. (Agricultural) ....AA
CONN.—Bridgeport
Bridgeport Brass Co. (Brass;
Jack; Safety, etc.)....AA
Bridgeport Chain Co. (Agricultural; Aluminum;
Awning; Brass Coil;
Cow Tie; Halter; Hydrant
Sets; Plumbers'; Railroad; Safety; Sash;
Tieout; Triumph; Well;
Windmill; Jack; Hanging
Basket; Tettering; Picture; Harness; Post;
Hitching; Rein; Trace;
Bicycle; Dog; Kennel
Key; Transom; Wagon;
Fancy; Weldless; Flat
Link; Bronze; Iron;
Steel; Pump; Cast; Heel;
Picket; Stake, etc.)....A
Locke Steel Belt Co. (Tempered Steel; Detachable
Sprocket Wheel) .....B
Smith & Egge Mfg. Co.
(Brass; Cable; Jack;
Plumbers'; Sash; Dog;
Key; Flat Link) ....A
CONN.—Deep River
Williams & Marvin Co.
(Plumbers') ....D
CONN.—Derby
Birmingham Brass Co.
(Brass; Jack; Plumbers')
...........................A
CONN.—Greystone
Greystone Mfg. Co. (Coil;
Cow; Tie; Halter) .....E
CONN.—Hartford
Whitney Mfg. Co. (Automobile; Bicycle) ....B
CONN.—Meriden
Chapman Mfg. Co. (Dog)..A
CONN.—Middletown
Douglas, W. & R. (Pump;
Galvanized Pump) ......A
Wilcox, Crittenden Co.
(Coil) ....A
CONN.—New Britain
Judd, Oliver S. (Halter;
Hitching) ....B
North & Judd Mfg. Co.
(Curb; Rein) ....AA
Union Mfg. Co. (Pump;
Well) ....AA
CONN.—New Haven
Hendryx & Co., Andrew B.
Brass; Iron; Jack;
Bronze; Steel; Safety;
Harness) ....A
CONN.—Norwich
Crescent Fire Arms Co.
(Bicycle) C
Hopkins & Allen Arms Co.
(Bicycle; Automobile) .AA
McKee Chain & Stamping
Co. (Bicycle) X
Thames Chain & Stamping
Co. (Bicycle) ....D
CONN.—Torrington
Turner & Seymour Mfg. Co.
(Brass; Jack; Plumbers';
Curtain; Drapery) .....A
CONN.—Wallingford
Wallace Sons Mfg. Co., R.
(Key) ....AAA
CONN.—Waterbury
American Ring Co. (Jack;
Key) ....A
Holmes, Booth & Haydens
Co. (Brass; Jack; Brass
Picture; Iron; Sash)....
...........................AAAA

CHAINS (Con.)

Plume & Atwood Mfg. Co.
(Brass; Jack; Plumbers';
Drapery; Safety) ...AAA
Scovill Mfg. Co. (Jack;
Safety, etc) .....AAAA
Steele & Johnson Mfg. Co.
(Brass; Jack; Plumbers')
...........................A
DEL.—Wilmington
Remington Machine Co.
(Halter; Hitching) .....A
ILL.—Chicago
American Steel & Wire Co.
(Railway) ....AAAA
Borden & Selleck Co., 48
Lake (Crane; Cable, etc.)
...........................B
Carpenter & Co., Geo. B.
(Iron) ....AA
Ewart Mfg. Co. (Detachable
Drive) ....A
Excelsior Supply Co. (Bicycle; Automobile) ......A
Link Belt Machinery Co.,
39th & Stewart Av.
(Power Transmission;
Transfer; Flat Riveted;
Steel) ....A
Smith Iron & Wire Wks.,
F. P. (Iron) ....AA
Taylor & Son, S. G., 98
Indiana (Block; Break;
Coal; Cow Tie; Crane;
Differential Pulley Block;
Dredge; Log; Railroad;
Trace; Wrecking) .....B
ILL.—St. Charles
Crown Electric & Mfg. Co.
(Bicycle; Automobile) ..D
Moline Malleable Iron Co.
(Transfer) ....B
IND.—Greenfield
U. S. Chain Co. (Coil) ..D
IND.—Indianapolis
Ewart Mfg. Co. (Br. Chicago, Ill.), 515 Holmes
Av. (House; Bull; Power
Transmission; Sprocket
Wheel; Steel Bushed) ..A
Indiana Chain Wks. (Agricultural; Brake; Coil;
Cow Tie; Halter; Log;
Rafting; Railroad;
Wagon; Well; Bicycle).C
IND.—New Albany
Todd-Obenchain Co. (Agricultural; Coil; Harness;
Log; Wagon) ....D
IND.—Richmond
Starr & Sons, W. C. (Agricultural; Coil; Crane;
Harness; Log; Railroad;
Wagon) C
MASS.—Boston
Boston Gear Wks. (Bicycle;
Automobile) ....B
Brown & Wales (Bicycles)
...........................A
Estabrook's Sons, R. (Railway) ....D
Harvey, H. H. (Mining;
Quarry) ....B
MASS.—Chicopee
Ames Sword Co. (Key; Jack;
Safety; Baggage) .....B
MASS.—Northboro
Farwell & Co., Walter M.
(Horn) X
MASS.—Southbridge
American Optical Co. (Eye
Glass) ....AAA
MASS.—Springfield
Duckworth Chain Mfg. Co.
(Bicycle; Automobile)...D
MASS.—Worcester
Baldwin Automobile Detachable Chain Co. (Automobile; Bicycle) .....B
Hale Bros., 65 Beacon
(Brass; Jack) X
Parker Wire Goods Co.
(Jack; Safety; Bird Cage)
...........................E
Wire Goods Co. (Jack;
Plumbers'; Sash; Safety;
Dog; Halter; Flower Basket) ....B
Wright Wire Co. (Jack;
Safety, etc.) ....AA
MICH.—Detroit
Buhl Malleable Co. (Agricultural; Cable; Marine;
Drag; Dredge; Log,

CHAINS (Con.)
Sprocket Wheel; Transfer; Detachable) ....A
MICH.—Manistee
Manistee Iron Wks. Co. (Convoyor) ....B
MICH.—Port Huron
Port Huron Engine & Thresher Co. (Sprocket Wheel) ....AAAA
MO.—St. Louis
Leschen & Sons Rope Co., A. (Coil; Crane; Cable, etc.) ....AAA
Zeinicker Supply Co., W. A. (Convoyor) C
N. J.—Fieldsboro
Robinson & Fosbrook (Agricultural; Block; Crane; Dredge; Log; Rafting; Safety) ....E
N. J.—Kearney
Marshall & Co. (Carpet).AA
N. J.—Newark
Baldwin & Co. (Halter; Hitching) .....:....D
Celluloid Co. (Celluloid)..B
Peters Harness & Saddlery Co. (Trace) C
N. J.—Trenton
Enterprise Chain Wks. (Agricultural; Block; Brake; Brass; Cable; Marine; Cow Tie; Crane; Dredge; Halter; Log; Railroad; Well) X
Trenton Iron Co. (Br. N. Y. City) (Agricultural; Cable; Crane; Harness; Halter; Wagon) ......AA
N. Y.—Brooklyn
Pollard, Jos. G., 141 Raymond (Stone fitted with Steel Hook) ....F
N. Y.—Buffalo
McKinnon Dash Co. (Bicycle; Automobile) ....AA
Western Wire Goods Co. (Jack; Safety, etc.) ....D
N. Y.—Cadwallader
Herbertson's Sons, J. (Hitching) X
N. Y.—Farmer
Covert's Saddlery Wks. (Breast; Halter; Hitching; Harness) ......AAA
N. Y.—Homer
Phoenix Hardware Mfg. Co. (Brass; Jack; Sash) ....D
New York City
Creamer Co., W. G., 96 John (Railway) ....B
Glauber, M., 317 E. 58th (Plumbers') ....B
Gould-Mersereau Co., 43 E. 19th (Curtain) C
Hungerford Brass & Copper Co., U. T., 479 Pearl (Jack; Plumbers') .....A
Hunt Co., C. W., 45 B'way (Laminated Hoisting; Crane; Cable, etc.) ....A
Ingersoll & Bro., R. H., 51 Maiden Lane (Key) ...A
Judd & Co., H. L., 87 Chambers (Brass Picture; Drapery; Curtain; Hanging Basket) ....AA
Keuffel & Esser Co., 127 Fulton (Measuring) ...A
Kroeder, John, & Henry Reubel Co., 254 4th Av. (Drapery) ....B
McNab & Harlin Mfg. Co., 56 John (Jack; Safety, etc.) ....AA
Manhattan Brass Co., 332 E. 28th (Brass) ....AA
Morton, Thos., 169 Elm (Sash; Steel; Flat Link; Transom) ....B
Newhall Chain Forge & Chain Co., 15 Murray (Crane; Dredge; Hoist; Steam Shovel; Trace; Wrecking) ....D
New Jersey Foundry & Mach. Co., 9 Murray (Brake; Railroad; Coil; Crane; Cable, etc.; Flat Link; Ice; Elevator; Log, Rafting, etc.; Ship; Stud) ....D
Russell & Erwin Mfg. Co.

CHAINS (Con.)
43 Chambers (Jack; Safety, etc.; Sash; Transon) ....AAAA
Sargent & Co., 151 Leonard (Jack; Safety, etc.; Dog; Halter; Harness; Transom) ....AAAA
Trenton Iron Co., 17 Burling Slip (Agricultural; Cable; Crane; Harness; Halter; Wagon) ....AA
N. Y.—Niagara Falls
Metal Stamping Co. (Harness; Key; Tubular Steel; Breast) ....B
Oneida Community (Ltd.) (Aluminum; Awning; Coil; Cow Tie; Halter; Log; Plumbers'; Railroad; Sash; Windmill; Pump; Cart; Dog; Jack; Safety; Harness; Heel; Hydrant; Agricultural; Flat Link; Key; Picket; Picture; Post; Stake; Trace; Wagon; Well; Fancy; Weldless) ....AAA
N. Y.—Rochester
Pullman Sash Balance Co. (Sash) ....B
N. Y.—Rome
Rome Brass & Copper Co. (Brass; Plumbers').AAAA
N. Y.—Troy
Carr & Co., Jno. B. (Agricultural; Brake; Cable; Marine; Crane; Dredge; Log; Railroad; Trace; Iron; Wrecking; Jack; Mining; Steel; Wagon) E
Gurley, W. & L. E. (Surveyors') ....AA
Taylor Electric Co. (Brake) B
N. Y.—Trumansburg
Morse Chain Co. (Power Transmission; Transfer; Bicycle; Rocker Joint)..B
N. Y.—Watervliet
Covert Mfg. Co. (Halter; Log; Harness; Breast Cart Back; Heel; Rein; Trace; Post; Hitching))A
OHIO—Canon
Aultman Co. (Drag; Sprocket Wheel; Steel Bushed) A
Elbel & Co. (Halter) ....B
OHIO—Cincinnati
Schreiber & Co., O. P., 208 Elm (Galvanized Pump) C
OHIO—Cleveland
Bartlett & Snow Co., C. O. (Crane; Cable, etc.) ....B
Cleveland Galvanizing Wks. (Pump; Well) ....B
Cleveland Hardware Co. (Wagon) ....A
Federal Mfg. Co., Amer. Tract Bldg. (Agricultural; Automobile; Awning; Bicycle; Block; Brass; Cable; Marine; Hoist; Laminated Hoist; Machinery; Plumbers'; Power Transmission; Sash; Sprocket Wheel; Steel Bushed) ....AAAA
H. P. Nail Co. (Coil; Iron; Trace; Wagon) X
Round & Son, David (Brake; Coil; Crane; Differential Pulley Block; Dredge, Log; Railroad; Sprocket Wheel; Trace; Wrecking) C
Woodhouse, Samuel, 2 Stafford (Block; Brake; Coil; Crane; Dredge; Railroad; Trace; Wrecking) ......H
OHIO—Columbus
Columbus Chain Co. (Agricultural; Block; Brake; Cable; Marine; Coil; Crane; Differential Pulley Block; Dredge; Harness; Log; Railroad; Safety; Sprocket Wheel; Trace; Wrecking; Wagon) AA
Hayden-Corbett Chain Co. (Agricultural; Brake; Cable; Marine; Crane;

CHAINS (Con.)
Dredge; Log; Rafting;
Sprocket Wheel; Wagon,
B
Hayden Saddlery Hardware
Co. (Harness) .....AAAA
Jeffrey Mfg. Co. (Drag;
Dredge; Sprocket Wheel;
Transfer; Coil; Iron; Log;
Mining; Roller; Special;
Detachable; Bushed).....
AAAA
OHIO—Cuyahoga Falls
Turner, Vaughn & Taylor
(Machinery) ....B
PA.—Allegheny
Baker Chain & Wagon Iron
Mfg. Co. (Cable; Crane;
Wagon) X
Chillcott-Evans Chain Co.,
652 Preble Av. (Cable;
Marine; Crane; Dredge).D
PA.—Hope Church
Monongahela Iron & Steel
Co. (Ball-bearing; Cable;
Marine; Railroad) .....B
PA.—Howard
Jenkins Iron & Steel Co.
(Brake; Cable; Marine;
Coil; Hitching; Mine;
Log; Railroad; Sprocket
Wheel) C
PA.—Lebanon
Lebanon Chain Wks. (Block;
Cable; Marine; Crane;
Dredge; Steam Shovel)..X
West End Rolling Mill &
Chain Wks. (Block;
Brake; Coil; Crane; Dif-
ferential Pulley Block;
Dredge; Log; Railroad;
Sprocket Wheel; Trace;
Wrecking; Iron; Mining;
B
PA.—McKee's Rocks
Kidd Bros. & Burgher Steel
Wire Co. (Bicycle) ....B
PA.—Milesburg
McCoy & Linn (Agricultur-
al; Coil; Cow Tie; Halter;
Log; Wagon; Well) ..AA
PA.—New Castle
New Castle Forge & Belt Co.
(Agricultural; Brake;
Coil; Cow Tie; Crane;
Dredge; Hitching; Mine;
Rafting; Railroad; Steam
Shovel; Cable) ....A
PA.—Philadelphia
Bradlee & Co., 1621 Beach
Av. (Iron; Steel; Cable;
Marine; Coil; Crane;
Dredge; Marine; R'way;
Mining; Log; Rafting;
Sling; Stud)
Hoopes & Townsend Co.,
1330 Butterwood (Crane;
Dredge; Elevator; Car-
rier; Log; Iron) ....AAA
Link Belt Engineering Co.,
Nicetown (Power Trans-
mission; Transfer; Crane;
Cable, etc.: Driving;
Bushed Log; Detachable)
A
Phila. Roll & Mach. Co.
(Dredging) ....A
Phosphor Bronze Smelting
Co. (Ltd.) (Jack; Sash)A
Queen Co. (Surveyors')..AA
Simons Bros. & Co.
(Plated) ....A
PA.—Pittsburg
Baker Mfg. Co., Jas. H.,
Park Bldg. (Brake; Coil;
Log; Rafting; Safety)..A
Eclipse Mfg. Co. (Hitch-
ing; Mine) ....D
Garland Chain Co., Frick
Bldg. (Plumbers'; Pump)
B
Jones & Laughlins Steel Co.
(Agricultural; Cable; Ma-
rine; Coil; Crane; Log;
R a i l r o a d; Sprocket
Wheel) ....AAAA
Lanz & Sons, M. (Hog)...B
McKay & Co., Jas. 20th
& Liberty Av. (Brass;
Coil; Crane; Railroad;
Brake; Conveyor; Stud;
Log; Rafting; Wagon;
Fancy) ....AAA
Pittsburg Chain Co., 32nd

CHAINS (Con.)
& Liberty Av. (Crane)..D
Robson & Son, John (Crane)
X
Standard Chain Co., Frick
Bldg. (Agricultural;
Brake; Cable; Marine;
Coil; Cow Tie; Crane;
Differential Pulley Block;
Dredge; Halter; Log;
Railroad; Sprocket Wheel;
Sling; Steam Shovel;
Trace; Wrecking; Wagon;
Well; Windmill; Convey-
or; Machinery; Binding;
Harness; Hobble; Cart;
Heel; Ship; Galvanized;
Rafting; Stud; Switch;
Well; Wagon; Fancy)..
AAAA
Union Chain Wks., People's
Saving Bank Bldg.
(Brake; Coil; Cow Tie;
Crane; Galvanized Pump;
Log; Railroad; Wagon).X
PA.—Pittston
Exeter Machine Wks.
(Drag) ....AA
PA.—Rankin Station
Garland Nut & Rivet Co.
(Br. Stand. Chain Co.,
Pittsburg, Pa. (Pump)..
AAAA
PA.—Reading
Chantrell Tool Co. (Bicycle;
Automobile) ....B
Duryea Power Co. (Drive).D
Reading Hardware Co.
(Transom) ....AAA
Reading Screw Co. (Bicycle)
D
PA.—So. Bethlehem
Bethlehem Foundry &
Mach. Co. (Bushed).....C
PA.—York
Nes Chain Mfg. Co. (Br.
Standard Chain Co., Pitts-
burg, Pa.) (Agricultural;
Cable; Coil; Crane; Iron;
Log; Mining; Safety;
Steel; Harness; Breast;
Halter; Heel; Hitching;
Rein; Trace; Wagon;
Railway) ....AAAA
Schmidt & Co., John C. (Br.
Standard Chain Co., Pitts-
burg, Pa.) (Agricultural;
Cable; Coil; Iron; Log;
Steel; Harness; Breast;
Cart; Back; Halter; Heel;
Hitching; Rein; Trace;
Wagon) ....AAAA
R. I.—Pawtucket
Fuller & Son, Geo. H.
(Bracelet) ....A
Haskell Mfg. Co., Wm. H.
(Flat Link; Ice; Elevator)
AA
R. I.—Providence
Eastern Bolt & Nut Co.
(Flat Link; Ice Elevator)
A
Rhode Island Tool Co. (Iron;
Steel; Punched; Ice Ele-
vator) ....AAA
WIS.—Milwaukee
Chain Belt Co. (Agricul-
tural; Sprocket Wheel)..B
Filer & Stowell Co. (Crane;
Cable, etc.) ....AAA
WIS.—So. Milwaukee
Stowell Mfg. & Foundry Co.
(Dog; Detachable) .....A

CHAIRS

See Furniture

CAL.—San Francisco
Hoey & Co., John 716 Madi-
son (Camp) ....A
CONN.—Meriden
Parker Co., Chas. (Piano)..
AAA
CONN.—New Haven
Dann Bros. & Co. (Invalid
Rolling) ....B
ILL.—Chicago
Adams & Westlake Co., On-
tario & N. Franklin (Rail-
way Car) ....AAAA
Barbee Wire & Iron Wks.
(Iron; Lawn; Rocking)..B
Chicago Chair & Wheel Co.

CHAIRS (*Con.*)

Wharton & Co.— Wm., Jr.,
25th & Washington Av.
(Rail) ....AAA
White Dental Mfg. Co., S. S.
(Dentists') ....AAAA
PA.—South Bethlehem
Bethlehem Foundry & Mach.
Co. (Lawn) C
PA.—Steelton
Penna. Steel Co. (Rail)...
...............AAAA
PA.—Wilkesbarre
Vulcan Iron Wks. (Head)..
...............AAAA
TENN.—Chattanooga
Ornamental Iron & Wire
Co. (Iron) X
VT.—Brattleboro
Smith & Co., S. A. (Swing)
...............AAA
VA.—Norfolk
Whitehurst Co., R. W.
(Lawn) ....B
WIS.—Milwaukee
Kipp Co., B. A. (Barbers')
...............B
WIS.—Racine
Gold Medal Camp Furniture
& Novelty Co. (Camp;
Folding;   Hammock;
Lawn; Reclining) .....D

CHALK

ILL.—Chicago
Spinks & Co., Wm. A., 93
Erie (Billiard) C
KY.—Louisville
Currie & Co., Chas. E....A
MD.—Baltimore
Thomas Mfg. Co. ....F
MASS.—Boston
Harvey, H. H. ....D
MICH.—Detroit
Acme White Lead & Color
Wks. (Lump) .....AAA
N. Y.—Buffalo
Schoellkopf, Hartford &
Hanna Co. ....AAA
New York City
Edison Chemical Co.. Thos.,
Jr., 14 Stone (Antiseptic)
...............X
Taintor Mfg. Co., H. F., 200
Water (Lump) ....B
OHIO—Cincinnati
Jackson & Co., E. S.
(French) ....F
OHIO—Sandusky
American Crayon Co. (Billiard; Bowling; Carpenters') ....AAA
Sandusky Crayon Co. (Billiard; Carpenters'; Coopers'; Finger; Foot)....D

CHAMBERS

CONN.—Meriden
Manning. Bowman & Co.
(Enamelled; Covers) ..AA
ILL.—Batavia
U. S. Wind Engine & Pump
Co. (Pump) ....AA
ILL.—Monmouth
Weir Pottery Co. (Porcelain) ....A
MASS.—Springfield
Emory Mfg. Co., P. P.
(Pump) C
Hercules Float Wks. (Air;
Copper) ....D
MO.—St. Louis
St. Louis Stamping Co.
(Enamelled; Covers)
...............AAAA
New York City
Cordley & Hayes, 172 Duane (Fibre; Hospital)..A
Goodyear Rubber Co., 787
Broadway (Rubber; Covers) ....AAAA
Goodyear's India Rubber
Glove Mfg. Co., 503 B'way
(Rubber; Covers) ..AAAA
PA.—Philadelphia
Kensington Engine Wks.,
Beach & Berk (Disinfecting) ....A
R. I.—Providence
Davol Rubber Co. (Rubber;
Covers) ....AA

CHAMBRAYS

See Cotton Goods

CHAMOIS

MASS.—Boston
White Son Co., 540 Atlantic
Av. ....A
New York City
National Sponge & Chamois
Co., 158 William .....A
Neumann & Co., R., 76 Duane (Imitation) ....A
Young Co., Richard, 36
Spruce (Imitation) ..AA
OHIO—Cincinnati
Fuchs-Budde Co. ....D
Trautman & Co., C. (Imitation) ....A
PA.—Philadelphia
Drueding Bros. Co., 433
Master ....AA

CHAMOMILE

New York City
Hopkins & Co., J. L., 100
William ....A

CHAMPAGNE

See Liquors

CHANDELIERS

See Fixtures

CHANNELERS

N. J.—Newark
Osborne Co., C. S.
(Saddlers') ....B
New York City
Ingersoll-Sargeant Drill Co.,
26 Cortlandt (Stone)....
...............AAAA

CHANNELS

See Angles, also Iron & Steel; Brass; Copper.

CHAPERAJOS

MINN.—Minneapolis
Dodson - Fisher - Brockman
Co. ....AA
New York City
Abercrombie & Fitch, 314
B'way ....B

CHAPLETS

OHIO—Cincinnati
Hill & Griffith Co. (Foundry) ....D
Obermayer Co.. S. .....AA
PA.—Philadelphia
Paxson Co., J. W., 102 N.
Delaware (Foundry).AA

CHARCOAL

ILL.—Chicago
Berger Bros., 1217 State..E
IOWA—Davenport
Halligan Co., W. P. X
MASS.—Springfield
Brown & Co., L. S., 33
Lyman C
Springfield   Facing   Co.
(Brass Founders' Facing;
Ground) C
MICH.—Cadillac
Commer, Diggins & Co.....
...............AAAA
MICH.—Onota
Onota Charcoal Mfg. Co...B
MICH.—Thompsonville
Immerman & Co., A. ....B
MICH.—Traverse City
Desmond Chemical Co. ..B
MO.—Noel
Mountain Coal Co. C
MO.—St. Louis
Harry Steel Wks., O. K.
(Furnace) ....B
N. Y.—Binghamton
Ballard, J. W. C
N. Y.—Brooklyn
Wiarda & Co., John C.
(Powdered) ....AA
New York City
Binney & Smith Co. 81 Ful-

CHARCOAL (Con.)

ton (Animal; Powdered)
    AA
Kelly & Co., Thos. P., 544
  W. 22nd ....B
N. Y.—Peekskill
Mackellar's Sons Co., R.
  (Powdered) ....D
N. Y.—Syracuse
Will & Baumer Co. .....AA
OHIO—Cincinnati
Obermayer Co., S. (Drug-
  gists'; Glasshouse;
  Ground; Filtering) ..AA
OHIO—Cleveland
Smith Foundry Supply Co.,
  J. D., 40 S. Water .....D
PA.—Bradford
American Charcoal Co...B
Bradford Chemical Co. ..C
Lewis Run Mfg. Co. C
Smith Chemical Co., A. B..B
PA.—Kane
La Mont Chemical Co.....C
PA.—Mt. Alton
Bartley & Co., John .....B
PA.—Pittsburg
Hillman & Son, J. H.,
  Frick Bldg. ....A
Hooker & Co., H. M.
  Farmers' Bank Bldg. ..C
McCormack Co., J. S., 25th
  & A. V. R'way ....B
PA.—Rockwood
Wolf, Penrose, Mariners' &
  Merchants' Bldg. C
S. C.—Summerville
Taylor, J. W. ....F

CHARGERS

IOWA—Ottumwa
Hardsocg Mfg. Co. (Coal
  Miners') ....B
OHIO—Cleveland
Standard Sand Machine Co.,
  32 S. Water (Conveyors;
  Cupola) C

CHARMS

See Jewelry

CHARTS

ILL.—Chicago
Andrews & Co., A. H. ..AA
Evans & Co., R. O., 210
  Madison (Arithmetical;
  Historical) ....A
KANS.—Lawrence
Williams, W. R. (Dress-
  makers') ....D
MASS.—Boston
Rand-Avery Supply Co.
  (Railway) ....AA
MASS.—Springfield
Bradley Co., Milton (Dis-
  sected) ....A
MINN.—Minneapolis
Diamond Publishing Co., 104
  N. 2d (School) ....D
MO.—St. Louis
Feld Music Co., John (Har-
  mony) X
Parson & Co., 1010 Pine
  (Masonic) ....E
New York City
Bliss & Co., John, 128 Front
  D
Spencer Optical Co. (Opti-
  cal) C
PA.—Philadelphia
Noll & Co., E. P........D

CHASERS

MASS.—Mansfield
Card Mfg. Co., S. W.
  (Screw) ....B
N. Y.—Brooklyn
Nebel. M. A., 72 Grand Av.
  (Putty) ....D
Ross & Son Co., 16 Steuben
  (Drug) ....D
New York City
Bookhop, F. H., 115 War-
  ren (Fly) ....E
N. Y.—Trenton
Crossley Mfg. Co. (Fret).B
OHIO—Cincinnati
Day Co., J. H. (Putty)...A
PA.—Millersburg

CHASERS (Con.)

Polk & Son, A. J. (Screw) C
  C

CHASES

CONN.—New London
Babcock Printing Press Mfg.
  Co. (Printing Press)....C
ILL.—Chicago
Latham Machinery Co.
  (Printing Press) C
MASS.—Boston
Golding & Co. (Printing
  Press) C
N. Y.—Brooklyn
Wesel Mfg. Co., F. (Print-
  ing Press) ....AA
New York City
Cottrell & Sons' Co., C. B.,
  41 Park Row (Printing
  Press) ....AAA
Hoe & Co., R., 504 Grand
  Printing Press) .....AAAA
OHIO—Cleveland
Chandler & Price Co. (Print-
  ing Press) ....B

CHECKERS

See Games

CHECKS

See also Cotton Goods

CAL.—San Francisco
Moise-Klinkner Co. (Pool)
  D
CONN.—Bridgeport
Bridgeport Brass Co. (Bag-
  gage; Key, &c.) ......AA
Schwerdtle Stamp Co., 39
  Fairfield Av. (Baggage;
  Brass; Key; Time; Pay)
  G
CONN.—Meriden
Jopson, Geo. W. (Metal).X
CONN.—New Haven
Hoggson & Pettis Mfg. Co.
  (Baggage; Key. &c.)....A
CONN.—Wallingford
Wallace Sons' Mfg. Co., R.
  (Sterling Silver Bag; Ho-
  tel Key) ....AAA
CONN.—Waterbury
Holmes, Booth & Haydens
  Co. (Brass) ....AAAA
Plume & Atwood Mfg. Co.
  (Brass) ....AAA
Scovill Mfg. Co. (Brass;
  Baggage; Key, &c.)
  AAAA
Waterbury Brass Co.
  (Brass) ....AAAA
ILL.—Chicago
Swisher Mfg. Co., R. D., 152
  5th Av. (Aluminum
  Trade) X
Tenney Co., J. F., 5th Av. &
  Monroe (Baggage) ....E
Wilcox Co., W. W., 201
  Lake (Baggage) ......B
MASS.—Boston
Robbins Mfg. Co., John, 58
  Kneeland (Baggage;
  Metal; Time) ....F
Woodman Mfg. Supply Co.,
  R. (Baggage; Key; Time)
  F
MASS.—Fitchburg
Dodge Mfg. Co. (Locomo-
  tive Boiler) ....B
MICH.—Detroit
Detroit Rubber Stamp Co.,
  99 Griswold (Baggage)..E
Thorpe Mfg. Co., 50 Wood-
  ward Av. (Baggage) ...F
MICH.—Grand Rapids
Hardware Supply Co. (Door)
  F
N. J.—Newark
Celluloid Co. (Br. N. Y.
  City) (Soda; Celluloid).B
Peters Harness & Saddlery
  Co. (Bridle) C
Sacks Iron Foundry, Louis
  (Repair) ....A
N. Y.—Buffalo
Gibson Co., A. C., 338
  Washn. (Baggage) .....D
Johnson & Co., J. G., 29
  Seneca (Baggage) ....AA

CHECKS (Con.)
New York City

American Railway Supply Co., 24 Park Pl. (Baggage; Hotel Key; Metal; Plantation; R u b b e r; Time) ....H

Bardsley, Jos., 147 Baxter (Door) ....B

Brass Goods Mfg. Co., 7 Warren (Baggage; Brass; Hotel Key) ....B

Dennison Mfg. Co., 11 Dey (Paper; Cloth Baggage; Garment; Restaurant) ....AAAA

Fulton Rubber Type, Ink & Pad Mfg. Co., 31 Frankfort (Metal) ....D

Goodyear's India Rubber Mfg. Co., 503 B'way (Rubber) ....AAAA

Ness, Geo. M. Jr., 61 Fulton (B a g g a g e; Key; Brass) ....A

New York Stencil Wks., 100 Nassau (Baggage; Cash Sale) ....D

Russell & Erwin Mfg. Co., 43 Chambers (Door) ....AAAA

Sargent & Co., 151 Leonard (Door; Dumb Waiter) ....AAAA

Stafford-Nelson Co., 66 Fulton (Baggage; Hotel Key; Metal; Plantation) .....F

Yale & Towne Mfg. Co., 9 Murray (Door Liquid) ....AAAA

N. Y.—Niagara Falls

Metal Stamping Co. (Coin; Identification; Dog; Time) ....B

N. Y.—Rochester

Caldwell Mfg. Co. (Door).E

Rome Brass & Copper Co. (Brass) ....AAAA

N. Y.—Utica

Balch Bros. & West Co. (Metal) ....D

OHIO—Cincinnati

Cressler, Wm. T. (Pool)..C

Spencer, Wm. W., 206 Longworth (Baggage) ......E

OHIO—Cleveland

Upson Nut Co. (Door).AAAA

OHIO—Dayton

Howard, Wm. H. (German Silver; Hotel Key) ....E

PA.—Philadelphia

Quint & Son, S. H., 15 S. 4th (Brass; Metal) .....B

PA.—Pittsburg

Pittsburg Supply Co., 439 Water (Gas Light).....A

PA.—Reading

Reading Hardware Co. (Door Liquid) ....AAAA

PA.—West Chester

Denny Tag Co. (Metal)...C

W. VA.—Wheeling

Wheeling Hinge Co. (Brass) ....AA

WIS.—Milwaukee

Schwab Stamp & Seal Co. (Metal) C

CHEESE
See Butter & Cheese in Appendix.

ILL.—Chicago

Moxley, W. J. (Inc.)......A

ILL.—Elgin

Cornell Bros. ....B

IOWA—Monticello

Farmers' C o-o p e r a t i v e Creamery Co. ....F

MASS.—Boston

Simpson, McIntire & Co..Aa

MICH.—Fruit Ridge

Horton, G. B. ....B

MICH.—Northville

Power & Son, A. D. .....E

MO.—Cameron

Gem Cheese Factory .....B

MO.—St. Louis

Bayle, Geo. A. (Devilled).B

N. Y.—Antwerp

Baumert & Co., F. X.....A

N. Y.—Denmark

Cook, H. E. ....D

CHEESE (Con.)
N. Y.—Goshen

Howell Condensed Milk & Cream Co. ....B

OHIO—Aurora

Harmon & Sons, C. R. ...B

Hurd, Frank ....A

WIS.—Burlington

McCanna & Fraser Co.....A

WIS.—Kaukauna

Lempke, M. A. ....F

WIS.—Kekoskee

Roll, Emil ....H

WIS.—Monroe

Karlen & Son, Jacob.....A

Regez, Jacob ....B

WIS.—Pigeon Falls

Eckern Co., P. C

WIS.—Waterloo

Roach & Sieber Co. .....A

Waterloo Butter & Cheese Co. ....F

CHEMICALS
See also Specific Headings

COLO.—Denver

Western Chemical Mfg. Co. (Battery) ....AA

MASS.—Boston

Atteaux & Co., F. E. (Tanners) ....A

Balch, Bailey & Co. (Tanners) ....A

Beach-Treiber Co. (Tanners) ....B

Merrimac Chemical Co., 75 Broad (Battery) ....AAA

MO.—St. Louis

Mallinckrodt Chemical Wks. (Photographers') ..AAAA

N. J.—Newark

Dennis Chrome Tannage Co., Martin (Tanners) .....D

Hanson & Van Winkle Co. (Electro) ....AA

N. Y.—Brooklyn

Wiarda & Co., J. C., 259 Greene (Brickmakers'; Enamelers'; Glassmakers') ....AA

New York City

Cooper & Co., Chas., 194 Worth (Battery) ....A

Eimer & Amend, 211 Third Av. (Battery; Electroplating) ....AA

General Chemical Co., 25 Broad (Battery)...AAAA

Grasselli Chemical Co., 93 Wall (Battery) ....AAAA

Harrison Bros. & Co., 117 Fulton (Paper Makers') ....AAAA

Kalbfleisch Co., Franklin H., 35 Burling Slip (Battery) ....A

Kalbfleisch & Son, E. L., 56 Pine (Battery) C

Klipstein & Co., A., 122 Pearl ....AA

McKesson & Robbins (Pharm) ....AAAA

Wholesale Druggists and Manufacturing Chemists, Importers and Exporters of Drugs, Chemicals, Essential Oils and Pharmaceutical Preparations, Dealers in Druggists Sundries, etc.

We are headquarters for crude drugs of all kinds. We carry a complete line of chemicals and pharmaceutical preparations, also chemicals for use in the industrial arts. We also manufacture a full line of fluid extracts, gelatine coated pills, compressed tablets and other pharmaceutical specialties. The large stock we carry enables us to make prompt shipments at lowest possible figures. We also have an analytical department equipped for all kinds of

CHEMICALS (Con.)

commercial analysis and technical investigations. Our line of druggists' sundries, sponges, etc., is unusually large and we are also prepared to fill orders for proprietary preparations of all kinds.

Merck & Co., 15 University Pl. (Battery) ......AAA
Roessler & Haaslacher Chemical Co. (Enamellers, Incandescent Light; Potters; Mantle) ......AA
Zucker & Levett & Loeb Co., 528 W. 25th (Electro) . A
PA.—Philadelphia
Powers - Weightman - Rosengarten Co., 9th & Parrish (Battery) ....AAAA
WIS.—Milwaukee
Fiebing Chemical Co. (Tanners) ....D

CHEMISES

See Underwear

CHENILLES

See Silk Goods

CHERRIES

New York City
Reboulin Fils & Co., E. (Maraschino) ....A
OHIO—Cincinnati
Rheinstrom Bros. (Maraschino) ....AA

CHESSMEN

See Games

CHESTNUT

See Lumber

CHESTS

CONN.—New Haven
Harrison, Lenoard D. (Bolting) ....H
CONN.—Willimantic
Vanderman Plumbing & Heating Co. (Steel Tool) C
ILL.—Chicago
Besley & Co., Chas. H., 10 Canal (Tool) ....AA
Cowan & Co., W. K., 213 Mich. Av. (Cedar) ....A
IND.—Richmond
Richmond City Mill Works (Bolting) ....B
KANS.—Enterprise
Ehrsam Machine Co., J. B. (Bolting) ....B
KANS.—Leavenworth
Great Western Mfg. Co. (Bolting) ....AA
MASS.—Boston
Paine Furniture Co., 48 Canal (Tool; Cedar) ......A
White & Son, W. B. (Cedar) ....D
MASS.—North Easton
New England Specialty Co. (Boys' Tool) ....F
MO.—St. Louis
St. Louis Stamping Co. (Spice) ....AAAA
N. Y.—Buffalo
Shepard & Co., Sidney (Roessler) ....AAAA
New York City
American Tool Chest Co., 20 W. Houston (Tool; Machinists' Tool; Boys' Tool) C
Central Stamping Co., 24 Cliff (Spice) ......AA
Frasse Co., 38 Cortlandt (Tool) ....D
Herring - Hall - Marvin Co., 400 B'way (Iron) ......B
Jennings & Co., C. E., 101 Reade (Tool) ....B
Millers Falls Co., 28 Warren (Tool) ....AA
Stoutenborough, X., 277 Pearl (Spice) ....D

CHESTS (Con.)

OHIO—Canton
Diebold Safe & Lock Co. (Iron) ....AAA
OHIO—Cincinnati
Duchscher & Co., N. (Cedar) C
Hall's Safe Co. (Iron) ....A
Mitchell Furniture Co., Robert (Cedar) ......AAAA
OHIO—Columbus
Case Mfg. Co. (Bolting)...A
Jeffrey Mfg. Co. (Bolting) ....AAAA
OHIO—Hamilton
Macneale & Urban Co. (Iron) X
Mosler Safe Co. (Iron) ....AAAA
PA.—Downingtown
Downingtown Mfg. Co., Ltd. (Stuff) ....A
PA.—Philadelphia
Hall Son & Co., Amos H. (Stuff) C
PA.—Pittsburg
Barnes Safe & Lock Co. (Burglar Proof) X
PA.—York
York Safe & Lock Co. (Iron) ....A
R. I.—Pawtucket
Bliss Mfg. Co., R. (Boys' Tool) ....AAAA
TENN.—Nashville
Ransom & Co., John B. (Cedar) ....A

CHEVALS

See Furniture

CHEVIOTS

See Cotton Goods & Woolen Goods.

CHICORY

CAL.—Stockton
Bachmann & Brandt ......A
ILL.—Chicago
Habel, Aug., 502 Blue Island Av. X
MICH.—Ann Arbor
Ann Arbor Chicory Co.....D
MICH.—Bad Axe
Bad Axe Chicory Factory..X
MICH.—Bay City
Belgian Chicory Mills C
Buck, H. E. ....D
National Chicory Co. C
MICH.—Capac
Vanneste Bros. ....F
MICH.—New Haven
New Haven Evaporating Co. ....G
MICH.—Port Huron
Miller & Co., E. B. (Br. N. Y. City) ....A
NEBR.—Schuyler
Nebraska Chicory Co. ....D
NEBR.—Sioux
Soo Beet Syrup & Chicory Co. ....B
N. J.—Jersey City
Haesaert & Buysse, 35 Sussex ....B
N. Y.—Brooklyn
Floto's Sons, Geo. C
N. Y.—Flushing
Francke, Sohne & Co.....A
New York City
Blume, F. E., 103 Water..C
Blume & Co., 103 Water..A
Gillies & Co., E. J., 245 Washington ....AA
Muller & Co., E. B., 10 9th Av. ....A
Seggerman Bros., 91 Hudson ....B
PA.—Philadelphia
Johnson & Co., P. C., 25 Wash. Av. ....AAA
WIS.—Cedarbury
Frank Chicory Co. ....F

CHIFFON

See Silk

CHIFFONIERS

See Furniture

CHIMES

See also Bells

CONN.—East Hampton
Bevin Bros. Mfg. Co. (Saddle; Church; Band) ....A
Gong Bell Mfg. Co. (Sleigh Bell) ....AAAA
CONN.—Ivoryton
Comstock, Cheney & Co. (Orchestra) ....AA
CONN.—New Haven
Shoninger Co., B. (Orchestra) ....AAA
CONN.—Waterbury
American Ring Co. (Sleigh Bell) ....A
R. I.—Providence
Durfee & Co., W. H. (Organ; Stage) C

CHIMNEYS

CONN.—Bridgeport
Bridgeport Boiler Works (Iron) ....D
CONN.—New Haven
Eagle Flint Glass Co. (Lamp; Glass) X
GA.—Augusta
Lombard Iron Works & Supply Co. (Steel) ....A
ILL.—Chicago
Adams & Westlake Co. (Lamp; Glass) ....AAAA
Illinois Malleable Iron Co., 30 W. Monroe (Cast Iron) AAAA
ILL.—Ottawa
De La Chapelle & Co., E. & J. (Lamp; Glass)...AA
IND.—Alexandria
Lippincott Glass Co. (Lamp; Glass) ....A
IND.—Arcadia
Caylor-Ellis Glass Co. (Lamp; Glass) X
IND.—Ellwood
McCloy Glass Co., W. R. (Lamp; Glass) ....D
IND.—Evansville
Sargeant Glass Co. (Lamp; Glass) ....B
IND.—Matthews
Kauffeld Glass Co. (Lamp; Glass) X
IND.—New Albany
Heegewald Co., Chas. (Iron; Steel) ....B
MASS.—Boston
Huse & Son, Jos. (Mica)...A
North Carolina Mica Co. (Mica) ....D
Union Glass Co. (Lamp; Glass) ....B
MICH.—Detroit
Northern Engineering Works (Steel) ....A
MICH.—Saginaw
Wickes Bros. (Steel).AAA
N. Y.—Brooklyn
Williamsburg Flint Glass Co. (Lamp; Glass) .....E
N. Y.—Corning
Corning Glass Wks. (Lamp; Glass) ....A
New York City
Babcock & Wilcox Co., 85 Liberty (Iron; Steel) AAAA
Block Light Co., 17 Park Pl. (Incandescent Gas Light)
Feusterer & Ruhe, 47 Murray (Incandescent Gas).B
Gleason Mfg. Co., E. P., 20 W. Houston (Lamp; Glass; Mica) ....B
Kirchberger & Co., M., 50 Warren (Incandescent Gas Light) C
Koven, L. O., 50 Cliff (Steel) ....A
Lovell & Co., F. H., 92 William (Glass) ....A
Mica Mfg. Co., 307 W. B'way (Lamp; Mica) ...C
Noe, Thos. R., 53 Murray (Incandescent Gas Light) ....A
Turl's Sons, John, 534 W. 28th (Iron; Steel) ......D

CHIMNEYS (Con.)
N. Y.—Owego
Storrs Mica Co. (Lamp; Mica) C
N. Y.—Port Jervis
Brox & Ryall (Lamp; Glass) ....A
Orange Co. Flint Glass Wks. (Lamp; Glass) ....A
N. Y.—Tonawanda
Gillie Engine & Machine Co. (Iron; Steel) C
OHIO—Akron
Biggs Boiler Works Co. (Iron; Steel) C
OHIO—Bellaire
National Glass Co. (Lamp; Glass) ....B
Rodefer, T. A. (Lamp; Glass) ....A
OHIO—Cincinnati
Tudor Boiler Mfg. Co. (Steel) ....B
OHIO—Columbiana
Columbiana Boiler Co. (Steel) C
OHIO—Salem
Clark Co., W. J. (Steel).A
OHIO—Steubenville
Gill Bros. Co. (Acme Lead Glass Works) (Lamp; Glass) ....AA
OHIO—Youngstown
Pollock, Wm. B. (Steel).AA
PA.—Allegheny
Carlin's Sons, Thos. (Steel) A
PA.—Charleroi
Macbeth & Co., Geo. (Lamp; Glass) ....AAAA
PA.—Chester
Wetherill & Co., Robert (Steel; Self-Supporting) AAAA
PA.—Coraopolis
Consolidated Lamp & Glass Co. (Lamp; Glass) .....A
PA.—Ellwood City
Clark Bros. Glass Mfg. Co. (Lamp; Glass) ....A
PA.—Jeanette
McKee-Jeanette Glass Co. (Lamp; Glass) ....B
PA.—Monaca
Phoenix Glass Co. (Br. Pittsburg) (Lamp; Glass) A
PA.—New Castle
Pennsylvania Engineering Works (Steel) ....AA
PA.—Philadelphia
Gill & Co. (Lamp; Glass).A
Gillinder & Sons (Lamp; Glass) ....B
Lindsay & Co., W. W., 1502 Market (Steel) C
Murray & Co., Jas. J. (Lamp; Glass) ....A
Reichman, Geo., 1406 N 10th (Lamp; Mica)....F
PA.—Pittsburg
McKee & Co., S. (Lamp; Glass) ....D
National Glass Co. (Glass) X
Pittsburg Lamp, Brass & Glass Co. (Glass).AAAA
Macbeth-Evans Glass Co. (Lamp; Glass; Steel; Iron) ....AAAA
Phoenix Glass Co. (Lamp; Glass) ....A
Riter-Conley Mfg. Co. (Iron; Steel) ....A
Scaife & Sons' Co., Wm. B. (Steel) ....AAA
U. S. Glass Co. (Lamp; Glass) ....AAAA
PA.—Warren
Struthers, Wells & Co. (Steel) ....AA
PA.—Washington
Petroleum Iron Works Co. (Steel) ....A
PA.—White Mills
Dorflinger & Sons, C. (Lamp; Glass) ....AA
PA.—Williamsport
Keeler Co., E. (Steel)....A
PA.—York
Broomell, Schmidt & Steacy Co. (Steel) ....A
W. VA.—Salem
Rand Lamp Chimney Co.

CHINAWARE

MD.—Baltimore
Bennett Pottery Co., Edwin
(Decorated) ....A
Maryland Pottery Co. (Decorated) ....B
New York City
Ahrenfeldt & Son, Chas., 50
Murray ....B
Bawo & Dotter, 26 Barclay
(Art) ....AA
Borgfeldt & Co., Geo., 48
W. 4th (Art) .....AAAA
Davison Bros., 12 Barclay
B
Dwenger, C. L., 35 Park Pl.
(Art) ....D
Endemann & Churchill, 50
Murray (Art) ....D
Fondeville & Van Iderstine,
37 Warren (Art) C
Gerard, Dufraisseix & Abbott, 29 Barclay (Art).X
Haviland & Abbott Co., 29
Barclay (Art) C
Hollis. H. B., 64 Murray
(Art) ....
Lazarus, Rosenfeld & Lehmann, 62 Murray (Art).B
Parontaud & Watson, 37
Murray (Art) ....B
Rowland & Marcellus Co.,
41 Barclay (Art) X
Royal Copenhagen Porcelain
Co., 2 Hudson (Art)...X
Straus & Sons, L., 42 Warren (Art) ....AAAA
Vantine & Co., A. A., 20
E. 18th (Oriental) .AAA
Vogt & Dose, 43 Barclay
(Art) ....D
N. J.—Trenton
Cook Pottery Co. ....A
International Pottery Co.
(Decorated; Semi-Vitreous) ....B
Mercer Pottery Co. (Decorated; White) .....AA
Trenton Potteries Co. (Decorated) ....AAA
Willetts Mfg. Co. (Decorated; White) ....A
OHIO—Cincinnati
Rookwood Pottery Co. (Decorated) ....B
OHIO—East Liverpool
Brunt Pottery Co., Wm.
(Decorated) ....A
Burford Bros. Pottery Co.
X
Cartwright Bros. Co. (Decorated) ....
Croxall Pottery Co. (Decorated) ....B
East End China Co. (Decorated) .....B
East Liverpool Pottery Co.
(Decorated) ....A
Goodwin Pottery Co. (Decorated) ....AA
Harker Pottery Co. (Decorated) ....A
Knowles, Taylor & Knowles
Co. (Decorated; Semi-Vitreous) ....AAAA
Laughlin-Homer China Co.
(Decorated; Semi-Vitreous) ....AAAA
McNicol Pottery Co., D. E.
(Decorated) ....AA
Murphy & Co., Geo. C.
(Decorated) ....B
Potters' Co-operative Co.
(Decorated) ....AA
Standard Pottery Co. (Decorated) ....A
Thompson Pottery Co., C.
C. (Decorated) ......AA
Vodrey Pottery Co. (Decorated) ....A
West End Pottery Co. (Decorated) ....A
OHIO—East Palestine
East Palestine Pottery Co.
(Decorated) ....A
Ohio China Co. (Decorated)
B
OHIO—Steubenville
Steubenville Pottery Co.
(Decorated; Semi-Vit

reous) ....A
OHIO—Wellsville
Wellsville China Co. (Decorated) ....A
PA.—Beaver Falls
Mayer Pottery Co., Ltd.
(Decorated) ....A
W. VA.—Wheeling
Warwick China Co. (Decorated) ....A
Wheeling Pottery Co. (Decorated) ....AAA

CHINCHILLAS
See Wollen Goods

CHINOIDINE
New York City
McKesson & Robbins, 91
Fulton ....AAAA

CHIPPERS
ILL.—Evanston
Sheldon & Co., E. H.
(Rotary Ice) ....D
IOWA—Cedar Falls
Wagner Mfg. Co. (Ice)...D
MICH.—East Saginaw
Mitts & Merrill (Dye Wood)
B
OHIO—Cincinnati
Dana & Co. (Ice) ....A
PA.—Philadelphia
North Bros. Mfg. Co., Lehigh Av. & N. American
(Ice) ....A

CHIPS
See Games

CHISELS
CAL.—San Francisco
Doble Co., Abner, 200 Fremont (Brick; Stone Cutters') ....A
CONN.—Bridgeport
Hurwood Mfg. Co. (Socket)
B
Knapp & Cowles Mfg. Co.
(Carpenters'; Cold).....C
CONN.—Collinsville
Collins Co. (Brick; Stone
Cutters'; Track) .AAAA
CONN.—Hartford
Billings & Spencer Co. (Drop
Forged Cold; Cape; Carpenters') ....A
CONN.—Middletown
Wilcox, Crittenden & Co.
(Cold; Cape) ....A
CONN.—New Britain
Humason & Beckley Mfg.
Co. (Box) ....A
Landers, Frary & Clark
(Ice) ....AAA
Russell & Erwin Mfg. Co.
(Carpenters'; Socket;
Tanged; Box) ....AAAA
CONN.—New Haven
Hilborn & Bishop Co., 81
Lloyd (Cold; Cape; Box;
Brick; Calking; Diamond
Point) C
CONN.—Norwich
Rogers & Co., C. B. (Mortiser) ....A
CONN.—Seymour
Swan Co., James (Carpenters') ....A
CONN.—Southington
Peck, Stow & Wilcox Co.
(Carpenters'; Cold; Cape;
Box; Socket; Tanged;
Wire) ....AAAA
CONN.—Winsted
Winsted Edge Tool Works
(Carpenters'; Hot) ....B
ILL.—Chicago
Solid Tool Steel Co., 11 S.
Jefferson (Track) .....F
Vaughan & Bushnell Co., 877
Carroll Av. (Brick; Cold;
Cape) ....A
Whitman & Barnes Mfg. Co.,
West Pullman (Cold;
Cape) ....AAAA
ILL.—Decatur
Mueller Mfg. Co., H. (Calk-

ing; Floor) ....AAA
ILL.—Downer's Grove
Dicke Tool Co. (Cold; Cape)
.................................C
ILL.—Freeport
Stover Mfg. Co. (Ice) ...AA
ILL.—Rockford
Forrest City Bit & Tool Co.
(Mortising; Hollow;
Solid) ....U
IND.—Evansville
Evansville Tool Works
(Brick; Cold; Cape; Stone
Cutters'; Track) ......A
IOWA—Cedar Falls
Wagner Mfg. Co. (Ice) ..D
IOWA—Fort Madison
Iowa Farming & Tool Co.
(Ice) ....A
MASS.—Boston
Harvey, H. H., 608 Atlantic
Av. (Brick; Cold; Cape;
Stone Cutters'; Track;
Chipping) ....A
MASS.—Brockton
Tuck Mfg. Co., 74 Ames
(Cold; Cape) ....G
MASS.—Fiskdale
Snell Mfg. Co. (Cold; Cape;
Carpenters') ....B
MASS.—Kingston
Drew & Co., C. (Cold; Cape;
Box; Carpenters') C
MASS.—Millbury
Buck, Chas. (Carpenters';
Socket; Tanged; Cold;
Floor; Ripping) ....B
Buck Bros. (Carpenters';
Cold; Cape; Socket;
Tanged) ....A
MICH.—Detroit
Anderson & Sons, W. H.
(Brick; Calking; Cold;
Cape; Stone Cutters';
Track) C
Detroit Steel & Spring Co.
(Chipping; Drove; Hot;
Diamond; Pitching Tool;
Track) ....D
MICH.—Kalamazoo
Kalamazoo Railway Supply
Co. (Track) ....B
MINN.—Minneapolis
Therien, J. O., 116 First Av.,
N. (Cold; Cape) ....E
MO.—St. Louis
Crescent Novelty Mfg. Co.
(Brick; Cold; Cape)....D
Mound Tool & Scraper Co.,
710 Howard (Cold; Cape)
.................................X
Schueddig & Son, 525 S. Jef-
ferson (Stone Cutters').E
N. J.—Elizabeth
Atha Tool Co. (Brick; Cold;
Cape; Stone Cutters';
Track; Diamond) ......A
Braunsdorf - Mueller Co.
(Box; Brick; Cold; Floor;
Ripping) ....D
Bernz, Otto S., 13th & S.
Orange Av. (Brick; Calk-
ing; Cold; Cape; Floor).P
Heller Tool Co. (Track;
Hot) ....D
Johnson, Wm., 249 Plane
(Cold; Cape) ....D
Kraeuter & Co., 577 18th
Av. (Cold; Cape)......E
Osborne & Co., C. S. (Calk-
ing; Box; Gasket) ....B
N. J.—Smithville
Smith Machine Co., H. B.
(Mortiser) ....A
N. Y.—Brooklyn
Carver, John, 80 Wallabout
(Cold; Cape) X
N. Y.—Buffalo
Niagara Machine & Tool
Works (Wire) ......AAA
White Co., L. & I. J. (Car-
penters'; Socket; Tanged)
.................................A
N. Y.—Little Falls
Cheney Hammer Co., Henry
(Track) ....D
New York City
American Axe & Tool Co.,
253 B'way (Carpenters')
.................................AAAA
American Wood Working
Mach. Co., 136 Liberty

(Carpenters'; Mortiser)
.................................AAA
Grafrath, Charles, 218 W.
20th (Dental) ....E
Hammacher, Schlemmer &
Co., 209 Bowery (Carpen-
ters'; Stone Cutters')
.................................AAA
Jennings & Co., C. E., 101
Reade (Carpenters'; Cold;
Cape; Socket) ....D
Mead, I. V., 418 E. 110th
(Stone Cutters') ......F
Sargent & Co., 151 Leonard
(Box; Cold) .....AAAA
Tower & Lyon Co., 95 Cham-
bers (Socket) ....B
N. Y.—Syracuse
Syracuse Twist Drill Co.
(Cold; Cape) ....B
OHIO—Alliance
Transue & Williams Co.
(Cold) ....A
OHIO—Canton
Ney Mfg. Co. (Cold) ....B
OHIO—Cincinnati
Fay & Egan Co., J. A. (Mor-
tiser) ....AAAA
OHIO—Cleveland
Gerlach & Co., Peter (Alli-
gator) ....B
OHIO—Columbus
Ohio Tool Co. (Carpenters';
Gasket; Mortiser; Socket)
.................................A
OHIO—Defiance
Defiance Mach. Wks. (Mor-
tiser) ....A
OHIO—Ravenna
Williams, A. C. (Ice) ....A
PA.—Chester
Black & Co., H. B. (Car-
penter's) ....A
PA.—Corry
McInness Steel Co. (Track)
.................................C
PA.—Ogontz
Hammond & Son Co. (Cold;
Cape; Chipping) ....A
PA.—Philadelphia
Goodell & Waters (Mortiser)
.................................X
Pedrick & Ayer (Track)..A
Plumb, Fayette E., Fkfd.
(Brick; Carpenters'; Cold;
Cape; Stone Cutters';
Track) ....AA
Pugh, Job. I., 31st & Lud-
low (Hollow Mortising).C
Stortz & Son, Jno., 210 Vine
(Brick; Cold; Cape; Stone
Cutters'; Floor) ......F
PA.—Pittsburg
Hubbard & Co., Murtland
Bldg. (Cold; Cape; Track)
.................................A
Iron City Tool Works, 32d
& Smallman (Cold; Cape;
Track) ....B
Klein-Logan Co., S. 13th &
Breed (Cold; Cape; Track)
.................................A
Pittsburg Tool & Drop
Forge Co., Arrott Bldg.
(Track) ....E
PA.—Verona
Verona Tool Works (Cold;
Cape; Track) ....A
VT.—Barre
Trow & Holden (Granite).B
W. VA.—Wheeling
Wheeling Hinge Co. (Car-
penters'; Cold; Cape;
Coal) ....AA

CHLORAL

New York City
Boehringer & Soehme, 7
Cedar ....A

CHLORIDE
OF LIME

See Lime

CHLOROFORM

MD.—Baltimore
Thomsen Chemical Co. ..B

CHLOROFORM (Con.)

MASS.—Boston
Billings, Clapp & Co.....B
MO.—St. Louis
Larkin & Scheffer Chemical Co. ....A
Mallinckrodt Chemical Wks. AAAA

N. Y.—Albany
Albany Chemical Co. .....A
New York City
Merck & Co. ....AAA
New York Quinine & Chem. Wks. ....A
Pfizer & Co., Chas. ..AAAA
Roessler & Hasslacher Chemical Co., 100 William ....AA
Schieffelin & Co., W. H. AA
PA.—Philadelphia
Powers- Weightman - Rosengarten Co. ....AAAA

CHOCOLATE & COCOA

CAL.—San Francisco
Ghiradelli Co., D., 617 Sansome ....AA
Sherwood & Sherwood, 212 Market ....AAA
ILL.—Chicago
Baker & Co. (Ltd.) Walter, 38 Lake ....AAAA
Chocolate Menier, 64 Wabash Av. ....AAAA
Cobb Chocolate Co., 374 E. Illinois ....B
Huylers, 49 Lake (Br. N. Y. City) ....A
Runkel Bros., 42 River....A
Van Houten and Zoon, 45 Wabash Av. .....AAAA
Volkman, Stollwerck & Co., 27 Mich. Av. ....AAAA
Wilbur & Son, H. O., 15 River (Br. Phila.) ..AA
MD.—Baltimore
Blue Ribbon Candy Co., 749 W. Pratt ....A
Headley Chocolate Co., 11 S. Fredk. C
MASS.—Boston
Baker & Co. (Ltd.) Walter, 247 Atlantic Av. ..AAAA
Lowney Co., W. M., 447 Commercial ....A
Schraff & Sons, W. F., 94 Portland C
Wenz, H., 9 Harcourt C
MASS.—Cambridge
Sparrow Co., H. F......A
MASS.—Dorchester
Baker & Co. (Ltd.) Walter AAAA
MINN.—Minneapolis
Oatmeal Cocoa Co. ......B
MO.—St. Louis
Blanke & Bro. Candy Co., 608 Market ....AA
N. J.—Newark
Hallock, Denton & Co.....B
N. Y.—Annandale
Baker, (Ltd.) W. H. ....A
N. Y.—Brooklyn
Baker & Co., J. H., 89 Bedford Av. ....A
Bischoff, F., 32 St. Felix (Ess. Cocoa) C
Matchett & Co., J. J., 390 Wythe Av. C
N. Y.—Buffalo
Phelps Co. 101 Seneca....C
N. Y.—Lockport
Niagara Mfg. & Merc. Co. C
New York City
Auerbach & Sons, D., 334 W. 39th C
Baker & Co. (Ltd.) W., 105 Hudson ....AAAA
Baker, W. H., 198 W. B'way C
Baker, W. H., 80 Wall (Br. Syracuse, N. Y.) C
Baker Co., W. P., 131st & Park Av ....B
Beling & Co., L., 410 W. 13th C
Burchard & Co., 265 Washn. B
Crane & Martin Co., 309 E.

CHOCOLATE & COCOA

22d ....B
Gousset, C., 137 Prince...B
Greek-American Confectionery Co., 7 Main C
Hawley & Hoops, 271 Mulberry ....AAA
Hershey Chocolate Co., 23 Worth ....AAAA
Hess Bros., 502 W. 30th..B
Herron, Jas. M., 6 Hanover B
"Huylers", 64 Irving Pl...A
Leeming & Co., T., 73 Warren ....B
Maillard, H., 118 W. 35th B
Menier (Firm of), 95 5th Av. ....AAAA
Phelps Co., 105 Hudson ...C
Phillips Chemical Co., 128 Pearl ....B
Plasmon Co. of America, 116 Broad ....AAA
Rach Cocoa Co., 202 Bleecker C
Rockwood Co., 468 Cherry AAA
Runkel Bros., 447 W. 30th A
Smith & Co., J. P., 90 Hudson ....A
Van Houten & Zoon...AAAA
Volkman, Stollwerck & Co., 5 Worth ....AAAA
Wilbur & Son, H. O., 6 Hanover ....AA
N. Y.—Syracuse
Baker, Wm. H. C
PA.—Lancaster
Hershey Chocolate Co. AAAA
PA.—Philadelphia
Baker, W. H., 117 Walnut A
Croft & Allen Co., Market & 33d ....AA
"Huylers", 1320 Chestnut. A
Miller & Son Co., G., 255 S. 3d ....AA
Whitman & Son, S. F., 606 Cherry ....AA
Wilbur & Co., H., 235 N. 3d AA
VA.—Winchester
Baker, W. H. ....A
WIS.—Milwaukee
Ambrosia Chocolate Co. ..B

CHOP

KANS.—McPherson
Pearl Milling Co. (Corn)..D
KANS.—Marionville
Marionville Roller Mill Co. (Corn) ....B
KANS.—Oakgrove
Oakgrove Mill Co. (Corn)..E
KANS.—Willington
Hunter Milling Co. (Corn).A
PA.—Fertility
Groff, I. B. (Corn) ......F

CHOPPERS

CONN.—Branford
New York Lock Co. (Meat; Food; Vegetable) ......B
CONN.—New Britain
Landers, Frary & Clark (Meat; Food; Vegetable) AAA
CONN.—Southington
Peck, Stow & Wilcox Co. (Meat; Food; Vegetable) AAAA
IOWA—Burlington
Murray Iron Works Co. (Meat) ....A
MASS.—Athol
Athol Machine Co. (Meat; Food; Vegetable) .....B
MO.—St. Louis
Brecht Butchers' Supply Co., Gus. V. (Power; Meat)..A
N. J.—Newark
Osborne & Co., C. S. (Meat) B
N. J.—Raritan
Kenyon & Son, D. R. (Meat) A
N. Y.—Buffalo
Smith's Sons, John E.

CHOPPERS (Con.)
(Meat) ....B
New York City
Chatillon & Sons, John, 87
Cliff (Meat; Food; Vege-
table) ....A
Graham & Co., John H., 113
Chambers (Meat; Food;
Vegetable) ....AA
Jennings & Co., C. E., 42
Murray (Butchers') ....D
Russell & Erwin Mfg. Co.,
43 Chambers (Meat; Food;
Vegetable) ....AAAA
Sargent & Co., 151 Leonard
(Meat; Food; Vegetable)
...............AAAA
Smith & Hemenway Co., 296
Bway. (Meat; Food; Vege-
table) ....D
Staubach, B., 652 E. 12th
(Power; Meat) ....A
N. Y.—Rochester
Streeter & Co., N. R. (Meat)
..................B
OHIO—Salem
Silver Mfg. Co. (Power;
Meat) ....A
PA.—Allegheny
Renkin Co., W. W. (Meat)
..................G
PA.—Elizabethtown
Buch's Sons, A. (Meat)..B
PA.—Enterprise
Enterprise Mfg. Co. of Pa.
(Meat; Food; Vegetable)
...............AAAA
PA.—Mount Joy
Rollman Mfg. Co. (Meat;
Food; Vegetable) ......G
PA.—Philadelphia
Model Mfg. Co. of Pennsyl-
vania (Meat) ....F
Nittinger, August (Power;
Meat) ....A
North Bros. Mfg. Co. (Meat;
Food; Vegetable) ......A
Plumb, Fayette R., Tasker
(Butchers') ....AA
Stortz & Son, John (Meat).F
S. C.—Blacksburg
Blacksburg Machine & Iron
Works (Cotton) ....E

CHOW CHOW

ILL.—Chicago
Henning, Wm., 113 E. North
Av. ....A
Squire, Dingee Co., 218 E.
Kenzie X
IOWA—Cedar Rapids
Breecht, Henry G. X
IOWA—Keokuk
Keokuk Pickle Co. ......B
MASS.—Boston
Skilton, Foote & Co.......X
MO.—St. Louis
Bayle, Geo. A. ....B
New York City
Gulden, Chas., 46 Elizabeth
..................AA
PA.—Philadelphia
Philadelphia Pickling Co...C

CHROMOS

MASS.—Springfield
Taber-Prang Art Co.....AA
New York City
Tobin, Michael F., 373
Broadway ....B

CHRONO-METERS

MASS.—Boston
Bond & Son, Wm., 148 State
..................E
New York City
Bliss & Co., Jno., 128 Front
(Ship) ....D
Kohlbusch, Herman, 194
Broadway ....B
Regus, T. S. & J. D., 140
Water ....B

CHUCKS

CONN.—Bridgeport
Smith & Egge Mfg. Co.
(Drills) ....A

CHUCKS (Con.)
Springfield Mfg. Co. (Emery
Wheel) C
CONN.—Hartford
Cushman Chuck Co. (Drill;
Jaw; Lathe; Planer; Com-
bined; Compound Circular;
Cutting off; Eccentric
Lathe; Independent Jaw;
Planet; Self-Centering;
Turret Lathe; Universal
Lathe; Amateur Lathe)
..................AA
Dwight Slate Machine Co.
(Lathe; Centering).....C
Jacobs, A. I. (Drill) ...D
Pratt & Whitney Co.
(Lathe; Planer; Drill;
Wire) ....AAAA
CONN.—New Britain
Skinner Chuck Co. (Drill
Lathe; Planer; Combined
Lathe; Car Wheel; Turret
Lathe; Centering; Milling
Machine) ....B
Union Mfg. Co. (Drill;
Lathe Machine; Screw Ma-
chine; Box; Scroll; Bi-
cycle; Centering; Boring
Mills; Turning Mills; Mill-
ing Machine; Planer).AA
CONN.—New Haven
Brown & Co., R. H. (Drill;
Planer; Lathe) ....B
Hoggson & Pettis Mfg. Co.
(Drill; Lathe; Car Wheel;
Independent Jaw; Univer-
sal Lathe) ....A
New Haven Mfg. Co. (Screw
Machine; Planer; Lathe)
..................AA
CONN.—New London
Whiton Machine Co., D. E.
(Drill; Jaw; Lathe Ma-
chine; Milling Machine;
Combined Lathe; Cutting
Off; Independent Jawed;
Self-Centering; Universal
Lathe; Valve; Amateur
Lathe) ....A
CONN.—Norwalk
Le Count, Wm. G. (Drill).D
CONN.—Tolland
Clough, R. M. (Drill;
Spring) X
CONN.—Torrington
Hendey Machine Co. (Plan-
er; Shaper) ....A
CONN.—Windsor Locks
Horton & Sons' Co., E.
(Drill; Jaw; Lathe; Mill-
ing Machine; Screw Ma-
chine; Brass Finishers';
Car Wheel; Cut-Off; In-
dependent Jaw; Gravity
Slip; Universal Lathe;
Boring Mills; Turning
Mills; Tapping) ....A
DEL.—Wilmington
Trump Bros. Machine Co.
(Drill; Lathe) ....A
ILL.—Chicago
Massey Vise Co., 30 S. Ca-
nal (Milling Machine;
Planer) ....E
ILL.—Elgin
Moseley Lathe Co. (Gravity
Slip) ....D
ILL.—Freeport
Hoefer Mfg. Co. (Drill)..D
MASS.—Boston
American Tool & Machine
Co. (Box; Turret Lathe;
Drill; Planer) ....AA
Faneuil Watch Tool Co.
(Self-Centering) C
MASS.—Fitchburg
Fitchburg Machine Works
(Planer) ....A
Putnam Machine Co. (Drill;
Lathe Machine; Screw Ma-
chine; Combined Lathe;
Eccentric Lathe; Indepen-
dent Jawed; Turret Lathe;
Universal Lathe; Rack;
Scraper) ....AA
MASS.—Greenfield
Buttler Chuck Co. (Drill).D
Goodell-Pratt Co. (Drill)..B
Wiley & Russell Mfg. Co.
(Drill) ....AA

CHUCKS (Con.)

MASS.—Millers Falls
Millers Falls Co. (Drill).AA

MASS.—New Bedford
Morse Twist-Drill & Machine
Co. (Drill; Lathe Drill;
Twist Drill; Self-Center-
ing; Independent Jawed)
AAA

MASS.—Orange
Leavitt Machine Co. (Lathe)
D

MASS.—Waltham
American Watch Tool Co.
(Wire) ....D

MASS.—Worcester
Draper Machine Tool Co.
(Planer) ....A
Norton Emery Wheel Co.
(Lathe; Emery Wheel
Bushing) ....AAA
Reed Co., Francis (Planer;
Planet) ....D
Walker, O. S., Station D
(Magnetic) ....H

MICH.—Detroit
Detroit Twist Drill Co.
(Drill) C

MICH.—Grand Rapids
Fox Machine Co., 127 N.
Front (Planer) X

MO.—St. Louis
St. Louis Machine Tool Co.,
1114 S. 8th (Tapping)..X

N. J.—Newark
Gould & Eberhardt, 95 N. J.
R. R. Av. (Drill; Lathe;
Combined Lathe; Com-
pound Circular; Oval) ..A

N. J.—Plainfield
Pond Machine Tool Co. (Br.
Niles-Bement-Pond Co.,
N. Y. City) (Planer)
AAAA

N. J.—Smithville
Smith Machine Co., H. B.
(Wood Lathe) ....A

N. Y.—Brooklyn
Almond, T. R., 83 Washn.
(Drill) C
Bliss Co., E. W., 19 Adams
(Spinning) ....AAAA
Hay-Budden Mfg. Co., 254
N. Henry (Forged Tool
Steel Spinning) ......B

N. Y.—Frankfort
Pratt Chuck Co. (Driving
Drill; Lathe) ....A

N. Y.—Lockport
Trevor Mfg. Co. (Lathe)..B

New York City
Errington, F. A., 39 Cort-
landt (Screw Cutting;
Auto. Opening; Tapping;
Die; Gravity Slip)......D
Fairbanks Co., 416 Broome
(Boring Mills; Turning
Mills; Lathe) ....AAAA
Garvin Machine Co., 137
Varick (Drill; Screw Ma-
chine Lathe) ......AAA
Jennings Co., C. E., 42
Murray (Drill) ....D
Niles-Belmont-Pond Co., 111
B'way (Centering; Drill;
Boring Mills; Turning
Mills; Independent; Uni-
versal Lathe; Milling Ma-
chine; Planer) ....AAAA
Peck, Stow & Wilcox Co.
(Lathe) ....AAAA
Tower & Lyon Co., 95 Cham-
bers (Planer) ....B

N. Y.—Oneida
Oneida National Chuck Co.
(Drill; Jaw; Lathe; Mill-
ing Machine; Planer;
Screw Machine; Twist
Drill) ....AAA
Westcott Chuck Co. (Drill;
Lathe; Car Wheel; Com-
bined Lathe; Cutting Off;
Eccentric Lathe; Inde-
pendent Jawed; Self-Sen-
tering; Turret Lathe; Uni-
versal Lathe; Boring;
Turning Mills; Milling
Machine) ....A

N. Y.—Seneca Falls
Seneca Falls Mfg. Co.
(Drill) ....B

N. Y.—Yonkers
Saunders' Sons, D. (Drill;

CHUCKS (Con.)
Tap; Lever; Concentric
Three Jawed; Independent
Jawed; Key Nippel; Uni-
versal Lathe) ....A

OHIO—Cleveland
Cleveland Twist Drill Co.
(Cox & Prentiss) (Drill)
A
Standard Tool Co. (Drill;
Lathe) ....AAA
Warner & Swasey, 57 E.
Prospect (Jaw; Lathe).A

OHIO—Shelby
Brightman Mfg. Co. (Drill)
AA

PA.—Erie
Holland's Mfg. Co. (Planer)
C
Modern Tool Co. (Drill, for
Reamers & Counterbores;
Tapping) ....E

PA.—Philadelphia
Harrington & Sons Co., E.
1515 Penna. Av. (Lathe;
Planer) ....AA
Pedrick & Ayer Co., 1001
Hamilton (Planer) .....A

PA.—Pittsburg
American Tool Wks. Co., 6th
& Empire Bldg. (Drill;
Planer) ....AA

R. I.—Pawtucket
Potter & Johnston Machine
Co. (Lever; Independent;
Universal) ....A

CHURNS

ILL.—Chicago
Barber Creamery Supply Co.,
A. H. (Butter Workers
Combined) ....B
Boyd, John (Dairy) ......B
Creamery Package Mfg. Co.
(Dairy; Power) ...AAAA
Sturges & Burn Mfg. Co..A

ILL.—Elgin
Barclay, D. F. (Dairy)....A

ILL.—Monmouth
Milne Mfg. Co. (Butters
Workers Combined)....C

ILL.—Rockford
Dobson Mfg. Co. (Dairy).B
McDermaid, John (Dairy;
Barrel) ....A
Palmer Co., H. H. (Dairy)
D

IND.—Fort Wayne
Wayne Mfg. Co., Anthony
(Dairy) X

IND.—Goshen
I. X. L. & Goshen Pump Co.
(Dairy) ....B

IOWA—Clinton
Moseley & Pritchard Mfg.
Co. (Dairy) ....D

IOWA—Davenport
Brammer Mfg. Co., H. F.
(Dairy) ....A

IOWA—Fort Dodge
Fort Dodge Stoneware Co.
(Stone) C

MASS.—Boston
American Tool & Machine
Co. (Rubber) ....AA
Ames Plow Co. (Dairy; Box;
Thermometer) .....AAAA

MICH.—Bay City
Bousfield & Co. (Inc.)
(Dairy) ....AA

MICH.—Flint
Flint Cabinet Creamery Co.
(Dairy) ....E

MICH.—Jackson
Aspinwall Mfg. Co. (Dairy)
B

MINN.—Owatonna
Owatonna Mfg. Co. (Butter
Workers Combined) ...B

N. Y.—Fort Edward
Hilfinger Bros. (Pottery).G

N. Y.—Little Falls
Burrell & Co., D. H.
(Dairy) ....AAAA

N. Y.—South Stockton
Fenner, R. W. (Dairy; Barrel; Box) ....H

N. Y.—Syracuse
Gowing, D. H. (Dairy;
Power) C

N. Y.—Union Center
Edson, Wyman L. (Dairy;

CHURNS (Con.)
Oil Test) ....H
N. Y.—Utica
Jones, Frank L. (Dairy)..C
OHIO—Hamilton
Deuscher Co., H. P. (Dairy)
A

OHIO—Sidney
Anderson & Carothers (But-
ter) C
Buckeye Churn Co. (Dairy)
B
OHIO—Wapaconeta
Brown & Co., M. (Dairy).A
Standard Churn Co. (Dairy;
Barrel; Revolving).....B
PA.—Philadelphia
Reid, A. H. (Dairy; Bar-
rel; Box; Factory; Power)
A

PA.—York
Farquhar Co., A. B. (Ltd.)
(Dairy) ....AAA
TENN.—Nashville
Prewitt, Spurr & Co.
(Dairy) ....A
VT.—Bellows Falls
Vermont Farm Machine Co.
(Dairy; Barrel; Box; Fac-
tory; Power; Swing)...C
VT.—Rutland
Stoddard Mfg. Co. (Dairy;
Barrel; Box; Factory;
Power) ....B
VT.—St. Albans
St. Albans Foundry Co.
(Dairy) ....D
W. VA.—Richmond
Richmond Cedar Wks.
(Ltd.) (Dairy) ....AAAA
WIS.—Fort Atkinson
Cornish, Curtis & Greene
Mfg. Co. (Dairy; Box;
Factory; Oil Test; Butter
Workers Combined).....A
WIS.—Menasha
Menasha Woodenware Co.
(Dairy) ....AA
WIS.—Racine
Racine Malleable & Wrought
Iron Co. (Dairy).......A
WIS.—Whitewater
Wisconsin Dairy Supply Co.
(Dairy) ....D

CHUTES

DEL.—Wilmington
McCullough Iron Co. (Coal)
AA
ILL.—Chicago
Allis-Chalmers Co., Home
Ins. Bldg. (Coal)..AAAA
Borden & Selleck Co., 118
Lake (Coal) ....A
Fairbanks, Morse & Co.,
Franklin & Monroe (Loco-
motive Loading Coal)
AAAA
Hoisting & Conveying Mach.
Co., 44 N. Elizabeth
(Coal) ....H
Kasper Oats Cleaner Co.
(Oat Cleaning for Stables)
F
ILL.—Moline
Williams, White & Co. (Lo-
comotive Loading Coal;
Automatic Coal) ....A
MASS.—Holyoke
Connor Steel Plate Ash
Chute Co. (Steel Plate
Ash) ....F
MASS.—Worcester
Hill Dryer Co., (Garbage).D
MICH.—Lansing
Lansing Wheelbarrow Co.
(Coal) ....AAA
N. J.—Hoboken
Union Iron Works (Coal).C
New York City
Hunt Co., C. W., 45 Bway.
(Coal) ....A
Koven & Bro., L. O., 50
Cliff (Coal; Grain, &c.).A
N. Y.—Rochester
Cutler Mfg. Co. (Mail)..AA
OHIO—Cleveland
Garry Iron & Steel Co.
(Coal) ....A
Wellman-Seaver-Morgan Co.,
(Coal) ....AAAA

CHUTES (Con.)
OHIO—Youngstown
Pollock Co., Wm. B. (Coal)
B
PA.—Monongahela
Monongahela Mfg. Co.
(Coal) C
PA.—New Castle
Pennsylvania Engineering
Wks. (Coal) ....A
PA.—Pittsburg
Riter-Conley Mfg. Co.
(Coal; Ore) ....AAA
Scaife & Sons Co., W. B.
(Coal) ....AAA
PA.—Scottdale
Kenney & Co. (Coal) .....A
W. VA.—Wheeling
Wheeling Hinge Co. (Coal)
AA

CIDER, VINE-
GAR, PICKLES
SAUERKRAUT

ALA.—Birmingham
Nabers, Morrow & Sinnige,
(C.; V.) ....A
ALA.—Ft. Smith
Oklahoma Vinegar Co. (C.;
V.; P.) C
ARK.—Little Rock
Lasker Bros. (C.).........A
CAL.—Los Angeles
Hill & Sons Co., Jas. (C.;
V.; P.) C
Keppler & Tamm, 235 San
Pedro ....B
Los Angeles Pickle Co., 737
San Fernando (P.).....C
Vache & Co., T. (V.)....B
CAL.—San Francisco
Calif. Vinegar Co., 431 7th
(C. & V.) C
Fisher Packing Co. 509
Coml. (C.; V.; P.).....C
Lewis Packing Co. Vinegar
Wks., 635 Front (C.; V.;
P.) C
Loeffler, John, 422 5th...C
Pacific Vinegar & Pickle
Wks, 122 Davis........A
Phila. Mfg. Co., 431 7th
(V.; P.) C
Phila. Vinegar Wks. Bryant
& 7th (C.; V.) C
Sherwood & Sherwood, 212
Mkt. (C.; V.; P.)....AAA
South End Pickle Works,
422 5th (P.)...........C
COLO.—Denver
Beebe-Cranel Pickle Co.,
11th & Bayard (C.; V.;
P.) C
Kuner Pickle Co., 22d &
Blake ....B
COLO.—Longmont
Empson Packing Co. (P.).A
CONN.—Hartford
Fitzgerald, R. N., 44 Mar-
ket (P.)...............B
CONN.—Melrose
Thompson & Son, J. A. (C.;
V.) ....A
CONN.—New Haven
Bates Co., L. (The) (P.).A
Dillon & Douglass (V.; P.)
A
CONN.—Nichols
Fairchild, E. S. (C.; V.)..C
CONN.—Windsor
Ellsworth & Filley (P.)..A
GA.—Albany
Albany Mfg. Co. (C.) .....A
GA.—Atlanta
Oklahoma Vinegar Co. (Br.
Ft. Smith, Ark.) (C.; V.)
C
GA.—Augusta
Grocers' Mfg. Co. (C.)....B
GA.—Macon
Mohawk Cider & Vinegar
Wks. (C.; V.)..........C
GA.—Savannah
Solomon & Son, H. (C.;
V.) ....AA
ILL.—Belleville
St. Clair Vinegar Co. (C.;
V.) ....A
ILL.—Bloomington
Bloomington Can Co. (S.,

CIDER, VINEGAR, &C.
(Canned) ....B
Bloomington Cider & Vinegar Co. (C.; V.; P.)...C
ILL.—Blue Island
Henke & Hoffner (S.)....A
ILL.—Brighton
Hilliard, Geo. W. (C.)....B
ILL.—Chicago
Barrett & Barrett, 260 Kinzie (C.; V.)........AAA
Budlong, L. A., Lincoln & Foster Av. (P.; S.)...A
Bunge Co., Wm. H., 71 N. Ann (C.; P.; S.).......A
Callahan & Co., A. P., 2407 La Salle (C.; V.).....A
Chicago Consolidated Bottling Co., 14 Lomax Pl. (C.) ....A
Claussen & Sons, C. F., N. Av. Boul. & 52d ......A
Dingee Squire Co., 175 Clybourn ....AA
Heinz Co., H. J., 1812 So. Clark (C.; V.; P.).AAAA
Hennig, Wm., 117 E. North Av. (C.; V.; P.)......A
Huss-Edler Preserve Co., 75 W. Kinzie (P.).......B
Illinois Vinegar Mfg. Co., 19th & Rockwell (C.; V.) ....AA
Prussing Vinegar Co. (A. P. Callahan), 135 Kinzie (C.; V.) ....A
Reid, Murdoch & Co., Lake & Mkt. ....AAAA
Spielman Bros. Co., 93 North Av. (C.; V.)....A
Stafford & Goldsmith, 698 Austin Av. (P.) ....A
Van Deursen, C. S. & M., 6 Dearborn (S.) ......B
Waidner Co., F. A., 42 River (S.) C
Wichert & Co., H., 1205 So. Paullina (P.) C
Wolff & Sons, M., 218 W. Lake (V.; P.; S.).....C
ILL.—Evanston
Dingee & Son, Saml. M. (P.) ....B
ILL.—Freeport
Burrell Bros. (C.; V.)....B
ILL.—Hampshire
Squire Dingee Co. (P.)..AA
ILL.—Kishwaukee
Johnson. F. C. (C.; V.)....A
ILL.—Lansing
Meeter, John (S.) C
ILL.—M'Henry
Stafford & Goldsmith Co. (Br. Chicago (P.)......B
ILL.—Norton Grove
Henning, W. (V.; P.)....A
ILL.—Nunda
Goodwin Sons, J. (P.)....C
ILL.—Quincy
Flynn & Co., J. J. (C.; V) ....A
Globe Pickle Co. (Br. St. Louis, Ill.) (C.; V.; P.) C
ILL.—Rockford
Johnson. F. C. (V.)......A
ILL.—Woodstock
Dingee Squire Co. (P.)..AA
IND.—Churnbusco
Gandy & Co., O. (P.).....A
IND.—Delphi
Great Western Canning Co. (S.) C
IND.—Ft. Wayne
Hoffman, C. A. (C.; V.)..C
IND.—Indianapolis
Heinz Co., H. J., 33 S. Del. (P.) ....AAAA
Huffman Packg. Co., W. D., 24 Dunlop (C.; V.).....C
Van Camp Packg. Co., 600 Kentucky Av. (S.)...AA
IND.—Lafayette
Cruikshank Bros. Co. (Br. Allegheny City, Pa.) (C.; V.; P.) ....B
Heinz Co. (The) (C.; V.; P.) ....A
IND.—Marble Hill
Dean Cider & Vinegar Co., Chas. B. (C.; V.).......B

CIDER, VINEGAR, &C.
IND.—Terre Haute
Stark, C. (C.. V.).......C
IOWA—Burlington
Blaul Sons Co., John (S.) ....AA
Lagomarcino & Co., A. (C.) ....B
IOWA—Council Bluffs
Smith Refining Co., (V.).C
IOWA—Davenport
Amazon Vin. & Pickg. Co. ....B
IOWA—Des Moines
Mennig & Slater, 120 2d (C.; V.; P.).........A
Rollins Vin. & Pickle Co..A
IOWA—Glenwood
New Glenwood Can Co. (C.; S.) C
IOWA—Keokuk
Keokuk Canning Co. (V.; P.) ....A
Keokuk Pickle Co. (V.; P.) ....B
IOWA—Marshalltown
Marshall Vinegar Co.......C
IOWA—Ottumwa
Ottumwa Pickle Co. (P.)..B
KANS.—Enterprise
Enterprise Vinegar Wks. (C.; V.) C
KANS.—Topeka
Kuehne Pres. Co., O. (C.; V.; P.) ....B
KY.—Covington
Ahlers Co. (The) (C.; V.; P.) ....B
KY.—Louisville
Gast & Crofts, 1004 W. Main (C.; V.; P.).....B
Heinz Co.. H. J., 1110 W. Main (P.) ....AAAA
Hirsch Bros. & Co., 700 14th (C.; V.; P.) ....B
Hughes & Co.. R. M., 10th & Ormsby (C.; V.).....A
Hyman Pickle Co. (The), 232 Pearl Av. (P.; S.)...
Jones Bros. & Co., 100 15th (C.; V.) ....B
Louisville Cider & Vinegar Wks., 1721 High Av. (C.; V.) ....A
Price & Lucas Cider & Vinegar Co. (C.; V.).......A
KY.—Millvale
Weller Co., J. (The), (P.) ....A
KY.—Paducah
Gregory Vinegar Co., O. L. (C.; V.) ....B
MAINE—Portland
Pettingill & Co.. E. D., 46 York (C.; V.; P.).......B
MD.—Baltimore
Baltimore Mfg. Co., 649 Buren (C.; V.).....AAAA
Elmer & Sons, Lewis, 104 South (C.; V.).........A
Gibbs Presg. Co., 2305 Boston (S.) ....AA
Heinz Co., H. J., 112 S. Howard (P.) ......AAAA
Langrall & Bro., J., 211 Aliceanna (P.) C
Numsen & Sons, W., 18 Light (V.; P.).........A
Van Lill Presg. Co., 108 Concord (P.) ....B
MASS.—Ayer
Haynes-Piper Co. (Br. Boston) (C.; V.).........C
MASS.—Boston
Barker, H., 88 Coml. (C.; V.) C
Budlong & Son Co., J. A., 9 Com. Whf. (Br. Prov., R. I.) (V.) ....A
Haynes-Piper Co., 124 Broad (C.; V.) C
Sherman Mfg. Co., R. I., 290 State (P.) C
Skilton, Foote & Co., Grocers' Exch. (V.; P.)...A
Von Laer & Co., J. P. W.. 383 Atlantic Av. (P.)..C
Walker. C. W., 108 Coml. (C.; V.) C
MASS.—Lynnfield Center
Gerry, E. F. (Cider) C

MASS.—South Acton
Barker, H. (C.; V.)......A

MASS.—South Sherborn
Holbrook & Sons, J. (C.;
 V.) ....AA

MICH.—Benton Harbor
Benton Fruit Products Co.
 (C.; V.; P.) C
Robinson Cider & Vinegar
 Co. (C.; V.) ....B

MICH.—Birmingham
Erity & Nixon (C.; V.)....C

MICH.—Caro
Caro Vinegar Co. (C.; V.)
          B

MICH.—Detroit
Greenslade Oil Co., 38 Jef-
 ferson Av. (C.; V.)....A
Vaughan & Co., Wm. W.,
 316 River (P.).........B
Williams Bros. Co., River
 Av. (C.; V.; P.)........A

MICH.—Holly
Heinz Co., H. J. (P.).AAAA

MICH.—Lansing
Genesee Fruit Co. (C.; V.)
          AA

MICH.—Muskegon
Muskegon Bottling Wks.
 (C.; V.) ....A

MICH.—Owosso
Thomas, A. T. (C.; V.)..C

MICH.—Plainwell
Williams Bros. Co. (Br.
 Detroit) (C.; V.; P.)...A

MICH.—Pontiac
Watson & Gordon Vinegar
 Co. (C.; V.) C

MICH.—Quincy
Bunge & Kirby (P.)....A

MICH.—Saginaw
Heinz Co., H. J. (P.).AAAA
Oakland Vinegar & Pickle
 Co. (C.; V.; P.).......C

MICH.—Shelby
Mikesell & Co., J. (C.; V.)
          B

MICH.—South Haven
Barrett & Barrett (Br. Chicago, Ill.) (C.; V.).AAA

MICH.—West Bay City
Beutel Pickling & Canning
 Co. ....A

MINN.—Minneapolis
Gedney Pickling Co., M.
 A., 32d Av. (C.; V.; P.)
          A

MINN.—St. Paul
Barret & Barrett, 242 E.
 4th (C.; V.) C
Bock, C F. A., 5th (C.;V.)
          C
Drewry & Sons, 702 Payne
 Av. (C.; V.) C
Gedney Pickling Co., M. A.,
 59 S. Wab. Av. ....A
Heinz Co., H. J., 45 E. Fill-
 more Av. (C.; V.; P.)
        AAAA

MISS.—Natchez
Natchez Mol. & Vinegar Co.
 (C.; V.) ....AA

MO.—Alexandria
Anchor Pickle & Canning
 Works (P.)............A
Keokuk Pickle Co. (P.)..C

MO.—Caribou
Dobson-Braun Mfg. Co., (P.)
          A

MO.—Clarksville
Clarksville Cider Co. (C.;
 V.) C

MO.—Independence
Coombs Bro. & Cromwell
 (C.) ....A

MO.—Kansas City
Byers, Wm. 1st & Char-
 lotte (C.; V.) ....A
Coombs & Bros. B. F., 421
 Walnut (C.; V.).......A
Heinz Co., H. J. (Br.
 Pittsburg, Pa.) (P.)
        AAAA
Monarch Vinegar Wks.
 Kemper Bldg. (C.; V.).C

MO.—Kirksville
Kirksville Canned Goods &
 Pickle Factory (P.).....B

MO.—St. Joseph
Fuelling, L. (C.; V.)....B

MO.—St. Louis
Bayle, Geo. A., 113 So. 2d
 (V.; P.) ....B
Beiser & Co., Fred., 2d &
 Hempstead (S.).........A
Clarksville Cider Co., 213
 N. 2d (C.; V.) C
Dodson-Braun Mfg. Co., 3d
 & Cedar (C.; V.; P.) ..AA
Globe Pickle Co., 1004 Col-
 lins (P.) C
Gregory Vinegar Co., O. L.,
 1125 Poplar (C.; V.)....B
Haase & Sons, A. C. L., 415
 N. 2d (P.) ....A
Haueisen Bros., 1017 N. 3d
 (S.) ....A
Heinz, H. J. Co., 1446 N.
 Bway. (Br. Pittsburg,
 Pa.) (P.) ....AAAA
Kaufman Mfg. Co., F. A.,
 106 S. 2d (C.; V; S.)...C
National Molasses Co., 204
 S. Main (C.; V.) ......A
Red Cross Vinegar Co. 204
 S. Main (C.; V.) ......B
Schopp & Co., G. P., 721
 N. 3d (S.)............B
Wagoner, J., 514 N. 2d
 (C.; V.; P.) ....A

MO.—Springfield
Scholten, Henry (C.; V.)..C

NEBR.—Nehawka
Pollard & Son, Isaac (C.;
 V.) C

NEBR.—Omaha
Haarmann Bros., 1914 S.
 20th (C.; V.; P.).......B
Haarmann Vinegar Co., 214
 S. 12th (C.; V.) ......B

N. H.—Concord
Haynes Piper Co. (C.; V.)
          C

N. H.—Durham
Griffith & Sons, J. B. (C.;
 V.) C

N. J.—Irvington
Ball, P. (C.; V.) ....B

N. J.—Jersey City
Steinberger, L., 496 Pavonia
 Av. (C.; V.) C

N. J.—Mt. Holly
Chances Sons, R. C. (P.) ..C

N. J.—Newark
Reitzel & Co., J. (C.; V.;
 P.) C

N. J.—Williamstown
Alart & McGuire (Br. N.
 Y. City) C
Souder & Clark (P.)......C

N. Y.—Albany
Heinz Co., H. J. (Br. Pittsburg, Pa.) (P.) ....AAAA

N. Y.—Albion
Rogers, L. R. (C.)........C

N. Y.—Brooklyn
Bergen-Monagle Co., 45
 Newell (P.) C
Dowst's Sons, J. A., 181
 Meserole (C.; V.) .....B
Schlegal, John, 132 22d
 (C.; V.) ....B

N. Y.—Buffalo
Buffalo Vinegar & Pres. Co.,
 642 Mich. ....B
Erie Preserving Co., 941 W.
 Feury (S.)..........AAAA
Geutsch, S., 395 Hickory
 (C.; V.) C
Geutsch's Sons, B. F., 232
 Walnut C
Heinz Co., H. J., 106 Main
 (Br. Pittsburg, Pa.)
        AAAA

N. Y.—Canastota
Harrison & Co., (C.; V.)..A
Hubbard. F. F. (C.; V.)..C

N Y.—Central Park
Central Park Pickle Wks.
 (P.; S.) ....B

N. Y.—Clarendon
Genesee Fruit Co. (C.; V.)
          AA

N. Y.—Cortland
Cortland Pickling Co. (P.;
 S.) ....B

N. Y.—Deansboro
Northrup, G. B. (C.; V.).C

N. Y.—Elmira
Eagle Bottling Works (C.)
................................C

N. Y.—Falconer
Geutsch's Sons, B. F. (P.)
................................C

N. Y.—Farmingdale
Central Park Pickle Wks.
(P.; S.) ....B

N. Y.—Holley
Genesee Fruit Co. (C.; V.)
................................AA

N. Y.—Islip
Islip Mustard & Pickle Co.
(P.) C

N. Y.—Kingston
Deyo, S. R.. (C.; V.) C

N. Y.—Le Roy
Le Roy Canning Co. (S.)..C

N. Y.—Liverpool
Woerner Presg. & Packg.
Co. (P.; S.) ....AA

N. Y.—Lockport
Erie Presg. Co. (S.) ....AA
Geutsch's Son, B. F. (C.;
V.; P.) C
Niagara Mfg. & Merc. Co.
(S.) C

N. Y.—Long Island City
Pryor Bros. (C.; V.; P.)..B

N. Y.—Mattituck
Alart & McGuire (Br. N. Y.
City) ....A

N. Y.—Medina
Heinz Co., H. J. (Br. Pittsburg, Pa.) (P.)....AAAA

N. Y.—Merrits Corners
Allen, H. C. (C.; V.)....C

N. Y.—Millwood
Allen, H. C. (C.; V.)......C

N. Y.—Montrose
Sherwood, C. K. (C.; V.)
................................B

New York City
Alart & McGuire ....A
American Fruit Product Co.,
497 West (C.; V.).AAAA
Apgar & Garretson, 83 Dey
(C.; V.) C
Central Park Pickle Wks.,
239 Bway. (P.; S.)......B
Erie Preserving Co.. 107
Hudson (S.) ....AA
Fahey, P., 223 E. 20th
(P.) ....B
Falcon Packing Co., 158
Franklin (V.) ....B
Fleischmann Vinegar Wks.,
630 W. 34th (C.; V.).AAA
Fuerst Bros. & Co., 2 Stone
(C.; V.) C
Genesee Fruit Co., 501 West
(C.; V.) ....AA
Harrison & Co., 45 Harrison
(C.; V.) C
Heinz Co.. H. J., 206 Spring
(Br. Pittsburg, Pa.)
................................AAAA
Israel & Cro.. C., 490 Canal
(P.) ....B
Kaufmann Bros., 50 Harri-
son (V.; P.; S.)..........B
Keller & Son, 319 E. 40th
(P.) C
Ross & Bro., W. A., 11 S.
William (Rasp.; V.)...B
Seville Packing Co., 202
Franklin (P.) ....B
Sherwood, C. K., 139
Franklin ....B
Williams Bros. C., 105 Hud-
son (P.) ....A

N. Y.—North Bloomfield
Ideson, J. (C.; V.) ......B

N. Y.—Pen Yan
Borgmann, B. (C.)........C

N. Y.—Port Dickinson
Ely Co., S. M. (P.).....AA

N. Y.—Riverhead
Alart & McGuire (P.)....A

N. Y.—Rochester
Albion Cider & Vinegar Co.,
32 White (C.; V.).......C
Doyle & Co.. M. (V.)......A
Fetzner, J. P.. 220 N.
Clinton (C.; V.)........C
Genesee Fruit Co. (C.; V.)
................................AA

N. Y.—Spencerport
Pettingill-Foster Co., (C.;
V.) ....A

N. Y.—Syracuse
Windholz, L. (C.; V.)...B

N. Y.—Tonawanda
Niagara Cider & Vinegar
Wks. (C.; V.) ....A

N. Y.—Voorheesville
Empire Cider & Vinegar Co.
(C.; V.) C

N. Y.—Wantagh
Kaufman Bros. (P.; S.)..B

N. Y.—Webster
Webster Pres. Co. (S.)....B

N. Y.—West Charlton
Gilchrist, A. & T. M. (C.;
V.) ....A

OHIO—Cincinnati
Heinz Co., A. J., 918 Syca-
more (Br. Pittsburg, Pa.)
(C.; V.; P.) ....AAAA
Miller Vin & Pickle Co.,
1272 Harrison Av.......C
Weller Co., J., Spring Grove
& Ala. Avs. ....A

OHIO—Cleveland
Heinz Co., H. J., 99 Wood-
land Av. (Br. Pittsburg,
Pa.) ....AAAA
Jankovsky, F. J., 1284
Bway. (V.; P.).........B
Williams Bros. (C.; V.)..B

OHIO—Clyde
Comstock & Hessman (S.).B

OHIO—Columbus
Heinz Co., H. J. (Br. Pittsburg, Pa.) (P.) ....AAAA

OHIO—Creston
Lutz & Schramm Co. (C.;
V.; P.) ....A

OHIO—Hill Grove
Denlinger, J. (C.; V.) C

OHIO—Oak Harbor
Weller Co., J. (P.).......A

OHIO—Shinrock
Hine, W. H. (C.; V.)....B

OHIO—Smithville
Weller Co., J. (P.).......A

OHIO—Toledo
Hine, T. B. (C.; V.)....B
Leroux Cider & Vinegar Co.
................................B

OHIO—Wooster
Wooster Pres. Co. (P.; S.)
................................B

PA.—Allegheny
Cruikshank Bros. Co. (C.;
V.; P.) ....B
Lurtz & Schramm Co.....AA
Vogel Co., Frank (C.; V.;
P.) C

PA.—Allentown
Gossler Oil Co., J. R. (C.;
V.) ....B
Schaadt & Co., T. (P.)...B

PA.—Erie
Werner Vinegar & Pickling
Wks. ....A

PA.—Fairview
Hauck, Jos. H. (C.; V.)..C

PA.—Philadelphia
Alart & McGuire, 126 Cuth-
bert ....A
Chance's Sons, R. C., 433
Spruce (P.)..............C
Erdmanns Sons, H., 1811
Fkd. Av. (C.; V.).......C
Fehrley, J. F., 2024 E.
Fletcher (C.; V.)......C
Haney, S. W., 2313 Ridge
Av. (C.; V.; P.).......C
Philadelphia Vinegar Co.,
1523 S. Front (V.)......B
Ritter Conserve Co., P. J.,
2156 E. Dauphin (C.; V.)
................................A

PA.—Pittsburg
Continental Pickle & Can-
ning Co., Monon Bank
Bldg. (P.; S.)...........A
Hirsch Bros. & Co., 59
Carson (C.; V.; P.)....B
Heinz Co., H. J.......AAAA

PA.—Pleasant Hall
Minehart & Hoover (C.; V.)
................................C

PA.—Sonora
Macomber, G. A. & F. S.
(C.; V.; P.) ....A

PA.—Sterrettania
Hauck, J. H. (C.; V.)..C

PA.—Vinemont
Shearer, Sol. (C.; V.)....B

CIDER, VINEGAR, &C.

R. I.—Providence
Budlong & Son Co., J. A.
(C.; V.; P.)............A
S. C.—Charleston
Charleston Cider & Vinegar
Co. (C.; V.)...........B
TENN.—Bristol
Andrews Mfg. Co., (C.)..C
TENN.—Chattanooga
Heinz Co., H. J. (Br. Pittsburg, Pa.) ....AAAA
TENN.—Memphis
Bluff City Bottling Co. (C.;
V.) ....B
Chickasaw Cider & Vinegar
Co. (C.; V.) ....AA
Ozark Fruit Co. (C.; V.) C
TENN.—Nashville
Heinz Co., H. J. (Br. Pittsburg, Pa.) ....AAAA
TEXAS—Dallas
Hughes Bros. Mfg. Co., (C.;
V.; P.) ....A
TEXAS—Galveston
Southern Coffee Co. (V.)..C
VT.—Brattleboro
Brattleboro Jelly Co. (Inc.)
(C.; V.; P.)...........B
VT.—Fair Haven
Allen, S. (P.) ....B
VT.—Newport
Vermont Preserving Wks.
(P.) ....A
VA.—Craig City
Penna. Canning Co. (P.)..C
VA.—Portsmouth
Va. Chemical & Mfg. Co.
(C.; V.) ....B
VA.—Richmond
Gregory Vinegar Co. (C.;
V.) ....B
VA.—Springwood
Penna. Canning Co. (P.)..C
VA.—Suffolk
McAnge & Co., W. N. (P.)
...................C
VA.—Winchester
Unfermented Juice & Cider
Co. (C.; V.) C
Valley Cider & Vinegar Co.
(C.; V.)...............C
W. VA.—Wheeling
Exley, Watkins & Co......B
Flaccus Bros. (C.; V.; P.)
...................A
Flaccus Co., E. C. (C.; V.;
P.) C
McMechen & Son (P.)....A
WIS.—Cassville
Klindt & Geiger Canning
Co. (P.; S.) ....
WIS.—Duplainville
Roth Vinegar & Pickle Co.
(C.; V.; P.)...........C
WIS.—Green Bay
Alart & McGuire ....A
Larsen & Co., Wm. (S.)..A
WIS.—Janesville
Hohenadel & Co., P., Jr.
(P.) ....A
WIS.—Manitowac
Richter & Sons, A. M.
(C.; V.; P.)...........C
WIS.—Milwaukee
American Vinegar & Pickle
Wrks, 294 Bway. (C.; V.;
P.) C
Dahinden & Gallasch Mfg.
Co., 500 Mil. (C.; V.)..C
Grossenbach & Co., A. (S.)
...................C
Milwaukee Vinegar Co., 456
Va. (C.; V.) ....AAA
Roth Vinegar & Pickle Co.,
720 Poplar (C.; V.; P.).C
WIS.—Racine
Glaser, Kohn & Co. (P.)..A
Gunther Co., F. W. (S.)..B
WIS.—Ripon
Ripon Packing Co. (S.)...C
WIS.—Wauwatosa
Milwaukee Pickle Co. (P.)
...................C

CIGARETTES

CAL.—San Francisco
Bohls & Co., H., 244 Fremont C
Bollman & Co., J., 695 Front
...................C

CIGARETTES (Con.)

GA.—Atlanta
E. E. M. Co., 23 W. Ala...B
KY.—Louisville
American Tobacco Co.,AAAA
LA.—New Orleans
Irby, W. R. (Br. American
Tob. Co., Ltd.) 400 S.
Peters ....AAAA
MD.—Baltimore
Neudecker, L. H., 701 E.
Lombard ....A
MICH.—Detroit
Scotten-Dillon Co., Fort W.
& Campan ....AAAA
New York City
American Tobacco Co., 509
W. 22d ....AAAA
Amargyros, S., 111 5th Av.
...................A
Cork Tip Cigarette Co., 205
West ....F
Duke Sons & Co., W. (Br.)
513 W. 22d ....AAAA
Egyptian Tob. Co., 319 Bowery C
Kinney Bros. (Br.) ....AAA
Mackler M., 11 Essex ....H
Monopol Tob. Wks., 250 W.
27th C
Prudential Tob. Co., 182
Grand ....E
Schinasi Bros., 48 Broad..D
N. Y.—Rochester
Kimball & Co., Wm. S., 18
Court ....AAAA
N. C.—Durham
Duke Sons & Co., W .AAAA
N. C.—Wilson
Wells-Whitehead Tobacco
Co. C
OHIO—Cincinnati
Lucke & Co. J. H. (all Tob.)
Lucke Blk ....A
VA.—Richmond
Allen & Ginter (Br.) 100
Seventh South ....AAAA
Cameron & Cameron, 15
Twenty Four South AAA

CIGARS

ALA.—Mobile
Hahn & Co., S. L. ....A
CAL.—San Francisco
Bachman & Co., 418 Market
...................AAA
Gunst & Co., M. A., 23
Kearny ....A
Plageman & Co., H., 709
Market ....B
COLO.—Denver
Best & Son, J. D. ....A
Colorado Cigar Co. C
Fehr, Wm. ....B
Friedman & Co., A. ......B
Hyman Cigar & Imp. Co...C
Prince & Co., A. ......B
Silver State Cigar Co. ...C
Solis Cigar Co. ....A
Stickney Cigar Co., W. A..A
Theis, F. C
Weingartner & Sons C
CONN.—Hartford
Soby, C. ....A
CONN.—New Haven
Grave, F. D ....A
Matton, A. W...........C
Moeller, C. A. ....AA
Osterweiss & Son, L. ..AA
Stoddard & Co., G ......AA
D. C.—Washington
Henderson & Co., W. A, B
Offerdinger, H. T C
Pond, W. G., 1316 F. N. W.
...................C
FLA.—Tampa
Ballard & Co., A. B ......B
Benjamin, G. N. ....B
Cuesta & Co. ....B
Morey & Co. ....B
San & Co., M. P ....B
GA.—Cairo
Roddenbery, W. B. ......D
ILL.—Carlton
Armstrong, Co. ....B
Dean Co., W. O. ....B
De Vilbiss Co., J ....B
Eyerley & Bros., W. H..B
Savill & Rafferty ....B
ILL.—Chicago
Behrendt, H., 348 W. 12th
...................B
Berriman Bros., 155 Wash.
...................A

CIGARS (Con.)

Cohen & Bros., S., 134 Van
Buren C
Franklin & Co., H. B. C
Gonzaley, Mara & Co. ..AA
Heegaard & Co., W., H.
Lake & State ....B

ILL.—Peoria
Lewis, F. P. ....B

ILL.—Pittsfield
Hirsheimer & Bros., L. D., A

ILL.—Quincy
Kingshaker, M. ....A

ILL.—Rockford
Lewis & Bros., F. C

ILL.—Springfield
Schoettker & Gehring ...B

ILL.—Urbana
Cohen, N. H. ....B

ILL.—Winchester
Smith, D. ....B

IND.—Fort Wayne
Eckert J. C..............B

IND.—Indianapolis
Indiana Cigar Co.........C
Kaufman & Son, B ......A
Meyer & Bro., C. F. ....A
Patton Bros. C
Woodford & Pohlman ...B

IND.—Vincennes
Schmidt, Jos. ....B

IOWA—Dubuque
Myers & Co., Cox........A

KY.—Louisville
Bakrow & Bro., R. D. ...B
Bickel Co., C. C. (Inc.)..AA
Hetterman Bros. Co......AA
Resch Bros., E. E. .....AA
Stier & Son, J. T. C

MAINE—Portland
Guppy & Co., C. H. C

MD.—Baltimore
Bond & Co., 417 Exchange
Place C
Kraus & Co. ....B
Newdecker, L. H., 701 E.
Louisville ....A

MASS.—Boston
Waitt & Bond, 67 Endicott
..................AAAA

MASS.—Lynn
Hefferman & Co., E. ...AA
P. W. C. Cigars Co......B

MASS.—Westfield
American Cigar Co. .....B
Eastern Cigar Co. ......B
Towne, Fuller Co ....B

MICH.—Adrain
Moreland Bros. & Crane..B

MICH.—Detroit
Banner Cigar Mfg. Co. ..B
Brown Bros. Co. ......AA
Collins & Co., C. P. ....B
Detroit Cigar Mfg. Co. ..B
Gordon, A C
Moebs & Co., W. D. C., 92
Woodward Av. ....A
Stender, H. H. C
Woodhouse & Co., J. T..B

MICH.—Grand Rapids
Johnson Cigar Co., G. J..C
Reynolds, B. J...........C
Schneider Co., H C
Trensch & Bro., M. H....B

MICH.—Pontiac
Mascotte Cigar Co. .....B

MINN.—Minneapolis
Conrad & Co., 410 Nicollet
Av. ....B

MINN.—St. Paul
Conrad, W. S., 341 Jackson
......................C
Fetsch, A C
Hart & Murphy, 455 Jackson
......................B
Kuhles & Stock ....A
Mark Bros., 383 Wabasha, C
Sexton & Co. ....B

MO.—Hannibal
Holmes Dakin Cigar Co. ..B
Rendlen, T. G ....B

MO.—Kansas City
Hopkins & Woodbury, 425
Delaware ....B
Lederman. F. W.........B
Moores & Son, W. P C
Morrin Powers Merc. Co.,
610 Wyandotte ....A
Reardon & Co., E. J.....B
Stickney Cigar Co., W. A.
......................A
Switzer Cigar Co., 603 Main
......................A

MO.—St. Joseph
Stewart Bros. C

CIGARS (Con.)

MO.—St. Louis
Rice Merc. Cigar Co., F. R.,
305 N. 4th ....A
Shryock-Johnson Mfg. Co.,
21 S. 4th C

MONT.—Anaconda
Collins & Co., J. V. .....A

MONT.—Butte
Browne & Flanigan C
Cohn, L. S. ....A
Caplice Commercial Co. ..B
Pincus, A ....B

MONT.—Great Falls
Bateman-Switzer Co. .....B
Silverman-Wallenstein ...B

MONT.—Helena
Goodkin Bros. ....A
Oppenheimer & Asch C
Switzer Co., J. ....B

MONT.—Missoula
Garden City Bottling & Liq-
uor Co. ....B
Mentrum-Briggs Co. C

NEBR.—Lincoln
Brown & Co., F. A. C

NEBR.—Omaha
Kiplinger, O. D. C
Riley Bros. ....A

N. H.—Manchester
Sullivan, R. G. ....A

N. J.—Camden
Bosch, C C

N. J.—Jersey City
Edelstein, J. ....A
Gotthardt & Co., W. C
Mayer Bros ....B

N. J.—Newark
Osborn & Co., D ....A

N. J.—New Brunswick
Hirschhorn, Mack & Co., AA

N. J.—Rutherford
Muehling. T C

N. J.—Trenton
Grumbacher, J ....B

N. MEX.—Albuquerque
Abel, D. J. ....B

N. Y.—Albany
Levy & Bros., S. ....B
Van Slyke & Horton ....A

N. Y.—Binghamton
Barlow-Rood Co. ....AA
Barnes, Smith & Co. C
Binghamton Cigar Co. ...B
Hummell & Co. ....A
Hull, Grummond & Co..AA
Kent & Co., G. A. .....AA
Wells & Co., C. C. C

N. Y.—Brooklyn
Dressner Bros., 183 Fulton
......................B
Mugge & Treckman, 105 Lib-
erty ....B
Schwager, L., 325 Wash...B
Sullivan, P. J., 56 Fulton..C

N. Y.—Buffalo
Breitwieser, H. & J ......A
Donovan, C. J. ....B
Levyn, S. C
Superior Cigar Co. C
Wagner & Son ....B

N. Y.—Elmira
Brown & Co., T. A. C

N. Y.—Glens Falls
Hitchcock & Co., C. H. ..C

N. Y.—Ithaca
Platts & Co., A. H. .....A
Stewart & Co., D. B. ....A

N. Y.—Jamestown
Heineman, L C
Tinkham Bros. C

N. Y.—Lansingburg
Mills, T. ....A

N. Y.—Lockport
Moore, H. H. C

N. Y.—Medina
Cook & Co., S. A. ......B

New York City
Adrain, M. J., 472 Grand
...................AAAA
Amo, Ortz & Co., 135 Front
......................A
Barranco, L. A., 192 Water
......................A
Batt & Co., S., 47 Murray.A
Castro & Co., M. J., 136
Water ....B
Cohen Cigar Co., 176 E.
127th ....A
Condit, S. G., 445 E. 10th..A
Davis & Co., S. I., 520 E.
81st ....B
Faber, G. W., 36 Beaver..B
Falk's Sons S., 5 Burling
Slip ....B
Foster & Co., M., 1059 3d

214

CIGARS (Con.)

Meyer, J. D C
PA.—Adamstown
Stork & Son, W. R C
PA.—Allentown
Jarrett Benj. C
Ruhe Bros. Co. ....B
PA.—Altoona
Blake Tobacco Co. ....B
Blumenthal, J ....B
Cunningham Tobacco Co., A
Reid Tobacco Co. ....A
Wolfe & Bro., W. H. ......A
PA.—Bethlehem
Applegate, W. M. ....B
PA.—Boyertown
Erb & Co., D. S. C
PA.—Braddock
Rosenbloom, M. C
PA.—Bradford
Collins & Co., P. R. ......B
Mayer & Co., A ....B
PA.—Carlisle
Livingston & Co., J ......A
PA.—Chester
McClure, W. J. ....A
PA.—Clarion
Selker Cigar Co. C
PA.—Coopersburg
Stephens, John S. C
PA.—Corry
Hull & Co., N. W. ......B
PA.—Cressman
Reiter, J. W ....B
PA.—Dallastown
Heckert, J. C. ....B
Minnich, J. W. C
Peters, Jr., W. H. C
Spatz & Son, J. F. C
PA.—East Prospect
Oleweller, L. E. C
PA.—Ephrata
Eshleman, J. W. C
Mentzer & Sons, A. W. ..A
Walker, J. H. ....B
PA.—Erie
Wingerten Bros. ....B
PA.—Hanover
Blair & Co., H. E. C
Frysinger, Jr., J. C
PA.—Hanover Junction
Glatfelter, H. J. C
PA.—Hazleton
Schwartz Co., Wm. ......B
PA.—Hellam
Gable & Co. C
PA.—Hopeland
Bingeman, S. H. C
PA.—Lancaster
Albright & Bros., J. C
Banner Cigar Co. ......AA
Dosch, J. J. C
Metzger Cigar Co., J. L. ..A
Moss Cigar Co., S. R. ..AA
Oblinger Bros. Co. ....A
Penn Cigar Co. ....A
Schnader & Sons ....B
Slater & Co., J ....B
Weaver Isaac H. ....A
Zook, J. G. ....B
PA.—Lebanon
Long & Son, D. B. ......A
Meredith & Rebstock C
PA.—Lititz
Bricker & Co., J. R. C
PA.—Lock Haven
Harmon, T. H. ....B
Sterner, A C
PA.—McSherrytown
Johns, S. L. ....AA
Poist & Co., J. A ....A
Smith Sons & Co. C
PA.—Mansfield
Ross Cigar Co. ....A
PA.—Meadville
Stern, S. C
PA.—Media
Burdsall & Adams C
PA.—Newmanstown
Witte, J. H. C
PA.—Norristown
Gresh & Sons, W. K. ...A
PA.—North Wales
Weingartner's Sons, J. ...C
PA.—Olyphant
Lackawanna Cigar Co....C
PA.—Philadelphia
Blanco, W., 439 Arch....C
Duncan & Moorhead, 511
  Chestnut ....B
Dunn & Co., T. J., 210 N.
  Broad ....A
Eisenlohr & Bros., 940 Mar-
  ket ....A
Fulweiler & Bro., P. C., 927
  Sansome ....B

CIGARS (Con.)

Granley, H. B., 527 Chest-
  nut ....B
Hoch & Sons, G., 248 N. 8th
  ....A
Holland, J., 2203 South ..C
Koenig, A., 203 Callowhill, C
Kuhn & Bro., F., 437 Girard
  Av. ....B
Langsdorf's Sons, J., 553 N.
  5th ....A
Lowengrund, I., 248 Market
  ....B
Miller Bros., 411 Market..B
Narrigan & Co., H. D., 617
  Arch ....A
Nolan & Co., H. C., 134 N.
  3d C
Oblinger Bros., 615 Market
  ....A
Portuondo Cigar Co., 1116
  Sansome ....A
Portuondo, V., 806 Chestnut
 C
Quinn, A. F., 2619 Ktn. Av.
  ....A
Roig & Langsdorf (Ltd.) 317
  N. 7th ....B
Stewart Newburger & Co.,
  29 N. 4th ....B
Teller & Co., F., 125 S. 2d, A
Theobald & Oppenheimer,
  111 N. 3d ....AA
Tuck & Co., J. E., 12 Mar-
  ket C
Viana & Son, D., 1334 Col-
  mubia Av. C
Warnbach, F., 2213 N. Front
  ....B
Warner, C. J., 820 Green..B
PA.—Pittsburg
Goldsmith Bros. & Co. ...B
Jenkinson & Co., R. W. ..A
Locke, A. J. C
McClurg Co., J., 414 6th Av.
  ....AA
Vockrodt & Wagner, 210
  Wood ....A
Zeugschmidt Bros. ....B
PA.—Pottstown
Evans, J. W ....B
PA.—Pottsville
Boyer, W. E. (Est.) ....AA
Hause, F. ....A
PA.—Reading
Dibert Bros. ....B
Fehr, J. U. C
Yocum Bros. ....AA
PA.—Reamstown
Root, J. G. C
PA.—Red Hill
Miller, L. B. C
PA.—Red Lion
Rost & Co., C. A. C
PA.—Richland Station
Klopp, S. C
Moore & Lanning C
PA.—Rothsville
Usner, J. G. ....B
PA.—Scranton
Garney, Brown & Co. ....A
Stoll & Co., O. P. C
PA.—Sellersville
Cressmans Sons C
PA.—Somneytown
Shively, C. F. ....B
PA.—Terre Hill
Watts, S. S. C
PA.—Titusville
Westheimer & Bros C
PA.—Washington
Slater, John ....B
PA.—West Manchester
Baer, Sprenkle Co. ....A
Natl. Cigar Mfg. Co. ......A
PA.—Wilkesbarre
Cohen, S. ....B
Horn & Son, M. C
Tisch, L. ....A
PA.—Womelsdorf
Fidler & Co., H. F. ......B
Hackman, H. D. ....B
Shaffner & Co., W ....B
PA.—Yeo
Kohler & Co., G. A. ......B
PA.—York
Baylor, C. A. ....B
Beck & Sons, E. C. C
Celestino & Co., C ....A
Frysinger, C ....B
Leiphart, H. C. ....B
Mayer & Bros., J. A. ....A
Myers, Adams & Co. ....A
Myers & Co., F. E. ......A
Sonneman, A C
Stallman, C. H. ....B

CIGARS (Con.)

Stiles, J. H. C
R. I.—Providence
Anthony & Co., J. M. C
Rose & Co., R. L. ....A
S. C.—Charleston
Follin Bros. ....B
TENN.—Chattanooga
Peeples & Pitner Bros ....B
TENN.—Memphis
Botto, V. F. & D. ....A
Goodman Bros. ....AA
Harpmann & Bro. ....B
Lee & Marton C
Podesta Bros. ....B
Samelsow & Co., I ....A
Sternberg & Sons ....A
Vaccaro Cigar & Liquor Co.
   C
TEXAS—Dallas
Block Bros ....A
Eppstein & Co., E ....A
Martinez, P. P. ....A
TEXAS—El Paso
Kohlberg Bros ....B
Pfaff, Hy. ....B
TEXAS—Fort Worth
Casey, Martin & Co. C
Casey, Swasey Co ....A
TEXAS—Houston
Japhet & Co. ....B
Loewenetein, James C
TEXAS—Waco
Archenhold Co ....B
UTAH—Salt Lake City
Hewlett Bros. & Co. ......A
Kahn Bros. ....A
Neldon Judson Drug Co. ..A
Rogers Cigar Co. ....B
Symns Utah Grocer Co....B
VT.—Burlington
Arbuckle Co. ....B
Reed & Co., J. G. ....B
VA.—Alexandria
Old Dominion Cigar Co....C
VA.—Chatham
Riddle & Hargrave ......A
VA.—Norfolk
Davis, L. W. C
Oberndorfer & Co. C
Straus, Gunst & Co. ......B
VA.—Winchester
Evans & Co., E. J. ....B
WASH.—Seattle
Coblentz, D. & A. C
Gottstein, M. & K ....A
Kreiselsheimer Bros ......B
Levy Co., M C
Schwabacher Bros. & Co.
    ....AA
WASH.—Spokane
Durkin, James C
Grinsfelder & Co., W. S. ..B
W. VA.—Wheeling
Pollack, Augustus ....AA
Marsh & Son, M C
Miller, J. F. C
Muhn & Brandfass C
WIS.—Appleton
Schmidt, L. C. C
WIS.—La Crosse
Pamperin & Wiggenharm
    Cigar Co. ....B
WIS.—Milwaukee
Goodrich & Co., A. C. C
Graf & Bauerlein ....A
Kindling & Co., L. C
Roth, L. ....A
WIS.—Platteville
Sickle & Co., M. S. C
WIS.—Watertown
Wiggenhorn Bros. ....B
WYO.—Cheyenne
Idleman Bros. ....A

CINCHES

See also Saddlery & Harnes

MO.—St. Louis
Straus Saddlery Co., Jacob.
N. J.—Newark
Peters Harness & Saddlery
    Co. C
WIS.—Milwaukee
Gem Hammock & Fly Net
    Co. ....A

CINCHONA

New York City
Hopkins & Co., J. L., 100
    William ....A

CINEOGRAPHS

MASS.—Braintre
Dow Portable Electric Co., C

CINNAMON

See Teas, Coffees and Spices

CIRCLES

CONN.—Bridgeport
Bridgeport Brass Co. (Brass;
    Copper) ....AA
CONN.—Waterbury
Holmes, Booth & Haydens
    Co. (Inc.) (Brass), AAAA
Plume & Atworth Mfg. Co.
    (Brass) ....AAA
Scovill Mfg. Co. (Brass)
    ....AAAA
MD.— Baltimore
Baltimore Copper Smelt &
    Rolling Co. (Copper)AAAA
MASS.—Lowell
Bagshaw, W. H. ....B
N. J.—Bloomfield
Hudson Rolling Mill Coi
    (Copper) ....E
New York City
Ansonia Brass & Copper Co.,
    99 John (Brass; Copper)
    ....AAAA
OHIO—Dayton
Dayton Folding Box Co.(Cor-
    rugated) ....B
OHIO—Van Wert
Van Wert Spoke & Bending
    Wks. (Wagon) X
PA.—Philadelphia
Phosphor Bronze Smelting
    Co. (Phos. Bronze).....A
R. I.—Providence
Holbrook, A. & C. W. (Mal-
    let) X

CISTERNS

ILL.—East St. Louis
New Process Steel & Wire
    Co. (Steel) ....A
ILL.—Galesburg
May Bros. ....B
IOWA—Waterloo
Tallerday Steel Pipe & Tank
    Co. (Steel Tank) C
LA.—New Orleans
Lewis & Co., H. F. (Cy-
    press) ....D
LA.—Shreveport
Allen Mfg. Co. (Cypress)..B
PA.—Erie
Fleming Slate Co. (Slate At-
    tic) C

CITRATES

MASS.—Boston
Billings, Clapp & Co. (Com-
    pound) ....B
New York City
Cooper & Co., Chas., 194
    Worth (Compound) ...AA

CITRONELLA

New York City
Hill's Sons Co., Edw....AA

CLAMPS

CONN.—Bradford
Hammer & Co. (Malleable
    Iron; Adjustable; Cabinet;
    Carpenter; Machinists;
    Woodworking) X
CONN.—Bridgeport
Armstrong Mfg. Co. (Iron;
    Steel; Adjustable; Machin-
    ists' Carriage Makers;
    Wood) ....A
Belknap Mfg. Co. (Hose)..C
Smith & Egge Co. (Adjust-
    able) ....A
CONN.—Bristol
Sessions & Son, J. H. (Case;
    Box) ....AAA
CONN.Hartford
Billings & Spencer Co. (Ad-
    justable; Bell; Machinists;
    C Clamps; Cabinet; Car-
    penters; Woodworkers;
    etc.) ....A

CLAMPS (Con.)

Stebbins Mfg. Co., E. (Basin) ....B

MASS.—Worcester
Wakefield J. E. (Vise, Wrench) ....B
Wire Goods Co. (Wire Rope) ....A

MICH.—Battle Creek
Sherman Mfg. Co., N. B. (Basin; Hose) ....B

MICH.—Detroit
Anderson & Sons, W. H. (Belt; Guy)..........C
Ideal Mfg. Co. (Basin)...A
Michigan Bolt & Nut Wks. (Patent Pressed Steel Guy; Plow; Pole)......A
Park & McKay Co., 53 Bagley (Basin) ....D

MICH.—Grand Rapids
Baldwin, Tuthill & Bolton (Saw; Saw Brazing; Saw Filing) ....B
Grand Rapids Clamp & Tool Co. (Adjustable) ......F
Grand Rapids Hand Screw Co. (Cabinet Makers'; Carpenters'; Carvers'; Wooden) ....A
Grand Rapids Hardware Co. (Cabinet; Carpenters; Machinists'; Woodworking, etc) ....D
Wolverine Brass Wks. (Basin; Hose) ....B

MICH.—Saginaw
Wickes Bros. (Flanging; Saw Brazing) ....AA

MICH.—Three Rivers
Roberts Car & Wheel Co. (Air Brake Hose) ......B

MINN.—Minneapolis
Nat'l Brass & Metal Co. (Basin) C

MINN.—St. Paul
American Hoist & Derrick Co. (Guy; Wire Rope)..A
Union Brass & Metal Mfg. Co. (Closet) ....A

MO.—St. Louis
Acme Pipe Clamp Co. (Pipe) X
Broderick & Bascom Rope Co. (Wire Rope) ......AA
Kupferle, John C., 2nd & Mound (Hose) ....AA
Leschen & Sons Rope Co., A., 920 N. 1st (Wire Rope) ....AAA
Pleuger & Henger Mfg. Co., 1015 Herbert (Hose) ..A
Ranz-Lambrecht Stamping Tool Co. (Machinists')..F

N. J.—Boonton
Lincoln Iron Wks. (Floor Laying) ....B

N. J.—Newark
Jenkinson & Co., R. C. (Box; Case) ....A
Lowentraut Mfg. Co., P., 36 Brenner (Linemen's Splicing) ....A
McIntire Co., C. (Linemen's Splicing; Twisting) ...D

N. J.—Trenton
Roebling's Sons Co., John A. (Wire Rope) ......AAAA
Trenton Brass & Machine Co. (Basin) ....B
Trenton Iron Co. (Br. N. Y. City) (Wire Rope) ..AA
Union Brass & Machine Co. (Basin) ....A

N. Y.—Batavia
Batavia Clamp Co. (Steel Bar Cabinet; Carpenters'; Carriage Makers') .....E

N. Y.—Brooklyn
Connolly Specialty Wks., 1071 Atlantic Av. (Basin) X

N. Y.—Buffalo
Pratt & Letchworth Co., 189 Tonawanda (Machinists'; Screw; Carriage Makers') ....AAA

N. Y.—Clifton Springs
Judd & Leland Mfg. Co. (Basin) C

N. Y.—Elmira
Cronk & Carrier Mfg. Co. (Linemen's Splicing) ....B

CLAMPS (Con.)

N. Y.—Fulton
Hunter Fan & Motor Co. (Hose) ....B

N. Y.—Homer
Phoenix Hardware Mfg. Co., 189 Homer (Screw; Adjustabl Screw; Steel; Machinists') ....D

New York City
American Woodworking Machine Co., 136 Liberty (Door; Sash; Blind).AAA
Brown Co., A. & F., 26 Cortlandt (Beam) ....A
Colwell Lead Co., 63 Centre (Basin) ....AA
Fee & Mason, 66 Beekman (Basin) ....F
Folmer & Schwing Mfg. Co., 271 Canal (Camera) ....B
Gould Coupler Co., 20 West 34th (Break Beam) ..AA
Graham & Co., John H., 113 Chambers (Hose) ......B
Hall's Sons, Samuel, 229 W. 10th (Pipe) ....A
Haydenville Co., 150 Nassau (Hose) ....A
McNab & Harlin Mfg. Co., 56 John (Hose; Basin).AA
Macomber - Whyte - Moon Co., 131 Worth (Wire Rope) ....H
Mott Iron Wks., J. L., 88 Beekman (Basin) ....AA
New Jersey Foundry & Mach. Wks., 9 Murray (Guy) ....D
Niles-Bement-Pond Co. 136 Liberty (Blicksmiths'; Fitters') ....AAAA
Phillips Mfg. Co., 215 E. 34th (Basin) ....E
Prentiss Vise Co., 44 Barclay (Vise) C
Roberts & Bros., Geo. I., 473 Fourth Av. (Steam Joint) ....B
Sargent & Co., 151 Leonard (Cabinet; Carpenter; Machinists'; Woodworkers'; Carriage; Saw) ....AAAA
Schrader's Sons, A., 30 Rose (Hose) ....A
Sheridan, T. W. & C. B., 2 Reade (Book) ....A
Simmons Co., Jno., 110 Centre (Beam) ....AA
Smith & Hemenway Co., 296 B'way (Lineman's; Splicing) ....D
Taylor, Geo., 98 Cliff (Basin) ....F
Tower & Lyon Co., 95 Chambers (Saw) ....B
Weed, Reiley & Co., 11 Gold (Machinists') .....D
Wood, Henry P., 20 Reade (Trunk) ....E

N. Y.—Niagara Falls
Dobbie Foundry & Machine Co. (Wire Rope) ......B

N. Y.—Schenectady
General Electric Co. (Linemen's Splicing) ...AAAA

N. Y.—Syracuse
Clancy, J. R., 247 N. Salina (Wrought Steel Hose) ....D
Stearns & Co., E. C. (Adjustable; Cabinetmakers'; Wooden; Carpenters'; Door; Saw; Screw; Carriagemakers'; Quilt Frame; Sash; Blind; Tire Bolt) ....AA

OHIO—Akron
Akron Belting Co. (Belt)..B

OHIO—Canton
Kohler & Co., F. E. (Hose) C

OHIO—Cincinnati
American Brass Wks., 426 Plum (Basin) ....D
American Valve & Meter Co. (Guard Rail) C
Cincinnati Tool Co., Norwood (Adjustable; Cabinetmakers'; Carpenters'; Linemen's Splicing; Machinists'; Screw; Carriage Makers'; Door; Sash; Blind) ....A

CLAMPS (Con.)

Creaghead Engineering Co., 313 Walnut (Malleable Iron Cross Arm) ......D

Fay & Egan Co., J. A., Front & John (Door; Sash; Blind) ....AAAA

Tatum Co., Samuel C., 414 Water (Iron; Steel; Carpenters'; Cabinetmakers'; Quilt Frame; Screw) ...B

OHIO—Cleveland

Bronson-Walton Co., 119 Shore Lane (Guy; Wire Rope) ....B

Central Brass Mfg. Co. (Basin) C

Crescent Mfg. Co., 24 Centre (Belt) X

Eberhard Mg. Co. (Wooden; Machinists'; Screw; Machinists' Heavy Steel; Wheel Flanging) ....AA

Fanner Mfg. Co. (Cabinet; Carpenters'; Machinists'; Woodworking) ......A

Forrest City Brass Wks. (J. V. Kennedy) (Basin) ...B

Glauber Brass Mfg. Co. (Basin) ....A

Superior Mfg. Co. (Basin) .C

Upson Nut Co. (Br. Unionville, Conn.) (Plow; Nutted) ....AAA

OHIO—Columbus

Case Mfg. Co. (Belt) ...AA

Columbus Brass Co. (Basin) .B

Ohio Tool Co. (Wooden; Cabinetmakers'; Carpenters'; Woodworkers') ....A

OHIO—Cuyahoga Falls

Falls Rivet & Machine Co. (Beam for Power; Belt) A

OHIO—Dayton

Dayton Malleable Iron Co. (Screw) ....AA

Fletcher Mfg. Co. (Insulated) ....D

OHIO—Leetonia

Crescent Machine Co. (Saw) C

OHIO—Mansfield

Ohio Brass Co. (Linemen's Splicing) ....B

OHIO—Plymouth

Root Bros. Co. (Harness) B

OHIO—Ravenna

Williams, A. C. (Cabinet; Carpenters'; Machinists'; Woodworkers', etc) ....A

OHIO—Sandusky

Sandusky Tool Co. (Bookbinders'; Wooden; Cabinetmakers'; Carpenters'; Flask) ....A

OHIO—Toledo

Bissel & Co., F. (Insulated) D

PA.—Chester

American Steel Casting Co. (Steel Pipe) ......AAAA

Chester Steel Casting Co. (Br. Phila.) (Machinists') AAA

PA.—Erie

Jarecke Mfg. Co. (Beam).. AAAA

Reed Mfg. Co. (Beam)...B

PA.—Lebanon

American Iron & Steel Mfg. Co. (Guy; Pole) ...AAAA

PA.—Mount Joy

Grey Iron Casting Co. (Iron; Steel) ......AAA

PA.—New Brighton

Logan & Strobridge Iron Co. (Curtain Frame) ......B

PA.—Philadelphia

Atlantic Works, 22nd & Arch (Saw Brazing) ....B

Blessing, C. A., 516 Montgomery Av. (Adjustable; Basin) ....AA

Bonney Vise & Tool Co., 3015 Chestnut (Quilting Frame) C

Cresson Co., Geo. V., 18th & Allegheny Av. (Beam for Power; Girder) ...AAA

Disston & Sons, Henry (Saw Filing) ....AAAA

Fairmount Machine Co., 22d

CLAMPS (Con.)

& Wood (Beam for Power) A

Frick, Horace E., 715 St. James's (Pipe) X

Haines, James & Cadbury, 1136 Ridge Av. (Basin).. AA

Hoopes & Townsend Co., 1330 Buttonwood (Pole)... AAA

Johnson, Israel H., Jr., 1424 Callowhill (Screw) ....A

McCambridge & Co., 527 Cherry (Basin) ....B

Penn Engineering Co., 312 Cherry (Basin) ....D

Pennsylvania Steel Co. (Guard Rail) ....AAAA

Smith, W. Clifford, 45 N. 2d (Pipe) ....F

PA.—Pittsburg

Bailey Farrell Mfg. Co., 619 Smithfield (Basin)....AA

Collins Mfg. Co., 104 First Av. (Beam) X

Hubbard & Co. (Malleable; Wrought Guy; Plate)...A

Lanz & Sons, Matthew, 101 S. 29th (Wire Rope; Guy) ....B

Oliver Iron & Steel Co. (Guy; Pole) ......AAAA

Standard Sanitary Mfg. Co., Arrott Bldg. (Basin).... AAAA

PA.—Reading

Penn Hardware Co. (Flooring; Quilt Frame) ...AA

Reading Hardware Co. (Saw; Cabinet; Carpenters'; Machinists'; Woodworkers'; Carriage, etc).. AAA

PA.—Sharon Hill

Pickering, R. S. ....F

PA.—Wilkesbarre

Hazard Mfg. Co. (Wire Rope) ....AAA

Vulcan Iron Works (Bell; Dock; Timber) ....AAAA

PA.—Wrightsville

Wrightsville Hardware Co. (Cabinetmakers'; Carpenters'; Machinists'; Wheel Flanging) C

R. I.—Pawtucket

Bliss Mfg. Co., R. (Cabinetmakers'; Carpenters'; Wood; Belt) ......AAA

Pawtucket Mfg. Co. (Cast Steel Screw; Steel) ....A

R. I.—Woonsocket

Woonsocket Machine & Press Co. (Girder) ....AA

WIS.—Cudahy

Power & Mining Machinery Co. (Boilermakers') AAA

WIS.—Milwaukee

Filer & Stowell Co. (Ltd.) (Saw Filing) ....AAA

Hoffman-Billings Mfg. Co. (Basin) ....AA

Milwaukee Foundry Supply Co. (Hugh J. Horrigan) 258 Lake (Hask) X

Rundle-Spence Mfg. Co. (Br. Century Foundry Co., N. Y. City) (Basin) ..AAAA

CLAPBOARDS

ARK.—Brinkley

Brinkley Car Works & Mfg. Co. ....D

MAINE—Locke's Mills

Tebbets & Co., C. L. C

MAINE—Portland

Berlin Mill Co. ......AAAA

MASS.—Boston

Stearns Lumber Co., A. T. AA

N. Y.—Binghamton

Roberson & Son, A. ....AA

VT.—North Duxbury

Elliott, W. R. ....G

CLARIFIERS

See also Machinery

CAL.—San Francisco

Riston Iron & Locomotive

CLARIFIERS (*Con.*)
Works ....AAA
DEL.—Wilmington
Pusey & Jones Co. ....AAA
ILL.—Chicago
Wolf Co., Fred W., 139
Rees ....AAA
KANS.—Fort Scott
Fort Scott Foundry & Mach.
Co. (C. Eller) ....H
LA.—New Orleans
Haubtman & Loeb Co.
(Ltd.) 217 Gravier ....B
Murphy, Jno. H., 643 Maga-
zine ....A
Payne & Joubert, 423 Ca-
rondelet C
N. J.—Jersey City
Flynn, W. S., 74 Hudson.D
N. Y.—Brooklyn
Pioneer Iron Wks., 151
William ....A
N. Y.—Buffalo
Squier Mfg. Co., Geo. L. 420
Niagara (Sugar) .....AAA
New York City
Bartlett, Hayward & Co.,
100 B'way ....B
Cornell, J. B. & J. M. Co.,
26th & 11th Av. ....AA
Deeley & Co., Robert, 507
W. 32nd ....E
Krajewski, Pesant & Co., 32
B'way ....AA
Mason & Co., Marcus, 329
Prod. Exch. ....A
Turl's Sons, Jno., 536 W.
38th ....A
OHIO—Cincinnati
Blymyer Iron Wks. Co. ...D
OHIO—Cleveland
Kilby Mfg. Co. ....AA
PA.—Philadelphia
Morris, Henry G., Phila.
Bourse ....F

CLARINETS

See Musical Instruments

CLASPS

CONN.—Bridgeport
Warner Bros. Co. (Br. N.
Y. City) (Corset) ..AAAA
CONN.—Greystone
Greystone Mfg. Co. .....E
CONN.—Meriden
Meriden Curtain Fixture Co.
(Curtain) ....AAAA
CONN.—Waterbury
American Pin Co. (News-
paper) ....A
Lane Mfg. Co. X
Novelty Mfg. Co. (Belt)...A
Waterbury Buckle Co.
(Belt) ....A
Waterbury Button Co.
(Belt) ....A
ILL.—Chicago
Acme Flexible Clasp Co.,
175 Clark (Wooden Box)
.......................A
Mackie-Lovejoy Mfg. Co.,
54 N. Clinton (Trousers)
.......................C
MD.—Baltimore
Catch-On Clasp Co. (Pants)
.......................B
MASS.—Attleboro
Regnell, Bigney & Co.....B
MASS.—Boston
Frost & Co., Geo. (Gar-
ment) ....A
MASS.—North Attleboro
Whiting Co., F. M. .....A
MASS.—Waltham
Thomson Mfg. Co., Judson
L. (Garment) ....A
MASS.—Worcester
Royal Worcester Corset Co.
(Corset) ....AA
N. J.—Hoboken
Schimpfer & Co., Wm.
(Book) ....AA
N. J.—Newark
Bowers & Co., James (Cor-
set) ....AA
Hartshorn Co., Stewart
(Curtain) ....AAA
Wright, Chas. C. (Corset)
.......................B
N. Y.—Binghamton
Titchener & Co., E. H.

CLASPS (*Con.*)
(Hoop; Pail) ....B
New York City
Cary Mfg. Co., 19 Roosevelt
(Hoop; Pail; Box) ....B
Frank & Gutmann, 274 W.
B'way ....B
Judd & Co., H. L., 87 Cham-
bers (Curtain; Album;
Bible) ....AA
Ludwig, A., 75 Spring
(Book) ....B
Normal Corset Co. (Corset)
.......................B
Standard Metal Strap Co.,
336 E. 38th (Box) .....F
Strouse, Adler & Co., 412
Broadway (Corset) .AAAA
Zonophone Co., 28 Warren
(Box) X
R. I.—Providence
Luther & Son, Wm. H.....B

CLASSIFIERS

MICH.—Saginaw
Farmers' Handy Wagon Co.
(Coffee) ....B
N. Y.—Buffalo
Buffalo Forge Co. ....AAA
Squier Mfg. Co. (Coffee)
.....................AAA
N. Y.—Silver Creek
Howes Co., S. (Coffee) ...A
N. Y.—Syracuse
Engelberg Huller Co. ....D
OHIO—Cincinnati
Blymer Iron Wks. Co., 2933
Spring Grove Av. (Cof-
fee; Rice) ....B

CLAWS

CONN.—Bridgeport
American Specialty Co.
(Tack) X
Bridgeport Hardware Mfg.
Co. (Tack) ....B
Knapp & Cowles Mfg. Co.
(Tack) C
CONN.—Hartford
American Specialty Mfg. Co.
(Tack) X
CONN.—Meriden
Nickel Plate Mfg. Co.
(Tack) X
CONN.—New Britain
Humason & Beckley Mfg.
Co. (Tack) ....A
ILL.—Freeport
Arcade Mfg. Co. (Tack)..B
MASS.—Shelburn Falls
Mayhew Co., H. H. (Tack)
.......................C
MASS.—Springfield
Springfield Mach. Ccrew Co.
(Tack) ....D
N. J.—Elizabeth
Braunsdorf-Muller Co.
(Tack) ....D
N. J.—Newark
Kraeuter & Co., 577 18th
Av. (Tack) ....E
Osborne & Co., C. S.
(Tack) ....B
N. Y.—Brooklyn
Williams & Co., J. H.
(Tack) ....AAA
New York City
Jennings & Co., C. E., 42
Murray (Tack) ....D
Peck, Stow & Wilcox Co., 27
Murray (Tack) ....AAA
Sargent & Co., 151 Leonard
(Tack; Nail) ......AAAA
Smith & Hemenway Co., 296
Broadway (Tack) ....B
N. Y.—Utica
Utica Drop Forge & Tool
Co. (Tack) C
PA.—Chester
Keystone Drop Forge Works
(Tack) ....A
PA.—Philadelphia
Stortz & Son, Jno., 219
Vine (Tack) ....F
PA.—Wrightsville
Wrightsville Hardware Co.
(Tack) C

CLAYS

See also Kaolin

CLAYS (Con.)

Paxson & Co., J. W., 1021 N. Delaware Av. (Fire) AA

Sweeney & Co., Geo., 1334 Ridge Av. (Fire) .....AA

PA.—Pittsburg

Gardner, Jr. Co., Jas. (Fire) B

Harbison & Walker Refractories (Fire) ......AAAA

Lincoln Fire Brick & Shape Co. (Fire) ....A

Stuart Fire Brick Co., Conestoga Bldg. (Fire).....D

Welch Fire Brick Works, House Bldg. (Fire) ....B

PA.—Sandy Ridge

Sandy Ridge Fire Brick Co. (Fire) ....B

S. C.—Langley

Lamar Kaslin Co. (China).B

TENN.—Chattanooga

Montague & Co. (China; Milled) ....A

VT.—Bennington

Lyon & Bro., S. C. (China) B

VT.—Rutland

Rutland Fire Clay Co. (Fire; Foundry) ....B

WASH.—Little Falls

Little Falls Fire Clay Co. (Fire) ....B

WASH.—Seattle

Denny Clay Co. (Fire) ....A

WASH.—Spokane

Washington Brick, Lime & Mfg. Co. (Fire; Milled; Screened) ....A

CLEANERS

CONN.—Naugatuck

Goodyears' India Rubber Glove Mfg. Co. (Rubber Window) ....AAAA

CONN.—New Britain

Humason & Beckley Mfg. Co. (Hoof) ....A

Judd, Oliver S. (Hoof) ...B

North & Judd Mfg. Co. (Hoof) ....AA

ILL.—Chicago

Bosley & Co., D. W., 210 Wash'n Boul. (Rubber Window) ....B

ILL.—Decatur

Oakes, Wm. L. (Boiler) ..D

ILL.—Freeport

Stover Mfg. Co. (Corn Sheller) ....AA

ILL.—Moline

Barnard & Leas Mfg. Co. (Corn Sheller; Malt; Flax Seed) ....AA

MASS.—Chicopee Falls

Stevens Arms & Tool Co., J. (Shot Gun) ....AAA

MASS.—Worcester

National Mfg. Co. (Wire Sink) ....A

Wire Goods Co. (Chain Pot) A

N. Y.—Brooklyn

Sudlow, Jno. W., 986 Halsey (Sink) X

N. Y.—Buffalo

Power Specialty Co. (Boiler Tube) X

Stewart Heater Co., 5 Norfolk Av. (Flue) ...D

Western Wire Goods Co. (Window) ....D

N. Y.—Cortland

Continental Tool Co. (Pavement) ....A

New York City

Beekman Novelty Co., 9 N. Moore (Fountain Pen)..X

Burns & Sons, Jabez, 554 Greenwich (Coffee) ....B

Goodyear Rubber Co. 787 Bway. (Window) .AAAA

Gutta Percha & Rubber Mfg. Co., 126 Duane (Window) AAAA

Hungerford Bros. & Co., 29 Cortlandt (Coffee) ....B

Jenkins Bros. 71 John (Flue) ....A

Millers Falls Co., 28 Warren (Flue) ......AA

Newell Mfg. Co., 149 Bway. (Boiler Tube) ....D

CLEANERS (Con.)

Parson Mfg. Co., 320 Bway. (Flue) C

Robertson & Son, Jas. L., 204 Fulton (Flue) .....D

Stoutenborough, X., 277 Pearl (Sink) ....D

N. Y.—Rochester

Streeter & Co., N. R. (Wire Pot) ....A

N. Y.—Schenectady

Westinghouse Co. (Thresher) ....AAAA

N. Y.—Syracuse

Lefever Arms Co. (Shot Gun) ....B

N. Y.—Troy

Barnum Bros. Co. (Boiler) E

Palmer Hdw. Mfg. Co. (Sidewalk) ....D

Troy Stamping Wks. (Sink) ....AAAA

OHIO—Canton

Kohler & Co., F. E. (Sidewalk) ....B

OHIO—Cincinnati

Bromwell Brush & Wire Gd's. Co. (Wire Pot)..AA

OHIO—Cleveland

American Fork & Hoe Co. (Drain; Sidewalk) AAAA

Cleveland Flue Cleaner Co. (Flue) C

Cleveland Stamping & Tool Co. (Chain Pot) ....A

Fanner Mfg. Co. (Flue)...A

Osborn Mfg. Co. (Flue, Sewer; Sink) ....B

OHIO—Columbus

Case Mfg. Co. (Corn) ....A

OHIO—Hamilton

Meyers Mfg. Co., Fred. J. (Wire Pot; Lamp Chimney) ....B

OHIO—Mansfield

Aultman & Taylor Mach. Co. (Thresher) ....AAAA

PA.—Erie

Jarecki Mfg. Co. (Flue) AAAA

PA.—Mt. Plesant

Mt. Plesant Tool Co. (Drain) ....D

PA.—Philadelphia

Darby & Sons, Edward (Chain Pot) ....A

Paxson Co., J. W. (Flue) AA

Pedrick & Ayer, 1001 Hamilton (Flue) ....A

Ruffner & Son, 3521 Bowman (Flue) ....D

PA.—Pittsburg

Gem Mfg. Co. (Flue) ....D

PA.—Williamsport

Darling Pump & Mfg. Co. (Ltd.) (Flue) ....B

Keeler Co., E. (Flue) ....AA

R. I.—Providence

Nicholson File Co. (File) AAAA

Towel Rack & Novelty Mfg. Co. (Rubber Window) ..X

VT.—Middletown Springs

Grays' Sons, A. W. (Thresher) ....AA

VA.—Richmond

Cardwell Mach. Co. (Thresher) ....A

WIS.—Racine

Dickey Mfg. Co. (Bean Grader) ....F

Johnson & Field Co. (Bean Grader; Seed; Coffee; Flax Seed; Corn; Rice) F

CLEANOUTS

ILL.—Quincy

Modern Iron Wks. (For Extra Heavy Pipe) ....B

MASS.—Chelsea

Carr & Co., J. H. ....D

MO.—St. Louis

Nelson Mfg. Co., N. O. ....D 409 CLEATS.

CLEATS

See also Hardware; Carriage

CONN.—Bridgeport

Bryant Electric Co. (Brass Wiring) ....B

CONN.—Derby

Shelton Co. (Boat) ......A

CLEATS (Con.)

CONN.—Hartford
Hartford Faience Co. (Porcelain) ....B
CONN.—Middletown
Wilcox Crittenden & Co. (Rope) ....A
CONN.—New Britain
Corbin, P. & F. (Line)
.................AAAA
DEL.—Wilmington
Pusey & Jones Co. (Boat)
..................AAA
IND.—Peru
Peru Electric Mfg. Co. (Porcelain) ....A
MAINE—Portland
Laughlin Co., Thos. (Boat) ..X
MASS.—Boston
Bellevue Porcelain Wks., 131 State (Porcelain or Clay) X
MASS.—West Somerville
New England Electric Mfg. Co. (Porcelain or Clay) X
MASS.—Worcester
Wire Goods Co. (Line; Rope) ....A
MICH.—Fenton
Phillips Co., A. J. (Wardrobe) X
N. J.—Trenton
Brian Pottery Co. (Porcelain) ....D
Diamond Porcelain Co. (Porcelain) X
Electric Porcelain & Mfg. Co. (Porcelain) ....A
Greenwood Pottery Co. (Porcelain) ....A
Hudson Porcelain Co. (Porcelain) ....F
Imperial Porcelain Wks. (Porcelain) ....AA
Standard China Wks. (Kimble Warren) (Porcelain) D
Star Porcelain Co. (Porcelain) ....B
Trenton Porcelain Co. (Porcelain) ....F
Union Electrical Porcelain Wks. (Duncan Mackenzie's Sons) (Porcelain) ....A
N. Y.—Brooklyn
Empire China Wks., 156 Greene (Porcelain) ..D
Union Porcelain Wks. (C. H. Smith) 300 Eckford (Porcelain) ....A
New York City
Sargent & Co., 151 Leonard (Line; Rope) ....AAAA
Tiebout, W. & J., 118 Chambers (Line; Rope) .B
N. Y.—Syracuse
Pass & Seymour (Porcelain) ....A
OHIO—Akron
Akron Insulator & Marble Co. (Clay) ....B
Amer. Marble & Toy Mfg. Co. (Porcelain or Clay) .X
OHIO—Canton
Canton Insulator & Clay Co. (Clay or Porcelain) ...X
OHIO—East Liverpool
Brunt Porcelain Wks., G. F. (Porcelain) ....B
Electric Porcelain Co. (Porcelain) ....B
Thomas & Sons Co., R. (Porcelain) ....B
OHIO—Mogadore
Bowers Mfg. Co. (Porcelain or Clay) ....F
OHIO—Ravenna
Williams, A. C. (Line; Rope) ....A
PA.—Reading
Reading Hdw. Co. (Line; Rope) ....AAA
PA.—South Bethlehem
Bethlehem Fdry. & Mach. Co. (Line; Rope) C
VA.—Norfolk
Whitehurst Co., R. W. (Line; Rope) ....B
W. VA.—Wheeling
Wheeling Hinge Co. (Rope)
..................AA

CLEAVERS

CONN.—Bridgeport
Knapp & Cowles Mfg. Co. .C

CLEAVERS (Con.)

CONN.—Southington
Peck, Stow & Wilcox Co. (Butcher &c.) ......AAA
ILL.—Chicago
Born Packers Supply Co., H. A. ....F
IND.—Lawrenceburg
Bishop & Co., Geo. H. (Family) ....A
MASS.—Greenfield
Nichols Bros. (Pork Packers') C
MASS.—Southbridge
Richard Co., Stephen .....E
N. Y.—Buffalo
White Co., L. I. & J. (Butcher &c.) ....A
New York City
American Axe & Tool Co. 253 Bway. ....AAAA
Chatillon & Sons, Jno., 85 Cliff (Butcher, &c.) ....A
Jennings & Co., C. E., 42 Murray ....B
N. Y.—Rochester
Mack & Co. ....AAAA
OHIO—Cincinnati
Bishop & Co., Geo. H. (Butcher) ....A
PA.—Chester
Black & Co., H. B.......AA
PA.—Philadelphia
Hoffman, C. & A., Frankford (Butcher, &c.) .....E
Nittinger Senr. Aug., 826 N. 4th ....A
Plumb, Fayette R. (Inc.)
..................AA
VT.—Wallingford
Wallingford Mfg. Co. (Butchers') X

CLEVISES

See also Hardware; Carriage

ILL.—Alton
Hapgood Plow Co. (Plow)A
ILL.—Chicago
Illinois Malleable Iron Co., 30 W. Monroe (Malleable)
..................AAAA
ILL.—Rockford
Weyburn & Briggs Co. (Plow) ....B
IND.—South Bend
South Bend Chilled Plow Co. (Plow) ....AAA
KY.—Louisville
Avery & Sons, B. F. (Plow)
..................AAA
MO.—Higginsville
Kruse, Kross, Klevis Co. (Malleable) X
N. Y.—Buffalo
Pratt & Letchworth Co. (Plow) ....AAA
New York City
Tiebout, W. & J., 118 Chambers (Malleable) ....B
OHIO—Cincinnati
Haven & Co., Jas. L. .....B
OHIO—Cleveland
Cleveland Hdw. Co. .....A
Eberhard Mfg. Co. (Plow)
..................AA
WIS.—Racine
Racine General Mfg. Co. ..E
Racine Malleable & Wrought Iron Co. (Plow; also Joint hooks) ....B
WIS.—South Milwaukee
Stowell Mfg. & Fdry. Co. (Malleable) ....A

CLIMBERS

CONN.—Branford
Donnelly, Jno. (Linemens')
..................F
ILL.—Chicago
Klein & Son, Mathias, 87 W. Van Buren (Linemens') .A
ILL.—Downer's Grove
Dicke Tool Co. (Linemens')
..................C
N. J.—Newark
Lowentraut Mfg. Co., P., 26 Bremen (Linemens') ...A
New York City
Smith & Hemenway Co., 296 Bway. (Linemens') ...C
N. Y.—Utica
Utica Drop Forge & Tool Co. (Linemens') C

CLIMBERS (Con.)

OHIO—Cincinnati
Cincinnati Tool Co., Norwood (Linemens') ......A
OHIO—Mansfield
Ohio Tool Co. (Linemens') A
OHIO—Toledo
Nagel Electric Co., W. G. (Electric) ....B
WIS.—Oshkosh
Oshkosh Logging Tool Co. (Linemens') C

CLINCHERS

PA.—Wyalusing
Lightning Hoof Shear Co. (Horse Nail) X

CLINOMETERS

N. Y.—Troy
Gurley, W. & L. E........A

CLIPPERS

CONN.—Ansonia
Cook Co., H. C. (Fingernail) E
CONN.—Bridgeport
Hotchkiss, Edward S. (Barbers'; Horse) ......A
CONN.—Seymour
Little River Mfg. Co. (Fingernail) ....E
CONN.—Southington
Peck, Stow & Wilcox Co. (Bolt; Rivet) ....AAAA
ILL.—Chicago
Chicago Flexible Shaft Co., 158 Huron (Barber; Power; Horse) ....B
Chicago Pneumatic Tool Co., Fisher Bldg. (Pneumatic Staybolt) ....AAAA
ILL.—Freeport
Stover Mfg. Co. (Ice) ...AA
IND.—Evansville
Halsey, C. W. (Ice) ....G
MASS.—Everett
Porter, Henry K. (Bolt) B
MASS.—Greenfield
Wiley & Russell Mfg. Co. (Bolt; Rivet) ....AA
MASS.—Orange
Chase Turbine Mfg. Co. (Board) ....A
MASS.—Springfield
Moore Drop Forging Co. (Bolt) C
MASS.—Worcester
Coates Clipper Mfg. Co. (Barber; Horse) ......D
Hobbs Mfg. Co. (Barbers') A
MINN.—St. Paul
Helwig Mfg. Co., Nat'l. Ger. Am. Bank Bldg. (Bolt or Rivet, Pneumatic Staybolt) ....F
N. H.—Nashua
American Shearer Mfg. Co. (Barbers'; Horse; Power) B
N. J.—Newark
Heinisch's Sons Co., R. (Horse) ....A
Peters Harness & Saddlery Co. (Horse) C
N. Y.—Brooklyn
Reinhardt & Co., 72 Stagg (Barber) ....F
New York City
Boker, Hermann & Co., 101 Duane (Horse) ....AA
Graham & Co., John H., 113 Chambers (Horse) ....AA
Smith & Hemenway Co., 290 Bway. (Nail) ....D
Snow, L. S. 296 Bway. (Nail) X
Wiebusch & Hilger, 157 Chambers (Horse) .....A
N. Y.—Rochester
Klip-Klip Co. (Nail) .....B
Standard Mfg. Co. (Fingernail) X
OHIO—Columbus
Columbus Bolt Wks. (Bolt; Rivet) ....A
PA.—Philadelphia
Chambers Bros. Co., N. 52nd & Lancaster Av. (Bolt; Rivet) ....AA
North Bros. Mfg. Co. Lehigh Av. (Ice) ....A

CLIPPERS (Con.)

PA.—Pomeroy
Phillips, M. T. (Dehorning) D
R. I.—Providence
Brown & Sharpe Mfg. Co. (Barbers'; Horse) AAAA
WIS.—Milwaukee
Chain Belt Co., 766 Park (Bolt; Rivet) ....B

CLIPS

See also Hardware; Carriage

CAL.—San Francisco
Leschen & Sons Rope Co., A. 920 N. 1st (Wire Rope) AAA
CONN.—Bridgeport
Smith & Egge Mfg. Co. (Toe) ....A
CONN.—East Hampton
Bevin Bros. Mfg. Co. (Toe) A
CONN.—Hartford
Billings & Spencer Co. (Trolley Wire; Wire Rope) AA
CONN.—Middletown
Wilcox Crittenden & Co. (Wire Rope) ....A
CONN.—Mt. Carmel
Woodruff & Sons, Walter W. ....A
CONN.—New Britain
North & Judd Mfg. Co. (Hame) ....AA
CONN.—New Haven
Cowles & Co., C. (Axle; Neck Yoke) ....A
North & Co., O. B. (Halter) AA
Seward & Son Co., Moses (Saddle; Axle; Spring Bar) ....A
CONN.—Plantsville
Atwater Mfg. Co. (Neck Yoke; Saddle) ....A
Blakeslee Forging Co. (Axle; Spring Bar) ....B
Smith & Co., H. D. ......A
CONN.—Southington
Peck, Stow & Wilcox Co. (Stationers) ....AAAA
CONN.—Unionville
Upson Nut Co. (Axle; Spring Bar) .....AAAA
CONN.—Winsted
Moore Co., Franklin (Axle; Spring Bar) ....A
ILL.—Chicago
Macomber-Whyte-Moon Co. 19 S. Canal (Wire Rope) A
Streeter, H. A., 41 Indiana (Structural Steel) ......A
ILL.—Freeport
Stover Mfg. Co. (Damper) AA
IND.—Elkhart
Buescher Mfg. Co. (Toe; Bicycle) ....E
IOWA—Dubuque
Adams Co. (Damper) ....A
MASS.—Boston
Durable Wire Rope Co., 288 Congress (Wire Rope) ..D
MASS.—Worcester
Wire Goods Co. (Toe) ....A
MICH.—Detroit
Bookkeeper Publishing Co. (Paper) ....A
MINN.—St. Paul
American Hoist & Derrick Co. (Wire Rope) ....AAA
MO.—St. Louis
Broderick & Bascom Rope Co., 809 N. Main (Wire Rope) ....AA
N. J.—Bloomfield
Consolidated Safety Pin Co. (Stationery) ....AA
N. J.—Jersey City
Williams & Son, E. A. (Hose) ....AA
N. J.—Newark
Newark Cycle Specialty Co. (Saddle) X
Peters Harness & Saddlery Co. (Saddle) C
N. J.—Trenton
Roeblings Sons Co. (Wire Rope) ....AAAA
Trenton Iron Co. (Wire Rope) ....A

CLIPS (Con.)

N. Y.—Auburn
Clapp Mfg. Co., E. D. (Axle; Saddle) ....B
Eccles, Richard (Saddle; Axle) ....A

N. Y.—Buffalo
Contractors' Plant Mfg. Co. 129 Erie (Wire Rope) B
Shepard & Co., Sidney (Damper) ....AAAA

N. Y.—Interlaken
Covert's Saddlery Works (Hame) C

N. Y.—Lockport
Merritt Mfg. Co. (Veneer) D

New York City
Attleboro Stock Co., 520 Bway. (Stationery) ...X
Cushman & Dennison, 174 9th Av. (Stationers') ...B
Faber, Eberhard, 545 Pearl (Paper) ....AAA
Hurd & Co., 570 Bway. (Sleeper; Timber) ...D
Judd & Co., H. L.,87 Chambers (Stationers') ...A
Niagara Clip Co., 37 Park Pl. (Paper) ....A
Pratt Mfg. Co., 167 Wooster (Stationers') ....B
Spencerian Pen Co., 450 Broome (Stationers')..AA

N. Y.—Niagara
Dobbie Fdry. & Mach. Co. (Wire Rope) ....D

OHIO—Canton
Elbel & Co. (Hame) .....A

OHIO—Cincinnati
Cincinnati Railway Supply Co., 13 E. 2nd (Wire Rope) ....A
Globe-Wernicke Co. (Stationers') ....AAAA
Tatum Co., Saml. C. (Paper; Stationers') ....B

OHIO—Cleveland
Cleveland Hdw. Co. (Neck Yoke) ....AA
Cleveland Wire Spring Co. (Connecting; Upholstering Spring) ....A
Taylor & Boggis Fdry. Co. (Damper ....AA

OHIO—Columbus
Columbus Belt Wks. (Saddle) ....AA
Lanman, E. B. ....B

OHIO—Ravenna
Byers Machine Co., Jno. F. (Wire Rope) ....B

OHIO—Toledo
Weis Binder Co., 168 La Grange (Stationers') ...D

PA.—Philadelphia
Berger Bros. Co., 231 Arch (Damper) ....A
Philadelphia Novelty Mfg. Co., 13th & Noble (Paper; Stationers') ....D

PA.—Pittsburg
Lanz & Son, Mathew, 101 S. 20th (Wire Rope) ....AA

PA.—Scranton
Scranton Forging Co. (Axle; Spring Bar) ....A

PA.—Wilkesbarre
Hazard Mfg. Co. (Wire Rope) ....AAAA

PA.—Williamsport
Williamsport Wire Rope Co. (Wire Rope) ....A

R. I.—Providence
Barstow & Williams (Paper) C
Textile Finishing Mchry. Co. (Tenter) ....AAA
Winsor & Jerauld Mfg. Co. (Tenter) C

VT.—Montpelier
U. S. Clothes Pin Co. (Carriage Trimmers') ......D

CLOAKINGS
See Wollen Goods

CLOAKS
See Clothing; Ladies'

CLOCKS

CONN.—Ansonia
Phelps & Bartholomew Co. (Marine; Alarm; Calen-

CLOCKS (Con.)
der; Hanging; Lever; Nickel; Office; School; Fancy) C

CONN.—Bridgeport
Bridgeport Brass Co. .....A

CONN.—Bristol
Bristol Brass & Clock Co. AAA
Ingraham Co., E. (Marine; Wooden Case; Calender; Gallery; Hanging; Lever; Mantle) ....AAA
Natural Self Winding Clock Co. (English Hall; Self Winding Electric, Synchronized Systems) .X

CONN.—Forrestville
Sessions Clock Co. (Wooden Case; Fancy) ....AA
Welch Mfg. Co., E. N. (Calender; Alarm; Hanging; Locomotive; Mantle; Marine; Ships Bells; Office; Regulator) X

CONN.—Meriden
Parker Clock Co. ....A

CONN.—Middletown
Annual Wind Clock Co. ...X

CONN.—New Haven
New Haven Clock Co. (Marine; Alarm; Cabinet; Calender; Elect. Street Post; Gallery; Hanging; Lever; Mantle; Night; Novelty; Office; Watchmaker's Regulator; Watchmen's Electric; Window; Chiming; Bronze; Fancy; Nickel; Astronomical) ...AA
Reeves Mfg. Co. (Electric; Self Winding Electric).C

CONN.—Plainville
Plainville Clock Co. X

CONN.—Thomaston
Thomas Clock Co., Seth (Astronomical; Chiming; Street; Tower; Wooden Case) ....AAA

CONN.—Waterbury
Standard Electric Time Co. (Programme; Self Winding Electric; Tower) ...E
Waterbury Clock Co. (Marine; Fancy; Iron Case; Nickel; Wooden Case; Alarm; Cabinet; Calender; Fancy Brass; Gallery; Hanging; Lever; Mantle; Nickel; Novelty; Office; Regulator; School; Street; Watchmakers') ..AAAA

CONN.—Winsted
Gilbert Clock Co., W. L. (Wooden Case; Iron Case; Locomotive; Marine; Calender; Alarm; Carriage Alarm; Hanging; Lever; Mantle; Nickel; Office; Regulator) ....AA
Goodwin & Kintz Co. ....D

ILL.—Chicago
Altman & Co., 69 Dearborn (Watchmans') X
American Clock Co., Wabash Av. & 20th (Electric; Pneumatic) ....B
Baird Mfg. Co. (Advertising; Hall; Novelty; Placque; Wooden Case) C
Crown Mfg. Co., 84 Wabash Av. ....D
Kuehl & Co., Geo., 178 E. Randolph (Cuckoo) .....B
Marsh & Co., J. P., 224 Wash'n. (Locomotive; Marine) ....B
Turnquist, C. M., 442 Van Buren (Electric; Electric Alarm) ....H

ILL.—La Salle
Western Clock Mfg. Co. (Novelty; Nickel Traveling; Alarm; Fancy) ..AA

MASS.—Boston
American Steam Gauge & Valve Mfg. Co. (Marine; Engine Room; Locomotive) C
Ashton Valve Co. (Marine) A
Automatic Time Stamp & Register Co., 160 Congress (Time Recording System) E
Blodgett Bros. & Co., 141

CLOCKS (Con.)
Franklin (Electric; Programme; Self Winding Electric) ....E
Chelsea Clock Co., 16 State (Ship Bell Striking) C
Crosby .Steam Gauge & Valve Co., 95 Oliver (Locomotive; Marine) .....AA
Eco Magnetic Clock Co., 620 Atlantic Av. (Watchmans') C
Gilbert Clock Co., Mrs. L., 373 Washington ......AA
Hersey Mfg. Co., 314 W. 2d (Watchman's) ......AA
Howard Clock Co., E. 403 Washington (Electric; Office; House; Locomotive; Engine Room; Marine; Programme; Watchman's; Tower) ....B
Stevens. G. M., 15 Chardon (Tower) ....B
Ziegler Apparatus Co., 200 Summer (Electric Alarm; Watchman's) ....E

MASS.—Brookline
Holtzer-Cabot Electric Co. (Watchman's) ....A

MASS.—Gardner
Simplex Time Recorder Co. (Watchman's) ....D

MASS.—South Boston
Hersey Mfg. Co. (Watchmen's Electric; Watchmen's Time Detectors) AA

MASS.—Waltham
Waltham Clock Co. C

MICH.—Detroit
King & Rogers ....D

MICH.—Grand Rapids
Grand Rapids Clock & Mantle Co. (English Hall) ..D
Waggoner Watchman Clock Co. (Watchman's) X

MO.—St. Louis
Sempire Clock Co., 1308 N. 16th (English Hall; Self Winding; Electric; Synchronized Systems) .....D

N. J.—East Orange
Export Specialty Co. (Electric Alarm) X

N. J.—Jersey City
New York Standard Watch Co. (Electric Alarm) AAA

N. Y.—Binghamton
International Time Recorder Co. (Time-Recording System) ....B
Star Electric Co. (Electric Alarm) ....D

N. Y.—Brooklyn
Schaffer & Budenberg, 10 Division (Locomotive; Marine) ....A
Self Winding Clock Co., 163 Grand Av. (Electric: Programme; Self Winding Electric; Synchronized Systems; Tower; Watchman's) ....B

N. Y.—Ithaca
Ithaca Calendar Clock Co. (Hall; Calendar) ......B

N. Y.—Kingston
Moore Bronze & Plate Co., E. M. ....D

New York City
American Watchman's Time Detector Co., 234 B'way (Self Winding Electric; Synchronized Systems; Time Recording System; Watchman's; Electric Street Post; School)...F
Ansonia Clock Co., 11 Cliff (Marine; Alarm; Bank; Cabinet; Calendar; Chiming; Elect. Street Post, Hall; Hanging; Lever; Mantle; Nickel; Novelty; Office; Precision; Regulator; School; Swinging; Watchmaker's Regulator; Window; Bronze; Chiming; Fancy) ......AAAA
Ashcroft Mfg. Co., 111 Liberty (Locomotive; Marine) ....A
Bing & Co., Ferd., 10 Wash. Pl. (Art) ....A
Bogart Co., A. L., 123 Liberty (Electric) ....F

CLOCKS (Con.)
Bunnell Co., J. H., 20 Park Pl. (Electric Alarm; Watchmans') ....A
Bunnell Telegraphic & Electric Co., 110 Beekman (Synchronized Systems).X
Edwards & Co., 144th & 4th Av. (Electric; Electric Alarm; Programme; Self Winding Electric; Synchronized Systems; Time Recording Systems; Watchmans'; School)....C
Glaenzer Freres & Rheinbolt, 26 Washington (Art) ....A
Globe Clock Co., 50 Maiden Lane (Nickel) X
Harris & Harrington, 32 Vesey (Art) ....B
Hausberg, E. O., 45 Maiden Lane (Watchmens') ....E
Herzog Teleseme Co., 51 W. 24th (Electric; Programme; Self Winding; Electric; Synchronized Systems) ....D
Hoppe, Paul S., 34 Church (Watchmans') ....D
Howard Clock Co., E., 41 Maiden Lane (Electric; Secondary Electric; Marine; Programme; Synchronized Systems; Time Recording System; Watchman's; Electric Tower).A
Imhauser & Co., E. 206 B'way (Watchman's; Watchman's Electric) .C
Jones & Son, J., 64 Cortlandt (Electric Alarm; Electric Light; Cut-out)F
Kilbourne Mfg. Co., 45 Maiden Lane X
Kroeber Clock Co., F., 360 B'way (Alarm; Bank; Cabinet; Electric Street Post; Hanging; Lever; Locomotive; Mantle; Nickel; Novelty; Office) X
Manhattan Electrical Supply Co., 32 Cortlandt (Electric Alarm) ....A
Myers Co., S. F., 48 Maiden Lane (Nickel) ....D
Nanz, G., 127 Duane (Watchman's) ....F
Ostrander & Co., W. R. 22 Dey (Electric Alarm; Watchman's) ....B
Pattengell Son & Co., C. E., 51 Cliff (Watchman's).X
Pearce, Frederick, 18 Rose (Electric; Electric Alarm) ....B
Pettes & Randall Co., 150 Nassau (Electric; Synchronized Systems; Watchman's) ....F
Prentiss Clock Improvement Co., 49 Dey (Electric; Programme; Synchronized Systems; Tower; Watchman's; Calendar; Frying Pan; School) ....D
Roche, Wm., 42 Vesey (Electric Alarm) ....D
Rousseau's Electrical Wks., 329 4th Av. (Watchman's) X
Stanley & Patterson, 93 Liberty (Electric Alarm)A
Strauss & Sons, L., 42 Warren (Art) ....AAAA
Sussfeld, Lorsch & Co., 37 Maiden Lane (Art) ..AA
Swiss Clock Co., 65 Barclay (Cuckoo; Minature) ...X
Thomas Clock Co., Seth, 49 Maiden Lane (Electric; Locomotive; Marine; Tower; Alarm; Cabinet; Astronomical; Calendar; Chiming; Gallery; Hall; Hanging; Lever; Luminous Dial; Mantle; Novelty; Office; Precision; Regulators; School; Street) ....AAA
Year Clock Co., 79 Crosby.D

CLOCKS (Con.)

N. Y.—Poughkeepsie
Wells & Coutant Co.
(Marine) C

N. Y.—Rochester
Bradley & Co., E. C., 15
Stone (Electric Alarm)..H

N. Y.—Syracuse
Automatic Clock Co.
(Automatic) X
Dey Time Register Co., 305
N. State (Time Recording
System) ....B

OHIO—Cincinnati
Herschede Hall Clock Co.,
1011 Plum ....B

OHIO—Cleveland
American Watchman's Time
Detector Co., 45 Sheriff
(Electric; Self Winding
Electric; Synchronized
Systems; Watchman's)..E

OHIO—Woodsville
Shields Universal Clock Co.
X

PA.—Danville
Rempe Mfg. Co. ....B

PA.—Philadelphia
American Cuckoo Clock Co.,
628 N. 5th ....B
Belfield & Co., H., 435 N.
Broad (Locomotive) ..AA
Patrick, Carter & Wilkins,
1231 Callowhill (Electric
Alarm) ....B
Riggs & Bros. 310 Market
(Watchman's; Electric &
Portable House; Office;
Locomotive; Engine
Room; Marine; Non-Magnetic; Programme) ...E
Smith & Co., Geo. W., 3904
Powelton Av. ....A
Sommer Clock Mfg. Co.,
1027 Columbia Av.
(Cuckoo) ....G

PA.—Pittsburg
Byers & Co., A. M. (Calendar) ....AA

PA.—Waynesboro
Frick Clock Co., Fred.
(Programme; Self Winding; Electric) ....F

R. I.—Pawtucket
Killam & Co. (Banjo) ....E

R. I.—Providence
Durfree & Co., Walter H.
(Hall) ....D

W. VA.—Wheeling
Poole Clock Co. (Electric) X

WIS.—Milwaukee
Johnson Electric Service
Co. (Pneumatic; Programme; Time Recording
System; Tower) ......AA

CLOGS

N. Y.—Buffalo
Buffalo Sash Works .....B

CLOSETS

See also Furniture

CAL.—San Francisco
Holbrook, Merrill & Stetson,
221 Market (Water Combinations) ....AAAA

CONN.—Hartford
Howard & Co., James L.
(Car) ....A

CONN.—New Haven
Peck Bros. & Co. (Water
Combinations) ....AA

DEL.—Wilmington
Speakman Supply & Pipe
Co., 113 Market (Water)B

ILL.—Chicago
Adams & Westlake Co., Ontario & N. Franklin
(Car) ....AAAA
Clow & Sons, Jas. B., 344
Franklin (School; Institution, etc.; Water)....
AAAA
Ill. Malleable Iron Co., 30
W. Monroe (Water;
School; Institution, etc.)
AAAA
Kelly & Bros., Thos., 76 W.
..Jackson Boul. (Water;
Self-acting) ....B

CLOSETS (Con.)

McDonald Co., A. Y., 111
Lake (Water) ....B
Sprague, Smith & Co., 72-84
Moffat (China) C
Wolff Mfg. Co., L., 117 W.
Lake (Water) .....AAAA

ILL.—Rockford
Central Furniture Co.
(China) ....A

IND.—Ft. Wayne
Knott-Van Arnam Mfg. Co.
(Water) ....B

IND.—Wabash
Wabash Cabinet Co. (Telephone; Cabinet) ....A

MD.—Baltimore
Robertson Mfg. Co., Jas. 30
Hanover (Water) ......A

MASS.—Boston
Bangs Druggists' Fixture
Co. (Poison) ....B
Dalton-Ingersoll Co., 171
High (Water) X
Deceo Co., 146 High
(Water) ....D
Grundy Brass Wks., 50
Sudbury (Water; Yacht)F
Hercules Iron & Supply Co.,
427 Coml. (Water) ....A
Phillips Flushing Tank Co.,
197 High (Water) .....E
Sanitas Mfg. Co. (Smith &
Anthony Co.), 48 Union
(Water) ....A.A
Sumner & Goodwin Co., 287
Congress (Water) .....B
Vannevar & Co., Edmund B.,
58 Fulton (Water) .....H

MICH.—Detroit
Hamilton, Jno. H., 22 Laf.
Av. (Water) ....H
Park & McKay Co., 55 Bagley Av. (Water) C
Standard Sanitary Mfg. Co.,
of Mich., 942 Champlain
Water) ....AAAA
Walker & Son, Jas. (Water)
A

MICH.—Grand Rapids ....
New England Furniture Co.
(China) ....A

MICH.—Muskegon
Heap, Wm. (Water; Dry
Earth) ....D

MO.—St. Louis
Nelson Mfg. Co., N. O., 424
N. 8th (Water; School; Institution, etc.) .....AAAA
White Sanitary Co., Peter
(Water) ....D

N. J.— Jersey City
Jersey City Supply Co., 12
Mercer (Water) C

N. J.—Trenton
Maddock & Sons, Thos.
(Water) ....AA
Trenton Potteries Co.
(Water) ....AAAA

N. Y.—Albany
Hyde, Clinton (Water) ...X

N. Y.—Brooklyn
Ronalds & Johnson Co., 51
Boerum Place (Water) AA

N. Y.—Buffalo
Jewett Mfg. Co., Jno. C.
(Cake) ....AA
Zero Valve & Brass Mfg.
Co., 296 Seneca (Water) F

New York City
Adee & Co., Fred., 92 Beekman (Water; School; Institution, etc.) C
American Steel House Co.,
796 11th Av. (Park) ...D
Colwell Lead Co., 63 Centre
(Water) ....AA
Dimock & Fink Co., 220 E.
125th (Water) ....AA
DuBois & Co., F. N., 245 9th
Av. (Water) ....AAA
Haydenville Co., 73 Beekman (Water) ....A
Hoffman, Jr. Co., Chas., 242
Water (Water) X
Huber Co., Henry, 244 5th
Av. (Water; School; Institution, etc.) ....D
Hussey & Son, Wm. H., 150
W. 35th (Water) ......AA
Kenney Mfg. Co., 36 E. 22d
(Water; School; Institution, etc.) ....D
McNab and Harlin Mfg. Co.,
56 John (Water) ....AAA

CLOSETS (Con.)

Mason & Co., J. W., 406 Pearl (China) ....D
Mayor, Lane & Co., 128 White (Water) ....A
Meyer-Sniffen Co. (Ltd.) 5 E. 19th (Water; School; Institution, etc.) ......A
Mott Iron Wks., J. L., 88 Beekman (Water; School; Institution, etc.) ....AA
Reynolds Plumbers' Supply Co., M., 25 Centre (Water) ....B
Schloss & Co., E., 504 Cherry (China) ....A

N. Y.—Troy

Aird-Don Co. (Water) ....A

OHIO—Cincinnati

Crane & Hawley Co., Court cor. Syracuse (Water) ..A
Douglas Co., Jno., 906 Poplar (Water) ....A
Gibson Co., Thos., 633 Walnut (Water) ....D
Lipp Co., Louis (Water) ..A
Mitchell Furn. Co., Robert. 111 W. 4th (China) AAAA
Peck-Williamson Heating & Ventilaing Co. (Water) AA
Pfau Mfg. Co., 536 Reading Rd. (Water) ....B
Tygart Fire Brick Co., 706 Burns (Fire) C
Wiggers & Sons Furn. Co., H. H. (China) ....B

OHIO—Cleveland

Fisher Co., E. W., 251 Superior (Water) ....B

OHIO—Columbus

Columbus Brass Co. (Water) A

OHIO—Dayton

Dayton Mfg. Co. (Car) ..A

OHIO—Hamilton

Sanitary Mfg. Co. (Water) B

OHIO—Toledo

National Supply Co., 1 St. Clair (Water) ....AAAA

PA.—Philadelphia

Blessing, C. A., 515 Montgomery (Water) ......AA
Cooper Brass Wks., W. S. (Water) ....B
Fleck Bros., 44 N. 5th (Water) ....A
Froelish Bros., 142 N. 7th (Water) ....A
Haimes, Jones & Cadbury Co., 1136 Ridge Av. (Water) ....AA
McCambridge & Co., 527 Cherry (Water) ....B
Walls & Pearsall, 307 N. 12th (Water) ....A

PA.—Pittsburg

Bailey-Farrell Mfg. Co. (Water) ....AA
Fort Pitt Supply Co., 525 Wood (Water) ....A
Pittsburg Brass Mfg. Co., 107 Wood (Water) ....D
Pittsburg Supply Co., 226 1st Av. (Water) ....A
Standard Mfg. Co. (Range; Water) ....AA
Standard Sanitary Mfg. Co., Arrott Bldg. (Water; School; Institution, etc.) AAAA

R. I.—Providence

Brown & Sharpe Mfg. Co. (Factory Sanitary), AAAA
Tillinghast Supply Co., L. H. (Water) C

WIS.—Milwaukee

Rundle-Spence Mfg. Co. (Water) ....A

WIS.—Sheboygan

Kohler Sons Co., J. M. (Water; School; Institution, etc.) ....A

CLOTH

See also Cotton Goods; Woolen Goods; Oil Cloth; see also Cloths

CAL.—San Francisco

California Artistic Metal & Wire Co., 539 Missouri (Wire) ....D
California Wire Cloth Co., 8 Pine (Wire) ....D

CLOTH (Con.)

COLO.—Denver

Denver Wire & Iron Wks. Co. 1403 Market (Wire) D

CONN.—Georgetown

Gilbert-Bennett Mfg. Co. (Wire; Brass Wire; Copper Wire; Galvanized Wire; Iron Wire; Lathing Wire; Rice Wire; Smut Wire; Spark Wire; Steel Wire; Tanning Mill Wire; Tinned Wire; Window Screen Wire) ......AAA

CONN.—Middletown

Palmer, I. E. (Hammock Wire; Screen Wire; Decorated; Window Screen Wire; Imitation Wire; Piano) ....AAA

CONN.—New Haven

McClusky & Sons, H. & T. (Brass Wire; Papermakers' Wire) ....F

CONN.—Southport

Jelliff Mfg. Corp'n (Wire) C

ILL.—Chicago

Allis-Chalmers Co., Home Ins. Bldg. (Bolting) AAAA
Barbee Wire & Iron Wks., 44 Dearborn (Wire; Screen Wire ....B
Booth, Jno., 116 E. Lake (Wire) ....B
Smith Wire & Iron Wks., F. P., 100 Lake (Wire) AA
Voss, Fred., 617 Austin Av. (Wire) ....B

ILL.—Dixon

Reynolds Wire Co. (Wire) B

IND.—Indianapolis

Nordyke & Marmon Co., 1101 W. Morris (Silk; Wire Bolting ....AAA

KANS.—Leavenworth

Great Western Mfg. Co. (Bolting) ....AA

KY.—Louisville

Dow Wire Wks. Co., 730 W. Market (Wire) ....D

MD.—Baltimore

Dufur & Co., 311 N. Howard (Wire; Bolting) ....B

MASS.—Boston

American Cotton Mills Co. (Cheese) ....F
Morss and Whyte, 75 Cornhill (Wire) ....AAA
Whyte & Co., Oliver, 17 Cornhill (Wire) C

MASS.—Clinton

Clinton Wire Cloth Co. (Wire; Bolting; Brass Wire; Copper Wire; Crimped Wire; Galvanized Wire; Iron Wire; Lathing Wire; Locomotive Spark Wire; Malt Kiln Wire; Mining Wire; Rice Wire; Screen Wire; Smut Wire; Spark Wire; Steel Wire; Strainer Wire; Sugar Wire; Tanning Mill Wire; Tinned Wire; Window Screen Wire) ......AAA

MASS.—Holyoke

Buchannan & Bolt Wire Co. (Wire) ....B

MASS.—Leeds

Northampton Emery Wheel Co. (Emery) ....A

MASS.—Springfield

Bigelow-Cheney Wire Wks. (Wire; Brass Wire; Copper Wire; Crimped Wire; Galvanized Wire; Iron Wire; Lathing Wire; Papermakers' Wire; Sugar Wire) X

MASS.—Worcester

Deane & Co., Henry E., 233 Arch (Wire) ....E
Nat'l Mfg. Co. ;(Wire; Strainer Wire) ....A
Wright Wire Co. (Wire; Battery Wire; Bolting Wire; Brass Wire; Copper Wire; Crimped Wire; Fruit Drying Wire; Galvanized Wire; Iron Wire; Lathing Wire; Locomotive

CLOTH (Con.)

Wire; Malt Kiln Wire;
Mining Wire; Rice Wire;
Spark Wire; Steel Wire;
Strainer Wire; Tanning
Mill Wire; Tinned Wire;
Window Screen) ......AA

MICH.—Detroit

Barnum Wire & Iron Wks.,
. T., 99-105 Shelby (Wire)
D

Michigan Wire Cloth Co.,
500 Howard (Steel, Brass,
Copper Wire; Bolting
Wire; Fruit Drying Wire;
Galvanized Wire; Iron
Wire; Malt Kiln Wire;
Tanning Mill Wire)... AA

MO.—Kansas City

Kansas City Wire & Iron
Wks., 1428 Oak (Wire) A

MO.—St. Louis

Lasar-Letzig Mfg. Co., 1124
Wash. Av. (Wire) C

Ludlow-Saylor Wire Co.,
16th & O'Fallon (Wire;
Window Screen Wire)
AA

N. J.—Belleville

De Witt Wire Cloth Co.
(Wire; Brass, Copper,
Iron, Mining Wire;Paper-
makers' Wire; Strainer,
Sugar Wire; Window
Screen) ....A

Eastwood Wire Mfg. Co.
Wire; Battery Wire; Bolt-
ing; Copper, Crimped, Gal-
vanized Wire; Iron Wire;
Papermakers' Wire; Rice
Wire; Smut Wire; Spark
Wire; Strainer, Sugar
Wire; Twilled Brass) ...A

N. J.—Harrison

Staniar & Laffey Wire Co.
(Wire) ....A

N. J.—Newark

Heath & Son, E. F. (Rub-
ber; Enamel Carriage) AA

N. J.—Trenton

Consolidated Rubber Co.
(Rubber; Carriage) C

New Jersey Wire Cloth Co.
(Wire; Window Screen
Wire) ....A

N. Y.—Brooklyn

Richardson, F. G., 403
Hewes (Wire; Brass, Cop-
per, Iron Wire; Bolting)
A

N. Y.—Buffalo

American Buffalo Robe Co.,
1 Howell (Astrakhan Fur)
A

Buffalo Weaving & Belting
Co. (Bolting; Webs) ...A

Buffalo Wire Wks. Co.
(Window Screen Wire;
Wire) ....A

N. Y.—Cortland

Wickville Bros. (Wire; Galvanized Wire; Iron; Win-
dow Screen Wire) .AAAA

New York City

American Cotton Mills Co.
(Cheese) ....B

Am. Felting Wks. (Asbes-
tos) ....D

Behr & Co., Herman (Em-
ery) ....AA

Cable Excelsior Wire Mfg.
Co., Wm., 44 Fulton
(Wire; Brass, Copper,
Iron, Galvanized Wire;
Lathing Wire; Fruit Dry-
ing Wire) ....B

Estey Wire Wks. Co., 59
Fulton (Wire; Bolting) .D

Gilbert & Bennett Mfg. Co.,
277 Bway. (Wire; Brass,
Copper, Iron, Galvanized
Wire; Lathing Wire; Rice,
Smut, Spark, Steel Wire;
Tanning Mill Wire; Tin-
ned Wire; Window Screen
Wire) ....AAA

Howard & Morse, 45 Fulton
(Wire; Batery Wire; Bolt-
ing; Brass, Copper, Gal-
vanized, Iron Wire; Lath-
ing Wire; Locomotive
Spark Wire; Malt Kiln
Wire; Mining Wire; Pa-
permakers' Wire; Phos-
phor Bronze Wire; Rice,
Smut, Spark Wire; Steel

CLOTH (Con.)

Wire; Sugar Wire; Steel,
Tinned Wire; Tanning
Mill Wire) ....D

Johns H. W.-Manville Co.,
100 William (Asbestos)
AAAA

Keuffel & Esser Co., 127
Fulton (Tracing) .....AA

Lloyd Co., W. H. S., 26 W.
22d (Grass Decorative) .F

Mica Insulator Co., 218
Water (Insulating) ....B

Mineralized Rubber Co., 18
Cliff (Brattice) ....A

Moses, Lionel, 36 E. 22d
(Japanese Grass) .....D

New York Wire Cloth Co.,
102 Chambers (Wire; Iron
Wire; Tinned, Window
Screen Wire) ....AA

Roeblings Sons Co., Jno. A.,
117 Liberty (Wire; Cop-
per, Crimped, Galvanized,
Iron Wire; Lathing Wire;
Locomotive Spark Wire;
Mining Wire; Rice, Smut,
Spark Wire; Strainer
Wire; Tanning Mill Wire;
Window Screen Wire)
AAAA

Roberts, Edw. Craig, 13 E.
30th (Grass) X

Standard Paint Co., 100 William (Insulating; Moth) A

Standard Table Oil Cloth
Co., 320 Bway. (Oil)
AAAA

Williams & Sons, Geo. A., 85
Fulton (Wire) X

N. Y.—Niagara Falls

Carborundum Co. (Carcorun-
dum) ....A

N. Y.—Rochester

Snow Wire Wks. Co., 76 Exchange (Wire) ....D

N. Y.—Rockville Centre

Tristram, Jas. J. (Wire) . .E

N. Y.—Syracuse

Syracuse Wire Wks. (Wire)
D

OHIO—Cincinnati

Bromwell Brush & Wire Gds.
Co. (Wire) ....AA

Cincinnati Mfg. Co., 512
Main (Wire) ....B

OHIO—Cleveland

Bartlett & Snow Co., C. O.
(Bolting) ....A

Tyler Co., W. S., 1150 St.
Clair (Wire; Window
Screen Wire) .....AAAA

OHIO—Columbus

Case Mfg. Co. (Bolting) .A

OHIO—Hamilton

Myers Mfg. Co., Fred'k J.
Wire; Window Screen
Wire) ....B

OHIO—Newark

Reed Wire Cloth Co. (Wire)
B

OHIO—Tiffin

Sterling Emery Wheel Mfg.
Co. (Emery) ....A

PA.—Hanover

Hanover Wire Cloth Co.
(Wire) ....A

PA.—Muncy

Sprout, Waldron & Co.
(Silk; Wire Bolting) ...A

PA.—New Freedom

New Freedom Wire Cloth Co.
(Wire Screen) ....A

PA.—Philadelphia

Baeder, Adamson & Co.
(Emery) ....AAAA

Barton Son & Co., H. H.
(Emery) ....A

Darby & Sons, Edw., 233
Arch (Wire; Brass, Cop-
per, Iron, Galvanized
Wire; Steel Wire) .....A

Haulfen & Co., Jno. E., Sav-
ery & East Thompson (As-
trakhan) ....AA

Latimer & Co., R. L., 21 N.
Front (Boling) C

Merritt & Co., 1024 Ridge
Av. (Wire; Copper Wire)
B

Phosphor Bronze Smelting
Co. (Ltd.) 2200 Wash. Av.
(Wire; Phosphor Bronze
Wire) ....A

Strawbridge & Chase Co.
(Ltd.), 228 Arch (Wire),F

230

CLOTH (Con.)

Weigand, C. A. (Window Shades) ....F

PA.—Pittsburg

Pittsburg Insulating Co. (Insulating Linen) ....b

R. I.—Bristol

National India Rubber Co. (Insulating) ......AAAA

R. I.—Pawtucket

American Hair Cloth Co. (Fibre) ....AA

R. I.—Providence

What Cheer Wire Wks. (Wire) ....F

CLOTHING CARD

CONN.—Stafford Springs

Beckwith Card Co. ....B

ILL.—Chicago

Street & Co., R. R., 186 Wash. ....A

MASS.—Boston

English Co., C. R., 204 Summer ....E
Leigh Evan Arthur, Mason Bldg. ....B
McKerrow & Co., H. G., 31 State X
Riley & Co., C. E., 65 Franklin ....A
Stoddard, Haserick, Richards & Co., 152 Congress B

MASS.—Fall River

Ashworth, Elijah X

MASS.—Leicester

Watson Mfg. Co., L. S...B

MASS.—Lowell

Bagshaw, W. H. (Est. of) B
Kitson Machine Co.....AAA
Stott, S. E. & T. X

MASS.—N. Andover Depot

Davis & Furber Mach. Co. AA

MASS.—Walpole

Walpole Card Clothing Co. D

MASS.—Worcester

American Card Clothing Co. AAA
Howard Bros. Mfg. Co...A

N. J.—Newark

Crabb & Co., Wm ....A

PA.—Philadelphia.

Booth & Co. (Ltd.) Benj. 1715 Bodine C
Hammer, Jr. & Co., C. H. 423 Belgrade ....D
Jefferson & Bro., Edw., 127 So. 2d C
Smith & Co., James, 411 Race ....B
Smith Woolen Mchry. Co., James, 411 Race ......AA

CLOTHING LADIES', CHILDREN'S & INFANT'S

CAL.—Los Angeles

Coulter Dry Gds. Co. (Suits, Dresses, Skirts) ......A

CAL.—San Francisco

Juda Bros. (Silk, Woolen & Wash Waists)..........D
Kelly & Liebes (Cloaks, Dresses, Silk Waists) ..B
Konig Max & Co. (Waists) D
Neubauer Bros. (Silk & Wash Waists) ....D
Rothschild, A. & Co. (Skirts, Suits, Cloaks, Waists)..B

COLO.—Denver

Daniels & Fisher Stroes Co. (Wrappers, Waists, Suits) AAA

CONN.—Bridgeport

Hatheway Mfg. Co. ......D

CONN.—Hartford

Wise, Smith & Co. (Cloaks) A

CONN.—Norwalk

Hutchinson, Pierce & Co. (Waists) ....AAA

ILL.—Chicago...

Abramhamson & Klein

CLOTHING, LADIES' &C (Cloaks, Jackets, Capes) B

Bartlett-Lincoln Co. (Shirtwaists', Coats, Skirts)..D
Beifield, Kirsch & Kline (Cloaks) ....A
Chicago Novelty Cloak Co. (Suits, Cloaks) ....AAAA
Dernberg Mfg. Co. (Dress, Walking Skirts) C
Farwell, John V., Co. (Suits, Cloaks, Wrappers, Dresses) ....AAAA
Friend, Henry ....B
Ginsburg Bros. (Silk Dress Skirts, Waists, Petticoats) C
Grossman, Edward B. & Co. (Suits, Cloaks, Skirts)..B
Grossman, Herman & Co. (Chicago Cloak Co.) (Cloaks) ....B
Harshberger, Chas. R. (Shirt Waists) ....D
Heilprin, L. & Co. (Suits; Cloaks) ....AAA
Hoyt & Co., G. W. (Wrappers, Waists, Skirts) ..B
Marcus Solms & Son (Suits; Skirts) ....B
Leeser & Co., Levi (Shirt Waists) C
Neelands, T. D. (Waists, Suits) ....D
Opoznauer & Lipman (Waists; Suits) ....D
Palmer, Percival B. & Co.; also Childrens' (Suits; Cloaks) ....A
Parkside Mfg. Co. (Shirt Waists) C
Samson & Jacobs (Skirts, Cloaks, Suits) C
Schram, B. & Co. (Wrappers, Dressing Sacques, Night Robes) ....D
Schwartz & Kline (Suits; Shirts) ....B
Shoninger Bros. Mfg. Co. Infants Coats)..........C
Siegel, F. & Bros. (Suits, Cloaks, Waists, Underskirts) ....AA
Stevens, Chas. A. & Bros. AA
Strasberg & Asher (Night Gowns, Dressing Sacques, Wrappers) ....D
Strauss, Eisendrath & Co. (Skirts; Waists; Wrappers) ....AA
Teasdal, F. L. & Co. (Shirt Waist Suits, Silk Waists, Skirts) ....D

ILL.—Decatur

Home Mfg. Co. (Aprons, Wrappers, Night Robes) D

ILL.—Quincy

Defiance Garment Mfg. Co. (Silk, Morreen, Sateen, Wash Petticoats; Dress, Walking Skirts C

ILL.—Waukegan

Alshuler, M. Co. (Wrappers, Dressing Sacques, Wash Skirts) C

IND.—Evansville

Leonard & Co., James (Skirts) ....B

IND.—Fort Wayne

Foster, Samuel M. (Shirt Waists) ....B
Merit Mfg. Co. (Waists; Suits) C
Paragon Mfg. Co. (Waists; Suits) C

IND.—Indianapolis

American Trousers Co. (Walking Skirts) C
Gem Garment Co. (Shirt Waists; Shirt Waist Suits) C
Kirshbaum, R. & Son (Cotton; Flannel Shirt Waists) A
Merritt, Geo. & Co. (Lustre Wool; Homespun; Flannel Petticoats; Dress Skirts) B

IND.—New Albany

Robinson J. M. Morton & Co. (Skirts) ....AAA

IOWA—Cedar Rapids

Talt, John H. & Co. (Skirts) B

IOWA—Davenport
Davenport Garment Mfg. Co. (Wrappers) ....D
IOWA—Des Moines
Capital City Woolen Mills (Scheuerman Bros. Props.) (Skirts) ....A
Des Moines Skirt & Corset Mfg. Co. (Skirts; Waists) ....E
IOWA—Dubuque
Rider-Wallis Co. (Wrappers) ....AA
KY.—Louisville
Gem Mfg. Co. (Skirts) ...C
Straus, Herman & Sons Co. (Dresses) ....A
LA.—New Orleans
Heidenheimer, Levy & Co. (Skirt & Coats, Boys Waists; Pants) ....A
Lehman, A. & Co. (Skirts; Shirt Waists) ....AA
Katz & Co., S. & J. (Waists & Skirts) ....A
Nick, H. L. & Co., (Shirt Waists; Skirts; Petticoats) ....D
MAINE—Portland
Cheney Mfg. Co. (Skirts; Waists; Wrappers; Suits) ....B
MD.—Baltimore
Gehrman & Co., P. F. (Aprons) C
Holzman Mfg. Co. (Waists) ....A
Levy, D. & Sons (Waists), B
Lowenstein, L. & Co. (Waists) ....D
Mayer, J. & Co. (Silk Waists; Cotton; Silk Suits) C
Mendels Bros. (Wrappers) ....D
Steppacher & Stern (Shirt Waists) C
MASS.—Boston
Aronson, N. (Waists; Skirts; Wrappers, Capes) C
Charlton, John G. Co. (Silk; Cotton; Cashmere Waists; Suits) X
Harvard Rubber Mfg. Co. (Silk Waists) ....D
Hollander, L. P. & Co. (Cloaks, etc.) ....AA
Howe, Lovejoy Mfg. Co. (Wrappers; Tea Gowns; Suits; Aprons) ....D
Ideal Shirt Waist Co. (Silk; Flannel Waists) ....D
Langley, Burr & Co. (Wrappers; Aprons) ....A
National Waist & Skirt Co. (Shirt Waists) ....D
Puritan Waist Co. (Silk Waists; Gowns, etc.)...D
Rosenfield Myer (Wrappers; Tea Gowns; Shirt Waist Suits) ....A
Slatery, E. T. Co. (Suits; Cloaks; Wraps; Waists) ....B
Standard Mfg. Co. (See J. P. Morse) (Waists) ....B
Sudbury Mfg. Co. (Silk; French Flannel; Mercerized Waists) C
MASS.—Natick
Randall Bros. (Skirts)....D
MASS.—Needham
Brooks Co., John F. (Knit Sacques) C
MASS.—Springfield
Bay State Corset Co. (Corset Waists) ....B
MASS.—Worcester
Burns Co., Wm. H. (Lawn Waists) ....A
MICH.—Ann Arbor
Crescent Works (Walking Skirts; Petticoats)......D
Randall Skirt & Corset Co. (Skirts) ....E
MICH.—Bay City
Victory Mfg. Co. (Silk; Cotton; Lawn; Velvet Waists) ....D
MICH.—Detroit
American Suit & Corset Co. (Suits, Skirts, Petticoats) ....AA
Babbitt, Taylor, Lane Co. (Dress Waists) C

Detroit Stay Co. (Waists), C
Edson, Moore & Co. (Waists; Skirts; Wrappers) ....AAA
Standard Skirt Co. (Skirts) C
Strong, Lee & Co. (Skirts; Wrappers, Shirt Waists) ....A
Zacharias & Mason Co. (Black, White Colored Flannel; Silk Waists; Suits) ....B
MICH.—Grand Rapids
Standard Mfg. Co. (Fancy Waists) ....B
MICH.—Jackson
Bortree Corset Co. (Underskirt) C
Pandora Corset Co. (Skirts) C
Reliance Corset Co. (Dressing Sacques; Underskirts) C
MICH.—Marshall
Cronin, S. E. (Skirts) C
MICH.—Saginaw
Robertson, E. A. & Co. (Silk; Mercerized Cotton; Velvet Waists) ....D
MINN.—Minneapolis
Clerihew, A. M. & A. E. (Shirt Waists; Wrappers) C
Minneapolis Knitting Works (Knit Waists, Children) ....B
MINN.—St. Paul
Finch, Young & McConville (Shirt Waists; Skirts; Wrappers) ....AAA
Lindek, Warren & Schurmeier (Shirt Waists; Skirts) ....AAAA
Macpherson & Langford (Walking & Dress Skirts) C
Tibbs, Hutchins & Co. (Skirts; Shirt Waists) ..A
MO.—Kansas City
Bell Waist & Shirt Co. (Waists; Skirts; Silk, Wool, Cotton Petticoats; Wrappers; Dressing Sacques) ....D
MO.—St. Joseph
Englehart, Davison Merc. Co. (Skirts) ....B
MO.—St. Louis
Bry & Bro. Cloak Co. (Suits; Cloaks; Skirts; Petticoats) ....A
Carlton Dry Goods Co. (Skirts) ....AAAA
Ely & Walker Dry Goods Co. (Shirt Waists; Skirts; Wrappers) ....AAAA
Ferguson-McKinney Dry Goods Co. (Skirts), AAAA
Friedman, & Sons (Suits; Cloaks; Skirts) ....A
Herzog, L. & Bro., Dry Gds. Co. (Cloaks; Suits) ...A
Hughes, John Co. (Skirts), C
Macdonald Mfg. Co. (Silk, Wool Waists; Silk, Wool, Wash Skirts) ....D
Olga Mfg. Co. (Silk; Lawn; Flannel; Satin Waists)..C
Olian Bros. (Silk; Wash Waists) C
Progress Mfg. Co. (Dress Skirts; Suits) C
Rosenfield, A., Skirt & Waist Co., (Skirts; Waists) ....D
St. Louis Corset Co. (Skirts; Petticoats) ....B
Singer Bros. (Jackets; Skirts; Capes; Collarettes) ....A
Western Corset Co. (Skirts) C
Williamson Corset & Brace Co. (Skirts; Petticoats).D
N. H.—Lebanon
Carter & Churchill Co. (Aprons) ....B
N. H.— Manchester
New York Store Co. (Skirts) C
N. H.—Newport
Peerless Mfg. Co. (Flannel Gowns; Skirts) ....A

N. H.——Tilton
Ideal Mfg. Co. (Wrappers)
....................B
N. J.——Millville
Dix, Henry A. & Sons
(Wrappers; Dressing
Sacques; Maids' Dresses)
....................D
N. J.——Newark
Best & Co., L. H. (Infants
Dresses) X
Cogswell & Boulter Co. (Infants Dresses) ....A
De Bevoise Waist Co.
(Waists) ....D
Delsarte Mfg. & Supply Co.
Dresses; Coats; Wraps)
....................D
Jackson & Co., T. W. (Petticoats) ....B
Shiner, Alexander W. (Shirt
Waists) C
N. J.——New Brunswick
Barkelen & Co., J. M.
(Aprons) ....D
N. Y.——Albany
Albany Garment Co. (Skirts;
Wrappers) C
Hubbard, G. A. & Co. (Calico Wrappers; Wash
Skirts; Dressing Sacques)
....................D
Munson, S. L. (Aprons;
Waists) ....A
N. Y.——Auburn
Parker Mfg. Co. (Wrappers;
Tea Gowns; Kimonas;
Suits; Dressing Sacques)
....................B
Romig Mfg. Co. (Tea
Gowns; Wrappers)......A
N. Y.——Binghamton
Bennett, Morgan Co. (Wrappers; Children's Dresses)
....................B
N. Y.——Brooklyn
Manheim, Julius (Shirt
Waists) C
Lowe & Sons, R. E. (Wrappers; House Dresses;
Waists; Wash Suits)...B
Parker & Co., J. K.
(Waists) ....D
Phillips & Co., S. (Children's Dresses) C
Zeman Bros. (Cotton Shirt
Waists; Suits) C
N. Y.——Buffalo
Hengerer Co., Wm. (Skirts)
....................AAA
Schwaegler Co., J. B. (Shirt
Waists; Shirt Waist Suits)
....................C
N. Y.——Elmira
Doolittle, F. E. (Aprons).B
Freudenheim & Bro., L.
(Dress Skirts) C
N. Y.——Glens Falls
Robertson & Co., D. L.
(Waists) C
Weill Haskell Co. (Waists)
....................AAA
N. Y.——Johnstown
Grewen Bros. & Co. (Skirts)
....................C
N. Y.——McGraw
McGraw Corset Co., A. P.
(Dress; Uunderskirts;
Waists) C
N. Y.——Milton
Bells' Sons Co., Henry H.
(Wrappers; Sacks) ....B
New York City
Acme Underwear Co.
(Skirts; Gowns) C
Adam, Hugo S. (Dressing
Sacques) C
Apfelbaum, M. (Shirt
Waists) ....D
Aronson Bros. (Cloaks;
Suits) ....B
Asch & Jaeckel (Golf; Pedestrian Suits) ....A
Bamberger & Son (Infants'
Dresses; Cloaks) ......B
Bauman, H. (Wrappers;
Shirt Waist Suits, Kimonas) ....D
Bauman & Sperling (Cloaks)
....................AA
Beekman & Hays (Wrappers) C

Beller & Co., A. (Cloaks;
Suits) ....A
Berman, Jacob (Cotton;
Woolen Waists) C
Biermann, Henry (Wrappers; Waists) ....D
Birkenfeld, Srauss & Co.
(Cotton Shirt Waists)..B
Blan, Jules (Shirt Waists)
....................D
Blauner Bros. & Co. (Suits;
Cloaks) ....B
Bloch, M. (Waists) ......D
Blum, Herman A. (Waists)
....................D
Blumenthal Bros. (Waists)
....................D
Bonwit, John (Skirts)...X
Borgenicht & Scharff
(Dresses) ....D
Brady & Co., J. M. (Suits;
Skirts) ....B
Brill, R. B. (Silk Waists;
Suits) ....D
Brill & Kriegsman (Waists)
....................B
Brody & Co., N. (Dress;
Walking Skirts) C
Brookstone & Sons, S.
(Waists) ....D
Brown & Co. (Waists)...D
Citron Bros. (Waists)....C
Claflin Co., H. B. (Suits;
Cloaks; Capes; Skirts;
Waists; Wrappers).AAAA
Cohen & Co., Henry
(Waists) ....A
Cohen, Joseph H. (Suits;
Cloaks) ....B
Cohen & Co., M. (Suits;
Cloaks) ....B
Cohen, J. & M. (Silk; Cotton Shirt Waists; Suits)
....................B
Comfort Waist Co. (Waists)
....................D
Cooper, Michael (Wrappers;
Dressing Sacques; Bath
Robes) ....B
Corn, Joseph (Skirts) ...C
Crawford, Andrew (Suits;
Cloaks; Skirts) ....B
Crystel, Bernard (Wrappers)
....................C
Dannenbaum Bros. (Waists;
Silk Petticoats) ......A
Daulton, Peter (Silk Petticoats) ....A
Denbusky Bros. (Waists).D
Diamond, Wm. J. (Dressing
Sacques) C
Eagle Skirt Co. (Petticoats)
....................C
Economist Waist Co. (Silk
Waists) C
Erlich & Co., Jacob (Wrappers; Tea Gowns) C
Ettelson, Henry Co. (Wrappers) ....D
Eureka Waist Co.. (Waists)
....................D
Feist Bros. (Jobbers)
(Cloaks; Capes; Skirts).X
Fisk, Clark & Flagg
(Waists) ....A
Flaherty, Joseph B. (Wrappers; Dressing Sacques).B
Floersheimer, Roman &
Hahn (Waists; Suits)..B
Forsythe, John (Waists)..A
Frank & Schloss (Waists).D
Frankenthal Bros. Co.
(Shirt Waists) ....B
Franklin, Julius (Wrappers;
Skirts; Suits; Sacques).B
Freeman & Son, H. (Wrappers) ....D
Friedlander & Co., A....AA
Fuld Bros. (Shirt Waists;
Children's Dresses) ...D
Gans Sons & Co., Myer,
(also Children's) .....A
Garfield & Bernstein (Peerless Cloak Mfg. Co.)
(Cloaks; Suits) ....B
Gershel & Son, H. (Cloaks;
Suits) ....B
Ginsburg & Bro., S......B
Gitskey & Bastianelli (Infants' Wash Dresses)..D
Goetz, J. & W. (Waists;

Jerseys) ....B
Goldberg & Sons, M.
(Cloaks) ....B
Goldberg & Sons, M.
(Shirt Waists) ....B
Goldman, J. & E. (Waists)
   B
Goldschmidt & Co. (Waists)
   C
Goldstein & Co., R.
(Waists) C
Gootman & Co., M. (Cotton; Flannel Shirt Waists)
   D
Gratz, Kohn & Sperber....D
Gross & Weiss (Shirt
Waists) ....D
Harburger, Henry L.
(Dresses; Aprons) .....D
Harris, Geo. (Dressing
Sacques) ....D
Harris & Blank (Waists)..C
Hartley Bros. (Shirts)....C
Heimerdinger, Geo. C.
(Skirts) ....D
Heiss & Co., S. W. (Skirts)
   D
Heller & Co., M. (Suits;
Cloaks; Skirts) ....B
Heller & Nyburg (Cotton;
Woolen Waists) ......D
Henle & Co., John (Shirt
Waists; Suits) ....D
Herzig & Knapp (Petticoats) ....B
Herzig & Co., Joseph (Children's Dresses) C
Herzig & Co. L. (Children's
Cloaks & Reefers) C
Hirsch Bros. (Wrappers)..D
Hirsch & Sons, A. (Wrappers) ....D
Horwitz Bros. & Serling
(Cotton; Flannel Shirt
Waists) ....D
Inbender & Cohen (Waists)
   C
Jaburg, Fuhs & Lovin (Infants' Coats; Cloaks)..B
Japanese Silk Garment Co.
(Wrappers; Tea Gowns).C
Kalisher & Bro., H. B.
(Tea Gowns) ....D
Kaplon, I. (Wrappers, &c.)
   D
Kaplon & Wien (Shirt
Waists) ....B
Kashowitz, M. & J. (Cloaks;
Suits) ....B
Katz, S. (Dress Skirts)...C
Kean & Schwed (Waists).C
Kitzinger & Zelenko (Infants' Reefers; Jackets)
   B
Klatzco & Miskend (Silk;
Sateen Petticoats) C
Klinger & Bach (Waists)..C
Kottler & Co., H. (Waists)
   D
Kupfer Bros. (Waists)...D
Kurzroh Bros. (Waists)...C
Laird & Bonwit (Suits;
Cloaks; Skirts) ....A
Levy & Co., Herman
(Cloaks; Mantles) .....B
Levy Co., H. H. (Tea
Gowns; Summer Suits).D
Lewis Bros. (Cotton; Wool
Shirt Waists) ....D
Lewyn & Co., A. (Shirt
Waist; Shirt Waist Suits)
   C
Libman, Mrs. B. (Infants'
Coats; Reefers) C
Livingston & Lieberman
also Misses (Waists)...B
Lindon & Bannin Co.
(Children's Dresses)....C
Lord & Taylor (Suits;
Cloaks) ....AAAA
Lublang & Beck (Dress
Skirts) C
Lurie & Co., G. (Children's
Dresses) ....B
Lyons & Co. (Misses Suits;
Children's Dresses) ....D
McLaughlin, W. A. (Waists)
   B
Maloney & Co., J. T.
(Wrappers; Waists) ...C
Manchel, Frank (Waists).D

Markowitz, H. (Suits;
Cloaks) ....B
Martin & Co., M. (Shirt
Waists) ....AA
Mayers & Lister (Colored
Petticoats) C
Melnick, Max (Waists)..D
Menaker, Bernheim & Menaker (Wrappers; Dressing
Sacques; Kimonas).....D
Messner, Emil (Silk Waists)
   B
Metropolitan Wrapper Co.
(Wrappers; Kimonas;
Dressing Sacues) ......D
Mikola & Bro. J. (Waists;
Suits) ....D
Mirsky & Co., M. D. (Wrappers) ....B
Mitchell & Gross (Waists)
   D
Model Mfg. Co. (Cloaks;
Skirts; Shirt Waists)...B
Morris & Co., Joseph A.
(Waists) C
Nathan, M. I. (Silk Waists;
Suits) C
National Cloak & Suit Co.
(Cloaks; Suits; Skirts)
   AAA
National Shirt Waist Co.
(Waists) C
Nessler & Whitehead
(Dresses; Children's)..D
Obermeier & Co., C. (Dress
Skirts) C
Oppenheim, Collins & Co.
(Cloaks; Suits) ....A
O'Hare, T. J. (Tea Gowns;
Silk; Negligee Waists).D
Palmer, R. D. (Waists;
Skirts; Wrappers).....D
Platt, S. (Wrappers; Tea
Gowns; Dressing Sacques)
   C
Price & Willgerodt (Cloaks;
Suits) ....B
Reutlinger & Bro., Max
(Cotton; Silk Waists) .C
Rohtman, Harry A.
(Waists) ....D
Roseff, Samuel (Cloaks)..B
Rosenbaum, H. (Children's
Dresses) ....D
Rosenberg, Joseph (Waists)
   D
Rosenblatt, A. (Wrappers)
   D
Rosenbloom & Kourcik
(Shirt Waists; Capes;
Children's Cloaks; Reefers) ....D
Rosenbloom & Lubell
(Waists) C
Rosenfeld & Co., L. E.
(Misses'; Children's Garments) ....B
Rosenthal Bros. Co. (Shirt
Waists; &c.) ....AA
Roth, Max (Shirt Waists).B
Rothschild & Bro., S.
(Suits; Cloaks) ....A
Rothschild, M. & L. F...B
Rothschild Co., V. Henry
(Waists) ....B
Rubin Bros. & Baron
(Cloaks & Suits)......D
Rutenburg, Miller & Lowenstein (Dress Skirts)..B
Ryan, Andrew (Petticoats)
   B
Samek Bros. (Children's
Dresses) ....D
Sandall & Neustadt
(Skirts) C
Scheyer & Co., Philip
(Cloaks & Suits) ......B
Schlang & Livingston
(Waists) ....D
Schneer's Son & Co., Isaac
(Shirt Waists; Blouses)
   B
Schwab Mfg. Co. (Waists)
   D
Schwartz & Scheer (Cloaks;
Suits) ....AA
Schwed & Co., R. (Petticoats) C
Shidlovsky & Bro., M.
(Cloaks; Suits; Skirts).B
Shrier, Samuel (Silk Petticoats) ....B

Sidenberg & Co., G.
(Waists) ....AA

Siemons, Chas. F. (Waists)
B

Siegel Bros. (Shirt Waists)
AAA

Sieradzki, Julius (Waists;
Skirts) ....D

Silverberg Bros. (Cotton;
Flannel Waists) C

Silverstein Bros. (Skirts)
A

Simon Julius (Waists)..C

Singer & Co., M. (Wrappers; Tea Gowns) ....B

Smith, A. H. (Silk Waists;
Suits) ....D

Sofranski Bros. (Skirts).C

Solinsky, Louis (Suits;
Cloaks) ....B

Solomon, Leopold (Children's Dresses) ....D

Solomon, Max (Dress
Skirts) ....A

Sondheim, Stein & Co.
(Waists) ....B

Sperling & Barin (Wrappers) ....D

Stein & Co., Julius (Suits;
Cloaks; Skirts) ....A

Stein, Levy & Co. (Waists)
B

Steinfeld & Co., S. (Cloaks;
Waists) ....A

Stern, S. & M. (Suits;
Cloaks; Capes) ....B

Stern, M. & Co. (Silk; Cotton Waists) C

Stern & Adler (Suits;
Cloaks; Skirts) ....B

Stiefel Bros. (Arlington
Skirt Mfg. Co.) (Silk;
Cloth; Flannel; Cotton;
Mohair Skirts) ....B

Stiglitz & Dinkelspiel
(Suits; Cloaks) ....B

Stone Bros. & Co. (Waists)
C

Stratton & Co., J. C.
(Misses'; Children's)
(Cloaks; Dresses) ....B

Tausig & Co. (Infants'
Dresses) C

Traubner & Co., B. (Cotton;
Woolen; Silk Waists)..D

Ullmann, M. (Dress Skirts)
C

Vesell, Meyer (Suits;
Cloaks) ....A

Weil & Grosz (Wrappers;
Dresses) ....D

Weiler Bros. (Silk; Cotton;
Flannel Waists) ....D

Weintraub, M. (Wrappers;
Skirts; Petticoats)...D

Weisman & Son, M.
(Waists) ....A

Welpen & Co. (Waists)..D

Whitehead & Asiel (Infants' Dresses) ....A

Wiener & Bossin (Suits;
Cloaks) ....B

Wightman & Co. (Misses'
Cloaks; Suits) ....A

N. Y.—Rochester

Sibley, Lindsay & Curr Co.
(Skirts) ....AAAA

N. Y.—Saratoga

Crippen & Reid (Wrappers;
Dressing Sacques; Shirt
Waist Suits) ....A

N. Y.—Sidney

Clark Textile Co. (Women's
Vests) ....A

N. Y.—Syracuse

Goodstock Mfg. Co. (Shirt
Waists) ....D

Lovell Wrapper & Overall
Co. (Percale; Flannelette
Wrappers) C

Wood & Co., J. E. (Petticoats) C

N. Y.—Troy

Coon Bros. (Waists) ....B

Corliss, Coon & Co. (Shirt
Waists) ....B

Stettheimer & Co., J. J.
(Waists) C

Tim & Co. (Waists) ....A

N. Y.—Waterford

American Shirt & Collar Co.

(Shirt Waists) ....D

N. Y.—Weedsport

Weedsport Shirt & Waist
Co. (Overskirts; Petticoats; Waists) ....B

OHIO—Akron

O'Neil & Co., M. (Suits).A

OHIO—Cincinnati

Bishop, Sterne & Stein
(Cloaks; Suits; Skirts).A

Cincinnati Cloak & Suit Co.
(Cloaks; Suits; Capes;
Skirts) ....B

Crescent Garment Co.
(Skirts) C

Fabian Mfg. Co. (Skirts)
A

Haas, B. & A. (Cloaks;
Suits; Reefers; Skirts).A

Jackman & Co., S. (Suits;
Cloaks) ....A

Shillito Co., John (Cloaks;
Capes) ....AAAA

Siefert Co. (Skirts; Wrappers) ....B

Stix & Co., Louis (Skirts)
AAAA

Veith & Brandt (Petticoats;
Skirts; Cloaks; Suits)..C

OHIO—Cleveland

Anisfield Co., John (Cloaks;
Suits) ....A

Bell Garment Co. (Skirts)
B

Black & Co., H. (Cloaks).A

Einstein, Guggenheim &
Co. (Shirt Waist; Suits)
B

Emsheimer & Co., Daniel
(Waists; Suits) C

Goldman & Co., M. (Skirts)
C

Landesman, Hirschheimer
Co. (Suits; Cloaks; Skirts)
AA

Printz, Biederman & Co.
(Suits; Cloaks; Skirts).A

Root & McBride Co. (Wrappers; Petticoats; Shirt
Waists) ....AAAA

Sampliner Cloak Co.
(Cloaks; Suits; Skirts).B

Silver & Co., M. T. (Suits;
Cloaks; Skirts) ....A

Silber & Gross (Waists)..C

Stein, Schwarz, Huebschman & Co. (Suits;
Cloaks; Skirts; Capes).A

Sunshine Cloak & Suit Co.
(Misses'; Children's
Cloaks; Suits) ....B

Taylor, Son & Co., Wm.
(Petticoats; Wrappers)
AAA

OHIO—Mansfield

Ditwilers' Sons, J. (Shirt)
D

OHIO—Napoleon

Napoleon Woolen Mills
(Flannel Skirts) C

OHIO—Toledo

Black Cloak Co., Alex.
(Suits; Cloaks; Skirts).B

Cohen, Friedlander & Martin Co. (Cloaks; Suits).B

Perfection Shirt Waist Co.
(Arthur Block & Co.)
(Shirt Waists & Wrappers) ....B

OREGON—Portland

Olds, Wartman & King..A

PA.—Allentown

Kline, Chas. (Waists;
Skirts) C

PA.—Altoona

Kline Bros. (Skirts;
Waists) ....B

PA.—Carlisle

Plank Co., J. W. (Ltd.)
(Wrappers; Dressing
Sacques, Children's Suits)
D

PA.—Harrisburg

Sun Mfg. Co. (Wrappers).D

PA.—Johnstown

Nathan & Bro., M. (Wrappers; Skirts) ....D

PA.—Nazareth

Nazareth Mfg. Co. (Children's Waists) ....B

PA.—Philadelphia

Alien, J. B. (Jerseys)...AA

Axford, John (Infants' Knit Wrappers) ....A

Beckman & Co., S. (Silk Waists; Suits) C

Behal, Jos. L. (Knit Skirts) ....D

Bernstein, Baum, Cravis & Co. (Suits; Cloaks).....B

Blum Bros. (Suits; Cloaks; Skirts; Silk Waists).AAA

Bowers & Co., A. J. S. (Phila. Cloak & Suit Co.) (Suits; Cloaks; Shirt Waists; Dressing Sacques) ....B

Branson & Co., Howard I. (Infants' Dresses) C

Brawerman Mfg. Co. (Eiderdown Dressing Sacques; Suits; Waists)...D

Cohn & Co., Alex. B. (Shirt Waists; Shirt Waist Suits) ....D

Feld & Co., Louis (Shirt Waists) ....B

Greenwald Bros. (Skirts).B

Haber & Co., M. (Shirt Waists) ....B

Hagedorn-Merz Co. (Shirt Waists) ....B

Harrison & Co., L. (Silk Waists) ....B

Heyman Bros. & Baum (Suits; Cloaks; Silk Waists) ....B

Horn & Co., P. (Silk; Mohair; Flannel; Cotton Waists) ....D

Hygienic Fleeced Underwear Co. (Wrappers; Eiderdown Terry: Blanket Robes) ....A

Kaufman & Rubin (Dressing Sacques; Waists; Infants' White) ....A

Kauffman & Harris (Wrappers; Waists) ....D

Leicester & Continental Mills Co. (Wrappers; Sacques) ....AA

Margolies & Harris (Progress Skirt Mfg. Co.) (Skirts) C

Meyerhoff & Co., M. S. (Misses'; Children's; Suits; Cloaks) ....B

Penn. Mfg. Co. (Waists).D

Penn. Waist & Suit Co. (Waists; Suits) ....B

Philadelphia Corset Co. (Infants' Waists) ....B

Rand Bros. (Waists) C

Rosenblatt, A. (Infants' Long and Short Dresses) C

Reinish, Son & Feld (Waists) ....D

Rothschild & Co., S. (Infants' Coats) C

Sacks Bros. (Suits; Cloaks) ....B

Schlein, S. (Waists) ....D

Schoenfeld, Tuck & Co. (Shirt Waists) ....B

Shatz, L. A. (Wrappers; Tea Gowns) C

Shenkin Bros. (Dresses).C

Stecher, L. (Silk Waists).C

Stein & McLoughlin (Skirts) C

Stein & Co., David (Star Novelty Co.) (Shirt Waists; Shirt Waist Suits; Dressing Sacques; Golf Vests) ....B

Strawbridge & Clothier (Suits; Cloaks; Skirts; Silk Waists; Petticoats) ....AAAA

Warshaw, Abraham (Wrappers; Skirts; Shirt Waists; Cloaks; Suits; Capes)..D

PA.—Pittsburg

Arbuthnot-Stephenson Co. (Silk Waists; Wrappers; Skirts) ....AAA

Pittsburg Dry Goods Co. (Wrappers; Aprons).AAA

Sidenburg & Rich (Cloaks;

CLOTHING, LADIES' &C

Suits; Misses'; Children's Coats). X

PA.—Reading

Brumbach, A. J. (St. Lawrence Woolen Mills) (Skirts) ....AA

Mercer, James R. (Wrappers) ....B

PA.—Wilkes Barre

Autocrat Shirt Waist Mfg. Co. (Shirt Waists; Suits) ....D

Galland Bros. (Dressing Sacques; Waists) ......B

PA.—York

Bear Mfg. Co. (Aprons; Skirts) C

R. I.—Pawtucket

Lumb, Geo. H. (Infants' Knit Bands; Wrappers) ....B

R. I.—Providence

Taylor, Symonds & Co. (Wrappers) ....AA

S. C.—Charleston

Wilbur & Son, T. A. (Skirts) ....A

TENN.—Knoxville

Arnstein & Co., M. B. (Skirts) C

TENN.—Memphis

Jiedel & Bro., I. (Skirts).B

VT.—Brattleboro

Hooker Corser & Mitchell Co. (Aprons) C

VT.—Rutland

Rutland Wrapper & Shirt Co. (Wrappers; Waists; Petticoats; Skirts) .....D

W. VA.—Parkersburg

Case Mfg. Co. Wrappers; Wash Petticoats) .....D

WIS.—La Crosse

La Crosse Rubber Mills Co. (Rubber Skirts) ......B

WIS.—Sheboygan

Excelsior Wrapper Co. (Wrappers; Dresses)...B

CLOTHING MEN'S, BOYS' & YOUTHS'

ALA.—Mobile

Bloch & Newburger (Overalls) C

Jacobson Clothing Co., G...B

Pollock & Bernheimer (Pants; Overalls) ...AAA

ALA.—Montgomery

Rice, Alex. ....B

CAL.—Los Angeles

Cohn, Goldwater & Co. (Pants; Overalls) ......B

Hoegee Co., W. H. (Hunting; Ball Suits) ....B

Jacoby Bros. ....A

Klein, Norton & Co. (A. F. Norton) (Overalls) ...B

CAL.—San Francisco

Brown Bros. & Co. ......AA

Dinkelspiel & Sons, L. (Overalls) ....A

Goldstein Bros. (Pants; Overalls) ....A

Hastings Clothing Co. .....A

Heynemann & Co. (Overalls; Pants) ....A

Hirsch, Leopold (Overalls) ....B

Hoffman, Rothchild & Co. ....AAA

Lowenberg & Co. (Overalls; Pants) ....AAA

Mandel & Wiener ....A

Meyerstein Co. (Overalls) ....AA

Newstadter Bros. (Suits; Pants; Overalls) ...AAA

Rosenthal, Maurice (Overalls) C

San Jose Woolen Mfg. Co. ....A

Scharlin & Co. (Overalls).D

Strauss & Co., Levi (Overalls; Riveted Clothing) ....AAAA

Summerfield, H. ....B

Wood, S. N. & Co. ......A

COLO.—Denver

Howe, Allen & Kaull Merc. Co. (Duck; Corduroy Pants) C

Underhill Mfg. Co. (Overall; Pants; Duck Clothing)..B

FLA.—Jacksonville

Kohn, Furchgott Co. (Pants) ....A

GA.—Atlanta

Loeb & Co., Marcus (Pants; Overalls) C

Nunnally Bros. (Pants; Overalls) C

Robinson Co., A. M. (Jeans; Cassimere Pants; Overalls; Duck Coats)......A

Wolf, H. (Pants; Overalls) C

GA.—Columbus

Georgia Mfg. Co. (Pants; Overalls; Jackets; Coats; Duck Coats) C

Rothschild & Co., D. (Pants; Overalls) C

Union Mfg. Co. (Andrews Co.) (Pants; Overalls)...C

GA.—Dalton

Smith, M. D. & H. L. (Overalls) ....D

GA.—Macon

Waxelbaum Co. (Pants)..B

GA.—Milledgeville

Evans, Samuel ....B

GA.—Rome

Kuttner & Co., J. (Pants; Overalls) ....B

GA.—Savannah

American Mfg. Co. (Pants; Overalls) ....B

ILL.—Bloomington

Klemm, C. W. (Overalls; Coats; Pants; Jumpers).A

ILL.—Chicago

Abt & Sons, L. ....A

Becker, Mayer & Co. (Youths) ....A

Bernstein, Cohen & Co. (Pants; Overalls) C

Born & Co., M. ....A

Cahn, Wampold & Co. ..A

Capps & Sons (Ltd.), J...A

Cook & Bro., E. C. (Hunters') ....A

Daube, Cohn & Co. (Youths') ....A

Dreyfus, Mayer & Co. (Knee Pants; Duck Coats) .....B

Edelman, Hyman (Overalls) ....D

Ederheimer, Stein & Co. (Youths') ....A

Farwell Co., John V. (Overalls; Duck Coats) ..AAAA

Freytag, M. (Overcoats; Furs) ....B

Hart Bros. (Overalls)...AA

Hart, Schaffner & Marx ....AAA

Hefter, Livingston & Co. (Youths) ....AA

Hirsh, Wickwire & Co. (Youths') ....AA

Hub, The (Inc.) ....A

Isador & Sons, J..........B

Jerrems, W. G. ....A

Kahn & Co., Felix ......B

Kaufman & Bros., Chas. (Suits; Overcoats) ...AA

Kaufmann, Fred ....B

Kling Bros. & Co. (Specialties) ....AA

Kohh Bros. ....AAAA

Kuh, Nathan & Fischer Co. ....AA

Kuppenheimer & Co., B. ....AAA

Lamm & Co. ....AA

Leopold, Solomon & Eisendrath ....A

Lewin & Son, A. (Overalls) C

Lindenthal & Goodman (Youths') ....B

Loeb's Sons, L. (Pants)..C

Marcus, Solms & Son (Pants) ....A

Marks & Co., H. M.....AA

Meyer & Co. ....A

Miller & Co., John G......A

Morris, Goldsmidt & Co....A

Opper & Co. ....B

Peck & Co., W. S.......A A

Pfaelzer & Co., David M. (Youths') ....A

Price & Co., Ed. V......A

Race Clothing Mfg. Co. (Jackets, Covert; Duck Coats; Overalls) ....B

Reliance Mfg. Co. (Pants; Overalls) ....A

Rose & Co., Edward .....B

Rosenwald & Weil (Inc.) (Summer Goods; Smoking Jackets; Pants; Fancy Vests) ....AA

Rothschild & Co., E. .....B

Rothschild & Co., Felix (Youths') ....B

Shauer & Bro., G. G. (Overalls; Jackets) ....D

Solomon & Co., J. ....A

Spitz & Schoenberg Bros. (Youths') ....A

Sterling Mfg. Co. (Men's Overalls; Youths' Overalls) ....A

Stern & Shohl Co., D. S. (Youths') ....B

Stern, Schafer & Co. (Youths') ....B

Strauss Bros. ....A

Strauss, Eisendrath & Co. (Boys' Waists; Pants) ....AA

Weil, Pflaum & Co. (Youths') ....B

Whitney, Christenson & Bullock ....B

Wurzburg & Co., H. J.....C

ILL.—Jacksonville

Columbia Mfg. Co. (Pants; Duck Goods; Overalls)..C

ILL.—Peoria

Peoria Merc. Co. (Overalls; Pants) X

True Fit Mfg. Co. (Overalls; Pants) C

ILL.—Quincy

Hargadine-McKittrick Dry Goods Co. (Pants; Overalls) ....AAAA

Menke Dry Goods Co. (Overalls; Pants; Duck Coats; Covert Coats) C

Whitney, White Co. (Overalls) ....D

ILL.—Rockford

Rockford Overalls Mfg. Co. (Overalls; Pants; Duck Coats) ....D

ILL.—Springfield

Hall & Herrick (Overalls; Pants) C

ILL.—Streator

Stauber Mfg. Co., A. (Pants; Overalls; Overcoats) ....A

IND.—Bluffton

Hunsicker, Henry (Bluffton Overall Co.) (Overalls)..D

IND.—Evansville

Gans Co., I. (Overalls; Pants) ....B

Goodwin Clothing Co. (Pants) X

Leonard & Co., James (Overalls; Drawers; Duck Coats) ....B

Mackey, Nisbet Co. (Overalls; Pants; Shirts)..AAA

IND.—Ft. Wayne

Hirsh & Co., A. (Overalls; Pants; Duck Coats)....D

Hoosier Mfg. Co. (Overalls; Pants; Duck Lined Coats) ....A

IND.—Greenfield

Thayer, H. B. (Overalls)..D

IND.—Indianapolis

American Trouser Co. (Pants) C

Cones & Son Mfg. Co., C. B. (Overalls; Pants; Engineers' Coats) ....B

Efroymson & Wolf (Overalls) ....A

Havens & Geddes Co. (Overalls; Pants; Duck Coats) ....AA

Jackson, J. W. (Overalls; Pants; Jackets) ....D

Kahn Tailoring Co. ......A

Lion Clothing Mfg. Co. (Pants; Duck Coats)...C

Meier & Co., Lewis

(Workingmens'; Overalls;
Pants) ....B

IND.—Lafayette
Curtis Sons' & Co., S. C.
(Overalls) C
Lion & Deer Mfg. Co. (Over-
alls; Pants; Duck Coats)
..............................C

IND.—Logansport
Uhl Bros. & Co. (Overalls;
Pants; Jackets; Duck
Coats) ....A

IND.—New Albany
Robinson, Norton & Co., J.
M. (Pants; Overalls; Duck
Coats; Corduroy Suits;
Hunting Suits) ....AAA

IND.—Richmond
Bartel Co., Adam H. (Per-
fection Mfg. Co.) (Over-
alls; Work Pants; Duck
Coats; Covert Coats)...X
Richmond Overall & Shirt
Co. (Successors to Rosser
& Calvin Mfg. Co.) (Over-
alls; Pants) ....D

IND.—Terre Haute
Ehrmann Mfg. Co. (Pants;
Overalls) ....A
Stahl-Urban & Co. (Cassi-
mere Pants; Cotton Pants;
Duck Coats; Covert Coats;
Overalls) ....A

IOWA—Bonaparte
Meek Bros. Co. (Pants)..B

IOWA—Burlington
Connor Merc. Co. (Overalls;
Pants; Duck Lined Coats)
..............................C

IOWA—Cedar Falls
Cedar Falls Mfg. Co. (Over-
alls; Pants; Duck Coats)
..............................D

IOWA—Cedar Rapids
Clark-McDaniel Co. (Over-
alls; Duck Coats; Pants)
..............................D

IOWA—Davenport
Krause Co., Robert (Inc.)
(Duck Pants; Overalls).B

IOWA—Des Moines
Capial City Woolen Mills
(Sheuerman Bros., Inc.,
Props.) (Pants) ....A

IOWA—Dubuque
Bell Bros. Co. (Overalls;
Pants; Duck Clothing)..B
Glover Co., H. B. (Pants;
Vests; Jackets; Overalls)
..............................A
Rider-Wallis Co. (Overalls;
Pants; Duck Coats)...AA

IOWA—Ft. Dodge
Mulroney Mfg. Co. (Over-
alls; Pants; Duck Coats)
..............................C

IOWA—Keokuk
Irwin-Phillips Co. (Overalls;
Pants; Duck Coats).....A

IOWA—Oskaloosa
Baker, H. A. (Jeans; Duck
Pants; Overalls) ......B

KANS.—Atchison
Howard Mfg. Co., Frank
(Pants; Overalls; Duck
Lined Coats) ....B

KANS.—Kansas City
Wesern Gents' Union Mfg.
Co. (Overalls; Pants;
Jackets; Duck Coats)..D

KANS.—Topeka
Topeka Woolen Mill Co.
(Pants) ....B
Western Woolen Mill Co.
(Pants) C

KANS.—Wichita
Johnson & Larimer Dry Gds.
Co. (Overalls) ....B

KY.—Bowling Green
Nahm & Co., E. ....A

KY.—Henderson
Henderson Woolen Mills
(Cotton; Worsted; Cassi-
mere; Jean Pants) .....B

KY.—Louisville
American Clothing Co.
(Inc.) (Suits; Pants)..B
Bray Clothing Co. (Cassi-
mere; Corduroy; Jean
Pants) ....A
Carter Dry Goods Co.
(Pants) ....AAA
Coleman Bros. Clothing Co

(Youths' Suits; Men's
Suits; Pants; Duck Coats;
Covert Coats; Serge Coats;
Serge Vests) ....B
Kentucky Jeans Clothing Co.
(Inc.) (Jeans; Duck
Coats) ....A
Mayfield Woolen Mills Co.
..............................AAAA
Moses & Co., L. (Men's;
Youths') ....A
Ox Breeches Mfg. Co.
(Pants) ....B
Richardson & Co., E. A.
(Men's; Youths') ......B
Robinson, Norton & Co., J.
M. (Pants) ....AAA
Shapinsky & Co., S. (Pants;
Overalls; Duck Coats)..B
Shuttleworth & Co., J. A.
..............................AAA
Tapp, Leathers & Co.
(Men's; Youths') ......A

KY.—Mayfield
May Pants Co. C
Old Woolen Mills, The
(Pants; Suits) ....B

KY.—Paducah
Famous Pants Factory
(Pants) ....B
Forked Deer Pants Co.
(Pants) C

LA.—New Orleans
Fraenkel, Max, (Men's
Coats; Boys' Coats;
Pants; Overalls) C
Frelich & Badt (Jeans;
Cashmere Pants) C
Godchaux Clothing Co., Ltd.,
Leon (Men's; Youths')
..............................AAAA
Israel & Co., Mayer (Men's;
Youths') ....
Kory & Sons, A. (Pants;
Coats; Overalls) ......A
Lehmann & Co., A. (Over-
alls; Pants) ....AA
Mercier's Sons, D. ....AAA
Picard, Kaiser & Co. (Pants)
..............................B
Weil, Leopold ....A
Weiss Mfg. Co. (Overalls)
..............................C
Wolf & Sons, B. J. (Men's;
Youths') ....A

MD.—Baltimore
Adler, L. & D. (Waterproof;
Oiled) ....B
Baltimore Bargain House
..............................AA
Brent, Bull & Co. (Pants)
..............................A
Burger & Co., Chas. .....B
Burgunder Bros. & Co...AA
Burk, Fried & Co......AA
Cohn & Bro., Alex. (Men's;
Youths') ....B
Epstein, Jacob (Men's;
Youths') ....AA
Erlanger Bros. (Overalls)
..............................AA
Frank & Bro., E. ....B
Friedman & Sons, M.
Youths') ....B
Grief & Bro., L. ......AA
Hamburger & Sons, Isaac..A
Hamburger Bros. & Co.
(Men's; Youths') ......A
Harzberg & Co., J.......B
Heilner, M. ....AA
Jacobson & Baker (Pants)
..............................C
Kiehne & Co., E. A. (Over-
alls) ....D
Lauchheimer & Sons, M. H.
(Men's; Youths') ......A
Likes & Co. ....B
Lowman & Co., S. ......B
Miller & Co. S. F. & A. F.
(White Vests; Fancy
Vests) ....B
Morris & Co. (Overalls;
Jumpers) ....B
Myer & Co., Henry (Over-
alls) C
Phoenix Mfg. Co. (Overalls)
..............................AAA
Reinhard, Meyer & Co....B
Ring & Sons, M. ....A
Rosenstein Bros. ....B
Schenthal & Sons, Jos.
(Overalls) C
Schloss Bros. & Co. (Men's;

Youths') ....AAA
Schoeneman, Jacob (Men's
    Pants; Boys' Pants)....B
Sonneborn & Co., H. (Men's;
    Youths') ....AAA
Standard Overall Co. (Over-
    alls) ....D
Strauss Bros. (Overalls)
    AAA
Strauss & Co., A. J. (Pants)
    B
Strouse & Bros. (Men's;
    Youths') ....AAAA
Stuart & Keith (Overalls;
    Jackets).............B
Thalheimer Bros. (Suits;
    Overcoats) ....B
Witz Bros. & Co. (Overalls;
    Jumpers) ....B
MASS.—Beverly
Carter Co., John F. (Water-
    proof; Oiled) ....D
MASS.—Boston
American Rubber Co.
    (Mackintoshes) ....AAAA
Bailey & Co., C. J. (Rain
    Coats) C
Broadway Coat Co.. (Leath-
    er; Sheep lined Coats;
    Vests) ....A
Co-operative Rubber Co.
    (Mackintoshes) C
Davies Payson & Co.
    (Men's; Youths') .....B
Franklin Rubber Co.
    (Mackintoshes) ....A
Freeland-Loomis Co. .....A
Hawley, Folsom & Ronimus
    (Overalls) ....A
Hodgdon, Anderson & Merry
    B
Loomis & Co., S. W. (Men's;
    Youths') ....B
Macullar-Parker Co. (Men's
    Youths') ....AA
Miner & Beal ....AAA
Morse, Leopold & Co.
    (Men's; Youths') .....AA
Oak Hall Clothing Co.
    (Men's; Youths') .....B
Pearson Co.. J. B. (Men's
    Overalls; Childrens' Over-
    alls; Suits; Pants).....C
Peavy & Bros. J. (Men's;
    Youths') ....AA
Pelonsky, N. A. (Overalls)
    A
Rhodes & Ripley Clothing
    Co. (Men's; Youths')...A
Rice. Sayward & Whitten
    (Men's; Youths') .....A
Shuman & Co., A. (Men's;
    Youths') ....AAAA
Simon Mfg. Co., The (Over-
    alls; Sheepskin lined
    Coats) ....D
Simons, Hatch & Whitten
    Co. (Overalls) ....A
Talbot Co. (Men's; Youths)
    AA
Tower Co.. A. J. (Water-
    proof; Oiled) ....A
Union Rubber Co. (Mackin-
    toshes) ....B
MASS.—Cambridge
Sayer & Son, H. M. (Water-
    proof; Oiled) C
MASS.—Hudson
Apsley Rubber Co. (Rub-
    ber) ....AA
MASS.—Hyde Park
Boston Gossamer Rubber Co.
    (Mackintoshes) ....A
MASS.—Lynn
Globe Mfg. Co. (Leather)
    .X
MASS.—Milford
Clapp, Huckins & Temple
    (Leather) X
Milford Shoe Co. (Duck)..B
MASS.—Pittsfield
Berkshire Mfg. Co. (Pants)
    C
MASS.—South Framingham
Conant Gossamer Rubber
    Co., W. H. (Cravenette;
    Waterproof) ....A
MASS.—Stoughton
Stoughon Rubber Co. (Crav-
    enette; Waterproof) ...A
MASS.—Worcester
Hildreth & Co., A. G. (Over-
    alls) C

Rowell & Co., W. P. (Duck
    Coats; Butcher Frocks).D
MICH.—Detroit
Carhartt, Hamilton (Duck)
    B
Fink & Co., Wm. M. (Over-
    alls; Pants) ....B
Imerman Bros. (Pants;
    Overalls) C
Krolik & Co., A. (Jackets;
    Mackinaws; Pants; Over-
    alls) ....AA
Peerless Mfg. Co. (Pants;
    Overalls; Duck Coats;
    Mackinaw Coats) ....B
Rosen & Co., A. D. (Over-
    alls; Pants) ....B
Rosenfield-Monroe Co.
    (Overalls; Pants) C
Schloss Bros. (Youths';
    Men's) ....A
Stanton & Co., M. M. (Over-
    alls; Pants; Lumbermens'
    Clothing) ....AAA
MICH.—Grand Rapids
Fasoldt Bros. (Overalls;
    Pants; Duck Coats)....D
Ideal Clothing Co. (Pants;
    Overalls; Duck Coats)..B
MICH.—Howell
Garland, A. (Pants)......C
MICH.—Kalamazoo
Henderson-Ames Co. (Band;
    Police Uniforms; Fire-
    men's Uniforms) ......A
MICH.—Lansing
Flint Pantaloon Co. (Pants;
    Overalls; Jackets; Duck
    Coats) C
MICH.—Saginaw
Wylie Mfg. Co. (Overalls;
    Pants; Duck Coats; Mack-
    inaws) C
MICH.—Wyandotte
Bishop Co., J. H. (Fur
    Coats) ....A
MINN.—Duluth
Christensen, Mendenhall &
    Graham (Overalls; Pants)
    C
MINN.—Minneapolis
Patterson & Stevenson Co.
    (Fur Coats) ....A
Plymouth Clothing House
    (Furs) ....AA
Robitshek, Frank & Heller
    (Pants; Overalls; Duck
    Coats) ....A
Wyman, Partridge & Co.
    (Overalls; Pants; Duck
    Coats; Mackinaws)
    AAAA
MINN.—St. Paul
Finck, Young & McConville
    (Overalls; Pants; Duck
    Coats; Covert Coats;
    Mackinaws) ....AAA
Guiterman Bros. (Duck;
    Bar Goods; Mackinaws;
    Pants; Overalls) ......A
Lindeke, Warner & Schur-
    meier (Overalls; Pants)
    AAAA
Sternberg, Herman & ..B
Sternberg, Weil & Co.
    (Duck; Mackinaw) .....B
Sternberg & Gottschall
    (Overalls; Pants; Duck
    Coats) C
Tibbs, Hutchins & Co. (Over-
    alls; Coats) ....A
MINN.—St. Peter
Johnson & Co. (Men's Pants;
    Boys' Pants; Overalls;
    Duck Coats) ....B
MISS.—Corinth
Alcorn Woolen Mfg. Co.
    (Pants; Suits) ....B
Corinth Clothing Mfg. Co.
    (Pants) C
MISS.—Meridian
Marks, Rothenberg & Co.
    (Jean Pants) ....AAA
MO.—Jefferson
Star Clothing Co. (Jean
    Pants; Overalls; Duck
    Coats) C
MO.—Kansas City
Barmon, Wm. (Pants) ...A
Burnham-Munger Mfg. Co.
    Duck Overalls; Cottonade
    Pants) ....AAAA
Smith-McCord-Townsend Dry

Goods Co. (Pants; Overalls; Duck) ....AAA

Standard Mfg. Co. (Overalls) ....D

Swofford Bros. Dry Goods Co. (Overalls; Pants; Jumpers) ....AAA

MO.—St. Joseph

August, Albert J. (Pants; Overalls) X

Brittain Dry Goods Co., John S. (Duck Overalls; Pants) ....AA

Hundley-Smith Dry Goods Co. (Overalls; Pants; Duck Clohing) ....AA

McDonald & Co., R. L. (Overalls; Pants; Duck Clothing) ....AAA

Richardson-Roberts Dry Gds. Co. (Pants; Overalls) ....AAA

Tootle, Wheeler & Motter Mercantile Co. (Overalls; Pants; Duck Clothing) ....AAAA

MO.—St. Louis

Bohm Bros.. Furnishing Gds. Co. (Overalls) ....A

Carleton Dry Gds. Co. (Overalls) ....AAAA

Ely & Walker Dry Goods Co. (Overalls; Pants)..AAAA

Epstein & Co., I. (Pants; Overcoats) C

Everett Mfg. Co. (Overalls; Jumpers) ....D

Ferguson - McKinney Dry Goods Co. (Overalls) ....AAAA

Gilmore & Ruhl (Men's; Youths') ....A

Haas & Son Pants Co., A. (Men's Pants; Boys' Pants) ....B

Hagadine-McKittrick Dry Goods Co. (Coats)..AAAA

Harris Bros. Clothing Co. (Men's; Youths') ......A

Leichtman, Goodman & Co. ....B

Lippman, Joseph M. C

Loth Jeans Clothing Co. (Pants; Duck Coats)....C

Marglous & Co. (Overalls) C

Marx & Haas Clothing Co. (Duck Coats; Duck Pants) ....A

Mayfield Woolen Mills Co. ....AAAA

Mills & Averill Tailoring Co. ....A

Premium Mfg. Co. (Pants; Overalls; Jumpers; Duck Coats) ....AAAA

Red Diamond Clothing Co. (Overalls; Jumpers) C

Rice-Stix Dry Goods Co. (Overalls; Pants) ..AAAA

Rosenthal & Desberger (Men's; Youths') .....A

Rosenthal & Co., M. (Woolen) ....B

Russack & Sons, Isaac....A

Schwab Clothing Co. (Men's; Youths') ....AAAA

Zittlosen Mfg. Co. (Leather; Oiled; Rubber) C

MO.—Sedalia

Cain Mfg. Co., J. M. (Pants) C

Lamy Mfg. Co., J. A. (Overalls; Pants; Blanket lined Duck Coats) ....B

MONT.—Butte

Connell Co., M. J.........A

MONT.—Helena

Greenhood-Benn Co. (Overalls; Pants; Jackets; Mackinaws) ....B

NEBR.—Lincoln

Herman Bros. Mfg. Co. (Overalls; Pants; Duck Coats) ....A

Lincoln Overall & Shirt Co. (Overalls; Jackets) ....D

NEBR.—Omaha

Byrne & Hammer Dry Goods Co. (Pants; Overalls) ....AAAA

King & Smead (Duck; Overalls; Pants) C

Smith & Co., M. E. (Pants; Overalls; Jumpers; Duck) ....AA

N. H.—Canaan

Barney Bros. (Overalls; Pants; Duck Coats) C

N. H.—Lebanon

Carter & Churchill Co. (Overalls; Barber Coats; Bar Coats; Hunting Coats) ....B

Carter & Sons, H. W. (Overalls; Pants; White Coats) ....B

N. H.—Nashua

Burbank Mfg. Co. (Overalls; Jumpers; Sacks) ....D

N. J.—Dover

Peters & Moore (Overalls; Pants) ....D

N. J.—Newark

Kraft, Mrs. T. (Pants)...C

Loewenberg & Cohn (Bar Coats; Butcher Gowns; Sportsmens' Goods)....A

Stoutenburgh & Co. (Men's; Youths') ....AA

N. J.—Paterson

Levi & Co., Jacob (Overalls; Pants; Jumpers)...C

N. J.—Somerville

Somerville Woolen Mills (Men's; Youths') ......A

N. J.—Trenton

Murray, Griffith & Messler (Overalls; Sporting Coats) ....B

Rice Clothing Co. (Institution) ....B

N. J.—Woodbine

Daniel & Blumenthal .....B

N. Y.—Binghamton

Binghamton Overall Co. (Overalls; Duck Coats; Covert Coats) ....B

Freeman Overall Co. (Overalls; Duck Lined Coats).C

Smith, Crary & Davidge (Overalls; Pants; Aprons) ....B

Smith, Kinney & Co. (Overalls; Pants; Coats).....B

N. Y.—Brooklyn

Barnard & Co., Geo. (Inc.) (Sportsmens') ....B

Gomers' Sons, Chas. (Men's; Youths') ....B

Kenyon Co., C. (Rain Coats; Outing Suits; Smoking Jackets; Fancy Vests)..AA

N. Y.—Buffalo

American Buffalo Robe Co. (Fur; Cloth Ulsters; Reefers; Driving) ....B

Beyer Bros. (Pants; Overalls) ....B

Cohn & Co., Frank (Men's; Youths') ....B

Cohn & Co. (Pants; Overalls) ....B

Lepper & Ellwood (Overalls; Pants; Duck Coats; Mackinaws) ....D

La Due-Tatre Mfg. Co. (Pants; Overalls; Duck Coats) ....B

Niagara Overall & Pants Co. (Overalls; Pants; Duck Coats) ....B

Wile Bros. & Weill (Men's; Youths') ....A

Wile & Co., M. (Men's; Youths') ....B

N. Y.—Cayuga

Cummings, Frank (Overalls; Jackets) ....D

N. Y.—Chestertown

Faxon Mfg. Co., C. H. (Overalls; Pants; Coats) ....A

N. Y.—Dansville

Hubertus & Sons, H. (Pants; Overalls; Coats) ....D

N. Y.—Ephratah

Yanney, Levi (Pants) C

N. Y.—Gloversville

Leak Fur Mfg. Co. (Fur Coats) ....D

Steele Bros. (Fur Coats).D

N. Y.—Madrid

Madrid Woolen Mill (Pants) C

Rothschild Co., V. Henry (Pants) ....B
Sampter Sons' & Co., M. (Youths') ....AA
Samuels & Bros., J. ...AAA
Scharps & Simon (Boys' Shirt Waists; Blouses) ..D
Schattman Bros. (Men's; Youths') ....B
Schleestein, Cohn & Co.....A
Schneers' Son & Co., Isaac (Boys' Wash Suits)....B
Shretski, Wm. ....B
Shuter & Adler Bros. (Pants) ....B
Siff & Bros., L. ....B
Simon, Julius (Blouses) ...C
Sohn, Oppenheimer & Co. (Men's Pants; Boys' Pants) ....A
Solomon & Sons, J. ....A
Spero & Son, Michael....A
Standard Oiled Clothing Co. (Waterproof Oiled) ....A
Stern & Son, B. ....A
Sternberg Bros. (Pants)..A
Swartz, Jerkowski & Co...B
Sykes & Ab. Kirschbaum & Co. ....AA
Valenstein & Co., J. (Men's; Youths') ....B
Valentine & Rabinowitz (Pants) ....AA
Vogel Bros. ....AA
Vogel & Son, Wm. .....AA
Wald, Walker & Co, (Summer Pants) ....B
Weigert, Meyer, Gross & Co. (Pants) C
Wener & Co., J. ....B
Werner & Co., A. L. (Pants) ....A
Werner Bros. (Pants) ....A
Werner & Sons, Julius ...A
Wolf & Abrahams ....B
Worcester Pants Mfg. Co. (Bicycle Pants) ....B
Wronker & Weil (Summer; Pants; Vests) ....B
Yeska, Joseph (Summer; Fancy Vests; Waiters' Jackets; Bar Coats).....B
Yost & Co., Chas. A. (Summer) ....B

N. Y.—No. Tonawanda
Becker Bros. (Overalls)..D
N. Y.—Poughkeepsie
Dutchess Mfg. Co. (Pants; Overalls) ....v..A
N. Y.—Rochester
Adler Bros. & Co., L...AA
Black & Co. (Men's; Suits; Youths' Overcoats).....A
Garson, Meyer & Co. (Men's; Youths') ....AA
Goldwater & Co. (Men's; Youths') ....A
Goldwater & Bros., N. (Pants; Overalls) ....A
Hershberg & Co. ....B
Holtz & Sons, Louis (Men's; Youths') ....B
Lowenthal & Bro., Max (Athletic) ....&C
Menter, Rosenbloom & Co..A
Meyer & Simon ....B
Michaels, Stern & Co. (Men's; Youths') ...AAA
Moore & Beirs (Men's; Youths') ....A
Solomon Bros. & Lempert.B
Stein-Bloch Co. (Inc.) (Men's; Youths') ..AAAA
Tichner & Jacobi ....B
N. Y.—Sidney
Clark Textile Co. ....A
N. Y.—Syracuse
Freeman & Co., Geo. (Specialty in Overcoats)....A
Kearney Bros. (Men's; Youths') ....B
Lovell Wrapper & Overall Co. (Overalls) ....D
Syracuse Clothing Co. (Overcoats) ....A
Woodhull, Goodale & Bull ....A

N. Y.—Utica
Cooper & Co., H. H. (Men's; Youths') ....B
Crouse & Brandegee (Men's; Youths') ....AA
Pixley & Son, H. D.......A

Riverside Mfg. Co. (Rathbun & Co.) (Overalls; Cotton Pants) ....A
Roberts-Wicks Co. ......A
N. Y.—Walden
Wooster Mfg. Co., H. B. (Overalls; Pants) ......D
N. Y.—Warrensburg
Warrensburg Woolen Co. (Pants) ....A
N. C.—Charlotte
Charlotte Clothing Mfg. Co. (Pants) ....B
Charlotte Trouser Co. (Pants) ....A
Junior Clothing Mfg. Co. (Pants) C
Piedmont Clothing Mfg. Co. (Pants; Overalls) C
N. C.—Graham
Scott-Mebane Mfg. Co. (Overalls) C
N. C.—Highpoint
Highpoint Overall Co. (Overalls) ....D
N. C.—Wilmington
Bear & Co., I. M. (Overalls) C

OHIO—Cincinnati
Bettmann Bros. & Co.....A
Bing. I. & S. (Men's Suits; Youths' Suits; Overcoats; Odd Pants) ....AA
Bloch & Co., Abe.......AA
Bloom Bros. & Co........A
Bloom, Cohn & Co........A
Capital Mfg. Co. (Overalls) D
Eisenman & Co., Chas. (Boys' Waists; Blouses).A
Fallers Sons' Co., Isaac AAA
Fechheimer Bros. Co. (Uniforms) ....A
Fechheimer, Kiefer & Co. (Men's; Youths'; Pants) A
Feder, Silberberg & Co....A
Geiershofer Clothing Co., Henry (Men's; Youths') AA
Globe Overall Mfg. Co. (Successors to Julius Felbelman) (Overalls) ......D
Globe Tailoring Co. ......A
Goldman, Beckman & Co. (Men's; Youths') ....AA
Hanke Bros. (Overalls).AAA
Hart & Co., E. ....A
Hart & Co., Isaac (Suits; Overcoats) ....B
Heilbrun & Nussbaum (Pants) C
Heidman, Heldman & Co. (Men's; Youths') .....A
Levy, Price & Co. (Boys').A
Loebs' Sons & Co., L. (Pants; Overcoats) C
Marks & Co., M. H. (Summer; Overcoats; Fancy Vests; Wash Vests)....A
Mayer, Scheuer, Offner & Co. (Men's; Youths').AAA
Ochs, Goodman & Co. (Men's; Youths') ...AAA
Oppenheimer, Seasongood & Co. (Men's Overcoats; Youths' Overcoats; Pants) A
Reiter & Co., Peter (Overalls; Pants) ....D
Rosenthal & Mayer (Globe Tailoring Co.) ....A
Sanford, Storrs & Varner (Suits; Overcoats) ....A
Seinsheimer & Co., H. A. (Boys'; Childrens')......A
Shillito Co., John (Overalls; Pants) ....AAAA
Sommerfield & Co., A. A. W. (Summer; Overcoats; Pants) ....B
Steifel, Holstein & Falk (Overalls) ....A
Stern, Lauer, Shohl & Co. (Men's; Youths') ....AA
Stricker, Beitman & Co. (Pants) ....B
Sturm & Sons, G. (Summer; Overcoats; White Vests; Fancy Vests; Bar Coats; Barber Coats; Smoking Jackets) ....B

United States Overall &
Pants Mfg. Co. (Overalls;
Pants; Jumpers) ......D
Verkamp & Sons, G. H.
(Men's; Youths') .....B
Weiler, S. L. (Pants) ....B
Wolfson Bros. & Co. (Boys';
Childrens') ....B
Wyler, Akerland & Co.
　　　　　　　　AAAA

OHIO—Cleveland

Enterprise Mfg. Co. (Over-
alls; Jumpers) ....D
Epstein & Co., B. ....A
Fisher & Son, B. (Overalls)
　　　　　　　　　　C
Goldsmith, Feiss Co., Jos.
(Men's; Boys') ....AAAA
Hall, Schwartz & Skall
(Overalls) ....A
Klein, Lichtenstadter & Co.
(Overalls) ....A
Kohn Bros. & Heller (Sum-
mer; Bicycle) ....A
Kornhauser, D. H. (Men's;
Youths') ....B
Metropolitan Mfg. Co. (Over-
alls; Pants) ....D
Miller, Weizenhof & Co....A
Schwartz & Co. (Overalls;
Pants) ....b

OHIO—Columbus

Ambach & Co., D. S......B
Burgunder Bros. & Co.
(Men's; Boys') ....A
Columbus Mdse. Co. (Over-
alls; Pants) ....A
Lilley & Co., M. C. (Uni-
forms) ....AAAA

OHIO—Dayton

Gem Shirt Co. (Overalls;
Pants) ....A
Legler & Co. (Overalls;
Pants; Duck Coats;
Aprons) ....A

OHIO—Hamilton

Sommers Mfg. Co., J. A.
(Overalls; Pants; Duck;
Corduroy Coats) C

OHIO—Portsmouth

Eisman & Co., J. (Pants) .C

OHIO—Toledo

Littman & Hoffstadt ....B
Stern & Bloch (General
Line) ....A
Shaw & Sassman Co. (Pants;
Overalls; Duck Coats)..B

OREGON—Portland

Fleischner, Mayer & Co.
(Overalls; Duck Clothing)
　　　　　　　　AAA
Newstadter Bros. (Overalls;
Pants) ....A
Wolf & Bro., H. (Overalls)
　　　　　　　　　　D

PA.—Allentown

Bittner, Hunsicker & Co.
(Overalls) ....AA

PA.—Brookville

Brookville Woolen Mills
(Pants; Overalls) .....B

PA.—Dillsburg

Harrisburg Mfg. Co. (Overalls; Pants; Coats) ....D

PA.—Easton

Correll, J. W. (Overalls;
Pants) ....B
Standard Mfg. Co. (Pants;
Overalls; Coats) C

PA.—Erie

Baker & Son, Isaac ....B
Straus Mfg. Co. (Pants;
Overalls) ....B
Freeland Overall Mfg. Co.
(Overalls; Pants) C

PA.—Harrisburg

Goodman, Oscar (Overalls;
Pants) ....D

PA.—Montoursville

Meyer & Co., L. I. (Pants;
Overalls; Knee Pants)..C

PA.—Philadelphia

Allen & Co., W. & T.....A
Arnold, Louchheim & Co..AA
Bacharach & Co., M. (Men's;
Boys') ....B
Blumenthal Bros. & Co...AA
Brubaker & Son, E. (Over-
alls) ....B
Chester, Bodek & Co. (Over-
alls) ....D
Daniel & Blumenthal
Men's; Childrens') ....ᵀ

Delaware Rubber Co., 631
Market (Rubber) X
Detwiler & Son, I. L.
(Men's; Youths') .....B
Eckstein, Wm. (Boys' Suits;
Pants; Overalls) ......B
Fleisher Bros. (Men's;
Boys') ....AAA
Frank Bros. & Co. (Men's;
Boys') ....A
Gantert & Carpenter (Over-
alls; Pants; Coats)....D
Greenebaum Bros. (Boys'
Shirt Waists; Blouses)..D
Harris, Isaac & Co. (Men's
Suits; Boys' Suits; Over-
coats) ....B
Hexter Bros. (Summer
Goods; Bar Coats) ....AA
Kirschbaum & Co., A. B.
　　　　　　　　AAAA
Lang, Morris ....A
Leicester & Continental
Mills Co. (Smoking Jack-
ets; Bathing Suits) ...AA
Lisberger & Wise (Pants).B
Liveright, Greenewald & Co.
(Men's; Boys') .....AAA
Meyers & Co., Wm. (Men's;
Youths') ....B
Moldawer & Sons, M.
(Men's; Youths') .....A
Reed's Sons, Jacob (Civil-
ian; Uniform) ......AA
Schoeneman & Salsburg
(Men's; Youths') .....B
Snellenburg & Co., N. Dept.
A. Goldsmith Sons) (Out-
ing Suits; Bar; Waiter
Coats, Fancy Vests)
　　　　　　　　AAAA
Treacy, Morris & Co.
(Men's; Youths') .....A
Underdown, A. R. (Overalls)
　　　　　　　　　　C
Yates & Co., A. C. (Men's;
Boys') ....A

PA.—Pittsburg

Arbuthnot-Stephenson Co.
(Pants; Overalls) .AAA
Bennett & Co., Joseph
(Pants) ....B
Hannach Bros. (Overalls).D
Lehman & Kingsbaker
(Pants) ....A
Oppenheimer & Co., M.
(Men's; Boys') ....A
Pittsburg Dry Goods Co.
(Overalls) ....AAA
Rosenburg & Co., J.
(Pants) C

PA.—Reading

Brumbach, A. J. (St. Law-
rence Woolen Mills)
(Pants; Vests; Knee-
Pants) ....AA
Leimbach & Co., J. G.
(Pants) ....A
Mercer, James R. (Over-
alls) ....B

PA.—Scranton

White Mfg. Co., Thos. A.
(Overalls; Pants) .....B

PA.—Shamokin

English & Henry (Over-
alls only) ....D

PA.—Shippensburg

Rummel Hines & Co., (Suc.
to Shippensburg Mfg. Co.)
(Suits; Pants; Blouses;
Overcoats) C

PA.—Waynesboro

Waynesboro Mfg. Co. (Overalls; Jackets) ....D

PA.—York

Hartman, L. M. (Overalls;
Blouses) C

R. I.—Bristol

National India Rubber Co.
(Rubber) ....AAAA

S. C.—Charleston

Wilbur & Son, T. A. (Overalls; Pants) ....A

TENN.—Chattanooga

Geismar Bros. & Bissinger
Chattanooga Pants Fac-
tory) (Overalls) C

TENN.—Cleveland

Cleveland Woolen Mills
(Jean Pants; Overalls).B

TENN.—Jefferson

Jefferson City Woolen Mills
(Pants; Overcoats; Duck

Pants) ....B
TENN.—Knoxville
Briscoe Mfg. Co. (Overalls;
Pants) C
Claiborne, Tate & Cowan
(Men's; Boys') ....B
McTeer Clo. Co., J. T...AA
TENN.—McMinnville
Faulkner, Clay (Mountain
City Woolen Mills)
(Pants; Overalls) C
TENN.—Memphis
Jiedel & Bro., J. (Jeans;
Pants) ....B
Lowenstein & Bros., B.
(Pants) ....AAAA
Morris & Bro., H. (Cassi-
mere; Jean Pants) .....A
TENN.—Nashville
National Woolen Co. (Duck
Pants; Overalls) ....B
O'Bryan Bros. (Suits;
Pants; Overalls; Duck-
lined Coats) ....A
TEXAS—Dallas
Rose Mfg. Co. (Pants;
Overalls; Jumpers).....B
Sanger Bros. (Duck Pants;
Overalls; Jumpers) AAAA
TEXAS—Galveston
Pierson, A. L. (Pants;
Overalls; Jumpers) C
TEXAS—Waco
Slayden-Kirkey Woolen Mill
(Cassimere; Worsted
Pants) ....AA
UTAH—Salt Lake City
Rosenbaum Bros. ....B
Zion's Co-operative Merc.
Institution (Overalls;
Duck-Lined Goods; Jump-
ers) ....AAAA
VT.—Brattleboro
Hooker, Corser & Mitchell
Co. (Overalls; Pants;
Coats) C
VT.—Derby Line
Pike Bros. (Standard Mfg.
Co.) (Overalls; Pants).D
VA.—Abingdon
Palmer & Co., L. A.
(Overalls) ....B
VA.—Charlottesville
Marchant Mfg. Co., H. C.
(Overalls) C
VA.—Lynchburg
Knight Clo. & Mfg. Co...B
VA.—Norfolk
Steel's Union Overall Co.
(Overalls) ....D
VA.—Richmond
Cohen Son & Co., M.
(Overalls) ....A
VA.—South Boston
Boston Mfg. Co. (Pants;
Overalls) ....A
VA.—Staunton
Fulton Witz & Co. (Over-
alls) ....AA
WASH.—Spokane
Spokane Dry Goods Co. (In-
land Mfg. Co. (Overalls;
Mackinaw Suits) ....A
Spokane Dry Goods Co.
(Mackinaw) ....A
W. VA.—Charleston
Schwabe & May ....A
W. VA.—Huntington
Biggs, Watts & Co. (Peer-
less Mfg. Co. (Overalls;
Pants) ....B
W. VA.—McMechen
McMechen Mfg. Co. (Over-
alls) ....A
W. VA.—Moundsville
Klee's Sons, Joseph (Pants)
B
WIS.—Appleton
Appleton Shirt & Pants Co.
(Pants; Suits) C
WIS.—Fond du Lac
Badger Sewing Co. (Over-
alls; Duck Coats)......D
Fond Du Lac Shirt & Overall
Co. ....D
WIS.—Janesville
Janesville Clothing Co.
(Overalls; Pants; Duck
Coats) ....D
WIS.—La Crosse
La Crosse Rubber Mills Co.
(Rubber) ....B
Martin Bros. Co. (Overalls;

Pants; Duck Clothing).C
WIS.—Milwaukee
Abeles, F. E. & Co. (Over-
alls) ....D
Adler & Sons Clothing Co.,
David (General Line)...A
Bellack Co., Chas. H.
(Men's; Youths') ....B
Fein Bros. & Co., S. S.
(Overalls; Pants) C
Friend Bros. Clothing Co.
(Suits; Overalls; Ulsters;
Pants) ....A
Goll & Frank Co. (Overalls;
Pants; Duck Coas; Mack-
inaws) ....AAAA
Landauer & Co. (Overalls;
Pants) ..|..|.........AA
Mahler, Albenberg & Co.
(Pants; Overalls; Duck
Coats; Mackinaws)...AA
Rice & Friedman Co., J. H.
(Mackinaws; Duck Coats;
Overalls; Pants) .....A
White, N. Y. (Pants)....AA
WIS.—Racine
Alshuler Mfg. Co., Chas.
(Overalls; Jackets; Duck
Coas) ....B
Hilker-Wischers Mfg. Co.
(Overalls) ....D

CLOTHES PINS
See Pins

CLOTHS

CAL.—San Francisco
California Jute Mill Co..A
Neville & Co. (Jute)......A
CONN.—Fairfield
Fairfield Rubber Co. (Car-
riage) C
CONN.—Meriden
Meriden Curtain Fixture Co.
(Shade) ....B
CONN.—Middletown
Arawana Mills (I. E. Palm-
er) (Cotton Piano; Screen)
AA
Palmer, J. L. (Screen).AAA
CONN.—Norwich
Clinton Mills Co. (Carriage;
Broad; Billiard).........A
Falls Co. (Awning) ...AA
CONN.—Torrington
Warrenton Woolen Co. (Car-
riage). ....A
GA.—Augusta
Sibley Mfg. Co. (Awning)
AAA
ILL.—Chicago
Western Shade Cloth Co.
(Shade) ....A
MAINE—Dexter
Morrison Woolen Co. (Wool-
en Carriage) C
MAINE—Lewiston
Bates Mfg. Co. (Table)....X
Libbey & Dingley (Woolen
Carriage) ....A
MAINE—So. Berwick
Newichanick Co. (Wool
Clearer; Slasher) ... .A
MD.—Baltimore
Garry & Son. Jas. S. (Awn-
ing) ....AAAA
Hooper & Son, Wm. E.
(Awning) ....AAAA
Laurel Mills, 9 W. German
(Awning) X
MASS.—Billerica
Talbot Mills (Carriage).AA
MASS.—Boston
Chase & Co., L. C., 129
Washn. (Carriage).AAA
Floyd Bros. & Co. (Water-
proof, Com.).........AA
Stohn, C. G. (Corset).....C
MASS.—Colerain
Griswoldville Mfg. Co.
(Butter) X
MASS.—Methuen
Knitted Fabrics Co. (Jer-
sey) ....B
MASS.—Pittsfield
Helliwell & Co. (Carriage;
Cap; Casket).........D
Russell Mfg. Co., S. N. &

CLOTHS (Con.)
C. (Carriage) ....B
MASS.—Thorndike
Thorndike Co. (Awning)
.............AAA
MASS.—Webster
Slater Woolen Co. (Carriage) ....AAAA
MICH.—Dearborn
Arna Mills (Astrachan) ..D
MICH.—Detroit
Pioneer Woolen Mills (Elderman; Jersey)...D
MO.—St. Louis
Zittlosen Mfg. Co. (Enameled) ....B
N. J.—Newark
Heath & Son, Edmond F. Carriage; Enameled; Waterproof) X
N. J.—Trenton
Empire Rubber Mfg. Co. (Carriage; Enameled).AA
N. Y.—Amsterdam
Waldron & Cassidy (Knit Jersey) ....D
N. Y.—Brooklyn
Brautigam, Robt. (Filter for Sug. Ref.; &c)...C
N. Y.—Honeoye Falls
Hunt, A. H. (Carriage)..D
N. Y.—Jamestown
Chautauqua Towel Mills (Face; Wash; Terry)..C
New York City
Behr & Co., Herman, 75 Beekman (Emery; Flint)
.............AA
Boyle & Co., John, 112 Duane (Filter).......AA
Columbus Shade Cloth Co., 41 Union Sq. (Shade)...D
Derby & Co., W. E. (Carriage, Com.) ....A
Dusenberry & Son, C. Coles (Com.; Carriage; Livery)
.............B
Faber, Eberhard, 545 Pearl (Tracing) ....AAA
H. W. Johns & Manville Co. 100 William (Asbestos)
.............AAAA
Howells Bros. (Carriage; Com.) ....B
Rothschild, Co., V. Henry, 43 Leonard (Moleskin).A
Patterson & Greenough (Com.; Carriage).......B
Sullivan, Vail & Co. (Uniform; Com.) ....AAA
N. Y.—Niagara Falls
Carborundum Co. (Carborundum) ....A
N. Y.—Oswego
Minetto Shade Cloth Co. (Shade) ....AAA
N. Y.—Skaneateles
Glenside Woolen Mills (Carriage) ....A
N. Y.—Waterloo
Waterloo Woolen Mfg. Co. (Carriage) ....A
OHIO—Dayton
Barney & Smith Car Co. (Emery) ....AAAA
PA.—Clifton Heights
Kent Mfg. Co., Thomas (Uniform) ....AA
PA.—Lancaster
Farnum & Co., John (Awning) ....AAAA
PA.—New Castle
Elliott-Blake Steel Co. (Enameled) ....A
PA.—Philadelphia
Baeder, Adamson & Co., 730 Market (Emery; Flint) ....AAAA
Barton & Son Co., H. H. (Emery; Flint).......A
Boylston Turkish Towel Co. (Terry) C
Cox & Bro., Geo. S. (Hair)
.............AA
Fritz, S. S. (Umbrella)
.............B
Green & Co., Henry W., 1715 Market (Shade)..A
Kaestner & Co., 241 So. Jeff. (Flange) ....A
Leicester & Continental Mills Co. (Eiderdown).AA
Schvehm & Sons, J. M.

CLOTHS (Con.)
(Hair) ....AA
Star & Crescent Mills Co. (Terry) ....A
Sumner & Co., T. (Damask Table) ....D
R. I.—Coventry
Interlaken Mills (Bookbinders') ....AAA
R. I.—Lonsdale
Lonsdale Co. (Holland Curtain) ....AAAA
R. I.—Pawtucket
American Cloth Co. (Hair; Fibre) ....AA
French Hair Cloth Co. (Hair) ....D
R. I.—Warwick
Centreville Cotton Mill (Window Shade) ....AA
R. I.—Woonsocket
Hamlet Textile Co. (Bookbinders') ....AA
S. C.—Seneca
Seneca Cotton Mills (Cotton Print) ....AA
UTAH—Manti
Hoggan, James E. (Damask Table) C
VA.—Buena Vista
Buena Vista Mills (Woolen Carriage) ....B

CLUBS

See also Sticks

CONN.—Bridgeport
Bridgeport Gun Implement Co. (Golf).........AA
Ives Mfg. Corp'n (Indian)
.............C
CONN.—New Haven
Dann Bros. & Co. (Golf).B
MICH.—Grand Rapids
Rademaker & Sons, H. (Indian) ....E
N. J.—Newark
Sommer's Sons, John (Indian) ....A
New York City
Estes & Sons, E. B., 45 John (Indian) ....AA
Spalding & Bros. (Inc.), A., 126 Nassau (Indian)
.............AAAA
Tower & Lyon Co., 95 Chambers (Police) ....B
OHIO—Piqua
Piqua Handle & Mfg. Co. (Indian) ....A
R. I.—Providence
Narragansett Machine Co. (Indian) ....A
WIS.—Milwaukee
Meinecke & Son, A. (Indian) ....AA

CLUSTERS

CONN.—Bridgeport
Bryant Electric Co. (Fixture) ....A
Hubbell, Harvey (Fixture)
.............C
CONN.—Seymour
Matthews Mfg. Co. (Seat Post) ....B
ILL.—Chicago
Benjamin Electric Mfg. Co., 1992 W. Van Buren (Fixture) ....D
ILL.—Decatur
Faries Mfg. Co. (Fixture).A
MASS.—Boston
Wheeler Reflector Co., 156 Pearl (Fixture) C
N. Y.—Brooklyn
White Mfg. Co., J. H., 127 N. 10th (Fixture)......B
New York City
Dale Co., 22 Thames (Fixture) ....B
Frink, I. P., 551 Pearl (Fixture) ....AA
Holloway, Bentz & Co., 80 Cortlandt (Fixture)....E
Walsh, Owen, 117 Walker (Fixture) ....D
OHIO—Cincinnati
Post-Glover Electric Co., 311 Perry (Fixture)....A

CLUSTERS (Con.)

OHIO—Dayton
Dayton Mfg. Co. (Fixture) ....A

PA.—Philadelphia
Roberts Electrical Supply Co., H. C., 831 Arch (Fixture) ....A

CLUTCHES

CONN.—Hartford
Hartford Machine Screw Co. (Friction) ....AAAA
Helix Gear Co. (Friction; Gas Engine) X
Johnson Carlyle Machine Co. (Friction) X
Pratt & Whitney Co. (Friction) ....AAAA

CONN.—New Haven
Eastern Machinery Co. (Friction; Jaw) ......B
New Haven Mfg. Co. (Friction) ....AA

ILL.—Chicago
Allis-Chalmers Co., Home Ins. Bldg. (Friction) ....AAAA
Caldwell & Son Co., H. W., 17th & Western Av. (Friction) ....AA
Fairbanks, Morse & Co. (Friction) ......AAAA
Link-Belt Machy. Co., W. 39th & Stewart Av. (Friction; Spring; Jaw) .AAA
Skillen & Richards Mfg. Co., 147 Fulton (Friction) ..C
Turner Brass Wks. (Arc Lamp) ....A
Webster Mfg. Co., 1076 W. 15th (Friction) ......AA
Weller Mfg. Co., 118 E. North Av. (Friction) ..A

IND.—Mishawaka
Dodge Mfg. Co. (Friction; Flange; Jaw; Wood Split Pulley) ....AAA

MD.—Baltimore
Poole Eng. & Machine Co. (Friction; Jaw) ......AA

MASS.—Boston
American Tool & Machine Co., 109 Beach (Friction) ....AA
Boston Gear Wks. (Friction) ....B
Faneuil Watch Tool Co., 1 Brooks (Friction).....B

MASS.—Fitchburg
Fitchburg Steam Engine Co. (Friction) X

MASS.—Lawrence
Emerson Mfg. Co. (Friction) C

MASS.—North Adams
Hunter Machine Co., Jas. (Friction) ....A

MASS.—Springfield
Springfield Fdy. Co. (Friction) ....A

MASS.—Worcester
McMahon & Co. (Friction) ....E

MINN.—Minneapolis
Minneapolis Steel & Machy. Co. (Friction) ......AAA

MO.—St. Louis
Essmueller Mill Furnishing Co. (Friction) C
Medart Patent Pulley Co., 3500 De Kalb (Friction) ....AAA

N. H.—Lakeport
Cole Mfg. Co. (Friction) .A

N. J.—Garwood
Whitman Mfg. Co. (Friction; Gas Engine) ......F

N. J.—Newark
Blevney, Jno. C. (Friction) X

N. J.—Raritan
Kenyon & Son, D. R. (Friction) ....B

N. Y.—Brooklyn
Bliss Co., E. W. (Friction) ....AAAA

N. Y.—Hudson
Gifford Bros. (Friction).A

N. Y.—Jamestown
Smith Cotton Mill. T. H. (Friction; Gas Engine).C

CLUTCHES (Con.)

New York City
Brown Co., A. & F., 26 Cortlandt (Friction)...B
Fairbanks Co., 416 Broome (Wood Split Pulley) ....AAAA

N. Y.—Sandy Hill
Sandy Hill Iron & Brass Wks. (Friction) ....A

OHIO—Akron
Webster Camp & Lane Mach. Co. (Friction) ....AAAA

OHIO—Bycyrus
American Clay Working Machy. Co. (Friction).X

OHIO—Canton
Aultman Co. (Friction) ....AAAA

OHIO—Cincinnati
Oesterlein Machine Co., Elam & Garrard Av. (Friction) ....B

OHIO—Cleveland
Brightman Machine Co. (Friction) ....D
Brown Hoisting Machy. Co. (Friction) ....AAAA
Electric Controller & Supply Co., Central & Giddings (Magnetic; Electric)...A
Hill Clutch Co., ft. Waverly Av. (Friction) ....B
Wellman - Seaver - Morgan Co. (Friction) ....AAAA

OHIO—Columbus
Case Mfg. Co. (Friction; Jaw; Wood Split Pulley) ....H
Jeffrey Mfg. Co., (Jaw) ....AAAA

OHIO—Cuyahoga Falls
Falls Rivet & Machine Co. (Friction) ....A

PA.—Erie
Taper Sleeve Pulley Wks. (Friction) C

PA.—Grove City
Carruthers-Fithian Clutch Co. (Friction; Gas Engine) ....B

PA.—Philadelphia
Cresson Co., Geo. V., 18th & Allegheny Av. (Friction) ....AA
Klein, Chas. C., 2850 Marshall (Friction) ....D
Link-Belt Engineering Co., Nicetown (Friction)..AA
Moore & White Co., 15th & Lehigh Av. (Friction).AA
Paiste Co., H. T., 3101 Ludlow (Arc Lamp)....B
Philadelphia Electrical & Mfg. Co., 2011 Market (Arc Lamp) ....E
Sellers Co., Wm., 1600 Hamilton (Friction) .....AAAA
Smith Woolen Machy. Co., Jas., 421 Race (Friction) ....AA
Wolf Co. (Friction) ....AA

PA.—Pittsburg
Jones & Laughlins Steel Co. (Friction) ....AAAA

PA.—Warren
Jacobson Machine Co. (Friction; Gas Engine).C

PA.—Wilkesbarre
Vulcan Iron Wks. (Friction; Umbrella Friction) ....AAAA

PA.—York
Smith Co., S. Morgan (Friction) ....AAA

R. I.—Providence
Brown & Sharpe Mfg. Co. (Friction) ....AAAA

R. I.—Woonsocket
Woonsocket Machine & Press Co. (Friction) ....AA

WIS.—Milwaukee
Nordberg Mfg. Co. (Friction) ....AAA

COACHES

See Carriage & Wagon

COAL

See also Coke

COAL (Con.)
ALA.—Birmingham
Sloss-Sheffield Steel & Iron
Co. (Anthracite; Bituminous) ....AAAA
ALA.—Mobile
Mobile Coal Co. (Bituminous) ....A
New York City
Berwind-White Coal Mining
Co. (Anthracite; Bituminous) ....AAAA
N. Y.—Rochester
Rochester & Pittsburg Coal
& Iron Co. (Anthracite;
Bituminous) ......AAAA
PA.—Philadelphia
Castner, Curran & Bullitt
(Anthracite) .....AAAA
Philadelphia & Reading Coal
& Iron Co. (Anthracite)
...........................B
Rockhill Iron & Coal Co.
(Bituminous) ....B
Virginia Coal & Iron Co.
(Bituminous) ....A
Westmoreland Coal Co.
(Bituminous) ......AAAA
Ziegler Bros., 119 N. 5th
(Bituminous) ....AA

COASTERS

IND.—Elkhart
Buescher Mfg. Co. (Bicycle)
...........................E
N. Y.—Buffalo
Forsyth Mfg. Co. (Bicycle)
...........................C

COATERS

MICH.—Detroit
Cotton, Arthur (Pill) ...C

COATINGS ..

ILL.—Chicago
Chicago Fire Proof Covering
Co . (Anti-Flame; Tin
Roof; Roof) ....E
MO.—St. Louis
Leschen & Sons Rope Co.
(Wire Rope) ......AAA
N. J.—Jersey City
Stowell Mfg. Co. (Liquid
Asphalt) ....B
New York City
Preservaline Mfg. Co. (Preservative) ....AA
Smith & Co., Edward (Preservative) ....A
Standard Paint Co. (Preservative) ....A
OHIO—Cincinnati
Moore Oil Co., Chas. H.
(Cable) ....B
OHIO—Columbus
Ironsides Co. (Wire Rope)
...........................O
PA.—Erie
Watson Co., H. F. (Asbestos; Roof) ....AAA
PA.—Freedom
Freedom Oil Wks. (Cable)
...........................A
PA.—Philadelphia
Bean & Co., Lewis U.
(Preservative) ....D
Rhoads & Son, J. E. (Preservative) ....A
S. C.—Summerville
Summerville Fernoline
Wks. (Preservative)....F

COATS

See also Men's Clothing

New York City
Reichman, Wm. (Stockinet)
...........................B
OHIO—Cincinnati
Pettibone Bros. Mfg. Co.
(Armor) ....A

COCAINE

MICH.—Detroit
Parke, Davis & Co. .AAAA
MO.—St. Louis
Mallinckrodt Chemical
Wks. ....AAAA

COCAINE (Con.)
New York City
Bischoff & Co., C. ......B
Boehringer & Soehne, C.
F. ....A
Merck & Co. ....AAA
New York Quinine & Chemical Wks. (Ltd.) ......A
Phair, R. W. ....F
Roessler & Hasslacher
Chemical Co. ......AA
Schieffelin & Co., W. H...
...........................AA
PA.—Philadelphia
Powers - Weightman - Rosengarten Co. ......AAAA

COCKEYES

CONN.—New Britain
North & Judd Mfg. Co.
(Screw; Triangular) ..AA

COCKS & BIBBS

CAL.—San Francisco
Roylance Brass Fdry.,
114 Main (Compression;
Fuller Work) ....B
CONN.—Bridgeport
Belknap Mfg. Co. (Gauge;
Steam; Stop; Waste
Cocks) C
CONN.—Hartford
Birkey, Cornelius J. (Ball
Cocks) X
Jones Co., Owen H. (Ball
Cocks) ....G
Noppel Pump Co. (Ball
Cocks) ....D
Pratt & Cady Co. (Gauge;
Stop; Waste Cocks) .AAA
CONN.—New Britain
Landers, Frary & Clark
(Ale; Beer; Compression;
Corporation; Fuller Work;
Ground Key; Stop; Waste
Cocks; Compression; Fuller Work; Ground Key
Bibbs) ....AAA
CONN.—New Haven
Peck Bros. & Co. (Ale;
Beer; Ball Compression;
Corporation; Gas Service;
Fuller Work; Ground Key;
Self-Closing; Waste Stop
Cocks; Compression; Fuller Work; Ground Key;
Waste; Stop Bibbs) .AA
DEL.—Wilmington
Speakman Supply & Pipe
Co. (Compression) .....B
ILL.—Chicago
Chicago Faucet Co., 224
Washington (Fuller Work;
Self Closing) ....F
Chicago Pneumatic Tool Co.,
Fisher Bldg. (Blow-Off
Cocks) ....AAAA
Clow & Sons, J. B., 344
Franklin (Compression;
Fuller Work; Self Closing) ....AAA
Crane Co., 10 N. Jefferson
(Ball; Compression; Gas
Service; Ground Key;
Gauge; Steam; Stop;
Waste Cocks; Compression; Ground Key Bibbs)..
...........................AAAA
Federal Co., 231 Washington
(Ground Key) ....A
Illinois Malleable Iron Co.,
30 W. Monroe (Ball; Fuller Work Cocks; Fuller
Work Bibbs) ......AAAA
Jerome & Elliott, 35 S. Canal (Blow-Off Cocks) ..B
Ryan & Co., J. J., 68 W.
Monroe (Compression;
Fuller Work, Self Closing;
also Ball; Stop; Waste
Cocks) C
Scott Valve Co., 32 W. Randolph (Gauge Cocks) ..D
Street & Kent Mfg. Co., 109
Jefferson (Compression;
Fuller Work; Gas Service;
Ground Key; Self Closing; also Ball; Corporation; Stop; Waste Cocks)
...........................B
Weir & Craig Mfg. Co., 2423

COCKS & BIBBS (Con.)

Wallace (Compression; Fuller Work; Ground Key; also Corporation; Gas Service; Stop; Waste Cocks) ....D

Western Valve Co., 43 Randolph (Gauge Cocks) ..B

Wolff Mfg. Co., 117 W. Lake (Compressin; Fuller Work; Ground Key; Self Closing; also Ale; Beer; Bell; Corporation; Stop; Waste Cocks) ....AAAA

ILL.—Decatur

Muller Mfg. Co., H. (Compression; Fuller Work; Ground Key; Self Closing; also Ball; Corporation; Gas Service; Stop; Waste Cocks) ....AAA

ILL.—Edwardsville

Edwardsville Brass Co. (Compression; Ground also Ball; Gas Service; Stop; Waste Cocks) ....B

ILL.—Kewanee

Western Table Co. (Corporation; Meter; Steam; Stop; Waste Cocks) .....AAA

ILL.—Oak Park

Goelitz, H. C. (Ball Cocks) ....B

ILL.—Peoria

Kinsey & Mahler Co. (Ground Key; also Corporation; Gas Service; Stop; Waste Cocks) ....A

ILL.—Waukegon

Thomas Brass & Iron Co. (Compression; Fuller Work; Ground Key; Self Closing; also Ball; Corporation; Gas Service; Gauge; Waste Cocks)...A

IND.—Evansville

Healey, Peter (Compression; Ground Key; also Gas Service; Soft; Waste Cocks) C

IND.—Fort Wayne

Knott-Van Arman Mfg. Co. (Ball Cocks) ....B

IND.—Indianapolis

Pioneer Brass Wks. (Ground Key; also Ale; Beer; Corporation; Gas Service; Stop; Waste Cocks) C

IOWA—Cedar Rapids

Dearborn Brass Co. (Fuller Work; Self Closing; also Ball Cocks) C

IOWA—Dubuque

McDonald, A. T. & Morrison Mfg. Co. (Compression; Fuller Work; Ground Key; Hose; Ball; Corporation; Gas Service; Stop; Waste Cocks) ..AA

KANS.—Wichita

Walterscheid Bros. (Corporation Cocks) ....B

KY.—Louisville

Ahrens & Ott Mfg. Co. (Corporation; Fuller Work; Self Closing; also Ball; Corporation; Gas Service; Ground Key; Stop; Waste Cocks) ....AAAA

Caldwell Co., W. E. (Stop; Waste Cocks) ....AA

MD.—Baltimore

Register's Sons Co., J. (Compression; also Ball; Corporation; Gas Service; Stop; Waste Cocks) ..A

Weiskittel & Son, A., Aliceanna and Washington (Compression; Fuller Work) ....A

MASS.—Boston

American Steam Gauge & Valve Mfg. Co., 195 High (Gauge Cocks) ....A

Ashton Valve Co., 271 Franklin (Gauge Cocks)A

Barrett Mfg. Co., 48 Pearl (Ball Cocks; Compression Bibbs) C

Boston Brass Co., 36 Oliver (High Pressure Ball Cocks) C

Boston Steam Specialty Co.,

COCKS & BIBBS (Con.)

35 Hartford (Gas Service; Stop; Waste Cocks) ....D

Crosby Steam Gauge & Valve Co., 95 Oliver (Gauge Cocks) ......AA

Dalton & Ingersoll Co., 175 High (Compression; Fuller Work; Ground Key; Self Closing; also Ball Cocks) X

D'Este & Co., Julian, 24 Canal (Compression; also Ball; Stop; Waste Cocks) ....B

Foster Mfg. Co., F. W., 6 Portland (Ball Cocks)..X

Grundy Brass Works, 50 Sudbury (Compression; Fuller Work; also Ball; Stop; Waste Cocks) ....F

Hamlin & Emery Brass Co., 26 Island (Compression; Ground Key; also Ball; Corporation; Gas Meter; Gas Service; Steam; Stop; Waste Cocks) ....D

Libbey Co., H. N., 143 Pearl (Ball Cocks) X

McKenney & Waterbury, 18 Franklin (Corporation Cocks) ....D

Smith & Anthony Co., 52 Union (Self Closing)..AA

Star Brass Mfg. Co., 103 E. Dedham (Three Way Indicator Cocks) ....A

Starter & Sons, Herman, 74 Sudbury (Ale; Beer Cocks) ....A

Sumner & Goodwin Co., 287 Congress ....B

Walworth Mfg. Co., 132 Federal (Compression; Ground Key; also Corporation; Gas Service; Stop; Waste Cocks) ......AAAA

Webb Mfg. Co., F. W., 50 Elm (Waste Cocks) ....A

Young, Jas. H., 224 Franklin (Ball Cocks) ....E

MASS.—Haydenville

Haydenville Co. (Compression; Fuller Work; Ground Key; Self Closing; also Ale; Beer; Ball; Corporation; Gas Service; Stop; Waste Cocks) ..A

MASS.—Springfield

Stebbins Mfg. Co., E. (Compression; Fuller Work; Ground Key; Self Closing; also Ball; Corporation; Gas Service; Stop; Waste Cocks) ....A

MICH.—Detroit

Detroit Brass Wks., Brooklyn Av. & M. R. R. (Ground Key; also Corporation; Stop; Waste Cocks) ....B

Globe Brass Works, 15 Macomb (Ground Key; also Ball; Corporation; Stop; Waste Cocks) ....E

Ideal Mfg. Co., 546 Franklin (Ball Cocks) ....A

McRae & Roberts Co., 227 Campbell Av. (Compression; also Corporation; Gas Meter; Gauge; Stop; Waste Cocks) ....A

Michigan Lubricator Co., 661 Beaubien (Self Closing) ....B

Park & McKay Co., 55 Bagley Av. (Ball; Stop; Waste Cocks) ....D

Penberthy Injector Co., 218 Abbott (Gauge Cocks)..A

Scully Mfg. Co., W. J., Beecher Av. & M. C. R. R. (Compression; Fuller Work; Ground Key; Self Closing Bibbs) ....B

Standard Brass Wks., 528 Woodbridge (Corporation Cocks) ....F

MICH.—Grand Rapids

Wolverine Brass Wks. (Ball; Ston; Waste Cocks) ....A

MICH.—Muskegon

Heap, Wm. (Ball Cocks)..D

COCKS & BIBBS (Con.)

MINN.—Minneapolis

National Brass & Metal Co., 256 3rd Av. (Compression; Fuller Work; Ground Key; also Ball; Corporation; Gas Service; Stop; Waste Cocks) ....B

Plumbing & Steam Fitting Supply Co., 212 N. 1st (Ball Cocks) ....A

MO.—Kansas City

Crampton-Farley Brass Co. (Compression; Fuller Work; Self Closing; also Stop; Waste Cocks) ....E

MO.—St. Louis

Cahill Swift Mfg. Co. (Ball Cocks) ....B

Kupferle, Jno. C., 2nd & Mound (Stop; Waste Cocks) ....AA

Nelson Mfg. Co., N. O., 8th & St. Charles (Compression; Fuller Work; also Ball; Gas Service Cocks) AAA

Pleuger & Henger Mfg. Co. (Compression) ....A

Rumsey Mfg. Co., L. M., 804 N. 2nd (Ball; Gas Service; Waste; Stop Cocks) ....AAA

N. H.—Exeter

Exeter Brass Works (Compression; Fuller Work; Ground Key; Self Closing; also Ball; Gas Service; Stop; Waste Cocks) C

N. J.—Belleville

Eastwood Wire Mfg. Co. (Corporation; Stop; Waste Cocks) ....A

N. J.—Newark

Chambers & Ainslee, 2 Commerce (Compression; Fuller Work; Ground Key; Self Closing; also Ale; Beer; Corporation; Gas Service; Stop; Waste Cocks) C

Jost's Sons, Edmund, 352 Plane (Ground Key; also Stop; Waste Cocks) C

Smith Mfg. Co., A. P., Passaic Av. & Brill (Gas Service Cocks) ....B

N. J.—Paterson

Asbell Co., S. J. (Ale; Beer Cocks) ....E

N. J.—Trenton

Trenton Brass & Machine Co. (Compression; Ground Key; also Ball; Stop; Waste Cocks) ....A

N. Y.—Albany

Albany Brass & Iron Co. (Ball Cocks) ....D

Cox Brass Mfg. Co. (Compression; also Gas Service Cocks) C

N. Y.—Brooklyn

Clarke, Robt., 93 Schermerhorn (Gas Service Cocks) F

Coyne & Delaney, 303 Rodney (Ball Cocks) C

Schaffer & Budenberg Mfg. Co., 10 Division (Gauge Cocks) ....D

N. Y.—Buffalo

Sherwood Mfg. Co., 34 Washington (Gauge Cocks) ....B

Zero Valve & Brass Mfg. Co. F

N. Y.—Elmira

Swift Lubricator Co. (Gauge Cocks) ....B

New York City

American Meter Co., 561 W. 47th (Gas Meter Cocks).B

Ashcroft Mfg. Co., 85 Liberty (Gauge Cocks) ....A

Bishop's Sons, Wm. (Ship Cocks) ....D

Dubois & Co., Fdk., 247 9th Av. (Compression; Self Closing) ....AAA

Eaton, Cole & Burnham Co., 253 B'way (Compression; Ground Key; also Hose; Gas Service; Gauge;

COCKS & BIBBS (Con.)

Stop; Waste Cocks) ....AAAA

Gleason Mfg. Co., E. P., 20 W. Houston (Ale; Beer; Corporation Cocks) .....B

Huber Co., Henry, 244 5th Av. (Compression; Fuller Work; Self Closing) ..B

Jenkins Bros., 71 John (Gauge Cocks) ....A

McNab & Harbin Mfg. Co., 56 John (Compression; Ground Key; also Ale; Beer; Corporation; Gas Service; Gauge; Steam; Stop; Waste Cocks) .AAA

Mayer, Lane & Co., 128 White (Compression; also Comporation; Gas Service; Stop; Waste Cocks).....A

Meyer-Sniffen Co., 5 E. 19th (Compression; Fuller Work; Ground Key; Self Closing; also Ball; Corporation; Gas Service; Stop; Waste Cocks) ....A

Morrison Co., David, 55 W. 16th (Compressin) ....E

Mott Iron Wks., J. L., 88 Beekman (Compression; Fuller Work; Ground Key; Self Closing; also Ball; Stop; Waste Cocks) AA

Mullany's Sons, James, 141 E. 25th (Compression; Ground Key; Self Closing; also Ale; Beer; Corporation; Stop; Waste Cocks) D

Standard Steam Specialty Co., 111 5th Av. (Blow-Off Cocks) ....D

United Metal Mfg. Co., 186 Wooster (Ground Key)..D

Victor Exchange Brass Wks. 42 Mott (Gas Service Cocks) ....A

N. Y.—Rochester

Clark Novelty Co. (Ale; Beer Cocks) ....D

Nunn Brass Wks. (Stop; Waste Cocks) ....F

N. Y.—Rome

Rome Sanitary Wks. (Wilson Mfg. Co., R. M.) (Compression) ....B

N. Y.—Syracuse

Syracuse Faucet & Valve Co. (Ball; Stop; Waste Cocks) X

OHIO—Cincinnati

American Brass Wks., 426 Plum (Compression; Fuller Work; Ground Key; Self Closing; also Ball; Corporation; Stop; Waste Cocks) ....D

Central Brass Wks. 322 W. Pearl (Compression; Ground Key; also Corporation; Steam; Stop; Waste Cocks) ....D

Douglass. Co., John, 906 Poplar (Ball Cocks) ....A

Lunkenheimer Co., Beekman & Waverly (Ale; Beer; Corporation; Gauge; Stop; Waste Cocks) ....AA

Nichol & Co., Theo. J., Pearl & Ludlow (Compression; Ground Key; also Corporation; Stop; Waste Cocks) ....D

Powell Co., Wm., 2525 Spring Grove Av. (Ground Key; also Ball; Corporation; Gas Service; Steam; Stop; Waste Cocks) ....A

Queen City Brass Wks., Spring Grove & Garrard Avs. (Compression; Ground Key; also Ale; Ball; Corporation; Gas Service; Indicator; Stop; Waste Cocks) C

Varwig Mfg. Co., 715 W. Court (Ale; Beer Cocks).A

OHIO—Cleveland

Bishop & Babcock Co., cor. Hamilton & Kirtland (Ship Cocks) ....AAA

COCKS & BIBBS (Con.)

Brookside Brass Fdry. & Mfg. Co., (Compression; Self Closing) ....E

Cleveland Bronze & Brass Wks. (Compression; Ground Key; Fuller Work; also Stop; Water Cocks) C

Cleveland Faucet Co., 21 Frankfort (Ale; Beer Cocks) ....AAA

Empire Brass Mfg. Co., 125 Viaduct (Compression; Fuller Work; Self Closing) ....E

Farman Brass Works, 23 Centre (Compression; Ground Key; also Corporation; Gas Service; Stop; Waste Cocks) ....A

Fisher Co., E. W. (Ground Key) C

Forest City Brass Works, 440 Huron (Compression; Fuller Work; Ground Key; also Corporation; Gas Service; Stop; Waste Cocks) ....B

Glauber Brass Mfg. Co. (Compression; Fuller Work; Ground Key; Self Closing; also Corporation; Gas Service; Stop; Waste Cocks) ....A

Ohio Brass & Mfg. Co., 1201 Franklin Av. (Ground Key) ....E

Reliance Gauge Column Co., 76 E. Prospect (Lever Chain Gauge Cocks) ....D

Russ Mfg. Co., A. E., 87 Wade Park Av. (Ground Key) ....B

Sanitary Co.. 1 Water (Compression; Self Crossing).B

Superior Foundry Co., Echo & Union (Self Closing).C

United Brass Mfg. Co., 958 Hamilton (Compression; Fuller Work; Ground Key; also Corporation; Stop; Waste Cocks) ....E

OHIO—Columbus

Columbus Brass Co., 94 N. 6th (Compression; Fuller Work; Ground Key; also Brass Ball; Corporation; Gas Service; Stop; Waste Cocks) ....B

Ohio Pump & Brass Co. (Ground Key; also Ball; Corporation; Gas Service; Stop; Waste Cocks) C

OHIO—Dayton

Buckeye Iron & Brass Wks. (Ground Key; also Corporation; Gauge; Stop; Waste Cock).........AA

OHIO—Mansfield

Humphrey Mfg. Co. (Fuller Work; Ground Key; also Corporation; Stop; Waste Cocks) ....B

Ohio Brass Co. (Gauge Cocks) ....AA

OHIO—Springfield

Nolte Brass Co. (Compression; also Corporation Cocks) ....D

Springfield Brass Co. (Hose) D

Victor Supply Co. (Corporation Cocks) ....B

OHIO—Toledo

National Supply Co. (Compression; also Ball; Gas Service Cocks) ....AAAA

PA.—Erie

Campbell Brass Works, J. B. (Compression; Ground Key; also Corporation; Gas Service; Stop; Waste Cocks) ....A

Erie Mfg. & Supply Co. (Gauge Cocks) ....B

Hays Mfg. Co. (Compression; Ground Key; also Gas Service; Stop; Waste Cocks) ....A

Jarecke Mfg. Co. (Corporation; Gas Service; Gauge; Stop; Waste Cocks)AAAA

COCKS & BIBBS (Con.)

PA.—Philadelphia

Belfield & Co., H., 435 N. Broad (Compression; also Corporation; Gauge; Stop; Waste Cocks) ....AA

Cooper Brass Wks., W. S., 437 N. 3rd (Compression; Self Closing; also Ball; Stop; Waste Cocks) ...B

Excelsior Brass Wks.. 1518 Florist (Plumbers' Brass; Ground Key) ....E

Eynon-Evans Mfg. Co., 1519 Clearfield (Blof-Off Cocks) ....A

Haines, Jones & Cadbury Co., 1136 Ridge Av. (Compression; Fuller Work; Ground Key; Self Closing; also Ball; Corporation; Gas Service; Stop; Waste Cocks) ....AA

Hartman Co., 1231 N. Front (Corporation Cocks) ....B

Homer Brass Works, 231 Race (Compression; Ground Key; also Ale; Beer; Ball; Corporation; Gas Service; Stop; Waste Cocks) C

Huyette, Paul R.. Betz Bldg. (Gauge Cocks) ...E

McCambridge & Co.. 537 Cherry (Compression; Ground Key; Self Closing; also Ale; Beer; Corporation; Gas Service; Stop; Waste Cocks) ....B

Perkes, Chas.. 627 Arch (Compression; Self Closing; also Gas Service; Stop; Waste Cocks) ...B

Savill, Thos.. 11th & Wood (Compression; Ground Key; Self Closing; also Ball; Stop; Waste Cocks) C

Webb & Son, Elisha. 142 S. Del. Av. (Gauge Cocks) D

PA.—Pittsburg

Bailey-Farrell Mfg. Co.. 619 Smithfield (Compression; Fuller Work; also Ale; Beer; Ball; Gas Service; Stop; Waste Cocks) ...AA

Bonar & Co.. Jas., Carnegie Bldg. (Gauge Cocks) ...B

Cadman Mfg. Co.. A. W., Smallman (Gauge Cocks) C

Chaplin-Fulton Mfg. Co.. 30 Penn Av. (Blow-Off) ...A

Kelly & Jones Mfg. Co.. 315 1st Av. (Compression; Ground Key; also Corporation; Gauge; Stop; Waste Cocks) ....AA

Oil Well Supply Co.. 219 Water (Corporation Coks) ....AAAA

Standard Sanitary Mfg. Co., Arrott Bldg.(Fuller Work; Ground Key; Self Closing; also Gas Service; Corporation; Stop; Waste Cocks) AAAA

PA.—Scranton

American Safety Lamp & Mine Supply Co. (Gas Service Cocks) ....F

Everhart Brass Wks. (Corporation; Gas Service Cocks) ....A

PA.—Williamsport

Darling Pump & Mfg. Co. (Corporation Cocks) ...B

R. I.—Providence

Dart Mfg. Co.. E. M.. 136 Clifford (Ground Key; also Corporation; Gas Service; Stop; Waste Cocks) ....D

Field Automatic Valve & Faucet Co., 168 Dorrance (Self Closing) ....B

TEXAS—San Antonia

Collins Mfg. Co., F. F. (Corporation) ....B

W. VA.—Charlestown

Powhatan Brass & Iron Wks. (Compression; Ful-

COCKS & BIBBS (Con.)
ler Work; Ground Key;
Self Closing; also Ale;
Beer; Ball; Corporation;
Gas Service; Stop; Waste
Cocks) ....B
WIS.—Kenosha
Badger Brass Mfg. Co.
Ball) C
WIS.—Milwaukee
Hoffman-Billings Mfg. Co.
Compression; Ful-
ler Work; Ground Key;
Self-Closing; also Ball;
Corporation; Gas Service;
Stop Cocks; Water Cocks)
AA
Hoffman Mfg. Co., B., 257
6th (Ball Cocks) ......A
Lamp & Miller Mfg. Co.
(Compression; Ful-
ler Work; Ground Key;
Stop; Waste; also Ale;
Bar; Corporation; Self-
Closing Cocks) ....B
Loeffelholz & Co., 170 Clin-
ton (Self-Closing) .....A
Milwaukee Brass Mfg. Co.,
241 Lapham (Compression;
Fuller Work; Self-Clos-
ing; also Ball Cocks)...C
Milwaukee Valve Co., 881
Robinson Av. (Fuller
Work; Self-Closing)....D
Rundell-Spence Mfg. Co., 63
2d (Compression; Fuller
Work; Ground Key; Self-
Closing; also Corporation;
Gas Service; Stop; Waste
Cocks) ....AAAA
Spence Mfg. Co. (Compres-
sion; also Corporation;
Gas Service; Stop; Waste
Cocks) ....D

COCOA

See Chocolate

COCOANUTS

ALA.—Birmingham

Douglas Bros., 2105 Morris
Av. ....F
Melton, P. O. ....G
CAL.—San Francisco
Sresovich & Co., L. G., 521
Sansom (Dessicated) ...X
ILL.—Chicago
Barrett & Co., M. L., 219
Lake (Oil) ....A
Pooley, S., 91 Hudson ...G
Puhl-Webb Co., 119 W. Ran-
dolph (Des.) C
MD.—Baltimore
Nat. Cocoanut Co., 307 Mc-
Elderry's Wharf) .....E
MO.—St. Louis
Dunham Mfg. Co., 511 N.
Main (Des.) ....A
MO.—Springfield
Missouri Fruit Co. ......F
N. J.—Jersey City
Graef, E. A. (Des.) ......D
N. J.—Brooklyn
Floto Cocoanut Co., 163
Union Av. (Des.) C
New York City
Brazeau, F., 244 Wash....F
Dunham Mfg. Co., 377 Pearl
(Des.) ....A
Fuerst Bros. & Co.,, 2 Stone
B
Schepp, L., 165 Duane.....
AAAA
PA.—Philadelphia
Baker, Franklin Co., 700 N.
Del. Av..............D
Croft & Allen Co., 33rd &
Market ....AA
Crowell & Co., C. S., 122
N. Del. Av. (Des.).....A
Keystone Co. Cocoanut Co.,
122 N. Del. Av. (Des.).D
Wetmore Mfg. Co., 1308 N.
Orianna (Prepared) ....B

CODEINE

MO.—St. Louis
Mallinckrodt Chemical Wks.
AAAA

CODEINE (Con.)
N. Y.—Brooklyn
Wiarda & Co., John C...AA
New York City
Boehringer & Soehne, C. F.
A
PA.—Philadelphia
Powers - Weightman - Ros-
engarten Co. ....AAAA

COD

See Fish

CODES

MASS.—Boston
Houghton & Co., F. O.
(Cable) ....D
New York City
American Code Co.(All
Kinds) C
Hartfield Telegraphic Code
Pub. Co. (Cable)......X
Lieber Code Co., 2 Stone
(Cable) ....D

COFFEE

See Teas; Coffees & Spices

COFFINS

See Cases; Burial

COGGING

IND.—South Bend
Bowsher, N. P. (Wood)...B
KANS.—Enterprise
Ehrsam Mach. Co., J. B.
(Wood) ....B
KANS.—Leavenworth
Great Western Mfg. Co.
(Wood) ....AA
N. Y.—Buffalo
Noye Mfg. Co., John T.
(Wood) X
OHIO.—Salem
Clark Co., W. J. (Wood).A

COGS

ILL.—Springfield
Aetna Fdry. & Machine Co.
(Self Dumping) ....B
IND.—Indianapolis
Nordyke & Marmon Co.
(Gear) ....AAA
IND.—Richmond
Richmond City Mill Wks.
(Mill) ....B
IND.—South Bend
Bowsher Co. (Mill) ......B
Cover, H. S. (Mill) ......F
WIS.—Menasha
Menasha Wood Split Pulley
Co. (Wooden) ....D

COILERS

CONN.—Waterbury
Manville Machine Co., E. J.
(Wire) C
MASS.—Worcester
Morgan Construction Co.
(Wire) ....A
N. Y.—Lockport
Merritt Mfg. Co. (Hoop).D
New York City
Garvin Machine Co., cor.
Spring & Varick (Wire).
AA
OHIO—Cuyahoga Falls
Turner, Vaughan & Taylor
Co. (Chain Link; Wire).B

COILS

COL.—Denver
Carstarphan Electric Co.
(Induction) ....E
CONN.—Ansonia
Ansonia Electrical Co. (In-
duction; Resistance;
Spark) ....A
Cameron Elect. Mfg. Co.,
H. P. (Armature) .....E
CONN.—Elmwood
Whitlock Coil Pipe Co.
(Brass; Brome; Bronze;
Compound; Copper; Silver;
Steel) ....AA

COILS (Con.)

CONN.—Hartford
Whitlock Coil Pipe Co.
(Iron; Brass; Copper
Pipe) ....A

CONN.—New Haven
National Pipe Bending Co.
(Pipe; Brass; Copper; Ice
Machine; Iron; Steel; Refrigerator Mach.) ......B

CONN.—Waterbury
Electrical Appliance Mfg.
Co. (Spark) ....G

DEL.—Wilmington
Morris Electric Co. (Spark)
.......................X

GA.—Atlanta
Wothen Electric & Mfg. Co.
(Gas Engine; Lighting
Spark) ....B

ILL.—Chicago
American Electric Fuse Co.,
50 Jackson Boul. (Electric
Heat) ....A
American Electric Telephone
Co., Canal & Jackson
Boul. (Induction) ......B
Harris & Bro., Geo. P.
(Copper) ....A
Harvard Electric Co., 224
S. Clinton (Induction)...D
International Telephone
Mfg. Co. (Induction, Resistance; Spark) X
McDermid Mfg. Co., 118 W.
Jackson Boul. (Induction)
.......................C
McIntosh Battery & Optical
Co., 39 W. Randolph (Induction) ....D
Western Electric Co., 259 S.
Clinton (Resistance;
Spark; Induction) .AAAA
Wolf & Co., Fred. W. (Ice;
Refrigerating Mach.;
Iron; Brass; Copper Pipe)
.......................AAA

IND.—Anderson
Remy Electric Co. (Spark)
.......................D

IND.—Fort Wayne
Fort Wayne Electric Corporation (Induction) ....
.......................AAAA

KANS.—Fort Scott
Fort Scott Fdry. & Mach.
Co. (Copper) ....H

MASS.—Andover
Tyer Rubber Co. (Abdominal) ....AA

MASS.—Boston
Badger & Sons Co. (Copper
Steam) ....B
Barney Ventilating Fan
Wks. (Iron; Brass; Copper Pipe) X
Boston Electric Co., 29
Harrison (Snark) ......B
Electric Gas Lighting Co.,
195 Devonshire (Induction Spark) ....A
Walworth Mfg. Co. (Pipe)
.......................AAAA

MASS.—Braintree
Dow Portable Electric Co.
(Jump Spark) C

MASS.—Brookline
Haltzer-Cabot Electric Co.
(Spark) ....B

MASS.—Cambridge
Crest Mfg. Co. (Spark)...X

MASS.—Somerville
American Coil Co. (Jump
Spark) ....D

MICH.—Lansing
Capital Electric Engineering Co. (Gas Engine: Igniting; Spark; Induction)
.......................E

MICH.—Menominee
Menominee Elect. Mfg. Co.
(Induction) ....E

N. H.—Penacook
Whitney Electric Instrument
Co. (Resistance) ......D

N. Y.—Brooklyn
Graham Chemical Pottery
Wks., 1018 Met. Av.
(Stoneware) ....D

N. Y.—Buffalo
Wilhelm Telephone Mfg.
Co., 45 N. Division (Induction) X

COILS (Con.)

New York City
Bunnell & Co., J. H., 20
Park Pl. (Induction; Resistance; Spark) ......B
Edison Phonograph Agency
(Ruhmkorff) ....D
Edwards & Co., 144th & 4th
Av. (Induction; Resistance; Spark) C
Foote, Pierson & Co., 82
Fulton (Spark) C
International Brass & Electric Co., 76 Beekman (Induction; Resistance;
Spark; Faradic; Ruhmdorff) ....D
MacNab & Hanlin Mfg. Co.,
56 John (Pipe).......AAA
Manhattan Electrical Supply Co., 32 Cortlandt (Induction) ....F
Mayer, Lane & Co., 128
White (Brass; Copper;
Iron Pipe) X
Pearce, Frederick, 20 Rose
(Induction) ....B
Roche, Wm., 42 Vesey
(Spark) ....D
Splitdorf, C. F., 27 Vandewater (Induction; Spark;
Resistance) ....E

N. Y.—Rochester
Bradley & Co., E. C. (Induction; Spark) ....H

N. Y.—Schenectady
General Electric Co. (Resistance) ....AAAA

N. Y.—Syracuse
Williams, E. Q. (Induction)
.......................F

OHIO—Akron
Akron Rubber Co. (Abdominal) ....AAAA

OHIO—Cincinnati
Electrical Appliance Co.
136 Longworth (Spark).C
Fischer Specialty Mfg. Co.,
229 W. 6th (Spark) ....H

OHIO—Cleveland
Nungesser Electric Battery
Co., 29 King (Spark)....B
Van Dorn-Elliott Electric Co.
(Armature; Field) .....F

OHIO—Columbus
Columbus Iron Works Co.
(Brass; Copper; Iron Pipe)
.......................A
Columbus Storage Battery
Co. (Gas Engine Spark).F

PA.—Allentown
Allbright's Sons & Co.
(Pipe) ....AA

PA.—Harrisburg
Harrisburg Pipe & Pipe
Bending Co. (Ltd.) (Pipe;
Brass; Copper; Ice; Refrigerating Machine; Iron;
Steel) ....AAA

PA.—Philadelphia
Biddle, James G., Stephen
Girard Bldg. (Induction;
Resistance) C
Patrick, Carter & Wilkins,
1231 Callowhill (Induction; Resistance; Spark)
.......................B
Philadelphia Pipe Bending
Wks. (Iron) ....D
Queen & Co., 1010 Chestnut
(Induction; Resistance)..
.......................AA

PA.—Pittsburg
Best Mfg. Co. (Pipe) ..AA

R. I.—Philipsdale
Varley Duplex Magnet Co.
(Induction; Resistance;
Spark) ....A

WIS.—La Crosse
Vought-Berger Co. (Induction) C

WIS.—Milwaukee
Allis-Chalmers Co. (Ammonia Expansion) ....AAAA
Mechanical Appliance Co.
(Armature) C

COKE

ALA.—Birmingham
Alabama Consolidated Coal
& Iron Co. ....AAAA
Ivy Coal & Coke Co.....B

COKE (Con.)

Palos Coal & Coke Co....X
Sloss-Sheffield Steel &
  Iron Co. ....AAAA
Tennessee Coal, Iron &
  R. R. Co. ......AAAA

COLO.—Denver
Colorado Fuel & Iron Co...
  ....AAAA
Northern Coal & Coke Co..A

GA.—Atlanta
Campbell Coal & Coke Co..A
Lookout Mountain Coal &
  Coke Co. C

ILL.—Chicago
Pickards, Brown & Co.
  Rookery Bldg. ....AAAA
Republic Iron & Steel Co.,
  108 La Salle ......AAAA

KY.—Middlesboro
Bryson Mountain Coal &
  Coke Co. C
Fort Ridge Coal & Coke Co.
 C
Mingo. Coal & Coke Co...A

MD.—Baltimore
Despard Gas Coal Co. ..X

MASS.—Boston
Ginn & Co., 7 Tremont....
  ....AAAA

MICH.—Detroit
Graham Coal & Coke Co..X

New York City
Chapman Iron, Coke & Coal
  Co., 80 B'way ....B
New York & Philadelphia
  Coal & Coke Co., Produce
  Exch. ....D
Virginia Iron, Coal & Coke
  Co. ....A

N. Y.—Rochester
Rochester & Pittsburg Coal
  & Iron Co........AAAA

OHIO—Cleveland
Drake Coal Co. ....A
Stewart Iron Co., Perry
  Payne Bldg. ....AAA

OHIO—Columbus
Columbus Iron & Steel Co.
  ....AAAA
Maynard Bros. ....A
New Pittsburg Coal Co.....
  ....AAAA

OHIO—Steubenville
La Belle Iron Wks. .AAAA
Steubenville Coal & Mining
  Co. ....B

PA.—Altoona
Altoona Coal & Coke Co...A

PA.—Blairsville
Blairsville Coke Co.......D

PA.—Carnegie
Verner Coal & Coke Co....A

PA.—Connellsville
Indian Ridge Coal & Coke
  Mfrs. ....B
Opekiska Coal & Coke Co..C

PA.—Dawson
Washington Coal & Coke
  Co. ....AAA

PA.—Greensberg
Donohue Coke Co. ....B
Mount Pleasant Coke Co...A

PA.—Hastings
Oak Ridge Coal & Coke Co.
  ....A

PA.—Latrobe
Latrobe - Connellsville Coal
  & Coke Co. ....A
Taxman Coal & Coke Co...A
Superior Coal & Coke Co...A

PA.—Loyal Hanna
Loyal Hanna Coal & Coke
  Co. ....AA

PA.—Philadelphia
Dimmick & Co. J. K.,
  2023 New Land Title
  Bldg. ....A
Stineman Coal & Coke Co.,
  421 Chestnut ....B

PA.—Pittsburg
Bessemer Coke Co., Lewis
  Blk. ....AAAA
Blair & Co., Reed F., Frick
  Bldg. C
Brown & Cochran, Conestoga
  Bldg. ....AAAA
Carnegie Steel Co., Carnegie
  Bldg. ....AAAA
Cherry Valley Iron Co., Peo-
  ple's Sav. Bank Bldg...A
Frick Coke Co., H. C.. Car-
  negie Bldg. ......AAAA

COKE (Con.)

Goff, Horner & Co., Frick
  Bldg. ....A
Hecla Coke Co., Arrott
  Bldg. ....AA
Hillman & Son, J. H., Frick
  Bldg. ....A
Hooker & Co., Howard M.,
  Farmers' Bank Bldg....C
Hostetter-Connellsville Coke
  Co., Frick Bldg. ...AAAA
Mansfield Coal & Coke Co..A
Monongahela River Consoli-
  dated Coal & Coke Co...
  ....AAAA
Oliver & Snyder Steel Co.,
  Carnegie Bldg. ...AAAA
Pittsburg & Buffalo Co.,
  Frick Bldg. ......AAAA
Pittsburg Coal Co., 232
  5th Av. ....AAAA
Virginia Coal & Iron Co...A

PA.—Scottdale
Keister & Co., A. L. ..AAA
Stauffer & Co., J. R....AA

PA.—Uniontown
Sackett Coal & Coke Co.,
  H. R. ....E
Taylor & Co., Isaac .....A
Uniontown Coke Co. .....E

PA.—Upland
Crozer Coal & Coke Co...AA
Upland Coal & Coke Co....A

PA.—Wampun
Beaver Coal & Coke Co...B

TENN.—Bristol
Virginia Iron, Coal & Coke
  Co. (Foundry; Furnace).A

TENN.—Chattanooga
Durham Coal & Coke Co..AA

TENN.—Clouse Hill
Sewanee Coal, Coke & Land
  Co. ....A

TENN.—Nashville
Bon Air Coal & Iron Co.....
  ....AAAA

VA.—Lynchburg
Arlington Coal & Coke Co.A
Gillam Coal & Coke Co...A

VA.—Norton
Norton Coal Co. ....A

VA.—Richmond
Ellison & McCaw ....E

VA.—Roanoke
Roanoke Coal & Coke Co...
  ....AA

VA.—Virginia City
Russell Creek Coal & Coke
  Co. ....B

W. VA.—Algoma
Algoma Coke & Coal Co...A

W. VA.—Bramwell
Buckeye Coal & Coke Co..A
Sagamore Coal & Coke Co..A

W. VA.—Caperton
Victoria Coal & Coke Co..A

W. VA.—Fairmount
Fairmount Coal Co. ..AAAA

W. VA.—Fire Creek
Fire Creek Coal & Coke Co.
  ....A

W. VA.—Glen Jean
McKell Coal & Coke Co....B

W. VA.—Godfrey
Crystal Coal & Coke Co...A

W. VA.—Goodwill
Goodwill Coal & Coke Co..B
Louisville Coal & Coke Co..A

W. VA.—Grafton
Tygarts River Coal Co...AA

W. VA.—Kyle
Lynchburg Coal & Coke Co.
  ....A

W. VA.—Raleigh
Raleigh Coal & Coke Co...B

W. VA.—Stonecliff
Benry Coal & Coke Co.....A

W VA.—Thacker
Thacker Coal & Coke Co..B

W. VA.—Thomas
Davis Coal & Coke Co.....
  ....AAAA

W. VA.—Vivian
Peerless Coal & Coke Co..A
Tidewater Coal & Coke Co.
  ....A

W. VA.—Worth
Rolfe Coal & Coke Co.....A

COLANDERS

MO. St. Louis

COLANDERS (Con.)

St. Louis Stamping Co. ..
AAAA

N. Y.—Albany
Hoy & Co. ....A
N. Y.—Buffalo
Shepard & Co., Sidney ....
AAAA
New York City
Lalance & Grosjean Mfg. Co.
AAAA

COLCHICUM

New York City
Hopkins & Co., J. L., 100
William ....A

COLCOTHER

N. Y.—Brooklyn
Wiarda & So., John C....AA

COLLAR-ETTES

See Clothing; Ladies'

COLLARS & CUFFS

CAL.—Oakland
Keller Co., M. J. ....A
CONN.—Windsor
Windsor Collar & Cuff Co.
(Rubber) C
MASS.—Boston
Reversible Collar Co.
(Linene) ....AA
MASS.—Cambridge
Reversible Collar Co. ..AA
MICH.—Detroit
Norris Co. ....B
MICH.—Grand Rapids
Kelly Shirt Co. ....D
N. Y.—Albany
Empire Collar & Cuff Co..A
Munson, S. L. ....A
N. Y.—Brooklyn
Goodman & Mandel C
Manheim, Julius C
Roach & Co., John C.....E
N. Y.—Glens Falls
Fowler Collar Co. C
Peyser Collar Co., Eugene
P. ....B
Robertson & Co., D. L....C
N. Y.—Lockport
Dumville & Co. C
New York City
Hauptner & Co., Chas. ...C
Keep Shirt Co., H. V....D
Moseley & Moody ....E
Sidenberg & Co., G. ....AA
United Mfg. Co., 636 B'way
(Paper) ....A
N. Y.—Troy
American Collar Co. C
Bowman & Sons, Joseph...F
Brown, E. H. ....F
Chapman-Harper Co. .....D
Cluett, Peabody & Co..AAA
Coon Bros. ....D
Corliss, Coon & Co......B
Curtis & Co., H. H......B
Dingman, J. B. ....F
Earl & Wilson C
Enugh & Straub.........C
Fellows & Co. ....B
Ferguson Co., C. W......D
Goodman, Saperstein & Co.
F
Hall, Hartwell & Co. ....A
Holmes, Henry C
Ide & Co., Geo. P. ......A
International Shirt & Collar
Co. ....B
McClellan Co., C. H......D
Marvin, E. W. C
Miller-Hale Shirt & Collar
Co. ....B
Searle, Gardner & Co.....B
Stettheimer & Co., J. J.
(Womens') C
Tim & Co. (Mens';
Womens') ....A
Troy Collar Co. ....E
United Shirt & Collar Co.
(Mens'; Womens').AAAA
Van Zandt. Jacobs & Co..B
Wilber - Campbell - Ste-

COLLARS & CUFFS
phens Co. ....A
N. Y.—Waterford
American Shirt & Collar Co.
D
N. Y.—West Troy
Barker Co., Wm. ....A
OHIO—Cincinnati
Gofton, Frank ......,...B

COLLARS

Miscellaneous

ALA.—Huntsville
Huntsville Fdry. & Machine
Wks. (Shafting) ......B
CONN.—Bristol
Smith, Ira B. (Shafting).E
CONN.—Willimantic
Thread City Collar Co.
(Rubber) ....B
IND.—Indianapolis
Hoosier Sweat Collar Co.
(Felt Sweat) C
IND.—Mishawaka
Dodge Mfg. Co. (Shafting)
AAA
IOWA—Keokuk
Weber-Hirch Mfg. Co.
(Pipe) ....E
MD.—Baltimore
Poole Engineering & Ma-
chine Co. (Shafting) ..AA
MASS.—Newburyport
Fiberloid Co. (Waterproof)
B
MASS.—Springfield
M. & M. Mfg. Co. (Rubber)
E
MASS.—Worcester
Matthews Mfg. Co. (Steam
Pipe) ....D
Worcester Ferrule & Mfg.
Co. (Steam Pipe) C
MICH.—Detroit
Buhl Malleable Co. (Shaft-
ing) ....A
MINN.—St. Paul
Scheffer & Rossum, 172 E.
4th (Dog) ....A
MO.—St. Louis
Brauer Bros. Mfg. Co. (Dog)
E
Medart Patent Pulley Co.
(Shafting) ....AAA
N. J.—Newark
Premo-Hall Mfg. Co. (Bath
Tub) X
N. Y.—Brooklyn
Smith & Son, Jas., 40
Franklin Av. (Dog)....D
Williams & Co., J. H., 9
Richards (Shafting) ..AA
New York City
Brown Co., A. & F., 25 Dey
(Shafting) ....B
Medford Fancy Goods Co..
75 Duane (Brass Dog)..E
PA.—Chester
Keystone Droy Forge Works
(Shafting) ....B
PA.—Pittsburg
Columbia Bridge Co.
(Shafting) ....AA
R. I.—Providence
Manchester Co., J. B. (Cop-
per Roof) ....E

COLLECTORS

CONN.—Hartford
Stirling Blower & Pipe Mfg.
Co. (Dust) ....A
IND.—Richmond
Richmond City Mill Wks.
(Dust) ....B
MASS.—Boston
Sturtevant Co., B. F.
(Dust) ....AAA
MICH.—Detroit
American Blower Co. (Dust)
AA
N. Y.—Buffalo
Buffalo Forge Co. (Dust)..
AAA
New York City
Fairbanks Co., 416 Broome
(Dust) ....AAAA
OHIO—Columbus
Case Mfg. Co. (Dust) ...A

COLLETS

CONN.—Hartford
Whitney Mfg. Co. (Spring)
A

CONN.—Waterbury
White Co., L. C. (Button)
C

R. I.—Providence
Brown & Sharpe Mfg. Co.
(Spring) ....AAAA

COLLODION

MASS. Boston
Billings, Clapp & Co. ....B
MO.—St. Louis
Larkin & Scheffer ......A
Mallinckrodt Chemical Wks.
AAAA
New York City
Cooper & Co., Chas. ....AA
McKesson & Robbins. AAAA
New York Quinine & Chemical Wks. (Ltd.) ......A
Schieffelein & Co., W. H.
AA
PA.—Philadelphia
Powers - Weightman - Rosengarten Co. ......AAAA

COLOCYNTH

PA.—Philadelphia
Drueding Bros. Co. ....AA

COLOGNE

See Perfumery

COLORS

See also Paints; Dyestuffs;
Dyes; Extracts.

CAL.—San Francisco
Blumenthal & Co., M.
(Sugar) ....E
Fuller & Co., W. P. (Car;
Coach; Japan; Oil) ....
AAAA
COLO.—Denver
James Mercantile & Mfg.
Co., B. L. (Car; Coach;
Graining; Oil) ....B
CONN.—Essex
Essex Paint Wks. (Artists'
Dry; Tube; Car; Coach;
Dry; Japan; Scene Painters' Dry) ....A
CONN.—Hartford
Beach & Co. (Analine). AAA
GA.—Augusta
Augusta Sienna & Ochre Co.
F
ILL.—Aurora
Akron Mining, Milling &
Mfg. Co. (Paint) ....B
ILL.—Chicago
Alston Mfg. Co., 177 Randolph (Agricultural; Artists' Tube; Dry) ....A
American Steel & Wire Co.,
The Rookery (Venetian
Red; Oil) ....AAAA
Baltimore Chemical Co.
(Canned Goods) ....B
Barrett & Co., M. L.
(Canned Goods; Cider;
Vinegar) ....A
Beekler Co., J. G. (Canned
Goods) ....D
Bode, Gustave A. (Cider;
Vinegar) ....D
Chapman & Smith Co.
(Confectioners') ....B
Chicago Wood Finishing Co.
(Car; Coach) ....A
Creamery Package Mfg. Co.
(Butter; Cheese) .. AAAA
Heath & Milligan Mfg. Co.
(Car; Coach; Ceramic;
Oil) ....AAA
Heller & Co., B. (Food) ..D
Hutchinson & Son, W. H.
(Sugar) ....A
Kohnstamm & Co., H.
(Canned Goods) ......AA
McMahon & Durlacher Co.
(Food) ....D
Ottens, H. H. (Confectioners'; Bakers') C
Rubber Paint Co. (Agricul-

COLORS (Con.)
tural; Car; Coach; Fresco;
Japan; Oil; Moist Water;
Paper Makers'; Pulp)..A
Senour Mfg. Co. (Oil) ....A
ILL.—East St. Louis
Illinois Mineral Milling Co.
C
ILL.—Sterling
Carolus Co., J. K. (Butter)
D
IOWA—Fort Dodge
Iowa Paint Mfg. Co.
(Dry) C
LA.—New Orleans
McWilliams, R. (Car;
Coach; Japan; Oil).....X
MD.—Baltimore
Macneal & Co., Jas. B., 34
S. Calvert (Paint) ....A
Sonneborn's Sons, L. (Aniline) C
MASS.—Boston
American Soda Fountain Co.
(Fruit) ....AAAA
Babcock & Co., John (Oil).B
Briggs & Co., John, 14
Washington (Oil) C
Cabot, Samuel (Mortar) ..A
Metcalf Co., Theodore
(Aniline) ....A
Murray Co. (Food) C
Swift & Co., 75 Broad
(Dry) ....B
Wadsworth - Howland Co.
Artists' Tube; Car;
Coach; Oil; Dry Paint;
Fresco; Japan) ....A
MASS.—Lynn
Hadley Cement Co. (Cement) ....D
MASS.—Springfield
Hampton Paint & Chemical
Co. (Japan; Oil; Paper
Makers') ....B
MASS.—Worcester
Ferric Chemical & Color
Co. ....AAAA
MICH.—Detroit
Acme White Lead & Color
Wks. (Brick; Car; Coach;
Decorators'; Dry; Distemper; Fresco; Graining;
Japan; Oil; Striping)....
AAA
Boydell Bros. White Lead &
Color Co., 18 Congress
(Oil; Mortar) ....AA
Crown Color Co. (W. E.
Heames & Co.) (Confectioners') ....D
Detroit White Lead Wks.,
532 Milwaukee (Agricultural; Car; Coach; Brick;
Dry; Graining; Japan;
(Oil; Striping) ......AAA
Eaton & Son, Thos. H.
(Aniline) ....AAAA
Peninsular Paint & Varnish
Co. Aubin Av. (Paint)..A
MICH.—Grand Rapids
Alabastine Co. (Dry) X
MICH.—Sebewaing
Sebewaing Sandstone Brick
Co. (Brick) ....D
MO.—Kansas City
Continental Varnish & Color
Co. (Paint) ....D
MO.—Poplar Bluff
Mamolith Carbon Paint Co.
(Mineral) X
MO.—St. Louis
Appelgren, F. (Sugar) ..D
Mepham, Geo. S. & Klein,
2106 Lafayette Av. (Dry)
A
Mound City Paint & Color
Co. (Dry; Papan; Oil)..
AA
Vane-Calvert Paint Co., 823
Locust (Oil) ....B
N. J.—Jersey City
Woolsey Paint & Color Co.,
C. A. (Car; Coach; Distemper; Dry; Fresco;
Graining; Japan; Oil; Paper Makers') ....A
N. J.—Lincoln
Atlas Co. (Miners'; Refiners') ....B
N. J.—Newark
Cawley, Clark & Co., 278
Passaic (Paint) ....A

COLORS (Con.)

N. J.—West Hoboken
Palisade Mfg. Co. (Burnt
  Sugar) ....D
N. Y.—Albany
Hudson River Aniline Color
  Wks. (Aniline) ....B
N. Y.—Brooklyn
Ansbacher & Co., A. B., 310
  N. 7th (Paint) X
Dryden & Palmer (Food)..A
Moore & Co., Benj. (Car;
  Coach; Japan; Oil)...AA
N. Y.—Buffalo
McLennan Paint Co. (Dry;
  Oil; Mineral; Mortar)..A
Schoellkopf, Hartford &
  Hanna Co. (Aniline; Dye;
  Dry) ....AAA
N. Y.—Clinton
Clinton Metallic Paint Co.
  (Motor) C
N. Y.—Little Falls
Burrell & Co., D. H. (But-
  ter; Cheese) ....AAAA
Hansen's Laboratory, Chr.
  (Butter; Cheese) ......B
McKinnon, Robt (Bottlers)
                      AAA

N. Y.—Long Island City
Long Island Paint & Color
  Works ....AAAA
N. Y.—New Brighton
Muralo Co. (Fresco) ....A
New York City
Adler Color & Chemical
  Wks., 100 William (Agri-
  cultural; Artists' Dry;
  Decorators'; Distemper;
  Dry; Oil; Papermakers';
  Pulp; Ham Canvas; Scene
  Painters' Dry) ....A
American Bronze Powder
  Mfg. Co. (Dry) ....B
Ansbacher & Co., A. B.
  (Agricultural; Pulp).AAA
Bartels, Ernest C. (Aniline)
                         B
Berlin Aniline Wks., 213
  Water (Aniline) ....B
Billings, King & Co., 438
  Pearl (Paint) ....B
Binney & Smith Co., 81 Ful-
  ton (Dry) ....AAA
Bischoff & Co., C. (Sulfa-
  mine for Leather) .....A
Breidbach & Son, E. J. Mott
  Av. & 144th (Paint) ...B
Bush & Co., W. J. (Confec-
  tioners') ....AA
Cassella Color Co. (Aliza-
  rine; Aniline) ....A
Chaskel Chemical Co. (Ci-
  gar; Sugar; Vinegar; Bot-
  tlers) X
Childs & Co., Chas. M. (Oil)
                        AA
Chilton Paint Co. (Japan;
  Oil) ....B
Coulston & Co., J. W., 81
  West (Paint) ....A
Delisser & Co. (Bottlers) B
Devoe, F. W. & C. F. Rey-
  nolds Co., 103 Fulton
  (Agricultural; Artists'
  Dry; Tube; Car; Coach;
  Chromo-Photograph; Deco-
  rators'; Distemper; Dry;
  Fresco; Graining; Ham
  Canvas; Japan; Marble-
  izers'; Moist; Pulp; Oil;
  Scene Painters' Dry; Wax
  Flower) ....AAAA
Döggett, Stanley, 101 Beek-
  man (Dry) ....A
Emken Chemical Co. (Sugar)
                         B
Fox & Co., M. Ewing, E.
  136th & Ridge Av. (Dry)
                         D
Frank & Co., R. (Food) ..E
Fries Bros. (Food for Tan-
  ners, &c.) ....A
Gabriel & Schall, 305 Pearl
  Dry; Lithophine) C
Geisenheimer & Co., 189
  Front (Aniline) ....A
Gennert, G. (Photographic)
                         B
Holliday, Read & Sons,
  William & John (Aniline)
                         B
Gerstendorfer Bros. (Car;
  Coach) ....B
Hammell & Gillespie, 240

COLORS (Con.)

  Front (Importers) ....A
Heller & Merz Co., 22 Cliff
  (Aniline; Dye) ....AA
Hemingway & Co., 135 Front
  (Dry; Mineral) ....B
Herrman & Co., Morris, 255
  Pearl (Dry) ....B
Huber, J. M., 275 Water
  (Dry) ....B
Johns-Manville Co., H. W.
  (Car; Coach; Japan; Oil)
                      AAAA
Kalle & Co., 530 Canal (Ani-
  line; Dye) ....A
Keppelmann, A., 192 Fulton
  (Paint) ....AA
Keuffel & Esser Co., 127
  Fulton (Artists' Water)
                        AA
Klipstein & Co., A. (Inc.)
  (Aniline; Dye; Paper-
  makers') ....AA
Koechl & Co., V. (Food) ..A
Kohnstamm & Co., H., 87
  Park Pl. (Paint; Food)AA
Kuttroff & Pickhardt Co.
  (Alizarine-Aniline) ...A
Lavanburg, Fred. L., 100
  William (Dry; Pulp) ..A
Lieber & Co., H. (Food) ..C
Longman & Martinez, 207
  Pearl (Car; Coach; Deco-
  rators'; Distemper; Dry;
  Fresco; Graining; Japan;
  Oil) ....AAA
McKesson & Robbins
  (Sugar) ....AAAA
Maas & Waldstein (Food) A
Matthews, John (Firm of)
  (Fruit) ....AA
Mergentime & Lamm (Fruit)
                         D
Metz & Co., H. A. (Aniline)
                         A
Matheson & Co., Wm. J.
  178 Front (Aniline; Dye)
                         A
Messner Paint & Color
  Works, 383 Pearl .....A
Pfeiffer, Isaac, 174 Fulton
  (Paint) ....A
Pierce Co., F. O. 170 Fulton
  (Car; Coach; Decorators';
  Distemper; Graining) .A
Prince Mfg. Co., 71 Maiden
  Lane (Paint) ....B
Preservaline Mfg. Co., 41
  Warren (Food) ....AA
Reichard, F. A. (Food) ..A
Roessler & Hasslacher
  Chemical Co. (Ceramic)
                        AA
Sartorius & Co., A. (Artists
  Tube; Ceramic) ....AAA
Shultze Co. A. H., 198 W.
  Bway. (Bottlers; Confec-
  tioners') X
Sinclair & Valentine, 149
  Baxter ....B
Smith & Co., E. (Artists'
  Tube; Car; Coach) ....A
Smith & Co., J. Lee (Vene-
  tian Reds) ....AA
Tiemann & Co., D. F., 44
  Duane (Agricultural; Ar-
  tists' Dry; Car; Coach;
  Decorators'; Distemper;
  Dry; Fresco; Graining;
  Ham Canvas; Jap; Marble-
  izers'; Oil; Moist; Water;
  Papermakers'; Pulp) ..A
Toch Bros, 85 Pearl (Dry;
  Mortar) ....A
Tompkins, Calvin (Mortar)
                         B
Ullman Co., Sigmund (Dry)
                         A
Valentine & Co., 257 Bway.
  (Artists' Dry; Car; Coach;
  Distemper; Graining;
  Moist Water; Scene
  Painters' Dry; Wax
  Flower) ....AAAA
Whitaker, W. H., 245 Front
  (Importer) ....G
Williamson & Co., D. D.
  (Cider; Sugar) ....B
Wix & Co., Charles, 53
  Dey (Dry) ....A
Wood & Selick (Bottlers;
  Confectioners') ....A
Woods, Robt. L. (Sugar) .A
N. Y.—Potsdam
Thatcher Mfg. Co. (Butter)
                         A

COLORS (Con.)

N. Y.—Syracuse
Gowing, D. H. (Cheese) **O**

N. Y.—Troy
Connors Paint Mfg. Co., W.
(Distemper; Dry Paint;
Oil; Mortar) ....**A**

N. Y.—Utica
Jones, Frank L. (Butter;
Cheese) ....**C**

OHIO—Cincinnati
Alexander Co., M. H.
(Sugar) ....**A**
Ault & Wiborg Co., 7th &
Calvert (Dry) ....**AAAA**
Eagle White Lead Co., 1030
Bway. (Agricultural; Dry;
Ham Canvas) ....**AAAA**
Fries & Bros. Alex. ......**A**
Moser Co., Chas. (Artists'
Tube; Car; Coal; Ham
Canvas; Oil) ....**AA**

OHIO—Cleveland
Billings-Chapin Co., 37
Case Av. (Car; Coach;
Dry) ....**A**
Cleveland Color Co., Mason
& Belden (Lake) ......**B**
Forest City Paint & Var-
nish Co., Hamilton &
Kirkland (Coach; Oil) ..**B**
Garry Iron & Steel Co. (Dry
Paint; Mortar) **9**
Glenmore Color Works
(Paint) ....**A**
Sherwin & Williams Co., 100
Canal (Car; Coach;Oil)
........**AAAA**

OHIO—Dayton
Sachs-Pruden Ginger Ale Co.
(Confectioner') ....**D**

OHIO—Marietta
Hasty & Son Co., J. M
(Confectioners') ......**H**

PA.—Alburtis
Bass Paint Co. (Dry) .....**C**

PA.—Allegheny
Eagle Paint & Varnish
Works, 225 Grant Av.
(Oil) ....**B**

PA.—Easton
Williams & Co., C. K. (Dry,
Mortar; Papermakers') ..**A**

PA.—Johnstown
Cambria Paint & Color·
Works ....**B**

PA.—Philadelphia
Bird Co., F. J., 122 Arch
(Aniline) ....**H**
Clinton & Co. (Oil) ....**A**
French Co., S. H., 4th Cal-
lowhill (Mortar) ......**A**
Harrison Bros. & Co., 35th
and Gray's Ferry Rd.
(Decorators'; Distemper;
Dry) ....**AAAA**
Jewel Mfg. Co. (Food) ...**A**
Keller, Robert (Beer) ....**D**
Lang & Son, Wm. (Sugar) .**B**
Johnson & Co., Chas. E. 509
So. 10th (Dry) ....**AA**
Lewis & Bros., John H., 231
So. Front (Dry) ...**AAAA**
Lucas & Co., John, 322 Race
(Agricultural; Artists'
Dry Tube; Car; Coach;
Dry; Decorators'; Distem-
per; Fresco; Graining;
Ham Canvas; Japan; Mar-
bleizers'; Oil; Paper Ma-
kers' Pulp; Scene Paint-
ers' Dry) ....**AAA**
Nice, E. E., 272 S. 2d (Dis-
temper; Dry Paint; Japan;
Oil) ....**A**
Ottens, Henry H. (Bakers';
Confectioners') ....**C**
Putzel, Abert S. (Food) ..**F**
Savage, Mahlon L., "Frank-
fort" (Pulp) ....**A**
Twitchell Co., S. (Burnt
Sugar; Fruit) ....**A**
Weber & Co., F. (Artists'
Tube; Moist Water; Pas-
tel) ....**A**
Woodhouse, S. F., Unity &
Franklin, Fkd. (Paint) .**D**

PA.—Pittsburg
Lawrence & Co., W. W.
(Inc.) Car; Coach; Strip-
ing) ....**AA**

PA.—Reading
Reading Paint Mills (Coach;
Oil) ....**AA**
Wilhelm Co., A. (Car;
Coach; Graining; Oil) **AA**

COLORS (Con.)

PA.—Williamsport
National Paint Wks. (Oil)
........**B**
United States Paint Co.
(Oil) ....**F**

R. I.—Providence
Arnold, Hoffman & Co. **AA**
United States Gutta Percha
Paint Co., 34 Mathewson
Decorators'; Oil) ......**A**

TEXAS—Dallas
Star Mfg. Co. (Food) .....**G**

VT.—Burlington
Wells & Richardson Co.
(Butter; Aniline; Dye) **AA**

WIS.—Lake Mills
Fargo & Co., F. B. (Butter)
B

COLUMNS

See also Woodwork

CONN.—Bristol
Sessions Fdry. Co. (Bench,
Cast) ....**AAA**

CONN.—East Berlin
Berlin Iron Bridge Co., Br.
Am. Bridge Co. (Steel)
........**AAAA**

CONN.—Hartford
Hartford Woven Wire &
Mattress Co. (Extension)
........**A**

GA.—Augusta
Lombard Iron Wks. & Sup-
ply Co. (Iron) ....**A**

ILL.—Batavia
U. S. Wind Engine & Pump
Co. (Railroad Water) ...**A**

ILL.—Chicago
Amberg Granite Co., Mar-
quette Bldg. (Polished
Granite) ....**E**
Blake & Co., Chas. G., 720
Women's Temple (Pol-
ished Granite) ....**B**
Dearborn Foundry Co.
(Iron) ....**A**
Foster & Hosler, 415 Wabash
Av. (Polished Granite) **D**

IOWA—Clinton
Curtis Bros. & Co. (Porch)
AAA

KANS.—Emporia
Emporia Fdry. & Machine
Wks., (J. C. Jones & Son
Prop.) (Iron) ....**D**

KY.—Covington
Ohio Scroll & Lumber Co.
(Twisted Wood) ......**D**

KY.—Louisville
Shead Architectural Iron
Works (Iron) ....**B**

MAINE—Hallowell
Hallowell Granite Wks.
(Polished Granite) ...**AA**

MAINE.—Portland
Maine & New Hampshire
Granite Co. (Polished
Granite) ....**B**

MAINE—Red Beach
Main Red Granite Co. (Pol-
ished Granite, in Red,
Gray, Black, Green &
White) ....**B**

MAINE—Rockland
Bodwell Granite Co. (Pol-
ished Granite) ....**AA**

MASS.—Boston
Granite Railway Co., 150
Devonshire (Polished
Granite) ....**AA**
Jones Bros., 161 Summer
(Polished Granite) ...**AA**
Stearn's Lumber Co., A. L.
AA

MASS.—Quincy
Mitchell Granite Wks. (Pol-
ished Granite) ....**E**
Richards, Jno. R. (Polished
Granite) ....**E**
Smith & Co., Thos. W. (Pol-
ished Granite) ....**E**

MASS.—Rockport
Rockport Granite Co. (Polished Granite) ....**A**

MASS.—Worcester
Algonquin Red Slate Co.
(Slate) ....**B**
Norcross Bros. Co. (Polished
Granite) ....**AA**

MICH.—Detroit
Michigan Lubricator Co.
(Water) ....**A**

COLUMNS (Con.)

MICH.—Three Rivers
Sheffield Car Co. (Railroad
Water) ....AA
MINN.—Minneapolis
Gillette-Herzog Mfg. Co.
(Iron; Steel) X
MINN.—St. Cloud
St. Cloud Granite Wks. (Pol-
ished Granite) X
Simmers & Campbell
(Turned; Polished Gran-
ite) ....E
MO.—Kansas City
Kansas City Wire & Iron
Wks. (Iron) ....B
N. J.—Trenton
MacKenzie, Duncan (Iron) A
N. Y.—Brooklyn
Taylor & Co. (Inc.) (Iron)
D
N. Y.—Long Island City
White Granite Co., West Av.
(Polished Granite) .....F
New York City
Ashcroft Mfg. Co. (Combi-
nation Water) ....A
Booth Bros. & Hurricane
Isle Granite Co., 207
Bway. (Polished Granite)
A
Cornell, J. B. & J. M.
(Bench; Cast; Iron) ..AA
Dimond, Thomas (Iron) ..A
Jackson Architectural Iron
Wks. (Iron) ....AA
Leopold & Co., Jos., 18
Bway. (Polished Granite)
C
Milford Pink Granite Co.,
1133 Bway. (Polished
Granite) X
N. Y.—Oswego
Kitts Mfg. Co. (Water) F
OHIO—Cincinnati
Laidlaw-Dunn-Gordon & Co.,
Br. Intn. Steam Pump Co.,
N. Y. City (Railroad
Water) ....AAAA
OHIO—Kenton
Champion Iron Co. (Iron)
AA
OHIO—Mansfield
Mansfield Mach. Wks.
(Iron) X
PA.—Bangor
American Slate Co. (Slate)
AA
PA.—East Bangor
East Bangor Consolidated
Slate Co. (Slate) ....AA
PA.—Harrisburg
Hickok Mfg. Co., W. O.
(Bench; Cast) ....AA
PA.—Middletown
American Tube & Iron Co.
(Pump) ....AAAA
PA.—Philadelphia
Novelty Iron Wks. (Iron) X
Phoenix Bridge Co. (Iron) A
PA.—Pittsburg
Best, Fox & Co. (Water) A
Riter-Conley Mfg. Co.
(Lattice) ....AAA
PA.—Wilkesbarre
Vulcan Iron Wks. (Iron;
Shaft) ....AAAA
PA.—York
Variety Iron Wks. (G. Im-
ser's Sons) (Iron) ......A
R. I.—Providence
Brown & Sharpe Mfg. Co.
(Bench; Cast) .....AAAA
R. I.—Waverly
New England Granite Wks.
(Polished Granite) ...AA
TENN.—Memphis
Chickasaw Iron Wks.
(Iron) ....A
VT.—Barre
McDonald & Buchan (Pol-
ished Granite) ....D
Wells, Lamson & Co. (Pol-
ished Granite) C
VT.—Hydeville
Hydeville Marbleized Slate
Mantel Co. (Slate) .....D
VT.—Woodbury
Woodbury Granite Co. (Pol-
ished Granite) C

COMBERS

MASS.—Taunton
Mason Machine Wks. (Cot-
ton) ....AA

COMBERS (Con.)

MASS.—Whitinsville
Whitin Machine Wks. (Cot-
ton) ....AAAA

COMBS

**See Celluloid Goods; Jew-
elry; Tortoise Shell Goods;
Horn Goods, etc.)**

CONN.—Bridgeport
Hotchkiss, Edward S. (Cur-
ry) ....A
CONN.—Danielson
Larkin & Wood (Slasher) G
CONN.—Deep River
Pratt, Reed & Co. (Horn;
Ivory) ....AA
CONN.—New Britain
Landers, Trary & Clark
(Curry; Mane) ......AAA
North & Judd Mfg. Co.
(Mane) ....AA
CONN.—New Haven
Fitch Co., W. & E. T.
(Curry) ....A
CONN.—Plainville
Hills, Edwin (Curry) .....A
CONN.—Southington
Peck, Stow & Wilcox Co.
(Curry) ....AAAA
Southington Cutlery Co.
(Curry) ....AA
CONN.—Wallingford
Wallace & Sons, Mfg. Co.
(Celluloid, Pocket; Shell)
AAAA
ILL.—Freeport
Stover Mfg. Co. (Curry) AA
ILL.—Lemont
Illinois Pure Aluminum Co.
(Metal; Aluminum) ...X
MASS.—Attleboro
Allen Smith & Thurston Co.
(Imitation Shell) X
MASS.—Boston
Bailey & Co., C. J. (Rubber)
B
Burton & Co., A. & E. (Cur-
ry) ....B
Leigh, E. A., Mason Bldg.
(Wool; Cotton) ....B
Lowe, Stephen C., 186 Dev-
onshire (Cotton) ......B
Riley & Co., C. E. 65 Frank-
lin (Wool) ....A
Stoddard, Haserick, Rich-
ards & Co., 152 Congress
(Wool; Cotton) ....B
MASS.—Fall River
McGregor & Sons (Slasher)
F
Sylvester & Co., C. F.
(Weavers') ....E
MASS.—Hopedale
Draper Co. (Wool) ..AAAA
MASS.—Lawrence
Austin & Co., M. E. (Wool)
D
MASS.—Leominster
Blodgett & Co., B. F.
(Celluloid) C
Earl & Co., W. D. (Horn) C
Kingman Co., E. B. (Cellu-
loid; Horn; Ivory) C
MASS.—Lowell
Bagshaw, W. H. (Wool) ..B
Stott, Samuel E. & T.
(Wool) X
MASS.—North Attleboro
Sadler Bros. (Celluloid) ..X
MASS.—Northboro
Farwell & Co., Walter M.
(Horn; Pocket) X
MASS.—Taunton
Mason Machine Works (Cot-
ton) ....AA
MASS.—Whitinsville
Whiton Machine Works
(Cotton) ....AAAA
MASS.—Worcester
Cleveland Machine Wks.
(Doffer) ....A
Crompton & Knowles Loom
Wks. (Wool) .....AAAA
N. J.—Newark
Celluloid Co. (Celluloid;
Pocket) ....B
Crabb & Co., Wm. (Wool;
Metal) ....A
Peters Harness & Saddlery
Co. (Curry) C
N. Y.—Binghamton
Noyes & Co., Jos. P. (Horn;
Ivory) ....B

258

COMBS (Con.)
N. Y.—Brooklyn
Adams & Co., J. J., 122 Greenpoint Av. (Graining) ....A
Eddy & Co., Geo. M. (Rubber) ....A
New York Stamping Co. (Curry) ....A
N. Y.—Interlaken
Coverts Saddlery Wks. (Mane; Tail) ....C'
New York City
American Hard Rubber Co. (Hard Rubber) ....AAAA
Borgfelt & Co., Geo., 48 W. 4th (Rubber) ......AAAA
Goodyear India Rubber Glove Mfg. Co., 503 Bway. (Rubber) ....AAAA
Goodyear Rubber Co. (Rubber Curry) ....AAAA
Grote & Co., F. (Tortoise Shell) ....D
Hanlon & Goodman (Graining) ....A
Hodgman Rubber Co. (Rubber) ....AA
Lalance & Grosjean Mfg. Co. (Curry) ....AAAA
Mechanical Rubber Co. (Rubber) ....A
Medford Fancy Goods Co. 75 Duane (Dog) ....E
Reilley Bros. (Graining) ..D
Sargent & Co. (Mane; Tail) ....AAAA
Sloan & Co. (Side) ......B
Smith & Son, J. Finley (Graining) ....B
N. Y.—Watervliet
Covert Mfg. Co. (Curry) ..A
N. C.—Charlotte
Southern Card Clothing & Reed Co. (Slasher) .....E
OHIO—Akron
Akron Rubber Wks. (Rubber) ....AAAA
OHIO—Canton
Gibbs Mfg. Co. (Curry) A
Kohler & Co., F. E. (Curry) B
PA.—Bloomsburg
Richards Mfg. Co. (Curry) B
PA.—Kane
Holgate Bros. Co. (Wooden Curry) ....B
PA.—Philadelphia
Barker, James, Sixth & Cayuga (Doffer) ....A
Bradford Wool Comb Co., 2630 Mascher (Wool) ..X
Fitzgerald Loom Reed Co., N. 2nd & Diamond (Slasher) X
Hood, R. H., 1424 Callowhill (Wool) ....E
Jefferson & Bro., Edw., 127 S. 2nd. (Wool) ....D
Philadelphia Textile Mchry. Co., Hancock & Somerset (Doffer; Striking) ..AA
Smith Woolen Mach. Co., Jas. (Doffer) ....AA
R. I.—Providence
American Supply Co. (Slasher) ....AA
Foster & Bros. Co., Theo. W. (Silver) ....AA
Gowdy Reed & Harness Mfg. Co., J. A. (Slasher) ..F
Miller, Wm. (Wool) .....F
Providence Machine Co. (Cotton; Doffer) ....AA
Textile Finishing Mchry. Co., 17 Exch. Pl. (Slasher) ....AAA
Townsend, Thomas, 157 Orange (Wool) ....E
WIS.—Two Rivers
Aluminum Mfg. Co. (Metal) ....A

COMFORTERS
See Bedding

COMMODES
See also Furniture

ILL.—Chicago
Chicago Chair & Wheel Co. ....A
IND.—Indianapolis
Udell Wks. ....A

COMMODES (Con.)
MASS.—Boston
Davenport, Albert H....AA
MICH.—Muskegon
Heap, Wm. ....G
MO.—St. Louis
Logeman Chair Mfg. Co., F. H. ....AA
Scarritt-Comstock Furniture Co. ....A
N. Y.—Brooklyn
Cooper & McKee ....A
New York City
Mace & Co., L. H. ......B
Sargent Co., Geo. F. (Sanitary) X
OHIO—Cincinnati
Ballman Cabinet Co. C
PA.—Philadelphia
Hale & Kilburn Mfg. Co. ....AAAA
McCracken & Hall ......A
WIS.—Milwaukee
Kipp & Co., B. A. ......B
WIS.—Oshkosh
Bucktaff-Edwards Co. ..AA
WIS.—Sheboygan
Crocker Chair Co. ....AAA

COMMUTATORS
ILL.—Chicago
Western Electric Co. (Mercury) ....AAAA
IND.—Ft. Wayne
Ft. Wayne Electric Wks. (Electric) ....AAA
IND.—South Bend
Miller-Knoblock Elect. Mfg. Co. (Electric) X
New York City
Burnett & Co., J. H., 20 Park Pl. (Mercury) ..A
N. Y.—Utica
Utica Electrical Mfg. & Supply Co. X
OHIO—Cleveland
Homer & Co.. F. E. (Generation; Special) ....D
PA.—North East
Eureka Tempered Copper Co. Electric; Assembled; Refilled) ....B
PA.—Pittsburg
Simonds Mfg. Co. (Electric) B
Supply Mfg. Co. (Electric) X
VA.—Richmond
Richmond Electrical Wks. A

COMPASSES
See also Dividers

CONN.—Bridgeport
Smith & Egge Mfg. Co. (Pencil) ....A
CONN.—New Haven
Schollhorn, Wm. (Pencil) B
CONN.—Southington
Peck, Stow & Wilcox Co. (Pencil) ....AAAA
ILL.—Chicago
Martin Co.. Edw. P. C
MASS.—Athol
Athol Machine Co. ......B
Starrett Co., L. S. ......A
MASS.—Boston
Thaxter & Son, S., 125 State ....B
MASS.—Fitchburg
Sawyer Tool Co. C
MASS.—Springfield
Bemis & Call Hardware & Tool Co. ....A
N. J.—Newark
Osborne & Co., C. S......B
N. Y.—Buffalo
West Mfg. Co. ....D
New York City
Eagle Pencil Co. (Pencil) AAA
Faber, Eberhard (Pencil) AAA
Graham & Co., J. H., 113 Chambers ....AA
Ingersoll & Bro., R. H., 51 Maiden Lane (Pencil) A
Keuffel & Esser Co., 127 Fulton ....AAAA
McAllister, T. H. (Boat; Pocket) ....B
Merrill's Sons, Robt.

COMPASSES (*Con.*)
(Ships'; Sperit; Tell Tale)

Smith & Hemenway .....D
N. Y.—Troy
Gurley, W. & L. E. (Pocket;
 Solar; Surveyors'; Ver-
 nier) ....AA
PA.—Philadelphia
Queen & Co. (Inc.) (Survey-
 ors') ....AA
Riggs & Bro., 310 Market
 (Marine) ....B
Young & Sons (Pocket; So-
 lar; Surveyors') ......B
R. I.—Providence
Brown & Sharpe Mfg. Co.
 AAAA

COMPOSITION

ILL.—Chicago
Armour Glue Wks. (Book-
 binders' Flexible) .AAAA
MASS.—Boston
Golding & Co. (Printers'
 Roller) ....B
Osgood & Co., J. H. (Prin-
 ters' Roller) X
Wild & Stevens (Printers'
 Roller) ....B
New York City
Gardiner, George N. (Anti-
 Corrosive) ....F
OHIO—Cincinnati .
Van Bibber Roller Co.
 (Printers' Roller) .....D
PA.—Philadelphia
Godfrey & Co. (Printers'
 Roller) ....F

COMPOUND

N. J.—Trenton .
Home Rubber Co. (Splicing)
 AA

COMPOUNDS

CONN.—New Haven
Standard Supply Co. (Pla-
 ters' Cleansing) ....H
DEL.—Wilmington
American Vulcanized Fibre
 Co. ....AAAA
ILL.—Chicago
Frazer Lubricator Co.
 (Lubricator) ....AA
Stuart & Co., D. A. (Inc.)
 (Boiler; Lubricating) ..C
MASS.—Boston
Bowdlear & Co., W. H.
 (Insulating) ....B
India Alkali Wks. (Car
 Cleansing) C
Macallan Co., W. T. C., 338
 Congress (Insulating) AA
Massachusetts Chemical Co.,
 200 Sumner (Insulating;
 Armature) ....A
MASS.—New Bedford
Nye, Wm. F. (Lubricating)
 A
MICH.—Detroit
Stevens, F. B. (Buffing) A
MO.—St. Louis
Aquart, A. D., Chemical
 Bldg. (Car Cleansing) F
N. J.—Boonton .
Loanto Hard Rubber Co.
 (Insulating) ....B
N. J.—Jersey City
Dixon Crucible Co., Jos.
 (Graphite; Pipe Joint)
 AAA
Smooth-On Mfg. Co. (Iron)
 A
N. J.—Newark
Duranoid Mfg. Co. (Com-
 position Insulating) ....B
N. J.—Paterson
Welding Compound Co.
 (Welding) ....E
N. Y.—Binghamton
Binghamton Oil Refining
 Co. (Lubricating) ......A
N. Y.—Brooklyn
Electrose Mfg. Co., 127 N.
 10th (Insulating) .....AA
Miller Co., Wm. P. (Lubri-
 cator) ....D
New York City
Bishop Gutta Percha Co.
 (Insulating) ....B
Cooks Sons, Adam (Lubri-
 cating) ....B

COMPOUNDS (*Con*)
De Ronde Co., Frank S., 46
 Cliff (Car Cleansing) ..B
Ilsley, Doubleday & Co.
 (Lubricating) ....B
Johns-Manville Co., H. W.
 (Insulating) ....AAAA
Kalbfleisch Co., Franklin H.
 (Boiler) ....AA
New York Insulated Wire
 Co. (Splicing) ....D
Pulver & Sons, Peter (Lubri-
 cating) ....D
Standard Paint Co. (Insula-
 ting) ....A
Williamson & Co., D. D.
 (Boiler) ....B
OHIO—Cincinnati
Modoc Soap Co. (Car
 Cleansing) ....D
Obermayer Co., S. (Core)
 AA
OHIO—Cleveland
Reliance Oil & Grease Co.
 (Boiler; Lubricating) ..X
Smith Fdy. Supply Co., J. D.
 (Core) ....D
OHIO—Columbus
Ironsides Co. (Insulating) C
OHIO—Toledo
National Cement & Rubber
 Mfg. Co. (Lubricating) C
OHIO—Troy
Ohio Electric Specialty Mfg.
 Co. (Lubricating) ......G
PA.—Easton
World Refining Co. (Lubri-
 cating) X
PA.—Franklin
Galena Signal Oil Co.
 (Lubricating) .....AAAA
PA.—Philadelphia
Keystone Lubricating Co.
 (Lubricating) X
Lord Co., Geo. W. (Boiler)
 B
Paxon Co., J. W. (Core) AA
Stevenson Bros. & Co.
 (Boiler) ....B
R. I.—Bristol
National India Rubber Co.
 (Insulating) ....AAAA
R. I.—Providence
American Oil Co. (Lubri-
 cating) ....B
W. VA.—Parkersburg
Upson's Oil & Soap Co.
 (Lubricating) ....B
WIS.—Milwaukee
Delaney Oil & Lubricant Co.
 (Boiler) X
WIS.—Racine
Racine Malleable & Wrought
 Iron Co. (Buffing) ....A

COMPRESSES

ALA.—Birmingham
Continental Gin Co. (Cotton)
 AAAA
GA.—Elberton
Elberton Cotton & Com-
 press Co. (Cotton) .....B
LA.—Minden
Webb Press Co. (Cotton) A
New York City
Planters Compress Co.
 (Cotton) ....B
PA.—Chester
Vulcan Works (Cotton) ...B
PA.—Reading
Reading Iron Co. (Cotton)
 AAAA
TEXAS—Houston
Dickson Car Wheel Co.
 (Cotton) ....A

COMPRESSORS

CAL.—San Francisco
Doble & Co., Abner (Air) A
Garratt & Co., W. T. (Inc.)
 (Air) ....AA
Risdon Iron & Locomotive
 Wks. (Air) ....AAA
CONN.—South Norwalk
Norwalk Iron Wks. Co.
 (Gas; Air) ....AA
ILL.—Aurora
American Well Works
 (Gas; Air) ....AA
ILL.—Chicago
Allis-Chalmers Co. (Ammo-
 nia; Gas) ....AAAA
Burton & Son, A. G. (Air) D
Chicago Pneumatic Tool Co.

COMPRESSORS (Con.)
Fisher Bldg. (Gas) .AAAA
Crane Co. (Air) .....AAAA
Fairbanks, Morse & Co.,
Franklin & Monroe (Gas-
oline) ....AAAA
Kroeschell Bros. Co., 55
Erie (Gas) ....B
Murphy & Co., Christopher,
204 Dearborn (Gas; Gaso-
line) C
IND.—Indianapolis
Chandler & Taylor Co. (Air)
AA
MASS.—Boston
Blanchard Machine Co. (Air)
D
MASS.—Springfield
Emory Mfg. Co., P. P.
(Air) C
MICH.—Detroit
Northern Engineering Wks.
(Air) ....A
MICH.—Saginaw
Wickes Bros. (Ammonia)AA
MINN.—Minneapolis
Minneapolis Steel & Machy.
Co. (Air).............A
MO.—Kansas City
Weber Gas & Gasoline En-
gine Co. (Air) ....B
MO.—St. Louis
Curtis & Co. (Air) .....A
General Compressed Air
House-Cleaning Co., 3933
Olive (Portable Air) ..X
St. Louis Steam Engine Co.
(Air) ....E
MO.—Springfield
Crescent Iron Wks. (Air;
Ammonia) X
N. J.—Dover
Morris County Machine &
Iron Co. (Air) ....B
N. J.—Elizabeth
Moore & Sons Co., Samuel L.
(Air) ....AA
N. J.—Smithville
Smith Machine Co., H. B.
(Air) ....A
N. Y.—Brooklyn
Bliss Co., E. W. (Air)
AAAA
Guild & Garrison, Kent Av.
cor. S. 10th (Ammonia;
Air) ....AA
New York City
American Air Compressor
Wks., 26 Cortlandt (Air;
Gas) X
Blake Mfg. Co., Geo. F. (Br.
Int. Steam Pump Co.)
(Air) ....AAAA
Clayton Air Compressor
Wks., 116 Liberty (Gas;
Carbonic Acid Gas; Air) B
Ingersoll-Sergeant Drill Co.,
26 Cortland (Corliss; Gas;
Air) ....AAAA
McKiernan Drill Co., 120
Liberty (Air) ....B
Niles-Bement-Bond Co., 136
Liberty (Air) .....AAAA
Pedrick & Ayer Co., 87 Lib-
erty (Air) ....A
Rand Drill Co., 128 Bway.
(Gas; Air) ....A
N. Y.—Rochester
Clark Novelty Co. (Air) D
N. Y.—Schenectady
General Electric Co. (Air)
AAAA
N. Y.—Troy
Hammett, M. C. (Air; Au-
tomatic Air) ....D
OHIO—Cincinnati
Laidlaw-Dunn-Gordon Co.
(Air; Gas) ....AAAA
Lane & Bodley Co., John &
Water (Air; Gas.) .....A
McGowan Co. John H. (Air)
A
Triumph Ice Mach. Co., 610
Baymiller (Ammonia) ..A
OHIO—Cleveland
Cleveland Faucet Co. (Air)
AA
OHIO—Columbus
Columbus Machine Co. (Gas;
Gasoline) ....A
Rarig Engineering Co. (Air)
A
OHIO—Mansfield
Barnes Mfg. Co. (Air) ...B
PA.—Bradford
Blaisdell Mfg. Co. (Air;

COMPRESSORS (Con.)
Gas.) ....A
Gray & Blaisdell Co. (Gas.)
X
PA.—Philadelphia
Cox & Sons Co. (Air) .....B
Eynon-Evans Mfg. Co., 1507
Clearfield (Air) ....B
Philadelphia Engineering
Wks. (Air) ....A
PA.—Pittsburg
Baird Machinery Co., U.
(Portable; Air) ....A
Hall Steam Pump Co. (Br.
Allegheny) (Air) ......A
PA.—Reading
Reading Iron Co. (Air)
AAAA
PA.—Scottdale
Kenney & Co. (Air) ......A
PA.—York
Dempwolf & Co., C. H.
(Air) ....B
R. I.—Providence
Builders' Iron Fdry. (Air)
AA
WIS.—Milwaukee
Allis-Chalmers Co. (Ammo-
nia; Air) ....AAAA
Filer & Stowell Co., Becher
cor. Ziemer (Gas; Air)
AAA
Nordberg Mfg. Co. (Gas.)
AA

COMPTO-METERS
ILL.—Chicago
Felt & Tarrant Mfg. Co., 56
Illinois ....B

CONCENTRA-TORS
CAL.—San Francisco
Hendy Machine Co. Wks. J.
(Ore) ....AA
COLO.—Denver
Stearns-Rogers Mfg. Co.
(Ore) ....A
ILL.—Chicago
Gates Iron Wks. (Allis-Chal-
mers N. Y. City) (Ore)
AAAA
KANS.—Fort Scott
Fort Scott Fdy. & Mach. Co.
(C. Eller) (Ore) ....H
N. J.—Garwood
Beckley & Co. (Ore) .....D
OHIO—Akron
Webster, Camp & Lane
Mach. Co. (Ore) ....A
WIS.—Milwaukee
Allis-Chalmers Co. (Ore)
AAAA

CONDENSERS
See also Feeders & Con-
densers

CONN.—Elmwood
Whitlock Coil Pipe Co.
(Steam Engine) ....B
GA.—Atlanta
Wotton Electric & Mfg. Co.
(Electric; Electric Tele-
phone) ....B
ILL.—Batavia
Sperry & Co., D. R. (Br.
North Aurora, Ill.) (Amal-
gam) C
ILL.—Chicago
Allis-Chalmers Co., Br. N.
Y. City (Steam) AAAA
Baragwanath & Son, Wm.,
52 W. Division (Steam) X
Fairbanks, Morse & Co.,
Franklin & Monroe
(Steam) ....AAAA
Kellogg Switchboard & Sup-
ply Co., 225 S. Green
(Electric Telephone) AA
Swedish-American Telephone
Co., 71 W. Jackson Boul.
(Electric Telephone) ..A
Western Electric Co., 259 S.
Clinton (Electric) ...AAAA
Wolf Co., Fred. A., 139 Rees
(Ammonia) ....AAA
IND.—Fort Wayne
Kerr-Murray Mfg. Co. (Gas)
A

CONDENSERS (Con.)

IND.—Lafayette
Sterling Electric Co. (Electric Telephone) ....A
IND.—Muncie
Warner Electric Co. (Electric) C
IOWA—Burlington
Murray Iron Wks. (Steam Engine) ....A
KANS.—Fort Scott
Fort Scott Fdy. & Mach. Co. (C. Eller) ....H
KY.—Louisville
National Fdy. & Mach. Co. (Steam) ....B
MD.—Baltimore
Bartlett, Hayward & Co. (Gas) ....AAA
MASS.—Fitchburg
Blake Steam Pump Co., W. H. (Independent Steam; Air) ....E
MASS.—Springfield
Springfield Elev. & Pump Co. (Steam) ....B
MASS.—Taunton
Taunton Locomotive Mfg. Co. (Steam) ....AA
MASS.—Waltham
Davis & Farnum Mfg. Co. (Gas Works) ....B
MASS.—Warren
Warren Steam Pump Co. (Steam) ....A
MASS.—Worcester
American Card Clothing Co. (Apron; Roll) ......AAA
MICH.—Detroit
Great Lake Engineering Works (Steam) ....A
MICH.—Manistee
Manistee Iron Works Co. (Steam Engine) ....B
MINN.—Minneapolis
Minneapolis Steel & Mchy. Co. (Steam) ....A
Twin City Iron Works (Br. Minn. Steel & Mchy. Co.) (Steam Engine) ......A
N. J.—Garwood
Beekley & Son, A. J. (Br. N. Y. City) (Amalgam).D
N. J.—Jersey City
Conover Mfg. Co., Princeton Av. (Steam Jet) ......D
Flynn, W. S., 74 Hudson (Steam) ....D
N. J.—Trenton
Throop Sons' Co., John E. (Steam) ....A
N. Y.—Brooklyn
Continental Iron Works (Steam Engine) ....A
Guild & Garrison (Steam Engine) ....AA
N. Y.—Buffalo
Stewart Heater Co. (Steam) D

New York City
Alberger Condenser Co., 95 Liberty (Barometric; Surface; Steam Jet; Self-Closing, &c.) X
Bunnell & Co., J. H., 20 Park Pl. (Electric) ....A
Colwell, A. W. ....A
Deeley & Co., Robt. ......A
Floyd's Sons, James R. (Gas Works) ....A
Foote, Pearson & Co., 82 Fulton (Eleitric) ......D
International Steam Pump Co., 114 Liberty (Steam) AAAA
Isbell-Porter Co., 245 B'way (Gas) ....AA
Kelley & Son, B. F., 91 Liberty (Steam) ......B
Wheeler Condenser & Engineering Co. 120 Liberty (Steam; Surface) ......A
Willyoung, Elmer G., 11 Frankfort (Electric) ....F
Worthington Pumping Engine Co. (Br. Internatl. Steam Pump Co.) (Steam Engine) ....AAAA
N. Y.—North Tonawanda
Buffalo Steam Pump Co. (Steam; Jet; Surface, &c.) ....A
N. Y.—Rochester
Stromberg - Carlson Tele-

CONDENSERS (Con.)

phone Mfg. Co. (Electric Telephone) ....AAA
N. Y.—Rome
Doyle, W. J. (Ale) ......E
N. Y.—Schenectady
General Electric Co. (Electric) ....AAAA
OHIO—Cincinnati
Electric Railway Equipment Co. (Electric) ....A
Laidlaw-Dunn-Gordon Co. (Br. Int. Steam Pump Co., N. Y. City) (Jet; Combined; Independent) AAAA
McGowan Co., John H. (Steam) ....A
Stacey Mfg. Co., 239 Mill (Gas) ....A
Triumph Ice Mach. Co., 610 Baymiller (Ice Machine) A
Tudor Boiler Mfg. Co. (Steam) ....B
OHIO—Cleveland
Snider-Hughes Co. (Steam) B
OHIO—Mt. Vernon
Cooper Co., C. & G. (Steam, for large plants) .....AA
OHIO—Upper Sandusky
National Steam Pump Co. (Steam) C
OHIO—Youngstown
Pollock Co., W. B. (Steam) B
OHIO—Zanesville
Griffith & Wedge Co. (Amalgam) ....A
PA.—Bridgeport
Wilkinson Mfg. Co. (Steam) C
PA.—Carbondale
Carbondale Machine Co. (Ammonia) ....AA
PA.—Harrisburg
Harrisburg Pipe & Pipe Bending Co. (Ammonia) AA
PA.—Philadelphia
Barr Pumping Engine Co. (Steam) ....A
Biddle, James G. (Electric; Electric Telephone) C
Electro Dynamic Co. of Phila. (Electric) ......A
Eynon-Evans Mfg. Co. (Steam) ....B
Furbush & Son Mach Co., C. A. (Apron; Roll) ....A
Philadelphia Engineering Works (& Air Pumps; Independent) ....A
Queen & Co., 1010 Chestnut (Electric) ....AA
Schutte & Co., L., 1251 N. 12th (Steam) X
Shaw, Thomas, 1419 Robinson (Steam Engine)....A
Southwark Fdy. & Mach. Co. (Steam) ....AAA
Wood & Co., R. D. (Gas; Steam) ....AAAA
PA.—Pittsburg
Epping-Carpenter Co. (Ammonia) ....A
Riter - Conley Mfg. Co. (Steam Engine) .....AAA
PA.—Warren
Struthers, Wells & Co. (Oil Refinery) ....AA
WIS.—Milwaukee
Allis-Chalmers Co. (& Air Pumps, Combined; Air Pumps, Independent) AAAA
Filer & Stowell Co. (Ltd.) (Jet; Steam; Air Pumps, Combined; Independent) AAA
Nordberg Mfg. Co. (Steam) AA

CONDIMENTS & RELISHES

ARK.—Ft. Smith
Okla. Vinegar Co. (Catsup; Mustard; Sauces) C
ARK.—Springdale
Springdale Canning Co. (Catsup) ....F

CONDIMENTS &C.

CAL.—Los Angeles
Pioneer Green Chili Packing Co. (Sauces) ....A
CAL.—Reedsburg
Ramsey & Co., S. (Horse Radish) ....B
CAL.—San Francisco
Burr & Co., C. C. (Prepared Mustard) ....A
California Packing Co. (Celery Salt; Salad Dressing; Sauces) ....A
Fisher Packing Co., 509 Commercial (Catsup; Mustard; Sauces) C
Ghiradelli & Co. (Cake; Flour Mustard) ......AA
Loeffler, John, 422 5th (Horse Radish; Salad Dressing; Sauces) C
Pacific Preserve Co., 1200 Battery (Catsup) ......E
Pacific Vinegar & Pickle Works. 122 Davis (Catsup; Sauces; Horse Radish; Salad Dressing; Prepared Mustard) ......A
Phila. Mfg. Co., 431 7th (Catsup; Prepared Mustard; Horse Radish; Sauces) C
Sherwood & Sherwood (Prepared Mustard Agts.) ....AAA
South End Pickle Works (Sauces) C
COLO.—Denver
Beebe-Cravel Pickle Co. (Sauces) C
Cannon, W. F. (Sauces) ..D
COLO.—Longmont
Empson Packing Co. (Catsup; Sauces) ....A
CONN.—Guilford
Knowles-Lombard Co. (Catsup) ....D
CONN.—Hartford
Fitzgerald, R. N. (Sauces) ....B
CONN.—New Haven
Doyle Co., J. T. (Catsup) .D
CONN.—Windsor
Ellsworth & Filley (Catsup) ....A
D. C.—Washington
Mundell Hygeia Relish Co. ....B
GA.—Atlanta
Cold Springs Packing Co. (Sauces) ....D
ILL.—Bloomington
Bloomington Cider & Vinegar Co. C
ILL.—Chicago
Atwood & Steele (Celery Salt; Salad Dressing)..C
Bause Bros., 799 W. 14th (Catsup) ....E
Claussen & Sons. C. F.., W. Av. Boul. & 52d (Catsup; Mustard) ....A
Darby, B. L., 681 W. Lake (Catsup) ....F
Dickinson Co., A. (Mustard) ....AA
Dress & Co., P. J. (Horse Radish) ....D
Huss-Edler Preserve Co.. 75 W. Kinzie (Catsup; Salad Dressing; Horse Radish; "Mustomat"; Mustard).B
My Wife's Salad Dressing Co ....D
Paprica Sauce Mfg. Co. (Sauces) ....B
Puhl-Webb Co., 119 W. Randolph (Catsup; Salad Dressing; Sauces; Mustard) C
Reid, Murdock & Co., Lake & Market (Salad Dressing) ....AAAA
Sherman Bros. & Co. (Mustard) ....A
Wichert Co., H.. 1205 S. Paulina (Catsup; Mustard) C
ILL.— East St. Louis
Triumph Sauce & Pickle Co. (Catsup) X
ILL.—Peoria
Central City Pickle Co.

CONDIMENTS &C.

(Sauces; Mustard) ....D
ILL.—Petersburg
Va. Canning Co. (Catsup).D
ILL.—Woodstock
Dingee, Squire Co. (Sauces) ....AA
IND.—Brookville
Brookville Mfg. Co. (Catsup) ....B
IND.—Churubusco
Gandy & Co., O. (Catsup).A
IND.—Greenwood
Polk Co., J. T. (Catsup).AA
IND.—Indianapolis
Columbia Conserve Co.. S. Meridian & Belt Av. (Catsup; Salad Dressing) ...A
Faulkner-Webb Co. (Sauces) ....D
Huffman Packing Co. (Sauces) C
Van Camp Packing Co.. 600 Ky. Av. (Catsup; Sauces) ....AA
IND.—Lafayette
Heinz Co. (Horse Radish; Prep. Mustard) ....A
IND.—Michigan City
Old English Chutney Works ....E
IOWA—Davenport
Davenport Vinegar & Pickle Works (Sauces) ......D
IOWA—Dubuque
Toussant-Trexler Company (Sauces) ....D
IOWA—Glenwood
New Glenwood Canning Co. (Catsup) C
IOWA—Keokuk
Keokuk Canning Co. (Catsup; Sauces) ....A
Keokuk Pickle Co. (Catsup; Mustard; Sauces) ....B
KY.—Louisville
Gast & Crofts, 1004 W. Main (Catsup; Sauces).B
Hirsch Bros. & Co., 700 14th (Catsup; Sauces) .....A
Price & Lucas Cider & Vinegar Co. (Catsup; Mustard; Sauces) ....A
Thornton & Co.. R. J. (Prepared Mustard) ....A
KY.—Owensboro
Blue Grass Canning Co. (Catsup) ....B
LA.—New Iberia
McIlhenny's Sons, E. (Tobasco Sauce) ....B
LA.—New Orleans
Erath, E. C. (Sauces)....D
King & Saint, 210 St. Peters (Sauces) ....D
MAINE—Portland
Pettingill Co.. E. D. (Catsup; Mustard; Horse Radish) ....B
MD.—Baltimore
Gibbs Preserving Co., 2305 Boston (Catsup) .....AA
McCormick & Co. (Mustard) C
Parrish Bros. (Mustard)..B
Van Lill Preserving Co.. 108 Concord (Catsup; Mustard; Sauces) ....B
MASS.—Boston
Bell Co.. W. G. (Sauces)..D
Halford Sauce Co. (Sauces) C
Sherman Mfg. Co. (Sauces) C
Skilton, Foote & Co. (Horse Radish; Salad Dressing; Sauces) ....A
Slade Co.. D. & L. (Celery Salt; Prep. Mustard)..A
Stickney & Poore Spice Co. (Celery Salt; Prepared Mustard) ....AA
MASS.—Chelsea
Slade Co.. D. & L. (Celery Salt; Prep. Mustard)..A
MASS.—Springfield
Castle, W. A. (Salad Dressing) ....B
MICH.—Detroit
Horton-Cato Mfg. Co. (Salad Dressing; Sauces) .....D
Johnson, T. H. (Horse Radish) ....D

Phelps, Brace & Co.
(Sauces) ....AA
Vaughn Co., W. W. (Catsup; Mustard; Sauces)..B
Williams Bros. Co. (Catsup; Mustard) ....A

MICH.—Marshall
Scribner Co., A. E. (Catsup; Mustard) ....D

MICH.—Munroe
Floral City Preserving Co. (Catsup) ....D

MICH.—Saginaw
U. S. Horse Radish Co....D

MICH.—South Haven
Dunkley Co. (Celery Salt; Celery Mustard) ......B

MICH.—West Bay City
Beubel Pickling & Canning Co. (Sauces) ....A

MINN.—Minneapolis
Gedney Pickling Co., M. A. (Horse Radish; Mustard; Sauces) ....A

MINN.—St. Paul
Gedney Pickling Co., M. A. (Horse Radish; Mustard; Sauces) ....A

MO.—St. Louis
Bayle, G. A., 113 S. 2d (Catsup; Salad Dressing; Celery Salt; Sauces; Mustard) ....B
Dodson - Braun Mfg. Co. (Catsup) ....AA
Eddy & Eddy (Sauces)..AA

NEBR.—Omaha
Haarman Bros. (Catsup; Mustard; Sauces) ......B

N. J.—Bridgeton
Brady Co., J. F. (Catsup).C

N. J.—Camden
Campbell Preserving Co. (Catsup; Salad Dressing) ....AA

N. J.—Mt. Holly
Chances' Sons, R. C. (Sauces) C

N. J.—Newark
Hallock, Denton & Co. (Sauces) ....B

N. Y.—Brooklyn
Garrett-Bergen Co., 45 Newell (Catsup; Mustard; Sauces) C
Green & Sons, J. H. (Sauces) ....D
Taft Bros. (Mustard) ...C
Voss, H. F. 68 Washn. Av. (Catsup; Sauces) .....D

N. Y.—Buffalo
Brennison & Son, F. (Horse Radish) ....B
Buffalo Vinegar & Preserving Co. (Sauces; Mustard) B
Erie Preserving Co. (Catsup; Celery Salt) ..AAAA
Gentsch's Son, B. F. (Mustard; Sauces) C
Hasselbeck, M. (Prepared Mustard) ....B
Klipfel Vinegar Co. (Mustard; Sauces) ....D
McCready, Mrs. J. T. (Sauces) ....B
Mersman, F. (Prepared Mustard) ....B

N. Y.—Islip
Islip Mustard & Pickle Co. (Mustard) C

New York City
Alart & McGuire, 70 Madison ....A
Ams, Max., 372 Greenwich ....AA
Archibald & Lewis (Mustard) C
Bennecke & Bro., E. (Sauces) ....AA
Burton & Co., W. (Celery Salt) ....B
Cohen & Co., W. H. (Sauces) C
Dean & Son, W. G. (Prep. Mustard) ....A
Duncan Sons', John (Sauces) ....AAAA
Durkee & Co., E. R.....AA
E v a n s & S o n s (Ltd.) (Sauces) ....A
Fischer & Co., B. (Prepared

(Mustard) ....AAAA
Fitzpatrick & Co., A. C. (Salad Dressing) .....B
Fuerst Bros. & Co. (Salad Dressing) ....B
Gillies & Co., E. J. (Prep. Mustard) ....AA
Gordon & Dilworth, 563 Greenwich (Catsup) ...A
Gruman, J. B. (Prep. Mustard) ....B
Gulden, Chas., 46 Elizabeth (Catsup; Mustard; Salad Dressing; Sauces) AA
Hayes & Co., Jas. A. (Mustard) ....A
Hazard & Co., E. C., 117 Hudson (Catsup) ....AA
Heinz Co., H. J. (Horse Radish; Catsup, &c.) AAAA
Israel & Bro., C. (Salad Dressing) ....B
Luedemann, A. (Prep. Mustard) ....A
Manheimer & Eben (Salad Dressing) C
Mason & Co., J. (Sauces).D
Moos & Co. (Salad Dressing) D
Seville Packing Co. (Sauces) B
Sherwood, C. K., 141 Franklin (Catsup; Sauces)....B
Smith & Co., Jas. P. (Mustard) ....AAA
S n i d e r Preserving Co. (Sauces, &c.) ....A
Soper & Co., A. C., 156 Maiden Lane (Sauces)...D
Taft Bros. (Cake; Oil Mustard) C
Tyler & Finch Co. (Mustard Seed) ....A
Williams Bros. Co., 105 Hudson (Catsup; Sauces; Mustard) ....A

N. Y.—Rochester
Clark & Co., W. N. (Chili Sauce; Relishes) ......D
Curtice Bros. Co. (Catsup) AA
French Co., R. T. (French Mustard) ....A

N. Y.—Skaneateles
Skaneateles K r a u t C o. (Sauces) ....D

OHIO—Akron
Smith Bros. (Salad Dressing) ....B

OHIO—Barnesville
Barnesville Canning & Packing Co. (Catsup) ......D

OHIO—Cincinnati
Derham, S. G., 204 Sycamore (Sauces) ....A
Droste & Co., H. R. (Mustard) ....A
Harrison & Co., W. H. (Mustard) C
Lippincott & Cree Co., 42 Main (Catsup) ....D
Loudon, C. F., Court & Sycamore (Catsup) C
Miller Vinegar & Pickle Co., 1272 Harrison Av. (Catsup; Mustard; Sauces)..C
National Pure Food Co., 920 Sycamore (Catsup) ...C
Ritter Conserve Co., P. J., 32 W. Conrt (Catsup)..A
Snider Pres. Co., T. A., 209 S y c a m o r e (Catsup; Sauces) ....A
Spencer & Son, W. M., 324 E. 2d (Catsup; Sauces).D
Ullman, Dreifus & Co. (Sauces) ....B
Weiler Co., J., Spring Grove & Ala. Av. ....A

OHIO—Cleveland
Heinz Co., H. J. ....AAAA

OHIO—Columbus
Andrus, Scofield & Co., 42 W. State (Sauces; Mustard) C
Citizens' Whol. Supply Co. (Celery Salt) ....D

OHIO—Creston
Lutz & Schramm Co. (Horse Radish; Mustard) ......A

OHIO—Toledo
Pepsin Relish Co. (Sauces;
Salad Dressing) ....D
OHIO—Van Wert
Royal Packing Co. (Sauces)
........................D

OHIO—Wooster
Wooster Pres. Co. (Catsup)
........................B

PA.—Allegheny
Lutz & Schramm Co. (Horse
Radish; Mustard; Salad
Dressing) ....AA
PA.—Erie
Werner Vinegar & Pickling
Co. (Horse Radish; Prep.
Mustard; Sauces) ......A
PA.—Philadelphia
Alart & McGuire, 126 Cuth-
bert (Catsup; Dressing;
Sauces; Mustard) ....A
American Preserve Co., 946
Beach (Catsup) ....A
Chance's Sons, R. C., 433
Spruce (Catsup; Prepared
Mustard; Sauces).......C
Clawson Co. (Celery Salt).C
Colbourn Co., A. (Ltd.)
(Sauces; Prep. Mustard)
........................AA
Harvey, T. D. (Sauces) ..D
Keystone Mustard & Pickle
Works, 110 Spruce (Horse
Radish; Sauces) ......D
Phila. Pickling Co., 262 S.
2d (Sauces; Prep. Mus-
tard) ....A
Philadelphia Vinegar Co.
(Mustard) ....B
Read & Co., H. (Sauces)..D
Ritter Conserve Co., P. J.,
309 Green (Catsup; Prep.
Mustard; Sauces) ......A
Weikel & Smith Spice Co.
(Celery Salt; Prep. Mus-
tard) ....A
PA.—Pittsburg
Heinz Co., H. J. .....AAAA
Hirsch Bros. & Co., 59 Car-
son (Sauces; Mustard)..B
R. I.—East Providence
Huntington Maple Syrup &
Sugar Co. (Celery Salt).D
S. C.—Waccaman
Donaldson Bros. (Tabasco)
........................C
TEXAS—Dallas
Hughes Bros. Mfg. Co. (Cat-
sup; Sauces) ....A
W. VA.—Wellsburg
Central Supply Co. (Mus-
tard) ....B
W. VA.—Wheeling
Exley, Watkins & Co. (Cat-
sup; Prep. Mustard; Cel-
ery Salt; Sauces) .....B
Flaccus Bros. (Catsup; Prep.
Mustard) ....A
Flaccus Co., S. C. (Catsup;
Mustard; Sauces) C
McMechen & Son, G. K.
(Catsup; Prep. Mustard;
Sauces) ....A
WIS.—Manitowoc
Richter & Sons, A. M. (Mus-
tard) C
WIS.—Milwaukee
American Vinegar & Pickle
Co. (Mustard) C
Jewett & Sherman Co. (Mus-
tard) ....A
Pahl & Co., E. R. (Horse
Radish) ....D
WIS.—Ripon
Ripon Packing Co. (Catsup;
Sauces) C

CONDUCTORS

ILL.—Sterling
Novelty Iron Wks. (Water)
........................E
MASS.—Boston
Stearns Lumber Co., A. T.
........................AA
Van Noorden & Co., E.
(Roof Water) C
MASS.—Worcester
Cummings, J. B. (Corru-
gated) ....D
New York City
Wheeling Corrugating Co.

CONDUCTORS (Con.)
(Roof Water) ....AAAA
OHIO—Cleveland
Garry Iron & Steel Co.
(Pipe) ....A
OHIO—Piqua
Standard Mfg. Co. (Elbow)
........................X
PA.—Philadelphia
Merchant & Co., 517 Arch
(Pipe) ....AA
Opdyke, Benj. P., 218 New
(Corrugated) ....A
WIS.—Milwaukee
Bursach & Niedermeyer Co.
(Galvanized Iron) .....B

CONDUITS

DEL.—Wilmington
Delaware Hard Fibre Co.
(Fibre) ....A
D. C.—Washington
Potomac Terra Cotta Co.
(Vitrified Salt Glazed
Terra Cotta) ....B
GA.—Macon
Stevens Sons' Co., H. (Clay
for Tel. & Tile Lines;
Electrical) ....A
ILL.—Chicago
Pioneer Fire Proofing Co.,
204 Dearborn ....AA
Walworth & Neville Mfg.
Co., 84 Van Buren (Creo-
soted Pine) ....AA
IND.—Brazil
McRoy Clay Works (Vitri-
fied Clay) X
IND.—Indianapolis
Edgecombe Co. (Pipe Joint)
........................D
KANS.—Pittsburg
Pittsburg Sewer Pipe &
Conduit Co. (Vitrified Salt
Glazed) ....B
MASS.—Boston
Clifton Mfg. Co. ....B
Cunningham Iron Co.
(Wrought Iron) ....B
MASS.—Chelsea
American Circular Loom Co.
(Flexible Interior; Elec-
trical) ....A
MICH.—Bay City
Michigan Pipe Co. (Creo-
soted Wood; Electrical)
........................AA
MO.—St. Louis
Blackmer & Post Pipe Co.
(Electrical) ....AA
Evans & Howard Fire Brick
Co. (Clay) ....AAAA
New York City
Alphaduct Mfg. Co., 522 W.
22d (Fireproof Fibre Flex-
ible Interior) ....B
American Vitrified Conduit
Co., 170 B'way (Vitrified
Salt Glazed, interior & un-
derground) ....B
Camp Co., H. B., 170 B'way
(Vitrified Clay) ....A
Eppinger & Russell Co., 66
Broad (Wooden) X
Federal Clay Mfg. Co., 170
B'way (Vitrified Clay).B
National Conduit & Cable
Co., 41 Park Row..AAAA
Osborn Flexible Conduit Co.,
15 Park Row (Flexible)
........................B
Sprague Electric Co. (Elec-
trical) ....AAAA
N. Y.—Orangeburg
Fibre Conduit Co. (Fibre)
........................B
N. Y.—Rochester
Standard Sewer Pipe Co.
(Clay; Camp; Electric).A
N. Y.—Schenectady
General Electric Co...AAAA
PA.—Catasauqua
Davis & Thomas Co. (Cast
Iron) ....AA
PA.—New Kensington
American Conduit Mfg. Co.
(Electric Wire) ....D
PA.—Philadelphia
Rittenhouse-Miller Co.,
Witherspoon Bldg. (Flex-
ible Waterproof Interior)
........................D

CONDUITS (Con.)

PA.—Pittsburg
American Sewer Pipe Co., 2d National Bank Bldg. ....AAAA
National Fire Proofing Co. (Vitrified Glazed)..AAAA
Safety - Armorite Conduit Co., Frick Bldg. (Iron Armored Flexible Metallic Interior) ....AA
U. S. Fireproofing Corporation, 326 4th Av. (Clay).X
TENN.—Chattanooga
Montague & Co. (Clay)...A

CONES

CONN.—Hartford
Hartford Mach. Screw Co. (Bicycle) ....AAAA
CONN.—Seymour
Matthews Mfg. Co., H. A. (Bicycle) ....B
ILL.—Carpenterville
Illinois Iron & Bolt Co. (Blacksmiths') ....AA
ILL.—Chicago
Chicago Screw Co. (Bicycle) AA
MD.—Baltimore
Poole & Son Co., Robt. (Wire Rope) ....A
N. Y.—Buffalo
Crosby Co. (Ball Bearing) A
OHIO—Elyria
Western Automatic Mach. Screw Co. (Bicycle)...AA
PA.—Bangor
Flory Mfg. Co., S. (Logging) ....A
PA.—Wilkesbarre
Vulcan Iron Works (Wire Rope) ....AAAA
VT.—East Corinth
Jackman Co. (Evener; Knitter Evener) ....E

CONFECTION-ERY

ALA.—Mobile
Stolla, L. C. (Mfr.; Job.).C
ALA.—Montgomery
Manegold & Co., J. C
ARK.—Little Rock
Karcher Candy Co., A.....C
CAL.—Los Angeles
Bishop & Co. (Crys. Fruit) AA
Christopher & Sparks, 241 S. Spring ....B
Kahn-Beck Co., 465 Aliso (Mfg.) C
Southern California Cracker Co. ....B
CAL.—San Francisco
G r u e n h a g e n Bros., 20 Kearny C
Haas & Son, G., 810 Market A
Hromada, A., 220 Battery B
Maskey, F., 32 Kearny....A
Pacific Coast Biscuit Co., 2d. & Folsom ....AA
Roberts & Co., G. F., Bush & Polk C
Rothschild & Ehrensport, 33 Main ....A
Saroni, Louis (Br. P. C. Bis. Co.) ....
Seidl & Co., J., 658 Mission C
Thain Bros., 781 Market..C
Townsend, W. S., 715 Market C
COLO.—Denver
Baur & Co., O. P., 1512 Curtis ....B
Hewitt Candy Co., 1613 Market (W. & M.) ....A
Nevin & Co., W. C., 1641 Blake ....B
Sauer Mfg. Co., C. L., 1385 Market (Mfg.; Job.)....C
CONN.—Bridgeport
Lane & Booth C
N. E. Peanut Taffy Co....C
CONN.—Hartford
Backes, F. W. ....A

CONFECTIONERY

Hoadley, E. J. ....A
CONN.—New Haven
Hillman, H. C
CONN.—Norwich
Perkins, J. C. ....B
CONN.—Waterbury
Trott Baking Co. C
DEL.—Wilmington
Morrow & Son, J. ....A
D. C.—Washington
Mueller, G. J., 336 Pa. Av., N. W. ....B
GA.—Atlanta
Atlanta Steam Candy Factory ....B
Johnson, G. E. C
Numally Co. (The) C
Schlessinger, H. L. (W. & Mfg.) ....B
GA.—Augusta
Clark Candy Co. ....B
Claussen, H. H. C
GA.—Savannah
Furber, J. H. C
ILL.—Aurora
Mason Factory (Br. N. B. Co.) ....AAAA
ILL.—Bloomington
Bloomington Caramel Co...B
ILL.—Chicago
Bunte, Spoehr & Co., 139 W. Monroe ....AA
Dawson Co., Martin (The), 1520 State ....B
Farley Branch National Candy Co., 130 E. Superior ....AAAA
Frank & Co., G., 131 La Salle C
Fritsch & Williams, 85 Ontario C
Gottman & Kretchmer, 158 W. Jack. Boul. C
Guest-Sullivan Candy Co., 11951 S. Halsted C
Gunther, C. F., 212 State AAA
Kehoe & Co., 45 Lake....A
Kranz, John, 74 Randolph AAAA
Lowney Co., W. M., 45 Wabash Av. ....B
Lyon & Co., 51 S. Union..A
Manierre-Yoe Syrup Co., 30 River (Rock Candy)...B
Morris & Gottman, 158 W. Jackson Boul. ....B
National Biscuit Co. .AAAA
Pan Conf. Co., 248 Illinois.A
Rueckheim Bros. & Eckstein, 261 S. Desplaines.A
Shields & Co., M., 51 S. Jefferson ....A
Slauson & Co., A., Unity Bldg. (Br. N. Y. City)..A
Swanson, A. C., 92 State..B
ILL.—Danville
Feldkamp Candy Co. C
Shields & Co., M. (Br. Chicago) ....A
ILL.—Quincy
Clark & Morgan C
Quincy Confec. Co. (W. & Mfg.) C
ILL.—Rockford
Leonard & Ward C
ILL.—Rock Island
Gansert, W. S. ....B
IND.—Brookville
Brookville Mfg. Co. .....B
IND.—Evansville
Herman, H. C
IND.—Ft. Wayne
Fox Bakery (Br. Nat. B. Co., Chicago) ....AAAA
Heit-Miller-Lau Co. C
IND.—Indianapolis
Daggett Factory (National Candy Co.) 18 W. Ga. AAAA
Darmody Co., J. F., 132 S. Penn C
Nicholls-Krull Factory, 112 S. Penn ....AAAA
IND.—Lafayette
Lafayette Cracker & Confec. Co. ....B
IND.—Terre Haute
Mewhinney Co., A. B. (The) B
IOWA—Burlington
Clinton-Copeland Co. C

National Biscuit Co. (Br. Chicago) ....AAAA
IOWA—Council Bluffs
Woodward & Co., J. G.....C
IOWA—Davenport
Roddewig-Schmidt Factory (Br. Natl. Bis. Co., Chicago) ....AAAA
IOWA—Dubuque
Lawther & Co., W. ......A
IOWA—Sioux City
National Biscuit Co. ....AAAA
Shenkberg Co., C. ....AAA
IOWA—Waterloo
Dickson-Graff Co. (Mfrs. & Jobbers) C
KANS.—Atchison
Hausner Merc. Co., H....B
KANS.—Salina
Salina Candy Co. (Whol. & Mfg.) C
KY.—Louisville
Bradas & Gheens C
Klein & Son ....A
Menne Factory, F. A. (Natl. Candy Co.) ....AAAA
LA.—New Orleans
Biedenharn-Burnett Candy Co. (Ltd.) C
Domecq & Son. Julius, 835 Canal ....B
Jaeger & De Pass, 535 Magazine ....B
Nelson & Berdon Candy Co., 323 Magazine C
LA.—Shreveport
Rose Merc. & Mfg. Co., Ltd. ....A
MAINE—Auburn
Huston & Co., T. A. (Mfg.) ....B
MAINE—Belfast
Pierce & Co., G. G........C
MAINE—Portland
Sawyer. G. E. (W. & R.)..C
Shaw & Co., G. C.........B
MD.—Baltimore
Baltimore Candy Co., 306 Spears' Wharf C
Birkmeyer & Sons, J. F., 868 W. Baltimore C
Blome & Son Co., G. (The) 617 W. Baltimore .....A
Blue Ribbon Candy Co., 749 W. Pratt ....A
Clarke & Jones, 17 Light Hillen ....AA
Darby Candy Co. (The), 700 Hillen ....B
Foos, F. E., 1505 W. Baltimore ....B
Gibbs Candy Co., 2319 Boston ....AA
Headley Choco. Co., 11 S. Frederick C
Lauer & Suter, Lombard & Frederick ....A
Maryland Mfg. & Candy Co, 115 South ....B
Pfeil Mfg. Co., H. (The), 557 Robert ....B
Pracht & Co., C., 406 Franklin C
Stolpp Fred C., 311 W. Saratoga ....B
MD.—Frederick
McCardell, A. C. ....B
MASS.—Boston
Aldrich & Smith, 21 Portland ....A
Eagle Candy Co., 460 Harrison Av. ....AAAA
Foss & Co., H. D., 87 Union (Mfg.) C
Hildreth, H. L., 42 Batterymarch ....A
Lewis, E. P., 36 Portland..C
Lowney Co., W. M. (The), 447 Commercial ....A
New England Confectionery Co., 253 Summer .....AA
Schrafft & Sons, W. F., 94 Portland Av. C
Stuber Co.. E. W., Barristers' Hall (Mfg.) ......A
Trowbridge Chocolate Chip Co . 142 Commercial ..B
Wenz. H.. 9 Harcourt....C
MASS.—Brockton
Washburn & Co., F. B....A
MASS.—Cambridge
Am. Confec. Co. ....A

Bay State Confec. Co.....B
Bell Confec. Co., J. S. (Mfg.) C
Clark & Co., B. P........C
Close Co., George C
Hazen Co., D. M.........C
Russell & Co. C
Sparrow Co., H. F.......A
Stuber Co., E. W........A
MASS.—North Adams
Sperry & Co., W. H......A
MASS.—Peabody
Pepper Co. (W. Mfg.)....B
MASS.—Springfield
Kibbe Bros. Co. ....A
MICH.—Adrian
Moreland Bros. & Crane...B
MICH.—Battle Creek
Honey Comb Choco. Chip Co. B
Purity Confec. Co. ......A
MICH.—Detroit
Gray. Toynton & Fox Factory (Natl. Candy Co.) AAAA
MICH.—Grand Rapids
Brooks & Co., A. E.......C
Putnam Factory (Natl. Candy Co.) ......AAAA
MICH.—Kalamazoo
Hanselman Candy Co. C
MINN.—Faribault
Theopold, Morris & Co. (Mfg.) ....A
MINN.—Mankato
Rosenberger & Currier ...C
MINN.—Minneapolis
Lillibridge-Bremner Factory (Br. National Biscuit Co.) AAAA
McXusic-Towle Co., 1st & 3d Av. (Mfg.) ....B
Paris-Murton Co., 29 N. 2d B
MINN.—St. Paul
McFadden Candy Co. (W. Mfg.) C
Menk Bros., 241 E. 6th...A
Roach Factory. J. H., 264 E. 6th (Natl. Candy Co.) AAAA
Ziegler-Egan Co., 55 E. 3d B
MINN.—Wadina
Wadina Cracker Co. (Job.) C
MISS.—Meridian
Lyon & Co., A. J.........C
MO.—Kansas City
Bliss Syrup Mfg. Co., 1329 St. Louis Av. (Rock Candy) ....B
Loose Bros. Factory, 200 Main (Natl. Biscuit Co.) AAAA
MO.—St. Joseph
Douglas & Son, C. W. (W. Mfg.) ....B
MO.—St. Louis
Blanke & Bro. Candy Co., 608 Market ....AA
Candy Bros. Mfg. Co., 215 Chestnut ....A
Hartman, C. A., 321 Clark Av. ....
Oakes Candy Co., 303 N. B'way C
Peckham Factory, O. H., 7th & Spruce (Natl. Candy Co.) ....AAAA
Seward Factory, F. D., 522 N. Main (Natl. Candy Co.) ....AAAA
St. Louis Candy Mfg. Co.. 9th & Gratiot ....B
Walter Factory, A. J., 114 Walnut (Natl. Candy Co.) AAAA
Wennecker - Morris Candy Co. 20 S. 3d. ....B
MONT.—Butte
Morris & Co. C
Stromberg & Co., J. A....C
NEBR.—Omaha
Voegel & Dinning........A
N. H.—Concord
Norris & Co.. J. C.......A
N. H.—Nashua
Folman. C. V. (Lozenges).B
N. J.—Jersey City
Causse Mfg. Co., A. L. (Candied Fruits) ......B

CONFECTIONERY

N. J.—Newark
MacAndrews & Forbes (Licorice) ....AAAA
Walsh & Co., R. ....B
N. Y.—Albany
Colburn & Son, E. S. C
N. Y.—Brooklyn
Dryden & Palmer, Bedford Av. & N. 12th (Rock Candy) ....B
Gardiner-Lucas Co., 52 Columbus Heights ....B
Kloster, A. A., 83 Fulton..C
Kuchler & Son, F. X., 248 Park Av. C
Mason, Au & Magenheimer, 22 Henry ....A
Matchett & Co., J. J., 390 Wythe Av. C
National Licorice Co., 375 Lorimer ....A
Standard Rock Candy Co., 15 Rush ....B
N. Y.—Buffalo
Buffalo Candy Co., 79 Ellicott (W. Mfrs.) ......AA
Burt & Sindele Factory, 113 Seneca (Natl. Candy Co.) ....AAAA
Huyler's, 350 Main ....A
Menker Co., H. A., 67 Seneca ....A
Sibley & Holmwood Factory, 149 Swan (Natl. Candy Co.) ....AAAA
N. Y.—Malone
Symonds & Allison C
New York City
Auerbach & Sons, D., 334 W. 39th C
Carenou & Tur, 3 Union Sq. ....B
Causse Mfg. Co., A. L., 105 Hudson ....B
Cella, G., 25 Wooster ....B
Cohen & Co., A. E., 15 Wooster ....B
Essing, A., 380 Pearl....C
New York City
Gardiner-Lucas Co., 99 John ....B
Greek-Am. Confec. Co., 7 Marion ....B
Hawley & Hoops, 271 Mulberry ....AAA
Heide, H., 88 Vandam..AA
Helmstetter, G., 504 Broome ....A
Hoefler & Co., C. M., 27 Wooster ....B
Humbert, F. J., 9 Wooster C
Huyler's, 64 Irving Pl.....A
Lertora, A., 7 Wooster...B
Maillard, H., 118 W. 25th ....B
Ode & Gerbereux, 419 W. B'way ....B
Powell, A. M., 152 Chambers (Caramels) ....A
Ridley & Co., 255 Greenwich ....B
Slauson & Co., A., 32 Dey ....A
Smith, E., 154 G'wich....B
Stern & Saalberg, 311 W. 40th C
United Conf. Assn., 43 Jay ....B
Wallace & Co., 160 Monroe ....A
N. Y.—Poughkeepsie
Smith Bros. (Cough Drops) ....AA
N. Y.—Rochester
Deininger Bros. ....B
Neun, H. P. (Mfg.) ....B
Rochester Candy Wks...A
Williams & Werner Co....B
N. Y.—Rockville Centre
Long Island Confec. Co. (Mfg.) C
N. Y.—Syracuse
Young & Larrabee (Natl. Biscuit Co.) ......AAAA
N. Y.—Utica
Young Bakery, G. (The)..B
N. C.—Raleigh
Royster & Bro., A. D.....C
OHIO—Cincinnati
Buhr, Pfaff Co., 2d. & Race (W. Mfrs.) ....B

CONFECTIONERY

Echert Co., P. (The), 25 W. Court ....A
Peebles Sons' Co., J. R. (The), Government Sq...A
Reinhart, C. H., 51 Vine..C
Reinhart & Newton, 10 W. 2d. ....B
Sauerston & Brown, 920 Elm ....B
Smith Co., H. D. (The), 206 Main ....B
OHIO—Cleveland
Kraus' Sons, J., 127 Water ....B
Kraus, L. G., 51 Woodland Av. C
OHIO—Columbus
Busy Bee Candy Kitchen (The) ....A
Snyder, Chaffee & Co.....B
OHIO—Lima
Banta & Son, F. J. (W. Mfg.) C
OHIO—Tiffin
Harter & Co. C
OHIO—Toledo
Banta-Lavey Co. C
Smith-Kirk Candy Co.....C
OREGON—Portland
Bishop & Co. ....A
Pacific Coast Biscuit Co. ....AA
PA.—Gettysburg
Gettysburg Confec. Co....C
PA.—Hazleton
Schwartz Co., Wm. (Whol. Mfg.) ....B
PA.—Johnstown
Hinchman, J. V. C
Love & Sunshine Co.....AA
PA.—Lancaster
Adams, C. F. (W. & Mg.).C
Dosch, J. J. C
Hershey Choc. Co....AAAA
PA.—Lititz
Kendig Mfg. Co. ....B
PA.—Meadville
Trowbridge Choc. Chip Co. ....B
PA.—Oxford
Williams Caramel Co. ....B
PA.—Philadelphia
Blank & Son, L., 1024 Chestnut ....B
Brandle & Smith, 9th & Dauphin (Mfg.) C
Croft & Allen Co., 33d. & Market ....AA
Lang & Son, W., 323 S. Lawrence (Rock Candy) ....B
Laurent & Sons, F., 1306 Chestnut ....B
Meyer, Herman, 844 N. 3d ....B
Miller & Son Co., Geo., 255 S. 3d (Whol. Mfg.) ..AA
Miller & Son, J. M., 335 N. 3d (Whol. Mfg.)...A
Nuss & Co., H., 223 N. 13th ....B
Pflaum, Jr., C., 2074 N. 4th ....B
Phila. Caramel Co., 1217 Beach C
Quaker City Choc. & Confec. Co., 2148 G'town Av...A
Schappert & Levick, 205 N. Front C
Smith & Peters, 483 N. 5th ....B
Temple Confec. Co., 701 Spring Garden (Mfg.'..B
Whitman & Son, S. F., 606 Cherry ....A
Wunderle, P., 130 Pegg.AA
PA.—Pittsburg
McClurg & Co., J., 414 6th Av. ....AA
McKee Co., J. K., 711 Grant (W. Job.) ....B
Novelty Candy Co., Grant.B
Ross, Shannon & Staving..A
Ward-Mackey Co., 3212 Liberty Av. (Job.) ......A
PA.—Reading
Reading Confec. Co......B
PA.—Williamsport
Williamsport Candy Mfg. Co. C

CONFECTIONERY

PA.—York
American Caramel Co. ..AA
York Candy Mfg. Co.....C
S. C.—Charleston
Claussen & Co., J. C. H..B
TENN.—Chattanooga
Triggs, Dobbs & Co.......A
Trotter Bros. ....A
TENN.—Clarksville
Ely, E. B. C
TENN.—Memphis
Heinrich & Co., J. J.....C
Maer Mfg. Co. C
Novelty Candy Co. ......B
TENN.—Nashville
Hoggins-Murkin Mfg. Co...C
Kemker-Woolwine Candy &
 Cracker Co. ....B
Mitchell, C. ....B
Zickler & Co., G. C
TEXAS—Austin
Austin Candy Mfg. Co.. .A
TEXAS—Fort Worth
Ft. Worth Candy & Cracker
 Co. C
Montgomery & Co. .....AA
TEXAS—Galveston
Southern Coffee Co. C
TEXAS—Houston
Heim, C. C
TEXAS—San Antonio
Duerler Mfg. Co., G. A.
 (Mfr. Pecan Candy Spec.)
 ....A
UTAH—Ogden
Shupe, Williams Candy Co.
C
UTAH—Salt Lake City
McDonald Candy Co., J. G.
C
National Biscuit Co. ..AAAA
Salt Lake Candy Co.......C
VT.—Burlington
Crystal Confectionery Co..C
VT.—Montpelier
Cross & Son, C. H. ......B
VT.—White River Junction
Smith & Son ....B
VA.—Alexandria
Hill Bakery (Natl. Biscuit
 Co.) ....AAAA
VA.—Lynchburg
Crescent Candy Works ...C
VA.—Norfolk
Bosman & Lohman C
Obendorfer & Co. C
VA.—Petersburg
Harrison, H. P. ....B
VA.—Richmond
Christian & Winfree Co...C
Fleming & Christian Co...B
Hardesty & Co., R. H....C
WASH.—Seattle
Jacobs, Trenholme & Co.
 (B'krs.) ....B
Seattle Cracker & Candy Co.
C
Superior Candy & Cracker
 Co. (W. & Mfg.) C
WASH.—Spokane
Washington Cracker Co...B
WASH.—Tacoma
Stardiamond Candy Factory
 (W. Mfg.) C
W. VA.—Charleston
Prince, Mahon & Keeny..B
W. VA.—Fairmont
West Virginia Gro. & Candy
 Co. (Mfg.) ....A
W. VA.—Wheeling
Dwist & Son, A. ....-...C
WIS.—Green Bay
Annen Candy & Biscuit Co.
C
Brenner, Gazett Co. C
WIS.—La Crosse
Funke Co., J. B. (Chocolate
 Bonbons) ....A
Kratchwil, M. C
La Crosse Cracker & Candy
 Co. ....B
WIS.—Madison
Teckmeyer Candy Co. (W.
 & Mfg.) C
WIS.—Milwaukee
Ambrosia Choc. Co. .....B
Amer. Candy Co. ....B
Carpenter-Underwood Fac-
 tory (Natl. Biscuit Co.)
 ....AAAA

CONFECTIONERY

Fernekes Co., J. (W. Mfg.)
C
Ziegler & Co., G. (W. &
 Mfg.) ....A

CONNECTIONS

ILL.—Chicago
Morgan & Wright (Inc.), 33
 W. Lake (Rubber) ..AA
ILL.—Decatur
Mueller Mfg. Co. (Brass;
 Water; Gas Meter) .AAA
N. Y.—Auburn
Leather & Brass Mfg. Co
 (Closet Repair) ......E
N. Y.—Brooklyn
Clonbrock Steam Boiler Co.
 (Boiler; Flue) ....D
New York City
Eaton, Cole & Burnham, 253
 B'way (Hose) ....AAAA
T r a g e s e r Steam Copper
 Works, John (Boiler)...A
N. Y.—Utica
Blasier & Co., M. E.
 (Closet) C
OHIO—Canton
Berger, Mfg. Co. (Sewer)
 ....AA
OHIO—Springfield
Rogers Iron Co. (Sewer)...C
PA.—Pittsburg
Steel Car Forge Co. (Air
 Brake) ....B
R. I.—Providence
Allen Fire Dept. Supply Co.
 (Hose) ....D
WIS.—Milwaukee
Milwaukee Brass Mfg. Co.
 (Siamese with Automatic
 Valve, for Fire Escapes,
 Stand Pipes, Bath, &c.).C

CONNECTORS

CONN.—Ansonia
Ansonia Electrical Co.
 (Wire, &c.) ....A
CONN.—Bridgeport
Bridgeport Brass Co. (Wire,
 &c.) ....AA
CONN.—Hartford
Veeder Mfg. Co. (Wire, &c.)
 ....B
CONN.—Plainville
T r u m b u l l Electric Co.
 (Wire, &c.) C
ILL.—Chicago
American Electric Fuse Co.,
 48 W. Jackson (Wire,
 &c.) ....A
Atkinson Co., J. M., 2427
 Calamut Av. (Wire, &c.)
 ....F
Chicago Die & Electric Co.,
 87 W. Lake (Wire, &c.)
X
Lang Electric Co., J., 44
 Michigan (Trailer) ....D
Turner Brass Wks., Michi-
 gan & Franklin (Wire;
 Trailer) ....D
MASS.—Boston
Electric Gas Lighting Co.,
 195 Devonshire (Wire,
 &c.) ....A
Stuart Howland Co., 281
 Devonshire (Wire &c.)..B
MASS.—Springfield
Springfield Electric Mfg.
 Co. (Wire, &c.) ......F
MO.—St. Louis
Central Union Brass Co., 811
 N. 2d (Trailer) ....E
Emerson Electric Mfg. Co.,
 718 St. Charles (Wire,
 &c.) ....B
N. J.—Newark
McIntire Co., C. H., 13
 Franklin (Wire, &c.)...D
New York City
Bunnell & Co., J. H., 20
 Park Pl. (Wire, &c.)...A
Johns-Manville Co., H. W.,
 100 William (Trolley
 Wire) ....AAAA
Jones & Son, J., 64 Cort-
 land (Wire, &c.) ....E
Manhattan Electrical Supply

CONNECTORS (Con.)

Co., 32 Cortland (Wire, &c.) ....A
Ostrander & Co., W. R., 22 Dey (Wire, &c.).......B
Zimdars & Hunt, 127 5th Av. (Wire, &c.) .....D
OHIO—Cincinnati
Kisinger-Ison Co. (Trolley Wire) ....D
OHIO—Mansfield
Ohio Brass Co. (Trailer; Trolley Wire) ....B
PA.—Philadelphia
Patrick, Carter & Wilkins (Wire, &c.) ....A

CONSERVA-TORIES

See also Greenhouses

CONSTRUCT-ORS

MINN.—Minneapolis
Northwestern Fireproofing Works (Fireproofing)...C
MO.—St. Louis
Bruner Granitoid Co., P. M. (Fireproofing) C
New York City
Metropolitan Fireproofing Co., 13 Burling Slip (Fireproofing) ....D
Norman Fireproof Construction Co. (Fireproofing).E
Roebling Construction Co. (Fireproofing) ....B
OHIO—Cincinnati
Ferro-Concrete Construction Co. (Fireproofing) ......B
OHIO—Cleveland
National Concrete Fireproofing Co., New England Bldg. (Fireproofing) ...C
OHIO—Columbus
International Fence & Fireproofing Co., Buttes Av. (Fireproofing) ....A
PA.—Chester
Keystone Fireproofing Co. (Fireproofing) ....B
PA.—Philadelphia
Drehmann Paving Co., 2629 Parrish (Fireproofing; Concrete Floors, &c.)...H
Merritt & Co., 1024 Ridge Av. (Fireproofing) .....B
PA.—Pittsburg
Columbian Fireproofing Co. (Fireproofing) ....A

CONSUMERS

OHIO—Cleveland
B r i g h t m a n Stoker Co. (Smoke; Gas) ....D
PA.—Philadelphia
Schulte & Roerting Co., 12th & Thompson (Smoke) ....A

CONTRACT-ORS

OHIO—Cleveland
Garrett-Cromwell Engineering Co., New England Bldg. (Blast Furnace; Steel Works) ....AA
Wellman-Seaver-Morgan Engineering Co. (Blast Furnace; Steel Works)...AA
OHIO—Columbus
R a r i g Engineering Co. (Blast Furnace; Steel Works) ....A
OHIO—Girard
Girard Boiler & Mfg. Co. (Blast Furnace; Steel Works) ....B
OHIO—Youngstown
Davis, Walker & Cooper Co. (Blast Furnace; Steel Works) ....E
Pollock Co., Wm. R. (Blast Furnace; Steel Wks.)...B

CONTRACTORS (Con.)

PA.—Pittsburg
Carroll-Porter Boiler & Tank Co., Empire Bldg. (Blast Furnace; Steel Wks.)...B
Ferguson, Hugh, Smith Bldg. (Blast Furnace; Steel Wks.) ....F
Laughlin & Co., Alex., 706 Lewis Blk. (Blast Furnace; Steel Wks.) ....D
McClure & Co., Smith Blk. (Blast Furnace; Steel Works) ....D
McNeil & Bro. Co., James, 29th & A. V. Ry. (Blast Furnace; Steel Wks.).AA
Petroleum Iron Works Co. (Blast Furnace; Steel Works) C
Riter-Conley Mfg. Co., 50 Water (Blast Furnace; Steel Works) ....AA
Scaife & Sons' Co., Wm. B., 221 1st Av. (Blast Furnace; Steel Wks.) ....A
PA.—Washington
Petroleum Iron Works Co. (Blast Furnace; Steel Works) C

CONTROL-LERS

ILL.—Chicago
Burdette-Rountree Mfg. Co., 87 W. Jackson Boul. (Electric Elevator) C
Instantaneous Water Heating Co., 90 Ohio (Gas)..D
McGuire Mfg. Co., 122 Sangamore (Electric Speed).A
Perfect Gas Controller Co., 170 Madison (Gas) X
Schureman & Hayden, 138 South Clinton (Electric Speed) C
IND.—Indianapolis
Commercial Electric Co. (Electric) ....A
Jenney Electric Mfg. Co. (Motor) ....A
IOWA—Keokuk
Garton-Daniels Co. (Railway) ....D
MASS.—Pittsfield
Stanley Electric Mfg. Co. (Railway Motor) ....AA
MASS.—Springfield
Elektron Mfg. Co. (Electric Elevator; Pump) ......B
N. Y.—Bronxville
Ward-Leonard Electric Co. (Electric; Ventilating Fan; Speed) ....B
New York City
Crane Co., Wm. M., 1133 B'way (Gas) ....A
General Incandescent Arc Light Co., 572 1st Av. (Electric Speed) ....A
Gordon Battery Co., 439 E. 144th (Electric Speed)..D
Marine Engine & Machine Co., 1123 B'way (Electric Elevator) ....A
Niles-Bement-Pond Co., 136 Liberty (Electric Speed) AAAA
N. Y.—Schenectady
General Electric Co. (Railway Motor) ......AAAA
OHIO—Alliance
Morgan Engineering Co. (Electric Speed) .....AA
OHIO—Cincinnati
Bullock Electric Mfg. Co., E. Norwood (Electric Speed) ....AAAA
OHIO—Cleveland
Electric Controller & Supply Co., Central & Giddings Avs. (Elec. Speed, for Series Motors) C
Elwell-Parker Electric Co., 1066 Hamilton (Electric Speed) ....A
OHIO—Columbus

CONTROLLERS (Con.)
Case Mfg. Co. (Electric)
...........................AA

OHIO—Mansfield
Phoenix Electric Mfg. Co. (Electric Elevator; Speed)
.............................B

OHIO—Troy
Ohio Electrical Specialty Mfg. Co. (Electric Speed; Fan Motor) ....G

PA.—Erie
Keystone Electric Co. (Electric Elevator; Speed; Reversing Motor) ....A

PA.—Philadelphia
Wirt Electric Co., 4523 Tacomy (Electric Speed)..D

PA.—Pittsburg
Supply Mfg. Co. (Electric)
.............................X
Westinghouse Electric & Mfg. Co. (Br. N. Y. City) (Railway Motor; Electric)
..........................AAAA

WIS.—Milwaukee
Cutler-Hammer Mfg. Co. (Electric Speed; Motor Reversing; Press Motor; Electric Elevator; Electric Crane; Ventilating Fan) ....AAAA
Johnson Electric Service Co. (Cumulative Draft.) .AA

CONVERTERS

ILL.—Chicago
Allis-Chalmers Co., Home Ins. Bldg. (Bessemer)
..........................AAAA

IND.—Ft. Wayne
Fort Wayne Electric Corp. (Induction Coil) .....AA

OHIO—Akron
Biggs Boiler Works Co...C

OHIO—Cleveland
Elwell-Parker Electric Co., 1066 Hamilton (Electric)
.............................A

OHIO—Youngstown
Pollock Co., W. B. (Bessemer) ....B
Tod Co., Wm. (Bessemer)
.............................AA

PA.—New Castle
Penn. Engineering Works (Bessemer) ....A

PA.—Philadelphia
Ott, Geo. F., 207 Buttonwood (Electric Rice) ..A

PA.—Pittsburg
Carroll-Porter Boiler & Tank Co., Empire Bldg. (Bessemer) ....B
Riter-Conley Mfg. Co. (Bessemer) ....AAA
Westinghouse Electric & Mfg. Co. (Induction Coil; Electric) ....AAAA

PA.—Washington
Petroleum Iron Works Co. (Bessemer) ....B

WIS.—Cudahy
Power & Mining Mach. Co. (Bessemer) ....AAA

CONVEYORS

COLO.—Denver
Mine & Smelter Supply Co. (Belt) ....AAAA

ILL.—Chicago
Allis-Chalmers Co., Home Ins. Bldg. (Belt; Log; Slat; Pan) ....AAAA
Borden & Selleck Co., 48 Lake (Belt; Freight; Grain Elevateor; Pan)..X
Caldwell & Son Co., H. W. Western & 17th (Spiral; Screw) ....AAAA
Gates Iron Works (Br. Allis-Chalmers Co., N. Y. C.) (Rock; Ore) ......AAAA
Hoisting & Conveying Mach. Co., 44 N. Elizabeth (Belt; Freight; Gravel; Pan; Sand) ....H
Link Belt Machinery Co., W., 39th & Stewart Av.

CONVEYORS (Con.)
(Belt; Brick; Fertilizers; Flour; Freight; Grain Elevator; Hot Metal; Log; Slab; Sawdust; Spiral; Screw; Wire Cable)....A
Moore & Lorenz Co., 123 S. Clinton (Grain Elevator; Spiral; Screw) ....D
Skillin & Richards Mfg. Co., 147 Fulton (Grain Elevator; Spiral; Screw; Wire Cable) C
Thornburg-Creel Co. (Grain Elevator) X
Webster Mfg. Co., 1075 W. 15th (Belt; Brick; Grain Elevator; Spiral; Screw; Wire Cable) ....AA
Weller Mfg. Co., 118 E. North Av. (Belt; Grain Elevator; Spiral; Screw; Wire Cable) ....A

ILL.—Harvey
Whiting Fdy. Equipment Co. (Hot Metal) ......AA

IND.—Indianapolis
Nordyke & Marmon Co., 1101 W. Morris (Grain Elevator) ....AAA

IND.—Mishawaka
Dodge Mfg. Co. (Belt; Spiral; Screw) ......AAA

IND.—Richmond
Richmond City Mill Works (Grain Elevator) ......A

IND.—Terre Haute
Prox & Brinkman Mfg. Co. (Coal) ....A

KANS.—Leavenworth
Great Western Mfg. Co. (Spiral; Screw) ......AA

MAINE—Bangor
Union Iron Wks. (Sawdust)
.............................A

MD.—Baltimore
Pool & Son Co., Robt. (Fertilizer) ....A

MASS.—Boston
American Tool & Machine Co., 109 Beach (Belt; Spiral; Screw) ......AA
Steel Cable Engineering Co., 92 State (Apron; Sorting; Throughed; Flat Belt; Freight; Pan; Wire Cable) X
Sturtevant Co., B. F. (Cotton; Wool; Light Material) ....D

MICH.—Bay City
Garland Co., M. (Cable; Steel Wire; Log; Slab; Sawdust; Steel Chain, &c.) C
Industrial Works (Freight)
.............................AA

MICH.—Detroit
Buhl Malleable Co., cor. Wright & Adair (Belt; Brick; Flour; Freight; Link Belt; Log; Slab; Sawdust; Spiral; Screw)
Huettemann & Cramer Co. (Clay) ....B
Northern Engineering Wks. Chene & Atwater (Hot Metal) ....A

MICH.—Saginaw
Koehler Bros. (Log; Slab; Sawdust) ... .E
Wickes Bros. (Sawdust).AA

N. J.—Trenton
Trenton Iron Co. (Br. N. Y. City) (Cable Hoist)...AA

N. Y.—Brooklyn
Logan & Son, Farrell (Coal)
.............................A

N. Y.—Buffalo
Mey Chain Belting Engineering Works, 14 Perry (Fertilizer; Link Belt; Sawdust; Spiral; Screw) ...F
Noye Mfg. Co., Jno. T., 50 Lakeview (Flour) ......D

New York City
New Jersey Fdy. & Machine Co., 9 Murray (Cable Hoist) ....D
Robins Conveying Belt Co.,

CONVEYORS (Con.)

15 Park Row (Belt)....C
United Telpherage Co.. 20
   Broad (Automatic Elec-
   tric) X

OHIO—Akron
Webster, Camp & Lane
   Mach. Co. (Clay) .....A
Whitman & Barnes Mfg. Co.
   (Canvas; Harvester; Bin-
   der) ....AAAA

OHIO—Bucyrus
Am. Clay Working Machin-
   ery Co. ....AAAA

OHIO—Canton
Aultman Co. (Fertilizer;
   Freight; Link Belt; Log;
   Slab; Sawdust; Spiral;
   Screw) ....B
Bonnot Co. (Belt) ......B

OHIO—Cleveland
Bartlett & Snow Co., C. O.
   (Belt; Brick; Freight;
   Grain Elevator; Hot
   Metal; Spiral; Screw) .B
Cleveland Elev. Bucket Co.,
   225 St. Clair (Brick;
   Grain Elevator; Gravel;
   Sand) ....D

OHIO—Columbus
Jeffrey Mfg. Co. (Apron;
   Belt; Brick; Endless Pan;
   Spiral; Screw; Wire Ca-
   ble; Cable; Coal; Special;
   Clinker) ....AA

OHIO—Wellington
Wellington Machine Co.
   (Brick) ....B

PA.—Allegheny
Carlin's Sons, Thos. (Belt)
   ....A

PA.—Muncy
Sprout, Waldron & Co.
   (Flour; Grain Elevator).A

PA.—Philadelphia
Campbell, Peter F., 51 Lau-
   rel (Flour; Freight) ....D
Klein, Chas. C., 2850 N.
   Marshall (Belt) ....D
Link Belt Engineering Co.
   (Link Belt; Sawdust)...A
Thompson & Campbell
   (Flour; Freight) X

PA.—Pittsburg
Tate, Jones & Co. (Inc.)
   Empire Bldg. (Belt; Spi-
   ral; Screw; Cable Wire)
   ....E

PA.—Scottdale
Kenney & Co. (Coal).....A

PA.—So. Bethlehem
Bethlehem Fdy. & Machine
   Co. (Belt) C

PA.—Wilkesbarre
Vulcan Iron Works (Coal;
   Freight; Rock; Ore)
   ....AAAA

TENN.—Chattanooga
Wheland Machine Works
   (Refuse) ....A

TENN.—Jackson
Southern Engine & Boiler
   Wks. (Inc.) (Sawdust)..A

WIS.—Cudahy
Power & Mining Machinery
   Co. (Belt; Sawdust).AAA

WIS.—Milwaukee
Allis-Chalmers Co. (Log;
   Slab) ....AAAA
Chain Belt Co., 766 Park
   (Belt; Flour; Freight;
   Grain Elevator; Spiral;
   Screw; Saw Dust; Coal) B
Ffler & Stowell Co. (Log;
   Slab; Saw Dust; Coal)
   ....AAA
Grotenrach, F., 111 Water
   (Belt; Link Belt; Grain
   Elevator; Spiral; Screw)
   ....E

COOKERS

CONN.—Meriden
Manning, Bowman & Co.
   (Br. Internatl. Silver Co.)
   (Steam) ....AAAA

ILL.—Arlington Heights
Bray & Kates (Steam)...D

ILL.—Chicago
Henlon & Hubbell (Feed).B
Sinclair Laundry Machinery

COOKERS (Con.)
   Co., 60 North Clinton
   (Starch) X

ILL.—Quincy
Electric Wheel Co. (Feed) A

IND.—Indianapolis
Nordyke & Marmon Co.
   (Feed) ....AAA

IOWA—Waterloo
Kelly & Taneyhill (Feed).G
Litchfield Mfg. Co. (Feed)
   ....A

MAINE—Portland
Conant Co., R. O. (Corn).F

MICH.—Kalamazoo
Clark Engine & Boiler Co.
   (Steam) ....B

MICH.—Tecumseh
Helsen Bros. & Co. (Feed)
   ....D

MINN.—Minneapolis
Howell & Co., R. R. (Feed)
   ....B

MINN.—St. Paul
Woltersdorff-Haskell Range
   & Furnace Co. (Steam
   Vegetable) ....E

N. J.—Bridgeton
Cox Bros. & Co. (Corn)..E

N. Y.—Cortland
Lewis, L. R. (Feed) X

New York City
Bramhall-Deane Co. (Steam)
   ....D
Central Stamping Co.
   (Steam) ....AA
Dietz Co., R. E. (Steam).A
Gorton & Lidgerwood Co.
   (Feed) ....B
Stoutenborough, X. (Steam)
   ....D

N. Y.—Rochester
Castle & Co., Wilmot
   (Steam) ....B
Werner, John (Syrup) ...D

N. Y.—Syracuse
Hemingway Mfg. Co. (Corn)
   ....A

OHIO—Cincinnati
Am. Copper & Brass Co.
   (Steam) ....A
Francis & Bro., Chas. E.
   (Glue) ....B
Park Specialty Co. (Steam)
  X
Van Range Co., Jno. (Corn)
   ....A

OHIO—Mt. Gilead
Hydraulic Press Mfg. Co.
   (Apple Butter) ....A

OHIO—Toledo
Ohio Steam Cooker Co.
   (Steam) ....E
Toledo Cooker Co. (Steam)
  C

PA.—Allentown
Grammes & Sons, E. F.
   (Glue) ....A

PA.—Columbia
Wilson Laundry Machinery
   Co. (Starch) ....A

PA.—Royersford
Royal Gas Stove & Fdy. Co.
   (Gas) C

COOLERS

CONN.—Meriden
Manning, Bowman & Co.
   (Water; Wine) ......AA
Meriden Britannia Co.
   (Wine) ....AAAA

ILL.—Batavia
U. S. Wind Engine & Pump
   Co. (Milk) ....AA

ILL.—Chicago
Sturges & Burns Mfg. Co.
   (Water) ....A
Wilson & Co., F. C. (Water)
   ....B

ILL.—Elgin
Barclay, D. F. (Milk)....A

MASS.—Boston
Hersey Mfg. Co. (Brewers'
   Beer) ....AA
Strater & Sons, Herman
   (Milk; Beer) ....A
Whitman & Co., Orrin M.
   (Milk) ....D

MASS.—Chelsea

COOLERS (Con.)
Low Tile Co. (Water; Wine)
...............................F

MASS.—Lowell
Woods, Sherwood & Co.
(Wire; Bread; Cake)...E
MICH.—Flint
Cook Car Journal Co. (Car
Journal) C
MO.—St. Louis
Brecht Butchers' Supply Co.,
G. V. (Lard) ....AAA
St. Louis Stamping Co.
. (Wine) ....AAAA
N. J.—Flemington
Fulper Pottery Co. (Stone-
ware Water) ....D
N. Y.—Brooklyn
Cooper & McKee (Water).A
N. Y.—Buffalo
Aldrich Mfg. Co. (Water)
...............................A
Buffalo Mfg. Co., 442 Nia-
gara (Water) ....B
Heinz & Munschauer
(Water) ....A
Jewett Mfg. Co., John C.
(Water; Wine) ......AA
Pierce Co., Geo. N. (Water)
...............................AA
Shepard & Co., Sidney
(Water) ....AAAA
Smith's Sons, John E.
(Lard) ....B
Vogt, Peter A. (Beer)...B
N. Y.—Cattaraugus
Oakes & Burger (Curd;
Milk) ....B
New York City
Appert Glass Co., 277 Bway
(Glass; Water) X
Brunswick - Balke Collen-
der Co. (Beer) ....AAAA
Cordley & Hayes (Fibre;
Wine; Water) ....A
Jochum, Andrew (Brewers'
Beer) ....E
Koven & Bro., L. O., 50 Cliff
(Water) ....A
Lalance & Grosjean Mfg. Co.
(Water; Wine) ...AAAA
Mace & Co., L. H. (Wooden;
Water) ....B
Nichthauser & Levy, 96
Beekman (Ice) C
Stoutenborough, X. (Water)
...............................D
U. S. Mineral Wool Co.
(Fibre; Water) ....D
N. Y.—Utica
Jones, Frank L. (Milk)...C
OHIO—Cleveland
Harris Mfg. Co. (Lard)...C
OHIO—Hamilton
Black & Clawson Co. (Lard)
...............................AAA
OHIO—Toledo
Stevens, B. A. (Beer)....A
PA.—Philadelphia
Hall, Son & Co., Amos H.
(Brewers' Beer) C
Nittinger, August (Lard).A
Reid, A. H. (Milk) ......A
VT.—Bellows Falls
Vermont Farm Machine Co.
(Milk) C
WIS.—Fort Atkinson
Cornish, Curtis & Greene
Mfg. Co. (Milk) ....A

COOPERAGE

ALA.—Demopolis
Demopolis Cooperage Co..C
ALA.—Mobile
Kennedy Stove & Cooperage
Co. (Staves) X
ALA.—Montgomery
Montgomery Cooperage &
Hardwood Co. ....B
ARK.—Black Rock
Black Rock Lumber &
Cooperage Co. C
ARK.—Camden
Anderson & Co. ....B
ARK.—Crawfordsville
Foley Stave Co., W. R.
(Whiskey Staves; Wine
Staves; Pork Staves)..D
Gilt Edge Cooperage Co.

COOPERAGE (Con.)
(Slack Stock; Elm Hoops)
...............................D

ARK.—De Queen
De Queen Stave & Lumber
Co. ....E
O'Neil & Son, J. H.......E
ARK.—Dermott
Bodenheim, M. B.........B
ARK.—Draughon
Draughon Stove Co......B
ARK.—Fayetteville
Fayetteville Cooperage Co.E
ARK.—Fordyce
Hampton, J. E. & G. M..B
Hampton Stave Co. .....D
ARK.—Greenfield
Greenfield Lumber & Coop-
erage Co. ....A
ARK.—Hamburg
Hamburg Stave Co. .....D
ARK.—Jonesboro
Alfrey, Henry ....AA
Jonesboro Stave & Hard-
wood Co. ....D
ARK.—Judsonia
Stecher Cooperage Works..A
ARK.—Junction
Cornil Stave Co. (Staves).C
ARK.—Little Rock
Gibson & Cunningham
(Staves) C
Greenville Stave Co. (Light
Staves) ....D
Hamlen & Son Co., J. H.
(Light Staves) ....A
Little Rock Cooperage Co..A
Willson Stave Co., W. W.
(Light Staves) ....B
ARK.—Nettleton
Kiech, Ferdinand (Staves)
...............................B
ARK.—Newport
Pond-Decker Mfg. Co. ....A
ARK.—Paragould
Wrape Hy. Co. ....A
ARK.—Stephens
Texarkana Cooperage Mfg.
Co. ....E
ARK.—Wilmar
Wilmar Stave Co. ....A
ARK.—Wynne
Kennedy & Morelock Stave
Co. ....B
CAL.—Los Angeles
Los Angeles Cooperage Co.
...............................C
CAL.—San Francisco
Carl, Andrew, 217 Commer-
cial ....E
Pacific Woodenware & Coop-
erage Co. ....B
D. C.—Washington
Gaskins, W. H., 1006 32nd
N. W. ....B
Kuhn, J. O. R., 3129 K.
N. W. ....D
GA.—Moultree
Colquett Co. Cooperage Co.
...............................E
ILL.—Alton
Alton Steam Cooperage Co.
...............................E
ILL.—Aurora
Aurora Cooperage Co. ....B
ILL.—Cairo
Nordman, F. (Staves)...B
ILL.—Carlyle
Patterson, P. (Staves)...E
ILL.—Chicago
Burkhartmeier Bros., 27 N.
Peoria C
Clayton, Chas., 576 25th..B
Gates, A. & H., 205 La
Salle C
Hemming & Co., E., 145
La Salle (Light; Slack
Staves) ....B
Maxwell Bros., Loomis &
21st ....AA
Rothwell, H. R., 337
Michigan (Bbls.).......E
Washburn & Co., C. G., 169
Jackson (Light Staves;
Heads; Hoops) ....D
Winterbotham & Son, 226
La Salle ....A
ILL.—Hutsonville
Hussong, McNutt & Co.
(Staves) ....E
ILL.—Mound Center

273

COOPERAGE (Con.)

Meyer, C. F. (White Oak
  Staves; Headings) .....A
ILL.—New Athens
Newman & Probst (Staves')
                         E
ILL.—Pekin
Pekin Stave & Mfg. Co...B
ILL.—Peoria
Empire Cooperage Co. ...E
Madigan & Walsch Co....C
Nat'l Cooperage & Wooden-
  ware Co. ....B
ILL.—Sandoval
Hall, H. R. C
ILL.—Shibonier
Shibonier Mfg. Co. C
ILL.—Vandalia
Walker Stave Co. ....E
IND.—Angola
Linder & Ramsey ....E
IND.—Aurora
Wymond Cooperage Co....A
IND.—Bern
Bern Hoop Mfg. Co......D
IND.—Birds Eye
Hubbard Bros. (Hoops)..D
IND.—Bluffton
Adams, F. P. (Staves)..E
Bluffton Hoop Co. ......E
IND.—Clay City
Clay City Mfg. Co. (Staves)
                         E
IND.—Evansville
Schultze, Waltman &Co..B
IND.—Ft. Wayne
Convoy Hoop Co. (Coiled
  Elm Hoops) X
Noble, W. K. ....B
Yergens & Son, W. C
IND.—Frankfort
Frankfort Hoop Co. .....E
IND.—Goblesville
Goble, J. H. ....E
IND.—Greencastle
Hirt, Alfred (Staves) C
IND.—Hoagland
Houser Bros. (Headings).F
IND.—Huntingburg
Partenheimer & Link ....E
IND.—Huntington
Griffith & Son, G. V.
  (Hoops) ....B
IND.—Kokomo
Snider, L. (Staves) .....D
Wright & Knight (Hoops).D
IND.—Lafayette
Peck & Abbott ....B
IND.—Lawrenceburg
Bauer Cooperage Co......A
IND.—Madison
Thomas, J. W. (Bbls.)..B
Tower Mfg. Co. C
IND.—Marion
Ackerman, B. C. (Headings)
                         E
IND.—Martinsville
Davis Cooperage Co. ....B
IND.—Michigan City
Winterbotham & Sons, J. H.
                         A
IND.—Mount Vernon
Ford & McGregor (Staves)
                         B
Moeller, J. M. ....E
IND.—New Carlisle
Hofman, F. (Pork Barrels)
                         E
IND.—New Castle
New Castle Coiled Hoop Co.
                         D
IND.—New Haven
Schnelker & Co., H. F.
  (Staves) ....B
IND.—Portland
Adams, D. L. (Staves;
  Headings) ....B
IND.—Rushville
Anderson Coiled Hoop Co.D
IND.—Sheldon
Eagle Hoop Co. ....D
IND.—South Bend
Bemis, Chas. (Bbls) ....D
IND.—Sullivan
Otto, John ....D
IND.—Terre Haute
Adair, Stephen ....D
Blair & Farley Co. (Staves)
                         B
Griffith & Stone ....D
IND.—Tipton

COOPERAGE (Con.)

Bowlin & Co., M. L. .....D
IND.—Troy
Anderson River Stave Works
  (Butter Tub Staves) ...X
IND.—Wakarusa
Liniger & Harris (Hoops).F
IND.—Washington
Creager, L. H. ....D
IOWA—Burlington
Moehn, Adam...........D
IOWA—Cresco
Owens, W. R............C
IOWA—Davenport
Bremer & Son, Hy. .....D
Woodruff-Kroy Co. (Slack
  Barrel; Butter Tub Stock)
                         B
IOWA—Dubuque
Key City Cooperage & Mfg.
  Co. ....D
IOWA—Keokuk
Keokuk Barrel & Hoop Co.
                         F
IOWA—Sioux City
Barker Cooperage Co. ....D
KANS.—Kansas City
Hauber Bros. Cooperage Co.
                         C
Kansas City Cooperage Co.D
KANS.—Leavenworth
Rothenberger, J. H. ......B
KANS.—Wichita
Wichita Cooperage Co. ..B
KY.—Burnside
Taylor-Mitchell (Oak Whis-
  key; Beer Stock) ......B
KY.—Campbellsville
Goudy, J. E. ....D
KY.—Clay City
Clay City Lumber & Stave
  Co. ....D
Eastern Kentucky Stave Co.
                         E
Russell, F. B. ....E
KY.—Columbus
Columbus Stave Co. ......D
KY.—Greensburg
Braden & Co., L. P.
  (White Oak Staves) ..X
KY.—Lawrenceburg
Dowling, John ....B
KY.—Livermore
Quigg Mfg. Co. (Gum
  Staves) ....E
Smith Bros. (Hoops) ....D
KY.—Louisville
Bergen & Meehan Co.
  (Staves) ....D
Chess & Wymond Co.
  (Staves) ....AA
Henry, F. (Bbls.) ....D
Hubbard Bros. (Beer; Whis-
  key; Staves; Heads)....C
Hyatt, J. J. ....B
Kentucky Cooperage Co.
  (Slack Stock; Shaved
  Hoops) ....F
Kentucky Stave Co. ......D
Ohio Valley Cooperage Co.
  (Slack Stock) ....E
Russell, Frank R. (Beer
  Staves; Headings) ....B
Schwarzenwalder & Sons..
                      AAAA
Sengel, P. ....D
Stafford Cooperage Co. (For
  Whiskey; Pork; Lard)..X
Vandiver & Hilte ....D
KY.—Newport
Kronk Barrel Co. ....F
KY.—Paducah
Kilgore & Co., J. L.
  (Headings) ....A
LA.—Jonesboro
Louisiana Stave Co. (Ltd.)
                         X
LA.—New Orleans
Albert, C., 618 Montegut
  (For Molasses; Rice)...X
Beck's Sons, T. A. (For
  Sugar; Molasses; Rice).B
Bobert Bros. (Staves)...AA
Brooklyn Cooperage Co.
  Peters & Erato ....A
Hirsh, P., 335 N. Front..C
Keegan, N., 1710 Tchoup
  (For Flour; Sugar; Mo-
  lasses) ....F
Louisiana Mfg. & Cooper-
  age Co., 221 S. Peters..B

COOPERAGE (Con.)
LeBlanc, P. A., 515 Conti
  (For Sugar; Molasses) ..F
Long, N. J., 208 S. Peters.D
McEnamy, M., 541 S.
  Peters C
Magner, L. J., 217 S. Front
  (For Sugar; Rice; Mo-
  lasses) X
Moore & Co., Lucas E.
  (White Oak Staves) ...B
Union Stave Co. ....A
MAINE—Appleton
Sherman, W. (Staves)....E
MAINE—Bangor
Sweet & Co. C
MAINE—Bristol
Robbins, C. C. (Bbls.) ..D
MAINE—Brownfield
Marstin, J. G. (Staves)..G
MAINE—Bucksport
Perkins & Co., F. G.
  (Staves) ....B
MAINE—Chisholm
Garden Bros. (Bbls) ....D
MAINE—Dennyville
Lyons Bros. (Staves)....D
MAINE—No. Sedgwick
Durgis' Son, J. N. (Staves)
                         E
MAINE—Portland
Hamlin & Son Co........A
Portland Cooperage Co...C
MAINE—Searsmont
Ripley, A. B. ....E
MD.—Baltimore
Gilkin & Co., 920 E. Front
                         C
Kunker, H. F. (Bbls.)...G
Pensel, Geo., 1024 Plum Al-
  ley ....G
Revier, H. G. (Bbls.)...E
MD.—Cambridge
Cambridge Mfg. Co. (Bbls.)
                         A
MASS.—Boston
Am. Stave & Cooperage Co.,
  156 State ....D
Fisher & Co., J., 17 Cald-
  well ....D
Hull & Co., C. E., 39 Hart-
  ford ....A
MASS.—Somerville
Armstrong & Co. ....D
MICH.—Benton Harbor
Colby-Hinkley Co. (Fr.
  Pkgs.) ....B
MICH.—Detroit
Althouse, C. W. (Stock).A
Crescent Mfg. Co. (Staves;
  Hdgs.) ....B
Detroit Steel Cooperage Co.
  (Steel) ....B
Hasty & Sons, J. F. ....A
Kelsey, E. L., 11 Wood-
  ward Av. C
Mich. Cooperage Co. (Slack
  Stock) ....D
National Mfg. Co. (Slack
  Staves; Headings)......D
Sauer & Son, W. ....D
MICH.—Gladstone
Northwestern Cooperage &
  Lumber Co. (Staves;
  Hoops; Headings) ....AA
MICH.—Grand Rapids
Grand Rapids Stave Co.
  (Bbls.) C
Michigan Barrel Co. (Bbls.)
                         A
Michigan Elm Hoop Co.
  (Elm Hoops) X
MICH.—Kalamazoo
Smith, J. G. ....E
MICH.—Quincy
Globensky, F. (For Pork).D
MICH.—Saginaw
Wylie & Co., J. T. (Hoops;
  Staves; Hdgs.) C
MICH.—Ypsilanti
Moore, W. A. ....G
MINN.—Aiken
Gyde, E. A. (Hoops) ....G
MINN.—Fosston
Heuss, F. (Staves) ......D
MINN.—Ronneby
Wood & Son, J. M. (Hdgs.)
                         D
MINN.—St. Paul
Gruber, N. ....D
St. Paul Barrel Co. .....B

COOPERAGE (Con.)
MISS.—Corinth
Adams, W. T. (Headings)
                        AA
MISS.—Friar's Point
Miller & Co. (Slack Staves)
                         D
MISS.—Greenwood
Sutherland, Innes & Co.
  (Staves) ....A
MISS.—Sunflower
Pittman, Baker & Grimes
  (Staves) ....D
MISS.—Vernon
Stuart & Co., F. P.
  (Staves) ....D
MO.—Alexandria
Bott Bros. Mfg. Co. ....D
MO.—Ardeola
Ardeola Stave Co. ......B
MO.—Bloomfield
Pioneer Cooperage Co. ..AA
MO.—Brownwood
Pioneer Cooperage Co....AA
MO.—Burfordville
Cape Co. Milling Co. .....A
MO.—Cape Girardeau
Cape Stave & Heading Co.
                         C
MO.—Caruthersville
Worst, Weirman & Brinker-
  hoff X
MO.—Dexter
Hoffman Heading & Stave
  Co. ....D
MO.—Harviell
Marigold & Co. (Staves;
  Hdgs.) ....B
MO.—Hayti
Worst, Weirman & Brinker-
  hoff ....A
MO.—Jackson
Cape Co. Milling Co.
  (Staves) ....A
MO.—Kansas City
Kansas City Cooperage Co.D
MO.—Malden
Nimmons, B. (Hdgs.)....B
MO.—Morehouse
Riepe & Co. (Staves; Hdgs.)
                         D
MO.—Parma
Payne Stave & Lumber Co.
  (Elm; Gum, etc., Staves)
                         B
MO.—Poplar Bluff
Palmer, L. M. ....AA
Williams Cooperage, H. D.
                         A
MO.—St. Joseph
Hougan, R. ....D
Southern Cooperage Co. ..A
MO.—St. Louis
Columbia Cooperage Co. ..D
Stecher Cooperage Co.(Beer;
  Wine Casks; Barrels;
  Kegs) ....AA
Union Cooperage Co. (Fish;
  Pickles) ....B
MO.—Springfield
Springfield Hoop Co. ....D
Wenderlich Cooperage Co.B
NEBR.—South Omaha
Omaha Cooperage Co. ...C
N. H.—East Ware
Fessenden & Lowell ....AA
N. H.—Fremont
Spaulding & Frost Co. ...C
N. H.—Hollis
Worcester Bros. ....B
N. H.—Keene
Impervious Package Co..B
N. H.—Milford
Gilson, H. S. ....D
N. H.—Reeds Ferry
Fessenden & Lowell ....AA
N. H.—Spofford
Spofford Mfg. Co. ....E
N. J.—Hoboken
Ryan, J. (Bbls.) ....D
Stanley, J. & W. C
N. J.—Jersey City
Day & O'Donnell ....D
Central Cooperage Co. ...C
Heldt & Son, C. ....B
Mathison Cooperage Co. ..C
O'Connor, J. J. ....B
Proctor Bros. & Co. .....A
N. J.—Trenton
White, E. A. ....D
N. Y.—Akron

COOPERAGE (Con.)

Jackson, T. W. (Staves)..C
N. Y.—Albany
Le Gallez, A. C
Pennie, John C
N. Y.—Brooklyn
Brooklyn Cooperage Co., 142
  Kent Av. ....A
O'Donnell, A., 110 Classon
  Av. ....D
Schwalb, F., 34 Garden ..C
Weidman Cooperage Co., N.
  1st & Berry ....A
N. Y.—Buffalo
Bogner, Jos., 94 Kingsley
                   F
Buffalo Pail & Barrel Co.,
  500 Babcock ....D
Church & Bro., Thompson &
  Parish ....A
Seitz Bros., 345 East ...D
Tindale & Jackson, 1318
  Niagara ....AA
N. Y.—Canastota
N. Y. Cooperage Co. ....D
N. Y.—Catskill
Jones, H. P. ....A
N. Y.—Chatham
Haviland & Son, R. S.
  (Staves) ....D
N. Y.—Crown Point
Snyder & Barringer
  (Staves) ....D
N. Y.—Eagle Harbor
Bennett & Co., C. ....D
N. Y.—East Hamlin
Union Cooperage Co. .....D
N. Y.—Elba
Staples & Son, J. A.
  (Staves; Hdgs.) ....D
N. Y.—Ellenville
Hornbeck, S. E. D. (Hoops)
                   F
Marshall, Mrs. F. ....D
N. Y.—Evergreen
Schmidt & Co. ....D
N. Y.—Fairport
Defendorf, F. A. ....D
N. Y.—Fillmore
Brooks, W. P. C
Young & Young ....D
N. Y.—Germantown
Coons, C. C. ....D
Snyder & Barringer ......D
N. Y.—Jamestown
Shaver & Hall ....AA
N. Y.—Liverpool
Smith, J. & P. (Bbls.)...D
N. Y.—Lockport
Bishop, J. P. ....D
Little & Son, J. W. (Bbls.)
                   F
N. Y.—Lyons
Bashford, S. ....D
N. Y.—Medina
Acer, V. A. (Staves) ....B
Smith, J. (Bbls.) ....B
N. Y.—Medusa
Smith, J. (Bbls.).........B
N. Y.—Middleport
Sterritt & Granes (Hdgs.;
  Bbls.) C
N. Y.—Newark
Perkins Cooperage Co., C.
  H. ....A
New York City
Bergen & Co., 9 Old Slip
  (Staves) ....A
Brooklyn Cooperage Co., 184
  Front ....A
Centenan & Son, L., 4 Stone
  (Staves) ....A
Church Cooperage Co., 13
  Park Row (Staves;
  Heads) ....A
Daniels, M. S., 24 State..B
Fisher, H. C., Produce Exch.
                   C
Getz, J., 303 E. 64th......D
Keys, Chas. H., 42 B'way
  (Slack; Light Staves,
  etc.) ....A
Keys & Son, J. G., 198 W.
  B'way ....B
Lapham & Co., 150 Nassau
                   B
Maguire Bros., 527 W. 55th
  (Lime Barrels)........E
O'Donnell, N. & H., 202
  Henry C
Schwarzwalder & Sons, 629

COOPERAGE (Con.)

W. 51st ....AAAA
Spencer & Son. W., 16 S.
  William ....B
Stanley, J. & W., 61 Laight
                   C
Sutherland, Innes Co., 29
  B'way ....AA
N. Y.—Niagara Falls
Glir, E. F. X
N. Y.—N. Germantown
Ham, Wilson & Co. .....D
N. Y.—North Rose
Union Cooperage Co. ....D
N. Y.—Ogdensburg
Northrup. H. D. (Staves).C
N. Y.—Palmyra
Burns, O. ....D
N. Y.—Poughkeepsie
Lown & Son ....B
N. Y.—Ripley
Richenbrode, W. B. ......D
N. Y.—Rochester
Esse, P. ....D
Skuse, T. G. ....B
N. Y.—Summerville
Adams, S. A. (Hoops) ...C
N. Y.—Syracuse
Burkhardt, L. ....D
Union Cooperage Co. ....D
N. Y.—Waterford
Hempstead, J. ....D
N. Y.—Wayne Centre
Putnam & Co., J. N. (Bbls.)
                   D
N. Y.—Webster
Billings & Son, L. J......B
N. C.—Bayborough
Bayborough Barrel Factory
                   D
N. C.—Lexington
Gray, M. K. (Staves) ....D
OHIO—Albany
Kiger, O. (Staves) ......E
OHIO—Alger
Grief Bros. Co. (Staves)..
                  AA
OHIO—Alvordton
Geesey, W. H. ....F
OHIO—Archbald
Gotshall Bros. C
OHIO—Arlington
Allen, Clark & Co. ......A
Showan & Co., G. W.
  (Hoops; Staves) ....E
OHIO—Ashland
Martieu, B. & G. (Staves).C
OHIO—Ashley
Dickson, Joseph ....G
OHIO—Batavia
Glancy & Breeding ......F
OHIO—Beach City
Camp, Alex. ....F
OHIO—Bell Brook
Killian, C. A. ....H
OHIO—Bellefontaine
Bose. John ....F
OHIO—Belleville
Retter, Philip (Staves) ..H
OHIO—Bellevue
Erdrick, W. H. (Staves,
  etc.) ....E
OHIO—Berlin
Grotthouse, Harmon .....G
OHIO—Berlin Centre
Baith & Sons, Wm. (Hoops)
                  H
OHIO—Birmingham
Henry, C. H. ....H
OHIO—Briceton
Magee, J. H. (Staves) ...A
Tank, Fred. (Staves) ....H
OHIO—Canal Dover
Hagner, C. L. ....H
OHIO—Carey
Perkins & Wallace (Staves)
                  E
OHIO—Celina
Celina Hoop Co. (Hoops)..G
OHIO—Chillicothe
Heimburger, Geo. ....H
OHIO—Cincinnati
Becker Veneer Barrel Co.,
  2nd & John X
Cinn. Cooperage Co. ..AAA
Hauser, Brenner & Fath Co.,
  McLean & Bank.......A
Oker & Sons, Jos., 409
  Charlotte ....B
Van Agthoven, A., 307 W.
  Front ....A

COOPERAGE (Con.)

OHIO—Circleville
Eagle Cooperage Works ..D
Richards, Conrad ....E
Sapp, George ....H
OHIO—Clarendon
Keppler, J. P. ....H
OHIO—Cleveland
Cleveland Barrel Co., 1396
St. Clair ....F
Grief Bros. Co. (Staves;
Bbls.) ....AA
OHIO—Columbiana
Shanner, J. ....H
OHIO—Columbus
Lapp, Jacob ....D
OHIO—Columbus Grove
Buckeye Stave Co. (Staves;
Hdgs.) ....AA
OHIO—Continental
Bruckeye Stave Co. (Staves;
Hdgs.) ....AA
OHIO—Convoy
Convoy Hoop Co. (Hoops) .C
OHIO—Creston
Kerr, A. E. ....E
OHIO—Cuyahoga Falls
Turner, Vaughan & Taylor
Co. (Chain; Nail Kegs) X
OHIO—Defiance
Dicus, Geo. H. X
Marshal & Son, John ....D
Rowe, John (Hoops) ....H
OHIO—Delphos
Weger, Thos. A. ....E
OHIO—Dowling
Garrill, M. R. (Staves)..D
OHIO—East Liverpool
Bough, M. H. ....G
Dawson, N. F. ....G
Faulk Bros. Co. ....D
Hill, Robert ....F
McCain Bros. ....G
McKinnon, T. B. ....G
Williams & Co., F. P. ...G
Williams & Co., S. C. ...B
OHIO—Elmore
Magee, J. H. ....A
OHIO—Findlay
Walter, J. E. ....G
OHIO—Fostoria
Fostoria Stave & Barrel Co.
B
OHIO—Fremont
West, N. C. (Hoops) X
OHIO—Geyer
Bose, John (Staves) .....F
OHIO—Gibsonburg
Zorn, Horning Co. (Staves;
Hdgs.) ....A
OHIO—Greenville
Kilgore & Co., J. L. (Staves)
A
OHIO—Grover Hill
Lenhart Cooperage Co., W.
S. C
OHIO—Hagerman
Burns & Co., D. (Staves) A
OHIO—Harrison
Richter, F. ....H
OHIO—Hicksville
Buckeye Stave Co. .....AA
OHIO—Holgate
Shelby & Bro. ....A
OHIO—Leipsic
Buckeye Stave Co. ......AA
OHIO—Lindsay
Lindsay Hoop & Stave Co. A
OHIO—Louisville
Nichols, James ....E
OHIO—Luckey
Eddy & Co., N. B. (Staves;
Hdgs.) ....F
OHIO—McGill
Gideon Bros. (Hdgs.) C
OHIO—Madison
Gale, L. ....H
OHIO—Maria Stein
Kleinhenz & Son (Hoops) G
OHIO—Marietta
Courath, Jacob..........F
OHIO—Marion
Morganthaler, Wm. ......G
Schweinfurth, Adam .....E
OHIO—Martins Ferry
Bettis & Co., H. (Kegs) ..B
Martins Ferry Keg & Barrel
Wks. ....E
OHIO—Metamora
Ries, Conrad (Headings) X
OHIO—Minster
Minster Cooperage Co. ...D
Haas, Hy. ....H

COOPERAGE (Con.)

OHIO—Mt. Vernon
Park, Colville & Herrick Co.
(Staves) ....E
OHIO—Mungen
Dewey Stave Co. ....AA
OHIO—Napoleon
Bruner & Son, A. (Hoops) D
OHIO—Navarre
Baetzer, C. ....H
OHIO—New Bavaria
Horning, Jacob (Staves;
Hoops) ....D
OHIO—New Bremen
Schneider, Aug. ....G
OHIO—New Richmond
Hoh, B. ....H
Schuler, H. A. ....H
OHIO—New Springfield
Reash, Andrew (Bbl. Hds.)
E
OHIO—New Washington
New Wash. Mfg. Co. (Bbls.)
E
OHIO—Oak Harbor
Dorset Cooperage Co.....A
Mylander, W. H. ....E
Oak Harbor Cooperage &
Lumber Co. ....A
Roose, Chas. Sr. (Staves;
Hds.) ....B
OHIO—Ottawa
Lenhart Cooperage Co., W.
S. C
OHIO—Paulding
Weidman Stave & Heading
Mills C
OHIO—Payne
Payne Stave Co. C
Schnelker & Co., H. F.
(Staves) ....B
OHIO—Piqua
Elbert, Fred'k. ....H
OHIO—Pleasant Bend
Buckeye Stave Co. ......AA
OHIO—Pomeroy
Morton, C. M. ....G
OHIO—Richwood
Marks, A. (Hoops) ....F
OHIO—Rockford
Adams & Son, T. C. (Staves)
C
OHIO—Sandusky
Brumm, Aug. ....D
Kilbourn & Co. ....A
Michel Bros. C
Ritter, Lewis ....G
Sandusky Cooperage & Lum-
ber Co. C
Zimmerman, Christ. .....G
OHIO—Somerset
Flaut, G. B. ....H
OHIO—Southington
Houghton & Straup (Staves)
E
Hurd, Frank (Staves) ....E
OHIO—South New Lyne
Berg, C. A. (Hoops) .....G
OHIO—Springfield
Geier, Joseph ....H
Lisch, J. J. ....H
Schnorbus, Jos. F. ......F
OHIO—Styker
Brun, H. F. (Hoops; Staves)
C
OHIO—Tiffin
Schweickhards & Dunn
(Staves) ....F
OHIO—Tippecanoe City
Sweeney, Edward ....H
OHIO—Troy
Brady, George ....H
OHIO—Van Wert
Eagle Stave Works ..AAAA
OHIO—Versailles
Fritschull, Henry ......G
OHIO—Wauseon
Wauseon Mfg. Co. (Staves)
D
OHIO—Wellington
Paul, Husted & Co. .....G
OHIO—Wellsville
Blackburn, W. F. ....H
OHIO—West Unity
Burkhart, Joseph ....F
OHIO—Winesburg
Sterzbach, Geo. ....H
OHIO—Woodville
Bittinger, D. H. (Staves) E
OHIO—Yondata
Teachont, Albert (Staves) E
OHIO—Zanesville
Basehart, J. H. ....F
OREGON—Astoria
Kearney Bros. ....F

COOPERAGE (Con.)

OREGON—Clatskamie
Aldridge, D. C. ....H
OREGON—Gales Creek
Miller, David ....H
OREGON—Langlois
Haagensen, O. P. ....G
OREGON—Mt. Angel
Schaffer Bros ....F
OREGON—Nehalem
Alley, H. V. ....H
PA.—Adamsville
Palmanteer & Ellis ....G
PA.—Allegheny
Menke, G. ....D
PA.—Allentown
Rice, W. H. ....E
Trexter Cooperage Co. ...G
PA.—Beaver Falls
Bell & Sons Co., E. .....A
PA.—Belleville
Hostetler, J. E. (Staves) F
PA.—Brodbeck
Werner, John ....G
PA.—Canonsburg
Budke Mfg. Co. (Kegs) ..A
PA.—Catasauqua
Treaster, L. F. (Staves) ..D
PA.—Corseca
Jones, J. B. (Staves) ....B
PA.—Corry
Westley, D. & F. E. (Butter
  Pails) ....G
PA.—Coudersport
Dieffenbachen, J. F. (Slack
  Bbl. Hds.) C
PA.—Diminsville
Brown, T. J. (Hoops)....H
PA.—Falkton
Kennedy, M. T. & C. (Kegs)
                          A
PA.—Foltz
Hill, John ....F
PA.—Flora Dale
Wert. R. S. ....G
PA.—Freedom
Menke, J. J. ....D
PA.—Galeton
Galeton Stave & Mfg. Co. D
PA.—Honesdale
McKenna's Sons, P. ......F
PA.—Kingsville
Burnham & McClune
  (Staves) ....F
PA.—Lawrenceville
Brown, W. E. (Hds.) ....F
PA.—Loysburg
Geibel, J. W. (Agt.) X
PA.—Mertztown
Trexter Stave & Lumber Co.
                          D
PA.—Milroy
Treaster, L. F. (Staves) ..D
PA.—Mt. Joy
Greenawald, B. F. ....F
PA.—New Baltimore
Warner, J. F. ....G
PA.—New Brighton
Kennedy & Son, M. T.
  (Kegs) ....A
PA.—Newburg
Heffelfinger, D. ....F
PA.—North East
Wagoner, F. X
PA.—Oil City
Rush, H. G. ....B
PA.—Pennsylvania Furnace
Knepp & Wert (Staves) ..D
PA.—Pittsburg
Bell & Co., Edwin (Nail;
  Spike; Bolt &c. Kegs;
  Lime; Flour &c. Barrels)
                          A
Walsh-Morris (Slack Bar-
  rels; Casks; Tierces)....A
Walsh Mfg. Co. (Nail Kegs)
                          A
PA.—Rupert
Monroe, W. M. (Kegs) ..E
PA.—Titusville
Stephens, W. J. (Staves;
  Hds.) ....A
PA.—Wagner
Gibboney, S (Staves) ...D
PA.—Warren
Knabb & Co., A. (Bbls.;
  Hds) ....A
PA.—Wilkinsburg
Goldie, Wm. (Hoops) ....A
PA.—York
Everhart, Geo. W. ......E
Lehn, D. & P ....E
Rehmeyer, C. W. ....D
S. C.—Charleston
Bainbridge Cooperage &
  Supply Co. ....D

COOPERAGE (Con.)

Palmer Mfg. Co. (Bbls.) ..A
TENN.—Beach Bluff
Laws Bros. ....B
Thompson & Co., I. W. ...C
TENN.—Bristol
Williams & Sons, Jno. T.
  (Slack Staves; Heads;
  Hoops)................B
TENN.—Dyersburg
Dyersburg Stave & Heading
  Co. (Slack Stock) X
Hall & Dawson (Staves;
  Heads; Hoops) ....A
Volterman & Co., F. H.
  (Oak; Poplar; Ash; Gum;
  Elm; Keg Stock) X
Wood, S. A. (Staves) .....E
TENN.—Erie
Harris, V. R. C
Hayes, A. L. (Staves) ...D
Ross, W. P. (Stave) ...E
TENN.—Gleason
Bynum, W. B. (Slack Stock)
                          D
TENN.—Greenfield
Coats Bros. (Staves) .....D
TENN.—Halls
Wilson & Co., W. F.
  (Staves; Hds.) ....E
TENN.—Holladay
Harrison, W. F. (Staves) D
TENN.—Huntingdon
Dalton, G. B. (Staves) ...C
TENN.—Jackson
Coleman Co., W. H.
  (Headings) ....B
TENN.—Johnson City
Exum & Boring (Hds.)....D
Wilson, J. A. (Staves) C
TENN.—Memphis
Chickasaw Cooperage Co. AA
Fleischer, Max (Tank;
  Claret Staves) X
TENN.—Milan
Keaton Bros. (Oil; Pork;
  Whiskey Staves).......G
Todd & Roper (Staves) ..D
TENN.—Mixie
Hurdle Bros. & Co. (Staves)
                          D
TENN.—Monterey
Monterey Stave & Lumber
  Co. (Staves) ....E
Kayes Co., A. L. (Light
  Barrel Stock) X
TENN.—Nashville
Mocker, C. H. ....D
Werne, R. (Bbl.).......D
TENN.—New River
Keen, J. M. (Staves) ...D
TENN.—Oneida
Shaver, Hall & Cross
  (Staves) ....AA
TENN.—Ripley
Cinn Cooperage Co. ....AA
TENN.—Sherwood
Gager Lime & Mfg. Co. ..C
TENN.—Trenton
Harlan & Co., T. (Light Bar-
  rel Stock) ....B
TENN.—Trezevant
Harris & Fuqua (Staves) D
TENN.—Union City
Howard, J. F. ....D
TENN.—Whitfield
McLean & Hall (Staves) ..D
TENN.—Winfield
Shaver Hall & Cross
  (Staves) ....AA
TEXAS—Dallas
Dallas Cooperage Co. ....E
TEXAS—Houston
Houston Barrel & Cistern
  Factory ....D
TEXAS—Sherman
Sherman Cooperage Co. ..F
TEXAS—Texarkana
Little Rock Cooperage Co. A
VA.—Belfield
Enterprise Co. (Bbls.) ...E
VA.—Bodley
Bell, J. A. ....D
VA.—Browntown
Rappahannock Lumber Co.
  (Slack Stock) X
VA.—Exmore
Gladstone & Nicholson ..E
VA.—Keizletown
Va. Stave & Heading Co. D
VA.—Lee
Anderson, J. R. ....A
VA.—Lynchburg
Yates, J. T. ....D
VA.—McKenney
McKenney Mfg. Co. (Slack

COOPERAGE (Con.)
Barrel Stock) ....F
VA.—Norfolk
Farmers Mfg. Co. (Bbls.) B
Reed Bros. & Co. (Staves) C
Reids, Sons, E. ....A
Stires, R. W. (Bbls.; Hdgs.)
　　　　　　　　　　　　B
WASH.—Aberdeen
Western Cooperage Co.
(Tubs) C
WASH.—Brookfield
Finke Bros. (Staves; Bbls.)
　　　　　　　　　　　　D
WASH.—Colby
Feas, A. S. (Bbls.) ......F
WASH.—Fairhaven
Spratt, A. C. ....H
WASH.—Mukilteo
Graville, Peter ....F
WASH.—Roche Harbor
Staveless Barrel Co. X
WASH.—Sherlock
Card & Sons, M. L. (Tubs)
　　　　　　　　　　　　E
W. VA.—Charlestown
Courtney, D. G. (White
Oak) ....A
Jefferson Cooperage Co. ..D
W. VA.—Wheeling
McConnell, W. W. ....D
WIS.—Antigo
Antigo Mfg. Co. (Staves;
Hdgs.) ....D
Kingsbury & Henshaw
(Staves) ....E
WIS.—Athens
Braun & Sons (Staves) ..E
WIS.—Beldenville
Brimmer, W. D. (Hdgs.) .E
WIS.—Boyd
Boyd Mfg. Co. (Staves) D
WIS.—Butternut
Benjamin, Fred. ....D
WIS.—Chippewa Falls
Kuntz, H. (Staves) ......D
WIS.—Cumberland
Keyes & Cole (Hdgs.) ...D
WIS.—Green Bay
Britton, D. W. ....A
WIS.—Hillsboro
Hammer Bros. (Staves) D
WIS.—La Crosse
Doud, Sons & Co. (Bbls.) A
Meininger, S. ....D
WIS.—Loyal
Ruplinger Stave & Hdg. Co.
　　　　　　　　　　　　C
WIS.—March
Doud Sons & Co. (Bbls.) A
WIS.—Marshfield
Saenile L. (Ash Hoops) ..C
Marshfield Stave Co. .....B
Wisconsin Hoop Co. C
WIS.—Milwaukee
Delta Cooperage Co. ....AA
Stolper Cooperage Co., Chas.
(Brewers') ....A
WIS.—Superior
American Barrel Co. .....D
WIS.—West Superior
Doud Sons & Co. (Bbls.) ..A

COOPS

ILL.—Chicago
Barbee Wire & Iron Wks.
(Wire; Poultry) ....B
IND.—Ligonier
Banta Mfg. Co. (Brood) ..D
N. Y.—Whitney Point
Otselic Mfg. Co. (Exhibi-
tion) X
OHIO—Difiance
Defiance Box Co. (Poultry)
　　　　　　　　　　　AA
OHIO—Hamilton
Myers Mfg. Co., Fred. J.
(Wire Poultry) ....B

COPING

CONN.—New London
Burch & Co., H. O. (Stone)
　　　　　　　　　　　　X
MINN.—Crookston
Crookston Marble Wks.
(Cemetery) ....D
MO.—St. Louis
Laclede Fire Brick Mfg. Co.
(Wall) ....AAA
N. J.—Perth Amboy
Perth Amboy Terra Cotta
Co. (Terra Cotta) .....AA
New York City

COPING (Con.)
Henry & Co., M. C. (Stone)
　　　　　　　　　　　　B
N. Y.—Oxford
Clark Bluestone Co., F. G.
(Stone) ....A
OHIO—Akron
Robinson Clay Product Co.
(Wall) ....AAAA
OHIO—Cleveland
Malone Stone Co. (Stone)..A
OHIO—Haydenville
Haydenville Co. (Wall) ..A
PA.—Philadelphia
Cortright Metal Roofing Co.
(Metal) ....B
PA.—Reading
Reading Terra Cotta & Stove
Lining Wks. (Terra Cot-
ta) C

COPPER

CONN.—Ansonia
Ansonia Brass & Copper Co.
(Angles) ....AAAA
CONN.—Bridgeport
Bridgeport Brass Co. (An-
gles) ....AAA
CONN.—Bristol
Bristol Brass Co. (Sheet)
　　　　　　　　　　　AAA
CONN.—Seymour
New Haven Copper Co.
(Sheet) ....AA
Seymour Mfg. Co. ....AAA
CONN.—Torrington
Coe Brass Mfg. Co. (Sheet)
　　　　　　　　　　　AAAA
CONN.—Waterbury
Benedict & Burnham Mfg.
Co. (Angles, etc.)..AAAA
Chase Rolling Mill Co.
(Sheet) ....AAAA
Holmes, Booth & Haydens
Co. (Sheet) ....AAAA
Plume & Atwood Mfg. Co
(Sheet) ....AAA
Randolph-Clowes Co. (Roll;
Sheet) ....AAAA
Scovill Mfg. Co. (Roll;
Sheet) ....AAAA
Waterbury Brass Co., (An-
gles; Sheet) ....AAAA
ILL.—Chicago
Goetz & Flodin Mfg. Co.
(Brewers') ....A
Magnus Sons Co., A. (Brew-
ers') ....B
Stier Mfg. Co., H. (Brew-
ers') ....D
Trenkhorst, Frank (Brew-
ers') ....F
MD.—Baltimore
Baltimore Copper Smelting
& Rolling Co. (Sheet)
　　　　　　　　　　　AAA
MASS.—Boston
Livermore, Honer, C. (Roll;
Sheet) ....E
MASS.—New Bedford
Taunton-New Bedford Cop-
per Co. (Sheet) ....AAA
MICH.—Bay City
Wilson & Wanless (Sheet)
　　　　　　　　　　　　E
MICH.—Detroit
Detroit Copper & Brass Roll-
ing Mills Angles; Sheet)
　　　　　　　　　　　AAAA
Henison Mfg.Co.(Sheet)...E
Huelteman & Cramer Co.
(Brewers') ....A
MO.—St. Louis
Aufrichtig, Alois (Brewers')
　　　　　　　　　　　　D
N. Y.—Brooklyn
Wiarda & Co., Jno. C. (Sul-
phate) ....AA
New York City
General Chemical Co. (Sul-
phate) ....AAAA
Hendricks Bros., 40 Cliff
Cake; Bar; Ingot)..AAAA
Hungerford Brass & Copper
Wks., U. S., 497 Pearl
(Ingot; Sheet) ....AA
Manhattan Brass Co. (Sheet)
　　　　　　　　　　　　A
Orford Copper Co., 74 Bway.
Cake; Bar; Ingot) ..AAA
Roos Sons, August (Brew-
ers') ....B
Selling Co. (Sulphate) C

COPPER (Con.)

Sholes Co., C. E. (Sulphate)
.... X

N. Y.—Rome
Rome Brass & Copper Co.
(Anges); Sheet) ....AAA
OHIO—Cincinnati
Deckebach Son Co., F. C.
Brewers') C
OHIO—Cleveland
Grasselle Chem. Co. (Sulphate) ....AAAA
PA.—Connellsville
Riverside Metal Refining Co.
(Ingot) ....D
PA.—Easton
Baker & Adamson Chemical
Co. (Clippings) ....A
PA.—Philadelphia
Fergerson Bros. (Sulphate)
.... A
Merchant & Co. (Anges;
Roll) ....AA
PA.—Pittsburg
Crucible Steel Co., of Am.
(Cake; Bar; Ingot; Sheet)
.... AAAA
Hussey & Co., C. G. (Sheet)
.... AAA
McKenna Bros. Brass Co.
(Roll; Sheet) ....A
Maloney Bronze Mfg. Co.
(Ingot) ....D
WIS.—Kenosha
Chicago Brass Co. (Sheet)
.... AA
WIS.—Milwaukee
Koss & Bros. Co., Chas.
(Brewers') ....A
Toepfer & Sons, Wm. (Perforated) ....B

COPPERAS

COLO.—Denver
Western Chemical Mfg. Co.
.... AA
DEL.—Wilmington
Atlantic Dynamite Co. .AAA
MASS.—Plymouth
Edes Mfg. Co. C
New York City
Am. Steel — Wire Co., 71
Bway. ....AAAA
General Chemical Co., 25
Broad ....A
New York Quinine & Chemical Wks. (Ltd.) ......A
OHIO—Cleveland
Harshuer, Fuller & Goodwin
Co. ....AA
PA.—Easton
Williams & Co., C. K. ....A
PA.—Philadelphia
Jordan, Jr., W. H. (Powdered) ....AA
Pennsylvania Salt Mfg. Co.
.... AAAA
Powers - Weightman-Rosengarten Co. ....AAAA
Welherell Co., S. P., 925
Chestnut ....B

COPPERS

See also Ingots

CONN.—Ansonia ..
Anonia Brass & Copper Co.,
Br. N. Y. C. (Soldering)
.... AAAA
CONN.—Bridgeport
Bridgeport Brass Co. (Soldering) ....AA
CONN.—Seymour
New Haven Copper Co. (Soldering) ....AA
Seymour Mfg. Co. (Battery)
.... AA
CONN.—Southington
Peck, Stow & Wilcox Co.
(Soldering) ....AAAA
CONN.—Torrington
Coe Brass Mfg. Co. (Battery) ....AAAA
Union Hdw. Co. (Soldering)
.... A
ILL.—Chicago
Atchison Perforated Metal
Co., Robt. (Perforated), X
Bryant Zinc Co., 71 W.
Adams (Battery) C
Harrington & King Perforating Co. (Perforated), A
White Mfg. Co., 93 Mich.
Av. (Soldering) ......D

COPPERS (Con.)

ILL.—Freeport
Stover Mfg. Co., 165 River
(Soldering) ....AA
MD.—Baltimore
Baltimore Copper Smelting
& Rolling Mill Co., Keyser
Bldg. (Battery) ......AA
Clendenin Bros., 111 S. Gay
(Soldering) ....A
Kemp Mfg. Co., Clarence M.
1501 Guilford Av. (Soldering) C
Schultz & Co., A. (Soldering) ....A
MASS.—Boston
Boston Electric Co., 29 Harrison Av. (Battery) ....B
Isele & Son, A. W., 51 Pitts
(Soldering) ....F
MASS.—Plymouth
Ede's Mfg. Co. (Battery), D
MASS.—Reading
Beattie Zinc Wks. Co. (Battery) ....D
N. J.—Kearney
McArthur, Archibald (Soldering) ....F
N. J.—Newark
Osborne & Co., C. T., 96
Mechanic (Soldering) ..B
N. J.—Salem
Ayars Machine Co. (Soldering) ....B
Salem Glass Works (Battery) ....A
N. Y.—Brooklyn
Bliss Co., E. W. (Soldering)
.... AAAA
N. Y.—Buffalo
Niagara Machine & Tool
Wks. (Soldering) ..AAA
Shepard & Co., Sidney (Soldering) ....AAAA
Waterbury Brass Co. (Soldering) ....AAAA
West Mfg. Co. (Soldering)
.... D
Wiarda & Co., Jno. C. (Soldering) ....AA
New York City
Hungerford Brass & Copper
Co., U. T., 497 Pearl (Soldering) ....A
Millers Falls Co. (Br. Millers
Falls, Mass.), 28 Warren
(Soldering) ....AA
Mundt & Son, Chas., 441
Pearl (Soldering) ......B
N. Y.—Watervliet
Covert Mfg. Co. (Soldering)
.... A
OHIO—Mansfield
Mansfield Tempered Copper
Co. (Soldering) ....A
OHIO—Plymouth
Root Bros.. Co. (Soldering
Seats) ....B
PA.—Northeast
Eureka Tempered Copper
Wks. (Soldering) ......B
PA.—Philadelphia
Merchant & Co., 517 Arch
(Battery) ....AA
Stortz & Son, Jno., 210 Vine
(Soldering) ....F
PA.—Pittsburg
Hussey & Co., C. G. (Soldering) ....AAA

CORD

CONN.—Georgetown
Gilbert & Bennett Mfg. Co.
(Wire; Picture) ....AAA
CONN.—New Haven
Hendryx & Co., Andrew B.
(Wire; Picture) ....A
CONN.—Norwich
Ossawan Mills Co. (Bell;
Macramé Lace; Worsted;
Wire Picture; Shade;
Sash; Signal; Suspender;
Venetian Blind; Ventilator; Bicycle Lacing; Solid
Braided; Upholstery; Cotton; Hemp) ....B
Turner Mfg. Co., E. P. (Bicycle Lacing; Picture;
Shade; Ventilator; Signal)
.... X
CONN.—Torrington
Turner & Seymour Mfg. Co.
(Wire; Picture) ....A
CONN.—Westport
Lees Mfg. Co. (Macramé

CORD (Con.)
Lace; Cable)............A
DEL.—Wilmington
Rhoades & Son, J. E. (Bell)
.............................A
GA.—Athens
Mallison Braided Cord Co.
(Trolley; Arch Lamp;
Bell) ....B
American Steel & Wire Co.
(Wire; Sash) .....AAAA
Carpenter & Co., G. B., 1
5th Av. (Sash) ......AA
Macomber & Whyte Rope
Co. (Sash; Signal)
Seller Mfg. Co. (Bell) ....B
MASS.—Attleboro
Union Braiding Co. (Silk Eye
Glass) ....D
MASS.—Boston
Boston Belting Co. (Rubber)
.......................AAAA
Hub Gore Makers (Rubber)
.............................A
Samson Cordage Wks., 115
Congress (Bell; Picture;
Sash; Shade; Signal; Sus-
pender; Venetian Blind;
Ventilator; Cotton; Hemp;
Solid Braided; Upholstery;
Trolley) ....A
MASS.—Easthampton
Colton, Geo. S. (Rubber) ..A
Glendale Elastic Fabrics Co.
(Elastic) ....A
MASS.—Fall River
Estes & Sons (Sash) ......A
MASS.—Hyde Park
Gould Wire Cord Co. (Trol-
ley; Window Shade; Sash)
.............................F
MASS.—Newtonville
Silver Lake Co. (Bell; Rail-
road Bell; Braided; Shade;
Sash; Signal; Suspender;
Ventilator) ....A
MASS.—Plymouth
Plymouth Cordage Co. (Cot-
ton; Hemp) ......AAAA
MASS.—Springfield
Union Braiding Co. (Silk) .C
MASS.—Westfield
Warren Thread Wks., W.
(Jute; Suspender; Upholst-
ery) ....A
MASS.—Worcester
Parker Wire Goods Co. (Pic-
ture) ....D
Wire Goods Co. (Wire, Pic-
ture) ....A
Wright Wire Co. (Sash), AA
MICH.—Belding
Belding Bros. & Co. (Inc.)
(Silk) ....AAAA
MO.—St. Louis
Buodenck & Bascom Rope
Co. (Wire; Sash; Signal)
.............................AA
Leschen & Sons Rope Co.
(Wire; Sash; Signal) AAA
N. H.—Concord
Page Belling Co. (Bell) ..AA
N. J.—Trenton
Trenton Iron Co. (Sash) ..A
Trenton Rubber Co. (Rub-
ber) ....A
United Rubber Co. (Rubber)
.............................E
N. Y.—Buffalo
Western Wire Goods Co.
(Picture) ....D
N. Y.— Harrison
Moosehead Silk Co. (Silk), X
New York City
Bishop Gutta Percha Co.,
420 E. 25th (Wire) ....B
Cathcart & Co., Jno. 115
Franklin (Silk for Book-
binders') ....E
Ellison & Co., A. S. (Silk) B
Graham & Co., J. H., 113
Chambers (Sash) .....AA
Gutta Percha & Rubber Mfg.
Co. (Rubber) .....AAAA
Hoffman-Corr Mfg. Co., 107
Duane (Trolley; Arc
Lamp; Bell) ....A
Johns-Manville Co., H. W.,
100 William (Asbestos)
.......................AAAA
Judd & Co. H. L. (Wire;
Picture) ....AA
Lawrence Cordage Wks.
(Inc.) (Manila; Sisal) ..A
N. Y. Belting & Packing Co.
(Rubber) ....AAAA

CORD (Con.)
Rubber Goods Mfg. Co., 253
Bway. (Ruber) ....AAAA
Schmitzer, B. (Silk) C
Spencer Optical Co. (Eye
Glass) C
Stine & Co., J. R. (Bell) .A
Sutro Bros. Braid Co. (Up-
holstery) ....A
Travers Bros. Co., (Sash)
.............................AA
Tucker & Carter Rope Co.,
76 South (Trolley; Arc
Lamp; Bell)...........B
Union Upholstery Trimming
Co. (Upholstery) ......D
Wemple Co., Jay C. (Shade)
.............................AA
N. Y.—Rochester
Pullman Mfg. Co. (Wire
Sash) ....B
N. Y.—Schaghticoke
Cable Flax Mills (Builders')
.............................A
N. Y.—Schenectady
General Electric .., (Trol-
ley) ....AAAA
N. Y.—Unadilla
Tie Company (Bicycle) ...D
OHIO—Ashland
Ashland Flax Mill Co. (Jute)
.............................E
OHIO—Canton
Canton Surgical & Dental
Chair Co. (Dental) C
OHIO—Cincinnati
Jacobs Cordage Co. (Sash) A
Rettibone Bros. Mfg. Co.
(Gold; Silver) ....A
OHIO—Hamilton
Meyers Mfg. Co., Fred. J.
(Wire; Picture) ....B
OHIO—Mansfield
Ohio Brass Co. (Trolley) AA
PA.—Philadelphia
Horstmann Co., Wm. H.
(Bell; Upholstery; Silk)
.......................AAAA
Loeb, Lipper & Co. (Skirt) A
Mayer & Englund (Trolley)
.............................A
Perry, Fergus (Elastic;
Wire) ....D
Phosphor Bronze Smelting
Co. (Sash; Wire; Picture)
.............................A
Schlicter Jute Cordage Co.
(Jute) ....AA
Schrack & Sherwood (Up-
holstery; Bicycle Lacing)
.............................A
PA.—Reading
Jackson & Son, Thos. (Jute)
.............................AA
PA.—Williamsport
Williamsport Wire Rope Co.
(Wire; Sash) ....A
R. I.—Pawtucket
Phillips Insulated Wire Co.
(Electric Lamp) ......AA
R. I.—Providence
Davol Rubber Co. (Rubber)
.............................AA
VA.—Richmond
Wortendyke Mfg. Co. (Car-
riage Seaming) ....B

CORDAGE

ALA.—Prattsville
Prattsville Cotton Mills &
Banking Co. (Cotton
Rope) ....A
CAL.—Oakland
California Cotton Mills Co.
(Rope; Twine, etc.) ..AA
CAL.—San Francisco
California Jute Mill Co.
(Twine) ....A
Tubbs Cordage Co., 607
Front (Manila; Sisal ;Rope
Binder Twine) .....AAA
CONN.—Moodus
Brownell & Co. (Seine
Twine) ....D
New York Net & Twine Co.
(Twine) ....B
Undine Twine Mills (Purple,
A. E.) (Seine; Sail Twine;
Cord) ....A
CONN.—New Haven
Hendryx Co., Andrew B.
(Braided) ....A
CONN.—Norwich
Ossawan Mills Co. (Braided)
.............................B

CORDAGE (Con.)

CONN.—Westport
Less Mfg. Co., (Seine; Sail; Gilling; Sea Island, etc., Twines) ....A

DEL.—Wilmington
Planet Mills Mfg. Co. (Jute Rope; Twines) ....AAAA

GA.—Athens
Mallison Braided Cord Co., B

GA.—Atlanta
Fulton Bag & Cotton Mills (Cotton; Jute Twine), AA

GA.—Augusta
Hutcheson Mfg. Co. (Cotton Rope) ....B

GA.—Columbus
Eagle & Phenix Mills (Cotton; Manila; Sisal), AAAA

GA.—Macon
Bibb Mfg. Co. (Seine Twine; Rope) ....AAAA
Manchester Mfg. Co. (Seine; Twine) ....B

IND.—Madison
Eagle Cotton Mills Co. (Twine) ....A

IOWA—Dubuque
Bestoval Mills (Rope; Twine) ....D

KANS.—Independence
Kansas Cotton Twine Co. (Cotton; Sewing, etc.)..D

KY.—Covington
Overman & Schrader Cord Co. (Jute; Hemp; Flax; Rope; Twine) ....A

KY.—Frankfort
Kentucky River Mills (Hemp Binder; Commercial Twines) ....A

KY.—Louisville
January & Wood Co. (Cotton Rope; Twine) ....A

MAINE—Kennebunk
Lord & Co., R. W. (Fishing Twine) ....A

MD.—Baltimore
Mount Vernon-Woodberry Cotton Duck Co. (Cotton Twine) ....AAAA

MASS.—Andover
Smith & Dove Mfg. Co. (Flax; Twine) ....AA

MASS.—Boston
Lockwood Mfg. Co. (Machinery) X
Lord, H. & G. W. (Manila; Sisal) ....A
Ludlow Cordage Co. (Rope; Binder Twine) ....A
Ludlow Mfg. Associates (Rope; Twine) ....AAAA
Sampson Cordage Works, 115 Congress (Braided; Cotton; Hemp; Manila; Sisal) ....A
Sewal & Day Cordage Co. (Rope; Binder Twine)..B
Silver Lake Co., 78 Chauncey (Braided; Cotton) ..A

MASS.—Fall River
Estes & Sons, J. H. (Rope) ....B

MASS.—Gloucester
Gloucester Net & Twine Co. (Twine) ....A

MASS.—Lawrence
Lawrence Duck Co. (Cotton Twine) ....A

MASS.—New Bedford
Lambeth Rope Co. (Manila; Sisal) ....B
New Bedford Cordage Co. (Hemp; Flax; Manila; Sisal Twine; Rope)...AAAA

MASS.—Newburyport
Bay State Cordage Wks. (Manila Sisal Rope; Binder Twine) ....A

MASS.—Newton
Silver Lake Co. (Braided Cords) ....A

MASS.—No. Grafton
Paton, Wm. (Cotton Twine) ....AA

MASS.—Plymouth
Plymouth Cordage Co. (Rope; Binder Twine) ....AAAA

MASS.—Westport
Westport Mfg. Co. (Cotton Twine) ....A

MICH.—Monroe
Boehme & Rauch Cordage Co. (Rope; Twine) C

CORDAGE (Con.)

MINN.—St. Paul
American Grass Twine Co. (Twine) ....AAA

MISS.—Columbus
Tombigbee Cotton Mills (Cotton Rope) ....B

MISS.—Laurel
Laurel Cotton Mills (Cotton Rope) C

MISS.—Water Valley
Yocomo Cotton Mills (Cable Cord; Wrapping Twine) B

MO.—St. Louis
American Mfg. Co. (Jute Rope) ....A
Broderick & Bascom Rope Co., 809 No. Main (Braided) ....AA
Macgowan & Finigan (Binder Twine) ....A
St. Louis Cordage Co. (Sisal Rope; Binder Twine) .AA

N. J.—Paterson
Dolphin Jute Mills (Jute Twine) ....AA
Sutherland & Edwards Co. (Jute Twine) ....A

N. Y.—Auburn
Columbian Cordage Co. (Manila; Sisal) ....AA

N. Y.—Brooklyn
American Mfg. Co. (Jute; Sisal; Manila Rope) ....AAAA
Allen's Sons Rope Co., D. (Manila; Sisal) ....B
Chelsea Jute Mills (Rope; Twine) ....AAAA
Empire State Bag Co. (Rope; Twine) C
Planet Mills Mfg. Co. (Rope; Twine) ....AAA

N. Y.—Maspeth
Catling, Jas. (Manila; Sisal Rope) C

New York City
American Mfg. Co. (Rope; Binder Twine) ....AAAA
Buckingham, Paulsen & Co. (Com. Twines) ....A
Halstead & Co., E. S., 75 Pearl (Sisal; Tarred Twine) ....A
Hamilton & Co., E. H. (Com. Twine) ....A
Hart Co., A. H. (Twine) ....AAA
Hoffman-Corr Mfg. Co., 107 Duane (Braided) ...AA
Kelley & Co., Hy. C. (Com. Rope; Twine) ....B
Lawrence Cordage Wks. (Manila; Sisal) ....A
Nawrath & Co., J. P. (Com. Twine) C
Reynolds & Co., Jas. E. (Com Twine) ....A
Standard Rope & Twine Co. (Rope; Binder Twine) ..A
Travers Bros. Co. (Hemp; Jute; Flax Rope; Twine) ....AA
Tucker & Carter Rope Co., 76 South (Braided) ...B
Turner Co., J. Spencer (Com. Twine) ......AAA
Wall Rope Works (Hemp; Manila; Sisal) ....A
Winne Co., D. P. (Com. Twine) C

N. Y.—Schaghticoke
Cable Flax Mills (Twine)..B

N. Y.—Valley Falls
Thompson & Co., Jas. (Twine) ....AA

N. C.—Charlotte
Charlotte Cordage Co. (Braided) ....D

N. C.—Cleveland Mills
Cleveland Cotton Mills (Rope; Clothes Lines) .B

OHIO—Cincinnati
Jacobs Cordage Co. (Hemp; Flax Cordage; Twine) ..B

OHIO—Dayton
Bradley Cordage Co. (Binder Twine) ....B

OHIO—Miamisburg
Miamisburg Twine & Cordage Co. ....A

OHIO—Xenia
Hooven & Allison Co. (Twine; Rope; Sash; Bell Cord) ....D
Kelley Co., R. (Sisal; Ma-

282

CORDAGE (Con.)
nila Rope) ....B
OREGON—Portland
Portland Cordage Co. (Rope;
Binder Twine) ....B
PA.—Beaver Falls
Keystone Driller Co. (Wall
Drilling) ....A
PA.—Easton
Easton Cordage Co. (Rope) ∪
PA.—Hanover
Bonte Cordage Co. (Jute;
Hemp; Twine) C
PA.—Hoboken
Flocker & Co., Jno. (Cotton
Rope; Hemp; Twine) ...C
PA.—Hulmeville
Fricke, Co.. J. E. (Cotton
Rope; Twine; Yarn)....A
PA.—New Brighton
Bently & Gerwig (Rope;
Hemp; Flax; Twine; Bind-
er Twine) ....A
PA.—Philadelphia
Baily, Christopher (Rope;
Twine) ....A
Bailey & Co.. Jno. T. (Rope;
Twine; Binder Twine)
AAAA
Fitler & Co., Edwin H.
(Rope; Binder Twine)
AAAA
Hooper Sons' Mfg. Co.
(Rope) ....B
Schlichter Jute Cordage Co.
(Rope; Twine, etc) ..AA
PA.—Reading
Jackson & Son, Thos. (Ma-
nila; Sisal; Cotton; Jute
Rope; Twine) ....A
R. I.—Pawtucket
Greene & Daniels Mfg. Co.
(Seine; Druggists' Twine)
AA
Kenyon Mfg. Co., John J.
(Braided) ....B
R. I.—Providence
American Electrical Works
(Incandescent Light)
AAAA
S. C.—Cherokee Falls
Cherokee Falls Mfg. Co.
(Cotton Rope) ....AA
S. C.—Clinton
Clinton Cotton Mills (Cotton
Cords) ....A
S. C.—Columbia
Columbia Mills Co. (Mt. Ver
Duck Co.) (Cotton Rope;
Twine) ....AAAA
S. C.—Orangeburg
Cornelson. Geo. H. (Cotton
Twine; Rope) ....A
S. C.—Pelham
Pelham Mills (Cotton Twine)
A
S. C.—Spartanburg
Beamont Mfg. Co. (Cotton
Twine) ....B
TENN.—Pine Wood
Pine Wood Cotton Mills
(Woolen Rope, etc.) ....A
TEXAS—Galveston
Galveston Bagging & Cord-
age Co. (Jute) ....AA
Galveston Rope Co. (Sisal
Rope; Binders Twine)..A
S. C.—Strathmore
Laurel Hill Mill (Cotton
Twine) ....A
WIS.—Janesville
Rock River Cotton Co. (Cot-
ton Twine) ....B

CORDIALS
See Liquors

CORDONNETS
CONN.—South Manchester
Cheney Bros. (Inc.)..AAAA

CORDOVAN
See Leather

CORDS
See Trimmings. Dress: also
Trimmings, Upholstery

CORDUROY CLOTHING
Clothing; see Clothing,
Men's

CORDUROYS
New York City
Folkard & Lawrence (Com.)
E
New York Mills ....AAAA
PA.—Catasauqua
Wahnetah Silk Co. ......A
PA.—Philadelphia
Baker & Co., A. T. (Plush;
Velour) ....B
Collins & Aikman Co. ..A
PA.—Swarthmore
Victory Plush Mill ......B
R. I.—Warwick
Crompton Co....:....AAA

CORERS
MD.—Baltimore
Sinclair-Scott Co. (Fruit;
Parers; Slicers Combined)
E
MASS.—Leominster
Hudson Parer Co. (Fruit;
Parers; Slicers Combined)
X
MASS.—Worcester
Hamblin & Russell Mfg. Co.
(Wire) ....B
Parker Wire Goods Co. (Ap-
ple) ....F
N. H. —Antrim
Goodell Co. (Fruit Parers;
Slicers Combined) ......A
New York City
Stoutenborough, X. (Apple)
D
PA.—Mount Joy
Rollman Mfg. Co. (Apple) C

CORES
CONN.—Hartford
Hartford Machine Screw Co.
(Armature; Magnet) AAAA
ILL.—Chicago
Western Electric Co. (Arma-
ture; Magnet) ....AAAA
New York City
Bunnell & Co., J. H. (Arma-
ture; Magnet) ....A
N. Y.—Palmyra.
Crandall Packing Co. (Gun)
D
OHIO—Cleveland
Federal Mfg. Co. (Telephone
Magnet) ....AAAA

CORIFIERS
COLO.—Denver
Denver Fire Clay Co. ....AA

CORKERS
ILL.—Chicago
Redlich Mfg. Co. (Wooden;
Bottle) ....A
MICH.—Bellaire
Richardi & Bechtold (Wood-
en Bottle) ....B
N. J.—Newark
Sommer's Son, John (Hand)
A

CORKS
CAL.—San Francisco
Illinois Pacific Glass Co., 10
Main ....A
CONN.—Norwich
Goodman Cork Co. (Granu-
lated Cork) ....F
D. C.—Washington
Wallace & Menchine, 1208 E.
N. W. ....D
ILL.—Chicago
Armstrong Cork Co. (Br.) 20
Market ....AAAA
Chicago Cork Wks.. Plym-
outh & Polk) C
Excelsior Cork Cutting Co..
61 Market ....D
McCready Cork Co.. R. W. A
Redlich Mfg. Co.. 2 Oak
Druggists': Brewers':
Bottlers') ....B

283

CORKS (Con.)

MD.—Baltimore
Armstrong Cork Co. (Br.) 7
  N. Howard ....AAAA
Crown Cork & Seal Co., AAA
McCormick & Co. (Rubber)
  ....D

MASS.—Boston
American Cork Co., 67
  Blackstone ....A
Boston Cork Wks., 52 Pur-
  chase X
Grosman & Co., E. (Imp.)
  127 Broad ....D
MO.—St. Louis
Armstrong Cork Co. (Br.) 12
  No. 2d ....AAAA
N. J.—Hoboken
Truslow & Fulle :........B
N. J.—Newark
Meinecke Cork Co. ....E
N. Y.—Brooklyn
Thompson & Norris Co.,
  Prince & Concord .....AA
Paddock Cork Co., DeKalb
  Av. (Granulated & Curled
  Cork) ....B
N. Y.—Buffalo
Buffalo Cork Factory (F.
  Bender, Prop.), 429 Gene-
  see ....A
Wright & Co., R. G., 52
  Terrace ....AA

New York City
Armstrong Cork Co., 57 Mur-
  ray ....AAAA
Boera & Co., J., 192 Pearl
  ....D
Budde & Westermann
  (Imps.) 50 Vesey ......B
Calm & Co., H., 67 Murray
  (Granulated Cork) ....A
Colgan, J. B., 675 Hudson, C
Danssa & Co., A., (Imp.) 100
  Maiden Lane..........AAA
Farrell, W. J., 115 Maiden
  Lane ....A
Frankel Co., Max, 212 Pearl
 C
Gudwill & Bucknell (Imps.)
  193 Water ....AAA
Mattson Rubber Co., 26
  Bway. (Rubber) ....B
Meinecke & Co., 48 Park Pl.
  (Druggists) ....B
Moehring & Co., W. G., 151
  Cedar ....B
Mundet & Son, L., (Imps.)
  278 Pearl C
Nonpareil Cork Mfg. Co.,
  Chambers & W. Bway.
  (Split; Granulated) AAAA
Strohmeyer & Arpe Co., 33
  Water ....AA
Wildman & Preherne, 57 N.
  Moore ....D
Wittermann Bros. (Imps.)
  188 William ....A
N. Y.—Rochester
Campbell, J. H., 11 Bartlett
  ....A

OHIO—Cincinnati
Cinn. Bottlers Supply Co., 32
  Main C
Schivell & Son, F. A., 339
  Main ....D
PA.—Lancaster
Lancaster Cork Wks..AAAA
Warren & Co., M. W.......D
PA.—Philadelphia
Armstrong Cork Co., 408 N.
  3d ....AAAA
Blaese & Co., G., 127 Walnut
 C
Brauer & Son, J., 248 N.
  Front ....B
Bruckman & Son, J. G., 133
  N. 3d ....B
Butz Cork Co., A. L., 829 N.
  3d ....B
Curran, P., 306 Race C
Wilkie. S., 842 N. 3d ....B
PA.—Pittsburg
Armstrong Cork Co., 23d &
  Alleys River (Split; Gran-
  ulated. etc.) ....AAAA
Banar & Wieland, 210 1st
  Av. C
R. I.—Providence
Davol Rubber Co. (Rubber)
  ....AA

CORKSCREWS

CONN.—Meriden
Meriden Britannia Co.
  ....AAAA

CORKSCREWS (Con.)

Meriden Cutlery Co. ....AA
CONN.—New Britain
Humason & Beckley Mfg.
  Co. ....A
CONN.—Plainville
Hills Edison ....A
CONN.—Wallingford
Wallace Sons Mfg. Co., R.
  ....AAAA
CONN.—Winsted
Empire Knife Co. ....B
MASS.—N, Attleboro
Blackinton & Co., R.......A
MASS.—Worcester
National Mfg. Co. ....A
N. H.—Alton
Rockwell-Clough Co. (Ad-
  vertising; Pocket; Vial) E
N. J.—Newark
Crabb & Co., Wm. ....A
Williamson Wire Novelty
  Co., C. T. ....B
N. Y.—Troy
Gorham Mfg .Co., Bway. &
  19th ....AAAA
Parks & Parks ....D
Smith & Hemenway Co., 296
  Bway. ....D
Walbridge & Co., J. H., 387
  Bway ....B
PA.—Erie
Erie Specialty Co. ....B
Reed Mfg. Co. ....A

CORN, BROOM

ILL.—Arcola
Lyons & Co., Thos. ......A
Woodworth, S. L. C
ILL.—Casey
Johnson & Young C
ILL.—Charleston
Griffen, Geo. B. ....E
Marshall, C. T. ....F
ILL.—Chicago
Ferry & Co., A. D. C
Gross & Co., J. P. ....A
Lande & Co., S. ....A
ILL.—Humbolt
Danner, J. ....E
ILL.—Mattoon
Checkley & Co. C
Gasaway, Chas. D. ....F
Phillips Broom Corn Co....D
ILL.—Oakland
Carter & Son, L. D. ......D
ILL.—Sullivan
Duncan, W. A. ....D
KANS.—Lindsburg.
Anderson, G. A. X
Anderson, John X
KANS.—Sterling
Findlay & Co., Robt. C
KANS.—Topeka
Supple, Wm. ....D
MO.—St. Louis
Boggs Broom Corn Co. ...E
Loewen Broom Corn Co....C
OHIO—Dayton
Chambers, M. W. C
OHIO—Sidney
Donaldson & Boal Broom Co.
  ....B
TENN.—Nashville
Cooley & Co., J. S. ......A

CORN, CANNED

See Canned Goods

CORN, EVAPO-RATED

CAL.— San Francisco
Guggenhime & Co. (Evapo-
  rated; Veg.) ....A
MICH.—East Tawas
National Milling & Evap. Co.
  (Evaporated) C
OHIO—Ada
Peterson, Hugh (Evapor-
  ated) ....D
OHIO—Alger
Thompson & Son, C. P.
  (Evaporated) ....F

CORN, POP

See Popcorn

CORNMEAL

Cereals (also Appendix)

CORNERS

CONN.—Bristol
Sessions & Son, J. H.
(Trunk) ....AAA
ILL.—Chicago
Golden Novelty Mfg. Co.,
194 So. Clinton (Metal) ..C
MD.—Baltimore
Monumental Mfg. Co.
(Crate) ....D
MASS.—Worcester
Warren Leather Goods Co.
(Leather) ....B
MICH.—Grand Rapids
Waddell Mfg. Co. (Casket)
..............B
N. J.—Newark
Jenkinson & Co., R. C.
(Box; Sample Case;
Trunk) ....A
N. Y.—Brooklyn
De Haven Mfg. Co., 50 Columbia (Box) ....A
Prahar, L. P., 124 Pearl
(Metal) Pocket Book) ..C
New York City
Cary Mfg. Co., 19 Roosevelt
(Box) ....B
Gould-Mersereau Co. (Carpet) ....B
Judd & Co., H. L. (Stair)
..............AA
N. Y.—Northville
Hubbell, Ray (Stair) C
OHIO—Cleveland
Cleveland Hardware Co.
(Dash) ....A
PA.—Columbia
Columbia Grey Iron Co.
(Window Screen)......C
PA.—Philadelphia
Weaver Mailing. E. & B. Co.
(Book Mailing) ....D
VT.—Burlington
Porter Screen Mfg. Co.
(Screen Frame) C
Queen Anne Screen Co.
(Screen Frame) ......A

CORNICES

Galvanized Iron, etc.

ALA.—Bessemer
Bessemer Cornice Wks. ...C
CAL.—Fresno
Kutner-Goldstein Co. ...AAA
CAL.—San Francisco
Conlin-Roberts ....A
CAL.—San Jose
Mangrum & Otter Co. ....A
CAL.—Santa Barbara
Boeseke-Dawe Co. ....B
COLO.—Glenwood Springs
Dongan, Wm. ....B
CONN.—Bridgeport
Drouve Co. G., 40 Tulip ..B
CONN.—Meriden
Griswold Richmond & Glock
Co., 2 W. Main ....B
CONN.—New Haven
Corbett. T. W., 29 Bway..A
ILL.—Batavia
U. S. Wind Eng. & Pump Co.
..............AA
ILL.—Chicago
Allen's Cornice & Corrugating Wks., 424 W. Randolph ....B
Bremer & Bielenberg, 1136
W. 13th ....B
Knisely Bros., 28th & 5th
Av. ....B
McFarland & Co., J. C., 27th
& 5th Av. ....B
Sykes Steel Roofing Co., 611
So. Morgan ....B
ILL.—Peoria
Bushnell & Son, A. A., 1317
So. Washington ....B
Hunter & Strehlow, 114 So.
Adams ....B
IND.—Evansville
Mesker & Co., Geo. L. ...AA
IND.—Indianapolis
Indianapolis Steel Roofing
& Cornice Co., 25 E. South
..............C
MD.—Baltimore
Hetzell & Son, John G. ...A
MASS.—Boston
Warren Bros. Co., 143 Federal ....AA
MASS.—Lowell
Castello & Co., T., 211 Central ....AA

CORNICES (Con.)

MICH.—Detroit
Burton & Co., W. J., 164 W.
Larned C
Detroit Cornice & Slate
Wks. 145 St. Antoine ...A
MINN.—Duluth
Duluth Corrugating & Roofing Co., 126 E. Michigan
..............B
MINN.—Minneapolis
Strenel Bros., 1215 Washington Av. No. C
MINN.—St. Paul
St. Paul Roofing, Cornice, &
Ornament Co., Water &
Wabash ....B
MO.—St. Louis
Banantine Galv. Iron Mfg.
Co. 113 Soulard ....A
Gerock Bros. Mfg. Co., 1252
Old Manchester Rd. C
Mesker & Bro., 421 So. 6th
..............AA
N. J.—Jersey City
N. Y. Iron Roofing & Corrugating Co. C
Ringle & Son, Jacob, 83
Newark Av. ....A
N. J.—Newark
Herpers Bros., 18 Crawford
..............B
N. J. Trenton
Trenton Archt. Cornice
Wks. 101 S. Warren C
N. Y.—Albany
Ackroyd. James ....A
N. Y.—Brooklyn
Seton, J., 78 Wash Av...B
New York City
Berger Mfg. Co., 210 E.
23rd ....AA
Moseley Iron, Bridge & Roof
Co., 39 Cortland ....A
Nugent, Thos., 223 E. 80th
..............A
N. Y.—Rochester
Goggin & Knowles, 50
Franklin ....B
N. Y.—Utica
Metal Roofing & Cornice Co.,
71 Main ....AA
OHIO—Akron
May & Fieberger ....A
OHIO—Cambridge
Cambridge Roofing Co. ..B
OHIO—Canton
Berger Mfg. Co. C
Canton Steel Roofing Co...A
Eller & Co. J. H. ....A
Kanneberg Roofing & Ceiling Co. ....B
OHIO—Cincinnati
Freund Roofing Co., J.,
Mitchell Av. & B. & O.
S-rb Ry. ....B
Kiechler Mfg. Co., Armory
Av. & Clinton C
Scott & Co., 234 E. Front..B
OHIO—Cleveland
Cleveland Galvanizing Wks.,
18 Cooper C
Garry Iron & Steel Co., Coe
& Lake ....A
OHIO—Columbus
Kinnear & Gager Co. ....A
OHIO—Forest
Dickelman Mfg. Co. ......A
OHIO—Salem
Mullins, W. H. ....A
PA.—Allegheny
Irwin, Thos. W., 411 Rebecca ....A
PA.—Philadelphia
Gara, McGinley & Co., 23
S. 17th ....A
Lunton's Sons, David, Allegheny Av. & Tulip ....B
Meade Roofing & Cornice
Co., 3717 Filbert C
Thorn Co., J. S., 1227 Callowhill ....A
PA.—Pittsburg
Keighley Metal Ceiling &
Mfg. Co., 819 Locust ..B
Rasner & Dinger Co., 100
2nd Av. C
R. I.—Providence
Clason Arch'l Metal Wks.
(Inc.) 428 Kinsley Av..C
TENN.—Chattanooga
Chattanooga Roofing &

CORNICES (Con.)
Fdry. Co., 720 Montgomery Av. ....A
Mountain City Stove & Mfg. Co., 623 Market ....A
TENN.—Nashville
Phillips & Buttorff Mfg. Co., 217 N. College ..AAA
W. VA.—Wheeling
Wheeling Corrugating Co..A
WIS.—La Crosse
La Crosse Steel Roofing & Corrugating Co. ....B
WIS.—Milwaukee
Milwaukee Corrugating Co., S. Bay & Aldrich ......A

CORNUCOPIAS

New York City

Meyer, Bernard ....D

CORSETS
& Corset Waists

CAL.—San Francisco
Corner R. Co...........E
CONN.—Bethel
Senior Corset Co., A. H. (Waists) ....E
CONN.—Bridgeport
Birdsey & Somers ......A
Downer, Hawes & Co. ...C
Warner Bros. ......AAAA
CONN.—Derby
Brewster Corset Co. C
CONN.—New Haven
Hickok Co. (Custom) ....E
Koch, Isaac ....D
Newman & Sons, I. .....A
Ottenheimer Bros. Co....A
Strause, Adler & Co. .AAA
Strause & Co., I. ....A
Todd, Henry H. (Custom-made) ....E
CONN.—South Norwalk
R. & G. Corset Co. ....A
ILL.—Aurora
Aurora Corset Co. ((& Waists) ....AA
Chicago Corset Co. (S. Florsheim & Son) (Ladies; Children's; Waists) ...A
ILL.—Chicago
Gage, Downs Co. (& Waists) ....B
IOWA—Des Moines
Des Moines Shirt & Corset Mfg. Co. ....E
KY.—Louisville
Peter & Co., Arthur .....B
MD.—Baltimore
Brinkman & Co., A. H...C
Pohl & Co., E. C
MASS.—Boston
Frost Co., Geo. (& Waists) ....B
MASS.—Springfield
Bay State Corset Co. ....B
MASS.—Worcester
Globe Corset Co. (& Waists) ....A
Royal Worcester Corset Co. (& Waists) ....AA
MICH.—Ann Arbor
Crescent Works (& Waists) ....D
Goodspeed Mfg. Co. ......E
Randall Skirt &Corset Co. ....E
MICH.—Detroit
American Lady Corset Co..C
American Suit & Corset Co. ....AA
MICH.—Jackson
Bortree Corset Co. (& Waists) C
Coronet Corset Co. (& Waists) ....B
Her Ladyship Corset Co...C
Jackson Corset Co. (& Waists) ....B
Michigan Corset Co. C
Pandora Corset Co. (& Waists) C
Reliance Corset Co. (& Waists) C
MICH.—Kalamazoo
Kalamazoo Corset Co. (& Waists) ....AA

CORSETS (Con.)
Puritan Corset Co. ....B
MINN.—Albert Lea
Case Corset Co. (& Waists) ....E
MO.—St. Louis
St. Louis Corset Co. (& Waists) ....B
Western Corset Co. C
Williamson Corset & Brace Co. ....D
N. J.—Hoboken
Horwood & Co., E. H. (& Waists) ....E
N. J.—Newark
Benjamin Bros. ....D
Bowers & Co., James ...AA
Delsarte Mfg. & Supply Co. (& Waists) ....D
Ferris Bros. Co. (Waists)..AA
Heilmer & Herzog C
Jackson & Co., T. W. ....B
Pfeiffer & Co.. H. A. (& Waists) ....E
Weingarten Bros. .....AAA
N. Y.—Brooklyn
California Corset Co. ....E
Menahan, Patrick J. C
N. Y.—McGraw
McGraw Corset Co., A. P..C
New York City
Binner, Madame R: (Custom) ....D
Cohn & Co., M. ....E
Courtney, Mrs. T. J. ....D
Kops Bros. ....A.
Normal Corset Co. ......B
Pansy Corset Co. (Importers') ....E
Viau, B. ....D
Wade Corset Co. (& Waists) ....AAAA
Weeks Co., E. J. ....B
Wolfe, Miss Fannie .....E
N. Y.—Syracuse
Wood & Co., J. E. C
N. Y.—Weedsport
Weedsport Skirt & Waist Co. ....B
PA.—Philadelphia
Anderson & Barry ....A
Baratet, M. A. ....D
Eastburn, Channing .....B
Philadelphia Corset Co...B
Western & Wells Mfg. Co. ....B
R. I.—Providence
Gould Corset Co. ....E

CORUNDUM

ILL.—Chicago
Chicago Wheel & Mfg. Co. C
IND.—Plymouth
Abrasive Mining & Mfg. Co. ....B
MASS.—Boston
Ashland Emery & Corundum Co., 100 Boylston ......A
MASS.—Chester
Hamilton Emery & Corundum Co. C
MASS.—North Grafton
Washington Mills Emery Mfg. Co. ....B
MASS.—Springfield
Hampden Corundum Wheel Co. X
MASS.—Westfield
Vitrified Wheel Co. C
MASS.—Worcester
Norton Emery Wheel Co...AA
N. H.—Pike
Pipe Mfg. Co. ....A
New York City
Best, L. C
PA.—Philadelphia
Keystone Emery Mills....C
R. I.—Providence
American Emery Wheel Wks. ....B

COSMETICS

MICH.—Detroit
Seelye Mfg. Co. C
New York City
Colgate & Co. ....AAA
Wetmore Co., S. H. ......D

COSMETICS (Con.)

OHIO—Cincinnati
Freeman Perfume Co.
(Manicure) ....D
PA.—Philadelphia
Vail Bros. C

COSTUMES

ILL.—Greenville
De Moulin & Bro., Ed.
(Burlesque; Lodge; Re-
galia) ....A
LA.—New Orleans
Alaban, Mrs. Julia X
MASS.—Boston
Curtis & Weld.........E
New York City
Koehler & Co., A., 54 Union
Sq. (Theatrical) C
Warnock Uniform Co., 19
W. 31st (Theatrical)...C
OHIO—Cincinnati
Beck & Sons, Wm. C
OHIO—New London
Ward & Stetson (Lodge)..C

COTS

See Beds; Furniture

ILL.—Chicago
Cold Blast Feather Co.
(Folding) ....AA
Fowler, John P. (Wire)..D
Haggard & Marcusson Co.
(Folding.. Wire)......B
Union Wire Mattress Co.
(Iron) ....AA
IND.—Indianapolis
Laycock Mfg. Co., T. B.
(Canvas; Wire)
IOWA—Cedar Rapids
Adams Mfg. Co., A. L.
(Folding) ....E
MICH.—Muskegon
Sargeant Mfg. Co. (Army)
B
MINN.—Minneapolis
Minneapolis Bedding Co...A
MO.—Kansas City
Lloyd, J. H. (Canvas; Wire)
D
MO.—St. Louis
Missouri Tent & Awning Co.
(Canvas) ....B
Scarritt-Comstock Furniture
Co. (Folding) ....A
Smith & Davis Mfg. Co.
(Folding) ....AA
N. J.—Trenton
Bloom & Godley (Wire)..A
N. Y.—Buffalo
Hard Mfg. Co. (Canvas;
Folding) ....B
New York City
Hall, Frank A. (Folding).B
McHugh, John F. (Ambu-
lance) C
N. Y.—Rochester
Sisserand Mfg. Co., Essex
Bldg. (Finger) ....F
N. Y.—Utica
Foster Bros. Mfg. Co. (Can-
vas; Folding; Iron; Wire)
A
OHIO—Akron
Miller Rubber Mfg. Co.
(Seamless Tissue) .....B
OHIO—Barberton
Pure Gum Specialty Co.
(Rubber) C
PA.—Philadelphia
Pack, W. H. X
WIS.—Racine
Gold Medal Cacm Furniture
& Novelty Co. (Army;
Folding) ....B

COTTERS

CONN.—Chester
Brooks & Sons, M. S.
(Spring) ....B
MASS.—Plymouth
Cobb & Drew (Spring).AA
MASS.—Worcester
Wire Goods Co. (Spring)..A
OHIO—Akron
Whitman & Barnes Mfg. Co.
(Spring) ....AAAA
OHIO—Cincinnati
Cincinnati Screw & Tap Co.

COTTERS (Con.)
(Spring) ....A
OHIO—Cleveland
Standard Tool Co. (Spring)
AA
OHIO—Dayton
Climax Tag Co. (Spring)..X
PA.—Pittsburg
McKay & Co. (Chain) .AAA
PA.—Sharon Hill
Pickering, R. S. (Spring).E
R. I.—Pawtucket
Jenckes Mfg. Co., E.
(Spring) ....A
R. I.—Valley Falls
Hindley Mfg. Co. (Spring)
D

COTTON DEALERS

ALA.—Birmingham
Brown, W. S. ....A
Drennan & Co. ....A
Earle, Terrell & Co. ...A
Hood, Fielding & Co. ...A
ALA.—Eufaula
Shorter, E. S. (Warehouse)
B
ALA.—Mobile
Burgess & Co.. D. R. ..A
Bush & Co., J. C. .....AAA
Heurin, Morriss & Co.....A
Ross Bros. & Co. ......B
Tonat, L. ....A
Watters & Co., J. A. ....B
ALA.—Montgomery
Marks & Gayle ....B
ALA.—Selma
Hooper & Co., C. W. ....A
Lamar, L. & E. ....A
Woolsey. M. ....B
ALA.—Tuskegee
Campbell & Wright ......A
ARK.—Little Rock
Carl & Tobey Co. ....B
Geyer & Adams Co. .....B
Penzel Grocery Co., C. F...B
ARK.—Pine Bluff
Blumenthal & Co., S....B
Gillespie & Bro. Co.....B
Hammett Grocery Co. ....B
GA.—Athens
Moss & Co.. R. L. .....B
Phinizy, Billups ....B
GA.—Augusta
Nixon & Danforth ......A
O'Dowd Sons & Co., M...B
Phinizy & Co. ....A
Pope & Fleming ....A
Whitney, S. M. ....A
GA.—Blackshear
Brantley Co., A. P. .....A
GA.—Carrollton
Mandeville & Co., L. C....A
GA.—Columbus
Blanchard. Humber & Co..A
Bradley Co., W. C. ......A
Davis & Co., J. T. Jr....A
GA.—Griffin
Boyd, Douglas ....A
GA.—Macon
English, Johnston & Co...
AAAA
Heard Bros. ....A
Jones, B. L. ....A
Mayer & Watts ....B
Willingham, C. B. ......A
GA.—Savannah
Butler, Stevens & Co. ....A
Ellis, Chas. ....A
Flannery. John ....A
Gordon & Co., W. W. ...A
Hunter, Pearce & Battery
A
Leffler Co.. A. ....AA
William & Co., J. P. .....AA
Wood & Bro., J. S......B
GA.—Senoia
Couch & Co.. M. H.......A
KY.—Louisville
McCord & Wright, 631 Main
B
LA.—Alexandria
Taylor Co., W. F. ....A
LA.—New Orleans
Abraham & Son, Hy., 216
Broome ....A
Atkinson & Co., Wm., 824
Gravier ....A
Frankenbush & Son, J. M.,
806 Perdido ....A

COTTON DEALERS

Gumbel & Co., F., 812 Perdido ....AAA

Gumbel & Co., S., 824 Gravier ....AAAA

Hardies' Sons & Co., J. T., 843 Union ....A

Hardie & Co., W. T., 938 Gravier ....A

Hyman, Hiller & Co., 829 Union ....AA

Lehman, Stern & Co., 839 Gravier ....A

Levy & Sons, M., 830 Gravier ....A

Lichtenstein & Son, H., 843 Union ....B

Minge & Co., C. H., 845 Union ....A

Newman, H. & C., 932 Union ....AA

Parker & Co., J. M., 819 Perdeda ....A

Peale & Co., W. A., 838 Union ....A

Putnam & King, 926 Gravier ....A

Richardson & May, 820 Perdido ....A

Stewart Bros. & Co., 836 Union ....AAAA

Thomas & Co., S. O. ....A

Thompson & Co., W. B., 808 Perdedo ....B

Walmsley, S. P., 812 Perdedo ....A

Weis & Co., J., 817 Gravier AAAA

MD.—Baltimore

Elliot Bros., 21 S. Gay....A

Turnbull & Morris, German & Calvert ....B

MASS.—Boston

Beebe & Co., Lucius, 89 State ....A

Emerson & Co., A., 683 Atlantic Av. (Waste) ...B

Hill & Cutler, 567 Atlantic Av. (Waste) ....B

Purdy & Co., O. N., 290 Sumner (Peruvian) ....B

Remick & Co., T., 489 Atlantic Av. (Waste) ....A

MASS.—Springfield

Mayo & Co., A. N., 156 Lyman (Waste) ....B

MASS.—Taunton

Carr, Peter H. (also Waste) AA

MISS.—Corinth

Corinth Cotton Com. Co..AA

MISS.—Greenville

Blum, A. ....B

Crittenden & Co., O. B. ..B

Ireys & Co., Henry T. ..B

MISS.—Jackson

Hart, J. & B. ....AA

Johnson-Taylor Co. ......B

MISS.—Meridian

Lyle, J. T. ....B

Marks, Rothenberg & Co... AAA

Threefoot Bros. & Co....AA

Winner & Meyers ......AA

MISS.—Natchez

Carpenter & Co., J. N....A

Lowenburg & Co., I. ....A

Postlewait & Chase......B

MISS.—Tupelo

Clark & Co. ....B

MISS.—Vicksburg

Brown, Sam. ....AAAA

Vicksburg Cotton Press Assn. ....A

Willis, Moore & Co. .....A

MISS.—Yazoo City

Powell, J. F. ....B

MO.—St. Louis

Adler-Goldman Com. Co., 108 S. Main ....AAAA

Allen-West Com. Co., 104 S. Main ....A

Hill Cotton Co., Napoleon, 116 S. Main ....A

Senter Comm. Co., 3rd, cor. Walnut ....B

N. C.—Waxhaw

Heath Co., A. W. ....A

Rodman, Heath & Nivens B

N. C.—Wilmington

Calder Bros. ....A

COTTON DEALERS

Sprunt & Son, Alex. ..AA

Worth Co., The ....B

OHIO—Cincinnati

Railway Supply & Mfg. Co., 1242 Harrison Av. (also Waste) ....B

OKLA.—Oklahoma City

Amer. Cotton Co....AAAA

Oklahoma Compress Co...B

PA.—Philadelphia

D'Olier & Co., Wm., 3rd & Chestnut ....A

Hoffman, Geo. E., 248 Chestnut ....A

Hyde, Edw. S., 223 Chestnut ....B

McFadden & Bro., G. H., 121 Chestnut ....AAA

McCloskey, John J., 34 N. Front (Waste) ......A

O'Neil, Chas., 57 N. Front.. AA

Sloan & Co., N. P., 241 Chestnut ....B

PA.—Pittsburg

Childs & Co., Harvey L. (Waste) ....A

R. I.—Pawtucket

Briggs & Co., H. A. (Waste) ....A

R. I.—Providence

Brooks, Geo. B., 297 Canal (Waste) ....B

Deming & Co., R. H., 10 S. Water ....A

Emerson & Co., A., 176 W. Exchange (also Waste) ....B

R. I.—Woonsocket

Ray, E. K. (Waste) ..AAA

S. C.—Charleston

Inman & Co...............AA

Seignious, James M. ....B

Wagener & Co., F. W. AAA

Whaley & Rivers ....B

TENN.—Memphis

Ball & Co., W. M., 286 Front ....A

Bowdre Bros. & Co., 272 Front ....A

Boyd & Son, Irby, 352 Front B

Brown & Perkins, 266 Front ....B

Chism Bros. & Co., 332 Front ....B

Delta Cotton Co., 8½ Madison ....A

Dillard & Coffin Co., 306 Front ....A

Dockery & Donelson, 320 Front ....B

Duffin Bros. & McGehee, 272 Front ....A

Fargason & Co., J. T., 369 Front ....A

Frank & Co., J. T., 282 Front ....A

Fulmer & Co., 348 Front..A

Gage & Co., W. A., 300 Front ....A

Goodlett & Co., 282 Front..A

Hill Cotton Co., Jerome, 334 Front ....B

Hughes & Mercer, 224 Front ....B

Knight, Nelson & Co., 304 Front ....A

Lundee, Chapman & Co., 334 Front ....A

Mallory & Sons Co., 381 Front ....AA

Palk, Spinning & Co., 268 Front ....A

Pritchett, McCormack & Co., 9 Union ....B

Sledge-Norfleet Co., 372-374 Front ....A

Stewart, Gwynne & Co., 356-358 Front ....A

Tate Bros., 336 Front.....B

Taylor & Co., W. F., 314 Front ....A

Wilson-Ward Co., 4 W. Court ....B

Wyme, Love & Co., 361 Front ....B

Schloss, Miller & Malone (Comm. Brokers) ..AAAA

TEXAS—Anna

Shirley & Bro., A. (Dealers)
...................................B

TEXAS—Arlington
Rogers-McKnight Co. .....B
TEXAS—Galveston
Heye & Co., Gustave ...AA
Kempner, H. ....AAAA
Mensing Bros. & Co.......A
Moody & Co., W. L..AAAA
Rogers & Co., John D. ..A
Wallis, Landes & Co...AAA
TEXAS—Houston
Carson, Sewall & Co....A
Cleveland & Sons, W. D..A
Dorrance & Co. ....B
Henke & Pillet ....AAA
House, T. W. ....AAAA
Inman, Nelms & Co. .....A
Taylor & Sons, H. D....B
TEXAS—Paris
Paris Oil & Cotton Co...B
TEXAS—San Antonio
Oppenheimer, D. & A...AA
TEXAS—Taylor
Melasky, J. ....A
VA.—Norfolk
Arps & Co., Geo. L.......A
Grandy & Sons, C. W.....
...................................AAAA
Harreil & Co., S. B......B
Jones, Son & Co. ....B
Lee Bros. & Co..........B
Perry Co., J. W........B
VA.—Petersberg
Hartley & Bro., E. A....B
VA.—Richmond
Branch & Co., Thos. ..AAA
Scott & Stringfellow....B

COTTON, BALL
See Thread

COTTON, GUN
CAL.—San Francisco
California Cap Co. ....A

COTTON, MISCELLANEOUS
MD.—Baltimore
Burroughs Bros. (Absorbent)
...................................A
MASS.—Boston
Billings, Clapp & Co. (Soluble)
...................................B
MASS.—Fall River
Estes & Son, J. H. (Absorbent)
...................................B
Maplewood Mills (Absorbent)
...................................A
MASS.—Walpole
Lewis Batting Co. (Batting)
...................................B
N. J.—Cedar Grove
Bowden, Anthony (Calking)
...................................C
N. J.—East Orange
Seabury & Johnson (Absorbent)
...................................AA
N. J.—Newark
Todor & Co., Geo. (Soluble
for Incandescent Mantles)
...................................D
N. J.—New Brunswick
Johnson & Johnson (Absorbent)
...................................A
New York City
Cooper & Co., Charles (Soluble)
...................................AA
Erkenbrach, Geo. A. (Soluble)
...................................D
Maas & Waldstein (Soluble)
...................................A
N. Y.—Yonkers
Drane Plaster Co. (Absorbent)
...................................C
PA.—Conshohocken
Lee Co., J. Elwood (Absorbent)
...................................AA
PA.—Philadelphia
Hance Bros. & White (Absorbent)
...................................AA

COTTON GOODS
ALA.—Anniston
Anniston Mfg. Co. (Brown
Sheetings;   Shirtings;

Drills) ....A
ALA.—Birmingham
Avondale Mills ....AA
ALA.—Cordover
Indian Head Mills of Ala.
Sheetings;   Shirtings;
Drills; Cotton Flannels) A
ALA.—Enterprise
Enterprise   Cotton   Mills
(Flat,   Twisted   Filling
Duck; Osnaburgs) ......A
ALA.—Florence
Cherry Cotton Mills (Yarns;
Skeins; Warp) ....A
ALA.—Huntsville
Dallas   Mfg.   Co.,   The
(Brown; Bleached Sheetings) ....AAAA
ALA.—Mobile
Barker   Cotton   Mill   Co.
(Brown Sheetings; Drills)
...................................AA
ALA.—Montgomery
People's Cotton Factory (4
yd.   Hydro   Sheetings;
Shirtings) ....A
ALA.—Pell City
Pell City Mfg. Co. (Denims)
...................................AA
ALA.—Piedmont
Coosa Mfg. Co. (Warps) A
ALA.—Prattsville
Prattsville Cotton Mills &
Banking   Co.   (Duck;
Sheetings; Shirtings; Osnaburgs) ....A
CAL.—Oakland
California Cotton Mills Co.
(Duck) ....AA
COLO.—Overland
Overland Cotton Mill Co.
(Sheetings; Shirtings; Cotton Flannel) ....A
CONN.—Baltic
Baltic Mills Co. (Fine) AAA
CONN.—Danielson
Danielsonville   Cotton   Co.
(Sheetings; Print Cloths)
...................................A
Quinebaug Co., (Sheetings;
Shirtings) ....AAA
CONN.—Greenville
Shetucket   Co.   (Denims;
Ducks; Cheviots; Domets;
Ticks; Shirtings) .....AA
CONN.—Jewett
Ashland Cotton Co. (Cambrics; Sateens; Twills) AA
CONN.—Killingly
Attawaugan Co. (Sheetings;
Shirtings; Cambrics; Satins, &c.) ....AAA
CONN.—Montville
Palmer Bros. Co. ....AAAA
CONN.—Moosup
Union Mills (Aldrich Mfg.
Co.) (Plain) ....B
**CONN.—North Grosvenor
Dale**
Grosvenor Dale Co. (Cambrics; Shirtings; Sateens;
Fancies) ....AAAA
CONN.—Norwich
Falls Co. (Cottonades; Coatings;   Ticks;   Awnings;
Domets; Denims; Shirtings; Fancy Stripes) ..AA
Shetucket Co. (Denims) AA
Totokett Mills Co. (Fine) A
CONN.—Putnam
Monohansett Mfg. Co.
(Bleached Shirtings)...B
Morse   Mills   (Sheetings;
Shirtings; Twills) .....A
Nightingale Mills (Sheetings; Shirtings; Twills) A
Powhatan Mills (Sheetings;
Shirtings; Twills) .....A
Putnam   Mfg.   Co.,   The
(Sheetings;   Shirtings;
Twills) ....A
CONN.—Shelton
Derby Cotton Mill (Robert
Franklyn Adams) Crown
Linings;   Buckram;   Silk
Finish; China Silk) ....A
CONN.—Taftsville
Ponemah   Mills   (Fancy
Woven; Fine Goods for
Printing) ....AAAA
CONN.—Uncasville
Uncasville Mfg. Co. (Fancy
Shirtings; Cheviots; Denims) ....A

COTTON GOODS

CONN.—Voluntown
Briggs Mfg. Co. (Sateens; Twills) ....A
CONN.—Waterbury
American Mills Co. (Narrow Elastic; Non-Elastic Fabrics) ....B
CONN.—Wauregan
Wauregan Co. (Lawn; Fancy) ....AAA
CONN.—Willimantic
Willimantic Cotton Mills Corp. (Plain three & four leaf Twills; Sateens; Fancy Goods) ....AA
Windham Mfg. Co. (Twills; Sheetings; Prints) ....B
CONN.—Wilmington
Brancroft Sons & Co. Joseph (Window Shade Fabrics; Window Hollands; Book Cloths) ....AAAA
GA.—Athens
Athens Mfg. Co. (Plaids; Convict Stripes) ....A
GA.—Atlanta
Atlanta Cotton Mills (Sheetings; Drills) .....A
Elizabeth Cotton Mills (Drills; Sheetings) ...B
Exposition Cotton Mills (Sheetings; Shirtings; Drills) ....AAA
Fulton Bag & Cotton Mills (Light Sheeting; Batting) ....AA
GA.—Agusta
Agusta Factory, The (Sheetings; Shirtings; Drills) ....AAA
Enterprise Mfg. Co. (Brown Sheetings; Shirtings; Drills) ....AA
Globe Cotton Mills (Duck; Sheetings; Osnaburg; Drills) C
Graniteville Mfg. Co. (Sheetings; Shirtings) ....AAAA
Langley Mfg. Co. (Sheetings; Shirtings; Drills) ....AAA
Riverside Mills (Batting; Machinery Waste Paper Stock; Waste) ....A
Sibley Mfg. Co. (Stripes; Ducks; Plaids; Brown Goods; Cheviots; Crashes) ....AAA
Warren Mf. Co. Cotton Standard Print) ......AA
GA.—Carrollton
Mandeville Mills (Sheetings) ....A
GA.—Columbus
Columbus Mfg. Co. (Sheetings) ....AA
Eagle & Phenix Mills (Plaids; Ginghams; Denims; Domets; Cotton Worsteds; Cottonades; Kerseys; Tickings; Prison Stripes; Cheviots) .AAAA
Muscogee Mfg. Co. Cheviots; Fancy Shirting; Denims; Kerseys) ....A
Swift Mfg. Co. (Cottonades; Plaids; Checks) ....A
GA.—Dalton
Crown Cotton Mills (Duck; Osnaburgs) ....A
GA.—Dublin
Dublin Cotton Mills (Sheetings) ....B
GA.—Eastman
Eastman Cotton Mills ...B
GA.—Gainesville
Gainesville Cotton Mills (Sheetings; Drills) ....A
GA.—Greensboro
Mary-Leila Cotton Mills (Sheeting; Drills) ......B
GA.—Griffin
Boyd-Mangham Mfg. Co. (Fancy Weaves) ....A
Griffin Mfg. Co. (Hickory Stripes; Cottonades; Plaids; Cheviots; Denims; Fancy Ducks) ....AA
Kincaid Mfg. Co. (Damasks; Crashes) ....AA
Rushton Cotton Mills (Brown Sheetings; Domets; Momie, &c.) ....A

COTTON GOODS

GA.—Harmony Grove
Harmony Grove Mills (Brown Shirtings; Sheetings; Drills) ....A
GA.—Hartwell
Witham Cotton Mills (Sheetings; Drills) ....B
GA.—High Shoals
High Shoals Mfg. Co. (Shirtings; Stripes) ....A
GA.—Hogansville
Hogansville Mfg. Co. (Duck) ....AAAA
GA.—Jefferson
Jefferson Cotton Mills (Brown Sheetings) .....A
GA.—La Fayette
Union Cotton Mills (Fine Sheetings; Drills) ......A
GA.—La Grange
Dixie Cotton Mills (Duck; Sheeting; Drills) ....A
United Cotton Mills (Duck) ....AA
GA.—Lindale
Mass. Mills in Georgia (Sheetings; Drills; Duck) ....AAAA
GA.—Macon
Willingham Cotton Mills (Sail; Hose; Belting Duck) ....A
GA.—Monroe
Monroe Cotton Mills (Sheetings) ....A
Walton Cotton Mills Co. (Drills; Sheetings) .....B
GA.—Moultrie
Moultrie Cotton Mills (Sheetings; Drills) .....A
GA.—Pelham
Pelham Mfg. Co. (Duck; Osnaburgs; Drills) ...B
GA.—Poulan
Poulan Cotton Mills (Sheetings) ....B
GA.—Rome
Anchor Duck Mills (Duck) ....B
GA.—Roswell
Roswell Mfg. Co. (Sheetings; Shirtings) ....A
GA.—Valdosta
Strickland Cotton Mills (Sheetings; Drills) .....A
GA.—West Point
Lanett Cotton Mills (Duck; Sheetings; Drills; Sateens) ....AAA
Riverdale Cotton Mills (Duck) ....B
GA.—Winder
Winder Cotton Mill (Denims) ....B
ILL.—Aurora
Aurora Cotton Mills (Brown Sheetings) ....AA
ILL.—Chicago
Bliss, Fabyan & Co. (Commission Print G'ds.)AAAA
Burton Co., J. (Bats; Felts) ....B
Catlin & Co. (Commission) ....AAAA
Converse, Stanton & Co. (Commission) ......AAA
Faulkner, Page & Co. Commission Denims; Dress Goods) ....AAA
Foster & Co., F. A. (Comm. Sheetings; Shirtings) .AA
Jenkins, Kreer & Co. (Comm.) ....B
Lawrence & Co. (Com. Prints; Sheetings; Dress Goods) ....AAAA
Minot, Hooper & Co. (Com. Sheetings; Shirtings; Drills) ....AAAA
Record & Co., M. L. (Com.) ....AAA
Shaw & Co., T. A. (Com.) ....AAA
Slater & Sons, S. (Com.) ....AAAA
Wellington, Sears & Co. (Com. Duck; Bunting; Cotton Goods) ....AAAA
Wood & Son, Jos. W. (Com.) ....A
IND.—Cannelton
Indiana Cotton Mills (Brown Sheetings) ....A

290

IND.—Evansville
Evansville Cotton Mfg. Co. (Sheeting; Drills; Batting) ....A
Lincoln Cotton Mills Co. ..A
IND.—Indianapolis
Brower & Love Bros. (Brown Sheeting) ....A
IND.—Madison
Eagle Cotton Mills Co. (Brown Sheetings; Drills; Carpet Warps) ....A warps) ....A
LA.—Monroe
Ouachita Cotton Mills (Sheetings) ....A
LA.—New Orleans
Lane Mills of New Orleans (Denims; Camlets; Drills; Stripes) ....AA
Maginnis Cotton Mills (Sheetings; Shirtings; Osnaburgs; Twills; Duck; Canton; Drills) ......AA
MAINE—Auburn
Barker Mill (Sheeting; Shirting) ....A
MAINE—Augusta
Edwards Mfg. Co. (Print Clths; Sheeting) ..AAAA
MAINE—Biddeford
Pepperell Mfg. Co. (Sheetings; Flannels; Drills; Jeans; Shirtings) .AAAA
MAINE—Brunswick
Cabot Mfg. C. (Fine Shirtings) ....AAA
MAINE—Lewiston
Androscoggin Mills (Sheetings; Shirtings; Sateens; Seersuckers) ....AAA
Bates Mfg. Co. (Gingham; Seersuckers) ....AAAA
Continental Mills (Sheetings; Twills; Lawns; Sateens; Muslin; Momie Cloth) ....AAAA
Hill Mfg. Co. (Sheetings; Twills; Shirtibgs; Sateens) ....AAAA
MAINE—Lisbon
Farwell Mills (Fine Sheetings; Shirtings; Fancy Gods) ....AA
MAINE—Saco
York Mfg. Co. (Denims; Dress Goods; Ginghams) AAA
MAINE—Waterville
Lockwood Co. (Sheetings; Shirtings) ....AAAA
MD.—Alberton
Alberton Cotton Mills; (Duck; Drills; Twills; Osnaburgs) ......AAAA
MD.—Baltimore
Ashland Mfg. Co. (Duck) AAA
Carey; Bayne & Smith Co. (Com.) ....AA
Dickey & Sons, W. J. (Com.) AAA
Mount Vernon - Woodberry Cotton Duck Co. (Duck) AAAA
Woodward, Baldwin & Co. (Com.) ....AAAA
MD.—Ilchester
Thistle Mills Co. (Cottonades; domets; Crashes) A
MD.—Millington
Unicorn Mills (Fancy Weaves; Crashes, etc.) ..A
MD.—Olella
Dickey & Sons (Oella Mills) (Duck) ....AAA
MD.—Warren
Warren Mfg. Co. (White; Colored Duck; Cottonades) A
MASS.—Adams
Berkshire Cotton Mfg. Co. (Fine) ....AAAA
Renfrew Mfg. Co. (Dress Goods; Turkey Red Demasks; Demasks; Madras Shirtings) ....AAA
MASS.—Amesbury
Hamilton Woollen Co. (Print Cloths; Sheetings) AAA
MASS.—Blackstone
Blackstone Mfg. Co. (Sheetings; Shirtings) ....AA

MASS.—Boston
Amory, Browne & Co. (Com. Sheetings; Ticks; Ginghams) ....AAA
Battelle, Hurd & Co. (Com. Duck; Sheeting; Shirting; Gingham) ....A
Bishop, Robt. (Est. of) (Nat. Carp. Lining Co.), 157 W. 6th (Dyed; Carded) A
Bliss, Fabyan & Co. (Com-Print Gods) ......AAAA
Catlin & Co. (Com.) AAAA
Faulkner, Page & Co. (Com. Denims; Dress Goods) AAA
Floyd Bros. & Co. (Com.) AA
Foster & Co., F. A. (Com. Sheeting; Shirting) ..AA
Howard Mfg. Co., Ch'town (Elastic) ....A
Joy, Langdon & Co. (Com. Prints) ....AAAA
Lane & Co., J. H. (Com.) AAA
Lawrence & Co. (Com. Prints; Sheetings; Dress Goods) ....AAAA
Minot, Hooper & Co. (Com. Sheeting; Shirting; Drills) AAAA
Nevins Co. (Com. Ticks; Cotton Flannels) .....A
Parker, Wilder & Co. (Com. Sheetings) ....AAAA
Smith, Hogg & Co. (Com.) AAAA
Wellington, Sears & Co. (Com. Duck; Bunting; Cotton Gods) ......AAAA
MASS.—Chicopee
Dwight Mfg. Co. (Sheetings; Sheetings; Dress Goods) AAAA
MASS.—Chicopee Falls
Chicopee Mfg. Co. (Sheetings) ....AAA
MASS.—Clinton
Lancaster Mills (Gingham; Cheviots; Dress Goods) AAAA
MASS.—Colerain
Griswoldville Mfg. Co. (Shirtings; Sheetings; Absorbent Gauze) ....A
MASS.—Dodgeville
Hebron Mfg. Co. (Dodgeville Mills) (Fine Sheeting; Twills) ....A
MASS.—Exeter
Exeter Mfg. Co. (Shirtings; Sheetings, etc.) ....A
MASS.—Fall River ..
American Linen Co. (Print Cloths) ....AAAA
Arkwright Mills (Spec.) AA
Barnaby Mfg. Co. (Fine Colored) ....AA
Barnard Mfg. Co. (Plain Twill; Sateen; Fancy) AAA
Borden Mfg. Co., Rich (Print Cloths) ......AAA
Borden City Mfg. Co (Wide Gods; Spec.) ......AAAA
Bourne Mills (Sateen; Twills) ....AA
Chace Mills (Twills; Print Cloths) ....AA
Conanticut Mills ....A
Cornell Mills (Print Cloths) AA
Davis Mills (Fine; Fancy) A
Davol Mills (Sheetings; Shirtings; Fancy Cottons) AA
Durfee Mills (Print; Odd Goods) ....AAA
Fall River Iron Wks. Co. (Print Cloths) ...AAAA
Fall River Mfg. ....A
Flint Mills ....AA
Granite Mills (To order) AAAA
Hargrave Mills (Fine Goods) AAA
King Phillip Mills (Cambric; Muslin; Sateens; Lawns) ....AAAA
Laurel Lake Mills (Print Cloths) ....AA

Merchants Mfg. Co. (Print Cloths) ....AAA
Metacomet Mfg. Co ..AAAA
Narragansett Mills (Corset Jeans; Sateens; Print Cloths) ....AA
Osborn Mills (Print Cloths) AAA
Parker Mills (Fine Goods) AAA
Pocasset Mfg. Co. (Sheetings; Print Cloths; Shirtings) ....AAA
Robeson Mills ....B
Sagamore Mfg. Co. (Print Cloths) ....AAA
Seaconnet Mills (Odd Goods) AAA
Shove Mills (Print Cloths) AAA
Slade Mills (Print Cloths; Twills; Satens) ......AA
Stafford Mills (Print Cloths) AAAA
Tecumseh Mills (Odd Goods) AAA
Troy Cotton & Woolen Mfry. (Print Cloths) ......AAA
Union Cotton Mfg. Co. (Print Cloths) ......AAA
Wampanoag Mills (Print Cloths; Twills; Sateens) AAA
Wheetsmoe Mills (Print Cloths) ....AAA

MASS.—Fitchburg
Fitchburg Duck Mills (Sail; Belting; Hose Duck)....A
Nockeve Mill (Plain; Fancy Cloths) ....A
Parkhill Mfg. Co. (Fine Dress Gods) ....AA

MASS.—Grafton
Fisher Mfg. Co. (Fancy) AAA
Saunders Cotton Mills (Twills; Sateens; Sheetings; Shirtings) ......B

MASS.—Holyoke
Lyman Mills (Sheetings; Shirtings; Drills; Lawns) B

MASS.—Lawrence
Atlantic Cotton Mills (Sheetings; Sateens) ......AAA
Everett Mills (Dress Goods; Cottonades; Shirtings; Denims) ......c ..AAA
Lawrence Duck Co. (Duck) A
Pacific Mills (Prints; Fancy; Denims; Delaines) AAAA
Pemberton Mfg. Co. (Cottonades) ....AA

MASS.—Lowell
Appleton Co. Sheeting; Drills) ....AA
Boott Cotton Mills (Drills; Sheetings; Shirtings; Fancy Dress Goods)...AAAA
Hamilton Mfg. Co. (Prints; Shirtings; Stripes; Drills; Flannels) ....AAAA
Lowell Weaving Co. (Sail Duck; Fire Cloths) .....D
Mass. Cotton Mills (Sheetings; Shirtings; Drills; Canton Flannel; Denims; Duck, etc.) ......AAAA
Merrimack Mfg. Co. (Prints) AAAA
Tremont & Suffolk Mills (Sheetings; Shirtings; Drills; Cotton Flannels) AAA

MASS.—Mechanics Mills
Mechanics Mills (To order) AAA

MASS.—Methuen
Methuen Co. (Ginghams; Ticks; Shirtings; Duck) A

MASS.—Millbury
Cordis Mills (Ticks) ......A

MASS.—Montague
Turners Falls Cotton Mills (Sheetings; Shirtings) ..A

MASS.—New Bedford
Acushnet Mill Corp (Bleached; Brown) ..AAA
Bristol Mfg. Corp. (Print Clths) ....AAA
Butler Mill ....AAA
Dartmouth Mfg. Corp. (Fine Goods) ....AAA

Grinnell Mfg. Corp. (Fine Goods) ....AAAA
Pierce Mfg. Co. ....AAA
Potomsker Mills Corp. (Fine Soule Mill (Fine) .....AAA
Wamsutta Mills (Shirtings; Sheetings; Muslin; Lawns; Sateens) ....AAAA
Whitman Mills ......AAAA

MASS.—No. Adams
Beaver Mill (Fine) ..AAAA
Eclipse Mill (Fine) ..AAAA
Greylock Mills (Lawns; Sateens; Sheetings) ......A
Johnson-Dunbar Mills Co. (Gingham; Dress Goods; Madras) ....A

MASS.—Northbridge
Whiting Mfg. Co., Paul (Cambrics; Lawns; Sateens) ....A
Whitinsville Cotton Mills (Fine) ....A

MASS.—Palmer
Boston Duck Co. (Duck) AA
Otis Co. (Dress Goods; Denims; Shirting) ...AAAA
Thorndike Co. (Ticks; Stripes; Shirtings) .AAA

MASS.—Plymouth
Plymouth Woolen & Cotton Co. (Sail Duck) ......D

MASS.—Salem
Naumkeag Steam Cotton Co. (Shirtings; Sateens; Sheetings; Drills) ......AAAA

MASS.—Sturbridge
Fiskdale Mills (Print Cloths) AA

MASS.—Taunton
Coer Mfg. Co. (Plain; Fancy) ....AA
Poole Mills, Elizabeth (Cotton Flannels) ....B
Whittenton Mfg. Co. (Dress Goods) ....AAA

MASS.—Thorndike
Thorndike Co. (Denims) AAA

MASS.—Three Rivers
Palmer Mills (Otis Co.) (Fancy Denims)....AAAA

MASS.—Uxbridge
Uxbridge Cotton Mills (Fine Sheetings; Shirtings)...A

MASS.—Waltham
Boston Mfg. Co. (Sheetings; Colored Fabrics; Cotton; Silk Mixtures) ....A

MASS.—Ware
Otis Co. (Checks; Denims; Awnings) ......AAAA

MASS.—Warren
Thorndike Co. (Ticking; Husking Clth; Linings; Shirtings) ....AAA

MASS.—Webster
Slater Mills, H. N. (Silesias; Jaconets; Lawns; Sateens; Cambrics) ....AAAA

MASS.—White Valley
White Valley Mills (Blue Denims) ....AA

MASS.—Winchendon Springs
White Bros. (Denims) .AAA

MASS.—Worcester
Wachuset Mills (Fancy)...C

MISS.—Columbus
Tombridge Cotton Mills (Shirting; Sheeting; Osanburgs) ....B

MISS.—Meridian
Meridian Cotton Mills (Plain; Fancy Weaves), B

MISS.—Natchez
Natchez Cotton Mills (Brown Sheetings; Shirtings; Drills) ....B

MISS.—Stonewall
Stonewall Cotton Mills (Sheetings; Drills; Osnaburgs; Madras) ......AA

MISS.—Tupelo
Tupelo Cotton Mills (Sheetings; Drills; Denims)..B

MISS.—Wesson
Mississippi Mills (Domets; Fancy Cotton, Worsteds) AAA

MISS.—Winona
Winona Cotton Mills (Sheetings; Drills; Shirtings)..B

MO.—St. Louis
Home Cotton Mills (Sheet-

ing) ....AAAA
N. H.—Claremont
Monadnock Mills (Sheetings)
A
N. H.—Dover
Cocheco Mfg. Co. (Cloths for
Printing) ....AAA
N. H.—Greenville
Columbian Mfg. Co. (De-
nims; stripes Cheviots;
Ticks) ....A
N. H.—Jaffray
Jaffray Mills (Denims)...A
N. H.—Manchester
Amory Mfg. Co. (Sheetings;
Jeans; Shirtings; Sateens)
AAAA
Amoskeag Mfg. Co. (Ging-
ham; Denims; Ticks)
AAAA
Manchester Mills (Prints)
AAAA
Stark Mills (Sheetings;;
Shirtings; Ducks; Drills)
AAAA
N. H.—Nashua
Jackson & Co. (Sheetings;
Shirtings) ....AAAA
Nashua Mfg. Co. (Shirtings;
Sheetings) ....AAAA
N. H.—Newmarket
Newmarket Mfg. Co. (Shirt-
ings; Sheetings; Pongees)
AAAA
N. H.—Pembroke
China Mfg. Co. (Print
Cloths) ....B
Webster Mfg. Co. (Print
Cloths) ....AA
N. H.—Salmon Falls
Salmon Falls Mfg. Co.
(Fine; Fancy Goods; Sa-
teens) ....AAAA
N. H.—Somersworth
Great Falls Mfg. Co. (Shirt-
ings; Sheetings; Drills)
AAAA
N. J.—May's Landing
May's Landing Water Power
Co. (Print Cloths) ....A
N. J.—Yardville
Morris & Co. (Duck) ....A
N. Y.—Cohoes
Harmony Mills (Print
Cloths; Sateens) ..AAAA
N. Y.—Elmira
Call Mfg. Co. (Interlinings)
C
N. Y.—Newburgh
Newburgh Steam Mills
(Print Cloths) .....AAAA
New York City
Amory, Browne & Co. (Com.
Sheetings; Ticks; Ging-
hams) ....AAA
Bailey & Co., Joshua L.,
(Com.; Jeans; Cotton;
Worsteds; Ginghams;
Sheetings; Denims; Flan-
nelettes) ....AAAA
Baker, Carver & Morrell
(Com. Duck) ....A
Battelle, Hurd & Co. (Com.)
A
Bausher & Co., C. L. (Com.;
Ticks; Denims; Ginghams;
Mapped Fabrics; Brown;
Bleached Cottons, AAAA
Bernhard & Son, B., (Com.)
A
Bernheimer & Bro., Jacob S.
(Com.) ....AAA
Bernheimer & Walter
(Com.) ....AAA
Bliss, Fabyan & Co. (Com.
Prints) ....AAAA
Brown Sons & Co., M.
(Com.; Jeans; Cottonades)
B
Burgess & Co., W. H.
(Com.) ....AAA
Carey, Bayne & Smith Co.
(Com.) ....AA
Catlin & Co. (Com.).AAAA
Childs & Co., H. C. (Com.;
Dress Goods; Prints, etc.)
A
Cone Export & Com. Co.
AAA
Conrad &·Co., W. B. (Com.)
AA
Converse, Stanton & Co.
(Com.) ....AAA
Cooke & Co., Jas. W. (Com.;
Ginghams, etc.) ....A

Cooley, Martin I. (Com.**)**
A
Creighton & Burch (Com.)
AA
Curtis & Warren (Com.)..B
Danforth, Clarke & Co.
(Com.) ....A
Deering, Milliken & Co.
(Com.) ....AAAA
Dickey & Sons, W. J. (Com.)
AAA
Eldredge, Lewis & Co.
(Com.; Sheetings; Drills)
White Goods; Dress
Goods) ....AAAA
Elms & Co. (Com.) .....B
Farber Drewry & Co., H. J.
(Com.; Dress Goods) ...C
Farish Stafford Co. (Com.)
B
Farnum & Co., Jno. (Com.;
AAAA
Faulkner, Page & Co. (Com.;
Shirtings; Cottonades; Un-
bleached Goods, etc.) AAA
Fillebrown & Co., C. B.
(Com.) ....A
Fish & Co., Wm., Jr.
(Com.) ....B
Fithian & Co., J. H. (Com.)
A
Forstman & Co. (Com.**)**
AAA
Foster & Co., F. A. (Com.;
Sheetings; Shirtings), AA
Galey & Lord (Com.) ....A
Garnet & Co. (Com.; Sa-
teens; Shirtings; Prints;
Dress Goods; Percales;
Lawns) ....AAAA
Haines & Bishop (Com.) ..A
Hamilton & Co., E. H.
(Com.) ....A
Harding, Whitman & Co.
(Com.) ....AAAA
Hardt, von Bernuth & Co.
(Com.) ....AAAA
Heller & Long (Com.;
Prints) ....AA
Hinchman & Co., W. H.
(Com.) ....B
Jenkins, Kreer & Co. (Com.)
A
Joy, Langdon & Co. (Com.;
Prints, etc.) .....AAAA
Juilliard & Co., A. D. (Com.)
AAAA
Kohlman & Co., Chas.
(Com.) ....A
Kremer & Steubing (Com.;
Prints) ....AAAA
Lane & Co., J. H. (Com.)
AAA
Langley & Co., W. H.
(Com.) ....AAAA
Lawrence & Co. (Com.;
Prints; White Goods;
Dress Goods, etc.) .AAAA
Libby & Co., H. J. (Com.;
Dress Goods) ....A
Masters & Co., Francis R.
(Com.; Madras; Dress;
Wash Goods) ....B
Meyer & Goetz (Com.)....B
Milius & Bros., E. (Com.), A
Minot Hooper & Co. (Com.;
Fancy White Goods;
Prints; Sheetings; Drills)
AAAA
Moss, Taylor & Co. (Com.;
Prints; White Goods, etc.)
AAA
Nevins Co., The (Com.)...A
Oelbermann, Dommerich &
Co. (Com.; Dress Goods)
AAAA
Parker, Wilder & Co. (Com.;
Sheetings, etc.)....AAAA
Poor & Co., J. Harper
(Com.; Colored; White;
Printed; Madras) ......A
Remy, Schmidt & Pleissner
(Com.; Dress; White
Goods) ....AA
Reynolds & Co., Jas. E.
(Com.; Sheetings) ......A
Riggs & Co., Geo. (Com.)..A
Robinson-Hughes Co. (Com.)
A
Rothschild & Hein (Com.), **B**
Schwab & Co., S. M., **Jr.**
(Com.) ....A
Sheridan & Co., G. K.
(Com.; Duck) ....**A**

Slater & Sons, S. (Com.) AAAA

Smith, Alb. D. (Com.)....A

Smith, Hogg & Co. (Com.) AAAA

Southern Cotton Mills & Com. Co. (Com.)..........A

Stevens & Co., J. P. (Com.) A

Strusburg & Co., W. Shell (Com.) ....B

Talcott, James (Com.; Jeans; Cottonades) AAAA

Townsend & Montant (Com.) ....AAA

Townsend & Co., E. M. (Com.) ....A

Treat & Converse (Com.; Prints) ....AAA

Turner Co., J. Spencer ((Com.; Duck; Bunting) AAA

Victor & Archelis, Fred. (Com.) ....A

Watson, Porter, Giles & Co. (Com.) ....A

Weed & Bro. (Com.) ...AAA

Wellington, W. L. (Com.) A

White & Co., Jas. F. (Com.) ....AAAA

Whiteside, Jos. S. (Com.; Damask; Ticks; Crashes) B

Whitin & Collins (Com.; Shirting; Sheetings) ....A

Whitman & Phelps (Shirtings; Denims; Ticks) AAA

Whitman & Co., Clarence (Com.; White Goods; Gingham) ....AA

Willis Grinnell & Co. (Com.; Sheeting; Shirtings; Muslin; ancy Goods) ...AAA

Wilmerding & Bisset (Com.) AA

Wilmerding, Morris & Mitchell (Com.) ......AA

Wilson & Bradbury (Com.) AAA

Woods & Son, Jos. W. (Com.) ....A

Woodward Baldwin & Co. (Com.) ....AAA

Yelland, Wm. (Com.); Cottonades; Worsted; Shirtings) ....B

New York Mills
New York Mills (Shirtings; Sheetings; Cottonades; Camlets) ....AAAA

N. Y.—Niagara Falls
Cataract Hair Cloth Co. (French; Herringbone; Twilled Hair Cloth) ....B

N. Y.—Stuyvesant Falls
Van Alen Cotton Mills (Print Cloths) ....A

N. Y.—Utica
Utica Steam & Mohawk Valley Cotton Mills (Sheetings; Shirtings) AAA

N. Y.—Victory Mills
Saratoga Victory Mfg. Co. (Silesia; Sleeve Linings) AAA

N. C.—Ashville
Ashville Cotton Mill (Plaids; Cheviots; Stripes; Tickings) ....A

N. C.—Bessemer City
Bessemer City Cotton Mills (Madras Cloth) C

Southern Cotton Mills (Brown; Colored) ......A

N. C.—Burlington
Alamance Cotton Mills (Plaids) ....B

Aurora Cotton Mills (Gingham) ....AAA

Carolina Cotton Mills (Plaids) ....B

Elmira Cotton Mills (Colored Goods) ....A

Glencoe Mills (Shirtings; Cheviots; Stripes; Domets) A

N. C.—Caroleen
Henrietta Mills ....AA

N. C.—Cedar Falls
Cedar Falls Mfg. Co. (Sheetings) ....B

N. C.—Charlotte
Chadwick Mfg. Co. (Sheetings) ....B

Highland Park Mfg. Co. (Gingham) ....A

High Shoals Co. (Sheetings) Louise Mills (Fine Cloth)..A

Orient Mfg. Co. (Sateens; Madras; Dimities) .....B

N. C.—China Grove
Patterson Mfg. Co. (Plain White) ....A

N. C.—Cliffside
Cliffside Mills (Ginghams) B

N. C.—Concord
Cabarrus Cotton Mill (Sheetings) ....A

Cannon Mfg. Co. (Sheetings) A

Gibson Mfg. Co. (Madras) A

N. C.—Cooleemee
Cooleemee Cotton Mills (Sheetings; Drills), AAA

N. C.—Durham
Durham Cotton Mfg. Co. (Chambrays; Ginghams; Domets; Shirtings) ...AA

Erwin Cotton Mills Co. (Denims; Camlets; Chambrays) ....AAA

Golden Belt Mfg. Co. (Sheetings) ....AA

N. C.—East Durham
Pearl Cotton Mills (Sheetings) ....A

N. C.—Elm College
Williamson & Sons, Jas. N. (Plaids; Cottonades; Flannelettes) ....AAA

N. C.—Fayetteville
Hope Mills Mfg. Co. (Madras; Shirtings) ......AA

Holt-Morgan Mills (adras; Shirtings; Ginghams; Tickings) ....A

N. C.—Forest City
Florence Mills (Sheetings; Drills; Print Cloths) ..A

N. C.—Franklinville
Randolph Mfg. Co. (Sheetings) ....B

N. C.—Gastonia
Avon Mills (Sheetings) ...A

Loray Mills (Sheetings; Drills) ....AAA

N. C.—Gibsonville
Minnola Mfg. Co. (Ginghams; Plaids; Checks)..B

N. C.—Goldsboro
Wayne Cotton Mills (Sheetings) ....B

N. C.—Graham
Bellemont Cotton Mills (Plaids) ....AAA

Holt, L. B. (Twills; Cheviots; Chambrays) ...AAA

N. C.—Greensboro
Hucomuga Mills (Ginghams; Blues; Browns) ......A

Proximity Mfg. Co. (Colored Goods) ....A

Revolution Cotton Mills (Canton Flannels) ....B

N. C.—Haw. River
Holt-Granite Mfg. Co. (Plaids; Dress Goods; Cheviots; Chambrays)...A

N. C.—Hickory
Shuford Mfg. Co., E. L. (Twills; Saterns) .....

N. C.—Hope Mills
Hope Mills Mfg. Co. (Cheviots; Cottonades) .....AA

N. C.—Huntersville
Anchor Mills (Ginghams)..B

N. C.—Kings Mo. ntain
Crowder Mountain Cotton Mills (Sheetings) ......B

Diling Cotton Mills (Brown Sheetings) ....A

Kings Mountain Mfg. Co. (Plain) ....B

N. C. Lexington
Nokomis Cotton Mills (White Goods) ....A

Wennonah Cotton Mills (Plaids; Checks; Stripes; Sheetings) ....A

N. C.—Lowell
McAdam Mills (Plaids; Denims; Cheviots) ....AA

N. C.—Mooresville
Mooresville Cotton Mills Sheetings) ....A

N. C.—Neuse
Neuse River Mills (Brown

Sheetings) ....A
N. C.— Patterson
Gwyn-Harper Mfg. Co.
(Plaids) ....B
N. C. —Raleigh
Caraleigh Mills Co. (Dress
Ginghams) ....A
Pilot Cotton Mills (Colored
Goods) ....A
N. C.—Ramseur
Columbia Mfg. Co. (Sheetings) ....A
N. C.—Randleman
Naomi Falls Mfg. Co. (Colored) ....B
Randleman Mfg. Co.
(Plaids; Checks; Stripes;
Denims) ....B
N. C.—Reidsville
Edna Cotton Mills (Drills)
AA
N. C.—Rhodhiss
Rhodhiss Mfg. Co. (Drills;
Sheetings) ....B
N. C.—Roanoke Rapids
Roanoke Mills Co. (Fine Colored) ....B
Rosemary Mfg. Co. (Damasks) ....B
N. C.—Rockingham
Steeles Mill (Prints) ..A
N. C.—Salisbury
Kisler Mfg. Co. (Sheetings)
B
N. C.—Sanford
Sanford Cotton Mills (Sheetings) ....A
N. C.—Saxapahaw
White, Williamson & Co.
(Piece Goods) ....A
N. C.—Shelby
Shelby Cotton Mills (Sheetings) ....A
N. C.—Spray
Leaksville Cotton Mills
(Plaids; Ginghams) ...A
Morehead Cotton Mills Co. B
Nantucket Mills (Colored
Goods) ....A
N. C.—Statesville
Statesville Cotton Mills
(Brown Sheetings)......A
N. C.—Swepsonville
Virginia Cotton Mills
(Plaids; Denims; Sheetings) ....B
N. C.—Troy
Smitherman Cotton Mills
(Sheetings) ....B
N. C.—Wilmington
Delgade Mills ....AA
N. C.—Winston-Salem
Fries, F. & H. (Shirtings;
Cheviots) ....AAAA
South Side Mfg. Co. (Shirtings) ....A
OHIO—Cincinnati
Goodin, Weaver, Reid & Co.
(Com.) ....B
Putnam, Hooker & Co.
(Com.) ....A
PA.—Chester
Aberfoyle Mfg. Co. (Dress
Goods) ....AAA
Chester Mfg. Co. (Table
Damask; Tickings)....A
Galey & Lord Mfg. Co.
(Fine Goods) ....A
Jordan Mfg. Co. ....A
PA.—Lancaster
Conestogo Steam Mills
(Ticks; Sheetings; Awnings) ....AAAA
PA.—Philadelphia
Bacon & Co. (Corn)....AAA
Bailey & Co., Joshua L.
(Com. Dress Goods)..AAA
Blankenburg & Co., R.
(Com.) ....A
Bradbury Bros. (Table Damask; Dress Goods).....B
Burton Bros. & Co. (Com.)
A
Carruth & Co., Jno. G.
(Seersuckers; Shirtings;
Madras; Chambreys; Cotton Worsteds) ....AAA
Connelly & Sons, Jas. (Ginghams) ....B
Frankford Co-operative Mfg.
Co. (Table Damask)..B
Glasgow Mills (Madras)..B
Greer, Benj. W. ....B
Hewett, C. G. (Table Dam-

ask) C
Kerr, Jas. H. (Ginghams;
Cheviots; Madras) ....A
King, Hillman & Gill
(Com.) ....AA
Kneedler & Co. (Sateens;
Tickings; Worsted Cloth)
B
Kremer & Strubing (Com.)
AAAA
Lane & Co., J. H. (Com.)
AAA
Lanne & Co., Frank D.
(Com. Dress Goods)..AAA
Milne & Sons, C. J. (Shirtings) ....AAAA
Neff & Co., Robt. K. (Com.)
B
O'Neill, Wm. (Damask)...C
Porter & Son, Chas. (Men's
Wear) ....AAA
Providence Mills Mfg. Co.
(Damasks; Crashes) ...C
Schadewald & Sons, Henry
(Turkey Red Damask)..B
Taylor & Scott (Turkey Red
Damask) ....D
Thorpe, Richard (Turkey
Red; Bleached Damask)
B
Wardlow, J. & W. (Table
Damask) ....E
Whitaker & Sons, Wm.
(Tickings; Stripes) ....A
Wilson & Bradbury (Com.)
AAA
Wittr & Co. Charles
H. (Turkey Red Damask)
A
PA.—Reading
Garner & Co. (Shirtings;
Sheetings; Twills)..AAAA
R. I.—Bristol
Richmond Mfg. Co. (Print
Cloths) ....A
R. I.—Coventry
Coventry Co. (For Converters) ....AAA
R. I.—Crompton
Quidnick Mfg. Co. (For Converters) ....AAA
R. I.—Cumberland
Berkeley Co. (Cambrics; India Lawns; Nainsooks)
AAA
R. I.—Hopkinton
Nichols & Langworthy Machine Co. (Print Cloths).A
R. I.—Lincoln
Samoset Co. (Sheetings;
Lawns) ....A
R. I.—Lonsdale
Lonsdale Co. (Bleached
Goods; Silesias, &c.)
AAAA
R. I.—Manville
Manville Co. (Plain; Fancy)
AAAA
R. I.—Pawtucket
American Yarn Mfg. Co.
(Twills; Sateens; Zanillas) ....A
Royal Wearing Co. ......AA
Slater Cotton Co. (Sheetings; Shirtings; Cambrics;
Muslins; Lawns) ...AAA
U. S Cotton Co. (Print
Cloths) ....AA
R. I.—Providence
Hebron Mfg. Co. (Shirtings;
Sheetings) ....AAAA
Nottingham Mills (Sheetings; Prints) .....AAAA
R. I.—Scituate
Fiskeville Mills (Sheetings)
AAAA
Jackson Mills (Shirtings;
Twills) ....AAAA
Hope Co. (Shirtings) ..AAA
R. I.—Smithfield
Bernon Mills (Print Cloths;
Twilled Goods; Sateens).A
Enfield Mills (Light; wide;
Fancy Goods) ....A
Forestdale Mfg. Co. (Sheetings; Shirtings) ....A
R. I.—Warren
Warren Mfg. Co. (Sheetings; Shirtings; Twills;
Sateens) ....AAAA

R. I.—Warwick
Centreville Cotton Mill (Sheetings) ....AAA

Crompton Co. (Print Cloths) ....AAA

Lippitt Mill (Sheetings; Twills) ....AAAA

Natick Mills (Shirtings; Twills) ....AAAA

Warwick Mills (Plain; Fancy) ....AAA

R. I.—Westerly
Solway Mills (Fancy Colored) ....AAA

White Rock Mill (Fine Sheetings) ....AAAA

R. I.—Woonsocket
Clinton Mfg. Co. (Sheetings; Shirtings) ....AAAA

Eagle Mills (Fancy Dress Goods; Sateens; Brocades) ....A

Naushon Co. (Dress Goods) ....A

S. C.—Bamberg
Bamberg Cotton Mills (Sheetings) ....A

S. C.—Batesburg
Middleburg Mills (Sheetings) ....B

S. C.—Bath
Aiken Mfg. Co. (Shirtings; Sheetings; Cotton Print) ....A

S. C.—Belton
Belton Mills (Brown Shirtings; Cotton Drills)..AAA

S. C.—Camden
Camden Cotton Mills ....B

S. C.—Cateechee
Norris Cotton Mills Co. (Sheetings) ....A

S. C.—Cherokee Falls
Cherokee Falls Mfg. Co. (Brown Sheetings) ...AA

S. C.—Chester
Eureka Cotton Mills (Filling; Hard Twist) ....AA

Springstein Mills (Ginghams; Madras) ....A

Wylie Mills (Skein; Warp) ....B

S. C.—Clifton
Clifton Mfg. Co. (Sheetings; Shirtings; Drills) ....AAAA

S. C.—Clinton
Clinton Cotton Mills (Fancy Stripes; Specialties)....A

S. C.—Clover
Clover Cotton Mfg. Co. (Combed Egyptian; Carded Peeler) ....A

S. C.—Columbia
Capital City Mills (Sheetings) ....B

Columbia Mills Co. (Duck) ....AAAA

Granby Cotton Mills (Cotton Print Cloths) ...AAA

Olympia Cotton Mills (Fine Sheetings; Print Cloths) ....AAAA

Palmetto Cotton Mills (Welts; Dress Goods; Print Cloths) ....B

Richland Cotton Mills (Twills; Sheetings).....A

S. C.—Cowpens
Cowpens Mfg. Co. (Sheetings) ....B

S. C.—Darlington
Darlington Mfg. Co. (Sheetings; Drills) ....AAA

S. C.—Easley
Easley Cotton Mills (Sheetings) ....A

S. C.—Edgefield
Edgefield Mfg. Co. (Sheetings) ....B

S. C.—Enoree
Enoree Mfg. Co. (Brown Drillings; Sheetings) .AA

S. C.—Fairmont
Tyger Cotton Mills (Sheetings) ....A

S. C.—Fort Mill
Fort Mill Mfg. Co. (Ginghams) ....A

S. C.—Gaffney
Gaffney Mfg. Co. (Dress;

Fancy Weaves; Madras; Cloth) ....AAAA

Limestone Mills (Cloth)...A

S. C.—Glendale
Converse Co., D. E. (Shirtings; Sheetings; Drills) ....AA

S. C.—Graniteville
Graniteville Mfg. Co. (Brown Shirtings; Sheetings; Drills) ......AAAA

S. C.—Greenville
American Spinning Co. (Cloth) ....AA

Brandon Mills (Converters; Cloth; Sheetings) ..AA

Huguenot Mills (Cottonades; Cheviots; Plaids; Outing Cloth) ....B

Mills Mfg. Co. (Fine White) ....AA

Monaghan Mills (Print; Oil Cloth Convertibles)....AA

Poe Mfg. Co. F. W. (Gray, for converting and mfg. trade) ....AA

S. C.—Greenwood
Greenwood Cotton Mills (Standard Drills; Sheetings) ....AA

Grendel Mills (4-yd. Goods) ....AA

S. C.—Greers
Victor Mfg. Co. (Sheetings; Print Cloth) ....AA

S. C.—Hartsville
Hartsville Cotton Mill (Print Cloth) ....A

S. C.—Inman
Inman Mills ....A

S. C.—Irene
Saxe-Gotha Mills (Sheetings; Drills) ....B

S. C.—Lancaster
Lancaster Cotton Mills (Sheetings) ....AAA

S. C.—Lando
Manetta Mills ....B

S. C.—Langley
Langley Mfg. Co. (Shirtings; Sheetings; Drills) ....AAA

S. C.—Laurens
Laurens Cotton Mills (Bedford Cords; Twills)...AA

Watts Mills (Fine Sheetings) ....A

S. C.—Lexington
Lexington Mfg. Co. (Tickings) C

S. C.—Lockhart
Lockhart Mills (Brown Sheetings) ....A

S. C.—Newberry
Newberry Cotton Mills (Brown Sheeting; Drills) ....AA

S. C.—Newry
Courtany Mfg. Co. (Sheetings) ....A

S. C.—Ninetysix
Ninetysix Cotton Mills (Sheetings) ....A

S. C.—Orangeburg
Orangeburg Mfg. Co. (Brown Sheetings) ....A

S. C.—Pacolet
Pacolet Mfg. Co. (Standard Sheetings; Drills)..AAAA

S. C.—Pelzer
Pelzer Mfg. Co. (Sheetings; Shirtings; Drills) ..AAAA

S. C.—Reedy River
Reedy River Mfg. Co. (Sheetings; Drills) ....A

S. C.—Rock Hill
Highland Park Mfg. Co. (Ginghams; Checks; Fancies) ....A

Manchester Cotton Mills Co. (Brown Sheetings) ...A

Victoria Cotton Mills (Ginghams) ....B

S. C.—Spartanburg
Arcadia Mills (Fine) .....A

Arkwright Mills (Sheeting; Drills) ....AA

Saxon Mills (Print Cloth) ....A

Spartan Mills (Sheetings;

COTTON GOODS

Shirtings; Print Cloth)
AAAA
S. C.—Union
Aetna Cotton Mills (Print
Cloth) ....B
Buffalo Cotton Mills (Sheet-
ings) ....AAA
Monarch Cotton Mills (Con-
verters' Goods) ....A
Union Cotton Mills Co. (Fine
Sheeting) ....AAA
S. C.—Walhalla
W a l h a l l a Cotton Mills
(Sheetings) ....A
S. C.—Walterboro
Colleton Cotton Mills ....B
S. C.—Warrenville
Warren Mfg. Co. (Print
Cloths) ....AA
S. C.—Westminster
Cheswell Cotton Mills Co.
(Sheetings; Twills) ....A
S. C.—Whitmires
Glenn-Lowery Mfg. Co.
(Sheetings) ....AA
S. C.—Whitney
Whitney Mfg. Co. (Shirt-
ings; Sheetings) ......A
S. C.—Williamston
Williamston Mills (Sheet-
ings) ....A
TENN.—Columbia
Columbia Cotton Mills Co.
(Heavy Brown Twills;
Sheetings) ....A
TEXAS—Covington
Tipton Cotton Mills (Plain)
B
TEXAS—Cuero
Cuero Cotton Mill (Sheet-
ings; Converting Cloth).A
TEXAS—Dallas
Dallas Cotton Mills (Duck)
AA
TEXAS—Gonzales
G o n z a l e s Cotton Mills
(Sheetings; Dress Ducks)
B
TEXAS—Hillsboro
Hillsboro Cotton Mill Co.
(Sheetings; Ducks) ....B
TEXAS—Waxahachie
Waxahachie Cotton Mills
(Duck) ....B
VT.—Burlington
Burlington Cotton Mills
(Prints) ....AA
Queen City Cotton Co.
(Print Cloth) ......AAA
VT.—North Pownal
North Pownal Mfg. Co.
(Prints) ....AA
VA.—Danville
Riverside Cotton Mills
(S h e e t i n g s; Plaids;
Checks; Stripes; Cheviots)
AAAA
VA.—Lynchburg
Lynchburg Cotton Mill Co.
(Canton Flannels; Drills;
Sheetings) .. ..A
WIS.—Beaver Dam
Beaver Dam Cotton Mills
(Sheetings) ....A
WIS.—Janesville
Rock River Cotton Co. (Bat-
ting) ....B

COTTON: SEW-
ING: SPOOL

See Thread

COTTONADES

See Cotton Goods

COUCHES

See Furniture

COULTERS

CAL.—Benicia
Benicia Agricultural Wks.,
Baker & Hamilton (Plow)
AAA
CONN.—Collinsville
Collins Co. (Plow) ..AAAA

COUNTERS (Con.)
IND.—Evansville
Blount, Henry F. (Plow)
AAAA
IOWA—De Witt
Cyclone Works (Plow) ..H
KY.—Louisville
Avery & Sons, B. F. (Plow)
AAA
N. Y.—Auburn
Osborne & Co., D. M. (Plow)
AAAA
OHIO—Canton
Buckeye Mfg. Co. (Plow
Rolling) ....D
Canton Saw Co. (Plow)...D
PA.—Beaver Falls
Beaver Falls Steel Works
(Plow) X

COUNTERS

See also Fixtures for Store
Counters

CONN.—Bridgeport
Grant Mfg. & Mach. Co.
(Revolution) ....E
Hubbell, Harvey (Revolu-
tion) C
CONN.—Bristol
Root, C. J. (Revolution)..B
CONN.—Hartford
Pratt & Whitney Co. (Revo-
lution) ....AAAA
Veeder Mfg. Co. (Revolu-
tion) ....A
ILL.—Chicago
Ball & Bro., A. (Game;
Card) ....AA
Brewers' & Bottlers' Machy.
Wks. (Beer Barrel)....G
McDonnell Odometer Co., S.
Kedzie Av. & W. 35th
(Revolution; Tally; Spe-
cial) X
Marsh & Co., Jas. P., 224
Washn. (Revolution) ..B
Warren Mfg. Co., J. D.
(Store; Wrapping) ....B
MASS.—Boston
American Steam Gauge &
Valve Mfg. Co. (Revolu-
tion) ....A
A s h t o n Valve Co., 271
Franklin (Revolution)..A
Boston Counter Co. (Boot;
Shoe) C
Crosby Steam Gauge &
Valve Co., 95 Oliver (Rev-
olution) ....AA
Dennison Mfg. Co. (Game;
Card) ....AAAA
Fuller, F. T., 16 Lincoln
(Boot; Shoe) C
Mousam Mfg. Co. (Boot;
Shoe) ....D
Star Brass Mfg. Co., 103
E. Dedham (Revolution)
A
National Fibre Board Co.
(Boot; Shoe) ....A
MASS.—Lynn
Hilliard & Merrill (Boot;
Shoe) ....A
Parker Bros. (Boot; Shoe).E
MASS.—Taunton
Campbell Printing Press &
Mfg. Co. (Printing Press)
B
MASS.—Townsend Harbor
Spaulding Bros. Co. (Boot;
Shoe) ....AA
MASS.—Worcester
Graton & Knight Mfg. Co.
(Boot; Shoe) ......AAAA
MICH.—Battle Creek
Hart, R. A. (Revolution).E
N. Y.—Brooklyn
Schaffer & Budenberg, 10
Division (Revolution)..D
N. Y.—Frankfort
Utica Steam Gauge Co.
(Revolution) X
New York City
Ashcroft Mfg. Co., 85 Lib-
erty (Revolution) ....A
Brunswick-Balke - Collender
Co. (Card; Game).AAAA
Grote & Co., F., 14th St.
Card; Game) ....D

COUNTERS (Con.)

PA.—Erie
Exhibition Show Case Co.
  (Glass) ....B
PA.—Philadelphia
Belfield & Co., H., 435 N.
  Broad (Revolution) ...AA
Tabor Mfg. Co., 1742 Ham-
  ilton (Revolution) ....B
R. I.—Providence
Standard Machinery Co.
  (Revolution) ....B
VA.—Glen Allen
Cussons, May & Co. (Card)
  ....B
WIS.—Milwaukee
Durant, Walter N. (Revolu-
  tion; Printing Press) ..E

COUNTER-SHAFTS

CONN.—Hartford
Pratt & Whitney Co..AAAA
Quint, A. D. ....D
CONN.—Waterbury
Blake & Johnson ....A
ILL.—Chicago
Chicago Wheel & Mfg. Co.,
  39 W. Randolph ....D
ILL.—Joliet
Bates Machine Co. ......A
IND.—Columbus
Reeves Pulley Co. ......A
IND.—Mishawaka
Dodge Mfg. Co. .....AAA
MASS.—Boston
Cutter, Wood & Stevens Co.
 C
Sturtevant Co., B. F., 34
  Oliver ....AAA
MASS.—Greenfield
Wells Bros. Co. ....A
Wiley & Russell Mfg. Co.
  ....AA
MICH.—Grand Rapids
Wilmarth & Morman Co.
  (Wilmarth Friction) ...C
MINN.—Minneapolis
Minneapolis Steel & Machy.
  Co. ....A
MO.—St. Louis
St. Louis Machine Tool Co.,
  1114 S. 8th X
N. Y.—Brooklyn
Almond, T. R., 83 Washn..C
N. Y.—Buffalo
Buffalo Forge Co. ......AA
Holmes Machy. Co., E. &
  B., 59 Chicago (Variable
  Speed, &c.) ....B
Oliver Mfg. Co., W. W.,
  1483 Niagara C
New York City
Fairbanks Co., 416 Broome
  (Friction) ....AAAA
Garwin Machine Co., 137
  Varick (Friction) ..AAA
Manning, Maxwell & Moore,
  89 Liberty ....AAA
Niles-Bement-Pond Co., 136
  Liberty ....AAAA
Prylbil, P., 512 W. 41st..AA
Zucker & Levett & Loeb
  Co., 526 W. 25th ......A
OHIO—Ashland
Myers & Bro., F. E......AA
OHIO—Canal Fulton
Fulton Machine Co. (Self-
  Oiling) ....F
OHIO—Cincinnati
American Tool Works, 6th
  & Eggleston Av. ....AAA
Lodge & Shipley Mach. Tool
  Co., 3055 Colerain Av...A
National Mach. Tool Co.,
  308 Lawrence ....E
Oesterlein Mach. Co., Elam
  & Garrard Av. (Friction
  Clutch) C
OHIO—Cleveland
Bardons & Oliver (Double
  Friction) ....A
Warner & Swasey Co., E.
  Prospect (Double Fric-
  tion) ....A
OHIO—Columbus
Case Mfg. Co. ....AA
OHIO—Mansfield
Humphreys Mfg. Co. ....A

COUNTERSHAFTS

OHIO—Salem
Deming Co. ....A
OHIO—Tiffin
Sterling Emery Wheel Mfg.
  Co. ....B
PA.—Harrisburg
Hickok Mfg. Co., W. O...AA
PA.—Philadelphia
Challenge Machine Co., 3223
  Turner ....D
Cresson Co., Geo. V., 18th
  & Allegheny Av. .....AA
Fairmount Machine Co.,
  2108 Wood ....A
Stow Flexible Shaft Co...B
PA.—Waynesboro
Frick Co. ....AAA
R. I.—Central Falls
Mossberg Wrench Co. C
R. I.—Providence
Brown & Sharpe Mfg. Co.
  ....AAAA
Builders' Iron Foundry..AA
Diamond Machine Co. ...A
Standard Machy. Co. ....A
VT.—Montpelier
Lane Mfg. Co. ....A
WIS.—Milwaukee
Kempsmith Mfg. Co. ....A

COUNTER-SINKS

CONN.—Bridgeport
Knapp & Cowles Mfg. Co..C
Smith & Egge Mfg. Co....A
CONN.—Chester
Deuse, J. S. ....E
CONN.—Hartford
Billings & Spencer (Drop
  Forged) ....A
Pratt & Whiting Co. .AAAA
CONN.—New Britain
Stanley Rule & Level Co.
  ....AA
CONN.—Rockfall
Smith, Otis A. (For Wood-
  workers') ....B
CONN.—Seymour
Humphreysville Mfg. Co...E
Swan Co., James ....A
ILL.—Chicago
Vaughan & Bushnell Mfg.
  Co. ....B
Whitman & Barnes Mfg. Co.
  ....AAAA
ILL.—Rockford
Forest City Bit & Tool Co.
 C
MASS.—Boston
Atlantic Machine Screw Co.
  ....F
Hunter & Co., J. B.......B
MASS.—Brockton
Tuck Mfg. Co. ....E
MASS.—Chicopee Falls
Stevens Arms & Tool Co., J.
  ....A
MASS.—Fiskdale
Snell Mfg. Co. ....B
MASS.—Greenfield
Goodell-Pratt Co. ....B
Reece Co., E. F..........E
Wells Bros. & Co........A
Wiley & Russell Mfg. Co.
  ....AA
MASS.—Millbury
Buck, Charles ....A
Buck Bros. (Flat; Rose;
  Snail) ....A
MASS.—New Bedford
Morse Twist Drill & Ma-
  chine Co. ....AAA
MASS.—Shelburne Falls
Mayhew Co., H. H.......C
MASS.—Springfield
Springfield Mach. Screw Co.
  ....D
MICH.—Detroit
Detroit Twist Drill Co....C
N. J.—Eliabeth
Braunsdorf-Mueller Co. ..D
N. J.—Newark
Johnson, Wm., 249 Plane..D
New York City
Russell & Erwin Mfg. Co.
  ....AAAA
N. Y.—Syracuse
Syracuse Twist Drill Co...B

COUNTER-SINKS

OHIO—Cincinnati
Cincinnati Tool Co. ......A
Tatum Co., Samuel C....B
OHIO—Cleveland
Cleveland Twist Drill Co.
(Cox & Prentiss) cor.
Lake & Kirtland ......A
Standard Tool Co. .....AAA
OHIO—Wilmington
Irwin Auger Bit Co......B
PA.—Millersburg
Polk & Son, A. J. (For
Drilling Machines, &c.).D
VT.—Derby Line
Butterfield & Co........B

COUPES

See Carriages & Wagons.

COUPLERS

See also Hardware; Carriage.

CONN.—New Haven
North & Co., O. B. (Collar)
AA
ILL.—Chicago
Van Dorn Co., W. T. (Car)
D
ILL.—Jerseyville
Jerseyville Novelty Works
(Shaft; Pole) X
ILL.—Monmouth
Milne Mfg. Co. (Wire Rope)
C
IND.—Muncie
Whiteley Malleable Castings
Co. (Car) ....AA
MASS.—Reading
Pierce Organ Pipe Co.,
Samuel (Octave) C
MASS.—Springfield
Bemis Car Box Co. (Car)..D
MO.—St. Louis
American Steel Founders
Co. (Car) ....AAAA
Helmbacker Forge & Rolling Mills Co. (Car)...AA
N. J.—Newark
Peters Harness & Saddlery
Co. (Collar) C
N. Y.—Auburn
Eccles Richmond Co. (Ball
Bearing) ....B
N. Y.—Buffalo
Pratt & Letchworth Co.
(Car; Collar; Freight Car)
AAA
N. Y.—Dunkirk
Mulholland Co. (Shaft;
Pole) ....B
New York City
Gould Coupler Co. (Car).AA
Standard Coupler Co. (Car)
B
N. Y.—Syracuse
Bradley & Son, C. C. (Shaft;
Pole) C
N. Y.—Utica
Empire State Shaft Coupling Co. (Shaft; Pole)...D
OHIO—Cincinnati
Queen City Forging Co.
(Shaft; Pole) ....B
OHIO—Cleveland
National Malleable Castings
Co. (Car) ....AAAA
OHIO—Dayton
Dayton Malleable Iron Co.
(Car) ....AA
OHIO—Springfield
Springfield Malleable Iron
Co. (Car) ....A
PA.—Philadelphia
Latrobe Steel Co. (Steel)
AAAA
PA.—Pittsburg
Carnegie Steel Co. (Ltd.)
(Freight Car) .....AAAA
Hammon Coupler Co., Farmers' Bank Bldg. (Gas
Main) ....D
McConway & Torley Co.
(Car; Automatic; Freight;
Tender) ....AA
PA.—Thurlow
American Steel Castings Co.
(Car; Freight Car).AAAA

COUPLERS (Con.)

WIS.—Racine
Racine Malleable &
Wrought Iron Co. (Wire
Fence) ....B

COUPLINGS

See also Hardware; Carriage.

ALA.—Huntsville
Huntsville Fdy. & Machine
Works (Nolan & Jones)
(Clutch; Compression;
Flange; Shaft) ....B
ARK.—Little Rock
Thomas-Fordyce Mfg. Co.
(Compression) ....A
CONN.—Bridgeport
Belknap Mfg. Co. (Pipe).C
CONN.—Hartford
Billings & Spencer Co.
(Belt) ....AA
CONN.—New Haven
Eastern Machinery Co. (Cutoff; Friction Clutch)....B
Hotchkiss Co., E. M. (Hose)
A
New Haven Mfg. Co. (Friction Clutch) ....AA
New Haven Novelty Mach.
Co. (Pipe) ....B
Peck Bros. & Co. (Hose)
AA
CONN.—Norwich
Ossawan Mills Co. (Bell
Cord) ....B
CONN.—Plantsville
Smith & Co., H. D. (Pole;
Shaft) ....A
GA.—Augusta
Lombard Iron Works & Supply Co. (Shaft) ....A
GA.—Columbus
Golden's Fdy. & Mach. Co.
(Shaft) ....A
ILL.—Chicago
Allen Mfg. Co., W. D., 151
Lake (Plain; Automatic
Hose) ....A
Allis-Chalmers Co., Home
Ins. Bldg. (Flange; Shaft;
Friction Clutch) ..AAAA
Borden & Selleck Co., 48
Lake (Flange; Shaft)...B
Caldwell & Son Co., H. W.
(Shaft; Friction Clutch;
Universal Joint) ....AA
Crane Co. (Hose; Pipe;
Pump Rod) .....AAAA
Illinois Malleable Iron Co.,
30 W. Monroe (Closet;
Pipe; Pump Rod; Flange;
Shaft) ....AAAA
Jones Fdy. & Mach. Co., 143
North Av. (Cut-off) ..A
Monash-Younker Co., 203 S.
Canal (Pipe) ....B
Plamondon Mfg. Co., A., 57
S. Clinton (Compression;
Flange; Shaft; Friction
Clutch) ....A
Whitman & Barnes Mfg. Co.
(Hose) ....AAAA
ILL.—Decatur
Mueller Mfg. Co., H. (Boiler; Lead Flange; Pipe;
Automatic; Cone; Gas
Meter) ....AAA
ILL.—Kewanee
Western Tube Co. (Iron;
Brass; Boiler; Drill Rod;
Pipe Line; Tubing)..AAA
ILL.—Moline
Barnard & Leas Mfg. Co.
(Shaft) ....AA
ILL.—Sterling
Charter Gas Engine Co.
(Shaft) ....A
Novelty Iron Works (Hose)
E
IND.—Evansville
Vandergrift Coupling Co.
(Compression; Compression Shaft; Flange Shaft)
E
IND.—Indianapolis
Nordyke & Marmon Co.
(Shaft) ....AAA
Pioneer Brass Works (Expansion Ring; Hose)....C

COUPLINGS (Con.)

IND.—Mishawaka
Dodge Mfg. Co. (Clamp; Shaft; Friction Clutch; Universal Joint; Flange Shaft) ....AAA

KANS.—Enterprise
Ehrsam Machine Co., J. B. (Shaft) ....B

KANS.—Leavenworth
Great Western Mfg. Co. (Clamp; Friction Clutch; Shaft) ....AA

MD.—Baltimore
Cuyler & Mohler, 2324 Boston (Pipe) ....A
Ellicott Machine Co., cor. Bush & Severn (Shaft) ..C
Hutton & Co., G. H. (Pole; Shaft) ....F

MD.—Cumberland
Cumberland Steel Company (Flange Shaft) ....A

MASS.—Amesbury
Bailey & Co., S. R. (Pole; Shaft) ....A

MASS.—Boston
American Tool & Mach. Co., 109 Beach (Clamp; Flange; Friction Clutch) AA
Boston Coupling Co., 156 Pearl (Fire Hose) ......E
Boston Gear Works (Flange Shaft; Joint) ....B
Callahan Co., C., 127 Purchase (Hose) ....D
Durable Wire Rope Co. (Wire Rope) ....D
Edson Mfg. Co., 257 Atlantic Av. (Hose) ......B
Morse & Son, Andrew J., 140 Congress (Hose) ....A
Samson Cordage Wks. (Bell Cord; Belt) ....A
Strater & Sons, Herman, 74 Sudbury (Pipe) ....A
Walworth Mfg. Co., 132 Federal (Hose; Flange Shaft) ....AAAA

MASS.—Cambridge
Boston Woven Hose & Rubber Co. (Hose) ....AAAA

MASS.—Holyoke
Holyoke Mach. Co. (Shaft) AA

MASS.—Lexington
Jefferson Mfg. Co. (Flange) X

MASS.—Newtonville
Silver Lake Co. (Bell Cord; Belt; Round Belt) ......A

MASS.—North Adams
Hunter Machine Co., James (Shaft) ....A

MASS.—Woburn
Smith & Wallace (Register Cord, for Street Railways) ....D

MASS.—Worcester
Union Machine Co. (Cutoff) X

MICH.—Battle Creek
Sherman Mfg. Co., H. B. (Hose) ....A

MICH.—Bay City
Garland Co., M. (Compression) C

MICH.—Detroit
Buhl Malleable Co., cor. Wright & Adair (Clutch; Shaft; Flange Shaft)..A
Co-operative Foundry Co. (Shaft) X
Diamond Stamped Ware Co. (Garden Hose) ....A
Globe Brass Works (Hose) D
Park & McKay Co. (Closet) C

MINN.—Minneapolis
Howell & Co., R. R. (Horse Power) ....B
Minneapolis Steel & Machy. Co. (Flange Shaft; Friction Clutch; Universal Joint) ....AAA

MO.—Kansas City
Witte Iron Works Co. (Shaft) ....B

MO.—St. Louis
Broderick & Bascon Rope

COUPLINGS (Con.)
Co., 809 N. Main (Mine Car; Wire Rope) ....AA
Handlan-Buck Mfg. Co., 212 N. 3d (Bell Cord; Hose) AA
Kupferle, John C., 2d & Mound (Hose) ....AA
Leschen & Sons Rope Co., A. (Wire Rope) .....AAA
Medart Patent Pulley Co., 3500 De Kalb Av. (Clutch; Friction Clutch; Shaft) AAA
Missouri Tent & Awning Co. (Wagon) ....B
Plenger & Henger Mfg. Co., 1015 Herbert (Hose) ...A

N. H.—Exeter
Exeter Brass Works (Boiler) C

N. J.—Newark
Gould & Eberhardt (Joint) A

N. J.—Salem
Salem Brass & Iron Mfg. Co. (Rubber Closet)...B

N. Y.—Auburn
Clapp Mfg. Co., E. D. (Pole; Shaft) ....B
Eccles Co., Richard (Pole; Shaft) ....A

N. Y.—Brooklyn
Bliss Co., E. W. (Friction Clutch) ....AAAA
Krantz Mfg. Co., H., Boerum Pl. & State (Insulator) ....B

N. Y.—Buffalo
Noye Mfg. Co., 50 Lakeview Av. (Shaft) X

N. Y.—New Hamburg
Stuart, R. J. (Wedge Compression; Shaft) ......A

New York City
Acme Brass Works, 147 Baxter (Hose) ....F
American Railway Supply Co. (Bell Cord) X
Brown Co., A. & F., 26 Cortland (Cut-off; Friction Clutch; Shaft; Universal Joint) ....B
Creamer & Co., W. G., 96 John (Bell Cord) .....A
Eaton, Cole & Burnham Co., 253 B'way (Hose) .AAAA
Empire Rubber Mfg. Co. (Expansion Ring; Shank) AA
Eureka Fire Hose Co., 13 Barclay (Hose) ....AAAA
Fairbanks Co., 416 Broome (Shaft; Flange; Universal Joint) ....AAAA
Goodyear's India Rubber Glove Mfg. Co., 503 B'way (Hose) ....AAAA
Graham & Co., John H., 113 Chambers (Hose) ....B
Haydenville Co., 150 Nassau (Hose) ....A
Hunt & Co., C. W. (Rope) AA
McNab & Harlin Mfg. Co., 56 John (Hose) ......AA
Waterbury Rubber Mfg. Co., 49 Warren (Hose) .....D

N. Y.—Rochester
Davis Machine Co., W. P. (Shaft; Flange Shaft; Compression) ....A
Estes Mfg. Co., 301 State (Compression) C
Nunn Brass Works (Inc.) (Boiler) ....F

N. Y.—Syracuse
Shaw Coupling Co. (Compression) ....E

N. Y.—Troy
McMurray Co., C. F. (Shaft) A

OHIO—Ashland
Myers & Bro., F. E. (Pump Rod) ....AAAA

OHIO—Canton
Kohler & Co., F. E. (Hose) C

OHIO—Cincinnati
Lane & Bodley Co., cor. John & Water (Shaft)...B
Oesterlein Mach. Co., Gar-

COUPLINGS (Con.)

rard Av. & Elam (Friction
Clutch) ....B
Queen City Brass & Iron
Works (Expansion; Hose,
&c.) ....B

OHIO—Cleveland
Bartlett & Snow Co., C. O.
(Clutch) ....A
Cleveland City Forge & Iron
Co. (Railroad) ....AA
Cleveland Hardware Co.
(Pole; Shaft) ....AA
Cudell, F. E. (Cut-off)....B
Hill Clutch Co., ft. Waverly
Av. (Friction Clutch)...B
Upson Nut Co. (Flange
Shaft) ....AAAA

OHIO—Columbus
Case Mfg. Co. (Shaft; Belt;
Flange; Flexible Shaft;
Friction Clutch; Universal
Joint) ....A
Columbus Bolt Co. (Pole;
Shaft) ....AA
Ohio Pump & Brass Co.,
18th & Oak (Expansion
Rod; Lead Flange) C

OHIO—Cuyahoga Falls
Falls Rivet & Mach. Co.
(Clutch; Friction Clutch;
Cut-off; Shaft) ....A

OHIO—Mansfield
Barnes Mfg. Co. (Pump
Rod) ....A

OHIO—Massillon
Hess-Snyder Co. (Cut-off;
Flange Shaft; Friction
Clutch) ....AA

OHIO—Salem
Clark Co., W. J. (Hose)..A

OHIO—Shelby
Brightmann Mfg. Co. (Friction Clutch; Cut-off)..AA

OHIO—Springfield
Springfield Brass Co. (Hose)
E

OHIO—Toledo
Baker Bros. (Flange Shaft)
A

OHIO—Youngstown
Republic Rubber Co.
(Closet) ....AA
Sennett Co., Geo. B. (Com-
pression) ....B

PA.—Beaver Falls
Standard Gauge Steel Co.
(Clutch; Compression;
Shaft) ....A

PA.—Braddock
Braddock Mach. & Mfg. Co.
(Compression; Flange).A

PA.—Bradford
Dresser, S. R. (Cast Iron
Pipe) ....AA

PA.—Ellwood City
Standard Engineering Co.
(Pipe) ....AA

PA.—Erie
Campbell Brass Works, J. B.
(Boiler) ....A

PA.—Grove City
Carruthers-Fithiam Clutch
Co. (Cut-off) ....B

PA.—Nazareth
Nazareth Fdy. & Mach. Co.
(Flange Shaft) ......B

PA.—Philadelphia
Cresson Co., Geo. V., 18th
& Allegheny Av. (Inter-
nal; Clutch; Cut-off;
Friction Clutch; Shaft;
Universal Joint) ......AA
Dallett & Co., Thos. H.
(Flexible Shaft) ......B
Hydraulic Specialty Co., 427
Walnut (Closet) ......B
Klein. Chas. C., 2850 N.
Marshall (Clamp) ....B
Moore & White Co., 15th &
Lehigh Av. (Cut-off)..B
Philadelphia Pneumatic Tool
Co., 21st & Allegheny Av.
(Air Hose) ....B
Sellers & Co., Wm., 1600
Hamilton (Shaft; Flange
Shaft) ....AAAA
Stow Flexible Shaft Co.
(Universal Joint) .....B
Wolf Co. (Flange Shaft;
Friction Clutch) .....AA

COUPLINGS (Con.)

PA.—Pittsburg
Columbia Bridge Co., Park
Bldg. (Flange; Shaft).AA
Jones & Laughlins Steel Co.
(Clutch; Compression;
Cut-off; Shaft; Friction
Clutch; Universal Joint)
AAAA
Kelly & Jones Co., 135
Water (Pipe) ....AA
McKay & Co., James (Coal
Car) ....AAA
Standard Chain Co. (Mine
Car) ....AAAA

PA.—Tamaqua
Tamaqua Mfg. Co. (Com-
pression; Face; Flange).B

PA.—Warren
Jacobson Mach. Mfg. Co.
(Cut-off) C

PA.—Waynesboro
Frick Co. (Clutch; Face)
AAAA

PA.—Wilkesbarre
Nicholson & Co., W. H.
(Shaft; Flange Compres-
sion) C
Vulcan Iron Works (Clutch;
Friction Clutch; Shaft)
AAAA

PA.—Williamsport
Darling Pump & Mfg. Co.
(Hose) ....B
Valley Iron Works (Com-
pression; Flange; Pole;
Shaft) ....A

R. I.—Providence
Allen Fire Dept. Supply Co.
(Hose) ....D
Combination Ladder Co.,
366 Fountain (Hose)...B
Franklin Machine Co.
(Shaft) ....A

TENN.—Memphis
Chickasaw Iron Works
(Shaft) ....A

VT.—Montpelier
Lane Mfg. Co. (Shaft;
Friction Clutch) ......A

WIS.—Milwaukee
Filer & Stowell Co. (Shaft;
Flange Shaft; Friction
Clutch; Universal Joint)
AAA
Hoffman & Billings Mfg.
Co., 96 2d (Boiler) ....AA
Spence Mfg. Co., 279 Park
(Boiler) ....D

WIS.—South Milwaukee
Stowell Mfg. & Fdy. Co.
(Bell Cord) ....A

COUPONS

IND.—Indianapolis
Allison Coupon Co. (for Re-
tail Stores) ....A

COVERERS

MASS.—Chicopee Falls
Belcher & Taylor Agricultural Tool Co. (Potato)...A

N. Y.—Geneva
Herendeen Mfg. Co. (Pota-
to) ....AA

N. Y.—Greenwich
Eddy Plow Co., W. (Potato)
B

COVERINGS

CONN.—Hartford
Jewell Pad Co. (Harness)
AAA

ILL.—Chicago
Chicago Fire Proof Cover
Co. (Boiler; Steam Pipe)
E
Mackolite Fireproofing Co.,
109 Randolph (Column).B

MASS.—Boston
Nightingale & Childs Co.
(Boiler; Steam Pipe)....C
Trainer Mfg. Co., Chas. W.
(Boiler; Steam Pipe)..E

N. J.—Paterson
Peerless Plush Mfg. Co.
(Furniture) ....A

N. Y.—Albany
Huyck & Sons, F. C. (Wool-
en Mangle) ....AA

COVERINGS (Con.)

New York City

Bhumgara Co., F. P. (Furniture) C

Federal Clay Mfg. Co., 170 B'way (Column) ....B

Griffing Iron Co., A. A. (Boiler; Steam Pipe)..AA

Johns-Manville Co., H. W. (Asbestos; Sectional) AAAA

Person, O. D., 160 5th Av. (Column) X

Standard Table Oil Cloth Co. (Washable Hall) AAAA

N. Y.—Troy

Conners Paint Mfg. Co., Wm. (Asbestos) ....A

OHIO—Cincinnati

Cincinnati Roofing Co. (Asbestos) ....H

OHIO—Haydenville

Haydenville Co. (Column) A

OHIO—Lockwood

Carey Mfg. Co., Philip (Asbestos; Sectional) ..AAA

OHIO—Logan

Hocking Clay Mfg. Co. (Column) ....B

PA.—Allegheny

De Long & Co., Julius (Boiler; Steam Pipe)...B

PA.—Ambler

Keasby & Mattison Co. (Asbestos; Magnesia) .AAAA

Magnesia Covering Co. (Magnesia) C

PA.—Erie

Watson Co., H. F. (Boiler; Steam Pipe; Asbestos; Sectional) ....AAA

PA.—Philadelphia

Cortright Metal Roofing Co. (Metallic Hip) ....B

Merritt & Co., 1025 Ridge Av. (Column) ....B

Schofield, Mason & Co. (Furniture) ....A

Stead, Miller & Co. (Furniture) ....AA

PA.—Pittsburg

McConnell Asbestos & Covering Co. (Boiler; Steam Pipe; Sectional) ....B

Turner, C. A. (Boiler; Steam Pipe) ....B

COVERS

for Horse Covers, see Blankets; Horse.

ALA.—Birmingham

Dimmick Pipe Co. (Sewer Manhole) ....AA

ARK.—Little Rock

Little Rock Tent & Awning Co. (Wagon) C

CAL.—Los Angeles

Hoegee Co., W. H. (Wagon) B

CAL.—San Francisco

Henrix, C. (Wagon) C

Neville & Co. (Wagon)....A

CONN.—Bristol

Sessons Foundry Co. (Sewer Manhole) ....AAA

CONN.—Danielson

Jacobs & Co., E. H. (Roll) B

CONN.—Georgetown

Gilbert & Bennett Mfg. Co. (Wire; Dish; Barrel).AAA

CONN.—Meriden

Manning, Bowman & Co. (Dish; Molasses Jug; Enamelled Chamber)..AA

CONN.—New Britain

National Spring Bed Co. (Fabrics & Length or Width for Couches, Divans, Spring Beds, &c.)..F

CONN.—New Haven

McLagon Fdy. Co. (Coal Hole) C

CONN.—Waterbury

Steele & Johnson Mfg. Co. (Piano) ....A

CONN.—Woodbury

Curtis' Sons, D. (Table)...A

COVERS (Con.)

GA.—Columbus

Muscogee Mfg. Co. (Couch) A

ILL.—Chicago

Barbee Wire & Iron Works (Orange; Lemon Box; Wire; Barrel) ....B

Carpenter & Co., Geo. B. (Horse; Wagon; Truck; Stack; Waterproof)..AA

Chicago Sidewalk Light Co., 501 Washn. (Coal Hole).F

Clow & Sons, Jas. B., 344 Franklin (Sewer Manhole) AAA

Cook & Bro., E. C. (Binder; Fishing Rod; Gun; Haystack; Wagon) ....A

Dauchy Iron Works, 84 Illinois (Coal Hole) ......A

Illinois Malleable Iron Co. (Catch Basin; Cistern) AAAA

International Harvester Co. (Binder) ....AAAA

Kimball Co., W. W. (Piano) AAAA

Lyon & Healy (Piano) AAAA

Tengwall File & Ledger Co. (Loose Leaf Catalogue) B

U. S. Cast Iron Pipe & Fdy. Co., 317 La Salle (Sewer Manhole) ....AAAA

Vassar Swiss Underwear Co. (Knit Corset) C

Vierling, McDonald & Co., 23d & Stewart Av. (Coal Hole) ....A

Vulcan Iron Works, 63 Milwaukee Av. (Sewer Manhole; Catch Basin) .AAAA

Wilt, Chas. T. (Trunk)...B

ILL.—Freeport

Stover Mfg. Co. (Catch Basin; Cistern) ......AA

ILL.—Quincy

Modern Iron Works (Sewer Manhole) ....B

IND.—Evansville

Mesker & Co., Geo. L. (Coal Hole) ....AA

IND.—Fort Wayne

Central Foundry Co. (Cistern) ....F

IND.—Indianapolis

Over, Ewald, 426 S. Penn. (Sewer Manhole) C

IND.—Muncie

Adamson Typewriter Press Co. (Disk) ....H

Muncie Fdy. & Mach. Co. (Sewer Manhole) X

IND.—South Bend

South Bend Fdy. Co. (Sewer Manhole) ....B

IOWA—Dubuque

Adams Co. (Stove) ....A

MAINE—Lewiston

Dickey & Son, H. H. ....D

MD.—Bank

Baldwin Mfg. Co. (Couch) C

MASS.—Boston

Coffin Valve Co. (Sewer Manhole) ....D

Leigh, Evan Arthur (Roll) X

Stoddard, Haserick, Richards & Co. (Roll) ......B

Sturtevant Co., B. F. (Catch Basin; Trench) .....AAA

Tower Co., A. J. (Boat; Sail) ....AA

MASS.—Fall River

Union Belt Co. (Roll)...B

Wetherell, Orrin B. (Roll) B

MASS.—Holyoke

Holyoke Belting Co. (Roll) C

MASS.—Lynn

Hayes Foundry Co., J. A. (Sewer Manhole) ......F

MASS.—Milford

Milford Iron Foundry (Cistern) C

MASS.—Newburyport

Russell & Sons' Co., Albert (Sewer Manhole) C

COVERS (Con.)

MASS.—Pittsfield
Hubbell, F. W. (Sewer Manhole) X

MASS.—Springfield
Dickinson Hard Rubber Co. (Battery Jar) X
Iroquois Mfg. Co. (Wagon) X
Springfield Foundry Co. (Sewer Manhole) ......A

MASS.—Worcester
National Mfg. Co. (Dish; Wire Dish) ....A
Wire Goods Co. (Barrel)..A
Wright Wire Co. (Barrel) AA

MICH.—Detroit
Amos & Co., Chas., 94 W. Larned (Coal Hole) ....F
Anderson & Sons, W. H. (Sewer Manhole) C
Co-operative Fdy. Co., Junction Av. & Wabash R. R. (Safety Manhole) X

MICH.—Grand Rapids
Michigan Barrel Co. (Barrel) ....A
Rempes & Gallmeyer Fdy. Co. (Sewer Manhole) ..B

MINN.—Minneapolis
Minneapolis Steel & Machy. Co. (Sewer Manhole; Catch Basin) ......AAA
Northwestern Fdy. (S. T. Ferguson), 312 S. 10th Av. (Sewer Manhole) ......A

MINN.—St. Paul
South Park Fdy. & Mach. Co., Gilfillan Blk. (Sewer Manhole) ....B

MO.—St. Louis
Koken Iron Works, Koken Bldg. (Sewer Manhole)..B
Morrison Tent & Awning Co. (Wagon) C
St. Louis Stamping Co. (Enamelled; Saucepan; Chamber) ....AAAA
Wenzel, Herman (Wagon) C

NEBR.—Omaha
Paxton & Vierling Iron Wks., 17th & U. P. Ry. (Sewer Manhole); Coal Hole) ....AA

N. H.—Concord
Concord Fdy. & Mach. Co. (Sewer Manhole) ......B

N. J.—Jersey City
Dixon Crucible Co., Joseph (Crucible) ....AAA

N. J.—Newark
Duranoid Mfg. Co., 28 Prospect (Battery Jar) ....B
Hay Fdy. & Iron Works (Sewer Manhole) ....AA
Maher & Flockhart, 60 Polk (Sewer Manhole) ......A
Metcalf & Co., Jas. (Sewer Manhole) ....E
Peddie & Co., T. B. (Inc.) (Trunk) ....AA

N. Y.—Brooklyn
Sweeney Mfg. Co., W. H. (Molasses Jug) ....A

N. Y.—Buffalo
Buffalo Wire Works Co. (Barrel) ....A
Shepard & Co., Sidney (Boiler; Pail; Tea Kettle) AAAA

N. Y.—Cortland
Wickwire Bros. (Wire Dish) AAAA

N. Y.—Newburg
Coldwell-Wilcox Co. (Sewer Manhole; also Pivot)...B
New York City
American Hard Rubber Co., 11 Mercer (Battery Jar) AAAA
Brunswick-Balke - Collender Co. (Billiard Table) AAAA
Campbell & Co., John (Book) ....D
Central Stamping Co. (Boiler; Bucket; Kettle; Tea Kettle; Tin Pot) ....AA
Cornell Co., J. B. & J. M.,

COVERS (Con.)

26th & 11th Av. (Sewer Manhole) ....AA
Dimond, Thomas (Vault; Iron) ....A
Dobbie Fdy. & Mach. Co., 42 Dey (Sewer Manhole)..D
Drummond & Co., M. J., 192 B'way (Sewer Manhole) ....A
Fiske Iron Works, J. W. (Coal Hole) ....B
Fitzpatrick & Co., J. J., 481 Canal (Dynamo; Engine) F
Goodyear Rubber Co. (Billiard Table; Gun; Piano) AAAA
Goodyear's India Rubber Glove Mfg. Co. (Violin) AAAA
Hodgman Rubber Co. (Gun) AA
Hutchings Bros. (Wagon).D
Kloes, F. J. (Wagon) ....F
Lalance & Grosjean Mfg. Co. (Enamelled; Dish; Chamber) .....AAAA
Lissa, Henry (Trunk)....B
McHugh, John F. (Hamper; Boat; Sail; Trunk; Wagon) C
Neppert Jr., Francis (Piano) X
Ollesheimer & Bros., Theo. (Hamper) ....AA
Plant & Co., H. W., 56 Leonard (Lace Parasol; Piano) ....D
Richards & Co., E. Ira (Diamond Earring) .AAA
Sloan & Co. (Inc.) (Diamond Earring) ....B
Spalding & Bros., A. G. (Inc.) (Gun) .....AAAA
Stoutenborough, X. (Boiler; Bucket; Kettle; Pail; Perforated Frying Pan; Sauce Pan; Tea Kettle; Tin Pot; Wire Dish)...D
Von Lengerke & Detmold (Fishing Ring; Gun) ..A
Zinn & Co., Chas. (Hamper) B
Zittlosen Mfg. Co. (Wagon; Horse) ....B

N. Y.—Rochester
Enterprise Fdy. Co., 48 Olean (Sewer Manhole).B

N. Y.—Troy
Troy Stamping Co. (Tin Pot) AAAA

N. Y.—Utica
Miller & Son Co., Chas. (Sewer Manhole) .....AA
Palmer, C. F. (Sewer Manhole; Coal Hole)........C

OHIO—Akron
Whitman & Barnes Mfg. Co. (Binder) ....AAAA

OHIO—Ashtabula
Barber Mfg. Co. (Sewer Manhole; Coal Hole)....C

OHIO—Cincinnati
Bromwell Brush & Wire Goods Co. (Barrel; Wire Dish) ....AA
Buckeye Fdy. Co., 2257 Buck (Sewer Manhole)..A
Haney & Spieker, 125 W. 2d (Sewer Manhole) C
Haven Malleable Casting Co. (Coal Hole) ......B
Seinsheimer Paper Co. (Wagon) ....B

OHIO—Cleveland
Madison Av. Fdy. Co. (Sewer Manhole) ....D
Wagner Mfg. Co. (Wagon) C

OHIO—Columbus
Holtzman & Sons, Henry (Piano) ....A
McDonald Bros. (Sewer Manhole) C

OHIO—Dayton
Kramer Bros. Fdy. Co. (Sewer Manhole) C
Kuhns Bros. (Sewer Manhole) ....B

303

COVERS (*Con.*)

OHIO—Elyria
Topleff & Ely Co. (Kettle)
.....................................B

OHIO—Hamilton
Bentel & Margedant (Band
Saw Wheel) ....A
Meyers Mfg. Co., Fred. J.
(Dish; Barrel; Wire Dish;
Coal Hole) ....B

OHIO—Tiffin
Ohio Lantern Co. (Molasses
Jug) ....B

OHIO—Toledo
Toledo Fdy. & Mach. Co.
(Sewer Manhole) .....B
Wilcox Co., M. I. (Wagon)
..............................A

PA.—Beaver Falls
Co-operative Flint Glass Co.
(Cake; Glass) ....A

PA.—Bradford
Caldwell & Co., E. R. (Sewer Manhole) ....B

PA.—Catasauqua
Davis & Thomas Co. (Sew-
er Manhole) ....AA

PA.—Chelthenham
Pike, Mrs. E. V. (Chenille
Table) ....D

PA.—Chester
Bridge, John (Roll Top)...F
Howland, Wm. O. (Roll
Top) ....D

PA.—East Bangor
East Bangor Consolidated
Slate Co. (Slate Grave)
..............................AA

PA.—Meadville
Curry & Co. (Sewer Man-
hole) X

PA.—Mount Joy
Rollman Mfg. Co. (Apple)
..............................G

PA.—Nazareth
Nazareth Fdy. & Mach. Co.
(Catch Basin) ....B

PA.—Philadelphia
Armure Tapestry Mill (Ta-
ble; Couch Tapestry)...E
Ayres & Sons, Wm. (Cow)
..............................AA
Belmont Iron Works, 22d &
Washn. (Sewer Manhole)
..............................AA
Bromley Mfg. Co. (Chenille;
Raw Silk; Silk; Tapestry
Table) ....AAAA
Brooks & Son Co., Geo.
(Tapestry Table) .....B
Bruner, Francis A., Union
& Leiper (Tapestry Table)
..............................D
Campbell & Bro. Co., J. A.
(Table) ....AA
Darby & Sons, Edw., 233
Arch (Barrel) ....A
Gillinder & Son (Cake;
Cheese) ....A
Heide, Frank (Piano).....B
Hoyle, Harrison & Kaye, In-
diana Av. & Front (Che-
nille; Silk; Tapestry Ta-
ble) ....AAA
Humphry's Sons, Richard A.
(Wagon) ....B
Lewis, Robt., Bridesburg
(Table; Couch) ....B
Meehan-Mothes Co. (Tapes-
try Couch) ....A
Morse, Williams & Co.
(Elevator Hatch) ....AA
Moss, Rose Mfg. Co. (Tap-
estry Table) ....A
Newton, Herbert B. (Tapes-
try Table) ....A
Phila. Tapestry Mills, Alle-
gheny & Front (Raw Silk;
Tapestry) ....AAA
Pollitz, Kaufman & Co.,
1716 N. 5th (Lace Para-
sol) ....B
Ritchie Co., Robert J. & R.
(Tapestry; Table; Couch)
..............................D
Smith & Co., W. T. (Che-
nille Table) ....AA
Star & Crescent Mills Co.
(Table) ....A
Stead, Miller & Co. (Che-
nille; Tapestry) .....AA

COVERS (*Con.*)

Stroud, David H. (Chenille;
Table; Couch) ....A
Taylor & Scott (Tapestry;
Table) ....D
Thompson & Co., J., cor.
Van Horn & Sophia (Sew-
er Manhole) ....A

PA.—Pittsburg
McCullough-Dalzell Crucible
Co. (Crucible) ....A
Phoenix Steel Construction
Co., Penn. & 3d (Coal
Hole) ....D

PA.—Reading
Kitchen Specialty Co. (Perforated Frying Pan)...D

PA.—South Bethlehem
Bethlehem Foundry & Ma-
chine Co. (Sewer Man-
hole) C

R. I.—Pawtucket
Jenckes Mfg. Co., E. (Roll)
..............................A
Lumb, Geo. H. (Knit Cor-
set) ....B

R. I.—Providence
American Supply Co. (Roll)
..............................AA
Builders' Iron Foundry
(Sewer Manhole) .....AA
Greene & Co., Wm. C. (Dia-
mond Earring) ....D

TENN.—Chattanooga
Chattanooga Car & Foun-
dry Co. (Sewer Manhole)
..............................A

TENN.—Memphis
Chickasaw Iron Works (Coal
Hole) ....A

VA.—Hampton
Hampton Mfg. Co. (Cis-
tern) ....D

WIS.—Fond du Lac
Fond du Lac Tent & Awn-
ing Co. (Wagon)......B

WIS.—Kiel
Kiel Woodenware Co. (Bar-
rel) ....B

WIS.—Mayville
American Bottle Cover Co.
(Bottle) X

WIS.—Milwaukee
Am. Sign Co., 51 Erie
Horse; Advertising) ....A
Bagley & Sons, Wm., 732
Greenbush (Sewer Man-
hole) ....E
Kieckhefer Elevator Co., A.
(Elevator Hatch) C

WIS.—Racine
Secor Trunk Co., M. M.
(Trunk) ....A

WIS.—South Milwaukee
Stowell Mfg. & Fdy. Co.
(Catch Basin) ....A

COVERT
CLOTH

Woolen Goods

CRABS

See also Canned Goods
Pole Crabs see **Hardware;
Carriage.**

CONN.—Mount Carmel
Woodruff & Sons, Walter
W. (Pole) ....A

CONN.—New Haven
English & Mersick Co.
(Pole) ....B

CONN.—Stamford
Yale & Towne Mfg. Co.
(Safety) ....AAAA

ILL.—Chicago
Fairbanks, Morse & Co.,
Franklin & Monroe (Wind-
mill, &c.) ....AAAA
Standard Carriage Lamp Co.
(Pole) ....D

ILL.—Harvey
Whiting Ydry. Equipment
Co. (Horse Power) ...AA

MICH.—Detroit
Anderson & Sons, Wm. H.
(Hoisting) C

N. Y.—Niagara Falls
Dobbie Fdry. & Mach. Co.

304

CRABS (Con.)
(Hoisting) ....D
OHIO—Cleveland
Brown Hoisting Machy. Co.,
1345 St. Clair ......AAAA
Round & Son, D., 2287
Bway. (Hoisting) ......A
OHIO—Ravenna
Byers Machine Co. (Chain
Stone; Hook Stone) ....B
TENN.—Chattanooga
Gustafson Mfg. Co., Hoist-
ing) C
TENN.—Nashville
Union Machine Co. (Hoist-
ing) ....D
W. VA.—Fairmont
Helmick Fdy. & Machine Co.
(Derrick) ....D

CRACKERS

Bakers; Crackers, etc.

CRACKERS: NUT

CRACKERS: FIRE

See Fire Works

CONN.—Bridgeport
Acme Shear Co...........B
Bridgeport Hdw. Mfg. Co.
.......................B
Jennings Bros. Mfg. Co.
.......................AA
CONN.—New Britain
Landers, Frary & Clark
.......................AAA
ILL.—Chicago
American Cutlery Co., 193
Mather ....AA
ILL.—Freeport
Arcade Mfg. Co. ....A
New York City
International Silver Co., 9
Maiden Lane ......AAAA
Peck, Stow & Wilcox, 27
Murray ....AAAA
Sargent & Co., 151 Leonard
.......................AAAA
OHIO—Cleveland
Federal Mfg. Co.....AAAA
OHIO—Ravenna
Williams, A. C. ....A
PA.—Reading
Reading Hdw. Co. ..AAAA

CRACKLINGS

OHIO—Cincinnati
Conway, Daniel, 524 Poplar
(Tallow) ....D
VT.—Hyde Park
Page, Carroll S...........A

CRADLES

See also Furniture

IND.—ANDERSON
Fisher, Thos. C. (Grain)..C
IND.—Indianapolis
North Indianapolis Cradle
Works, 29th & Elmira
(Grain) C
IND.—Seymour
Seymour Mfg. Co. (Grain)
.......................B
IOWA—Fort Madison
Iowa Farming Tool Co.
(Grain) ....A
MICH.—Jackson
Withington & Cooley Mfg.
Co. (Grain) ....AA
N. Y. Conewango
Spear, W. D. (Grain) ....F
New York City
Fiske Iron Wks., J. W.
(Iron) ....B
Judd & Co., H. L. (Brass)
.......................AA
OHIO—Columbus
Brown, Hinman & Hunting-
don (Grain) ....A
OHIO—Kenton

CRADLES (Con.)
Champion Iron Co. (Iron)
.......................AA
PA.—Wilmore
McGuire, B. C. J. (Grain)
.......................F
VT.—Bellows Falls
Derby & Ball (Grain)....B
WIS.—Kenosha
Kenosha Crib Co. (Toy)..B
WIS.—Milwaukee
Meinecke & Son, A. (Toy)
.......................AA
WIS.—Sheyboygan
Garton Toy Co. (Toy)....A

CRANBERRIES

CAL.—Oakland
Pacific Cranberry Co......A
ILL.—Chicago
Weaver & Co., C. H., 129
So. Water ....A
IOWA—Burlington
Lagomarcino & Co., A.....B
IOWA—Cedar Rapids
Lagomarcino & Co., A.....B
IOWA—Sioux City
Haley & Lang Co.........A
KY.—Louisville
Allen & Co., J. T.........C
MASS.—Falmouth
Falmouth Cranberry Co....B
MASS.—Harwichport
Small, E. ....B
MASS.—West Barnstable
Makepeace, A. D.........A
N. J.—Elwood
Atlantic Co. for Culture of
Cranberries ....A
Champion, Saml. M.......B
N. J.—Hammonton
Hammonton Cranberry &
Imp. Ass'n ....B
N. J.—Laurel Springs
Collings, E. J............B
N. J.—Medford
Braddock Cranberry Co....C
Garwood, I. W...........C
Haines, C. A.............X
N. J.—Pemberton
Forsyth, John............C
N. Y.—Buffalo
Brennisen & Son, F., 156
Michigan ....B
New York City
Lane & Son, M., 252
Washn. ....B
WASH.—Ilwaco
Pacific Cranberry Co. (Br.)
.......................A
WIS.—Berlin
Stedman & Sons, H.......C
WIS.—Eureka
Trow, Rounds & Co.......B
WIS.—Grand Rapids
Briere & Pomanville......A
WIS.—Milwaukee
Pierce Co., A. J. W., 305
Bway. ....B
WIS.—Tunnel City
Winship, J. E. C

CRANES

CONN.—Ansonia
Farrell Fdry. & Mach. Co.
(Railroad; Swing; Power;
Jib; Traveling)....AAAA
CONN.—Derby
Birmingham Iron Frdy.
(Power) ....AA
Whitcomb Metallic Bedstead
Co. (Iron) ....A
CONN.—Hartford
Pratt & Whiting Co. (Light;
Movable Jib; Pillar; Pow-
er; Rectiliner; Rotary;
..Swing; Tram; Walking
.......................AAAA
CONN.—Stamford
Yale & Towne Mfg. Co.
(Bridge; Derrick; Jib; Pil-
lar; Rectiliner; Rotary;
Tram; Walking) ..AAAA
ILL.—Batavia
U. S. Wind Engine & Pump
Co. (Locomotive; Water)
.......................AA
ILL.—Chicago
Fairbanks, Morse & Co.,
cor. Franklin & Morse

CRANES (Con.)
(Locomotive; Water)....
AAAA

Hoisting & Conveying Machinery Co., 44 N. Elizabeth (Jib) ....E

Otto Gas Engine Wrks., 360 (Locomotive; Water) AAA

Shaw, Willis, N. Y. Life Bldg (New & Second Hand Traveling).......E

ILL.—Harvey
Whitney F'd'y Equipment Co. (Dock; Electric; Compressed Air; Belt; Hydraulic; Power; Jib; Traveling; Pillar; Traveling; Locomotive; Pneumatic...
AA

ILL.—Mount Vernon
Mt. Vernon Car Mfg Co. (Wrecking) ....AAA

IND.—Indianapolis
Commercial Electric Co. (Electric) ....A

IND.—New Albany
New Albany Mfg Co. (Electric Traveling).......C

KANS.—Fort Scott
Ft. Scott Fdy. & Mach. Co. (Traveling) ....H

MAINE—Portland
Maine Electric Co. (Variable & Fixed Radius; Electric Locomotive) ....E

MD.—Baltimore
Sinclar-Scott Co. (Power).E

MASS.—Boston
Boston Bridge Wks.,47 Winter(Traveling; Gantry & Hand Power).......AA

MASS.—Fitchburg
Putnam Machine Co. (Light)
A

HASS.—Worcester
Morgan Construction Co. (Hydraulic; Jib; Hand; Power; Traveling; Hydraulic; Jib; Steam) ...A

MICH.—Bay City
Industrial Wks. (Steam; Hand; Dock; Electric; Locomottve; Jib; Traveling; Pillar; Transfer; Wrecking; Derrick; Light; Locomotive) ....AA

MICH.—Detroit
Byram & Co. (Inc.), 435 Guvin (Hand; Power; Jib; Traveling; Ingot).......D

Northern Engineering Wks. Cantilever; Dock; Elect. Locomotive; Gantry; Hand Power; Hydraulic; Jib; Pillar; Pneumatic; Railroad; Tower Riveting; Elect. Traveling).......A

Russell Wheel & Fdy. Co. (Gantry) ....AA

Whitehead & Kales Iron Wks. (Jib; Hand Traveling) ....A

MICH.—Muskegon
Shaw Electric Crane Co. (Elec. Traveling; Revolving; Hand Power; Charging; Dock; Gantry; Jib; Power) ....A

MICH.—Saginaw
Wickes Bros. (Hand Traveling) ....A

MICH.—Three Rivers
Sheffield Car Co. (Locomotive ater; Wrecking)
AA

MINN.—Minneapolis
Kilgore Machine Co. (Steam Saw Mill)...........X

Minneapolis Steel & Mchy Co. (Jib; Hand Power)
AAA

MINN.—St. Paul
Amer. Hoist & Derrick Co. (Locomotive) ......AAA

MO.—St. Louis
American Car & Fdy. Co., 706 Chestnut (Wrecking)
AAAA

Curtis & Co. Mfg. Co., 2201 Washington Av. (Pneumatic Air Motor;l Air Traveling) ....A

N. J.—Jersey City
Smith & Sone Co., Theo., ft. of Essex (Dock).......A

CRANES (Con.)
N. Y.—Albany
Osgood Dredge Co. (Derrick; Power)..........B

N. Y.—Buffalo
Contractors Plant Mfg. Co., 127 Erie (Jib).......B

N. Y.—Montour Falls
General Pneumatic Tool Co. (Pneumatic) ....B

New York City
Fairbanks Co., 416 Broome (Hydraulic Jib).....AAA

Manning, Maxwell & Moore, 85 Liberty (Electric Traveling) ....AA

New Jersey Fdy. & Mach. Co., 15 Murray (Elec. Traveling; Jib; Locomotive; Dock; Hand Power; Hand Traveling)
D

Niles-Bement-Pond Co., 136 Liberty (Elec. & Hand Traveling; Hand Power; Jib; Swing) ......AAAA

Reilly Bros. (Wash Line).D

Shriver & Co., T., 333 E. 56th (Elec. Traveling; Hand Power) ....A

Watson-Stillman Co., 210 E. 43rd (Hydraulic)......A

N. Y.—Niagara Falls
Dobbie Fdy. & Mach. Co. (Dock; Hand Power; Jib; Traveling) ....D

N. Y.—Schenectady
General Elec. Co. (Elec. Traveling) ......AAAA

N. Y.—Troy
Ludlow Valve Mfg. Co. (Water; for sprinkling care, &c.).........AAA

N. Y.—Waterford
Eddy Valve Co. (Water for sprinklinng wagons, &c.) ....AA

OHIO—Alliance
Alliance Machine Co. (Charging; Drawing; Elec. Locomotive; Traveling; Forge; Gantry; Hand Power; Hydraulic; Hydraulic Jib; Pillar; Swing; Tower Riveting;
AA

Morgan Engineering Co. (Charging; Drawing; Elec. Traveling; Locomotive; Forge; Gantry; Hydraulic; Jib; Pillar; Tower Riveting; Derrick)..AAAA

OHIO—Cincinnati
American Valve & Meter Co. (Autimatic Locomotive Water) ....A

Bullock Electric Mfg. Co. (Electric Traveling; Locomotive ....AA

Obermayer Co. S. (Electric; Hand Power; Jib)..AA

Triumph Ice Mach. Co., 610 Baymiller (Elec. Traveling; Pnneumatic) ......A

OHIO—Cleveland
Brown Hoisting Mchy. Co., 1345 St. Clair (Cantilever; Dock; Steam; Electric Traveling; Locomotive; Gantry, Hand Travelinig; Gantry, Hand Traveling; Wrecking; Hand Traveling) ....AAAA

Electric Controller & Supply Co. (Automatic; Electric) ....A

Garry Iron & Steel Co. (Hand Power; Pneumatic Air Motor; Revolving; Dock; Electric; Electric Bridge Gantry; Hand Traveling; Hydraulic; Jib; Locomotive; Hand Travelinig) ....A

Kaltenbach & Griess (Traviing) ....B

Vana Dorn Iron Wks. Co. (Hand Power)........AA

Wellman-Seaver-Morgan Engraving Co. (Elec. Traveling; Revolving; Charging; Dock; Gantry; Hand Power; Hand Traveling; Hydraulic; Traveling Power) ....AAAA

OHIO—Collinwood
Browning Engineering Co.
(Dock; Electric Traveling;
Power; Steam; Elec. Jib;
Power and Steam Travel-
ing X

OHIO—Columbus
Case Mfg. Co. (Electric
Traveling; Hand Power;
Belt; Hand Power; Elec.
Jib; Locomotive; Over-
hanging Jib; Power;
Charging; Gantry; Hy-
draulic; Pneumatic;
Traveling Power; Wreck-
ing) ....A

OHIO—Cuyahoga Falls
Turner, Vaughn & Taylor
Co. (Hand; Traveling
Power) ....B

OHIO—Hamilton
Niles Tools Works Co. (Electric; Traveling) ..AAAA

OHIO—Marion
Marion Steam Shovel Co.
(Wrecking) ....AAA

OHIO—Springfield
Rogers Iron Co. (Electric
Traveling; Hydraulic)..B

OHIO—Toledo
Toledo Fdy. & Mach. Co.
(Traveling) ....B

OHIO—Wiskliffe
Cleveland Crane & Car Co.
(Elec. Locomotive; Travel-
ing; Brdge; Hand Power;
Jib; Hand Traveling)..B

OHIO—Youngstown
Tod Co., Wm., (Direct Self
Acting Hydraulic)....AA
Youngstown Engineering Co.
(Electric Travling).....H

PA.—Allegheny
Carlin's Sons, Thos (Traveling) ....A

PA.—Chambersburg
Chambersburg Engineering
Co. (Hand Power; Hydrau-
lic; Swing; Traveling)..A

PA.—Coatesville
Ridgway, Craig & Son Co.
(Hydraulic Direct Self
Acting &s., Jib; Swing;
Pneumatic; Power) ....A

PA.—Franklin
Franklin Portable Crane &
Hoist Co. (Portable, all
iron on wheels; Hand
Power) ....B

PA.—New Castle
Vulcan Fdy. & Mach Co.
Pillar; Center Post Jib;
Locomotive; Pillar, for
breaking large castings;
Swing; Wrecking; Ingot;
Derrick) ....A

PA.—Philadelphia
Bement, Niles & Co. (Power)
.................AAAA
Brill Co., J., G., 62nd &
Woodland Av. (Electric
Locomotive) ......AAAA
Dallett & Co., Thos H., cor.
York & Sedgley (Electric
Traveling) ....B
Dodge Coal Storage Co. (Re-
volving Locomotive) ....A
Harrington, Son & Co., Edw.
15th & Penn. Av. (Hand
Traveling; Electric) ..AA
Maris Bros.,56th & Gay's
Av. (Jib; Hand; Electric
Traveling) ....D
Pedrick & Ayer Co., 1001
Hamilton (Pneumatic Jib)
....................A
Pennsylvania. Iron Wks.
(Hydraulic) ....AAA
Phila. Engineering Co.
(Electric Traveling) ....
.................AAAA
Philadelphia Roll & Mach.
Co., So. 23rd & Washing-
tton Ave. (Hydraulic)..A
Sellers & Co., Wm. (Inc.),
1600 Hamilton (Charging;
Drawing; Dock; Electric;
Power Traveling; Gantry;
Hydraulic; Jib; Railroad;
Swing; Wrecking; Car)
.................AAAA
Southwark Fdy. & Mach.
Co. (Hydraulic)....AAA
Walton, P. M., 1023 Ger-
mantown Av. (Traveling

C
Wood & Co., R. D., 400
Chestnut (Hydraulic; Jib;
Traveling) ....AAAA

PA.—Pittsburg
Jones & Laughlin's Steel Co.
(Small Jib or Worm
Hoist) ....AAAA
Lewis Fdy. & Mach Co.,
1001 Bingham (Hand
Power; Hydraulic; Jib)..A
Mackintosh-Hemphill & Co.,
(Ltd.), ft. 12th (Hydrau-
lic) ....AAAA
Riter-Conley Mfg. Co. (Jib)
...................AAA
Scaife Fdy. & Mach. Co.,
28th & Smallman (Hand
Power; Hydraulic).....B
United Enginering & Fdy.
Co., 54th & A. V. Ry. Hy-
raulic; Jib; Whip).AAAA

PA.—Reading
Johnston Fdry. & Mach Co.
(Traveling) ....B
Reading Crane & Hoist
Wks. (Hand Power
Traveling) ....A
Speidel, J. G., cor. Button-
wood & Gordon (Hand
Power Traveling)......B

PA.—South Bethlehem
Bethlehm Fdy. & Mach Co.
(Traveling; Gantry)....C

VT.—Barre
Smith Whitcomb & Cook
Co. (Traveling) C
Whitcomb Bros. (Hand
Traveling) X

VT.—Montpelier
Lane Mfg. Co. (Traveling,
for marblestone yards &c.)
....................A

VT.—Rutland
Lincoln Iron Wks. (Swing;
Electric Traveling).....A

WIS.—Miiwaukee
Pawling & Harnischfeger
(Electric Traveling; Hand
Power; Jib; Locomotive;
Traveling Power; Ladle)
.................AAA

WIS.—So. Milwaukee
Bucyrus Co. (Wrecking)...
.................AAA

CRANKS

CONN.—New Britain
Corbin P. & T. (Bell) ....
.................AAAA

CONN.—New Haven
Sargent & Co. (Bell).AAAA

MASS.—Fairhaven
Babbitt Bros. (Loom)....D

MASS.—Worcester
Steele & Bros., A. H.
(Loom) X

MICH.—Detroit
Anderson & Sons. W. H.
(Gas Engine)..........C

N. Y.—Auburn
Ecceles Co., Richard .....A
Leather & Brass Mfg. Co.
(Bicycle) ....F

N. Y.—Buffalo
Pratt & Letchworth Co.....
.................AAA

New York City
Ostrander & Co., W. R.,
22 Dey (Bell).........A
Peck, Stow & Wilcox, 27
Murray (Bell).....AAAA
Sargent & Co., 151 Leonard
(Bell) ....AAAA
Russell & Erwin Mfg. Co.,
43 Chambers (Bell) AAAA

OHIO—Cleveland
Dyson & Sons, Jos........A

PA.—Reading
Reading Hdw. Co. (Bell)
.................AAAA

PA.—South Bethlehem
Bethlehem Steel Co. (Marine
Engine; Stationary En-
gine) ....AAAA

PA.—Wilkesbarre
Vulcan Iron Wks....AAAA

VT.—Bellows Falls
Vermont Farm Mach Co.
(Hoisting) C

WIS.—Evansville
Baker Mfg. Co. (Pumping)·
.....................AA

CRASHES

Cotton Goods

CRATES

See also Boxes

LA.—New Orleans
Pelican Box Factory.....D
MASS.—Greenfild
Rugg Mfg. Co............F
MICH.—Bay City
Vance Box Co., E. J. (Ltd.)
  (Bicycle) ....B
MICH.—Saginaw W. S.
Saginaw Basket Co. (Bicycle) C
N, J.—Jersey City
Dodge & Bliss ....AA
N. Y.—Brooklyn
Dykman, Jas. H. ....A
N. Y.—North Tonawanda
Butts & Co., Chas. G. ...D
OHIO—Berlin Heights
Berlin Fruit Box Co. ....D
OHIO—Cleveland
Smeed Box Co. ....B
854 6:5 '05 543 Register 229
TENN.—Greenfield
Ward-Kent Co. ....A
VA.—Petersburg
South Side Mfg. Co. (Fruit
  Nesting) C

CRAYONS

GA.—Spring Place
Cohutta Talc Co. (Blackboard; Boiler Makers';
  Metal Workers'; Railroad;
  Rolling Mill) ....E
MASS.—Pawtucketville
Lowell Crayon Co. ......B
N. J.—Jersey City
Dixon Crucible Co., Jos
  (Colored; Metal Workers')
                AAA
New York City
American Lead Pencil Co.
  (Colored) ....AA
Binney & Smith Co., 81
  Fulton (Artists') ......D
Chrystal. Chas. B. 51 Cliff
  (Metal Workers') ......D
Eagle Pencil Co. (Colored)
                AAA
Faber, Eberhard (Colored)
                AAA
Horn, Wm., 120 Centre
  (Lithographic; Marking)
                F
N. Y. Silicate Book Slate
  Co. (Silicate) ....D
N. Y.—Rochester
Franklin Crayon Co. (Checking; Civil Engineers') D
N. Y.—Syracuse
Will & Baumer (Wax) ..AA
N. C.—Hewett
North Carolina Talc & Mining Co. (Metal Workers')
                C
OHIO—Cincinnati
Obermayer Co., S. (Metal
  Workers') ....AA
OHIO—Girard
Greenwood, D. (Billiard
  Cue; Dustless) ....H
OHIO—Sandusky
American Crayon Co.
  (Artists') ....AA
TENN.—Chattanooga
American Lava Co.
  (Foundry) ....D
Steward Mfg. Co., D. M.
  (Colored; Dustless) ....B

CREAM

See Milk

CREAM, COLD

MAINE—Portland
Hinds, A. L.............A
MICH.—St. Louis
Pozzoni & Co., J. A.......B
Sellye Mfg. Co...........C
N. Y.—Binghamton
Simons Mfg. Co., W. E...D
N. Y.—Brooklyn
Chesebrough Mfg. Co..AAAA
N. Y.—Buffalo
Larkin Co. ....AAAA

CREAM, COLD (Con.)
New York City
Barclay & Co., 44 Stone..A
Caswell, Massey & Co.....X
Doggett & Ramsdell, W.
  34th C
Recamier Mfg. Co........F
OHIO—Toledo
Robinson Thermal Bath Co.
                C
PA.—Philadelphia
Shull, Wm. A., 142 N. 4th
                F
Vail Bros., 25 Broad......C
R. I.—Providence
Rumford Chemical Co.
                AAAA

CREAM TARTAR

MASS.—Boston
Slade Co., D. & L., 13
  India ....A
New York City
Pfizer & Co., Charles.AAAA
Tartar Chemical Co....AAA

CREASERS

N. J.—Newark
Heller Bros. Co. (Blacksmiths') ....AA

CREELS

MASS.—Lowell
Lowell Machine Shop (Revolving) ....AAAA
PA.—Philadelphia
Diamond Textile Machine
  Wks., 2d & Diamond....E
Smith Woolen Machy. Co.,
  Jas., 411 Race........AA

CREEPERS

CONN.—Torrington
Union Hdw. Co. (Ice) ....A
MAINE—Augusta
Gay, Geo. E. (Ice)........E
MD.—Baltimore
Sinclair-Scott Mfg. Co.
  (Ice) ....E

CREME-DE-MENTHE

Cordials

CREOSOTE

GA.—Savannah
Pine Products Co. (Crude)
                X
LA.—New Orleans
American Creosote Wks...B
LA.—Slidell
Southern Creosoting Co...A
MO.—St. Louis
Mallinckrodt Chemical Wks.
                AAAA
New York City
Barrett Mfg. Co.....AAAA
White Tar Co., 101 No.
  Moore ....E
N. C.—Wilmington
Spiritine Chem. Co. (Wood)
                C
VA.—Norfolk
Norfolk Creosoting Co....A

CREPE-DE-CHINE

See Silk Goods

CRESTING

OHIO—Canton
Berger Mfg. Co. (Galvanized Iron) ....AA
PA.—Pittsburg
Kratzer & Co., W. N. (Galvanized Iron) ....D
WIS.—Milwaukee
Bayley & Sons Co., Wm.
  (Galvanized Iron)......A

CRIBS

See also Furniture

ILL.—Joliet
Adam, W. J...............X
IND.—Richmond
Elliott & Reid Co. (Portable
Corn) ....D
IA.—Cedar Rapids
Denning Wire & Fence Co.
(Portable Corn) ....B
KANS.—Kansas City
Clippinger & Son, A. B.
(Portable Corn) ....B

CRIMPERS

CONN.—Waterbury
American Pin Co. (Hair)
AA
IND.—Richmond
Bartel & Co. A. H. (Hair)
A
MASS.—Boston
New England Novelty Mfg.
Co. (Hair) ....H
MASS.—Worcester
National Mfg. Co. (Pie)..A
MICH.—Sturgis
Berridge Shear Co. (Pipe)
C
N. J.—Smithville
Smith Mach. Co., H. B.
(Blind Slat) ....A
N. Y.—Buffalo
Buffalo Last Wks. ......B
New York City
American Wood Working Co.
(Blind Slat) ......AAAA
Dunlap Machinery Co.....F
Walbridge & Co., J. H., 337
Broadway ....B
PA.—Philadelphia
Philadelphia Novelty Mfg.
Co. (Hair) ....D

CRINOLINE

CONN.—Middletown
Palmer, I. E...........AA
N. Y.—New Brighton
Irving Mfg. Co. ....B
R. I.—Scituate
North Scituate Cotton Mills
C

CRIPPLES

OHIO—Elyria
Worthington Mfg. Co.
(Bicycles) ....B

CROCKERY

See also Stoneware; Earthenware, &c.

CONN.—New Haven
Elm City Mfg. Co. C
GA.—Atlanta
Lillienthal Crockery Co....D
ILL.—Chicago
Burley & Co., 118 Wabash
Av. ....AA
N. J.—Trenton
Greenwood Pottery Co.....A
Norris, James E...........A
Resolute Pottery Co.......X
New York City
Barth & Son, L., 87 1st
Av. ....A
OHIO—Cincinnati
Cincinnati Glass & Crockery
Co. C
OHIO—East Liverpool
Knowles, Taylor & Knowles
Co. ....AAAA
Laughlin, Homer China Co.
AAAA
Thompson Pottery Co., C.
C. ....AA
Vodray Pottery Co. ......A
OHIO—Toledo
Daudt Glass & Crockery Co.
A
OHIO—Toronto
American China Co........B

CROCKERY (Con.)
W. VA.—Wheeling
Wheeling Potteries Co.
AAA

CROCKS

542C CROCKS
CAL.—San Francisco
Gladding, McBean & Co.
(Acid) ....AA
COLO.—Denver
Denver Stoneware Co.
(Milk) X
IOWA—Fort Dodge
Fort Dodge Stoneware Co.
C
N. J.—Haddonfield
Wingender & Bro., Chas.
(Earthenware Chimneys)
E

CROCUS

MICH.—Detroit
Stevens, F. B. (English)..A
New York City
Smith & Co., J. Lee....AA

CROOKS

ILL.—Chicago
Burch & Co., F. S. (Shep-
herds') ....B
IOWA—Fort Madison
Iowa Farming Tool Co.
(Shepherds') ....A
MICH.—Jackson
Withington & Cooley Mfg.
Co. (Shepherds').....AA

CROPS: RIDING

New York City
830 6:6 '5 543 Register—230
Follmer, Clogg & Co., 395
Broadway ....AAA
Gorham Mfg. Co., 19th &
Broadway ....AAAA
Harrison, W. W., 1149
Broadway ....D
Ware & Co., Arthur W., 109
Leonard ....B
White & Major, 46 Howard
X
PA.—Philadelphia
Hirsh & Bro. ....A
Simons Bro. & Co. ....A

CROQUET

See Games

CROSSES

CONN.—Bridgeport
Belknap Mfg. Co..........C
N. J.—Newark
Durand & Co. (Inc.)....AA
New York City
Fiske Iron Wks., J. W.
(Iron) ....B
Hughes, Thos., 51 E. 9th
(Electric) ....D
Jones, Thos. W., 18
Fletcher (Church)......E
Lamb, J. & R. (Bronze;
Iron) ....D
Richards & Co., E. Ira
AAA
Sloan & Co. ....B
Westervelt, A. B. & W. T.
(Iron) ....B
R. I.—Providence
Lederer Co.. S. & B......C
WIS.—Sheboygan
Kohler Sons Co., J. M.
Enameled; Cast Iron)..A

CROSSINGS

See also Frogs

ILL.—Chicago
Ajax Forge Co., 138 E. Jack-
son Boul. (Railroad)..AA
Morden Frog & Crossing
Wks., The Rookery (Rail-
road) ....A
Pettibone, Mulliken & Co.

CROSSINGS (Con.)
(Railroad) ....AAAA
ILL.—East St. Louis
Elliott Frog & Switch Co.
(Railroad) ....AA
IND.—Elkhart
Elkhart Frog & Crossing
Wks. (Railroad C
MASS.—Boston
Harrington, Robinson & Co.
D
MASS.—Cambridge
Barbour, Stockwell Co.
(Railroad) ....A
MASS.—Springfield
Hawkins Iron Wks., R. F.
E
N. J.—Hoboken
New York Switch & Cross-
ing Co. (Railroad) .....A
New York City
Buckley & Co., L. J., 257
Bway. (Railroad)......B
Hunt Co., C. W., 45 Bway.
(Railroad) ....AA
Koppel, Arthur, 68 Broad
(Railroad) ....A
OHIO—Cincinnati
Weir Frog Co., Front &
Smith (Railroad)......A
OHIO—Cleveland
Bowler Mfg. Co. ....B
Cleveland Frog & Crossing
Co. (Railroad)........B
Fulton Foundry Co.......C
OHIO—Springfield
Indianapolis Switch & Frog
Co. (Railroad)........B
PA.—Allentown
Allentown Rolling Mills
Railroad) ....AAA
PA.—Philadelphia
Pennsylvania Steel Co.
AAAA
Wharton & Co., Wm., Jr.
(Inc.) (Railroad)....AAA
PA.—Steelton
Pennsylvania Steel Co.
(Railroad) ....AAAA
PA.—Swissvale
Union Switch & Signal Co.
(Railroad) ....AAAA
PA.—Wilkesbarre
Vulcan Iron Wks. (Rail-
road) ....AAAA
WIS.—Milwaukee
Falk Co. (Railroad.)..AAA

CROSSWALKS
547 CROSSWALKS
N. Y.—Oxford
Clarke Blue Stone Co., F. G.
(Stone) ....A
OHIO—Cleveland
Cleveland Stone Co. (Stone)
AAAA
OHIO—West Clarksfield
Warner Stone Co..........A

CROWFEET
CONN.—Guilford
Spencer's Sons, I. S. (Iron)
A

CROWNS
CONN.—Seymour
Matthews Mfg. Co. (Fork)
B
ILL.—Chicago
Lefort, Henry G., 153 Wa-
bash Av. (Watch)......C
N. J.—Newark
Nobs & Son, Chas. H.
(Watch) ....D
New York City
Consolidated Dental Mfg.
Co., 115 W. 42d (Gold
Dental) ....B

CROZER
OHIO—Cleveland
Oram, Jno. S., 1 N. Coe
(Hogshead) ....A

CRUCIBLES
COLO.—Denver

CRUCIBLES (Con.)
Denver Fire Clay Co...AA
CONN.—Bridgeport
Bridgeport Crucible Co....A
MASS.—Taunton
Phoenix Crucible Co..AAAA
Taunton Crucible Co.......B
N. J.—Jersey City
Dixon Crucible Co., Jos.
AAA
New York City
Peabody & Co., Henry W.
AAA
OHIO—Cincinnati
Obermayer Co., S......AA
PA.—Malvern
Bishop & Co., J. (Platinum)
D
PA.—Philadelphia
Seidel, Reuben B.........A
Taylor, Robert J., Inc., 19th
& Callowhill (Bleck Lead)
A
PA.—Pittsburg
McCullough-Dalzell Crucible
Co. (Brass Melting)....A

CRUCIFIXES
New York City
Lamb, J. & R., 59 Carmine
D
Sloan & Co. ....B

CRULLERS
MO.—St. Louis
St. Louis Stamping Co.
AAAA
New York City
Central Stamping Co....AA
Lalance & Grosjean Mfg.
Co. ....AAAA
Stoutenborough, X. ......D

CRUMBERS
N. H.—Antrim
Goodell Co. (Bread)......A

CRUPPERS
IND.—Charlestown
Bastian & Sussman.......H
Graf Crupper Co., J.......F
N. J.—Newark
Peters Harness & Saddlery
Co. C
New York City
Smith, Worthington & Co.
AA
OHIO—Dayton
Victor Crupper Co. ....H

CRUSHERS
See also Rollers; Pulver-
izers; Ag. Implements.

CAL.—Benicia
Benicia Iron Wks. (Barley;
Corn; Cob) ....AA
CAL.—Los Angeles
Calkins Co. (Rock; Ore).E
CAL.—San Francisco
Hendy Mach. Wks., Joshua,
38 Fremont (Rock; Ore)
AA
Marshutz & Cantrell, cor.
Main & Howard (Rack;
Ore) ....A
Union Iron Wks., 222 Mar-
ket (Rock; Ore)........X
COLO.—Denver
Denver Engineering Wks.
Co., cor. Blake & 30th
(Ore) ....A
Mine & Smelter Supply Co.
(Ore) ....AAAA
Stearns-Rogers Co. (Ore).A
CONN.—Ansonia
Farrell Fdry. & Machine Co.
(Portable; Ore; Rack;
Stone) ....AAAA
CONN.—New Haven
Harrison, Leonard D. (Corn;
Cob) ....H
CONN.—Thompsonville
Bushnell Press Co., G. H.
(Grape) ....A

CRUSHERS (Con.)

DEL.—Wilmington
Walker & Elliot (Phosphate; Rock; Stone) ....B

GA.—Atlanta
Van Winkle Gin & Mach. Wks., E. (Cotton Seed) ....AAA

ILL.—Aurora
Western Wheeled Scraper Co. (Rock; Stone)....AA

ILL.—Batavia
Appleton Mfg. Co. (Corn; Cob) ....A

ILL.—Chicago
Allis-Chalmers Co., Home Ins. Bldg. (Coal; Rock; Ore) ....AAAA
Austin Western Co., Manhattan Bldg. (Rock; Ore) ....B
Contractors' Supply & Equipment Co. (Rock; Ore)..B
Drake Standard Mach. Wks. (Clay) ....B
National Drill & Mfg. Co., Pullman Bldg. (Rock; Ore) ....B
Raymond Bros. Impact Pulverizer Co., 142 Laflin (Clay; Rock; Ore)......D
Shaw, Willis, N. Y. Life Bldg. (Rock; Ore)......E

ILL.—Decatur
Leader Iron Wks. (Clay).D

ILL.—Downers Grove
Dicke Tool Co. (Rock; Stone) C

ILL.—Freeport
Stover Mfg. Co. (Corn)..AA

ILL.—Galesburg
Frost Mfg. Co. (Clay)....A

ILL.—Harvey
Austin Mfg. Co., F. C. (Rock; Ore; Stone)..AAA

ILL.—Peru
Brunner, Chas. (Clay)....A

IND.—Anderson
American Bridge & Scraper Co. (Rock; Ore)........D
Anderson Fdry. & Mach. Wks. (Clay) ....B

IND.—Aurora
Stedman's Fdry. & Mach. Co. (Clay; Coal; Coke; Phosphate Rack).......D

IND.—Columbus
Kelier, C. M. (Coal; Coke) C

IND.—Fort Wayne
Indiana Road Machine Co. (Rock; Ore; Stone)....A

IND.—Frankfort
Wallace Mfg. Co. (Clay).C

IND.—Indianapolis
Nordyke & Marmon Co. (Barley; Corn; Cob).AAA
Over, Ewald (Clod).......C

IND.—Richmond
Richmond City Mill Wks. (Corn; Cob)............B

IND.—Rushville
Madden & Co. (Clay).....D

IND.—South Bend
Bowsher Co., N. P. (Corn).D

IOWA—Des Moines
Eagle Iron Wks. (Clay)..A

KANS.—Leavenworth
Great Western Mfg. Co. (Corn) ....AA

LA.—New Orleans
Whiting Iron Wks. Co. (Sugar Cane) ....AA

MD.—Baltimore
Sinclair-Scott Co. (Corn; Cob) ....E

MASS.—Boston
Ames Plow Co., Quincy Hall (Corn; Cob)..AAAA
Bradley Fertilizer Co. (Ore; Rock; Stone)......AAAA
Sturtevant Mill Co., Harrison Sq. (Rock; Ore; Plaster) ....B

MICH.—Detroit
Huettemann & Creamer Co. (Clay) ....A

MICH.—Grand Rapids
Butterworth & Lowe (Plas-

CRUSHERS (Con.)

ter) ....A

MICH.—Hancock
Portage Lake Fdry. & Mach. Co. (Rock; Ore)........D

MICH.—Marquette
Lake Shore Engine Wks. (Rock; Ore) ....A

MICH.—Monroe
Wilder Strong Impl. Co. (Fertilizer; Clod).......B

MICH.—Port Huron
Port Huron Engine & Thresher Co. (Rock; Ore) AAA

MICH.—Tecumseh
Brewer & Co., H. (Clay).B

MINN.—Minneapolis
Schutz-O'Neill Co. (Clay; Coal; Rock; Ore).......C

MO.—St. Louis
Fernholtz Brick Machy. Co., Boyle & Old Manchester Av. (Clay) ....D
Scott Mfg. Co. (Clay)....D
South St. Louis Fdry., 7516 S. Bdway. (Rock; Ore).C
Williams Patent Crusher & Pulverizer Co., 2705 N. Bdway. (Clay; Quartz Rock) ....B

N. H.—Nashua
White Mountain Freezer Co. (Ice) ....AA

N. J.—Garwood
Beckley & Co., A. J. (Rock; Stone) ....D

N. J.—High Bridge
Taylor Iron & Steel Co. (Rotary) ....AAAA

N. J.—Rockaway
Hoagland Son Co., M. (Rock; Stone).......A

N. Y.—Brooklyn
Nebel, M. A., 72 Grand Av. (Clay) ....D
Pioneer Iron Wks., 151 William (Sugar Cane)..A

N. Y.—Buffalo
Noye Mfg. Co., John T., 50 Lakeview Av. (Coal; Barley; Plaster; Corn; Cob) X
Squier Mfg. Co., Geo. L., 420 Niagara (Sugar Cane; Coffee) ....AAAA

N. Y.—Frankfort
Acme Road Machy. Co. (Rock; Ore) ....B

N. Y.—Marathon
Climax Road Machine Co. (Rock; Ore) ....B

N. Y.—Newburgh
Coldwell-Wilcox Co. (Rock; Ore; Sugar Cane).......B

New York City
American Road Roller Co., 156 5th Av. (Rock; Ore) B
Bacon, Earle C., 26 Cortlandt (Rock; Ore) ......B
Burns & Sons, Jabez (Coffee) ....B
Cornell Co., J. B. & J. M., 26th & 11th Av. (Sugar Cane) ....AA
Crandall & Godley Co. (Ice) AA
Deeley & Co., Robt., 507 W. 32d (Sugar Cane)..AA
Hunt Co., C. W., 45 Bway. (Coal; Rock; Ore).....AA
Krajewski-Pesant Co., 32 Bway. (Sugar Cane)..AA
Krom Machine Wks., 170 Bway. (Rolling Toggle).D
Mead & Co., John A., 11 Bway. (Coal) ....B
Mundt & Sons, Chas. (Ore; Rock) ....B
Newell Mfg. Co., 149 Bway. (Clay) ....D
Scholl & Co., Julian, 126 Liberty (Rock; Ore)...C
Turls' Sons, Jno., 536 W. 28th (Sugar Cane)....D

N. Y.—Syracuse
Boomer & Boschert Co. (Cotton Seed) ....A

CRUSHERS (Con.)

N. Y.—Walton
Hoyt & Co., L. E. (Rock; Ore) X

N. C.—Statesville
Steele & Sons, J. C. (Clay) B

OHIO—Akron
Taplin-Rice & Co. (Clay).B
Webster, Camp & Lane Mach. Co. (Clay)..AAAA

OHIO—Bucyrus
Amer. Clay Working Machy. Co. (Clay) ....:X

OHIO—Canton
Aultman Co. (Rock; Ore) AAAA
Bonnot Co. (Clay; Rock; Ore) ....A

OHIO—Cincinnati
Arnold-Creager Co. (Clay).B
Miller, L. J. (Cotton Seed) X
Stacey Mfg. Co., 239 Mill (Coke) ....AA

OHIO—Cleveland
Bartlett & Snow Co., C. O. (Ore; Rock) ....A
Kilby Mfg. Co. (Sugar Cane) X
Wellman-Seaver-Morgan Co. (Ore; Rock) .....AAAA

OHIO—Columbus
Jeffrey Mfg. Co. (Coal; Coke; Mining; Ore; Rock) AAAA

OHIO—Dayton
Raymond Co., C. W. (Clay) A

OHIO—Galion
Freese & Co., E. M. (Clay) A

OHIO—Hillsboro
Bell & Co., C. S. (Sugar Cane; Corn; Cob) ......A

OHIO—Springfield
Foos Mfg. Co. (Cotton Seed) ....A

OHIO—Tiffin
National Machy Co. (Ore; Rock; Stone) ....AA

OHIO—Wellsville
Stevenson & Co. (Clay)...B

OHIO—Zanesville
Griffith & Wedge. Co. (Rock; Stone) ....B

OREGON—Portland
Hammond Mfg Co. (Rock; Stone) X
Phoenix Iron Wks. (Rock; Ore) ....D

PA.—Allegheny
Carlin's Sons, Thos. (Rock; Stone) ....A

PA.—Allentown
Mosser & Son, Wm. F. (Rotary) ....A

PA.—Bausman
Bausman, David H. (Corn) C

PA.—Birdsboro
Diamond Drill & Machine Co. (Rock; Stone; Ore).A

PA.—Chambersburg
Woods' Sons, T. B. (Corn; Cob) ....A

PA.—Coatsville
Ridgway & Son, Craig (Corn; Cob) ....A

PA.—Danville
Curry & Co. (Ore; Rock).B

PA.—Kennett Square
American Road Machine Co. (Rock; Ore; Road)...AA
Good Roads Machy. Co. (Rock; Ore) ....D

PA.—Lancaster
Martin Brick Machine Mfg. Co., Henry (Clay; Ore).B

PA.—Muncy
Sprout-Waldron & Co. (Coal; Rock; Ore; Corn).......A

PA.—Philadelphia
Cresson Co., Geo. V., 18th & Allegheny Av. (Rock; Ore) ....AA
Enterprise Mfg. Co. (Ice) AAAA
Harrison Safety Boiler Wks.

CRUSHERS (Con.)
(Ice) ....A
Latrobe Steel Co. (Ore; , Rock) ....AAAA
Mills & Bros., Thos. (Ice) A
Morris, Henry G., Phila. Bourse (Sugar Cane)....B
Phila. Roll & Machine Co. (Rock; Stone).........A
Standard Steel Wks. (Mining) ....AAA

PA.—Pittsburg
Fischer Fdry. & Mach. Co. (Ore; Rock) ....AA
Garrison Fdry. Co., A. (Ore; Rock) ....AAA
Hogg Iron & Steel Fdry. Co., Geo. A. (Clay; Rock)..A
Mesta Machine Co. (Rock; Ore) ....AAAA
Phillips & McLaren, 24th & Smallman (Rock; Ore; Stone) ....B
United Engineering & Fdy. Co. (Ore; Rock)...AAAA
Yagle Fdry. & Machine Co., 400 32d (Rock; Ore)....C

PA.—Pittston
Exeter Machine Wks. (Rock; Ore) ....AA

PA.—Shamokin
Mullen & Son, John (Coal) AA

PA.—So. Bethlehem
Bethlehem Fdry. & Machine (Rock; Ore) C
Bethlehem Steel Co. (Spindle) ....AAAA

PA.—Tatamy
Messinger Mfg. Co. (Mining) ....B

PA.—Tyrone
Tyrone Fdry. & Machine Co. (Stone; Rock; Ore)....X

PA.—Wilkesbarre
Vulcan Iron Works (Coal; Rock; Ore; Coke; Rock Salt) ....AAAA

PA.—York
Dempwolf & Co., C. H. (Mining) ....A
Motter & Sons, Geo. F. (Rock; Stone; Ore; Plaster) C

TENN.—Chattanooga
Chattanooga Plow Co. (Cotton Seed) ....AA

VA.—Richmond
Cardwell Machine Co. (Cotton Seed) ....A

W. VA.—Fairmont
Wagner-Palmore Mfg. Co. (Coal) ....A

WIS.—Cudahy
Power & Mining Machy. Co. (Coal; Rock; Ore)...AAA

WIS.—Milwaukee
Allis-Chalmers Co. (Ore; Rock; Stone) ......AAAA

WIS.—Whitewater
Merriam, I. Z. (Corn)....E

CRUTCHES

MASS.—Boston
Codman & Shurtleff.......C
Hersey Mfg. Co. ......AA

New York City
Frees, C. A................X
Marks, A. A. ....AA
Pomeroy Co. ....B

N. Y.—Rochester
Fuller, Geo. R. ....E

OHIO—Elyria
Worthington Mfg. Co.....B

PA.—Philadelphia
Hastings & McIntosh Truss Co. ....B
Horn & Bro., Wm. H.....B
Philadelphia Truss & Bandage Co. X
Seeley, Isaac B. ....F

PA.—Pittsburg
Feick Bros. Co.............D

CRYSTAL-LIZERS

DEL.—Wilmington
Pusey & Jones Co.....AAA
ILL.—Chicago
Wolf Co., F. W., 139 Rees
................AAA
LA.—New Orleans
Whitney Iron Wks. Co..AA
MD.—Baltimore
Bartlett, Hayward & Co.,
Continental Trust Bldg.
................B
MASS.—Boston
Cochrane Chemical Co., 55
Kilby (Tin) ....AA
N. Y.—Brooklyn
Pioneer Iron Wks., 151 William ....A
New York City
Cornell Co., J. B. & J. M.,
26th & 11th Av. ......AA
Deeley & Co., Robt., 507
W. 32d ....AA
Turl's Sons, Jno., 536 W.
28th ....D
OHIO—Cleveland
Dyer & Co., E. H., New
England Bldg. .....AAA
PA.—Philadelphia
Morris, Henry G., Phila.
Bourse ....B

CRYSTALS

See also Glasses; Watch.

N. Y.—Syracuse
Solway Process Co. (Monohydrate; Snow Flake)
................AAAA

CUES

MASS.—Worcester
Blood, O. L. (Billiard)..H
New York City
Brunswick - Balke - Collender Co. (Billiard)..AAAA
Grote & Co., F., E. 14th
(Billiard) ....B
Kaldenberg Importing &
Trading Co. (Billiard)..D
Shardlow, Joseph (Billiard)
................D
OHIO—Toledo
Toledo Billiard Ball Co.
(Billiard) ....D

CUFFS

See Collars & Cuffs

CULLERS

MASS.—Worcester
Hamblin & Russell Mfg.
Co. (Wire Strawberry).B
OHIO—Maria Stein
Maria Stein Machine Works
(Flue) ....D

CULVERTS

IND.—Winamac
Winamac Bridge Co. ....G
MICH.—St. Johns
St. Johns Iron Works ....E

CULTIVATORS

See Agr. Implements

CUPBOARDS

See also Furniture

IND.—Indianapolis
Madden Son & Co., Thos..A
MO.—Kansas City
Abernathy Furniture Co..
................AA
MO.—St. Louis
Scarritt-Comstock Furniture
Co. ....A
OHIO—Defiance
Geiger Furniture Co. .....B
WIS.—Sheboygan
Mattoon Mfg. Co. ....A

CUPOLOS

ALA.—Birmingham
Means & Fulton Iron Wks.
(Foundry) X
CONN.—New Haven
Bigelow Co., 435 Guoin
(Foundry) ....B
ILL.—Harvey
Whiting Fdry. Equipment
Co. (Foundry) ....AA
MASS.—Worcester
Stewart & Son, C. (Foundry)
................B
MICH.—Detroit
Byram & Co. (Foundry)..D
Northern Engineering Wks.
(Foundry) ....A
OHIO—Cincinnati
Hill & Griffith Co. ......D
OHIO—Cleveland
Smith Fdry. Supply Co., J.
D., 40 S. Water (Foundry)
................D
OHIO—Lowellville
Meehan Boiler & Construction Co. ....B
OHIO—Portsmouth
Portsmouth Harbinson-
Walker Co. ....AAAA
OHIO—Youngstown
Pollock Co., Wm. B. ..AA
PA.—Allegheny
Carlin's Sons Co., Thos...A
PA.—Lebanon
Union Boiler & Mfg. Co.
(Foundry) ....B
PA.—Philadelphia
Etting, Edw. J., Land Title
Bldg. (Foundry) ....B
Hibbs, E. A., 209 Quarry
(Foundry) ....B
Paxson Co., J. W., 1021 N.
Delaware Av. (Foundry)
................AA
Sellers & Co., Wm. (Inc.),
1600 Hamilton (Foundry)
................AAAA
PA.—Pittsburg
Carroll-Porter Boiler & Tank
Co., Empire Bldg. (Foundry) ....B
McCormack Co., J. S., 25th
& A. V. Ry. (Foundry).B
Munroe & Son, R. ......AA
Riter-Conley Mfg. Co..AAA
PA.—Pottstown
Sotter Bros. (Foundry)....B
PA.—Washington
Petroleum Iron Works Co.
(Foundry; Calcining) ..A
TENN.—Chattanooga
Casey & Hedges Mfg. Co.
(Foundry) ....A

CUPS

See also Oilers; Aluminium
Ware; Chinaware; Glassware; Silverware; Tinware.

CONN.—Bridgeport
Belknap Mfg. Co. (Oil)...C
CONN.—Hartford
Hartford Machine Screw Co.
(Bicycle) ....AAAA
Tucker, W. W. & C. F.
(Self-Closing Rotary)...F
CONN.—Meriden
Manning, Bowman & Co.
(Drinking; Enamelled)AA
Meriden Britannia Co.
(Collapsible) ......AAAA
Wilcox Silver Plate Co.
(Drinking) ....AAAA
CONN.—New Haven
Harrison, Leonard D.
(Elevator) ....H
Peck Bros. & Co. (Oil)..AA
CONN.—Wallingford
Wallace & Sons Mfg. Co.,
R. (Collapsible) ...AAAA
CONN.—Waterbury
Novelty Mfg. Co. (Collapsible) ....A
Scovill Mfg. Co. (Aluminum;
Pocket) ....AAAA
ILL.—Chicago
Allen Mfg. Co., W. D., 151

CUPS (Con.)

Lake (Oil; Grease) ....A

Besly & Co., Chas. H. (Oil; Grease) ....AA

Chicago Screw Co. (Bicycle) AAA

Crane Co. (Brass; Copper; Oil; Grease) ......AAAA

Walker & Ehrman Mfg. Co. (Bicycle) ....A

Western Leather Mfg. Co. (Dice) ....D

ILL.—Elgin

Moseley Lathe Co. (Bicycle Oil) ....D

ILL.—Lemont

Illinois Pure Aluminum Co. (Aluminum) X

ILL.—Waukegan

Thomas Brass & Iron Co. (Oil; Grease) ....A

IND.—Indianapolis

Nordyke & Marmon Co. (Elevator) ....AAA

MASS.—Andover

Tyer Rubber Co. (Cupping) AA

MASS.—Boston

Crosby Steam Gauge & Valve Co., 97 Oliver (Oil; Grease) ....AA

New England Pottery Co. (Porous) C

Seibert Cylinder Oil Cup Co., 53 Oliver (Oil; Grease)..F

Star Brass Mfg. Co. (Oil).A

Walworth Mfg. Co. (Oil; Grease) ....AAAA

MASS.—Chelsea

Low Tile Co. (Sponge) ..F

MASS.—Whitinsville

Whitinsville Spinning Ring Co. (Travelers') .....AA

MASS.—Worcester

Bay State Stamping Co. (Oil; Grease; Self-Closing) ....E

MICH.—Detroit

American Injector Co., Congress & Brooklyn Av. (Brass; Oil Grease) ....D

Detroit Lubricator Co., Hedges Bldg. (Oil; Grease; Glass; Oil) X

Detroit Shipbuilding Co. (Brass; Oil; Grease) .... AAAA

Essex Brass Co., G. B. (Oil; Grease) C

Globe Brass Wks., 13 Macomb (Oil; Grease) ....D

Michigan Lubricator Co., 663 Beaubien (Oil; Grease) ....A

Penberthy Injector Co., 346 Holden Av. (Oil; Grease) A

MICH.—Port Huron

Lee Mfg. Co. (Oil; Grease) B

MICH.—Saginaw

Koehler Bros. (Grease) ..E

MINN.—Minneapolis

Stahl-Salter Lubricating Co., 983 17th Av. (Oil; Grease) X

MO.—St. Louis

Cahill-Swift Mfg. Co. (Oil) B

Ruppenthal & Son, J., 1602 B'way (Grease) ....F

St. Louis Stamping Co. (Drinking) ....AAAA

N. J.—High Bridge

Taylor Iron & Steel Co. (Elevator) ....AAAA

N. J.—Newark

Bernz, Otto, S. 13th, cor. S. Orange Av. (Plumbers' Soil) ....B

Sacks Iron Fdry., Louis (Shoemakers' Nail) ...A

N. J.—New Brunswick

Consolidated Fruit Jar Co. (Oil; Grease) ....AA

N. Y.—Auburn

Bowen Mfg. Co. (Oil; Grease) ....B

N. Y.—Brooklyn

Acton, Jno., 118 John (Oil;

CUPS (Con.)

Grease) ....D

Miller Co., Wm. P. (Grease) D

Schaffer & Budenberg (Compression Grease) ....D

Sweeney Mfg. Co., W. H. (Drinking; Tin) ....A

N. Y.—Buffalo

Crosby Co. (Ball Bearing) A

Shepard & Co., Sidney (Aluminum; Enamelled Marking; Measuring)..... AAAA

Serwood Mfg. Co., 34 Washington (Oil; Grease; Compression Grease) ....B

N. Y.—Elmira

Swift Lubricator Co. (Glass; Brass Oil; Compression Grease) ....B

N. Y.—Geneva

Chapman, C. A. (Measuring) E

New York City

Ashcroft Mfg. Co. (Oil)...A

Central Stamping Co. (Marking; Measuring; Muffin; Spit) ....AA

Cooks, Adams Sons Co., 313 West (Oil; Grease) ....A

Eaton, Cole & Burnham Co., 253 B'way (Oil; Grease).. AAAA

Edison Phonograph Agency (Porous) ....D

Estes & Sons, E. B. (Pin) AA

Goodyear Rubber Co. (Cupping) ....AAAA

Goodyear's Ind. Rub. Glove Mfg. Co. (Dice; Cupping; Pin) ....AAAA

Gordon Battery Co. (Porous) D

Hall Mfg. Co., R. H., 40 Cortland (Oil; Grease)..G

International Silver Co. (Silver Plated; Shaving; Children's) ....AAAA

Judd & Co., H. L. (Sponge) AA

Lalance & Grosjean Mfg. Co. (Drinking; Enamelled)... AAAA

Mace & Co., L. H. (Soap).B

McNab & Harlin Mfg. Co., 56 John (Oil; Grease) ... AAA

Montrose, Norman E. (Palette) ....F

Nathan Mfg. Co., 92 Liberty (Brass Oil; Grease) ...A

Pedrick & Ayer Co. (Oil)..A

Reilley Bros. (Painters'; Palette) ....D

Reilly Repair & Supply Co., James, 229 West (Oil; Grease) ....AA

Robins Conveying Belt Co. (Grease) ....A

Schieren & Co., Chas. A., 45 Ferry (Leather) ...AAAA

Stoutenborough, X. (Marking; Measuring; Muffin; Spit; Tin) ....D

N. Y.—Ogdensburg

Nash Bros. & Co. (Spring Compression Grease)....A

N. Y.—Rochester

Nunn Bros. Wks. (Inc.) (Oil; Grease) ....F

N. Y.—Troy

Troy Stamping Co. (Drinking; Tin Ar ny) ...AAAA

N. Y.—Wolcott

Curtis, O. M. (Bleechers) X

OHIO—Cincinnati

Bourbon Copper & Brass Wks. (Oil) ....A

Lunkenheimer Co., cor. Beekman & Waverly (Oil; Grease; Glass Oil) ...AA

Powell Co., Wm., 2525 Spring Grove Av. (Oil; Grease) ....A

Queen City Brass & Iron Wks. (Brass; Oil; Grease)

CUPS (Con.)

B

Tatum Co., Samuel C.
(Sponge) ....B

OHIO—Cleveland
Farnan Brass Wks., 25 Center (Brass Oil) ....A
Federal Mfg. Co. (Ball Bearing) ....AAAA
Forest City Brass Wks., 90 Merwin (Brass Oil; Grease) ....B

OHIO—Dayton
Buckeye Iron & Brass Wks. (Oil; Grease) ....AA
Dayton Malleable Iron Co. (Drinking) ....AAA

OHIO—Elyria
Western Automatic Mach. Screw Co. (Bicycle)...AA

OHIO—Mansfield
Ohio Brass Co. (Brass; Glass Oil; Grease) ....AA

OHIO—Salem
Clark Co., W. J. (Elevator) A

OHIO—Sidney
Wagner Mfg. Co. (Aluminum) ....A

OHIO—Springfield
Nolte Brass Co. (Plain Brass Oil) ....D
Springfield Brass Co. (Brass Oil; Grease) ....E

PA.—Beaver Falls
Co-Operative Flint Glass Co. (Sponge) ....A

PA.—Erie
Griswold Mfg. Co. (Aluminum) ....A
Jarecki Mfg. Co. (Oil; Grease) ....AAAA
Keystone Brass Co., 1017 Peach (Oil; Grease) ..A
Reed Mfg. Co. (Oil; Grease) A
Sims Co. (Crank Pin Oil)..D

PA.—Philadelphia
Belfield & Co., 435 N. Broad (Oil; Grease)...AA
Eynon-Evans Mfg. Co., 1519 Clearfield (Railroad Oil) A
France Packing Co. (Inc.), 6512 State Road (Oil; Grease) ....B
Lonergan & Co., J. E. (Oil) AA

PA.—Pittsburg
Cadman Mfg. Co., A. W. (Oil) C
Kelly & Jones Co., 135 Water (Oil; Grease)...AA

PA.—Williamsport
Darling Pump & Mfg. Co. (Oil) ....B

R. I.—Providence
Wall & Co., A. T. (Aluminum; Drinking) C

WIS.—Milwaukee
Chain Belt Co. (Elevator)D
Delaney Oil & Lubricating Co. (Grease) X
Wadham's Oil Co., National Av. (Grease) ....A

CURASOA

See Cordials

CURBING

CONN.—Middletown
Douglas, W. & B. (Well).A

IND.—Goshen
I. X. L. & Goshen Pump Co. (Well) ....B

PA.—Philadelphia
Blatchley, Chas. G. (Well) B

PA.—Warren
Red Star Brick Co. (Sidewalk) C

VT.—Fair Haven
Scotch Hill Slate Co. (Slate) ....D

W. VA.—Wheeling
Wheeling Corrugating Co. (Steel) ....AAAA

CURBS

CONN.—Bristol
Barrett, Wm. L. (Pump).D

CONN.—Stamford
Foster, E. H. (Well)....D

MO.—St. Joseph
St. Joseph Pump & Mfg. Co. (Pump) ....B

N. Y.—Dansville
Hubbard, H. E. (Well)...G

N. Y.—Lockport
American District Steam Co. (Valve; Cast Iron)..AAA

CURDS

ILL.—Elgin
Cornell Bros. (Dry) ......B

CURLERS

CONN.—Bridgeport
Gaynor & Mitchell Mfg. Co. (Hair) C

R. I.—Pawtucket
Luther & Co., C. A. (Hair) C

R. I.—Providence
Stayner & Co., T. B. (Hair) E

CURRENCY

New York City
American Bank Note Co. (Paper) ....AAAA

CURTAINS

See also Shades

CONN.—Bridgeport
Cylindrograph Embroidery Co. (Embroidered) .....B
Trolley Vestibule Shade Co. (Car) ....F

CONN.—South Manchester
Cheney Bros. (Silk) ..AAAA

CONN.—Tariffville
Tariffville Lace Mfg. Co..B

ILL.—Chicago
Adams & Westlake Co. (Car) ....AAAA
Curtain Supply Co., 87 Ohio (Car) ....AA
Forsyth Bros. Co., 50 S. Canal (Car) ....E

ILL.—Zion City
Zion Lace Industries (Lace) AAA

MAINE—Portland
Burrows Co., E. T. (Berth; Car; Carriage) ....AA

MASS.—West Newton
Martin Mfg. Co. ....D

N. J.—Camden
Loeb & Schoenfeld Co. (Lace) ....AAAA

N. J.—Paterson
Fulton, Smith & Co. (Silk Tapestry) ....F

New York City
Asbestos Felting Wks., 79 Maiden Lane (Asbestos Theatre) ....D
Boyle & Co., John, 203 Fulton (Car) ....AA
Creighton & Burch (Lace; Com.) ....AA
Empire Rubber Co., 115 Worth (Rubber; Bath)..D
Goodyear Ind. Rub. Glove Mfg. Co., 503 B'way (Rubber; Bath) ....AAAA
Greer & Hutton (Mfrs.' Agts.) ....D
Goodyear Rubber Co., 787 B'way (Rubber; Bath)...AAAA
Hodgeman Rubber Co., 593 B'way (Rubber; Bath)..AA
Johns-Manville Co., H. W. (Asbestos Theatre) AAAA
Pantosote Leather Co., 11 B'way (Car) ....AA
Ryan & McGahan (Mfrs.' Agt. Lace; Tapestry) ..D
Schwab & Co., S. M., Jr.

CURTAINS (Con.)

(Embroidered) ....A
Sloan, W. & J. (Inc.) (Silk)
AAAA
Whitman & Co., Clarence
(Com. Lace) ....AA
Wilson Mfg. Co., Jas., 3
W. 29th (Steel Rolling).A

N. Y.—Patchogue
Patchogue Mfg. Co. (Lace)
A

OHIO—Cleveland
Federal Mfg. Co. (Car)...
AAAA

OHIO—Lockland
Carey Mfg. Co., Philip (Asbestos Theatre) .....AAA

PA.—Ambler
Keasbey & Mattison Co.
(Asbestos Theatre) ....
AAAA

PA.—Cheltenham
Pike, E. V. (Chenille)...D

PA.—Chester
Birkin & Co., T. I. (Lace)
B

PA.—Columbia
Columbia Lace Mfg. Co.
(Lace) ....A

PA.—Eden
Eden Mfg. Co. (Silk) C

PA.—Erie
Watson Co., H. F. (Asbestos Theatre) .....AAA

PA.—Philadelphia
Amure Tapestry Mill (Tapestry) ....E
Barber & Co., J. W. (Upholstery) C
Barlow, Noah, 53rd & Westminster Av. (Tapestry).D
Binder & Ellis, 6th & Allegheny Av. (Upholstery).C
Bromley, Jos. H. (Lace)..
AAAA
Bromley Mfg. Co. (Chenille; Lace) ....AAAA
Brooks & Son Co., Geo.
(Tapestry; Berth; Chenille) ....B
Bruner, Francis A., Unity
& Leiper (Tapestry) ..D
Derk & Co., Joseph (Tapestry) ....D
Falk & Co., O. N. (Tapestry) ....E
Godshalk Co., E. H. (Chenille; Lace; Tapestry) ..B
Grange, Wm. G., Ktn. &
Ontario (Silk; Tapestry)
C
Hale & Kilburn Mfg. Co.
(Car) ....AAAA
Herbst, Jacob, 2149 N. Warnock (Silk; Tapestry)..D
Holdsworth & Arthur (Tapestry) ....D
Hoyle, Harrison & Kaye
(Tapestry; Chenille).AAA
Lewis, Robert, Richmond &
Brill (Car) C
Mawley, J. V. (Portieres)D
Meehan-Mothes Co. (Tapestry) ....A
Moss Rose Mfg. Co., Allegheny Av. & Hancock
(Tapestry) ....A
Newton, Herbert B., Ktn.
Av. & Venango (Tapestry) ....D
Orinoka Mills (Tapestry).A
Philadelphia Tapestry Mills,
Allegheny & Front (Tapestry) ....AAA
Pollitz, Kaufman & Co.,
1716 N. 5th (Lace) C
Regar & Oughton (Silk;
Cotton) C
Ritchie Co., Robt. J. & R.
(Tapestry) ....D
Schwehm & Sons, J. M.
(Tapestry; Silk; Turcoman) ....AA
Smith & Son, W. T. (Lace;
Chenille) ....AA
Stead, Miller & Co. (Tapestry; Chenille; Silk) ..AA
Stroud, David H. (Chenille)
A

CURTAINS (Con.)
Vigilant Mills (Silk Tapestry) C

PA.—Scranton
Scranton Lace Curtain Co.
(Nottingham Lace) ....A

PA.—Wilkesbarre
Wilkesbarre Lace Mfg. Co.
(Lace) ....AAA
Wyoming Valley Lace Mills
(Lace) ....A

R. I.—Bristol
National India Rubber Co.
(Rubber Bath) ....AAAA

CURVES

MINN.—Minneapolis
Peteler Portable Railway
Mfg. Co. (Portable; Railway) C

N. J.—Hoboken
New York Switch & Crossing Co. (Portable; Railway) ....A

New York City
Stoltmann, E. G., 125 E.
42d (Railroad) ....B

CUSHIONS

CONN.—New Haven
Seamless Rubber Co. (Air;
Rubber) ....AA

CONN.—Saugatuck
Wakeman, Rufus (Hall;
Church; Chair; Yacht)..C

GA.—Atlanta
Southern Spring Bed Co....C

ILL.—Chicago
Emmerich & Co., Chas.
(Art Down) ....A
Sanitary Feather Co.
(Down) C
Smith & Co., David A.
(Carriage) ....D

ILL.—Lincoln
Fisher & Co., Chas. A....D

MD.—Baltimore
Larrimore Buggy Top Co.
(Carriage; Wagon) ....G
Perfection Mattress Co....C

MD.—Hagerstown
Hagerstown Mattress Co...C

MASS.—Andover
Tyer Rubber Co. (Rubber;
Air; Invalid; Carriage)..
AA

MASS.—Boston
Bailey & Co., C. J. (Rubber Heel) ....B
Bent & Co., Geo. W. (Boat;
Chair; Church) ....B
Boston Belting Co. (Billiard) ....AAAA
Davidson Rubber Co. (Rubber; Air) ....A
Paine Furniture Co. ......A
Standard Wire Mattress Co.
D
Wheeler & Co., A. W......C

MASS.—So. Framingham
Avery, F. F. (Chair;
Church) ....E

MASS.—Worcester
Griffin, John J. (Estate of)
C
Wire Goods Co. (Steel
Wire) ....A
Wright Wire Co. (Wire).AA

MINN.—Minneapolis
Kilgore Machine Co. (Air;
Saw-Mill; Carriage)....D

MINN.—St. Paul
Union Mattress Co. C

MO.—St. Louis
Beck & Corbitt Iron Co.
(Carriage; Wagon) ....AA

N. J.—Bloomfield
Combination Rubber Mfg.
Co. (Billiard) ....B

N. J.—Jersey City
New Jersey Car Spring &
Rubber Co. (Billiard).AA

N. J.—Trenton
Bloom & Godley ....A
Trenton Rubber Mfg. Co.
(Billiard) ....A

N. Y.—Brooklyn
Brass Goods Mfg. Co. (Pin)
B

CUSHIONS (Con.)

N. Y.—Cortland
Newton & Son, W. H. (Carriage; Wagon) ....B
N. Y.—East Syracuse
Benedict Mfg. Co., M. S. (Pin) ....AA
N. Y.—Jamestown
Blystone, W. I. C
New York City
Abercrombie & Fitch, 314 B'way (Air) ....B
Boyle & Co., John (Boat).. AA
Brunswick - Balke - Collender Co. (Billiard).AAAA
Ellithorpe Safety Air Cushion Co. (Elevator Safety Air) ....D
Fogg, M. W. C
Goodyear Rubber Co. (Rubber Chair Leg; Air)AAAA
Goodyears' India Rubber Glove Mfg. Co. (Rubber; Billiard; Air) .....AAAA
Grote & Co., F. (Pin) ...D
Gutta Percha & Rubber Mfg. Co., 126 Duane (Billiard) ....AAAA
Hodgman Rubber Co. (Rubber Chair Leg; Air)...AA
McHugh, John F. (Boat; Wagon) C
Mattson Rubber Co. (Rubber; Air) ....B
New York Belting & Packing Co. (Billiard) ..AAA
New York Rubber Co. (Billiard) ....AA
Ostermoor & Co., 132 Bowery (Carriage; Wagon; Boat; Chair; Church)...A
Rehm & Co., 141 Fulton (Carriage; Wagon) .....D
Rogers & Co., Charles P..A
Sperry & Beale, 32 Union Sq. (Boat; Church) ...X
N. Y.—Rochester
Wegman, Wm. J. (Church; Windaw) ....D
OHIO—Akron
Akron Rubber Wks. (Goodrich Co., B. F.) (Billiard; Air) ....AAAA
Faultless Rubber Co. (Invalid Air) ....AA
OHIO—Cincinnati
Maish & Co., Chas. A. (Cotton) ....B
Perkins-Campbell Co. (Carriage; Wagon) ......AA
OHIO—Toledo
Kroh Co., C. Z. (Carriage) E
PA.—Harrisburg
Hickok Mfg. Co., W. O. (Gold) ....AA
PA.—Philadelphia
Dougherty & Co., H. L...C
Smith & Sons Co., Oscar (Church) C
R. I.—Providence
Davol Rubber Co. (Rubber; Air) ....AA
Providence Stock Co. (Pin) D
Sweeney Co., Wm. .....D
W. VA.—Wheeling
Wheeling Mattress Co. (Down) C
WIS.—Janesville
Rock River Cotton Co. ...A
WIS.—Milwaukee
Wergell, A. (Down) .....A
WIS.—Racine
Chicago Rubber Clothing Co. (Air) ....A
Racine General Mfg. Co. (Carriage) ....E

CUSPIDORS

CONN.—Bridgeport
Bridgeport Brass Co.(Brass; Self-righting) ......AAA
CONN.—Meriden
Manning, Bowman & Co. (Brass; Enamelled; Nickeled; Tin) ....AAA
Meriden Britannia Co.

CUSPIDORS (Con.)

(Brass) ....AAAA
CONN.—Nagatuck
Goodyear's Ind. Rub. Glove Mfg. Co. (Rubber).AAAA
ILL.—Chicago
Clark & Co., A. C. (Fountain) ....A
Sturges & Burn Mfg. Co..A
ILL.—Lemont
Illinois Pure Aluminum Co. (Aluminum) X
MD.—Baltimore
Rosenbery Co., A. (Physicians; Dentists; Flushing) H
MASS.—Boston
Boston Belting Co. (Rubber) AAAA
MICH.—Detroit
Ireland & Matthews Mfg. Co. (Brass; Nickel; Self-Righting) ....A
MO.—St. Louis
St. Louis Stamping Co. (Enamelled) ......AAAA
N. J.—Burlington
Stewart & Peterson Co...A
N. J.—Trenton
Trenton Potteries Co. (Sick-Bed) ....A
N. Y.—Brooklyn
Sweeney Mfg. Co., W. H. (Brass; Nickeled; Tin).A
N. Y.—Buffalo
Aldrich Mfg. Co. (Brass).A
Shepard & Co., Sidney (Aluminum) ......AAAA
N. Y.—Horseheads
Weller Hardware & Foundry Co. (Iron) ....D
N. Y.—Manlius
Cheney & Son, S. ....A
New York City
American Hard Rubber Co. (Rubber) ....AAAA
Cordley & Hayes (Fibre) .A
Fiske Iron Works, J. W. (Brass) ....B
Goodyear Rubber Co. (Rubber) ....AAAA
Gould-Mersereau Co. (Brass) ....B
Hodgman Rubber Co. (Rubber) ....AA
Lalance & Grosjean Mfg. Co. (Enamelled)...AAAA
Manhattan Brass Co. (Brass) ....A
Manhattan Rubber Mfg. Co., 18 Vesey (Rubber)AA
Seabury & Johnson (Sanitary) ....AA
Stoutenborough, X. (Nickeled; Self-Righting) ...D
N. Y.—Rome
Rome Mfg. Co. ....E
OHIO—Canton
Canton Surgical & Dental Chair Co. (Fountain) ..C
OHIO—Cincinnati
Haven Co., Jas. L. (Iron) B
OHIO—Sidney
Wagner Mfg. Co. (Aluminum) ....A
OHIO—Zanesville
Zanesville Art Pottery Co. (Pottery) ....B
PA.—Erie
Griswold Mfg. Co. (Aluminum) ....A
PA.—Marietta
Marietta Hollow Ware & Enamel Co. (Enamelled) B
PA.—Philadelphia
Hall & Carpenter, 518 Race AA
PA.—Pittsburg
Pittsburg Brass Mfg. Co. (Brass) ....D
PA.—So. Bethlehem
Bethlehem Fdry. & Mach. Co. C
R. I.—Providence
Wall & Co., A. T. (Aluminum) C

CUTLERY

See also Knives; Scissors; Razors, etc.

CUTLERY (Con.)
571 CUTLERY.
CONN.—Hotchkissville
Amer. Shear & Knife Co.
(Pocket) ....A
CONN.—Lakeville
Holley Mfg. Co. (Pocket) B
CONN.—Meriden
Meriden Cutlery Co. (Table)
AA
Miller Bros. Cutlery Co.
(Pocket) ....A
Parker Co., Chas. (Table)
AAA
CONN.—Naubuc
Williams Bros. Mfg. Co.
(Table) ....A
CONN.—New Britain
Humason & Beckley Mfg.
Co. (Pocket) ....A
Landers, Frary & Clark
(Kitchen; Table) ...AAA
CONN.—Northfield
Northfield Knife Co.
(Pocket) ....B
CONN.—Shelton
Silver Plate Cutlery Co.
(Table) ....B
CONN.—Southington
Southington Cutlery Co.
(Pocket) ....AA
CONN.—Thomaston
Thomaston Knife Co.
(Pocket) ....F
CONN.—Wallingford
Wallace Sons Mfg. Co., R.
(Kitchen; Table) ..AAAA
DEL.—Wilmmington
Walker & Elliot ....B
ILL.—Chicago
American Cutlery Co. (Sil-
ver Plated; Table) ..AA
ILL.—Decatur
Illinois Cutlery Co. (Min-
cing; Paring Knives) ...B
MASS.—Boston
Gilmore Electric Co.
(Pocket) ....AA
MASS.—Greenfield
Nichols Bros. (Table) ...C
Warner Mfg. Co. (Table) C
MASS.—Northampton
Northampton Cutlery Co.
(Kitchen; Table) ......A
MASS.—Shelburne Falls
Lamson & Goodnow Mfg. Co.
(Table) ....A
MASS.—Turners Falls
Russell Cutlery Co., Jno.
(Pocket; Table) ......A
N. H.—Antrim
Goodell Co. (Table; Silver
Plated) ....A
N. H.—Bennington
Kimball Co., C. J. (Kitchen)
B
N. J.—Newark
Bannister & Co., A. F.
(Pocket) ....A
N. Y.—Buffalo
White Co., L. & I. J., Perry
& Columbia (Mincing
Knives) ....A
N. Y.—Elmira
Cronk & Carrier Mfg. Co.
(Pocket) ....B
New York City
Boker & Co., Herman, 101
Duane (Pocket) ...AAA
Chatillon & Sons, J., 85
Cliff (Pocket) ....A
Russell & Co., J. 37 Reade
(Mincing; Paring Knives)
AA
Silberstein, A. L., 459
B'way (Pocket) ....A
Wiebusch & Hilger (Pocket)
A
N. Y.—Rochester
Robeson Cutlery Co.
(Pocket) ....A
OHIO—Canton
Gibbs Mfg. Co. (Mincing
Knives) ....A
PA.—Titusville
Schatt & Morgan Cutlery Co.
(Pocket) ....B

CUT-OFFS

ILL.—Peoria
Clark, Quien & Morse (Rain
Water) ....A
LA.—New Orleans
N. O. Roofing & Metal Wks.
(Cistern) ....B

CUT-OFFS (Con.)
MINN.—Minneapolis
Minn. Bedding Co. (Auto-
matic Loom) ....A
OHIO—Canton
Berger Mfg. Co. (Rain
Water) ....AA
Canton Steel Roofing Co.
(Rain Water) ....A
OHIO—Cleveland
Tarry Iron & Steel Co.
(Rain Water) ....A
OHIO—Lima
Smith & Son, W. A. (Rain
Water) ....F
OHIO—Massillon
Hess, Snyder & Co. (Rain
Water) ....AA
PA.—Philadelphia
Berger Bros., 231 Arch
(Rain Water) ....A

CUT-OUTS

CONN.—Bridgeport
Bryant Electric Co. ......A
Perkins Electric Switch Mfg.
Co. (Electric) ....A
CONN.—New Britain
Brady, L. H. (Electric) .B
IND.—Fort Wayne
Fort Wayne Electric Works
(Electric) ....AAA
IOWA—Sioux City
Electric Supply Co.
(Ceiling) ....E
MASS.—Boston
Gilmore Electric Co. (Elec-
tric) ....A
MASS.—Brookline
Holtzer, Cabot Electric Co.
(Electric) ....A
MO.—St. Louis
Emerson Electric Mfg. Co.
(Electric) ....A
Wagner Electric Mfg. Co.,
(Electric) ....AA
New York City
Jones & Son, J., 64 Cort-
landt (Electric) X
N. Y.—Syracuse
Crouse-Hinds Electric Co.
(Electric) ....A
Pass & Seymour (Electric)
A
OHIO—Cincinnati
Creaghead Engineering Co.
(Electric) ....D
OHIO—East Liverpool
Brunt Porcelain Wks.
(Electric) ....B
PA.—Philadelphia
Patrick, Carter & Wilkins
(Electric) C

CUTS

ILL.—Chicago
Hawtin & Co., W. (Stock;
Lithographers') ......F
New York City
Ringler Co., F. A. (Stock;
Lithographers') ......A
Schedler, Herman (Stock;
Lithographers') ......E

CUTTERS

See also Nippers; Agr.
Implements; Machinery.

CONN—Ansonia
Cook Co., H. C. (Sewing
Thread) ....E
CONN.—Bridgeport
American Tube & Stamping
Co. (Tube) ....AAAA
Armstrong Mfg. Co. (Pipe)
A
Bridgeport Hdw. Mfg. Co.
(Rod; Wire) ....B
Curtis & Curtis Co. (Pipe)
AA
Hubbell, Harvey (Round
Belt; Punch) C
Schwerdtle Stamp Co. (Let-
ter; Steel; Brass) .....F
CONN.—Bristol
Barrett, W. L. (Glass Tube)
D
CONN.—Hartford
Billings & Spencer Co. (Rod;
Wire; Cigar) ....AA
Dwight Slate Mach. Co.
(Milling; Pinion; Rock) B
Pratt & Whitney Co. (An-

318

CUTTERS (Con.)

gular; Turret Bolt; Convex; Concave; Gang; Metal Slotting; Milling; Screw Slotting; Sprocket; Epicycloidal; Involute; Rack; Pipe; Tube; Reamer; Twist Drill) ....AAAA
Sigourney Tool Co. (Milling) ....A
CONN.—Meriden
Bradley & Hubbard Mfg. Co. (Cigar Tip; Paper) AAAA
Kelsey Press Co. (Card) A
CONN.—New Britain
Landers, Frary & Clark (Meat; Slaw; Kraut) AAA
CONN.—New Haven
Barnes Tool Co. (Pipe; Moulding) ....B
Belden Machine Co. (Rod; Wire) ....D
Geometric Drill Co. (Milling) ....B
Hoggson & Pettis Mfg. Co. (Hand; Pipe) ....A
Kilborn & Bishop Co., 81 Lloyd (Rod; Wire) C
Mersick & Co., C. S., 286 State (Iron Bar; Rod) A
New Haven Mfg. Co. (Bolt) ....AA
Schollhorn & Co., W. (Cigar) ....A
Shuster Co., F. B. (Automatic, for Metal; Strip Stock Straighteners; Spiral Mill; Sprue; Wire) X
CONN.—New London
Whiton Machine Co., D. E. (Milling) ....AA
CONN.—Norwich
Rogers & Co., C. B. (Mouldings) ....AAAA
CONN.—Rockfall
Smith, Otis A. (Washer; Gasket) ....B
CONN.—Seymour
Swan Co., James (Plug) A
CONN.—Southington
Peck, Stow & Wilcox Co. (Hand; Tobacco; Meat; Sausage Meat; Vegetable; Slaw; Kraut) .....AAAA
CONN.—Tolland
Clough, R. M. (Angular; Convex; Concave; Milling; Gear; Screw Slotting) D
CONN.—Unionville
Monce, S. C. (Glass; Gauge Glass; Photo Print) ....D
CONN.—Williamantic
Vanderman Plumbing & Heating Co. (Lead Pipe) C
DEL.—Wilmington
Henderer's Sons, A. L. (Tube) ....E
Hillis & Jonen Co. (Sprue) ....AAAA
Pusey & Jonen Co. (Paper Stock) ....AAA
ILL.—Alton
Hapgood Plow Co. (Stalk) ....AA
ILL.—Aurora
Wilcox Mfg. Co. (Twine) B
ILL.—Batavia
Appleton Mfg. Co. (Ensilage; Fodder; Chaff; Hay; Straw) ....A
Challenge Wind Mill & Feed Mill Co. (Feed; Corn; Chaff; Ensilage; Fodder; Hay; Straw; Stalk) AAA
U. S. Wind Engine & Pump Co. (Chaff; Hay; Straw; Stalk) ....AA
ILL.—Belleville
Sucker State Drill Co. (Stalk) ....A
ILL.—Bradley
Bradley Mfg. Co., David (Cornstalk) ....AAA
ILL.—Canton
Parlin & Orendorff Co. (Feed; Stalk) ....AAAA
ILL.—Chicago
American Cutlery Co. (Fingernail) ....AA
Chicago Pneumatic Tool Co. Fischer Bldg. (Pneumatic; Flue; Stay Bolt) ..AAAA
Curtis & Co., Mfg. Co., 42 S. Canal (Combination Belt) C

CUTTERS (Con.)

Kelso & Co., 209 S. Clinton (Kraut) ....E
Latham Machry. Co. (Card; Rotary Board; Round Corner) C
Lovejoy, T. H., 90 Ohio (Flue Hole) ....D
McCrea & Co., James, 67 W. Washington (Washer; Gasket) ....E
Mark Mfg. Co. (Pipe) ..AA
Murphy & Co., Christopher 204 Dearborn (Tube, rapid operated by hand or motor) ....B
Porter & Berg, 309 Dearborn (Sleet) ....D
Reiss Bros. & Co. (Cigar Butt) ....AA
Rosback, F. P. (Index) ...E
Rouse & Co., H. B., 61 Ward (Lead; Rule) ....G
Sutherland & Dow (Computing Cheese) ....D
ILL.—Downers Grove
Dicke Tool Co. (Gauge Glass) C
ILL.—Edwardsville
Bignall & Keeler Mfg. Co. (Pipe) ....B
ILL.—Freeport
Stover Mfg. Co. (Chaff; Hay; Straw) ....AA
ILL.—Harvey
Austin Mfg. Co., F. C. (Ensilage; Chaff; Fodder; Hay; Straw) ......AAA
ILL.—Marseilles
Marseilles Mfg. Co. (Steam; Horse Power Feed; Cornstalk; Chaff; Ensilage; Fodder) ....A
ILL.—Moline
Deere & Mansur Co. (Cornstalk) ....AAAA
Moline Plow Co. (Stalk) ....AAAA
ILL.—Paxton
Paxton's Hardware Mfg. Co. (Cake; Biscuit) X
ILL.—Peoria
Avery Mfg. Co. (Spiral Knife; Stalk) ......AAA
Selby, Starr & Co. (Stalk) X
ILL.—Peru
Peru Plow & Wheel Co. (Single; Double Row Stalk) AA
ILL.—Rockford
Barnes Co., W. F. & John (Moulding) ....AA
Ingersoll Milling Machine Co. (Milling) ....D
ILL.—Rock Island
Rock Island Plow Co. (Stalk) ....AAAA
ILL.—Sandwich
Sandwich Mfg. Co. (Corn; Cornstalk) Chaff; Fodder; Ensilage) ....AA
ILL.—Sterling
Keystone Co. (Chaff; Ensilage; Fodder; Hay; Corn; Straw) ....AA
Sterling Mfg. Co. (Chaff; Ensilage; Fodder; Straw; Hay; Stalk) ....A
IND.—Anderson
Computing Cheese Cutter Co. ....G
Hoosier Cheese Cutter Co. (Computing Cheese) ...X
IND.—Aurora
Stamm Machine Wks. (Barrel Heading) C
IND.—Columbus
Reeves & Co. (Inc.) (Stalk) ....AAAA
IND.—Indianapolis
Atkins & Co.. E. C. (Saw Gummer; Slaw; Kraut) ....AAAA
Nordyke & Marmon Co. (Corn) ....AAA
Tucker & Dorsey Mfg. Co. (Slaw; Kraut; Vegetable; Smoked Beef) ....A
IND.—Richmond
Richmond City Mill Wks. (Corn) ....B
Wayne Works (Chaff; Hay; Straw) ....A
IND.—South Bend
Haberle & Graham (Open Die Head Bolt) ....D

CUTTERS (Con.)

IOWA—Burlington
Murray Iron Wks. Co. (Meat) ....A

IOWA—Dubuque
Adams Co. (Steel; Tubular Sprue; Milling) ....A

IOWA—Fort Madison
Iowa Farming Tool Co. (Chaff) ....A

KANS.—Enterprise
Ehrsam Mach. Co., J. B. (Chaff) ....B

KY.—Louisville .
Avery & Sons, B. F. (Spiral; Straight Knife; Stalk) ....AAA

MAINE—Portland
Hayes, Harrison (Tube) ..H

MD.—Baltimore
Adt Machine Wks., John B. (Tobacco) ....A
Detrick & Harvey Mach. Co. (Bolt) ....A
Mergenthaler-Ott Co. (Inc.) cor. Claggett & Allen (Flue, for boilers) X
Sinclair-Scott Co. (Chaff; Hay; Straw) ....B

MASS.—Athol
Athol Mach. Co. (Meat) ..B
Gay & Ward (Angular; Convex; Concave; Gang; Milling; Metal Slitting; Rack; Radial Duplex; Screw Slotting; Spiral Mill; Sprocket; T-slot; Tape; Reamer; Twist Drill; Worm Wheel) ....A
Starrett Co., L. S. (Boxmakers' Corner; Involute; Milling; Gear; Slotting; Sprocket Wheel) ....A

MASS.—Boston
Ames Plow Co. (Corn; Ensilage; Chaff; Fodder; Hay; Straw; Vegetable; Root; Meat) .....AAAA
Boston Gear Wks., 152 Purchase (Gear; Milling) ..B
Chandler & Farquhar, 36 Federal (Wire; Rod) ..B
Eyelet Tool Co. (Button Hole) X
Faneuil Watch Tool Co. (Pinion; Watch Wheel) E
Golding & Co. (Card; Paper) ....B
Livermore, H. F., 81 Pearl (Pipe) ....E
Lufkin, John W. (Button Hole) ....A
Seelye Mfg. Co. (Die) C
Sewing Machine Supply Co. (Buttonhole) ....B
Trimont Mfg. Co. (Hand; Pipe) ....A
Wadsworth, Howland & Co., 84 Washington (Fillet) ....A
Walker & Pratt Mfg. Co. (Bread) ....AA
Walworth Mfg. Co., 132 Federal (Pipe; Lead Pipe) ....AAAA

MASS.—Brockton
Tuck Mfg. Co. (Sole Leather) ....E

MASS.—Chicopee Falls
Belcher & Taylor Agricultural Tool Co. (Chaff; Ensilage; Fodder; Hay; Straw; Vegetable; Root) ....A

MASS.—Everett
Porter, H. K. (Wire) C

MASS.—Fitchburg
Putnam Machine Co. (Bolt; Epicycloidal; Involute; Rack; Paper Stock) ...A
Simonds Mfg. Co. (Cork; Cloth; Leather; Paper) ....AAA

MASS.—Greenfield
Goodell-Pratt Co. (Glass) .B
Reece Co., E. F. (Bolt) ...A
Wells Bros. Co. (Bolt) ...A
Wiley & Russell Mfg. Co. (Bolt) ....AA

MASS.—Holyoke
Holyoke Machine Co. (Paper Stock; Strop) ....AA

MASS.—Hyde Park
Becker, Brainard Milling Mach. Co. (Milling) AA

CUTTERS (Con.)

MASS.—Lawrence
Horne & Sons Co., J. H. (Paper Stock) ....A

MASS.—Lowell
Dennis & Co., John (Plush) ....E
Lowell Machine Shop (Stop) ....AAAA

MASS.—Marlboro
Parsons & Son, Henry (Knit Fabric) ....A

MASS.—New Bedford
Morse Twist Drill & Mach. Co. (Angular; Convex; Concave; Gang; Metal Slitting; Milling Side; Screw Slotting; Spiral Mill; Sprocket; Stay-Bolt; T-Slot) ....AAA

MASS.—Northampton
Herrick, Chas. E. (Epicycloidal; Involute) ......D

MASS.—North Attleboro
Codding & Heilborn Co. (Cigar Tip) ....A

MASS.—Orange
Leavitt Machine Co. (Disk) ....D

MASS.—Shelburne Falls
Mayhew Co., H. H. (Glass) ....D

MASS.—Springfield
Bradley Co., Milton (Card) ....A
Bullock Mfg. Co., O. W., 172 Dwight (Pinion; Glass; Watch Wheel) ....A

MASS.—Watertown
Waterproof Paint Co. (Fillet) ....E

MASS.—Worcester
Blaisdell & Co., P. (Gear; Milling) ....A
Boynton & Plummer (Hand; Power, Bolt) ....B
Burlingame, A. (Sole Leather) ....D
Coates Clipper Mfg. Co. (Fingernail) ....D
Curtis & Marble Mach. Co. (Flock; Ray; Paper Stock) ....A
Rice, Barton & Fales Mach. & Iron Co. (Paper Stock) ....AA
Wire Goods Co. (Fingernail; Nail) ....A

MICH.—Albion
Gale Mfg. Co. (Stalk) AA

MICH.—Battle Creek
Advance Thresher Co. (Chaff) ....AAAA
Amer. Steam Pump Co. (Solid Steel Moulding) ....AAA

MICH.—Detroit
McRae & Roberts Co. (Glass Tube; Gauge Glass) ..A
Metal Novelty Co. (Computing Cheese) C
Northern Engineering Wks. (Sprue, for brass fdry.) A

MICH.—Grand Rapids
Baldwin, Tuthill & Bolton (Lap) ....B
Fox Mach. Co. (Pipe; Tube) ....A

MICH.—Jackson
Aspinwall Mfg. Co. (Vegetable) ....B
Withington & Cooley Mfg. Co. (Corn; Thistle) ..AA

MICH.—Lansing
Clark & Co. (Vehicle) ....B

MICH.—Monroe
Wilder Strong Impl. Co. (Chaff) C

MICH.—Muskegon
Morton Mfg. Co. (Key-Way) ....B

MICH.—Tecumseh
Brewer & Co., H. (Brick; Drain Tile) ....B

MICH.—Three Rivers
Sheffield Car Co. (Track Weed) ....AA

MINN.—St. Paul
Helwig Mfg. Co. (Bolt) D

MINN.—St. Joseph
Saint Joseph Plow Co. (Single; Double Row Stalk) A

MO.—Kansas City
Russell Hdw. & Implement Mfg. Co. (Wire) X

CUTTERS (Con.)

MO.—St. Louis
American Roll Paper Co. (Roll Paper) ....B
Brecht Butchers' Supply Co., Gus. V. (Back Fat; Meat) AAA
Ludlow-Saylor Wire Co. (Paper) ....AA
Sawyer Paper Co., F. O. (Roll Paper) X
Standard Railway Equipment Co., Union Trust Bldg. (Pneumatic Casting) ....G
Swain Co., F. J., 930 N. Main (Milling) ....B
Universal Cutter Co., 4565 Scott Av. (Knit Fabric) E
Whitman Agricultural Co. (Chaff; Ensilage; Fodder; Hay; Straw) ....AA
Zelnicker Supply Co., Walter A., 408 N. 4th (Continuous or Spline) X

NEBR.—Hastings
Rose, J. A. (Washer; Gasket) X

N. H.—Antrim
Goodell Co. (Chaff; Vegetable) ....

N. H.—Concord
Ford & Co., Wm. P. (Chaff; Ensilage; Fodder) ......B

N. J.—Elizabeth
Braunsdorf - Mueller Co. (Lace; Leather; Rod; Wire) ....D

N. J.—Gloucester
Rogers Boat, Gauge & Drill Wks., Jno. M. (Milling) A

N. J.—Newark
Bernz, Otto, S. 13th n. S. Orange Av. (Lead Pipe; Washer; Gasket; Registering &c.) ....B
Celluloid Co. (Paper) .B
Durand & Co. (Die) ....AA
Gould & Eberhardt, 95 N. J. R. R. Av. (Gang; Milling; Radial Duplex; Rack; Epicycloidal; Involute) A
Heinisch Sons Co., R. (Button Hole) ....A
Johnson, Wm., 249 Plane (Washer; Gasket) .....D
Kraeuter & Co., 577 18th Av. (Washer; Gasket; Button Hole) X
Natl. Saw Co. (Cork; Cloth; Leather; Paper; Slaw; Kraut) ....B
Obl & Co., G. A. (Bar) .B
Osborne & Co., C. S. (Champagne; Washer) .B
Smith Mfg. Co., A. P. (Cast Iron Pipe) ....B
Williamson Wire Novelty Co., C. T. (Champagne) B

N. J.—Paterson
Royle & Sons, John (Automatic Peg; Lac Hole)..A

N. J.—Riegelsville
Taylor, Stiles & Co. (Glue Stock; Moulding; Paper Stock; Rag; Shaper)...A

N. J.—Smithville
Smith Mach. Co., H. B. (Moulding) ....A

N. J.—Trenton
MacKenzie Sons Co., Duncan (Meat) ....A

N. Y.—Amsterdam
Inman Mfg. Co. (Boxmakers' Corner) ....A

N. Y.—Auburn
Osborne & Co., D. M. (Stalk) AAAA

N. Y.—Brooklyn
Bliss Co., E. W., 19 Adams (Sprue; Card; Boxmakers' Corner; Solder) ....AAAA
Oldham & Sons, Joshua (Inc.) 26th (Moulding) D
Williams & Co., J. H. (Pipe; Tube) ....AA

N. Y.—Buffalo
Buffalo Forge Co. (Metal Bar; Axle) ....AAAA
Eastman Machine Co., 45 N. Division (Cloth) ......B
Holmes Mch'r'y. Co., E. & B. (Lock) ....B
Howard Iron Wks. (Bolt; Paper) ....A
Niagara Mach. & Tool Wks.

CUTTERS (Con.)

(Gang; Metal Slitting; Rod; Wire; Bar) ......A
Oliver Mfg. Co., W. W., 1483 Niagara (Jewelers' Rod; Wire) C
Shepard & Co., Sidney (Cake; Biscuit) ..AAAA
Smith's Sons, John E. (Meat; Sausage Meat; Kraut; Core) ....B
White Co., L. & I. J. (Moulding) ....A

N. Y.—Cohoes
Beattie & Son, Wm. (Rib) D
Kennedy, Thos. (Knit Fabric) ....E

N. Y.—Cortland
Keator & Wells (Vehicle) C

N. Y.—Fulton
Dilts Machine Wks. (Automatic Ream; Rag) ....B

N. Y.—Gowanda
Gowanda Agr'l. Wks. Co. (Hand Feed) X

N. Y.—Greenwich
Eddy Plough Co., W. (Root; Chaff; Vegetable) .....B

N. Y.—Ithaca
Williams Bros. (Chaff) AA

N. Y.—Newburgh
Coldwell Lawn Mower Co. (Smoked Beef) ....A

New York City
Abbe Engineering Co. (Root) ....D
Alling & Co. (Cigar) ....AA
American Wood Working Mach. Co. (Moulding) AAAA
Ashcroft Mfg. Co., 85 Liberty (Pipe) ....A
Boker, Hermann & Co., 101 Duane (Wood Screw) AAA
Brunswick - Balke - Collender Co. (Cue) ......AAAA
Chatillon & Sons, J., 85 Cliff (Meat) ....A
Crandall & Godley (Cake; Biscuit; Candy) .....AA
Dickinson, J. (Est. of) (Glass; Diamond; Glass Tube) ....B
Erlandsen, Julius, 172 Centre (Milling) ....F
Fairbanks Co., 186 Elm (Pipe; Milling) ...AAAA
Garvin Machine Co., 137 Varick (Gear; Bolt; Milling) ....AA
Grote & Co., F. (Cue) .D
Hoe & Co., R. (Card; Rule; Lead) ....
Jenings Co., C. E., 42 Murray (Pipe; Tube)..B
Judd & Co., H. L. (Paper) AA
Kaldenberg Importing & Trading Co. (Cigar Butt) D
Kaufmann Bros. & Bondy (Cigar Tip) ....AA
Millers Falls Co., 28 Warren (Glass) ....AA
Niles-Bement-Pond Co., 136 Liberty (Bolt; Milling; Sprue; Stay-Bolt; Pipe; Tube) ....AAAA
Pels. & Co., Henry, 66 B'way (Bar) C
Russell & Erwin Mfg. Co. (Meat) ....AAAA
Sargent & Co., 151 Leonard (Meat) ....AAAA
Schwartz, Jos. (Cigar Butt) D
Shardlow, Joseph, 116 Fulton (Paper) ....D
Sheridan, T. W. & C. B. (Card; Bookmakers' Corner; Die; Round Corner) A
Singer Mfg. Co. (Button Hole) ....AAAA
Smith & Hemmenway Co., 296 B'way (Glass) ....D
Staubach, B. (Meat; Sausage; Vanilla Bean) ..A
Stimpson & Son, Edwin B. (Leather Strip; Shoe Lace) ....B
Thomson, W. S., 418 W. 27th (Moulding) ......F

CUTTERS (Con.)

Tower & Lyon Co. (Washer) ....B

Watson-Stilman Co. (Rod) ....A

N. Y.—Oswego
Oswego Tool Co. (Improved Three Wheel & One Wheel Pipe) ....B

N. Y.—Poughkeepsie
Lane Bros. Co. (Root; Vegetable) ....A

N. Y.—Richford
Hilts' Wrench & Mfg. Co. (Roll Paper) ....F

N. Y.—Rochester
Klip, Klip Co. (Finger Nail) ....B

Streeter & Co., N. R. (Roll Paper) ....A

N. Y.—Seneca Falls
Seneca Falls Mfg. Co. (Moulding) ....B

Westcott Jewell Co. (Advertising Paper) ....D

N. Y.—Stapleton
Warth, Mrs. G. (Cloth) ..B

N. Y.—Troy
Troy Carriage Wks. (Vehicle) C

Troy Stamping Co. (Cake; Biscuit) ....AAAA

N. Y.—Union Centre
Edson, Wyman L. (Vegetable; Root) ....H

N. Y.—Utica
Eureka Mower Co. (Hand Fodder) ....A

Smith & Co., D. B. (Hay; Chaff) ....B

Utica Drop Forge & Tool Co. (File) ....B

N. Y.—Warsaw
Warsaw-Wilkinson Co. (Ensilage) C

N. Y.—Waterford
Holroyd & Co. (Axle) ....A

King & Co., J. M. (Rod; Wire) ....A

N. Y.—Yonkers
Saunders Sons, D. (Boiler Tube; Lead Pipe; Tube; Pipe) ....A

N. C.—Greensboro
Glascock & Sons, G. T. (Feed) ....D

Sergeant Mfg. Co. (Chaff) ....D

N. C.—Statesville
Steele & Sons, J. C. (Brick) ....B

OHIO—Akron
Whitman & Barnes Mfg. Co. (Milling) ....AAAA

OHIO—Bucyrus
Amer. Clay Working Mach. Co. (Brick) X

OHIO—Canton
Bonnot Co. (Revolving Brick; Drain Tile) ....A

Dick Agri'l Wks., Jos. (Ensilage; Feed; Fodder; Chaff; Hay; Straw) ...A

Ney Mfg. Co. (Feed; Ensilage) ....B

OHIO—Cincinnati
American Tool Wks. Co., 6th & Eggleston (Bolt)...AA

Brickford Drill & Tool Co., Front & Pike (Milling Multiple Spindle) .....A

Cincinnati Milling Mach. Co. (Universal) ....AA

Cinn. Screw & Tap Co. (Milling) ....A

Day & Co., J. H. (Slaw; Kraut) ....A

Fay, J. A. & Egan Co. (Moulding) ....AAAA

Lunkenheimer Co., Beekman & Waverly (Gauge Glass) ....AA

Miller, L. J. (Vegetable; Root) X

Miller, Dubrul & Peters Mfg. Co. (Cigar) .....B

Obermayer Co., S., 647 Evans (Foundry) .....AA

Randall & Co. (Die) ....B

CUTTERS (Con.)

Tatum Co., Samuel C. (Washer) ....B

Triumph Elect. & Ice Mach. Co. (Electric Cloth) ....A

OHIO—Cleveland
Acme Machry. Co. (Bolt).. ....AA

Ajax Mfg. Co. (Bolt) ..AA

American Fork & Hoe Co. (Cabbage) ....AAAA

Chandler & Price Co. (Rule; Lead) ....A

Cleveland Twist Drill Co. (Milling) ....A

Reliance Mach. & Tool Co., 31 W. Center (Bolt) ...D

Standard Tool Co. (Angular; Convex; Concave; Milling; Spiral Mill; Sprocket).AA

OHIO—Columbus
Columbus Mach. Co. (Bolt) ....A

Jeffrey Mfg. Co. (Coal)... ....AAAA

OHIO—Cuyahoga Falls
Turner, Vaughan & Taylor Co. (Chain Link) .....B

OHIO—Dayton
National Automatic Tool Co. (Cane) ....D

Seybold Machine Co. (Boxmakers' Corner) ....A

OHIO—Tremont
Lehr Agr'l Co. (Feed; Stalk; Chaff) ....B

OHIO—Galion
Freese & Co., E. M. (Automatic Brick) ....A

OHIO—Hamilton
Advance Mfg. Co. (Chaff). X

Black & Clawson Co. (Automatic Ream; Paper Stock; Rag; Stop) ..AAA

Long & Allstatter Co. (Chaff; Ensilage; Fodder) ....AA

Meyers Mfg. Co., Fred. J. (Cigar Butt) ....B

Niles Tool Wks. Co. (Bolt) .. ..AAAA

OHIO—Lancaster
Eagle Machine Co. (Chaff; Ensilage; Fodder) ....A

Hocking Valley Mfg. Co. (Chaff) ....A

OHIO—Massillon
Harrison & Co., W. R. (Fodder) ....B

OHIO—Middletown
McSherry Mfg. Co. (Chaff) ....A

OHIO—Norwood
Cinn. Tool Co. (Washer; Gasket) ....B

OHIO—Piqua
Champion Paper Cutter Co. (Paper) X

OHIO—Salem
Silver Mfg. Co. (Power Ensilage; Hand; Power Feed; Chaff; Hay; Straw; Fodder; Lever Feed)..AA

OHIO—Sebring
Farmers Mfg. Co. (Feed).X

OHIO—Springfield
Ross Co., E. W. (Ensilage; Feed; Chaff; Fodder; Hay; Straw; Vegetable; Root) ....A

Webster & Perks Tool Co. (Bolt) C

OHIO—Tiffin
National Mchry. Co. (Bolt; Pipe; Tube) ....AA

OHIO—Toledo
Baker Bros. (Key-Way)..A

PA.—Bausman
Bausman, David H. (Corn) C

PA.—Beaver Falls
Emerson, Smith & Co. (Ltd.) (Molding) ......A

PA.—Elizabethtown
Buch's Sons, A. (Chaff; Vegetable; Root) ......A

CUTTERS (Con.)

PA.—Ellwood City

Standard Eng. Co. (Bolt) .. AA

PA.—Erie

Erie Specialty Co. (Rod; Wire; Cigar; Cigar Tip)B

Hollands Mfg. Co. (Pipe) .B

Reed Mfg. Co. (Pipe) ....A

PA.—Harrisburg

Hickok Mfg. Co., W. O. Rotary Board; Round Corner) ....AA

PA.—Lancaster

Mast Mfg. Co., J. M. (Slaw) X

PA.—Lansdale

Heebner & Sons (Ensilage; Fodder) ....

PA.—Mechanicsburg

Comstock, Geo. S. (Chaff; Ensilage; Fodder; Hay; Straw; Stalk) C

PA.—Millersburg

Polk & Son, A. J. (Milling; Side) C

PA.—Mount Joy

Rollman Mfg. Co. (Apple; Meat; Potatoes) ......G

PA.—Norristown

Wildman Mfg. Co. (Knit Fabric; Rib) ....A

PA.—Philadelphia

Altemas, Jacob, 2816 N. 4th (Chenille) C

Anderson & Co., J. P. (Candy) X

Andress, Thos. J., 821 Cherry (Glass) X

Bonny Vice & Tool Wks., 3015 Chestnut (Glass; Washer; Gasket) C

Carver Co., Cephas R. (Rule; Lead) X

Chambers Bros. Co., 52nd below Lancaster Av. (Bolt; Round Corner; Board) ....AA

Disston & Sons, Henry (Inc.) (Screw Slotting; Saw Gummer; Cork; Cloth; Leather; Paper; Slaw; Kraut) .....AAAA

Enterprise Mfg. Co., 3rd (Tobacco, hand for counter use; Vegetable; Root; Meat; Slaw; Kraut).... AAAA

Lever, Oswald, Lehigh Av. & Masher (Chenille) ..C

Mills & Bro., Thomas, 1301 N. 8th. (Vegetable) ...A

Moore & White Co. (Paper) AA

Morris, P. H. (Pipe; Tube) C

Natl. Specialty Mfg. Co. (Tobacco) ....AA

Newton Machine Tool Wks. (Inc.), 2343 Vine (Milling; Perforated for Internal Lubrication) ..AA

Nittinger, August (Meat; Slaw; Kraut) ....A

North Bros. Mfg. Co., Lehigh Av. & America (Hand; Tobacco; Meat).. AA

Pancoast & Co., H. B., 243 S. 3rd (Gauge Glass; Pipe) ....B

Phila. Novelty Mfg. Co. (Washer) ....D

Phila. Roll & Machine Co., 23rd & Washington Av. (Pinion) ....A

Sellers & Co., Wm. (Inc.), 1600 Hamilton (Bolt; Milling) ....AAAA

Stortz & Son, Jno., 210 Vine (Glass; Washer; Gasket) E

Stow Flexible Shaft Co., N. 26th & Buttonwood (Boiler Tube; Stay-Bolt)B

Underwood & Co., H. B., 1023 Hamilton (Stay-Bolt) B

Waterall & Co., Wm., 200 N. 4th (Fillet) ....A

CUTTERS (Con.)

Woodhouse, Sam'l F. (Liquid; Paste Fillet) ....D

PA.—Pittsburg

Nuttall & Co., H. (Milling) A

PA.—Reading

Penn. Hardware Co. (Tobacco, hand for Counter) AA

Reading Standard Cycle Mfg. Co. (W. F. Remppis) (Milling Face, etc.)B

PA.—Scranton

Hunt, Alex. E., 434 Lack. Av. (Gauge Glass) .....B

PA.—Tatamy

Messinger Mfg. Co. (Ensilage; Fodder; Chaff; Hand; Power Feed) ...B

PA.—Wrightsville

Wrightsville Hdw. Co. (Tobacco, hand for counter)B

PA.—York

Farquhar Co., A. B. (Feed; Chaff; Hay; Straw).AAA

Keystone Farm Mach. Co. (Hand; Power Feed; Ensilage; Fodder; Hay; Straw) ....B

Spangler Mfg. Co. (Feed; Chaff; Hay; Straw) ...C

R. I.—Providence

Brown & Sharpe Mfg. Co. Angular; Convex; Concave; Gear; Milling; Screw; Slotting; Spiral Mill; Sprocket; T-Slot; Tape; Reamer; Twist Drill; Worm Wheel; Involute; Epicycloidal; Chain Link) ......AAAA

Johnson & Co., C. A. (Cloth) D

New England Pearl Co. (Paper) ....F

Standard Mchry. Co. (Jewelers') ....B

Thurston Mfg. Co. (Jewelers') C

VT.—Bennington

Cooper, Chas. (Rib) ......B

VT.—Derby Lane

Butterfield & Co. (Axle; Pipe; Gummer) ......A

VT.—St. Albans

St. Albans Fdry. & Implement Co.(Ensilage; Stalk; Fodder) ....D

VT.—Woodstock

Daniels Machine Co. (Paper Stock) ....F

VA.—Danville

Westbrooks Fdry. & Mach. Co., J. B. (Feed) ......F

VA.—Norfolk

White & Bro., S. R. (Feed) A

Whitehurst Co., R. W. (Root; Vegetable) .....B

VA.—Richmond

Cardwell Mach Co. (Hay; Straw) ....A

WIS.—Beloit

Beloit Iron Wks. (Automatic Ream; Stop) ...A

Berlin Machine Wks. (Excelsior) ....AAAA

WIS.—Eau Claire

McDonough Mfg. Co. (Excelsior) ....A

WIS.—Manitowoc

Smalley Mfg. Co. (Ensilage; Feed; Chaff; Fodder; Hay; Straw; Vegetable; Root) ....B

WIS.—Milwaukee

Chain Belt Co. (Bolt) ....B

Milwaukee Fdry. Supply Co., 258 Lake (Fillet)...F

WIS.—North Milwaukee

Luther Bros. Co. (old Rubber) C

WIS.—Racine

Belle City Mfg. Co. (Ensilage; Feed; Chaff; Hay; Straw; Root; Vegetable; Lever Feed) ....B

Case Plow Wks., J. I. (Stalk) ....AAA

CUTTERS (Con.)

Foster & Williams Mfg. Co.
 (Ensilage; Fodder) ....B
Freeman & Son Mfg. Co., S.
 (Feed; Chaff; Ensilage;
 Fodder; Hay; Straw; Lev-
 er Feed) ....A
WIS.—Sheboygan
Kohler Sons Co., J. M.
 (Chaff; Ensilage; Fodder;
 Hay; Straw) ....A
WIS.—Whitewater
Merriam, I. Z. (Corn) ...E

CYANIDE

New York City
Roessler & Hasslacher
 Chemical Co., 100 William
 AA
PA.—Philadelphia
Harrison Bros. & Co. (Inc.),
 35th & Gray's Ferry Road
 (of Soda) ....AAAA

CYCLOME-TERS

CONN.—Bristol
New Departure Bell Co....A
CONN.—Hartford
Veeder Mfg. Co. (Bicycle)B
CONN.—Waterbury
New England Watch Co..AA
ILL.—Chicago
McDonnell Odometer Co..X
N. J.—Trenton
Trenton Watch Co. .....A
New York City
Graham & Co., J. H., 113
 Chambers ....AA

CYLINDERS

ALA.—Birmingham
Dimmick Pipe Co. (Com-
 press) ....A
ILL.—Batavia
Challenge Wind Mill & Feed
 Mill Co. (Brass; Pump)
 A
U. S. Wind Engine & Pump
 Co. (Brass; Iron; Pump)
 A
ILL.—Chicago
Aermotor Co. (Pump) .AAA
Fairbanks, Morse & Co. ..
 AAAA
Temple Pump Co. (Pump).A
ILL.—Freeport
Woodmanse & Hewitt Mfg.
 Co. (Pump) ....B
ILL.—Sandwich
Sandwich Mfg. Co. (Pump)
 AA
ILL.—Sterling
Novelty Iron Wks. (Pump)
 X
IND.—Anderson
Hill Machine Co. (Pump).D
IND.—Kendallville
Flint & Walling Mfg. Co.
 (Foster; Iron; Pump)..AA
IOWA—Davenport
Red Jacket Mfg. Co.
 (Pump) ....B
IOWA—Dubuque
A. Y. McDonald & Morri-
 son Mfg. Co. (Br. Cent.
 Fdry. Co., N. Y. City,
 N. Y.) (Pump) ...AAAA
MD.—Baltimore
Poole & Son Co., Robt.
 (Iron) ....A
MASS.—Boston
National Tube Wks. Co.
 (Br. U. S. Steel Corpn.)
 (Iron; Steel) .....AAAA
MASS.—Chicopee Falls
Lamb Mfg. Co. (Needle)..B
MASS.—Westfield
Crane Bros. (Linenoid Seam-
 less) ....AAA
MASS.—Worcester
Wheeler Fdry. Co. (Engine)
 D
MICH.—Detroit
Detroit Lubricator Co.
 (Locomotive) ....AA

CYLINDERS (Con.)

NEBR.—Beatrice
Dempster Mill Mfg. Co.
 (Pump) ....A
N. J.—Belleville
Eastwood Wire Mfg. Co.
 (Papermakers') ....A
N. J.—Jersey City
Eastern Carbon Wks. (Car-
 bon) ....A
N. Y.—Brooklyn
Continental Iron Wks.
 (Welded Steel; Iron) ..X
N. Y.—Dunkirk
Brooks Locomotive Wks.
 (Br. Amer. Locomotive
 Wks., N. Y. City) (Loco-
 motive) ....AAAA
N. Y.—Little Falls
Stafford & Holt (Knitting
 Machine) ....B
New York City
Cent. Foundry Co. (Pump)..
 AAAA
Int. Steam Pump Co.
 (Pump) ....AAAA
Koven & Bro., L. O., 50
 Cliff (Hydraulic) .....A
U. S. Cast Iron Pipe &
 Fdry. Co. 80 B'way
 (Large Cast Iron) ....A
Worthington Pumping En-
 gine Co. (Br. Int. Steam
 Pump Co.) (Pump).AAAA
N. Y.—Seneca Falls
Rumsey & Co. (Ltd.)
 (Pump) ....A
OHIO—Cleveland
Avery Stamping Co. ....A
Tyler Wire Wks. Co., W.
 S. (Papermakers') ...AA
OHIO—Hamilton
Black & Clawson Co.
 (Papermakers') ......AA
OHIO—Warren
Trumbull Mfg. Co. (Gaso-
 line Engine) C
OHIO—Youngstown
Pollock Co., W. B. (Ammo-
 nia; Carbolic Acid) ....B
PA.—Harrisburg
Harrisburg Pipe & Pipe
 Bending Co. (Anhydrous;
 Ammonia; Carbolic Acid
 Gas; Iron) ....AA
PA.—Philadelphia
Branson Machine Co., 506
 N. American (Knitting
 Machine; Needle) ......A
Cook, Stephen S., 624 Race
 (Knitting Machine;
 Forged Steel; also Dials)
 F
Janney, Stimmetz & Co.,
 Drexel Bldg. (Cold Drawn
 Seamless Steel; also
 Tanks) ....D
Paxton & O'Neil, 127
 Bread (Knitting Machine)
 A
Phila. Steel & Iron Co.
 (Steel Hydraulic) .....B
Phoenix Bridge Co. (Iron)A
PA.—Pittsburg
National Tube Co. (Ammo-
 nia; Carbolic Acid) .AAA
Scaiffe & Sons Co., Wm. B.,
 221 1st Av. (Calcium
 Light; Hydraulic; Hydro-
 gen; Oxygen; Ammonia;
 Carbolic Acid; Steel) ..A
Sterrit-Thomas Fdry. Co.,
 32nd & Smallwood (Hy-
 draulic) ....A
PA.—South Bethlehem
Bethlehem Fdry. & Machine
 Co. (Ammonia; Carbolic
 Acid) C
PA.—Washington
Petroleum Iron Wks. Co.
 (Caisson) ....B
PA.—Wilkesbarre
Vulcan Iron Wks. (Iron;
 Engine) ....AAAA
R. I.—Providence
Hill Mfg. Co., Jas. (Spin-
 ning) ....B
WIS.—Beloit
Beloit Iron Wks. (Paper-
 makers') ....A

CYLINDERS (Con.)
WIS.—Milwaukee
Pressed Steel Tank Co. (Calcium Light; Hydrogen; Oxygen; Seamless Steel; also Shells; Tanks) X

CYMBALS
See Musical Instruments

CYPRESS
See Lumber

DADOS
ILL.—Chicago
Phoenix Trimming Co., 577 Clybourn Av. ....D
MASS.—Boston
Mathews Consolidated Slate Co., 199 Washington (Slate) X

DAMASK
See Cotton Goods

DAMPENERS
See Machinery; Laundry.

DAMPERS
ILL.—Freeport
Arcade Mfg. Co. (Stove; Pipe) ....B
Stover Mfg. Co. (Stove)..A
IOWA—Dubuque
Adams Co. (Stove) ......B
MASS.—Boston
Howes Co.. S. M. (Pipe)..C
MASS.—Milford
Milford Iron Foundry (Stoveplace) C
MO.—St. Louis
Pleuger & Henger Mfg. Co. (Pipe) ....A
N. Y.—Albany
Troy Nickel Wks. (Stove; Pipe) C
N. Y.—Buffalo
Shepard & Co., Sidney (Stove) ....AAAA
N. Y.—Manlius
Cheney & Son, S. (Pipe).A
New York City
Jackson & Bro., Edwin A., 50 Beekman (Fireplace, etc.) C
Peck. Stow & Wilcox Co., 27 Murray (Pipe)..AAAA
Tuttle & Bailey Mfg. Co. (Stove) ....A
N. Y.—Utica
Millar & Son, Chas. (Stove) ....AA
OHIO—Cleveland
Fanner Mfg. Co. (Pipe) ..A
Taylor & Boggis Fdry. Co. (Pipe) ....AA
OHIO—Columbus
Patton Mfg. Co. (Stove).X
OHIO—Plymouth
Root Bros. Co. (Pipe) ...B
OHIO—Ravenna
Williams, A. C. (Pipe)...A
PA.—Erie
Griswold Mfg. Co. (Stove) ....A
PA.—Philadelphia
Berger Bros. Co. (Stove).A
W. VA.—Fairmount
Hemlock Fdry. & Machine Co. (Coke Oven) ......D

DAMS
MASS.—Andover
Tyer Rubber Co. (Rubber) ....AA
N. J.—Menlo Park
Elliott Mfg. Co. (Dental) X
New York City
Hodgman Rubber Wks. 806 Bway. (Rubber) ...AA
Kleinert Rubber Co., I. B., 725 Bway (Dental) .....A
OHIO—Cleveland
Cleveland Rubber Co.

DAMS (Con.)
(Rubber) ....AAAA
R. I.—Providence
Davol Rubber Co. (Dental) AA

DARNERS
MASS.—North Attleboro
Gilbert, F. S. (Glove) ...D
New York City
Estes & Son, E. B. 45 John (Stocking) ....AA
OHIO—Akron
Baker, McMillan Co. (Glove; Stocking) ....B

DASHERS
MICH.—Bellaire
Richards & Bechtold (Churn) ....B
MICH.—Kalkaska
Freeman Mfg. Co. (Churn) B
N. J.—Hoboken
Woodman, Joel H. (Sleigh) A

DASHES
See Woodwork; Carriage.

DATES
See Figs & Dates

DAUBERS
See Brushes

DAVENPORT
See Furniture

CONN.—Mt. Carmel
Woodruff & Sons Co. (Screen) ....A
New York City
Mundt & Sons, Chas. (Screen) ....B

DECAL-COMANIE
ILL.—Chicago
Meyercord Co.. 618 Chamber of Commerce ....A
Palm, Fechteler & Co. ..A
N. J.—Hoboken
American Decalcomanie Wks. ....D
OHIO—Cincinnati
Palm Bros. & Co. (Inc.) A
PA.—Philadelphia
Nat'l. Decalcomanie Co. .F

DECANTERS
See Glassware

DECKING
FLA.—Pensacola
Thornton. H. H. (Ship) ..F
GA.—Savannah
Southern Pine Co. of Ga. (Car) ....AAA
N. C.—Abbotsburg
Cashwell, J. C. (Ship) ...F
OHIO—Toledo
Smith & Co., W. H. H. (Ship) ....B
TEXAS—Houston
Emporia Lumber Co. (Car) AAA
WASH.—Tacoma
Washington Mfg. Co. (Porch; Ship) ....E

DECKS
MICH.—Bay City
Garland Co., M. (Log) ...C
VT.—Montpelier
Lane Mfg. Co. (Log) ....A
WIS.—Milwaukee
Filer & Stowell Co. (Ltd.) (Log) ....AAA

DECORATIONS
CONN.—Beacon Falls
Bronson Co.. Homer D. (Bronze; Silver Plate) C

DECORATIONS (Con.)
CONN.—Hartford
Root, C. R., 286 Sheldon
(Plastic Relief) ......G
ILL.—Chicago
Architectural Decorating Co.
204 Illinois (Carton Pierre;
Plastic Relief; Theatre)
........................C
Decorators' Supply Co.,
209-219 S. Clinton (Carton
Pierre; Plastic Relief;
Theatre) ....B
Plastic Relief Mfg. Co., 298
N. Halsted (Carton
Pierre; Plastic Relief;
Theatre) ....E
MASS.—Boston
Dolan, W. J., 181 Tremont
(Church) ....E
Emmel, Chas., 383 Albany
(Carton Pierre; Plastic
Relief; Theatre) ......B
Vogt & Sons, Paul, 97 Haverhill (Plastic Relief) ..A
MICH.—Detroit
Bailey Co., 224 21st (Plastic
Relief) ....E
MO.—St. Louis
Siefert, Frank A. (Carton
Pierre; Plastic Relief;
Theatre) ....D
N. J.—New Brunswick
Janeway & Carpenter
(Ceiling) ....AA
N. Y.—Brooklyn
Arnold & Locke, 250 Fulton (Theatre) ....A
Forman Bros., 645 Gates Av.
(Plastic Relief).....D
Halbert, G. & W., 455 Fulton (Church; Theatre) .F
Heilmann Co., R., 207 State
(Carton Pierre; Church;
Plastic Relief; Theatre)
........................E
New York City
Benziger Bros., 36 & 38
Barclay (Church) .....A
Church Glass & Decorating
Co., 253 4th Av. (Theatre)
........................B
Fuchs, Henry, 34 W. 37th
(Theatrical) ....D
Geissler, R., 56 W. 8th
(Church) ....F
Koster Co., C. H. (for Celebrations) ....D
Lamb, J. & R., 59 Carmine
(Church; Ceiling) ....A
Righter & Kold, 156 5th Av.
(Church; Plastic; Relief;
Theatre) ....E
Rudolph, Oscar, 3 Marion
(Carton Pierre) ......D
Stoltzenberg Co., 51 Barclay
(Church) ....B
Tiffany Studios, 333 4th Av.
(Church) ....AA
N. Y.—Syracuse
Wood Glass Co., 226 N. Salina (Church) C
OHIO—Cincinnati
Marks Plaster Ornament
Mfg. Co., W. A., 726 W.
5th (Carton Pierre) ....E
PA.—Philadelphia
Busse Sculptured Leather
Co., 1221 Samson ......F
De Planque, F. R., 1349
Ridge Av. (Carton Pierre;
Plastic Relief; Theatre) D
Whitman & Co., J. Franklin,
212 S. 5th (Carton Pierre;
Plastic Relief) C

DECOYS
ILL.—Monmouth
Allen, F. A. ....F
MICH.—Detroit
Dodge, Jasper N. ....E
TENN.—Union City
Canvass Decoy Co. (Ducks,
etc.) ....E

DEERSKINS
See Leather

DEES
CONN.—New Britain
North & Judd Mfg. Co.
(Breeching; Harness; Riv-

DEES (Con.)
et) ....AA
CONN.—New Haven
North & Co., O. B. (Harness) ....AA
N. J.—Newark
Jenkinson & Co., R. C. ..AA
OHIO—Canton
Elbel Co. (Breeching; Halter; Harness; Hull) .....B
OHIO—Cleveland
Eberhard Mfg. Co. (Harness) ....AA

DEFECATORS
594 DEFECATORS
CONN.—Ansonia
Farrell Fdry. & Machine Co.
......................AAAA
DEL.—Wilmington
Pusey & Jones Co. ....AAA
ILL.—Chicago
Wolf Co., Fred. W., 139
Rees ....AA
KANS.—Fort Scott
Fort Scott Fdry. & Machine
Co. (Chas. Eller) ......H
LA.—New Orleans
Haubtman & Loeb Co.
(Ltd.) 217 Gravier ....A
Murphy, Jno. H., 643
Magazine ....A
Payne & Joubert, 433 Carondelet C
N.J.—Jersey City
Flynn, W. S., 74 Hudson ..D
N. Y.—Brooklyn
Pioneer Iron Wks., 151 William ....A
N. Y.—Buffalo
Squier Mfg. Co., Geo. L.,
420 Niagara (Sugar) ...A
N. Y.—Newburgh
Coldwell-Wilcox Co. .....B
New York City
Cornell Co., J. B. & J. M.,
26th & 11th Av. ......AA
Deeley & Co., Robert, 507
W. 32d ....AA
Krajewski-Pesant Co., 32
Bway. (Sugar) ....A
Reilly Repair & Supply Co.,
Jas., 229 West (Sugar)
......................AA
Turl's Sons, Jno., 534 W.
28th ....A
OHIO—Cincinnati
Blymyer Iron Wks. Co.
(Sugar) ....D
OHIO—Cleveland
Kilby Mfg. Co. ....AA
PA.—Philadelphia
Morris, Henry G. (Phila.
Bourse) ....F

DEFLECTORS
New York City
Reconstructed Granite Co.,
14 Dey (Arc for Controllers) C

DEGERMINATORS
IND.—Indianapolis
Nordyke & Mormon Co.,
(Corn) ....AA
OHIO—Columbus
Case Mfg. Co. (Corn) ...AA

DEGRAS
MASS.—Boston
Leonard & Co., Geo. H. ..A
New York City
Fuerst Bros. & Co. ......D
Klipstein & Co.. A ......AA

DEHORNERS
ILL.—Chicago
Pratt Mfg. Co., 91 Lake
(Cattle) ....B
ILL.—Decatur
Brown Mfg. Co., H. H.
(Cattle) ....D
IND.—Lawrenceburg
Bishop & Co., Geo. H. (Cattle) ....A
MO.—Kansas City
Russell Hdw. & Implement
Mfg. Co. X

DELAINES

See Cotton Goods

DEMAGNET-
IZERS

IND.—South Bend
Knoblock-Heideman Mfg.
Co. (Watch) ....D
MASS.—Brookline
Holtzer-Cabot Electric Co.
(Watch) ....B
New York City
Green & Co., W., 6 Maiden
Lane ....B
Jones & Son J., 64 Cortlandt
X

DEMIJOHNS

See also Carboys; Bottles.

New York City
Boley Mfg. Co., 52 Cannon D
Brookfield Glass Co., 220
Bway. ....B
N. Y.—Poughkeepsie
Poughkeepsie Glass Wks...A
PA.—Philadelphia
Burgin & Son Glass Co...A

DENIMS

See Cotton Goods

DENTRIFICE

See Powder; Tooth.

DEPILA-
TORIES

CONN.—Hartford
Bailey Mfg. Co. C
New York City
Recamier Mfg. Co. ....F
Stone, Tunlow & Co., 4 Warren ....A
PA.—Philadelphia
Fricke, Arthur C

DE-RAILS

ILL.—Chicago
Pneumatic Gate Co., 100
Wash. (Street Railway) D
MICH.—Kalamazoo
Kalamazoo Railway Supply
Co. (Street Railway) ...B
MICH.—Three Rivers
Sheffield Car Co. (Street
Railway) ....AA
N. J.—Hoboken
New York Switch & Crossing
Co. (Street Railway) ...A

DERRICKS

CAL.—San Francisco
Hendy Machine Wks.,
Joshua ....AA
CAL.—Stockton
Shaw Plow Wks., H. C.
(Hay) ....A
GA.—Augusta
Lombard Iron Wks. & Supply Co. (Hay).........A
ILL.—Batavia
U. S. Wind Engine & Pump
Co. (Hay) ....A
ILL.—Chicago
Carpenter & Co., Geo. B.
(Construction) .....AA
Shaw, Willis, N. Y. Life
Bldg. (Traveling) .....D
Vulcan Iron Wks., 57 Milwaukee Av. (Pile Driving;
Coal) ....AA
ILL.—Ottawa
Porter Co., J. E. (Hay)..A
IND.—New Albany
New Albany Mfg. Co.
(Steam) C
KANS.—Fort Scott
Ft. Scott Fdry. & Machine
Co. (C. Eller) (Mining;
Quarry) ....H
KY.—Louisville
Brennan & Co. (Construction) ....AA
Vogt Machine Co., Henry
(Revolving Steam)....AA

DERRICKS (Con.)
MICH.—Bay City
Industrial Wks. (Construction) ....AA
MICH.—Detroit
Northern Engineering Wks.
A
MINN.—St. Paul
American Hoist & Derrick
Co. (Traveling) ....A
MO.—St. Louis
Broderick & Bascom Rope
Co. ....AA
Leschen & Sons Rope Co., A.
AAA

N. J.—Jersey City
Smith & Sons Co., Theodore,
ft. of Essex (Pile Driving;
Wrecking) ....A
N. J.—Newark
Mundy, J. S., 22 Prospect. A
N. Y.—Albany
Osgood Dredge Co. (Construction) ....A
N. Y.—Brooklyn
Pollard. Jos. G., 141 Raymond (Ash Hoisting) ...F
N. Y.—Buffalo
Contractors' Plant Mfg. Co.,
127 Erie (Pile Driving;
Steam; Construction) ...B
N. Y.—Dunkirk
Brooks Locomotive Wks.
(Br. Amer. Loco. Wks., N.
Y. City) (Wrecking)
AAAA
N. Y.—Lockport
Norman & Evans (Steam), B
New York City
American Locomotive Wks.
Wrecking) ....AAAA
Dobie Fdry. & Machine Co.,
42 Dey (Pile Driving;
Steam; Traveling) ....D
Hayward Co., 97 Cedar
(Traveling) ....B
Lidgerwood Mfg. Co. 96
Liberty (Pile Driving;
Mining; Quarry) ....AAA
New Jersey Fdry. & Mach.
Co. ....D
N. Y.—Schenectady
General Electric Co. (Electrical) ....AAAA
OHIO—Akron
Webster Camp & Lane Machine Co. (Revolving
Steam) ....A
OHIO—Alliance
Morgan Engineering Co.
(Traveling; Electric)..AA
OHIO—Cleveland
Kaltenbach & Griess (Steam;
Traveling) ....B
McMyler Mfg. Co., 180 Columbus (Steam; Ore; Revolving Steam) ....A
OHIO—Warren
Excelsior Hoisting Mchry.
Co. (Pile Driving; Steam;
Traveling; Wrecking)..X
PA.—Allegheny
Carlin's Sons, Thos. (Coal;
Construction; Pile; Wooden) ....A
PA.—Nazareth
Nazareth Fdry. & Mach. Co.
B
PA.—Pittsburg
Oil Well Supply Co. (Steel;
Wooden) ....AAAA
Riter-Conly Mfg. Co. ...AAA
PA—Reading
Reading Crane &Hoist Wks.
(Portable Folding) C
Sneidel, J. G. ....D
TENN.—Memphis
Bodley Wagon Co. (Crane)
A
VT.—Barre
Whitcomb Bros. (Boom)..F
VT.—Rutland
Patch Mfg. Co., F. R. ....A
WIS—Racine
Case Threshing Machine Co.,
J. J. (Construction) AAAA

DERRINGERS

See Fire Arms

DESIGNS

MASS.—Worcester
National Mfg. Co. (Floral
Wire) ....A

DESIGNS (Con.)
Wright Wire Co. (Floral Wire) ....AA
New York City
Jansen, Edward (Florists') ....A
OHIO—Cincinnati
Griffith & Sons, Jas. (Floral Wire) ....A
OHIO—Dayton
Dayton Art Glass Wks. (Art Glass) ....F
OHIO—Hamilton
Meyers Mfg. Co., Fred. J. (Floral Wire) ....B
TEXAS—Dallas
Cunningham, I. E. (Odd Furniture) ....D

DESKS

See Furniture

DESTROYERS

MASS.—Chicopee Falls
Belcher & Taylor Agr'l Tool Co. (Potato Bug) ......A
New York City
Adler Color & Chemical Wks. (Potato Bug) ....A

DETACHERS

N. Y.—Troy
Trojan Button Fastener Co. (Inc.) (Button) ......B

DETECTORS

See also Watches

IND.—Ft. Wayne
Fort Wayne Electric Wks. (Ground) ....AA
MASS.—Boston
Boston Electric Co. 29 Harrison (Ground; Battery) B
MASS.—Pittsfield
Stanley Electric Mfg. Co. (Ground) ....AA
N. H.—Penacook
Whitney Electrical Mfg. Co. (Ground) ....D
New York City
American Watchman's Time Detector Co., 234 & 235 Bway. (Time) ....F
Empire Elect. Instrument Co., 656 Hudson (Ground) D
Kinsman Elec. & Railway Supply Co., 91 Liberty (Phonoscopic or Electric) E
N. Y.—Schenectady
General Electric Co. (Ground) ....AAAA
N. Y.—Syracuse
S. E. I. Co. (Ground) X
N. Y.—Utica
Utica Electrical Mfg. & Supply Co. (Ground)...X
PA.—Philadelphia
Keystone Elec. Instrument Co., 901 Montgomery Av. (Ground) ....B

DETINNING

New York City
Vulcan Detinning Co., 157 Cedar (Tin Scrap) .....A

DEVELOPERS

MO.—St. Louis
Cramer Dry Plate Co., G. (Photo. Eikonogen; Pyro) A
Hammer Dry Plate Co., Ohio Av. & Miami (Powder)..A
New York City
Tolmer & Schwing Mfg. Co., 407 Broome (Photographic) ....B
Gennert, G. (Photo. Eikonogen; Pyro) ....B

DEVICES

CONN.—Hartford
Whitney Mfg. Co. (Wheel Truing for Water Tool Grinders ....B

DEVICES (Con.)
IND.—Anderson
Hill Tool Co. (Crank Turning) ....E
IND.—Fort Wayne
Fort Wayne Electric Corpn. (Truing; Commutator) AA
MICH.—Ovid
Folding Casket Lowering Device Co. (Coffin Lowering) E
N. J.—Irvington
Howlett & Co., J. (Lead Sealing) ....B
N. J.—Vineland
Gage Tool Co. (Truing & Bench Plane) ....A
OHIO—Cincinnati
Globe-Wernicke Co. (Filing) AAAA
OHIO—Fremont
Simple Account File Co. (Filing) ....B
PA.—Philadelphia
Standard Elevator Interlock Co., S. Girard Bldg. (Elevator) ....F
WIS.—Racine
Bishop & Son, A. W. (Fish Reel Spooling) ....B

DEXTRINE

See also Starch

DEL.—Wilmington
Delaware Glue Co. ....B
ILL.—Chicago
Fuller & Fuller ....AAA
MD.—Baltimore
Bloede Co., Victor G.......B
MASS.—Boston
Glover & Son, H. N., 355 River C
New York City
National Gum & Mica. Co., 502 W. 45th ....A

DIALS

CONN.—Waterbury
Waterbury Clock Co. (Clock; Watch; Meter) .....AAA
MASS.—Boston
Thaxter & Son, S. (Sun) .B
MASS.—Waltham
O'Hara Waltham Dial Co. (Watch; Meter; Clock) .B
N. J.—Newark
Plumb, D. S. (Watch; Clock; Meter) ....D
N. Y.—Brooklyn
Manhattan Dial Co. (Enameled Clock) ....E
New York City
Caesar Bros. (Watch; Meter; Clock; Instrument)....D
VA.—Norfolk
Whitehurst & Co., R. W. (Instrument) ....B

DIAMONDS

See Jewelry

DIAPERS

CONN.—Bridgeport
Canfield Rubber Co. (Rubber) ....AA
MASS.—Andover
Tyre Rubber Co. (Rubber) AA
New York City
Goodyear India Rubber Glove Mfg. Co. (Rubber) AAAA
Goodyear Rubber Co. (Rubber) ....AAAA
Kleinert Rubber Co., I. B., 795 Bway. (Rubber) ...A
R. I.—Providence
Davol Rubber Co. (Rubber) AA

DIAPHORETIC

N. Y.—Brooklyn
Wiarda & Co., Jno. C. (Antimony) ....AA

DIAPHRAGMS

ILL.—Chicago

DIAPHRAGMS (Con.)

Railway. Appliances Co.,
Old Colony Bldg. (Car), A
Ward Co., E. J., 100 Lake
(Car, made from Cotton
Belting) ....D
Wood & Co., G. S., 100 Lake
(Car, sewed or sewed &
riveted) ....D

MASS.—Boston

Boston Belting Co., 256 Devonshire (Vestibule; Car;
Rubber) ....AAAA

MASS.—Cambridge

Boston Woven Hose & Rub-
ber Co. (Rubber)...AAAA

New York City

Gutta Percha & Rubber.Mfg.
Co. (Rubber) ......AAAA
New York Belting & Pack-
ing Co. (Rubber) ....AAA
New York Rubber Co., 84
Reade (Rubber) ......AA

OHIO—Cleveland

National Carbon Co. (Telephone) ....AAAA

R. I.—Providence

Davol Rubber Co. (Rubber)
AA

DIARIES

MASS.—Cambridge

Cambridgeport Diary Co....A

WIS.—Milwaukee

Milwaukee Blank Book Mfg.
Co. (Vest Pocket) ......B

DIATESE

MICH.—Detroit

Parke. Davis & Co. ..AAAA

DICE

See Games

DICTIONA-RIES

ILL.—Chicago

Laird & Lee, 263 Wabash
Av. ....A

MASS.—Springfield

Merriam Co., G. & C.......A

New York City

Funk & Wagnalls Co., 30 Lafayette Place........AAA

PA.—Philadelphia

Syndicate Publishing Co.,
234 S. 8th ....A

DIES

See Plates

COLO—Denver

Denver Novelty Works &
Electric Co. ....E

CONN.—Bridgeport

American Tube & Stamping
Co. ....AAA
Armstrong Mfg. Co. (Pipe;
also Stocks; Pipe Thread-
ing) ....A
Connecticut Tool Co. (&
Stocks; Adjustable; Pipe
Threading) ....D
Curtis & Curtis Co. (Pipe)
A
Hatheway Mfg. Co. .....E
Schwerdtle Stamp Co. (Or-
namental; Embossing;
Stencil) ....G

CONN.—Bristol

Smith, Ira B. (Cutting;
Stamping) ....E

CONN.—East Hampton

Brown & Co., H. B. (Bolt
Threading) ....E

CONN.—Hartford

Billings & Spencer Co.
(Screw Plate; Stocks)..A
Hartford Machine Screw Co.
(Automatic) ......AAAA
Sigourney Tool Co. (Cut-
ting) ....A
Pratt & Whitney Co. (Ad-
justable Expanding; Cut-
ting; Stamping; Opening;
Punching: also Stocks;
Solid Pipe) ......AAAA
Tucker, W. W. & C. F., 302

DIES (Con.)

Asylum (Cutting; Stamp-
ing; Opening) ....F

CONN.—New Haven

Belden Machine Co. .....D
Griswold, Geo. M. ......D
Hoggson & Pettis Mfg. Co.
(Cutting; Stamping;
Press; Stencil; Leather
Cutting; Boot; Shoe)...A
Kilborn & Bishop Co.
(Blanking; Cutting;
Pressing; Punching;
Stamping) C
Miner & Peck Mfg. Co.
(Press) X

CONN.—Plainville

Clark & Cowles (Cutting;
Stamping) ....B

CONN.—Waterbury

Blake & Johnson (Blanking;
Cutting; Embossing; Die
Sinkers; Pressing; Punch-
ing; Stamping) ....A
Cross & Spiers Machine Co.
D
Draher, Jno., 70 N. Elm..F
Waterbury-Farrell Fdy. &
Machine Co. (Wire;
Press) ....AA
Waterbury Machine Co.
(Forming) ....B
Waterbury Wire Die Co.
(Wire Drawing) ......F

CONN.—Westville

Geometric Drill Co. (Au-
tomatic; Opening) X

DEL.—Wilmington

Hilles & Jones Co. (Cutting;
Stamping) ....AA

ILL.—Chicago

American Can Co., Mer-
chants' Loan & Trust
Bldg. (Cutting; Stamp-
ing) ....AAA
Chicago Last & Die Co., 194
S. Clinton (Boot; Shoe).B
Chicago Model Works, 181
E. Madison X
Christy & Co., F. C. (Boot;
Shoe) ....F
Consolidated Press & Tool
Co., 96 N. Clinton (Ad-
justable Expanding; Auto-
matic; Blanking; Cutting;
Embossing; Pressing;
Punching; Stamping) ..D
Crane Co., 10 N. Jefferson
(& Stocks; Pipe Thread-
ing) ....AAAA
Crowe Metal Mfg. Co. ...E
Elmes Engineering Works,
Chas. F. (Punching;
Stamping) ....A
Lovejoy, T. H., 90 Ohio
(Punching) ....G
Mooney & Bereter (Boot;
Shoe) ....F
Van Pelt, Geo. H., 45 Hu-
ron (Boot; Shoe) C
Wold, Torris & Co., 66 N.
Jefferson C

ILL.—Ottawa

American Hdw. Mfg. Co.
(Cutting; Stamping) ...D

ILL.—Sandwich

Enterprise Windmill Co.
(& Stocks; Rachet Pipe
Threading) ....B

IND.—Elkhart

Buescher Mfg. Co. C

IND.—Indianapolis

Union Embossing Machine
Co. (Wood; Leather Em-
bossing) C

KY.—Louisville

Koehler. Hy. L. (Wooden
Box Printing) ....G

MAINE—Portland

Hayes, Harrison (Adjust-
able Pipe) ....H
Lang Co., E. M. (Tinners')
C

MD.—Baltimore

Brown, F. S. & G. L., 20 E.
Fort Av. ....D
Dorman Co., J. F. W., 121
E. Fayette (Press) .....F
Kemp Mfg. Co., C. M., 1501
Guilford Av. (& Stocks;

DIES (Con.)
  Ratchet Stocks) C
MASS.—Attleboro
Mossberg Co., Frank
  (Stamping) ....B
MASS.—Boston
Barrett Bros., 43 Haverhill
 C
Becker Engineering Co.,
  August, 247 Atlantic Av.
  (Cutting; Stamping)...E
Burke, P. F., Dow, cor.
  Dorchester (Welding)..E
Dalton-Ingersoll Co., 175
  High (Expanding) .....A
Lang & Sons, J. A., 280
  Dover ....E
National Machine & Tool
  Co., 253a, (Forming)...A
Seelye Mfg. Co. (Boot;
  Shoe) ....D
Walworth Mfg. Co., 132
  Federal (Halls' Pipe, &c.;
  Pipe; Press; Pipe Thread-
  ing) ....AAAA
Woodman Mfg. & Supply
  Co., R. (Ticket Punch).F
MASS.—Brockton
Brockton Die Co. (Boot;
  Shoe) ....F
MASS.—Greenfield
Reece Co., E. F. (Adjustable
  Expanding; Pipe; Solid;
  Cutting) ....E
Warner Mfg. Co. C
Wells Bros. Co. (Pipe;
  Cutting) ....A
Wells & Son, F. E. (Pipe;
  Pipe Threading) ....B
Wiley & Russell Mfg. Co.
  (& Stocks; Opening)..AA
MASS.—Lynn
Lynn Die Co. X
MASS.—Mansfield
Card Mfg. Co., S. W.
  (Round Adjustable; Ex-
  panding; Stocks) ......B
MASS.—New Bedford
Morse Twist Drill & Ma-
  chine Co. (Adjustable;
  Expanding; Bolt Thread-
  ing; Pipe; Screw Plate;
  Stocks) ....AAA
MASS.—Waltham
Ames & Co., B. C. (&
  Punches) ....G
Waltham Machine Works
  (& Punches) ....F
MASS.—Worcester
Smith & Co., Thos. W.
  (Press) ....D
Wilson & Smith (Cutting;
  Stamping; Punching;
  Press) ....D
MASS.—Wrentham
Winter Bros. Co. (Solid
  Square Bolt Threading;
  Pipe; Die Stocks) .....E
MICH.—Detroit
Detroit Brass & Iron Novel-
  ty Co., 14 Atwater ....F
Skareen & Ericsson, 58 1st
  (Cutting; Stamping) ...H
Voelkner & Reinke Mfg. Co.
  123 W. Woodbridge (Cut-
  ting; Stamping) ....E
MICH.—Grand Rapids
Grand Rapids Brass Co....A
MICH.—Kalamazoo
Kalamazoo Fdy. & Machine
  Co. (Cutting; Furring;
  Forming) ....D
MICH.—Lansing
Western Tool Co. ....F
MINN.—St. Paul
N. W. Stamp Wks. (Wooden
  Box Printing) ....E
MO.—St. Louis
Columbia Novelty Mfg. Co.,
  1537 N. B'way (Press)..D
Crescent Novelty Mfg. Co.,
  703 S. B'way ....D
Fernholtz Brick Machy. Co.,
  Boyle & Manchester Avs.
  (Brick; Clay Workers').E
Knight & Co., W. B., 1518
  Olive ....F
Phillips Bros., 19 N. 2d...H
Ranz-Lambrecht Mfg. Co.,
  522 Spruce (Cutting;

DIES (Con.)
  Stamping) ....F
Swaine Co., Fred J. (Cut-
  ting; Stamping; Forming;
  Punching) ....E
N. J.—Bridgeton
Ferracute Machine Co.
  (Sheet Metal; Cutting;
  Stamping) ....A
N. J.—Newark
Burroughs Co., Chas., 143
  Commerce C
Ohl & Co., Geo. A. (Press-
  ing; Punching) ....B
Osborne & Co., C. S.
  (Leather Cutting) .....B
Riley-Klotz Mfg. Co., 17
  Mulberry (Cutting;
  Stamping) ....A
Rudman Iron Fdy. Co., 49
  Hermon (Cutting; Stamp-
  ing) ....F
Schlueter & Co., A., 34
  Ward (Cutting; Stamp-
  ing) ....E
Standard Machine Works, 61
  N. J. R. R. Av. (Cutting;
  Stamping) X
Stone, Thos. & Geo. M.,
  Mulberry & Murray (Cut-
  ting; Stamping) C
N. J.—Salem
Ayars Machine Co. (for Can
  Makers') ....B
N. J.—Trenton
McFarland Fdy. & Machine
  Co. (Wire Drawing)....E
N. Y.—Auburn
Clapp Mfg. Co., E. D.....A
N. Y.—Brooklyn
Adriance Machine Works,
  254 Van Brunt (Cutting;
  Stamping; Embossing;
  Pressing; Punching) ...A
Bliss Co., E. W., 19 Adams
  (Adjustable Expanding;
  Automatic; Blanking;
  Cutting; Stamping; Em-
  bossing; Pressing; Punch-
  ing) ....AAAA
Chrome Steel Works, Kent
  Av. & Keap (Chrome
  Steel; Stencil) .....AAA
Hay-Budden Mfg. Co., 254
  N. Henry (Press) ......B
Hibbard, Wm. H., 79
  Washn. (Blanking; Com-
  bination; Embossing;-
  bination; Embossing;
  Pressing; Punching; Wir-
  ing) ....B
Leffler & Co., Chas., 63
  Clymer (Cutting; Stamp-
  ing; Adjustable Expand-
  ing; Automatic; Blank-
  ing; Cutting; Embossing;
  Die Sinkers; Pressing;
  Punching) ....D
Standard Stamping & Die
  Co. (Press) ....F
V. & O. Press Co. (Auto-
  matic; Blanking; Emboss-
  ing; Pressing; Punching;
  Stamping) ....D
Williams & Co., J. H.
  (Stamping) ....AA
N. Y.—Buffalo
Diamond Saw & Stamping
  Works, 357 7th ....D
Forsyth Mfg. Co., 308 Ter-
  race C
Howard Iron Works ....AA
Niagara Machine & Tool
  Works (Cutting; Stamp-
  ing; Embossing; Forming;
  Press; Punching; Blank-
  ing) ....AAA
West Mfg. Co., 374 7th
  (Tinners') ....D
White Co., L. & I. J. (Cut-
  ting; Stamping) ....A
New York City
Ashcroft Mfg. Co., 85 Lib-
  erty (Pipe; Stocks) ...A
Bender & Sons, Ph. J., 87
  Frankfort (Cutting; Em-
  bossing; Stamping; Form-
  ing) ....H
Eaton, Cole & Burnham Co.,

DIES (*Con.*)

253 B'way (Pipe) .AAAA

Etna Mfg. Co. (Adjustable; Expanding; Solid Bolt; Solid Pipe) ....D

Fairbanks Co., 186 Elm (& Stocks) ....AAAA

Hanan, Marcus (Boot; Shoe) ....F

Lewthwaite, T. H., 142 Centre ....G

Loyd Co., Jno., 558 Water (Leather Cutting) .....B

McCabe Hanger Mfg. Co., 425 W. 25th C

Ness, Jr., Geo. M., 61 Fulton (Embossing; Stencil Cutting) ....G

Newton, J. W., 81 John (Wire Drawing) X

New York Stencil Works (Stencil) ....D

Niles - Bement - Pond Co. ....AAAA

Olden, Geoffrey J. (Boot; Shoe) ....D

Peck, Stow & Wilcox Co. (Cutting; P u n c h i n g) ....AAAA

Steel Set Diamond Co., 275 Water (Wire Drawing; Diamond) X

N. Y.—Oswego

Oswego Tool Co. (& Stocks; Malleable Solid Die for Pipe) C

N. Y.—Rochester

Clark Novelty Co., 380 Exchange ....D

Erdle & Schenck (Stamping) ....D

N. Y.—Waterford

Holroyd & Co. (Bicycle, &c.; Pipe; Stocks)...A

King & Co., J. M. (& Stocks) ....A

N. Y.—Yonkers

Saunders' Sons, D. (Adjustable Expanding; Pipe; Pipe Threading) ....A

N. C.—Statesville

Steele & Son, J. C. (Brick; Clay Workers') C

OHIO—Bucyrus

American Clay Working Machy. Co. (Brick; Clay Workers'; Tile) .....B

OHIO—Canton

Canton Fdy. & Machine Co. (for Metal Ceiling Work) ....B

Canton Roll & Machine Co. ....B

OHIO—Cincinnati

Cincinnati Screw & Tap Co., 2442 Beekman (all kinds) C

Cincinnati Specialty Mfg. Co., 22 E. 3d ....G

Eagle Tool Co., 5th & Elm ....E

Keene & Co., Geo. C., 502 E. Front (C u t t i n g; Stamping) ....F

Rapid Tool & Machine Co., 814 B'way (& Tools)...X

Robinson Mfg. Co., J. M., 2d & Central Av......B

Ross-Meyer Mfg. Co., 634 Sycamore (Leather Cutting) ....A

Standard Die Co., 456 E. 2d ....F

OHIO—Cleveland

Acme Machy. Co., Hamilton & Belden (& Stocks; Adjustable; Opening; Expanding) ....AA

Avery Stamping Co. (Cutting; Stamping) ....A

Bardons & Oliver, Case Av. & Hamilton ....A

Bultman & Co., F. H., 106 Canal ....F

Cleveland Galvanizing Wks. (Cutting; P u n c h i n g; Stamping) ....B

Cleveland Punch & Shear Works (Punching; Stamping) ....A

DIES (*Con.*)

Cleveland Stamping & Tool Co., cor. Hamilton & Coe (Cutting; Press; Stamping; Blanking) C

Globe Machine & Stamping Co., 970 Hamilton (Forming; Punching; Blanking; Die Sinkers; Stamping).E

Hart Mfg. Co., Wood & St. Clair (& Stocks; Ratchet Die Stocks) C

Konigslow & Bro., E., 184 Champlain (C u t t i n g; Stamping; F o r m i n g; Punching) ....E

Oster Mfg. Co., 85 E. Prospect (& Stocks) ....B

Reliance Machine & Tool Co., 31 W. Center (Automatic) C

Reserve Press Co. (Inc.), 83 Lake ....B

Standard Tool Co. ....AAA

OHIO—Mansfield

Humphreys Mfg. Co......A

OHIO—Springfield

Webster & Perks Tool Co. (Cutting) ....D

OHIO—Steubenville

Means Fdy. & Machine Co. (Brick; Clay Workers').B

OHIO—Toledo

Heartley, G. W. (Sheet Metal; Cutting; Forming; also Tools) ....D

Toledo Machine & Tool Co. (Sheet Metal Cutting; Stamping) ....A

OHIO—Wellsville

Stevenson Co. (Brick; Clay Workers') ....B

OHIO—Youngstown

Sennett Co., Geo. B. (Cutting; Die Sinkers; Punching) ....A

PA.—Bloomsburg

Richards Mfg. Co. (Ltd.), F. J. (Cutting; Stamping; Press) C

PA.—Erie

Hollands Mfg. Co. (& Stocks; Pipe) C

Jarecki Mfg. Co. (& Stocks; Pipe Threading) .AAAA

Modern Tool Co. (Self-opening Adjustable) ....E

PA.—Lancaster

Champion Blower & Forge Co. (Blacksmiths') ....B

PA.—Millersburg

Brubaker & Bros., W. L. (& Stocks; Pipe Threading) ....D

Polk & Son, A. J. (Bolt Threading; Solid Pipe).D

PA.—Philadelphia

Chester Steel Casting Co. ....AAA

Chesterman & Co., F. E., 243 Arch (C u t t i n g; Stamping) ....D

Ellison Bros., 2213 Bridge ....E

Falkenau-Sinclair Machine Co., 109 N. 22d (Cutting; Stamping; Press; Blanking) ....B

Gordon, W. J., 225 Bread.C

Hoopes & Townsend Co., 1330 Buttonwood ..AAAA

Keystone Drop Forge Works, 19th & Clearfield ....B

Nack & Son, A., 240 S. 9th ....F

Pancoast & Co., Hy. B., 243 S. 3d (& Stocks; Pipe Threading) ....B

Philadelphia Machine Tool Co., 445 N. Darien .....A

Philadelphia Roll & Machine Co. (Chilled Cast Wire) ....A

Stortz & Son, Jno., 210 Vine (Cutting; Punching) ...F

Wootten & Peckworth, 231 N. Front (C u t t i n g; Stamping) ....F

Wright Mfg. Co., H. T., 323

DIES (Con.)
Race (Cutting; Stamping) ....E
PA.—Pittsburg
Crucible Steel Co. of America, Frick Bldg. (Drop Forging) ....AAAA
Matthews & Co., Jas. H. (Wooden Box) C
Pittsburg Mfg. Co., 28th & Railroad (Chilled Hammer) ....A
Sterrit-Thomas Fdy. Co., 32d & Smallman (Chilled Hammer) ....A
Tretheway & Co. (Ltd.) Samuel. 47th near Butler (Blanking; Press) ......F
Westmoreland Steel Co., 424 4th Av. (Wire Drawing) ....B

R. I.—Pawtucket
Carpenter Tap & Die Co., J. M. (& Stocks; Adjustable; Expanding) C
Pawtucket Mfg. Co. (& Stocks) ....A

R. I.—Providence
Lange & Fischer X
Standard Machy. Co. (Adjustable Expanding; Automatic; Blanking; Cutting; Pressing; Punching; Stamping) ....A

VT.—Derby Line
Butterfield & Co. (Screw Plate; Stocks) ....B

VT.—Springfield
Jones & Lamson Machine Co. (Automatic) ....AA

W. VA.—Wheeling
Wheeling Mold & Fdy. Co. ....A

WIS.—Milwaukee
Milwaukee Automatic Machine Co. (Punches; Tools) ....D
Krueger Mfg. Co., 463 Front ....G

DIGESTORS

MAINE—Portland
Portland Co. (Paper Making) ....AA
MASS.—Boston
Atlantic Works ....AA
N. J.—Belleville
Eastwood Wire Mfg. Co. (Paper Making) ....A
N. J.—Burlington
Stewart & Peterson Co. (Paper Making) ....A
N. J.—Jersey City
Smith & Sons' Co., Theodore, ft. of Essex ......A
N. J.—Phillipsburg
Tippett & Wood ....B
N. Y.—Buffalo
Dopp & Son. H. Wm.....D
OHIO—Cincinnati
American Copper & Brass Works. 427 E. Front....A
Tudor Boiler Mfg. Co. (Pulp) ....B
PA.—Pittsburg
Munroe & Son, R. (Paper Making) ....AA
Riter-Conley Mfg. Co. (Paper Making) ....AAA
PA.—Washington
Petroleum Iron Works Co. (Pulp) ....A
PA.—York
Dempwolf & Co., C. H. (Paper Making) ....A

DIGGERS
See Agr. Implements

CAL.—San Francisco
Doble Co., Abner (Post Hole) ....A
ILL.—Chicago
Eureka Digger Co. (Post Hole) ....F
Pratt Mfg. Co., Wm. E., 91 Lake (Post Hole)..B
Vaughan & Bushnell Mfg. Co. (Post Hole) ......B

DIGGERS (Con.)
ILL.—Ottawa
Porter Co., J. E. (Post Hole) ....A
ILL.—Rockford
Rockford Tack & Nail Co. (Post Hole) C
ILL.—Streator
Iwan Bros. (Post Hole)..D
IND.—Indianapolis
Tucker & Dorsey Mfg. Co. (Post Hole) ....A
IND.—Montpelier
Jackson Shovel & Tool Co. (Earth; Post Hole) ....B
MO.—St. Louis
Ludlow-Saylor Wire Co. (Post Hole) ....A
N. Y.—Elmira
Cronk & Carrier Mfg. Co. (Post Hole) ....B
OHIO—Akron
Whitman & Barnes Mfg. Co. (Post Hole) ....AAAA
OHIO—Canton
Gibbs Mfg. Co. (Post Hole) ....A
Kohler & Co., F. E., 120 S. 4th (Post Hole) C
Ney Mfg. Co. (Post Hole).B
OHIO—Cleveland
Avery Stamping Co. (Post Hole) ....A
OHIO—Mansfield
Ohio Brass Co. (Post Hole) ....B
PA.—Pittsburg
Klein-Logan Co., S. 13th & Breed (Post Hole) .....A
Oliver Iron & Steel Co. (Post Hole) ....AAAA
PA.—Tacony
Disston & Sons (Inc.), Hy. (Post Hole) ....AAAA

DIGITALIS
New York City
Hopkins & Co., J. L., 100 William ....A

DILATORS
See also Rubber Goods

OHIO—Akron
Akron Rubber Co. (Rubber) ....AAAA
R. I.—Providence
Davol Rubber Co. ......AA

DIMITIES
See Cotton Goods

DIMMERS
ILL.—Chicago
Western Electric Co., 259 S. Clinton (Theatre) ....AAAA
MASS.—Boston
Simplex Electrical Co., 75 Cornhill (Theatre) ....A
Ziegler Electric Co., 200 Summer (Theatre) ....E
N. Y.—Bronxville
Ward Electric Co...Leonard (Theatre) ....B
OHIO—Troy
Ohio Electric Specialty Mfg. Co. '(Theatre)....G
PA.—Philadelphia
Wirt Electric Co., 4523 Tacony (Theatre) ....D
WIS.—Milwaukee
Cutler-Hammer Mfg. Co. (Lamp) ....A

DINGEYS
See Boats

DI-OXIDE
N. Y.—Newburgh
Newburgh Ice Mach. & Engine Co. (Sulphurous; Anhydrous) ....A

DIPPERS

See Enamelled Ironware;
Silverware; Tinware.

CONN.—Meriden
Manning, Bowman & Co.
(Enameled) ....AA
ILL.—Paxton
Paxton Hdw. Mfg. Co...X
KANS.—Coffeyville
Pioneer Flint Glass Co.
(Glass) ....A
MICH.—Bellaire
Richardi & Bechtold (Wood-
en Pickle) ....B
MICH.—Kalkaska
Freeman Mfg. Co. (Grocers'
Wooden; Wooden Pickle)
...........................B
MO.—St. Louis
St. Louis Stamping Co.
(Enameled) ......AAAA
N. H.—Henniker
Wilkins, Chas. A. (Wooden)
...........................F
N. Y.—Albany
Hoy & Co. (Tin) ....A
N. Y.—Buffalo
Aldrich Mfg. Co. (Copper)
...........................A
Shepard & Co., Sidney (Tin)
......................AAAA
New York City
Central Stamping Co. (Egg;
Vegetable; Milk) ....A
Lalance & Grosjean Mfg. Co.
(Enameled) ......AAAA
Reilley Bros. ....D
Stoutenborough, X. (Copper;
Egg; Vegetable; Milk).D
N. Y.—Rome
Rome Mfg. Co. (Nickel
Plated) ....B
N. Y.—Troy
Troy Stamping Works (Tin)
......................AAAA
OHIO—Cincinnati
Bromwell Brush & Wire
Goods Co. (Egg; Vege-
table) ....AA

DIPS

MINN.—Minneapolis
Chemical Mfg. Co. (Sheep)
...........................X
MO.—St. Louis
Nicotine Mfg. Co. (Sheep)
...........................X
NEBR.—Omaha
Lee & Co., Geo. H. (Car-
bolic) ....B
N. C.—Wilmington
Spirittine Chemical Co.
(Sheep) C
WIS.—Cuba
Cuba City Remedy Co.
(Sheep) ....F

DISCS

ILL.—Chicago
Crane Co. (Valve) ..AAAA
Johnston & Chapman Co.,
1345 Carroll Av. (Arma-
ture) ....B
IND.—Evansville
Bernardin Bottle Cap Co.
(Tin) ....B
IND.—Indianapolis
Barry Saw & Supply Co., W.
B. (Iron Cutting) .....D
Indianapolis Drop Forging
Co. (Armature) X
MASS.—Boston
Walworth Mfg. Co. (Valve)
......................AAAA
MASS.—Worcester
Wilson & Smith (Armature)
...........................D
MICH.—Detroit
Buscoe Mfg. Co., 1427 Wood-
ward Av. (Auto. Radia-
tor) ....A
Detroit Oak Belting Co.
(Valve; Leather) .....A
MICH.—Port Huron
Draper Mfg. Co. (Brass
Valve) ....D

DISCS (Con.)
N. Y.—Brooklyn
Bischoff, F. (Homoeopath-
ic) ....B
New York City
Empire Bottle Supply Co.,
7 Murray (Paper Milk
Bottle) ....E
Jenkins Bros. (Valve)..AA
N. Y.—Oneida
Smith-Lee Co. (Paper Milk
Jar) ....A
N. Y.—Potsdam
Thatcher Mfg. Co. (Paper
Milk Bottle) ....A
OHIO—Cleveland
Avery Stamping Co. (Arma-
ture; Metallic) ....A
PA.—Cheswick
Cheswick Mfg. Co. (Har-
row; Plow) ....D
PA.—Corry
Whittlesey & Sons, H. E.
(Leather) ....B
PA.—Philadelphia
Disston & Sons, Henry (Hot
or Cold Iron Cutting)
......................AAAA

DISHES: (MIS-CELANEOUS

See also Chinaware; Glassware; Woodenware.

CONN.—Meriden
International Silver Co.
(Silver Plated) ...AAAA
Manning, Bowman & Co.
(Baking; Butter; Chaf-
ing; Meat; Pudding;
Soap; Enameled Soap;
Enameled Sponge; Enam-
eled Vegetable) ......AA
Meriden Brittannia Co.
(Baking; Butter; Meat;
Enameled Sponge) .AAAA
CONN.—Wallingford
Wallace & Sons Mfg. Co.,
R. (Butter; Chafing;
Meat) ....AAAA
CONN.—Winsted
Goodwin & Kintz Co. (Chaf-
ing) ....B
ILL.—Chicago
Barbee Wire & Iron Works
(Pudding) ....B
MASS.—Boston
Bailey & Co., C. J. (Rub-
ber; Soap) ....B
MO.—St. Louis
St. Louis Stamping Co.
(Meat; Pudding; Soap;
Enameled Soap; Enameled
Vegetable) ....AAAA
N. Y.—Brooklyn
Empire Silver Plate Co.,
258 Washington X
Kreamer, A. (Soap) ....B
New York Stamping Co.
(Baking; Chafing) ....A
Sternau Co., S. (Soap)....A
Sweeney Mfg. Co., W. H.
(Chafing; Pudding) ..A
N. Y.—Buffalo
Jewett Mfg. Co., Jno. C.
(Baking; Chafing) ..AA
Shepard & Co., Sidney
(Aluminum; Chafing).
......................AAAA
New York City
American Hard Rubber Co.
(Rubber Soap) ...AAAA
Central Stamping Co. (Soap;
Tin Soap) ....AA
Fiske Iron Works, J. W.
(Iron; Soap) ....B
Gorham Mfg. Co. (Silver
Plated) ....AAAA
International Silver Co.
(Berry; Butter; Fruit;
Meat; Chafing) ...AAAA
Lalance & Grosjean Co.
(Chafing; Enameled Soap;
Enameled Sponge; Enam-
eled Vegetable) ...AAAA
Stoutenborough, X. (Soap;
Iron; Tin Soap) ......D

DISHES: MISC. (Con.)

N. Y.—Rochester
Rochester Stamping Co. (Metal) ....AAA

OHIO—Cleveland
Avery Stamping Co. (Soap) ....B

OHIO—Columbus
Columbus Brass Co. (Soap) ....A

OHIO—Ravenna
Williams, A. C. (Soap) ..A

PA.—Erie
Griswold Mfg. Co. (Aluminum; Chafing) ....A

PA.—Pittsburg
Standard Mfg. Co. (Soap) AA

PA.—Reading
Reading Hdw. Co. (Soap) AAAA

PA.—Wrightsville
Wrightsville Hardware Co. (Soap) ....B

DISHES & PLATES

Wood; Paper; Butter; Lard, etc.

DEL.—Frankford
Diamond Basket Co. (Butter Dishes, &c.; Wooden) D

ILL.—Chicago
Sefton Mfg. Co., J. W. (Wooden; Paper Dishes) AAA

IND.—Marion
Economy Butter & Pie Plate Co. (Pulp Plates) .....D

MICH.—Escanaba
Escanaba Wooden Ware Co. (Wooden) ....A

MICH.—Holland
King & Co. (Inc.), C. L. (Wooden) ....A

MICH.—Saginaw
Berst Mfg. Co. (Wooden) .C

MICH.—St. Joseph
Mullen Bros. (Paper Dishes) C

N. Y.—Black River
Jefferson Paper Co. (Pulp Plates) ....A

N. Y.—Brooklyn
Gair Co., Robert (Paper Dishes) ....AAA
Tompkins & Tuttle (Wooden) C

N. Y.—Newark
Bloomer Bros. Co. (Paper Dishes; Pulp Plates) C
Drake, H. R. (Paper Dishes) ....D

New York City
Fortgang, E. (Paper Dishes) G
McClusky, J. J., 248 Greenwich (Wooden) ....A
Sanford Mfg. Co., W. P. (Paper; Wooden Dishes; Pulp Plates) ....B

N. Y.—Sandy Creek
Sandy Creek Wood Mfg. Co. (Ltd.) (Paper; Wood Plates) ....A

OHIO—Dayton
Aull Bros. Paper & Box Co. (Paper Dishes) ....B
Dayton Paper Novelty Co. (Paper Dishes) C
Weston Paper & Mfg. Co. (Paper Dishes) ....B

OHIO—Delta
Oval Wood Dish Co. (Wooden) ....A

VT.—Richford
Manuel & Son, C. C. (Wooden) ....E

VA.—Petersburg
Southside Mfg. Co. (Wooden) C

VA.—Richmond
Richmond Cedar Works (Wooden) ....AAAA

DISHES & PLATES

VA.—Suffolk
Virginia Mfg. Co. (Wooden) C

DISINFECT-ANTS

CONN.—Westport
Embalmers' Supply Co.....C

ILL.—Chicago
Burch & Co., F. S........D
Red Cross Hygienic Co., 242 S. Robey ....D
West Disinfecting Co., 325 Wabash Av. ....B

MASS.—Boston
Egyptian Chemical Co....X
Jenkins Mfg. Co. X

MASS.—Pittsfield
Bromo Chloralum Co. ....D

MICH.—Detroit
Parke, Davis & Co....AAAA
Zenner Disinfectant Co., 27 Bates ....B

MICH.—Grand Rapids
Durfee Embalming Fluid Co. ....B

N. J.—Kearney
Cromwell-Walker Co. C

N. Y.—Brooklyn
Coal Tar Products Co., 71 Commerce ....D

New York City
Dusenberry, H. C., 95 Gold E
Fuerst Bros. & Co., 2 Stone B
Platt, Henry B., 42 Cliff (Chloride) ....B
Preservaline Mfg. Co., 41 Warren ....AA
Pulsford, A. J., 97 Water F
Royal Lubricating Oil Co., 116 Broad X
West Disinfecting Co., 26 E. 59th ....B

N. Y.—Rochester
Robachers' Disinfect. Co., 77 Kenil Av. ....F
Rochester Germicide Co..F

N. Y.—Syracuse
Syracuse Ext. Co. X

OHIO—Cincinnati
Thompson, Nuhring Chem. Co., 907 Walnut ......F
Werner & Simonson, 9th & Race ....F
West Disinfecting Co. (Inc.) 515 Main (Br.) .....B

OHIO—Cleveland
Atlantic Refining Co. ....A
Prescott Chem. Co., 1691 Pearl ....E

PA.—Philadelphia
Barrett Mfg. Co. .....AAAA
West Disinfecting Co., 262 N. 13th ....B

S. C.—Summerville
Summerville Fernoline Wks. F

WIS.—Milwaukee
Delaney Oil & Lubricant Co. X
Weller Mfg. Co. ....A

DISINFECTORS

New York City
Hospital Supply Co. (Hospital) ....A
Kny-Scheerer Co., 225 4th Av. C

PA.—Philadelphia
American Aromatic Disinfector Co., 430 Walnut..B
Lentz & Sons, Chas., 18 N. 11th ....A

DISINTEGRA-TORS

See also Mills

DEL.—Wilmington
Walker & Elliott (Clay)..B

ILL.—Chicago
Raymond Bros. Imp. Pul-

DISINTEGRATORS

verizer Co. ....D
Stroud & Co., H., 36 La
Salle ....D
IND.—Aurora
Stedman's Fdy. & Machine
Works (Clay) ....B
IND.—Indianapolis
Potts & Co., C. & A. (Clay)
B
Rockwood Mfg. Co. (Clay)
A
MICH.—Morenci
Michigan Brick & Tile
Mach. Co. (Clay) .....D
MICH.—Tecumseh
Brewer & Co., H. (Clay) ..B
MO.—St. Louis
Ross-Keller Triple Pressure
Brick Machine Co., Ful-
lerton Bldg. ....D
N. Y.—Brooklyn
Abbe Engineering Co. ...D
Alsing & Co., J. R. X
Houchin & Huber, 39 53d
(Clay) ....D
Ross & Son Co., Chas., 20
Steuben ....D
N. C.—Statesville
Steel & Son, J. E........B
OHIO—Bucyrus
American Clay Working
Machy. Co. (& Crushers
Combined; Clay) X
OHIO—Cincinnati
Day Co., J. H., 1144 Harri-
son Av. (Clay) ....A
OHIO—Cleveland
Standard Sand & Machine
Co. (Sand) C
OHIO—Columbus
Jeffrey Mfg. Co. (Coal)
AAAA
OHIO—Wellington
Wellington Machine Co.
(Clay) ....B
PA.—Lancaster
Martin Brick Machine Mfg.
Co., Henry (Clay) .....B
PA.—Philadelphia
Campell, Peter F., 51 Laurel
(Mill) ....D
Paxson Co., J. W., 1021 N.
Del. Av. (Sand) ......AA

DISPENSERS

OHIO—Delphos
Delphos Can Co. (Drug-
gists') ....B

DISPLAYERS

CONN.—Norwich
Norwich Nickel & Brass Co.
(Dry Goods) ....B
N. Y.—Buffalo
Du Mont Tool Co. (Dry
Goods) X

DISTILLERIES: WHISKEY

See Liquors

DISTRIBU- TORS

See also Agr. Implements

IOWA—Ottumwa
Ottumwa Iron Works (Coal)
AA
MASS.—Boston
Carters Ink Co. (Mucilage)
A
New York City
Davids Co., Thaddeus (Mu-
cilage) C
Stafford, S. S. (Mucilage)
B

DITCHERS

ILL.—Aurora
Western Wheeled Scraper
Co. (Grader; Loader Com-
bined) ....AA

DITCHERS (Con.)

ILL.—Harvey
Austin Mfg. Co., F. C.
(Railroad) ....AAA
MINN.—Stephen
Stockland, C. K. (Elevating
Road) ....E
N. Y.—Buffalo
Contractors Plant Mfg. Co.
(Railroad) ....B
N. Y.—Oswego
Kingsford Fdy. & Mach.
Works ....AAAA
OHIO—Carey
Van Buren's Sons & Co., S.
C. (Traction) X
OHIO—Marion
Marion Steam Shovel Co.
(County; Railroad) .AAA
PA.—Kennett Square
American Road Machine Co.
(Grader; Loader Com-
bined) ....AA

DIVANS

See Furniture

DIVIDERS

See also Compasses

CONN.—Bridgeport
Gaynor & Mitchell Mfg. Co.
(& Brass Compasses)....C
CONN.—East River
Munger & Son (Blackboard)
C
CONN.—New Haven
Schollhorn Co., Wm. ....A
CONN.—Southington
Peck, Stow & Wilcox Co.
(& Compasses, &c.)
AAAA
MASS.—Athol
Athol Machine Co. (Exten-
sion Spring) ....B
Starrett Co., L. S. (Exten-
sion Spring; Combination)
A
MASS.—Boston
Johnson & Co., H. A.
(Dough) ....A
MASS.—Chicopee Falls
Stevens Arms & Tool Co., J.
(& Compasses, &c.).AAA
MASS.—Springfield
Bemis & Call Hdw. & Tool
Co. (& Compasses, &c.).A
MASS.—Worcester
Eagan, Thos. F. (Extension
Spring) ....G
N. J.—Newark
Johnson, Wm. ....D
Kracuter & Co., 577 18th
Av. (& Compasses, &c.)
X
Sayre & Co., L. A........B
New York City
Keuffel & Esser Co., 127
Fulton (& Compasses,
&c.) ....AA
McAllister, T. H., 49 Nas-
sau (& Compasses, &c.).B
New York Silicate Book
Slate Co., 68 Church
(Blackboard) ....D
Soltmann, E. G., 125 E.
42d (& Compasses, &c.).B
Tower & Lyon Co., 95 Cham-
bers (& Compasses, &c.).B
N. Y.—Rochester
Taylor Bros. Co. (& Com-
passes. &c.) ....AA
OHIO—Cincinnati
Pfister, Herman, 428 Plum
(& Compasses, &c.) ...E
PA.—Philadelphia
Altoneder & Sons, Theo.,
945 Ridge Av. ....D
Queen & Co. (Inc.), 1010
Chestnut (& Compasses,
&c.) ....AA

DOBBIES

See also Machinery

CONN.—Stonington
Atwood-Morrison Co. ....AA

DOBBIES (Con.)

MASS.—Readville
Stafford Co., Geo. W...A

MASS.—Taunton
Mason Machine Works..AA

MASS.—Worcester
Crompton-Thayer Loom Co.
...........AAA
Crompton & Knowles Loom
Co. ....AAAA

N. J.—Paterson
Paterson Machine Wks....F
Royle & Sons, John .....A

DOESKIN

See Woolen Goods

DOGS

CONN.—Bridgeport
Armstrong Mfg. Co. (Lathe)
........A

CONN.—Hartford
Billings & Spencer Co.
(Drop Forged Clamp; Die;
Lathe) ....AA
Pratt & Whitney Co. (Drop
Forged Lathe) ...AAAA

CONN.—South Norwalk
Le Count, Wm. G. (Bolt;
Clamp; Heavy Steel
Lathe; Straight Tail with
Steel Screws) ....D

ILL.—Chicago
Allis-Chalmers Co. (Saw
Mill) ....AAAA
Armstrong Bros. Tool Co.,
617 Austin Av. (Lathe;
Clamp) ....B
Barbee Wire & Iron Works
(Iron) ....B
Besly & Co., Chas. H.
(Lathe) ....AA
Mark Mfg. Co. (Lathe)..AA

IND.—Anderson
Hill Tool Co. (Drop Forged
Lathe) ....E

IND.—Indianapolis
Atkins & Co., E. C., 402 S.
Illinois (Saw Mill).AAAA
Chandler & Taylor Co. (Saw
Mill) ....AA
Rockwood Mfg. Co. (Saw
Mill ....A
Sinker-Davis Co., 230 S.
Missouri (Saw Mill)....B

IND.—Jefferson
Indiana Chain Wks. (Chain;
Ring) ....B

LA.—Shreveport
Henderson Iron Wks. Supply
Co. (Saw Mill) ....AA

MAINE—Bangor
Bangor Edge Tool Co. (Saw
Mill) ....D

MD.—Baltimore
National Supply Co., 7 W.
Lombard (Timber) ....B

MASS.—Fitchburg
Fitchburg Machine Wks.
(Clamp; Die) ....B
Putnam Machine Co. (Die)
........A

MICH.—Bay City
Garland Co., M. (Double
Grip Saw Mill) C

MICH.—Evart
Champion Tool & Handle
Wks. (Rafting; Timber)
........AA

MICH.—Saginaw
Wickes Bros. (Saw Mill;
Timber) ....AAAA

MINN.—Minneapolis
Howell & Co., R. R., 30th
Av. & S. E 5th Saw Mill)
........B

MISS.—Meridian
Soule Steam Feed Wks.
(Saw Mill) C

MO.—St. Louis
Fisher & Davis. 1024 N.
Main (Saw Mill) ....B
Zelnicker Supply Co., Wal-
ter A.. 408 N. 4th (Raft-
ing; Chain; Ring; Saw
Mill) X

N. J.—Plainfield
Pond Machine Tool Co.

DOGS (Con.)
(Lathe) ....AAAA

N. Y.—Brooklyn
Williams & Co., J. H., 9
Richards(Dropped Forge
Lathe; Milling Machine)
........AA

N. Y.—Homer
Phoenix Hdw. Mfg. Co.
(Lathe) ....D

N. Y.—Malone
Hinds, Thos. (Saw Mill)..D
New York City
Fairbanks Co., 416 Broome
(Lathe) ....AAA
Niles-Bement-Pond Co., 136
Liberty (Clamp; Lathe)
........AAAA

N. Y.—Seneca Falls
Seneca Falls Mfg. Co.
(Clamp; Lathe) ....B

OHIO—Canton
Canton Saw Co. (Saw Mill)
........C
Knight Mfg. Co. (Saw Mill)
........B

OHIO—Cincinnati
American Tool Wks. Co.
(Drop Forged Lathe)..AA
Lane & Bodley Co. (Saw
Mill) ....B

OHIO—Columbus
Hayden-Corbett Chain Co.
(Chain; Ring) ....A

PA.—Allegheny
Carlin's Sons Thomas
(Stone) ....A

PA.—Bennett
Lippert, E. T. (Saw Mill)
........A

PA.—Chester
Chester Steel Castings Co.
(Lathe) ....AA

PA.—Erie
Standard Saw Mill Machy.
Co. (Saw Mill) ....B
Stearns Mfg. Co. (Saw Mill)
........B

PA.—New Castle
New Castle Forge & Bolt Co.
(Rafting; Chain; Ring;
Timber) ....AA

PA.—Philadelphia
Bonney Vise & Tool Wks.,
3015 Chestnut (Lathe).C

PA.—Pittsburg
Oliver Iron & Steel Co.
(Timber) ....AAAA
Standard Chain Co., Frick
Bldg. (Timber; Ring;
Chain) ....AAAA

VA.—Richmond
Old Dominion Iron & Nail
Wks. Co. (Timber)....AA

WIS.—Eau Claire
Phoenix Mfg. Co. (Saw
Mill) ....A

WIS.—Milwaukee
Filer & Stowell Co., cor.
Becher & Ziemer (Saw
Mill) ....AAA

DOLLIES

ILL.—Chicago
Union Elevator & Machine
Co., 144 Ontario (Lumber)
........C

MICH.—Lansing
Lansing Wheelbarrow Co.
(Timber) ....AAA

MICH.—Saginaw
Morley Bros. (Timber)..AA

MINN.—Minneapolis
Clark Co., J. R. (Timber)
........B

MISS.—Meridian
Soule Steam Feed Wks.
(Timber) C
New York City
Fairbanks Co. (Timber)
........AAAA

N. Y.—Niagara
Dobbie Fdry. & Machine Co.
(Lumber) ....D

OHIO—Cleveland
Gerlach Co., Peter (Tim-
ber) ....A

OHIO—Columbus
Kilbourne & Jacobs Mfg.

DOLLIES (Con.)

Co. (Pipe; Timber).AAAA
PA.—Philadelphia
Disston & Sons, Henry
(Saw Mill) ....AAAA
PA.—Tarentum
Baker Mfg. Co., James H.
(Timber) ....AA
PA.—Waynesboro
Frick Co. (Saw Mill).AAAA
PA.—York
Farquhar Co., A. B. (Ltd.)
(Saw Mill) ....AAA
TENN.—Chattanooga
Wheland Machine Wks.
(Saw Mill) ....A
TENN.—Jackson
Southern Engine & Boiler
Wks. (Inc.) (Saw Mill)
AA

DOLLS

N. J.—Jersey City
Rucholl, Adolph ....E
N. Y.—Brooklyn
Hayward, S. M., 1104 Fulton (Rag) ....F
New York City
American Doll & Toy Mfg.
Co., 55 Great Jones....X
Edison Mfg. Co. (Talking)
A
Fischer & Co., Alfred, 43
W. 4th (Dresden Heads)
D
Mace & Co., L. H., 111 E.
Houston ....B
New York Rubber Co., 84
Reade (Rubber) ......AA
OHIO—Akron
Whitman & Barnes Mfg. Co.
(Rubber) ....AAAA

DOMES

ILL.—Chicago
Clinton, Hass Co., Morgan
& 21st (Art Glass).....F
New York City
Husted, Henry, 74 Murray
(Clock) ....F
PA.—Pittsburg
Kratzer & Co., W. N. (for
Observatories) ....D
McCullough-Dalzell Crucible
Co. ....A

DOMETS

See Cotton Goods

DOMINOES

See Games

DONGOLA

See Leather

DOORS

See also Woodwork

ILL.—Aurora
Wilcox Mfg. Co. (Automatic
Fire) ....B
ILL.—Chicago
American Bronze Fdry. Co.,
73d & Woodlawn Av.
(Bronze) ....D
Bolter & Sons, A. (Iron)..B
Braumoeller & Son, Henry
D. (Fireproof; Iron; Ash
Pit; Jail) ....B
Burdett-Rowntree Mfg. Co.,
76 W. Jackson Boul.
(Hatch; Automatic; in
case of fire only) .....B
Chicago Grain Door Co.,
Monadnock Bldg. (Car).C
Chicago Ornamental Iron Co.
37th & Stewart Av.
(Bronze) C
Dodge & Co., H. B., 108 La
Salle (Winding; Sliding)
D
Gardner Sash Balance Co.,
164 Dearborn (Elevating;
Heavy Doors with Chain;
Ball Bearing Pulleys)..C

DOORS (Con.)

Jones Car Door Co., 234 La
Salle (Car) C
Landon & Eggers, 103 S.
Canal (Automatic Elevator) ....D
McCord & Co., Old Colony
Bldg. (Hopper) ....B
McGuire-Cummings Mfg. Co.
122 N. Sagamore (Car;
Freight Car; Grain Car)
AA
Natl. Railway Specialty Co.,
Old Colony Bldg. (Car).D
Smith Wire & Iron Wks. &
Co., 100 Lake (Bronze).B
Underwriters Hatch · Door
Co., 58 N. Jefferson (Automatic Hatch; Electric
Hatch, automatic in case
of fire only) ....B
Variety Mfg. Co., 77 W.
Lake (Automatic Elevator; Folding) ....D
Winslow Bros. Co., 368 Carroll Av. (Bronze) ...AA
IND.—Goshen
I. X. L. & Goshen Pump
Co. (Screen) ....B
IND.—Indianapolis
American Car Door Co., Ingalls Blk. (Car).......X
Sinker-Davis Co. (Ash Pit;
Boiler; Furnace) ......B
IND.—Richmond
Richmond Safety Gate Co.
(Automatic Elevator)...C
IOWA—Des Moines
Central Iron Wks., Equitable Bldg. (Automatic
Elevator) ....H
KY.—Newport
Higgin Mfg. Co. (Screen)
A
MAINE—Portland
Burrows & Co., E. T.
(Screen) ....AA
MASS.—Boston
Beckwith Elevator Co., 123
Pearl (Automatic Elevator; Automatic Hatch)..H
Coffin Valve Co. (Iron)..D
Murdock Corp't (Bronze).X
Stearns Lumber Co., A. T.
(Cold Storage; Winding;
Sliding; Car) ....AA
MASS.—Cambridgeport
Kanaly Co., M. E. (Car).E
MASS.—Chicopee
Ames Foundries (Bronze).F
Mosman, M. H. (Bronze).C
MASS.—Gardner
Heywood Bros. & Wakefield Co. (Swing).AAAA
MASS.—Holyoke
Coburn Trolley Track Mfg.
Co. (Automatic Fire)...A
MASS.—Salem
Salem Elevator Wks. (Automatic Hatch) ......B
MASS.—Westfield
Smith Co., H. B. (Iron).AA
MASS.—Worcester
Wheeler Fdry. Co. (Ash Pit;
Boiler) ....D
MICH.—Detroit
Amos & Co., Chas. A., 94
Larned (Bronze) ....E
Bolles Iron & Wire Wks.,
J. E. (Iron; Vault; Ash
Pit; Jail) X
Huebner Mfg. Co., 236 E.
Front (Hardwood; Veneered) ....D
Vulcan Co. (Bronze).....F
MICH.—Fenton
Phillips Co., A. J. (Screen)
A
MICH.—Grand Rapids
Grand Rapids Brass Co.
(Vault) ....A
MICH.—Three Rivers
Sheffield Car Door Co. (Car;
Grain Car) ....AAA
MINN.—Minneapolis
Fireproof Door Co. (Metal
Covered) ....B
Lagerquist, Gust., 18 1st
Av. (Automatic Hatch).E

DOORS (Con.)

MO.—Kansas City
Swearingen Mfg. Co. (Automatic Fire) X

MO.—St. Louis
Ludlow-Saylor Wire Co.
(Iron) ....AA
Standard Railway Equipment Co., Union Trust
Bldg. (Car) ....D
Western Railway Equipment
Co., Union Trust Bldg.
(Car) ....D

N. J.—Newark
Ohl & Co., Geo. A. (Iron;
Steel) ....B

N. Y.—Brooklyn
Hecla Iron Wks., N. 11th
& Berry (Bronze; Iron)
AA
Kleinschmitz & Co., K., 61
Noble (Mausoleum) ....E
White Co., James, 446 Adelphi (Automatic Dumb
Waiter) ....D

N. Y.—Buffalo
Buffalo Wire Wks. Co.
(Screen) ....A
Heiser, Wm. (Manhole)..C

N. Y.—Cohoes
Griffin & Son, A. J.
(Screen) ....A

N. Y.—Long Island City
Richey, Browne & Donald
(Bronze) ....A

N. Y.—Medina
Swett Iron Wks., A. L.
(Ash Pit) ....A

New York City
Bardsley Bros., 147 Baxter
(Automatic Elevator; Automatic Hatch) ....A
Brodie & Co., Wm. H., 45
Vesey (Automatic Fire)
E
Cabaret & Co., Paul E.,
342 W. 14th (Bronze)..D
Cornell Co., J. B. & J. M.
(Iron) ....AA
Dimond, Thos. (Iron).....A
Fiske Iron Works, J. W., 39
Park Pl. (Bronze) ....A
Gorman Mfg. Co., Bdway.
& 19th (Bronze)...AAAA
Herring-Hall-Marvin Co.
(Vault; Safe) ....B
Hubbard Portable Oven Co.
(Oven) C
Jackson Co., Wm. H., 29
E. 17th (Bronze; Iron;
Safe) ....A
Jackson & Bro., Edwin A.,
50 Beekman (Ash Pit)..C
Manhattan Brass Co., 338
E. 28th (Bronze).....AA
Moseley Iron Bridge & Roofing Co. (Iron) ....B
Mott Iron Wks., J. L., 84
Beekman (Bronze) ...AA
Newhall, Henry B., 9 Murray (Automatic Fire;
Folding) ....B
Pitt Composite Iron Wks.,
Wm. R., 111 5th Av.
(Iron; Glass Front; Vestibule) ....D
Rapp, Jno. W., 156 5th Av.
(Dumb Waiter Fireproof;
Metal Covered) X
Sedgwick Machine Wks.,
110 Liberty (Automatic
Hatch) ....D
Union Equipment & Bronze
Co., 514 W. 36th (Bronze)
E
Va.n Kannel Revolving Door
Co., 524 E. 134th (Hardwood; Veneered Revolving; Revolving Fireproof)
B
Webb, J. R., 414 Bleecker
(Automatic Dumb Waiter;
Automatic Elevator; Automatic Hatch).........D
Williams, Jno., 556 W. 27th
(Bronze) ....B
Wilson Mfg. Co., Jno. G.,
3 W. 29th (Swing for
Freight Sheds; Warehouses) ....A

DOORS (Con.)

N. Y.—Poughkeepsie
Lane Bros. Co. (Screen)..A

N. Y.—Rochester
Rochester Automatic Elevator Door Co., 291 Mill
(Fire Proof Safety Fire)
E

N. Y.—Syracuse
Edwards Co., O. M. (Car
Ext. Platform Trap)...E

N. Y.—Warsaw
Warsaw Elevator Co. (Automatic Hatch) ....B

OHIO—Ashtabula
Barber Mfg. Co. (Ash Pit)
C

OHIO—Bucyrus
American Clay Wkg. Machinery Co. (Brick Kiln)
X

OHIO—Canton
Berger Mfg. Co. (Iron;
Steel) ....AA
Diebold Safe & Lock Co.
(Vault; Safe; Jail)..AAA

OHIO—Cincinnati
Halls' Safe Co. (Vault;
Safe) ....A
Schreiber & Sons Co., L.,
8th & Eggleston Av.
(Steel Cellar; Bronze).AA
Stewart Iron Wks. (Iron;
Steel) ....A

OHIO—Cleveland
Forest City Steel & Iron
Co. (Iron; Steel).......A
Garry Iron & Steel Roofing
Co. (Iron) ....A
National Safe & Lock Co.
(Vault) ....A
Van Dorn Iron Wks. Co.
(Iron; Jail; Cemetery
Vault) ....AA

OHIO—Columbus
Kinnear Mfg. Co. (Folding;
Fireproof; Steel Rolling;
Warehouse) ....AA

OHIO—Dayton
Dayton Malleable Iron Co.
(Car) ....AA

OHIO—Galion
Freese & Co., E. M. (Brick
Kiln) ....A

OHIO—Hamilton
Macneale & Urban Co.
(Vault) X
Meyers Mfg. Co., Fred. J.
(Iron; Steel) ....B
Mosler Safe Co. (Vault;
Safe; Cemetery Vault)
AAAA

OHIO—Kenton
Champion Iron Co. (Iron)
AA

OHIO—Lancaster
Eagle Machine Co. (Screen)
A

OHIO—New London
Arnold, Creager Co., B.
(Brick Kiln) ....B

OHIO—Salem
Mullins, W. H. (Copper
Vault) ....A

OHIO—Springfield
Rogers Iron Co. (Ash Pit)
B

OHIO—Toledo
Donovan Wire & Iron Co.
(Iron; Steel) C
Stevens, Benj. A. (Cold
Storage) ....A

PA.—Allegheny
Rieseck, P., Allegheny Av.
& Rebecca (Cellar) C

PA.—Chester
Stevenson Co. (Ltd.) (Air;
Fireproof Cold Storage).B

PA.—Ellwood City
Glen Mfg. Co. (Iron; Steel;
Bronze) C

PA.—Harrisburg
Harrisburg Fdry. & Machine
Wks. (Steel Cellar) ..AA

PA.—Indiana
Indiana Foundry Co. (Oven)
C

PA.—Lancaster
Welchans, A. C., 202 W.

DRAFT (Con.)
chanical) ....AA

N. Y.—Buffalo
Buffalo Forge Co. (Forced;
Exhaust; Mechanical).AA

OHIO—Dayton
Dayton Malleable Iron Co.
(Gear, for Steel; Wooden
Cars) ....AA

VT.—Fair Haven
Dalrymple Iron Wks.
(Tuber) ....F

WIS.—Milwaukee
Natl. Blower Wks., 17th &
St. Paul Av. (Mechanical)
B

DRAGS

KY.—Louisville
Avery & Sons, B. F...AAA
Brennan & Co. ....A

MD.—Baltimore
Friedenwald Bros., 216 N.
Holliday (Cellar) .....D
Kemp Mfg. Co., C. N., 1501
Guilford Av. (Cellar)..B
Sinclair-Scott Mfg. Co...E

MASS.—Boston
Edson Mfg. Co. (Ship)...E

MO.—St. Louis
Nelson Mfg. Co., N. O.
(Cellar) ....AAA

PA.—York
Farquhar & Co., A. B..AAA

TENN.—Chattanooga
Chattanooga Plow Co....A

DRAINERS

CONN.—Meriden
Manning, Bowman & Co.
(Br. Int. Silver Co.)
(Tumbler) ....AAAA

ILL.—Chicago
Barbee Wire & Iron Wks.
(Br. Lafayette, Ind.)
(Dish) ....B
Erwin & Welch Hydraulic
Machy. Co., 37 S. Canal
(Cellar Automatic) ....B

ILL.—Paxton
Paxton Hdw. Mfg. Co.
(Dish) X

MD.—Baltimore
Friedenwald Bros., 216 N.
Holliday (Cellar Automa-
tic) ....D
Kemp Mfg. Co., C. M., 1501
Guilford Av. (Cellar Au-
tomatic) C

MASS.—Boston
D'Este Co., Julian (Cellar)
D
Prescott, Edwin (Dish)..D
Stratter & Sons, Herman
(Tumbler) ....A

MASS.—Lowell
Woods, Sherwood & Co.
(Dish) C

MASS.—Worcester
Natl. Mfg. Co. (Tumbler)
A
Parker Wire Goods Co.
(Dish) ....E
Wire Goods Co. (Dish)...B

N. Y.—Brooklyn
Sweeney Mfg. Co., W. H.
(Tumbler) ....A

N. Y.—Buffalo
Jewett Mfg. Co., Jno. C.
(Tumbler) ....AA
Western Wire Goods Co.
(Dish) ....E

N. Y.—Cortland
Wickwire Bros. (Dish)
AAAA
New York City
Braender, Philip, 47 W.
125th (Cellar Automatic)
B
Lalance & Grosjean Mfg.
Co. (Tumbler) ....AAAA

OHIO—Cincinnati
Geldreich, Adolph (Bar)..F

OHIO—Cleveland
Cleveland Stamping & Tool
Co. (Dish) ....B

OHIO—Hamilton
Meyers Mfg. Co., Fred J.
(Dish) ....B

DRAINERS (Con.)
PA.—Philadelphia
Darby & Sons, Edw., 233
Arch (Dish) ....A
Hall & Co., Amos H.
(Papermakers') C

PA.—Pittsburg
Standard Mfg. Co. (Dish)
AA

DRAPERIES:
UPHOLSTERY
See Trimmings

DRAWERS
See also Underwear

ILL.—Chicago
Chicago Scale Co. (Money)
A

IND.—Indianapolis
Tucker & Dorsey Mfg. Co.
(Money) ....A

MASS.—Cambridge
Auld, Francis L. (Money).D

N. H.—Nashua
Wood, Egbert O. (Money).D

New York City
Stephens, Alfred, 258 W.
28th ....F

OHIO—Columbus
Sun Mfg. Co. (Money)....A

R. I.—Providence
Presbrey & Son Co., W. A.
(Alarm Money Till).....C

DRAWHEADS

OHIO—Cleveland
Atlas Bolt & Mfg. Co. (Car)
A

DRAYS
See Carriages & Wagons

DREDGES
See also Excavators; Machi-
nery.

CAL.—San Francisco
Risdon Iron & Locomotive
Wks., Stewart & Folsom
(Gold; Placer Mining)
AAA
Yeatman & Co., Jno. A., 13
1st (Gold; Placer Mining)
X

ILL.—Chicago
Nicol & Co. (Flour) .....D
Shaw, Willis, N. Y. Life
Bldg. (Second Hand) ..D

MAINE—Portland
Portland Co. ....AA

MD.—Baltimore
Poole & Son Co., Robt.
(Steam) ....A

MICH.—Detroit
Mitskun Co., M., Chamb. of
Com. Bldg. (Second Hand)
C
MO.—Kansas City
Urie Boiler & Machine Co.,
607 W. 5th (Gold; Placer
Mining) ....B

N. J.—Garwood
Beckley & Co., A. J. (Placer
Mining) ....D

N. J.—Newark
Mundy, J. S. (Steam) ....A

N. Y.—Albany
Osgood Dredge Co. (Broom)
A
N. Y.—Buffalo
Buffalo Scale Co. (Flour)
AA
N. Y.—New York
Morris & Cummings Dredg-
ing Co. X

OHIO—Marion
Marion Steam Shovel Co.
(Gold; Placer Mining
Boom; Steam) ....AA

OHIO—Toledo
Ohio Steam Shovel Co.
(Gold; Placer Mining)..D

OREGON—Portland
Hammond Mfg. Co., 100 1st
(Gold; Placer Mining) ..X

PA.—Erie
Stearns Mfg. Co. ....AA

DREDGES (Con.)

PA.—Wilkesbarre
Vulcan Iron Wks. (Steam)
..................AAAA
WIS.—Milwaukee
Sheriff Mfg. Co. ....B
WIS.—South Milwaukee
Bucyrus Co. (Gold; Placer
Mining) ....B

DRESSERS

See also Furniture

CONN.—Bridgeport
Bridgeport Safety Emery
Wheel Co. (Emery Wheel)
...................F
CONN.—New Britain
New Britain Hdw. Mfg. Co.
(Emery Wheel) ....B
CONN.—Southington
Southington Cutlery Co.
(Emery Wheel) ......AA
CONN.—Waterbury
Blake & Johnson (Grind-
stone ....A
ILL.—Chicago
Chicago Screw Co. (Emery
Wheel) ....AA
Chicago Wheel & Mfg. Co.
(Emery Wheel) ....B
Standard Screw Co., 2 N.
Canal (Emery Wheel) ..E
Walker & Ehrman Mfg. Co.
(Emery Wheel) ....B
Wrigley, Thos., 300 Dear-
born (Emery Wheel) ..F
ILL.—Edwardsville
Bignall & Keeler Mfg. Co.
(Emery Wheel) ....B
ILL.—Moline
Barnard & Leas Mfg. Co.
(Flour) ....AA
IND.—Indianapolis
Nordyke & Marmon Co.
(Flour) ....AAA
IND.—New Albany
New Albany Mfg. Co.
(Stone) C
KANS.—Enterprise
Ehrsam Machine Co., J. B.
(Flour) C
KANS.—Leavenworth
Great Western Mfg. Co.
(Flour) ....AA
MD.—Baltimore
Poole & Son Co., Robt.
(Grindstone) ....A
MASS.—Boston
Cutter, Wood & Stevens Co.
(Emery Wheel) C
Sewing Machine Supplies Co.
(Emery Wheel) ....B
MASS.—Leeds
Northampton Emery Wheel
Co. (Emery Wheel) ....A
MASS.—Westfield
Vitrified Wheel Co. (Emery
Wheel) ....B
MASS.—Whitinsville
Whitin Machine Wks. (Cot-
ton) ....AAAA
MASS.—Worcester
American Card Clothing Co.
(Wool) ....AAA
Bay State Stamping Co.
(Emery Wheel) ....E
Cleveland Machine Wks. (J.
H. Whittle) (Cotton;
Yarn) ....A
Norton Emery Wheel Co.
(Emery Wheel) ....AAA
MICH.—Detroit
Star Corundum Wheel Co.
(Ltd.) (Emery Wheel)..E
MICH.—Grand Rapids
Hayden & Co., J. M. (Emery
Wheel) ....D
MICH.—Ypsilanti
Ypsilanti Machine Wks.
(Flour) ....D
N. J.—Elizabeth
Braunsdorf-Mueller Co.
(Emery Wheel) ....D
N. J.—Newark
Bernz, Otto, S. 13th Cor. S.
Orange Av. (Bib Seat)..B
N. Y.—Buffalo
Diamond Saw & Stamping
Wks., 357 Seventh (Emery
Wheel) ....D
Noye Mfg. Co., Jno. T.
(Floor) ....D
Osgood, J. L. (Emery
Wheel) ....D

DRESSERS (Con.)

N. Y.—Gloversville
Curtin Herbert Mfg. Co.
(Emery Wheel) ....D
New York City
Baylis Co., 140 Wash.
(Emery Wheel) ....D
Best, L. Emery Wheel) ..D
Dickinson, Jno. (Est. of), 64
Nassau (Diamond Pointed
Emery Wheel) ....B
Dickinson, Thos. L., 45
Vesey (Emery Wheel) ..H
Steel Set Diamond Co.
(Emery Wheel) X
Zucher & Levett & Loeb Co.
(Emery Wheel) X
OHIO—Cleveland
Auld & Conger (Slate) ....A
Globe Machine & Supply Co.
970 Hamilton (Emery
Wheel) ....E
Standard Tool Co. (Emery
Wheel) ....AAA
OHIO—Columbus
Case Mfg. Co. (Flour) ..AA
Columbus Bolt Wks., Ran-
dolph & Gorman (Emery
Wheel) ....A
Dayton Malleable Iron Co.
Emery Wheel) ......AA
OHIO—Tiffin
Sterling Emery Wheel Co.
(Emery Wheel) ....B
OHIO—Urbana
Desmond-Stephan Mfg. Co.
(Emery Wheel) ....D
PA.—Erie
Hollands Mfg. Co (Emery
Wheel) C
Reed Mfg. Co. (Emery
Wheel) ....B
PA.—Lancaster
Calder, Geo. H. (Emery
Wheel) ....H
Lancaster Peerless Emery
Wheel Co. (Emery Wheel)
...................B
PA.—Muncy
Sprout, Waldron & Co.
(Flour) ....A
PA.—Philadelphia
Abrasive Material Co.
(Emery Wheel) ....B
Butterworth & Sons Co., H.
W. (Wool) ....A
Challenge Machine Co., 3223
Turner (Emery Wheel) ..D
Furbush & Son Mach. Co., C.
A. (Warp; Wool; Yarn) A
Smith Woolen Mchry., Jas.,
411 Race (Warp) ....A
PA.—Stroudsburg
Tanite Co. (Emery Wheel)
R. I.—Pawtucket
Luther & Co., C. A. (Thread;
Yarn) C
R. I.—Providence
American Emery Wheel
Wks. (Emery Wheel)..C
Builders' Iron Foundry
(Emery Wheel) ......AA
Diamond Machine Co.
(Emery Wheel) ....A
Franklin Machine Co. (Yarn)
...................A
Textile Finishing Mchry. Co.
(Warp) ....AAAA
WIS.—Appleton
Valley Iron Wks. Mfg. Co.
(Stone) C
WIS.—Beloit
Berlin Machine Wks. (Tim-
ber) ....AAAA
WIS.—Milwaukee
Allis-Chalmers Co. (Flour)
..................AAAA

DRESSES

See Clothing; Ladies.

DRESSING

See also Polish; Blacking.
For Salad Dressing see Condiments & Relishes

657 DRESSING
CAL.—San Francisco
Nason & Co., R. N., 115
Front (Wire Rope) .....A
CONN.—Bridgeport
Palmer & Co., N. (Oak Belt)
...................B

DRESSING (Con.)

CONN.—Hartford
Jewell Belting Co. (Belt) AAA

ILL.—Chicago
Arnstein, Eugene (Shoe)..A
Bauer & Black (Antiseptic) A
Beltine Mfg. Co., 55 W. Jackson Boul. (Belt)....F
Blichert Mfg. Co., P. A. (Shoe) C
Carpenter Co., Geo. B. (Rope) ....AA
Chicago Belting Co., 67 S. Canal (Belt) ....A
Kilby & Co., G. W. (Shoe) C
Leather Preserve Mfg. Corp. 27 W. Monroe (Belt) ....D
Martell Co. (Harness; Shoe) E
Munson Belting Co., Chas. (Belt) ....B
Reliance Shoe Polish Co. (Shoe) ....G
Whitman & Barnes Mfg. Co., 60 S. Canal (Belt), AAAA

ILL.—Rockford
Sovergin Co., C. E. (Carriage Top; Harness) ...C
West Mfg. Co., L. M. (Carriage Top; Harness)....X

IND.—Mishawaka
Dodge Mfg. Co. (Rope) AAA

MASS.—Boston
Baker & Co., Chas. F. (Shoe) B
Boston Blacking Co. (Harness) ....AA
Brown & Co., B. F. (Shoe) A
'Eagle Oil & Supply Co., 104 Broad (Belt) ....D
Egyptian Chemical Co. (Harness) X
Hauthaway & Sons, Chas. L. (Harness; Shoe) ....A
Richmond & Co., Chas. C. Harness ....D
Viscol Co., A., E. Cambridge (Belt; Harness; Leather; Shoe) ....A
White Co., Saml. A. (Harness) C
Wood Co., Geo. H. (Shoe) C

MASS.—Cambridge
Sawyer Belting Co. (Belt, for Leather or Canvas), C
Whittemore Bros. & Co. (Leather; Shoe)......AA

MASS.—New Bedford
Nye, Wm. F. (Harness)...A

MASS.—Springfield
Young, W. F. (Hoof) ....D

MASS.—Watertown
Waterproof Paint Co. (Belt) E

MASS.—Worcester
Hudson Belting Co. (Belt) B
White & Bagley Co. (Belt) C

MICH.—Detroit
Acme White Lead Wks. (Carriage Top) .....AAA
Detroit White Lead Wks. (Carriage Top).....AAA

MICH.—Grand Rapids
Hayden & Co., J. M. (Belt) E

MO.— St. Louis
Leschen & Sons Rope Co., A., 920 N. 1st (Rope) AAA
Shultz Belting Co., 402 Barton (Belt)...........AA

N. H.—Concord
Page Belting Co. (Belt; Leather) C

N. J.—Jersey City
Dixon Crucible Co., Jos. (Belt) ....AAA
Gillespie & Sons, Chas. H. (Carriage Top) ....B

N. J.—Lincoln
Franklin Co. (Belt) ......G

N. J.—Newark
American Oil Supply Co. (Hoof) ....A
Peters' Harness & Saddlery Co. (Harness) ....A
Porsch Mfg. Co., 6 Lum (Leather for Bag, Cases, etc.) ....G
Rossendale-Reddaway Belting & Hose Co. (Belt)...A

DRESSING (Con.)

N. J.—New Brunswick
Johnson & Johnson (Inc.) (Antiseptic) ......AAAA

N. Y.—Albany
Stephenson Mfg. Co. (Bar Belt) ....D

N. Y.—Buffalo
Buffalo Specialty Mfg. Co., 375 Ellicott (Belt)....B
Cling-Surface Mfg. Co., 146 Virginia (Belt) ......D

New York City
Beldon & Co., A. G., 145 Maiden Lane (Belt) ...C
Bixby & Co., S. M. (Shoe) B
Bradford Belting Co., 88 Dey (Belt)...........A
Callahan & Co., Geo., 218 Front (Belt) ....F
Cowles & Co., 231 Fulton (Belt; Shoe) ....D
Fay Belting Co., 3 Jacob (Belt) ....D
Gallaway, G. W., 322 Pearl C
Gerstendorfer Bros., 235 E. 42d (Carriage Top) ....B
Hunt Co., C. W., 45 Bway. (Rope) ....AA
Loeb Bros., Leather Belting Co., 38 Ferry (Belt) ...D
Miller Co., Frank (Carriage Top; Harness; Hoof; Shoe) ....A
New York Mfg. Co., 38 Park Row (Belt) ....F
Post & Co., E. L., 50 Cliff (Belt) X
Restorff & Bettman (Leather; Shoe)........B
Royal Lubricating Co., 116 Broad (Harness) X
Schieren & Co., Chas. A., 45 Ferry (Belt) .....AAAA
Seabury & Johnson (Antiseptic) ....AA
Southwick Co. (Inc.), Geo. W., 149 Centre (Belt) ..E
Wolff, Norbert, 14 Jay (Belt) ....F

N. Y.—Palmyra
Garlock Packing Co. (Belt) A

N. Y.—Rochester
Rochester Chemical Co. (Harness) C

N. Y.—Syracuse
Baums Castorine Co. (Carriage Top) X

N. Y.—Tonawanda
Tallismanic Co. (Belt) ....D

N. Y.—Troy
Barnum Bros. Co. (Belt) ..E

OHIO—Akron
Akron Belting Co. (Belt)..B
Whitman & Barnes Mfg. Co. (Belt) ....AAAA

OHIO—Cincinnati
Atkins & Pearce Mfg. Co., 5th & Eggleston (Belt)..D

OHIO—Cleveland
Plomo Specialty Mfg. Co. (Belt) ....D
Smith Fdry. Supply Co., J. D. (Pattern) ....D

OHIO—Columbus
Ironsides Co., The Wyandotte (Belt) C

OHIO—Toledo
Allen Mfg. Co. (Hoof)....X

OHIO—Youngstown
American Belting Co. (Belt) C

PA.—Allentown
Garnet Belt Dressing Co. (Liquid; Bar Belt) ......B

PA.—Easton
World Refining Co. (Carriage Top; Hoof; Belt; Shoe) X

PA.—Philadelphia
Continental Mfg. Co. (Shoe) D
Diamond, McDonnell & Co. (Shoe) ....A
Eclipse Cement & Blacking Co., 1238 Belmont Av. (Harness; Leather; Shoe) A
Estweiler, Wm., 230 N. 3d (Belt) C
Felton, Sibley & Co., 136 N. 4th (Carriage Top) ..AAA
Gold, Walter C., 235 Race

DRESSING (Con.)
(Belt) ....E
Harkinson & Co., Robert (Leather) ....E
Houghton & Co., E F., 240 W. Somerset (Belt) ....B
Imperial Leather Preserve Mfg. Co., 212 S. 3d (Belt) C
Keystone Lubricating Co., 20th & Allegheny Av. (Grease Belt) X
Link Belt Engineering Co. (Rope) ....AA
Mason & Co., Jas. S. (Shoe) A
Mulford Co., H. K. (Antiseptic) ....AAA
Nice, Eugene E. (Canvas Oil) ....A
Rhoads & Son, J. E., 239 Market (Belt) ....A
PA.—Pittsburg
Feick Bros. Co. (Antiseptic) D
Pittsburg Rubber & Leather
PA.—Reading
Wilhelm Co., A. (Belt) AA
R. I.—Providence
Amer. Oil Co. (Belt) ....B
Providence Oil W'ks (Belt) ....B
WASH.—Seattle
Tolsma & Co., R. B. (Belt) ....F
WIS.—Menasha
Little Pulley Coating Co., O. C. (Softener; Preserver for Rubber; Canvas Belts) D
WIS.—Milwaukee
Delaney Oil Lubricant Co. 45 Third (Belt) ....D

DRIERS

See Dryers

DRIFTS

CONN.—Plantsville
Blakeslee Forging Co. (Key) B

DRILLS

See also Machinery; Cotton Goods; Agr. Implements.

CAL.—San Francisco
Compressed Air Machy. Co. (Compressed Air; Rock; Steam) ....E
Doble Co., Abner (Steam Stone) ....B
Rix Compressed Air & Drill Co., 396 Mission (Compressed Air) ....D
San Frans. Tool Wks., 27 Stevenson (Autoniatic) ..F
Union Iron Wks., 222 Market (Rock steam) .AAAA
COLO. Denver
Denver Engineering Wks. Co. (Electric 'Box' nonflexible Shaft) ....A
Jackson Drill & Mfg. Co., 1756 Larimer (Rock Hand) ....D
Leyner Engineering Wks Co., J. Geo. (Compressed Air) ....D
Mine & Smeltter Supply Co. (Electric Rock) ......AAA
CONN.—Bridgeport
Curtis & Curtis Co. (Ratchet, Flat; Pipe) .....A
Fray & Co., Jno. S. (Breast; Hand) C
CONN.—Bristol
Barttholomew, H. S. (Breast) ....B
Turner & Deegan (Breast) E
CONN.—Collinsville
Collins & Co. (Stone) AAAA
CONN.—Hartford
Billings & Spencer Co. (Ratchet, Flat; Pipe) ......A
Dwight Slate Machine Co. (Automatic; Bench; Multiple Spindle; Sensitive Self Feeding) C
Fenn-Sadler Machine Co. (Four Spindle Adjustable

DRILLS (Con.)
Hand; Multiple) ....F
Pratt & Whitney Co. (Automatic; Blacksmith's; Gang; Multiple Spindle; Rail; Railway Track; Ratchet, Flat; Pipe; Sensitive; Traverse; Upright; Taps, Pipe; Bench; Bicycle) ....AAAA
Quint, A. D. (Turrent) ....D
Sidowrney Tool Co. (Bench; Multiple Spindle; Upright; Self-Feeding; Sensitive) A
Woodward & Rogers Co. (Multiple Spindle; Sensitive) ....D
CONN.—Meriden
Parker Co., Chas. (Ratchet Flat; Pipe; Geared) AAAA
CONN.—New Haven
Geometric Drill Co. (Geometric; Collapsible Tap) ..C
New Haven Mfg. Co. (Suspension; Upright with Automatic Power Feed) AA
Shuster Co., F. B. (Multiple Spindle) X
CONN.—Oakville
Smith & Son, Seymour (Breast) ....D
CONN.—Plainville
Norton & Jones Machine Tool Wks. (Automatic Power Feed Multiple Spindles; Sensitive; Upright) ....F
CONN.—Seymour
Swan Co., Jas (Twist) ..A
CONN.—Southington
Peck, Stow & Wilcox Co. (Blacksmith's; Breast; Ratchet, Flat: Pipe; Geared) ....AAAA
CONN.—Waterbury
Cross & Spiers Machine Co. (Gang; Upright) ......D
Waterbury Tool Co. (Ratchet, Flat; Pipe) .....F
DEL.—Wilmington
Betts Machine Co. (Radial) A
GA.—Atlanta
May & Spalding (Rock) ..B
ILL.—Belleville
Belleville Pump & Skein Wks. (Rock, Steam) ....A
ILL.—Carpentersville
Illinois Iron & Bolt Co. (Blacksmith's Horizontal & Upright; Hand; Post) AA
ILL.—Chicago
Allis-Chalmers Co., Home Ins. Bldg. (Rock Steam) AAAA
Armstrong Bros. Tool Co., 617 Austin Av. (Ratchet Flat; Pipe) C
Austin Mfg. Co., Manhattan Bldg (Artesian Well) AAA
Chicago Flexible Shaft Co., La Salle Av. & Onario (Flexible Shaft; Hand; Portable) ....B
Chicago Pneumatic Tool Co., Fisher Bldg. (Pneumatic Rock) ....AAAA
Chicago Screw Co. (Taps, Pipe) ....AA
Contractor's Supply & Equipment Co., 232—5th Av. (Compressed Air; Rock Steam) C
Fairbanks, Morse & Co., Franklin & Monroe (Self-Feeding Rail; Railway Track) ....AAAA
Goodman Mfg. Co., Halstead & 48th Pl. (Electric) ..A
Hardinge Bros., 1036 Lincoln Av. (Sensitive) C
Helmold & Bro., J. F., 32 S. Jeff'n (Sensitive) ...E
Link—Belt Machine Co. (Coal, Auger Type) ....B
Lovejov, T. H., 90 Ohio (Railway Track) ......G
Morgan-Gardner Elec. Co., 2632 Shields Av. (Electric) ....AA
Pettibone, Mulliken & Co.,

DRILLS (Con.)

204 Dearborn (Railway Track) ....A
Railway Appliance Co., Old Colony Bldg (Pneumatic; Railway Track) ....A
Schuttler Ratchet Drill Co., 242 W. Lake (Railway Track; Ratchet, Flat; Pipe) ....B
Shaw, Willis, N. Y. Life Bldg. (Rock Steam)....D
Standard Diamond Drill Co., Monadnock Bldg., (Core Capacity 350 to 6000 ft.) C
Standard Screw Co., 2 N. Canal (Taps, Pipe) AAAA
Sullivan Machy. Co., 35 Adams (Core; Prospecting, Hand or Power; Rock Steam) ....AAA

ILL.—Downers Grove
Dicke Tool Co. (Hollow; Jamper Brick) C

ILL.—Edwardsville
Bignall & Keeler Mfg. Co. (Ratchet) ....B

ILL.—Evanston
Mark Mfg. Co. (Expansion) ....AA

ILL.—Freeport
Hoefer Mfg. Co. (Automatic; Bench; Gang; Upright; Multiple; Vertical; Multiple Spindle) ......D

ILL.—Harvey
Buda F'dry & Mfg. Co. (Br. Chicago, Ill) (Railway Track) ....A

ILL.—Moline —
Moline Tool Co. (Gang) ..D
Williams, White & Co. (Multiple Spindle)......A

ILL.—Ottawa
Porter Co., J. E. (Hand; Ratchet) ....A

ILL.—Rockford
Barnes Co., B. F. (Bench Multiple Spindle; Sensitive; Hand & Foot Power Upright; Horizontal; Vertical) ....B
Barnes & Co., W. F. & Jno. (Bend; Mulutiple Spindle; Sensitive; Upright; Bench; Radial; Self-Feeding; Bicycle) ......AA
Forest City Bit & Tool Co. (Bit Stock; Wood Boring Brace; Wood Boring)..C
Mechanics Machine Co. (Vertical) ....E

ILL.—Streator
Iwan Bros. (Hand Coal) ..D

IND.—Aurora
Aurora Tool Wks. (Boilermaker's; Radial; Upright) C

IND.—Elkhart
Buescher Mfg. Co. (Sensitive) C

IND.—Indianapolis
Everitt, J. A. (Hand)....B

IND.—South Bend
Sibley & Ware (Sensitive; Upright) ....A

KY.—Louisville
Clarke, Jr. & Co., Jas. (Electric) C

MAINE—Dexter
Fay & Scott (Upright)...C

MD.—Baltimore
Detrick & Harvey Machine Co. (Radial; Universal; Boiler Shell; Horizontal) ....AA

MASS.—Boston
Harvey, H. H. (Bow; Machine Bit; Stone)......B
Walworth Mfg. Co., 132 Federal (Railway Track) ....AAAA

MASS.—Fitchburg
Fitchburg Machine Wks. (Gang; Traverse; Upright; Radial; Self-Feeding; Special) ....A
Putnam Machine Co. (Radial; Tap; Traverse; Gooseneck; Increase Twist)..A

MASS.—Greenfield
Goodell-Pratt Co. (Automatic; Bench; Breast; Hand; Ratchet; Tap;

DRILLS (Con.)
Twist) ....B
Wells Bros. & Co. (Blacksmith's; Automatic)....A
Wiley & Russell Mfg. Co. (Automatic; Fluted; Blacksmith's Hand; Post) ....AA

MASS.—Lowell
Upton & Gilman (Hand, with Screw Feed & Chain attachment) ....D

MASS.—Miller's Falls
Miller's Falls Co. (Breast; Hand; Rail; Railway Track; Ratchet, Flat & Pipe; Automatic; Bench) ....AA

MASS.—New Bedford
Morse Twist Drill & Machine Co. (Bit Stock; Blacksmith's; Hand; Hollow; Ratchet, Flat; Pipe; Taps, Pipe; Twist; for Ratchets; Increase Twist; Shank; Taper Shank; Straightway; Bit Brace; Combination Center Fluted; Oil; Tap)......AAA

MASS.—North Adams
Hunter Machine Co., Jas. (Hand; Ratchet, Flat; Pipe) ....A

MASS.—Pittsfield
Jones & Sons Co., E. D. (Hand; Railway Track; Ratchet) ....B

MASS.—Shelburne Falls
Mayhew Co., H. H. (Bit Stock; Twist; Wood Boring Brace) C

MASS.—Springfield
Baush Machine Tool Co. (Automatic; Multiple Spindle; Radial; Suspension; Universal; Self Feeding) ....B

MASS.—Taunton
New Process Twist Drill Co. (Blacksmith's; Ratchet Flat; Pipe; Tap; Twist; Straightway; Wire Gauge) ....E

MASS. Webster
Barr & Co., Henry G. (Multiple Spindle; Sensitive; Spindle Upright; Bench; Geared; Vertical) ....D
Blaisdell & Co., P. (Traverse; Upright; Gooseneck; Self-Feeding; Bicycle; Multiple; Electric Driven; Vertical) ......A
Boynton & Plummer (Blacksmith's; Upright; Bench; Breast; Hand; Horizontal; Post; Rail; Vertical; Clamp; Horizontal) ....B
Fish Machine Wks Co., H. S. (Radial) ....D
Prentice Bros. Co. (Automatic; Boilermaker's; Boiler Shell; Gang; Hand; Multiple Spindle; Radial; Suspension; Upright) ..A
Prescott & son, J. B. (Blacksmith's) C
Reed Co., Francis (Bench; Blacksmith's; Clamp; Hand; Multiple Spindle; Portable; Rail; Railway Track; Sensitive; Upright; Automatic; Vertical; Post) ....D
Snyder; J. E. (Gang; Portable; Upright) C

MASS.—Wrentham
Winter Bros. Co. (Tap; Twist) ....E

MICH.—Bay City
Industrial Wks. (Rail) ..AA

MICH.—Detroit
Anderson & Sons, W. H. (Ratchet, Flat; Pine)..C
Detroit Twist Drill Co. (Twist; Wood Boring Brace; Wood Boring) ..C

MICH.—Grand Rapids
Fox Machine Co., 127 N. Front (Multiple Spindle; Sensitive; Upright; Bicycle; Vertical) x

MICH.—Kalamazoo
Kalamazoo Railway Supply Co. (Railway Track)....B

DRILLS (Con.)
MICH.—Saginaw
Wickes Bros. (Rock) ..AA
MICH.—Three Rivers
Sheffield Car Co. (Rail).AA
MICH.—Ypsilanti
Michigan Mchry. Mfg. Co.
  (Railway Track) .....AA
MINN.—St. Paul
Helwig Mfg. Co., Natl. Ger-
  man-Amer. Bldg. (Pneu-
  matic; Reversible; Port-
  able) ....F
MO.—Kansas City
Weber Gas & Gasoline En-
  gine Co., (Electric Driven)
  ....B
MO.—St. Louis
Ellison & Sons Mfg. Co.,
  Wm., 1018 N. 6th (Core)
  ....B
Handlan-Buck Mfg. Co., 212
  N. 3rd (Self-Feeding Rail-
  way Track) ....AA
Pleuger & Henger Mfg. Co.,
  11th & Hebert (Black-
  smiths'; Tire) ....A
St. Louis Machine Tool Co.,
  1114 S. 8th (Bench; Sensi-
  tive) X
St. Louis Screw Co., 3017 N.
  13th (& Taps; Pipe) ..A
Standard Railway Equip-
  ment Co., Union Trust
  Bldg. (Breast; Hand;
  Pneumatic) ....D
MONT.—Butte
Western Electric Drill Co.
  (Electric Rock) ....B
N. H.—Manchester
Forsaith Machine Co., S. C.
  (Radial; Suspension) ..X
N. H.—Tilton
Lord Bros. Mfg. Co. (Sensi-
  tive) ....B
N. J.—Elizabeth
Braunsdorf-Muller Co. (Star;
  Brick; Cement; Stone) .D
N. J.—Gloucester City
Rogers Boat Gauge & Drill
  Wks., J. M. (Compressed
  Air; Rock Steam) .....B
N. J.—Hasbrouck Heights
Olmsted, L. H. (Bench; Up-
  right) ....B
N. J.—Newark
Atha Tool Co. (Stone Cut-
  ters'; Ratchet; Flat;
  Pipe) ....A
Gould & Eberhardt, 95 N. J.
  R. R. Av. (Multiple Spin-
  dle; Twist; Automatic;
  Vertical) ....A
Johnson, Wm., 249 Plane
  (Ratchet; Flat; Pipe) ..D
N. J.—Plainfield
Pond Machine Tool Co. (Br.
  Niles-Bement-Pond Co.)
  (Radial) ....AAAA
N. Y.—Binghamton
Marvin Electric Drill Co
  (Electric Rock) ....B
Stow Mfg. Co. (Breast; Elec-
  tric; Flexible Shaft; Rail;
  Hand; Elec. Railway
  Track; Portable Power)B
N. Y.—Brooklyn
Pollard, Jos. G., 141 Ray-
  mond (Hollow; Jamper
  Brick to Drill Holes in
  Brick for Expansion Bolts)
  ....F
N. Y.—Buffalo
Buffalo Forge Co. (Black-
  smiths'; Hand) ......AA
Keystone Mfg. Co. 308 Ter-
  race (Ratchet; Flat; Pipe;
  Single Acting; Reversible;
  Hand) ....AA
Oliver Mfg. Co., W. W. 1483
  Niagara (Bench; Sensi-
  tive; Jewelers', &c.) ..C
Union Mfg. & Specialty Co.
  (Foot Power) ....D
West Mfg. Co., 374 7th
  (Breast) ....D
N. Y.—Frankfort
Acme Road Mchry Co.
  (Rock; Steam) C
N. Y.—Medina
Swett Iron Wks., A. L.
  (Blacksmiths' Steel
  Spindle) ....A

DRILLS (Con.)
New York City
American Diamond Rock
  Drill Co., 95 Liberty (Dia-
  mond Prospecting Core;
  (Rock) ....D
American Wood Working
  Mach. Co. (Machine Bit)
  ....AAA
Ashcroft Mfg. Co., 85 Lib-
  erty (Ratchet; Flat; Pipe)
  ....A
Clayton Air Compressor Wks
  118 Liberty (Compressed
  Air) ....B
Davis Calyx Drill Co., 128
  Bway. (Core, without Dia-
  monds) ....B
Dickinson, John (Est. of)
  64 Nassau (Glass) .....B
Eckstein, Chas. G., 249
  Center (Clamp) ....D
Etna Mfg. Co., 253 B'way
  (Bit Stock; Blacksmiths;
  Fluted; Ratchet; Twist)
  ....D
Fairbanks Co., 416 Broome
  (Blacksmiths'; Breast)
  ....AAAA
Fox Bros. & Co., 24 Vesey
  (Railway Track) ......H
Garvin Machine Co., 143
  Varick (Bench; Multiple
  Spindle; Sensitive; Up-
  right; Automatic; Self-
  Feeding; Bicycle)...AAA
Hercules Elec. Drill Co., 32
  Bway. (Electric Rock)
 X
Ingersoll-Sergeant Drill Co.,
  26 Cortlandt (Compressed
  Air; Rock Steam; Pneu-
  matic) ....AAAA
Jennings Co., C. E., 42 Mur-
  ray (Hand) ....B
McCabe, J. J., 14 Dey (Ra-
  dial; Vertical) ....B
McDougall & Potter Co., 606
  W. 55th (Rock Steam)
  ....D
McKiernan Drill Co., 170
  Bdway. (Compressed Air;
  Rock Steam) ....B
Manning Maxwell & Moore,
  85 Liberty (Radial) .AAA
Motley Co., Thornton N., 14
  John (Rock Hand) X
Niles-Bement-Pond Co., 136
  Liberty (Automatic
  Blacksmiths'; Boilermak-
  ers'; Electric; Multiple
  Spindle; Portable; Radial;
  Rail; Sensitive; Suspen-
  sion; Turrent; Universal;
  Upright; Boiler Shell;
  Electric Driven; Geared;
  Horizontal; Vertical;
  Wheel Car) ....AAAA
Pierce Well Engineering &
  Supply Co. (Rock) C
Rand Drill Co., 128 Bdway.
  (Compressed Air; Rock
  Steam; Pneumatic) ....A
Sargent & Co., 151 Leonard
  (Blacksmiths') .....AAAA
Slotkin & Praglin (Automa-
  tic; Bench; Sensitive;
  Foot Power) C
Tower & Lyon Co., 95 Cham-
  bers (Hand) ....B
N. Y.—Orangeburg
Empire Engine & Motor Co.
  (Breast) ....B
N. Y.—Rochester
Davis Machine Co., W. P.
  (Sensitive; Vertical) ..B
N. Y.—Schenectady
General Electric Co. (Elec-
  tric Rock) ....AAAA
N. Y.—Spuyten Duyvil
Johnson & Co., Isaac G.
  (Railway Track) .....AA
N. Y.—Syracuse
Kane & Roach, Niagara &
  Shonnard (Radial) C
Stearns & Co., E. C.
  (Bench) ....AA
Syracuse Twist Drill Co.
  (Bit Stock; Twist; Bit
  Brace) ....B

345

DRILLS (Con.)

OHIO—Akron
Star Drilling Machine Co. (Artesian Well; Radial) ......A

Whitman & Barnes Mfg. Co. (Bit Stock; Blacksmiths'; Boilermakers'; Fluted; Garden Seed; Ratchet; Flat; Pipe; Twist; Taps; Pipe) ....AAAA

OHIO—Cincinnati
American Tool Wks. Co. (Multiple Spindle; Radial; Sensitive; Universal; Upright; Boiler Shell; Vertical) ....AAA

Andrew & Co., M. L., 118 W. 2d (Multiple Spindle) ......D

Bickford Drill & Tool Co., Front & Pike (Boilermakers'; Multiple Spindle; Portable; Radial; Suspension; Traveling; Universal; Upright; Bicycle).A

Cincinnati Screw & Tap Co., 2442 Beekman (Pipe; Twist) ....B

Cincinnati Machine Tool Co. (Upright; Bit Brace; Machine Bit; Vertical).D

Dietz Machine Tool Co. (Upright) ....B

Dreses, Mueller Machine Tool Co. (Radial; Universal) ....B

Fosdick Machine Tool Co. (Bicycle; Boiler Shell; Electric Driven; Multiple; Radial; Horizontal; Multiple; Vertical) C

Fosdick & Halloway Machine Tool Co. (Radial; Upright) C

Gang Co. Wm. E., 1543 Queen City Av. (Radial)

Haven Co., Jas. L. (Fire) X

Hisey-Wolf Machine Co. (Breast; Electric-Driven; Hand; Portable) X

Knecht Bros. Co., 2442 Beekman (Friction Sensitive; Upright) ....D

Lodge & Shipley Mach. Tool Co. (Radial; Upright) ....A

Muller Mach. Tool Co. (Radial) ....D

Presler-Crawley Mfg. Co., 219 W. 2nd (Prospecting Core; Hand; Power) ..F

Roos & Mill (Radial) ....F

Schumacher & Boye, Queen City Av. & Buck (Sensitive; Upright) ....A

OHIO—Cleveland
Cleveland Punch & Shear Wks., 156 Case Av. (Portable; Radial; Suspension; Multiple; Post) ......A

Cleveland Twist Drill Co., Lake & Kirtland (Bit Stock; Fluted; Hollow; Twist; & Taps; Pipe; Blacksmiths; Bit Brace; Wood Boring Brace)....A

Foote, Burt & Co., 269 St. Clair (Gang; Multiple Spindle; Sensitive; Adjustable Universal; Arch Bar; Automatic; Bench; Boiler Shell; Locomotive Frame; Rail; Vertical; Locomotive; Mud Ring; Flue Steel) ....D

Gardner Elec. Drill & Mchry. Co. (Electric Rock) ....A

Lucas Machine Tool Co. (Multiple Spindle) C

Standard Tool Co. (Bit Stock; Blacksmiths'; & Taps; Pipe; Increase Twist; Shank; Bit Brace; Fluted; Hollow; Oil Tube) ....AAA

DRILLS (Con.)

Strong. Carlisle & Hammond (Bench; Bracket; Portable; Radial) ......A

OHIO—Columbus
Jeffrey Mfg. Co. (Compressed Air; Electric; Rock; Steam; Coal; Augur Type; Hand Coal; Power Coal) ....AA

Rhoades Mfg. Co. (Sensitive Press) X

OHIO—Dayton
Nat'l Automatic Tool Co. (Two-Nutting Full Automatic Multiple Spindle).C

Patterson Tool & Supply Co. (Bench; Sensitive; Vertical) ....B

OHIO—Hamilton
Hamilton Machine Tool Co. (Radial; Upright) ......A

Niles Tool Wks. Co. (Automatic; Multiple Spindle; Radial; Rail; Upright)... ....AAAA

OHIO—Mansfield
Ohio Brass Co. (Railway Track) ....B

OHIO—Nelsonville
Nelsonville Fdry. & Machine Co. (Coal; Augur Type).B

OHIO—Norwood
Cincinnati Tool Co. (Bit Stock; Blacksmiths') ..A

OHIO—Salem
Edwards Co., M. S. (Hand) ....F

Silver Mfg. Co. (Bench; Blacksmiths'; Boilermakers'; Machine Bit) .....A

OHIO—Springfield
Foos Mfg. Co. (Blacksmith's; Hand) ....A

OHIO—Toledo
Baker Bros. (Bicycle; Multiple; Vertical) ....A

OREGON—Merlin
Keyte, H. L. (Rock; Hand) X

PA.—Beaver Falls
Beaver Falls Mfg. Co. (Coal; Augur Type; Hand Coal; Hand Rock) ....D

PA.—Birdsboro
Diamond Drill & Machine Co. (Artesian Well; Core; Prospecting; Hand; Power; Rock; Steam) ......B

PA.—Lancaster
Champion Blower & Forge Co. (Blacksmiths'; Hand) ......B

Potts, David H. (Upright) ......D

PA.—Philadelphia
Bement, Miles & Co. (Automatic; Multiple Spindle; Radial; Rail; Self-Feeding; Suspension; Upright) (see Niles-Bement-Pond Co., N. Y. City).

Borton & Tierney Co., Stephen Girard Bldg. (Mfrs.' Agts.—Rock; Steam)...F

Box & Co., Alfred, 813 N. Front (Radial) ....D

Dallett & Co., Thos. H., York & Sedgley Av. (Electric Duplex; Boiler Shell; Electric Breast; Hand; Pneumatic; Portable Electric Rope Driven; Electric Railway Track) ......A

Dwight. E. P. (Rail) X

Eppen-Lucas Machine Wks. (Rail) X

Harrington Son & Co., E., 1515 Penn Av. (Multiple Spindle; Portable; Radial; Sensitive; Post) ......AA

Nazel Machine Tool Wks., 1042 Ridge Av. (Portable) ......F

Newton Machine Tool Wks., 2343 Vine (Multiple Spindle; Portable Electrically Driven) ....A

North Bros. Mfg. Co., cor.

DRILLS (Con.)

Amer. & Lehigh Av. (Automatic; Reciprocating; Hand, for Carpenters'; Hand) ....A
Olsen, Tinius & Co., 500 N. 12th (Hand) ....B
Philadelphia Pneumatic Tool Co., 21st & Allegheny Av. (Pneumatic; Rotary; Portable) C
Phillips Rock Drill Co. (Compressed Air Rock).X
Rutschmann Bros., N. 5th & Berks (Hand) C
Sellers & Co. (Inc.), Wm., 1600 Hamilton (Boilermakers'; Multiple Spindle; Radial; Rail; Universal; Upright; Reaming; Countersinking; Cotter; Boiler Shell) ......AAAA
Steward & Romaine Mfg. Co., 124 N. 6th (Star; Brick; Cement) ....D
Stortz & Son, Jno., 210 Vine (Radial; Flat; Pipe; Star) ....F
Stow Flexible Shaft Co., N. 26th & Buttonwood (Breast Clamp; Flexible Shaft; Electric Hand; Pneumatic Portable; Rail; Suspension; Universal; Bicycle; Hand; Portable; Radial; Rock; Sensitive) ....B

PA.—Pittston
Muirhead & Son, Jno. (Prospecting Core) .....B
PA.—Plymouth
Bittenbender, Geo. H. (Mine Ratchet) ....D
Howell's Mining Drill Co. (Compressed Air; Electric; Hand Rock; & Coal; Coal; Auger Type; Steam; Powder Coal) C
PA.—Wilkesbarre
Le Grand Mine Drill Wks. (Coal; Rock Mine; Steam) ....F
R. I.—Pawtucket
Carpenter Tap & Die Co., J. M. (& Taps; Pipe) ..C
Jackson Patent Shell Roll Co. (Clamp) X
Pawtucket Mfg. Co. (& Taps; Pipe) ....A
R. I.—Providence
Langelier Mfg. Co. (Sensitive; Upright) ....E
Slocomb & Co., J. T. (Combination Centre) ......E
Standard Machineery Co. (Bench; Sensitive) ....E
TENN.—Chattanooga
Nixon-Ratchet Mining Drill Co. (Mine Ratchet) ....D
VT.—Derby Line
Butterfield & Co. (Tap) ..B
VT.—Rutland
Patch Mfg. Co., F. R. (Marble) ....A
WIS.—Milwaukee
Pawling & Harnischfeger (Horizontal) ....AA
WIS.—Racine
Tecktonius, E. C. (Clamp) ....F
WIS.—Sheboygan
Optenberg & Sonneman (Radial) ....D

DRIPS

IND.—Fort Wayne
Kerr Mfg. Co., Murray (Street) ....A

DRIVERS

CONN.—Bridgeport
Bridgeport Hdw. Mfg. Co., 481 Iranistan Av. (Screw) ....B
Hurwood Mfg. Co. (Screw) C
Smith & Egge Mfg. Co. (Cycle Screw, of Steel

DRIVERS (Con.)

Wire) ....A
CONN.—Bristol
Clayton Bros. (Screw)....D
Turner & Deegan (Screw) ....E

CONN.—Guilford
Spencer's Sons, I. S. (Staple) ....A
CONN.—Hartford
Billings & Spencer Co. (Screw; Screw Magazine) ....AA
CONN.—Meriden
Meriden Mfg. Co. (Self Adjustable Screw)......X
CONN.—New Britain
Russell & Erwin Mfg. Co. (Screw) ....AAAA
Stanley Rule & Level Co. (Screw) ....AAA
CONN.—New Haven
Brown & Co., R. H. (Screw) ....B
CONN.—Seymour
Swan Co., James (Screw) ....A
CONN.—Southington
Peck, Stow & Wilcox Co. (Screw) ....AAAA
CONN.—Torrington
Union Hdw. Co. (Screw).AA
ILL.—Chicago
Bartlett & Son, M. J., 196 S. Clark (Screw) .....F
Nicol & Co. (Screw)......D
Vulcan Iron Wks., 36 No. Clinton (Pile)........AA
ILL.—Decatur
Mueller Mfg. Co., H. (Screw; Reversible Bit Screw; Combined Screw; Drill) ....AAA
ILL.—Downers Grove
Dicke Tool Co. (Screw, for Electrical and Machinery Work) C
ILL.—Freeport
Arcade Mfg. Co. (Screw).A
ILL.—Harvey
Austin Mfg. Co., F. C. (Pile) ....AAA
IND.—Indianapolis
National Dry Kiln Co. (Brick) ....A
MASS.—Athol
Starratt Co., L. S. (Pocket Screw) ....A
MASS.—Brockton
Tuck Mfg. Co. (Screw)..E
MASS.—Fiskdale
Snell Mfg. Co. (Screw)..B
MASS.—Fitchburg
Sawyer Tool Mfg. Co. (Screw) C
MASS.—Greenfield
Goodell-Pratt Co. (Screw; Screw Automatic; Ratchet Screw) ....B
MASS.—Kingston
Drew & Co., C. (Coopers').C
MASS.—Millbury
Buck, Chas. (Screw) ....B
Buck Bros. (Screw).......A
MASS.—Miller Falls
Miller Falls Co. (Screw; Screw Automatic; Ratchet Screw; Spiral Screw) ....AA
MASS.—New Bedford
Morse Twist Drill & Machine Co. (Screw) ......AAA
MASS.—Northampton
Clement Mfg. Co. (Hollow Handle Screw).......B
MASS.—North Easton
New England Specialty Co. (Screw) ....F
MASS.—Shelburne Falls
Ducharmes & Co. (Screw).F
Mayhew Co., H. H. (Screw) ....D
MASS.—Springfield
Bemis & Call Hdw. & Tool Co. (Screw) ....A
Smith & Wesson (Pocket Screw) ....AAAA
Waltham Watch Tool Co. (Screw) ....B

DRIVERS (Con.)

MASS.—West Mansfield
Standard Tool Co. (Screw) .... H

MICH.—Bay City
Industrial Wks. (Pile) ..AA

MINN.—Minneapolis
Howell & Co., R. R. (Pile) .... B

N. H.—Bennington
Kimball Co., C. J. (Screw) .... D

N. H.—Lebanon
Kendrick & Davis (Small Screw) .... A

N. J.—Newark
Bernz, Otto S., 13th, cor. So. Orange Av. (Screw) .... B
Johnson, Wm. (Screw) .D
Mundy, J. S. (Pile) ..... A
Osborne & Co., C. S. (Screw) .... B
Seymour & Whitlock, 43 Lawrence (Brad, for Boarding or Nailing Door Mouldings) .... B

N. Y.—Buffalo
Union Mfg. & Spec. Co. (Screw; Screw Leather Handled) C
White, L. & I. J. (Coopers') .... A

New York City
Ingersoll-Sargent Drill Co., 26 Cortlandt (Pile) .AAAA
Jennings & Co., C. E. (Screw; Spiral Screw) .B
Lidgerwood Mfg. Co., 96 Liberty (Pile) .....AAA
New Jersey Fdry. & Machine Co. (Pile) ....D
Prentiss Vise Co., 44 Barclay (Screw, full line) ..C
Sargent & Co., 151 Leonard (Screw) ....AAAA
Smith & Hemenway Co., 296 Bway. (Screw) ....D
Tower & Lyon Co., 95 Chambers (Screw; Screw, Holder) ....B
Wilbusch & Hilger, 9 Murray (Adjustable Screw) .A

OHIO—Akron
Whitman & Barnes Mfg. Co. (Screw) ....AAAA

OHIO—Cleveland
Federal Mfg. Co., Amer. Trust Bldg. (Screw) AAAA

OHIO—Ravenna
Williams, A. C. (Screw) .A

PA.—Allegheny
Carlins Sons, Thos. (Pile) A

PA.—Philadelphia
Disston & Sons (Inc.) Henry (Screw) ....AAAA
Miller Lock Co. (Pocket Screw) .... B
North Bros. Mfg. Co., Lehigh Av., cor. Amer. (Ratchet; Pocket; Magazine Screw; Screw Automatic; Ratchet Screw; Spiral Screw) ....AA
Smith Co., J. Barton, N. 4th & Somerset (Screw) .D
Stortz & Son, Jno., 210 Vine (Screw) ....E
Stow Flexible Shaft Co. (Ratchet Screw) ....B
Sutterley & Co., Gilbert T. (Screw) C

PA.—Seitzland
Vaughn, Chas. A. (Screw) G

DRIVES

ILL.—Chicago
Borden & Selleck Co., 48 Lake (Rope) ....B
Caldwell & Son, H. W., Western Av. & 17th (Belt; Chain) ....AA
Roth Bros. & Co., 29 S. Clinton (Electric) .....B

N. Y.—Poughkeepsie
Adriance, Platt & Co. (Mower Chain) ....AAAA

DRIVES (Con.)

OHIO—Cleveland
Electric Controller & Supply Co., Central & Giddings (Magnetic Clutches) ....A

DROPPER

MASS.—Andover
Tyer Rubber Co. (Medicine) AA

New York City
Mattson Rubber Co. (Medicine) ....B

OHIO—Akron
Akron Rubber Wks. (Medicine) ....AAAA

OHIO—Barberton
Pure Gum Specialty Co. (Rubber Medicine) C

PA.—Philadelphia
Ware Co., Walter F. (Medicine) ....B

DROPS

See Jewelry

DROSS

ILL.—Chicago
Loraine Smelting & Refining Co., 115 Dearborn (Tin; Zinc) ....F

New York City
Nassau Smelting & Refining Wks., 607 W. 29th (Refiners'; Smelters') AAA

DRUGS & HERB

See also Barks; Herbs.

MASS.—Boston
Stickney & Poor Spice Co. (Cooking Herbs) ....A

MICH.—Detroit
Parke Davis & Co. (Crude) AAAA

New York City
Dodge & Olcott (Crude) AAA
Hopkins & Co., J. L. (Crude) ....A
Lehn & Fink (Crude) ..AAA
McKesson & Robbins (Crude) ....AAAA
Peck & Velsor (Crude) C
Schieffelen & Co. (Crude) AA
Thurston & Braidich (Crude) ....AA

WIS.—Fond du Lac
Huber & Fuhrman Drug Mills (Powdered; Ground Herbs) ....A

DRUMS

See also Musical Instruments

CONN.—New Haven
Eastern Machinery Co. (Friction Winding) .....B

ILL.—Chicago
Allis-Chalmers Co., Home Ins. Bldg. (Hoisting; Single; Double) ..AAAA
Chicago Pneumatic Tool Co., Fisher Bldg. (Pneumatic Winding) ....AAAA
Crane Co., 10 No. Jefferson (Car Heater) ......AAAA

ILL.—Decatur
Leader Iron Wks. (Winding; Cable) ....D

IND.—Brazil
Crawford & McCrimmon Co. (Hoisting) ....A

IND.—Indianapolis
Potts & Co. (Inc.) C. & A. (Winding) ....B

IOWA—Ottumwa
Ottumwa Iron Wks. (Hoisting) ....AAAA

KANS.—Fort Scott
Fort Scott Fdry. & Machine Co. (Hoisting; Winding) H

DRUMS (Con.)

MAINE—Portland
Portland Cooperage Co.
(Fish Shipping).......C

MASS.—Boston
Hersey Mfg. Co. (Hoisting)
AA

MASS.—Cambridge
Rawson & Morrison Mfg. Co.
(Hoisting; Single; Double)
A

MASS.—Northampton
Williams Mfg. Co. (Veneer;
Coffee, &c.) ....A

MICH.—Grand Rapids
Michigan Barrel Co. (To-
bacco Shipping) ....A

MICH.—Morenci
Michigan Brick & Tile Ma-
chine Co. (Winding)....D

MINN.—St. Paul
American Hoist & Derrick
Co. (Hoisting) ......AAA

MO.—Kansas City
Weber Gas & Gasoline En-
gine Co. (Friction Wind-
ing) ....A

MO.—St. Louis
St. Louis Basket & Box Co.,
Arsenal & 2d (Packing) A

N. J.—Newark
Lambert Hoisting Engine
Co., 115-121 Poinier
(Hoisting) ....A
Mundy, J. S., 22 Prospect
(Hoistin) ....A

N. J.—Trenton
Trenton Iron Co. (Rope
Driving) ....A

N. Y.—Albany
Dederick's Sons, P. K.
(Hoisting; Single; Double)
A
Townsend Furnace & Ma-
chine Shop Co. (Cable)..A

N. Y.—Buffalo
Contractors Plant Mfg. Co.,
129 Erie (Hoisting)....B
Shephard & Co., Sidney
(Botanizing) ......AAAA

New York City
Bacon, Earle C., 26 Cort-
landt (Hoisting) .....B
Johns-Manville Co., H. W.,
100 William (Liquid)
AAAA
Koven & Bro., L. O., 50
Cliff (Mud) ....A
Lidgerwood Mfg. Co., 96
Liberty (Hoisting; Single;
Double) ....AAA

N. Y.—Niagara Falls
Dobbie Fdry. & Machine Co.
(Hoisting) ....D

N. C.—Statesville
Steele & Son, J. C. (Winding) ....B

OHIO—Bucyrus
American Clay Wkg. Machy.
Co. (Winding) X

OHIO—Canton
Bonnot Co. (Winding)...A

OHIO—Cleveland
Cleveland Wire Spring Co.
(Steel Oil) ....A

OHIO—Ravenna
Byers Machine Co., Jno. F.
(Hoisting) ....A

OHIO—Zanesville
Griffiths & Wedge Co.
(Winding) ....B

PA.—Allegheny
Carlins Sons, Thos. (Gravity Incline) ....A

PA.—Bangor
Flory Mfg. Co., S. (Hoisting; Double; Single)...A

PA.—Erie
Erie City Iron Wks. (Mud)
AAAA
Stearns Mfg. Co. (Mud).B

PA.—Philadelphia
Link Belt Engineering Co.
(Rope Driving) ......AA

PA.—Pittsburg
Riter-Conley Mfg. Co. (Gas)
AAA
Scaife & Sons Co., Wm. B.,
221 1st Av. (Glycerine;
Oil; Steel Oil) ......AAA

DRUMS (Con.)
Union Fdry. & Machine Co.
(Winding) ....B

PA.—Sharon
Sharon Boiler Wks. (Mud)
A

PA.—Wilkesbarre
Vulcan Iron Wks. (Rope
Driving; Winding; Hoist-
ing; Conical; Cylindrical)
AAAA

R. I.—Woonsocket
Woonsocket Machine & Press
Co. (Rope Driving)....AA

WIS.—Milwaukee
Filer & Stowell Co. (Rope
Driving) ....AAA

DRYERS

See also Kilns; Machinery

CAL.—San Francisco
Hendy Machine Works,
Joshua, 38 Fremont (Ore)
AA
Union Iron Wks., 222 Mar-
ket (Ore) X

COLO.—Denver
Mine & Smelter Supply Co.
(Ore) ....AAAA

CONN.—Derby
Birmingham Iron Fdry.
(Cloth) ....AA

CONN.—Windsor Locks
Clark Co., Geo. P. (Warp)
C

GA.—Rome
Georgia Fdry. & Machine
Wks. (Ore) ....D
Morrison, Trammell Brick
Co. (Brick) ....D

ILL.—Chicago
Allis-Chalmers Co., Home
Ins. Bldg. (Ore)..AAAA
Andrews Co., A. H. (Lum-
ber) ....AA
Barron Dryer Co., Temple
Court Bldg. (Brick)....D
Chicago Clothes Dryer Wks.
346 Wabash Av. (Clothes;
Steam; Hot Air; Hot Wa-
ter; Gas) ....D
Hess Warming & Ventilat-
ing Co., 135 La Salle
(Pneumatic System Grain;
Malt) ....D
Steel Roll Machine Co. 142
Washn. Boul. (Laundry)
F

IND.—Indianapolis
Nordyke & Marmon Co. (Ce-
ment; Asphalt; Meal;
Grain) ....AA
Standard Dry Kiln Co.
(Brick) ....A

IOWA—Davenport
Davenport Foundry & Ma-
chine Co. (Cane Continu-
ous) X

KANS.—Leavenworth
Great Western Mfg. Co.
(Meal; Grain) ....AA

KY.—Louisville
Turney Drier Co., Columbia
Bldg. (Cement; Asphalt;
Grain; Malt; Ore) X

MAINE—Brunswick
Fairfield Lawn Swing Co.
(Clothes) ....E

MASS.—Boston
Hersey Mfg. Co., 314 W.
2d (Rotary; Fertilizer;
Grain; Malt; Salt; Sand;
Sugar; Starch Refuse;
Coffee) ....AA
Riley & Co., C. E., 65
Franklin (Wool) ......A
Sturtevant Co., B. F.
(Cloth; Wood; Yarn;
Grain; Lumber; Cotton)
AAA

MASS.—Cambridge
Rawson & Morrison Mfg.
Co. (Inc.) (Fertilizer;
Grain) ....A

MASS.—Lowell
Kitson Machine Co. (Wool)
AAA

349

DRYERS (Con.)

MASS.—North Adams
Hunter Machine Co., Jas
(Wool) ....A
MASS.—Westford
Sargents' Sons, C. G. (Cotton; Wool) ....A
MASS.—Worcester
Cleveland Machine Wks.
(Cloth) ....A
Curtis & Marble Machine Co.
(Carpet) ....A
Hill Dryer Co. (Clothes).D
MICH.—Detroit
American Blower Co.
(Brick; Cement; Asphalt;
Wool; Lumber; Cloth;
Cotton; Grain) ......AA
Berry Bros. (Ltd.) (Japan;
Liquid) ....AAAA
N. H.—Manchester
Campbell, Jno. (Clothes).H
N. H.—Nashua
Nashua Novelty Wks. (Wall
Clothes) ....B
N. H.—Pike Station
Pike Mfg. Co. (Boot Soapstone) ....A
N. J.—Cedar Brook
Bailey, Frank (Yarn)...E
N. J.—Jersey City
Griffing Iron Co., A. A.,
449 Communipaw Av.
(Brick) ....AA
Smith & Sons Co., Theodore,
ft. of Essex (Cement; Asphalt) ....A
Woolsey Paint & Color Co.,
C. A. (Transparent) ...A
N. J.—Newark
Murphy Varnish Co. (Japan; Transparent).AAAA
N. J.—Raritan
Kenyon & Son, D. R.
(Cloth) ....B
N. Y.—Buffalo
Buffalo Dental Mfg. Co.
(Clothes Airers; Gas)...B
Buffalo Forge Co. (Brick;
Cloth; Cotton; Grain;
Leather) ....AAA
Mey Chain Belting Engineering Wks., 14 Perry
(Grain; Malt) ....F
Smiths' Sons, Jno. E. (Lard)
B
Squier Mfg. Co., Geo. L.
(Coffee) ....
N. Y.—Munnsville
Munnsville Plow Co.
(Clothes) ....B
New York City
Abbe Engineering Co., 220
Bway. (Cement; Asphalt)
D
Calman & Co., Emil
(Liquid) ....AA
F. W. Devoe & C. T. Raynolds Co. (Liquid; Transparent) ....AAAA
Hungerford Bros. & Co.
(Coffee) ....B
Longman & Martinez (Japan; Liquid) ......AAA
Mace & Co., L. R.
(Clothes) ....B
Mayer & Loewenstein (Japan; Liquid; Transparent)
AAA
Pierce Co., F. O. (Japan)
A
Pratt & Lambert (Inc.)
(Japan; Liquid) ....B
Reilley Bros. (Clothes)..D
Ruggles-Coles Engineering
Co., 39 Cortlandt (Cement; Asphalt; Grain;
Malt; Ore; Pebbles)....X
Staubach, B. (Lard) ....A
Steel Cable Engineering Co.,
120 Liberty (Rotary)..B
N. Y.—Silver Creek
Hower Co., S. (Grain) ..A
N. Y.—Warsaw
Warsaw Elevator Co. (Salt
Well) ....B
N. C.—Winston-Salem
Salem Iron Wks. (Coffee)
A

DRYERS (Con.)

OHIO—Bucyrus
American Clay Wkg. Machy.
Co. (Brick) X
OHIO—Cincinnati
American Laundry Machy.
Co. (Clothes Airers; Gas)
AA
Ault & Wiborg Co. (Japan)
AAAA
Blymer Iron Wks. Co.
(Hop) ....B
Day & Co., J. H. (Sand)..A
Littleford Bros., 453 E.
Pearl (Pebble) ....B
Miller Range & Furnace Co.,
Wm., 125 E. 5th (Laundry) ....A
Peck-Williamson Heating &
Ventilating Co., 337 W.
5th (Laundry) ....AA
OHIO—Cleveland
Bartlett & Snow Co., C. O.
(Cement; Asphalt; Grain;
Malt; Coal) ....A
Cleveland Varnish Co.
(Japan; Liquid; Transparent) ....AA
Crown Dryer Co., New England Bldg. (Cement; Asphalt; Grain; Malt) ...D
Cummer & Son Co., F. D.,
413 Arcade (Brick; Cement; Asphalt; Grain;
Malt; Ore) ....A
Mannen & Esterly, 811 St.
Clair (Clothes; Hot Air;
Steam; Hot Water; Gas)
D
Ohio Ceramic Engineering
Co. (Hot Air Brick) ..B
OHIO—Columbus
Case Mfg. Co. (Grain; Corn)
A
Jeffrey Mfg. Co. (Grain)..
AAAA
OHIO—Dayton
Thresher Varnish Co.
(Japan) ....A
OHIO—Hamilton
Black & Clawson Co.
(Lard) ....AAA
OHIO—Steubenville
Means Fdry. & Machine Co.
(Brick) C
OHIO—Zanesville
Griffith & Wedge Co.
(Revolving) ....B
PA.—East Stroudsburg
Stauffer, Geo. E. (Revolving) C
PA.—Lancaster
Martin Brick Mchry. Mfg.
Co. (Sand) ....B
PA.—Philadelphia
American Drying Mchry. Co.
(Cotton; Wool; Yarn)...D
Atlantic Drier & Varnish Co.
(Japan; Liquid) ....B
Morris, Henry G., Phila.
Bourse (Grain; Malt) ..B
Nittinger, August (Lard) A
Philadelphia Drying Mchry.
Co. (Wool; Yarn) ....D
Philadelphia Textile Mchry.
Co., Hancock & Somerset
(Cloth; Cotton; Wool;
Yarn; Tobacco; Underwear) ....AA
PA.—Pittsburg
Velte Fdry. & Machine Co.
(Sand) ....A
PA.—South Bethlehem
Bethlehem Fdry. & Machine
Co. (Cement; Asphalt)..B
PA.—Union City
Novelty Wood-work Co.
(Cloth; Clothes) ....B
PA.—Warren
Struthers Wells & Co.
(Fertilizer) ....AA
PA.—York
Dempwolf & Co., C. H.
(Tankage; Bone) ......A
R. I.—Providence
Textile Finishing Mchry.
Co., 17 Exchange Pl.
(Cloth; Warp; Yarn)...
AAA

DRYERS (Con.)

WIS.—Cudahy
Power & Mining Mchry. Co.
(Ore) ....AAA
WIS.—Milwaukee
Allis-Chalmers Co. (Ore)..
..................AAAA
Morris & Co., F. R. (Grain;
Malt) ....F
Nat'l Blower Wks., 17th &
St. Paul Av. (Brick;
Wool) ....A
Pawling & Harnischfeger
(Grain) ....AAA

DUCKS

See Cotton Goods ....

DULCIMERS

See Musical Instruments

DUMBWAIT-
ERS

See also Elevators

ILL.—Chicago
Union Elevator & Machine
Co., 144 Ontario C
MASS.—Springfield
Electron Mfg. Co. (Electric)
...........................A

New York City
Sedgwick Machine Wks., 110
Liberty ....D
See Electric Elevator Co.,
A. B., 220 B'way ..AAA

DUMPS

ILL.—Bloomington
Portable Elevator Mfg. Co.
(Wagon) ....B
ILL.—Chicago
Weller Mfg. Co., 118 North
Av. (Wagon) ....A
IND.—Indianapolis
Nordyke & Marmon Co.
(Wagon) ....AAA
MASS.—Milford
Milford Iron Foundry
(Ash) C
MINN.—Minneapolis
Howell & Co., R. R.
(Wagon) ....B
Moulton & Evans (Wagon)
...........................F
N. Y.—Buffalo
Buffalo Scale Co. (Coal)..
..........................AA
OHIO—Cincinnati
Triumph Ice Machine Co.,
610 Baymiller (Ice) ....A
PA.—Wilkesbarre
Vulcan Iron Wks. (Coal)..
........................AAAA

DUPLICATORS

ILL.—Chicago
Dick Co., A. B. (Letter)..
..........................AA
New York City
Beck Duplicate Co., 72
Beaver (for Reproduction
of Manuscripts) ....D
Bensinger Co., 245 B'way
(Letter) X
Daus Duplicator Co., 111
John C
Hektograph Co. (for Re-
production of Manu-
scripts, etc.) ....D
Neostyle Co., 30 Reade
(Letter) ....A
Soltmann, E. G., 125 E.
42nd (for Reproduction of
Manuscripts, etc.) .....B

DUST

COLO.—Denver
Western Chemical Mfg. Co.
(Marble) ....AA
ILL.—Chicago
Hutchinson & Son, W. H.
(Inc.) (Marble) ....AA
Sherman & Flavin
(Marble) ....B

DUST (Con.)

MD.—Baltimore
Bullock & Son, John (Bone)
...........................X
MASS.—Worcester
Winslow Skate Mfg. Co.
(Boxwood) ....A
MICH.—Bay City
Vance Box Co., E. J. (Ltd.)
(Saw) ....B
MICH.—Detroit
Michigan Carbon Works
(Bone) ....AAA
MO.—St. Louis
Mathiason Mfg. Co., P. B.
(Bone) ....A
N. J.—Newark
Lister Agricultural Chemical
Works (Bone) ....AAAA
Sommer's Son, John (Saw)
...........................A
N. Y.—Brooklyn
Wiarda & Co., John C.
(Marble) ....AA
New York City
Baker & Bro., H. J.
(Bone) ....AA
Cooper & Co., Chas. (Bone)
..........................AA
King & Co., J. B. (Mar-
ble) ....AAAA
OHIO—Cleveland
Cleveland Dryer Co. (Bone)
........................AAAA

DUSTERS

See also Brushes

CAL.—San Francisco
Atlantic Brush Co.
(Feather) ....D
Buchanan Bros. (Feather)
...........................E
ILL.—Chicago
Chicago Feather Duster Co.
(Turkey Feather) .....E
Dearborn Duster Co. (Feath-
er; Turkey Feather;
Hemp) ....D
Woven Down Duster Co.
(Turkey Feather) ......G
ILL.—Moline
Barnard & Leas Mfg. Co.
(Bran) ....AA
IND.—Fort Wayne
Hoosier Mfg. Co. ......AA
IND.—Indianapolis
Nordyke & Marmon Co.
(Bran) ....AAA
IND.—Richmond
Richmond City Mills Works
(Bran) ....B
IOWA—Davenport
Lee Broom & Duster Co.
(Feather; Turkey Feath-
er) ....A
KANS.—Leavenworth
Great Western Mfg. Co.
(Bran) ....AA
KY.—Louisville
Falls City Duster Co.
(Feather) ....E
Fisher Duster Co. (Feather)
...........................D
MASS.—Athol
Gerry & Son, Geo. (Rag;
Wool; Waste) X
MASS.—Boston
Boston Feather Duster Co.
(Feather) ....D
MASS.—Florence
Norwood Engineering Co.
(Rag) ....B
MASS.—Holyoke
Holyoke Machine Co. (Rag)
..........................AA
MASS.—Lowell
Bagshaw, W. H. (Est. of)
(Rag) ....B
Kitson Machine Co. (Rag)
.........................AAA
Lowell Machine Shops
(Rag) ....AAAA
MASS.—North Adams
Hunter Machine Co., Jas.
(Wool; Waste) ....A
MASS.—Pittsfield
Jones & Sons Co., E. D.
(Rag) ....B

DUSTERS (Con.)

MASS.—Westford
Sargent's Sons. C. G. (Rag; Wool; Waste) ....A

MASS.—Worcester
American Card Clothing Co. (Wool) ....AAA
Cleveland Machine Works (Wool; Waste) ....B
Curtis & Marble Machine Co. (Wool; Waste) ......A

MICH.—Grand Rapids
Grand Rapids Brush Co. (Artisans'; Moulders'; Counter) ....A

MICH.—Jackson
Knickerbocker Co. (Bran).C

MICH.—Wyandotte
Bishop Co., J. H. (Wool)..A

N. J.—Belleville
Atlas Foundry & Machine Co. (Wool; Waste) ...D

N. Y.—Brooklyn
Adams & Co., J. J. (Crepe; Parasol; Mantel) ......A
American Duster Co. (Turkey Feather) ....F

N. Y.—Lockport
Richmond Mfg. Co. (Bran) A

New York City
Bradley & Smith (Barbers'; Furniture; Plush; Painters') ....AA
F. W. Devoe & C. F. Reynolds Co. (Painters')AAAA
Hanlon & Goodman (Furniture; Plush; Painters'; Moulders') ....A
Hayes Duster Co. (Feather; Turkey Feather) ......B
Martin's Sons. J. M. C. (Barbers'; Painters') ..A
Mitchell, E. (Painters') ..E
New York Feather Duster Co. (Feather) C
Smith & Son, J. Finley (Counter; Furniture; Plush; Painters') .....B
Tonk & Bro., Wm. 452 10th Av. (Piano) C

N. Y.—Troy
Dennin & Sons. Owen (Barbers'; Furniture; Plush; Painters') ....B

OHIO—Cincinnati
Cincinnati Mfg. Co. (Feather) ....B

OHIO—Cleveland
Osborn Mfg. Co. (Turkey Counter) ....B

OHIO—Columbus
Case Mfg. Co. (Bran) ..A

OHIO—Hamilton
Black & Clawson (Rag).. AAA

PA.—Easton
Pollock Brush Co. (Radiator; Wire-drawn) ....D

PA.—Philadelphia
Levy, S. (Feather) ......F
Smith Woolen Machinery Co., Jas. (Rag) ......AA
Star & Crescent Mills Co..A

VT.—St. Albans
Willard Mfg. Co. ....A

WIS.—Beloit
Beloit Iron Works (Rag).A

WIS.—Milwaukee
Allis-Chalmers Co. (Bran) AAAA

DYES & DYE-STUFFS

See also Anilines; Colors; Logwood, etc.

CONN.—Hartford
Beach & Co. ....AAA

MAINE—Foxcroft
Cushing & Co., W. (Egg).X

MASS.—Boston
Boston Belting Co. .AAAA
Cochrane Chemical Co...AA
Metcalf Co., Theo. ....A

MASS.—Lowell
Talbot Deywood & Chemical Co. ....B

DYES & DYESTUFFS

MICH.—Detroit
Eaton & Son, Theo. H. .... AAAA

MO.—St. Louis
Donnell Mfg. Co., 612 S. 6th (Egg) ....B

MO.—Unionville
Monroe Drug Co. (Egg)..C

N. J.—Newark
Paas Dye Co. ....B

N. Y.—Albany
Hudson River Aniline Color Wks. ....B

N. Y.—Buffalo
Schoellkoff, Hartford & Hanna Co. (Coal Tar).. AAA

N. Y.—Massena
Handy Package Dye Co. (Egg) ....F

New York City
Barclay & Co., 44 Stone (Hair) ....A
Bartels Co., Ernest C. ..B
Berlin Aniline Wks. .....B
Bischoff & Co., C. ....B
Bredt & Co., F. ....B
Cassela Color Co. ....A
De Bruenn Chemical & Dyestuff Co. ....D
Dillon & Co., 20 Cedar ..X
Fezandie, Felix ....D
Fuerst Bros. & Co. ......D
Geigy Aniline & Ext. Co., 69 Barclay (Aniline; Dyewood; Sumac Extracts).A
Heller & Merz Co. ......AA
Kalle & Co. ....A
Klipstein & Co., A. (Inc.), 122 Pearl ....AA
Kuttroff, Jickhardt & Co. A
Matheson & Co.. Wm. J..A
Metz & Co., H. A. ....A
New York & Boston Dyewood Co., 55 Beekman (Hematines; Fustics; Crystals) ....AAAA
Stamford Mfg. Co. .AAAA
Tult Mfg. Co. ....B
West Indies Chemical Wks., 20 Cedar (Logwood Ext.) X

OHIO—Tiffin
Fleck, J. J. (Egg) .....B

PA.—Bedford
Heckerman Drug & Dye Co. (Egg) ....B

PA.—Easton
Baker & Adamson Chemical Co. ....A

PA.—Philadelphia
Sharpless Dyewood Ext. Co., Bourse (Hematine; Logwood) X

R. I.—Providence
Arnold, Hoffman Co. ...AA
Lewis, John D. ....AA

VT.—Burlington
Wells & Richardson Co. (Egg) ....AA

DYNAMITE

CAL.—San Francisco
California Powder Wks...A

DEL.—Wilmington
Hercules Torpedo Co. ....B
Repauno Chemical Co. AAAA

ILL.—Chicago
Aetna Powder Co. ......AA

New York City
Laflin & Rand Powder Co., 99 Cedar X

OHIO—Cincinnati
King Powder Co. .....AAA

OHIO—Toledo
Great Western Powder Co.X

PA.—Philadelphia
International Smokeless Powder & Dynamite Co. B

PA.—Pittsburg
Kirk & Son Co., Arthur..X

PA.—Tamaqua
Repauno Chemical Co..... AAAA

DYNAMOM-ETER

ILL.—Chicago
Western Electric Mfg. Co. (Electric) ....AAAA
MASS.—Lawrence
Lawrence Machine Co. ..X
N. H.—Penacook
Whitney Electrical & Instrument Co. ....D
N. Y.—Brooklyn
Schaeffer & Budenberg Mfg. Co., 10 Division..B
New York City
Kohlbusch, Herman, 194 Broadway ....B
Manning, Maxwell & Moore, 85 Liberty ....AA
N. Y.—Schenectady
General Electric Co. (Electro) ....AAAA
OHIO—Cleveland
Elwell-Parker Electric Co. C

DYNAMOS

See also Generators; Motors.

CAL.—San Francisco
California Electrical Works (Direct Electric Lighting) ....A
CONN.—Windsor
Eddy Electric Mfg. Co. (Direct Electric Power; Copper Refining; Electro-Incandescent Lighting; Plating; Electrotyping; Power) ....D
ILL.—Chicago
Central Electric Co. (Incandescent Lighting) .....A
Chicago Edison Co. (Incandescent Lighting) .AAAA
Chicago Flexible Shaft Co., 124 La Salle Av. .....B
Roth Bros. & Co., 29 S. Clinton (Electric Lighting; Arc Lighting; Electro-Plating) ....B
Western Electric Co., 259 S. Clinton (Direct; Alternating; Electric Lighting; Arc Lighting; Telegraph) AAAA
ILL.—Peoria
Royal Electric Co. (Direct and Alternating Electric Lighting) ....D
IND.—Fort Wayne
Fort Wayne Electric Works (Inc.) (Direct and Alternating Electric Lighting, Arc Lighting; Direct Connected; Direct Current).. AAA
IND.—Indianapolis
Commecial Electric Co. (Direct Electric Lighting; Street Railway) ....A
Jenney Electric Mfg. Co. (Direct and Alternating Electric Lighting; Belted; Copper Refining; Direct connected; Electro-Plating Electrotyping) ....A
IND.—Terre Haute
Kester Electric Co. (Street Railway) ....D
KY.—Owensboro
Kentucky Electrical Co. (Direct Electric Lighting).B
MAINE—Portland
Maine Electric Co., 25 Commercial (Electric Lighting) ....E
MASS.—Boston
Cutter, Wood & Stevens Co. (Electro-Plating) ......E
Sturtevant Co., B. F. (Direct Electric Power).AAA
MASS.—Brookline
Holtzer-Cabot Electric Co. (Plating) ....A
MASS.—Lynn
Littlefield & Co., H. A. (Direct and Alternating

DYNAMOS (Con.)
Electric Lighting.......X
MASS.—Pittsfield
Stanley Electric Mfg. Co. (Alternating Electric Power) ....AAAA
MASS.—Springfield
Elecktrom Mfg. Co. (Electric Power) ....A
MICH.—Three Rivers
Sheffield Car Co. ......AA
MINN.—Minneapolis
Electric Machinery Co. (Induction Type Alternating Electric Power) ....A
MO.—St. Louis
Wagner Electric Mfg. Co. Direct and Alternating Electric Lighting) ...AA
N. J.—East Orange
Crocker-Wheeler Electric Co. (Direct Electric Lighting; Street Railway; Electro-Plating; Direct Connected) ....AAAA
N. J.—Elizabethport
Diehl Mfg. Co. (Direct Electric Lighting; Incandescent Lighting) ....B
N. J.—Newark
Hanson & Van Winkle Co. .(Plating) ....AA
N. Y.—Buffalo
Averill, Francis E., 680 Main (Plating) ....H
N. Y.—Eldridge
Eldridge Electrical Mfg. Co. (Arc Lighting; Electro-Plating; Experimental).D
N. Y.—Hornellsville
Bartz, Wygant & Brown (Electric Lighting) ....D
New York City
Bunnell Co., J. H. (Incandescent Lighting) ....B
C. & C. Electric Co., 143 Liberty (Direct Electric Lighting; Street Railway) AA
General Incandescent Arc Light Co., 572 1st Av. (Electric Power; Oil; Electric) ....A
La Roche & Co., F. A., 656 Hudson (Direct Electric Lighting) ....A
Sprague Electric Co., 527 W. 24th (Direct and Alternating up to 1000 K. W. Electric Lighting; Electric Lighting; Street Railway; Direct Connected ....AAAA
Zucker & Levett & Loeb Co., 526 W. 25th (Plating) ....A
N. Y.—Rochester
Rochester Electric Motor Co. (Direct Current) C
N. Y. Schenectady
General Electric Co. (Direct and Alternating Electric Lighting; Street Railway; Incandescent Lighting; Telegraph) AAAA
N. Y.—Syracuse
Powell, E. C. (Electric Lighting) ....B
N. Y.—Troy
Bernard Co., E. G. (Belted; Direct Connected) .....D
N. Y.—Watertown
Eager Electric Co. (Direct Current Electric Lighting) D
OHIO—Akron
Akron Electrical Mfg. Co. (Electric Lighting; Direct Curent; Belted or Direct Connected, 1 to 500 K. W.; Electro-Plating).D
OHIO—Cincinnati
Bullock Electric Mfg. Co. (Direct and Alternating Electric Lighting; Street Railway) ....AA
Jantz & Leist Electric Co. (Plating; Electroplating) B

DYNAMOS (Con.)

Triumph Electric Co., 610
Baymiller (Direct Current
Electric Lighting; Street
Railway) ....A

OHIO—Cleveland
Elwell-Parker Electric Co.
(Direct Electric Lighting;
Street Railway) C

OHIO—Columbus
Jeffrey Mfg. Co. ....AAAA

OHIO—Dayton
Thresher Electric Co. (Direct Electric Lighting;
Street Railway) X

OHIO—Mansfield
Phoenix Electric Mfg. Co.
(Electric Lighting; Street
Railway; Electro-Plating)
..............B

OHIO—Sandusky
Warren Electric Mfg. Co.
(Alternating Electric
Lighting; Alternating Current; Incandescent Lighting) ....A

OHIO—Springfield
Robbins & Myers Co. .....A

PA.—Erie
Keystone Electric Co. (Direct Electric Lighting;
Street Railway) ......B

PA.—Grove City
Bessemer Gas Engine Co.
(Electric Power) ......A

PA.—Philadelphia
Dallett & Co., T. H. ....B
Quaker City Electric Co.
(Arc Lighting; Electro-Plating; Incandescent
Lighting; Marine; Power)
..............D

PA.—Pittsburg
Westinghouse Electric &
Mfg. Co. (Direct; Alternating Electric Lighting;
Street; Railway; Alternating Current; Arc Lighting; Incandescent Lighting; Power) .....AAAA

PA.—Ridgway
Ridgway Dynamo & Engine
Co. (Street Railway).AA

R. I.—Providence
Bowen Electric Co. (Electric
Lighting) X

WIS.—Madison
Northern Electrical Mfg.
Co. (Direct and Alternating Electric Lighting)
..............AAAA

WIS.—Milwaukee
Christensen Engineering
Co. (Alternating; Direct)
..............A
Mechanical Appliance Co.
(Electrical Power) C
Milwaukee Electric Co.
(Direct Electric Lighting)
..............X
Pawling & Harnischfeger
(Incandescent Lighting;
Marine; Power) .....AAA

DYNAMOTORS

ILL.—Chicago
Roth Bros. & Co., 29 S.
Clinton (Ringing) .....B
New York City
Crocker-Wheeler Co., 39
Cortlandt ....AAA
OHIO—Akron
Akron Electrical Mfg. Co..D
OHIO—Cleveland
Elwell-Parker Elec. Co.,
1066 Hamilton C

EAGLES

MICH.—Detroit
Barnum Wire & Iron Wks.,
E. T. (Flag Pole) ......B
New York City
American Flag Co. (Flag
Pole) ....A

EARRINGS

See Jewelry

EARS

CONN.—Bridgeport
Bridgeport Brass Co.
(Brass Pail) ......AAA
CONN.—Waterbury
Plume & Atwood Mfg. Co.
(Pail) ....AAA
Waterbury Brass Co. (Brass
Pail) ....AAAA
KY.—Louisville
Horan Stay Hanger Co.
(Tin, for Tin Buckets) F
MASS.—Worcester
Wire Goods Co. (Tub) ....A
MICH.—Detroit
Hutchins & Sons, C. B., 1383
12th (Trolley) ....D
N. Y.—Albany
Troy Nickel Works (Jno. G.
Gaitley Prop.) (Pan; Kettle, &c.) C
N. Y.—Binghamton
Titchenor & Co., E. H.
(Pail; Tubs) ....B
N. Y.—Brooklyn
Columbia Machine Works &
Malleable Iron Co., 169
Chestnut (Trolley) ....A
N. Y.—Buffalo
Forsyth Mfg. Co. (Pail) ..C
N. Y.—Troy
Troy Stamping Co. (Pail)
..............AAAA
OHIO—Cincinnati
Creagland Engineering Co.,
313 Walnut (Trolley) ..D
OHIO—Mansfield
Ohio Brass Co. (Trolley) AA
OHIO—Troy
Ohio Electric Specialty Mfg.
Co. (Trolley) ....A
PA.—Philadelphia
Berger Bros. Co. (Pail) ...A

EARTH

New York City
Fuerst Bros. Co. (Fullers) D
Taylor & Co., G. F.
(Fullers) ....F
Waddell & Co., R. J.
(Fullers) ....A
Whittaker, W. H. (Fullers)
..............E

EARTHEN-WARE

See also Pottery; Stoneware,
etc.

IND.—Kokomo
Great Western Pottery Co.
(Plumbers' Sanitary) AA
MASS.—Boston
Dalton-Ingersoll Co. (Sanitary) X
MO.—St. Louis
Nelson Mfg. Co., N. O. AAA
N. J.—Bordentown
Iron Sides Pottery Co.
(Plumbers' Sanitary) ..C
N. J.—Elizabeth
Standard Sanitary Pottery
Co. (Plumbers' Sanitary)X
N. J.—Trenton
Acme Sanitary Pottery Co.
(Plumbers' Sanitary) ..D
Belmark Pottery Co. (Car
Builders'; Plumbers' Sanitary) ....B
Economy Pottery Co.
(Plumbers' Sanitary) ...E
Keystone Pottery Co.
(Plumbers' Sanitary) ...B
Maddock & Sons, John
(Plumbers' Sanitary) ...A
Maddock & Sons, Thos.
(Plumbers' Sanitary) .AA
Mercer Pottery Co.
(Plumbers' Sanitary) .AA
Monument Pottery Co.
(Plumbers' Sanitary) ...A
Sanitary Earthenware Specialty Co. (Plumbers' Sanitary) ....B
Trenton Fire Clay & Porcelain Co. (Plumbers' Sanitary) ....A
Trenton Potteries Co.
(Plumbers' Sanitary) AAA
Willetts Mfg. Co.
(Plumbers' Sanitary) ...A

EARTHENWARE (Con.)
New York City
Meyer-Sniffen Co. (Ltd.)
(Sinks) ....A
OHIO—East Liverpool
Thompson Pottery Co., C. C.
....AA
Vodry Pottery Co. ....A
OHIO—Findlay
Bell Pottery Co. (Decorated;
Plain) ....A
PA.—New Castle
Universal Sanitary Mfg. Co.
(Plumbers' Sanitary) ...B
PA.—Philadelphia
Owen & Slater (Sanitary) A
W. VA.—Wheeling
Wheeling Potteries Co.
(Plumbers' Sanitary) AAA

EARTHERS

PA.—Philadelphia
Allen & Co., S. L. (Celery)
....AA

EASELS

See also Furniture; Pictures; etc.

CONN.—Chester
Brooks & Sons, M. S. (Wire)
....B
CONN.—Meriden
Bradley & Hubbard Mfg. Co.
(Brass) ....AAAA
ILL.—Chicago
Barbee Wire & Iron Wks.
(Wire) ....B
Dietzgen Co., Eugene
(Artists') ....A
MASS.—Gardner
Heywood Bros. & Wakefield
Co. (Rattan; Wicker)
....AAAA
MASS.—Lowell
Woods, Sherwood & Co.
(Wire) ....E
MASS.—Worcester
Hamblin & Russell Mfg. Co.
(Wire Cup & Saucer) .B
National Mfg. Co. (Wire) A
Wire Goods Co. (Wire) ..A
MICH.—Detroit
Twitchell Bros. Mfg. Co., 69
National Av. (Crockery;
Photograph) ....H
N. J.—Hoboken
Ferguson Bros. Mfg. Co.
(Wire) ....A
N. Y.—Lockport
Oliver Bros. Co. (Brass) AA
New York City
Abels & Co., 137 E. Houston
(Wire) ....D
Aimone Mfg. Co. (Bamboo)
....B
Friedrichs, E. H. (Artists')
....A
Judd & Co., H. L. (Brass;
Wire) ....AA
New York Silicate Book
Slate Co., 68 Church
(Blackboard) ....D
N. Y.—Rochester
Yawman & Erbe Mfg. Co.
(Rattan; Wicker) ....AA
PA.—Allegheny
Pittsburg Lamp & Brass &
Glass Co. (Brass) ..AAAA
WIS.—Milwaukee
Meinecke & Son, A. (Bamboo; Ratan; Wicker) AA

EBONY GOODS

Toilet, etc.

ILL.—Rockford
Ash, J. B. ....F
New York City
Avirbick, M. J., 19 Maiden
Lane ....A
Gorham Mfg. Co., 19th &
Broadway ....AAAA
Dietsch Bros., 14 E. 17th X
Harrell Leather Goods Co.,
554 Broadway C
Langsdorf & Co., S., 13
Crosby ....AA
Selwyn Importing Co., 18 E.
17th ....A
Trout & Co., Chas. L., 7
Maiden Lane ....
Whiting Mfg. Co., 18th &

EBONY GOODS (Con.)
Broadway ....AAA
OHIO—Akron
Goehring Mfg. Co. ....B

ECONOMIZERS

MASS.—Boston
Sturtevant Co., B. F.
(Fuel) ....AAA
MICH.—Detroit
Burton & Co., W. J., 164 W.
Larned (Fuel) C
N. Y.—Matteawan
Green Fuel Economizer Co.
(Fuel) ....B
New York City
Steam Boiler Equipment Co.,
20 W. Houston (Fuel;
Hydro-Carbon System) ·D
PA.—York
Broomell, Schmidt, Steacy &
Co. (Fuel) ....A

ECRASEURS

ILL.—Chicago
Haussmann & Dunn
(Cautery) C
New York City
Seabury & Johnson
(Cautery) ....AA

EDGERS

CAL.—San Francisco
California Saw Wks. (Gang
Saw) ....A
GA.—Atlanta
DeLoach Mill Mfg. Co.
(Gang Saw) ....B
IND.—Indianapolis
Sinker-Davis Co. (Rotary)
....B
IND.—Montpelier
Jackson Shovel & Tool Co.
(Turf) ....B
IOWA—Fort Madison
Iowa Farming Tool Co.
(Turf) ....A
LA.—Shreveport
Henderson Iron Wks., W. K.
(Gang Saw) ....AA
MAINE—Bangor
Union Iron Wks. (Double;
Gang Saw) ....A
MASS.—Orange
Chase Turbine Mfg. Co.
(Board) ....A
MICH.—Alpena
Klein, Lewis T. (Gang Saw)
....D
MICH.—Bay City
Garland Co., M. (Gang Saw;
Lumber) C
MICH.—Grand Rapids
Butterworth & Lowe (Gang
Saw) ....A
MICH.—Greenville
Gordon Hollow Blast Grate
Co. (Gang Saw) ....B
MICH.—Jackson
Withington & Cooley Mfg.
Co. (Turf) ....AA
MICH.—Kalamazoo
Hill & Co., W. E. (Gang
Saw) ....B
MICH.—Menominee
Prescott Co., D. Clint.
(Gang Saw; Lumber) ..A
MICH.—Saginaw
Wickes Bros. (Gang Saw)
....AAA
MINN.—Minneapolis
Howell & Co., R. R. (Gang
Saw; Single) ....B
MISS.—Corinth
Adams Machine Co., W. F.
(Gang Saw) ....AA
MO.—St. Louis
Johnson Machinery Co.,
Moses B. (Gang Saw) ..F
N. J.—Paterson
Royle & Sons, John (Single)
....A
N. Y.—Belmont
Clark Bros. Co. (Gang Saw)
....A
N. Y.—Buffalo
Frank Machinery Co. (Gang
Saw) C
Holmes Machinery Co., 59
Chicago (Gang Saw) ..B

EDGERS (Con.)

N. Y.—Frankfort
Continental Tool Co. (Solid
Steel; Bronze Finish Turf)
.....................................A

N. Y.—Newburg
Chadborn & Caldwell Mfg.
Co. (Turf) C

New York City
Amer. Woodworking Machine Co., 136 Liberty
(Double; Gang Saw; Lumber) ....AAAA

OHIO—Canton
Knight Mfg. Co. (Gang Saw;
Single) ....B

OHIO—Cincinnati
Fay & Egan Co., J. A., cor.
Front & John (Gang Saw)
.....................................AAAA
Lane & Bodley Co. (Rotary)
.....................................B
Smith Meyers & Schnier Co.
(Gang Saw; Lumber) ..B

OHIO—Cleveland
Amer. Fork & Hoe Co.
(Turf) ....AAAA

OHIO—Columbus
Crown Hinman & Huntington Co. (Rotary) ....A

PA.—Erie
Standard Saw Mill Machinery Co. (Gang Saw) ...B
Stearns Mfg. Co. (Gang
Saw; Lumber) ....B

PA.—Williamsport
Moltz, Jacob J. (Gang Saw)
.....................................C
United States Machine Co.
(Gang Saw) ....D

TENN.—Chattanooga
Wheland Machine Works
(Rotary; Gang Saw) ...A

TENN.—Jackson
Southern Engine & Boiler
Wks. (Inc.) (Gang Saw)
.....................................AA

VT.—Bennington
Scott, Olin (Single) .....A

VT.—Montpelier
Lane Mfg. Co. (Double;
Gang Saw; Lumber; Rotary) ....A

WASH.—Seattle
Vulcan Iron Wks. Co.
(Gang Saw) ....A

WIS.—Eau Claire
Phoenix Mfg. Co. (Gang
Saw) ....A

WIS.—Milwaukee
Allis-Chalmers Co. (Gang
Saw) ....AAAA
Filer & Stowell Co. (Gang
Saw; Double; Lumber)
.....................................AAA

WIS.—Stevens Point
Cook, R. A. (Gang Saw) B

WIS.—Wausau
Murray Mfg. Co., D. J.
(Double; Gang Saw) A

EDGES

CONN.—Hartford
Pratt & Whitney Co.
(Straight) ....AAAA

IND.—Indianapolis
Atkins & Co., E. C., 402 S.
Illinois (Straight) AAAA
Barry Saw Co., 228 S. Penn.
(Straight) ....B

MASS.—Athol
Athol Machine Co.
(Straight) ....B
Starrett Co., L. S. (Straight)
.....................................A

MASS.—Fitchburg
Putnam Machine Co.
(Straight) ....A
Sawyer Tool Mfg. Co.
(Straight) C
Simonds Mfg. Co. (Straight)
.....................................AAA

MICH.—Grand Rapids
Baldwin, Tuthill & Bolton
(Straight) ....B

New York City
Keuffel & Esser Co., 127
Fulton (Straight) .....AA

OHIO—Cleveland
Standard Tool Co. (Straight)
.....................................AA

PA.—Philadelphia
Campbell, Peter F.

EDGES (Con.)
(Straight) ....D
Disston & Sons, Henry (Inc.)
(Straight) ....AAAA

R. I.—Providence
Brown & Sharpe Mfg. Co.
(Straight) ....AAAA

EGGS

CONN.—Hartford
Sturtevant, F. C. (Glass
Nest) ....D

New York City
Demuth Glass Mfg. Co., 89
Walker (Glass) X

PA.—Philadelphia
Gill & Co. (Inc.) (Nest) ..A

S. C.—Charleston
Valk & Murdock Iron Wks.
(Acid) ....B

EIKONOGEN

MO.—St. Louis
Mallinckrodt Chemical Co.
.....................................AAAA

EJECTORS

See also Sujectors

ILL.—Chicago
Shone Co., 455 N. 46th (Jet
Pump or Syphons; Pneumatic) ....B

ILL.—Du Quoin
Blakeslee Mfg. Co. (Jet
Pumps or Syphons) ...B

MICH.—Detroit
Penberthy Injector Co., 346
Holden Av. (Jet Pumps
or Syphons) ....A

MICH.—Port Huron
Lee Injector Mfg. Co. (Jet
Pumps or Syphons) ...B

MO.—St. Louis
Nelson Mfg. Co., N. O. 8th
& St. Charles (Jet Pumps
or Syphons) ....AAA

N. Y.—Brooklyn
Munkenbeck Bros., 88 Hamilton (Jet Pumps or Syphons) ....D
Schaffer & Budenberg Mfg.
Co., 10 Division (Jet
Pumps or Syphons) ...D

N. Y.—Buffalo
Sherwood Mfg. Co., 34
Wash'n (Jet Pumps or Syphons) ....B

New York City
Bushnell Co., Jno. S., 120
Liberty (Jet Pumps or
Syphons) ....E
Fairbanks Co., 416 Broome
.....................................AAAA
McNab & Harlin Mfg. Co.,
56 John ....AAA
Manning, Maxwell & Moore
85 Liberty ....AA
Nason Mfg. Co. 71 Beekman (Jet Pumps or Syphons) ....B
Nathan Mfg. Co., 92 Liberty
(Jet Pumps or Syphons) A

N. Y.—Ogdensburg
Nash Bros. & Co. (Jet
Pumps or Syphons) ...A

OHIO—Cincinnati
McGowan Co., Jno. H., 56
Central Av. (Jet Pumps
or Syphons) ....A

OHIO—Wadsworth
Ohio Injector Co. (Jet Pumps
or Syphons) ....A

PA.—Erie
Watson, N. A. (Jet Pumps
or Syphons) ....A

PA.—Philadelphia
Belfield & Co., H., 435 N.
Broad (Jet Pumps or Syphons) ....AA
Eynon-Evans Mfg. Co., 1519
Clearfield (Jet Pumps or
Syphons) ....A
Lonergan & Co., Jas. E., 211
Race (Jet Pumps or Syphons) ....AA
Pancoast & Co., Henry B.,
243 S. 3rd (Jet Pumps or
Syphons) ....B
Rue Mfg. Co. 215 Race (Jet
Pumps or Syphons) C
Schutte & Koerting Co., 1251

EJECTORS (Con.)
N. 12th (Jet Pumps or Syphons) ....A
Watson & McDaniel Co., 146 N. 7th (Jet Pumps or Syphons) C
PA.—Pittsburg
Chaplin-Fulton Mfg. Co., 28 Penn. Av. (Jet Pumps or Syphons) ....A

ELASTICS
See Webbing

ELBOWS
CONN.—Bridgeport
Belknap Mfg. Co. (Radiator; Brass) C
DEL.—Marshallton
Marshallton Iron & Steel Co. (Pipe) ....B
ILL.—Chicago
Excelsior Steel Furnace Co., 40 W. Monroe (Adjustable &c.) ....A
Morgan & Wright (Inc.) 333 W. Lake (Plumbers' Rubber) ....AA
Sturges & Burn Mfg. Co. (Stove Pipe) ....A
Tressing & Co., E., 179 Lake (Adjustable) ....E
ILL.—Peoria
Clark, Queen & Morse (& Shoes) ....A
IND.—Fort Wayne
Kerr Mfg. Co., Murray (Pipe) ....A
MD.—Hagerstown
Hunter, C. S. (Furnace) E
MASS.—Boston
Howes Co., S. M. (Stove Pipe) ....B
MASS.—Cambridge
Lamb & Ritchie (Corrugated; Galvanized Iron) .AA
MASS.—Worcester
New England Steel Roofing Co. (Corrugated) .....F
MICH.—Detroit
Stephens-Roe Mfg. Co. (Brass Union) ....A
N. Y.—Buffalo
Shepard & Co., Sidney (Stove Pipe; Pipe; Conductor) ....AAAA
New York City
Corwin, M. M. (Adjustable Stove Pipe) ....D
Froehlich, A. (Est. of) (Adjustable Stove Pipe) B
Good Mfg. Co., 88 Lincoln Av. (Rubber) ....B
Marcy Stove Repair Co. (Adjustable Stove Pipe) B
Stoutenborough, X. (Adjustable Stove Pipe) ....D
Stove Manufacturers Repair Ass'n. (Adjustable Stove Pipe) ....F
N. Y.—Troy
Troy Stamping Co. (Stove Pipe) ....AAAA
N. Y.—Utica
International Heater Co. (Stove Pipe) ....AAA
OHIO—Canton
Berger Mfg. Co. (Pipe; Conductor; Shoes) ......AA
Canton Steel Roofing Co. (Pipe; Conductor; Shoes)A
OHIO—Cincinnati
Corrugated Elbow Co., 114 E. Liberty (Corrugated) D
Edwards Mfg. Co. (Stove Pipe) C
OHIO—Cleveland
Cleveland Elbow Co. (Adjustable Stove; Galvanized Stove) C
Garry Iron & Steel Co. (Pipe Conductor; Shoes) A
OHIO—Festoria
Fostoria Novelty Co. (Lead Pipe) C
OHIO—Hamilton
Kahn & Bros., F. & L. (Stove Pipe) ....A
Myers Mfg. Co., F. J. (& Shoes) ....B
OHIO—New Philadelphia
Ohio Stove Pipe Mfg. Co.

ELBOWS (Con.)
(Corrugated Stove Pipe) B
OHIO—Niles
Bostwick Steel Lath Co. (Galvanized) C
OHIO—Piqua
Standard Mfg. Co. (Corrugated) X
OHIO—Warren
Winfield Mfg. Co. (Stove Pipe) ....B
PA.—Philadelphia
Berger Bros. Co. (Stove Pipe; Pipe; Conductor; Shoes) ....A
Pfeifer & Co., John (Ltd.) (Stove Pipe) ....A
PA.—Pittsburg
Budke Mfg. Co. (Stove Pipe) B
TENN.—Chattanooga
Chattanooga Roofing & Foundry Co. (Stove Pipe) A
W. VA.—Wheeling
Wheeling Corrugating Co. (Pipe) ....AAAA

ELECTRODES
ILL.—Chicago
Birtman & Co., C. F. (Cautery) C
Friedlander & Co., R., 43 State (Glass) ....D
Scheidel & Co., W., 171 E. Rand (Glass; Metal) ..D
MD.—Baltimore
Chloride of Silver Dry Cell Battery Co. (Medical) ..B
New York City
Bunnell & Co., J. H., 20 Park Row (Galvanic; Faradic; Vacuum) V
Van Houten & Ten Broeck Co., 300 4th Av. (Galvanic; Faradic; Vacuum) ..D
OHIO—Cleveland
National Carbon Co. (Smelting) ....AAAA
PA.—Washington
Washington Carbon Co. (Carbon) ....A

ELECTROM-ETERS
ILL.—Chicago
Western Electric Co. AAAA
New York City
Bunnell & Co., J. H. ......B
N. Y.—Schenectady
General Electric Co...AAAA

ELEVATORS
ARK.—Little Rock
Thomas-Fordyce Mfg. Co. (Cotton) ....A
CAL.—San Francisco
California Electrical Wks., 547 Mission (Electric) A
Hammond & Co., Jno., 2nd & Townsend (Electric) B
Hendy Machine Wks., Joshua (Hydraulic) .....AA
San Francisco Tool Wks. (Passenger) ....E
CONN.—New Haven
Eastern Machinery Co. (Freight; Belt) ....B
Harrison, Leonard D. (Grain) ....H
GA.—Atlanta
Van Winkle Gin & Machine Wks., E. (Seed; Cotton) ....AAA
ILL.—Batavia
U. S. Wind Engine & Pump Co. (Grain) ....AA
ILL.—Chicago
Adams Bros. & Co., 355 31st (Hod) ....F
Allis-Chalmers Co., Home Ins'ce. Bldg. (Quicksilver; Belt) ....AAAA
Caldwell & Son Co., H. W., Western Av. & 17th (Automatic Barrel; Grain; Water; Belt) ....AA
Eaton & Prince Co. 76 Michigan (Electric; Hand Pow-

ELEVATORS (Con.)

Noye Mfg. Co., John T. (Flour Mill; Grain) X

Steel Storage & Elevator Construction Co. (Fire Proof Grain) ....A

N. Y.—Cohoes

Cohoes Iron Foundry & Machine Co. (Freight; Hydraulic) ....B

N. Y.—Hudson

Gifford Bros. (Bucket; Ice) A

N. Y.—Long Island City

Stuebner, G. L. (Coal) ....B

New York City

Bowes, John J., 227 W. 29th (Sidewalk) ....D

Cornell Co., J. B. & J. M., 26th & 11th Av. (Sidewalk; Hand Power) .AA

Diamond Bros. (Sidewalk) A

Dowdall, Chas., 152 W. Bway. (Sidewalk) ....F

Edelmeyer & Morgan Hod Elevator Co., 333 W. 49th (Hod) ....E

Edwards & Co., Joseph (Freight; Steam Power) F

Gordon Bros., 176 Wooster (Sidewalk) ....B

Hoffman Co., Chas. W., 223 W. 28th (Sidewalk) ..D

Hunt Co., C. W. (Coal) AA

Marine Engine & Machine Co., 1132 Bway. (Electric; Automatic Plunger) ....B

Mundt & Sons, Chas., 441 Pearl (Automatic Barrel) B

Murtaugh Co., Jas., 202 E. 42d (Carriage; Invalid; Hand Power; Sidewalk) D

N. Y. Foundry & Machine Co., 9 Murray (Automatic Barrel; Hand Power; Electric Freight) ....D

Otis Elevator Co., 71 Bway (Electric; Plunger; Factory; Freight; Hydraulic; Passenger) ......AAAA

Pelham Hod Elevating Co., 416 W. 26th (Hod) .....B

Reedy Elevator Co., 407 W. 15th (Electric; Belt Power) ....A

See Electric Elevator Co., A. B., 220 Bway. (Electric) AAA

Sommerville, John, 50 Mc Dougal (Sidewalk) .....F

Sprague Electric Co. (Electric) ....AAAA

Standard Plunger Elevator Co., 1 Bway. (Plunger) B

Thomas & Buckley Hod Elevator Co., 317 W. 64th (Hod) X

N. Y.—North Tonawanda

Armitage & Herschell Co. (Electric; Hydraulic) ..B

N. Y.—Poughkeepsie

Sedgwick Machine Wks. (Carriage; Hand; Invalid; Hand Power; Sidewalk) D

N. Y.—Rochester

Kohlmetz, Chas E., 180 N. Water (Sidewalk) ....B

Michel Machine Co., 25 S. Water (Sidewalk) .....H

N. Y.—Syracuse

Houser Elevator Co. (Electric) C

N. Y.—Troy

Bernard Co. E. G. (Electric) ....D

N. Y.—Warsaw

Warsaw Elevator Co. (Barrel; Package; Carriage; Combination; Hand; Power; Electric Sidewalk; Hand; Invalid; Hand Power Traveling Coal; Passenger; Vehicle; Water; Belt; Electric; Freight) ....B

OHIO—Akron

Webster, Camp & Lane Mach. Co. (Clay) ..AAAA

OHIO—Bucyrus

Amer. Clay Working Mach.

ELEVATORS (Con.)

Co. (Clay; Tile) X

OHIO—Canton

Aultman Co. (Barrel; Package) ....AAAA

OHIO—Cincinnati

Curran Elevator Co., Jas. H. (Electric Sidewalk).D

Fritch Mfg. Co., Francis (Malt; eer) X

Lane & Bodley Co. (Freight; Steam Power; Hydraulic; Brick) ....B

Miller, L. J. (Freight) X

Obermayer Co., S. (Foundry) ....AA

Reedy Co., H. J., 8th, Lock & Reedy (Barrel; Package; Carriage; Combination; Hand; Power; Electric; Foundry; Hand; Invalid; Hand Power; Sidewalk; Belt Power; Factory; Freight; Hydraulic; Passenger; Warehouse) C

Triumph Electric Co., 610 Baymiller (Electric) ..A

Warner Elevator Mfg. Co., Spring Grove Av., Alfred & Valley (Carriage; Belt; Electric; Hand; Invalid; Hand Power; Sidewalk; Freight; Hydraulic; Passenger; Steam Power)AA

OHIO—Cleveland

Bartlett & Snow Co., C. O. (Barrel; Package; Water for Mine; Quarry) ....A

National Iron & Wire Co. (Passenger) ....B

O'Donnel Elevator Co., 22 Johnson (Electric; Freight) ....B

Oram, Jno. S., 160 Coe (Barrel; Package) ....A

OHIO—Columbus

Case Mfg. Co. (Grain; Belt) ....A

Jeffrey Mfg. Co. (Barrel; Package; Brick; Tile; Belt; Water for Mine; Quarry) ....AAAA

OHIO—Dayton

Roberts & Co., Geo. J. (Hydraulic) ....A

OHIO—Ravenna

Byers Machine Co., John F. (Hod; Double Platform) AA

OHIO—Salem

Clarke Co., W. J. (Grain).A

Silver Mfg. Co. (Ensilage Cutter) ....AA

OHIO—Toledo

Haughton Elevator Mach. Co., 124 S. Huron (Electric Sidewalk; Foundry; Hand; Invalid; Hand Power) C

OHIO—Warren

Trumbull Mfg. Co. (Sawdust) C

OHIO—Wellsville

Stevenson & So. (Clay)...B

PA.—Coatsville

Ridgway & Son Co., Craig (Steam Hydraulic) .....A

PA.—Muncy

Sprout, Waldron & Co. (Flour Mill) ....A

PA.—Philadelphia

Chambers Bros. Co. (Clay) AA

Cresson Co., Geo. V., 18th & Allegheny Av. (Belt) AA

Dallett & Co., Thos. H. (Electric) ....B

Energy Elevator Co., 408 Cherry (Hand Power; Vehicle; Belt; Freight) ..D

Harrington Son & Co., E. (Hand Power) ......AA

Link Belt Engineering Co. (Freight) ....AA

Morse, Williams & Co., West End Trust Bldg. (Carriage; Combination; Hand Power; Cotton;

ELEVATORS (Con.)
 Electric; Hand; Invalid
 Hand Power; Sidewalk
 Belt Power; Freight; Hy
 draulic; Passenger; Steam
 Power; Brick; Belt)..AA
Schnitzler, Chas. H. (Spool)
 ....D

Stokes & Parrish Elevator
 Co. (Freight; Hydraulic;
 Passenger) ....A
U. S. Elevator Co., Bourse
 Bldg. (Automatic Safety;
 Hand; Sidewalk) ......D
PA.—Pittsburg
Heyl & Patterson, 51 Wa
 ter (Travelling; Coal).AA
Marshall Bros. (Freight).
 ....AA
Riter-Conley Mfg. Co.
 (Grain) ....AAA
PA.—Pittston
Exeter Machine Works (Bar
 rel; Package) ....AA
PA.—Reading
Reading Crane & Hoist
 Wks. (Sidewalk) ....A
Speidel, J. G., cor. Button
 wood & Gordon (Hand;
 Invalid; Hand Power;
 Sidewalk; Belt) ......B
PA.—Scranton
National Elevator & Ma
 chine Co. (Electric) ....A
PA.—South Bethlehem
Bethlehem Foundry & Ma
 chine Co. (Sidewalk;
 Hand Power) C
PA.—Wilkesbarre
Vulcan Iron Wks. (Coal;
 Gas Works Coal)..AAAA
R. I.—Providence
Mason & Co., Volney W.
 (Carriage) ....D
VA.—Richmond
Cardwell Machine Co.
 (Warehouse) ....A
WIS.—Cudahy
Power & Mining Machinery
 Co. (Bucket) ....AAA
WIS.—Milwaukee
Allis-Chalmers Co. (Quick
 silver) ....AAAA
Barth Mfg. Co., 15th & St.
 Paul (Carriage; Electric;
 Hand; Sidewalk) C
Brodesser Elevator Mfg. Co.
 (Electric; Hand) X
Filer & Stowell Co. (Ltd.)
 (Sawdust) ....AAA
Kieckhefer Elevator Co., A.
 (Electric; Hod; Belt Pow
 er; Carriage; Factory;
 Freight Hand Power; Hy
 draulic; Passenger; Side
 walk; Steam Power;
 Street Car; Warehouse).C

ELIMINATORS

New York City
Robertson & Sons, Jas. L.,
 205 Fulton (Oil) ....E
OHIO—Springfield
Hoppes Mfg. Co. (Oil)...A
PA.—Wilkesbarre
Nicholson & Co., W. H.
 (Automatic) C

ELIXIRS

ILL.—Chicago
Baker & Co., Chas. S. C
IND.—Indianapolis
Lilly & Co. Eli ....AA
MD.—Baltimore
Resinol Chem. Co. .....B
Sharp & Dohme ......AAA
MASS.—Cambridge
Thayer & Co., Henry......A
MICH.—Detroit
Parke, Davis & Co. ..AAAA
Stearns & Co., Fdk. ..AAA
MICH.—Kalamazoo
Upjohn Co. ....AA
N. Y.—Albany
Moore, J. ....D
New York City
Caswell, Massey & Co....X
Fairchild Bros. & Foster.AA
Keith & Co., B. ....F

ELIXIRS (Con.)
McKesson & Robbins.AAAA
Riker & Son Co., Wm. B..
 ....AA
Schieffelin & Co., W. H.AA
PA.—Philadelphia
Hance Bros. & White ..AA
Mulford Co., H. K...AAA

ELLS

ELM
See Lumber

MO.—St. Louis
Nelson Mfg. Co., N. O.
 (Closet; Flush) ....AAA
OHIO—Cincinnati
Eureka Brass Wks.
 (Union) ....E

EMBLEMS

See also Jewelry

ILL.—Chicago
Amer. Terra Cotta & Cera
 mic Co. (Terra Cotta).A
MASS.—Attleboro
Robbins Co., Chas M. (Ma
 sonic; Society) C
N. J.—Newark
Durand & Co. (Inc.) (Ma
 sonic; Society) .....AA
N. J.—Perth Amboy
Perth Amboy Terra Cotta
 Co. (Terra Cotta) ...AA
New York City
Braxmar Co., C. G. (Ma
 sonic; Society; Masonic
 Society Cuff Button) ...B
Excelsior Terra Cotta Co.
 (Terra Cotta) ....A
Lamb, J. R. (Masonic; So
 ciety) ....D
Myers Co., S. F. (Masonic;
 Society) ....D
Richardson & Co., J. W.
 (Masonic; Society) ....D
Sinnock & Sherrill (Masonic;
 Society) ....B
PA.—Philadelphia
Bingham, James (Masonic;
 Society) ....H
Cassel, Jacob C. (Terra
 Cotta) ....D
Englehart, Wm. F. (Ma
 sonic; Society) ....B
Parry & Sons, Thos. (Ma
 sonic; Society) ......B
PA.—Reading
Reading Terra Cotta &
 Stove Lining Wks. (Terra
 Cotta) C
R. I.—Providence
Darling & Co., C. C. (Ma
 sonic; Society) ......B
Irons & Russell (Masonic;
 Society) ....A
Waite, Mathewson & Co.
 (Masonic; Society) .....B

EMBOSSERS

CAL.—San Francisco
Ingerson & Glasier Co.
 (Glass) ....D
Schmitz & Hopps, 62 8th
 (Glass) ....F
ILL.—Chicago
Rawson & Evans, 151 W.
 Washington (Glass) ...C
Suess Ornamental Glass Co.,
 48 N. Clinton (Glass)..D
Western Sand Blast Co., W.
 Jackson Boul. & South
 Clinton (Glass) C
MASS.—Boston
Redding, Baird & Co., 83
 Franklin (Glass) .....B
N. Y.—Brooklyn
Jones Decorative Glass Co.,
 Thos., Concord & Hudson
 Av. (Glass) C
New York City
Carter, C. W. H. (Stamping
 Varnish) ....A
Dougherty, James, 435
 B'way (Glass) ....B

EMBOSSERS (Con.)

Potts Bros., 210 Center (Glass) ....F
Rae & Co., G., 436 W. B'way (Glass) ....F
Schaefer Bros., 457 B'way (Glass) ....F
Van Horne & Co., D. A., 44 Vestry (Glass) .....B
OHIO—Dayton
Seybold Machine Co. (Paper) ....A
PA.—Philadelphia
French & Co., Saml. H., York Av., 4th & Callowhill (Glass) ....A
Gillinder & Sons (Inc.), 135 Oxford (Glass) ....A
Reith, Wm., 134 N. 7th (Glass) C
Smith & Sons, H. J., 271 S. 5th (Glass) ....D
PA.—Pittsburg
Pittsburg Plate Glass Co., Frick Bldg. (Glass)AAAA
WIS.—Milwaukee
Van Horn, Danl., 537 17th (Glass) ....H

EMBROIDER-IES

CAL.—San Francisco
Higginbotham & Co. (Silk) B
CONN.—Bridgeport
Cylindrograph Embroidery Co. (Silk) ....B
ILL.—Chicago
Chicago Braiding & Embroidery Co., 116 Market (Silk) ....B
Chicago Embroidery Co., 492 W. Ohio (Silk) ....D
Garden City Embroidery Wks. (Swiss) C
Wilson Braiding & Embroidery Co., 183 Wabash Av. (Silk) ....D
MASS.—Haverhill
Dalrymple & Co., J. A...B
N. J.—Camden
Loeb & Schoenfeld Co. .... AAAA
N. J.—Newark
Borneman, Herman (Lace) AA
New York City
Benziger Bros. (Church)..A
Brunner & Dreifuss (Silk) D
Cox, Sons & Vining (Church) ....D
Kursheedt Mfg. Co. (Lace; Silk) ....AA
Lamb, J. & R. (Church)..D
Locke & Altherr (Com.).B
Oehle & Braeker (Silk)...C
Schiess, Theodore (Silk)..C
N. Y.—Tarrytown
Husted, A. P. (Silk) ...B

EMERALDS

See Jewelry

EMERY

CONN.—Bridgeport
Bridgeport Safety Emery Wheel Co. ....F
CONN.—Derby
Oriental Emery Co. (Turkish) ....D
ILL.—Chicago
Chicago Wheel & Mfg. Co., 39 W. Randolph C
MASS.—Boston
Ashland Emery & Corundum Co., Boyleston (Corundum) ....A
MASS.—Leeds
Northampton Emery Wheel Co. ....A
MASS.—North Grafton
Washington Mills Emery Mfg. Co. ....B
MASS.—Westfield
Vitrified Wheel Co. C

EMERY (Con.)

N. Y.—Croton-on-Hudson
Crescent Abrasive Co......X
New York City
Sheridan, Wm. H., 48 Centre ....D
PA.—Philadelphia
Abrasive Material Co. ...A
Keystone Emery Mills (Corundum) C
PA.—Stroudsburg
Tanite Co. ....A
R. I.—Providence
American Emery Wheel Wks. ....B

EMULSIFIERS

OHIO—Cincinnati
Day & Co., J. H. ....A

EMULSION

CONN.—Glenbrook
Phillips Chem. Chas. H...B
MAINE—Portland
Frye, Geo. C. ....A
MD.—Baltimore
Sharp & Dohme. .....AAA
MICH.—Detroit
Parke, Davis & Co...AAAA
New York City
McKesson & Robbins.AAAA
Riker & Son Co., Wm. B... AA
Scott & Bowne ......AAAA

ENAMELLED WARE

CONN.—Meriden
Manning, Bowman & Co... AA
CONN.—Middletown
New England Enamelling Co. (Cooking) ....B
ILL.—Chicago
Wolff Mfg. Co., 93 W. Lake AAAA
Sturges & Burn Mfg. Co., A
IND.—Terre Haute
Columbian Enameling & Stamping Co. ......AAA
MO.—St. Louis
Geisel Mfg. Co. ....A
St. Louis Stamping Co. AAAA
N. Y.—Buffalo
Shepard & Co., Sidney AAAA
N. Y.—Canandaigua
Lisk Mfg. Co. (Cooking)... AAA
New York City
Central Stamping Co., 24 Cliff ....AA
Iron-Clad Mfg. Co., 2 Cliff (Cooking) ....AA
Lalance & Grosjean Mfg. Co. (Cooking, etc.).AAAA
Markt & Co., 193 West (Imported White) ......AAA
National Enamelling & Stamping Co., 81 Fulton (Cooking) ....AAAA
Rothschild, Meyers & Co., 524 B'way (Cooking).AA
N. Y.—Rochester
Rochester Stamping Co.AAA
N. Y.—Rome
Rome Sanitary Wks. (Plumbers' Cast Iron)..B
OHIO—Bellaire
Bellaire Enamel Co. .....E
OHIO—Cleveland
Avery Stamping Co. ......B
Bowman Co., Geo. H. (White Cooking, etc.)..A
Cleveland Stamping & Tool Co. (Agate Cooking)..A
OHIO—Mansfield
Humphries Mfg. Co. (Cast Iron Sanitary) ....B
OHIO—New Philadelphia
Belmont Stamping & Enamelling Co. (Iron) ....B
PA.—Allegheny
Star Enamelling & Stamping Co. ....B

ENAMELLED WARE

PA.—Marietta
Marietta Casting Co. ....B
Marietta Holloware & Enam-
　elling Co. ....B
PA.—New Castle
New Castle Stamping Co.
　(Cooking) ....A
PA.—Pittsburg
Standard Mfg. Co. .....AA
R. I.—Providence
Narragansett Machine Co.
　(Iron) ....A
W. VA.—Moundsville
United States Stamping Co.
　　　　　　　　　　　　A
WIS.—Sheboygan
Vollrath Mfg. Co., Jacob J.
　(Cooking, &c.) ....A

ENAMELLERS

ILL.—Chicago
Rawson & Evans, 151 Wash-
　ington (Glass) C
Suess Ornamental Glass Co.,
　48 N. Clinton (Glass)...D
KY.—Louisville
Plum Art Glass Co., 308 7th
　(Glass) X
MD.—Baltimore
Gernhardt & Co., H. T., 409
　E. Fayette (Glass) .....H
New York City
Dougherty, James, 435 W.
　B'way (Glass) ....B
OHIO—Dayton
Stevens Art Glass Co., 28 S.
　St. Clair (Glass) ......H
PA.—Philadelphia
French & Co., Saml. H.
　(Glass) ....A
R. I.—Providence
Amer. Enamel Co. (of
　Wood; Metal, etc.) ...B
Narragansett Machine Co.
　(Iron; Wood) ....A

ENAMELS

See also Paints

CONN.—New Milford
Bridgeport Wood Finishing
　Co. ....AA
ILL.—Chicago
Adams & Elting Co., 155 W.
　Wash'n. (Bedstead) ..A
Arnstein, Eugene, 35th &
　Shields Av. (Air Drying;
　Aluminum; Baking; Bath
　Tub; Radiator) ....A
Bradley & Vrooman Co.,
　2633 Dearborn ....A
Chicago Varnish Co., Dear-
　Born Av. & Kinzie ..AA
Chicago Wood Finishing Co.,
　261 Elston Av. ....A
Ernecke & Salmstein, 295
　Loomis (Marble Paint for
　Walls & Ceilings; Bath
　Tubs) C
Nat'l. Fire Proof Paint Co.,
　40 Dearborn ....D
Nubian Paint & Varnish Co.
　(Brewers) ....B
Rubber Paint Co., 154 W.
　Van Buren (Baking) ..A
Wadsworth-Howland　Co.,
　Indiana Av. & 13th ...A
ILL.—Rockford
Sovereign Co., C. E. (Rock-
　ford Top Dressing) ...C
IND.—Indianapolis
Burdsal Co., A., 102 S. Meri-
　den (Porcelain; Bath
　Tub) ....A
Lily Enamel & Paint Co. E
MICH.—Detroit
Acme White Lead & Color
　Wks. (Bath Tub; Brew-
　ers'; Radiator) ....AAA
Detroit White Lead Wks.
　(Bicycle) ....AAA
N. J.—Jersey City
Woolsey Paint & Color Co.,
　C. A. (Bicycles) ......A
N. J.—Newark
Bigelow Varnish Co., 356
　Mulberry (White) C
Cawley Clark & Co., 272

ENAMELS (Con.)

　Passaic ....AA
Stiles, Chas. ....D
N. Y.—Buffalo
Buffalo Enamel & Stain Co.,
　Ellicott Square (Paint) F
McLennan Paint Co. (Ltd.)
　175-195 Rano. (Baking;
　Bath Tub) ....AA
New York City
Aspinwall, Edwin, 98 Beek-
　man (Importer) ....B
Behlen & Bro., Herman, 5
　N. William (Bath Tub) C
Bensinger Co., C., 245 Bway
　(Boiler; Smoke Stack) X
Billings, King & Co., 438
　Pearl ....A
De Ronde Co., Frank S., 46
　Cliff ....B
De Voe & Raynolds Co. ..
　　　　　　　　　　AAAA
Engel & Co., Jno., 137 W.
　Bway. (Stove Pipe) ...E
Gestendorfer Bros., 43 Park
　Pl. (Stove Pipe; Bath
　Tub; Gold; Aluminum;
　Radiator) ....B
Pierce & Co., F. O. (Bicycle)
　　　　　　　　　　　　A
Schlegel Mfg. Co., Oscar,
　182 Grand ....B
Smith Co., Edw., 45 Bway.
　　　　　　　　　　　　A
Standard Varnish Wks., 29
　Bway. (Air Drying; Bak-
　ing; Bicycle) ....AA
Toch Bros., 468 W. Bway. A
N. Y.—Unionport
Feil Co., Edward (Watch) X
OHIO—Cleveland
Billings-Chapin Co., 37 Case
　Av. ....A
Forest City Paint & Var-
　nish Co., Hamilton &
　Kirkland ....B
OHIO—Toledo
National Cement & Rubber
　Mfg. Co. (Bicycle) ...C
PA.—New Castle
New Castle Paint & Varnish
　Co. (Rubber Paint) ...E
PA.—Philadelphia
Binswanger & Co., B., 115
　N. 4th ....B
Bowens' Sons, S., N. 4th
　cor. Sedgely Av. ......B
Felton, Sibley & Co., 136 N.
　4th (Bicycle) ....AAA
French & Co., Saml. H., 4th
　& Callowhill (Baking;
　Bath Tub; Brewers'; Ra-
　diator) ....A
Hamrich Tank & Barrel
　Hard Shell Enameling Co.,
　(Brewers) ....D
Harrison Bros. & Co., (Inc.)
　35th & Grays Ferry Rd.
　　　　　　　　　　AAAA
Lucas & Co., Jno., 4th &
　Race (Bath Tub; Brew-
　ers'; Radiator; Bicycle)
　　　　　　　　　　　AAA
Phoenix Paint & Varnish
　Co., 124 Market ......A
Rinald Bros., 1142 N. Han-
　cock (Porcelain, &c.; Bak-
　ing; Bath Tub; Iron) ..B
Thomson Wood Finishing
　Co., 115 N. 4th (Air Dry-
　ing; Baking; Bath Tub;
　Iron) ....B
Waterall & Co., Wm., 200
　N. 4th ....A
PA.— Pittsburg
Atlas Paint Co. (Ltd.) 2638
　Liberty Av. X
Hommel Co., O., 110 Mar-
　ket (Aluminum) ....D
Lawrence & Co., W. W.
　(Bicycle) ....AA
PA.—Reading
Wilhem Co., A. (Baking;
　Bath Tub) ....AA
R. I.—Providence
Amer. Enamel Co. (Japan;
　&c.; Baking; Celluloid
　Color) ....B
Carpenter & Wood (Jewel-
　ers') ....D
United States Gutta Percha

ENAMELS. (Con.)
Paint Co., 24 Matthewson (Bath Tub) ....A
WIS.—Milwaukee
Smith Paint & Varnish Co., 329 Chestnut (Air Drying; Baking) ....D

ENCLOSURES

CAL.—Los Angeles
Fruhling, Wm. A., 218 S. Los Angeles (Elevator) C
CAL.—San Francisco
Cahill & Hall Elevator Co., 133 Beale (Elevator) ..B
Pioneer Iron & Wire Wks. Co., 1433 Market (Elevator) ....D
CONN.—Meriden
Bradley & Hubbard Mfg. Co. (Elevator) ....AAAA
ILL.—Chicago
Barbee Wire & Iron Wks., 44 Dearborn (Elevator; Office) ....B
Booth, Jno., 114-116 E. Lake (Elevator) .....B
Chicago Ornamental Iron Co., 37th & Stewart Av. (Elevator) ....A
Gilbert & Bennett Mfg. Co., 153 Lake (Elevator) AAA
Smith Wire & Iron Wks., F. P., 100 Lake (Elevator) AA
Voss, Fred'k., 621 Austin Av. (Elevator) ......B
Winslow Bros. Co., 368 Carroll Av. (Elevator) ..AA
ILL.—Peoria
Lucas & Sons, A., cor Cedar & Wash'n. (Elevator) ..B
KY.—Louisville
Dow Wire Wks. Co., 730 W. Market (Elevator) ....D
MD.—Baltimore
Dufur & Co., 311 N. Howard (Elevator) ....B
MASS.—Boston
Hub Wire Cloth & Wire Work Co., 13 Devonshire (Elevator) ....F
MASS.—Clinton
Clinton Wire Cloth Co. (Elevator) ....AAA
MASS.—Springfield
Bigelow-Cheney Wire Wks. (Elevator) ....A
MASS.—Worcester
Dean & Co., Henry E. (Elevator) C
Nat'l. Mfg. Co. (Elevator) A
Wright Wire Co. (Elevator) AA
MICH.—Detroit
Art Brass & Iron Wks., cor. 4th & Porter (Elevator) C
Barnum Wire & Iron Wks., 99-105 Shelby (Elevator) B
MINN.—Minneapolis
Flour City Ornamental Iron Wks., 27th Av. & 27th (Elevator) ....B
MINN.—St. Paul
Perkins Mfg. Co., 1121 E. 7th (Elevator) ....D
MO.—Kansas City
Kansas City Wire & Iron Wks. (Elevator) ......A
MO.—St. Louis
Globe Iron & Fdry. Co., 9th & Victor (Elevator) ....B
Koken Iron Wks., Koken Bldg. (Elevator) ......B
Ludlow-Saylor Wire Co., 4th & Elm (Elevator) ....AA
N. J.—Jersey City
Snead & Co. Iron Wks., ft. of Pine (Elevator) .....A
N. Y.—Brooklyn
Eagle Iron Wks. (Inc.) 850 DeKalb Av. (Elevator) .C
Hecla Iron Wks., N. 11th & Bway (Elevator) ...AA
N. Y.—Buffalo
Buffalo Wire Wks. Co. (Elevator) ....A

ENCLOSURES (Con.)
New York City
Dimond, Thomas, 128 W. 33rd (Elevator) ....A
McMurray & Bro., Robt. T., 105 E. 22nd (Elevator) C
Sterling Bronze Co., 12 E. 30th (Elevator) ......B
Union Equipment & Bronze Co., 514 W. 36th (Elevator) ....D
Westervelt, A. B. & W. T., 102 Chambers (Elevator) B
N. Y.—Rochester
Snow Wire Wks. Co., 76 Exchange (Elevator) ..B
N. Y.—Syracuse
Houser Elevator Co., 314 E. Water (Elevator) C
OHIO—Cincinnati
Cinn. Mfg. Co., 512 Main (Elevator) ....B
Schreiber & Sons Co., L., 8th & Eggleston Av. (Elevator) ....AA
Stewart Iron Wks. (Elevator) ....A
OHIO—Cleveland
Nat'l. Iron & Wire Co. (Elevator) ....B
Tyler Co., W. S. (Elevator) AAAA
Van Dorn Iron Wks. Co. (Elevator) ....AA
OHIO—Hamilton
Meyers Mfg. Co., Fred. J. (Elevator) ....B
OHIO—Kenton
Champion Iron Co. (Elevator) ....AA
OHIO—Springfield
Webster & Perks Tool Co. (Elevator) C
OHIO—Toledo
Donovan Wire & Iron Co. (Elevator) C
OREGON—Portland
Portland Wire & Iron Wks., 147 Front (Elevator) ..D
PA.—Allegheny
Albree Iron Wks., Chester B. (Elevator) ....B
Rieseck, P., Allegheny Av. & Rebecca (Elevator) ..C
PA.—Ellwood City
Glen Mfg. Co. (Elevator) C
PA.—Philadelphia
Darby & Sons, Edw., 233 Arch (Elevator) .....A
Gaumer Co., Jno. L., 19th & Hamilton (Elevator) C
Merritt & Co., 1024 Ridge Av. (Elevator) ....B
PA.—Pittsburg
Taylor & Dean, 205 Market (Elevator) ....B
PA.—Reading
Remppis Co., Wm. F. (Elevator) ....B
WIS.—Milwaukee
Bayley & Sons Co., Wm., 782 Greenbush (Elevator) A

ENDS

CONN.—Hartford
Billings & Spencer Co. (Bicycle Fork) ....AA
CONN.—Milldale
Clark Bros & Co. (Bolt) A
CONN.—New Haven
Cowles & Co. (Inc.) C., (Joint) ....A
CONN.—Plantsville
Atwater Mfg. Co. (Joint) A
Blakeslee Forging Co. (Joint; Perch) ....B
Smith & Co., H. D. (Bolt; Pole; Joint; Perch; Stay) A
CONN.—Unionville
Upson Nut Co. (Bolt) AAA
DEL.—Wilmington
Diamond State Steel Co. (Bolt) ....AAA
Wilmington Malleable Iron Co. (Brake) ....AAA
ILL.—Chicago
Continental Bolt & Iron

ENGINES

ENGINES (Con.)

sene Burning Launch) ..B

CAL.—San Leandro

Best Mfg. Co. (Gas; Gasoline; Oil; Traction Logging; Steam Traction), A

CAL.—Stockton

Holt Mfg. Co. (Traction; Steam) ....AA

Sampson Iron Wks. (Gas) C

COLO.—Denver

Davis Iron Wks. Co., F. M., Larimer Cor. 8th (Steam Hoisting; Steam).......A

Denver Engineering Wks. Co., Blake Cor. 30th (All kinds Hoisting; Direct Acting Mining; Steam)..A

Hendri & Bolthoff Mfg. Supply. Co. (Steam Hoisting) AAA

Mine & Smelting Supply Co. (Steam Hoisting)....AAA

Stearns-Roger Mfg. Co. Steam Hoisting; Steam) A

CONN.—Bridgeport

Acme Oil Engine Co. (Oil) F

Amer. & British Mfg. Co. (Gas or Gasoline, in quantities only; Steam in quantities only) ....AAA

Coulter & McKenzie Mach. Co. (Steam; Steam Hoisting)..............C

Locomobile Co., of America (Steam & Gasoline Automobile) ....B

Pacific Iron Wks. (Hoisting Steam) ....A

CONN.—Cea e Brook

Connecticut Valicy Mfg. Co. (Gasoline Marine) C

CONN.—Cos Cob

Palmer Bros. (Gasoline Marine; Gas or Gasoline)...C

CONN.—Hartford

Colt's Pat. Firearms Mfg. Co. (Oil Well; Steam; Portable Steam) ..AAAA

Pitkin Bros. & Co., 152 State (Steam) ....B

Vanderbeck Tool Wks. (Compound Steam) .....B

CONN.—New Britain

New Britain Mach. Co. (Steam Corliss; Automatic Steam) ....A

CONN.—New Haven

Rowland, F. C. & A. E., 413 Chapel (Automatic Steam) C

Twiss. Nelson W. (Marine 15 to 100 h. p.) ....E

CONN.—New London

New London Gas & Electric Co. (Steam) ....B

CONN.—Norfolk

Norwalk Iron Wks. Co. (Steam) ....AA

CONN.—Stamford

Brooklyn Railway Supply Co. (Gasoline) ....A

International Power Vehicle Co. (Oil) ....D

Stamford Motor Co. (Gasoline) ....A

CONN.—Torrington

Eagle Bicycle Mfg. Co. (Gas, Marine; Stationary 4 to 6 h. p.; Stationary Steam) A

CONN.—Windsor Locks

Windsor Locks Machine Co. (Rag) ....E

DEL.—Wilmington

Amer. Machine Co. (Hot Air Pumping) ....D

Stamford Motor Co. (Gasoline)

Harlan & Hollingsworth Co. (Marine) ....AAAA

Pool Co., J. Morton (Beating) ....AA

Pusey & Jones Co. (Beating; Marine; Stationary Steam) AAA

Remington Machine Co. (Corliss Steam) ....A

FLA.—Jacksonville

Merrill-Stevens Engineering Co. (Steam Marine) ....B

GA.—Augusta

Lombard Iron Wks. & Supply Co. (Gas; Horizontal Steam; Farm Steam)....A

ENGINES (Con.)

GA.—Macon

Schofield Sons Co., J. S. (Steam) ....A

GA.—Newnan

Cole Mfg. Co., R. D. (Steam) ....A

GA.—Savannah

Kehoe & Sons, Wm. (Marine; Steam) ....A

McDonough & Ballington (Steam) ....B

GA.—West Point

West Point Iron Wks. (Portable Steam; Farm Steam) B

ILL.—Aurora

Amer. Wells Wks. (Gas; Gasoline; Gasoline Portable; Artesian Well Steam) ....AA

ILL.—Batavia

Feedmill Co. (Gasoine)..A

ILL.—Belleville

Harrison Machine Wks. (Traction Steam) ....AA

ILL.—Chicago

Allis-Chalmers Co., Home Ins. Bldg. (Blowing; Steam Corliss; Steam Hoisting; Steam Portable Steam; Steam Vertical) AAAA

Amer. Blower Co., 1550 Marquette Bldg. (Automatic Steam) ....AA

Amer. Well Wks., 45 W. Randolph (Gasoline; Steam) ....AA

Ames. Iron Wks. (of Oswego, N. Y.) Monadnock Blk. (Steam 16 to 100 h. p.) AA

Anderson Co., Carl, 27 N. Clinton (Gas; Gasoline) C

Atlas Engine Wks. (of Indianapolis, Ind.) 55 S. Canal (Steam 10 to 500 h. p.) ....AAAA

Borden & Selleck Co., 48 Lake (Gas; Gasoline; Steam; Hoisting).......B

Caldwell & Son, H. W., Western Av. bet. 17th & 18th (Gas; Gasoline)....A

Chicago Ship Bldg. Co., Rookery Bldg. & 101st & Calumet River (Steam Marine) ....AAAA

Contractors' Supply & Equipment Co., 232 5th Av. (Steam Hoisting) C

Elmes Engineering Wks., Chas. F., Cor. Fulton & N. Morgan (Automatic Marine; Yacht or Launch), A

Fairbanks, Morse & Co. (Gas; Gasoline; Gasoline Launch; Naphtha Launch) AAAA

Ft. Wayne Fdry. & Mach. Co. (of Ft. Wayne, Ind.) The Rookery (Automatic Steam) C

Garden City Fan Co., 43 S. Clinton (Steam Vertical) C

Latham Mchry. Co., 199 S. Canal (Gas; Gasoline)..C

McMullin Motive Power & Construction Co. (Gas; Gasoline) ....B

Marine Iron Wks. (Steam Marine) ....B

Moniglians Machine Wks., 813 Carroll Av. (Steam Hoisting; Logging; Portable Hoisting) C

Perrin & Co., Wm. R., 1500 46th (Blowing) .....A

Scott Valve Co., 32 W. Randolph (Deep Well Pumping) ....D

Strang Engine Co., 140 Dearborn (Kerosene) ...D

Skillin & Richards Mfg. Co., 147 Fulton (Gas; Gasoline) C

Sturtevant Co., B. F. (of Boston, Mass.) 218 S. Clinton (Automatic Steam; Steam Vertical) .....AA

Sullivan Mchry. Co., 135 Adams (Steam Corliss;

ENGINES (Con.)
Steam; Steam Hoisting)
..........................AAA

Temple Pump Co., 15th Place (Gasoline, 2 to 10 h. p.) ....A

Webster Mfg. Co., 1075 W. 15th (Gas; Gasoline) ..AA

Willard & Co., Chas. P. (Horizontal Steam; Steam Marine Gasoline; Steam Launch; Steam Yacht; Steam Portable; Compound Condensing Steam; Vertical Steam) ......D

Wolf Co., Fred. W. (Freezing) ....AAA

ILL.—Danville

Danville Fdry. & Machine Co. (Haulage; Steam Hoisting) C

ILL.—East Moline

Root & Van Devoort Engine Co. (Gas) C

ILL.—Freeport

Stover Engine Wks. (Gasoline) ....A

ILL.—Galesburg

Frost Mfg. Co. (Steam Corliss 30 to 900 h. p.; Automatic Steam 7 to 150 h. p.) ....A

ILL.—Joliet

Bates Machine Co. (Corliss; Steam; Street Railway) ..AA

ILL.—Litchfield

Litchfield Fdry. & Machine Co. (Steam Corliss; Haulage; Steam Hoisting; Steam) ....A

ILL.—Mattoon

Chuse Engine & Mfg. Co. (Steam) C

ILL.—Moline

Moline Pump Co. (Gas) ...A
Williams White & Co. (Inc.) (Portable Steam) ....AA

ILL.—Peoria

Armstrong, Jas. C. (Steam) C

Avery Mfg. Co. (Steam Traction) ....A

Colean Mfg. Co. (Steam Traction) ....A

ILL.—Peru

Brunner, Chas. (Gas; Gasoline) ....A

ILL.—Quincy

Central Iron Wks. (Gas; Gasoline; Steam Hoisting; Marine Gas; Gasoline; Yacht or Launch Gas or Gasoline) ....B

Quincy Engine Wks. (Vertical, Compound, Triple Expansion Steam 40 to 2,500 h. p.) ....AA

ILL.—Rockford

National Engine Co. (Gasoline) C

ILL.—Springfield

Ide & Sons, A. L. (High Speed, Automatic, Steam; Compound Steam; Compound Condensing Steam; Street Railway) ......AA

ILL.—Sterling

Charter Gas Engine Co. (Gas; Gasoline; Portable Gasoline) ....A

IND.—Anderson

Anderson Fdry. & Machine Wks. (Horizontal Steam) ....B

Buckeye Mfg. Co. (Gas; Gasoline; Gasoline Launch; Naphtha Launch; Compound Launch; Vertical Launch) ....AA

Wooley Fdry. Machine Co. Gas; Gasoline) ....B

IND.—Auburn

Model Gas Engine Co. (Gas; Gasoline) C

IND.—Brazil

Crawford & McCrimmon Co. (Hoisting Steam; Friction Hoisting; Steam; Hauling Steam) ....A

IND.—Columbus

Reeves & Co. (Traction Steam; Portable Steam; Farm Steam) ......AAAA

ENGINES (Con.)

IND.—Connersville

Roots Co., P. H. & F. M. (Blowing) ....AA

IND.—Evansville

Heilman Machine Wks. (Horizontal Steam; Traction Steam; Portable Steam; Corliss Steam; Corliss Steam; Farm Steam) ....A

Kratz Bros. (Portable Steam) X

IND.—Ft. Wayne

Brass Fdry. & Machine Wks. (Horizontal Steam) X

Western Gas Construction Co. (Gas; Gasoline) ....B

IND.—Indianapolis

Atlas Engine Wks. (High Speed, Automatic, Steam; Corliss Steam; Hoisting Steam; Mining Steam; Double Steam; Quarry Steam; Horizontal Steam; Farm Steam; Winding Steam; Portable Steam; Portable Steam, or Skids; Portable Steam on Wheels; Automatic Cut-off Steam) ....AAAA

Capital Gas Engine Co. (Gas; Gasoline) ...AAA

Chandler & Taylor Co. (Horizontal, Steam; Electric Steam; Portable Steam; Automatic Cut-off Steam; Compound Steam; Double Steam) ......AA

Monarch Gas Engine Co., E. New York Cor. Belt Ry. (Gas; Gasoline) C

Nordyke & Marmon Co. (Portable Steam)....AAA

Potter Mfg. Co., 2010 Northwestern Av. (Steam Hoisting) ....B

Sinker-Davis Co. (Horizontal Steam; Vertical Portable Steam; Portable Steam) B

IND.—Kendallville

Flint & Waling Mfg. Co. (Gasoline) ....AA

IND.—La Porte

Rumely Co., M. (Steam, Straw Burning, Farm; Steam Traction; Steam Portable; Steam Farm) ....AAA

IND.—Marion

Gemmer Engine & Mfg. Co. (Gas & Gasoline) ..AAAA

IND.—Mishawaka

Western Gas Engine Co. (Gas; Gasoline Yacht, etc.) C

IND.—Muncie

Muncie Gas Engine & Supply Co. (Gas) ....B

IND.—New Albany

Goetz-Coleman Mfg. Co. (Gas; Gasoline) ....B

IND.—Richmond

Gaar, Scott & Co. (Traction Steam; Straw Burning Traction Steam; Portable Steam; Portable on Skids, Steam; Portable on Wheels; Steam; Farm Steam) ....AAAA

Quaker City Machine Co. (Steam) C

Richmond Machine Wks. (Automatic Steam 6 to 75 h. p.) ....B

Robinson & Co. (Traction, Steam; Portable Steam; Farm Steam) ....AA

IND.—Terra Haute

Prox & Brinkman Mfg. Co. (Gas; Gasoline; Hoisting Steam: Mining, Steam), A

IOWA—Burlington

Murray Iron Wks. Co. (Gas; Gasoline; Hoisting Steam; Marine Steam; Hauling Steam; Portable Steam; Automatic Cut-off Steam; Corliss Steam; Vertical Steam) ....A

IOWA—Cedar Rapids

Carmody. J. T. (Steam)...C
Cherry Co., J. G. (Dairy) A

366

ENGINES (Con.)

IOWA—Charles City
Hart-Parr Co. (Gasoline Traction) ....A
IOWA—Davenport
Davenport Fdry. & Machine Co. (Steamboat; Automatic Steam 30 to 400 h. p.) ....B
IOWA—Des Moines
Chemical Fire Engine Co. (Chemical, Fire)......H
Des Moines Gas Engine Co. (Gas; Gasoline) ....B
Des Moines Mfg. & Supply Co. (Steam) ....A
Eagle Iron Wks. (Steam Hoisting) ....B
IOWA—Lyons
Pelton & Son, T. G. (Gasoline) ....B
IOWA—Marshalltown
Lennox Machine Co. (Stationary; Mounted Gas; Gasoline) C
Shorthill & Co., A. E. (Gas; Gasoline; Steam) C
IOWA—Ottumwa
Ottumwa Iron Wks. (Haulage; Steam Hoisting; Steam, also Air)......AA
IOWA—Waterloo
Waterloo Gasoline Engine Co. (Gasoline, Marine; Traction Steam) ....B
Waterloo Motor Wks. (Gasoline) ....A
KANS.—Enterprise
Ehrsam & Sons Mfg. Co., J. B. (Steam) C
KANS.—Kansas City
Riverside Iron Wks. Co. (Steam) ....A
KANS.—Topeka
Western Fdry. & Mach. Wks. (Steam) ....B
KY.—Covington
Houston, Stanwood & Gamble Co. (Throttling, Standard Duty, etc., Steam)..A
KY.—Louisville
Grainger & Co., 129 E. Main (Steam) ....A
National Fdry. & Machine Co. (Blowing) ....A
LA.—New Orleans
Coleman Mach. Co. (Ltd.), H. Dudley (Portable Steam) ....D
Shakespeare Iron Wks., 913 Girod (Steam) ....A
Whitney Iron Wks. Co. (Steam Marine) ......AA
MAINE—Bath
Bath Iron Wks. (Marine; Steam) ....AA
MAINE—Hallowell
Davenport, S. F. (Yacht; Launch) ....H
Fullers' Sons, G. (Steam)..C
MAINE—Mechanics Falls
Penney & Sons Co., J. W. (Automatic Steam 8 to 35 h. p...) ....B
MAINE—Portland
Maine Electric Co. (Direct Connected; Belted) .....E
Portland Co. (High Speed, Automatic, Steam; Hoisting, Steam; Horizontal, Steam; Marine Steam; Portable Steam; Corliss Steam) ....AA
Stickney, Henry R. (Marine Steam) ....D
MD.—Baltimore
Brown, F. S. & G. L. (Steam Yacht) ....E
Murray & Son, James, 102 E. York (Steam) ....B
Rosenberg Co., A. (Gas; Gasoline) ....A
White & Middleton Engine Co. (Gas; Gasoline) ....B
MD.—Cumberland
McKaig, Merwin (Steam 10 to 100 h. p.) ....A
MD.—Sparrows Point
Maryland Steel Co. (Steam Marine) ....AAAA
MASS.—Boston
Atlantic Wks., 70 Border (Marine Steam) ......AA
Clark, Edward S. (Oil Well,

ENGINES (Con.)

Steam) X
Cunningham Engineering Co., Tremont Bldg. (Marine; Steam) ....B
Fitzhenry & Co., E. L., 36 Wash. (Yacht or Launch) ....E
Lockwood Mfg. Co. (Marine) X
Star Brass Mfg. Co. (& Pumps Combined; Gas) A
Sturtevant Co., B. F. (Blowing; Automatic Cutoff; Steam; Double Steam) ....AAA
MASS.—Cambridge
Kendall & Sons, Edward (Hoisting Steam).....AA
Rawson & Morrison Mfg. Co. (Hoisting Steam; Logging; Steam) ....B
MASS.—Fitchburg
Brown & Co., C. H. (Corliss Steam; Automatic Steam) ....A
Fitchburg Steam Engine Co. (High Speed, Automatic, Steam; Horizontal Steam; Automatic Cut-off, Steam; Compound Steam; Compound Condensing Steam; Vertical Steam) X
Putnam Machine Co. (Automatic Steam 20 to 650 h. p.) ....AA
Union Machine Co. (Rag), B
MASS.—Florence
Norwood Engineering Co. Vertical Steam 2 to 50 h. p.) ....B
MASS.—Holyoke
Dean Steam Pump Co. (Pumping) ....AAAA
Holyoke Machine Co. (Beating; Rag) ....AA
Perkins & Son, B. F. (Steam) ....B
MASS.—Hyde Park
Boston Blower Co. (Steam) ....B
MASS.—Lawrence
Horne & Son Co., J. H. (Beating; Washing Combined; Jordan) ....A
Lawrence Machine Co. (Direct Connected ; Belted) X
MASS.—Marlboro
Parsons & Son, Henry (Steam) ....A
MASS.—New Bedford
Weeden Mfg. Co. (Toy Steam) ....D
MASS.—Pittsfield
Jones & Sons Co., E. D. (Beating; Beating & Washing Combined; Rag) ....B
MASS.—Quincy
Fore River Ship & Engine Co. (Marine; Steam) ....AAAA
MASS.—Taunton
Mason Machine Wks. (Steam) ....AAA
Taunton Locomotive Mfg. Co. (Steam) ....AA
MASS.—Worcester
Greendale Gas Engine Co. (Oil) X
Morgan Construction Co. (Rolling Mill) ....A
MICH.—Adrian
Adrain Brick & Tile Mach. Co. (Hoisting, Steam)..C
MICH.—Battle Creek
Advance Thresher Co. (Steam, Straw Burning, Farm Traction Steam; Farm Steam) ......AAAA
Amer. Steam Pump Co. (Deep Well Pumping) ....AAA
Nichols & Shepard Co. (Steam Straw Burning, Farm; Traction, Steam; Portable Steam; Portable on Skids, Steam; Portable on Wheels, Steam; Farm Steam) ....AAAA
Union Steam Pump Co. (DeepWell Pumping) AA

ENGINES (Con.)

MICH.—Bay City

Industrial Wks. (Hoisting, Steam) ....A

MacKinnon Mfg. Co. (Marine, Steam) C

Marine Iron Co. (Hoisting, Steam; Steam) C

Smalley Bros. & Co. (Steam) B

MICH.—Comstock

Comstock Mfg. Co. (Automatic Steam) C

MICH.—Detroit

Amer. Blower Co. (Blowing) AA

Detroit Shipbuilding Co. (Marine; Steam) ..AAAA

Dodge Bros., 137 Beaubien (Marine; Steam).......B

Fisher Electrical Wks., 183 Larned (Direct Connected; Belted) ....E

Great Lakes Engineering Wks., Rivard & Detroit River (Marine; Gas or Gasoline; Steam) ......A

Leland & Faulconer Mfg. Co. (Gasoline) ....B

Michigan Steel Boat Co. (Marine; Gas or Gasoline) C

Mitshkun Co., M., Chamb. of Commerce (Second Hand Hoisting Steam)..C

Murphy Iron Wks., ft. Walker (Steam) ....B

Northern Engineering Wks., Chene & Atwater (Gas; Gasoline) ....A

Olds Motor Wks., Jeff Cor. Concord (Gas; Gasoline 1 to 75 h. p.) ....AA

Sintz Gas Engine Co., 1524 Jeffn. Av. (Gas) ....B

Strelinger Co., Chas. A., 98 Bates (Gas) ....

Wilson & Co., J. B., Cor. W. Fort & 13th (Steam)....A

MICH.—Grand Rapids

Austin & Son (Gasoline Automobile; Gasoline Automatic; Launch) ....A

Grand Rapids Gas Engine & Yacht Co. (Gas; Gasoline; Marine, Gas or Gasoline) A

Leitelt Iron Wks., Adolph (Steam) ....B

Wolverine Motor Wks. (Gas; Gasoline; Marine, Gas or Gasoline; Gas; Gasoline Yacht or Launch) C

MICH.—Kalamazoo

Clark Engine & Boiler Co. Geo. (Steam, 10 to 100 h. p.) C

Dutton Co., C. H. (Vertical Steam 2 to 10 h. p.) ..B

Kalamazoo Railway Supply Co. (Gasoline Pumping) B

MICH.—Lansing

Bates & Edmonds Motor Co. (Gas; Gasoline) C

Lansing Boiler & Engine Wks. (Gas; Gasoline; Automatic Steam 10 to 300 h. p.) ....B

Olds Gasoline Engine Wks. (Gas; Gasoline; Gasoline Launch) ....AA

MICH.—Manistee

Manistee Iron Wks. Co. (Marine; Twin Feed Steam) ....B

MICH.—Marquette

Lake Shore Engine Wks. (Inc.) (Gas; Gasoline; Hoisting Steam; Gasoline; Hoisting; Pumping; Marine; Gasoline; Steam; Gasoline Yacht or Launch) A

Lakeside Iron Wks. Co. (Steam) ....B

MICH.—Montague

Montague Iron Wks. Co. (Marine, Gasoline; Pumping Gasoline; Steam; Steam; Gasoline Yacht or Launch) ....B

MICH.—Morenci

Michigan Brick & Tile Mach. Co. (Gas) C

ENGINES (Con.)

MICH.—Muskegon

Rodgers Iron Mfg. Co. (Steam) ....A

MICH.—Port Huron

Jenks Ship Bldg. Co. (Marine; Stationary Steam) A

Port Huron Eng. & Thresher Co. (Simple; Compound Steam Traction) ...AAAA

MICH.—Saginaw

Bartlett & Co., A. F. (Steam Corliss 50 to 1,000 h. p.; Steam Hoisting; Marine; Slide Valve Steam).....A

Jackson & Church Co. (Steam Hoisting; Steam) A

Wickes Bros. (Marine; Steam; Vertical Steam) AA

MICH.—St. Joseph

Engberg's Electric & Mechanical Wks. (Direct Connected; Belted) ....D

Truscott Boat Mfg. Co. (Gasoline Marine; Gasoline Yacht or Launch) ..A

MICH.—Ypsilanti

Michigan Mfg. Co. (Gas; Gasoline) ....AA

MINN.—Duluth

Kelley Hdw. Co. (Gasoline) C

Northwestern Steam Boiler Wks. (Steam) C

MINN.—Hastings

Stroud & Son, H. K. (Marine) ....F

MINN.—Minneapolis

Globe Iron Wks. Co. (Inc.), 2429 University Av. (Stationary, Portable, Marine, Electric Light; Steam; Gasoline Yacht or Launch) C

Minneapolis Steel & Mchry. Co. (Steam Corliss) ...A

Minneapolis Threshing Mach. Co. (Traction, Steam; Thresher; Farm Steam) AAAA

Nutting Fire Extinguisher Co., H. S., 13 N. E. 5th (Fire, Chemical) X

MINN.—St. Paul

Stickney Co., Chas. A. (Gas; Gasoline Direct Connected; Belted Pumping Gas; Gasoline, for Railroad Service, etc.) ....A

Waterous Engine Wks. (Fire, Steam) ....B

MISS.—Corinth

Adams Machine Co., W. T. (Steam) ....AA

MO.—Kansas City

Kansas City Hay Press Co. (Stationary; Portable Gas; Gasoline) ....AA

Weber Gas & Gasoline Engine Co. (Gas; Gasoline; Gasoline Hoisting; Steam; Gasoline Launch; Petroleum; Portable Steam)..A

Witte Iron Wks. Co. (Gas) B

MO.—St. Louis

Cook-Well Co., 15 S. 4th (Deep Well Pumping) ..C

Ellison & Sons Mfg. Co., Wm., 1018 N. 6th (Steam Hoisting; Steam) ......B

Fritz, Geo. J. (High Feed, Automatic. Steam; Portable Steam) ....B

Fulton Iron Wks. (Steam Corliss 30 to 5,000 h. p.; Steam; Vertical Steam) AA

Kingsland Mfg. Co., 1521 N. 11th (Steam) ....B

Meyrose Lamp & Mfg. Co., F. (Chemical) X

St. Louis Iron & Machine Co. (Steam Marine; Steam Corliss) ....AA

South St. Louis Fdry., 121 E. Stein's (Steam Corliss; Slide Valve Automatic Steam) C

Stempel Fire Extinguisher Mfg. Co. (Chemical Fire) D

NEBR.—Fremont
Fremont Fdry. & Machine
Co. (Steam) C

N. H.—Concord
Concord Machine Co.
(Steam) ....B

N. H.—Exeter
Exeter Machine Wks. (Horizontal, Steam) ....B

N. H.—Lancaster
Thompson Mfg. Co. (Steam)
B

N. H.—Manchester
Johnson Gasoline Motor Co.
(Gasoline Automobile;
Marine; Gas; Gasoline), X

N. H.—Nashua
Rollins Engine Co. (Steam
Corliss; Automatic, etc.;
Steam 20 to 600 h. p.)..B

N. J.—Bound Brook
Amer. Engine Co. (Direct
Connected; Belted; American Ball Duplex Compound
Steam) ....A

N. J.—Camden
Dialogue & Son, Jno. H.
(Marine Steam) .....AA

N. J.—Dover
Morris County Mach. &
Iron Co. (Hoisting, Steam)
B

N. J.—Gloucester City
Rogers Boat, Gauge &
Drill Wks., Jno. M. (Marine; Steam) ....B

N. J.—Hoboken
Fischer Motor Vehicle Co.,
1311 Hudson (Comb. Gas;
Electric; Yacht or Launch)
X
Fletcher Co., W. & A., Hudson & 14th (Marine;
Steam) ....B
Forbes & Co., W. D., 1300
Hudson (Marine) ....D

N. J.—Jersey City
Brown & Miller (Marine;
Steam) ....A
Russell, M. J., 42 Morris
(Marine) ....D
Smith & Sons Co., Theodore,
ft. of Essex (Marine)...A
Standard Motor Mfg. Co.
(Marine; Gas or Gasoline)
B

N. J.—Newark
Backus Water Motor Co., 174
Penn Av. (Gas; Gasoline)
B
Currier & Sons, Cyrus (Beating; Hoisting; Steam;
Horizontal, Steam; Jordan) ....AA
Hewes & Phillips Iron Wks.
(Steam Corliss 50 to 2,000
h. p.;Steam) ....A
Lambert Hoisting Engine
Co. (Deep Well Pumping; Logging; Mining;
Steam Portable; Portable
Hoisting; Steam; Steam
Traction; Vertical Steam)
C
Mundy, J. S., 22 Prospect
(Bridge Erecting; Hoisting; Steam; Mining,
Steam; Quarry, Steam;
Horizontal, Steam; Hauling Steam; Winding
Steam) ....A
Seymour & Whitlock, 43
Lawrence (Vertical
Steam) ....B
Watts-Campbell Co., 298
Ogden (Steam Corliss 40
to 1,000 h. p.; Steam), AA

N. J.—New Brunswick
Lea, Thos. (Marine) ......F

N. J.—Perth Amboy
Schantz & Eckert (Marine)
E

N. J.—Riegelsville
Taylor Stiles & Co. (Paper
Mill, Steam; Rag) ....A

N. J.—Trenton
DeLaval Steam Turbine Co.
Steam Turbine) X
MacKenzie, Duncan, Hamilton Av. Cor. Clark
(Steam) ....A
Reeves Engine Co., Parker &
Randolph (Steam) .....A

Thropp Sons Co., Jno. E., ft.
Lewis (Marine; Stationary
Steam) ....A
Trenton Iron Co. (& Pumps
Combined, Farm) ......A

N. Y.—Albany
Dederick Agr'l & Machine
Wks. (Steam Hoisting)
AA
Dederick's Sons, P. K.
(Hoisting, Steam; Portable Skids, Steam; Portable on Wheels, Steam;
Farm Steam) ....A
Skinner & Arnold Co.
(Steam, Marine) C

N. Y.—Auburn
McIntosh, Seymour & Co.
(Direct Connected; Belted;
Compound, Triple, Expansion Tandem, etc., Steam;
Vertical Steam) .....AAA
New Birdsall Co. (Traction,
Steam; Portable Steam;
Farm, Steam) ....AA

N. Y.—Baldwinsville
Morris Machine Wks. (High
Speed, Automatic, Steam;
Horizontal Steam; Marine
Steam; Yacht Steam; Automatic Cut-off Steam; Compound Steam; Double
Steam; Vertical Steam)
AA

N. Y.—Belmont
Clark Bros. & Co. (Automatic Cut-off Steam; Corliss Steam) ....A

N. Y.—Binghamton
Shapley & Wells (Steam 8 to
20 h. p.) ....A

N. Y.—Brooklyn
Bliss Co., E. W., 19 Adams
(Hot Air Pumping) AAAA
Guild & Garrison (Pumps
Combined; Farm; Horizontal; Steam; Freezing;
Cane Mill Beam; Steam)
B
Houchin & Huber (Gas;
Gasoline) ....D
National Meter Co., 42nd
cor. 1st Av. (Gas; Gasoline ....A
Pioneer Iron Wks., 151 William (Steam; Vertical
Steam) ....A
Pioneer Machine Wks. (Jas.
Hartley, Prop.), 75 Delevan (Marine; Steam)....B
Riley & Cowley, Richards
cor. Bowne (Steam; Yacht
or Launch also Tow Boat)
B

N. Y.—Buffalo
Alberger Co. (Four Cycle;
Two Cylinder; Tandem;
Gas;Gasoline, 25 to 250 h.
p.) ....B
Buffalo Forge Co., 480
B'way (Automatic Steam;
Steam Traction) ....AAA
Buffalo Gasoline Motor Co.
(Steam; Gasoline Automobile) ....D
Buffalo-Pitts Co. Hauling
Steam; Traction Steam;
Straw Burning Traction
Steam; Portable Steam;
Steam Portable on Skids;
Steam Portable onWheels;
Steam Farm.......AAAA
Contractors' Plant Mfg. Co.
(Steam Hoisting; Portable
Hoisting) ....B
Farrar & Trefts (Gas;
Steam 4 to 30 h. p.)..AAA
Frontier Engine Wks., ft of
Illinois (Steam).........B
Keim, Jno. R. Kensington
Av. & Erie R. R. (Steam;
Gasoline; Automobile).AA
Noye Mfg. Co., Jno. T.
(High Speed Automatic
Steam; Horizontal Steam;
Automatic Cut-off Steam;
Compound Steam; Compound Condensing Steam;
Compound Steam).......X
Olin Gas Engine Co. (Gasoline Launch)..........D
Ruger Mfg. Co., J. W. (Gas;
Gasoline) ....B

ENGINES (Con.)

Thomas Motor Co., E. R., B'way & Elm (Gas)....A

Tront & Co., H. G., 226 Ohio (Marine; Steam).......B

N. Y.—Canandaigua

Lesk Mfg. Co. (Portable Oil Country) ....AAA

N. Y.—Clyde

Wood & Son, S. W. (Steam) C

N. Y.—Corning

Hood Furnace & Supply Co. (Hot Air)..............B

N. Y.—Elmira

American-La France Fire Engine Co. (Fire Steam)B

Payne Co. (Inc) (Gas; High Speed Automatic Steam; Yacht Steam; Petroleum; Portable Steam; Compound Steam; Corliss Steam) X

N. Y.—Fishkill-on-Hudson

Fishkill Landing Machine Co. (Corliss Steam; Vertical Steam) ....A

N. Y.—Frankfort

Acme Road Mchy Co. (Gasoline) C

N. Y.—Fulton

Dilts Machine Wks. (Beating) ....B

Pearman, James (Paper Mill Steam) ....F

N. Y.—Geneva

N .Y. Central Iron Wks. Co. (Steam 15 to 100 h. p.) B

N. Y.—Groton

Groton Bridge Co. (Portable Steam) ....B

N. Y.—Ithaca

Williams Bros. (Vertical Portable Steam; Portable Steam; Portable on Skids Steam; Portable on Wheels Steam; Farm Steam) ....AA

N. Y.—Little Falls

Burrel & Co., D. H. (Vertical Steam).......AAAA

N. Y.—Lockport

Holly Mfg. Co. (Pumping) X

Norman & Evans (Marine; Steam) ....B

N. Y.—Long Island City

Daimler Mfg. Co. (Fire; Gas Marine) ....D

N. Y.—Malone

Hinds, Thomas (Gasoline).D

N. Y.—Marathon

Climax Road Mach. Co. (Portable on Wheels)..D

N. Y.—Newburgh

Coldwell-Wilcox Co. (Steam) B

Marvel & Co., T. S. (Marine) B

Newburgh Ice Mach. & Engine Co. (Steam) ....B

New York City

Abendroth & Root Mfg. Co., 99 John (Corliss Steam; Steam) ....A

Amer. Hoist & Derrick Co., 26 Cortlandt (Hoisting Steam) ....A

Amer. Locomotive Co. 25 Broad (Fire Steam) AAAA

Automatic Fire Alarm Co. (Ltd.) (Fire Chemical) AA

Bacon, Earle C., 26 Cortlandt (Bridge Erecting) D

Ball & Wood Co. (Street Railway) ....AA

Brown Hoisting Mchy Co., 26 Cortlandt (Hoisting Steam) ....AAAA

Buckeye Engine Co., 39 Cortlandt (Automatic Steam) ....AA

Colwell, Augustus W. Cane Mill Beam Steam)......D

Deeley & Co., Robert (Cane Mill Beam Steam; Pumping) ....AA

De La Vergne Mach. Co., ft. E. 188th (Oil)..;..AAAA

Diesel Engine Co., 11 B'way (Steam) ....AA

Edwards & Co., Joseph

ENGINES (Con.)

(Hoisting Steam)......B

Fairbanks Co. (Gas; Gasoline) ....AAAA

General Power Co., 81 Fulton (Automobile Gas; Gasoline; Marine; Oil)...B

Gas Engine & Power Co. & Chas. L. Seabury & Co., 11 B'way (Gas; Gasoline; Marine; Steam; Gasoline; Naphta Yacht or Launch) AAA

Hayward & Co., S. F. (Fire Chemical) ....D

Howard & Morse (High Speed Automatic Steam) D

Hunt Co., C. W. (Hoisting Steam; Electric Hoisting Steam) ....AA

Imperial Engine Co., 128 B'way (Steam).........C

International Power Co., 72 B'way (Corliss Steam; Steam) ....AA

Lidgerwood Mfg. Co., 96 Liberty (Bridge Erecting; Hoisting Steam; Mining Steam; Quarry Steam; Horizontal Steam; Winding Steam; Portable Steam) AAA

Lozier Motor Co., 1 B'way (Naptha) ....D

Marine Engine & Machine Co., 1123 B'way. (Yacht or Launch) ....B

Mietz, August, 87 Elizabeth (Alcohol; Gas; Petroleum) A

Morgan Iron Wks., ft. E. 9th (Marine; Steam)....B

National Meter Co. (Pumps Combined Gas; Gas)...A

N. Y. Blower Co., 39 Cortlandt (Steam; Vertical Steam) ....A

N. Y. Kerosene Oil Engine Co., 31 Burling (Oil)....D

New York Safety Steam Power Co., 118 Liberty (Direct Connected; Belted; Vertical Marine; Automatic Steam 15 to 200 h. p.; Vertical Steam 2 to 100 h. p.; Yacht or Launch) B

Oil City Boiler Wks. (of Oil City, Pa.), 39 Cortlandt (Corliss Steam; Gas; Gasoline; Steam Portable 4 to 40 h. p.; Steam 20 to 150 h. p.; Vertical Steam) AAAA

Palmer, N. F.,742 E. 12th (Marine Steam) ....A

Pelham Hod Elevating Co., 416 W. 26th (Hoisting; Steam) ....B

Penn. Iron Wks. Co. (of Phila., Pa.) (Corliss, Steam; Gas; Gasoline; Stationary; Marine; Four Cycle 1 to 100 h. p.; Automatic Steam, 75 to 1,000 h. p.; Vertical Steam, 25 to 100 h. p.) ....AAAA

Pierce Well Engineer & Supply Co. (Artesian Well Steam) ....D

Rae, Robt., 442 Water (Marine) ....F

Rand Drill Co. (Portable Steam) ....AAA

Rider-Ericsson Engine Co., 35 Warren (Hot Air Pumping) ....A

Stearns Mfg. Co., 95 Liberty (Autotmatic Steam 18 to 1,000 h. p.; Vertical Steam) ....AA

Struthers, Wells & Co., 26 Cortlandt (Gas; Gasoline; High Speed Steam 30 to 70 h. p.).............AA

ENGINES (Con.)

Sullivan, Jno. W., 385 South
Marine) ....B
Welch & Lawson, 210 Centre
(Gas; Gasoline).......B
Worthington Pumping Engine Co. (Pumping) AAAA

N. Y.—Niagara Falls
Dobbie Fdy. & Machine Co.
Hoisting Steam; Portable
Hoisting) ....B

N. Y.—Oneida
Oneida Iron Wks. (Steam)
B

N. Y.—Orangeburg
Empire Engine & Motor Co.
(Pneumatic Steam Hoisting) ....B

N. Y.—Ogdensburg
Nash Bros. &Co. (Marine
Steam) ....A

N. Y.—Oswego
Ames Iron Wks. (Traction
Steam; Portable Steam;
Farm Steam; Street Railway) ....AA
Kingsford Fdy. & Mach.
Wks. (Marine Steam;
Automatic Cut-of Steam;
Vertical Steam).AAAA
Lozier Motor Co. (Marine, 2
Cycle Gasoline) ....D

N. Y.—Rochester
Rochester Mach. Tool Wks.
(Ltd) (Kerosene Burning
Launch; Kerosene Burning
Yacht; Petroleum)......C

N. Y.—Rome
Adams & Son, S. (Yacht;
Launch) C

N. Y.—St. Johnsville
Rumsey-Williams Co. (Gas;
Gasoline) ....B

N. Y.—Salamanca
Benedict Mfg. Co. (Steam)
C

N. Y.—Schenectady
General Electric Co. (Electric; Steam Turbine)....
AAAA
Westinghouse Co. (Dairy;
Traction Steam; Vertical
Portable Steam; Portable
Steam; Portable on Skids
Steam; Portable on
Wheels Steam; Farm
Steam) ....AA

N. —Seneca Falls
Amer.-La France Fire Engine Co. (High Speed
Automatic Steam; Fire
Steam; Steam Launch;
Compound Vertical Steam;
Vertical Steam) ......B
Rumsey Co. (Ltd.) (Chemical) ....A

N .Y.—Syracuse
Mc.Millan Engine & Mach.
Co., 613 E. Water (Steam)
C
Moore Mfg. Co., 102 N.
Beech (Hoisting Steam) C
Sanderon & Bros., P. W.,
309 W. Willow (Yacht or
Launch) ....F
Straight Line Engine Co.,
218 S. Geddes (Steam)..A

N. Y.—Troy.
Knowlson & Kelly (Corliss
Steam 40 to 2,000 h. p.;
Direct Connected; Belted;
Steam) ....B

N. Y.—Utica
Millar & Son Co., Chas.
(Portable Steam; Farm
Steam; Vertical Steam)..
AA
Utica Steam Engine & Boiler
Wks. (Steam).........C

N. Y.—Watertown
Bagley & Sewall Co. (Washing) ....AA
Watertown Engine Co.
(Simple Compouned; Triple Expansion Steam Corliss 300 to 1,500 h. p.;
Portable Steam 6 to 40 h.
p.; High Speed Throttling; Automatic Steam;
Traction Steam 7 to 15 h.
p.) C

N. Y.—Wellsville
McEwen Bros. (Portable
Steam) ....A

ENGINES (Con.)

N. C.—Charlotte
Liddel Co. (Inc.) (Automatic
Steam) ....A
Mecklenburg Iron Wks.
(Portable Steam)......X

N. C.—Winston-Salem
Salem Iron Wks. (Portable
on Wheels)............A

OHIO—Akron
Star Drilling Machine Co.
(Upright Steam).......A
Taplin, Rice & Co. (Steam)
A

Webster Camp & Lane Mach.
Co. (Hoisting Steam;
Mining Steam; Hauling
Steam; Winding Steam
Automatic Cut-off Steam;
Compound Steam; Corliss
Steam) ....AAAA

OHIO—Alliance
Morgan Engineering Co.
(Steam) ....AA

OHIO—Bucyrus
Pilling Air Engine Wks.
Compressed Air Hoisting)

OHIO—Canton
Aultman Co. (Oil; Portable
Steam; Steam; Traction
Steam; Vertical Steam)
A
Canton Surgical & Dental
Chair Co. (Dental)....C
Knight Mfg. Co. (Gas; Gasoline) ....B

OHIO—Cincinnati
Blettner & Co., Joseph B.,
1976 Central Av. (Steam)
C
Blymer Iron Wks. Co. (Vertical Portable Steam;
Portable Steam; Portable
on Skids Steam; Portable on Wheels Steam)..B
Greenwald Co., I. & E., 720
E. Pearl (Automatic
Steam) ....A
Johnson Co., W. T., 522
Main (Vertical Steam) C
Kinsey Co., E. A., 331 W.
4th (Vertical Steam)..B
Laidlaw-Dunn-Gordon Co.
(Artesian Well Steam;
Pumping) ....AAAA
Lane & Bodley Co. (Carliss
Steam 50 to 1,000 h. p.;
Direct Connected; Belted;
Rolling Mill; Slide Valve;
&c. Steam)............A
McGowan Co., Jno. H.
(Deep Well Pumping)..A
McKeown, H. J. (Hoisting
Steam) ....B
Presler-Crawley Mfg. Co.,
219 W. 2nd (Marine Gas
or Gasoline)...........D
Smith, Myers & Schnier
(Portable Steam)......B
Van Duzen Co., E. W., 428
E. 2nd (Gas; Gasoline)..C
Watkins Mfg. Co., F. M.,
857 W. 6th (Gas; Gasoline) C

OHIO—Cleveland
Amer. Ship Building Co.
(Blowing; Steam Hoisting; Marine; Steam)....
AAAA
Brown Hoisting Mchy Co.
(Hoisting Steam).AAAA
Chase Machine Co. (Gas;
Gasoline Marine; Stationary; Haulage).........B
Kilby Mfg. Co. (Steam) AA
Mac Beth Iron Co. (Blowing) ....A
Manning-Stovering Mach.
Co, 100 Merwin (Fire
Steam) C
Merian-Abbott Co., 60 E.
Prospect (Gas; Gasoline)
B
Snider-Hughes Co., cor Coe
& Hamilton (Blowing)..B
Strong, Carlisle & Hammond
Co., 61 Frankfort Gas;
Gasoline) ....A
Union Machine & Boiler Co.,
108 River (Marine)....X

OHIO—Columbiana.
Enterprise Mfg. Co. (Portable Steam; Steam)......B

ENGINES (Con.)

OHIO—Columbus

Columbus Machine Co. (Gas; Gasoline; Steam) A

Pulling & Co., Jas. G. (Pumping) ....B

Rarig Engineering Co., A. K. (Blowing; Haulage; Steam Hoisting; Rolling Mill; Steam)..........A

OHIO—Dayton

Brownell & Co. (Portable Steam 2 to 40 h. p.; Steam) ....AAA

Callahan & Co., W. P. Hoisting Steam; Gasoline Launch; Naphta Launch) AA

Dayton Engine Wks (Steam) C

Dayton Globe Iron Wks. Co. (Beating) ....B

New Era Gas Engine Co. (Gas; Gasoline)........A

Stoddard Mfg. Co. (Gas; Gasoline) ....AAA

OHIO—Defiance

Defiance Machine Co. (Portable Steam; Portable on Skids Steam; Portable on Wheels Steam) ......A

OHIO—Elyria

Elyria Engine Co. (Gas; Gasoline) ....A

OHIO—Fostoria

Fostoria Fdry. & Machine Co. (4 Cycle Gas; Gasoline) C

OHIO—Fremont

June & Co., D., (Steam Portable, 6 to 20 H. P.; Steam, 12 to 40 H. P.; Traction, 10 to 16 H. P.) AA

OHIO—Hamilton

Black & Clawson (Beating; Washing; Jordan; Refining; Pulp Refining).AAA

Hooven, Owens & Rentschler Co. (Steam Corliss, 30 to 3,000 H. P.; Rolling Mill; Steam, 100 to 500 H. P.).....AAAA

OHIO—Lima

Bessemer Gas Engine Co. (Gas;; Gasoline).......B

Golley & Finley Iron Wks. (Steam) ....A

OHIO—Lorain

Brown-Cochran Co. (Gas; Gasoline) ....A

OHIO—Mansfield

Aultman & Taylor Machy. Co. (Steam Straw-Burning Farm; Traction Steam; Portable Steam; Farm Steam) ......AAA

Barnes Mfg. Co. (Pumping) B

Mansfield Engineering Co. (Corliss Steam) ......B

OHIO—Marietta

Pattin Bros. Co. (Gas; Steam Hoisting; Steam) B

OHIO—Marion

Huber Mfg. Co. (Portable on Wheels; Steam, 5 to 25 H. P.; Steam Traction, 2 to 16 H. P.) ......AAA

Marion Mfg. Co. (Traction Steam; Portable Steam) AA

OHIO—Martins' Ferry

Spence & Sons, L. (Steam Portable, 30 H. P.; Rolling Mill; Steam; Steam Traction, 10 to 16 H. P.) A

OHIO—Massillen

Russell & Co. (Steam Straw Burning Farm; Steam Traction; Steam Traction Straw Burning; Steam Portable; Steam Automatic Cut-Off; Steam Farm; Street Railway) AAA

Russell Engine Co. (Steam) A

OHIO—Middleport

Ohio Machine Co. (Steam

ENGINES (Con.)

Marine) C

OHIO—Mount Vernon

Cooper Co., C. & G. (Hoisting Steam; Traction Steam; Portable Steam; Compound Condensing Steam; Compound Corliss Steam; Compound Farm Steam; Street Railway) AA

OHIO—Nelsonville

Nelsonville Fdry. & Machine Co. (Haulage Steam)...B

OHIO—Newark

McNamar Machine Wks. (Steam Portable, 8 to 40 H. P.; Steam; Steam Traction) ....B

Scheidler Machine Wks. (Steam Portable, 8 to 40 H. P.) ....B

OHIO—Pomeroy

Pomeroy Machine Co. (Steam Farm) ....B

OHIO—Ravenna

Byers Machine Co., Jno. F. (Steam Hoisting; Mining; Vertical Steam) ....B

OHIO—St. Marys

St. Mary's Machine Co. (Gas; Gasoline) ......A

OHIO—Salem

Buckeye Engine Co. (Blowing; Automatic Cut-Off Steam; Compound Steam) AAA

OHIO—Sandusky

Klotz Machine Co. (Steam, 10 to 150 H. P.; Vertical Steam, 10 to 50 H. P.).B

OHIO—Springfield

Amer. Engraving Co. (Gas; Gasoline) C

Bauroth & Bro., W. F. (Gas; Gasoline) C

Foos Gas Engine Co. (Gasoline, 1½ to 250 H. P.).A

Kelly Co., O. S. (Heavy Traction Steam; Portable Steam; Farm Steam)..AA

Leffel & Co., James (Horizontal Steam; Vertical Portable Steam; Portable Steam; Portable on Skids Steam; Portable on Wheels Steam; Automatic Cut-Off Steam; Farm Steam; Vertical Steam; Throttling Cut-Off Steam) AA

Springfield Gas Engine Co. (Gas; Gasoline) ....D

Trump Mfg. Co. (Portable on Skids Steam) ....A

OHIO—Swanton

Baker Co., A. D. (Steam Traction) ....B

OHIO—Toledo

Ricard Boiler & Engine Co., 700 Water (Steam)....B

Toledo Fdry. & Machine Co. (Steam Hoisting; Marine Steam) ....B

OHIO—Warren

McMyler Mfg. Co. (Haulage Steam Hoisting) ....A

OHIO—Wellington

Wellington Machine Co. (Steam) ....B

OHIO—Wellsville

Stevenson Co. (Steam)...B

OHIO—Youngstown

Sennet Co., Geo. B. (Steam 20 to 40 H. P.)........A

Tod Co., Wm. (Blowing; Steam Corliss; Reversing; Roll Mill; Steam, 75 to 5,000 H. P.).........AA

United Engineering & Fdry. Co. (Steam) ....A

OHIO—Zanesville

Griffith & Wedge Co. (Hoisting Steam; Quarry Steam; Horizontal Steam; Hauling Steam; Winding Steam; Portable Steam; Portable on Skids Steam; Portable on Wheels Steam; Farm Steam)...B

ENGINES (Con.)

OREGON—Astoria
Astoria Iron Wks. (Inc.)
(Marine Gas; Gasoline;
Steam) ....A

OREGON—Portland
Arthur & Co., J. M., 40 1st
(Steam Hoisting) ....B
Columbia Engineering Wks.
(Steam Hoisting; Marine;
Steam) ....B
Honeyman & Co., J. (Marine) ....D
Portland Iron Wks., 495
Northrop (Steam Hoisting; Steam) ....A
Tatum & Bowen (Logging)
X
Willamette Iron & Steel
Wks., 123 3d N. (Steam)
B

PA.—Allegheny
Carlin Machy. & Supply Co.
(Steam Hoisting) ....A
Carlins' Sons Co., Thomas
(Steam Hoising) ......A
National Gear Wheel & Fdy.
Co., South Av. & Walker
(Gas) C
Porter Fdry. & Machine Co.
(Vertical Steam. 2 to 35
H. P.) ....A

PA.—Allentown
Allentown Fdry. & Machine
Wks. (Hoisting Steam;
Mining Steam) ....A
Mosser & Son, Wm. F.
(Steam) ....A
Nadig & Bro. Mfg. Co.,
Chas. H. (Gasoline; Automatic Single; Double Acting Steam) ....A

PA.—Avonmore
West Penn. Fdry. & Mach.
Co. (Rolling Mill; Steam)
B

PA.—Bangor
Flory Mfg. Co., S. (Haulage;
Steam Hoisting; Logging;
Steam) ....A

PA.—Beaver Falls
Champion Saw & Gas Engine Co. (Gas; Gasoline)
C
Keystone Driller Co. (Vertical Steam) ....B

PA.—Birdsboro
Diamond Drill & Mach. Co.
(Steam) ....B

PA.—Bradford
Bovaird & Co. (Steam)....A
Bovaird & Seyfang Mfg. Co.
(Steam) ....A
Caldwell & Co., E. R.
(Steam) ....B
McElwaine Co. (Gas) .....A

PA.—Brownsville
Herbertson's Sons, J. (Hoisting Steam; Marine Steam)
D

PA.—Butler
Evans Mfg. Co. (Steam)..B
Palm Gas Engine Co. (Gas)
A

PA.—Chambersburg
Chambersburg Engineering
Co. (Steam) ....A

PA.—Chester
Delaware River Iron Ship
Bldg. & Engine Wks. (Marine; Steam) ......AAA
Niagara Hydraulic Engine
Co. (Hydraulic Pumping)
B
Wetherill Machine Co., Jas.
P. (Steam) C
Wetherill & Co., Robt.
(Steam Corliss, 25 to 2,000
H. P.; Stationary Steam)
AAAA
Wetherill & Co., R. (Compound Corliss; Steam;
Street Railway; Pumping)
AAAA

PA.—Connellsville
Connellsville Machine & Car
Co. (Steam) ....A

PA.—Corry
Ajax Iron Wks. (Gas; Gasoline, 4 to 40 H. P.; Steam)
B
Climax Mfg. Co. (Double

FIGURES (Con.)

Cylinder High Speed
Steam; Vertical Steam, 6
to 100 H. P.)........AA

PA.—Downingtown
Downingtown Mfg. Co.
(Ltd.) (Beating) ......A

PA.—Du Bois
Dubois Iron Wks. (Steam)
AAAA

PA.—East Stroudsburg
Stauffer, Geo. E. (Steam)
C

PA.—Erie
Ball Engine Co. (High Speed
Automatic Steam; Horizontal Steam; Automatic Cut-Off Steam; Compound
Steam; Vertical Seam)
AA
Bay State Iron Wks. (Horizontal Steam; Marine
Steam; Portable Steam;
Automatic Cut-Off Steam;
Vertical Steam; Vertical
Cut-Off Steam) ......F
Erie City Iron Wks. (High
Speed Automatic Steam;
Horizontal Steam; Throttling; Oil Well Steam;
Portable Steam; Portable
on Skids Steam; Portable
on Wheels Steam; Automatic Cut-Off Steam;
Double Steam; Farm
Steam) ....AAAA
Erie Engine Wks. (Steam
Portable, 6 to 50 H. P.;
Steam) ....A
Erie Mfg. & Supply Co. (Direct Connected; Belted;
Horizontal; Vertical;
Plain; Automatic Steam;
Steam Vertical) .....A
Erie Pump & Engine Co.
Steam Vertical) C
Lake City Engineering Co.
(Marine) X
Link Machy Co., E. M.
(Steam) C
Nagle Engine & Boiler
Wks. (High Speed; Automatic Steam; Horizontal
Steam; Portable Steam;
Farm Steam; Vertical
Steam) ....AAAA
Skinner Engine Co. (Direct
Connected; Belted; Steam
Portable, 8 to 40 H. P.;
Automatic Steam, 8 to 60
H. P.) ....B
Stearns Mfg. Co. (High
Speed Automatic Steam)B

PA.—Franklin
Franklin Supply Co. (Gas)
C
Sheperd Engineering Co.
(Steam) ....B

PA.—Grove City
Bessemer Gas Engine Co.
(Gas) ....A

PA.—Harrisburg
Harrisburg Fdry. & Machine
Wks. (Steam Corliss; Automatic Steam, 40 to 1,000
H. P.) ....A

PA.—Kennett Square
Amer. Road Machine Co.
(Steam Portable; Steam)
AA

PA.—Lancaster
Best, Jno. (Hoisting Steam;
Horizonal Steam; Portable
Steam; Portable on Skids
Steam; Portable on
Wheels Steam; Farm
Steam; Vertical Steam).B

PA.—Lebanon
Weimer Machine Wks. Co.
(Blowing, 30 to 2,000 H.
P.; Steam Corliss; Steam
Hoisting for Furnaces and
Mines; Steam) ....AA

PA.—Mauch Chunk
Stroh. W. H. (Est. of)
(Haulage; Steam Hoisting) ....B

PA.—Meadville
Phoenix Iron Wks. Co.
(Portable Steam; Automatic Cut-Off Steam; Street

ENGINES (Con.)

Railway) ....A
PA.—Monongahela
Monongahela Mfg. Co.
(Haulage) ....B
Robinson Machine Co.
(Haulage; Steam Hoist-
ing; Steam) ....B
PA.—New Brighton
Pierce-Crouch Engine Co.
(Gas; Gasoline) ....B
PA.—Norristown
Newbold & Son, Co., R. S.
(Rolling Mill; Slide Valve
Steam) ....A
PA.—Oil City
Oil City Boiler Wks. (Inc.)
(Portable Steam) .....AA
Reid Gas Engine Co., Jno.
(Gas) ....A
PA.—Philadelphia
Baisley Iron Wks., Jno., 514
N. 3d (Steam) ....AA
Barr Pump Co. (Pump)..A
Box & Co., Alfred (Hoist-
ing Steam) ....B
Cox & Sons Co., 215 Race
(Steam Corliss; Steam).B
Cramp & Sons Ship & En-
gine Bldg. Co., Wm. (Ma-
rine Steam) ....AAAA
D'Ollier Engineering Co.,
119 S. 11th (Steam Tur-
bine) ....A
Fairbanks Co., 701 Arch
(Gas; Gasoline) ..AAAA
Kensington Engine Wks.
Ltd.) (Horizontal Steam;
Automatic Cut-Off Steam)
A
Midvale Steel Co. (Marine)
AAAA
Motor Vehicle Power Co.,
1221 Spg. Garden (Marine;
Gas; Gasoline; Gasoline
Yacht; Launch) X
Naylor, Jno. H., Front, cor.
Girard Av. (Steam)....A
Nittinger, August (Horizon-
tal Steam; Vertical
Steam) ....A
Otto Gas Engine Wks. (Gas;
Gasoline; Pumps Com-
bined; Gas; Gasoline
Launch) ....AAA
Penna. Iron Wks. Co. (Gas;
Gasoline) ....AAA
Phila. Engineering Wks.
(Ltd.) (Blowing; Corliss
Steam) X
Phillips & Sons Co., F. R.,
Penna. Bldg. (Rolling
Mill) ....D
Rich, J. & G., 120 N. 6th
(Steam; Vertical Steam)
B
Sibley, Gideon (Dental) .AA
Southwark Fdry. & Machine
Co. (Blast; Blowing; High
Speed Automatic Steam;
Horizontal Steam; Port-
able Steam; Automatic
Cut-Off Steam; Compound
Condensing Seam; Double
Steam; Farm Steam) AAA
White Dental Mfg. Co., S.
S. (Dental) ....AAAA
Williamson Bros. Co., E.
Cumberland, cor. Thomp-
son (Steam Hoisting) .AA
York Mfg. Co. (Ltd.) (of
York, Pa.) North Amer:
Bldg. (Steam Corliss;
Steam Vertical) .....AA
Fischer Fdry. & Mach. Co.
(Automatic Steam) ....A
PA.—Pittsburg
Hogg Iron & Steel Fdry. Co.,
Geo. A., 24th & R. R.
(Steam Corliss; Reversing;
Steam for Rolling Mill).A
Macintosh, Hemphill & Co.,
ft. of 12th (Steam) .AAA
Mesta Machine Co. (Blow-
ing; Steam Corliss; Roll-
ing Mill) ....AAA
Oil Well Supply Co., 21st &
A. V. Ry. (Gas; Steam)
AAAA
Phoenix Steel Construction
Co., Penn. Av. & 3d
(Haulage; Logging) ...D

ENGINES (Con.)

Pittsburg Electrical &
Mach. Wks. (Vertical
Steam) ....E
Porter & Co., H. K. (Auto-
matic Cut-Off Steam)
AAA
Westinghouse Electric Mfg.
Co. (Electric) .....AAAA
Westinghouse Machine Co.
(Steam Corliss; Steam
Portable, 5 to 25 H. P.;
Steam) ....AAAA
PA.—Pittston
Exeter Machine Wks.
(Haulage; Steam Hoist-
ing) ....AA
PA.—Pottsville
Sparks & Parker (Steam) .C
PA.—Reading
Johnston Fdry. & Machine
Co. (Gas; Gasoline) ....B
Orr & Sembower (Inc.) (Ma-
rine; Steam; Vertical
Steam) ....A
Reading Iron Co. (Steam
Corliss; Rolling Mill;
Steam) ....AAAA
PA.—Ridgway
Ridgway Dynamo & Engine
Co. (Direct Connected;
Belted; Steam) ....A
Ridgway Mfg. Co. (Steam)
C
PA.—Scottdale
Kenney & Co. (Haulage;
Steam Hoisting; Automa-
tic Slide Valve Steam).A
PA.—Scranton
Finch Mfg. Co. (Haulage;
Steam Hoisting; Steam)
AA
PA.—Shamokin
Mullen & Son, John (Haul-
age; Steam Hoisting;
Steam) ....A
PA.—Spring Forge
Glatfelter, P. H. (Vertical
Portable Steam; Automa-
tic Cut-Off Steam).AAAA
PA.—Stroudsburg
Stroudsberg Engine Wks.
(Steam Hoisting; Steam)
C
PA.—Tamaqua
Tamaqua Mfg. Co. (Vertical
Steam) ....B
PA.—Tatamy
Messinger Mfg. Co. (Steam
Portable; Portable on
Wheels; Automatic Steam,
3 to 25 H. P.; Vertical
Steam) ....B
PA.—Titusville
Titusville Iron Co. (Gas;
Gasoline; Steam) .AAAA
Young & Sons, E. R.
(Steam) ....B
PA.—Troy
Troy Engine & Mach. Co.
(Jno. A. Parsons, Prop.)
(Steam) ....B
PA.—Warren
Struthers, Wells & Co. (Gas;
Gasoline; Portable on
Wheels Steam; Artesian
Well Steam) ....AA
PA.—Waynesboro
Frick Co. (High Speed Au-
tomatic Steam; Hoisting
Steam; Horizontal Steam;
Traction Steam; Vertical
Portable Steam; Portable
Steam; Portable on Skids
Steam; Portable on
Wheels Steam; Automatic
Cut-Off Steam; Corliss
Beam Steam; Compound
Steam; Compound Corliss
Steam; Compound Horizon-
tal Steam; Farm Steam;
Vertical Steam) ...AAAA
Geiser Mfg. Co. (Steam
Portable on Wheels; Sills;
Steam, 8 to 30 H. P.;
Wood; Coal Traction)
AAA
PA.—Wilkesbarre
Vulcan Iron Wks. (High
Speed Automatic Steam;
Hoisting Steam; Duplex
Hoisting Steam; Mining

ENGINES (Con.)
Steam; Friction Hoisting
Steam; Horrizontal Steam;
Hauling Steam; Winding
Steam; Double Steam;
Vertical Steam; Pumping)
.... AAAA

PA.—Williamsport
Larzelere Machine Co.
(Steam) .... B
Valley Iron Wks. (High
Speed Automatic Steam;
Electric; Automatic Cut-
Off Steam) .... A

PA.—York
Farquhar Co. (Ltd.), A. B.
(Steam Corliss; Steam
Portable, 4 to 40 H. P.;
Portable on Wheels; Cen-
tre Crank Steam; Steam
Traction; Steam Vertical)
.... AAA
Hench & Dromgold Co.
(Portable Steam) ...... B
Motter & Sons, Geo. F.
(Hoisting Steam; Hori-
zontal Steam; Portable
Steam; Farm Steam; Ver-
tical Steam) C
York Mfg. Co. (Horizontal
Steam; Corliss Steam;
Vertical Steam) ....AAA

R. I.—Bristol
Herreshoff Mfg. Co. (Steam
Marine; Yacht; Launch)
.... R

R. I.—Hope Valley
Nichols & Langworthy
Mach. Co. (Steam) ....AA

R. I.—Providence
Amer. & British Mfg. Co.
(Automobile) .....AAAA
Bowen Electric Co., 58
Point (Kerosene Oil) ..X
Fuller Iron Wks., 40 Tock-
wotton (Steam Hoisting;
Steam Portable; Steam) . A
Harris Steam Engine Co.,
Wm. A. (Steam Corliss,
20 to 2,000 H. P.; Auto-
matic Steam) .... B
Providence Engineering Co.
(Steam Corliss; Marine
Steam) .... A

S. C.—Charleston
Valk & Murdock Iron Wks.
(Steam) .... B

S. C.—Columbia
Palmetto Iron Wks. (Steam)
.... B
Tozer Engine Wks. (Steam)
.... C

TENN.—Chattanooga
Casey & Hedges Mfg. Co.
(Steam) .... A
Chattanooga Engine & Boil-
er Wks. (Steam) .... A
Lookout Boiler Mfg. Co.
(Steam) C
Walsh & Weidner Boiler Co.
(Steam Portable; Steam)
.... A
Wheland Mach. Wks. (Cen-
tre; Slide Valve Steam). A

TENN.—Jackson
Southern Engine & Boiler
Wks. (Inc.) (Steam Cor-
liss; Direct Connected;
Belted; Logging; Steam
Portable on Wheels;
Steam) .... A

TENN.—Memphis
Chickasaw Iron Wks. 2d,
cor. Winchester (Hoisting
Steam; Steam) .... A
Ellis & Sons, Wm. C., 439
Shelby (Steam) C

TENN.—Nashville
Nashville Machine Co.
(Steam) .... B
Stewart & Bruckner, 157 N.
College (Steam) C

TEXAS—Galveston
Astall Iron Wks. Co., 2615
Strand (Steam) C

TEXAS—San Antonio
Collins Mfg. Co., F. F.
(Steam) .... A

VT.—Rutland
Howe Scale Co. (Gas; Gasoline) .... AA

ENGINES (Con.)
VT.—Westminster Station
Abenaque Machine Wks.
(Gas; Gasoline) .... A

VA.—Newport News
Newport News Ship Bldg. &
Dry Dock Co. (Marine
Steam) .... AAAA

VA.—Norfolk
Godwin & Co., Thos. W.
(Gas; Gasoline; Steam) . B

VA.—Petersburg
Petersburg Iron Wks. Co.
(Marine) .... D

VA.—Richmond
Smith-Courtney Co. (Gas;
Gasoline) .... B

WASH.—Seattle
Hefferman Engine Wks.
(Marine; Steam) .... B
Mitchell Lewis & Staver
Co. (Logging) .... B
Moran Bros. Co. (Marine;
Steam) .... AAAA
Northwestern Iron Wks.
(Steam Hoisting; Marine;
Steam) C
Washington Iron Works Co.
(Logging) ....AA

WASH.—Spokane
National Iron Wks. (Inc.)
(Steam) C

WASH.—Tacoma
Puget Sound Dry Dock &
Mach. Co. (Marine;
Steam) .... B
Puget Sound Iron & Steel
Wks., A, cor. 21st
(Steam) .... B

W. VA.—Parkersburg
U. S. Engine Co. (Gas; Gasoline; Traction Steam) .. B

WIS.—Beloit
Thompson & Sons Mfg. Co.,
J. (Gas; Gasoline) ....AA

WIS.—Corliss
Brown-Corliss Engine Co.
(Steam Corliss, heavy
duty up to 8,000 H. P.;
Steam) ....AA

WIS.—Eau Claire
Phoenix Mfg. Co. (Steam)
.... A

WIS.—Fond du Lac
Giddings & Lewis Mfg. Co.
(Steam) .... B

WIS.—Manitowoc
Smalley Mfg. Co. (Portable
Steam; Farm Steam) ... B

WIS.—Marinette
Stevens Co., A. W. (Steam
Traction) ....AA

WIS.—Milwaukee
Allis-Chalmers Co. (Gas;
Blowing; Hoisting Seam;
Mining Steam; Electric;
Portable Steam; Com-
pound Steam; Corliss
Steam; Vertical Steam;
Street Railway; Pump-
ing) ....AAAA
Bayley & Sons Co., Wm.,
732 Greenbush (Steam;
Vertical Steam) .... A
Filer & Stowell Co. (Ltd.)
(Hoisting Steam; Hosi-
zontal Steam; Compound
Steam; Compound Con-
densing Steam; Compound
Corliss Steam; Compound
Horizontal Steam; Street
Railway; Pumping) AAA
Hoffman & Billings Mfg.
Co. (High Speed Corliss
Steam; Horizontal Steam;
Corliss Beam Steam; Com-
pound Corliss Steam) . AA
National Blower Wks., 17th
& St. Paul Av. (Steam;
Steam Vertical) .... B
Nordberg Mfg. Co. (Steam
Corliss; Steam Hoisting;
Automatic Steam) ....AA
Pawling & Harnischfeger
(Duplex Hoisting Steam;
Steam Steering) .....AAA
Sheriffs Mfg. Co. (Steam
Marine; Triple Steam
Steering; Compound
Steam; Dredge Steam) . B
Vilter Mfg. Co. (Steam Cor-

ENVELOPES (Con.)

Broome ....AA
Improved Mailing Case Co.,
158 W. Broadway (Let-
ter & Package).......F
Meyers, H. N., 102 Cham-
bers C
Neostyle Envelope Co., 88
Reade (Merchandise)..D
Powers Paper Co., 290
Bdway. ....AA
Raynor & Perkins Env. Co.,
115 William (Letter)...A
Tension Envelope Co., 22
Reade (Package) X
U. S. Env. Co., 339 Bdway
AAAA
Whiting, F., 85 William..C
Whiting Paper Co., 150
Duane ....AAAA

N. Y.—Rochester
Karle Lithographic Co...B

N. Y.—Saugerties
Saugerties Mfg. Co.......A

OHIO—Cincinnati
Carpenter & Co., W. B., 310
Walnut ....B
Chatfield & Woods, Central
Av. & 4th ....A
Globe-Wernicke Co., The,
4th & Elm ....AAAA

OHIO—Dayton
Dayton Env. Mfg. Co......C

OHIO—Springfield
Thomas Stationery Co.....C

OHIO—West Carrellton
American Env. Co.........A
Friend Paper & Tablet Co.,
Geo. H. ....AAA

OREGON—Portland
Pacific Paper Co.........B

PA.—Huntington
Blair Co., J. C.........A

PA.—Philadelphia
Cohen, Chas. J., 312 Chest-
nut ....B
Molten & Co., R. R., 23 S.
6th C
Reyburn Mfg. Co., 19th &
Allegheny C
Royal & Co., Thos. M., 3d
& Locust ....B
Spangler & Co., E. J., 507
Ludlow C

R. I.—Providence
American Env. Co.........A

VA.—Richmond
Union Env. Co...........C

WIS.—Milwaukee
U. S. Env. Co. (National
Env. Co. Div.)....AAAA

EPAULETTES

PA.—Philadelphia
Horstmann Co., Wm.

EQUALIZERS

GA.—Rome
Towers & Sullivan Mfg. Co.
(Plow) ....B

ILL.—Chicago
Turner Brass Wks. (Wind
Mill) ....A

MO.—Sawyer
Implement Woodstock &
Mfg. Co. (Horse).......X

OHIO—Cleveland
Oram, John S., Hamilton &
Coe (Horse; Stave).....A

ERADICATORS

ILL.—Chicago
Eureka Blotter Bath Co.
(Ink) ....E

MASS.—Boston
Cutter-Tower Co. (Ink)..B

MO.—St. Louis
Levison & Blythe Mfg. Co.
(Ink) ....D

New York City
Collins Ink Eradicator Co.,
H. H., 60 Perry (Ink)..F

ERASERS

CONN.—Bridgeport
Challenge Cutlery Corpn.
(Ink) ....A

ERASERS (Con.)

CONN.—East River
Munger & Son (Blackboard;
Slate) C

CONN.—Meriden
Miller Bros. Cutlery Co.
(Steel) ....A

CONN.—Naugatuck
Goodyears' India Rubber
Glove Mfg. Co. (Rubber)
AAAA

CONN.—Wallingford
Wallace & Sons Mfg. Co.,
R. (Steel) ....AAAA

ILL.—Chicago
Andrews Co., A. H. (Dust-
less; Blackboard).....AA
Londergan & Son, W. H.
(Blackboard) X
Sanford Mfg. Co. (Ink,
Liquid) ....B

MASS.—Boston
Allen-Solman & Co. (Black-
board) ....F
Bailey & Co., C. J. (Rub-
ber) ....B
Carter's Ink Co. (Rubber)
A
Cutter & Tower Co. (Rub-
ber) ....B
Davidson Rubber Co. (Rub-
ber) ....A

MASS.—Worcester
Coes, Loring & Co. (Inc.)
(Draughtman's) ....A

N. J.—Jersey City
Dixon Crucible Co., Jos.
(Rubber) ....AAA

N. Y.—Jamestown
American Mfg. Concern
(Blackboard) ....A

New York City
Amer. Lead Pencil Co. (Rub-
ber) ....AA
Eagle Pencil Co. (Rubber)
AAA
Faber, Eberhard (Steel;
Rubber) ....AAA
Goodyear India Rubber
Glove Mfg. Co., 500 Bway.
(Rubber) ....AAAA
Goodyear Rubber Co. (Rub-
ber) ....AAAA
Keuffel & Esser Co., 127
Fulton (Rubber) .....AA
N. Y. Silicate Book Slate
Co. (Blackboard; Chamois)
D
Spencerian Pen Co. (Rub-
ber) ....AA
Wicbusch & Hilger (Ltd.), 9
Murray ....A

OHIO—Akron
Akron Rubber Wks. (Rub-
ber) ....AAAA

OHIO—Barberton
Pure Gum Specialty Co.
(Rubber) C

PA.—Philadelphia
Philadelphia Novelty Mfg.
Co. (Rubber) ....D

R. I.—Providence
Beno Co., William (Silver
Mounted) ....B

WIS.—La Crosse
Monroe Eraser Mfg. Co.
(Rubber) X

ERGOT

New York City
Hopkins & Co., J. C., 100
William ....A
Lehn & Fink (Spanish).AAA
Schieffelin & Co. (Spanish;
Russian) ....AA

ERGOTINE

MD.—Baltimore
Sharp & Dohme.......AAA

New York City
Boehringer & Sons, C. F...A
McKesson & Robbins.AAAA

ESCALATORS ..

See Stairways: Moving

377

ESCAPES: FIRE

CAL.—San Francisco
Western Iron Wks., 123 Beale ....B

COLO.—Colorado Springs
Hassell Iron Wks., 1401 Market ....B

D. C.—Washington
Barber & Ross, 614 11th N. W. ....A

ILL.—Chicago
Barbee Wire & Iron Wks., 44 Dearborn ....B
Booth, Jno., 114 E. Lake..B
Braumoeller & Son, Hy., 92 W. Van Buren ....B
Smith Wire & Iron Wks., F. P., 100 Lake ....B
Vierling, McDowell & Co., 23d & Stewart Av.......A

IND.—Lafayette
Barbee Wire & Iron Wks..B

IOWA—Davenport
Schneider, Chris. ....B

IOWA—Des Moines
Des Moines Bridge & Iron Wks. ....B

IOWA—Ottumwa
Fair-Williams Bridge & Mfg.

KY.—Louisville
Snead Arch'l Iron Wks., 10th, cor. Hill....... ..C

MAINE—Portland
Megquier & Jones Co., 31 Pearl ....B

MD.—Baltimore
McLaughlin Co., Geo. T., 120 Fulton ....A
Smith Iron Co., G. W. & F., Gerard, cor. Leland....A

MASS.—Everett
New England Structural Co. ....A

MASS.—Holyoke
Coburn Trolley Track Mfg. Co. ....B

MASS.—Medford
Boston Steel & Iron Co...B

MASS.—Springfield
Springfield Iron Wks., 106 Taylor C

MICH.—Detroit
Barnum Wire & Iron Wks., E. T. 99 Shelby ....B
Russel Wheel & Fdry. Co. ...A
Whitehead & Kales Iron Wks., Beecher Av. & M. C. R. R. ....B

MINN.—Minneapolis
Crown Iron Wks. Co., 109 2d Av., S. E..........B
Flour City Ornamental Iron Wks., 27th Av. & 27th S. ...B
Twin City Fence & Wire Wks., 223 E. 6th....AA

MO.—Kansas City
Kansas City Wire & Iron Wks., 1428 Oak ....B

MO.—St. Louis
Banner Iron Wks., 715 Locust ....B
Christopher & Simpson Arch'l. Iron & Fdry. Co., Park Av. & 9th.......AA
Globe Iron & Fdry. Co., 9th & Victor ....B
Koken Iron Wks., Koken Bldg. ....AA
Ludlow-Savlor Wire Co., 4th, cor. Elm ....A
St. Louis Arch'l Iron Co...C
Union Iron & Fdry. Co., 1458 S. 2d ....B

N. J.—Jersey City
Snead & Co. Iron Wks....A

N. J.—Newark
Burns Iron Wks. 201 Commerce ....A
Hay Fdry. & Machine Wks., 306 Fairmont Av. ......A

N. Y.—Brooklyn
Hecla Iron Wks., N. 11th & Berry ....AA

ESCAPES: FIRE (Con.)

N. Y.—Buffalo
Ernest, Chas. F., 311 Walnut ....A
Jones Iron Wks., 308 Terrace ....B
Machwirth Bros. Co., 201 Oak ....A

N. Y.—Newburgh
Coldwell-Wilcox Co......B

New York City
Bowes, Jno. J., 227 K. 29th ....A
Cornell, J. B. & J. M., 26th & 11th Av. ....AA
Dimond, Thomas, 128 W. 33d ....A
Happel, Adam, 1803 1st Av. ....B
Harris Safety Co., 1133 Bdway. (Portable) ...B
Jackson Arch'l Iron Wks., 315 E. 28th ....AA
Vreeland, G. A., 229 W. 36th ....B

N. Y.—Long Island City
Richey, Brown & Donald.A

N. Y.—Troy
Mahony Mfg. Co., 5th Av. & Liberty ....B
West Side Foundry Co., 3d Av. N. 28th..........A

OHIO—Cincinnati
Schrieber & Sons Co., L., 8th & Eggleston Av.....A
Stewart Iron Wks., 3d & Culvert ....A

OHIO—Cleveland
Forest City Steel & Iron Co., 10 Ramsey ....A
Variety Iron Wks. Co., Case Av., cor. Hamilton.....B

OHIO—Kenton
Champion Iron Co........AA

OREGON—Portland
Phoenix Iron Wks., Hawthorne. cor. E. 3d......C

PA.—Allegheny
Albree, Chester B., 1129 Market ....A

PA.—Philadelphia
Baisley Iron Wks., Jno., 514 So. Del. Av........AA
Belmont Iron Wks., 22d & Wash. Av. ....A
Cresswell Iron Wks., Saml., 23d & Cherry ....B
Darby & Sons, Edw., 231 Arch ....A
Hitzeroth, C., 3124 Market ....B
Remppis Co., Wm. F., 331 Witherspoon Bldg......C
Thompson Bros., 112 Bread ....B

PA.—Pittsburg
Marshall Bros., 341 Diamond ....B
Taylor & Dean, 201 Market ....B

PA.—Reading
Remppis Co., Wm. F., Water, at Lancaster Bridge.C

PA.—Scranton
Scranton Iron Fence & Mfg. Co., 1335 Capouse......C

R. I.—Providence
Tower, J. H., 52 Borden..B

TENN.—Chattanooga
Cahill Iron Wks., 102 Boyce ....B

TENN.—Memphis
Chickasaw Iron Wks.....A

WIS.—Milwaukee
Bayley & Sons Co., Wm., 732-736 Greenbush......A
Pietsch, Ferd., 619 Cedar.B
Skobis Bros., 955 30th....B

ESCUTCHEONS

CONN.—Bridgeport
Gayner & Mitchell Mfg. Co. (Keyhole) C

CONN.—Meriden
Foster Merriam & Co. (Door; Keyhole; Drawer)....AA

CONN.—New Haven
Mallory, Wheeler & Co. (Door; Keyhole; Sliding Door) ....AA

ESCUTCHEONS (Con.)

Sargent & Co. (Door).AAAA

CONN.—Stamford

Yale & Towne Mfg. Co.
Cup; Door; Drawer; Keyhole; Sliding Door).AAAA

CONN.—Waterbury

Amer. Ring Co. (Door;
Keyhole; Drawer)......A

Plume & Atwood Mfg. Co.
(Door; Drawer; Sliding
Door) ....AAA

MICH.—Grand Rapids

Grand Rapids Brass Co.
(Door; Drawer; Keyhole;
Sliding Door) ....A

Waddell Mfg. Co. (Wood).B

Hardware Supply Co.....X

New York City

Bardsley, Joseph, 147 Baxter ....B

Ludwig, A., 75 Spring
(Box) ....B

Peck, Stow & Wilcox Co.,
27 Murray ....AAAA

Russell & Erwin Mfg. Co.,
43 Chambers ....AAAA

OHIO—Cleveland

Taylor & Boggis Fdry. Co.
AA

OHIO—Piqua

Piqua Handle & Mfg. Co.
(Door; Drawer)........A

PA.—Reading

Reading Hardware Co.
AAAA

R. I.—Providence

New England Butt Co.
(Door; Drawer; Keyhole;
Sliding Door) ....AA

ESSENCES

See also Extracts

CAL.—San Francisco

Folger & Co., J. A. (Coffee) ....AA

Grandjean, Hy. (Coffee).D

Sherwood & Sherwood (Coffee) ....AAA

MASS.—Boston

Beach & Clarridge Co. (Coffee) ....B

Oriental Tea Co. (Coffee)
AA

N. J.—Maywood

Standard Essence Co. (Coffee) ....A

N. Y.—Brooklyn

Floto's Sons, Geo. (Coffee)
C

Moller & Bro., G. H.
(Coffee) ....D

N. Y.—Buffalo

Buchert, Philip (Coffee)..A

Mersman, F. (Coffee).....B

N. Y.—Flushing

Francke, Sohne & Co., Heinrich (Coffee) ....A

New York City

Ackerman, Mary (Coffee).B

Hachelmacher & Bohmer
(Coffee) C

Schmittmann, Wm. F. (Coffee) ....A

PA.—Philadelphia

Natl. Essence for Coffee Co.
(Coffee) ....A

Tomson & Co., P. C. (Coffee) ....AAA

Weikel & Smith Spice Co.
(Coffee) ....A

Wilde Bros. (Coffee) ....B

WASH.—Seattle

Crescent Mfg. Co. (Coffee)
C

WIS.—Milwaukee

Markhoff, W. (Coffee)...G

ETCHINGS

ILL.—Chicago

Blomgren Bros. & Co.
(Zinc) C

Hawtin Engraving Co.
(Zinc) ....E

MASS.—Boston

Art Brass Co., 110 High
(Art) X

ETCHINGS (Con.)

New York City

Gill Engraving Co. (Zinc)
C

Ringler & Co., F. A. (Zinc)
A

OHIO—Dayton

Dayton Art Glass Wks.
(Glass) ....F

ETHER

MD.—Baltimore

Thomsen Chemical Co.
(Nitrous) ....B

MASS.—Boston

Billings, Clapp & Co.....B

MO.—St. Louis

Larkin & Scheffler Chem.
Co. ....A

Mallinckrodt Chem. Wks.
AAAA

N. J.—Woodbridge

Trubek Chemical Works, M.
(Acetic; Butyric; Nitrous;
Rum; Sulphuric; Valerianic) ....E

New York City

Chaskel Chemical Wks....X

Cooper & Co., Chas., 194
Worth ....A

Erkenbrach; Geo. A......D

Franco-American Chemical
Works, 90 W. Bdway...D

Heyden Chemical Wks., 40
Pine (Fruit) ....A

N. Y. Quinine & Chem. Wks.
Ltd. ....A

Schieffelin & Co., W. H., AA

Warner Chemical Co., 141
Bdway. (Acetic; Benzoic;
Butyric; Formic)....AAA

PA.—Easton

Baker & Adamson Chemical
Co. ....A

PA.—Philadelphia

Powers-Weightman-
Rosengarten Co. ...AAAA

VA.—Richmond

American Ether Co.......B

ETHYL:
CHLORIDE

New York City

Franco-American Chemical
Wks., 90 W. Bdway...D

EVAPORATORS

CAL.—Petaluma

Petaluma Incubator Co.
(Fruit) ....B

DEL.—Wilmington

Pusey & Jones Co. (Multiple
Effects; Salt) ......AAA

ILL.—Chicago

Am. Foundry & Machine Co.
(Chemical) ....AA

Wolf Co., Fred W. (Multiple Effects) ......AAA

ILL.—Noble

Palmer & Co. (Fruit).....B

ILL.—Odin

Sebastian Bros. (Fruit)..E

ILL.—Quincy

Shahl Evaporated Co., Wm.
(Fruit) ....D

IND.—Bloomington

Oakes Mfg. Co. (Fruit)...D

Stutzman, D. (Fruit).....F

KANS.—Fort Scott

Fort Scott Fdry. & Machine
Co. (Sugar) ....H

KY.—Louisville

Avery & Sons, B. F. (Multiple Effects) ......AAA

LA.—New Orleans

Connell Iron Works, J. D.
(Iron) ....●

Haubtman & Loeb Co., Ltd.
27 Gravier (Multiple Effects; Sorghum) ......B

Murphy, John H., 643 Magazine (Multiple Effects)
AA

Payne & Joubert, 423 Carondelet (Multiple Effects)
A

EVAPORATORS (Con.)

MO.—St. Louis
Cook Cane Mill & Evaporator Co. (Multiple Effects)
..........................D
Kingsland Mfg. Co. (Sorghum) ....B

N. Y.—Auburn
New Birdsall Co. (Fruit)
..........................AA

N. Y.—Brooklyn
Burkhard, Thomas (Chemical) C
Pioneer Iron Wks., 155 William (Multiple Effects).A

N. Y.—Buffalo
Dopp Co., H. W. (Chemical)
..........................D
Squier Mfg. Co., Geo. L., 420 Niagara (Multiple Effects; Sugar; Fruit).AAA

N. Y.—Newburgh
Coldwell-Wilcox Co. (Multiple Effects) ....B

New York City
Bartlett, Hayward & Co., 100 Bdway. (Multiple Effects) ....B
Cornell Co., J. B. & J. M., 26th & 11th Av. (Multiple Effects) ....AA
Deeley & Co., Robert, 507 W. 32d (Multiple Effects; Sugar) ....AA
Krajewski-Pesant Co., 32 Bdway. (Multiple Effects; Sugar) ....AA
Reilly Repair & Supply Co., 229 West (Sugar) ....AA
Turl's Sons, Jno., 536 W. 28th (Multiple Effects; Sugar) ....D
Wheeler Condenser & Engineering Co. (Multiple Effects; Sugar) ....A
Yaryan Co., 41 Park Row (Sugar) ....B

N. Y.—Syracuse
Boomer & Boschert Press Co. (Fruit) ....A

OHIO—Cincinnati
Blymyer Iron Works Co., 2933 Spg. Grove Av. (Multiple Effects; Fruit Sap; Sorghum; Sugar) ......B

OHIO—Cleveland
Bartlett & Snow Co., C. O. (Chemical) ....A
Dyer & Co., E. H. (Multiple Effects) ....AAA
Kilby Mfg. Co. (Multiple Effects) X

OHIO—Hamilton
Black & Clawson Co..AAA

OHIO—Hillsboro
Bell Co., C. S............A

OHIO—Hudson
Bouton & Son, Charles (Cider; Fruit; Jelly)..X
Champion Evaporator Co. (Cider; Fruit; Jelly)..E

OHIO—Mt. Gilead
Hydraulic Press Mfg. Co. (Steam; Salt) ....A

OHIO—Warren
Warren Evaporator Wks..D

PA.—Bloomsburg
Harman-Cogger Co. (Acid; Sugar) C
Morris, Henry G., Phila. Bourse (Double; Single; Sorghum; Sugar) ....B
Oat & Sons, Jos., 230 Quarry (Copper; Iron).A
Sugar Apparatus Mfg. Co., 326 Chestnut (Multiple Effects) ....A
Wood & Co., R. D., 400 Chestnut (Multiple Effects) ....AAAA

TENN.—Chattanooga
Casey & Hedges Mfg. Co. (Multiple Effects; Sugar)
..........................A
Chattanooga Plow Co. (Cider; Sorghum) .....AA

VT.—Bellows Falls
Vermont Farm Machine Co. (Cider; Fruit; Sap; Sugar)
..........................C

EVAPORATORS (Con.)

VT.—Rutland
Grimm & Co., G. H......D

EWERS

See Pottery

EXALGINE

New York City
McKesson & Robbins..AAAA

EXCAVATORS

See also Dredges

ILL.—Aurora
Western Wheeled Scraper Co. ....AA

ILL.—Harvey
Austin Mfg. Co., F. C. (Steam) ....AA

MASS.—Boston
Souther & Co., Jno., 671 Dorchester Av. (Steam).D

MICH.—Bay City
Industrial Works (Steam)
..........................AA

MINN.—Minneapolis
Hilgore Machine Co. (Steam) X

MO.—St. Louis
Leschen & Sons Rope Co., A., 920 N. 1st (Steam)..
..........................AAA

N. Y.—Albany
Osgood Dredge Co. (Steam)
..........................B
Townsend Furnace & Mach. Shop Co. (Steam) ......B

New York City
Hayward Co., 97 Cedar (Steam) ....B
Lidgerwood Mfg. Co., 96 Liberty (Steam) .....AAA

N. Y.—Oswego
Kingsford Foundry & Machine Wks. ....AAAA

OHIO—Columbus
Hilbourne & Jacobs Mfg. Co. (Steam) ......AAAA

OHIO—Marion
Marion Steam Shovel Co. (Steam) ....AAA

OHIO—Toledo
Ohio Steam Shovel Co. (Steam) ....D
Toledo Fdry. & Machine Co. (Steam) ....B
Vulcan Iron Wks. Co. (Steam) ....A

PA.—Philadelphia
Noble, Henry A. (Odorless)
..........................X

WIS.—So. Milwaukee
Bucyrus Co. (Steam) .AAA

EXCELSIOR

ARK.—Pine Bluff
Pine Bluff Bedding Co...D

FLA.—Jacksonville
American Fibre Co. C

ILL.—Chicago
Cold Blast Feather Co...AA

ILL.—Lincoln
Lincoln Excelsior Co. ...F

IND.—South Bend
Russell & Ober ....D

KANS.—Fort Scott
Bearman, John M. ......F

KANS.—Wichita
Wichita Furniture & Mfg. Co. (Mattress) ....B

LA.—Shreveport
Shreveport Mfg. Co. (Ltd.)
..........................D

MD.—Baltimore
Winchester, V. W. .....E

MASS.—Boston
Boston Excelsior Co. ...A
Sammet & Son, G. W. ...D

MASS.—South Hanson
Foster, John C

MICH.—Grand Rapids
Fox Excelsior Co., J. W..X

New York City
Huffman & Co., Theo. P..B

OHIO—Cincinnati
Lounsbury & Sons, G. H..D

380

EXCELSIOR (Con.)
WIS.—Marshfield
Marshfield Bedding Co...D

EXCHANGE

MASS.—Boston
Lowell & Co., John A.
  (Bills of) ....D
New York City
Amer. Bank Note Co.
  (Bills of) ....AAAA
International Bank Note
  Co. (Bills of).........B
N. Y. Bank Note Co.
  (Bills of) ....A

EXCITERS

IND.—Ft. Wayne
Ft. Wayne Electric Corporation ....AAAA

EXERCISERS

N. Y.—Buffalo
Whitely Exerciser Co.
  (Elastic) ....B
New York City
American Exerciser Co.,
  1123 B'way ....B
Ingersoll & Bro., R. H., 51
  Maiden Lane (Elastic) ..A
R. I.—Providence
Narragansett Machine Co..
                        A

EXHAUSTERS

CONN.—Hartford
Hartford Blower Co.
  (Planing Mill, etc.) ...X
Sterling Blower & Pipe Mfg.
  Co. (Planing Mill, etc.)
                        A
ILL.—Chicago
Andrews & Johnson Co., 256
  Washington Boul. (Plan-
  ing Mill, etc.) ....B
Garden City Fan Co., 43 S.
  Clinton (Planing Mill;
  Gas) ....B
IND.—Connersville
Connersville Blower Co.
  (Gas) ....A
Roots Co., P. H. & F. M.
  (Gas) ....AA
IND.—Ft. Wayne
Kerr-Murray Mfg. Co.
  (Steam Jet; Rotary) ...A
MASS.—Boston
Banister, A. W., 35 Ware-
  ham (Planing Mill, etc.)
                        D
Sturtevant Co., B. F. (Gas;
  Air; Planing Mill, etc.)
                      AAA
MASS.—Hyde Park
Boston Blower Co. (Air;
  Gas; Planing Mill, etc.), A
MICH.—Detroit
Amer. Blower Co. (Gas;
  Planing Mill, etc.) ..AA
Lloyd Construction Co.
  (Steam Jet) C
MICH.—Saginaw
Allington & Curtis Mfg. Co.
  (Planing Mill, etc.)....A
N. J.—Newark
Isbell-Porter Co., 46 Bridge
  (Gas; Steam Jet) ......D
N. Y.—Brooklyn
Continental Iron Wks., West
  & Cayler (Steam Jet)...A
N. Y.—Buffalo
Buffalo Forge Co. (Gas;
  Planing Mill, etc.)..AAA
New York City
Connelly Iron Sponge & Gov-
  ernor Co. (Gas) ....B
Cornell, J. B. & J. M.,
  26th & 11th Av. (Gas;
  Planing Mill, etc.) ..AA
N. Y.—Utica
Giblin & Co. (Gas) ......B
OHIO—Bucyrus
New York Blower Co.
  (Planing Mill, etc.)....A
OHIO—Cleveland
Elwell-Parker Electric Co.
  (Air) C

EXHAUSTERS (Con.)
PA.—Lancaster
Champion Blower & Forge
  Co. (Planing Mill, etc.)..
                       AA
PA.—Philadelphia
Wilbraham-Green Blower
  Co. (Gas) ....B
WIS.—Milwaukee
Bayley & Sons Co., Wm.
  (Planing Mill, etc.) ...X
National Blower Wks. (Gas;
  Planing Mill, etc.) .....A

EXHIBITORS

CONN.—Bridgeport
Model Machine Co. (Rug)
                        D
IOWA—Keokuk
Strickler Store Furniture
  Co. (Curtain) ....E
New York City
Reilly Bros. (Wall Paper)
                        D
PA.—Philadelphia
Petersen Carpet Co., 1919
  Market (Carpet) ......B

EXPANDERS

DEL.—Wilmington
Henderer's Sons, A. L.
  (Tube) ....E
ILL.—Aurora
Aurora Automatic Mchry.
  Co. (Tube) ....A
MAINE—Portland
Hayes, H., 41 Cross (Tube)
                        H
MINN.—St. Paul
Helwig Mfg. Co. (Tube)..D
Lee & Hoff Mfg. Co. (Tube)
                        D
MO.—Moberly
Faesseler Mfg. Co., J.
  (Roller Tube) ....B
New York City
Dudgeon,   Richard,   82
  Broome (Roller Tube) ..A
McCoy Co., Jos. F., 157
  Chambers (Tube) ......B
Prosser & Son, Thos., 15
  Gold (Tube) ....A
Watson-Stillman Co., 210 E.
  43d (Tube) ....A
N. Y.—Oswego
Oswego Tool Co. (Tube)..B
PA.—Allegheny
Ajax Mfg. Co., 848 Jack-
  son (Tube) ....D
PA.—Philadelphia
Bullock, Chas. K., 1361
  Ridge Av. (Boiler Tube)C
PA.—Pittsburg
Ajax Mfg. Co. (Tube)....X

EXPECTOR-ANTS

New York City
Riker & Son Co., Wm. B.
                       AA
PA.—Philadelphia
Jayne & Son, Dr. D. ....A

EXPLODERS

N. Y.—Kingston
Nitro Powder Co. (Electric)
                        B
PA.—Wrightsville
Susquehanna Casting Co.
  (Cartridge; Cane Tip).AA

EXTENSIONS

N. J.—Newark
Sommer's Son, John (Fau-
  cet) ....A
New York City
Frees, C. A. (Shortened
  Limb) X

EXTINGUISH-ERS

CONN.—Meriden
Miller & Co., Edw. (Candle)
                      AAAA

EXTINGUISHERS (Con)

CONN.—Waterbury
Randolph-Clowes Co. (Fire)
..........AAA

ILL.—Chicago
Harden Hand Grenade
(Fire) ....D
Lindgren-Mahan Fire Apparatus Wks. (Fire) ..X
Liquid Carbolic Acid Mfg.
Co. (Fire) ....AAAA
B
Wilson & Co., F. C. (Fire)
B

ILL.—Quincy
Stahl, Geo. H. (Fire) ...B
MASS.—Boston
Badger & Sons Co., E. B.
(Fire) ....B
Walworth Mfg. Co. (Fire)..
AAAA
MO.—St. Louis
Stempel Fire Extinguisher
Mfg. Co. (Fire) ....D
New York City
Automatic Fire Alarm Co.
(Fire; Automatic Fire)..
AA
Hayward & Co., S. F.
(Fire) ....D
Judd & Co., H. L. (Candle)
AA
Nathan Mfg. Co. (Fire)..A
N. Y.—Seneca Falls
Rumsey & Co. (Ltd.) (Fire)
A
PA.—York
Spangler Mfg. Co. (Fire) .C
R. I.—Providence
General Fire Extinguisher
Co. (Automatic Fire)....
AAAA
WIS.—Racine
Racine Fire Engine Co.
(Fire) X

EXTRACT-RENNET

See Rennet

EXTRACT: WITCH HAZEL

See Witch Hazel

EXTRACTORS

See also Machinery
CONN.—Meriden
Manning, Bowman & Co.
(Cork) ....AA
MASS.—Boston
Amer. Tool & Machine Co.
(Hydro; Centrifugal) .AA
Empire Laundry Machine
Co. (Centrifugal) C
Harvey, H. H. (Spike) ...D
MASS.—Worcester
Cleveland Machine Works
(Hydro) ....A
MICH.—Gladstone
Marble Safety Axe Co.
(Broken Shell) ....B
MINN.—Minneapolis
Minnesota Beekeepers' Supply Mfg. Co. (Honey;
Wax) ....G
N. J.—Newark
Alba Tool Co. (Spike) ....A
N. Y.—Brooklyn
U. S. Bung Mfg. Co. (Bung)
A
N. Y.—Buffalo
Buffalo Scale Co. (Mineral)
AA
Squier Mfg. Co., Geo. L.
(Centrifugal) ......AAA
N. Y.—Little Falls
Burrell & Co., D. H. (Centrifugal) ....AAAA
New York City
Hepworth Co., S. S., 92
William (Centrifugal) ..D
Krajeroski, Pesant & Co., 32
B'way (Centrifugal) .AA
Reilly Repair & Supply Co.,
James, 229 West (Grease)
AA
Robertson & Son, Jas. L.,
204 Fulton (Centrifugal;

EXTRACTORS (Con.)

Grease) ....D
N. Y.—Troy
Adams Laundry Machinery
Co. (Centrifugal) ......B
Solhurst & Son, W. H. (Centrifugal; Hydro) ......B
Troy Laundry Machinery
Co. (Centrifugal) .....AA
N. Y.—Utica
Jones, Frank L. (Butter) .C
N. C.—Winston-Salem
Salem Iron Works (Centrifugal) ....A
OHIO—Alliance
Morgan Engineering Co.
(Ingot) ....AAAA
OHIO—Cincinnati
Amer. Laundry Machinery
Co. (Centrifugal; Hydro)
AA
Blymer Iron Wks. Co. (Centrifugal) ....B
Watkins Mfg. Co., F. M.
(Centrifugal) ....B
Watkins Laundry Machinery
Co. (Laundry Starch)...A
PA.—Columbia
Wilson Laundry Machinery
Co. (Centrifugal) ......A
PA.—Erie
Chapman Cream Separator
Wks., C. L. (Centrifugal)
D
PA.—Philadelphia
Enterprise Mfg. Co. of Pa.
(Meat Juice) ....AAAA
Harrison Safety Boiler Wks.
(Grease) ....A
Schaum & Uhlinger (Hydro; Centrifugal) ...AAA
PA.—Pittsburg
Lewis Fdry. & Machine Co.
(Ingot) ....A
Mesta Machine Co. (Ingot)
AAAA
PA.—West Chester
Sharpless, P. M. (Centrifugal) ....AAA
VT.—Bellows Falls
Vermont Farm Machine Co.
(Butter) C
WIS.—Fort Atkinson
Cornish, Curtis & Green
Mfg. Co. (Butter) ......A

EXTRACTS: FLAVORING

See following Heading for Miscellaneous Extracts
ARK.—Little Rock
Fletcher Coffee & Spice Co.,
The ....D
CAL.—Los Angeles
Newmark Bros. ....B
Southern California Supply
Co. ....B
CAL.—San Diego
Calif. Cream of Lemon Co.
D
Jewell Lemon Product Co.
D
CAL.—San Francisco
Ceylon Tea Co. ....D
Cohen & Son, Louis .....A
Folger & Co., J. A. .....AA
Herrmann & Co. (Oil; Essential) ....D
Levy & Co., Simon ......D
Man, Sadler & Co. ....A
Merten & Co. C
Phila. Mfg. Co. C
Price Flavoring Ext. Co. .AA
Rieger & Co., P. C
Schilling & Co., A. ...AAA
Scott & Gilbert ....D
Sherwood & Sherwood .AAA
Standard Soda Water Co. .C
Thompson's Union Soda
Wks. ....D
Tyler & Son, S. H. C
Quiros Soda Water Co. ...B
COLO.—Denver
Cannon, W. F. ....D
Hardesty Mfg. Co. ......D
Miller-Osborn Spice Co.
(The) ....D
COLO.—Littleton
Sterne & Martin ....D

Smith & Co., C. B. .....B

N. J.—West Hoboken

Palisade Mfg. Co. (Vegetable; Fruit Syrup) .....P

N. Y.—Albany

McEwan, Walter ....A

N. Y.—Binghamton

Harris, F. E. ....D

N. Y.—Brooklyn

Livingston, Jr., Wm. J.
(Flavoring; Essential Oil) C

Moller & Bro., G. H. ....D

N. Y.—Buffalo

Abwender, E. E. C
Favorite Mfg. Co. ......D
Granger & Co., W. H...AAA
House & Son, Jacob ....D
Liebetrieb, E. J. ....D
Pickering Mfg. Co. .....D
White Cap Mfg. Co. ...D

N. Y.—Catskill

Vincent Mfg. Co. ....D

N. Y.—Elmira

Thomas Co., N. S. ....A

N. Y.—Jamestown

Jones & Co., J. F. .....D
Keeler, C. S. & W. A....C

N. Y.—Le Roy

Bennett Chemical Co. ....A

N. Y.—Middletown

McMonagle & Rogers (Flavoring; Fruit Syrup) ..A

N. Y.—Montour Falls

Tilden Co. ....D

New York City

Amer. Extract & Supply Co. C
Andrews, Gulick & Sillcocks .....D
Archibald & Lewis C
Baron & Co., M. ....D
Bastine & Co. ....A
Budde & Westermann ...B
Burton & Co., C. L. (Flavoring; Essential Oil) ...D
Bush & Co., W. J. (Flavoring; Essential Oil) ..AA
Cohen & Co., Wm. H. X
Colgate & Co. (& Cooking) .....AAAA
Colton & Co., Jno. W. C
Cook, G. W. ....D
Crown Cordial & Extract Co. .....B
Delisser & Co. (Flavoring; Ginger) ....B
Durkee & Co., E. R. .....AA
Fries & Bro. ....AAA
Gillies & Co., E. J. .....AA
Goodheart & Co., R. M....C
Hickok, Jno. N. C
Johnston & Co., E. L. ...B
Kienzler, H. C
Knapp Extract Co. (Flavoring) ....B
McKenzie Bros. (Flavoring; Essential Oil) ....B
McKesson & Robbins (Flavoring) ....AAAA
Mergentime & Lamm ...D
Miller Mfg. Co. (The) C
Moss, G. A. ....B
Palmer, Solon ....D
Paturel & Co., F. C
Peloubet Mfg. Co., A. H..D
Price Flavoring Extract Co. .....AA
Royal Baking Powder Co.. .....AAAA
Rudkin Co., W. H. (Flavoring; Essential Oil) ....A
Rudkin's Sons, Wm. (Flavoring; Essential Oil) ....D
Selwyn Importing & Trading Co. (Flavoring; Essential Oil) C
Union Extract Wks......D
United Confectioners' Assn. ....B
Van Duzer Extract Co....B
Wertheim, S. ....D
Wood & Selick (& Cooking Flavoring) ....A

N. Y.—Penn Yan

Snow Grape Juice Co....D

N. Y.—Rochester

French & Co., R. T. ....A
Smith, Hungerford Co., J., A
Van De Carr Spice Co....D
Wright, A. (& Essential

Oil) ....AA

N. Y.—Syracuse

Gowing, D. H. C

N. Y.—Ushers

Anthony, Joshua ....A

N. Y.—Utica

Hitzelberger, Paul ......D

OHIO—Akron

Smith Bros. ....B

OHIO—Cincinnati

Berghausen Chem. Co. (The) (& Essential Oil) ....D
Echert Co., P. (The) ....A
Frank Tea & Spice Co. ..C
Fries & Bro., A. (Essential Oil) ....AAA
Garlick Co., H. C
Hilker & Bletsch ......B
Kingery Mfg. Co. ....D
Webster & Co., E. R.....C

OHIO—Cleveland

Bruce & West Mfg. Co.
Fruit Syrup) ....D
Palmer, Arthur L. ....D
Palmer Mfg. Co. C
Royce Co., Abner ....D
Sacks, Kirkpatrick Co.
(Root Beer) ....D
Schondorfer & Eberhard Co. C
Zipp Mfg. Co. (Root Beer) C

OHIO—Columbus

Citizen's Whol. Supply Co.
(The) ....D
Kentucky Extract Co. C

OHIO—Dayton

Burkhardt & Rotterman..D
Royal Remedy & Extract Co. .....B
Sachs-Pruden Ginger Ale Co. (Bottlers'; Confectioners') ....D
Sigretz, G. A. ....D
Wire Coffee Co., C. F....A

OHIO—Findlay

Hopper & Co., C. H. ....B

OHIO—Marietta

India Spice & Drug Co. ..D

OHIO—Newark

Styron, Beggs & Co. .....A

OHIO—Toledo

Lorenz Co., Geo. ....D

OHIO—Youngstown

Averbeck Drug Co. C

OREGON—Portland

Closset & Devers ....A
Northrop & Sturgis Co. ..D

PA.—Philadelphia

Clawson Co. (The) C
Cartwright & Co., W. A..B
Favorite Mfg. Co. (Flavoring) C
Fker & Co., F. ....AA
Ingersoll & Co. (Essential Oil) ....D
Jewel Mfg. Co. (Essential Oil) ....A
Knight Cooking Extract Co. .....D
Phila. Ext. Mfg. Co. (Essential Oil) C
Phila. Pickling Co. C
Ritter Conserve Co., Philip J. ....A
Stevenson, Jr., R. ......D
Sulzberger, D. C
Thayer & Co., P. W.....B
Twitchell, S. ....A
Whittle & Mutch ....D

R. I.—Providence

Fraser Bros. Co. ....B
Nichols & Co., C. E. ....D

TENN.—Bristol

Andrews Mfg. Co. C

TENN.—Knoxville

Knoxville Drug Co. ......B

TENN.—Nashville

Webb Mfg. Co. C

TEXAS—Dallas

Hughes Bros. Mfg. Co. ..A

TEXAS—Galveston

Galveston Coffee & Spice Co. ....AAA
Southern Coffee Co. C

TEXAS—Waco

Artesian Mfg. & Bottling Co. .....D

VA.—Norfolk

Haynor Mfg. Co. ....D

VA.—Portsmouth
Virginia Chem. & Mfg. Co.
B
VA.—Richmond
Sauer Co., C. F. C
VA.—Rocky Mount
Angle & Co. (Essential Oil)
D
WASH.—Seattle
Crescent Mfg. Co. C
Oriental Spice Co. ......B
WASH.—Spokane
Spokane Ext. & Spice Co..D
W. VA.—Wheeling
Exley, Watkins & Co. ...B
WIS.—Milwaukee
Hilbert & Co., A. J. .....D
Ladwig & Schranck Co...B
Meissner, Bergwell Co....D
Nat'l Extract Works C
Schleuter & Co., A. C
WIS.—Oshkosh
Roewekamp Bros. ....D

EXTRACTS: MISSCELLANEOUS

See also Dyes; Colors, etc.

CAL.—San Francisco
California Tanning Extract
Co. (Tanning) ....D
CONN.—Essex
Dickinson & Co., E. E.
(Fluid) ....A
CONN.—Hazardville
Gordon Bros. (Shoddy) ..A
CONN.—So. Coventry
Tracey, E. A. (Wool) ...A
FLA.—Jacksonville
Southern Mfg. Co. (Tanning) ....D
ILL.—Chicago
Armour & Co. (Beef).AAAA
Baker & Co. (Fluid; Solid
Bark) C
Morris, & Co., Nelson (Beef)
AAAA
Nutriment Co. (Beef) ...B
Swift & Co. (Beef) ..AAAA
Thompson Phosphate Co.
(Root Beer) ....B
Westermann Co., F. (Malt)
D
IND.—Hammond
Hammond Co., G. H. (Beef)
AAAA
IND.—Indianapolis
Lilly & Co.. Eli (Fluid;
Powder; Solid) ......AA
MAINE—Portland
Baker Extract Co. (Fluid)
B
MD.—Baltimore
Sharp & Dohme (Fluid;
Solid) ....AAA
Young Co., J. S. (Ltd.)
Tanners' Bark) ....B
MASS.—Boston
Burkhardt Brewing Co.
(Malt) ....AA
Gahm, J. (Malt) ....A
Menzel Malt Coo. (Malt)..D
Spencer, C. A. (Oak Bark;
Quebracks; Tanilla) ....D
MASS.—Cambridgeport
Thayer Co., Hy. A.
(Fluid; Solid) ....A
MASS.—Franklin
Norfolk Woolen Co. (Wool)
A
MASS.—Hyde Park
Gray & Co., T. H. (Wool)
C
MASS.—Northbridge
Riverside Woolen Co.
(Wool) ....A
MASS.—Methuen
Klaus, Hy. (Wool) C
MASS.—Salem
Bovox Co. (Beef) ....D
MICH.—Alpena
Northern Extract Co. (Hemlock) ....B
MICH.—Detroit
Horton-Cato Mfg. Co. (Root
Beer) ....D
Ingram & Co., F. F. (Beef;

Root Beer) ....B
Lambert & Lowman (Root
Beer) C
Parke, Davis & Co. (Fluid;
Malt; Solid) .....AAAA
Stearns & Co., Fredk.
(Fluid; Solid) .....AAA
MICH.—Kalamazoo
Upjohn Co. (Fluid; Solid)
AA
MINN.—Minneapolis
Bertrand Mfg. Co. (Root
Beer) ....D
MO.—St. Louis
Anheuser-Busch Brewing
Co. (Malt) ......AAAA
Tilden Co., The (Beef) ...A
NEBR.—So. Omaha
Cudahy Packing Co. (Beef)
AAAA
N. J.—Newark
Hoff, Jno. (Malt) ....B
N. Y.—Brooklyn
Huber Brewing Co., Otto
(Malt) ....AA
Leibmann's Sons Brew. Co.,
S. (Malt) ....AAA
Wiarda & Co., Jno. C.
(Fluid) ....AA
N. Y.—Lebanon
Tilden Co. (Beef) ....A
N. Y.—Little Falls
Hansen's Laboratory, Chr.
Rennett) ....B
Little Falls Wool Extract
Co. (Wool) ....A
N. Y.—Lowville
Crawford & Co., Lewis
(Bark) X
New York City
Burnham & Co., E. C.
(Beef) ....B
Burton & Co., W. (Root
Beer) ....B
Caswell Massey & Co.
(Fluid) ....AA
Chaskell Chem. Wks.
(Bottlers'; Tobacco) ...X
Corneille & Co., David
(Beef) ....B
Doherr, Grimm & Co.
(Quebracho) X
Eisner & Mendelson (Malt)
AA
Harvey Deywood & Extract
Co. (Deywood) ....A
Jones Chemical Co. (Tanning) ....B
Klipstein & Co., A. (Indigo;
Ink; Quebracho) .....AA
Knapp Extract Co. (Root
Beer) ....B
Lanmann & Kemp (Fluid)
AAA
McKesson & Robbins (Solid;
Fluid) ....AAAA
Matheson & Co., Wm. J.
(Indigo; Logwood; Tanning) ....A
Mosquera-Julia Food Co.
(Beef) ....A
N. Y. & Boston Dyewood
Co. (Fustic; Logwood;
Quebracho; Tanning) ..
AAAA
Royal Spec. Co. (Beef)...C
Schieffelin & Co. (Fluid;
Solid) ....AA
Smith & Co., Jas. R.
(Beef) ....A
N. Y.—Rochester
Rochester Brewing Co.
(Malt) ....AA
OHIO—Cleveland
Acme Woolen Mills Co.
(Wool) C
OHIO—Fremont
Trommer Extract of Malt
Co. (Malt) ....B
OHIO—Hamilton
Am. Maltine Co. (Malt)...
AAAA
PA.—Hanover
Young & Co., J. S. (Tanning; Dyewood) ....A
PA.—Malvern
Hires Co., Chas. E.
(Root Beer) ....AA
PA.—Philadelphia
Adams & Co., Jos. M.
(Wool) ....A

Favorile Mfg. Co. (Root
Beer) C
Hance Bros. & White
(Fluid; Solid) ....AA
Hires Co., Chas. E. (Root
Beer) ....AA
Mulford Co., H. K. (Fluid)
AAA
Shoemaker & Co., Robt.
(Fluid) ....AA
Wyeth & Bro., Jno. (Fluid)
AAAA
PA.—Allegheny
Am. Extract Co. (Bark)...A
PA.—Smithport
Smithport Extract Co.
(Hemlock Bark) ....A
TENN.—Bristol
Andrews Mfg. Co. (Drug-
gists') ....B
VT.—Springfield
Slack & Bro., W. H. H.
(Wood) ....A
VA.—Buena Vista
Buena Vista Extract Co.
(Tanning Bark) ....A
VA.—Lynchburg
Heald & Co., Jno. H.
(Tanning Bark) ......AA
VA.—Richmond
Valentine Meat Juice Co.
(Beef) ....A
W. VA.—Charleston
Tanners' & Dyers' Extract
Co. (Tanning Chest.; Oak
Bark) ....B
WIS.—Milwaukee
Blatz Brewing Co., Val.
(Malt) ....AAAA
Pabst Brewing Co. (Malt)..
AAAA

EYEGLASSES

See Optical Goods

EYELETS

See also Hardware; Carriage

CONN.—Seymour
Rimmon Mfg. Co. (Brass).B
CONN.—Waterbury
American Ring Co. (Brass)
A
Platt Bros. & Co. (Brass)
B
Waterbury Brass Co.
(Brass) ....AAAA
Waterbury Button Co. (But-
ton) ....A
IND.—Goshen
Goshen Eyelet Co. (Curtain)
F
MASS.—Boston
Eyelet Tool Co., 40 Lincoln
(Brass) X
MASS.—Fairhaven
Atlas Tack Co. (Shoe)
AAAA
MASS.—New Bedford
Rhodes & Co., J. C.
(Shoe) ....AA
N. J.—Newark
Agatine Shoe Hook & Eye-
let Co. (Shoe) ....D
N. Y.—Binghamton
Crandall Stone Co. (&
Knobs) ....A
New York City
Metal Stamping Co., 468 W.
B'way (Brass) ....A
Stimpson & Sons, Edwin B.
(all Kinds) ....B
OHIO—Cincinnati
Monarch Carriage Goods Co.
(& Knobs) ....B
PA.—Philadelphia
Horne & Bro., Wm. H.
(Sets) ....B
Smith Machinery Co., Geo.
A., 415 Arch (Brass) ..X

EYES

CONN.—Chester
Brooks & Sons, M. S.
(Screw; Brass; Iron Wire
stair Rod; Harness) ..B
CONN.—Middletown
Rogers & Hubbard Co.

EYES (Con.)
(Button) ....:.A
CONN.—New Britain
Corbin, P. & F. (Stair Rod)
AAAA
Humason & Beckley Mfg.
Co. (Screw) ....A
Landers, Frary & Clark
(Screw) ....AAA
North & Judd Mfg. Co.
(Screw; Loop &c.) ....AA
CONN.—New Haven
Cowles & Co. (Screw) ....A
Sargent & Co. (Screw;
Transom) ....AAAA
CONN.—Norwich
Ossawan Mills Co. (Screw)
B
CONN.—Waterbury
American Pin Co. (Button)
AA
Lane Mfg. Co. (Button) X
Steele & Johnson Mfg. Co.
(Button) ....A
White Co., L. C. (Button) C
ILL.—Chicago
Barbee Wire & Iron Wks.
(Shutter) ....B
Fowler, E. S. & W. S.
(Artificial) ....D
Haussmann & Dunn (Arti-
ficial) C
MASS.—Boston
Boston Belting Co.
(Bleachery) ......AAAA
Boston & Lockport Block
Co. (Dead Bulls') .....A
MASS.—Hyde Park
Webster Co., F. B. (Artifi-
cial Glass) ....D
MASS.—Worcester
Parker Wire Goods Co.
(Hot House or Garden) D
Wire Goods Co. (Screw;
Stair Rod) ....A
MICH.—Northville
Dubawi Mfg. Co. (Dead) X
MINN.—Minneapolis
Hoffman, C. A., 624 Nicol-
let Av. (Artificial) ...D
MO.—Kansas City
Kansas City Bolt & Nut Co.
(Screw) ....A
MO.—St. Louis
Moran Bolt & Nut Mfg. Co.
(Screw) ....A
N. Y.—Buffalo
Western Wire Goods Co.
(Hot House or Garden) D
New York City
Judd & Co., H. L.
(Screw) ....AA
Hoehn Co., R., 82 Chambers
(Artificial) ....B
Mager & Gouglemann (Tax-
idermists'; Artificial), D
Peck Stow & Wilcox Co.
(Cock) ....AAAA
OHIO—Cleveland
Cleveland Hdw. Co. (Neck
Yoke) ....AA
OHIO—Findlay
Findlay Axe & Tool Co.
(Pick) ....A
PA.—Howard
Howard Iron & Tool Co.
(Coal Pick) ....B
PA.—Lebanon
Amer. Iron & Steel Mfg. Co.
(Screw) ....AAAA
PA.—Philadelphia
Hoopes & Townsend Co.
1330 Buttonwood (Screw)
AAA
TEXAS—Terrill
Terrill Foundry & Machine
Co. (Hinge) ....F

FABRIC

MASS.—Chicopee Falls
Knit Goods Specialty Co.
(Incandescent Mantle) G

FACERS

MD.—Baltimore
Detrick & Harvey Mach. Co.
(Flags) ....AA
MICH.—Port Huron
Draper Mfg. Co. (Pump
Valve) ....D

FACES

PA.—Philadelphia
Philadelphia Electric & Mfg.
Co. (Electric Ceiling) ..E

FACINGS

MASS.—Springfield
Springfield Facing Co.
(Foundry) C
N. J.—New Jersey
Dixon Crucible Co., Jos.
(Foundry) ....AAA
N. J.—Pompton Lakes
German Artistic Weaving
Co. (Silk Shoe) ....B
N. Y.—Geneva
Geneva Woven Label Wks.
(Silk Shoe) C
New York City
Pettit Chemical Co.
(Foundry) ....B
OHIO—Cincinnati
Obermayer Co., S. (Foundry)
AA
OHIO—Cleveland
Smith Fdy. & Supply Co.,
J. D. (Foundry) ....D
PA.—Philadelphia
Paxson Co., J. W. (Foundry)
AA
PA.—Pittsburg
McCormick Co., J. S.
(Foundry) ....B

FAIENCE

See Pottery

FAILLES

See Silk Goods

FANS:
MACHINERY

CAL.— San Francisco
Brooks-Follis Electric Corp.
523 Mission (Electric) ..C
CONN.—Bridgeport
Bridgeport Brass Co.
(Revolving Fly) ....AAA
CONN.—Clintonville
Vibbert & Co., Geo. S. (Advertising) ....F
CONN.—Windsor Locks
Clark Co., Geo. P. (Drying;
Exhaust; Ventilator) ..C
DEL.—Wilmington
Baker & Co., G. W. (Ventilating) ....A
ILL.—Belleville
Belleville Pump & Skein
Wks. (Ventilation; Mine)
AA
Herzler & Henninger Machine Wks. (Ventilating;
Mine) ....D
ILL.—Chicago
Allis-Chalmers Co. (Ventilating; Mine) ......AAAA
Andrews & Johnson Co., 256
Washn. Boul. (Power;
Ventilating; Engine Connected) ....B
Central Electric Co. 268 5th
Av. (Ceiling; Electric;
Portable) ....A
Chicago Water Motor & Fan
Co., 22 S. Canal (Ceiling;
Water Motor) ....D
Electric Appliance Co., 92
W. Van Buren (Ceiling) B
Garden City Fan Co. (Ventilating; Elevator; Exhaust) ....B
Sullivan Machinery Co., 135
Adams (Ventilating;
Mine) ....AAAA
Watson Electric Co., 259 S.
Clinton (Ceiling; Electric)
AAAA
ILL.—Danville
Danville Fdy. & Machine
Co. (Ventilating; Mine) C
ILL.—Litchfield
Litchfield Fdy. & Machine
Co. (Ventilating; Mine) A
ILL.—Moline
Barnard & Leas Mfg. Co.

FANS (Con.)
(Suction) ....AA
IND.—Brazil
Crawford & McCrimmon Co.
(Ventilating; Mine; Engine Connected) ....A
IND.—Fort Wayne
Ft. Wayne Electric Wks.
(Electric) ....AAAA
IND.—Indianapolis
Commercial Electric Co.
(Electric Ventilating) A
Nordyke & Marmon Co. (Exhaust; Suction) ....AAA
Specialty Mfg. Co. (Ceiling;
Column Belt Power; Water Motor) ....D
IOWA—Des Moines
Eagle Iron Wks. (Ventilating; Mine) ....A
IOWA—Ottumwa
Ottumwa Iron Works (Ventilating; Mine) ....B
MASS.—Amherst
Hills & Co. (Palm Leaf) ..B
MASS.—Boston
Barney Ventilating Fan Co.
165 Ft. Hill Sq. (Power;
Ventilating) C
Boston Electric Co., 29 Harrison Av. (Electric) ...B
Sturtevant Co., B. F. (Disk;
Direct Connected Engine;
Electric; Power; Propeller; Ventilating; Engine
Connected; Exhaust) AAA
MASS.—Brookline
Holtzer-Cabot Elect. Co.
(Ceiling; Electric; Direct
Current, &c.) ....A
MASS.—Holyoke
Perkins & Son, B. F., 10
Crescent (Ventilating) A
MASS.—Hyde Park
Boston Blower Co. (Direct
Connected Engine; Electric Power; Ventilating;
Exhaust; Shaving; Dust)B
MASS.—Springfield
Elektron Mfg. Co., 60 Wilbraham Rd. (Electric Exhaust) ....A
MASS.—Westford
Sargent's Sons, Chas. G.
(Exhaust) ....A
MICH.—Bay City
Marine Iron Wks. (Ventilating; Mine) C
MICH.—Detroit
Amer. Blower Co. (Disk;
Electric Power; Ventilating; Engine Connected;
Disc; Exhaust; Malting;
Seed Cotton Elevator;
Shavings; Dust) .....AA
Fuller Co., 1565 Russell (Exhaust; Elastic; Ventilating) C
MICH.—Saginaw
Allington & Curtis Mfg. Co.
(Power; Ventilating) ..A
MO.—Kansas City
Bledsoe Fan & Supply Co.
(Exhaust) ....F
MO.—St. Louis
Commercial Electrical Supply Co., 1007 Market (Ceiling) ....B
Emerson Elastic Mfg. Co.,
718 St. Charles (Ceiling;
Alternating Current; Electric Portable) ....A
St. Louis Blower & Heater
Co., 1628 N. 9th (Ventilating) ....B
Wagner Elect. Mfg. Co.
(Ventilating; Belted;
Electrically Driven) ..AA
N. J.—Belleville
Eck Dynamo & Motor Wks.
(Bracket) C
N. J.—Elizabethport
Diehl Mfg. Co. (Ceiling;
Electric; Disk; Ventilator) ....B
N. J.—Newark
Backus Water Motor Co.,
182 Pa. Av. (Ceiling; Ventilating; Exhaust, &c.) B
Seymour, Jr., J. M., 43 Lawrence (Ceiling; Power;
Belted; Ventilating) ..B
Seymour & Whitlock
(Exhaust) ....B

FANS (Con.)

N. Y.—Buffalo
Buffalo Forge Co. (Power; Disk; Electric; Elevator; Exhaust; Mechanical Draft; Suction; Ventilator, &c.) ....AAA

N. Y.—Fulton
Hunter Fan & Motor Co. (Ceiling; Electric Ventilating; Column; Exhaust) B

New York City
Baker Smith & Co., 83 W. Houston (Ventilating) AA
C. & C. Electric Co., 143 Liberty (Electric Portable; Exhaust; Ventilating; Revolving Fly) ....AA
Cornell, J. B. & J. M., 26th & 11th Av. (Ventilating) AA
Crocker-Wheeler Co.. 39 Cortlandt (Electric Portable, &c.) ....AAA
Edison Mfg. Co., 83 Chambers (Electric) ....A
Howard & Morse, 45 Fulton (Power; Ventilating; Engine Connected) ....D
Power Specialty Co., 126 Liberty (Ventilating) ...E
Simonds Furnace Co.. 2768 Bway. (Ceiling; Disk; Exhaust; Seed Cotton Elevator) C
Sprague Electric Co.. 527 W. 34th (Electric; Ventilator) AAAA

N. Y.—Schnectady
General Electric Co. (Ceiling; Electric; Ventilating; Mine) ....AAAA

N. Y.—Syracuse
Engleberg Huller Co., The (Coffee; Rice) ....D

N. Y.—Troy
Grant & Ferris Co. (Coffee; Rice) X
Tollhurst & Son, W. H. (Exhaust) ....B

OHIO—Cincinnati
Macleod & Co., Walter, 463 E. Front (Ventilating) B
Standard Electric Co., 113 W. 3d (Portable Electric) B

OHIO—Cleveland
Ohio Electric Works (Electric) ....D

OHIO—Dayton
Bates & Bro.. D. L.. St. Clair & Kenton (Electric Ceiling; Portable Electric; Water Motor) ....D
Dayton Fan & Motor Co. (Ceiling; Electric Portable) C

OHIO—Nelsonville
Nelsonville Fdy. & Machine Co. (Ventilating; Mine) B

OHIO—Ravenna
Colonial Electric Co. (Electric Ceiling) ....B

OHIO—Springfield
Foos Mfg. Co. (Exhaust) A
Robbins & Myers Co. (Electric Desk; Bracket; Direct Current) ....A

PA.—Connellsville
Connellsville Machine & Car Co. (Ventilating; Mine) A
Connellsville Mfg. & Mine Supply Co. (Ventilating; Mine) ....B

PA.—Erie
Link Machinery C., E. M. (Power; Ventilating; Mine) C

PA.—Jeannette
Clifford Cappell Fan Co. (Ventilating; Mine) ....B

PA.—Lancaster
Champion Blower & Forge Co. (Ventilating; Exhaust) ....AA
Fidelitty Electric Co. (Bracket; Desk) ....D

PA.—Marietta
Penna. Electric Co. (Ceiling) C

PA.—Mauch Chunk
Stroh. W. M. (Est.) (Ventilating; Mine) C

PA.—Monongahela
Monongahela Mfg. Co. (Ven-

FANS (Con.)
tilating; Mine) ....B
Robinson Machine Co. (Ventilating; Mine) ....B

PA.—Osceola Mills
Stine & Son, S. B. (Ventilating; Mine) ....B

PA.—Philadelphia
Dallett & Co., Thos. H. (Electric) ....B
Delaware Rubber Co., 631 Market (Water Motor) X
Fleck Bros., 44 N. 5th (Fly) ....A
Jandus Electric Co. Real Est. Trust Bldg (Electric) B
Snediker, James F., 139 N. 7th (Ceiling) ....D

PA.—Pittsburg
Baird Machinery Co. (Exhaust) ....B
Westinghouse Electric & Mfg. Co. (Electric) AAAA

PA.—Pittston
Exeter Machine Wks. (Ventilating; Mine, &c.; Exhaust) ....AA

PA.—Scranton
Finch Mfg. Co. (Ventilating; Mine) ....AA

PA.—Shamokin
Mullen & Son, Jno. (Ventilating; Mine) ....AA

PA.—Wilkesbarre
Vulcan Iron Works (Ventilating; Mine; Exhaust) AAAA

PA.—York
Broomell Schmitt & Co. Ltd. (Induced Draft) ......A

R. I.—Providence
New England Ventilating & Heating Co. (Ventilator) D

VA.—Richmond
Richmond Electrical Wks. (Electric) ....AA

WIS.—Milwaukee
Allis-Chalmers Co. (Mine; Ventilating) ......AAAA
Bayley & Sons Co., 732 Greenbush (Ventilating; Ceiling; Electric) X
Mechanical Appliance Co. (Electric) ....A
National Blower Wks. (Electric Power; Ventilating; Engine Connected; Disc; Exhaust; Seed Cotton Elevator; Wool Elevating) A

WIS.—Watertown
Watertown Electric Co. (Electric) ... .D

FANS: LADIES

New York City
Steiner & Co.. Louis, 520 Bway. (Fancy Ivory; Shell; Pearl, &c.) ...X
Strauss & Co.. Ignatz, 621 Bway. (Fancy Ivory; Tortoise Shell; Pearl, &c.) B
Vantine & Co., A. A., 20 E. 18th (Fancy Ivory; Tortoise Shell; Pearl, &c.) AAA

FARINA

DEL.—Wilmington
Lee Milling Co. ......AAA

FLA.—Lake Mary
Planters Mfg. Co. ....A

ILL.—Chicago
American Cereal Co. AAAA

MO.—St. Louis
Stobie Cereal Mills ....B

New York City
Durkee & Co., E. R., 534 Washn. ....AA
Leggett & Co., Francis H. AAAA
Pulsford. A. J.. 97 Water F

OREGON—Portland
Albers Bros. Milling Co. ..C

N. C.—Raleigh
Farina Roller Mills ......E

WASH. Seattle
Centenn. ' Mill Co. .....AA

FASTENERS

See also Jewelry; Hardware; Carriage

CONN.—Bridgeport
Weld Mfg. Co. (Shoe) C
CONN.—Hartford
Billings & Spencer Co.
(Belt) ....AA
Jewell Belting Co. (Belt)
AAA
CONN.—Meriden
Meriden Curtain Fixture Co.
(Curtain) ....B
Parker Co., Chas. (Blind)
AAA
CONN.—Middletown
Palmer, I. E. (Hammock)
AAA
CONN.—Mt. Carmel
Woodruff & Sons Co., W. W.
(Storm Window; Seat) A
CONN.—New Britain
Corbin, P. & F. (Sash)
AAAA
Judd, O. S. (Sash) .....B
Russell & Erwin Mfg. Co.
(Blind; Sash) ....AAAA
Stanley Wks. (Box; Corrugated Steel; Sash; Window) ....AAA
CONN.—New Haven
Cowles & Co., C. (Inc.)
(Apron; Curtain) ......A
English & Mersick Co.
(Apron; Curtain) .....B
Fitch & Co., W. & E. F.
(Rope) ....A
Ives Co., Hobart B. (Sash)
A
Mallory-Wheeler Co. (Sash;
Casement) ....AA
North & Co. (Hame) ....AA
Sargent & Co. (Blind;
Sash) ....AAAA
CONN.—Norwich
Ossawan Mills Co. (Picture
Frame) ....B
CONN.—Southington
Peck, Stow & Wilcox Co.
(Sash) .:........AAAA
CONN.—South Norwalk
Norwalk Lock Co. (Sash) A
CONN.—Stamford
Yale & Towne Mfg. Co.
(Sash; Door) .....AAAA
CONN.—Unionville
Upson Nut Co. (Belt) AAAA
CONN.—Waterbury
American Pin Co. (Button)
AA
Bristol Co. (Belt) ....B
Holmes Booth & Haydens
Co. (Paper) ......AAAA
Waterbury Button Co.
(Glove) ....A
ILL.—Chicago
Chicago Crossing Co., Monadnock Bldg. (Bolt) ....F
Curtis & Co. Mfg. Co., 42 S.
Canal (Belt) C
Pratt Mfg. Co., 91 Lake
(Wire Belt) ....B
ILL.—Freeport
Stover Mfg. Co. (Curtain)
AA
ILL.—Paxton
Paxton Hdw. Mfg. Co.
(Clothes Line; Rope) X
ILL.—Streator
Iwan Bros. (Conductors') C
IOWA—Red Oak
Kretchmer Mfg. Co.
(Foundation) C
KY.—Newport
Higgin Mfg. Co. (Apron) A
MAINE—Rockland
Torrey & Son, J. G. (Ship) E
MASS.—Attleboro
Horton Angell & Co. (Cuff)
A
MASS.—Boston
Consolidated Fastener Co.,
95 Milk ....AA
Dennison Mfg. Co. (Card;
Paper) ...:......AAAA
Farquhar's Sons, John, 20
East (Slate) C
Hosmer, Codding & Co.
(Button) ....AA
MASS.—Cambridgeport
Lamb & Ritchie (Conductors') ....AA

FASTENERS (Con.)

MASS.—Fiskdale
Snell Mfg. Co. (Refrigerator) ....B
MASS.—Fitchburg
Merriam Mfg. Co. (Bottle)
F
MASS.—Lynn
Anchor Neckwear Fastener
Co. (Neckwear) ....H
MASS.—Plymouth
Bradford Joint Co. (Bedstead) ....D
MASS.—Salem
Crown Woven Wire Brush
Co. (for Round; Sewing
Machine Belts) X
MASS.—South Easton
Purinton Co., C. F. (Blind)
F
MASS.—Worcester
Brownsville Maine Slate Co.
(Slate) ....B
Eagan, Thos. F. (Storm
Window) ....G
MICH.—Detroit
Universal Button Fastening
& Button Co. ....D
MICH.—Grand Rapids
Elliott Button Fastener Co.
(Button) ....E
Hayden & Co., J. M. (Wire
Belt) ....E
MINN.—St. Paul
Schroeder Bros., 85 Inglehart (Storm Sash) .....F
MO.—St. Louis
American Novelty & Mfg.
Co. (Box) X
Miller Lock Co., 219 N. 4th
(Sash) ....B
N. Y. Auburn
Clapp Mfg. Co. (Seat) ..B
N. Y.—Binghamton
Crandall, Stone & Co. (Curtain) ....A
N. Y.—Brooklyn
De Haven Mfg. Co. 50 Columbia Heights (Box) ..A
N. Y.—Buffalo
Buffalo Belting Wks., 122
Washn. (Belt) ....F
Buffalo Specialty Mfg. Co.,
375 Ellicott (Belt) .....B
Pratt & Letchworth (Mitre)
AAA
N. Y.—Gowanda
Smallwood Mfg. Co., W. W.
(Corrugated Steel) C
N. Y.—Homer
Phoenix Hdw. Mfg. Co.
(Sash) ....D
New York City
Cary Mfg. Co., 19 Roosevelt
(Box) ....B
Cushman & Denison, 240 W.
23d (Paper) C
Green, Tweed & Co., 17
Murray (Belt) ....A
Judd & Co., H. L. (Sash;
Curtain) ....AA
Kerr & Co., 171 Bway.
(Metallic Belt) ....D
Lawrence Stationery Co., B.
(Paper) ....D
Metal Stamping Co. (Apron;
Curtain) ....A
Peck, Stow & Wilcox Co., 27
Murray (Door Chain) ..
AAAA
Richards & Co., E. Ira
(Cuff) ....AAA
Russell & Irwin Mfg. Co.,
43 Chambers (Bedstead;
Door Chain) ......AAAA
Sargent & Co., 151 Leonard
(Bedstead; Casement;
Door Chain) ......AAAA
Southwick Co., Geo. W., 149
Centre (Belt) ....E
Spencerian Pen Co. (Card)
AA
Standard Metal Strap Co.,
336 E. 38th (Box) ....E
N. Y.—Rochester
Pullman Mfg. Co. (Sash) B
N. Y.—Troy
Troyan Button Fastener Co.
(Button) ....B
N. Y.—Unadilla
Tie Co. (Curtain) ....D
OHIO—Canton
Elbel & Co. (Hame) .....A

FASTENERS (Con.)

OHIO—Cincinnati
Cincinnati Cooperage Co.
(Hoop) ....A
Robertson Steel & Iron Co.
(Basket; Hoop) ....A
OHIO—Cleveland
Cleveland Hardware Co.
(Seat) ....AA
Garry Iron & Steel Co.
(Conductors') ....A
Kenehan Steel Belt Fasten-
er Co., 307 Arcade (Belt)D
Strong, Carlisle & Hammond
Co., 61 Frankfort (Belt) A
Thacher Belting Hook Co.,
245 Crawford Rd. (Belt)D
OHIO—Dayton
Dayton Malleable Iron Co.
(Freight Car Door) .AAA
OHIO—Springfield
Corrugated Steel Nail Co.
(Corrugated Steel) ....F
PA.—Lancaster
Chase Co. (Belt) ....G
PA.—Meadville
Wilkins Shoe Button Fasten-
er Co. (Shoe Button) ..D
PA.—Philadelphia
Acme Staple Co. (Ltd.)
(Welt) X
Berger Bros. Co. (Conduc-
tor) ....A
Conroy, P. J. (Door; Refri-
gerator Door; Refrigera-
tor) ....A
Pease Mfg. Co., 1347 River
(Belt) ....F
Penna. Steel Co. (Street
Rail) ....AAAA
Phila. Novelty Mfg. Co.
(Paper) ....D
PA.—Pittsburg
American Nut & Bolt Fas-
tener Co., Frick Bldg.
(Nut; Bolt) ....B
PA.—Reading
Penna. Hdw. Co. (Sash) AA
Reading Hdw. Co. (Sash)
AAAA
PA.—Williamsport
Wyland Mfg. Co. (Box) ..D
PA.—Wrightsville
Susquehanna Castings Co.
(Bedstead) ....AA
Wrightsville Hdw. Co.
(Blind; Corrugated Steel;
Bedstead) ....B
R. I.—Providence
Cory & Reynolds (Belt) ..C
Talcott, W. O. (Belt) ....D
TENN.—Chattanooga
American Mfg. Co.
(Bedstead) ....D
WIS.—Racine
Dickey Mfg. Co., A. P.,
(Tank Band) ....F

FAUCETS

See also Cocks & Bibbs

CAL.—San Francisco
Am. Faucet Co. ....D
CONN.—New Britain
Landers, Frary & Clark (Self
Closing; Brass; Bung)
AAA
CONN.—New Haven
Peck Bros. & Co. (Brass;
Lock; Self Closing) ..AA
ILL.—Chicago
Goetz & Flodin Mfg. Co.
(Beer) ....A
Rodecke Mfg. Co. (Wooden)
E
Redlich Mfg. Co. (Wooden;
Cork Lined; Wooden Rub-
ber Saturated) ....B
Stier Mfg. Co., Herman
(Beer) ....A
Trenkhorst, Frank (Beer) E
Wilson & Co., F. C. (Bung)
B
ILL.—Edwardsville
Edwardsville Brass Co.
(Brass) ....B
KY.—Burnside
Burnside Mfg. Co. (Wooden)
E
MASS.—Boston
Boston & Lockport Block
Co. (Wooden) ....A
Strater & Sons, Herman

FAUCETS (Con.)
(Ale; Beer) ....A
Union Brass Wks. (Bath
&c.) ....F
MICH.—Detroit
Buhl Stamping Co. (Cream
Can) ....AA
MICH.—Petoskey
Lovelace & Birkett
(Wooden) ....A
MO.—St. Louis
Aufrichtig, Alois (Beer) .D
Messner Mfg. Co., Ferd
(Ale; Beer) ....B
N. J.—Newark
Chambers & Ainslee (Brass)
C
Sommers' Son, Jno. (Wood;
Metal; Ale; Cider; Bung;
Cork Lined; Extension;
Leather Lined; Lock;
Wooden) ....A
N. Y.—Brooklyn
Graham Chemical Pottery
Wks., Chas., 1018 Met.
Av. (Stoneware) ....D
New York City
McNab & Harlin Mfg. Co.,
56 John (Brass) .....AA
Meyer Sniffen Co., 5 E. 19th
A
Mott Iron Wks., J. L., 88
Beekman (Metal) ...AA
United Metal Mfg. Co., 186
Wooster (Brass) ....D
N. Y.—Poughkeepsie
Lane Bros. Co. (Self Meas-
uring; Brass) ....A
N. Y.—Rochester
Clark Novelty Co. (Brass;
Metal) ....D
N. Y.—Syracuse
Stearns & Co., E. C. (Wood
Key;; Wooden; Measur-
ing) ....AA
Syracuse Faucet & Valve Co.
(Without Packing) X
OHIO—Canton
McLain Co., Jas. H. (Brass)
AA
OHIO—Cincinnati
Deckebach Sons Co. (Beer)
C
OHIO—Cleveland
Bishop & Babcock Co.
(Metal) ....AAA
Cleveland Faucet Co. (Ale;
Beer) ....AAA
Sanitary Co., 335 Huron ..B
OHIO—Dayton
Dayton Mfg. Co. (Metal) A
PA.—Philadelphia
Cooper Brass Wks., Wm. S.
(Metal) C
Devlin Mfg. Co., 437 N.
10th (Measuring) ....AA
Enterprise Mfg. Co., 3d &
Dauphin (Molasses; Self
Measuring, &c.) ......AAA
Nat. Spec. Mfg. Co. (Self
Measuring) ....AA
North Bros. Mfg. Co., Le-
high Av. & American
(Molasses; Metal; Self
Meas.) ....AA
PA.—Pittsburg
McKenna Bros. Brass Co.
(Metal) ....A

FEATHERBONE

ILL.—Chicago
American Featherbone Co.,
109 S. Jeff. ....D

FEATHERS

See also Bedding & Millinery

ILL.—Chicago
Cold Blast Feather Co
(Geese) ....AA
Rich & Co., H. & M., 122
Wabash Av. (Art) ....A
Sanitary Feather Co.
(Geese) C
IOWA—Dubuque
Dubuque Mattress Factory
(Geese) ....D
MO.—Kansas City
Lloyd, J. H. (Geese) ....D
MO.—St. Louis
Ely & Walker Dry Goods Co.
(Geese) ....AAAA

390

FEATHERS (Con.)

Kaiser & Co., Jacob (Geese)
                     A

New York City

Hall, Frank A. (Geese) B
Lewis & Co., Alfred, 31 E.
  10th (Ostrich) ....B
Lindheim & Son, R. (Artificial; Millinery) ......B
Moch & Co., E. (Millinery)
                     X
Motley Co., H. K., 649
  Bway (Ostrich) ......D
Patent Feather Trimming
  Co. 230 W. 30th (Millinery) ....F
Rogers & Co., C. P.
  (Geese) ....A
Taylor & Co., M. J., 30 E.
  10th (Ostrich) ....E
Waffenbach & Co., Wm.,
  55 E. 8th (Ostrich) ...D
Wurzburger & Hecht (Millinery) ....AA

PA.—Philadelphia

Baxter, Jennie & Lizzie
  (Millinery) ....A
Henly's Sons, David (Artificial; Ostrich; Millinery)
                     A
Thorn Co., J. T., 123 N. 7th
  (Ostrich) X

FEEDERS & CONDENSERS

ALA.—Prattville

Pratt Gin Co., Daniel
  (Cotton Gin) ....AAAA

CAL.—San Francisco

Harron, Richard & McCone
  (Ore) ....A
Hendy Machine Wks., Joshua (Feeders (Ore) ..AA
Union Iron Works (Feeders
  (Ore) X

COLO.—Denver

Davis Iron Wks. Co., F. M.
  8th & Larimer (Feeders
  (Ore) ....AA
Hendrie & Bothoff Mfg. Co.,
  1625 17th (Feeders (Ore)
                    AA
Mine & Smelter Supply Co.
  (Feeders (Ore) ....AAAA

CONN.—New London

Brown Cotton Gin Co. (Cotton Gin) ....AA

GA.—Atlanta

Van Winkle Gin & Machine
  Wks., E. (Cotton Gin)
                   AAA

ILL.—Chicago

Allis-Chalmers Co. (Feeders (Ore) ....AAAA
Davis Regulator Co., G. M.,
  145 Milwaukee Av. (Feeders (Boiler; Heater) ...C
Engel & Fagerstein Chem
  Co. (Feeders (Boiler Compound) ....D
Q & C Co. (Feeders (Boiler)
                     X

IND.—Columbus

Reeves & Co. (Feeders;
  Hullers (Clover) ..AAAA

IND.—Connersville

Roots Co., P. H. & F. M.
  (Feeders (Boiler) ...AA

IND.—Indianapolis

Nordyke & Marmon Co.
  (Feeders; Mixers (Flour)
                 AAA

IOWA—Muscatine

Barry Mfg. Co. (Feeders
  (Automatic) ....A

KANS.—Leavenworth

Great Western Mfg. Co.
  (Feeders; Mixers (Flour)
                   AA

LA.—Amite City

Gullett Gin Co. (Cotton Gin)
                     A

MD.—Baltimore

Sinclair-Scott Co. (Feeders
  (Automatic) ....E

MASS.—Boston

Cross Paper Feeder Co., 185
  Summer (For Printing
  Presses) X
Foster Mfg. Co., F. W.
  (Feeders (Boiler) X

MASS.—East Bridgewater

FEEDERS (Con.)

Carver Cotton Gin Co.
  (Cotton Gin) ....A

MASS.—Lawrence

Horne & Sons Co., J. H.
  (Feeders (Automatic) ..A
Watts Regulator Co. (Feeders (Boiler Oil) X

MASS.—Warren

Warren Steam Pump Co.
  (Feeders (Boiler) ...A

MICH.—Battle Creek

Advance Thresher Co. (Feeders (Threshers) ....AAAA

MICH.—Bay City

Garland Co., M. (Feeders
  (Fuel) C

MICH.—Detroit

Amer. Injector Co.
  (Boiler) ....D
Detroit Lubricator Co. Hodge
  Bldg. (Feeders (Boiler
  Compound; Oil) ......AA
Lloyd Construction Co. Glenwood Av. & M. C. R. R.
  (Feeders (Boiler Compound) ....A
McRae & Roberts Co. (Feedpound) C
McRae & Roberts Co. (Feeders (Boiler Oil) ......A
Michigan Lubricator Co.
  (Feeders (Boiler Oil) A

MICH.—Port Huron

Lee Mfg. Co. (Feeders (Boiler Compound; Boiler Oil)
                   B

MO.—St. Louis

Kingsland Mfg. Co. (Cotton
  Gin & Automatic) .....B
Northrup Lubricating Co.
  (Feeders (Boiler Compound) ....F

N. J.—Jersey City

Krom Machine Wks., 10
  Essex (Feeders (Ore) X

N. Y.—Brooklyn

Bliss Co., E. W. (Feeders
  (Automatic) ......AAAA

N. Y.—Buffalo

Lake Erie Boiler Compound
  Co. (Feeders (Automatic
  Boiler Compound) ......D
Noye Mfg. Co., Jno. T.
  (Feeders; Mixers (Flour)
                   X

New York City

Creamer Steam Specialties
  Co., 123 Liberty (Feeders
  (Boiler) ....B
Lawler Water, Feed & Damper Regulator Co., 181
  Mercer (Feeders (Boiler)F
Rutzler Co., E., 178 Centre
  (Feeders (Low Pressure
  Automatic Boiler) ....A
Standard Steam Specialty
  Co., 542 W. Bway. (Feeders (Boiler, High & Low
  Pressure) ....D

N. Y.—Oswego

Kilts Mfg. Co. (Feeders
  (Boiler, High & Low)...D

N. Y.—Pearl River

Dexter Folder Co. (Paper for
  Printing Presses) .....B

N. Y.—Rochester

Hayner Co., Norman C.
  (Feeders (Boiler Compound) ....F

N. Y.—Syracuse

Merrell-Soule Co. (Feeders
  (Automatic) ....AA

N. C.—Charlotte

Mecklenburg Iron Wks.
  (Feeders (Ore) X

OHIO—Cincinnati

Day & Co., J. H. (Traders;
  Mixers (Flour) ....A
Lunkenheimer Co., Beekman
  & Waverly (Feeders
  (Boiler Compound; Boiler
  Oil) ....AA
Powell Co., Wm. (Feeders
  (Boiler Oil) ....A

OHIO—Steubenville

Steubenville Pottery Co.
  (Feeders (Sick) ....A

PA.—Erie

Sims Co. (Feeders (Boiler
  Oil) ....D
Watson, N. A., 1602 State
  (Feeders (Boiler) ......A

PA.—Philadelphia

Schutte & Koerting Co., 1251

FEEDERS (Con.)
N. 12th (Feeders (Boiler)
A
Smith Woolen Mchry. Co.,
Jas., 41 Race (Feeders
(Automatic Self Weighing
Scale) ....AA
PA.—Pittsburg
Chapin Fulton Mfg. Co., 28
Penn. Av. (Feeders (Boil-
er) ....A
Kelly & Jones Co., 135 Wa-
ter (Feeders (Stone Saw-
ing) ....AA
Pittsburg Reduction Co.,
Park Bldg. (Feeders (Alu-
minum Railway) ..AAAA
Scaife & Sons Co., W. B.
(Feeders (Boiler Com-
pound) ....AAA
PA.—Waynesboro
Frick Co. (Cotton Gin;
Fuel) ....AAAA
VT.—Rutland
Frenier, J. H. (Ore Feed-
ers) ....D
WIS.—Cudahy
Power & Mining Machinery
Co. (Feeders (Ore) .AAA
WIS.—Milwaukee
Allis-Chalmers Co. (Feed-
ers (Ore) ....AAAA
Filer & Stowell Co., Becker
(Feeders (Fuel) ...AAA
Steam Appliance Co. (Feed-
ers (Boiler Compound) .D

FEEDERS:
PTG. PRESS

See Machinery

FEEDS

ILL.—Moline
Barnard & Leas Mfg. Co.
(Automatic Shake) ..AA
KANS.—Leavenworth
Great Western Mfg. Co.
(Automatic Shake) ..AA
MICH.—Kalamazoo
Hill & Co., Wm. E. (Steam
Carriage) ....B
R. I.—Woonsocket
Woonsocket Machine & Press
Co. (Cord) ....AA
WIS.—Milwaukee
Allis-Chalmers (Steam Car-
riage) ....AAAA
Filer & Stowell Co. (Steam
Carriage) ....AAA
Pawling & Harnischfeger
(Steam Carriage) ...AAA

FEET

See also Limbs

CONN.—New Haven
Seward & Son, C. M. (Vehi-
cle; Dash) ....A
ILL.—Chicago
Merrick & Hopkins, 59 Dear-
born (Artificial) ......F
MASS.—Lowell
Andrews, Wm. (Rubber).E
MICH.—Grand Rapids
Waddell Mfg. Co. (Carved
Claw) ....B
New York City
Condell, A., 852 B'way
(Artificial) ....D
OHIO—Cleveland
Cleveland Hdw. Co. (Vehi-
cle; Dash) ....AA
OREGON—Portland
Portland Artificial Co.
(Artificial) ....F

FELDSPAR

N. J.—Trenton
Golding Sons' Co. (Ground)
AA
N. Y.—Belford
Kinkle Sons, P. H. (Crude)
X
PA.—Toughkenoman
Penna. Feldspar Co. ......D

FELLOES

See Woodwork; Carriage

FELT

See also Paper

CONN.—Meriden
Foster, Merriam & Co.
(Chair; Table) ....AA
CONN.—Winnipauk
Winnipauk Mills (Woolen)
A
ILL.—Chicago
Armour Glue Wks. (Hair;
Wood) ....AAAA
Barrett Mfg. Co., Merch.
Loan & Trust Bldg.
(Roofing) ....AAAA
Bosley & Co., D. W.
(Weather Strips) ......B
Bunker Saddle & Specialty
Co. (Shaped; Brown)...F
Burke, Augustus, 100 W.
Superior (Roofing) C
Carlyle Paper Co., 245
Sedgwick (Deadening).B
Chicago Asbestos Mfg. Co.
(Hair) ....E
Chicago Fire Proof Cover-
ing Co., 18 N. Canal
(Hair; Roofing; Asbestos)
E
Hopkins, H. H., 50 Dear-
born (Roofing) ....B
North Chicago Roofing Co.,
128 North Av. (Rofing) .G
Opaque Shade Clth Co.
(Shade Cloth) ....AA
Powell Co., M. W., 204
Dearborn (Roofing) ....B
Powell & Jones, Monadnock
Bldg. (Roofing) ....E
Sall Mountain Asbestos Co.,
128 Ontario (Roofing)..C
Western Felt Wks. (General
Line) C
IND.—Lafayette
Boyle Mfg. Co. (Deadening;
Roofing) ....D
MAINE—Camden
Knox Woolen Co. (Paper
Makers') ....A
Megunticook Woolen Co.
(Paper Makers') ......B
MASS.—Boston
New England Felt Roofing
Wks. (Roofing) ....A
Battelle, Hurd & Co. (Com-
mission) ....A
Trainer Mfg. Co., C. W.
(Hair; Roofing) ....E
Warren Bros. Co. (Roofing)
AA
MASS.—Canton
Draper Bros. (Paper Mak-
ers') ....A
MASS.—City Mills
Amer. Felt Co. (Cotton;
Elastic; Hat; Lining;
Piano; Organ; Polishing;
Saddlery; Upholstery;
Boot) ....AAAA
MASS.—East Walpole
Bird & Son, F. W. (Dead-
ening; Non-Inflammable;
Sanitary) ....AA
MASS.—Fitchburg
Fitchburg Duck Mills
(Paper Makers'; Wool)AA
MASS.—Lawrence
Lawrence Duck Co.
(Paper Makers') ......A
MASS.—Leeds
Northampton Emery Wheel
Co. (Polishing) ....A
MASS.—Millbury
Bowden Felting Mills Co.
(For all Purposes) ....B
MASS.—Springfield
Bigelow-Cheney Wire Wks.
(Guides) ....A
MASS.—Winchester
Bacon Bros. ....E
MASS.—Worcester
Cleveland Machine Wks.
(Cards) ....A
MICH.—Detroit
Burton & Co., W. J., 164

FELT (Con.)
Larned (Roofing) C
MICH.—Saginaw
Asphalt Roofing Co. (Wani-
gas Band Roofing) .....D
MINN.—Winona
Union Fibre Co. (Litho.
Board; Quilted; Flax
Fibre; Mineral Wool
Deadening) ....B
MO.—Kansas City
Midland Asbestos Mfg. Co.
(Hair) ....E
MO.—St. Louis
Sawyer Paper Co., F. O., 213
N. 3rd (Roofing) X
Trinidad Asbestos Mfg. Co.,
320 S. 21st (Deadening;
Roofing) ....A
N. H.—Peterborough
Noone's Sons Co., Jos.
(Ironing) ....D
N. J.—Belvidere
Crane Felt Mfg. Co.
(Piano) X
N. J.—Elizabeth
Rankin Co., W. H.
(Roofing) ....AA
N. J.—Jersey City
Stowell Mfg. Co., 114 Cul-
ver Av. (Roofing) ......B
N. J.—Newark
Peters Harness & Saddlery
Co. (Pads; Saddle Hous-
ings) C
N. J.—Orange
McGall Hat Co. (Hats)..X
N. Y.—Albany
Albany Felt Co. (Paper
Makers'). ....**B**
Huych & Sons, F. C.
(Paper Makers') ....AA
N. Y.—Amsterdam
Cons. Woolen Felt Mills
(Saddle; Shoe; Polishing)
C
N. Y.—Binghamton
Binghamton Felting Co.
(All Kinds) ....B
N. Y.—Brooklyn
Hatfield, Geo. E. (Roofing)
D
Nassau Mills ....AAA
N. Y.—Dolgeville
Am. Felt Co. (All Kinds)..
AAA
N. Y.—Lestershire
Faatz, Reynolds Felting Co.
(Shoe; Sad.; Laundry;
Millinery; Trimming)..A
N. Y.—Little Falls
Kingston's Sons, Wm.
(Deadening; Dry Roofing)
D
N. Y.—Middleville
Nelson-Dedicke Felt Co.
(Wool) ....B
N. Y.—Newburgh
Stroock Felt Co. (Hair;
Polishing; Roofing) ..AA
N. Y.—Newfane
Lockport Felt Co. (Paper
Mill) ....D
New York City
American Felt Co., 110 E.
13th (For Electrical Pur-
poses; Polishing) .AAAA
Asbestos Felting Wks., 79
Maiden Lane (Hair) ..D
Baeder, Adamson & Co., 67
Beekman (Hair) ...AAAA
Boyle & Co., John, 112 Du-
ane (Dryer) ....AA
Hewitt & Bros., C. B., 48
Beekman (Roofing) ...A
Johns-Manville Co., H. W.
Asbestos Fire; Building;
Deadening; Hair; Roof-
ing; Asbestos) ....AAAA
Jonas & Naumberg, 2 Wash-
ington Pl. (Hatters')..AA
Martin Co., 192 Water
(Hair) ....D
Mineralized Rubber Co., 18
Cliff (Roofing) ....A
Ostermoor & Co. (Elastic;
Mattress) ....A
Rauft, Richard (Piano;
Organ) ....A
Russian Hair Felt Co.
(Hair) ....A
Smith & Co., Thos. F., 16

FELT (Con.)
Cedar (Hair) ....F
Sperry & Beale Co. (Cotton;
Elastic; Mattress) .....B
Stewart Mfg. Co., W. H., 81
Fulton (Roofing) C
Stroock & Co., S. (Commis-
sion) ....A
Taylor, W. J., 341 B'way
(For Electrical Purposes)
A
Tingue, Brown & Co. (Elas-
tic; Hat; Lining; Paper
Makers'; Piano; Organ;
Polishing; Saddlery; Shoe;
Upholstery, etc.) ......D
N. Y.—Oriskany
Waterbury & Sons Co., H.
(Machine Paper Makers')
A
N. Y.—Syracuse
Single Paper Co., John
(Roofing) ....B
N. C.—Charlotte
Barnhardt Mfg. Co. (Cot-
ton Mattress) C
Southern Cotton Oil Co.
(Mattress) ....AAAA
N. C.—Goldsboro
Royall & Borden (Mat-
tress) ....D
OHIO—Cincinnati
Chalfield & Wood Co., 347
W. 4th (Deadening; Roof-
ing) ....A
Diem & Wing Paper Co., 320
Elm (Roofing) ......AA
OHIO—Columbus
Union Brick & Supply Co.
(Roofing) ....E
OHIO—Hamilton
Black & Clawson Co.
(Guides) ....AAA
Shuler & Benninghofen
(Paper Makers') .....AA
OHIO—Lockland
Carey Mfg. Co., Philip
(Deadening; Hair; Roof-
ing) ....AAA
Halderman Paper Co.
(Deadening) ....A
OREGON—Portland
Hammond Mfg. Co., 100 1st
X
PA.—Allegheny
De Long & Co., Julius
(Hair) ....B
McGraw Bros., J. A., 220
Sandusky (Roofing) C
PA.—Ambler
Keasby & Mattison Co.
(Asbestos) ....AAAA
PA.—Erie
Watson Co., H. F. (Dead-
ening; Hair; Roofing
Asbestos, etc.) .....AAA
PA.—Franklin
Franklin Mfg. Co. (Deaden-
ing; Hair) ....AA
PA.—Philadelphia
Baeder, Adamson Co., 730
Market (Hair) X
Garrett & Son Co., C. S.,
21 Decatur (Deadening;
Roofing; Wood) ......AA
Stelwagon Mfg. Co., 826
Schuylkill Av. (Roofing)
B
PA.—Pittsburg
McClintock & Irvine Co.,
Neville (Roofing) ......B
TENN.—Nashville
Nashville Chemical Co.
(Roofing) ....D
WIS.—Appleton
Appleton Woolen Mills
(Paper Makers') ....B

FENCES & FENCING

See also Wire

CAL.—San Francisco
Pacific Steel & Wire Co.
(Farm) ....A
CONN.—Georgetown
Gilbert & Bennett Mfg. Co.
(Wire) ....AAA
GA.—Atlanta
Atlanta Wire & Iron Works

FENCES (Con.)

Co. (Iron; Steel Picket;
Wire) ....F

ILL.—Chicago
Am. Steel & Wire Co.,
Rookery (Woven Wire)..
AAAA
Barbee Wire & Iron Wks.
(Coping; Jail; Lawn;
Poultry; School; Tubular)
B
Booth, Jas., 114 E. Lake
(Iron; Wire) ....B
Braumoeller & Son, Henry
(Iron) ....B
Expanded Metal Fireproof-
ing Co. (Steel) ....A
Page Woven Wire Fence
Co., 200 Monroe (Woven
Wire; Park; Game Pre-
serves; Iron; Ornamental)
A
Smith Wire & Iron Wks.,
F. P. (Metal) ....AA

ILL.—De Kalb
De Kalb Fence Co. (Steel
Web; Woven Wire; Steel
Picket; Poultry) .....AA
Union Fence Co. (Hog;
Lawn; Poultry) ......B

ILL.—Joliet
Adams Steel & Wire Co.
(Woven Wire) ....D

ILL.—Peoria
Keystone Fence Co.
(Woven Wire) ......AA

ILL.—Sterling
Dillon-Griswold Wire Co.
(Woven Wire) X

IND.—Anderson
Skinner Woven Wire Fence
Co. (Woven Wire) .....D

IND.—Indianapolis
Enterprise Fdry. & Fence
Co. (Iron; Wire) .....B
Over, Ewald (Barbed Wire;
Iron) C

IND.—Kokomo
Kokomo Fence Mach. Co.
(Ornamental; Farm).AAA

IND.—Lafayette
Barbee Wire & Iron Wks.
(Iron) ....B

IND.—Muncie
Kitselman Bros. (Woven
Wire) ....A

MD.—Baltimore
Balderston & Son, H. (Iron;
Wire) ....E

MASS.—Boston
Walworth Mfg. Co. (Iron)..
AAAA
MASS.—Clinton
Clinton Wire Cloth Co.
(Woven Wire) ......AAA

MICH.—Adrian
Page Woven Wire Fence Co.
A
MICH.—Detroit
Barnum Wire & Iron Works,
E. T. (Iron; Steel) ...B
Bolles Iron & Wire Works.
J. E. (Iron) X
Michigan Wire Cloth Co.
(Wire) ....AA

MICH.—Holly
Cyclone Woven Wire Fence
Co. (Woven Wire) C

MICH.—Oxford
Harris Wire Fence Co.
(Woven Wire) X

MINN.—Crookston
Crookston Marble Works
(Cemetery) ....D

MINN.—St. Paul
Minnesota Fence Works
(Woven Wire) ....E

MO.—St. Louis
Globe Iron Fdy. Co. (Iron;
Wire) ....B
Harry Steel Works, O. K.
(Iron) ....B
Ludlow-Saylor Wire Co.
(Iron; Wire) ....AA
St. Louis Wire & Iron Co..E

N. H.—Concord
Hill & Co., Jas. R. (Metal)
X
N. Y.—Hornellsville
Hollow Cable Mfg. Co.
(Metal) C

FENCES (Con.)

New York City
Anchor Post Co., 15 Cort-
landt (Cemetery) ......D
Clinton Wire Cloth Co.
(Wire) ....AAA
Dewitt Wire Cloth Co.
(Wire) ....A
Fiske Iron Works, J. W.
(Iron) ....B
Howard & Morse (Iron)...D
Lamb, J. & R. (Iron).....D
Pitt Composite Iron Works,
111 5th Av. (Iron; Steel
Picket) ....D

N. Y.—Rossman
McClellan & Connor (Woven
Wire) ....E

N. Y.—Syracuse
Syracuse Wire Works (Iron;
Wire) ....D

N. Y.—Utica
Palmer, C. F. (Iron; Wire)
C

OHIO—Cincinnati
Bromwell Brush & Wire
Goods Co. ....AA
Gholson Fence Co., W. C.,
1746 Reading Rd. (Metal
Portable; Iron; Wire)..X
Nimmo Fence Co., 334 E.
4th (Iron; Steel Picket).E
Schreiber & Sons' Co., L.
(Wire; Iron) ....AA
Stewart Iron Works, 3d &
Culvert (Iron; Metal;
Wire; Steel Picket) ...A

OHIO—Cleveland
Van Dorn Iron Works (Iron)
AA
OHIO—Dayton
City Forge & Iron Works
(Metal) ....D

OHIO—Hamilton
Meyers Mfg. Co., Fred J.
(Iron) ....B

OHIO—Kenton
Champion Iron Co. (Iron;
Steel; Wire; Punched
Rail; Metal) ....AA

OHIO—Sandusky
Boley Wire Fence Co. (Wov-
en Wire) C

OHIO—Springfield
Mast, Foos. & Co. (Iron;
Punched Rail; Metal).AA
Rogers Iron Co. (Iron;
Metal) ....B

OHIO—Westerville
Bennett & Co., H. L.
(Metal) ....E

PA.—East Bangor
East Bangor Mfg. Co.
(Metal) X

PA.—Philadelphia
Darby & Sons' Co., Edward
(Iron; Wire) ....A
Merritt & Co. (Iron; Wire)
B

PA.—Pittsburg
McDowell Mfg. Co. (Ex-
panded Metal) ....D
Phoenix Steel Construction
Co. (Iron; Steel Picket).D
Pittsburg Woven Wire
Fence Co. ....B
Taylor & Dean (Wire; Iron)
B

WIS.—Janesville
Janesville Barb Wire Co.
(Woven Wire) ....A

FENDERS

CONN.—Georgetown
Gilbert & Bennett Mfg. Co.
(Nursery) ....AAA

CONN.—Waterbury
Holmes, Booth & Haydens
Co. (Brass) ....AA

GA.—Rome
Towers & Sullivan Mfg. Co.
(Plow) ....B

ILL.—Chicago
Barbee Wire & Iron Works
(Nursery; Wire) ......B
McGuire-Cummings Mfg. Co.
122 N. Sagamon (Car)
AA
Tothill, W. S., 128 W. Web-
ster Av. (Baby) ......F

FENDERS (Con.)

KY.—Louisville
Dow Wire Works (Nursery) ....D

MD.—Baltimore
Baltimroe Car Wheel Co., Payson & Patterson (Car) .... B

MASS.—Boston
Elastic Tip Co. (Furniture) .... B

Murdock .Corporation, 156 Boylston (Fire Place)..X

Pfingst, .Louis, 31 State (Car) ....D

MASS.—Cambridge
Boston Woven Hose & Rubber Co. (Rubber; Furniture) ....AAAA

MASS.—Worcester
National Mfg. Co. (Fire Place) ....A
Wright Wire Co. (Fire Place) ....AA

MICH.—Detroit
Briscoe Mfg. Co. (Automobile) ....A

N. J.—Jersey City
New Jersey Car Spring & Rubber Co. (Rubber; Furniture) ....AA

N. Y.—Brooklyn
Smith & Son, James (Leather Boat) ....D

N. Y.—Buffalo
Buffalo Wire Works Co. (Fire Place) ....A
Jewett Mfg. Co., J. C. (Register) ....AA
McKinnon Dash Co. (Carriage) ....AA

New York City
Dewitt Wire Cloth Co. (Wire) ....A
Estey Wire Works Co. (Fire Place) ....D
Fiske Iron Works, J. W. (Nursery) ....B
Goodyear's India Rubber Glove Mfg. Co. (Rubber; Furniture) ....AAAA
Goodyear Rubber Co. (Rubber; Furniture) ...AAAA
Hodgman Rubber Co. (Rubber; Furniture) ......AA
Howard & Morse (Folding; Iron; Nursery) ......D
Jackson & Co., Wm. H. (Brass) ....A
Judd & Co., H. L. (Brass; Iron) ....AA
Manhattan Brass Co. (Brass) ....A
Mott .Iron .Works, J. L. (Brass) ....AA
Peck, Stow & Wilcox Co. (Fire Place) ......AAAA
Peckham Mfg. Co., 26 Cortlandt (Car) . . ..A

OHIO—Cincinnati
Bromwell Brush & Wire Goods Co. (Wire) ....AA
Hunter Automatic Fender Co. (Car) ....F

OHIO—Cleveland
Eclipse Car Fender Co. (Car) X

OHIO—Hamilton
Meyers Mfg. Co., F. J. (Brass; Wire) ....B

PA.—Philadelphia
Brill Co., J. G. 62 Woodland Av. (Car) .....AAA
Darby & Sons' Co., Edw. (Nursing; Fire Place)..A
Harrison's Sons, W. H. (Brass; Iron) ....E
Mayer & Englund, 1024 Filbert (Car) ....A
Phila. Lawn Mower Co., 3100 Chestnut (Lawn Mower) ....B

PA.—Pittsburg
Armstrong Cork Co. (Yacht) ....AAAA
Simonds Mfg. Co. (Car)...C

R. I.—Providence
Consolidated Car Fender Co. (Car) ....D

FERMENTS

MICH.—Detroit
Parke, Davis & Co. (Digestive) ....AAAA

N. Y.—Little Falls
Burrell & Co., D. H. (Lactic) ....AAAA
Hansen's Laboratory, C. (Lactic) ....B

New York City
Fairchild Bros. & Foster (Digestive) ....AA

FERRULES

CONN.—Bridgeport
American Tube & Stamping Co. (Brass) ......AAAA
Bridgeport Brass Co. (Brass) ....AAA
Gaynor & Mitchell Mfg. Co. (Brass) C

CONN.—Bristol
Bartholomew Co., H. S. (Iron) ....B

CONN.—Middletown
Wilcox Crittenden & Co. (Iron; Steel) ....A

CONN.—Mt. Carmel
Woodruff & Sons' Co., W. W. ....A

CONN.—New Haven
Peck Bros. & Co. (Brass) ....AA
Sargent & Co. (Sash Tool) ....AAAA

CONN.—Torrington
Union Hardware Co. (Iron; Steel; Brass) ....AA

CONN.—Unionville
Humphreys. H. W. (Solid Brass; Tin; Sheet Metal) ....D

CONN.—Waterbury
American Pin Co. (Brass) ....AA
American Ring Co. (Brass; Seamless) ....A

CONN.—Waterbury
Benedict & Burnham Mfg. Co. (Brass) ......AAA
Novelty Mfg. Co. (Brass; German Silver; Iron; Seamless; Table Cutlery) ....A
Plume & Atwood Mfg. Co. (Brass) ....AAA
Randolph - Clowes Company (Brass) ....AAA
Scovill Mfg. Co. (Brass) ....AAAA
Steele & Johnson Mfg. Co. (Brass) ....A
Waterbury Brass Co. (Brass) ....AAAA

ILL.—Chicago
Illinois Malleable Iron Co. (Iron) ....AAAA

ILL.—Decatur
Mueller Mfg. Co., H. (Brass) ....AAA

ILL.—Edwardsville
Edwardsville Brass Co. (Brass) ....B

MAINE—Brunswick
Brunswick Mfg. Co. (Steel; Plain; Nickel Plated)..C

MD.—Baltimore
Robertson Mfg. Co., Jas. (Iron; Lead) ....A

MASS.—Worcester
Bay .State .Stamping Co. (Brass; Iron; Steel)....F
Matthews Mfg. Co. (Brass; Steel) ....D
Parker & Co., Jno. L., 75 School (Brass; Iron; Steel; Seamless) ......B
Wire Goods Co. (Wire)...A
Worcester Ferrule & Mfg. Co. (Brass; Light Steel; Iron) C

MICH.—Detroit
Park & McKay Co. (Brass) C

MICH.—Jackson
McKeel & Co., Geo. A. (Brass; Steel; Hoe; Fork; Rake; Screw Driver, &c.) ....B

FERRULES (Con.) ..

Withington & Cooley Mfg.
Co. (Brass; Iron; Seam-
less) ....,...AA

MO.—St. Louis
Nelson Mfg. Co., N. O.
(Iron) ....AAA

N. J.—Newark
Green & Son, C. E. (Brass;
Wire) ....D
Newark Rivet Wks. (Brass)
AA

N. J.—New Brunswick
Consolidated Fruit Jar Co.
(Sheet Metal) ....AA

N. Y.—Fort Plain
Walrath. A. (Broom) ....D

N. Y.—Frankfort
Pratt Chuck Co. (Iron;
Steel; Seamless) .`....B

New York City
Ansonia Brass & Copper Co.
(Seamless) ....AAAA
Hungerford Brass & Copper
Co., 497 Pearl (Brass;
also Copper) ....AA
Lovell & Co., F. H., 92
William (Copper) ....A
McNab & Harlin Mfg. Co.
(Brass) ....AAA
Marks, A. A., 701 B'way
(Crutch; Brass) .....AA
Plume & Atwood Mfg. Co.,
29 Murray (Brass) ..AAA
Reilly Repair & Supply Co.,
James, 229 West (Copper)
AA

N. Y.—Rome
Rome Brass & Copper Co.
(Brass) ....AAAA

N. Y.—Syracuse
McVey & Kratz (Plumbers')
E

N. Y.—Troy
Troy Stamping Works (Tin;
Sheet Metal) .....AAAA

OHIO—Cincinnati
Queen City Brass & Iron
Works (Brass) ....B

OHIO—Cleveland
Sanitary Co. (Brass for
Plumbing) ....B

PA.—Erie
Campbell Brass Works, J.
B. (Brass; End Reducing;
Trap Screw) ....A
Hays Mfg. Co. (Brass)...A

PA.—Pittsburg
National Tube Co. ...AAAA
Shelby Steel Tube Co. (Iron;
Steel) ....AAAA

PA.—Scranton
Scranton Button Co. (Bi-
cycle; Hand) ....A

FERTILIZERS

See also Guano; Phosphate

CONN.—Bridgeport
National Fertilizer Co. ..A

CONN.—Hartford
Sturtevant Corpn., F. C.
(Potato; Tobacco) ....D

CONN.—Middletown
Roger & Hubbard Co. ...A

DEL.—Georgetown
Calhoun & Jones Co. .....D

GA.—Atlanta
Furman Farm Improvement
Co. ....A

GA.—Augusta
Georgia Chemical Works
(Ammoniated) ....AA

GA.—Blackshear
Blackshear Mfg. Co. .....A

GA.—Newnan
Coweta Fertilizing Co.
AAAA

GA.—Savannah
Savannah Guano Co. (Am-
moniated) ....A

ILL.—Chicago
Armour & Co. (Ammo-
niated) ....AAAA

KY.—Louisville
Currie Fertilizer Co. .....A

LA.—New Orleans
Planters' Fertilizer Mfg. Co.
B
Standard Guano & Chemical

FERTILIZERS (Con.)
Mfg. Co. (Ammoniated)
AA

MD.—Baltimore
Patapsco Guano Co. ......A

MD.—Elkton
Scott Fertilizer Co. ......A

MASS.—Boston
Bradley Fertilizer Co. (Ammoniated) ....AAAA

MASS.—Gloucester
Dodd & Co., Andrew W.
(Fish Scrap) ....B

MICH.—Detroit
Michigan Carbon Wks. (Am-
moniated) ....AAA

N. J.—Newark
Lister's Agricultural Chem-
ical Wks. (Ammoniated)
AAAA

New York City
Baker & Co., H. J. (Am-
moniated; Potato; To-
bacco) ....AA
Coe & Co., E. Frank.....A
Read Fertilizer Co. (Ammo-
niated; Potato; Tobacco)
AAAA
Williams & Clark Fertilizer
Co. ....AAAA

N. C.—Wilmington
Acme Mfg. Co. ....A
Navassa Guano Co. ...AAA

OHIO—Cleveland
Cleveland Dryer Co. .AAAA

PA.—Allentown
Allentown Mfg. Co.......A

PA.—Jermyn
Lackawanna Fertilizer &
Chemical Co. ....A

PA.—Philadelphia
Moro Phillips Wks...AAAA
Tygert Co., J. E. (Ammo-
niated) ....D

PA.—York
York Chemical Co. ......A

S. C.—Charleston
Ashepoo Fertilizer Co. ....A
Drayton, C. H. ....A
Etivan Fertilizer Co. ...AA
Florida Phosphate Co. ...B
Macmurphy Co., W. C.....A
Oakland Mining Co. ......D

S. C.—Columbia
Southern Cotton Oil Co.
AAAA

TENN.—Nashville
Read Phosphate Co. ....AA

VA.—Norfolk
Columbia Guano Co. .....A
Royster Guano Co., F. S.
(Guano) ....AAA

VA.—Richmond
Virginia Carolina Chemical
Co. ....AAAA

FIBRE

See also Pulp

DEL.—Elsmere
Diamond State Fibre Co.
(Insulating) ....B

DEL.—Wilmington
American Vulcanized Fibre
Co. (Insulating) .AAAA
Delaware Hard Fibre Co.
(Insulating) ....A

ILL.—Chicago
Brown & Besley (Letter;
Bill) C
Nicol & Co. (Letter; Bill).D

MAINE—Augusta
Cushnoc Paper Co. (Chemi-
cal) ....A

MAINE—Bangor
Eastern Mfg. Co. (Chemi-
cal) ....AA
Orono Pulp & Paper Co..AA

MAINE—Kennebunk
Leatheroid Mfg. Co. (Insulating) ....A

MAINE—Lincoln
Katahdin Pulp & Paper Co.
AA

MINN.—Jackson
Wallace, J. I. (Upholstery
Tow) ....F

MINN.—Spring Valley
Spring Valley Flax Fibre
Co. (Upholstery Tow)...D

FIBRE (Con.)

MINN.—Winona
Union Fibre Co. (Upholstery
Tow) ....B
MO.—St. Louis
St. Louis Stamping Co.
AAAA
N. H.—Berlin
Burgess Sulphate Fibre Co.
AAAA
N. J.—Boonton
Loando Hard Rubber Co.
(Insulating) ....B
N. Y.—Ausable Forks
Rogers Co., J. & J. (Chemical) ....AA
N. Y.—Brown Station
Hudson River Wood Pulp
Mfg. Co. (Chemical)...D
N. Y.—Buffalo
Oliver Mfg. Co., W. W...C
N. Y.—Carthage
Carthage Sulphite Pulp Co.
(Chemical) ....A
N. Y.—Lockport
United Indurated Fibre Co.
of New Jersey (Indurated
Wire) ....A
New York City
Wilkinson Bros. & Co.
(Chemical) ....A
N. Y.—Syracuse
Stearns & Co., E. C....A
N. Y.—Ticonderoga Pulp &
Paper Co. (Chemical).AA
N. Y.—Watertown
Remington & Son Pulp &
Paper Co., H. (Chemical)
B
N. Y.—West Carrollton
Friend Paper Co. (Chemical)
AAA
PA.—Easton
Pollock Brush Co. ....D
PA.—Lock Haven ·
N. Y. & Pennsylvania Co.
(Chemical) ......AAAA
PA.—Philadelphia
Jessup & Moore Paper Co.
(Chemical) ......AAAA
R. I.—Bristol
National India Rubber Co.
(Insulating) ......AAAA
R. I.—Pawtucket
Thayers' Son, Ellis (Brush)
X
WIS.—Appleton
Atlas Paper Co. (Chemical)
AA
WIS.—Combined Lock
Combined Lock Paper Co.
(Chemical) X
WIS.—Kaukauna
Kaukauna Fibre Co. (Chemical) ....A
WIS.—Nekoosa
Nekoosa Paper Co. (Chemical) ....A

FIBRE WARE

DEL.—Wilmington
Delaware Hard Fibre Co...A
N. Y.—Lockport
United Indurated Fibre Co.
X
New York City
Cordley & Hayes (Indurated) ....AA

FIGS & DATES

CAL.—Fresno
Hammond, T. J. (Packer).C
CAL.—San Francisco
Rosenberg Bros. & Co., 211
California ....A
IOWA—Burlington
Lagomarcino & Co., A. ....B
IOWA—Cedar Rapids
Lagomarcino & Co., A.....B
LA.—New Orleans
Dunbar Sons, G. W. .....A
New York City
Arquimbau & Ramee, 84
Thomas ....B
Cameron & Greenly, 228
Washington ....D
Garlick & Co., 268 Washington ....D
Hahn & Sons, Jos., 212
Washington ....B

FIGURES & LETTERS

CONN.—Bridgeport
Schwerdtle Stamp Company
(Steel) ....F
CONN.—Meriden
Bradley & Hubbard Mfg. Co.
(Brass; Bronze) ..AAAA
CONN.—New Haven
Hoggson & Pettis Mfg. Co.
(Steel) ....A
CONN.—Winsted
Goodwin & Kintz Co.
(House) ....B
ILL.—Chicago
Besley & Co., Charles H.
(House) ....AA
Chicago .Spring Butt Co.
(House) ....B
ILL.—Freeport
Arcade Mfg. Co. (House)..A
Stover Mfg. Co. (Brass).AA
MASS.—Boston
Dennison Mfg. Co. (Paper
Gummed) ....AAAA
Woodman Mfg. & Supply
Co., R. (Steel) ....F
MO.—St. Louis
St. Louis Electrotype Fdy.
(Metallic Pattern) .....D
New York City
American Railway Supply
Co. (House) X
Ansonia Clock Co. (Bronze)
AAAA
Brooks & Co., E. J. (Metallic Pattern; Steel)...B
Caesar Bros. (Enameled)..D
Judd & Co., H. L. (Bronze)
AA
Ness, Jr., Geo. M. (Steel).H
New York Stencil Works
(Brass; Steel) ....D
Russell & Erwin Mfg. Co.
(House) ....AAAA
Sargent & Co. (House)
AAAA
Stafford Co., N. (Brass)..F
Tiebout, W. & J. (House).B
Wiebusch & Hilger (House)
A
Yale & Towne Mfg. Co.
(House) ....AAAA
OHIO—Canton
Berger Mfg. Co. (Cornice;
Sign) ....AA
OHIO—Cincinnati
Obermayer Co., S. (Metallic
Pattern) ....AA
Taylor & Co., A. V. (House;
White Enamel) X
OHIO—Cleveland
Cleveland Galvanizing Wks.
(House) C
Globe Machine & Stamping
Co. (Steel) C
Konigslow Stamping & Tool
Works (Steel) ....D
Taylor & Boggis Fdy. Co.
(House) ....AA
OHIO—Dayton
Howard, Wm. H. (Brass).E
PA.—Philadelphia
National Decalcomania Co.
(Paper Gummed) ....F
Paxson Co., J. W. (Metallic
Pattern) ....AA
Quint & Sons, S. H. (Metallic Pattern) ....B
PA.—Reading
National Brass & Iron Wks.
(Bronze) ....A
Reading Hdw. Co. (House)
AAAA

FIGURES: SHOW ETC

MICH.—Lansing
Lyons & Co., Hugh (Wax)
A
MO.—St. Louis
Belle, Hickey Mfg. Co.
(Wax) C
New York City
American Figure Co., 27
Grand (Show) ....F
Baumann Co., F., 19 Howard (Show) ....E

FIGURES (Con.)

Demuth & Co., Wm., 507 B'way (Show) ......AAA
Spieles, J., 424 W. B'way (Wax) ....D
Stevens & Co., C. C., 57 W. 24th (Wax) ......F
OHIO—Akron
Enterprise Mfg. Co. (Block) ....A
PA.—Philadelphia
Schoenhut Co., A. (Show) .A
Straus, Wm. (Show) ....F
WIS.—Milwaukee
French Wax Figure Co. (Wax) ....D

FILBERTS

See Nuts; Edible

FILERS

MICH.—Grand Rapids
Baldwin, Tuthill & Bolton (Band Saw) ....D
MISS.—Columbus
Columbus Machine & Fdy. Co. (Saw) C
N. Y.—Buffalo
Rogers & Co., S. C. (Band Saw, &c.) C
N. Y.—Seneca Falls
Seneca .Falls Mfg. Co. (Saw) ....B
R. I.—Providence
Nicholson File Co. (Saw; Gummers) ....AAAA
WIS.—Milwaukee
Filer & Stowell Co. (Saw; Gummers) ....AAA

FILES

See also Furniture

CONN.—Bridgeport
Bridgeport Hdw. & Mfg. Co. (Bill; Letter; Paper) B
ILL.—Chicago
Chicago Wheel & Mfg. Co. (Emery; Corundum; Planer; Knife) C
Rockwell-Wabash Co., 151 Wabash Av. (Card Index) A
Tengwall File & Ledger Co. (Bill; Letter, &c.) ...B
ILL.—Freeport
Arcade Mfg. Co. (Paper; Horse Tooth) ....A
Stover Mfg. Co. (Paper) .AA
IND.—Indianapolis
Atkins & Co., E. C. (Mechanics') ....AAAA
MASS.—Attleboro
Blake Co., Jas. E. (Manicure) ....A
MASS.—Fitchburg
Fitchburg File Wks. (Iron) D
Simonds Mfg. Co. (Planer Knife) ....AAA
MASS.—Worcester
Wire Goods Co. (Paper) ...A
MICH.—Grand Rapids
Macey-Wernicke Co. (Letter; Bill) ....AA
N. J.—Elizabeth
Amer. Swiss File & Tool Co. ....A

Finest Grade "American Swiss" Files mainly for Tool Makers' and Die Sinkers' use, replacing the best foreign makes heretofore imported.

N. J.—Freehold
Stokes Bros. Mfg. Co. (Iron; Rasps) ....A
N. J.—Newark
Heller .Bros. Co. (Iron; Rasps; Mechanics) ...AA
Parkes File Co. (Manicure)
N. Y.—Brooklyn
Murcott & Campbell, 296 Union Av. (Jewelers')...C

FILES (Con..)

New York City
Forquignon Mfg. Co., E. (Manicure) ....D
Funk & Wagnalls Co., 30 Lafayette Pl. (Mechanics') ....AAA
Mayer, Lane & Co., 128 White (Mechanics') ...X
Patterson, Gottfried & Hunter, 146 Centre (Jewelers') ....A
Peck, Stow & Wilcox Co. (Paper) ....AAAA
Sargent & Co., 151 Leonard (Paper) ......AAAA
Shipman's Sons, A. L., 14 Warren (Letter; Bill)..A
Silberstein, A. L. (Manicure) ....A
Surpless, Dunn & Co., 55 Warren (Mechanics')...C
N. Y.—Troy
Troy File Works (Horse Tooth; Mechanics) ....D
OHIO—Akron
Whitman & Barnes Mfg. Co. (Iron; Rasps) ....AAAA
OHIO—Cincinnati
Globe-Wernicke Co. (Bill; Letter; Card Index; Newspaper) ......AAAA
Tatum Co., Samuel C., 266 Water (Letter; Bill)....B
OHIO—Hamilton
Meyers Mfg. Co., Fred J. (Paper) ....B
OHIO—Painesville
Globe Mfg. Co. (Hand Saw) E
OHIO—Toledo
Ohio Binder Co., 168 La Grange (Letter, &c.)...D
PA.—Philadelphia
Barnett Co., G. & H. (Iron; Mechanics') ....A
Disston & Sons, Hy. (Iron; Mechanics') .....AAAA
McCaffrey File Co., 5th & Berks (Iron; Rasps, all kinds) ....AAAA
Mayer & Co. (Iron) ....B
Philadelphia Novelty Mfg. Co. (Upright Wire).....D
PA.—Wrightsville
Wrightsville Hardware Co. (Paper) ....B
R. I.—Providence
Bens, Wm. (Manicure) ...B
Nicholson File Co. (Iron: all kinds) ....AAAA
WIS.—Milwaukee
Westfahl & Co., F. (Mechanics') C

FILLERS

See also Paints & Machinery

CONN.—Derby
Clark Cast Steel Cement Co. (Iron) ....G
CONN.—Hartford
Winkley Co. (Oil Can) ...P
GA.—Columbus
Sauls Bros. (Can) ....D
ILL.—Chicago
Creamery Package Mfg. Co. (Egg Case) ......AAAA
Devoe & Raynolds Co. (Iron; Wood) ....AAAA
Marine Iron Works (Package) ....B
National Fire Proof Paint Co., 40 Dearborn (Iron; Steel) ....D
Wadsworth-Howland Co., Ind. Av. (Iron; Steel)...A
Warren Mfg. Co., J. D. (Nail Bin) ....B
IND.—Terre Haute
American Asbestos Co. (Wood) ....D
IOWA—Cedar Rapids
Cherry Co., J. G. (Egg Case) A
MAINE—Portland
Conant & Co., R. O. (Can) F
Stickney, Henry R. (Condensed Milk Can) ......D

FILLERS (Con.)
MD.—Baltimore
Sinclair-Scott Co. (Can)..E
MASS.—Boston
Edson Mfg. Co., 257 Atlantic Av. (Bottle) ....B
MICH.—Battle Creek
Johnson Foundry & Machine Works (Adjustable Package) ....D
MICH.—Detroit
Acme White Lead & Color Works (Iron; Steel).AAA
Eastman Capsule Filler Co. (Capsule) ....H
MO.—St. Louis
Leschen & Sons Rope Co., A. (Wire Rope) ......AAAA
N. J.—Bridgeton
Cox Bros. & Co. (Can)...D
N. J.—Haddonfield
Star Milk Cooler Co. (Milk Bottle) C
N. J.—Salem
Ayars Machine Co. (Tomato) ....B
N. Y.—Brooklyn
King Paint Mfg. Co. (Iron; Steel) ....B
Ross & Son, Charles, 16 Steuben (Can) ....D
N. Y.—Buffalo
McLennan Paint Co., Ltd., 175 Rano (Iron; Steel).AA
Shepard & Co., Sidney (Lamp; Oil Can) .AAAA
N. Y.—Cortland
Champion Milk Cooler Co. (Bottle) ....E
N. Y.—Newark
Grippin Mfg. Co. (Floor Crack) ....B
New York City
Central Stamping Co. (Oil Can; Lamp) ....AA
Chatillon & Sons, John (Bag) ....A
Knapp Mfg. Co., 24 Frankfort (Oil Can) ....D
Stoutenborough, X. (Lamp) ....D
Smith & Co., Edw., 45 B'way (Iron; Steel) ..A
OHIO—Cincinnati
Day & Co., J. H. (Can; Package) ....A
Obermayer Co., S. (Iron) ....AA
OHIO—Cleveland
Cleveland Steam Gauge Co. (Bag) ....B
Forest City Paint & Varnish Co. (Iron; Steel) ......B
PA.—Allegheny
Wisconsin Graphite Co. (Graphite) X
PA.—Muncy
Keystone Paint & Filler Co. (Iron; Steel) ....B
PA.—Philadelphia
Barrett, Lindeman Co., 1402 Frankford Av. (Iron; Steel) ....B
Binswanger & Co., B., 115 N. 4th (Iron; Steel)...B
Bowen's Sons, S., N. 4th (Iron; Steel) ....B
Cambria Steel Co., 15 Market (Frog) ......AAAA
Felton, Sibley & Co., 136 N. 4th (Iron; Steel) .AAA
French & Co., Samuel H., 4th & Callowhill (Iron; Steel) ....A
Grogan & Co., H. F., 2113 E. Sergent (Iron; Steel).D
Lucas & Co., Jno., 322 Race (Iron; Steel) ......AAA
Paxson Co., J. W. (Iron) ....AA
Phila. Scoop Co. (Bag)..X
Waterall & Co., Wm. (Iron; Steel) ....A
PA.—Pittsburg
Atlas Paint Co., 2638 Liberty Av. (Iron; Steel)..X
Emanuel & Ihrig, 501 2d Av. (Capsule) ....D
Gem Mfg. Co. (Oil) ....D
Suydam Co., M. B., 61st & Butler (Iron; Steel) ....A

FILLERS (Con.)
PA.—Reading
Wilhelm Co., A. (Iron; Steel) ....AA
PA.—Williamsport
United States Paint Co. (Iron; Steel) X
WIS.—Fort Atkinson
Cornish, Curtis & Green (Bottle) ....A
WIS.—Milwaukee
Smith Paint & Varnish Co. (Iron; Steel) ....D

FILLETS

New York City
Butler, A. G., 101 Beekman (Leather) ....D
N. Y.—Seneca Falls
Brunn, A. W. (Pattern)..F
Knight & Son, H. W. (Pattern) C
OHIO—Canton
Benskin Mfg. Co. (Pattern) D
Canton Fillet Co. (Pattern; Leather; Wood) C
OHIO—Cincinnati
Obermayer Co., S. (Leather) AA
PA.—Philadelphia
Paxson Co., J. W., 1021 N. Del. Av. (Pattern Metallic) ....AA

FILLING

See also Amalgams

CONN.—Hartford
Jewell Belting Co. (Pulley) AAA
CONN.—New London
Brainerd & Armstrong Co. (Silk) ....AAA
CONN.—Watertown
Hemingway & Sons Silk Co. (Silk) ....A
MASS.—Florence
Nonotuck Silk Co. (Silk) AAAA
MICH.—Belding
Belding Bros. & Co. (Silk) AAAA
N. J.—Trenton
Trenton Rubber Mfg. Co. (Pulley) ....A
N. Y.—Brooklyn
Doherty, Eugene (Dental).D
New York City
Bishop Gutta Percha Co. (Dental) ....B
PA.—Allentown
Garnet Belt Dressing Co. (Belt; Preserver) ......F
PA.—Philadelphia
Horstman & Co., Wm. H. (Silk) ....AAAA
Johnson & Lund .(Dental) AA
Justi & Sons, H. D. (Dental) ....AA
White Dental Mfg. Co. (Dental) ....AA
R. I.—Pawtucket
Slater Cotton Co. (Cotton) AA
WIS.—Milwaukee
Hendee Wire Brush Co., 127 Michigan (Belt) ....E

FILMS

N. J.—Orange
Wilson Mfg. Co., ...A
New York City
Edison Phonograph Agency (Animated Photograph).D
Johns-Manville Co., H. W. (Asbestos Filtering) AAAA
N. Y.—Rochester
Eastman Kodak Co. (Photograph) ....AAAA
PA.—Philadelphia
Carbutt Dry Plate & Film Co., Wayne Junct. (Photographic) X

FILTERS

CONN.—Ansonia
Farrell Fdy. & Machine Co.
  (Mechanical) .....AAAA
CONN.—Meriden
Manning, Bowman & Co.
  (Coffee) ....AA
CONN.—New Haven
Peck Bros. & Co. (Water)
  ....AA

ILL.—Chicago
Colles & Co., E. G. T., 42
  S. Clinton (Oil) ....B
Independent F i l t e r Co.
  (Beer) .... B
Metropolitan Filter Co.
  (Water) ....E
National Filter Co., 277
  Dearborn (Water) ....B
Perrin & Co., Wm. R. (Me-
  chanical) ....A
Warren Paint Co., 128 N.
  Jefferson (Oil) ....B
Wilson, Cortez & Co., F.,
  239 Lake (Oil) ....B
Wolf Co., Fred W., 139
  Rees (Bag; Mechanical;
  Ice Machine; Sugar).AAA
ILL.—Joliet
Bates Machine Co. (Oil).AA
ILL.—Peoria
Peoria Automatic Filter Co.
  (Automatic Oil) X
IND.—South Bend
Turner, M. A. (Oil)......E
KANS.—Ft. Scott
Fort Scott Fdy. & Machine
  Co. (Sugar) ....H
LA.—New Orleans
Gulf Bag Co., 746 Tchoup
  (Bag) ....AAAA
Haubtman & Loeb Co., 217
  Gravier (Bag; Mechan-
  ical) ....A
Payne & Joubert, 423 Ca-
  rondelet (Bag; Mechani-
  cal) ....A
MASS.—Boston
Boston Brass Co. (Faucet).A
Jones Mfg. Co., 243 Frank-
  lin (Water; Faucet).....E
Naiad Filter Co., Sudbury
  Bldg. (Water) ....D
New England Pottery Co.
  (Water) C
Walworth Mfg. Co. (Water)
  ....AAAA
S.—Chelsea
Boston Filter Co. (Water)
  ....D
MASS.—Florence
Norwood Engineering Co.
  (Water for mills; Pres-
  sure; Water) ....B
MASS.—Winchester
Eastern Felt Co. (Felt)....C
MICH.—Detroit
Hygeia Filter Co. (Water)
 C
MO.—St. Louis
Famous Filter Co., 316 N.
  Main (Oil) ....D
Flower & Co., Walter L.,
  721 Oliver (Oil) ......E
Handlan-Buck Mfg. Co. 213
  N. 3d (Oil) ....AA
Jackson Filter Mfg. Co.,
  Chemical Bldg. (Water;
  Gravity; Pressure) ....E
MO.—Seneca
Seneca Filter Co. (Tripoli)
  ....D
N. J.—Newark
Standard Machine Co., 61
  N. J. R. R. Av. (Water
  Portable) X
N. Y.—Albany
Albany Steam Trap Co.
  (Water; Feed Water).D
N. Y.—Brooklyn
Acton, John, 118 John
  (Grist; Mud Oil) .....D
Pioneer Iron Works, 151
  William (Mechanical).A
Sweeney Mfg. Co., W. H.
  (Coffee) ....A
Ward & Upright Engineer-
  ing Co., 41 York (Feed
  Water) ....D

FILTERS (Con.)
N. Y.—Buffalo
Heinz & Munschauer (Wa-
  ter) ....A
Jewett Mfg. Co., Jno. C.
  (Water) ....A
Shepard & Co., Sidney
  (Water) ....AAAA
Squier Mfg. Co., Geo. L.,
  420 Niagara (Water;
  Bag; Animal Bone; Coal)
  ....AAAA

N. Y.—Jamestown
Engineering & Power Co.
  (Oil) ....AA
New York City
American Felt Co., 110 E.
  13th (Bag) ....AAAA
Bartlett, Hayward & Co.,
  100 B'way (Bag) .....B
Buhring Water Purifying
  Co., 12 W. B'way (Water)
  ....F
Bushnell Co., Jno. S., 126
  Liberty (Oil) ....E
Cordley & Hayes (Water)..A
Cornell Co., J. B. & J. M.,
  26th & 11th Av. (Bag;
  Mechanical) ....AA
Deeley & Co., Robert, 507
  W. 32d (Bag; Mechanical;
  Sugar) ....AA
German-American Filter Co.
  (Beer) X
Hall Mfg. Co., 40 Cortlandt
  (Oil Waste) ....G
Haydenville Co. (Faucet).A
Koven & Bro., L. O., 50
  Cliff (Feed Water)....A
Krajewski-Pesant Co., 32
  B'way (Mechanical; Su-
  gar) ....AA
Linke & Co., T., 1559 B'way
  (Water; Portable Stone
  Tub) ....F
Matthews, John (Water)
  ....AA
Morris Co., Elmer P., 15
  Cortlandt (Oil) ....D
Mundt & Sons, Charles, 447
  Pearl (Water) ....B
N. Y. Continental Jewell
  Filtration Co., 15 Broad
  (Feed Water; Gravity;
  Pressure; Mechanical;
  Sand) ....B
Rapid Safety Filter Co.,
  359 B'way (Water) X
Robertson & Sons, Jas. L.,
  204 Fulton (Oil Waste).D
Seed Filter & Mfg. Co. (Fau-
  cet; Water) ....F
Shriver & Co., T., 333 E.
  56th (Mechanical) .....A
N. Y.—Troy
Ross Valve Co. (Oil; Feed
  Water; Water) C
OHIO—Akron
Akron Belting Co. (Oil)..A
Burt Mfg. Co. (Oil)......C
OHIO—Canton
Bonnot Co. (Bag) ......A
OHIO—Cincinnati
Blymyer Iron Works Co.
  (Bag) ....B
Lynn Filter Mfg. Co., 3250
  Spring Grove Av. (Grav-
  ity; Pressure; Water).D
OHIO—Cleveland
Cleveland Stamping & Tool
  Co. (Water) ....A
Cleveland Steam Gauge Co.
  (Barrel) C
Darling Filter Co., 299
  Prospect (Water) X
Dyer & Co., E. H., New
  England Bldg. (Mechani-
  cal) ....AAA
Loew Filter Co. (Beer;
  Water; Wine) ....B
OHIO—Dayton
Nusbaum, F. A. (Oil) ....H
PA.—Chester
Wetherill & Co., Robert
  (Water; Portable).AAAA
PA.—Erie
Jarecki Mfg. Co. (Automat-
  ic; Pressure; Oil).AAAA
Sims Co. (Oil) ....D
Watson, N. A. (Water)..A

FILTERS (Con.)

PA.—New Brighton
Pittsburg Clay Mfg. Co.
(Water) ....AAAA

PA.—Philadelphia
Buchanan, W. P., 1226
Arch (Photographers')..C
Coles Mfg. Co. (Water)...D
Gwilliam, Jos. R., 115 N.
6th (Oil) X
Haines Co., W. S., 136 S.
14th (Oil) ....**X**
Hibbs, E. A., 209 Quarry
(Oil) ....B
Lonergan & Co., J. E. (Oil)
AA
Loomis-Manning Filter Co.,
828 New Land Title Bldg.
(Feed; Water; Gravity;
Pressure; Waterworks).X
Morris, Henry G., Phila.
Bourse (Bag; Mechanical)
B
Moore & White Co. (Oil)
AA
Penn Engineering Co., 1421
Filbert (Water) ......E
Roberts Mfg. Co., 3011
Chestnut (Water) C
Wood & Co., R. D., 400
Chestnut (Bag) ...AAAA

PA.—Pittsburg
Bonar & Co., Jas., Carnegie
Bldg. (Oil) ....B
Liberty Mfg. Co. (Oil)...D
Pittsburg Filter Mfg. Co.,
Farmers' Bank Bldg.
(Gravity; Water; Pres-
sure) X
Purity Oil Filter Mfg. Co.
(Oil) C
Scaife & Son Co., W. B. 221
7th Av. (Charcoal; Feed
Water; Gravity; Pressure;
Mechanical; Oil; Sand;
Tripoli) ....AAA

PA.—Scranton
Union Steam Specialty Co.
(Oil) ....A

PA.—South Bethlehem
Bethlehem Fdy. & Machine
Co. (Mechanical) C

PA.—Waynesboro
Frick Co. (Ice Machine)
AAAA

FINGERS

N. Y.—Cortland
Cortland Specialty Co.
(Lamp) ....D

PA.—Middletown
Brinser & Sons, E. C.
(Grain Cradle) ....D

W. VA.—Moundsville
Schwab Co., J. A. (Spring
Repair) C

FINIALS

CONN.—Bridgeport
Drouve Co., G. (Metal)...B

ILL.—Chicago
Barbee Wire & Iron Works
(Hook) ....B

MASS.—Boston
Van Noorden & Co., E.
(Hook) C

MASS.—Worcester
New England Steel Roofing
Co. (Metal) ....F

MO.—St. Louis
Harry Steel Works, O. K.
(Hook) ....B

N. J.—Jersey City
National Sheet Metal Roofing Co. (Metal) C

New York City
Fiske Iron Works, J. W.
(Hook; Metal) ....B
Lamb, J. & R. (Hook)....D

OHIO—Canton
Berger .Mfg. Co. (Hook;
Metal) ....AA
Canton Steel Roofing Co.
(Metal) ....A

OHIO—Cleveland
Van Dorn Iron Works Co.
(Hook) ....AA

OHIO—Hamilton
Meyers Mfg. Co., Fred J.
(Hook) ....B

OHIO—Kenton

FINIALS (Con.)
Champion Iron Co. (Hook;
Metal) ....AA

OHIO—Salem
Mullins, W. H. (Hook;
Metal) ....A

OHIO—Toledo
Donovan Wire & Iron Co.
(Metal) C

PA.—Philadelphia
Merchant & Co. (Metal).AA

PA.—Pittsburg
Kratzer & Co., W. N. (Metal) ....D

FINISH

**See also Woodwork; Polish;
Paints**

CAL.—Los Angeles
Bowers & Sons, W. R.
(Floor) C

CONN.—Bridgeport
Crockett Co., David B. (Oil;
Wood) ....B

CONN.—Essex
Essex Paint Works (Oil).A

CONN.—New Milford
Bridgeport Wood Finishing
Co. (Floor; Wood).....AA

ILL.—Chicago
Adams & Elting Co. (Wood)
A
Chicago .Varnish Co., 41
Dearborn Av. (Floor;
Hard Oil) ....AA
Chicago Wood Finishing
Co., 259 Elston Av. (Floor;
Hard Oil) ....A
Devoe, F. W. & C. T. Rey-
nolds Co., 176 Randolph
(Hard Oil; Wax; Wood)
AAAA
U. S. Gypsum Co., 184 La
Salle (Wall) ....AAAA
Vilas Bros., 227 5th Av.
(Floor Varnish) ....B
Wadsworth - Howland Co.
(Floor) ....A

IND.—Indianapolis
Interior Hardware Co.
(Wax) ....A
Lilly Varnish Co. (Parque-
rie Floor Preservative).A

IOWA—Ft. Dodge
Cardiff Gypsum Plaster Co.
(Wall) ....B

MD.—Baltimore
Macneal & Co., Jas. B., 34
S. Calumet (Hard Oil)..B

MASS.—Boston
Butcher Polish Co., 356 At-
lantic Av. (Floor; Hard
Oil) ....F
Gilman, Chas. H., 103 Mer-
rimac (Floor) ....G
Morse Blacking Co. (Black-
ing; Leather) ....F

MICH.—Detroit
Acme White Lead & Color
Works (Floor; Hard Oil)
AAA
Berry Bros., Ltd. (Hard Oil)
AAAA

MICH.—Grand Rapids
Anti-Kalsomine Co., (Wall;
Plaster) ....AA
Diamond Wall Finish Co.
(Wall) ....B

MO.—Kansas City
Continental Varnish & Color
Co., 1315 W. 8th (Hard
Oil) X

N. J.—Jersey City
Gillespie & Sons, Chas. H.
(Hard Oil) ....B
Woolsey Paint & Color Co.,
C. A. (Oil; Wood) .....A

N. J.—Newark
Anglo-American Varnish Co.,
55 Johnson (Hard Oil)..B
Brooks & Co., Clarence, 249
Chestnut (Hard Oil)....A
Flood & Conklin Co., 132
Chestnut (Hard Oil).AAA
Mitchell-Mallon Co., 319 N.
J. R. R. Av. (Hard Oil)
D
Murphy Varnish Co. (Hard
Oil; Wood) ....AAAA

FINISH (Con.)

Palmer-Price Co., 270 Chestnut (Hard Oil) ....B

N. Y.—Brooklyn

Moore & Co., Benjamin, 256 Water (Wall) ....AA

Moller & Schumann Co., Marcy & Flushing Avs. (Hard Oil) ....A

N. Y.—Buffalo

McLennon Paint Co., Ltd., 175 Rano (Hard Oil) ..AA

N. Y.—New Brighton

Muralo Co. (Wall) ....A

New York City

Calman & Co., Emil (Oil) ....AA

Fox & Co., M. Ewing, 136 Rider Av. (Wall) ....D

Gillespie & Sons, L. C. (Oil; Wood) ....AA

Longman & Martinez (Oil; Wax) ....AAA

Mayer & Lowenstein (Oil; Wax) ....AAA

Pierce Co., F. O. (Oil)....A

Smith & Co., Edward, 45 B'way (Hard Oil) ....A

Somerville Sons', Wm., 66 Pine (Wax) ....A

Standard Varnish Works, 29 B'way (Gutta Percha) .AA

Water Paint Co. of America, 100 William (Wall) ....B

Whitaker, W. H., 215 Front (Wall) ....E

N. Y.—Syracuse

Paragon Wall Plaster Co. (Wall) ....A

N. Y.—Troy

Troy Cold Water Kalsomine Co., 22 Pine (Wall) ....E

Troy Oil Works (Floor) ..H

OHIO—Cleveland

Cleveland Varnish Co., 14 Rockland Av. (Floor; Oil; Wax; Wood) ....AA

Glidden Varnish Co., Williamson Bldg. (Floor; Hard Oil) ....AA

OHIO—Gibsonburg

Standard Lime Co. (Wall).X

PA.—Chester

Keystone Plaster Co. (Wall) ....A

PA.—Erie

Reed Mfg. Co. (Collar; Cuff) ....A

PA.—Philadelphia

Atlantic Drier & Varnish Co., Drexel Bldg. (Floor) ....B

Felton, Sibley & Co., 136 N. 4th (Hard Oil) ....AAA

French & Co., Samuel H., 4th & Callowhill (Hard Oil) ....AAAA

Harrison Bros. & Co., 35th (Hard Oil) ....AAAA

Lucas & Co., Jno., 322 Race (Floor) ....AAA

Nice, Eugene E., 272 S. 2d (Floor) ....A

Shoemaker & Co., Robert, 4th & Race (Wall) ..AA

PA.—Reading

Wilhelm Co., A. (Hard Oil) ....AA

VT.—Chester Depot

American Soapstone Finish Co. (Wall) ....F

FIR

See Lumber

FIRE ARMS

CONN.—Cromwell

Stevens Co., J. & E. (Toy; Paper Caps; Pistols) ....AAAA

CONN.—Derby

United States Rapid Fire Gun & Powder Co. ...AA

CONN.—Hartford

Colts' Arms Co. (Automatic; Revolving; Breech Loading; Military Repeating; Shooting Match Rifles;

FIRE ARMS (Con.)

Derringer Pistols; Revolvers) ....AAAA

Gatling Gun Co. (Gatling Guns) X

CONN.—Meriden

Parker Bros. (Shot; Breach Loading; Hammerless Guns) ....AAA

CONN.—New Britain

Landers, Frary & Clark (Toy; Paper Cap Pistols) ....AAA

CONN.—New Haven

Marlin Fire Arms Co. (Pistols; Repeating Rifles; Shot Guns; Revolvers) AA

Snow, L. T. (Cannon)....D

Winchester Repeating Arms Co. (Shot Guns; Rifles; Revolvers; Breach Loading; Hammerless; Repeating; Military; Sporting Rifles) ....AAAA

CONN.—Norwich

Crescent Fire Arms Co. (Rifles; Guns, &c.) C

Davenport Fire Arms Co. (Rifles; Guns, &c.) ....A

Hopkins & Allen Arms Co. (Rifles; Guns; Revolvers; Pistols) ....AA

CONN.—Rockfall

Smith, Otis A. (Revolvers; Pistols) ....B

MASS.—Chicopee Falls

Stevens Arms & Tool Co., J. (Rifles) ....AAA

MASS.—Assonet

Davis & Sons, N. R. (Hammerless Shot Guns) ....B

MASS.—Chicopee

Ames Sword Co. (Revolvers; Pistols) ....B

MASS.—Chicopee Falls

Stevens Arms & Tool Co. (Rifles; Revolvers; Pistols) ....AAA

MASS.—Fitchburg

Johnson Arms & Cycle Wks., Iver (Shot Guns; Pistols; Revolvers) ....AA

MASS.—Hatfield

Shattuck, C. S. (Shot Guns) ....D

MASS.—Springfield

Bradley Co., Milton (Toy Guns; Pistols) ....A

Smith & Wesson (Hammerless Revolvers) ....AAAA

MASS.—Worcester

Harrington & Richardson Arms Co. (Guns; Pistols; Revolvers) ....B

MICH.—Northville

Dubuar Mfg. Co., J. A. (Air Rifles) ....F

MICH.—Plymouth

Daisy Mfg. Co. (Air Rifles) ....B

Hamilton Rifle Co. (Air Rifles) C

Markham Air Rifle Co. (Air Rifles) ....B

N. H.—Keene

Wilkins Toy Co. (Top; Paper Cap Pistols)..AAA

N. Y.—Batavia

Baker Gun & Forging Co. (Rifles; Guns, &c.)....A

N. Y.—Fulton

Hunter Arms Co. (Shot Guns) ....AA

N. Y.—Herkimer

Quackenbush, H. M. (Pocket; Safety; Bicycle)....A

N. Y.—Ilion

Atlas Gun Co. (Air Rifles) ....D

Remington Arms Co. (Derringer Pistols; Shot; Breach Loading Guns; Repeating; Military; Shooting Match; Spanish; Sporting Rifles) ....AAA

N. Y.—Ithaca

Ithaca Gun Co. (Shot; Breach Loading Guns)..B

N. Y.—Syracuse

Syracuse Arms Co. (Shot; Hammerless) ....B

402

FIRE ARMS (Con.)

N. Y.—Utica
Savage Arms Co. (Rifles).A
OHIO—Dayton
Requarth Co., F. A. (Guns
for Drill Purposes) ....B
OHIO—Toledo
Union Fire Arms Co. (Shot
Guns) ....B
PA.—Hazelton
Koenig, M. F. (Toy Guns).X
PA.—Philadelphia
Cramp & Sons, Wm.
(Driggs-Schroeder Guns)
AAAA
Schoenhut & Co., A. (Drill;
Toy) ....A
PA.—South Bethlehem
Bethlehem Iron Co. (Can-
non) ....AAAA
R.I.—Pawtucket
Bliss Mfg. Co. (Toy Guns;
Pistols) ....AAAA

FIRE CRACKERS

See Fireworks

FIREPLACES

KY.—Louisville
Peerless Mfg. Co. ......AA
MASS.—Cambridge
Hall & Co., Chas. E.
(Soapstone) ....A
N. Y.—Brooklyn
Hecla Iron Works ......AA
New York City
Bradley & Hubbard Mfg.
Co., 21 Barclay (Brass)
AAAA
Manhattan Brass Co., 332
E. 28th (Brass) ....A
Janesch, F. G. (Est.), 750
E. 34th (Brass) C
Judd Co., H. L., 87 Cham-
bers (Brass) ....AA
Union Equipment & Brass
Co., 514 W. 36th (Brass)
B
PA.—Philadelphia
Harrison's Sons, W. H...E

FIREPROOFING

**See also Terra Cotta; Ex-
panded Metal Asbestos;
etc.**

CAL.—San Francisco
Gladding, McBean & Co.
(Porous Terra Cotta).AA
Western Expanded Metal
Co. (Expanded Metal)..A
ILL.—Chicago
Illinois Terra Cotta Lumber
Co., The Rookery, (Porous
Terra Cotta) ....AA
Imperial Expanded Metal
Co., Monadnock Blk. (Ex-
panded Metal) ....D
Mackolite Fire Proofing Co.,
Schiller Bldg. (Plastic).B
Northwestern Expanded
Metal Co., Old Colony
Bldg. (Expanded Metal)
B
Pioneer Fire Proofing Co.,
204 Dearborn (Porous
Terra Cotta) ....AA
ILL.—Rock Island
Lewis Roofing Co. (Plastic)
B
IND.—Terre Haute
Vigo Clay Co. (Clay).....B
MASS.—Boston
Amer. Fire Proofing Co.,
166 Devonshire (Sala-
mander) ....D
Eastern Expanded Metal
Co., 101 Tremont (Ex-
panded Metal) ....A
MO.—St. Louis
Parker & Russell Mining &
Mfg. Co. (Porous Terra
Cotta) ....AAA
St. Louis Expanded Metal
Fireproofing Co. (Expanded
Metal) ....B
N. J.—Boonton

FIREPROOFING (Con.)
Lincoln Iron Wks. (Hang-
ers'; Iron) ....B
N. Y.—Buffalo
Buffalo Expanded Metal
Co. (Expanded Metal)..B
New York City
Am. Wood Fire Proofing Co.
156 Fifth Av. (Wood)..B
Electric Fire Proofing Co.,
19th & E. R. (Wood)..B
Fireproofine Mfg. Co., 66
Beaver (Wood) X
Maurer & Son, Henry, 420
E. 23d (Porous Terra Cot-
ta) ....AA
Metropolitan Fire Proofing
Co., 13 Burling Slip (Plas-
tic) ....D
OHIO—Delaware
Delaware Fire Proofing Co.
(Porous Terra Cotta)..B
OHIO—Haydenville
Haydenville Co. (Porous
Terra Cotta) ....A
PA.—Philadelphia
Merritt & Co., 1024 Ridge
Av. (Expanded Metal)..D
PA.—Pittsburg
Natl. Fire Proofing Co.
(Porous Terra Cotta)
AAAA

FIREWORKS

CAL.—San Francisco
Calif. Fireworks Co. of San
Fran., 219 Front C
Mack, Simon, 119 Bush
(Japanese) ....A
CONN.—Hartford
Aetna Pyrotechnic Co.....X
MINN.—Minneapolis
Paris Murton Co. ....B
New York City
Champion & Standinger, 124
Pearl (Firecrackers)....A
Cons. Fireworks Co. of
America, 9 Park Pl...AA
Detwille & Street Fireworks
Mfg. Co., 172 Fulton...A
Koster & Co., C. H., Park
Pl. C
Lloyd, T., 22 Park Pl...C
Nordlinger, J. D., 143 W.
Bdway. ....AA
Pain Mfg. Co., 12 Park Pl.
D
N. Y.—Rochester
Rochester Fireworks Co..B
OHIO—Cincinnati
Due Fireworks Co., A. L..C
PA.—Philadelphia
Miller & Son Co., Geo., 255
S. 3d ....AA
VA.—Petersburg
Romaine Fireworks Co.,
Chas. N. ....D

FISH (PRESERVED)

See also Canned Goods

CAL.—Benicia
Carquinez Packing Co. (Sal-
mon) ....A
CAL.—Black Diamond
Sacramento River Packing
Assn. (Salmon)........C
CAL.—Los Angeles
Calif. Fish Co. ....A
CAL.—Requa
Klawath Packing & Trading
Co. (Salmon) C
CAL.—San Diego
San Diego Fish Co.
(Smoked) ....B
CAL.—San Francisco
Alaska Codfish Co. 17 Davis
(Salt; Smoked; Dried)..A
Alaska Packers' Assn. (Sal-
mon) ....AAAA
Alaska Salmon Co. (Salmon)
B
Alaska Salmon Assn. (Sal-
mon ....A
Bristol Packing Co. (Sal-
mon) ....A

FISH (*Con.*)

Carquinez Packing Co. (Salmon) ....A
Getz Bros. & Co., 111 Calif. (Salt; Smoked; Salmon) ....AAAA
Gibbs-Wilson Packing Co. (Salmon) ....B
Griffith-Durney Co. (Salmon) ....A
Hume & Co., R. D. (Salt; Smoked; Canned) ......A
Hume & Co., Geo. (Salmon) ....AAAA
Klawarth Pack. & Trading Co. (Salmon) ....A
Lynde & Hough Co., 40 Calif. (Salt; Smoked; Salmon) ....A
McCollam Fish & Trading Co., 24 Calif. (Salt; Smoked) ....A
Naknek Packing Co. (Salmon) ....A
No. Alaska Packing Co..AA
No. Pac. Trading & Packing Co. (Salmon) C
Paladini, A., 520 Merchant (Salt; Smoked) ....B
Red Salmon Canning Co. (Salmon) ....A
Sac. River Packers' Assn. (Salmon) ....A
Schlegel & Co., P., 326 Front (Salt; Smoked; Caviar) ....A
Union Fish Co., 24 Calif. (Salt; Smoked) C
Willand Bros., 12 Clay (Dr.; Salt; Canned)....A
CAL.—Vallejo
Gibbs-Chambers Packing Co. (Salmon) ....B
COLO.—Denver
Haskell & Co., 1625 Market ....B
CONN.—New Haven
Bates Co., L. (Salt; Smoked; Cod) ....A
Dillon & Douglas (Salt; Smoked) ....A
DEL.—Leipsic
Levin Sons, S. H. (Salt), AA
D. C.—Washington
Javins & Sons, C. H., 930 C., N. W. (Fresh) C
FLA.—Punda Garda
Fla. Fish & Produce Co..B
FLA.—St. Petersburg
Fla. Fish & Ice Co.......B
ILL.—Chicago
Beardsley's Sons, J. W., 34 Wabash Av. (Dried)....C
Boak & Co., R. B., 33 So. Water (Bkrs. Salt; Smoked) C
Booth & Co., A., 42 River (Salt; Smoked) ...AAAA
Schwennesen, H. P., 180 S. Water (Smoked).....B
Thorp & Co., O. A., 215 La Salle Av. (Imptrs.)....B
KY.—Louisville
Herndon-Carter Co., 313 Murrel Ct. (Salt; Smoked) C
MAINE—Bucksport
Nicholson, T. M. (Salt; Smoked) ....B
MAINE—Booth Bay Harbor
Maddocks Packing Co. (Sardines) C
Pickard Fish Co., L. (Sardines) ....D
MAINE—Eastport
Sea Coast Packing Co. (Sardines) ....AAAA
MAINE—Lubec
Lubec Sardine Co. (Sardines) ....A
Peacock, R. J. (Sardines).D
Sea Coast Packing Co. (Sardines) ....AAAA
MAINE—Machiasport
Dodge & Bangs (Sardines) ....D
Machiasport Packing Co. (Sardines) C
MAINE—No. Lubec
Globe Packing Co. (Sardines) ....D

FISH (*Con.*)

MAINE—Portland
Portland Packing Co. (Canned) ....AA
Twitchell Champlin Co. (Canned) ....AA
Webb Co., H. F. (Canned) ....B
MAINE—Rockland
Thorndike & Hix (Lobsters; Sardines) C
MAINE—West Pembroke
Sunset Packing Co. (Sardines) ....D
MAINE—West Tremont
Russell & Co., E. T. (Sardines) ....A
MD.—Baltimore
Bennett & Co., W. M., 221 South C
Booth & Co., A., 727 So. Wolfe ....AAAA
Coulehan & Hogan, 118 Coml. (Salt; Smoked)..C
Geyer & Co., E. C., P. O. Box 464 (Bkrs.)......C
Huntemuller & Son, H. W., 124 South (Salt; Smoked) C
Lawder & Sons, S. M., 2215 Boston C
MD.—Harve de Grace
Coulehan & Hogan C
Seneca, S. J. ....A
MASS.—Boston
Booth & Co., 12 T Wharf ....AAAA
Caswell, Livermore & Co., 428 Atl. Av. (Salt; Smoked) ....B
Consolidated Weir Co., 3 T Wharf ....B
De Long, Seaman & Co., 156 Milk ....AAA
Dorman Huxford & Co....D
Lyon, Dupuy & Co., Carleton Wharf (Salt; Smoked: Corn; Salt; Exp.) ....AA
Marston & Co., J. W., 42 Lewis Wharf (Lobsters) ....AA
Phillips & Co., B. F., 20 T Wharf C
Pickert Fish Co., New St. (Mack.; Salt; Smoked).B
Potter & Wrightington, 60 Coml. (Salt; Smoked).A
Russell & Co., E. T., 284 State (Salt; Smoked)...A
Scandinavian Impg. Co., 498 Coml. C
Stratton, Little & Co., 85 Water ....B
MASS.—Gloucester
Allen & Co., B. F. (Salt; Smoked) C
American Halibut Co......B
Ayers & Andrews Co. (Salt; Smoked; Mac.; Cod.)...A
Cunningham & Thompson (Salt; Smoked) ......AA
Davis Bros. (Salt; Smoked; Pickled) ....A
Gloucester Fresh Fish Co. ....A
Jordan, W. H. (Salt; Smoked) ....A
Lane & Bro., Saml.......B
McDonald, Jerome C
N. E. Fish Co. (Salt; Smoked) ....B
Parkhurst & Co., H.......C
Parsons Co., Wm. ....A
Perkins & Son, Geo. (Salt; Smoked) ....A
Pew & Son, J. (Salt; Smoked) ....AAA
Slade, Gorton & Co. (Salt; Smoked) ....B
Smith & Co., D. B........A
Smith & Co., Sylvanus (Salt; Smoked) ....A
Stanwood, Frank (Salt; Smoked; Pickled)......A
Stanwood & Co. (Salt; Smoked; Cod; Smoked Mack.) ....A
Steele & Co., Geo. (Salt; Smoked) C

404

Tarr & Co., G. J. (Salt;
Smoked) ....A
Tarr & Bro., J. G. (Salt;
Smoked) ....A
Treat, Leonard A.........C
Wonson & Son, W. H.
(Salt; Smoked) ....B
MASS.—Provincetown
Pickert Fish Co., L. (Salt;
Canned) ....A
MICH.—Au Sable
Au Sable Fish Co. ....B
MICH.—Bay Port
Ballard Fish Co., W.......C
Bay Port Fish Co........C
Carpenter, Cook & Co.
AAAA
MINN.—Minneapoils .
Preece & Dunham (Bkrs.)
B
MO.—Kansas City
Booth Packing Co., A.
AAAA
MO.—St. Louis
Haase & Sons Fish Co.
(Salt; Smoked)........A
N. J.—Penns Grove
Leonard. D. P. (Cavair) ..G
N. Y.—Albany
Smith Sons, W. E. (Salt;
Smoked) ....A
Wooster, S. E. (Salt;
Smoked) ....B
N. Y.—Brooklyn
Gutkes, A. H., 90 Van
Dyke (Salt; Smoked) ..B
Hoag, Werner & Co., 2
Taylor C
Lundy Bros., Sheepshead
Bay ....B
New York City
Ams, Max, 372 Greenwich
(Smoked; Salt; Cavair)
AA
Beardsley's Sons, F. W., 476
Greenwich (Salt; Smoked)
A
Bowers Co., B. O., 6
Harrison (Sardines) ....B
Ferris & Co.. E., 185 Wash.
(Salt; Smoked) ....B
Frye & Co., Jed., 47 Water
(Salt; Smoked; Sardines)
A
Haaker Co., W., 99 N.
Moore (Salt; Smoked) ..B
Hansen & Dickmann, 368
Washn. (Salt; Smoked;
Caviar) ....AA
Harvey & Outerbridge, 11
Bdway. (Com. Salt) ..AA
Hiscox, John (Est.), 271
Columbus Av. (Salt) ...B
Job & Co., W. & S., 68
Broad (Exptrs.Salt).....A
Kress & Co., A., 64 Dey
(Salt; Caviar).........B
La Manna, Azema & Farnan,
397 Washn. (Smoked;
Sardines) ....B
Leber & Meyer, 78 Wall
(Com. Salt) ....A
Lewis & Co., S. W., 24
South (Salt) C
Matlage & Sons, C. F., 335
Greenwich (Salt) ...AAA
Moos & Co., 171 Duane
(Caviar; Sardines) ....A
Rosenstein Bros. (Inc.), 96
N. Moore (Salt; Smoked;
Sardines) ....AA
Schaefer, J. W., 6 Harrison
(Imp. Salt; Sardines)..B
Schmidt & Co., S., 152 W.
19th (Salt; Smoked; Ca-
viar) ....A
Smith, T., 309 Wash. Mkt.
(Salt; Smoked) C
Stokes, Thos., 323 Green-
wich (Salt; Smoked)...A
Storer & Co., S. L., 16
Fulton Mkt. ....AA
Strohmeyer & Arpe Co., 33
Water (Salt; Smoked;
Sardines) ....A
Woodruff & Co., F., 49
Water (Exp. Salt).....C
Woodward & Son. Thos..
44 Front (Com. **Salt:**

Smoked) ....A
N. Y.—Rochester
Hasselbeck. M. (Herring).B
N. C.—Morehead City
Watson, C. T............C
OHIO—Cincinnati
Morgenthau & Son, H., 2d &
Walnut (Salt) ....B
OHIO—Lorain
Lorain Fish Co. C
OHIO—Sandusky
Lay Bros. ....B
Sandusky Fish Co. (Fresh)
A
OHIO—Vermillion
Kishman's Sons C
OREGON—Astoria
Alaska Fishermens' Packg.
Co. (Salmon) ......AAAA
Booth Packing Co., A. (Sal-
mon ....AAAA
Colo. River Packers' Assn.
(Salmon) ....AA
Elmore Packing Co. (Sal-
mon) ....B
Elmore & Co., S. (Salmon)
AA
Kinney, M. J. (Salmon)..A
McGowan & Sons, P. J. P.
(Salmon) ....A
Mehalem Packing Co. (Sal-
mon) ....B
Sanborn & Cutting Co. (Sal-
mon) ....A
Schmidt & Co., S. (Smoked)
A
Tallant-Grant Packing Co.
(Salmon) ....A
OREGON—Empire
Southern Oregon Co. (Sal-
mon) ....AA
OREGON—Florence
Meyer & Kyle (Salmon)..A
OREGON—Garibaldi
Elmore Packing Co. (Sal-
mon) ....B
OREGON—Nehalem
Nehalem Packing Co. (Sal-
mon) ....A
OREGON—Portland
Alaska Portland Packers'
Assn. (Salmon) ......A
Barnes, F. C. (Salmon)..B
Cook Pack. Co., J. W. & V.
(Salmon) ....AA
OREGON—The Dalles
Seufert Bros. & Co. (Sal-
mon) ....A
OREGON—Warrendale
McGowan & Sons, P. J.
(Salmon) ....A
Warren, F. M. (Salmon)..A
OREGON—Wedderburn
Hume, R. D. (Salmon).AA
OREGON—Yaquina
Barnes, F. C. (Salmon)..B
PA.—Erie
Keystone Fish Co. (Ltd.)
(Fresh; Salt; Frozen)..B
PA.—Philadelphia
Booth & Co., A., 13 Dock
AAAA
Ernst, B., 2920 N. 6th (Salt;
Smoked) ....B
Howlett, M., 12 Dock
(Fresh) ....A
Levins Sons, S. H., 238 N.
Del. Av. (Salt) ....AA
McCormick & Co., W. H.,
19 Del. Av. Fish Mkt.
(Fresh) ....A
Shriver & Co., J. N.,
32 N. Del. Av. (Salt;
Smoked) ....A
Warner & Co., C. E., 8 Dock
St. Fish Mkt. (Fresh)..A
Yost & Co., J. C., 223 N.
Water (Salt; Smoked)..B
R. I.—Providence
Midwood's Sons, H. ......B
VT.—Montpelier
Corry, F. M. ....B
VA.—Alexandria
King & Son, Chas. (Her-
rings) ....A
WASH.—Aberdeen
Gray's Harbor Packing Co.
(Salmon) ....B

FISH (Con.)

WASH.—Anacortes
Fidelgo Island Canning Co.
.............................A
Rosario Straits Pack. Co.
(Canned) C
WASH.—Blaine
Alaska Packers' Assn.
.........................AAAA
Cook Pack. Co., J. W. & W.
.............................B
WASH.—Brookfield
Megler & Co., J. G.
(Canned) ....B
Pacific Packg. & Naviga-
tion Co. ....AAAA
Pillar Rock Packing Co.
(Canned) ....B
WASH.—Cathlamet
Warren, F. M..........A
WASH.—Chinock
McGowan & Sons, P. J.
(Canned) ....A
WASH.—Cosmopolis
McGowan Bros. & Megler.B
WASH.—Fairhaven
Pacific Amer. Fisheries Co.
(Canned) ....AA
WASH.—Ilwaco
Aberdeen Packing Co.
(Canned) ....A
WASH.—McGowan
McGowan & Sons, P. J...A
WASH.—Port Angeles
Manhattan Packing Co....C
WASH.—Port Townsend
Port Townsend Packing Co.
.............................B
WASH.—Seattle
Chlopeck Fish Co. (Salmon)
.............................C
Kelley-Clarke Co. (Salmon
Dlrs.) ....A
Pacific Cold Storage Co.
.........................AAAA
Pacific Packg. & Naviga-
tion Co. ....AAAA
San Juan Fish & Packing
Co. (Salmon) ....B
WASH.—Semiahmoo
Alaska Packers' Assn.
(Canned) ....AAAA
WASH.—South Bend
Barnes, F. C. ....B
McGowan & Seaborg
(Canned) ....A
WASH.—Tacoma
Union Packing Co. (Salmon)
.............................A
WIS.—Green Bay
Hurlburt, Fred. (Salt;
Smoked) ....B
WIS.—Milwaukee
Birkenwald Co., S., 124
Fowler ....A

FISHERS

PA.—Philadelphia
Phila. Novelty Mfg. Co.
(Automatic) ....D

FISHING
TACKLE

**See also Rods; Reels; Lines
etc.**

CONN.—Bristol
Horton Mfg. Co. (Steel
Rods) ....B
CONN.—New Haven
Hendryx & Co., A. B.
(Reels; Trolling; Bait) A
MASS.—Boston
Dame, Stoddard & Kendall A
MASS.—Montague City
Montague City Rod Co.
(Rods; Reels) ....A
N. Y.—Buffalo
Lowe, William T. J. (Arti-
ficial; Luminous; Troll-
ing Bait; Flies) X
New York City
Abbey & Imbrie, 18 Vesey
(Rods; Reels. etc.)......C
Abercrombie & Fitch, 314
B'way (All Kinds) .....B
Plath & Son, Chas. (Arti-
ficial; Trolling; Bait;

FISH TACKLE (Con.)

Flies) ....F
Spaulding & Bros., A. G.,
126 Nassau (Rods;
Tackle) ....AA
N. Y.—Whitehall
Buell Co., Jno. T. (Spoons;
Spears; Spinners) ....D
N. Y.—Utica
Clark-Horrocks Co. (Trolling
Bait; Rods, etc.) .....A
PA.—Philadelphia
Shipley, Malcolm A. ......D
OHIO—Akron
Enterprise Mfg. Co. (Arti-
ficial; Luminous; Bait;
Devon;Fly; Floats; Hooks;
Rods; Reels) ....A
VT.—Post Mills
Chubb Rod Co. (Rods; Flies,
etc.) ....A

FITTINGS

See also Pipe

ALA.—Birmingham
Dimmick Pipe Co. (Pipe)
.............................AA
CAL.—Los Angeles
Pacific Clay Mfg. Co. (Drain
Pipe; Soil) ....A
CAL.—San Francisco
Union Iron Wks. (Electri-
cal) X
CONN.—Branford
Malleable Iron Fittings Co.
(Malleable Iron; Steam
Pipe) ....AA
CONN.—Bridgeport
Bridgeport Brass Co. (Bicy-
cle Frame; Hall Lamp)
.........................AAA
CONN.—Hartford
Howard & Co., Jno. L. (Rail-
way Car) ....A
Post & Lester Co. (Automo-
bile) ....B
CONN.—Meriden
Miller Edward & Co. (Bil-
liard Lamp ;Hall Lamp)
.........................AAAA
CONN.—Middletown
Wilcox, Crittenden & Co.
(Boat; Wire Rope) ....A
CONN.—New Haven
Cowler & Co., C. (Automo-
bile) ....A
Peck Bros. & Co. (Basin;
Bath Supply) ....AA
CONN.—Norwich
Ossawan Mills Co. (Bicycle
Guard) ....B
ILL.—Chicago
Adams & Westlake Co. On-
tario (Coach Vestibule;
Railway Car)......AAAA
Amer. Radiator Co. (Lake
& Dearborn) (Steam Pipe
H. O. & Distributors)
.........................AAAA
Amer. Spiral Pipe Wks.,
1173 S. Paulina (Flanged
for Spiral Rivetted Pipe,
etc.) ....B
Beckley- Ralston Co. (Bicy-
cle Frame) C
Carroll Iron Wks., 779 Car-
roll Av. (Malleable Iron
Steam Pipe) C
Clow & Sons, J. B., 344
Franklin (Cast Iron,
Drainage; Steam Pipe)
.........................AAA
Crane Co. (Air Brake. Car
Heater; Flanged; Green-
house; Malleable; Cast
Iron Steam Pipe also Drain
Pipe) ....AAAA
Davis & Co., Jno., 69 Mich
(Cast Iron Steam Pipe)
.........................AA
Elmes Engineering Wks.,
Chas. F., Fulton & Morgan
Hydraulic; Steam) ....A
Excelsior Steel Furnace Co.,
38 W. Monroe (Furnace
Pipe) ....A
Illinois Malleable Iron Co.,
30 W. Monroe (Malleable;
Cast Iron Steam Pipe; Wa-
ter Closet; Railing)
.........................AAAA
Kroeschell Bros. Co., 55 Erie

FITTINGS (Con.)
(Cast Iron Steam Pipe)
A
Swadkins, W. F., 143 Fulton (Flanged; Screwed ' Eccentric; Spiral ")..X
Turner Brass Wks. (Bicycle Guard)
Walker & Ehrman Mfg. Co. (Bicycle Frame) ......A
Wolf & Co., Fred. W., 139 Rees (Ammonia; Ice Machine) ....AAA
ILL.—Decatur
Mueller Mfg. Co., H., (Basin; Water Closet) ..AAA
ILL.—Edwardsville
Edwardsville Brass Co. (Fine Thread) ....B
ILL.—Kewanee
Western Tube Co. (Car Heater; Cross Over; Brass; Malleable Iron Railway; Cast Iron Steam Pipe) ....AAA
ILL.—Litchfield
Litchfield Fdy. & Machine Co. (Air Brake; Cast Iron Steam Pipe) ....A
ILL.—St. Charles
Glen Mfg. Co. (Cast Iron; Drainage; Greenhouse; Grey Iron Steam Pipe) ..D
ILL.—Sterling
Novelty Iron Wks. (Basin)
E
KANS.—Kansas City
Riverside Iron Wks. Co. (Ammonia) ....A
MAINE—Portland
Laughlin Co., Thomas (Boat) ....A
MASS.—Boston
Dalton Ingersoll Co. (Bath Supply) X
Durable Wire Rope Co. (Wire Rope) ....D
Harvey, Henry H. (Wire Rope) ....D
Howes Co., S. M. (Furnace) B
National Tube Wks. (Soil Pipe) ....AAAA
Walworth Mfg. Co., 132 Federal (Malleable; Cast Iron Steam Pipe also Flanged Pipe) ....AAAA
MASS.—New Bedford
New Bedford Boiler & Machine Co. (Flanged) ....B
MICH.—Detroit
Ideal Mfg. Co. (Fine Thread) ....B
Safety Furnace Pipe Co., 13 E. Atwater (Furnace Pipe) D
MINN.—St. Paul
South Park Fdy. & Machine Co. (Cast Iron Steam Pipe) B
MINN.—Stillwater
Stillwater Mfg. Co. (Bowling Alley) ....A
MO.—St. Louis
Leschen & Sons Rope Co., A. (Wire Rope; Tramway) AAAA
Nelson Mfg. Co., N. O. (Lavatory) ....AAA
Stockhoff Supply Co., 432 S. 12th (Furnace Pipe) ....E
N. J.—Belleville
Eastwood Wire Mfg. Co. Bronze; Cast Iron Steam Pipe) ....AA
N. J.—Jersey City
Griffing Iron Co., A. A. (Cast Iron Steam Pipe) AA
New Jersey Car Spring & Rubber Co. (Air Brake, Washers, etc.; Basin), AA
N. J.—Newark
Chase, Edward O. (Lathe) D
N. J.—Trenton
Stahl, Harry E. (Bicycle Frame) ....F
Trenton Iron Co. (Wire Rope) ....A
N. Y.—Brooklyn
Vosburgh Mfg. Co., W. C. (Ltd.) (Gas Fixtures; Bath) X
Williams & Co., J. H. (Am-

FITTINGS (Con.)
monia) ....AA
N. Y.—Buffalo
Crosby Co., (Bicycle) .....A
Forsyth Mfg. Co. (Bicycle Guard; Brake) C
N. Y.—Canton
Rushton, J. H. (Boat) ....F
N. Y.—Coxsackie
Newbury, J. G. (Steam Pipe) ....D
N. Y.—Lockhart
Amer. District Steam Co. (Flanged) ....AAA
N. Y.—Newburgh
Coldwell-Wilcox Co. (Cast Iron Greenhouse)) .....B
New York City
Brunswick - Balke-Collendor Co. (Billiard Lamp) AAAA
Common Sense Metallic Packing Mfg. Co. (Ltd.) (Valve) ....D
Crane Co., Wm. M. (Pipe) A
Creamer & Co., W. G. (Railway Car) ....A
Eaton, Cole & Burnham Co., 253 Bway. (Malleable Iron Steam Pipe) ......AAAA
Fairbanks Co. (Pipe; Steam) AAAA
Goodyear's India Rubber Glove Mfg. Co. (Basin) AAAA
Hunt Co., C. W. (Mast; Gaff) ....AA
Jenkins Bros. (Valve) .....A
Kennedy Valve Mfg. Co. (Pipe) ....A
McNab & Harlin Mfg. Co. (Cast Iron Steam Pipe) AAA
Manning, Maxwell & Moore (Pipe) ....AA
Mattson Rubber Co. (Nursery) ....B
Meyer-Sniffen Co. (Ltd.) (Basin; Bath Supply; Lavatory; Sink; Water Closet; Drinking Fountain) ....A
Mott Iron Wks., J. L. (Bath Supply; Lavatory; Sink; Drain Pipe; Soil) ....AA
New Jersey Fdry. & Machine Co., 15 Murray (Malleable Iron Steam Pipe) ......D
New York Air Brake Co., 66 Bway. (Air Brake Equipment) ....AAAA
Trageser Steam Copper Wks. (Water Closet) ....B
Watson-Stillman Co., 210 E. 43d (Hydraulic; Valve; High Pressure; Pipe)..AA
N. Y.—Towanda
Gille Engine & Machine Co. (Cast Iron Steam Pipe)..C
N. Y.—Troy
Curd-Don Co. (Cast Iron Steam Pipe) ....A
N. Y.—Utica
International Heater Co. (Furnace) ....AAA
Millar & Co., Chas. (Flanged Pipe; Pipe; Steam) ...AA
OHIO—Canton
Arctic Machine Co. (Ammonia) X
OHIO—Cincinnati
Knecht Co., Victor (Railway Car) ....B
Lunkenheimer Co. (Steam) AA
Triumph Ice Machine Co., 610 Baymiller (Steel Ammonia; Ice Machine)....A
Vanduzer Co., E. W. (Marine) ....B
OHIO—Cleveland
Cudell, F. E. (Basin) .....B
Ohio Brass & Iron Mfg. Co. (Basin) ....B
Strong Carlisle & Hammond Co.. 61 Frankfort (Steam Pipe) ....A
Universal Skirt Guard Co. (Bicycle Guard) ....F
Van Dorn Iron Wks. Co. (Stable) ....AA
OHIO—Columbus
Kilbourne & Jacobs Mfg. Co. (Sink) ....AAAA

FITTINGS (Con.)

OHIO—Dayton
Dayton Malleable Iron Co. (Air Brake Lever Guides, etc.) ....AAA
Kuhns Bros. (Steam Pipe) B

OHIO—Mansfield
Humphreys Mfg. Co. (Pipe) B

OHIO—Shelby
Shelby Steel Tube Co. (Soil Pipe) ....AAAA

OHIO—Toledo
Perfection Furnace Pipe Co. (Furnace Pipe) ....B

PA.—Allegheny
Carlin's Sons, Thomas (Wire Rope) ....A

PA.—Carnegie
Rome & Co. Geo. (Furnace Pipe Ventilating) ......E

PA.—Chester
Keystone Fire-Proofing Paper Stock Co. (Plastic) ..D

PA.—Erie
Jarecki Mfg. Co. (Malleable; Cast Iron Steam Pipe) AAAA

PA.—Mechanicsburg
Wilcox Mfg. Co., D. (Bicycle Frame) ....A

PA.—Middletown
Amer. Tube & Iron Co. (Drain Pipe; Soil) AAAA

PA.—Nazareth
Nazareth Fdy. & Machine Co. (Flanged Pipe; Steam; Pipe) ....B

PA.—Philadelphia
Belfield & Co., H., 435 N. Broad (Ammonia, Flanged; Malleable; Cast Iron Steam Pipe) ....AA
Devlin & Co. Mfg. Co., Thos. (Steam Pipe) ....AA
Flagg & Co., Stanley G., 19th & Pa. Av. (Malleable Iron Railway; Steam Pipe Blast Furnace; Ammonia) AAA
McCambridge & Co. (Basin; Bath Supply; Lavatory; Sink; Railing; Brass) ...B
Owen & Salter (Lavatory; Water Closet) ....A
Pancoast & Co., H. & B., 245 S. 3d (Malleable Iron, Steam Pipe; Awning Frame) ....B
Watson & McDaniel Co. (Suction) C
Wood & Co., R. D. (Flanged Pipe; Pipe) ....AAAA

PA.—Pittsburg
Bartlett Furnace & Range Co., 632 Liberty Av. (Furnace Pipe) ....B
Kelly & Jones Co. (Malleable; Cast Iron Steam Pipe) AA
Oil Well Supply Co., 213 Water (Malleable; Cast Iron Steam Pipe) ..AAAA
Pittsburg Malleable Iron Co. (Air Brake) ....A
Pittsburg Valve Fdy. & Construction Co. (Gasoline, Hydraulic; Pipe) ....AAA
Standard Mfg. Co. (Basin, Bath Supply, Lavatory, Sink, Water Closet; Soil Pipe) ....AA
Yagle Fdy. Mach. Co., 400 32d (Flanged) C

PA.—Scranton
Scranton Button Co. (Insulating) ....A

PA.—Tamaqua
Tamaque Mfg. Co. (Malleable Iron; Steam Pipe) ...B

PA.—Williamsport
Paling Pump & Mfg. Co. (Cast Iron Steam Pipe) ..B
Keeler Co., E. (Cast Iron Steam Pipe) ....A
Williamsport Wire Rope Co. (Wire Rope) /........A

PA.—York
York Mfg. Co., Ltd. (Ammonia) ....AAAA

R. I.—Providence
Builders Iron Foundry (Cast Iron Steam Pipe) .....AA

FITTINGS (Con.)

WIS.—Milwaukee
Allis Chambers Co. (Ammonia) ....AAAA
Hoffman-Billings Mfg. Co. (Malleable; Cast Iron Steam Pipe) ....AA
Hoffman Mfg. Co., B. (Cast Iron Steam Pipe) ......A
League Cycle Wks. (Bicycle Frame) ....D
Vilter Mfg. Co. (Ammonia) AA

WIS.—Racine
Racine Malleable & Wrought Iron Co. (Bicycle Frame) A

FIXATIVE

ILL.—Chicago
Dietzgen Co., Eugene ....A
New York City
F. W. Devoe & C. T. Reynolds Co. ....AAAA

FIXTURES

For Bank; Bar; Office, etc.
See also Furniture

ALA.—Birmingham
Wood, Dickerson & Putnam (Wood Office; Bank, etc.) B

CAL.—Los Angeles
Los Angeles Gas & Electric Mfg. Co. (Gas; Electric) A

CAL.—San Francisco
Day & Co., Thos.,725 Mission (Gas; Electric) ....A
Ickelheimer Bros., 20 Geary (Gas; Electric) ....B

CAL.—Lincoln
Gladding McBean & Co. (Chimney) ....AA

COLO.—Denver
Paulson, Jno. P. (Wood Office; Bank, etc.) ....B

CONN.—Meriden
Bradley & Hubbard Mfg. Co. (Extention Gas Lamp; Oil Chandeliers; Wrought Iron Gas; Electric Light; Oil; Lamp) ....AAAA
Meriden Curtain Fixture Co. (Window Shade) ....B
Miller & Co., Edward (Oil; Lamp; Chandeliers) AAAA
Parker Co., Chas. (Oil; Lamp; Extension Chandeliers) ....AAA

CONN.—New Britain
Corbin P. & F. (Blind Automatic) ....AAAA

CONN.—New Haven
Burgess, E. A. (Est. of), 67 Court (Stone Display) ..E
Dann Bros. & Co. (Butchers') ....B
English & Mersick Co. (Landau) ....B

CONN.—Norwalk
Arnold & Co. (Stable) C
Norwich Nickle & Brass Co. (Boot & Shoe Display; Store; Hatters') ....B

CONN.—Plantsville
Smith & Co., H. D. (Pole) A

CONN.—Southington
Peck, Stow & Wilcox Co. (Grindstone) ......AAAA

DEL.—Wilmington
Garrett, Miller & Co. (Water Tight Electrical) .....D

ILL.—Aurora
Wilcox Mfg. Co. (Grindstone) ....B

ILL.—Chicago
Adams & Westlake Co. (Berth & Car) ....AAAA
Andrews Co. A. H. (Court House; Office; Bank, etc.) AA
Baggot Co., E. (Lighting Combination; Electric Light; Gas) ....D
Barbee Wire & Iron Wks. (Butchers'; Stable) ...B
Becker Co., L. A. (& Drug Store; Saloon, etc.) .....B
Bender, Julius (& Store) ...C
Bodach, Chas. (Show Cases) C

FIXTURES (Con.)

Braun Mfg. Co., David J., 135 W. Wash. (Gas; Electric; Chandeliers) ......B

Chicago Gas & Elect.Fixture Mfg. Co., 19 S. Jeff. (Gas; Electric) ....B

Edwards Mfg. Co., 21 E. Lake (Gas; Electric)....B

Edwards Mfg. Co., W. S. (Lighting Combination Gas; Electric) ....A

Fairbanks, Morse & Co., Franklin & Monroe (Tank) AAAA

Keenan Hyland Mfg. Co. (& Office & Bar) ....B

Law, W. H. (Pullman Bldg.) (Gas; Electric) C

Melchior Bros., Furn. Co. (& Store) C

Merle & Heaney Mfg. Co. (Store; Bar) ....A

Reveal Co., A. H. (& Office; Store, etc.) ....A

Simonson & Co., R. A. (& Office; Store, etc.) .....A

Ward Co., E. J., 100 Lake (Car Window) ....E

Weiss, Sontag & Co. (& Store; Saloon) C

Williamson & Co., R., 54 E. Lake (Gas; Electric)....A

Wilmarth Co., T. W., 261 Wabash Av. (Gas; Electric) ....B

ILL.—Decatur

Faries Mfg. Co. (Store Display) ....A

ILL.—Freeport

Stover Mfg. Co. (Window Shade) ....AA

ILL.—Harvey

Buda Fdy. & Mfg. Co. (Switch) ....AA

ILL.—Joliet

Hacker & Co. (Office; Store) C

ILL.—Ottawa

Sanders Bros., Mfg. Co. (Office; Store) ....B

ILL.—Quincy

Knitted Show Case Co., Jos. (Office; Bank, Bar)....A

Stahl, Geo. H. (Bank; Saloon) ....B

ILL.—St. Charles

Crown Electric Mfg. Co. (Chandeliers) ....D

ILL.—Sterling

Novelty Iron Wks. (Chain Pump) ....E

IND.—Evansville

Ellert, C. H. (Boot; Shoe Display) X

IND.—Indianapolis

Aetna Cabinet Co. (Bank; Office) C

IOWA—Sioux City

Curtis Sash & Door Co. (& Bank; Store; Bar) ...AA

KY.—Louisville

Mansfield & Son, Robt. (Office; Store; Bank) C

MAINE—Bangor

Morse & Co. (Office) ....AA

MD.—Baltimore

Reinte Salmon Co. (Drug; Jewelry, etc.) ....A

Schultz & Co., A. (Light; Electric; Gas) ....A

Walther & Co., 208 W. Fayette (Gas; Electric) ....B

MASS.—Boston

Bangs & Co., Chas. H. (Store) C

Boston Electric Co., 29 Harrison Av. (Gas; Electric) B

Harvey, Henry H. (Derrick) D

Hollings & Co., R., 93 Summer (Gas; Electric) ....B

Office, Bank, & Library Co. (Office) ....B

MASS.—Holyoke

Barlow Mfg. Co. (Boot; Shoe Display) ....E

MASS.—Lowell

Woods, Sherwood & Co. (Toilet Paper) ....E

MASS.—Springfield

Morgan Envelope Co. (Toilet Paper) ....AAAA

FIXTURES (Con.)

MASS.—Worcester

Bishop & Co., Jno. W. (Bank; Store; Office) ..B

Wire Goods Co., (Awning Blind; Automatic Blind; Curtain Rod) ....A

MICH.—Belding

Belding-Hall Mfg. Co. (Butchers') ....AAAA

MICH.—Detroit

Acme Fancy Wire Wks. (Office Wire) ....D

Barnum Iron Wks., E. T. (Stable) ....B

MICH.—Flint

Lyons, Hugh (Shoe Display) F

Perfection Fixture Co. (Shoe Display) ....F

MICH.—Northville

Dubuar Mfg. Co., J. A. (Maple Sugar Making) ....K

MINN.—Minneapolis

Witte Mfg. Co., J. C. (Office) C

MISS.—Jackson

Enoch's Lumbar & Mfg. Co. (Office; Bank) ....A

MO.—Kansas City

Kansas City Wire & Iron Wks. (Stable) ....A

MO.—St. Louis

American Roll Paper Co. (Toilet Paper) ....B

Benderscheid Mfg. Co. (Office) C

Mechanics Iron Wks., 901 S. Ewing Av. (Office) ....F

Pauk & Sons Mfg. Co., H. (Office; Bar) ....A

Phoenix Planing Mill Co., Spruce & 12th (Office) ..A

Pleuger & Henger Mfg. Co., 11th & Hebert (Grindstone) ....A

Prutrock, Wm. (Barbers) A

N. H.—Manchester

Campbell, John (Stable)..H

N. J.—Boonton

Lincoln Iron Wks. (Stable) B

N. J.—Bound Brook

Standard Gas Fixture Co. (Gas; Electric) C

N. J.—Burlington

Stuart & Peterson Co. (Stable) ....A

N. J.—Bridgeton

Acme Gas Fixture Co. (Gas; Electric) ....B

N. J.—New Brunswick

New Jersey Lamp & Bronze Wks. (Chandeliers) ...AA

N. J.—Newark

Hemmer Bros. (Bank) ...B

Searls Mfg. Co. (Toilet Paper) ....B

N. J.—Trenton

Amer. Lamp & Brass Co. (Gas; Electric) ......AA

N. Y.—Albany

A. P. W. Paper Co., (Wall Paper; Toilet Paper)....A

N. Y.—Brooklyn

Hecla Iron Wks. (Wrought Iron Gas) ....AA

Nichols Fixture Mfg. Co., Geo., 56 Boerum (Gas; Electric) C

Vosburgh Mfg. Co., W. C., Ltd. (Electric; Gas; Chandeliers) X

N. Y.—Buffalo

Contractors Plant Mfg. Co. (Derrick) ....B

Noye Mfg. Co., Jno. T. (Millstone) X

Shepard & Co., Sidney (Creamery) ......AAAA

Wright & Co., R. G. (Grocers) ....AA

N. Y.—Chichester

Sshwarzwalder, L. A. (Bank; Office. etc.; Cabinet Work to order) ...A

N. Y.—Elmira

Cronk & Carrier Mfg. Co. (Grindstone) ....B

N. Y.—Hillburn

Ramapo Iron Wks. (Switch) AAA

409

FIXTURES (Con.)

N. Y.—Horsehead
Weller Hdw. & Fdy. Co. (Grindstone) ....D

N. Y.—Jamestown
Art Metal Construction Co. (Metallic; Bank; Office) ....B
Fenton Metallic Mfg. Co. Library; Steel; Bronze; Office; Banks; Vault)..A

New York City
Ansonia Brass & Copper Co. (Lighting Combination; Gas; Oil; Lamp) ...AAAA
Brunswick - Balke-Collender Co. (Bank; Bar; Saloon) ....AAAA
Caldwell & Co., Edw. F. (Gas; Electric) C
Carey Samuel (Millstone) C
Cassidy & Son Mfg. Co. (Lighting; Combination Gas; Electric) ....A
Cornell Co., J. B. & J. M. (Metallic; Bank; Office) ....AA
Farrell Thomas (Butchers') ....D
Fiske Iron Wks., J. W., 39 Park Pl. (Stable) ......B
Frink, I. P., 551 Pearl (Lighting; Electric School; Reflector Chandeliers) AA
Gleason Mfg. Co., E. P. (Lighting; Combination; Electric) ....B
Goetz Mfg. Co., 247 3d Av. Gas; Electric) C
Howard & Morse, 45 Fulton (Stable) ....D
Iden & Co. (Lighting; Electric; Gas) ....D
Jackson Co., Wm. H., 29 E. 17th (Wrought Iron Gas) ....A
Judd & Co., H. L. (Store Display; Pole; Window Shade) ....AA
Koehn Alfred, 159 W. 29th (Wrought Iron Gas) ....E
Kreig & Co., J. K. (Boot; Shoe Display; Store) ..B
Lamb, J. & R., 59 Carmine (Church Chandeliers) ..D
McCoy & Co., J. B., 126 W. 33d (Gas; Electric).....E
Manhattan Brass Co. (Pole) ....A
Marscheider Edward (Butchers) ....D
Mitchell-Vance Co. (Lighting; Combination; Electric; Gas) ....AA
Mott Iron Wks., J. L. (Grate; Stable) ..AA
Newhall, Henry B., Murray (Fire Door) ....D
Oxley-Enos Co., 91 7th Av. (Gas; Electric) ....B
Palmerbergs Sons, Jos. R., 210 Bway. (Boot; Shoe Display; Brass; Window; Store Display; Hatters') X
Plant & Co., L., 432 E. 23d (Gas; Electric) ....B
Porter's Sons Co., Wm. (Headlight) ....E
Safety Car Heating & Lighting Co., 60 Bway. (Car Chandeliers) ......AAA
Wemple Co., Jay C. (Window Shade) ......AA
Westervelt, A . B. & W. T. (Stable) ....B
Williams. Jno., 556 W. 27th (Gas; Electric) ....B

N. Y.—Rochester
Clark Novelty Co. (Headlight; Store Display).....D
Hofman Co., John (Office) C
Rochester Show Case Wks. (Office; Bar) ....D
Streeter & Co., N. R. (Toilet Paper) ....D
Yauman & Erbe Mfg. Co. (Court House; Office; Bank) ....AA

N. Y.—Saratoga Springs
Lawrence. C. W. (Bank)..B

N. Y.—Schenectady
General Electric Co. (Light;

FIXTURES (Con.)
Gas) ....AAAA

N. Y.—Seneca Falls
Rumsey & Co. (Chain Pump) ....A

N. Y.—Syracuse
Edwards Co., O. M. (Car Window) ....D
Stearns & Co., E. C. (Stable) ....AA

N. Y.—Utica
Jones, Frank L. (Creamery) C
Utica Fixture Co. (Gas; Electric) ....A

OHIO—Akron
Whitman & Barnes Mfg. Co. (Grindstone) ......AAAA

OHIO—Bryan
Bryan Novelty Mfg. Co. (Display) ....F

OHIO—Canton
Berger Mfg. Co. (Metallic Bank; Office) ....AA
Weaver & Sons, Jos. (Office; Bank) ....E

OHIO—Cincinnati
Brunswick - Balke-Collender Co. (Bar; Saloon; Office) ....AAAA
Cincinnati Butchers Supply Co. (Butchers') ....A
Huss Bros. Mfg. Co. (Bar; Store) ....D
Lage Joseph (Grocers) ..G
McCassy Bros. (Bar) ......B
Triumph Electric Co. (Headlight) ....A
Weir Frog Co. (Switch) ..A

OHIO—Cleveland
Caster-Alton-Clark Co. (Display) X
Cleveland Galvanizing Wks. (Lightning Rod) C
Cleveland Gas & Elect. Fixture Co. (Gas; Electric) A
Cleveland Stone Co. (Grindstone) ....AAAA
Morreau Gas Fixture Mfg. Co. 276 Huron (Gas; Electric) ....A
Selzer, C. A., Euclid Av. & Erie (Gas; Electric)....A
Taylor & Boggis Fdy. Co. (Chain Pump) ....AA
Tyler, Co., W. S., 1150 St. Clair (Wrought Iron Gas) ....AAAA
Van Dorn Iron Wks. (Stable) ....AA

OHIO—Dayton
Obmur's Sons Co., The M. (& Bank; Office) ......A

OHIO—Hamilton
Meyers Mfg. Co., Fred. J. (Stable) ....B

OHIO—Kenton
Champion Iron Co. (Stable) ....AA

OHIO—Ravenna
Byers Mach. Co., Jno. F. (Derrick) ....B

OHIO—Tiffin
Enterprise Mfg. Co. (Bank; Office; Store) ....E

OHIO—Toledo
Stevens, B. A. (Bar; Market) ....A
Yesbera Mfg. Co. (Stove)..A

OHIO—Youngstown
General Fire Proofing Co. (Metallic Bank & Office) ....AA

PA. Allegheny
Carlin's Sons, Thomas (Derrick) ....A

PA.—Lanesboro
Barnes Mfg. Co. (Derrick) B

PA.—Philadelphia
Cox Stove Co., Abram (Grate) ....AAA
Gaumer & Co., J. L., 19th & Hamilton (Gas; Electric) ....A
Gebson Gas Fixture Wks., 1426 Callowhill (Gas; Electric) ....A
Hall & Garrison Mfg. Co. (Bank; Bar) X
Horn & Brannen Mfg. Co. (Electric; Gas)........AA
Ledig Reinbold, G. (Gas;

FIXTURES (Con.)
Electric) X
Pennsylvania Steel Co.
(Switch) ....AAAA
Reid Creamery Supply Co.
(Creamery) ....A
Shaw & C., Geo. W., 1020
Walnut (Gas; Electric) B
Sulzer & Co., 821 Cherry
(Gas; Electric)........B
Shackara Mfg. Co., 1606
Chestnut (Gas Electric) C
Weldon & Kelly, 305 Wood
(Gas; Electric) ....B
PA.—Pittsburg
Aiken & Co. (Wood; Store,
&c.) ....B
McKenna Bros. Brass Co.
(Display) ....A
Pittsburg Brass Mfg. Co.
(Oil; Lamp)...........D
Pittsburg Lamp Brass Co.
Glass Co. (Chandeliers)
AAAA
Reineke-Wilson Co., 13
Wood (Gas; Electric)..B
PA.—Reading
National Brass & Iron Wks.
(Chandeliers) ....A
Penn Hdw Co. (Grindstone)
AA
PA.—Wrightsville
Susquehanna Casting Co.
(Grindstone) ....AA
Wrightsville Hdw. Co.
(Grindstone) ....B
TENN.—Nashville
Edgefield & Nashville Mfg.
Co. (Office; Bank)......A
VT.—Rutland
Lincoln Iron Wks. (Derrick)
A
W.VA.—Wellsburg
Riverside Glass Wks. (Crystal) C
WIS.—Milwaukee
Northweseran Funiture Co.
(Office) ....A
Polachek & Bros. Co. (Gas;
Electric) ....B
Ritter, Louis (Bar; Stove;
Office) C
Willer Mfg. Co. (Bank)..A
WIS.—Oshkosh
Brand & Son, R. (Bank; Office; Saloon).........D
WIS.—Sheboygan
Winter Lumber Co., M.
(Bank) ....B
WIS.—South Milwaukee
Stowell Mfg. & Fdy Co.
(Grindstone) ....A

FLAGONS

N. Y.—Brooklyn
New York Stamping Co.
(Alcohol) ....A

FLAGS

See also Awnings; Tents &
Flags
CAL.—San Francisco
Neville & Co.............A
CONN.—Bridgeport
Ives Mfg. Corpn.........C
CONN.—South Manchester
Cheney Bros. (Ltd.) (Silk)
AAAA
ILL.— Chicago
Carpenter & Co., Geo B.
(Bunting) ....AA
Cook & Bros., E. C. (of all
nations) ....A
MASS.—Boston
Lamprell & Marble........F
MASS.——Fall River
McLellan Chas. P. (Yacht)
F
MICH.—Detroit
Detroit Tent & Awning Co.
D
MO.—St. Louis
Handlan-Buck Mfg. Co.
(Metallic also Bunting;
Railway, &c.).........AA
Missouri Tent & Awning Co.
B
Zittlosen Mfg. Co.........B
New York City
Amer. Flag Co. (Embroidered; of all nations; Silk;
Yacht,&c.) ....A
Annin & Co. (Yacht)......D

FLAGS (Con.)
Boyle & Co., Jno. (Embroidered; Of all nations;
Silk; Yacht,&c.) ......
Coston Signal Co., 7 Water
(Burgess; Club; Decorating; International; Marine; Signal)..........X
De Graw, Aymar & Co. AA
Hemmenway & Sons (Yacht)
C
Horstman Co., Wm. H. (Of
all nations; Silk) ..AAAA
Joel & Co., J. A., 88 Nassau
(Boat) C
Koster Co., C. H. (Embroidered; Of all Nations; Silk;
Yacht) ....D
Lamb J. & R. (Embroidered;
Silk) ....D
McHugh Jno. F. (Est)....C
N. Y.—Rochester
Pulver Co., F. F. (Celluloid)
B
OHIO—Cincinnati
Beck & Sons Co., Wm....C
Palton & Co., R. J. (Railway; Signal, &c.).....C
Petibone Bros. Mfg. Co...A
OHIO—Columbus
Lilley Co., M. C. (Bunting; Silk).........AAAA
OHIO—Easton
Amer. Flag Mfg. Co. (Railway; Signal; Bunting;
Silk) C

FLANGERS

ILL.—Chicago
Board-Crosby Co., 175 S.
Clinton (Automatic)....X
IND.—Indianapolis
Barry Saw Co. (Shingle
Saw) C
PA.—Ridgway
Russel Car & Snow Plow Co.
D

FLANGES

ILL.—Chicago
Ryerson & Son, Jos. I.
(Forged Steel) ....AAAA
Sundberg Co., J. A., Kinzie
& Carpenter (Boiler)....C
ILL.—Decatur
Muller Mfg. Co., H. (Water
Closet Floor) ......AAA
ILL.—St. Charles
Glenn Mfg. Co. (Tapped
Floor; Ceiling)........D
MASS.—Worcester
Dwyer Machine Co. (Glass
Tube) ....F
Worcester Ferrule & Mfg.
Co. (Floor; Ceiling)...C
MO.—St. Louis
Nelson Mfg. Co., N. O. (Closet Floor) ....AAA
N.Y.——New York City
Good Mfg. Co., 88 Lincoln
Av. (Brass)...........B
N.Y.—Seneca Falls
Climax Specialty Co. (Closet) ....B
PA.—Millersburg
Millersburg Fifth Wheel Co.
(Forged Steel for Distilleries) ....D
PA.—Philadelphia
Belfield & Co., H. (Cast;
Malleable Iron).......AA
Latrobe Steel Co., Girard
Bldg (Soft Steel Weldless
for high pressure)..AAAA
PA.—Pitsburg
Riter-Conley Co. (Pressed
Weldless Steel)......AAA
PA.—Williamsport
Keeler & Co., E. (Pressed
Steel; Weldless Steel)..A
WIS.—Milwaukee
Pressed Steel Tank Co.
(Weldless Steel).......B
WIS.—Kencsha
Frost Mfg. Co. (Brass)....B

FLANNELS & FLANELETTES

See Woolen Goods & Cotton
Goods

FLAPPERS

CONN.—New Haven
Cowles & Co. (Carriage) ..A
English & Mersick Co. (Carriage) ....B

FLAPS

CONN.—New Britain
Corbin P. & F. (Shutter)....
.......................AAAA
Stanley Wks. (Shuter).....
.......................AAAA
CONN.—Stanford
Yale & Towne Mfg. Co.
(Shutter) ....AAAA
ILL.—Chicago
Braumoeller & Son, Henry
(Shutter) ....B

FLASHES

ILL.—Chicago
Reynolds Electric Flash Co.,
221 5th Av. (Electric
Sign) ....F
Reynolds Electric Flash Co.,
Adams (Electric Sign)..C
N.J.—Newark
Elect. Motor & Euipment Co.
(Electric Sign).........C
OHIO—Toledo
Bissell Co., F. (Electric
Sign) ....A
R.I.—Providence
Hamblen Co., Jno. A. (Electric Sign)..............X

FLASKS

See also Bottles

CONN.—New Haven
Ideal Mfg. Co. (Powder) B
CONN.—Waterbury
Waterbury Brass Co. (Powder) ....AAAA
ILL.—Harvey
Whiting Fdy Equipment Co.
(Molders') ....AA
IND.—Richmond
Diamond Clamp & Flask Co.
(Molders'; Floor)......D
IOWA—Dubuque
Adams Co. (Molders')....A
N. J.—Newark
Brass Founders Supply Co.
(Foundry) ....E
N. Y.—Albany
Hoy & Co. (Tin) ....A
N. Y.—Buffalo
Buffalo Dental Mfg. Co.
(Dental) ....B
Shepard & Co., Sidney (Tin)
.......................AAAA
New York City
Consolidated Dental Mfg. Co.
(Dental) ....B
Spalding & Bros., A. G.
(Inc.) (Powder)....AAAA
OHIO—Cincinnati
Hill & Griffith Co.........D
Obermayer Co., S. (Molders'; Snap)............AA
OHIO—Cleveland
Smith Fdy Supply Co., J. D.,
40 S. Water (Molders';
Snap) ....D
OHIO—Lowellville
Meehan Boiler & Locomotive
Co. (Steel) ....B
PA.—Harrisburg
Harrisburg Pipe Bending Co.
(Ammonia; Carbonic Acid)
.......................AAA
PA.—Philadelphia
Johnson & Lund (Dental)..
.......................AA
Paxson Co., J. W., 1021 Del
Av. (Molders').......AA
Rosenblatt & Co., H. M.,
1025 Vine (Pocket)....A
Sibley Gideon (Dental)..AA
White Dental Mfg. Co., S.
S. (Dental)........AAAA
TEXAS—Dallas
Cunningham I. C. (Foundry)
.......................H

FLAX

KY.—Covington
Overman & Schrader Cordage

FLAX (Con.)
Co. (Hemp).........AA
MASS.—Boston
Boston Excelsior Co. (Trow)
.......................A
MASS.—Melrose
Chesterton Co., A. W.
(Square) ....A
MICH.—Yale
Livingston Flax Co., Jos.
(Hackled) C
MINN.—Heron Lake
Minnesota Fabric Co. (Spining; Upholstery) ......D
N. Y.—Palmyra
Crandall Packing Co......D
OHIO—Ashland
Ashland Flax Mill Co. (Upholstery) ....E
OHIO—Dayton
Payne & Co..............B

FLESHERS

N. H.—Bennington
Kimball & Co., C. J. (Tanners') ....D
PA.—Philadelphia
Horn & Bros., Wm. H. (Tanners') ....B
PA.—Pittsburg
Amer. Axe & Tool Co. (Tanners') ....AAAA

FLIES

See Fish Tackle

FLINT

CONN.—New Milford
Bridgeport Wood Finishing
Co. ....AA
MD.—Concwingo
Hartford County Flint Co.
(Ground) X
N. Y.—Bedford
Kinkels Son, P. H. (Crude)
.......................X
N. Y.—Brooklyn
Wiarda & Co., Jno. C.
(Ground) ....AA
PA.—York
York Chemical Wks.
(Crushed) ....A

FLITTERS

New York City
F. W. Devoe & C. T. Raynolds Co. ....AAAA

FLOATERS

N. J.—Salem
Ayars Machine Co. (Can).B

FLOATS

Fish Tackle

CONN.—Hartford
Jones Co., O. H. (Glass)..O
CONN.—Naugatuck
Naugatuck Mfg. Co. (Seamless Copper; Copper Ball)
.......................E
ILL.—Chicago
Chicago Cork Wks. Co., 167
Plymouth (Cork)........F
ILL.—Evanston
Mark Mfg. Co. (Copper
Tank) ....AA
IND.—Kokomo
Great Western Pottery Co.
(Crockery) ....AA
KY.—Louisville
Kentucky Wagon Mfg. Co.
(Cotton) ....AAAA
MASS.—Boston
Boston Brass Co., 36 Oliver
(Copper) C
MASS.—Haydenville
Haydenville Co. (Copper), A
MASS.—Springfield
Hercules Float Wks. (Seamless Conper) ....D
MICH.—Detroit
Diamond Sample Ware Co.
(Copper) ....A
Ireland & Matthews Mfg.
Co. (Copper; Zink for

FLOATS (Con.)

Tanks) ....A

MICH.—Kalamazoo

Smith & Pomeroy Windmill
Co. (Copper)..........B

MICH.—Muskegon

Heap & Son, Wm (Glass).D

MICH.—Sturgis

Miller, Hubbard Mfg. Co.
(Copper) ....B

MINN.—St. Paul

Union Brass & Metal Mfg.
Co. (Copper)..........A

MO.—St. Louis

Nelson Mfg. Co., N. O.
(Copper) ....AAA

N. J.—Elizabeth

Standard Sanitary Pottery
Co. (Crockery).......X

N. J.—Newark

Sacks Iron Fdy, Louis
(Counter) ....A

N.J.—Trenton

Bellmark Potery Co. (Crockery) ....B

Maddock & Son, Jno. (Crockery) ....A

Trenton Potteries Co.
(Crockery) ....AAA

N. Y.—Brooklyn

Burr John M., 1939 Fulton
(Glass) ....F

New York City

McNab & Harlin Mfg. Co.,
56 John (Copper Ball..
.................AAA

Page Wm. E., E. 166th &
Walton Av. (Copper)..F

Ronalds & Johnson Co.,
54 Cliff (Copper)....AA

Steeger Henry, 143 E. 31st
(Copper) ....A

Trageser Steam & Copper
Wks., Jno., 447 W. 26th
(Copper) ....A

N.Y.—Rome

Wilson Mfg. Co., R. M.
(Copper) ....B

OHIO—Cincinnati

Douglas Co., Jno., 900
Poplar (Copper).......A

Pfau Mfg. Co. Copper)...B

OHIO—Cleveland

Cleveland Faucet Co., 25
Frankfort (Copper) AAAA

Reliance Gauge Column Co.,
70 E. Prospect (Seamless
Copper) ....D

PA.—Philadelphia

Blessing C. A., 516 Mont-
gomery Av. (Copper)..AA

Boekel & Co., Wm., 518 Vine
(Copper Tank) ....A

Watson & McDaniel Co.
(Copper for Steam Taps)
.................C

FLOCKS

CONN,— Rockville

Regan Mfg. Co., J. J....AA

CONN.—Somersville

Somerville Mfg. Co. ....AA

CONN.—Stafford

Smith & Cooley..........B

MASS.—Boston

Gray & Co., T. H ......D

MASSS.—Shirley

Gould Mfg. Co..........F

PA.—Chester

Bower's Sons, Jas. (Ltd.), B

FLOCONNES

MAINE—Lisbon Fallls

Worumbo Mfg. Co.....AAA

FLOORING

See Lumber

FLOORS

See also Tile; Carpet; Wood

CAL.—San Francisco

Bateman Wm., 835 Folsom
(Parquet) ....E

Bush & Mallett Co., 328
Post (Parquet)........C

Inlaid Floor Co. (Parquet)
.................D

ILL.—Chicago

Aitchison Perforated Metal
Co. (Drying).........X

FLOORS (Con.)

Barbee Wire & Iron Wks.
(Malt Kiln).........B

Chicago Floor Co., 151 Wabash Av. (Parquet)....E

Cooley Wm. H., 1160 Cly-
born (Parquet) C

Dunfee & Co., J., 104 Frankl
in (Parquet).........B

Moore & Co., E. B. (Par-
quet) ....B

Wolf Co., Fred. W. (Malt
Kiln) ....AAA

IND.—Indianapolis

Gall, Albert, 17 W. Wash'n
(Parquet) ....B

Interior Hardwood Co. (Parquet) ....A

IND.—New Albany

Wood Mosaic Flooring Co.
(Wood Mosaic) ......AA

MASS.—Boston

Adams R. F., 24 Bromfield
(Parquet) ....F

Allen, Hall & Co., 384 Boylston (Parquet).........C

Day & Co., Wm J., 46 Canal
(Parquet) ....D

MASS.—Clinton

Clinton Wire Cloth Co. (Malt
Kiln; Wire Cloth....AAA

MASS.—Worcester

Wright Wire Co. (Malt Kiln;
Wire Cloth).........AA

MICH.—Detroi

Michigan Wire & Cloth Co.
(Malt Kiln; Wire Cloth)..
.................AA

MINN.—St.Paul

Dumphy W. C., 116 W. 3d
(Parquet) ....H

MO.— St. Louis

Asphalt Roofing Co. (As-
phalt Mastic)........X

Herr Floor Co., 1203 Olive
(Parquet) ....D

Ludlow-Saylor Wire Co.
(Wire Cloth) ....AA

N. H.—Milford

Pierce & Co., W. E. (Wood
Block) ....D

N. Y.—Albany

Skinner & Arnold Co. (Malt
Kiln) C

N. Y.— Buffalo

Churchyard Jos. J. (Parquet)
.................X

N. Y.—Carthage

Carthage Lumber Co. (Par-
quet) ....B

New York City

Amer. Parquetry Co., 3 E.
42nd (Parquet) ....E

Boynton & Van Winkle,
186 5th Av. (Parquet)..D

Buttle Parquet Floor Co.,
36 W. 27th (Parquet)..D

Howard & Morse (Malt Kiln;
Wire Cloth)..........D

Maurer & Son. H. V., 420
E. 23d (Fire-Proof Hollow)
.................AA

Roebling's Sons Co.. Jno. A.
Malt Kiln; Wire Cloth), **B**

Sicilian Asphalt Paving Co.,
Times Bldg. (Malt Kiln)
.................A

Wilson Mfg. Co., Jas. G.
(Wood Block).........A

N. Y.—Rochester

Wood Mosaic Flooring Co.
(Parquet, Wood Mosaic)
.................AA

OHIO—Cincinnati

Schreiber & Sons Co., L. 8th
& Eggleston Av. (Malt
Knil) ....AA

OHIO—Cleveland

Cleveland Hardwood Floor
Co., Colonial Arcade (Parquet) ....A

Garry Iron & Steel Co. (Fire
Proof) ....A

OHIO—Norwalk

Boswick-Goodell Co. (Par-
quet) C

OHIO—Toledo

Schillinger Bros. Co., 412
City Park Av. (Malt Kiln)
.................C

OHIO—Youngstown

Youngstown Iron & Steel
Roofing Co. (Fire Proof;
Bridge) ....AA

FLOORS (Con.)

PA.—Philadelphia
Amer. Parquetry Floor Co., 143 S. 13th (Parquet)..C
Heaton & Wood (Mosaic; Parquet) ....D
Phoenix Bridge Co. (Iron) A
Wood & Co., R. D. (Iron) ....AAAA

PA.—Pittsburg
Star Encaustic Tile Co. (Tile) ....B

WIS.—Milwaukee
Am. Monolith Co. (Hospital; Sanitary; Fire Proof)..E
Toepper & Sons, 88 Menomonee (Malt Kiln) .....B

FLORENTINES

See Silk Goods

FLOSS

See also Silk Goods

CONN.—New London
Brainerd & Armstrong Co. (Silk) ....AAA

CONN.—Winsted
Winsted Silk Co. (Silk)...A

MASS.—Florence
Nonotuck Silk Co. (Silk)....AAAA

MASS.—Holyoke
Skinner Mfg. Co., Wm. (Silk) ....AA

MICH.—Belding
Belding Bros & Co. (Silk) ....AAAA

PA.—Bethlehem
Bethlehem Silk Co.. (Silk) AA

FLOUR: WHEAT

Numbers following names indicate approximately the daily output in bbls. For Rice Flour, see next Heading; For Buckwheat & Pancake Flour, see Cereals; See also Dust etc. for Marble Flour

ARK.—Little Rock
Little Rock Mill & Elevator Co. (1000).............D

CAL.—Fresno
Sperry Flour Co.(700) AAAA

CAL.—Hollister
Alliance Mill Co. (500)...G

CAL.—Los Angeles
Capitol Milling Co. (50) AA
Los Angeles Farming & Milling Co........AAAA
Sperry Flour Mills (600)....AAAA

CAL.—Paso Robles
Southern Pacific Milling Co. (300) ....A

CAL.—Sacramento
Phoenix Milling Co. (700)..A

CAL.—Salinas
Sperry Flour Co. (700)....AAAA

CAL.—San Francisco
Port Costa Milling Co. (2500) ....AAA
Southern Pacific Milling Co. (300) ....A

CAL.—Stockton
Farmers' Union & Milling Co. (1,000) ....AA
Sperry Milling Co. (1500)..AAAA
Stockton Milling Co. (2000) A

CAL.—Vallejo
Port Costa Milling Co. (2000) ....AAA

COLO.—Denver
Crescent Mill & Elevator Co. (400) ....A

COLO.—La Mar
La Mar Milling & Elevator Co. (500) ....A

COLO.—Longmont
Longmont Flour Milling Co. (500) ....AAAA

DEL.—Wilmington
Lea Milling Co. (2,500)....B

FLOUR (Con.)

GA.—Atlanta
Atlanta Milling Co. (1500) A

GA.—Augusta
Clark Milling Co. (300)...C

GA.—Cartersville
Etowah Milling Co. (350)..B

GA.—Columbus
City Mills Co. (500)......A

GA.—Dalton
Barrett, Denton & Lynn (600) ....A
No. Ga. Milling Co. (2000) C

GA.— Rome
Rome Milling Co. (800) ...D

ILL.—Alton
Alton Roller Milling Co. (300) ....B
Sparks Milling Co. (1500) A
Stanard Milling Co., E. O. (1500) ....AA

ILL.—Belleview
Crown Milling Co. (800)..A

ILL.—Bloomington
Hungarian Roller Mills (400) ....A

ILL.—Cairo
Halliday Milling Co., H. L. (600) ....AA

ILL.—Carlyle
Carlyle Mill & Grain Co. (300) ....B

ILL.—Chicago
American Cereal Co. (2400) AAAA
Eckart & Swan Milling Co. (1000) ....AAA
Norton & Co. (2000).....A
Northern Milling Co. (2000) A
Great Western Cereal Co. (1250) ....AAAA
Star & Crescent Milling Co. (1500) ....AA

ILL.—Collinsville
Tiedeman Chas Milling Co. (300) ....B

ILL.—Columbia
Columbia Star Milling Co. (500) C

ILL.—Decatur
Decatur Milling Co. (400) A
Shellabarger Mill & Elevator Co. (1000).............A

ILL.—Du Quoin
Du Quoin Mill Co. (300)..C

ILL.—East St. Louis
Hazel Milling Co. (500)..A
Kehlor Milling Co. (3000).. AAAA

ILL.—Golden
Emminga H. H. (300)....B

ILLL.—Highland
Highland Milling Co. (500) B

ILL.—Jacksonville
Fitzsimmons-Kreider Milling Co. (300).........A

ILL.—Lincoln
Gordon Mill & Grain Co. (400) ....B

ILL.—Lockport
Norton & Co. (2000)......A

ILL.—Marine
Valier & Spies Millling Co. (350) C

ILL.—Murphysboro
Southern Ill. Milling & Elevator Co. (400) ....A

ILL.—Nashville
Camp Spring Mill Co. (1000) A
Huegely Milling Co. (450) A

ILL.—New Athens
New Athens Milling Co. (300) ....B

ILL.—O'Fallon
Tiedeman. Chas. (400) B

ILL.—Pickneyville
Pickneyville Milling Co. (500) ....A

ILL.—Quincy
Dick Bros. Milling Co. (300) A

ILL.—St. Jacob
St. Jacob Enterpise Mill Co. (300) C

ILL.—Teutopolis
Uptmor & Siemer (300) ..B

ILL.—Warsaw
Warsaw Milling Co. (350) B

FLOUR *(Con.)*

ILL.—Waterloo
Koenigsmark, T. (400) ...A
IND.—Evansville
Aiken-Erskine Milling Co.
 (350) ....D
Inglehart Bros. (350) ..B
Melrose Milling Co. (600) A
Phoenix Flour Mill (350) B
IND.—Goshen
Goshen Milling Co. (700) B
IND.—Greensburg
Garland Milling Co. (300) D
IND.—Indianapolis
Acme Milling Co. (2500)..A
Blanton Milling Co. (500) B
IND.—Jeffersonville
Gathright, R. O. (300) ..A
IND.—Lawrenceburg
Lawrenceburg Roller Mills
 (1800) ....B
IND.—Madison
Trow Co., W. (1000)......A
IND.—Mt. Vernon
Fuhrer-Ford Milling Co.
 (300) ....B
IND.—Noblesville
Noblesville Milling Co.
 (1000) ....AA
IND.—Peru
Peru Milling Co. (300) ..A
IND.—Princeton
Moore Milling Co. (400) A
Witherspoon & Barr Co.
 (400) ....A
IND.—Seymour
Blish Milling Co. (1000) ..A
IND.—Terre Haute
Kidder, Willard (1000) ...A
Paddock, Wm. & Co. (350) B
IND.—Vincennes
Emisson, J. & S. (600) AA
IOWA—Alton
Alton Milling Co. (400) B
IOWA—Cedar Falls
Waterloo & Cedar Falls
 Union Mill Co. (600) AA
IOWA—Davenport
Phoenix Milling Co. (600) A
Riverside Milling Co. (500) B
IOWA—Des Moines
Shannon & Mott Co. (300) C
IOWA—Keokuk
Gate City Milling Co. (300)
 C
IOWA—Le Mars
Plymouth Milling Co. (500)
 B
IOWA—Sioux City
Mystic Milling Co. (800) C
IOWA—Waterloo
Waterloo & Cedar Falls
 Union Mill Co. (600) AA
KANS.—Abilene
Security Milling Co. (350) C
KANS.—Arkansas City
New Era Milling Co. (600)
 C
KANS.—Atchison
Blair Milling Co. (400) ..A
Cain Mill Co. (800) ......A
Lukens Milling Co. (1400)
 A
KANS.—Burlington
Wilson & Son (300) ......B
KANS.—Clay Center
Snell Mill & Elevator Co.
 (300) ....B
Williamson, F. L. & Co.
 (300) ....A
KANS.—Coffeyville
Grisham-Kiddro Milling Co.
 (500) C
McGrew Milling Co. (600) B
Rea-Patterson Milling Co.
 (800) ....B
KANS.—Ellsworth
Larkins' Sons (450) ......D
KANS.—Ft. Scott
Goodlander Milling Co. (400)
 B
KANS.—Great Bend
Walnut Creek Milling Co.
 (550) ....A
KANS.—Halstead
Halstead Milling & Elevator
 Co. (400) C
KANS.—Hays City
Yost Milling Co. (1000) ..B
KANS.—Junction City
Hogan, Thomas F. (300) ..H
KANS.—Kansas City
Rex Mills (5000) ..AAAA

FLOUR *(Con.)*

KANS.—Lawrence
Bowersock Milling Co. (600)
 B
KANS.—Leavenworth
Kelley & Lysle Milling Co.
 (1000) ....A
Snyder & Cassingham (1000)
 D
KANS.—McPherson
Colburn Bros. (300) ......B
KANS.—Manhattan
Manhattan Milling Co.
 (500) ....D
KANS.—Marysville
Hutchinson, Perry (300)..A
KANS.—Moundridge
Moundridge Milling Co.
 (300) ....B
KANS.—Newton
Newton Milling & Elevator
 Co. (300) ....A
KANS.—Olathe
Olathe Milling & Elevator
 Co. (300) ....B
KANS.—Oswego
Pearl Roller Mills Co. (500)
 B
KANS.—Rosedale
Arms & Kidder (700) ....B
KANS.—Salina
Lee-Warren Milling Co.
 (400) ....B
KANS.—Stafford
Stafford Milling & Elevator
 Co. (1000) C
KANS.—Topeka
Crosby Roller Milling Co.
 (1000) ....A
Inter Ocean Mills (800) ..A
Mid-Continent Mills (700) .A
Shawnee Milling Co. (300)
 B
Topeka Milling Co. (700)..A
Willis, Norton & Co.
 (1000) ....A
KANS.—Wellington
Hunter Milling Co. (700) ..A
Kramer Bros. (500)......A
KANS.—Wichita
Imboden Milling Co. (350)
 C
KANS.—Winfield
Alexander Milling Co. (300)
 C
Baden Produce Co., J. P.
 (650) C
Clarkson Milling Co. (300)
 C
KY.—Frankfort
Miles Milling Co., J. E.
 (500) C
KY.—Hopkinsville
Acme Mills Co. (350)....D
Crescent Milling Co. (300)
KY.—Lexington
Lexington Roller Mills Co.
 (600) ....A
KY.—Louisville
Ballard & Ballard Co.
 (2000) ....AA
Gathright & Co., R. O.
 (300) ....A
MD.—Baltimore
Gambrill Mfg. Co., C. A.
 (2200) ....AAA
MICH.—Adrian
Washington Milling Co.
 (400) C
MICH.—Albion
Albion Milling Co. (400).B
MICH.—Alma
Wright & Co., A. W. (300)
 AAAA
MICH.—Coldwater
Coombs Milling Co. (1000)
 B
MICH.—Detroit
Scott, David (1600).....AA
MICH.—Dowagiac
Colby Milling Co. (350)..B
MICH.—Grand Rapids
Model Mills (350) C
Valley City Milling Co.
 (350) ....G
Voigt Milling Co. (900)..AA
MICH.—Greenville
Middleton & Sons, E. (550)
 A
MICH.—Harbor Beach
Huron Milling Co. (365).A

FLOUR (Con.)

MICH.—Holland
Walsh-De Roo Milling Co.
(600) ....B
MICH.—Jackson
Eldred Mill Co. (600).....B
MICH.—Lansing
Thomas & Bro., F. (550).AA
MICH.—Niles
Niles Milling Co. (500)..A
MICH.—Saginaw
Brand & Hardin (300)...B
Saginaw Milling Co. (322)
B
MICH.—Sherman
Masqueston & Co. (640)..H
MICH.—Tecumseh
Heck, C. H. (516)........F
MICH.—Three Rivers
Harris Milling Co. (420)..C
MINN.—Albert Lea
Albert Lea Milling Co. (300)
B
MINN.—Anoka
Pillsbury-Washburn Flour
Mills Co. (1300)...AAAA
MINN.—Appleton
Jennison Co., W. J. (300), C
MINN.—Cannon Falls
Goodhue Mill Co. (500)...C
MINN.—Duluth
Duluth Universal Milling
Co. (800) ....B
MINN.—Eden , alley
Nerlien. Ludwig L. (350).C
MINN.—Elizabeth
Freeman Mill Co., A. A.
(300) ....D
MINN.—Elk River
Elk River Milling Co. (300)
C
MINN.—Faribault
Sheffield-King Milling Co.
(2000) ....AA
MINN.—Fergus Falls
Fergus Flour Mills Co.
(400) ....B
MINN.—Hastings
Carter Seymour (1100)..C
MINN.—Jordan
King & Co., H. H. (400).C
MINN.—Janesville
Jennison Bros. Co. (700, AA
MINN.—Lake Ci .
Tennant & Hoyt (500)...D
MINN.—Lake Crystal
Graif Bros. Milling Co.
(300) ....D
MINN.—Little Falls
Minnesota Mill Co. (500).C
MINN.—Madelia
Christensen Co., C. S. (500)
MINN.—Mankato
Hubbard Milling Co. (1200)
B
MINN.—Marshall
Marshall Milling Co. (400)
A
MINN.—Melrose
Melrose Milling Co. (300).B
MINN.—Minneapolis
Barber Milling Co. (1200).D
Christian. Geo. C. (1800).B
D
Elk Valley Mill Co. (500)
D
King & Co.. H. H. (400).C
National Milling Co. (700)
B
Nerlien, Ludwig L. (500).C
Northwestern Consolidated
Milling Co. (1800).....B
Phoenix Mill Co. (650)...A
Pillsbury-Washburn Flour
Mills Co. (Ltd.) (30,000)
AAAA
Russel-Miller Milling Co.
(1500) ....F
Sheffield-King Milling Co.
(2500) ....AA
Washburn-Crosby Co.
(25,000) ....AAAA
MINN.—Montevideo
Montevideo Roller Mill Co.
(400) ....A
MINN.—Montgomery
Quirk Milling Co., Jas.
(600) ....A
MINN.—Morton
Morton Merchants' Milling
Co. (500) ....B

FLOUR (Con.)

MINN.—New Prague
New Prague Mills Co.
(2000) C
MINN.—New Richland
Everett Aughenbaugh & Co.
(300) ....AA
MINN.—New Ulm
Eagle Roller Mill Co.
(2500) ....AA
New Ulm Roller Mill Co.
(500) C
MINN.—Osakis
Osakis Milling Co. (400).D
MINN.—Red Lake Falls
Red Lake Falls Milling Co.
(500) ....B
MINN.—Red Wing
Simmons Milling Co. (1200)
B
MINN.—St. Cloud
Carter, Wesley & Co. (700)
C
Tileston Milling Co., Geo.
(1000) ....A
MINN.—St. Peter
Sackett & Fay (350)....A
MINN.—Shakopee
Christian & Co., L. (900).A
MINN.—Sleepy Eye
Sleepy Eye Milling Co.
(1500) ....A
MINN.—Springfield
Springfield Roller Mill Co.
(300) ....A
MINN.—Wabasha
Wabasha Roller Mill Co.
(600) ....B
MINN.—Waseca
Everett, Aughenbaugh & Co.
(700) ....AA
MINN.—Waterville
Quirk Milling Co., Jas.
(500) ....A
MINN.—Wells
Zatzenbach Milling Co., W.
H. (400) ....B
MINN.—Winnebago
Parker, Leland Mill Co.
(400) ....D
MINN.—Winona
Bay State Milling Co.
(1500) ....A
MO.—Boonville
Sombart Milling & Merc.
Co. (300) ....A
MO.—Carthage
Cowgill & Hill Milling Co.
(500) ....A
MO.—Clinton
Bernheimer Milling & Merc.
Co.. M. (600) ....B
MO.—Hannibal
Carter, Shepard & Co. (500)
C
Hannibal Milling Co. (600)
B
MO.—Higginsville
Higginsville Milling Co.
(300) ....B
MO.—Independence
Waggoner-Gates Milling Co.
(500) ....A
MO.—Jackson
Cape Co. Milling Co. (1000)
A
MO.—Jefferson
Dulle Milling Co., G. H.
(500) ....A
MO.—Kansas City
Arms & Kidder (700)....B
Kansas City Milling Co.
(800) ....A
Kelley Milling Co. (2000).X
Kirk & Co., David B. (1000)
A
Zenith Milling Co. (900)..B
MO.—Lexington
McGrew Milling Co. (500)
B
MO.—New Haven
Wolff Milling Co. (300)..B
MO.—Rich Hill
Flanagan Mills & Elevator
Co. (400) ....D
MO.—St. Joseph
Davis Mill & Mfg. Co., R.
T. (1000) ....A
Faucett Mill Co., R. H.
(350) ....B

416

FLOUR (Con.)
Hauck, Geo. M. (350)....C
MO.—St. Louis
Bernet-Kraft-Kauffman
  Milling Co. (800)......D
Bernheimer Milling & Merc.
  Co., M. (600).........D
Buss Flour Mills, J. B.
  (350) ....AA
Camp Spring Mill Co. (1200)
  ....A
Carondelet Milling Co. (350)
  ....B
Eggers' Milling Co. (500).A
Engelke & Ferner Mill Co.
  (1500) ....A
Goddard Flour Co., E. (800)
  ....B
Kehlor Bros. (8000).AAAA
Meyer & Sons, Jno. F.
  (2000) ....AA
Plant Milling Co., Geo. P.
  (2000) ..,.........AAA
Regina Flour Mill Co. (1200)
  ....A
St. Jacob Enterprise Mill
  Co. (350) X
St. Louis Victoria Flour
  Mills (1200) ....A
Saxony Mills (1000)......B
Sessinghaus Milling Co.
  (450) ....B
Stanard Milling Co., E. O.
  (4000) ....AA
Washburn-Crosby Co
  (25,000) ....AAAA
MO.—Silkeston
Bowman-Matthews Milling
  Co. (350) ....AAA
Greer-Ebert Milling Co.
  (500) ....B
MO.—Silver Lake
Geile & Lorenz (300).....A
MO.—Springfield
Eisenmayer Milling Co.
  (600) ....B
Link Milling Co. (600)..B
Meyer & Sons, J. F. (1000)
  ....AA
MO.—Warrensburg
Markward, Isaac (300)...A
MO.—Washington
Washington Flour Mills Co.
  (400) C
MONT.—Bozeman
Story, Nelson & Co. (500)
  ....AAA
MONT.—Great Falls
Royal Milling Co. (500)..A
MONT.—Kalispell
Royal Milling Co. (300)..A
NEBR.—Crete
Crete Mills (500)........A
NEBR.—Omaha
Omaha Milling Co. (400)..B
NEBR.—Schuyler
Wells. Abbott & Newman
  (600) ....AA
NEBR.—Verdigris
Pavlik Bros. (500) ......D
N. Y.—Akron
Newman, H. L. & W. C.
  (300) ....B
N. Y.—Baldwinsville
Frazee Milling Co., Jas.
  (500) ....B
N. Y.—Binghamton
Moon & Co., Geo. I. (300).A
N. Y.—Brooklyn
Fulton Grain & Milling Co.
  (800) C
N. Y.—Buffalo
Banner Milling Co. (1000)
  ....AA
Husted Milling & Elev. Co.
  (500) ....A
Marine Milling Co. (300)
  ....AA
Niagara Falls Milling Co.
  (2000) ....A
Thornton & Chester Milling
  Co. (1000) ....AAAA
Urban Milling Co. (2000).A
N. Y.—Central Bridge
Becker & Co. (300)......C
N. Y.—Cohocton
Larrowe Milling Co. (800)
 C
N. Y.—Corning
Hoyt, S. T. (300) ....A

FLOUR (Con.)
N. Y.—Dresden
Ferenbaugh, C. H. (300).D
N. Y.—Fulton
Gage & Co., W. G. (500).B
Gilbert & Nichols (300)...C
N. Y.—Ithaca
Fall Creek Milling Co.
  (300) C
N. Y.—Lockport
Franklin Mills Co. (400)..A
Thompson Milling Co. (500)
  ....A
N. Y.—Moravia
Selover Milling Co. (300).B
N. Y.—Rochester
Chase & Co. (300).......B
Hinds & Co., J. A. (400).A
N. DAK.—Bismark
Missouri Valley Milling
  Co. (450) C
N. DAK.—Fargo
Fargo Roller Mill Co. (500)
 C
N. DAK.—Grafton
Leistikow, W. C. (500).AA
N. DAK.—Grand Forks
Diamond Milling Co. (850)
  ....B
N. DAK.—Kindred
Rastad & Cresse (350)...D
N. DAK.—Mandan
Missouri Valley Milling Co.
  (450) C
N. DAK.—Valley City
Russell Miller Milling Co.
  (300) ....B
OHIO—Akron
American Cereal Co. (2400)
  ....AAAA
Great Western Cereal Co.
  (1250) ....AAAA
Colton Bros. (500).......A
OHIO—Canal Dover
Hardesty Bros. (500)...AA
OHIO—Chillicothe
Marfield Milling Co. (700)
  ....D
OHIO—Cincinnati
Foulds Milling Co. (500).B
OHIO—Circleville
Smith Mill Co. (1000)...A
OHIO—Cleveland
Commercial Milling Co.
  (2000) ....B
OHIO—Columbus
Hardesty Bros. (500) ...AA
OHIO—Dayton
Durst Milling Co. (400)..A
OHIO—Hamilton
Carr Milling Co. (1500)..C
Semler Milling Co. (300).C
OHIO—Kent
Williams Bros. Co. (600)
  ....B
OHIO—Mansfield
Hicks-Brown Milling Co.
  (800) ....B
OHIO—Marietta
Phoenix Mill Co. (300)...B
OHIO—Mount Vernon
Northwestern Elev. & Mill
  Co. (450) ....AA
OHIO—Orrville
Orrville Milling Co. (800).A
OHIO—Roscoe
Lee. Edwin S. (300)....B
OHIO—Shelby
Davis Mill Co. (1000)....C
OHIO—Springfield
Ansted & Burk Co. (500).A
OHIO—Spring Valley
Barrett & Son (300).....D
OHIO—Tiro
Auburn Milling Co. (300).C
OHIO—Toledo
National Milling Co.
  (4,000) ....AA
Northwestern Elev. & Mill
  Co. (2000) ....AA
Toledo Grain & Milling Co.
  (350) ....B
OHIO—Troy
Allen & Wheeler (350)..AA
OHIO—Wauseon
Lyon, Clement & Greenleaf
  Co. (1,000) ....AA
OHIO—Youngstown
Baldwin, Homer (400)...A
OKLA.—El Reno
Canadian Co. Mill & Elev.

Co. (700) ....B
El Reno Mill & Elev. Co. (500) ....B
OKLA.—Enid
Enid Mill & Elev. Co. (400) ....B
OKLA.—Kingfisher
Oklahoma Mill Co. (300).C
OKLA.—Oklahoma
Acme Milling Co. (400)..B
OKLA.—Pawhuska
Osage Roller Mills (500).D
OKLA.—Perry
Perry Mill Co. (400).....A
OKLA.—Pond Creek
Pond Creek Mill & Elev. Co. (400) C
OREGON—Pendleton
Byers, W. S. (500)......A
OREGON—Portland
Portland Flouring Mills Co. (750) ....A
OREGON—Salem
Salem Flouring Mills Co. (500) ....B
PA.—Butler
Klingler & Co. (300).....A
PA.—Erie
Crouch Bros. Co. (300)..A
PA.—Lewisburg
Buffalo Milling Co. (350) A
PA.—Philadelphia
Milbourne Milling Co. (800) A
Quaker City Flour Mills Co. (600) ....A
PA.—Treichlers
Mauser Mill Co. (300) ....A
PA.—Warren
Warren Mills Co. ......AA
S. DAK.—Aberdeen
Aberdeen Mill Co. (400)..B
S. DAK.—Ashton
Christian, Geo. C. (350)...C
S. DAK.—Redfield
Christian, Geo. C. (500) ..B
S. DAK.—Watertown
Stokes Milling Co., W. H. (600) ....A
TENN.—Chattanooga
Mountain City Mill Co. (1.000) ....A
Shelton Mills (300) ......A
TENN.—Columbia
Columbia Mill & Elev. Co. (350) ....B
TENN.—Franklin
Lillie Mill Co. (300) .....A
TENN.—Knoxville
Smith & Co., J. Allen (1.000) ....A
TENN.—Lebanon
Farmers' Milling Co. (400) C
TENN.—Memphis
Cannon & Yates Co. (1.000) ....B
TENN.—Morristown
Reid Bros. (500) C
TENN.—Nashville
Cumberland Mills (2.500) AAA
Liberty Mills (3.500) ....A
Model Mills (1.500) ......A
TEXAS—Dallas
New Century Milling Co. (1.000) ....A
Stanard Milling Co., E. O. (2.000) ....AA
TEXAS—Denison
Denison Milling Co. (400).C
TEXAS—Denton
Alliance Milling Co. (800) A
TEXAS—Fort Worth
Anchor Roller Mills (550).A
Cameron Mill & Elev. Co. (2.000) ....AA
TEXAS—Gainesville
Whaley Mill & Elev. Co. (600) ....A
TEXAS—Galveston
Texas Star Flour Mills (850) ....AA
TEXAS—Greenville
Greenville Mill & Elev. Co. (300) C
TEXAS—Houston
Thompson Milling Co., T. H. (400) ....B

FLOUR (Con.)
TEXAS—New Braunfels
Landa Roller Mills (550) .. AA
TEXAS—San Antonio
Guenther Milling Co. (600) A
TEXAS—Sherman
Brennan & Son, J. B. (350) B
Diamond Milling Co. (350) B
TEXAS—Wichita Falls
Victory Milling Co. (300).D
Wichita Mill & Elev. Co. (650) ....B
UTAH—Ogden
Ogden Milling & Elev. Co. (400) ....A
UTAH—Salt Lake City
Inter Mountain Milling Co. (600) ....B
VA.—Lynchburg
Hurt & Son, S. C. (300)..A
VA.—Norfolk
Daisy Roller Mills (1.200).C
VA.—Richmond
Moore, Warner & Co. (700) AA
VA.—Staunton
White Star Mills (500) ...A
VA.—Winchester
Baker's Sons, W. B. (300) A
WASH.—Davenport
Big Bend Milling Co. (320) B
WASH.—Dayton
Portland Flouring Mills Co. (300) ....A
WASH.—Garfield
Tacoma Grain Co. (1.000) A
WASH.—Harrington
Harrington Milling Co. (300) C
WASH.—Reardon
Washington Grain & Milling Co. (350) ....D
WASH.—Rockford
Sheldon Milling Co. (350) D
WASH.—Seattle
Centennial Mill Co. (2.500) AA
WASH.—Spokane
Portland Flouring Mill Co. (600) ....A
WASH.—Sprague
Sprague Roller Mill Co. (300) ....B
WASH.—Tacoma
Puget Sound Flouring Mill Co. (1.800) ....A
Tacoma Grain Co. (1.000).A
WASH.—Waitsburg
Preston-Parton Milling Co. (350) ....B
WASH.—Wilbur
Columbia River Milling Co. (425) C
W. VA.—Parkersburg
Novelty Mills Co. (300) . B
WIS.—Appleton
Willy & Co. (400) ......B
WIS.—Beloit
Blodgett Milling Co. (300) B
WIS.—Berlin
Wright, Stillman & Co. (300) ....B
WIS.—Chippewa Falls
Consolidated Milling Elev. & Power Co. (350) .....B
WIS.—Green Bay
Ebeling, Jno. H. (500)....B
WIS.—Hortonville
Buchmann Bros. (350) ..G
WIS.—Janesville
Blodgett Milling Co. (500) B
WIS.—La Crosse
Listman Mill Co. (3.000)..A
WIS.—Manitowoc
Schuette, Jno. (300) ......A
WIS.—Milwaukee
Atlas Bread Factory (1.400) C
Faist, Kraus & Co. ......A
Kern & Sons, Jno. B. (2.500) AA
Manegold Milling Co., C.

FLOUR (Con.)
(900) ....B
WIS.—Neenah
Krueger & Lachman Milling
Co. (300) ....B
WIS.—Wauwatosa
Wauwatosa Milling, Fuel &
Lumber Co. (500) .....F
WIS.—West Superior
United States Flour Milling
Co. (2,000) ....AAAA

FLOUR: RICE

CAL.—San Francisco
Del Monte Milling Co.....A
LA.—New Orleans
Talmage, Jno. S.........A
New York City
Archibald & Lewis........C
Armstrong, Chas. E.......D
Talmage Sons & Co., Dan.A
S. C.—Charleston
Talmage, Dan ....A
West Point Mill Co......A
TEXAS.—Beaumont
Weiss-Kyle-McFadden Co..A
TEXAS—Eagle Lake
Eagle Lake Rice Milling
Co. ....A

FLOWERS

See also Plants & Millinery.

ILL.—Chicago
Botanical Decorating Co.
(Millinery) ....E
Nelson, Henry (Artificial;
Leaves) X
Netschert, Carl (Artificial)
D
N. J.—Jersey City
Dorbandt, Chas. (Paper).H
New York City
Gerard, S. (Artificial;
Leaves) ....D
Lindheim & Son, R. (Mil-
linery) ....A
Neumann, Alvina (Black
(Artificial) C
Schieffelin & Co., 24 E. 4th
(Arnica) ....AA
Winsburger & Hecht
(Millinery) ....AA
PA.—Philadelphia
Baxter, Jennie & Lizzie
(Artificial; Leaves) ....A
Henley's Sons, David (Arti-
ficial; Leaves) ....A
Thorn Co., J. T., 123 N. 7th
(Artificial) ....D

FLUES

IOWA—Burlington
Murray Iron Wks. Co.
(Boiler) ....A
MASS.—Boston
Chesterton & Co., A. W.,
64 India (Boiler) ......A
N. Y.—Brooklyn
Continental Iron Works
(Boiler; Corrugated) ..A
OHIO—Cleveland
Cleveland Flue Cleaner Mfg.
Co. (Boiler) C
PA.—New Brighton
Pittsburg Clay Mfg. Co.
(Chimney) ....AAAA
PA.—Philadelphia
Pedrick & Ayer Co., 1001
Hamilton (Boiler) .....A
PA.—Pittsburg
Riter-Conley Co. (Chimney;
Smoke) ....AAA

FLUIDS

CONN.—Westport
Embalmers' Supply Co.
(Embalming) C
MD.—Baltimore
Schultz & Co., A., 1016
E. Balto. (Soldering)...A
MASS.—Boston
Egyptian Chemical Co.
(Embalming) X
MASS.—Springfield
Dickinson, Frank W. (Em-

FLUIDS (Con.)
balming) C
MICH.—Grand Rapids
Durfee Embalming Fluid
Co. (Embalming)......B
Mills & Lacey Mfg. Co.
(Depilating; Embalming)
D
MO.—Kansas City
Bankers' Ink Co., 116 W.
6th (Bankers' Copying;
Bankers' Writing)......D
MO.—St. Louis
Hisey & Son, W. S.
(Soldering) ....D
N. J.—Newark
Schneider, Emil (Jewelers'
Soldering) ....D
N. Y.—Brooklyn
Seldner & Enquist, Leonard
& Richardson (Soldering)
F
N. Y.—Buffalo
Buffalo Specialty Mfg. Co.
(Tire) ....B
New York City
Callahan & Co., G. W.. 218
Front (Soldering)...,...F
OHIO—Dayton
Fansher Bros. (Bleachings)
E
OHIO—Toledo
National Cement & Rubber
Mfg. Co. (Enamel Clean-
ing) C
PA.—Philadelphia
Eckels & Co., H. S., 2005
Market (Embalming)...D

FLUMES

ALA.—Birmingham
Southern Bridge Co......D
CAL.—San Francisco
Risdon Iron & Locomotive
Works (Iron; Steel)
AAAA
OHIO—Youngstown
Pollock Co., W. B. (Steel)
AA
PA.—Hanover
Fitz Water Wheel Co.
(Iron) ....D
PA.—Williamsport
Keeler Co., E. (Steel)....**A**

FLUORO-SCOPES

MASS.—Boston
Swett & Lewis Co., 18
Boylston ....E
New York City
Edison Phonograph Agency
D

FLUORSPAR

OHIO—Cincinnati
Obermayer Co.. S. ......AA
PA.—Philadelphia
Lea & Co., J. T...........A

FLUSHERS

New York City
Reynolds Plumbers Supply
Co.. M. (Sewer) ....,.B
PA.—Pittsburg
Standard Mfg. Co. (Sewer)
AA

FLUTERS

See also Machinery

ILL.—Chicago
Sinclair Co., S. H., 8 S.
Canal ....F
N. Y.—Buffalo
Shepard Co., Sidney
(Hand) ....AAAA
New York City
Jones, Thos. W., 18
Fletcher ....F
N. Y.—Rochester
Streeter Co., W. R........A
N. Y.—Troy
Troy Laundry Machinery Co.
(Ltd.) (Hand)........AA
OHIO—Cincinnati
Am. Laundry Machinery Co.
(Hand) ....AA

FLUTERS (Con.)
Pease Mfg. Co...........F
PA.—Erie
Lovell Mfg. Co. (Hand).AA
PA.—Philadelphia
North Bros. Mfg. Co.
  (Hand) ....AA

FLUTES
See Musical Insts.

FLUX
COLO.—Denver
Colorado Lime & Fluxing
  Co. ....D
CONN.—New Haven
New Era Lustre Co. (Solder-
  ing) ....E
IND.—Asphaltum
Indian Asphalt Co. (As-
  phalt) ....B
MD.—Baltimore
Baltimore Chemical Co.
  (Soldering) ....D
Schultz & Co., A. (Solder-
  ing) ....A
Sonneborn's Sons. L., 801
  So. Wolfe (Soldering)..C
Thomson Chemical Co.
  (Soldering) ....B
MASS.—Boston
Massachusetts Chemical Co.,
  170 Summer (Rubber)..A
N. J.—Newark
American Oil & Supply Co.
  (Jewelers') ....B
OHIO—Cleveland
Graselli Chemical Co.
  (Soldering) ....D
OHIO—Columbus
Franklin Stone Co. (Bes-
  semer) ....D

FLYERS
CONN.—North Windham
Hartson Co., L. M. (Silk).X
MASS.—Boston
Riley & Co., C. E., 65
  Franklin ....A
MASS.—Fall River
Thurston & Son, A. G....E
MASS.—Hopedale
Westcott. A. W.........F
MASS.—Lawrence
Merriman Flyer Wks......F
MASS.—New Bedford
Baker Machine Co........D
N. H.—Manchester
Smith Co., J. A. V......E
N. J.—Paterson
Buckley's Son, B........E
R. I.—Bridgeton
Hopkins Machine Wks....X
R. I.—Providence
Providence Machine Co..AA

FOBS
See Jewelry

FOIL
See also Tinfoil

CONN.—Hartford
Ney & Co., J. M. (Gold..C
ILL.—Chicago
Hutchinson & Son, W. H.
  (Tin) ....A
MO.—St. Louis
Johnston Tin Foil & Metal
  Co. (Tin) ....A
New York City
Conley Foil Co., 521 W.
  25th (Tin; Paper-backed)
  ....AAA
Crooks Co., J. J. (Tin;
  Gold) ....A
Lehmaier, Schwartz & Co.
  (Tin) ....AA
Witteman Bros. (Tin)...AA
PA.—Erie
Baker & Adamson Chem.
  Co. (Copper) ....A
PA.—Malvern
Bishop Co., J. (Platinum)
  ....D
PA.—Philadelphia

FOIL (Con.)
Hastings & Co. (Gold).AA
Johnson & Lund (Gold).AA
White Dental Mfg. Co.
  (Gold) ....AAAA

FOLDERS
See also Machinery
ILL.—Chicago
Rand. McNally & Co. (Inc.)
  (Railway) ....AAAA
Western Bank Note Engrav-
  Co. (Railway) ....AA
MASS.—Boston
Rand-Avery Supply Co.
  (Railway) ....AA
New York City
Am. Bank Note Co. (Rail-
  way) ....AAAA
International Bank Note
  Co. (Railway) ......B

FOLIAGE
See also Flowers

New York City
Campomenosi, P., 542 W.
  Bdway. (Artificial)....D
Neumann, Alvin A., 24 E.
  4th (Artificial)......C

FOLIOS
See also Leather Goods

ILL.—Chicago
Keating Co. (Music)......F
MASS.—Foxboro
Fales Folio Co. (Music)..H
N. J.—Jersey City
Mehl & C., John (Music)
  ....AAA

FOLLOWERS
MASS.—Taunton
Taunton Locomotive Mfg.
  Co. (Locomotive) ......A

FONTS
MASS.—Stockbridge
Snyder, J. L. (Baptismal)
  ....H

FOOD-ANIMAL ETC
See also Seed; Bird

FLA.—Lake Mary
Planters Mfg. Co. (Cattle;
  Horse; Poultry).......A
GA.—Sandersville
Sandersville Enterprise Co.
ILL.—Chicago
Amer. Cereal Co., Railway
  Exch. (Cattle; Horse;
  Poultry) ....AAAA
Western Horse & Cattle
  Food Co., 438 N. Clark
  (Cattle) ....E
ILL.—Quincy
Stahl, Geo. H. (Poultry).B
ILL.—Waukegan
Barwell, J. W. (Cattle)..C
IOWA—Allerton
Allerton Caponizer Mfg. Co.
  (Poultry) ....H
KY.—Louisville
Menz Co., G. W. (Bird)..G
MASS.—Springfield
Bartlett & Holmes (Horse;
  Poultry) C
MICH.—Detroit
Ingram & Co., F. F. (Cattle;
  Horse; Poultry).......B
MINN.—Minneapolis
Amer. Standard Food Co.
  (Cattle) C
Chemical Mfg. Co. (Cattle;
  Horse; Poultry).......F
MO.—St. Louis
Stillwagon Food Co. (Cattle;
  Horse; Poultry).......E
NEBR.—Omaha
Sanborn Co., T. E. (Cattle;
  Horse; Poultry).......C
N. H.—Plaistow
Knight's Stock & Poultry

FOOD (*Con.*)

Food Co. (Poultry).....F

N. J.—Hoboken
Vanderbilt & Son, J.
(Cattle; Horse; Poultry)
................D

N. Y.—Ransomville
Curtis & Co., W. R.
(Poultry) ....G

OHIO—Newark
Styron, Beggs & Co.
(Cattle; Horse) ......A

OHIO—Piqua
Piqua Paint & Putty Co.
(Pearl Poultry).......D

OHIO—Tiffin
Capitol Food Co. (Animal)
................D

PA;—Burlington
Henry Johnson & Lord Co.
(Cattle; Horse; Poultry)
................D

PA.—Philadelphia
Pratt Food Co. (Cattle;
Horse, &c.) ....A

PA.—St. Albans
Capitol Soap & Mfg. Co.
(Poultry) X

PA.—York
York Chemical Wks.
(Poultry) ....A

VT.—Brattleboro
Peels Food Co. (Cattle;
Horse, &c.) ....H

VT.—Hyde Park
Page, Carroll S. (Poultry).A

VT.—North Bennington
Henry, B. T. (Poultry)..F

FOOD-PREPARED, CEREAL, BREAKFAST ETC

CAL.—Los Angeles
California Cereal Food Co.
(Cereals Prep.)......AAA
Pacific Pure Food Co.
(Prepared) ....AAA

CAL.—Oakland
Butler Co., Chas. H.
(Cereals) C

CAL.—Placerville
Pioneer Milling Co.
(Cereals) ....AAAA

CAL.—Sacramento
Phoenix Milling Co.
(Cereals) ....A
Sperry Flour Co. (Br. San
Fran., Cal.) (Cereals)
................AAAA

CAL.—St. Helena
St. Helena Sanitarium Food
Co. (Cereals Prep.)....B

CAL.—Salinas City
Sperry Flour Co. (Cereals)
................AAAA

CAL.—San Francisco
Amer.´ Milling Co., Battery
& Union (Cereals; Corn-
meal; Oatmeal) ....A
Capitol. Mills, 114 Sacra-
mento (Cereals; Corn-
meal; Oatmeal) .....AA
Del Monte Milling Co., 400
Front (Cereals; Rolled
Oats; Cornmeal; Oatmeal)
................A
Empire Milling Co., 310
Townsend (Cereals)...B
Hinz & Plageman, Mission
& Main (Cereals; Hominy;
Cornmeal; Oatmeal)...B
Sperry Flour Co. (Cereals)
................AAAA
Stockton Milling Co., 112
Calif. (Cereals) ......AA

CONN.—Fair Haven
Yankee Crisp Cereal Co.
(Cereals) ....B

CONN.—New Britain
Taco Milling Co. (Cereals)
................B

CONN.—New Haven
Imperial Granum Co. (Baby
Food Prep.) ....A
Ready Bits Co. (Cereals).C

FOOD (*Con.*)

CONN.—South Norwalk
New England Food Co.
(Cereals Prep.) ......A

DEL.—New Castle
Lea & Sons Co., Wm. (Br.)
(Cornmeal; Hominy).AAA

DEL.—Wilmington
Lea & Sons Co., Wm. (Cornmeal; Hominy) .....AAA

FLA.—Jacksonville
Elgin Butter & Pure Food
Co. (Prep) C

GA.—Atlanta
Atlanta Milling Co.
(Hominy) ....A
Shewmake & Murphey
(Cereals Gds.) C

GA.—Cartersville
Etowah Milling Co.
(Hominy) ....B

ILL.—Bloomington
Hooper & Son, B. T.
(Buckwheat) ....B
McCord, J. C. (Buckwheat)
................C

ILL.—Carlinville
St. Louis Milling Co.
(Cereals) ....A

ILL.—Chicago
Amer. Cereal Co., Monad.
Blk. (Cereals; Cornmeal;
Hominy; Oatmeal) ....
................AAAA
Amer. Hominy Co. (Cereals)
................AAAA
Continental Cereal Co., 163
Randolph (Cereals) ....B
Dickinson Co., A., W. Tay-
lor & The River (Buck
wheat) ....AA
Great Western Cereal Co., 77
Jackson (Cereals; Corn-
meal; Hominy; Oatmeal)
................AAAA
Knoke & Groll (Cereals;
Barley) C
Lenfestey Milling Co., J. T.,
27 Mich. Av. (Buckwheat;
Cereals) ....A
Martin & Co., 46 S. Water
(Oatmeal) ....AA
Rieser-Livingston Co., 233
Johnson (Buckwheat;
Pancake; Flour) ......A
Reifsnyder, Warren, 130
Kinzie (Cereals; Corn-
meal) C
Van Mills (G. J. Vandehou-
ten, Prop.), 1057 Grand
Av. (Buckwheat) ......D

ILL.—Danville
Amer. Hominy Co. (Hom-
iny) ....AAAA

ILL.—Decatur
Amer. Hominy Co. (Cereals;
Hominy) ....AAAA
Decatur Cereal Mill Co.
(Cornmeal) C
Decatur Milling Co. (Cer-
eals; Cornmeal; Hominy)
................A
Suffern, Hunt & Co.
(Cereals) ....A

ILL.—Elgin
Elgin Milkine Co. (Milk
Food) ....B

ILL.—Eureka
Dickinson & Co. (Hominy)
................C

ILL.—Joliet
Great Western Cereal Co.
(Br. Chicago.) (Cereals;
Oatmeal) ....AAAA

ILL.—Paris
Kidder & Co., F. L. (Cer-
eals; Hominy; Corn-
meal) ....B

ILL.—Peoria
Donmeyer, Gardner & Co.
(Cereals) ....B
Gift & Sons, J. W. (Cereals)
................B
Great Western Cereal Co.
(Br. Chicago) (Oatmeal)
................AAAA
Nat'l Cereal Milling Co.
(Cereals) ....A

ILL.—Quincy
Battle Creek Breakfast Food
Co. (Cereals) ....A
Long, E. (Buckwheat) ..F

FOOD (*Con.*)

Pape & Loos (Buckwheat)
           G

ILL.—Shelton
Bishopp Hominy Co. (Cereals; Hominy) C

IND—Delphi
Great Western Canning Co. (Hominy) C

IND.—Goshen
Goshen Milling Co. (Buckwheat; Cornmeal; Oatmeal) ....B

IND.—Ft. Wayne
Mayflower Mills (Cereals)
           C

IND.—Indianapolis
Amer. Hominy Co. (Cereals; Hominy) ....AAAA
Evans Milling Co. (Cereals)
           B
Van Camp Pack. Co., 600 Ky. Av. (Hominy) ...AA

IND.—Lafayette
Geiger Finney Co. (Pancake Flour) C
Lafayette Hominy Mills Co. (Cereals; Hominy) ....B

IND.—Mishawaka
Sheppard Cereal Co. (Cereals) ....AAA

IND.—Montezuma
Nordyke, A. H. (Montezuma Mills) (Cereals)..AA

IND.—Mt. Vernon
Amer. Hominy Co. (Hominy) ....AAAA

IND.—Newport
Newport Milling Co. (Cornmeal) ....A

IND.—Terre Haute
Amer. Hominy Co. (Cereals; Hominy; Cornmeal) ....
         AAAA

IND.—Vincennes
Emison & Co., J. & S. (Cereals; Corn Gds.; Hominy)
         AA

IOWA—Cedar Falls
Great Western Cereal Co. (Br. Chicago) (Cornmeal; Oatmeal) ....AAAA

IOWA—Cedar Rapids
Amer. Cereal Co. (Oatmeal)
         AAAA
White Cereal Co., P. G. (Buckwheat; Cereals)..C

IOWA—Davenport
Crescent Macaroni Co. (Pancake Flour) ....B
National Oatmeal Co. (Cereals; Oatmeal) ....A

IOWA—Ft. Dodge
Great Western Cereal Co. (Br. Chicago) (Cereals; Oatmeal) ....AAAA
Heath & Sons, H. R. (Pancake Flour) ....A

IOWA—Glenwood
New Glenwood Can. Co. (Hominy) C

IOWA—Independence
Independence Mills Co. (Buckwheat) C

IOWA—Keokuk
Gate City Milling Co. (Cereals; Prep.; Pancake Flour) C
Keokuk Cereal Co. (Cereals)
         B

IOWA—Le Mars
Plymouth Roller Mills (Buckwheat; Cereals)..B

IOWA—Muscatine
Great Western Cereal Co. (Br. Chicago) (Cereals; Oatmeal; Prep.) ..AAAA

IOWA—Sioux City
Great Western Cereal Co. (Br. Chicago) (Hominy)
         AAAA
Sioux Milling Co. (Pancake Flour) ....A

IOWA—Waterloo
Great Western Cereal Co. (Oatmeal) ....AAAA

KANS.—Atchison
Blair Milling Co. (Buckwheat) ....A

KANS.—Clay Center
Snell Mill & Elevator Co. (Cereals; Prepared) ...B

FOOD (*Con.*)

LA.—New Orleans
New Orleans Cereal Co., 509 Conti (Cereals) ....A

MD.—Baltimore
Baltimore Pearl Hominy Co., 335 McElderrys Wharf..C
Lea & Sons Co., Wm. (Br.) (Cornmeal) ....AAA

MD.—Cambridge
Cambridge Mfg. Co. (Hominy) ....A

MD.—Westminster
Smith, Yinghing & Co. (Hominy) ....A

MASS.—Boston
Amer. Cereal Co., Chamber of Com. (Cereals) .AAAA
Beardsley's Son's, J. W., 131 State (Prepared) C
Cole & Co., Benj. Jr., 46 Com. (Cereals) C
Great Western Cereal Co., Chamb. of Com. (Cereals)
         AAAA
Health Food Co., 199 Tremont (Cereals; Prep.)..C
Mellins Food Co. of North Amer., 291 Atlantic Av. (Infants' Food) .....AA
Murdoch Liquid Food Co., Huntington Av., cor Grinslow (Prep.) C
Potter & Wrightington, 60 Commerce (Cereals)..AA

MASS.—Crookston
Crookston Oatmeal Co. (Oatmeal) ....AA

MASS.—Worcester
Natural Food Co. (Br. Niagara Falls, N. Y.) (Cereals) ....AAAA

MICH.—Ann Arbor
Michigan Milling Co. (Buckwheat) ....AA

MICH.—Battle Creek
Battle Creek Flaked Food Co. (Cereals; Prepared).B
Battle Creek Sanitarium Food Co. (Cereals; Prep.)
         A
Cero-Fruto Co. (Ltd.) (Cereals) ....AAA
Fruit Cereal Health Assn. (Ltd.) (Cereals; Prep.)C
Hibbard Food Co. (Cereals)
         AA
Korn-Krisp Co. (Cereals; Prep.) ....B
Malta Vito Pure Food Co. (Cereals; Prep.) ....AA
Malt Too Flaked Food Co. (Cereals; Prep.) ......AA
Malted Food Co. (Cereals; Prep.) ....A
Michigan Sanitarium & Benevolent Assn. (Cereals; Prep.) ....A
Norka Food Co. (Ltd.) (Cereals; Prep.) .....AA
Postum Cereal Co. (Ltd.) (Cereals) ....AAA
Price Cereal Food Co. (Cereals; Prep.) ......A
Real Food Co. (Cereals)..B
Sanitary My. Food Co. (Cereals) ....AA
Sanitas Nut Food Co. (Cereals; Prep.) C
World's Fare Food Co. (Cereals; Prep.) ......B

MICH.—Bay City
Hammond Food Co. (Cereals) ....B

MICH.—Carleton
Kahlbaum, J. E. (Buckwheat) ....D

MICH.—Coldwater
Cream of Oats Co. (Cereals) ....A

MICH.—Detroit
Beck & Sons, J., 245 Congress (Cereals; Cornmeal)
         A
Commercial Milling Co., 45 Randolph (Cornmeal) ..B
Detroit Cereal & Nut Food Co. (Cereals; Prep.)....B
Manna Cereal Co. (Ltd.), 45 Fort E. (Cereals; Prep.)
         AAA
Nutrine Food Co. (Ltd.),

FOOD (*Con.*)

1300 Gratiot Av. (Cereals; Prep.) ....AAA

Standard Pure Food Co. (Ltd.), 16th & M. C. R. R. (Cereals; Prep.)..AAA

MICH.—Flint

Flint Cereal Co. (Cereals).A

MICH.—Grand Rapids

Globe Food Co. (Cereals)..B

National Pure Food Co. (Ltd.) Cereals; Prep.)..B

Volgt Cereal Food Co. (Ltd.) (Cereals; Prep.) ......A

Watson & Frost (Buckwheat) C

MICH.—Hastings

Hastings Union Food Co. (Ltd.) (Cereals; Prep.).. AA

MICH.—Holland

Walsh-De Roo Milling & Cereal Co. (Buckwheat; Cereals; Prepared) ......A

MICH.—Jackson

Celery Health Food Co. (Ltd.) (Prepared) ....AA

Crystal Food Co. (Cereals; Prep.) ....AAA

MICH.—Kalamazoo

Celery City Food Co. (Cereals) ....A

Kalamazoo Pure Food Co. (Prep.) C

Meat Substitute Co. (Ltd.) (Cereals) ....A

Premo Flake Food Co. (Cereals) ....B

MICH.—Lake Odessa

Lake Odessa Malted Cereal Co. (Cereals; Prep.) ..AA

MICH.—Owosso

Vigor-O-Health Food Co. (Ltd.) (Cereals; Prep.).. AAA

MICH.—Oxford

Mich. Pure Food Co. (Cereals; Prep.) ......B

MICH.—Plainwell

Eesley Milling, J. F. (Buckwheat) C

MICH.—Quincy

McKenzie Cereal Food & Milling Co. (Buckwheat; Prep.) C

MICH.—Waldron

Avis Milling Co. (Buckwheat) ....E

MINN.—Lanesboro

Spillain & Co., D. (Oatmeal) ....D

MINN.—Minneapolis

Amer. Cereal Co., Corn Exch. (Cereals) ...AAAA

Great Western Cereal Co. (Cereals; Oatmeal)AAAA

New Occidental Mill Co., 330 S. 1st (Buckwheat)

Pillsbury-Washburn Flour Co. (Cereals) ......AAAA

MINN.—St. Francis

St. Francis Milling Co. (Buckwheat) ....D

MINN.—Sleepy Eye

Sleepy Eye Milling Co. (Cereals; Prep.) ......A

MINN.—Waseca .

Great Western Cereal Co. (Cereals; Oatmeal) .... AAAA

MO.—Chapman

Neb. Cent. Milling Co. (Oatmeal) C

MO.—Kansas City

Amer. Cereal Co., 1220 W. 8th (Cereals) ......AAAA

Atlas Oats Co., 1200 W. 8th (Cereals; Oatmeal).A

Continental Cereal Co., 528 Walnut (Cereals) C

Kansas City Oatmeal & Cereal Co., 8th & Santa Fe (Cereals) ....B

Kimball-Fowler Cereal Co., Bd. Trade Bldg. (Cereals) C

MO.—La Grange

Real Food Co. (Br. Battle Creek, Mich) (Cereals).B

MO.—St. Joseph

FOOD (*Con.*)

Amer. Hominy Co. (Cereals; Hominy) ....AAAA

Aunt Sally Mfg. Co. (Cereals) ....B

Davis Mill & Mfg. Co., R. T. (Cereals) ....A

Faucett Mill Co., R. H. (Aunt Sally's; Pancake Flour) ....B

MO.—St. Louis

Blanke Tea & Coffee Co., C. F., Clark Av. & 7th (Cereals) ....AA

Engelke & Fenier Milling Co., 816 B'way (Hominy) AA

Flanagan Milling Co., 1911 S. 3rd (Hominy) ....A

Gandolfo-Ghio Mfg. Co., 104 S. 8th (Buckwheat) ....E

Great Western Cereal Co., 813 Spruce (Cereals) .... AAAA

Imbs Milling Co., J. F., Gay Bldg. (Cereals) ....A

Michigan Cereal Co., B'way & Poplar (Cereals) C

Purina Mills, 801 S. 8th (Hominy) ....B

Stobie Cereal Mills, 709 N. 2nd (Buckwheat; Flour; Hominy; Oatmeal) ....B

MONT.—Butte

Beebe Grain Co. (Cornmeal) A

MONT.—Great Falls

Royal Milling Co. (Cereals) B

NEBR.—Beatrice

Cummings Milling Co., M. T. (Cereals) C

NEBR.—Chapman

Nebr. Central Milling Co. (Cornmeal) C

NEBR.—Columbus

Columbus Milling Co. (Buckwheat) ....D

NEBR.—Kearney

Roby, F. F. (Buckwheat) C

NEBR.—Milford

Johnson & Co., F. S. (Cereal; Hominy) ......,..AA

NEBR.—Nebr. City

Great Western Cereal Co. (Br. Chicago, Ill.) (Cereals) ....AAAA

NEBR.—Norfolk

Sugar City Cereal Mills (Cereals) ....B

NEBR.—Schuyler

Wells, Abbott & Niemans (Cornmeal) ....AA

NEBR.—Seward

Seward Cereal Mills (Flaked Oats; Rolled Oats) C

N. J.—Matawan

Amer. Rice, Food & Mfg. Co. (Rice Flakes) ....AA

N. J.—Passaic

Amer. Comp. Food Co. (Tablets Prep.) C

N. Y.—Albany

Amer. Cereal Co. (Cereal) AAAA

N. Y.—Balston Spa

Curtis, Elmer A. (Buckwheat) ....D

N. Y.—Binghamton

Standard Food Co. (Cereals; Prep.) ....A

N. Y.—Buffalo

Buffalo Cereal Co., 41 Dun Bldg. (Cereals) ......B

Force Food Co., Mutual Life Bldg. (Cereals) ......AA

H.-O. Co. (The) (E. Elsworth & Co., Prop.), 46 Fulton (Cereals; Oatmeal) AA

Hygienic Food Co. (Ltd.), Fillmore & William (Cereals; Prep.) ....B

N. Y.—Camillus

Globe Milling Co. (Cereals) C

N. Y.—Cattaraugus

True & Young (Buckwheat) G

D (Con.)

N. Y.—Cobbleskill
France Milling Co. (Buckwheat Flour) C

N. Y.—Cohocton
Larrowe Milling Co. (Ltd.) (Buckwheat) C

N. Y.—Cohoes
Rogers & Son, C. (Buckwheat) ....D

N. Y.—Dansville
Hall Cereal Co. (Cereals) . B
Our House Granula Co. (Prepared) C

N. Y.—Fishkill Landing
Buffalo Cereal Co. (Cereals) B

N. Y.—Geneva
Patent Cereals Co. (Cereals) A

N. Y.—Lodi
Townsend, J. C. (Buckwheat) ....E

New York City
Amer. Cereal Co. (Br.), 11 B'way (Cereals)...AAAA
Beardsley's Sons, J. W., 476 Greenwich (Prepared) ..A
Cook's Flaked Rice Co., 1 Union Sq. W. (Cereals) AA
Cutting & Co., J. T., 151 W. 38th (Cereals; Prep.) C
Durkee & Co., E. R., 534 Washington (Cereals) ..A
Elsworth & Co., E., Prod. Exch. (Oatmeal; Buckwheat) ....AA
Force Food Co. (E. Elsworth & Co., Prop.), Prod. Exch. (Cereals) ....AA
Great Western Cereal Co., 90 W. B'way (Cereals) AAAA
Harlem River Milling Co., 227 E. 129th (Hominy) . B
Hecker's - Jones - Jewell Milling Co., Prod. Exch. (Buckwheat; Cereals)... AAAA
H.-O. Co. (E. Elsworth & Co., Prop.), Prod. Exch. (Cereals; Oatmeal)...AA
Hoyt, A. S., 90 W. B'way (Cereals) ....B
Lea, R., Prod. Exch. (Cereals) C
Leeming & Co., T., 73 Warren (Prep.) C
Mattie Mitchell Co. (Br. Cleveland, Ohio), 115 Hudson (Cereals) ....B
Miles & Holman, 115 Hudson (Cereals; Prep.) ...A
National Oatmeal Co., 105 Hudson (Oatmeal) .....A
Plasmon Co. of America 116 Broad (Cereals) ...AAA
Postum Cereal Co. (Br. Grand Rapids, Mich), 105 Hudson (Cereals; Prep.) AAA
Pure Gluten Food Co., 90 W. B'way (Gluten Bread) B
Rosenstein Bros. (Inc.), 96 N. Moore (Cereals)....C
Wheatena Co., 348 W. 12th (Cereals; Prep.) ......B

N. Y.—Niagara Falls
Natural Food Co. (Cereals; Prep.) ....AAAA

N. Y.—Oneonta
Oneonta Milling Co. (Buckwheat) ....A

N. Y.—Penn Yan
Birkett, C. T. (Buckwheat; Cereals) ....B

N. Y.—Rochester
Stone Co., H. D. (Cereals) C

N. Y.—Summitville
Adams, S. A. (Buckwheat) C

N. Y.—Syracuse
Justs Food Co. (Infants) AA

N. Y.—Ushers
Anthony, Joshua (Oatmeal) A

N. Y.—Watertown
Farwell & Rhines (Cereals;

FOOD (Con.)

Breakfast Food) ......B
Herrick & Sons, A. H. (Buckwheat) ....B

N. C.—Asheville
Wheat-Hearts Co. (Cereals) A

N. C.—Goldsboro
Carolina Rice Mills ......B

N. C.—Wilmington
Boney & Harper (Hominy) B
Carolina Rice Mills (Rice Flakes) ....B

OHIO—Akron
Amer. Cereal Co. (Br. Chicago, Ill.) (Cereals; Oatmeal) ....AAAA
Great Western Cereal Co. (Br. Chicago, Ill.) (Cereals; Oatmeal) ..AAAA
Pioneer Cereal Co. (Cereals) B

OHIO—Ashland
Ashland Cereal Co. (Cereals) B

OHIO—Bellefontaine
Johnson Co., F. N. (Buckwheat; Cereals) ....A

OHIO—Chillicothe
Standard Cereal Co. (Cereals) ....B

OHIO—Cincinnati
Great Western Cereal Co., 1675 Detroit (Cereals)... AAAA
Grotlisch Co., Hy., 315 Hunt (Cornmeal) .....B
Patterson & Evans, 52 Vine (Hominy) ....B
Perin Bros., 14 E. Front (Cornmeal) C
Weidler Co., S. W., 938 W. 6th (Cornmeal; Hominy) ....B

OHIO—Circleville
Crites Bros. & Co. (Cornmeal) ....A
Heffner & Co. (Cornmeal) A
Ohio Cereal Co. (Cereals) . A
Smith Mill Co. (Cornmeal) A

OHIO—Cleveland
Amer. Cereal Co. (Cereals) AAAA
Mattie Mitchell Co., 1925 Harvard (Buckwheat; Cornmeal; Cereals) .....B

OHIO—Dayton
Dayton Cereal Co. (Cereals) B

OHIO—McConnellsville
Elk Eye Milling Co. (Buckwheat) C

OHIO—New Bremen
Bakhaus & Kuenzel Co. (Buckwheat; Cornmeal.) B

OHIO—Portsmouth
Portsmouth Cereal Co. (Cereals) C

OHIO—Ravenna
Amer. Cereal Co. (Oatmeal) AAAA

OHIO—Toledo
Amer. Hominy Co. (Hominy) ....AAAA
Haskell & Co., Wm. H., 136 Neb. Av. (Cereals; Cornmeal; Hominy) C
Miami Maize Co. (Cereals) B

OHIO—Tuscarawas
Tuscarawas Cereal Co. (Cereals) C

OHIO—Youngstown
Thomas' Sons, Jno. R. (Cereals) ....B

OREGON—Hillsboro
Milne, Jno. (Oatmeal) ..B

OREGON—Portland
Acme Mills Co. (Cereals) .C
Albers Bros.' Milling Co. (Buckwheat; Cornmeal; Hominy; Oatmeal) C

PA.—Bloomsburg
White Milling Co. (Buckwheat) ....B

PA.—Butler
Klingler & Co., H. J. (Buckwheat) ....A

424

FOOD (Con.)

Walter & Sons, Geo. (Buckwheat) ....B

PA.—Mercer
Mercer Milling & Lumber Co. (Cereals) ....A

PA.—Philadelphia
Amer. Cereal Co. (Br.), 105 S. Water (Cereals).AAAA
Barker & Co., 321 N. Front (Oatmeal; Cornmeal; Hominy) C
Carter & Co., S. R., 33 S. Front (Cereals) C
Health Food Co., 47 N. 13th (Cereals) ....B
Klander, Jno. C. (Est. of), 1900 N. 6th (Cereals; Hominy) ....B
Koons, Schwarz & Co. (Cereals) ....A
Walker-Gordon Laboratory Co., 1721½ Chestnut (Cereals) C

PA.—Pittsburg
Great Western Cereal Co. (Cereals) ....AAAA

PA.—Wilkesbarre
Miner-Hilliard Milling Co., (Maize Flakes; Flour)..AA

PA.—Williamsport
Hopkins Hulled Cereals Co. (Cereals) ....B

R. I.—Providence
Reliance Mill Co., 208-16 Dyer (Pancake Flour).AA

S. C.—Charleston
Rohde & Co., D. (Hominy) C

TENN.—Chattanooga
Mountain City Milling Co., 204 King (Hominy) ....A

TENN.—Estill Springs
Tennessee Milling Co. (Hominy) ....A

TENN.—Nashville
Dixie Pure Food Co. (Cereals) C
Southern Flaked Food Co., (Cereals; Coffee; Prepared) C
Spotswood & Co., Geo. W. (Cornmeal; Hominy)....C

VT.—Burlington
Malted Cereal Co. (Cereals; Prep.) ....A

VA.—Norfolk
Bosman & Lohman (Peanut) C
Smith Mill Co. (Cornmeal) ....A

WASH.—Seattle
Centennial Mill Co. (Cornmeal) ....AA
Lehman Bros. (Cereals) ..A
Seattle Cereal Co. (Cereals; Oatmeal) ....A

WASH.—Spokane
Centennial Mill Co. (Br.) (Cereals) ....AA

WASH.—Tacoma
Cascade Cereal Co. (Oatmeal) ....B

WASH.—Walla Walla
Walla Walla Health Food Co. (Cereals; Prep.)....A

WIS.—Beloit
Salmon Cereal Co. (Cereals) ....B

WIS.—Eagle Point
Eagle Point Roller Mills (G. A. Young & Bro., Props.) (Buckwheat) ....E

WIS.—Janesville
Blodgett Milling Co. (Buckwheat) ....B

WIS.—Manitowoc
Kneipp Malt Food Co. (Prepared) ....B

WIS.—Racine
Horlick's Food Co. (Malted Milk) ....A

FOOTWEAR

See Boots & Shoes

FORGES

CAL.—San Francisco
Garratt & Co., W. T. (Inc.)

FORGES (Con.)

(Portable) ....AA

CONN.—Hartford
Billings & Spencer Co. (Portable; for Drop Forging Plants) ....AA

CONN.—New Haven
Miner & Peck Mfg. Co. (Blast for Drop Forging Plants) X

ILL.—Chicago
Chicago Pneumatic Tool Co., Fisher Bldg. (Rivet Heating) ....AAAA
Chicago Scale Co., 292 W. Jackson Boul. (Portable) ....A
Chicago Wheel & Mfg. Co., 39 W. Randolph C
Cumming, David, 787 W. Kinzie (Portable) ...D
Union Drop Forge Co., 66 E. Ohio (For Drop Forging Plants) ....A

ILL.—Chicago Heights
Canedyn-Otto Mfg. Co. (Portable) ....A

ILL.—Evanston
Comstock, A. S. (Automatic Power Gas Blast) C

ILL.—Ottawa
Porter Co., J. E. ....A

IND.—Connersville
Roots & Co., P. H. & F. M. (Portable) ....AA

MASS.—Boston
Beaudry & Co., 8 Oliver (Heating; Portable) ...D
Sturtevant Co., B. F. (Blast; Bridge Builders) ...AAA

MASS.—Hyde Park
Boston Blower Co. (Blast; Portable) ....B

MASS.—Worcester
Boynton & Plummer (Portable) ....B

MICH.—Marcellus
Chapman, H. L. (Portable) ....H
Amer. Gas Furnace Co. (Gas Blast for Drop Forging Plant) ....A

N. Y.—Auburn
Crane Fdry. & Machine Wks., W. W. (Heating) ....D

N. Y.—Brooklyn
Brown & Patterson, 33 Marcy Av. (Portable) ..A
Merrill Bros. ....A

N. Y.—Buffalo
Buffalo Forge Co. (Stationary; Portable Blast). AAA
Star Forge Co., 18 Lock (Portable Bridge Builders' Bellows) ....F

N. Y.—Ft. Plain
Burns Hydro-Carbon Burner Co. ....F

New York City
Fairbanks Co. (Portable)..AAAA
Parson Mfg. Co., 320 B'way C
Slotkin & Praglin, 210 Canal ....B

N. Y.—Syracuse
Bradley & Son, C. G. ....A
Bradley Co. (For Drop Forging Plants; also Portable) X

N. Y.—Troy
Empire Forge Co. (Portable) ....F

OHIO—Canton
Canton Fdry. & Machine Co. ....B

OHIO—Cincinnati
Hayden-Roth-Evans Co...F

OHIO—Cleveland
Acme Machinery Co. ...AA
Bullock Bellows Co., T. H., 130 Columbus (Portable) ....E
Cleveland Steam Gauge Co., 106 Merwin (Portable)..C

OHIO—Salem
Silver Mfg. Co. (Blacksmiths') ....AA

OHIO—Springfield
Foos Mfg. Co. (Portable).A

FORGES (*Con.*)

PA.—Lancaster
Champion Blower & Forge Co. (Portable) ......AA
Potts, David H. (Portable) ....D

PA.—Philadelphia
Cox & Sons Co., 215 Race (Portable) ....B
Evans' Sons, Jno., 13th & Buttonwood (Heating; Welding) ....B
Sellers & Co., Wm...AAAA

PA.—Rankin's Station
Duquesne Forge Co. (Blacksmiths') ....A

FORGINGS

See also Hardware; Carriage etc.

ALA.—Birmingham
Republic Iron & Steel Co. (Iron; Steel; Car Axle; Shafting, etc.) ...AAAA

ALA.—Huntsville
Huntsville Fdry. & Machine Wks. Light; Heavy Iron; Steel) ....B

ALA.—Mobile
Ala. Iron Wks. (Light; Heavy Iron; Steel) .....B

CAL.—San Francisco
Doble Co., Abner, 200 Fremont (Drop; all Kinds).A
Amon Iron Wks., 222 Market (Iron; Steel; Ship; Mining) ....AAAA

CONN.—Bridgeport
ridgeport Forge Co. (Iron; Steel) ....A
Farist Steel Co. (Steel; Railroad; Machinery).AA

CONN.Hartford
Billings & Spencer Co. .Automatic; Bicycle; Copper; Drop; Gem Handle; Iron Special; Manganese Bronze; Marine; Machine; Railroad; Shaft; Iron; Steel Carriage) ....A

CONN.—New Haven
Belden Machine Co. (Aluminum; Automobile; Copper; Drop; Iron; Steel; Bicycle; Carriage; Gun; Handle) ....D
Brown & Co., R. H. (Drop) ....B
Kilborn & Bishop Co. (Bicycle; Bronze; Carriage; Copper; Drop; Gun; Handle; Iron; Steel Specialties; Marine; Machine; Railroad; Shaft) C
Seward & Son Co., M. (Bicycle; Carriage; Drop; Iron; Steel Bicycle; General).A

CONN.—Plantsville
Atwater Mfg. Co. (Iron; Steel Carriage) ....A
Blakeslee Forging Co. (Bicycle; Bronze; Carriage; Drop; Copper; Gun; Iron Special; Marine; Steel; Machine; Railroad; Shaft) ....B
Smith & Co., H. D. (Drop, Iron; Steel Carriage) .AA
Thompson Drop Forge Co. (Automobile; Bicycle; Carriage; Drop; Gun; Iron Special; Steel; Marine; Machine; Railroad; Shaft) ....E

CONN.—Torrington
Union Hardware Co. (Drop) ....AA

CONN.—Waterbury
Waterbury Farrel Fdry. & Mach. Co. (Drop) ....AA

DEL.—Wilmington
Diamond State Steel Co. (Iron; Steel Car; Bridge, etc.) ....AAA
Johnson Forge Co. (Iron; Steel Car; Locomotive Axle) ....B

GA.—Savannah
Kehoe & Sons, Wm. (Heavy Iron; Steel) ....A

FORGINGS (*Con.*)
Rourke & Son, John (Heavy Iron; Steel) ....B

ILL.—Chicago
Ajax Forge Co., 138 Jackson Boul. (Iron; Steel) ...AA
Bethlehem Steel Co. (Iron; Steel; also Hollow)AAAA
Block-Pollak Iron Co. Marquette Bldg. (Iron; Steel Railroad) ....AA
Cambria Steel Co., 138 Jackson Boul. (Iron; Steel Railroad) ....AAAA
Carnegie Steel Co., The Rookery (Iron; Steel Heavy) ....AAAA
Chicago Drop Forge & Fdry. Co. (Bicycle; Bronze; Carriage; Copper; Drop; Handle; Iron Special; Marine; Machine; Railroad; Shaft; also Steel) .....B
Continental Bolt & Iron Wks. (Iron; Steel; Structural, etc.) ....B
Crucible Steel Co. of America, 64 S. Clinton (Steel of all kinds) ......AAAA
Dunne & Co., Geo. W., 68 W. Washington (Iron; Steel) C
O'Leary Iron Wks., Arthur J., 132 W. Lake (Iron; Steel Rod; Bolt; Vise; Railway; Quarry Tool)..B
Pittsburg Forge & Iron Co., Monadnock Bldg. (Iron; Steel Car; Locomotive; Heavy) ....A
Republic Iron & Steel Co., 108 La Salle (Iron; Steel Car Axle; Shafting; Machine; Railroad; Shaft)..AAAA
Union Drop Forge Co., 66 E. Ohio (Aluminum; Automobile; Bronze; Copper; Iron; Steel; Drop; Electric Railway; Gas Engines) ....A
Vulcan Iron Wks., 63 Milwaukee Av. (Iron; Steel; Marine; Machine; Railroad; Shaft) ....AA
Western Steel Car & Fdry. Co., Old Colony Bldg. (Iron; Steel; all kinds for Railroads) ....AA
Willard Sons & Bell Co. (Heavy Iron; Steel) ...A

ILL.—Harvey
Buda Fdy. & Mfg. Co. (Iron; Steel) ....A
Paigne Iron Wks. (Iron; Steel; Special Track Work) C

ILL.—Mt. Vernon
Mt. Vernon Car Mfg. Co. (Iron; Steel Car) .AAAA

ILL.—Quincy
Ellington Mfg. Co. (Heavy Iron; Steel) ....A

IND.—Anderson
Anderson Forging Co. (Iron; Steel) ....B

IND.—Evansville
Mesker & Co., Geo. L. (Structual Iron) .....AA

IND.—Indianapolis
Bates Forging Co. (Drop) X
Indianapolis Drop Forging Co. (Drop of all kinds; Iron Special) X

IOWA—Des Moines
Des Moines Mfg. & Supply Co. (Heavy Iron; Steel) A

KY.—Louisville
Drummond Mfg. Co. (Iron; Steel; Vehicle; Axle, &c.) ....A

LA.—New Orleans
Swoop, Julian W., 913 Girod (Light; Heavy Iron; Steel) ....A

MD.—Baltimore
Natl. Supply Co., 5 W. Lombard (Iron; Steel; Rod).B
Ryan, McDonald, 44 South (Iron; Steel) ....A

MD.—Cumberland
Cumberland Steel Co. (Iron; Steel) ....A

FORGINGS (Con.)

MASS.—Boston

Boston Bolt Co., 33 Purchase
(Iron; Steel) ....B
Boston & Lockport Block Co.
(Iron Special) ....B
Harvey, H. H., 606 Atlantic
Av. (Iron; Steel; Tool; Die
&c.) ....B
Livermore, Homer F. (Cop-
per; Drop) ....E
McLauthlin & Co., Geo. T.,
120 Fulton (Iron; Steel) A
New England Bolt & Nut Co.
263 Atlantic Av. (Iron;
Steel all kinds) C

MASS.—Canton

Kinsley Iron & Machine Co.
(Iron; Steel) ....AA

MASS.—Chicopee Falls

Page & Storms Drop Forge
Co. (Automobile; Bicycle;
Drop; Golf; Gun; Iron
Special; Steel; Marine;
Machine Railroad; Shaft)
            C

MASS.—East Boston

Boston Forge Co., 340 Ma-
verick (Electric; Iron;
Steel Railroad; Marine) A

MASS.—Gloucester

Cape Ann Anchor Wks.
(Iron; Steel) ....A

MASS.—Revere

Revere Drop Forge Co.
(Drop) ....D

MASS.—South Egremont

Dalzell Axle Co. (Iron;
Steel Carriage Special) A

MASS.—Springfield

More Drop Forging Co.
(Drop) C

MASS.—Taunton

Taunton Locomotive Mfg.
Co. (Iron; Steel) ....AA

MASS.—Worcester

Wyman & Gordon (Automo-
bile; Bronze; Copper;
Drop; Manganese Bronze;
Bicycle; Carriage; Gun;
Handle; Iron Special; Ma-
rine; Steel; Machine Railroad; Shaft) ....A

MICH.—Detroit

Anderson & Sons, W. H.
(Automobile; Copper;
Iron; Steel) C
Ireland & Matthews Mfg.
Co. (Drop) ....A
Lauer, Jno., 108 St. Antoine
(Iron; Steel) C

MICH.—Jackson

Lewis Spring & Axle Co.
(Iron; Steel Axle) C

MICH.—Manistee

Manistee Iron Wks. Co.
(Iron; Steel Railroad;
Heavy) ....B

MICH.—Sault Ste. Marie

Hickler Bos. (Iron; Steel) A

MICH.—Ypsilanti

Michigan Machinery Mfg.
Co. (Iron; Steel) ....AA

MO.—St. Louis

Amer. Car & Fdy. Co., 706
Chestnut (Iron; Steel Car;
Railroad; Merchant)
            AAAA
Helmbacher Forge & Rolling
Mill Co. (Iron; Steel;
Railroad; Marine; Machin-
ery) ....AA
Republic Iron & Steel Co.
(Iron; Steel Car Axle;
Shafting, &c.) ....AAAA
Union Iron & Fdy. Co., 1458
S. 2d (Iron; Steel) ....B
Western Forge Co., 520 Olive
(Iron; Steel) ....B

MONT.—Butte

Western Iron Wks. (Iron;
Steel) ....B

NEBR.—Omaha

Paxton & Vierling Iron Wks.
(Iron; Steel) ....A

N. H.—Lakeport

Cole Mfg. Co. (Iron; Steel
Light; Heavy) ....A

N. J.—Harrison

Crucible Steel Co. (Heavy
Iron; Steel) ......AAAA

N. J.—High Bridge

Taylor Iron & Steel Co.
(Iron; Steel Car; Locomo-

FORGINGS (Con.)

tive; Axle; Shaft) AAAA

N. J.—Hoboken

New York Switch & Cross-
ing Co. (Iron; Steel Railroad) ....A
Union Iron Wks. (Light;
Heavy Iron; Steel) AAAA

N. J.—Jersey City

Smith & Sons Co., Theo. ft.
Essex (Heavy Iron; Steel)
            A

N. J.—Newark

Currier & Sons, Cyrus (Iron;
Steel) ....AA
Hewes & Phillips Iron Wks.
(Iron; Steel) ....A
Strieby & Foote Co., 301
Ogden (Automobile; Bicy-
cle; Carriage; Drop;
Iron; Steel; Marine; Ma-
chine Railroad; Shaft) B

N. J.—Paterson

Passaic Steel Co. (Marine;
Machine Railroad; Shaft)
            A

N. Y.—Albany

Townsend Fdy. & Machine
Shop Co. (Iron; Steel) B

N. Y.—Auburn

Clapp Mfg. Co., E. D. (Bicy-
cle; Carriage; Drop; Gun;
Iron Special; Marine;
Steel; Machine Railroad;
Shaft) ....B
Eccles Co., Richard (Bicy-
cle; Carriage; Drop; Iron
Special; Steel) ....A

N. Y.—Batavia

Baker Gun & Forging Co.
(Gun; Iron; Steel) ....A

N. Y.—Brooklyn

Bliss & Co., E. W. (Seam-
less Steel) ......AAAA
Carpenter, Thos. D. (Iron
Special; Marine; Machine
Railroad; Shaft) ......B
Columbia Engineering Wks.,
William & Imlay (Iron;
Steel; Marine) .,......B
Columbia Machine Wks. &
Mall. Iron Co. (Copper;
Elect. Railway; Iron Spe-
cial) ....B
Gill & Sons, Phil. H., Lor-
raine & Otsego (Iron;
Steel; Piping) ....A
Hay-Budden Mfg. Co., 254
N. Henry (Drop; Marine;
Machine Railroad; Shaft)
            B
Merrill Bros., 465 Kent Av.
(Drop; Iron; Steel) ....B
Williams & Co., J. H. (Alu-
minum; Bronze; Copper;
Drop; Elect. Railway;
Iron; Steel; Bicycle; Gun;
Handle; Iron Special; Ma-
rine; Steel; Machine Rail-
road; Shaft) ....AAAA

N. Y.—Buffalo

Delaney Forge & Lyon Co.,
300 Perry (Iron; Steel) A
Iroquois Iron Wks., 178
Washn. Av. (Iron; Steel;
Crank Engine; Crank
Shaft, &c.) ....A
Sizer, W. S. (Locomotive
Iron; Steel Drawing Axle;
Marine; Engine) ....AA

N. Y.—Cortland

Cortland Forging Co. (Iron;
Steel Carriage) ....A

N. Y.—Hillburn

Ramapo Iron Wks. (Iron;
Steel Railroad) ......AA

New York City

Bethlehem Steel Co., 100
Bway (Iron; Steel; Hol-
low) C
Cambria Steel Co., 71 Bway.
(Iron; Steel Railroad)
            AAAA
Carbon Steel Co., 26 Cort-
landt (Iron; Steel) ....A
Carnegie Steel Co., 71 Bway
(Heavy Iron; Steel) AAAA
Cleveland City Forge &
Iron Co., 11 Bway (Heavy
Iron; Steel) ....AA
Cresson Co., Geo. V., 141
Liberty (Iron; Steel) AA
Crucible Steel Co. of Amer-
ica, 71 Bway (All Kinds

FORGINGS (Con.)

Co. (Steel; Special Iron) B

PA.—New Castle

New Castle Forge & Belt Co. (Drop; Telegraph; Telephone Pole; Iron; Steel; Car; Mine; Agricultural) A

PA.—Northumberland

Keystone Forging Co. (Carriage; Special Drop; Manganese Bronze) ....A

PA.—Philadelphia

Allison Mfg. Co. (Iron; Steel Car) ....AAAA

Bethlehem Steel Co., Bank Bldg. (Iron; Steel; Hollow) ....U

Cambria Steel Co., Arcade Bldg. (Iron; Steel Railroad) ....AAAA

Carnegie Steel Co., 1502 Market (Heavy Iron; Steel) ....AAAA

Cramp & Sons Ship & Engine Bldg Co., Wm. (Manganese Bronze; Iron; Steel Marine) ....AAAA

Cresson Co., Geo. V. (Iron; Steel) ....AAAA

Hoopes & Townsend Co., 1330 Buttonwood (Iron; Steel Car) ....AAA

Janney Steinnutz & Co. (Drop; Iron Special; Marine; Steel; Machine Railroad; Shaft) ....D

McGookin, D. H., 1630 N. 9th (Iron; Steel; Structural) C

Midvale Steel Co. (Car; Gun; Marine; Steel; Locomotive) ....AAAA

Morris, P. Hollingsworth, Phila. Bourse (Iron; Steel) ....A

Penna. Steel Co., Girard Bldg. (Heavy Steel) .. .. AAAA

Phillips & Sons Co., R. F., Penna. Bldg. (Iron; Steel) C

Phosphor Bronze Smelting Co., 2200 Washn. Av. (Bronze; Delta Metal; Drop) ....A

Roberts & Co., A. P., 261 S. 4th (Iron; Steel) ....AA

Standard Steel Works, Harrison Bldg. (Steel Locomotive) ....AA

PA.—Pittsburg

Baker Mfg. Co., Jas. H., Park Bldg. (Drop; Steel; Iron; Car; Wagon, &c.) A

Carbon Steel Co. (Nickel Steel) ....A

Carnegie Steel Co. (Nickel Steel; Steel) ......AAAA

Columbia Bridge Co., Park Bldg. (Iron; Steel) C

Crucible Steel Co of America (Nickel Steel; Steel of all Kinds) ......AAAA

Fort Pitt Forge Co. (Marine; Machine Railroad; Shaft) B

Heppenstall Forge & Knife Co. (Marine; Machine Railroad; Shaft) ......B

Jones & Laughlin's Steel Co. (Iron; Steel) .....AAAA

Keystone Smooth Forging Co., Hamilton Bldg. (Iron; Steel) C

Lanz & Sons, M., 101 S. 29th (Drop; Iron; Steel) B

Oliver Iron & Steel Co. (Elect. Railway) ..AAAA

Penna. Drop Forging Co., 937 Fayette (Drop) AAA

Phoenix Steel Construction Co., Penn Av. & 3rd (Bronze) ....D

Pelling & Crane, Farmers' Bank Bldg. (Iron; Steel) B

Pittsburg Forge & Iron Co., 10th & Penn Av. (Iron; Steel; Locomotive) ...A

Pittsburg Mfg. Co., 28th & Railroad (Iron; Steel)..A

Pittsburg Screw & Bolt Co., 25th & Liberty (Iron; Steel) ....B

FORGINGS (Con.)

Republic Iron & Steel Co., Frick Bldg. (Iron; Steel; Shafting) ....AAAA

Scaife & Sons Co., Wm. B. (Iron Special) ......AAA

Steel Car Forge Co. (Iron; Steel) ....B

Union Forge Co., 541 Wood (Iron; Steel) ......AAA

U. S. Aluminum Co. (Aluminum) ....B

Westmoreland Steel Co., 424 4th Av. (Steel) ....B

PA.—Rankin

Duquesne Forge Co. (Iron; Steel) ....A

PA.—Reading

Carpenter Steel Co. (Steel) AA

PA.—Scranton

Scranton Forging Co. (Drop; Carriage; Iron; Steel)..A

PA.—Shamokin

Mullen & Son, John (Iron; Steel; also Mine) ......A

PA.—South Bethlehem

Bethlehem Steel Co. (Hollow; Iron; Steel; Liquid Pressed) ....AAAA

PA.—Steelton

Penna. Steel Co. (Heavy Steel) ....AAAA

PA.—Tarentum

Baker Mfg. Co., Jas. H. (Iron; Steel; Car; Wagon, etc.) ....A

PA.—Titusville

Titusville Forge Co. (Iron; Steel; Drop; Marine; Machine; Railroad; Shaft). B

PA.—Waynesboro

Frick Co. (Iron; Steel)... AAA

PA.—Wilkesbarre

Sheldon Axle Co. (Iron; Stel) ....AAA

Vulcan Iron Works (Iron; Steel) ....AA

R. I.—Pawtucket

Pawtucket Mfg. Co. (Drop) A

R. I.—Providence

Rhode Island Tool Co. (Drop; Iron; Steel).AAA

TENN.—Chattanooga

Chattanooga Car & Fdry. Co. (Iron; Steel; Marine; Machine; Railroad; Shaft) A

TENN.—Knoxville

Knoxville Fdry. & Machine Co. (Iron; Steel) ......A

TEXAS—Dallas

Mosher Mfg. Co. (Heavy Iron; Steel) C

VA.—Norfolk

Godwin, Thos. W. (Iron; Steel; Marine) ....B

VA.—Richmond

Old Dominion Iron & Nail Wks. Co. (Iron; Steel)..A

Tredegar Co. (Iron; Steel; Car; Machinery) ....AAA

WASH.—Seattle

Moran Bros. Co. (Iron; Steel; Marine) ....AAAA

WIS.—Milwaukee

Bayley & Sons Co., Wm. (Marine; Machine; Railroad; Shaft) X

Wisconsin Bridge & Iron Co. (Iron; Steel) .....AA

FORKS

See also Silverware

CAL.—San Francisco

Jackson Mach. Wks., Byron (Hay) ....A

CONN.—Bridgeport

Acme Shear Co. (Steel; Table; Tinned) ......B

Knapp & Cowles Mfg. Co. (Strawberry) C

CONN.—Higganum

Scovill, D. & H. (Iron; Hand) ....A

CONN.—Meriden

Meriden Britannia Co. (Fish; Culinary) ..AAAA

FORKS (Con.)

Meriden Cutlery Co. (Table) .... AA

Rogers Bros. Co. (Forks
Tinned) .... AAAA

CONN.—Naubuc

Williams Bros. Mfg. Co.
(Table) .... A

CONN.—New Britain

Humason & Beckley Mfg.
Co. (Tuning) .... A

CONN.—Wallingford

Wallace & Sons, Mfg. Co.,
R. (Flesh; Vegetable;
Table; Culinary) .. AAAA

CONN.—Waterbury

Novelty Mfg. Co. (Olive;
Pickle) .... A

Rogers & Hamilton Co.
(Table) .... AAAA

ILL.—Batavia

U. S. Wind Engine & Pump
Co. (Horse; Hay) ..... AA

ILL.—Chicago

Gibson Co., W. D., 23 N.
Clinton (Hay; Tedder) B

Klein & Sons, Mathias, 87
W. Van Buren (Raising) B

Whitman & Barnes Mfg. Co.
(Hand Hay; Horse)
.... AAAA

ILL.—Decatur

Chambers - Bering - Quinlan
Co. (Horse; Hay) ..... A

ILL.—Downers Grove

Dicke Tool Co. (Raising) C

ILL.—Harvard

Hunt, Helm, Ferris & Co.
(Horse; Hay) .... AA

ILL.—Ottawa

Porter Co., J. E. (Horse;
Hay) .... A

ILL.—Plainsville

Hills, Edwin (Tinned) .... A

IND.—Columbus

Columbus Handle & Tool Co.
(Raising) .... B

IND.—Evansville

Evansville Tool Wks. (Rail)
.... A

IND.—Terre Haute

Terre Haute Shovel & Tool
Co. (Iron; Hand) ..... A

IOWA—Fairfield

Londen Machinery Co.
(Horse; Hay) C

IOWA—Fort Madison

Am. Hoe & Fork Co. (Hand;
Coal; Coke; Barley;
Sluice; Stone; Fodder;
Hay; Manure; Spading;
Wood) .... AAAA

MD.—Baltimore

Ives Mfg. Co., 203 Hanover
(Bicycle) .... E

MASS.—Greenfield

Nichols Bros. (Tinned) C

Warren Mfg. Co. (Tinned) C

MASS.—Lowell

Woods Sherwood Co. (Olive;
Pickle) .... E

MASS.—Newburyport

Towle Mfg. Co. (Table) AA

MASS.—Shelburne Falls

Lamson & Goodnow Mfg. Co.
(Kitchen) .... A

Mayhew Co., H. H. (Tinned)
.... D

MASS.—Turners' Falls

Russell Cutlery Co., Jno.
(Table) .... AA

MASS.—Worcester

National Mfg. Co. (Flesh;
Culinary; Olive; Pickle;
Toasting; Vegetable) .. A

Wire Goods Co. (Kitchen) A

MICH.—Detroit

Anderson & Sons, W. H.
(Rail; Raising) C

MICH.—Galion

Montrose, Richard W. (Barley; Grain; Wooden) .. B

MICH.—Jackson

Am. Hoe & Fork Co. (Hand
Barley; Hay; Manure;
Spading; Vegetable; Beet
Root; Coal; Coke; Fish
Handling; Header; Scoop;
Sluice; Stone; Iron;
Hand; Straw; Tanners')
.... AAAA

MICH.—Kalamazoo

Star Brass Wks. (Trolley) C

FORKS (Con.)

MICH.—Kalkaska

Freeman Mfg. Co. (Kraut) B

MO.—St. Louis

Central Union Brass Co.,
811 N. 2d (Trolley) .... E

N. H.—Antrim

Goodell Co. (Table) ...... A

N. J.—Bound Brook

Graphite Lubricating Co.
(Trolley) .... B

N. J.—Newark

Williamson Novelty Co., C.
T. (Olive; Pickle; Toasting; Vegetable) .... B

N. J.—Newton

Farrell & Son, John (Horse;
Hay) .... E

N. Y.—Auburn

Osborne & Co., D. M.
(Horse; Hay) .... AAAA

N. Y.—Brooklyn

American Stamping Co.
(Flesh; Culinary) X

N. Y.—Buffalo

Shepard & Co., Sidney
(Flesh; Culinary) .. AAAA

Strauss & Son, Jos., 694
Mich. (Bicycle) .... E

N. Y.—Cortland

Wickwire Bros. (Kitchen)
.... AAAA

N. Y.—East Syracuse

Benedict Mfg. Co., M. S.
(Table) .... AA

N. Y.—Frankford

Continental Tool Co. (Hand
Hay; Manure; Spading;
Header; Barley; Stone;
Coke; Coal; Sluice; Beet;
Potato; Digging; Tanners,
&c.) .... A

New York City

Chatillon & Sons, J., 85
Cliff (Kitchen) .... A

Lalance & Grosjean Mfg. Co.
(Fish; Flesh; Culinary)
.... AAAA

Marks, A. A. (Folding) AA

N. Y.—Rochester

Ricker Mfg. Co. (Horse
Hay) .... E

N. Y.—Syracuse

Syracuse Chilled Plow Co.
(Horse Hay) .... AA

N. Y.—Troy

Lane & Gale (Iron; Hand) A

N. Y.—Utica

Eureka Mower Co. (Horse
Hay) .... A

OHIO—Ashland

Myers & Bro. F. E. (Horse
Hay; Agricultural) AAAA

OHIO—Ashtabula

Ashtabula Tool Co. (Hand
Hay; Manure, &c.) .... A

OHIO—Canton

Ney Co., V. L. (Horse Hay)
.... B

Ney Mfg. Co. (Horse Hay)
.... B

OHIO—Cincinnati

Electric Railway Equipment Co., 433 E. Front
(Trolley) .... B

OHIO—Cleveland

Am. Fork & Hoe Co. (Bailing Press; Coal; Coke;
Cotton Seed; Fish; Fodder Hay; Manure; Spading; Ore; Sluice; Stone;
Tanners, &c.) ..... AAAA

Osborne Mfg. Co. (Coke;
Coal) .... B

OHIO—Columbus

Am. Hoe & Fork Co. (Hand;
Hay; Header; Manure;
Coal; Coke; Stone; Spading) .... A

OHIO—Dayton

Dayton Malleable Iron Co.
(Brake) .... AAA

OHIO—Hicksville

Kerr Bros. Mfg. Co. (Barley; Shavings) C

OHIO—Springfield

Economic Mfg. Co. (Trolley)
.... D

OHIO—Toledo

Nagel Electric Co., W. G.
(Raising) .... B

OHIO—Zanesville

Brown Mfg. Co. (Horse
Hay) .... AA

480

FORKS (Con.)

PA.—Philadelphia
Myers & Ervien Co. (Iron; Hand) ....B
PA.—Pittsburg
Hubbard & Co., Murtland Bldg. (Rail) ....AA
Nuttall Co., R. D. (Trolley) A
Oliver Iron & Steel Co. (Rail) ....AAAA
Pittsburg Tool & Drop Forge Co., Arrott Bldg. (Rail) D
Roberts, Geo., 1st & Liberty Av. (Raising) ....F
R. I.—Providence
Fessenden & Co. (Hand) B
Natl. Ring Traveler Co. (Loom) ....AA
TENN.—Harriman
Harriman Hoe & Tool Co. (Iron; Hand) ....A
TENN.—Nashville
Nashville Spoke & Handle Mfg. Co. (Hay) ......AA
VT.—Bellows Falls
Derby & Ball (Hay; Manure; Spading) ....B
VT.—Brookfield
Peck, Clark & Co. (Hand; Hay) ....D
VT.—Hartford
French, Watson & Co. (Iron; Hand) C
VT.— St. Johnsbury
Amer. Hoe & Fork Co. (Hay; Hand; Grain; Manure; Spading) ....AAAA
VT.—Wallingford
Amer. Hoe & Fork Co. (Hand, &c.) ....AAAA
Batcheller & Sons Co. (Iron; Hand) ....A
WIS.—Fort Atkinson
Hager, E. (Hand) ....D
WIS.—Janesville
Janesville Hay Tool Co. (Horse Hay) X
Rock River Machine Co. (Horse Hay) ....D
WIS.—Madison
Fuller & Johnson Mfg. Co. (Horse Hay) ....AAA
WIS.—Milwaukee
Milwaukee Hay Tool Co. (Horse Hay) ....A
Smith & Sons Co., C. S. (Bicycle) ....B
WIS.—Racine
Belle City Mfg. Co. (Horse Hay) ....B

FORMALD-EHYDE

N. J.—Perth Amboy
Perth Amboy Chemical Wks. C
N. Y.—Brooklyn
Wiarda & Co., Jno. C. ..AA
N. Y.—Buffalo
Schoelkopp, Hartford & Hanna Co. ....AAA
New York City
Bischoff & Co., C. ......B
Fries Bros., 92 Reade ....A
Fuerst Bros. Co. ....D
Heyden Chemical Wks., 40 Pine ....A
Klipstein & Co., A. ...AA
Merck & Co. ....AAA
Metz & Co., H. A. ....A
Roessler & Hasslacher Chemical Co. ....AA

FORMS

CONN.—Bridgeport
Taylor, Thos. P. (Dress) A
MASS.—Worcester
Hamblin & Russell Mfg. Co. (Baby Cap Display) ....B
MICH.—Three Oaks
Warren Featherbone Co. (Dress) ....AA
MO.—St. Louis
Ludlow-Saylor Wire Co. (Dress; Coat) ....AA
N. Y.—Buffalo
Henderson & Henderson (Pneumatic Bust Corset) C

RMS (Con.)

New York City
Ferris Bros. Co. (Dress) A
Palmenberg's Sons, J. R. (Dress) X
N. Y.—Syracuse
Wood & Co., J. E. (Shirt Waist) C
OHIO—Cincinnati
Bromwell Brush & Wire Co. (Dress) ....AA
PA.—Philadelphia
Darby & Sons, Edw., 233 Arch (Dress; Coat) ....A
Straus, Wm. (Stocking) ..F
Weston & Wells Mfg. Co. (Dress) ....B
TENN.—Chattanooga
Chattanooga Machinery Co. (Coffin Bending) C

FOULARDS

MASS.—North Adams
Windsor Co. ....AAA
N. H.—Dover
Cocheco Mfg. Co. ....AAA
New York City
McLean Co., Andrew ..AA

FOUNDATIONS

ILL.—Hamilton
Dadant & Son, Chas. (Beekeepers' Comb) ....B
OHIO—Medina
Root Co., A. I. (Beekeepers' Comb) ....AA
PA.—Philadelphia
Phoenix Bridge Co. (Bridge) A

FOUNDERS

See Castings

FOUNTAINS

COLO.—Denver
Denver Stoneware Co. (Chicken) X
ILL.—Carpentersville
Illinois Iron & Bolt Co. (also Vases) ....AA
ILL.—Chicago
Acorn Brass Mfg. Co. (Soda) D
Barbee Wire & Iron Wks., 44 Dearborn (also Vases) B
Becker Co., L. A. (Soda) AA
Both, John, 114 Lake (also Vases) ....B
Clow & Sons, Jas. B., 344 Franklin (also Vases) AAAA
Illinois Malleable Iron Co. 30 W. Monroe (Drinking; Park Lawn, &c.) ..AAAA
Liquid Carbonic Acid Mfg. Co. (Soda Water) ..AAAA
Middleby Oven Mfg. Co., 60 W. Van Buren (also Vases) ....D
Smith Wire & Iron Wks., F. P., 100 Lake (also Vases; Display) ....AA
Wilson Iron Wks. (Stock) X
Winslow Bros. Co., 368 Carroll Av. (Iron; Brass; Bronze Drinking) ..AA
ILL.—Sterling
Novelty Iron Wks. (Stock) E
IND.—Muncie
Glasscock Bros. Mfg. Co. (Poultry) ....B
IOWA—Waterloo
Cedar Valley Mfg. Co. (Soda) C
LA.—New Orleans
Hinderer's Iron Fence Wks. (also Vases) ....B
MD.—Baltimore
Smyser's Sons, E. G., 4 Light (also Vases) ...A
MASS.—Boston
Am. Soda Fountain Co. (Soda) ....AAAA
Jones & Co., M. D., 73 Portland (also Vases) ......G
Puffer Mfg. Co. (Soda Water) ....A

FOUNTAINS (Con.)

MASS.—Middleboro
Le Baron Foundry Co. (also Vases) ....D

MICH.—Detroit
Amos & Co., Charles, 94 W. Larned (also Vases) ....F
Barnum, E. T., 99 Shelby (also Vases) ....B
Vulcan Co. (also Vases) F

MICH.—Sturgis
Freeland Sons Co., B. F. (Poultry) ....D

MINN.—Minneapolis
Northwestern Foundry. 312 10th Av. S. (also Vases) ....A

MO.—St. Louis
International Steel Post Co. (Drinking; Park Lawn, &c.) ....A
Nelson Mfg. Co., N. O. (Display) ....AAA
Pleuger & Henger Mfg. Co. (Drinking) ....A

N. H.—Concord
Concord Foundry & Mach. Co. (also Vases) .....B

N. H.—Keene
Humphrey Machine Co. (Drinking; also Vases) A

N. Y.—Brooklyn
Eagle Iron Wks., 850 De Kalb Av. (also Vases) C
Hecla Iron Wks., N. 11th & Berry (also Vases) ..AA

N. Y.—Buffalo
Ginther's Sons. J., 417 Bway. (also Vases) ....A
Walbridge & Co., 392 Main (also Vases) ....A

N. Y.—Manlius
Cheney & Son, S. (also Vases) ....A

N. Y.—Medina
Swett Iron Wks., A. L. (also Vases) ....A

New York City
Fiske Iron Works, J. W., 39 Park Pl (also vases: display) ....B
Mott Iron Works, J. L., 88 Beekman (also Vases: drinking & display) ..AA
Westervelt. A. B. & W. F., 102 Chambers (also Vases) B

N. Y.—Utica
Palmer, C. F. (also Vases).C

OHIO—Canton
Harvard Co. (Dental Cuspidor) ....AA

OHIO—Cincinnati
Cincinnati Mfg. Co., 512 Main (also Vases) ....B
Stewart Iron Works (Park Lawn. &c.; also Vases) ..A

OHIO—Cleveland
Van Dorn Iron Works Co., 1793 E. Madison Av. (also Vases) ....AA

OHIO—Columbus
McDonald Bros. (also Vases) C

OHIO—Kenton
Champion Iron Co. (also Vases) ....AA

PA.—Ellwood City
Glen Mfg. Co. (Drinking; Park Lawn, &c.) C

PA.—Homer City
Prairie State Incubator Co. (Drinking) ....A

PA.—New Brighton
Pittsburg Clay Mfg. Co. (Hen) ....AAAA

PA.—Philadelphia
Creswell Iron Works Co., S. J., 23d & Cherry (also Vases) ....B
Darby & Sons. Edw., 233 Arch (also Vases) .....A
Green & Sons, R. M. (Soda Water) ....AA
Hitzeroth. C., 3124 Market (also Vases) ....B

PA.—Pittsburg
Phoenix Steel Construction Co. (also Vases) ......D
Standard Mfg. Co. (Drinking) ....AA
Taylor & Dean, 205 Market (also Vases) ....B

FOUNTAINS (Con.)

TENN.—Chattanooga
Cahill Iron Works (also Vases) ....B
Chattanooga Pipe & Foundry Co. (Drinking) ....A

VA.—Richmond
Carr, Jas. W., 2003 E. Main (also Vases) ....F

WIS.—Milwaukee
Globe Wire & Iron Wks., 136 Reed ....G
Hennecki Co., C., 103 Wisconsin (also Vases; Terra Cotta & other kinds)...A
Wisconsin Iron & Wire Works, 186 E. Water (also Vases) ....D

WIS.—Sheboygan
Kohler Sons' Co., J. M. (Drinking; Street) .....A
Winter Lumber Co., M. (Soda Water) ....B

FOUNTS

CONN.—Bridgeport
Bridgeport Brass Company (Lamp; Decorated Lamp; Metal Lamp) ....AAA

CONN.—Bristol
Bristol Brass Co. (Metal Lamp) ....AAA

CONN.—Meriden
Bradley & Hubbard Mfg. Co. (Metal Lamp) ....AAAA
Miller & Co., Edw. (Decorated Lamp) ......AAAA

CONN.—Waterbury
Benedict & Burnham Mfg. Co. (Metal Lamp).AAAA
Holmes, Booth & Haydens Co. (Inc.) (Lamp; Decorated Lamp; Metal Lamp) AAAA

MASS.—New Bedford
Smith Bros. (Decorated Lamp) X

PA.—Coraopolis
Consolidated Lamp & Glass Co. (Glass Lamp)......A

PA.—Philadelphia
Gillinder & Sons (Decorated Lamp; Glass Lamp) ...A
Murray & Co., Jas. J. (Glass Lamp) ....A

PA.—Pittsburg
Phoenix Glass Co. (Glass Lamp) ....A
Pittsburg Brass Mfg. Co. (Lamp) ....D

PA.—Reading
National Brass & Iron Wks. (Glass Lamp) ....A

FRAMES

See also Woodwork; Carriage & Wagon; Furniture Woodwork; Silverware; Pictures; for Spectacle Frames see Optical Goods & Jewelry; Millinery.

CONN.—Bridgeport
Bridgeport Hardware Mfg. Co. (Hack Saw) C
Springfield Mfg. Co. (Polishing) ....B

CONN.—Danielson
Jacobs Mfg. Co., E. H. (Harness) ....B

CONN.—Hartford
Pratt & Whitney Co. (Emery Wheel Polishing) AAAA

CONN.—Meriden
Meriden Brittannia Co. (Photograph) .....AAAA

CONN.—Middletown
Palmer, I. E. (Canopy; Brass Canopy. Self-adjusting; Hammock; Mosquito Canopy; Turn-over Canopy) ....AAA

CONN.—New Haven
Cowles & Co., C. (Inc.) (Curtain) ....A
Hendryx & Co., Andrew B. (Exhibit) ....A

CONN.—Pine Meadow
Chapin, Stephens Co. (Turn-

FRAMES (Con.)

ing Saw) ....A
CONN.—Stonington
Atwood-Morrison Co. (Redrawing; Silk Quilting; Spooling; Silk Warping)
.........AA
CONN.—Torrington
Union Hardware Co. (Hack Saw) ....AA
CONN.—Waterbury
American Pin Co. (Plush)
.........AA
ILL.—Chicago
Andrews Co., A. H. (Numeral) ....AA
Chicago Clothes Dryer Wks. (Clothes Drying) ......D
Continental Mfg. Co. (Furniture) ....B
Fairbanks, Morse & Co., Franklin & Monroe (Wood Saw; with Arbors).AAAA
Hausske & Co., Aug. (Inc.) (Furniture) ....B
Illinois Malleable Iron Co. (Manhole) ....AAAA
Knisely Bros., 5th Av. & 28th (Metallic Window)
.........A
Miller & Bro., Jas. A., 129 S. Clinton (Metallic Window) ....A
Mueller Bros. Art & Mfg. Co. (Picture) ....B
National Parlor Furniture Co. (Furniture) ....A
National Portrait Co. (Picture) ....E
Richter Co., August F. (Picture) ....B
Street & Co., R. R. (Harness) ....A
Western Parlor Frame Co. (Furniture) ....F
ILL.—Kankakee
Sheldon Novelty Co. (Photograph) ....A
IND.—Evansville
Linderschmidt, H. & G. (Awning) ....F
IND.—Indianapolis
Atkins & Co., E. C. (Band Saw; Brazing; Hack Saw)
.........AAAA
Chandler & Taylor Co. (Buck Saw) ....AA
Lieber Co., H. (Picture).AA
Tucker & Dorsey Mfg. Co. (Buck Saw; Hack Saw).A
KY.—Covington
Ohio Scroll & Lumber Co. (Furniture) ....D
MASS.—Athol
Athol Machine Co. (Grindstone) ....B
Starrett Co., L. S. (Hack Saw) ....A
MASS.—Boston
Badger & Sons' Co., E. B., 63 Pitt (Metallic Window) ....B
Boston Hat & Bonnet Frame Co., 42 Chauncey (Bonnet) X
Brown & Co., C. A., 94 Arch (Hat) ....AA
Coffin Valve Co. (Manhole)
.........D
Firth Co., Wm., 150 Devonshire (Cotton Drawing; Roving: Slubbing) ....D
Hicks & Sons, S. D., 9 Bowker (Metallic Window) ....B
Hill, Clarke & Co., 156 Oliver (Grindstone) ....A
Jameson & Co., J. M., 20 Chauncey (Hat) ....D
McKerrow & Co., H. G., 31 State (Cotton Drawing; Roving) X
Riley & Co., C. E., 65 Franklin (Jack; Roving; Spinning) ....A
Stoddard, Haserick, Richards & Co., 152 Congress (Cotton Fly; Gassing)..B
United Shoe Machinery Co. (Turning) ....AAAA

FRAMES (Con.)

MASS.—Everett
Faxon Co., Geo. H. (Piano)
.........D
MASS.—Fall River
Fall River Foundry & Machine Co. (Cotton Drawing; Cotton Fly; Ring Spinning; Roving; Spinning; Wool Spinning) ...F
MASS.—Fitchburg
Putnam Machine Co. (Grindstone) ....A
MASS.—Hopedale
Draper Co. (Roving).AAAA
MASS.—Lowell
Lowell Machine Shop (Cotton Drawing; Cotton Fly; Ring Spinning; Roving; Slubbing) ....AAAA
MASS.—Newton Upper Falls
Saco & Petee Machine Shops (Cotton Drawing; Cotton Fly; Ring Spinning; Roving; Slubbing; Spinning)
.........AAA
MASS.—Springfield
Taber-Prang Art Co. (Picture) ....AA
MASS.—Taunton
Mason Machine Works (Cotton Drawing; Ring Spinning; Spinning) .....AA
MASS.—Whitinsville
Whitin Machine Works (Cotton Drawing; Cotton Fly; Ring Spinning; Spinning)
.........AAAA
MASS.—Worcester
American Card Clothing Co. (Wool Spinning) ....AAA
Crompton & Knowles Loom Works (Harness) .AAAA
Hill Dryer Co. (Clothes Drying) ....D
Johnson & Bassett (Wool Spinning) ....A
MICH.—Battle Creek
Buechner Mfg. Co. (Display Case) ....E
MICH.—Detroit
Haberkorn & Co., C. H. (Furniture) ....A
Hargreaves Mfg. Co. (Photograph) ....A
Widman & Co., C. D. (Mirror) ....A
MICH.—Grand Rapids
Baldwin, Tuthill & Bolton (and Saw; Brazing) ...B
MO.—St. Louis
Baxter Moulding Co. (Picture) ....D
Hyatt, H. A. (Printers')..C
Southwestern Straw Works, Bennett & Leffingwell (Hat) ....D
Webber Moulding Co., J. R. (Picture) ....B
N. H.—Nashua
Maine Mfg. Co. (Door; Window Screen) ....A
N. J.—Elizabeth
Braunsdorf - Mueller Co. (Hack Saw) ....D
N. J.—Harrison
Headley & Farmer Co. (Bag) ....A
Heilmann Co. (Bag) .....B
Osborn Mfg. Co., J. A. (Chatelaine Bag) ......A
N. J.—Hoboken
Schimper & Co., Wm. (Photograph) ....AA
N. J.—Newark
Goertz & Co., Aug. (Satchel)
.........B
Jenkinson & Co., R. C. (Bag; Suit Case) ....AA
National Saw Co. (Cabinet; Turning Saw) ....B
Neumann & Co., R. (Bag)
.........B
Newark Purse Frame Mfg. Co. (Chatelaine Bag)...E
Peddie & Co., T. B. (Bag)
.........AA
Poeter & Co., E. (Chatelaine Bag) ....E
N. J.—Paterson
Royle & Sons, Jno. (Hand Lacing) ....A

FRAMES (Con.)

Fales & Jenks Machine Co. (Ring Spinning) ....AAA
Howard & Bullough American Machine Co. (Ltd.) (Cotton Drawing; Intermediate; Jack; Roving; Slubbing; Spinning) .AAA

R. I.—Providence
Barstow & Williams (Photograph) C
Brown Bros. Co. (Cotton Fly; Harness) ....B
Franklin Machine Co. (Cotton Drawing; Ring Spinning) ....A
Providence Machine Co. (Cotton Drawing; Cotton Fly; Ring Spinning; Roving; Slubbing) ......AA
Woonsocket Machine & Press Co. (Cotton Fly; Ring Spinning; Roving) AA

VT.—Post Mills
Chubb Rod Co., T. H. (Landing Net) ....A

VA.—Richmond
Richmond Wood Working Co. (Furniture) ..AAAA

WIS.—Milwaukee
Filer & Stowell Co. (Ltd.) (Band Saw; Brazing) AAA
Meinecke & Son, A. (Wool Spinning) ....AA

WIS.—Oshkosh
Gould Mfg. Co. (Doors; Window) ....A

WIS.—Racine
Belle City Mfg. Co. (Hack Saw) ....B
Gold Medal Camp Furniture Mfg. Co. (Hammock; Mosquito Bar) ....B

WIS.—Two Rivers
Hamilton Mfg. Co. (Roller) AA

FREEZERS

N. H.—Nashua
White Mountain Freezer Co. (Ice Cream) ....A

N. Y.—Ithaca
Treman, King & Co. (Ice Cream) ....A

New York City
Cordley & Hayes (Ice Cream) ....AAA
Crandall & Godley Co. (Ice Cream) ....AA
Slotkin & Praglin, 210 Canal (Ice Cream; Foot Power) ....B

N. Y.—Syracuse
Stearns & Co., E. C. (Ice Cream) ....AA

OHIO—Cincinnati
Dana Mfg. Co. (Ice Cream) A
Day & Co., J. H. (Ice Cream) ....A
Kingery Mfg. Co. (Ice Cream) C
Tatum Co. (The), Samuel C. (Ice Cream) ....B

PA.—Philadelphia
Anderson & Co., J. P. (Ice Cream) X
Mills & Bro., Thos. (Ice Cream) ....A
North Bros. Mfg. Co. (Ice Cream) ....A
Packer, Chas. W. (Ice Cream) ....D

FRETWORK:

See Grilles

FRICTIONS

ILL.—Chicago
Weller Mfg. Co. (Paper) ..A
IND.—Indianapolis
Rockwood Mfg. Co. (Paper) A

FRIERS

MASS.—Worcester

FRIERS (Con.)

National Mfg. Co. (Potato) A
Wire Goods Co. (Potato) ..A
MO.—St. Louis
St. Louis Stamping Co. (Potato) ....AAAA
N. Y.—Cortland
Wickwire Bros. (Potato) AAAA
New York City
Thurnauer & Bro., G. M., 35 Park Pl. (Egg) X
OHIO—Hamilton
Meyers Mfg. Co. (Potato) .B
PA.—Philadelphia
Darby & Sons, Edw., 233 Arch (Potato) ....A
PA.—Royersford
Royal Gas Stove & Fdy. Co. (Croquette) C

FRIEZES

See Woolen Goods

FRILLS

CONN.—Waterbury
American Mills Co. ......A
MASS.—Boston
Hub Gore Makers (Elastic) A
MASS.—Easthampton
Colton, Geo. S. (Elastic) ..A
Nashawannuck Mfg. Co. (Elastic) ....AA
PA.—Philadelphia
Adamson & Co., Joseph ...A

FRINGES:
SILK ETC

See Trimmings; Upholstery & Trimmings; Dress

FROGS

ALA.—Anniston
Alabama Frog & Switch Co. (also Switches; Crossings) C
ILL.—Chicago
Ajax Forge Co., 138 Jackson Boul. (also Switches; Crossings) ....AA
Morden Frog & Crossing Works, The Rookery (also Switches; Crossings) ..A
Tilden Co., B. F., Monadnock Blk. (Replacing) ...D
ILL.—East St. Louis
Elliott Frog & Switch Co. (Spring Frogs; Split Switches; Switch Stands; Wrecking) ....AA
ILL.—Harvey
Buda Foundry & Mfg. Co. (also Switches; Crossings) AA
ILL.—Elkhart
Elkhart Frog & Crossing Works (also Switches; Crossings) C
KY.—Louisville
Louisville Bridge & Iron Co., 11th & Oldham (also Switches; Crossings) ...A
MASS.—Cambridge
Barbour-Stockwell Co. (also Switches; Crossings; Street Railway) ....A
MASS.—Springfield
Wason Mfg. Co. (also Switches; Crossings) ..AA
MO.—St. Louis
Green's Car Wheel Mfg. Co. (also Switches; Crossings) A
Railway Supply Co., Bedford Bldg. (also Switches; Crossings) ....D
N. J.—Hoboken
New York Switch & Crossing Co., 15th & Madison (also Switches; Crossings) A
N. Y.—Hillburn
Ramapo Iron Works (also Switches; Crossings) .AAA

FROGS (Con.)

New York City
Cornell Co., J. B. & J. M., 26th & 11th Av. (also Switches; Crossings)..AA
Koppel, Arthur, 68 Broad (also Switches; Crossings) ....A
White Mfg. Co., 556 W. 34th (also Switches; Crossings) ....D

N. C.—Statesville
Steele & Son, J. C. (also Switches) ....B

OHIO—Cincinnati
Weir Frog Co., cor. Front & Smith (also Switches; Crossings) ....A

OHIO—Cleveland
Atlas Bolt & Screw Co. (Railroad) ....AA
Cleveland Frog & Crossing Co., 16 Bessemer Av. (Spring Rail; Wrecking) ....B

OHIO—Hamilton
American Frog & Switch Co. (also Switches; Crossings) ....A

OHIO—Springfield
Indianapolis Switch & Frog Co. (also Switches; Crossings) ....B

PA.—Allentown
Allentown Rolling Mills (also Switches; Crossings) AAA

PA.—Chester
Chester Steel Castings Co. (also Switches; Crossings) AA
Johnson Railroad Frog & Switch Co. (also Switches; Crossings) ....B

PA.—Johnstown
Lorain Steel Co. (also Switches; Crossings) AAAA

PA.—Philadelphia
Midvale Steel Co. (also Switches; Crossings) AAAA
Wharton, Jr. & Co., Wm. (Inc.) 25th & Washn. Av. (also Switches; Crossings) AAA

PA.—Steelton
Pennsylvania Steel Co. (also Switches; Crossings; Mine Track) ....AAAA

PA.—Swissvale
Union Switch & Signal Co. (also Switches; Crossings) ....AAAA

PA.—Wilkesbarre
Vulcan Iron Works (also Switches; Crossings; Mine Track) ....AAAA

WIS.—Milwaukee
Falk Co., foot 30th (also Switches; Crossings) AAA

FRONTS

ILL.—Chicago
Globe Iron Works (Store).B
IND.—South Bend
Studebaker Bros. Mfg. Co. (Bridle) ....AAAA
MASS.—Worcester
Wheeler Fdy. Co. (Store).D
MINN.—St. Paul
St. Paul Roofing, Cornice & Ornament Co. (Iron Building) ....B
MO.—St. Louis
Christopher & Simpson Architectural Iron & Fdy. Co. (Store) ....AA
Mesker & Bros. (Iron Buildings) ....AA
NEBR.—Omaha
Paxton & Vierling Iron Wks. (Store; Boiler) ......AA
N. J.—Jersey City
National Sheet Metal Roofing Co. (Building; Sheet Iron) C
New York City
Cornell Co., J. B. & J. M.

FRONTS (Con.)
(Iron; Building; Store) AA
Dimond, Thomas (Iron; Building) ....A
Mott Iron Works, J. L. (Grate) ....AA
Rutzler Co., E. (Boiler)..A
N. Y.—Syracuse
Frazer & Jones Co. (Bridle) AA

OHIO—Canton
Berger Mfg. Co. (Sheet Iron; Building) ......AA
Gilliam Mfg. Co. (Coach).A
OHIO—Cleveland
Avery Stamping Co. (Boiler) B

OHIO—New Berlin
Hoover, W. H. (Bridle)..A
PA.—Erie
Erie Engine Works (Engine) ....A
PA.—Harrisburg
Harrisburg Mfg. & Boiler Co. (Boiler) ....A
PA.—Kutztown
Kutztown Foundry & Machine Co. (Boiler) ....A
PA.—Lancaster
Best, John (Boiler) .....B
PA.—Philadelphia
Gara, McGinley & Co. (Iron; Building) ....A
PA.—Pittsburg
Munroe & Son, R. (Boiler) AA
PA.—Wilkesbarre
Vulcan Iron Works (Iron; Building; Store; Boiler) AAAA
PA.—Williamsport
Valley Iron Wks. (Boiler) A
TENN.—Chattanooga
Chattanooga Roofing & Fdy. Co. (Building; Sheet Iron) A
TENN.—Memphis
Chickasaw Iron Wks. (Iron; Building; Store; Boiler) A
TEXAS—Fort Worth
Fort Worth Iron & Steel Mfg. Co. (Iron; Building) A
WIS.—Racine
Freeman & Sons Mfg. Co., S. (Boiler) ....A

FRUIT: GREEN
See Produce List in Appendix

FRUIT: CANNED
See Canned Goods

FRUIT: DRIED
See also Prunes; Raisins For Preserved Fruit see Jams; Jellies, etc.

CAL.—Armona
Armsby Co., J. K. (Br. Chicago) ....A
Downing, Charles C
CAL.—Campbell
Campbell Fruit Growers' Union C
CAL.—Chico
Warren, E. A. C
CAL.—Colton
California Fruit Canners Association ....AAAA
CAL.—Courtland
California Fruit Canners Association ....AAAA
CAL.—Cupertimo
Le Quesne, E. C
CAL.—Fowler
Chaddock & Co. ....A
Phoenix Seeded Raisin & Packing Co. ....B
CAL.—Fresno
Bonner Vineyard Co. ....B
California Fruit Canners Association ....AAAA

FRUIT DRIED (Con.)

California Raisin Growers Association ....B
Griffin & Skelly Co. ......A
Hammond, T. J. (Packer).C
Inderrieden & Co., J. B. ....AA
Phoenix Seeded Raisin & Packing Co. ....B
Producers' Raisin Packing Co. ....B
CAL.—Geyserville
Walden & Co. ....A
CAL.—Glendora
Gregory Fruit Co. C
CAL.—Gubserville
Cox & Sons, W. C
CAL.—Hanford
California Fruit Canners Association ....AAAA
CAL.—Los Angeles
Armsby Co., J. K., 121 W. 3d (Brokers) ....A
Bishop & Co. ....AA
Germain Fruit Co. (Inc.).A
Inderrieden Co., J. B. (Br. Chicago) ....AA
Johnson Carvell Co., 251 San Pedro C
Ruddock, Trench & Co., 314 W. 4th ....AA
Simpson & Hack Fruit Co. (Inc.) C
CAL.—Los Gatos
Shaner & Co., J. J. C
CAL.—Madeira
Sayre, A. L. ....B
CAL.—Marysville
California Fruit Canners Association ....AAAA
CAL.—Modesto
McHenry Seeded Raisin Co. AA
CAL.—Niles
Niles Co-operative Fruit Association C
CAL.—Oakland
California Fruit Canners Association ....AAAA
CAL.—North Ontario
North Ontario Packing Co. C
CAL.—Oleander
Oleander Packing Co. C
CAL.—Pomona
Pomona Cured Fruit Union C
CAL.—Redlands
Gregory Fruit Co. C
CAL.—Riverside
Pattee & Lett Co. ...AAAA
CAL.—Sacramento
California Fruit Canners Association ....AAAA
Castle Bros. ....AA
CAL.—San Diego
Hersey, Ralph W. ....B
Levi, Simon ....B
CAL.—San Francisco
Alina Colony Corporation, Crosley Bldg. ....A
Balfour, Guthrie & Co., 316 California ....AAAA
California Commission Co., 124 California ....B
California Fruit Canners Association, Pine & Battery ....AAAA
California Green & Dried Fruit Co., 327 Market ..A
Castle Bros., 463 Mission AA
Dennison, Fieweger & Co., 117 Sacramento ....B
Getz Bros. & Co., 111 California ....AAAA
Gray & Barbieri, 309 Washington ....A
Gray, Lang & Stroh, Luning Bldg. ....A
Griffin & Skelley Co., 132 Market ....A
Ivancovich & Co., J., 211 Washington ....A
Johnson-Locke Mercantile Co., 123 California .....A
Lyden & Co. ....B
Phoenix Raisin Seeding & Packing Co., 3 California B

FRUIT DRIED (Con.)

Pike & Co., C. W., 124 California (Brokers) C
Rosenberg Bros. & Co., 211 California ....A
Russ, Early & Harville, 125-129 Davis ....A
Seropian Bros., 406 California (Brokers) ....A
Sorosis Fruit Co., 101 Sansome ....A
Ulrichs & Co., J. F., 120 Clay ....A
Wolf & Co., Philip, 419 Battery ....A
CAL.—San Jose
A. & C. Ham Co. ....A
California Cured Fruit Association ....B
California Fruit Canners Association ....AAAA
Castle Bros. ....AA
Costa Orchard Canning Co. A
Cured Fruit Assn. of California ....A
Frank & Co., George C
Griffin & Skelley Co. ...AA
Herbert, Geo. N. C
Inderrieden Co., J. B....AA
Losse & Co., H. E. ......A
Phoenix Dried Fruit Co....B
Santa Clara Co. Fruit Union B
Warren Dried Fruit Co....C
CAL.—Santa Clara
Cured Fruit Association of California ....A
Haines, S. S. C
CAL.—Santa Rosa
Merritt Fruit Co. C
CAL.—Saratoga
Saratoga Packing Co. ....B
Sorosis Fruit Co. ....A
CAL.—Sebastopol
Huntley, G. W. C
CAL.—Stockton
Thompson & Folger Co....B
CAL.—Suisun
Alden-Anderson Fruit Co...C
Luehning, E. C
CAL.—Toluca
Toluca Packing Co. C
CAL.—Vacaville
Buck & Co., F. H. ....A
Pinkham & McKevitt ....B
CAL.—Visalia
Armsby Co., J. K. (Br. Chicago) ....A
Downing, C. C
Pinkham & McKevitt ....B
CONN.—Hartford
Bentley Co., G. W. (Bkrs.) B

ILL.—Chicago

Armsby Co., J. K., 46 River (Br. Chicago) ....A
California Package Fruit Co., 53 River C
Durand & Kasper Co., 153 W. Lake ....AAA
Fry & Co., M., 34 Clark (Brokers) C
Holden, C. N. (Bkrs.)....A
Inderrieden Co., J. B., 36 River (Bkrs.) ....AA
Knight & Co., W. S., 2 Wabash Av. (Bkrs.)....B
Leslie & Co., J. H., 29 Michigan Av. (Bkrs.) ....A
Newhall & Sons, F., 131 S. Water ....AA
Reid, Murdock & Co., Lake & Market (Jobbers).AAAA
Smith Co., H. W., 189 S. Water (Brokers) ......A
Weaver & Co., C. H., 129 S. Water ....A
Webber & Co., C. M. (Bkrs.) A
Wing & Co., L. R., 2 Wabash Av. (Bkrs.) ......B
ILL.—Salem
Rogers & Schwartz (Evap.) C
IOWA—Des Moines
Peycke Bros. & Chancy ...A
IOWA—Glenwood
New Glenwood Canning Co. C

437

FRUIT DRIED (Con.)

IOWA—Sioux City
Haley & Lang Co. ......A
KY.—Louisville
Herndon, Carter Co., 313
  Murrell Ct. C
Sabel Sons', M. ....A
LA.—New Orleans
Dunbar Sons', G. W., 317
  Magazine (Figs) ......A
MD.—Baltimore
Continental Commercial Co.,
  1630 Bank ....B
Dix & Wilkins, 9 E. Lom-
  bard ....AA
Jackson & Co., R. S., 113
  S. Charles (Packers) ..B
Seward & Co., J. H., Pier,
  ft. Mill ....B
MASS.—Boston
Bently Co., Geo. W., 192
  State (Brokers) ....B
Chany, John, 12 India (Bkr.)
                          C
Dudley & Co., H., Board
  Trade ldg. (Bkrs.) ....A
Howe & Co., F. C., 156
  State (Brokers) C
MASS.—Lawrence
Slayton Co., E. M........A
MASS.—Worcester
Blodgett Co., W. H.......A
MICH.—Detroit
Braid & West, 149 Jeffer-
  son Av. (Bkrs.) C
Reynolds & Co., F. P., 16
  W. Woolbridge (Bkrs.).C
MICH.—East Tawas
National Milling & Evap.
  Co. C
MICH.—Grand Rapids
Moseley Bros. ....A
MICH.—Lansing
Genesee Fruit Co. ......AA
MICH.—Owosso
Thomas, A. T. (Evap.) ...C
MICH.—Sebewaing
Liken & Co., J. C. (Evap.)
                          A
MICH.—Stockbridge
De Puy Co., C. E. C
MINN.—Minneapolis
Park Co., L. M. 6 N. 3d..B
Potter Co., E. G. C
Preece & Co., T. J., 9 N.
  3d ....D
MINN.—St. Paul
Park Co., Louis M., Drake
  Bldg. (Bkrs.) ....B
MO.—Kansas City
Ford & Doan, 1209 W. 9th
  (Brokers) C
Ginocchio-Jones Fruit Co.,
  519 Walnut C
Goodlett & Bolles, 1422 St.
  Louis Av. (Bkrs.) .....A
Peycke Bros. Com. Co., 2d &
  Main (Bkrs.) ....A
Seavey & Flarsheim, 1324
  Union Av. ....B
MO.—Kirksville
Kirksville Canning & Pick-
  ling Factory ....B
MO.—St. Joseph
Seavey & Flarsheim, 1317
  St. Louis Av. ....B
MO.—St. Louis
Ford & Doan, 312 N. 2d
  (Brokers) C
Funsten & Co., R. E., 300
  N. Coml. ....B
Gettys & Gilbert, 806
  Spruce (Bkrs.) C
Hoffman Bros. Produce Co.,
  700 N. 2d ....B
Hudson Bros. Com. Co., 212
  N. 2d ....B
Triechlinger & Stern, 813
  Spruce (Bkrs.) ....B
NEBR.—Omaha
Peycke Bros. Com. Co., 1009
  Howard (Bkrs.) ....A
Russell Brokerage Co., 215
  S. 13th ....B
Seavey & Flarsheim, 1008
  Jackson (Bkrs.) ....B
N. J.—Newark
Johnson & Co., T. F., 77
  Mechanic ....A
N. Y.—Albion
Doyle & Co., M. ....A

FRUIT DRIED (Con.)

Rogers, L. R. (Evap. Apple)
                          C
N. Y.—Alton
Miles, G. B. C
N. Y.—Baldwinsville
Toll & Clark C
N. Y.—Buffalo
Brennisen & Son, F., 156
  Michigan ....B
Erie Preserving Co., 941 W.
  Perry ....AA
N. Y.—Cato
Hapeman & Goodfellow
  (Apples) C
N. Y.—Hilton
Upton & Co., E. M. ....AA
N. Y.—Holly
Genesee Fruit Co. (Evap.
  Apples) ....AA
Pettengall & Son, W. T...C
N. Y.—Lockport
Shaeffer, W. E. (Evap. Ap-
  ples) C
N. Y.—Mt. Morris
White, J. F. (Agt.) ......B
N. Y.—Naples
Hemenway, Geo. B. C
N. Y.—Newark
Perkins Co., C. H. ......AA
Pierson & Co., E. V. (Evap.)
                          B
Smith & Hyde (Raspberry)
                          B
New York City
Allen & Co., W. L., 19
  Jay ....AA
Armsby Co. J. K., 87 Hud-
  son (Br. Chicago) ......A
Arquimbau & Ramee, 84
  Thomas (Imptrs.) .....B
Bennett, Day & Co., 96 Hud-
  son (Imptrs.) ....A
Causse Mfg. Co., A. L., 105
  Hudson ....B
Dudley & Co., W. H., 49
  Hudson (Bkrs.) ....A
Erie Preserving Co., 107
  Hudson (Apples) .....AA
Genesee Fruit Co., 501 West
                         AA
Hartwig & Bennett, 61 N.
  Moore ....A
Hawkesworth, J. A., 10 Jay
  (Broker) ....A
Higgins & Co., W. A., 374
  Washington ....B
Hills Bros. Co., 377 Wash-
  ington ....AA
Howe & Co., C. T., 51
  Hudson (Bkrs.) C
Hurley & Co., J. B., 90 W.
  B'way. (Bkrs.) ....B
Johnston, North & Co., 21
  Harrison (Bkrs.) C
Kraus & Stettin, 105 Hud-
  son ....B
Lumsden, J. W., 260 Wash-
  ington C
Oettinger Bros., 336 Green-
  wich (Bkrs.) C
Rafferty & Hoosier, 67
  Front ....B
Rosenstein Bros. (Inc.), 96
  N. Moore ....AA
Schaefer, J. W., 6 Harrison
                          B
Seggerman Bros., 91 Hudson
                          B
Sneckner & Quimby, 146
  Reade ....B
Starace, A., 76 Pearl .....A
Stout, J. R. (Broker).....A
Thompson, G. H., 107 Hud-
  son ....B
Turle & Skidmore, 105 Hud-
  son (Bkrs.) ....B
Wakeman & Co., John, 65
  Broad ....A
Zucca & Co., 235 West ...A
N. Y.—Penfield
Brown Bros. C
N. Y.—Penn Yan
Birkett, C. T.............A
N. Y.—Port Byron
Gutchess Bros. C
N. Y.—Rochester
Doyle & Co., M. ....A
Genesee Fruit Co. (Apples)
                         AA

N. Y.—Sodus
Case & Norris Co. ......B
Williams, A. B. ....A
N. Y.—Victor
McCrea & Co., J.........C
N. Y.—Walworth
McCrea & Co., J.........C
N. Y.—Webster
Hallauer & Sons, J. W....B
N. Y.—Wolcott
Johnson & Northrup ......A
OHIO—Cincinnati
Brooks & Co., P., 39 Main
......................C
Davidson & Co., C. M.....C
Echert & Co., P., 25 W.
Court (Foreign) ....A
Flach Bros. Grocery Co., 2d
& Vine ....A
Glas. Bloom & Co., 115 E.
Front ....A
Holden, Jr. & Co., R. A.,
46 Main ....B
Hosea & Co., Main & Front
(Brokers) C
Peebles' Sons & Co., Jos. R.,
Government Sq. ......A
Shaw & Co., G. A., 42 Vine
(Brokers) C
Smith Co., H. D., 206 Main
(Foreign) ....B
Stevens & Co., S. J., 37
Walnut ....A
Threlkeld & Son, H. C., 59
Walnut (Bkrs.) C
OHIO—Cleveland
Banks & Co., W. A., 84
B'way C
Haserot Canneries Co., 39
Woodland Av. ....B
Haserot Company, 37 Wood-
land Av. ....A
Housum Co., B. W., The
Arcade (Bkrs.) C
OHIO—Marietta
Kirby, S. B. ....B
OHIO—Mt. Vernon
Bunn & Co., A. D.........C
OHIO—Salem
McNabob, J. B. ....B
OHIO—Urbana
Marvin & Co., W. H.
(Packers) ....A
OREGON—Carlton
Howe, W. A. C
PA.—Philadelphia
Armsby Co., J. K., 23 S.
Front (Bkrs.) ....A
Barker & Co. C
Cowan & Son, H., 28 S.
Front (Bkrs.) ....B
Howe & Co., C. T. (Bkrs.)
....
James & Washington, 21 S.
Front (Bkrs.) C
Wilson, Sherborne & Co.,
107 N. Water ....A
Yost & Co., J. C., 223 N.
Water ....A
PA.—Pittsburg
Woodruff Co., W. W., 1147
Penn. Av. (Bkrs.)......B
R. I.—Providence
Cooper & Sisson, 73 Dyer..C
TENN.—Knoxville
Scarborough & Henderson
Co. ....A
TENN.—Memphis
Ozark Fruit Co., 7 How-
ard Row C
TEXAS—Dallas
Jackson & Co., A. A.....B
Nigro & Co., N. ....B
TEXAS—Houston
Kirkland & Morrow .....B
VT.—Montpelier
Corry. F. M. ....B
WASH.—Seattle
Balfour, Guthrie & Co.
......................AAAA
Eagle Evaporating Co. ...B
Kelley-Clarke Co. (Bkrs.).A
WASH.—Tacoma
Balfour, Guthrie & Co.
......................AAAA
WASH.—Vancouver
Kelley-Clarke Co. (Bkrs.).A

FULLERS

IND.—Evansville
Evansville Tool Wks. (Top;
Bottom) ....A
MICH.—Detroit
Anderson & Sons, W. H.
(Top; Bottom) C
N. J.—Newark
Atha Tool Co. (Top; Bot-
tom) ....A
W. VA.—Charlestown
Powhattan Brass & Iron
Works ....B

FUNNELS

CONN.—Meriden
Meriden Britannia Co.
......................AAAA
CONN.—Wallingford
Wallace & Sons Mfg. Co.,
R. ....AAAA
ILL.—Chicago
Wilson & Co., F. Cortez,
239 Lake (Accurate) ...B
MASS.—Andover
Tyer Rubber Co. (Rubber)
......................AA
MASS.—Boston
Strater. & Sons, Herman
(Copper) ....A
MASS.—Worcester
New England Steel Roofing
Co. (Gravel Roof) .....F
MO.—St. Louis
St. Louis Stamping Co.
......................AAAA
N. J.—Newark
King & Hone (Rubber) ..F
N. Y.—Albany
Hoy & Co. ....A
N. Y.—Brooklyn
Sweeney Mfg. Co., W. H.
(Copper) ....A
N. Y.—Buffalo
Pierce & Co., Geo. N. (Cop-
per) ....AA
Shepard & Co., Sidney
......................AAAA
New York City
Cordley & Hayes ....A
Goodyear's India Rubber
Glove Mfg. Co. (Rubber)
......................AAAA
Hatch & Co., 92 Murray
(Counter) ....E
Lalance & Grosjean Mfg. Co.
......................AAAA
Mechanical Rubber Co.
......................AAAA
N. Y.—Troy
Troy Stamping Wks..AAAA
OHIO—Salem
Clark Co., W. J. (Charging)
......................A
PA.—Philadelphia
Disston & Sons, Henry
......................AAAA
WIS.—Milwaukee
Wallman Mfg. Co. ....E

FURNACES

See also Heaters

CAL.—Los Angeles
Braun & Co., F. W. (Smelt-
ing; Roasting; Calsing)
......................AAA
CAL.—San Francisco
Harron, Rickard & McCone
(Inc.) (Smelting; Roast-
ing; Calsing) ....AA
Hendy Machine Works,
Joshua. 38 Fremont
(Smelting; Roasting;
Calsing) ....AA
COLO.—Denver
Colorado Iron Works Co.
(Smelting; Roasting; Cal-
sing; Blast) ....AA
Davis Iron Works Co., F.
M. (Smelting; Roasting;
Calsing) ....AA
Denver Fire Clay Co. (As-
say) ....AA
Mine & Smelter Supply Co.
(Smelting; Roasting; Cal-
sing, &c.) ....AAAA

ʄURNACES (Con.)

Stearns-Rogers Mfg. Co. (Smelting; Roasting; Calsing) ....A

CONN.—Bristol

Turner Heater Co. (Hot Air) C

CONN.—Hartford

Billings & Spencer Co. (Forging) ....AA

CONN.—Putnam

Putnam Foundry & Machine Co. (Hot Air) ....B

CONN.—Stamford

Stamford Fdy. Co. (Heating; Combined Hot Air; Hot Water) ....A

Stamford Gas Stove Co. (Hot Air) C

CONN.—Waterbury

Kenworthy Engineering & Construction Co. (Annealing; Annealing Lead; Blast; Brass Melting; Brazing; Case Hardening; Chain Heating; Crucible; Forging; Gas Annealing; Gas Crucible; Heating; Malleable; Natural Gas; Gas Blast; Open Hearth) X

Waterbury, Farrell Foundry & Machine Co. (Annealing; Tempering; Casting; Brazing) ....AA

Waterbury Machine Co. (Wire Brazing) ....B

ILL.—Bloomington

American Foundry & Furnace Co. (Hot Air) ....A

ILL.—Chicago

Allis-Chalmers Co., Home Ins. Bldg. (Smelting; Roasting; Calsing, &c.; Roasting Ore; Blast) ....AAAA

Brand Stove Co., 177 E. Lake (Hot Air) ......A

Burke, Jas. V. (Smokeless) ....F

Chicago Flexible Shaft Co., 158 Huron (Gas Blast Tempering) ....B

Excelsior Steel Furnace Co. 40 W. Monroe (Hot Air) C

Hawley Dawn Draft Furnace Co., Superior & Townsend (Brass; Copper Melting; Smokeless) ...A

Klein & Son, Mathias, 87 W. Van Buren (Charcoal Plumbers'; Tinners') ..B

Lyman. W. C., 49 Michigan (Asphalt; Pitch; Tar)...D

McMillan & Co., Jas., 219 Washn. (Smokeless)....F

Railway Materials Co., Old Colony Bldg. (Annealing; Tempering; Boiler Shop; Oil as Fuel; Flue Welding; Roll Tapering; Spring Fitting) ....D

Robinson Furnace Co., 109 Lake (Hot Air) ......B

Rubel & Co. (Drying; Iron; Steel) ....A

Turner Brass Works, Franklin & Michigan (Gasoline; Crucible; Gasoline Porcelain; Brazing; Chain Heating) ....A

Union Drop Forge Co., 66 E. Ohio (Crucible; Forging, &c.) ....A

Wolf Co., Fred W., 139 Rees (Bagasse) ....AAA

ILL.—Decatur

Mueller Mfg. Co., H. (Lead) ....AAA

ILL.—Downers Grove

Dicke Tool Co. (Blast; Electric Soldering; Tinners'; Plumbers') C

ILL.—Harvey

Whiting Foundry Equipment Co. (Brass Moulders; Cupola; Brass; Copper Melting; Annealing; Malleable; Open Hearth) ....AA

FURNACES (Con.)

ILL.—Joliet

Bates Machine Co. (Annealing; Tempering) ....AA

ILL.—Peoria

Sandmeyer & Co., H., 215 S. Adams (Hot Air)...AA

ILL.—Quincy

Gem City Stove Mfg. Co. (Hot Air) ....B

IND.—Indianapolis

Kruse & Dewented, 427 E. Washn. (Hot Air) ...B

IOWA—Cedar Rapids

Economy Furnace Co. (Hot Air) ....B

IOWA—Dubuque

Smedley Steam Pump Co. (Hot Air) C

IOWA—Marshalltown

Lennox Machine Co. (Wood Burning; also for Hard & Soft Coal; Hot Air)....C

KANS.—Fort Scott

Fort Scott Fdy. & Machine Co. (Open Hearth; Ore Smelting) ....H

LA.—New Orleans

Babcock & Wilcox Co. (Bagasse) ....AAAA

Burt Co. (Ltd.), C. S., 726 Gravier (Bagasse) ...X

Haubtman & Loeb Co. (Ltd.), 217 Gravier (Bagasse) ....B

Payne & Joubert, 423 Carondelet (Bagasse) ......A

Swoop, Julian M., 913 Girod (Bagasse) ....A

MAINE—Bangor

Wood & Bishop Co. (Wood Burning; Hot Air).....A

MAINE—Portland

Portland Stove Fdy. Co. (Hot Air) ....B

MD.—Baltimore

Bibb Stove Co., B. C. (Heating; Hot Air) ....A

Hill Mfg. Co., J. S. (Tinners'; Plumbers') X

Leibrandt & McDowell Stove Co., 26 E. Pratt (Hot Air) ....AAA

Sexton & Son, S. B., 23 E. Lombard (Hot Air)..AA

MASS.—Boston

Carpenter & Co., Cyrus, 44 Hanover (Hot Air)....C

Chilson Furnace Co., 88 Washn. (Hot Air) C

Gurney Heater Mfg. Co. (Heating) ....B

Highland Foundry Co., 1301 Columbus Av. (Hot Air) ....B

Howes Co., S. M., 40 Union (Hot Air) C

Jarvis Engineering Co., 61 Oliver (Smokeless).....X

McDowell Oven Co. (Candy) ....E

Magee Furnace Co. (Heating; Hot Air) ....AA

Smith & Anthony Co., 48 Union (Hot Air) ......AA

MASS.—North Dighton

Dighton Furnace Co. (Hot Air) C

MASS.—Springfield

Gilbert & Barker Mfg. Co. (Plumbers'; Tinners')...A

MASS.—Taunton

Weir Stove Co. (Heating; Combined Hot Air; Hot Water) ....A

MASS.—Watertown

Walker & Pratt Mfg. Co. (Hot Air) ....AA

MASS.—Westfield

Smith & Co., H. B. (Heating) ....AA

MASS.—Worcester

Morgan Construction Co. (Annealing; Tempering; Billet Heating; Re-heating) ....A

MICH.—Adrian

Clauda, Meyer & Littleton (Wood Burning) ....D

MICH.—Battle Creek

Duplex Printing Press Co.

FURNACES (Con.)
(Stereotypers.) ....B
MICH.—Big Rapids
Michigan Heater Co. (Hot
Air) C
MICH.—Detroit
Byram & Co. (Brass Mould-
ers'; Cupola; Smelting;
Brass; Copper Melting).D
Clayton & Lambert Mfg. Co.
(Plumbers'; Tinners')..B
Michigan Stove Co., 1022
Jeff. Av. (Hot Air) AAAA
Northern Engineering Wks.
(Brass Melting).......A
Park & McKay Co., 52 Bag-
ley Av. (Plumbers'; Tin-
ners') ....B
Peninsular Stove Co., Fort
& 10th (Hot Air) ....AA
Union Heater Supply Co., 13
Macomb (Plumbers'; Tin-
ners') ....G
MICH.—Dowagiac
Beckwith, Philo. D. (Est.
of) (Heating) ......AAA
MICH.—Grand Rapids
Miller Furnace Co. (Wood
Burning) ....F
MICH.—Monroe
Monroe Foundry & Furnace
Co. (Wood Burning; Hot
Air) C
MINN.—Minneapolis
Peteler Portable Railway
Mfg. Co. (Heating).....C
MO.—St. Louis
Front Rank Steel Furnace
Co. (Laundry; Hot Air).B
Ringen Stove Co., 414 N.
6th (Quick Meal; Plumb-
ers'; Tinners)......AAAA
Wrought Iron Range Co.
(Heating; Hot Air)..AAA
N. J.—Burlington
Stewart & Peterson Co.
(Farm) ....A
N. J.—Elizabeth
Amer. Gas Furnace Co. (An-
nealing; Tempering; As-
say; Case Hardening; Gas;
Regenerating; Gas Cru-
cible; Gas Annealing;
Muffle; Crucible).......A
N. J.—Jersey City
Gautier & Co., J. H. (Gas
Generator) ....AA
N. J.—Newark
Bernz, Otto, So. 13th, cor.
So. Orange Av. (Plumb-
ers'; Tinners')..........B
Currier & Sons, Cyrus
(Smelting) ....AA
Thatcher Furnace Co., 42
St. Francis (Hot Air)..A
N. J.—Salem
Amer. Producer Gas Furnace
Co. (Glass) ....D
N. J.—Trenton
Mackenzie Sons Co., Duncan
(Annealing; Tempering;
Muffle) ....A
N. Y.—Albany
Littlefield Stove Co. (Heat-
ing) ....A
N. Y.—Auburn
Crane Foundry & Mach.
Wks., W. W. (Forging,
&c.) ....D
Leather & Brass Mfg. Co.
(Gas; Oil; Kerosene;
Plumbers'; Tinners)....F
N. Y.—Brooklyn
Bliss Co., E. W. (Plumb-
ers'; Tinners).....AAAA
Continental Iron Wks. (Boil-
er; Corrugated for Land
and Marine Boilers)....A
Guild & Garrison, ft. So.
10th (Bagasse) ....B
Pioneer Iron Wks., 151 Wil-
liam (Bagasse) ....A
Pollard, Jos. G., 141 Ray-
mond (Lead) ....F
N. Y.—Buffalo
Buffalo. Dental Mfg. Co.
(Assay;. Gas; Soldering;
Tempering) ....b
Buffalo Forge Co. (Heating)
AAA
Crosby Co. (Case Hardening;

FURNACES (Con.)
.....................A
Annealing) ....A
Ginthers' Sons, J., 417
Bdway. (Hot Air) .....A
Niagara Mach. & Tool Wks.
(Plumbers'; Tinners')..A
N. Y.—Fort Plain
Burns Hydro-Carbon Burner
Co. (Annealing; Brass
Melting; Forging; Lead
Bath Tempering; Muffle;
Case Hardening; Fuel Oil;
Spiral; Elliptical Car
Spring) ....F
N. Y.—Geneva
Herendeen Mfg. Co. (Heat-
ing) ....AA
N. Y.—Hoosick Falls
Brien Heater Co. (Hot
Air) C
N. Y.—Long Island City
Stuebner Iron Wks., G. L.
(Plumbers') ....B
N. Y.—Munnsville
Munnsville Plow Co. (Dry-
ing; Fruit Drying).....B
N. Y.—Newburg
Coldwell-Wilcox Co.
(Bagasse) ....B
New York City
Abendroth Bros. (Heating)
A
Am. Gas Furnace Co., 23
John (Gas Blast).......A

*Gas Blast Furnaces for
Industrial Heating Pro-
cesses only. Burners and
Positive Pressure Blow-
ers. Factory at Eliza-
beth, N. J.*

Bowsky, L., 164 E. 52d
(Plumbers'; Tinners')..E
Boynton Furnace Co. (Heat-
ing; Hot Air) ....A
Bramhall-Deane Co. (Heat-
ing) ....B
Cornell Co., J. B. & J. M.,
26th & 11th Av. (Bagesse;
Annealing) ....AA
Cottrell & Sons Co., C. B.
(Stereotypers') .....AAA
Crane Co., Wm. M., 1133
Bdway. (Hot Air; Gas for
Fuel; Plumbers; Tinners')
A
Deeley & Co., Robert
(Bagasse) ....A
Gesswein Co., F. W., 39
John (Kerosene; Brass;
Copper Melting).......A
Graff Furnace Co., 208 Wa-
ter (Heating; Hot Air).B
Hammacher, Schlemmer &
Co.. 209 Bowery (Plumb-
ers'; Tinners') ......AAA
Hydrocarbon Burner Co., 197
Fulton (Plumbers'; Tin-
ners') X
Koven & Bro., L. O.. 50
Cliff. (Asphalt; Pitch;
Tar; Portable; Lead;
Gravel) ....A
Lovejoy Co. (Stereotypers.)
B
Mott Iron Wks., J. L., 88
Beekman (Hot Air)..AA
Munsell Engine Co., 218
Water (Hot Air) ......B
Murray, Jno. A., 625 6th
Av. (Plumbers'; Tinners')
B
Nugent, Thos., 223 E. 80th
(Hot Air) ....A
Peck, Stow & Wilcox Co.,
27 Murray (Plumbers';
Tinners') ....AAAA
Reichhelm & Co., E. P.
(Gas) ....A
Richardson & Boynton Co.
(Heating; Hot Air)..AA
Rockwell Engineering Co.,
26 Cortlandt (Annealing;
Tempering; Brass; Copper
Melting; Case Hardening;
Regenerating Gas; Braz-
ing; Forging; Heating;
Wire Galvanizing; Wire
Tinning) C
Smith of New York Co., 352

442

FURNACES (Con.)

Evans Furnace Wks., 506 N. 13th (Hot Air) .....B

Gefrorer & Son, C., 248 N. 8th (Plumbers'; Tinners') ....F

Haines, Jones & Cadbury Co., 1136 Ridge Av. (Plumbers'; Tinners') .AA

Harrison's Sons, W. H. (Heating) ....E

Morris, Henry G., Phila. Bourse (Bagasse) .....B

Paxson Co., J. W. (Brass Moulders'; Cupola; Brass; Copper Melting; Annealing; Crucible; Natural Gas; Oil Melting; Open Hearth) ....AA

Phila. Engineering Wks. (Blast) ....AAAA

Phila. Roll & Machine Co. (Heating; Open Hearth Puddling) ....B

Phila. Stove & Iron Foundry Co. (Hot Air) ....B

Sheppard & Co., Isaac A. (Heating; Combined Hot Air and Hot Water) .AAA

Spear Stove & Heating Co., Jas., 1014 Market (Heating; Hot Air) ....A

PA.—Pittsburg

Amer. Furnace & Mach. Co. (Annealing; Boiler; Brass Melting; Brazing; Crucible; Forging; Glass; Malleable; Muffle; Open Hearth; Chain Heating; Heating; Puddling; Tube Welding) ....D

Amsler Engineering Co. (Annealing; Blast; Crucible; Glass; Heating; Muffle; Crucible; Open Hearth; Tube Welding) ....D

Carroll-Porter Boiler & Tank Co. (Blast) ......B

Fischer Foundry & Machine Co. (Blast) ....AA

Foster-Miller Engineering Co., Westinghouse Bldg. (Annealing; Tempering; Blast; Crucible; Heating; Muffle; Crucible; Open Hearth; Tube Welding).D

Huber & Co., S. V. (Blast; Heating; Open Hearth).D

Laughlin & Co., Alex. (Crucible; Heating; Open Hearth; Pubbling; Tube Welding) ....B

McClure Son & Co. (Blast; Heating; Open Hearth).D

McCullough Dalzell Crucible Co. (Blast; Open Hearth) ....A

Mackintosh. Hemphill & Co. (Ltd.) (Blast) ....AAAA

Munroe & Son, R. (Blast; Boiler) ....AA

Murphy. M. L., 426 4th Av. (Glass) ....D

Pittsburg Stove & Range Co. (Hot Air) ....AAAA

Prizer-Painter Stove & Heater Co., 717 Grant (Hot Air) ....A

Riter-Conley Mfg. Co. (Blast; Open Hearth; Brass Melting) .....AAA

Scaife & Sons Co., W. B. (Blast) ....AAA

Smythe Co., S. R. (Heating; Open Hearth) ....B

Standard Mfg. Co. (Plumbers') ....AA

Swindell & Bros., Wm. (Asphalt; Pitch; Tar; Regenerating Gas; Annealing; Brass Melting; Crucible; Heating) ......AAAA

Westinghouse Machine Co., Westinghouse Bldg. (Smokeless) ......AAAA

PA.—Pittston

Pittston Stove Co. (Hot Air) ....A

PA.—Pottsdown

March-Brownback Stove Co. (Hot Air) ....A

FURNACES (Con.)

PA.—Quarkertown

Roberts, Winner & Co. (Hot Air) ....B

PA.—Reading

Mt. Penn Stove Wks., 111 N. 2d (Heating; Hot Air) ....A

Reading Stove Wks. (Heating) ....AA

PA.—Royersford

Buckwalter Stove Co. (Hot Air) ....AA

Grandee Stove Co. (Hot Air) ....A

PA.—Bethlehem

Bethlehem Foundry & Machine Co. (Annealing; Tempering) C

PA.—Spring City

Yeager-Hunter Spring City Stove Wks. (Hot Air) ..A

PA.—Towanda

Loetzer Valve & Mfg. Co. (Lead; Furnace; Lead Pot mounted on wheels)....X

PA.—Warren

Jacobson Machine Mfg. Co. (Plumbers'; Tinners') ...C

Schellhammer & Son (Hot Air; Gas for Fuel)......E

R. I.—Pawtucket

Pawtucket Mfg. Co. (Revolving Forge) ....A

R. I.—Providence

Barstow Stove Co. (Heating; Hot Air) ....AA

Brown & Sharpe Mfg. Co. (Annealing; Tempering; Case Hardening) ....AAAA

Westmacot Co., J. M. (Annealing; Tempering; Case Hardening) X

S. C.—Charleston

Valk & Murdock Iron Wks. (Sulphur) ....B

TENN.—Chattanooga

Chattanooga Plow Co. (Bagasse) ....AAA

TENN.—Knoxville

Scates' Warm Air Furnace Co. (Hot Air) ....A

WIS.—Cudahy

Power & Mining Machine Co. (Smelting; Roasting; Calsing) C

WIS.—Milwaukee

Allis-Chalmers Co. (Muffle; Smelting; Ore Smelting; Roasting) ....AAAA

Johnson Service Co. (Brass; Copper Melting) ...AAA

Lindeman & Hoverson Co., A. J., 348 Florida (Hot Air) ....AA

Lindemann & Sons, J. P., 78 W. Water (Hot Air)....A

Schwab & Sons Co., R. J., 271 Clinton (Hot Air)..A

Sheriff's Mfg. Co. (Brass Moulders'; Tempering; Brass; Copper Melting).B

WIS.—Neenah

Bergstrom Bros. & Co. (Heating; Wood Burning; Hot Air) ....AA

FURNITURE

For Dental Furniture see following Heading. For Barbers Furniture see Chairs—See also Fixtures for Bar; Office, etc. Furniture

ALA.—Mobile

Mobile Spring Bed Co. (Woven Wire Springs, Cots) C

ARK.—Ft. Smith

Ballman Cummings Furn. Co. (Chamber Suits, Odd Dressers; Chiffoniers; Sideboards; Desks) .....D

Ft. Smith Folding Bed & Table Co. (Mantle Folding Beds; Extension; Library; Kitchen Tables; Kitchen Cabinets) C

McLoud & Sparks Furn. Co. (Bedsteads; Kitchen Safes; Cupboards; Glass Cup-

FURNITURE (Con.)

boards) C
Ward Furn. Mfg. Co. (Bedroom Suits; Chiffoniers; Odd Dresses; Sideboards)
................C

ARK.—Little Rock
Little Rock Furn. Mfg. Co. (Chamber Suits; Chairs; Rockers; Tables) C

ARK.—Pine Bluff
Home Furn. Mfg. Co. (Chamber Suits; Chiffoniers; Safes) C

CAL.—Los Angeles
Stearns Mfg. Co. (Dressers; Commodes; Chiffoniers; Bookcases; Folding Beds; Tables; Office Bank Fixtures) C
Van Vorst & Berman (Suits; Chiffoniers; Kitchen Furn.; Lounges; Couches; Top Mattresses; Wire Mattresses; Brass; Iron; Hospital Beds) C

CAL.—San Francisco
Bernhard Mattress Co. (The) Iron & Wire Beds) .....A
Crescent Feather Co. (Woven Wire Springs; Couch; Spring Frames) ....D
Frederichs, Henry (Kitchen; Bank Furn.) C
Fuller Desk Co., Geo. H. (Office; Bank Furn.)....C
Hoey, John (Upholstered Furn.; Mattresses; Parlor Suits; Davenport Safes; Turkish Chairs; Couches; Upholstered Box Spring; Woven Wire Mattresses)
................B
Pacific Coast Lumber & Furn. Co. ....A
Schrock W. A. (Mattresses; Iron Beds) ....D

CONN.—Bridgeport
Miller Wire Spring Co. (The) (Upholstering; Beds; Helical Compression; Extension Springs) ....A

CONN.—East River
Munger & Sons (School Furn.) ....D

CONN.—Hartford
Bishop & Co., E. C. (Chairs)
................F
Case & Co., O. D. (School Furn.) ....B
Hartford Woven Wire Mattress Co. (Bedsteads; Steel; Brass Trimmed; Steel Woven Wire; National Link Mattresses; Wire Work Aseptic Furn.; Hospital Bedsteads) ...B

CONN.—Meriden
Parker Co., Chas. (Piano Stools) ....B

CONN.—New Britain
National Spring Bed Co. (Rip Van Winkle Spring Beds) ....F

CONN.—New Haven
Connecticut Chair Co. (Cane Seat Chairs; Reed Rockers) ....A
Farren Bros. Co. (The) (Spring Beds) ....D
Rattan Mfg. Co. (Invalid; Morris Chairs; Folding Settees C
Savage & Co., B. B. (Spring Beds; Bedding) C
Shepard & Sons, N. G. (Bent Wood Chairs) ....B

CONN.—New Milford
Eastern Lounge Co. (Lounges; Couches; Sofas; Sofa Beds; Adjustable; Wardrobe Couches; Davenports, etc.) ......D

CONN.—Shelton
Whitcomb Metallic Bedsteads; Spring Mattresses)
................B

CONN.—Waterbury
National Wire Mattress Co. (Wire Mattresses) .....D

D. C.—Washington
Stumpf & Lyford (Couches)
................A

FURNITURE (Con.)

GA.—Atlanta
Atlanta Mfg. Co. (Iron; Brass Bedsteads) ....D
Atlanta Table Co. (Flat; Roll Top Desks; Office Tables) ....D
Beutell, H. H. (Music Cabinets; Bar; Bank Furn.)
................B
Capitol City Chair Co. (Medium Grade Chairs) ....D
Cooper Mfg. Co. (Double Cane Seats; Wood Seat Children's Chairs; Rockers) ....D
Golstin-Conningham Spring Bed Co. (Spring; Iron Beds; Cots; Mattresses) C
Hirsch & Spitz Mfg. Co. (Spring Beds; Mattresses; Cots) C
Ladder & Specialty Co. (Odd Dresses; Washstands; Beds; Chiffoniers; Dressing Tables; Cheap; Medium Suits; Ladies' Desks) ....D
National Furn. Co. (Bedroom Suits; Sideboards; Buffets; Hall Racks; Bookcases; Combination Cases) ....D
Southern Furn. Co. (Sideboards; Side Tables; Buffets; Chiffoniers; Chamber Suits; Dresses; Washstands) ....A
Southern Spring Bed Co. (Spring Beds) C
Ware Mfg. Co. (Chamber Suits; Odd Beds; Dressers; Sideboards; Wardrobes; Bookcases; Kitchen Safes; Cupboards, in Oak & Poplar) ....A

GA.—Dalton
Duane Chair Co. (Wood Seat Chairs) ....D

GA.—Dublin
Dublin Furn. Mfg. Co. (Chamber Suits) ......D

GA.—Griffin
Osborn & Walcott Mfg. Co. (Chairs) ....B

GA.—Macon
Willingham Mfg. Co. (Suits; Odd Dressers; Odd Beds; Chairs; Rockers; Centre Tables; Safes; Sideboards; Hat Racks) ....B

GA.—Marietta
Brumby Chair Co. (Wood; Cane; Cobbler Seat Chairs)
................A
Marietta Chair Co. (Open; Double Cane; Wood; Cobler Seat Chair; Rockers; Cane; Wood Seat Stools; Baby Cradles; Parlor Tables) ....B

GA.—Maysville
Maysville Mfg. Co. (Dining; Kitchen Chairs) ....D

GA.—Washington
Washington Mfg. Co. (Tables; Hat Racks; Ladies' Desks; Cribs) ....B

ILL.—Altamont
Hillemann, Geo. (Chamber Suits) ....A

ILL.—Bradley
Turk Furn. Co. (Iron Beds)
................C

ILL.—Chicago
Acme Co. (Acme Hygienic Couches; General Line of Furn.) C
Adams & Westlake Co., The (Brass; Iron Bedsteads)
................AAAA
Alsburg, Samuel (Ottomans)
.. ..D
American Metal Ware Co. (Brass Bedsteads) .....B
American Stool Co. (Piano Stools). X
Andrews, Co., A. H. (Office Desks; Tables; Desks; Chairs, etc.; Church; Auditorium Seatings; School Furn.; Steel Wire Chairs; Stools; Tables) ....AA
Art Bedstead Co. (Brass;

444

FURNITURE (Con.)

Iron Beds) ....B
Balkwill & Patch Furn. Co.
(Odd Dressers; Chiffon-
iers; Washstands; Toilet
Commodes; Princess Dress-
ers; Ladies' Dressing Ta-
bles; made in Mahogany,
Birdseye; White Maple,
Curly Birch; Enamel Fin-
ishes) ....B
Blonder Bros. (Brass; Iron
Beds) ....D
Borgwardt & Ernest Co.
(Upholstered Furn.) C
Calumet Metal Furn. Co.
(Metal Folding Beds) ..D
Cass & Co., B. T. (Screens)
........................C
Central Mfg. Co. (Roll Top;
Flat; Standing Desks;
Typewriter Cabinets; Of-
fice Tables; Office Furn.)
........................B
Century Seating Co. (School
Furn.; Tables;Office Fix-
tures) ....E
Chicago Chair & Wheel Co.
(Invalid Adjustable Re-
clining; Wheel Chairs)..A
Chicago Hassock Co. (Has-
socks; Ottomans; Foot
Rests; Commodes; Black-
ing Cases; Reed Novelties)
........................E
Chicago Table Wks. (Exten-
sion Tables) C
Chicago Willow & Rattan
Wks., The (Willow; Rat-
tan Ware) C
Clemetson Co., The (Office
Desks) C
Cold Blast Feather Co.
(Spring Beds) .....AAA
Columbia Parlor Frame Co.
(Parlor Furn. Frames;
Morris Chairs) C
Continental Mfg. Co. (Parlor
Furn.; Frames; Couch
Frames) ....B
Cowan & Co. (Inc.), W. K.
(High Grade Mahogany
Furn.; Colonial Reproduc-
tions; Special Furn. to
Order) ....B
Davis & Horwich (Brass;
Iron Bedsteads) ....B
Dunn Co., John A. (Chairs)
........................AA
Federal Iron & Brass Bed
Co. (Iron; Brass Beds)..B
Ford, Johnson & Co., J. S.
(Cane Seat Cairs: Settees;
Fibre; Reed; Rattan; Mis-
sion Furn.; Office Stools)
........................AAA
Fowler, John P. (Uphols-
tered Mattresses; Box
Springs; Couches; Shirt
Waist Boxes; Spring
Beds) C
Franke & Sievers (Folding;
Mantel Beds) ....D
Garvey Co., The (Steel Fold-
ing Beds; Couches; Divans;
Davenports; Steel Cots) C
Gibson-Petre Seating Co.
(Opera Chairs; Church
Furn.; School Desks) ...E
Globe Novelty Co. (Reed;
Rattan Specialties) C
Gramer Valentine (Church
Furn.) ....G
Hafner Furn. Co. (Uphols-
tered Furn.) ....B
Haggard & Marcusson Co.
(Spring Beds; Woven
Wire Mattresses; Cots;
Cribs) ....B
Hall, Miller & Son (Brass;
Iron Beds) ....B
Hanke Bros. (Parlor Desks;
Sideboards; China Closets;
Chiffoniers; Bureaus;
Washstands; Odd Dress-
ers; Chamber Suits) ....B
Hanson Co., Louis (Hall
Furn.; Mirrors) ....A
Hausske & Co., August (Par-
lor Furn.; Frames) .....B
Herhold & Sons, F. (Cane
Seat Chairs; Rockers; Set-
tees) ....A
Horn Bros. Mfg. Co. (Dress-

FURNITURE (Con.)

ers; Chiffoniers; Ladies'
Dressing Tables; Bed-
steads; Washstands; Com-
modes) ....B
Independent Steel & Wire
Co. (Couch Construction;
Spring Beds; Upholstery
Springs) C
Johnson Chair Co. (Chair)
........................AA
Johnson & Sons Furn. Co., A.
J. (China Closets; Buf-
fets; Sideboards; Plate
Racks; Bookcases) .....B
Judkins Co. (Folding Beds)
........................C
Karpen & Bros., S. (Uphols-
tered Furn.; Lodge; Pulpit
Furn.; Special Furn. from
Designs; Sofa Beds; Bed
Lounges) ....AA
Kaufman & Spencer (Ta-
bourettes; Pedestals; Ex-
tension Tables) ....F
Ketcham & Rothschild (Up-
holstered Furn.) C
Kimball & Chappell Co., The
(Brass; Enameled Iron
Beds) ....B

*We make nothing but
high-grade metal Bed-
steads.
Our goods have the
reputation of being the
best that money can buy.
Prompt shipments,
reasonable prices. (One
price to all).
Make us the factory to
buy your dependable
goods from.
Send for Catalogue.*
**VERNIS MARTIN
FINISH.**
*We are selling ten
Bedsteads in this finish
to one white or colored
enamel finish. The
popularity of our orig-
inal Vernis Martin Finish
as applied to the Iron
Bed is growing daily.
It is permanent, showy
and durable—better than
any Enamel finish that
you can buy. We ab-
solutely guarantee it will
not tarnish or fade.
Send for sample tube.
Sample Bed sent on ap-
proval.*

Kinley Mfg. Co. (Reed; Rat-
tan Furn.; Childrens
Chairs)) ....B
Klein Co., A. S. (Easels;
Screens) ....A
Koenig & Gamer Furn. Co.
(Folding Beds) ....A
Larson, Peter (Desks; Office
Furn.) ....B
Loeser & Co., John (Box
Springs; Upholstered Furn.
etc.) ....H
Mallen & Co., H. Z. (Parlor
Furn.; Frames) ....B
Merle & Heaney Mfg. Co.
(Desks) ....A
Metallic Folding Bed Co.
(Metallic Folding Beds;
Steel Couches) ....D
National Parlor Furn. Co.
(Upholstered Furn. of all
Kinds) ....B
Niemann & Weinardt Table
Co. (Tables) ....B
Nonnast, Louis F. (Exten-
sion Library; Parlor Ta-
bles) ....B
Olbrich & Golbeck (Side-
boards; Buffets) C
Olsen & Co., O. C. S. (Office
Desks; Typewriter Cabi-
nets) C
Passow & Son, Chas. (Office
Furn.; Bar Fixtures) ...B
Peterson & Co., A. (Roll
Top, Flat Top; Standing

FURNITURE (Con.)
Desks) C
Peterson Co., Geo. L. (Sideboards; Bookcases; Cabinets) ....B
Phoenix Parlor Frame Co. (Inc.) (Frames only for Parlor Suits; Davenports; Divans; Sofa Beds; Odd Chairs; Rockers; Box Couches) ....B
Rauch Mfg. Co. (Office Desks) ....B
Rivell & Co., Alex H. (Upholstered) ....AA
Roos Mfg. Co. (Easels; Screens; Hat Racks; Curtain Poles) C
Schmidt & Co., A. C. (Upholstered Furn.) ....A
Schultz & Hirsch Co. (Spring Beds) ....B
Sidway Mfg. Co. (Sidway Adjustable Tables) .....D
Sherwood Co. (School Desks) D
Simmons Mfg. Co. (Brass; Iron; Children's; Institution Beds; Canvas; Wire; Cradle Cots; Woven Wire Mattresses; all Wire Spring Beds; Folding Chairs; Metal Folding Couches) ....AAA
Sprague-Smith & Co. (China Closets; Cabinets) ....B
Tonk Mfg. Co. (Piano Stools; Benches; Scarfs) C
Union Wire Mattress Co. (Iron Bedsteads; Childrens' Beds; Woven Wire Mattresses; Spring Beds; Cots; Cribs; Couches; Hospital Beds; Bedside Tables) ....A
Valentine-Seaver Co. (Upholstered Furn.; Odd Chairs; Rockers; Divans; Foot Benches; Ottomans; Two & Three Piece Suits; Colonial Sofas; Davenports; Couches; Screens) C
Warren Mfg. Co., J. D. (Office Desks) ....B
Western Chair Co. (Wood; Cane; Rattan Chairs; Rockers) ....D
Windsor Folding Bed Co. (Dining; Bedroom; Library; Hall Furn.) ......B
Zangerle & Peterson Co. (Parlor Furn. Frames) .B
ILL.—Greenville
De Moulin & Bro., Ed. (Lodge Furn.) ....A
ILL.—Joliet
Illinois Rattan Co. (The) (Reed; Rattan Furn.)...C
Joliet Chair Co. (Veneer; Cane; Wood Seat Chairs; Polished Rockers) .....E
Wilcox Bros. (Couches; Davenports; Odd Pieces; Upholstered Furn.) ....B
ILL.—Kankakee
Sheldon Novelty Co. (The) (Ladies' Desks; Music; Medicine Cabinets; Foot Stools; Blacking Cases; Tabourettes; Easels; Screens; Grilles; Bookcases) C
Turk Mfg. Co., Joseph (Brass Bedsteads) C
ILL.—Morrison
Illinois Refrigerator Co. (School Furn.) C
ILL.—Mound
Mound City Furn. Co. (Suits; Wardrobes; Extension; Centre Tables; Stands; Safes in Imitation & Oak) C
ILL.—Naperville
Naperville Lounge Co. (Couches; Morris Chairs) B
ILL.—Peoria
Peoria Lounge & Mattress Co. (Lounges; Couches).D

FURNITURE (Con.)
ILL.—Plano
Earl Mfg. Co. (Metal Beds) C
Earle Metal Bed Co. (Iron; Brass Beds; Jardiniere Stands) C
Sears, Albert H. (Metal Beds) ....B
ILL.—Quincy
Schenck Altar Co. (Church Furn.) ....F
ILL.—Rockford
Central Furn. Co. (Bookcases; China Closets; Ladies' Desks) ....B
Forest City Furn. Co. (Libraries; Combination Cases; Music; Music Roll Cabinets; Ladies' Desks; Sectional Bookcases; Folding Tables; Washstands; Folding Mantel; Upright; Combination Beds) ....A
Mechanics Furn. Co. (Inc.) (Sideboards; China Closets; Combination Buffets; Buffets; Music; Parlor Cabinets, in Oak; Mahogany) ....B
Rockford Chair & Furn. Co. (Buffets; China Closets; Combination; Library Bookcases; Ladies' Desks) A
Rockford Desk Co. (Inc.) (China Closets; Parlor; Music Cabinets; Ladies' Desks; Libraries) C
Rockford Palace Furn. Co. (Buffets; Combination; Library Bookcases; China Closets; Sideboards; Music Cabinets; Ladies' Desks; Dressers) C
Rockford Standard Furn. Co. (China Closets; Combination Cabinets; Library Cases; Buffets; Parlor Desks) C
Skandia Furn. Co. (Bookcases; China Closets; Sideboards; Buffets) ......B
Union Furn. Co. (Oak; Walnut; Birch; Mahogany Furn.; Combination Cases; Closets; Buffets; Music; Parlor Cabinets) ......B
West End Furn. Co. (Combination; Library Bookcases; China Closets; Buffets; Music Cabinets) ..D
IND.—Anderson
Greenburg Chair Co. (Chair; Lawn Settees) C
IND.—Aurora
Cobb Chair Co. (The) (Wood Seat Chairs) ....B
Smith Chair & Furn. Co., H. W. (Medium Priced Wood Seat Dining Chairs; Rockers) ....D
IND.—Batesville
American Furn. Co. (Chamber Suits; Odd Dressers; Chiffoniers) C
Union Furn. Co. (Chamber Suits; Chiffoniers; Wardrobes to Match, in Mahogany; Oak) ....B
IND.—Bloomington
Showers Bros. Co. (Inc.) (Chamber Suits; Sideboards; Chiffoniers) ...C
IND.—Bluffton
Bluffton Folding Chair Co. (Folding Chairs) C
IND.—Brookville
Tucker Furn. Co., A. M. (Camber Suits; Chiffoniers; Dressing Tables; French Dressers; Cheval Glasses) C
IND.—Cambridge
Standard Mfg. Co. (The) (Folding Chairs) ....D
IND.—Cannelton
Cannelton Chair Co. (Double Cane; Split Bottom Chairs) ....E
IND.—Cochran
Cochran Chair Co. (Chairs; Rockers) C

446

FURNITURE (Con.)

IND.—Columbia

McNown Mfg. Co. (The)
(Cupboards; Kitchen Cabinets; Wardrobes; Bookcases) ....F

IND.—Columbus

Orinoco Furn. Co. (The)
(Parlor; Library; Dressing; Writing Tables; Antique; Colonial Reproductions) –.................C

IND.—Connersville

Connersville Furn. Co.
(Chamber Furn.; Chiffoniers; Sideboards) ....B

Indiana Furn. Co. (Sideboards; Buffets) .....A

IND.—Evansville

Bockstege Furn. Co. (Extension; Parlor; Library; Centre Tables; Mantel Folding Beds) C

Buehner Chair Co. (Chairs; Rockers; Wood; Cane; Cobbler; Leather Stuffed; Upholstered Spring Seats) C

Crown Chair Mfg. Co. (Medium Grade of Chairs) ..F

Crescent Furn. Co. (Sideboards; Buffets; Closets; Chamber Suits) C

Evansville Furn. Co. (Wood Bedsteads; Kitchen Safes; Cheap Wardrobes; Glass Cupboards; Oak Suits) ....B

Globe Furn. Co. (The)
(Chamber Suits; Kitchen Cabinets) ....B

Hasse Conrad (Lounges; Couches) ....D

Indiana Furn. Co. (Bedsteads; Chamber Suits; Extension Tables; Victoria Suits; Kitchen Safes; Cabinets) C

Karges Furn. Co. (Chamber Suits; Wardrobes; Dressers; Dressing Tables) ...B

Novelty Furn. Co. (Bookcases; Tables) C

Smith Chair Co., E. Q.
(Wood; Cane; Cobbler; Splint; Double Cane Seat Chairs; Rockers) C

Specialty Furn. Co. (Chamber Suits; Odd Dressers; Chiffoniers) C

Standard Chair Co. (Chairs; Rockers; Box Seat Diners) E

Stolz-Schmitt Furn. Co.
(Chamber Suits; Chiffoniers; Dressing Tables) ..B

IND.—Ft. Wayne

Paul Mfg. Co., The (Kitchen Cabinets) ....D

IND.—Franklin

Franklin Desk Co. (Flat; Roll Top Desks) ....D

IND.—Goshen

Banta Furn. Co. (Extension; Library Tables; Mission Furn. in Golden Antwerp; Weathered Oak; Mahogany) ....B

Gosher Novelty & Brush Co.
(Easels; Screens; Tabourettes; Music Racks; Cabinets; Hat Racks; Wall Pockets; Clock Shelves; Combination Cases; Bolsters; Plate Racks) ....E

Hawks Furn. Co. (Chamber Furn. in Mahogany; Birdseye; Maple; Oak) ......A

I-X-L & Goshen Pump Co.
(Kitchen Cabinets; Cupboards; Sinks; Wardrobes; Safes; Screen Door; Windows) C

IND.—Greenfield

National Adjustable Chair Co. (Automatic Morris Chairs) ....F

IND.—Indianapolis

Allison Co., W. D. (Physician's Office Furn.; Invalid; Reclining Chairs) ..D

Cabinet Maker's Union (Extension Tables) C

Capital Rattan Co. (The)

FURNITURE (Con.)

(Go-Carts; Reed Chairs; Reed Novelties) C

Central Chair Co. (Cane; Upholstered Chairs; Rockers) C

Clark & Roberts (Pysicians' Chairs; Tables; Instrument Cabinets; Aseptic Hospital Furn. of all Kinds) C

Clune & Sons, M. (Couches; Lounges; Sofa Beds; Davenports; Mattresses) ..AA

Combination Billiard Mfg.
Co. (Library; Dining; Billiard; Pool Tables; Dutch; Mission Furn.) C

Emrich Furn. Co. (Sideboards; Buffets; Tables) A

Fells, W. B. (Church Furn.) F

Huey Co., M. S. (Special Furn.) ....B

Indianapolis Chair & Furn. Co. (Dining; Office Chairs; Fancy; Cobbler; Weatered Oak Rockers; Hall Suits) ....A

Kramer Mfg. Co. (Sofas; Couches; Lounges; Wood Mantels) ....B

Lauter, Herman (Dressers; Chiffoniers; Dressing Tables; Commodes; Centre; Library Tables; Ladies'; Roll Top Desks; Music Cabinets) ....B

Laycock Mfg. Co., T. B.
(Brass; Iron Bedsteads; Children's Folding Cribs; Woven Wire Cribs; Mattresses; Furn. Springs; Spring Beds; Metallic Couch Bottoms) .....AA

McDougall & Son, G. P.
(Kitchen Cabinets; Cupboards; Wardrobes; China Closets) ....B

Madden Son & Co., Thos.
(Parlor Suits; Leather Rockers; Couches; China; Fancy Divans; Rockers; Chairs; Davenports; Single; Bed Couches; Bed Lounges) ....B

Neu, J. B. (Chairs) ....D

Ott Mfg. Co., L. W.
(Couches; Davenports; Upholstered Leather Chairs; Rockers) ....B

Piel Bros. Mfg. Co. (The)
(Reed Furn.) ....A

Puritan Bed Spring Co.
(The) Bed; Spiral; Woven Wire Springs; Iron Beds; Cots; Mattresses) C

Sander & Recker (Office; Bar Fixtures; Special Furn. to Order) C

Sheetz-Straughn Mfg. Co.
(Upholstered Furn.) .....D

Smith, Day & Co. (Ltd.)
(Cane; Cobbler; Saddle; Upholstered Rockers; Dining; Children's Chairs) ..A

Snow & Co., J. H. (Specialties) ....D

Thompson Mfg. Co., L. C.
(Special Post-Office Furn.) ....D

Udell Wks. (The) (Music Magazine; Medicine Cabinets; Ladies' Desks; Commodes; Blacking Cases; Folding Tables) ....A

Library Bookcases, Sheet Music Cabinets, Ladies' Parlor Desks, Magazine Cabinets, Piano Player Music Roll Cabinets, Cylinder and Disk Record Cabinets, Music Box Tune Sheet Cabinets, Medicine Cabinets, Toilet Room Cabinets, Sick Room Commodes, Blacking Cases, Folding Tables (Card and Sewing), Hook Racks, Clothes Bars, Folding Clothes

Racks, Towel Rollers and Arms, Ironing Stands and Boards, Step and Extension Ladders.

Our line is the largest of its kind made by any single manufacturer in the United States to-day.

We give particular attention to the selection of our veneers. the figure effects o° our Oak and Mahogany pieces are very fine, and we doubt if they could be matched outside of ourselves.

The workmanship and finish of our goods is brought up to the highest standard of perfection.

Write for Catalogs and prices, will be glad to mail them to you.

A mail order will receive just as great care and prompt attention as if taken throug.. one of our salesmen.

Western Furn. Co. (Chamber Suits; Chiffoniers; Odd Beds) ....:.........B

IND.—Jasper
Jasper Furn. Co. (Office Desks) C

IND.—Kendallville
Baker Sons Co.. J. R. (Adjustable Bedside; Reading Tables; Combined Baby Jumper; Rocking Chair) D

IND.—La Parte
Buck & Son. Robt. (Chamber Suits; Odd Dressers; Sideboards; Chiffoniers) ....D

IND.—Lebanon
Campbell. Smith & Ritchie (Kitchen Cabinets; Cupboards; Safes; Wardrobes) C
Lebanon Mfg. Co. (Kitchen Cabinets) C
Meyer, A. H. (Kitchen Cabinets) ....D

IND.—Logansport
Ash & Hadley (Extension Tables) C
Henderson & Sons, J. W. (Wood Mantels, a General Line of Furn.)........C
Logansport Furn. Co. (Dining Tables) ....B

IND.—Madison
McKim & Cochran Furn. Co. (Dressers; Stands; Beds; Chiffoniers; Wardrobes; Toilet Suits) ....D

IND.—Marion
Barley & Spencer Lumber Co. (Office Furn.) C
Indiana Brass & Iron Bed Co. (Iron; Brass Beds) ..C
Keller Chair Co. (Inc.), O. H. (Chairs) C
McCure Mfg. Co. (Kitchen Furn.) ....E
Marion Iron & Brass Bed Co. (Iron Beds) C
Union Cabinet Co. (Kitchen Cabinets) C

IND.—Martinsville
Hubbard, Cas. A. (Kitchen Furn.) ....D
Old Hickory Chair Co. (The) (Chairs; Rockers; Settees; Tables; Tabourettes; Swings; Seats; Log Chairs) ....E

IND.—Misahawka
Roper Furn. Co. (Sideboards; Buffets; Library Extension Dining; Library Tables; Odd Dressers; Dressing Tables; Chiffoniers; Oak Mahogany)...B

IND.—Munice
Glascock Bros. Mfg. Co. (Invalid Tables) C
Hickson Mfg. Co. (Iron Beds) ....B

FURNITURE (Con.)
IND.—New Albany
Klerner Furn. Co., Henry (Bedroom Suits; Wardrobes) ....B
Klerner, Peter (Cheap; Medium Bedroom Suits) ....D
New Albany Table Co. (Extension Tables; Folding Beds; Sideboards) ......D
Shrader Furn. Co., John (Mantel Folding Beds)..D

IND.—New Castle
Brass & Iron Bedstead Co., The (Iron; Brass Trimmed Iron Bedsteads) ....D
Hoosier Mfg. Co., The (Hoosier Kitchen Cabinets) C
Jennings, L. A. (Kitchen Cabinets) C

IND.—N. Manchester
Syracuse Screen & Grille Co. (Screens; Easels; Grille Work; Curtain Poles; Light Furn.) ....D

IND.—Ohio Falls
Union Carriage & Rattan Co. (Reed; Rattan Chairs)..C

IND.—Parker City
Vaught Sons & Co., H. C. (Church; Bank Office Furn.) C

IND.—Richmond
Richmond Chair Co. (Double Cane Chairs) ....D
Richmond Ind. Mfg. Co. (Brass; Iron Beds) ....B
Rowlett Desk Mfg. Co. (Roll; Flat Top Desks for Offices; Typewriter Cabinets) ....D

IND.—Rockport
Weiss Chair Co. (Chairs) .B

IND.—Rushville
Innis. Pearce & Co. (Chamber Suits; Chiffoniers) B
Park Furn. Co. (Extension; Library Tables; Pedestals) C

IND.—Seymour
Greenman & Co.. Louis F. (Combination Bookcases; Bookcases; Music Cabinets; Odd Dressers; Washstands; Ladies' Desks) C

IND.—Shelbyville
Blanchard-Hamilton Furn. Co. (Inc.) (China Closets; Bookcases; Novelties)..D
Campbell Furn. Co., C. H. (Hall Furn.)............C
Conrey-Davis Mfg. Co. (Costumers; Plate Racks; Wall Closets; Medicine Cabinets; Ladies' Desks; Extension; Directors Tables) ....D
Conrey & Birely Table Co. (Mission Furn. Parlor; Library Tables; Tabourettes; Ladies' Dressing Tables; Pedestals)........A
Conrey-Forster Furn. Co. (Combination Library; Sectional Cases; Music Cabinets; China Closets)....D
Hodell Furn. Co. (Mantel Folding Beds; Dressers; Chiffoniers; Ladies' Dressers; Commodes)........C
Shelbyville Desk Co. (Roll; Flat Top Desks).......D
Shelbyville Wardrobe Mfg. Co. (Sideboards; Buffets) C
Spiegel Furn. Co. (Chiffoniers; Dressers; Washstands) ....B

IND.—South Bend
Wells-Kriegbaum Mfg. Co. (Extension Tables).... D

IND.—Spiceland
Stigleman Mfg. Co. (Fold'g Chairs; Cupboards).....E

IND.—Tell City
Cabinet Makers' Union (Chamebr Suits)........C
Chair Makers' Union (Double Cane Bottom Cairs) C
South Western.....teA..liM
Fiscer Chair Co.. The (Double Cane Seat Chairs)..C
South Western Furn. Co.

FURNITURE (Con.)

(Chamber Suits, &c.....C
Tell City Desk Co. Office
Desks; Wood Mantels)..C
Tell City Furn. Co. (Chamber
Suits; Wardrobes)......C
IND.—Troy
Troy Chair Co. (Double Cane
Splint Seat Chairs).....D
IND.—Union City
Koontz Sons, Jno. (Kitchen
Cabinets) C
IND.—Vevay
Union Furn. Co. Bedroom
Suit; Wardrobes; Side-
boards; Chiffoniers; Victo-
ria Bedroom Suits).....C
IND.—Wabash
Wabash Cabinet Co. (Spe-
cial Cabinet Work to Or-
der) ....A
Walter & Co., B. (Extension
Tables) ....D
IOWA—Burlington
Chittenden & Eastman Co.
(Upolstered Gds; Mattres-
ses; Chairs).......AAA
Leopold Desk Co. (Office;
Typrweiter Desks; Office;
Directors' Tables).....B
Nort-Western Cabinet Co.
(Cobbination Bookcases;
Ladies' Desks; Sectional
Cases) ....D
IOWA—Cedar Rapids
Cedar Rapids Wood Wkg.
Co. (Couch; Chair Frames)
D
IOWA—Clinton
Anderson Furn. Co. (Tables;
Sideboards; Chiffoniers;
Kitchen Cabinets).....D
Anderson & Winter Mfg. Co.
(Chamber Suitts; Chiffon-
iers; Beds) ....E
Hemingway Furn Co.
(Lounges) C
Kelley & Bros., J.A. (Sofas;
Beds; Davenports; Reclin-
ing Chairs; Couches;&c.)
D
IOWA—Davenport
Knostman & Peterson Furn.
Co. (Chamber Suits; Side-
boards; Extension Tables;
Centre Tables; Beds)..D
IOWA—Des Moines
Scmittt & Henry Mfg. Co.
(Parlor Furn. Lounges;
Couches; Mattresses;
Woven Wire Springs;
Beds; Cots)...........A
IOWA—Dubucue
Dubuque Cabinet Makers'
Ass'n (Chairs; Rockers;
Lounges; Bedsteads; Cham-
ber Suits; Bureaus; Chif-
fonieers; Hall Racks; Ex-
tension; Kitchen; Saloon;
Centre Tables; Stands;
Washstands; Wardrobes;
Kitchen; Glass Cupboard;
Kitchen Cabinets; Flour
Bins; Desks Secretaries;
Combination Cases; Inter-
ior Finish; Colonial;
Flemish; Weathered Oak
Furn.) C
Key City Furn. Co. (Furn.;
Show Cases; Store Fix-
tures) ....D
IOWA—Ft Madison
Fort Madison Chair Co.
(Chairs; Rockers).....B
IOWA—Iowa Falls
Iowa Falls Mfg. Co. (Bank;
Office Furn.).........D
IOWA—Sioux City
Curtis Sash & Door Co.
(Church Pews; Screens)AA
KANS.—Atchinson
Atchinson Mfg. Co.. The
(Bedroom Suits; Kitchen
Cabinets)............D
KANS.—Leavenworth
Helmers Mfg. Co., The (Ex-
tension Tables; Kitchen;
Breakfast; Centre Tables;
Kitchen Safes; Cupboards;
Kitchen Cabinets; Ward-
robes; Cheap Suits; Dres-
sers) ....B
Klemp H. W. (Cupboards;
Wardrobes; Extension Ta-

FURNITURE (Con.)

bles) C
KANS.—Wichita
Western Furn. & Mfg. Co.,
The (Couches; Lounges;
Davenports; Parlor Furn.;
Bedding; Box; Hair
Mattresses; Tables; Kit-
chen Safes; Cabinets;
Chamber Suits)........C
KY.—Carrollton
Carrollton Furn. Mfg. Co.
(Bedroom Suits; Bureaus
Washstands; Chiffoniers;
Dressing Tables; Ward-
robes in Mahogany,
Birds's-eye Maple, Curly
Birch; Oak; Walnut)....C
KY.—Covington
Phoenix Mfg. Co. (Library;
Parlor Tables; Music Ca-
binets;China Cases; Ladies'
Desks) C
KY.—Frankfort
Frankfort Chair Co. (Chairs;
Furn.; Reed Gds.).....A
KY.—Henderson
Alles Bros. (Tables; Kitchen
Safes) ....D
Marstall Furn. Co. (Oak
and Walnut Wardrobes).C
KY.—Louisville
Gimnich Furn. Mfg. Co.
(Suits; Odd Dressers;
Chiffoniers; Sideboard;
Mantel Folding Beds)..C
Jacobson Peter (Kitchen
Furn. C
Koop Wm. (Wardrobes;
Glass Cupboards; Safes;
Kitchen Tables).......C
McElroy-Shannon Spring Bed
Mfg. Co. (Spiral Spring
Beds) C
Schupp & Smidt Mfg. Co.
(Parlor Suits).......D
Weikel Chair Co., Fred.
(Chairs) ....B
Wolke & Bros., H. (Bedroom
Suits; Wardrobes; Chif-
foniers; Chifforobes; Half
Canopy Suits) ....B
KY.—Owensboro
Price-Klein Co., (Plain
Quartered Oak Dining;
Library; Centre Tables;
Hardwood; Dining; Kit-
chen Tables) ....D
KY.—Paducah
Paduca Furn. Mfg. Co. (Bed-
room Suits; Odd Dressers;
Beds; Chiffoniers).....C
KY.—Seven Hills
Owensboro Chamber Suits Co.
Chamber Suits; Beds;
Dresses; Chiffoniers)....D
KY.—Warsaw
McDannell's Sons Co., J. H.
(Chamber Suits) .....B
Warsaw Furn. Mfg. Co., The
(Hall Furn.; Combination
Bookcases; Library Cases)
D
LA.—New Orleans
Crescent Bed Co. (Ltd.)
(Iron; Brass Beds; Child-
ren's Cribs; Surprise
Springs; Spiral Springs;
Woven wire Springs; Cots;
Hospital Beds) ....B
Gulf City Spring Bed & Matt-
ress Mfg. Co. (Spring
Beds) ....A
Lhote Lumber Mfg. Co.
Furn. Store; Bar Fixtures;
Interior Finish).......AA
Magee F. B. (Spring Beds)
C
Muller Furn. Mfg. Co. (Ltd)
(Medium; Common Ward-
robes; Beds; Safes; Cup-
boards; Tables; Wash-
stands) C
New Orleans Furn. Mfg. Co.
(Inc.) (Chamber Furn.;
Chairs; Kitchen Safes;
Tables; Wardrobes)....A
Seidel Furn. Mfg. Co. (Cheap
Kitchen; Bedroom Furn.)
A
Tebault W. G. (Spring
Beds) ....A
MAINE—Fairfield
Fairfield Furn. Co. (Exten-

449

sion; Kitchen; Saloon Tables) C

Knowles Furn. Co., The, C. H. (Adjustable **Sofas**; Parlor Suits Bed Lounges; Couches; Divans; Turkish; Fancy; Morris Chairs)..B

Nye Mfg. Co., S. A. (Desks; Chiffoniers; Fold'g Tables; Step Chairs; Bookcases; Stands; Centre Tables; &c................B

ME.—Portland

Beals Co. (Inc.), Thos. P. (Bedsteads; Dressers; Chiffoniers; Sideboards; Ladies'; Office Desks; **Spring**; Cot Beds; Chairs; Rockers) ....B

Berlin Mills Co. (**Office**; Bank Furn.; Desks; Chairs; Tables; Church Furn.; Fixtures)...AAAA

ME.—South Paris

Paris Mfg. Co. (Children; Ladies; Office Roll Top Desks) ....A

MD.—Baltimore

Bagby Furn. Co. (Chamber Suits; Hall Racks; Wardrobes; Buffets; Tables Chairs; Kitchen Safes; Bedsteads) C

Chipman & Son, Geo. (Chairs) ....A

Foster Bros. Mfg. Co. (Woven Wire Mattresses; Spiral Spring Beds; Woven Wire, Canvas; Upholstered Cots; Metallic Bedsteads; Cribs) ....D

Gleitsman, Herman (Parlor Suits; Couches; Lounges; Mattresses; Bedding....C

Goldstrom Bros. (Parlor Suits; Couches; Lounges; Morris Chairs; Odd Pieces) C

Hartwig & Kemper (Chairs; Fancy Rockers).......C

Hechinger Bros & Co. (Wood; Cobbler; Cane; Chairs; Rockers; Reed; Rattan Rockers; Centre Tables; Cribs; Cradles; Clothes-Trees; &c.).....A

Heywood Bros. & Wakefield Co. (Chairs; Chair Cane; Chair; Car Seats; Webbing; Reed; Rattan Furn.; Rattan Specialties.AAAA

Hughes Furn. Mfg. Co., The (Chamber Suits; Odd Dressers; Chiffoniers; Wardrobes; Hall Racks; Ladies' Toilet Table; Sideboards; Enamelled Dressers)....C

Yoyce Mfg. Co. (Spring Beds) ....D

Levenson & Zenitz (Upholstered Church; Club; Lodge Furn.) C

Pimes & Co., M. (**Parlor** Suits; Couches) C

Rawson Mfg. Co., The (Spring Beds; Woven Wire Mattresses; Cots; Crips; Cradles; Brass; Enameled Beds; Adjustable Bedsteads; Step Ladder Chairs; Tables; Clothes-Trees) C

Reliable Furn. Mfg. Co. (Oak Sideboards; Chamber Suits; Dressers)........B

Rich Bros. (Reed Rockers) ....E

Wilfson & Son, D. (Oak Sideboards; Chamber Suits; Chiffoniers; Dressing Tables; Odd Dressers)....B

MD.—Hagerstown

Brandt Cabinet Wks, The (Parlor Tables; Clothes-Trees) ....D

Hagerstown Furn. Co. (Extension Tables; Stands) A

Hagerstown Table Wks (Extension Tables; Small Stands) C

Hagerstown Woven Wire Mattress Co. (Woven

MASS.—Ashburnham

Pierce W. B. (Chairs; Cradles; Stools) ....D

Whitney & Co., W. F. (Wood; Cane; Reed Chairs) ....**AA**

MASS.—Athol

Morse & Sons, L. (Cradles; Cribs; Tables; Washstands) C

Stowell & Warrick (Tables; General Line of Furn.) B

MASS.—Baldwinsville

Bishop & Dickinson (Reed; Rattan; Chairs) C

Thompson & Co., E. L. (Children's; Dining; Arm; Rocking; Cobbler; Wheel Chairs) ....A

Waite Chair Co. (High; (Rocking; Dining Chairs) ....A

MASS.—Boston

Allen - Thompson - Whitney Co. (Children's; Office; Dining; Wood Seat; Bedroom Chairs; Rockers)..B

Bay State Bedstead Co. (Brass Trimmed Iron Beds) ....D

Bent & Co., G. W. (Brass; Steel Bedstead; Bed Springs; Couch Beds; Fold's Beds; Morris Chairs) ....B

Boston Bamboo Co. (Bamboo Furn.) ....E

Boston Metallic Bed Co. (Iron Beds; Springs)....D

Clifford Co. (Inc.) R. C. (Ash; Oak Furn.; Morris Chairs) C

Conant Ball & Co. (Dining Chamber; Office Chairs) C

Davenport Co., A. H. (Children's Cribs).....AA

Derby Desk Co. (Roll Top Office Desks)........AA

Doten-Dunten Desk Co., The (Commercial Furn. Desks; &c.) C

Dunn Co., John A. (Chairs) ....AA

Fellows Co. (The), J. B. (Adjustable Chairs; Settees) ....D

French & Heaid (Chamber Furn.; Chiffoniers; Sideboards) ....B

Kenney Co., A. E. (Spring Beds; Cots; Beds; Couch Beds; Bedding)........C

Lansing, E. H. (Piano Stools) C

Mellish, Byfield & Co. (Inc.) (Chamber Suits; Chairs; Sideboards) C

Merrimac Mattress Mfg. Co. (Spring Beds; Couches; Cots; Iron; Brass Beds) C

New England Reed Co. (Chairs; Reed; Rattan Furn.) ....F

Orpin Bros. (Office Furn.; Roll; Flat Top Desks; Cashiers'; Bookkeepers' Desks; Office; Directors' Table; Roll Top Cases; Filing Cabinets)........B

Paine Furniture Co. (Ladies; Office Desks)........A

Peabody-Williams Co. (Willow; Rush Furn.)........F

Phinney M. F. (Divans) ..H

Sammet & Son, G. W. (Morris Chairs)..............D

Shales & May (Hall; Dining Room; Parlor Furn.)....B

White Wm. (Invalid Chairs) ....E

MASS.—Cambridge

Cook & Co., C. A. (Piano Stools) ....F

Shaw Co., A. B. & E. L. (Parlor; Library; Church; Lodge; Shoe Store; Club; Hotel Furn.)............C

MASS.—Chelsea

Maine Furn. Co. (Inc.)

FURNITURE (Con.)

MICH.—Dowagiac

Dowagiac Furn. Co. (Iron Beds) ...... AA

MICH.—Grand Ledge

Grand Ledge Chair Co. (Chairs) ...... A

Grand Ledge Table Co. (Tables; Chairs) ...... A

MICH.—Grand Rapids

Berkey Furn. Co., Wm. A. (Parlor; Library Tables; House Desks; Chamber Furn.; Parlor; Music Cabinets; Bookcases; Dressing Tables) ...... B

Berkey & Gay Furn. Co. (Inc.) (Medium; High Grade Bedroom; Dining Room; Library Furn.) .. A

Grand Rapids Brass & Iron Bed Co. (Ltd.) (Brass; Iron Beds) C

Grand Rapids Chair Co. (House Desks, Music Cabinets, Cellarettes; Hall Racks, Hall Seats; Hall Glasses; Cedar Lined Boxes; Library; Breakfast; Hall; Directors'; Serving Tables; Stands; Sideboards; Buffets; China Closets; Bookcases; Bookshelves) ...... AA

Grand Rapids Fancy Furn. Co. (Ladies' Desks; Bookcases; Music Cabinets; Writing Tables) ...... B

Grand Rapids Table Co. (Parlor; Den; Library; Bedroom; Invalid; Café Tables) C

Gunn Furn. Co., The (Office Desks; Sectional Bookcases; Filing Devices) .. A

Haney School Furn. Co. (School Furn.; Office Desks; Artificial Blackboard; Sectional Bookcases) C

Imperial Furn. Co. (Tables; &c.) ...... A

Limbert & Co., Chas. P. (Art; Mission Furn.) C

Luce Furn. Co. (Chamber Suits; Sideboards; Buffets) ...... B

Macey-Wernicke Co. (Office; Library Furn.; Desks; Sectional Bookcases; Card Index Systems; Filing Cabinets; Office Chairs. Typewriter Cabinets; Desks; Leather Rockers; Chairs; Couches; &c.) ...... AA

Michigan Chair Co. (Inc.) **(Chairs; Hall Furn.;** Tables; Tabourettes; Stands; Ladies' Desks; &c.) .... B

Mueller & Slack Co. (Inc.) (Upholstered Furn. of all kinds) C

Nelson-Mater Furn. Co. (Bedroom; Dining Room Furn.) ...... AA

New England Furn. Co. (Sideboards; Buffets; Closets; Dining Room Suits) ...... B

Oriel Cabinet Co. (Inc.) (Music; Parlor Cabinets; Dining Room Suits Complete; Bookcases; Novelties; Fancy Furn.; Ladies' Desks) ...... A

Phoenix Furn. Co. (Bed; Dining; Hall; Den; Parlor Furn.) ...... AA

Retting & Sweet (Parlor; Lodge; Pulpit Furn.; Library; Directors' Tables) ...... B

Royal Furn. Co. (Bedroom; **Dining**; Library Furn.; Ladies' Desks) ...... B

Sligh Furn. Co. (Bedroom Furn.; Ladies Desks) AA

Stickly Bros. Co. (Inc.) (Fancy Chairs; Tables) ......

Stow & Davis Furn .Co. (Oak Dining; Directors'; Office Tables) C

FURNITURE (Con.)

Valley City Desk Co. (Roll Top Office Desks) C

Waddell Mfg. Co. (Carvings; Mouldings; Grilles) C

Welch Fold'g Bed Co. (Inc.) (Fold'g Beds) ...... B

Widdicomb Co. (Inc.) (Bedroom Furn.) ...... B

Widdicomb Furn. Co., The (Chamber Suits) ...... AA

MICH.—Greenville

Skinner & Steenman (Sideboards; Buffets) ...... B

MICH.—Holland

Holland Furn. Co. (Suits; Dressers; Chiffoniers) .. C

Ottawa Furn. Co. (Sideboards; Mahogany Suits; Ladies' Dressing Tables; Chiffoniers) C

West Michigan Furn Co. (Inc.) (Chamber Suits; Sideboards; Buffets; Chiffoniers; Combination Commodes; Odd Dressers; in Elm; Oak; Mahogany) .. A

CHAMBER AND DINING ROOM FURNITURE.

Suits, Dressers, Chiffoniers, Dressing Tables, Sideboards and Buffets. Ours is the largest Chamber Suite Factory in the world and our line is confined strictly to low prices and medium grade goods.

We have a great variety of patterns in both light and heavy weight goods. We make Suites ranging in price from $12 to $100, Dressers and Chiffoniers from $5.00 to $50.00, Sideboards from $9.00 to $75.00.

Our designs in low priced and medium grade goods are unexcelled. Our prices are extremely low for the quality of the goods, as is evidenced by the fact that we have a larger volume of business than any other factory in the United States.

Our new catalog will be ready for distribution about April 1st. We shall be glad to receive your inquiries and shall be pleased to send you catalog upon application.

MICH.—Kalamazoo

Kalamazoo Sled Co. (Bent; Folding Settees; Lawn Swings; Stools; Chairs; Patented Specialties) ... C

MICH.—Manistee

Manistee Mfg. Co. (Sideboards; Buffets; Chiffoniers) C

Manistee Novelty Co. (Furn. Novelties; Children's Furn. Fold'g Tables) C

MICH.—Muskegon

Grand. Rapids Desk Co. (Office; House Desks) .. C

Muskegon Valley Furn. Co. (Beds; Dressers; Chiffoniers; Toilet Tables; Cheval Mirrors; Dressers; Princess Dressers; Wardrobes; Washstands; Somnoes) .. B

Sargent Mfg. Co. (Inc.) Ladies Desks; Chiffoniers; Hall Trees Shaving Stands; Street Rolling Chairs; Revolving Bookcases; Book Holders; Dictionary Stands); &c. ...... D

Shaw-Walker Co., The, (Card System Cabinets; Filing Devices; Sectional

FURNITURE (Con.)

Bookcases; Office Fixtures; Special Furn.)...D

MICH.—Nashville
Lenz Table Co. (Extension Tables) C

MICH.—Niles
Earl-Storms Co. (Chairs).E

MICH.—Otsego
Otsego. Chair Co. (Cane; Wood; Cobbler; Upholstered Chairs; Rockers).B

MICH.—Owosso
Estey Mfg. Co. (Chamber Suits; Sideboards; Chiffoniers; Buffets; Odd Dressers, &c.) ....A
Robbins Table Co. (Inc.) (Extension Tables) ....D
Woodard Furn. Co. (Beds; Dressers; Washstands; Chiffoniers; Ladies' Dressing Tables) ....D

MICH.—Portland
Blandfield Furn. Co. (Extension; Library Tables; Ladies' Desks) ....E
Dellenbaugh-Alton Mfg. Co. (Morris Chairs) ......E
Ramsey-Alton Mfg. Co. (Morris Chairs) ....D

MICH.—Reading
Acme Chair Co. (Folding Chairs;. Tables; Folding Lawn Seats; Settees; Folding Opera Chairs).C
Schermerhorn, C. D. (Folding Chairs) C

MICH.—Saginaw
Herzog Art Furn. Co. (Ladies' Desks; Music Cabinets; Centre Tables) ......D

MICH.—St. Johns
St. Johns Table Co. (Extension; Breakfast; Kitchen; Parlor;. Library; Office; Saloon Tables) ....D

MICH.—Sturgis
Aulsbrook & Sturges (Suits; Sideboards; Dressers)...B
Grobhiser & Crosby Furn. Co. (Extension; Directors' Office; Library; Cafe Tables) ....E
Royal Chair Co. (Morris Chairs) ....E

MICH.—Traverse City
Beitner, Wm. (Chairs)...C
Fulghnam & Roberts Mfg. Co. (Chairs) C

MINN.—Faribault
Faribault Rattan Co. (Rattan Chairs) ....F

MINN.—Minneapolis
Barnard-Cope Mfg. Co. (Extension; Library; Centre; Combination Tables; Chamber Suits; Odd Dressers) ....B
Cree-Dickson Mfg. Co. (Sectional Book Cases) .....B
Gangelhoff ros. (Spring Beds; Cots) ....B
Levin.. Bros. (Couches; Lounges; Davenports; Sofa Beds; Parlor Suits; Odd Pieces) ....B
McLeod & Smith (Upholstered Furn.; Parlor Suits; Rockers; Easy Chairs; Couches; Bed; Single Lounges; Davenports; Divans; Sofa Beds; Foot Rests, &c.) C
Minneapolis Bedding Co. (Iron; Brass Bedsteads; Cots; Cribs; Wire Springs; Coil Springs; Excelsior Feathers; Iron Couches; Iron Foldg. Beds)......B
Minneapolis Furn. Co. (Chamber Suits; Chiffoniers; Sideboards; Folding Beds; Kitchen Cabinets) ....B
Minneapolis Office & School Furniture Co. (Flat; Roll Top; Standing Desks)...D
Salisbury & Satterlee (Spring; Iron Beds; Cots; Cribs; Cradles).........A

FURNITURE (Con.)

Webster Mfg. Co. (Chairs) ...... A

Witte Mfg. Co., J. C. (Office Furn.) C

MINN.—New Duluth
Thompson Furn. Co., H. J. (Bedroom; Suits; Chiffoniers; Sideboards)....C

MINN.—St. Paul
Amer. Folding Bed Co. (Folding Beds; Chamber Suits; Extension; Parlor Tables; Combination; Library Cases) ....A
Dunn, John A. (Chairs)...B
Luger Furniture Co. (Library Desks) ....A
Northwestern Bedding Co. (Springs; Cots, &c.)....B
St. Anthony Furn. Co. (Office; Club; Saloon; Restaurant; Library; Dining Room Tables) ....B
St. Paul Furn. Co. (Bank; Store; Church Furn.)...B
Twin City Reed & Rattan Co. (Reed; Rattan Chairs) ...... F
United States Bedding Co. (Iron; Spring Beds; Cots; Cribs; Cradles).........D

MINN.—Sauk Centre
Kellar Mfg. Co. (Tables).B

MISS.—Greenwood
Weems-Lockwood Furn. Co. (Chamber Suits; Odd Dressers; Odd Beds) ......B

MISS.—Vicksburg
Mississippi Furn. Mfg. Co. (General line of cheap and medium goods) ....A

MO.—Carthage
Leggett & Platt Spring Bed & Mfg. Co. (Spring Beds) ...... A

MO.—Kansas City
Abernathy Furn. Co. (Chamber Suits; Sideboards; Chiffoniers; Kitchen Safes; Cabinets; Couches; Parlor Furn.; Mattresses) ...... AA
Brown Mfg. Co. (Iron Beds) ...... F
Hettinger Bros. Mfg. Co. (General line) ....B
Lloyd, J. H. (Cots).......D
Sammons. V. K. (Spring Beds; Lounges) ....B

MO.—Lexington
Winkler Furn. Co. (Upholstered Furn.; Wood Mantels; Office Desks).....D

MO.—Martinsburg
Friedman & Co., N. M. (Frames; Mouldings)...C

MO.—St. Joseph
Talge Lounge Co.. Jno. H. (Couches; Folding Beds) C

MO.—St. Louis
Amer. Bed Co. (Brass; Iron; Stationary Folding Canopy Beds; Steel Couches; Cribs; Cots; Davenports) ....A
Special attention giv-

en to the export trade. Goods for export carefully crated and all custom house requirements carefully complied with. Our entire line was awarded the Gold Medal at the World's Fair, this being the highest award made, thus giving our production the world's highest endorsement. Send for catalogue.

Amer. Rattan Co. (Rattan; Willow Ware) ....B
Aude Furn. Co. (Extension; Parlor Tables; Kitchen Cabinets; Bedsteads)...C
Central Furn. Co. (Chamber Suits; Wardrobes)......C
Conrades. Chair & Parlor

FURNITURE (Con.)
  Couches; Tables) ......D
Dexter Chair Co., H. C.
  (Summer Chairs; Furn.;
  Fancy Chairs; Rockers;
  Mission Furn.) C
N. Y.—Brooklyn
Adler Veneer Seat Co. (Par-
  lor;. Library; Smokers'
  Tables; Mission Furniture;
  Chairs; Settees; Gilt
  Chairs) C
Brooklyn Chair Co. (Office;
  Dining; Bedroom; Mission
  Chairs; Ladies' Desks) .B
Greenpoint Metallic Bed Co.
  (Metallic Bedsteads;
  Washstands; Brass; Iron
  Cribs; Metallic Couches;
  Hospital Furn.) ....A
Medicus & Son, C. H. (Par-
  lor Furn.; Novelties) ...B
Namm, Adolph I. (Divans)
  AA
National Parlor Suit Co.
  (Parlor Furn.; Couches;
  Odd Pieces) ....D
Prairie Grass Furn. Co.
  ("Crux" Prairie Grass
  Furn.) ....B
Royal Metal Furn. Co.
  (Brass; Iron Beds) .. .B
Schneider & Son, F. (Par-
  lor Suit Frames) ....B
Whitney & Co., W. F.
  Maple; Oak Chairs; Rock-
  ers; Oak Box Seat Dining
  Chairs; Cobble Rockers;
  Reed Chairs; Rockers;
  Suits) ....A
N. Y.—Buffalo
Barcalo Mfg. Co. (Inc.)
  (Brass; Iron Beds; Cribs;
  Springs; Mattresses) ..C
Buffalo Desk & Table Co.
  (Parlor; Library Tables)
  C
Buffalo Lounge Co.
  (Lounges; Couches) C
Colie & Son (Upholstered
  Furn.; Couches; Parlor
  Suits; Odd Pieces; Mor-
  ris Chairs; Davenports) ..C
Cutler & Son, A. (Office
  Furn.; Typewriter Desks;
  Filing Cabinets; Letter
  Press Stands; Office
  Chairs; Directors' and Of-
  fice Tables) ....B
Hard Mfg. Co. (Malleable
  Iron Bedsteads; Children's
  Cribs; Hospital Beds;
  Spring Beds; Woven Wire
  Mattresses; Hair; Felt;
  Combination Pillows;
  Cushions; Mattresses;
  Couches; Toy Beds) ...C
Sikes Chair Co. (Cane;
  Leather Dining Chairs;
  Rocking Chairs) ....B
N. Y.—Camden
Camden Cabinet Co. (Hale
  Sectional Bookcases) ...C
Conants' Sons. F. H. (Fancy
  Rockers; Desk; Morris
  Mission; Dutch; Vernis
  Martin Reception Chairs)
  C
N. Y.—Canastota
Smith. Ellis & Joyce (China
  Closets; Buffets; Ladies';
  Roll Top Desks) ....B
N. Y.—Chichester
Schwarzwaelder. L. A.
  (Folding; Portable Chairs;
  Office Desks; Bank; Of-
  fice Fixtures; Special
  Cabinet Works to Order) .A

*My New York Sales-
room is at 13 East 16th
St., where samples of my
line may be inspected.*

*My factory is located
in the hardwood belt of
the Catskills, of which I
own more than 7,000
acres. Have my own saw
mills and am therefore
first hand, saving to my
customers lumbermen's*

*and lumber dealers' prof-
its.*

*A corps of draughts-
men are in attendance at
my New York office
ready at all times to
make special designs for
any and all kinds of cab-
inet work and special fixtures. Plans, sketches
and estimates furnished
upon request without
charge*

N. Y.—Cohoes
Standard Refrigerator Co.
  (The) (Music Cabinets;
  Ladies' Desks; Cellar-
  ettes) C
N. Y.—Eldridge
National Chair Mfg. Co.
  (Clark. Hunsiker & Co.)
  (Chairs; Novelties) C
N. Y.—Elmira Heights
Elmira Table Mfg. Co.
  (Extension Tables;
  Stands) C
N. Y.—Geneva
Geneva Furn. Mfg. Co. (Up-
  holstered Lounges;
  Couches; Sofa Beds) ...C
N. Y.—Gouverneur
Van Duzee Mfg. Co., S. B.
  (Folding; Typewriter;
  Extension Tables; Cham-
  ber Suits; Lapboards) ..D
N. Y.—Groton
Conger-Norton Chair Co.
  (Cane; Cobbler Seat Din-
  ing Chairs; Rockers; Of-
  fice Chairs) C
N. Y.—Herkimer
Horrocks Desk Co. (Inc.)
  (Office Furn.; Type-
  writer Roll; Flat Top Of-
  fice desks; Office; Type-
  writer Tables; Sectional
  Bookcases; Filing De-
  vices) C
Standard Furn. Co. (Inc.)
  (Office Desks) ....A
Wagner Couch Co. (Adjus-
  table Bed; Box; Leather
  Couches; Lounges; Couch
  Frames) ....F
N. Y.—Hornellsville
Deutsch & Co., J. M. (Par-
  lor; Library Tables; Tab-
  ourettes; Pedestals) ....B
N. Y.—Hudson
Winstian. Louis (Uphols-
  tered Furn.) ....B
N. Y.—Illion
Tucker File & Cabinet Co.
  (Special Furn. Made to
  Order; Filing Cabinets) .C
N. Y.—Jamestown
Atlas Furn. Co. (Chiffon-
  iers; Dressers) ....A
Bailey-Jones Co. (Inc.)
  (Parlor; Library; Bed-
  room; Directors'; Ladies'
  Sewing Tables; Pedestals)
  A
Curtis Co., F. M., The
  (Odd Dressers; Ladies
  Desks; Music Cabinets) .C
Diamond Furn. Co. (Parlor;
  Library Tables; Tabour-
  rettes; Pedestals) ......B
Fenton Metallic Mfg. Co.
  (Metallic Desks) ....A
Jamestown Longue Co.
  (Couches; Sofa Beds;
  Davenports; Adjustable
  Sofas; Box Divans; Bed
  Lounges) ....A
Maddox Table Co. (Parlor;
  Library Tables; Tabour-
  ettes; Pedestals; Vernis
  Martin Tables; Odd
  Pieces) ....A
Morgan Mfg. Co. (Parlor;
  Library Tables; Tabou-
  rettes; Pedestals) ......B
N. Y.—Keesville
Prescott & Son, R. (Cham-
  ber Suits; Dressers; Chif-
  foniers; Washstands; Bed-
  steads) ....B

FURNITURE (Con.)

N. Y.—Lestershire

Marshall Furn. Co. (Furniture Specialties) C

N. Y.—Lockport

Oliver Bros. Co. (Brass; Iron Bedsteads) ....A

N. Y.—Lowville

Haberer, John E. (Chamber Suits; Chiffoniers) .....B

N. Y.—Medina

Cook & Co., S. A. (Morris Chairs; Reclining Rockers; Patent Adjustable End Divans; Davenport Beds; Turkish Chairs; Specialties in Couches; Parlor Furn.) ....A

Maher Bros. (Parlor Suits; Sofa Beds; Couches; Davenports; Odd Pieces) ...B

N. Y.—Mt. Lebanon

Wagen & Co., R. M. (The Shakers) (Shaker Chairs) ....AA

New York City

Aimone Mfg. Co. (Bedroom; Dining; Library; Hall; Fancy Furn. in Mahogany; Inlaid) ....B

American School Furn. Co. (School; Church Furn.; Opera Chairs; Auditorium Seating) ....AAAA

Austrian Bent Wood Furn. Co. (The) (Bent Wood Chairs; Sofas; Settees; Clothes Stands; Costumers; Hat Racks; Rockers; Stools, etc.) ....AAA

Bhumgara Co. (The), F. P. (Oriental Carved; Inlaid Furn.; Furn. Coverings from India; Turkey; Syria) C

Corbett Chair Co. (Wood; Cane Seat Chairs; Rockers; Cobbler Rockers; Box Seat; Office Chairs) ...D

Cornell Co., J. B. & J. M., 20th & 11th Av. (Steel; Metallic Desks) ......AA

Cunningham Sons' Rattan Co. (Reed; Rattan) ...F

Derby & Co., P. (Chairs; Settees) ....A

Estabrook & Co., S. G. (Parlor; Library Furn.) ....A

Fennell, John (Parlor Suits) ....A

Fruauf, Jacob (Est. of) (Parlor Suits; Couches; Lounges) C

Hale & Kilburn Mfg. Co. (Telescope Parlor Beds; Convertible Sofas; Portable Reservoir Wash Stands; Polished Hardwood Odorless Commodes) ....AA

Hall, Frank A. (Bedding; Brass; Iron Bedsteads; Down Cushions; Woven Wire Mattresses) ......B

Helmsley. John (Parlor Frames) C

Herrmann Furn. & Plumbers' Cabinet Wks. (Bedroom Suits; Chiffoniers; Odd Dressers; Bedroom; Dining Tables; Wardrobes; Bookcases; Sideboards; Hall Stands; Music Cabinets; Parlor; Roll; Flat Top; Standing Desks) ....A

Hospital Supply Co. (Ward Furn.) ....A

Hunzinger & Son, Geo. (Chairs; Rockers; Platform Rockers; Tetes; Card Tables; Summer; Quaint Furn.) ....B

Jansen, Edward (Green Rush; Willow; Raffia Furn.; Fancy Baskets) ..E

Judd Co., H. L., (Metallic Bedsteads; Cribs; Curtain Poles; Upholsterers') .AA

Kiliam Bros. & Somma (Mahogany Inlaid Furn.) ....A

Kohn, Jacob & Joseph (Aus-

FURNITURE (Con.)

trian Bent Wood Furn.) ....AAAA

Madison Mfg. Co. (Brass Beds) ....E

Manhattan Bedding Co. (Brass; Iron; Enamel Beds; Woven Wire Mattresses; Cribs; Cots, etc.) ....B

Metal Stamping Co. (Metal Folding Chairs) C

Miller & Co., John (Dining; Office; Library Chairs)B

Mohr & Co., F. (Upholstered Parlor; Library Furn.; Gold; Mahogany Cabinets; Tables; Library; Dining-room Suits Complete) ....A

Nathan & Co., P. (Parlor Suits; Couches) ......B

New York Couch Bed Co. (Couch Beds; Mattresses) ....B

New York Woven Wire Mattress Co. (Woven Wire Springs; Institution Beds; Divans; Upholstered; Woven Wire Cots) C

Ostermoor & Co. (Metal Bedsteads) ....B

Palmer & Embury Mfg. Co. (Parlor; Library Sofas; Chairs; Tables; Tabourettes; Pedestals) .....A

Pomroy & Gambell Co. (Bed Springs) ....B

Pottier & Stymus Co. (Fine Furn. and Upholstery to Order) ....A

Preiser & Co., J. (Parlor Suits; Couches; Lounges; Odd Pieces; Leather Chairs) C

Rogers & Co., Chas. P. (Brass; Iron Bedsteads; Spring Beds) ....A

Rotner & Co., H. (Bamboo Furn.) ....F

Sargent Co., Geo. F. (Adjustable Reading Desks)B

Schwarzwaelder Co., Wm. (Office) X

Sellew, T. G. (Office; Roll Top Desks) ....B

Steinfeld Bros. (Lawn Furn.; Swings; Furn. Specialties) C

Strobel & Sons, Philip (Chairs; Sideboards; Tables) ....B

Thonet Bros. (Bent Wood Chairs; Settees; Tables; Costumers, etc.) ....AAAA

Tonk & Co. (Piano Stools)C

N. Y.—Phoenix

Sinclair Chair Co. (High Grade Folding Chairs) ..F

N. Y.—Poughkeepsie

Kaal Rock Chair Co. (Medium; High Grade Box Seat Dining; Library; Office Chairs in Cane; Leather) ....E

Poughkeepsie Chair Co. (Box Seat Dining; Typewriting Chairs; Store Stools; Special Chairs to Order) ....D

N. Y.—Rochester

Archer Mfg. Co., Geo. W. (Piano Stools; Barber; Physicians' Chairs) ....B

Barnard-Simonds Co. (Inc.) (Chairs) C

Brooks, Edw. (Ladies' Desks; Bookcases) C

Copeland & Durgin Co. (Extension Tables; Ladies' Desks; Combination; Bookcases; Dressers; Chiffoniers) ....B

Halstrick, Anthony (Church Furn.) ....E

Hubbard & Eldredge Co. (Fancy Chairs; Rockers)B

Langslow-Fowler Co. (Morris; Hall; Reception Chairs; Fancy Rockers; Mission Furn.; Den Settees; Tete-a-tetes, etc.) .B

Miller Cabinet Co. (Parlor; Library Tables; Hall

FURNITURE (Con.)

Seats; Hanging Glasses; Hall Racks; Pedestals; Tabourettes; Stands)....C

Rochester Hassock Co. (Hassocks) ....F

Straussman & Co., H. M. (Parlor; Library Suits; Davenports; Leather Chairs; Divans; Fancy Chairs; Lodge Furn.)...A

Vetter Desk Wks. (Desks; Filing Cabinets) ....A

Wegman, Wm. J. (Spring Beds) ....D

Yawman & Erbe Mfg. Co. (Files; Cabinets; Card Indexes; Commercial Report; Credit Systems; Vertical Filing Systems; Sectional Filing Cabinets; Devices) ....AA

N. Y.—Rome
Rome Metallic Medstead Co. (Brass; Iron Beds; Cribs, etc.) ....A

N. Y.—Salamanca
Salamanca Furn. Wks. (Inc.) (Chiffoniers; Dressers) ....D

N. Y.—Shandaken
Whitney, Hiram (Cane Seat; Rocking Chairs) C

N. Y.—Sherman
Sherman Chair Co. (Wood Seat Chairs) ....E

N. Y.—Silver Creek
Silver Creek Upholstering Co. (Parlor Furn.; Couches) ....D

N. Y.—Syracuse
Benson, Herbert H. (Couches Dining Chairs; Upholstered; Cobbler Rockers; Children's Rockers; Chairs) C

Brown Furn. Co., C. G. (China Cabinets; Bookcases; Ladies' Desks; Music Cabinets; Tabourettes, etc.) ....B

Butler Mfg. Co. (Parlor; Music Cabinets; Curios; Desks; Pedestals; Tea; Card Nested Work; Parlor Tables; Screens; Hall Clocks; Seats; Diningroom; Bedroom; Library Furn.) ....A

Onondaga Novelty Co. (Folding Tables; Step Ladders; Medicine Cabinets) .....D

Perry, Aziell D. (High Grade Folding Chairs for Church; Lodge Rooms; Halls; Undertakers) .....E

Simonds Co., Elgin A. (Chairs; Rockers) .....D

Wells Mfg. Co. A. J. (Letter Filing; Sectional; Catalogue; Card Index Cabinets; Special Furn. to Order) C

N. Y.—Truxton
Bryant Furn. Co. (Bedroom Suits; Tables; Commodes; Kitchen Cabinets) C

N. Y.—Utica
Foster Bros. Mfg. Co. (Inc.) (Iron Bedsteads; Divans; Mattresses; Spring Beds; Cots; Cribs; Woven Wire Mattresses) ....B

Latimer & Adams (Adjustable Chairs; Sofas; Adjustable Bed; Box Couchs; Odd Pieces) ...D

Lortz, Teuscher & Co. (Cots; Cribs; Woven Wire Mattresses, etc.; also Hospital Beds; Antiseptic Tables; Towel Racks)..G

Utica Couch & Mattress Co. (Couches) C

N. Y.—Waverly
Hall & Lyon Furn. Co. (Bedsteads; Dressing Cases; Princess Dressers; Chiffoniers; Ladies' Toilet Tables; Washstands; in Quartered Oak; Bird's-eye Maple; Mahogany)..C

Merriam, F. W. (Woven

FURNITURE (Con.)

Wire Mattresses) C

N. Y.—Wayland
Gunlocke Chair Co. (The), W. H. (Office; Morris; Rustic; Lawn; Veranda Chairs; Stools) ....D

N. Y.—Wellsville
Coats Mfg. Co. (Inc.) (Odd Dressers; Folding Beds; Chamber Suits) C

N. Y.—West Camden
Blount & Sprague (Chairs) ....E

N. Y.—Westmoreland
Hecla Reed Co. (Reed Rockers; Chair Settees; Couches; Book Racks; Music Stands) ....F

N. Y.—Whitesboro
Quigley Furn. Co., The (Office Furn.) ....D

N. C.—Asheboro
Asheboro Furn. Co. (Oak; Poplar Chamber Suits; Odd Dressers; Chiffoniers) ....D

Randolph Chair Co. (Chairs; Rockers) ....D

N. C.—Carthage
Carthage Furn. Co. (Cheap; Medium Oak Chamber Suits; Dressers; Bedsteads; Commodes) ....D

N. C.—Concord
Yorke Furn. Co. (Suits; Odd Dressers; Chiffoniers) ....D

N. C.—Dunn
South Dunn Mfg. Co. (Chamber Suits; Odd Dressers; Chiffoniers) C

N. C.—Goldsboro
Goldsboro Furn. Mfg. Co. (Oak; Mahogany Suits; Odd Dressers; Chiffoniers) C

N. C.—Greensboro
Gate City Furn. Mfg. Co. (The) (Chamber Suits; Odd Dressers; Chiffoniers) C

Greensboro Furn. Mfg. Co. (Chamber Suits; Dressers; Chiffoniers) C

Greensboro Table & Mantle Co. (Extension; Centre; Kitchen Tables) ....D

N. C.—Hickory
Hickory Furn. Co. (Suits; Dressers) ....D

Martin Furn. Co. (Sideboards; Buffets) ......D

N. C.—High Point
Alma Furniture Co. (Sofas; Tables) C

Continental Furn. Co. (The) (Chamber Suits; Chiffoniers; Buffets; Sideboards) C

Eagle Furn. Co. (Inc.) (Chamber Suits; Dressers) C

Globe-Home Furn. Co. (The) (Chamber Suits; Odd Dressers; Chiffoniers)..A

Grand Rapids Furn. Co. (Hall Racks) ....B

High Point Furn. Co. (Chamber Suits; Odd Dressers) ....A

High Point Mantel & Table Co. (Tables; Hat Racks; Kitchen Safes) ....D

High Point Metallic Bed Co. (Cheap; Medium Iron Beds) ....D

Lindsay Chair Co. (Inc.) Cane; Cobbler Seat; Diners; Rockers) C

Myrtle Desk Co. (Roll; Flat Top Desks) ....D

Piedmont Table Co. (Extension; Library; Office; Centre Tables) ....D

Smith Furn. Co. (Sideboards; Wardrobes) ....D

Southern Chair Co. (Dining; Office; Porch; Children's Chairs; Nurse; Arm; Porch Rockers) ....D

Tate Furn. Co. (Chamber Suits; Odd Dressers; Chif-

FURNITURE (Con.)

foniers in Oak; Imitation
Mahogany) C
Tomlinson Chair Mfg. Co.
(Chairs; Rockers; Cradles;
Tables ....B
Union Furn. Co. (Chamber
Suits; Odd Dressers; Odd
Beds; Washstands) ....D
Victor Chair Co. (Cane;
Split Seat Cottage Chairs;
Porch; Nurse Rockers;
Children's Rockers; Table
Chairs) ....D
Welch Furn. Co. (Chamber
Suits; Mantel Folding
Beds; Chiffoniers) ....D

N. C.—Kernersville

Kernersville Furn. Mfg. Co.
(Chamber Suits; Odd
Dressers; Commodes) ..D

N. C.—Lenoir

Harper Furn. Co. (Cheap;
Medium Price Oak Cham-
ber Suits; Odd Dressers;
Commodes) ....A

N. C.—Lexington

Elk Furniture Co. (Side-
boards; Chamber Suits;
Odd Dressers; Chiffoniers)
............................C
Oneida Chair Co. (Chairs)
............................D

N. C.—Marion

Blue Ridge Furn. Co. (Suits;
Chiffoniers; Beds) ....D
Catawba Furn. Co. (Suits;
Sideboards) ....A

N. C.—Mebane

White Furn. Co. (The)
(Suits; Dressers; Centre;
Library; Extension Ta-
bles) ....B

N. C.—Mocksville

Mocksville Furn. Co. (Chamber Suits; Odd Dressers;
Chiffoniers) C

N. C.—Mt. Airy

Mt. Airy Furn. Co. (Cheap;
Medium Chamber Suits;
Odd Beds; Dressers) ...C
Mt. Airy Mantel & Table
Co. (Extension; Centre
Tables; Hall Racks) ...D
Surry Lounge Co. (Lounges;
Couches; Davenports; Set-
tees) ....D

N. C.—North Wilkesboro

Oak Furn. Co. (Chiffoniers)
............................D

N. C.—Oxford

Oxford Furn. Co. (Oak
Chamber Suits; Odd
Dressers; Beds) C

N. C.—Ramseur

Alberta Chair Wks. (Chairs;
Cheap Furn.) ....D

N. C.—Sanford

Fitts-Crabtree Mfg. Co.
Co. (Parlor; Library; Ex-
tension Tables; Beds;
Washstands; Kitchen
Safes; Cupboards; Tables)
............................D

N. C.—Selma

Selma Mfg. Co. (General
Line) ....D

N. C.—Statesville

Imperial Furn. Mfg. Co.
(Sideboards; Hall Racks)
............................C
Key Furn. Co. (Odd Dress-
ers; Suits; Chiffoniers).D
Kincaid Furn. Co. (Bedroom
Suits; Odd Pieces; Chif-
foniers; Chevals) ......D
Statesville Furn. Co. (Bed-
room Suits; Odd Dressers)
............................D

N. C.—Thomasville

Cates Chair Co. (Caned Seat
Diners; Rockers) ......D
Climax Chair Co. (Chairs)E
Cramer Furn. Co. (Open
Cane; Cobbler Seat;
Turned Post Diners; Box
Seat Diners; Arm; Office
Chairs; Cobbler; Bent
Arm Open Cane Seat
Rockers) ....D

N. C.—Warrenton

Warrenton Furn. Co.
(Chairs) ....D

FURNITURE (Con.)

N. C.—Winston-Salem

Forsyth Iron Bed Co. (Iron;
Brass Beds) ....D
Oakland Mfg. Co. (Bed-
room Suits; Odd Dressers;
Chiffoniers; Sideboards)D
Winston Furn. Co. (Roll;
Flat Top Desks) ....D

OHIO—Ashland

Kauffman Mfg. Co. (The)
Woven Wire Mattresses;
Cots; Cribs; Folding
Tables; Chairs; Iron Beds;
Spring Beds, etc.) .....B

OHIO—Athens

Hudson School Furn. Co.
(School Furn.) ....B

OHIO—Bellefontaine

Elliott, A. C. (Church; Of-
fice; Hall; Lodge; School;
Opera Furn.; Chairs;
Hall; Lodge Settees;
Church Pews; Pulpits)..X

OHIO—Bucyrus

Roehr Co. (The), Chas.
(School; Office Furn;
Mantels) C
Berger Mfg. Co. (The)
(Steel Tables; Desks;
Counters; Card Index
Cases; Vertical Filing
Cabinets; Document Files;
Roller Shelves; Book-
cases; Library Shelves;
Stacks) ....A
Danner Mfg. Co. (The),
John (Sectional; Revolv-
ing Bookcases; Medicine
Cabinets; Store Stools).C

OHIO—Chillicothe

Arbenz Furn. Co. (Side-
boards; Buffets; Chiffon-
iers; Dressers in Oak and
Mahogany) ....D

OHIO—Cincinnati

Becker & Co., Wm. (Side-
boards; China Cases; Ex-
tension Tables; Buffets;
Chairs) C
Betts Street Furn. Co. (The)
(Mantel Folding Beds;
Cradles; Cribs) C
Cinn. Chair Co. (Chairs;
Rockers; Furn.; Mantels)
............................D
Cinn. Mattress & Spring Co.
(Woven Wire Bed Springs,
etc.) ....D
Cinn. Seating Co., 6th &
Vine Sts., (Church; Opera;
School) C
Closterman, Henry (Chairs;
Centre Tables; Hat
Racks; Parlor Furn.).AAA
Dietz & Co., J. F. (Office
Desks) ....A
Dornette & Bro. Co. (The)
J. (Office Desks) .....B
Globe-Wernicke Co. (Sec-
tional Bookcases; Filing
Appliances; Desks; Office
Furn.) ....AAAA
Kaipers' Sons, Charles (Up-
holstered Furn.) ....A
Kelsall Co., Thos. (Library;
Office; Teachers' Desks)
............................B
Lubke's Sons, Fred. (Cane
Seat Chairs) ....E
Luck, A., 1019 Main
(Divans) ....D
National Carriage & Reed
Co. (Reed; Rattan Chairs;
Furn.; Screens; Easels;
Novelties; Bamboo Goods;
Cane; Cobbler Seat Oak
Chairs) ....A
Newman-Kuhn Mfg. Co.
(Brass; Iron Bedsteads).C
Onken Co. (The), Oscar.
(Hall Clocks; Cellarettes;
Ladies' Desks; Sewing
Tables; Pedestals; Tabou-
rettes; Cheval Mirrors,
etc.) ....B
Renesch & Co., A. (Hall
Racks; Settees; Hanging
Racks; Cheval Mirrors;
Dressing Tables) ......B
Schmidt & Co., Henry (Up-
holstered Furn.; Church;
Lodge Work) C
Sextro Mfg. Co. (Hall

FURNITURE (Con.)

Furn.; Extension Tables)
.....................C
Standard Furn. Co. (The)
(Chairs) C
Steinman & Meyer Furn.
Co. (Sideboards; Exten-
sion Tables) ....B
Stille & Duhlmeier Furn.
Co. (The) (Bedroom Suits;
Wardrobes; Chiffoniers;
Dressing Tables) .....B
Streit Mfg. Co., C. F.
(Morris Chairs; Daven-
port Sofa Beds) C

OHIO—Cleveland

Cleveland Brass & Iron Bed-
Stead Co. (The) (Brass;
Malleable Iron; Steel
Enameled Children's and
Other Bedsteads; Springs;
Cribs) ....B
Forest City Bedstead Co.
(Brass; Malleable Iron;
Brass Trimmed Bed-
steads) ....AA
Janssen & Loeblein (Up-
holstered Furn.; Couches;
Parlor Suits; Morris
Shairs; Leather Work)..B
Marble & Shattuck Chair Co.
(The) (Dining; Office;
Cafe; Chamber; Fancy
Chairs; Rockers) ....B
Ohio Spring Bed Co.
(Woven Wire Mattresses;
Wire Fabrics; Wire Beds;
Couch and Lounge Bot-
toms; Cribs; Cots).....A
Sheier Furn. Co., D. L. (Par-
lor Suits; Turkish Leather
Rockers; Couches) C
Schulte Furn. Co. (The)
(Parlor Furn.; Couches;
Odd Pieces; Davenports;
Turkish Chairs; Leather
Work) C
Standard Metal Bedstead
Co. (Iron Bedsteads;
Cribs) ....E

OHIO—Columbus

Holtzman & Sons, Henry
(Piano Stools) ....A
Lilly Co., M. C. (Church;
Lodge Furn.) ......AAAA
Sun Mfg. Co. (Lawn Furn.
Chairs; Cots; &.) ......A

OHIO—Dayton

Burkhardt Furn. Co. (The)
(Parlor; Library Tables;
Pedestals; Tabourettes;
School Desks) C
Dayton Table Slide Co.
(The) (Extension Table
Slides; Dowels; Leaf Sup-
ports) C
Huler & Co., E. M.
Couches; Lounges) .....D
Ohio Rake Co. (School;
Teachers' Desks) .....AA
Ohmer's Sons Co. (The). ...
(Bank; Office Furn.; Fix-
tures; Special Furn. of all
kinds; Sectional Sliding
Door Bookcases; Filing
Devices of all kinds) ..A
Stengel & Co., John (Cham-
ber Suits; Sideboards;
Buffets; Chiffoniers; La-
Dies' Dressing Tables) ..B
Stomps-Burkhardt Co. (The)
(Chairs) ....AA

OHIO—Defiance

Geiger Furn. Co. (Beds;
Cupboards; Cabinets;
Wardrobes) ....D

OHIO—Eaton

Ohio Iron & Brass Bed Co.
(The) (Inc.) (Iron; Brass
Bedsteads) ....B

OHIO—Findlay

Findlay Table Mfg. Co.
(The) (Extension Tables:
..........................D

OHIO—Gallipolis

Gallipolis Chair Co. (The)
(Opera Cane; Cobbler
Seats; Chairs; Rockers;
Box Seat Diners) ......E
Gallipolis Furn. Co. (The)
(Chiffoniers; Dressers;
Washstands; Hotel Dress-
ers) ....B

FURNITURE (Con.)

Ohio Valley Furn, Co. (Oak
Chiffoniers; Dressers;
Washstands; Hall Racks;
Sideboards; Buffets; Man-
tel Beds) ....A

OHIO—Harrison

Cincinnati Seating Co.
(Church; Hall; Opera;
School Furn.) C

OHIO—Hillsboro

Globe Chair Co. (The)
(Cane; Upholstered Chairs;
Rockers) ....D

OHIO—Logan

Kesslers & Sons, Frank
(Chamber Suits; Ward-
robes; Double Cupboards;
Cupboard Safes) ....D
Snider Mfg. Co. (Bent
Wood; Lumber; Chairs).C

OHIO—Manchester

Manchester Chair Co. (Rin-
ing Chairs; Rockers) ...D
Manchester Furn. Co. (Gen-
eral Line of Cheap Furn.)
..........................A
Ohio Valley Furn. Co. (The)
(Bedroom Suits; Odd
Beds; Dressers; Stands;
Safes; Tables) C

OHIO—Marietta

Darby Furn. Co. (The) (Pil-
lar; Extension; Parlor; Li-
brary; Office Tables) ..C
Marietta Chair Co. (Cane;
Leather Seat Dining
Chairs; Rockers; Wood;
Leather Seat Office; Li-
brary; Bedroom Chairs).A

OHIO—Marysville

Marysville Cabinet Co.(The)
(Kitchen Cupboards; Cab-
inets; Tables; Special
Cabinet Work; Bank;
Store; Office Furn.) ....A

OHIO—Massillon

Ohio Table Co. (Extension
Tables) C

OHIO—New Bremen

Klanke Furn. Co. (The) (Extension Tables; Ward-
robes; Cupboards) C

OHIO—New Richmond

Fridman Seating Co. (The)
(Church; Bank; Office;
Counting House Furn.)..F

OHIO—Norwalk

Stewart Co., G. S. (Curtain
Poles; Wood Trimmings;
Grilles; Screens; Fret-
work; Decorated Furn.)A

OHIO—Piqua

Cron Co., The L. C. & W.
L. (Bedroom Suits; Odd
Beds; Dressers) ....A
Cron, Kills & Co. (Porta-
ble Wardrobes; Ladies'
Portable Desks; Cos-
tumers) ....A
Fritsch-Parker Furn. Co.,
The (Extension Tables).E

OHIO—Pomeroy

Probst Furn. Co. (Chamber
Suits; Sideboards; Buf-
fets; Odd Dressers) ....D

OHIO—Portsmouth

Wait Furn. Co.. The (Sideboards; Chiffoniers) ..A

OHIO—Springfield

Harris Mfg. Co.. The (High
Grade Leather Couches;
Chairs; Davenports) C

OHIO—Tiffin

Kishler & Son, F. D.
(Chairs) ....F
Tiffin Mfg. Co., The
(Church Furn.) ....D

OHIO—Tippecanoe City

Tipp Building & Mfg. Co.
(Kitchen Cabinets; Ta-
bles; Ironing Tables) ..B
Tipp Furn. Co., The (Cham-
ber Suits; Chiffoniers;
Sideboards) C

OHIO—Toledo

Gendron Wheel Co. (Reed
Furn.; Novelties; In-
valids and Rolling Chairs.
..........................AAA
Toledo Furn. & Mfg. Co.
(Upholstered Furn.) ...A
Toledo Spring & Mattress

FURNITURE (Con.)

Co. (Woven Wire Springs;
Cots; Cribs; Single; Double
Coil Springs; Sanitary
Bed Springs) ....E

Toledo Upholstering Co.
(Leather Goods; Parlor
Suits; Davenports; Sofas;
Odd Pieces; Sofa Beds).B

Uhl Bros. Co., The (Art
Steel Furn.; Chairs; Ta-
bles; Stools; Tabourettes;
Piano Stools; Typewrit-
er Chairs) ....E

Waldcutter & Kahlenberg
(Chairs) C

Williams & Co. (Wood
Seats; Cane Cobbler; Sad-
dle Seats; Upholstered
Rockers) ....D

Yesbera Mfg. Co. (Store
Stools; Combination Ta-
bles; Cloak Racks) .....A

OHIO—Urbana

Barlow & Kent Co., The
(Wardrobes; Extension
Tables) ....B

OHIO—Wapakoneta

Swink, Snyder & Co. (Ex-
tension Tables; Sofas,
etc.) C

OHIO—Warren

King Furniture Co. (Tables)
C

Western Reserve Furn. Co.
(Inc.) (Dressers; Chiffon-
iers; Fine Cabinet Ware)
C

**OHIO—Washington Court
House**

Washington Mfg. Co.
(Wood; Cane; Cobbler
Seat Chairs; Rockers;
Morris Chairs; Stands;
Odd Pieces) C

OHIO—West Farmington

Miller Table Co. (Exten-
sion Tables) C

OHIO—Williamsburg

White & Dillman (Chairs)D

Williamsburg Furn. Co.
(Chairs) C

OHIO—Youngstown

General Fireproofing Co.
(Metallic Desks) .....AA

Heller Bros. Co. (General
Line) C

OHIO—Zanesville

Zanesville Mantel & Furn.
Co., The (Sideboards;
Dressers; Washstands;
Chiffoniers) ....D

OREGON—Albany

Veal & Son, R. (Chairs)...D

OREGON—Baker City

Queen City Furniture Co.
(Couches) ....D

OREGON—Portland

Doernbecher Mfg. Co.
(Chamber Suits; Dressers;
Bureaus) C

Oregon Furn. Mfg. Co. (Bed-
room; Parlor Suits; Dress-
ers; Kitchen Furn.; Flat
Top Desks; Chiffoniers;
Mattresses; Couches; Bed
Lounges) ....B

Peters & Roberts Furn. Co.
(Parlor Suits; Fancy
Chairs; Lounges; Couches)
D

PA.—Allegheny

Amer. Baby Carriage Co.
(Rattan Chairs; Rockers;
Doll Cabinets) ....F

Gross & Hastings (Couches;
Lounges; Davenports; Par-
lor Suits; Mattresses;
Spring Beds; Bedding)..D

Hagmaier, John (Parlor
Furn.; Couches; Lounges)

PA.—Allentown

Bear Furn. Co. (Parlor
Tables; Hat Racks; Jardi-
niere; Hall Stands; Set-
tees) C

Buehler & Co., G. (Parlor
Furn. Frames) C

Dorney Furn. Co., C. A.
(Sideboards) ....A

Johnston & Swartz (Parlor
Frames in the White; ma-

FURNITURE (Con.)

ple; Mahogany) ....A

Kroll Furniture Co. (Ltd.)
(Upholstered Parlor Nov-
elties in Gold; Gilt; Ma-
hogany) ....AAAA

Schneck & Sons, E. J. (Parlor; Library Tables; Hall
Stands) ....D

Yeager Furn. Co., The (Par-
lor Furn.; Fancy; Easy
Chairs; Gold; Gilt Parlor
Pieces; Weathered Oak
Den Furn.) ....B

PA.—Athens

Athens Furn. Co. (Chamber
Suits; Chiffoniers; Side-
boards) ....B

PA.—Brookville

Deemer Furn. Co., A. D.
(Suits; Wood Beds; Kitch-
en Tables; Cupboards;
Sinks) C

PA.—Chambersburg

Sierer & Co. H. (China
Closets; Bookcases; Dress-
ing Tables; Hall Seats;
Glasses; Tabourette;
Special Order Cabinet
Work) ....D

PA.—Chester

New Farson Mfg. Co., The
(China Cabinets; Book-
cases; Music Cabinets)..D

PA.—Conneautville

Penn. Furn. Co. (Extension;
Centre & Kitchen Tables)
D

PA.—Corry

Bonnell & Lambing (Spring;
Beds; Cots; Cribs) .....D

Corry Chair Co. (Wood Seat
Chairs; Cobbler Seat; Up-
holstered Rockers) C

PA.—Erie

Erie City Carriage Wks.
(Reed Chairs, etc.) C

PA.—Hallstead

Amer. Chair Mfg. Co.
(Fancy Rockers; Chairs;
Settees) ....B

PA.—Hanover

Crandall-Long Furn. Co.
(Ltd.) (Extension Tables)
D

PA.—Harrisburg

Boll Bros. Mfg. Co. (Brass;
Iron; Hospital Beds; Cos-
tumers; Mattresses; Box;
Wire and Coil Springs;
Cots; Pillows; Bolsters;
Cribs) ....A

PA.—Hughesville

Hughesville Furn. Co. (Sideboards; Buffets) ....B

PA.—Johnstown

De Frehn & Sons, W.
(Chairs; Rockers) C

PA.—Kane

Chatauqua Desk Co. (Roll;
Flat Top; Typewriter
Desks; Letter Press
Stands) ....D

PA.—Lewisburg

Lewisburg Chair Co.
(Chairs; Rockers; Tables;
Office Chairs) ....E

PA.—Lock Haven

Clinton Furn. Co. (Chamber
Suits) C

PA.—Milton

West Branch Novelty Co.
(Bamboo Furn. Tabou-
rettes; Cheap Ladies'
Desks) ....B

PA.—Montgomery

Heilman Couch Co. (Inc.)
The (Couches) ....E

Montgomery Table Wks.
(Tables; Desks) ....B

Penn. Furn. Mfg. Co. (Sideboards; Buffets) ....B

PA.—Montoursville

Woolever Bros. (Extension
Tables) ....D

PA.—Mt. Union

Moudy Mfg. Co.. The Wm.
H.. (Wood Seat Chairs;
Rockers) C

PA.—Muncy

Muncy Mfg. Co. (Chamber
Suits; Chiffoniers; Side-
boards) ....D

FURNITURE (Con.)

PA.—Oil City

Kramer & Son, W. J. (Extension; Kitchen Tables) ....D

PA.—Philadelphia

Behrend, Jacob (Costumers or Clothes Trees; Commodes; Sanitary; Hanging Cabinets; Hanging Hat Racks; Plate; Stein Racks; Umbrella Stands; Mirrors in Oak; Gilt Frames) C

Bernstein Mfg. Co. (Brass; Iron Bedsteads; Aseptic Hospital Furn.) ......A

Bodenstein & Kuemmerle (Chamber; Dining; Office; Odd Chairs; Fancy Rockers) ....A

Bunting, J. R. (Mattresses; Springs; Enamel Beds) ....B

Burt Bros. (Chamber Suits; Sideboards; Chiffoniers; Dressing Tables; Odd Bureaus; Washstands) ...B

Clark & Co., Thos. (Cylinder; Office Desks)....D

Goff, R. W. P. (China Cabinets; Side Tables; Music; Parlor Pedestals; Library Tables; Hall Stands; Seats; Glasses) ....B

Hale & Kilburn Mfg. Co., (Telescope Parlor Beds; Convertible Sofas; Portable Reservoir Wash Stands; Polished Hardwood Odorless Commodes) ....AAAA

Harrington, Howard E. Church; Lodge Furn.; Sofa Beds) ....F

Knell, W. W. & H. H. (Parlor and Library Suits; Davenports; Couches; Easy Chairs; Odd Pieces) C

Knoell & Sons, John, (Parlor; Shakespeare Tables; Commodes; Costumers) ....A

Knowlton & Co. (Chairs) .C

Kraan Furn. Co., Henry (Chamber Suits; Chiffoniers; Dressing Tables) .C

Lincoln Furn. Co. (Bedroom Furn.; Bookcases; Chevals; Wardrobes; Nightstands; Center Tables) ....B

McCracken & Hall (China Closets) ....B

McElroy - Shannon Spring Bed Mfg. Co. (Spiral Spring Beds) ....A

Phila. Baby Carriage Factory (Invalid; Reclining Chairs) ....B

Phila. Metallic Bed Co. (Brass; Iron Beds; Woven Wire Springs; Cots; Cribs; Metal Couches) ....A

Quaker City Metallic Bedstead Co. (Brass and Iron Bedsteads; Woven Wire Spring Mattresses; Institution Beds) C

Rawson Mfg. Co., The (Spring Beds; Woven Wire Mattresses; Cots; Cribs; Cradles; Brass; Enameled Beds. Adjustable Bedsteads; StepLadder Chairs; Tables; Clothes Trees) C

Rossell Bros. & Co. (Chairs) C

Schwartz, C. E. (Upholstered Furn.; Parlor Suits; Couches; Easy Chairs; Library Suits in leather & fabrics) C

Sikes Co. The (Morris; Office; Rocking; Cane & Leather Dining Chairs; C

Smith & Co., Geo. W. (Divans) ....A

FURNITURE (Con.)

PA.—Picture Rocks

Burrow Bros. & Co. (Ltd.) (Chamber Suits; Sideboards) ... .B

PA.—Pittsburg

Stevens Chair Co. (Fold'g; Rolling Chairs) C

PA.—Railroad

Helb & Sons, F., (Bedroom Suits; Sideboards; Chiffoniers; Odd Dressers, etc.) ....D

PA.—St Marys

St. Marys Chair Co. (Library; Office Chairs, Rockers; Lawn Settees; Porch Rockers; Odd Fancy Rockers) C

PA.—Shippensburg

Bober & Phillips (Sideboards; Chiffoniers) ...E

PA. South Williamsport ..

Keystone Furniture Co. (Chamber Suits; Odd Dressers; Chiffoniers) .A

PA.—Titusville

Specialty Mfg. Co., The (Settees; Kitchen Tables) ....B

Titusville Elastic Chair Co. (Limited) (Upholstered and Dining Chairs Opera and Church Seats; Porch Chairs; Settees) ......D

PA.—Towanda

Frost's Sons, J. O. (Oak Chamber Suits; Odd Dressers; Sideboards; Chiffoniers) ....A

PA.—Union City

Keystone Chair Works (Wood Seat Chairs; Rockers) ....D

Novelty Wood W'ks. Co. (Inc.) (Desks; Bookcases; Music Cabinets; Chautauqua Drawing Boards; Book Racks; Shaving Stands) ......D

Penn Chair Co. (Wood Seat Chairs; Rockers) ......B

Standard Chair Co. (Wood; Cobbler Seat Chairs; Rockers) ....D

Union City Chair Co. (Wood Seat Chairs; Rockers) ..B

PA.—Warren

Conewango Furniture Co. (Odd; Princess Dressers; Chiffoniers; Commodes) C

Phoenix Furn. Co. (Childfoniers; Dressers; Dressing Tables) C

Warren Chair Works (Patent Wood Seat; Sadle Seat; Fine Upholstered Chairs; Rockers) ......A

Warren Table Works. (Homer Roll Top Extension &; Dressing Tables Dressers; Chiffoniers; Commodes; Beds) C

PA.—Watsontown

Watsontown Table & Furniture Co. (Extension Tables) C

PA.—Wilkes-Barre

Collins-Hale Mfg. Co. (Parlor Suits; Couches; Turkish; Easy Chairs; Rockers) C

PA.—Williamsport

Culler Furn. Co. (Chamber Furn.; Chairs; Extension Tables; Chiffoniers; Cupboards; Iron Beds; Sideboards; Sinks; Stands, &c.) ....D

Dittmar Furn. Co. (Church Pews; Church Furn.; Special Woodwork) ....D

National Furn. Co. (Extension; Office; Café Tables) ....B

Rishel Furn. Co., J. K. (Chamber Furn.; Oak Extension Tables) ....B

Williamsport Furn. Co. (Chamber Furn.; Dressers; Chiffoniers; Dressing Tables; Sideboards) ......B

FURNITURE (Con.)

PA.—York

Jacoby & Bro., Adam (Sideboards in Oak; Dressers; Chiffoniers; Washstands in Plain & Quartered Oak; Birds'-Eye Maple; Mahogany; Curly Birch) ....D

R. I.—Pawtucket

Bliss Mfg. Co., R. (School Desks) ....AAAA

R. I.—Providence

Brady, James Wm. (Couches) ....D

S. C.—Abbeville

Abbeville Furn. Factory (Plain; Quartered Oak Bedroom Suits; Odd Dressers; Chiffoniers) ......D

S. C.—Anderson

Anderson Mattress & Spring Bed Co. (Spring Beds) ..D

S. C.—Cheraw

Pee Dee Chair Co. (Chairs; Chair Stock) ....D

S. C.—Laurens

Laurens Furn. Mfg. Co. (Bedroom Suits; Chiffoniers; Odd Dressers; Beds) ....D

TENN.—Baxter

Putnam Mfg. Co. (Bedroom Suits; Chiffoniers; Sideboards; Tables; Odd Dressers; Washstands) ......B

TENN.—Bristol

Ordway Mfg. Co. (Chairs; Chair Stock; Lumber) ..B

We have spent a short life time in making Bentwood Chairs. We challenge the world to make Bent-wood Base-Rocking Chairs equal to ours and sell them at so low a price. Positively no glue joints. Artistically designed in both reed and leather

We make genuine twisted (not turned) woods for Balustrades, Palace Car and House-finishing material, Table legs, Office fixtures, Bedstead material, and bent stock for all purposes.

We are in the "Heart" of the Oak and Hickory district of the south. Low priced labor and material. $125,000 plant.

Let us know your wants.

TENN.—Chattanooga

Acme Kitchen Furn. Co. (Mantel Beds; Separate Dressers; Chiffoniers; Wardrobes; Combination Cases; Kitchen Cabinets; Safes; Cupboards; Kitchen Tables, etc.) C

Carlin Furn. & Mfg. Co. (Cottage Chairs) ......F

Chattanooga Furn. Co. (Extension; Library; Office and Parlor Tables; Hall Racks; Settees; Hanging Mirrors) C

Heron Iron Bedstead Co. (Iron Bedstead) ......E

Lomis & Hart Mfg. Co. (Bedroom Suits; Wardrobes; Sideboards; Dressers; Washstands; Tables) ....A

Wight Mfg. Co., The (Bed Springs; Cots; Couch Tops; Couches) ......E

TENN.—Cleveland

Milne, W. S. (Cane Seat Chairs; Rockers) ......D

TENN.—Elizabethton

Empire Chair Co. (Chairs; Rockers) ....D

TENN.—Jackson

Southern Seating & Cabinet Co. (Church Pews; School Desks, etc.) ....D

FURNITURE (Con.)

TENN.—Johnson City

Exum Furn. Co. (Oak Bedroom Suits; Chiffoniers) ....D

TENN.—Knoxville

Knoxville Rubber Tire

Knoxville Table & Chair Co. (Centre Tables; Chairs) C

Schaad & Rotach (Oak Chamber Suits; Odd Beds; Extension Tables) ......D

Utica Cabinet Co. (Roll; Flat Top Desks; Excelsior) C

TENN.—Loudon

Loudon Furn. Co. (Extension Tables) ....D

TENN.—Memphis

Memphis Furn. Mfg. Co. (Cheap Bed Suits; Extension Tables; Wardrobes; Safes; Glass Door Cupboards, etc.) ....B

Rose & Co., J. (Spring Beds; Woven Wire Mattresses; Cots; Cribs) ...B

Tennessee Furn. Mfg. Co. (General line) C

TENN.—Nashville

Montgomery Furn. & Mfg. Co. (Chamber Suits; Tables; Safes; Wardrobes; Springs) C

Nashville Chair & Carriage Co. (Rattan; Reed Furn.) ....F

TENN.—Newcomb

Newcomb Mfg. Co. (Bedroom Suits; Tables; Cupboards; Kitchen Sofas) C

TENN.—Tullohoma

Parker-Battle-Talbot Mfg. Co. (Kitchen Safes; Beds; Bureaus; Washstands; Bank and Office Furn.).D

TEXAS—Dallas

Olive & Myers Mfg. Co. (Couches; Lounges; Mattresses; Spring Beds; Cots) ....A

TEXAS—Texarkana

Southern Furn. Co. (Suits; Odd Beds; Dressers; Extension; Kitchen and Parlor Tables; Chiffoniers; Sideboards; Bookcases; China Closets; Wardrobes) ..C

TEXAS—Waco

Dennis Mfg. Co. (Cots) ..D

VT.—Barton

Percival Furn. Co. (Hygienic Couches; Adjustable Divans; Couches; Morris Chairs) ....E

VT.—Beecher Falls

Beecher Falls Co. (Birch Chamber Suits; Chiffoniers; Ladies' Desks; Dressing Tables; Odd Dressers; Mahoganized; Golden Birch) ....A

Our specialty is Birch Chamber Furniture and Ladies' Writing Desks in Curly Birch. Mahoganized Birch or Mahogany Veneer. Situated as we are in the heart of a Birch country with every facility for manufacturing goods, we are in a position to quote you prices that will interest you. Would be pleased to have your application for cuts and prices.

VT.—Battleboro

Smith & Co., S. A. (School Desks) ....AAA

VT.—Burlington

Champlain Mfg. Co. (Chairs) ....B

VT.—Ludlow

Fullam & Sons Co., L. G. (Porch; Saddle Seat; Rockers; Dining Chairs) D

VT.—North Bennington

Cushman Mfg. Co., H. T. (Decorative; Mission Furn.; Costumers; Clocks) C

FURNITURE (Con.)

VT.—Pompanoosuc
Patterson, L. S. (Cane; Wood Seat; Reed Chairs) E

VT.—Randolph
Salisbury Bros. Furn. Co. (Oak; Mission; Colonial Furn.; K. D. Dressers for Export) ....B

VT.—Readsboro
Readsboro Chair Mfg. Co. (Opera; Fold'g; Steamer Chairs; Lawn; Park Settees; Fold'g Card and Lunch Tables; Church and Lodge Furn.) ....D

VT.—Richford
Richford Mfg. Co. (Inc.) (Chamber Furn.; Odd Bureaus; Chiffoniers; Case Work) ....D
Sweat Comings Co. (Inc.) (Chamber Suits; Dressers; Chiffoniers) ....B

VT.—St. Albans
St. Albans Furn. Co. (Chiffoniers; Bookcases; Ladies' Desks; Fold'g Tables; Church Pews) ...B

VA.—Basic
Basic Furniture Co. (Chamber Suits; Sideboards; Chiffoniers) ....D

VA.—Bassett
Bassett Furn. Co. (Chamber Suits; Bedsteads) ..D

VA.—Chase City
Virginia Furn. Co. (Chamber Suits; Odd Dressers; Chiffoniers) ....D

VA.—Danville
Boatwright Furn. Mfg. Co. (Sideboards; Buffets) . C
Noell Mfg. Co., (Inc.) J. R. (Desks; Extension; Centre; Parlor; Saloon; Kitchen Tables) ....D

VA.—Manchester
James River Furn. & Mattress Co., (Couches; Sofas; Single; Bed Lounges, in Velour, Imitation & Genuine Leather) ....B
Manchester Furn. Co. (Wardrobes; Cupboards; Safes) ....D

VA.—Martinsville
Martinsville Mfg. Co. (Centre Tables) ....D

VA.—Port Norfolk
Air Line Mfg. Co. (Library; Kitchen Drop Leaf; Centre; Extension Dining Tables) C

VA.—Richmond
James River Furn. Co. (Couches; Sofas; Single; Bed Lounges, in Velour; Imitation; Genuine Leather) ....B
Toler & Sons (Bedroom Suits; Sideboards; Extension Tables; Tables; Wardrobes) ....D

VA.—Wakefield
Wakefield Mfg. Co. (Bedroom Suits) ....D

VA.—Waynesboro
Alexander & Bro., C. W. (Church Furn.; Store Fixtures; Bank Counters; Mantels; General Furn.) D
Lambert Bros. (Suits; Odd Dressers; Beds; Washstands; Tables; Commodes; Sofas) ....D

VA.—Winchester
Kurtz, Geo. W. (Tables; Sideboards) ....D

WASH.—Seattle
Carman Mfg. Co. (Mattresses; Bedroom Suits; Tables; Cupboards; Safes; Chiffoniers; Beds; Extension Tables; Woven Wire Mattresses; Cots; Cribs, etc.) ....A
Washington Mattress & Furn. Co. (Woven Wire Mattresses; Cots) ......D

WASH.—Tacoma
Carman Mfg. Co. (Bedroom Suits; Tables; Cupboards; Safes; Chiffoniers; Beds; Extension Tables; Woven Wire Mattresses; Cots; Cribs, etc.) ....A
Metal Bedstead Co. (Iron; Institution Beds; Cribs) C

W. VA.—Charleston
Morgan, J. & J. S. (Beds; Safes; Stands; Kitchen; Extension Tables; Store; Office Fixtures) C

W. VA.—Keyser
Richardson Furn. Co. (Chamber Suits; Sofas; Cupboards; Sideboards) C

W. VA.—Moundsville
National Bed Co. (Iron Beds) C

W. VA.—Parkersburg
Bentley & Gerwig Furn. Co. (Office Desks; Wardrobes) A
Parkersburg Chair Co., The (Wood; Cane; Cobbler; Upholstered Chairs; Rockers) C

WIS.—Algoma
Ahnapee Furn. Co. (Chamber Suits; Odd Dressers; Commodes) C

WIS.—Appleton
Appleton Chair Co. (Chairs) C

WIS.—Brooklyn
Capitol Chair Co. (Chairs; Desks; Extension Tables) C

WIS.—Eau Claire
Pioneer Furn. Co. (Chamber Suits; Chiffoniers; Sideboards) ....B

WIS.—Fond du Lac
Bowen Mfg. Co. (Desks) B
Winnebago Furn. Mfg. Co. (Chamber Suits; Sideboards; Chiffoniers; Odd Dressers; Office Desks; Cheap Beds) ....A

WIS.—Grand Rapids
Oberbeck Bros. Mfg. Co. (Sideboards; Buffets; Chiffoniers; Dressers; Chamber Suits) C

WIS.—Green Bay
Automatic File & Index Co. (The Automatic Letter Filing Cabinet; Sectional Bookcases) ....E
Kemnitz Furn. Co., Theo. (Chamber Suits; Odd Dressers) ....B

WIS.—Janesville
Choate-Hollister Furn. Co. (Extension Tables) C
Hanson Furn. Co. (Dining; Parlor; Library Tables) D

WIS.—Jefferson
Wisconsin Mfg. Co. (Wood; Cane; Veneer Seat Dining Chairs; Wood; Cane; Veneer Cobbler; Upholstered Spring Seat Floor; Swing Rockers) C

WIS.—Juneau
Peters' Furn. Mfg. Co. (Extension; Common; Centre Tables; Bedsteads; Suits; Washstands) C

WIS.—Kenosha
Kenosha Crib Co. (Parlor; Library Tables; Jardiniere Stands; Tabourettes; Cribs; Cradles; Beds) C
Simmons Mfg. Co. (Canvas Cots) ....AAA

WIS.—Kiel
Kiel Mfg. Co. (Dining; Library; Parlor; Kitchen Tables) ....D

WIS.—La Crosse
Hackner, E. (Church Furn.; Altars; Pulpits; Railings; Reading Tables; Pews, etc.; Statues) ....E
Tillman Bros. (Wardrobes; Cupboards; Kitchen Safes) C

WIS.—Marshfield
Upham Mfg. Co. (Bedroom Sets; Sideboards; Chiffoniers; Buffets; French Dressers) ....A

FURNITURE (Con.)

WIS.—Milwaukee

Berger Bedding Co. (Spring Beds) ....A

Bub Co., Jos. (Parlor Furn.; Divans) ....D

Cream City Woven Wire Wks. (Spring Beds; Cots; Cradles; Cribs) ....A

George & Heyer (Parlor Furn.; Couches) ....B

Hennecke Co., C. (Statuary; Busts; Metal Armor, etc.) ....B

Kipp Co., B. A. (Upholstered Furn.) C

Mayhew Mfg. Co. (Fine Upholstered Furn.; Chairs; Rockers; Mission Furn.; Trays; Tables, etc.) C

Meinecke & Son, A. (Willow Veranda Chairs; Settees; Toy Desks; Furn. Novelties in Bamboo; Punjab) A

Milwaukee Chair Co. (Wood Seat Chairs) ....A

Northwestern Furn. Co. (Desks; Office; Store Furn.; Bank Fixtures; Interior Cabinet Woodwork) ....B

Preuss Co., R. J., (Spring Beds; Cots; Cribs) C

Western Hdw. & Mfg. Co. (Brass; Iron Bedsteads) A

Wisconsin Furn. Co. (Extension; Breakfast; Kitchen; Library; Office; Saloon; Parlor Tables) C

Wollaeger Mfg. Co. (Bank; Office Fixtures; Interior Cabinet Work from Special Design) ....A

WIS.—North Milwaukee

Schneider Furn. Co. (Extension Tables) ....E

WIS.—Oshkosh

Banderob-Chase Co. (Suits; Chiffoniers; Dressing Tables) ....B

Buckstaff-Edwards Co., The (Chairs) ....A

Schram & Sons, A. W. (Patent Rockers) C

WIS.—Plymouth

Plymouth Furn. Co. (Chamber Suits; Odd Dressers; Chiffoniers; Sideboards) B

WIS.—Port Washington

Wisconsin Chair Co. (Rockers; Dining Chairs) ....A

WIS.—Racine

Gold Medal Camp Furn. Mfg. Co. (Fold'g Camp Beds; Cots; Chairs; Stools; Tabies; Settees) ....B

WIS.—Sheboygan

Amer. Folding Bed Co. (Folding Beds) ....B

Amer Mfg. Co. (Chairs; Fancy Rockers) ....D

Crocker Chair Co. (Wood; Cane; Leather Seat Chairs) ....AAAA

Dillingham Mfg. Co. (Furn. Specialties) ....B

Frost's Veneer Seating Co. (Built Up Veneered Woods; Depot Seating; Settees; Car Ceilings; Panels) ....A

Mueller Lumber Mfg. Co., H. G. (Centre; Library; Fold'g Tables; Wooden Ware Novelties) C

Northern Furniture Co. (Chamber Suits; Dressers; Chiffoniers; Buffets; Sideboards; Dining Tables; China Closets) ....A

Phoenix Chair Co. (Chairs; Rockers; Lawn Gds.; Children's Cradles) ..AA

Preussler & Sons, R. (Combination Bookcases; Desks) ....D

Richardson Bros. (Chairs) A

Sheboygan Chair Co. (Staple Chairs; Rockers) ......A

Sheboygan Novelty Co. (Book; Combination Cases; Ladies' Desks; Music Cabinets) C

Sheboygan Parlor Furn. Co.

FURNITURE (Con.)

(Couches) ....E

Spratt & Co., Geo. (Dining; Rocking; Cane; Wood Seat; Upholstered Chairs; Rockers; Children's Chairs; Rockers) C

Winter Lumber Co, M. (General Store; Bank; Drug; Jewelry Store; Office Fixtures; Desk; Show Cases; Kitchen Cabinets) ......B

WIS.—South Superior

Webster Mfg. Co. (Chairs) A

WIS.—Stevens Point

Coye Furn. Co., The (Chamber Suits; Sideboards; Buffets; Chiffoniers) ..A

WIS.—Two Rivers

American Cabinet Co., The (Furn. for Dentists; Physicians; Surgeons) AA

Hamilton Mfg. Co. (Office Desks) ....AA

FURNITURE: DENTISTS

ILL.—Chicago

Jessen & Rosberg, 405 W. Kinzie ....D

Kimball Dental Mfg. Co., 44 N. Clark ....E

N. Y.—Middletown

Hamilton Mfg. Co. ....AA

N. Y.—Rochester

Archer Mfg. Co. ....A

Ritter Dental Mfg. Co. ..B

OHIO—Canton

Gould Co., A. P. ....D

FURS

CAL.—San Francisco

Alaska Commercial Co. ....AAAA

Kelly & Liebes ....B

Liebes & Co., H. (Inc.) AAA

North American Commercial Co. ....A

North Pacific Trading & Packing Co. ....B

Sloss & Co., Louis ..AAAA

ILL.—Chicago

Glass, Samuel ....A

North American Transportation & Trading Co. ...B

Ziff & Sugarman C

MICH.—Detroit

Miller & Co., Wm. H. ..A

Schmidt & Co., Carl E. ..AA

Schmidt, Traugolt & Sons (Inc.) ....AA

MINN.—Minneapolis

N. W. Hide & Fur Co. ...C

McMillan Fur & Wool Co. X

MO.—St. Louis

Bry & Bro. Cloak Co. ....A

Hartman Hide & Leather Co. ....A

Landau & Co., A. ....A

Sachs, Isaac ....AA

Singer Bros. ....A

Warner & Co., W. F. ....D

New York City

Asch & Jaeckel ....A

Freystadt & Sons, J. .....B

Gunther's Sons, C. G. AAA

Markowitz, H. ....B

OHIO—Marietta

Strecker Bros. ....A

WASH.—Bellingham

Montague & McHugh ....B

FUSE

CONN.—Simsbury

Ensign, Bickford & Co. (Blasting; Safety) AAAA

ILL.—Aurora

Vindex Electric Co. (Boxes) X

ILL.—Chicago

Aetna Powder Co., Security Bldg. (Electric) ....AA

Amer. Electric Fuse Co., 50 W. Jackson Boul. (Wire) ....A

Electric Appliance Co., 92 W. Van Buren (Wire) B

Harvard Electric Co., 224 S. Clinton (Wire) ....D

FUSE (Con..)

ILL.—Peroia
Acme Railway Signal Mfg.
  Co. (Railway Signal) ..E
IND.—Fort Wayne
Fort Wayne Electric Corpor-
  ation (Boxes) ....AAAA
IND.—Lafayette
Sterling Electric Co. (Wire)
  AA
IND.—Peru
Peru Electric Mfg. Co.
  (Cartridge) ....A
MASS.—Boston
Gilmore Electric Co.
  (Plugs) ....AA
N. J.—Jersey City
Williams & Son, E. A.
  (Wire) ....AA
N. J.—Newark
McIntire Co., C. (Electric
  Wire) ....D
New York City
Climax Fuse Co., 271 Bway.
  (Blasting; Safety; Water-
  proof) ....B
Foote, Pierson & Co., 84
  Fulton (Wire) C
Laflin & Rand Powder Co.,
  99 Cedar X
Macbeth & Co., Jas (Elec-
  tric Platinum) ....D
Metalic Cap Mfg. Co., 271
  Bway. (Blasting) .....A
Rendrock Powder Co.
  (Blasting) ....B
N. Y.—Schenectady
General Electric Co. (Wire)
  AAAA
OHIO—Bucyrus
Columbia Fire Cracker Co.
  (Railway Signal) .....D
OHIO—Cincinnati
King Powder Co. ....AAA
OHIO—Fostoria
Western Railway Signal Co.
  (Railway Signal) .....B
PA.—Allegheny
Granite Railway Signal Co.
  (Railway Signal) .....B
R. I.—Providence
Amer. Electrical Wks.
  (Wire) ....AAAA

FUSTIC

CONN.—Hartford
Beach & Co. (Ground) AAA
New York City
Stamford Mfg. Co., 82
  Wall (Cut; Extract)
  AAAA
Suzarte & Whitney, 18
  State St. (Imp.) ......A

GADDERS

New York City
Ingersoll-Sergeant Drill Co.,
  26 Cortlandt (Air) AAAA
Rand Drill Co., 100 Bway.
  AAAA
VT.—Rutland
Patch Mfg. Co. ....B
Steam Stone Cutter Co. ..A

GALLERIES: RIDING

See Carousels

GALLEYS

ILL.—Chicago
Barnart Bros. & Spindler
  (Printers') ....AA
MICH.—Grand Haven
Challenge Machinery Co.
  (Plate Zinc) ....A
New York City
American Type Founders'
  Co. (Printers') ....AAAA
Hoe & Co., R. (Printers';
  Slice) ....AAAA
Liberty Machine Co. (Print-
  ers') ....E
R. I.—Providence
Hammond Printers Supply
  Co. (Printers' Brass) ..X
WIS.—Two Rivers
Hamilton Mfg. Co. (Print-
  ers') ....AA

GALLOONS

ILL.—Chicago
Phoenix Trimming Co., 577
  Clybourn Av. (Drapery) D
New York City
Bernhard Co., Morris, 35 W.
  19th ....D
Lindental, E. & P., 1648
  Bway. ....D
PA.—Philadelphia
Loeb, Lipper & Co. ......A
Oehrle Bros. & Co., 245 N.
  3d ....B

GALVANO-METERS

ILL.—Chicago
Western Electric Co., 259 S.
  Clinton (& Bridges) AAAA
MASS.—Boston
Gleeson, Thos. W., 106 Sud-
  bury (& Bridges) .....F
N. H.—Penacook
Whitney Electrical Instru-
  ment Co. (& Bridges) ..D
N. J.—Newark
Western Electrical Instru-
  ment Co. ....A
New York City
Bunnell & Co., J. H., 20
  Park Pl. (& Bridges) ..B
Foote, Pierson & Co., 82
  Fulton (& Bridges) C
Manufacturers & Inventors
  Electric Co., 84 Nassau (&
  Bridges) X
Pearce, Frederick, 18 Rose
  (& Bridges) ....B
Willyoung & Gibson Co., 11
  Frankfort (& Bridges) X
N. Y.—Schenectady
General Electric Co. AAAA
PA.—Philadelphia
Biddle, Jas. G., Stephen Gi-
  rard Bldg. (& Bridges) C
Keystone Electrical Instru-
  ment Co. ....E
Partrick, Carter & Wilkins E
Queen & Co. (Inc.) 1010
  Chesnut (& Bridges) A₄

GAMBOGE

New York City
Hopkins & Co., J. L., 100
  William ....A

GAMES

See also Boards

CONN.—Bridgeport
Ives Mfg. Co. (Parlor;
  Amusement) C
CONN.—New Haven
New Haven Toy & Game
  Co. ....D
ILL.—Chicago
Ball & Bro., A. (Poker
  Chips; Dice) ....AA
Continental Mfg. Co.
  (Croquet) ....AA
Mikkelsen, Edw., No. Jeff
  (Combination   G a m e
  Board) ....D
IND.—South Bend
South Bend Toy Mfg. Co.
  (Croquet) ....AA
MAINE—Dixfield
Stowell & Co., N. S.
  (Checkers) ....F
MAINE—Portland
Burrowes Co., E. T. (Port-
  able; Folding Billiard;
  Pool; Card Tables) ...A
MASS.—Charlemont
Frary Mfg. Co. (Checkers) E
MASS.—Leominster
Whitney Reed Chair Co.
  (Parlor; Amusement)
  AAAA
MASS.—Lowell
Merrimack Croquet Mfg. Co.
  (Croquet) ....B
MASS.—Salem
Parker Bros. (Children's;
  Parlor) ....A
MASS.—Springfield
Bradley Co., Milton (Check-
  ers; Chessmen) ....A
MICH.—Grand Rapids
Pademaker & Sons, H. (Cro-

GAMES (Con.) ..

quet) ....E

N. J.—Jersey City

Redgrave. M. (Parlor) ..D

N. J.—Newark

Celluloid Co. (Poker Chips;
Dice; Chessmen) .....B

N. Y.—Albany

Embossing Co. (Checkers;
Dominoes) ....B

New York City

Baumann, A. O., 112 University Pl. (Checkers) ....D

Estes & Sons, E. B., 45
John (Checkers) .....AA

Grote & Co., F., 14 E. 14th
(Ivory Checkers; Poker
Chips; Dice; Dominoes;
Chessmen) ....D

Horsman Co., E. I. (Parlor;
Amusement) C

McLoughlin Bros. (Parlor;
Amusement; Checkers)
...................AAA

New York Consolidated Card
Co., 6 W. 14th (Poker
Chips) ....B

Selchow & Richter (Parlor;
Amusement) ....AA

Spaulding & Bros., A. G.
(Croquet) ....AAAA

N. Y.—Seneca Falls

Westcott-Jewell Co. (Dominoes) ....D

OHIO—Columbus

Sun Mfg. Co. (Croquet) A

PA.—Scranton

Scranton Button Co. (Checkers; Poker Chips) ......A

R. I.—Pawtucket

Bliss Mfg. Co., R. (Croquet)
.................AAAA

VT.—Putney

Stowell & Co. (Croquet) D

WIS.—Casco

Casco Novelty Co. C

GANNISTER

PA.—Philadelphia

Paxson Co., J. W. (Ground)
...................AA

PA.—Pittsburg

Stuart Fire Brick Co.
(Ground) ....B

GARMENTS

See Clothing

GARNETS

See Jewelry

GARTERS

Suspenders, Garters, etc.

GARANTOSE

ILL.—Chicago

Fuller & Fuller ....AA

GAS

CAL.—San Francisco

Western Carbonic Acid Gas
Co. (Carbonic Acid) ..B

ILL.—Chicago

Chicago Oxygen Gas Co.
(Oxygen) ....E

MASS.—Chelsea

Hecla Compressed Gas Co.
(Liquefied) ....E

N. Y.—Buffalo

Buffalo Dental Mfg. Co.
(Nitrous Oxide) .....B

National Carbonic Gas Co.
(Carbonic Acid) C

New York City

American Carbonate Co., 430
E. 19th (Carbonic Acid).A

Murray Oxygen Co., 1345
Bway. (Oxygen) .....B

Walton Oxygen Works
(Oxygen) X

PA.—Philadelphia

Ross, Edw. K., 2402 N. 15th
(Nitrous Oxide) ....G

White Dental Mfg. Co., S. S.
Oxygen for Medical and
Chemical work and Calcium Light; also Nitrous
Oxide for Anaesthesia,

GAS (Con.)

and Oxygen and Nitrous
Oxide combined.) Branches at New York; Chicago;
Boston and Atlanta.

PA.—Pittsburg

National Liquid Gas Co.
(Liquefied) ....B

GASKETS

CONN.—Bridgeport

Canfield Co., H. O. (Rubber
Boiler) ....B

Hartford Rubber Wks. Co.
(Rubber) ....AAAA

DEL.—Wilmington

Amer. Vulcanized Fibre Co.
.................AAAA

Delaware Hard Fibre Co.
(Oil Proof) ....A

ILL.—Chicago

Guillot Metal Casket Co., 84
Market (Metal) ....D

Morgan & Wright (Inc.)
333 W. Lake (Rubber) AA

MD.—Baltimore

Patterson Regulator Co., 14
W. Barre (Metal) X

MASS.—Boston

Boston Belting Co. (Rubber)
.................AAAA

Chadwick-Boston Lead Wks.
(Metal) ....AAA

Revere Rubber Co., 63
Franklin (Rubber) AAAA

MASS.—Cambridge

Boston Woven Hose & Rubber Co. (Rubber) AAAA

MASS.—Taunton

Taunton Locomotive Mfg.
Co. (Corrugated Copper) A

MICH.—Battle Creek

Sherman Mfg. Co., H. B.
(Rubber) ....A

MO.—St. Louis

Hazzard Machinery Co., A.
B. (Lead) X

N. J.—Jersey City

New Jersey Car Spring &
Rubber Co. (Rubber) AA

Smooth-on Mfg. Co. (Iron) B

Voorhees Rubber Mfg. Co. A

N. J.—Milltown

International Automobile &
Vehicle Tire Co. (Rubber)
....................B

N. J.—Trenton

Crescent Belting & Packing Co. ....A

Empire Rubber Mfg. Co.
(Rubber) ....AA

Hamilton Rubber Mfg. Co. A

Home Rubber Co. (Rubber)
...................AA

Mercer Rubber Co. (Rubber)
...................A

Stokes Rubber Co., Jos. ..A

Trenton Rubber Mfg. Co.
(Rubber) ....A

United & Globe Rubber Mfg.
Co. ....AAA

New York City

Brandt, Randolph, 38 Cortlandt (Triple Expansion
for Boiler Wks.) ......E

Common Sense Metallic
Packing Co. ....D

Goodyear Rubber Co. (Rubber) ....AAAA

Gutta Percha & Rubber Co.,
126 Duane (Rubber)
.................AAAA

Hodgman Rubber Co., 806
Bway. ....AA

Jenkins Bros. ....A

Kinsman Electric & Railway Supply Co. (Copper)E

Johns-Manville Co., H. W.
(Asbestos) ....AAAA

McCord & Co., 101 Bway.
(Rubber encased in Copper) ....B

Manhattan Rubber Mfg. Co.,
18 Vesey ....AA

Mineralized Rubber Co., 18
Cliff ....A

New York Belting & Packing Co., (Ltd.) 25 Park Pl.
(Rubber) ....AAA

New York Rubber Co., 84
Reade (Rubber) .....AA

Peerless Rubber Co., 16
Warren (Rubber) ....AA

GASKETS (Con.)

Pulver & Sons, Peter, 214
Franklin ....D
U. S. Mineral Wool Co., 143
Liberty (Corrugated Copper; Asbestos) ....D
Waterbury Rubber Mfg. Co.,
49 Warren (Rubber) ...D
N. Y.—Palmyra
Garlock Packing Co. ...AA
OHIO—Akron
Diamond Rubber Co. AAAA
Goodrich Co., B. F. AAAA
Whitman & Barnes Mfg. Co.
AAAA
OHIO—Cincinnati
Van Duzen Co., E. W.
(Lead) ....B
OHIO—Cleveland
Mechanical Rubber Co.
(Rubber) ....AAAA
OHIO—Youngstown
Republic Rubber Co. (Rubber) ....AA
PA.—Erie
Watson Co., H. F. ....AAA
R. I.—Bristol
National India Rubber Co.
AAAA
WIS.—Milwaukee
Windsor Mfg. Co., 570 Clinton ....B

GASOLINE

CAL.—San Francisco
Pacific Coast Oil Co. AAAA
New York City
Standard Oil Co. ....AAAA
PA.—Bradford
Emery Mfg. Co. ....AAAA
PA.—Freedom
Freedom Oil Wks. Co. ....A
PA.—Philadelphia
Atlantic Refining Co. AAAA
Crew-Levick Co., 113 Arch
AAA

GATES

See also Valves
ALA.—Birmingham
Dimmick Pipe Co. (Sluice)
AA
CAL.—San Francisco
California Artistic Metal &
Wire Co., 539 Mission
(Folding) ....D
Pelton Water Wheel Co.
(Sluice) ....AA
CONN.—Georgetown
Gilbert & Bennett Mfg. Co.
(Automatic; Wire) ..AAA
CONN.—Hartford
Stirling Blower & Pipe Mfg.
Co. (Blast) ....A
CONN.—Meriden
Bradley & Hubbard Mfg. Co.
(Bronze; Ornamental Iron)
AAAA
Parker Co., Chas. (Oil;
Molasses) ....AAA
GA.—Atlanta
Atlanta Wire & Iron Wks.
Co., 64 N. Broad (Ornamental Iron) ....F
ILL.—Chicago
Allis-Chalmers Co.. Home
Ins. Bldg. (Ore Bin)
AAAA
Barbee Wire & Iron Wks.
(Drive; Folding; Iron;
Lawn; Walk; Wire; Ornamental; Cemetery; Cemetery Vault; Netting) ..B
Booth, Jno., 114 Lake (Ornamental Iron) ....B
Braumoeller & Son, Henry
(Iron) ....B
Chicago Ornamental Iron Co.
37th & Stewart Av. (Ornamental Iron) ....A
Expander Metal Fire Proofing Co. (Farm) ....A
Garden City Fan Co. (Blast)
B
Globe Iron Wks. (Iron) ..B
Hickey Wire & Iron Wks.,
M. H., 54 Dearborn (Ornamental Iron) ....B
Pneumatic Gate Co., 149 E.
Huron (Railway Crossing)
D
Smith Wire & Iron Wks., F.
P., 100 Lake (Ornamental

GATES (Con.)

Iron) ....AA
Vulcan Iron Wks., 63 Milwaukee Av. (Sluice) .AA
Winslow Bros. Co., 368 Carroll Av. (Bronze; Ornamental Iron) ....AA
ILL.—De Kalb
De Kalb Fence Co. (Drive;
Walk; Farm) ....AA
Union Fence Co. (Drive;
Walk) ....B
ILL.—Harvey
Buda Foundry & Mfg. Co.
(Railway Crossing) ..AA
ILL.—Joliet
Adams Sled & Wire Wks.
(Cemetery) ....D
ILL.—Quincy
Quincy Elevator Gate Co.
(Elevator) ....D
IND.—Connorsville
Connorsville Blower Co.
(Blast) ....A
IND.—Evansville
Grote Mfg. Co. (Ornamental
Iron; Park; Cemetery,
etc.) ....D
IND.—Indianapolis
Over, Ewald (Automatic) C
IND.—Kokomo
Kokomo Fence Machine Co.
(Farm; Ornamental Wire;
Yard) ....AAA
IND.—Richmond
Richmond Safety Gate Co.
(Automatic; Elevator) C
IOWA—Cedar Falls
Iowa Gate Co. (Railway) D
MASS.—Boston
Coffin Valve Co. (Sluice;
Sewer; Water Work) ..D
Sturtevant Co., B. F.
(Blast) ....AAA
MASS.—Indian Orchard
Chapman Valve Mfg. Co.
(Sluice; Gas; Water
Work) ....AAA
MASS.—Salem
Salem Elevator Wks.
(Safety Elevator) ......B
MASS.—Springfield
Springfield Foundry Co.
(Molasses; Oil) ....A
MASS.—Woburn
Smith & Wallace (Car) ...X
MASS.—Worcester
Wright Wire Co. (Wire) AA
MICH.—Adrian
Page Woven Wire Fence Co.
(Farm) ....A
MICH.—Birmingham
Wilson Railway Gate Co.
(Railway Crossing) ....F
MICH.—Detroit
Amer. Blower Co. (Blast) AA
Barnum Wire & Iron Wks.
(Ornamental Iron) ....B
Vulcan Co. (Ornamental
Iron) ....F
MICH.—Holly
Cyclone Woven Wire Fence
Co. (Farm) C
MICH.—Saginaw
Wickes Bros. (Blast) AAA
MO.—Kansas City
Kansas City Wire & Iron
Wks. (Wire) ....A
Kleeman, Trotter & Co.,
1327 Main (Ornamental
Iron) ....D
MO.—St. Louis
Brownell Co., 2300 N. Bway.
(Car) ....AAA
Koken Iron Wks., Koken
Bldg. (Ornamental Iron) B
Ludlow-Taylor Wire Co.
(Extension) ....AA
Union Iron & Foundry Co.,
1458 S. 2nd. (Ornamental
Iron) ....A
N. J.—Boonton
Lincoln Iron Wks. (Iron) B
N. J.—Jersey City
Snead & Co. Iron Wks.
(Bronze; Ornamental Iron)
A
N. Y.—Brooklyn
Ajax Iron & Wire Co., 75
York (Ornamental Iron) F
Hecla Iron Wks., N. 11th &
Berry (Bronze; Ornamental Iron; Wrought Iron)
AA

GATES (*Con.*)
N. Y.—Buffalo
Buffalo Forge Co. (Blast)
............................AAA
N. Y.—Cortland
Cortland Carriage Goods Co.
(Vehicle End) ....A
N. Y.—Horseheads
Weller Hardware & Foundry Co. (Molasses) ...D
N. Y.—Manlius
Cheney & Son, S. (Molasses)
............................A
Scoville, E. U. (Oil) C
N. Y.—Newburgh
Coldwell-Wilcox Co. (Sluice;
Pivot) ....B
New York City
Anderson, Henry C., 414
Bleecker (Folding) ....E
Barr Co., Edward (Water
Work) X
Bataille, Achille & Co., 587
Hudson (Folding) .....E
Cabaret, Paul E., 342 W.
14th (Bronze) ....D
Carpenter Co., F. E., 7-9
Warren (Ornamental Iron)
............................F
Cornell Co., J. B. & J. M.
26th & 11th Av. (Ornamental Iron; Farm) ....AA
Dewitt Wire Cloth Co.
(Wire) ....A
Diamond, Thos. (Folding;
Iron; Iron Stoop) .....A
Estey Wire Wks. Co., 59
Fulton (Extension) ....D
Fiske Iron Wks., J. W.
(Iron; Wire; Wrought
Iron) ....B
Fox & Co., Jno., 253 Bway.
(Sluice) ....B
Jackson Co., Wm. H., 29 E.
17th (Union Sq.) (Bronze;
Driveway; Entrance; Ornamental Iron) ....A
Kennedy Valve Mfg. Co., 57
Beekman (Sluice) ..AAA
Koehn, Alfred, 159 W. 29th
(Ornamental Iron) ....E
Manhattan Brass Co., 334 E.
28th (Bronze) ....A
Mott Iron Wks., J. L., 84
Beekman (Bronze; Ornamental Iron) ....AA
Pitt Composite Iron Wks.,
Wm. R., 111 5th Av.
(Bridge; Bronze; Car;
Driveway; Entrance; Patent Folding Ferryboat; Ornamental Iron; Folding
Elevator) ....D
Prince Iron Wks., 553 W.
33d (Ornamental Iron) C
Sargent & Co., 151 Leonard
(Oil; Molasses) ....AAAA
Union Equipment & Bronze
Co., 514 W. 36th (Bronze)
............................D
Williams, Jno., 556 W. 27th
(Iron) ....D
N. Y.—Syracuse
Stearns & Co., E. C. (Oil;
Molasses) ....AA
N. Y.—Troy
Ludlow Valve Mfg. Co.
(Sluice; Water Wk.) AAA
N. Y.—Warsaw
Warsaw Elevator Co. (Automatic Hatch) ....B
N. Y.—Waterford
Eddy Valve Co. (Sluice;
Water Work) ....AA
OHIO—Cincinnati
Bourbon Copper & Brass
Wks., 618 E. Front
(Sluice) ....A
Obermayer Co., S. (Blast)
............................AAA
Schreiber & Sons Co., L., 8th
& Eggleston Av. (Bronze;
Folding; Ornamental Iron)
............................AA
Stewart Iron Wks., 714 E.
3rd (Folding; Ornamental
Iron) ....A
OHIO—Cleveland
Taylor & Boggis Foundry Co.
(Molasses; Oil) .....AA
Tyler & Co., W. S., 1150 St.
Clair (Bronze; Ornamental
Iron) ....AAAA
Van Dorn Iron Wks. Co.

GATES (*Con.*)
(Ornamental Iron) ....AA
OHIO—Columbus
International Fence & Fire
Proofing Co., Buttles Av.
(Automatic Drive; Farm)
............................A
OHIO—Hamilton
Meyers Mfg. Co., Fred. J.
(Wrought Iron) ....B
OHIO—Kenton
Champion Iron Co. (Driveway; Entrance; Ornamental Iron) ....AA
OHIO—Middletown
Fetzer & Co. (Self Opening)
............................AAAA
OHIO—Springfield
Rogers Iron Co. (Ornamental Iron) ....B
Webster & Perks Tool Co.
(Safety Elevator) C
OHIO—Toledo
Donovan Wire & Iron Co.
(Electric; Cable Car;
Safety Elevator) C
PA.—Elwood City
Glen Mfg. Co. (Cemetery) C
PA.—New Castle
Vogan Bros. Mfg. Co. (Car)
............................B
PA.—Philadelphia
Brill Co., J. G., 62d & Woodland Av. (Car) .....AAA
Creswell Iron Wks., Samuel
J., 23d & Cherry (Ornamental Iron) ....B
Energy Elevator Co., 408
Cherry (Safety Elevator)D
Enterprise Mfg. Co., 3d &
Dauphin (Molasses; Oil)
............................AAAA
Eynon-Evans Mfg. Co.
(Blast) ....A
Gaumer & Co., Jno. L., 19th
& Hamilton (Bronze; Ornamental Iron) C
Merritt & Co., 1024 Ridge
Av. (Folding; Ornamental
Iron) ....B
North Bros. Mfg. Co. (Oil;
Molasses) ....AA
Paxson Co., J. W. (Blast)
............................AA
Wayne Iron Wks., (Inc.)
Arcade Bldg. (Ornamental
Iron) ....B
Wood & Co., R. D., 400
Chestnut (Sluice) AAAA
PA.—Pittsburg
Phoenix Steel Construction
Co., 3d & Penn Av.
(Bronze; Ornamental Iron)
............................D
Taylor & Dean, 205 Market
(Ornamental Iron) ....B
Vilsack Co., Martin (Ornamental Iron) ....E
PA.—Reading
Remppis Co., Wm. F. (Entrance; Driveway; Ornamental Iron) ....B
R. I.—Pawtucket
Bliss Mfg. Co., R. (Car;
Wood) ....AAA
VA.—Lynchburg
Glamorgan Pipe & Foundry Co. (Sluice) ....AAA
WIS.—Cudahy
Power & Mining Machinery
Co. (Ore Bin) ....AAA
WIS.—Milwaukee
Bayley & Sons Co., Wm.,
732 Greenbush (Blast) ..X
National Blower Wks.
(Blast) ....A
WIS.—Racine
Racine General Mfg. Co.
(Yard) ....E

GAUGES

See also Micrometers

CONN.—Bridgeport
Belknap Mfg. Co. (Tank) C
CONN.—Hartford
Billings & Spencer Co.,
(Pocket, etc.; Caliper;
Scratch without Screw Attachment; Snap; Universal Screw Cutting; Combination; Depth; Marking)
............................AA

GAUGES (Con.)

Pratt & Cady Co., 556 Capitol Av. (Water Pressure Self-Closing) .....AAA

Pratt & Whitney Co. (Caliper; Car Wheel, Circumference; Limit; Plug & Ring; Screw Pitch; Sheet Metal; Snap; Thread; Universal Screw Cutting Decimal Sheet Metal; Master Car Builders) .....AAAA

CONN.—New Britain

Stanley Rule & Level Co. (Carpenters'; Marking; & Squares Combined; Butt; Rabbett; Chisel; Clapboard) ....AAA

CONN.—New Haven

Hoggson & Pettis Mfg. Co. (Surface) ....A

Kilborn & Bishop Co., 81 Lloyd (Forged Saw) ...C

CONN.—Pine Meadows

Chapin-Stephens Co. (Carpenters'; Marking; Butt; Rabbett; Combination) A

CONN.—Rockfall

Smith, O. A. (Marking) B

CONN.—Southington

Peck, Stow & Wilcox Co. (Wire; Clapboard) AAAA

CONN.—Tolland

Clough, R. M. (Plug; Ring) D

CONN.—Waterbury

Bristol Co. (Compression; Recording Pressure; Recording Tide; Water Pressure; Self-Closing) D

Standard Electric Time Co. (Electric) ....D

CONN.—Winsted

Winsted Edge Tool Wks. (Carpenters') ....B

ILL.—Chicago

Baird Mfg. Co. (Battery) C

Crane Co. (Steam; Water Pressure; Self-Closing; Hydraulic) .....AAAA

Fairbanks, Morse & Co., Franklin & Monroe (Circular Radial, etc. Track) AAAA

Lovejoy, T. H., 90 Ohio (Track) ....D

Marsh & Co., Jas. P., 224 Washington (Steam; Electric; Ammonia; Illuminated; Test; Compound Pressure; Hydraulic; Vacuum) ....B

Pelouze Scale & Mfg. Co. (Hem) C

Scott Valve Co., 32 W. Randolph (Water Pressure Self-Closing) ....D

Star Brass Wks., 67 S. Canal (Syrup) ....F

Weiskopf, A. (Vacuum) E

Western Valve Co., 43 W. Randolph (Water Pressure Self-Closing) ....B

ILL.—Harvey

Buda Fdry. & Mfg. Co. (Tie Plate; Track) ....AA

ILL.—Waukegan

Thomas Brass & Iron Co. (Water Pressure Self-Closing) ....A

IND.—Indianapolis

Atkins Co., E. C. (Saw; Standard Size; Dimension) AAAA

MASS.—Athol

Athol Machine Co. (Caliper Open-Face; Screw Pitch; Surfaces; Universal Screw Cutting; Centre; Depth; Pocket Center) ....B

Richardson-Oliver Co. (Scratch) ....E

Starrett Co., L. S. (Caliper; Micrometer; S c r a t c;h; Screw; Pitch; Surface; Thread; Universal Screw Cutting; Wire; Circumference; Centre; Depth; Drill) ....A

MASS.—Boston

Amer. Steam Gauge & Valve Mfg. Co., 195 High (Recording Pressure; Steam; Water Pressure, Self-Clos-

ing; Combination; High Pressure, Alarm; Locomotive; Mercurial Pressure; Ammonia; Test; Thermo m e t e r; Hydraulic; Pump; Vacuum; Draft; Mercury) ....AA

Ashton Valve Co., 271 Franklin (Compression; Recording Pressure; Steam; Water Pressure; Self-Closing; Air Brake; Back Pressure; Locomotive; Ammonia; Compound; Test; Hydraulic; Vacuum) ......A

Boston Gear Wks. (Gear Tooth) ....E

Brainerd Steam Trap Co., Chamb. of Commerce (Gas Pressure; Mercurial Air Pressure) ....H

Crosby Steam Gauge & Valve Co., 95 Oliver (Gas; Recording Pressure; Water Pressure, Self-Closing; Steam; Air Brake; Back Pressure; Combination; Locomotive; Ammonia; Ordnance; Test; Gas Pressure; Hydraulic; Chemical; Brewers'; Vacuum) ....AA

Jones Gauge Co., 5 Broad (Recording Pressure) ..H

Star Brass Mfg. Co., 103 E. Dedham (Steam; Water Pressure, Self-Closing; Back Pressure; Combination; Indicating; Locomotive; Mercurial Pressure; Recording; Time Recording; High Pressure Alarm; Automatic Water Pressure; Vacuum) ....A

Sturtevant Co., B. F., 34 Oliver (Testing, Fan Pressure) ....AAA

Welch & Co., T. F., 65 Sudbury (Scratch) ....D

MASS.—East Boston

Wyke & Co., Jno., 898 Saratoga (Keyseat or Shipping; Combination Surface; Universal Screw Cutting) D

MASS.—Chicopee Falls

Stevens Arms & Tool Co., J. (Scratch; Surface; Universal Screw Cutting) AAA

MASS.—Fitchburg

Sawyer Tool Mfg. Co. (Surface; Planer; Scratch; Screw; Pitch; Thread; Graduated Universal Screw Cutting; Center; Depth) C

MASS.—Greenfield

Goodell-Pratt Co. (Planer; Combination; Marking) B

Massachusetts Tool Co. (Surface) C

Wells Bros. Co. (Bolt; Pipe) A

MASS.—New Bedford

Morse Twist Drill & Machine Co. (Caliper; Plug; Ring; Universal Screw Cutting; Worm Thread Tool; Drill) ....AAA

MASS.—Shelburne Falls

Mayhew Co., H. H. (& Squares Combined) ....D

MASS.—Springfield

Bemis & Call Hdw. & Tool Co. (Marking) ....A

Bullock & Co., O. W. (Chamferer) ....A

MASS.—Worcester

Union Water Meter Co. (Reservoir) ....B

Wright Wire Co. (Wire) AA

MICH.—Detroit

Buhl Stamping Co. (Gas Pressure) ....AA

Byram & Co. (Blast) ....D

McRae & Robberts Co., 227 Campbell Av. (Water Pressure Self-Closing) ..A

Michigan Lubricator Co. (Water Pressure Self-Closing) ....A

Penberthy Injector Co., 346 Holden Av. (Water Press-

GAUGES (Con.)

ure Self-Closing) ......A
Wright Mfg. Co., 57 W.
Woodbridge (Water Pressure Self-Closing) ......B

MICH.—Kalamazoo
Kalamazoo Railway Supply
Co. (Track) ....B

MICH.—Saginaw
Lufkin Rule Co. (Lumber)
........................AA

MICH.—Three Rivers
Sheffield Car Co. (Track)AA

MO.—St. Louis
Handlan-Buck Mfg. Co., 212
N. 3rd (Track) ......AA

N. J.—Calstadt
Vulcan Hdw. Co. (Wire) C

N. J.—Elizabeth
Braunsdorf-Mueller Co.
(Bit) ....D

N. J.—Gloucester City
Rogers Boat Gauge & Drill
Wks., Jno. M. (Caliper;
Limit; Cylindrical; Surface; Metric) ....A

N. J.—Newark
Gould & Eberhardt (Depth;
Gear Tooth) ....A
Seymour & Whitlock, 43
Lawrence (Saw) ....B

N. J.—Paterson
Trautvetter Bros. (Recording Pressure) ....G

N. J.—Smithville
Smith Machine Co., H. B.
(Saw) ....A

N. J.—Vineland
Gage Tool Co. (Carpenters';
Wheel) ....A

N. Y.—Albany
McDonald & Co., D. (High
Pressure Alarm; Gas
Pressure; Pocket Pressure) ....A

N. Y.—Brooklyn
Schaffer & Budenberg Mfg.
Co., 10 Division (Compression; Recording Pressure;
Steam; Water Pressure
Self-Closing; Test; Vacuum) ....D
Williams & Co., J. H.
(Caliper) ....AA

N. Y.—Buffalo
Sherwood Mfg. Co. 34
Washington (Water Pressure Self-Closing) ......B

N. Y.—Elmira
Swift Lubricator Co. (Water
Pressure Self-Closing)) B

N. Y.—Frankfort
Utica Steam Gauge Co.
(Steam) X

New York City
Ashcroft Mfg. Co., 85 Liberty (Recording Pressure;
Steam; Water Pressure
Self-Closing; Back Pressure; Locomotive; Test;
Vacuum) ....A
Bushnell Co., Jno. S. 120
Liberty (Recording Pressure) ....E
Etna Mfg. Co., 253 Bway.
(Drill) ....D
Fairbanks Co., 186 Elm
(Water Pressure Self-Closing) ....AAAA
Fox Bros. & Co., 24 Vesey
(Track) ....A
Hammacher, Schlemmer &
Co., 209 Bowery (Caliper;
Marking; Scratch; Screw
Pitch; Surface; Universal
Screw Cutting; Wire)AAA
Hoe & Co., R., 504 Grand
(Saw) ....AAAA
Koppel, Arthur, 68 Broad
(Track) ....A
Leavitt & Co., C. W., 15
Cortlandt (Track) ......D
McCoy Co., Jos., 157 Chambers (Track) ....B
McNab & Harlin Mfg. Co.,
56 John (Water Pressure
Self-Closing) ......AAA
Manhattan Electrical Supply
Co., 32 Cortlandt (Wireman's Calculating) ....AA
Millers Falls Co., 28 Warren
(Bit; Jointer) ....AA
Nelson, Charles, 439 E. 10th
(Water Pressure Self-Closing) ....D

GAUGES (Con.)

Tower & Lyon Co., 95 Chambers (Butt; Rabbett) ..B
Watson-Stillman Co. (Hydraulic) ....A

N. Y.—Rochester
Caldwell Mfg. Co., 8 Jones
(Carpenters') C
Taylor Bros. Co. (Rain; Hydraulic; Vacuum) ....AA

N. Y.—Syracuse
Standard Gauge Mfg. Co.
(Compression; Recording
Pressure; Steam; Water
Pressure Self-Closing) ..B

OHIO—Cincinnati
Cinn. Tool Co. Norwood
(Bit; Universal Screw
Cutting) ....A
Lunkenheimer Co., Beekman
& Waverly (Compression;
Dynamo; Motor Oil;
Recording Pressure;
Steam; Water Pressure
Self-Closing) ....AA
McGowan Co., Jno. H., 44
Central Av. (Water Pressure; Self-Closing) ....A
Powell Co., Wm., 2525
Spring Grove Av. (Water
Pressure Self-Closing) ..A
Queen City Brass & Iron
Wks. (Water Pressure
Self-Closing) ....B
Tatum Co., Saml. C.
(Bit) ....B
Vanduzen Co., E. W., 428
E. 2nd (Water Pressure
Self-Closing) ....B

OHIO—Cleveland
Cleveland Steam Gauge Co.,
106 Merwin (Recording
Pressure; Steam; Water
Pressure Self-Closing)...C
Cleveland Twist Drill Co.,
cor. Lake & Kirtland
(Snap; Universal Screw
Cutting; Drill) ....A
Farnan Brass Wks., 25
Center (Water Pressure
Self-Closing Safety) ....A
Reliance Gauge Column Co.,
76 E. Prospect (Reliance
Lever; Water Pressure
Quick-Closing) ....D
Standard Tool Co. (Universal Screw Cutting) ...AA

OHIO—Columbus
Ohio Tool Co. (Carpenters';
Marking) ....AA

OHIO—Dayton
Buckeye Iron & Brass Wks.
(Water Pressure Self-Closing) ....AA

OHIO—Mansfield
Ohio Brass Co. (Water Pressure Self-Closing) ....AA

OHIO—Mt. Gilead
Hydraulic Press Mfg. Co.
(Barrel) ....A

OHIO—Sandusky
Sandusky Tool Co. (Carpenters'; Marking) ....A

PA.—Columbia
Smith, E. H. (Caliper; Micrometer; Screw Pitch;
Universal Screw Cutting)
........................E

PA.—Eldred
Prouty & Co., C. (Saw) ..B

PA.—Erie
Jarecki Mfg. Co. (Water
Pressure Self-Closing)..
....................AAAA

PA.—Harrisburg
Hickok Mfg. Co., W. O.
(Case) ....AA

PA.—Montrose
Beach H. W. (Saw) ......D

PA.—Philadelphia
Atlantic Wks. (Inc.), 23rd
& Arch (Saw) ....B
Belfield & Co., H., 435 N.
Broad (Steam; Water
Pressure Self-Closing).AA
Brown, Edward (Mercury)
........................B
Disston & Sons (Inc.),
Henry (Carpenters';
Marking; Saw; Universal
Screw Cutting; Wire;
Combination) ....AAAA
Huyette, Paul B., Betz
Bldg. (Water Pressure

GAUGES (Con.)
Quick-Closing) ....E
Olsen & Co., Tinius
(Hydraulic) ....A
Paxson Co., J. W. (Blast)
.....................AA
Pedrick & Ayer (Adjusta-
ble Shrinking) ....A
Quimby Engineering Co.,
911 Ridge Av. (Recording
Pressure; Steam) .....F
PA.—Pittsburg
Kelly & Jones Co., 135
Water (Water Pressure
Self-Closing) ....AA
Mansfield Mfg. Co., 57 1st
Av. (Water Pressure Self-
Closing) X
Pittsburg Gauge & Supply
Co. (Water Pressure Self-
Closing) ....A
Verona Tool Wks., Murt-
land Bldg. (Track).....A
PA.—Scranton
Everhart Brass Wks.
(Safety) ....A
PA.—Susquehanna
Curran, F. (Wheel) .....F
PA.—Williamsport
United States Machine Co.
(Saw) ....D
R. I.—Providence
Brown & Sharp Mfg. Co.
(Caliper; Cylindrical;
Limit; Micrometer; Plug;
Ring; Rolling Mill;
Screw Pitch; Sheet Metal;
Thread; Universal Screw
Cutting; Wire; Worm
Thread Tool; Centre; Cor-
rective; Precision; Stand-
ard Size; Surface; Depth;
Drill; Gear Tooth; Metric)
.....................AAAA
Slocomb & Co., J. T. (Cali-
per; Micrometer; Uni-
versal Screw Cutting;
Depth) ....D
WIS.—Milwaukee
Filer & Stowell Co. (Lum-
ber; Timber) ......AAA

GAUNTLETS

See Gloves & Mittens

GAUZE:
SURGICAL

MASS.—Griswoldville
Griswoldville Mfg. Co.
(Hospital) ....A
MASS.—Walpole
Lewis Batting Co. (Ab-
sorbent) ....B
N. J.—New Brunswick
Johnson & Johnson (Anti-
septic) ....A
New York City
Seabury & Johnson (Anti-
septic; Absorbent)..AAAA
PA.—Conshohocken
Lee Co., J. Ellwood (Anti-
septic) ....AA

GAVELS

MASS.—Boston
Boston Regalia Co., 7 Tem-
ple Pl. (Military) ....F
New York City
Baumann, A. O., 112 Uni-
versity Pl. (Ivory) ....D
Estes & Son, E. B., 45
John ....AA
Grote & Co., F. ....E
Shardlow, Joseph, 116 Ful-
ton (Iron; Wood) .....D
N. Y.—Stony Brook
Stossel, Carl ....F

GEARS

**See also Woodwork; Car-
riage; also Hardware;
Carriage**

CAL.—San Francisco
Pacific Gear & Tool Wks.
(Spur; Worm) ....A
Union Iron Works (Steer-
ing) X

GEARS (Con.)
CONN.—Ansonia
Farrell Fdry. & Mach. Co.
(Machine Molded; Cast)..
.....................AAAA
CONN.—Derby
Birmingham Iron Fdry.
(Machine Molded; Cast)
.......................A
CONN.—Middlefield
Lyman Gunsight Corpora-
tion (Rowing) C
CONN.—New Haven
Reeves Mfg. Co. (Spur)..C
CONN.—Waterbury
Waterbury, Farrell Fdry. &
Cach. Co. ....AA
GA.—Atlanta
De Loach Mill & Mfg. Co.
(Mill) ....B
ILL.—Chicago
Allis-Chalmers Co. ..AAAA
Borden & Selleck Co. ....B
Caldwell & Son, H. W.,
17th & Western Av. (Ma-
chine Moulded; Worm;
Cast) ....A
Chicago Rawhide Mfg. Co.
75 E. Ohio (Rawhide; &
Pinions; Rawhide Electric
Railway) ....A
Dodge Mfg. Co., 168 S.
Clinton ....AAA
Ganschow, Wm., 35 S. Ca-
nal (Cut; Internal;
Worm) ....D
Hardinge Bros., 1036 Lin-
coln Av. (Cut) ....B
Kaestner & Co. (Inc.), 241
S. Jefferson ....A
Link Belt Mchry. Co., 39th
& Stewart Av. (Equaliz-
ing) ....A
McGuire-Cummings Mfg. Co.
(Street Car; Running)AA
Plamondon Mfg. Co., A., 59
S. Clinton (Machine
Moulded) ....A
Redington Co., F. B., 35 W.
Monroe (Cut) ....D
Stilwell-Bierce & Smith-
Vaile Co., 311 Dearborn
(Cast; Mortise) ...AAAA
ILL.—Edwardsville
Bignall Keeler Mfg. Co...B
ILL.—Litchfield
Litchfield Fdry. & Mach.
Co. (Cast) ....A
IND.—Indianapolis
Nordyke & Marmon Co.,
1101 W. Morris (Bevel)..
.....................AAA
IND.—Mishawaka
Dodge Mfg. Co. ......AAA
IND.—Richmond
Richmond City Mill Wks.,A
KANS.—Enterprise
Ehrsam Mach. Co. (Friction
Clutch) C
KANS.—Leavenworth
Great Western Mfg. Co.
(Bevel; Spur; Cast; Mor-
tise) ....AA
KY.—Louisville
Caldwell Co., W. E., Bran-
dies Av. & Brook ......A
MAINE—Portland
Laughlin Co., Thos. (Ma-
rine; Steering) ....A
Portland Co. (Bevel; Cast;
Mitre; Spur) ....AA
MD.—Baltimore
Morse, Williams & Co., 205
E. German ....AA
Poole Engineering & Ma-
chine Co. (Cut; Friction
Clutch; Worm; Bevel;
Internal; Machine Mould-
ed; Angler; & Pinions
Electric Railway; Mor-
tise) ....AA
MASS.—Boston
Boston Gear Wks., 152 Pur-
chase (Bevel; Mitre; Mor-
tise; Spur, etc.; also
Brass; Worm; Fibreoid;
Rawhide; Compensating
Bevel; Fibre; Rawhide)B
Dodge Mfg. Co., 137 Pur-
chase ....AAA
Edson Mfg. Co.. 257 Atlan-
tic Av. Steering Yacht;
Ship) ....B
Falls Rivet & Machine Co.,

GEARS (Con.)

54 Purchase ....A
Grant Gear Wks., 6 Portland (Cut) ....A
Holmes & Blanchard Co., 39 Wash. N. ....B
Morse, Williams & Co., 19 Pearl ....A
Welch & Co., T. F., 65 Sudbury (Brass Internal; Brass Worm) ....D

MASS.—Florence
Norwood Engineering Co. (Spur) ....B

MASS.—Holyoke
Holyoke Machine Co. (Cut; Friction Clutch; Bevel Cast; Mortise; Spur) ..AA

MASS.—Orange
Chase Turbine Mfg. Co. ..A
Hunt, Rodney Machine Co. (Friction Clutch) ....A

MASS.—Pittsfield
Jones Sons Co., E. D. (Bevel; Cast; Friction).B

MICH.—Detroit
Buhl Malleable Co., Wight & Adair (Cut; Worm)..A
Dodge Bros. (Cut) ....A
Leland & Faulconer Mfg. Co. (Reciprocating for Automobiles) ....A

MINN.—Minneapolis
Minneapolis Steel & Mchry. Co. (Cast) ....AAA
Twin City Iron Wks. ....A

MISS.—Meridian
Soule Steam Feed Wks....C

MO.—St. Louis
Medart Patent Pulley Co., 3500 De Kalb Av. (Plain; Mortise Cut; Friction Clutch; Worm) .....AA
Messmer Mfg. Co., Fred. (Cut; Worm) ....B

N. H.—Concord
Holt Bros. Mfg. Co. (Log) B

N. H.—Lakeport
Cole Mfg. Co. ....A

N. J.—High Bridge
Taylor Iron & Steel Co... AAAA

N. J.—Newark
Gould & Eberhard (Worm, etc.) ....A

N. Y.—Albany
Townsend Fdry. & Mach. Shop Co. ....B

N. Y.—Brooklyn
Bliss Co., E. W., 19 Adams (Cast Steel; Cut; Spur; & Pinions; Electric Railway) .....AAAA
New York Gear Wks., 57 Milton (Cut) C
Pioneer Mach. Wks. (Jas. Hartley, Prop.), 75 Delavan (Cut) ....B

N. Y.—Buffalo
Buffalo Gear & Pattern Wks. 18 Elk (Cut)......G
Noye Mfg. Co., 50 Lakeview Av. (Friction Clutch; Internal; Bevel; Cast; Mortise; Helical-Spur; Mitre) X
Pratt & Letchworth Co. (Cast; Steel) .....AAA
Queen City Engineering Co., 49 Illinois (Hydraulic Steering) C

N. Y.—Catskill
Catskill Fdry. & Mach. Wks. (& Pinions; Electric Railway) ....B

New York City
Arthur Co. (Cut; Worm).A
Brown & Co., A. & F., 26 Cortlandt (Cut) ......A
Cornell, J. B. & J. M., 26th & 11th Av. (Cast Iron)AA
Cresson Co., Geo. V., 141 Liberty (Cut; Machine Moulded; Bevel; Cast; Rawhide) ....AA
Dodge Mfg. Co., 45 Dey.. AAA
Durke & Co., Chas. D. (Marine; Steering) ....B
Falls Rivet & Mach. Co., 208 Fulton ....A
Shriver & Co., T., 333 E.

GEARS (Con.)

56th (Machine Moulded) A

N. Y.—Rochester
Gleason Wks. (Automobile; Automobile Equalizing; Machine Moulded; Rawhide; Compensating Bevel) ....AA
Sager Gear Co. (Changeable for Bicycles) X

N. Y.—Syracuse
Franklin Mfg. Co., H. H..C
New Process Rawhide Co., 248 W. Washington (Internal; Cut Rawhide; Spur; Automobile; & Pinions; Electric Railway).B

OHIO—Canton
Aultman Co. ....A

OHIO—Cincinnati
Dodge Mfg. Co., 128 W. 3rd AAA
Greenwald Co., I. & E., 720 E. Pearl (Cut; Machine Moulded; Cast) ....A
Straub Mchry. Co., 1956 W. 6th (Mill) C

OHIO—Cleveland
Bartlett & Snow Co. ....A
Bultman & Co., F. H., 106 Canal (Internal; Spur; Worm) ....F
Cleveland Gear Wks., 86 Seneca (Cut; & Pinions, Electric Railway) ....A
Federal Mfg. Co. (Automobile Equalizing) ..AAAA
Horsburgh & Scott, 108 Canal (Cut; Rawhide; Spur; & Pinions, Electric Railway) ....B
Van Dorn & Dutton Co., 1798 E. Madison Av. (Cut; Spur; & Pinions, Electric Railway) ....B

OHIO—Columbus
Case Mfg. Co. (Compensating Bevel; Rawhide; Automobile; Equalizing) ..A
Jeffrey Mfg. Co.....AAAA

OHIO—Cuyahoga Falls
Falls Rivet & Machine Co. (Cut) ....A

OHIO—Dayton
Stilwell-Bierce & Smith-Vaile Co. (Cut; Bevel; Friction Clutch; Cast; Mortise) ....AAAA

OHIO—Mansfield
Ohio Brass Co. (Spur) ..AA

OHIO—Springfield
Leffel & Co., Jas. ......AA

OHIO—Toledo
Milburn Wagon Co. (Lumber) ....AAA

OHIO—Portland
Portland Iron Wks. (Inc.).A

PA.—Allegheny
Eagle Tool & Machine Co., 120 Sandusky (Cut; also Rask) ....F
National Gear Wheel & Fdry. Co. (Friction Clutch; Machine Moulded) B

PA.—Allentown
Allentown Fdry. & Mach. Wks. Co. (Friction Clutch; Cast; Mortise)..A

PA.—Chambersburg
Woods Sons, T. B. ......A

PA.—Chester
Wetherill & Co., R. (Mill) AAAA

PA.—Muncy
Sprout, Waldron & Co. (Mill) ....A

PA.—Philadelphia
Albro-Clem Elevator Co. (Worm) ....A
Bilgram, Hugo, 440 N. 12th (Cut; Internal; Worm; Bevel) ....B
Brill Co., J. G. (Street Car; Running) ....AAAA
Chester Steel Castings Co., 407 Sansom (Bevel; Mitre) AAA
Cresson Co., Geo. V. (Mitre; Spur; Worm) ....AA
Davis. Rodney. 626 Race (All Kinds Cut) ......F

472

GEARS (Con.)

Earle Gear & Machine Co. (Automobile; Worm; Rawhide) ....D

Harrington, Son & Co., Edwin, 1505 Penn. Av. (Cut) ....AA

Link Belt Engineering Co., Nicetown) ....A

Morse, Williams & Co., West End Trust Bldg. (Worm) ....AA

Phila. Gear Wks., 127 N. 7th (Cut) ....B

Phila. Roll & Machine Co. (Cast; Cast Steel; Worm) ....A

Stow Flexible Shaft Co. ..B

Wolf Co. (Cast) ....AA

PA.—Pittsburg

Fawcus Machine Co., 2818 Smallman (Steel; Iron; Bronze; Rawhide; Spur; Worm; & Pinions, Electric Railway; Automobile; Compensating Bevel; Machine Moulded; Rawhide) ....B

Fischer Fdry. & Mach. Co., S. 21st, cor. Mary .....A

Garrison Fdry. Co. (Cast) .. ..AAA

Jones & Laughlins Steel Co. (Cut) ....AAAA

Link Belt Engineering Co., Park Bldg. ....A

Mesta Machine Co., Lewis Blk. (Machine Moulded). ....AAA

Nuttall Co., R. D., Fayette & Garrison Pl. (Bevel; Mitre; Mortise; Spur, etc.; Cut; Worm; Automobile; & Pinions, Electric Railway; Fibre; Rawhide)..A

Pittsburg Malleable Iron Co. (Spur) ....A

Pittsburg Steel Fdry., 541 Wood ....AA

Simonds Mfg. Co., 25th & Liberty Av. (Cut; Spur; Worm; & Pinions, Electric Railway) C

Sommerfield Mach. & Mfg. Co., 224 3rd Av. (Steel; Cast Iron; Brass Internal; Steel; Cast Iron; Brass Hobbed Worm) ....B

Union Fdry. & Mach. Co., W. Carson (Cut; Internal; Machine Moulded; Worm) ....B

PA.—Rankin Station

Duquesne Forge Co. (& Pinions, Electric Railway).A

PA.—Reading

Johnston Fdry. & Mach. Co. ....B

PA.—South Bethlehem

Bethlehem Fdry. & Mach. Co. (Cast) C

Bethlehem Steel Co. (Cast; Cast Steel; Forged Steel) ....AAAA

PA.—Tamaqua

Tamaqua Mfg. Co. (Mitre; Spur) ....B

PA.—Wilkesbarre

Vulcan Iron Wks. (Cut; Friction Clutch; Bevel; Steel; Mortise) ..AAAA

R. I.—Providence

Brown & Sharpe Mfg. Co., (Cut; & Pinions, Electric Railway; Compensating Bevel; Rawhide) ..AAAA

Franklin Mach. Co., 189 Charles ....A

Providence Machine Co. (Roving Frame) .....AA

Woonsocket Mach. & Press Co. (Roving Frame)..AA

TENN.—Memphis

Chickasaw Iron Wks. (Cut; Friction Clutch; Cast)..A

VT.—Montpelier

Lane Mfg. Co. (Cut; Bevel; Cast; Mortise) ....A

WIS.—Kenosha

Bain Wagon Co. (Lumber) ....AAA

WIS.—Madison

Gisholt Mach. Co. ......AA

GEARS (Con.)

WIS.—Milwaukee

Allis-Chalmers Co. ..AAAA

Falk Co., ft. 30th (Motor; & Pinions, Electric Railway) ....AAA

Filer & Stowell Co., Becher, cor Yilmer (Mill) ..AAA

Western Rawhide & Belting Co. (Rawhide; & Pinions, Electric Railway) .....A

WIS.—Racine

Freeman & Son Mfg. Co., S. (Wind Mill Foot)....A

GEESE

N. J.—Newark

Hess & Drake (Tailors')..A

TENN.—South Pittsburg

Blaclock Fdy. (Tailors')..C

TENN.—Union City

Canvas Decoy Co. (Collapsible Canvas Decoy) ...E

GELATINE

CAL.—San Francisco

Sherwood & Sherwood, 212 Market ....AAA

ILL.—Chicago

Armour Glue Wks. 205 La Salle ....AAAA

Barrett & Co., M. L., 219 Lake ....A

Lenfestey Milling Co., 27 Mich. Av. C

Puhl-Webb Co., 119 W. Randolph C

Zinkeisen & Co., 25 E. Lake (Japanese) C

MD.—Baltimore

Imperial Mfg. Co., 113 South ....F

MASS.—Boston

Amer. Glue Co., 415 Atlantic Av. ....AAAA

Plymouth Rock Gelatine Co., 68 Western Av. ....A

Swampscott Gelatine, 313 State ....E

Whitten & Co., J. O., 68 Western Av. ....A

MASS.—Marblehead

Marblehead Mfg. Co. C

MASS.—Orange

Whitman Grocery Co. ...C

MASS.—Swampscott

Swampscott Gelatine Co. (Br. Boston, Mass.) ...E

MICH.—Delray

Fishe Gelatine Wks. C

MICH.—Detroit

Mich. Carbon Wks., 5 Front ....AAAA

MO.—St. Louis

Amer. Glue Co., 410 Elm (Br.) ....AAAA

Reardon Mfg. Co., Ft. Bremen Av. ....B

N. J.—Bordentown

French Gelatine Co. ......D

N. Y.—Gardenville

Buffalo Gelatine Co. C

N. Y.—Gowanda

Amer. Tanners Glue Co. (for Confec. only) ...AA

N. Y.—Johnstown

Knox, C. B. ....B

New York City

Armour & Co. (Br.), 173 Duane ....AAAA

Beaumont, R. B., 125 Hudson ....E

Behrend, F., 54 Front.....D

Burnham Co., E. S., 61 Gansevort ....B

Coopers Glue Wks., Peter, 13 Burling Slip .....AA

Cromwell, G., 136 Water.E

Deike, Hy., 118 John ....A

Duche & Sons, T. M., 101 Water C

Dunn, T. W., 47 Beekman ....E

Falcon Packg. Co., 158 Franklin C

Gardner & Bro., A. K., 99 John ....D

Hayes & Co., Jas. A., 105 Hudson ....A

Herzfelder, Bernhardt & Co., 93 Crosby C

GILLS (Con.)
ishing) ....A
MASS.—Lowell
Bagshaw, W. H. ....B
Dean, John M. (Rotary).F
Lowell Machine Shop (Preparing; Finishing).AAAA
N. J.—Newark
Crabb & Co., Wm. ....A
R. I.—Pawtucket
Atherton Machine Co., A.
T. (Preparing; Finishing)
B

GIMLETS

CONN.—Centrebrook
Connecticut Valley Mfg. Co.
B
CONN.—Chester
Chester Mfg. Co. ....G
Deuse, J. S. ....E
CONN.—Seymour
Garrett & Beach ....E
Swan Co., Jas. ....A
MASS.—Fiskdale
Snell Mfg. Co. (Bell
Hanger) ....B
MASS.—Greenfield
Goodell-Platt Co. ....B
MASS.—Shelbourne Falls
Mayhew Co., H. H. .....D
New York City
Jennings & Co., C. E., 101
Reade ....B
Russell & Erwin Mfg. Co.,
43 Chambers .....AAAA
OHIO—Cincinnati
Cinn. Tool Co. ....A
PA.—Philadelphia
Stortz & Son, Jno. ....F

GIMPS

See also Trimmings; Upholstery

CONN.—Bridgeport
Salts' Textile Mfg. Co....A
MASS.—Boston
Ziegler & Sons Co., Alfred
(Silk) ....A
MASS.—Lynn
Parker Bros. Mfg. Co.
(Leather) ....E
MASS.—Worcester
Wilter & Co., H. M. (Cotton) ....A
N. Y.—Long Island City
Astoria Silk Wks. .....AAA
New York City
Eifert, Henry F., 284 4th
Av. (Leather) ....F
Ellison & Co., A. S. (Silk)
B
Federal Leather Co. (56
Union Sq. E. (Upholstery)
D
Siegman & Weil, 110 Greene
(Tinsel) ....A
Union Upholstery Trimming
Co. (Furniture) ....D
N. Y.—Tottenville
Barnard, Bella F. (Silk)..B
PA.—Philadelphia
Brooks & Son, Geo., Westminster Av. & 55th
(Furniture) ....F
Eastlake Mfg. Co., Adams
& Leiper (Cotton; Furniture) ....A
Horstmann Co., Wm. H.
(Silk) ....AAAA
Loeb, Lippen & Co. (Cotton;
Silk; Undertakers') ....A
Wright & Co., S. D. (Furniture; Undertakers') ....D

GINGER

See also Teas; Coffees &
Spices. For Ginger Ale
see Ale

ILL.—Chicago
Puhl--Webb Co. (Jamaica).A
MD.—Baltimore
Cook & Co., R. W.
(Jamaica) ....D
Crawford Co., W. H.
(Jamaica) ....E
Beach & Claridge Co.
(Jamaica) ....B

GINGER (Con.)
McCormick & Co. (Jamaica)
D
MASS.—Boston
Potter Drug & Chemical
Corpn. (Jamaica) ......A
MICH.—Saginaw
Ferrell & Co., A. T.
(Jamaica) ....B
MO.—St. Louis
Bayle, Geo. A. (Jamaica,
Essence) ....B
N. Y.—Brooklyn
Wiarda & Co., Jno. C...AA
New York City
Archibald & Lewis
(Jamaica) C
Hazard & Co., E. C., 117
Hudson (Jamaica) ...AA
Schultze Co., A. H. 198
W. B'way (Jamaica)..X
OHIO—Newark
Styron, Beggs & Co.
(Jamaica) ....A
PA.—Philadelphia
Favorite Mfg. Co. (Jamaica)
C

GINGHAMS

See Cotton Goods

GIN

See Liquors

GINS

See also Machy.; Agr. Imps.

ALA.—Prattville
Pratt Gin Co., Daniel (Cotton) ....AAAA
CONN.—Branchville
Gruman, G. G. (Ice
Hoisting) ....F
CONN.—New London
Brown Cotton Gin Co.
(Cotton) ....AA
GA.—Atlanta
Van Winkle Gin & Machine
Co., E. (Cotton) ...AAA
KY.—Louisville
Avery & Sons, B. F. (Cotton) ....AAA
LA.—Amite City
Gullett Gin Co. (Cotton)..A
MASS.—Arlington
Wood & Co., W. T. (Ice
Hoisting) ....A
MASS.—East Bridgewater
Carver Cotton Gin Co. (Cotton) ....A
MO.—St. Louis
Kingsland Mfg. Co. (Cotton)
B
PA.—Waynesboro
Frick Co. (Cotton)...AAAA
S. C.—Charleston
Valk & Murdoch Iron Wks.
(Cotton) ....B
VA.—Norfolk
White & Bro., S. R. (Cotton) ....A

GIRDERS

See also Beams; Iron & Steel

IOWA—Clinton
Clinton Bridge & Iron Wks.
(Steel) ....AA
IOWA—Des Moines
Des Moines Bridge & Iron
Wks. (Steel) ....B
MASS.—Boston
Boston Bridge Works, 47
Winter ....AA
MASS.—Holyoke
Walsh's Holyoke Steam
Boiler Wks. (Iron) ....D
MO.—St. Louis
Christopher & Simpson
Arch. Iron & Fdry. Co.
(Riveted) ....AA
NEBR.—Omaha
Paxton & Vierling Iron
Wks. (Steel) ....AA
OHIO—Girard
Girard Boiler & Mfg. Co.
(Steel) ....D
PA.—Philadelphia
Belmont Iron Wks. (Riveted) ....AA

GIRDERS (Con.)

PA.—Pittsburg
McClintic-Marshal Construction Co. ....AA
Riter-Conley Mfg. Co. (Lattice) ....AAA

GIRDLES

IND.—Vincennes
Vincennes Novelty Mfg. Co. D
MASS.—Springfield
Bay State Corset Co. ....A
N. J.—Newark
Delsarte Mfg. & Supply Co. (Bust) ....D

GIRTHS

See also Harness

KY.—Louisville
Louisville Girth & Blanket Mills (Saddle) C
N. J.—Newark
Peters' Harness & Saddlery Co. (Saddle) C
N. Y.—Buffalo
Buffalo Weaving & Belting Co. (Saddle) ....A
R. I.—Woonsocket
Perforated Pad Co. (Saddle) B

GLASS

See also Glassware

CAL.—San Francisco
Schmitz & Hopps, 62 8th (Leaded) ....F
COLO.—Denver
Baker, James W., 1836 Champa (Leaded) ....H
DEL.—Wilmington
Christiana Window Glass Co. (Window) ....B
ILL.—Chicago
Amer. Luxfer Prism Co., 346 Wabash Av. (Prismatic) ....B
Brown Bros. Mfg. Co., 22d & Campbell Av. (Prismatic) ....B
Chicago Sidewalk Light Co., 101 Washington (Prismatic) ....F
Dauchy Iron Wks., 88 Illinois (Prismatic) ...B
Flanagan & Biedenweg Co., 57 to 63 Illinois (Leaded; Ornamental) ....A
Ford Bros., 234 5th Av. (Leaded) ....D
Kinsella Co., John J. (French Mirror; Plate; Art) X
McCully & Miles Co., 88-90 Wabash Av. (Leaded; Mosaic; Stained) X
Schuler & Mueller Co., cor. Madison & Canal (Leaded; Ornamental) ....D
Suess Ornamental Glass Co. 54 N. Clinton (Art) ...D
Western Sand Blast Mfg. Co., cor. Clinton & Jackson (Chipped; Leaded; Ornamental; Sand Blast; Stained) C
ILL.—Ottawa
Peltier Bros. Glass Co. (Opalescent; Rough Ribbed; Figured Rolled Plate) ..X
ILL.—Streater
Western Glass Co. (Window) ....D
IND.—Anderson
Anderson Mirror & Bent Glass Wks. (Bent) ....E
IND.—Arcadia
Baker Bros. Glass Co. (Window) C
IND.—Dunkirk
Dunkirk Window Glass Co. (Window) ....A
IND.—Eaton
Baur Window Glass Co. (Window) X
IND.—Gas City
Amer. Window Glass Co. (Window) ....B
Diamond Window Glass Co.

GLASS (Con.)

(Window) ....A
IND.—Hartford City
Hartford City Flint Glass Co. (Window; Chipped; Ground) ....E
Snead Glass Co. (Vault; Sidewalk) ....B
IND.—Kokomo
Opalescent Glass Wks. (Cathedral; Rough Plate; Tile; Opalescent; Rough; Ribbed; Figured Rolled Plate; Vault; Sidewalk)B
IND.—Marion
Canton Glass Co. (Pressed Light; Vault; Sidewalk) B
Estep Glass Co. (Window) X
IND.—Matthews
Crown Glass Co. (Window) X
La Ruche Window Glass Co. (Window) ....D
Progress Window Glass Co. (Window) ....D
Star Co-oper. Glass Co. (Window) X
Van Camp Glass Co. (Window) ....B
Winslow Glass Co. (Window) ....B
IND.—Montpelier
National Window Glass Co. (Window) ....B
IND.—New Albany
Ohio Falls Co-oper. Window Glass Co. (Window) E
IND.—Pendleton
Pendleton Window Glass Wks. (Window) ....D
KY.—Louisville
Louisville Silvering & Beveling Co. (Mirror) ......B
MD.—Baltimore
Baker Bros. & Co. (Window) A
Chaudron & Peyton (Chipped) ....E
King & Bro., Wm., 113 W. Fayette (Window) X
Swindell Bros., cor. Bayard & Russell (Window) ...A
MASS.—Boston
Crosby Steam Gauge & Valve Co. (Scotch Gauge) ..AA
Redding. Baird & Co., 83 Franklin (Leaded; Ornamental; Prismatic; Baird's Hand-made Silver; Embossed; Jewelled; Mosaic; Stained; Enamelled .....B
MASS.—New Bedford
Smith Bros. (Mosaic) X
MASS.—Somerville
Union Glass Co. (Art)...B
MICH.—Detroit
Fredericks & Wolfram, 107 Gratiot Av. (Leaded) ...E
Windman & Co., C. D. (Mirror) ....A
MICH.—Jackson
Jackson Glass Wks. (Mirror) ....B
MICH.—Saginaw
Saginaw Plate Glass Co. (Window) ....AA
MO.—St. Louis
Daylight Prism Co. of Mo., Carleton Bldg. (Prismatic) F
Mississippi Glass Co. (Cathedral; Rough Plate; Tile; Rolled; Maze Pattern; Ribbed; Figured Rolled Plate; Wire, for Fire-Proofing Windows; Wire Skylight) ......AA
Missouri Glass Co. (Mirror) A
Oriel Glass Co. (Bent; Plate) ....B
Wallis, A. H. 2000-2002 Locust (Leaded) ......D
N. J.—Bridgeton
Cumberland Glass Mfg. Co. (Window) ....B
More-Jonas Glass Co. (Inc.) (Window) X
N. J.—Newark
Sharpe Bros., 927 Broad

GLASS (Con.)
(Leaded) ....H
N. J.—Paterson
Payne, Geo. H., 247 Market
(Leaded) ....F
N. J.—Trenton
Golding Sons Co. (Ground)
AA
N. Y.—Brooklyn
Dannehoffer Glass Wks.,
Jno., 389 Harmon (Cathe-
dral; Rough Plate; Tile;
Rough; Ribbed; Figured
Rolled Plate) ....B
Donnelly Co., J. R. (Air
Port; Bevelled Plate; Mir-
ror) ....D
Heidt, Jno. B., 278 Boerum
Pl. (Cathedral; Rough
Plate; Tile; Opalescent;
Ground) ....D
Jones Decorative Glass Co.,
Thos., Hudson Av. &
Concord (Decorated; Lead-
ed) C
Wiarda & Co., Jno. C.
(Ground) ....AA
N. Y.—Canastota
Canastota Glass Co. (Win-
dow) ....E
N. Y.—Durhamville
Durhamville Glass Mfg. Co.
(Window) X
N. Y.—Elmira
Elmira Glass Cutting Co.
(Window) ....E
N. Y.—Ithaca
Ithaca Glass Mfg. Co.
(Window) ....D
Mutual Glass Co. (Window)
D
New York City
Bache, Semon & Co., 7
Laight (Camera) .....AA
Carr-Lowrey Glass Co., 290
B'way (for Engineering
Specialties) ....B
Cowens Son, Newman
(Window) ....F
Decorative Stained Glass Co.
(Mirror) ....F
Geissler, R., 56 W. 8th
(Leaded) ....F
Henderson Bros., 343 W.
37th (Leaded; Orna-
mental) X
Kahn, Jacques (Mirror).AA
Lamb, J. & R., 59 Carmine
(Embossed; Jewelled;
Enamelled; Mosaic;
Stained) ....D
N. J. Fdry. & Machine Co.,
9 Murray (Prismatic)..D
N. Y. Prism Co., 473 B'way
(Prismatic) ....E
Popper & Sons, Leo., 7 Sulli-
van (Opalescent; Jew-
elled) ....A
Potts Bros., 116 Walker
(Mitre Cut) ....F
Rae & Co., G. 436 W.
B'way (Leaded) ......F
Righter & Kolb, 156 5th
Av. (Leaded) ....E
Spiers, Richard N., 859 6th
Av. (Leaded) ....A
Stoltzenberg Co., 51 Bar-
clay (Stained; Leaded).B
N. Y.—Syracuse
Wood Glass Co., 226 N. Sa-
lina (Leaded; Ornamen-
tal; Window) C
OHIO—Barnesville
Barnesville Glass Co. (Inc.)
(Window) ....A
Eastern Ohio Glass Co.
(Window) ....B
OHIO—Bellaire
Rodefer, T. A. (Opalescent;
Pressed Light; Prismatic,
for Architectural Iron
Works; Tiling, for Arch-
itectural Iron Works)..A
OHIO—Cincinnati
Riordan & Co., G. C., 133 E.
5th (Leaded) ....D
OHIO—Cleveland
Cleveland Window Glass
Co., 232 Champlain (Win-
dow; Prismatic) ......A
Solar Prism Co., Card Bldg.
(Prismatic) ....B

GLASS (Con.)
OHIO—Columbus
Columbus Plate & Window
Glass Co. (Window) ...B
Independent Window Glass
Co. (Window) ....AA
OHIO—Dayton
Dayton Art Glass Wks.
(Church Art) ....H
Stevens Art Glass Co.
(Leaded) ....A
OHIO—Findlay
Globe Window Glass Co.
(Window) ....D
OHIO—Quaker City
Cochran, Alex. (Window).B
OHIO—Rossford
Ford Plate Glass Co., Edw.
(Window) ....B
PA.—Beaver Falls
Co-operative Flint Glass Co.
(Vault; Sidewalk) .....A
PA.—Bradford
Tuna Glass Co. (Window).B
PA.—Butler
Standard Plate Glass Co.
(Bent; Cathedral; Rough;
Plate; Tile; Ground) ...
AAAA
PA.—Covington
Covington Glass Wks. (Win-
dow) ....D
PA.—Dubois
Mahler Glass Co., J.
(Window) ....B
PA.—Falls Creek
Fitzpatrick Glass Mfg. Co.,
(Window) ....AA
Gray & Son (Cathedral;
Rough Plate; Tile; Win-
dow) ....D
PA.—Harrisburg
Rudy Co., C. D. (Art,
Stained) C
PA.—Hazelhurst
Healy Window Glass Co.
(Window) ....B
PA.—Jeanette
McKee-Jeanette Glass Co.
(Window) ....B
PA.—Mt. Jewett
Boyd Glass Co. (Window)
B
PA.—New Bethlehem
New Bethlehem Window
Glass Co. (Window) ...B
PA.—New Eagle
Monongahela Window Glass
Co. (Window) ....D
PA.—Philadelphia
Amer. Prismatic Light Co.,
48 N. 11th (Prismatic) D
Daylight Glass Mfg. Co.,
Bourse Bldg. (Prismatic)
B
Dukes Glass Wks., Hy.
(Stained) ....D
French & Co., Saml. H.
(Leaded; Embossed) ...A
Gillinder & Sons. (Inc.) 135
Oxford (for Engineering
Specialties; Opalescent) A
Groves, R. S. (Stained) D
Lucas & Co., Jno., 322 Race
(Window) ....AAA
Whitall Tatum Co., 410
Race (for Elec. & Chem-
ical Use; for Engineer-
ing Specialties) .....AAAA
Young, W. C. (Imitation,
Stained) ....F
PA.—Pittsburg
American Window Glass Co.
(Window) X
Campbell Co., T. (Window)
H
Commercial Glass Co. (Art)
E
Cunningham Glass Co., D.
O., 123 S. 26th (Window)
AA
Cunningham's & Co. (Ltd.)
(Window) ....A
McKee Glass Co., S., S. 13th
& Carson (Window) D
National Glass Co., 806
Penn Av. (Pressed Light;
Vault; Sidewalk) X
Penn-Amer. Plate Glass Co.
(Bent) ....AAAA
Pittsburg Plate Glass Co.
(Window; Bent; Cathe-
dral; Rough; Rough

GLASS (*Con.*)
Plate; Tile) ......AAAA
U. S. Glass Co. (Window)
........................AAAA
Wightman Glass Co., Thos.,
104 Woods (Window) AA
PA.—Smethport .
Smethport Glass Co. (Window) ....A
PA.—Spring City
Phila. Window Glass Co.
(Window) ....D
PA.—Washington
Highland Glass Co. (Cathedral; Rough Plate; Tile)A
Pittsburg Window Glass Co.
(Window) ....A
PA.—Wilcox
Diamond Glass Co. (Window) ....A
George Window Glass Co.
(Window) C
R. I.—Providence
Gorham Mfg. Co. (Stained)
........................AAAA
W. VA.—Morgantown
Pressed Prism Plate Glass
Co. (Prismatic) ......B

GLASSES

**See .also .Optical .Goods;
Mirrors**

CONN.—Meriden
Meriden Britannia Co.
(Reading) ......AAAA
CONN.—New Britain
Stanley Rule & Level Co.
(Level) ....AAA
CONN.—Pine Meadow
Chapin-Stephens Co. (Level)
........................A
ILL.—Chicago
Fowler, E. S. & W. S.
(Eye; also Spectacles) D
Gordon & Morrison (Smoked
Eye) ....A
Young & Co., Otto (Eye;
also Spectacles; Blue Eye)
........................AAAA
MASS.—Boston
Crosby Steam Gauge &
Valve Co., 95 Oliver
(Gauge, Red Reflecting
Imported; Gauge, Scotch)
........................AA
MASS.—Leominster
Wetherbee, John W. (Eye;
also Spectacles) ......G
MASS.—Southbridge
Amer. Optical Co. (Eye;
also Spectacles) ..AAA
MICH.—Detroit
Black & Co., L. (Eye; also
Spectacles) ....B
Johnson Optical Co. (Eye;
also Spectacles; Magnifying; Reading; Watchmakers') ....A
Moore & Son, E. C., 103
Miami Av. (Magnifying)
........................F
MICH.—Grand Rapids
Nelson-Matter Furniture Co.
(Cheval) ....AA
Royal Furniture Co. (Cheval) ....A
N. H.—Tilton
Lord Optical Co., Albert C.
(Eye; also Spectacles;
Blue Eye; Smoked Eye)
........................H
N. Y.—Brooklyn
Donnelly & Co., J. R. (Cheval) ....D
Green, Henry J. (Opera) ..X
N. Y.—Geneva
Geneva Optical Co. (Eye;
also Spectacles) ......D
Standard Optical Co. (Eye;
also Spectacles) ......A
New York City
Fradley & Co. (Inc.), J. F.
(Opera) ....E
Gregg, Wm. F. (Pick) ...F
Hagerty Bros. & Co. (Graduated) ....
Herter Bros. (Inc.) (Cheval)
........................D
Hill Glass Co., 75 Nassau
(Watch; Clock) ......F
Keuffel & Esser Co., 127

GLASSES (*Con.*)
Fulton (Opera; Level;
Field) ....AA
King Optical Co., Julius, 4
Maiden Lane (Field; Marine; Opera) ....A
McAllister, T. H., 49 Nassau (Marine; Opera;
Field) ....B
Meyrowitz, E. B. (Eye; also
Spectacles) ....A
Pottier & Stymus Co. (Cheval) ....D
Schwarzwaelder & Co., Wm.
(Cheval) X
Seymour, Ernest, 60 Nassau
(Watch; Clock) X
Souto & Co., B. (Cheval) .B
Spencer Optical Co., 12
Maiden Lane (Eye; also
Spectacles; Field; Magnifying; Marine; Opera;
Reading; Spy) C
Swain & Son (Inc.), H. C.
(Cheval) ....D
N. Y.—Rochester
Bausch & Lamb Optical Co.
(Field; Marine; Opera;
Magnifying; Eye; also
Spectacles) ......AAA
OHIO—Cincinnati
Lunkenheimer Co., Beekman
& Waverly (Gauge; Red
Reflecting; Imported;
Gauge; Scotch) ......AA
Mitchell Furniture Co.,
Robert (Cheval) ..AAAA
OHIO—Cleveland
Warner & Swasey (Field;
Marine; Opera) ....A
PA.—Philadelphia
Belfield & Co., H. 435 N.
Broad (Gauge; Red Reflecting; Imported;
Gauge; Scotch) ......AA
Burgin & Sons Glass Co.
(Graduated) ....A
Disston & Sons, Henry
(Level) ....AAAA
McIntire, Magee & Brown
(Spy) ....A
National Optical Co. (Eye;
also Spectacles) ......B
PA.—Reading
Willson & Co. T. O. (Eye;
also Spectacles) ......AA

GLASSWARE

CONN.—Danbury
Handel Co. (Art) X
CONN.—Meriden
Bergen Co., J. D. (Cut) ..A
International Silver Co.
(Cut) ....AAAA
Monroe Co., C. F. (Art) ..A
ILL.—Chicago
Adams & Westlake Co., Ontario & Franklin (Railroad; Lamp; Lantern)
........................AAAA
Burley & Tyrrell, 238 Adams
(Cut) ....A
Burley & Co., 120 Wabash
Av. (Bar) ....AA
Peck & Co., Albert, 199 E.
Rand (Bar) ....A
Pitkin & Brooks, 60 Lake
(Cut) ....A
Foster & Co., A. M., 120
Lake (Druggists) ......A
Roch & Co., E. J., 40
State (Cut) C
IND.—Alexandria
Lippincott Glass Co. (Chemists) ....A
IND.—Hartford City
Sneath Glass Co. (Fancy
Colored) ....B
IND.—Marion
Canton Glass Co. (Bar;
Chemical; Druggists) ..B
IND.—Muncie
Hemingrey Glass Company
(Blown; Pressed Flint)
........................AA
MD.—Baltimore
Baker Bros. & Co. (Chemists) ....A
MD.—Cumberland
Maryland Glass Etching
Works (Bar; Ornamental)
........................C

GLASSWARE (Con.)

MASS.—Boston
Dean, Foster & Co., 14 Blackstone (Druggists') ... AA

MASS.—New Bedford
Blackner Co., A. L. (Cut) .B
Mt. Washington Glass Co. (Cut) X
Pairpoint Corporation (Cut) ... AA
Smith Bros. (Fancy Colored) ... X

MASS.—Somerville
Union Glass Co. (Chemists') ... B

MICH.—Lansing
American Cut Glass Co. (Cut) ....D

MINN.—Red Wing
Red Wing Stoneware Co. (Chemists') ....A

N. J.—Flemington
Empire Cut Glass Co. (Cut) ... D

N. J.—Newark
Newark Cut Glass Co. (Cut) ... C
Smith, M. A. (Bent Plate) ... D
Unger Bros. (Cut) ......A

N. Y.—Brooklyn
Dannenhoffer Glass Works, Jno. (Pressed Flint) ...B

N. Y.—Corning
Corning Glass Wks. (Blown; Cut; Pressed Flint) ....A
Egginton Co., O. F. (Cut) ... E
Hawkes & Co., Thos. G. (Cut) ....A
Hoare & Co., J. (Cut) ....A
Hunt & Sullivan (Cut)....D
Ahrenfeldt & Son, Chas., 50 Murray (Decorated) ...B
Alford & Co., C. G., 11 John (Cut) ....A
Bawo & Dotter, 26 Barclay (Art Decorated) .....AA
Brookfield Glass Co., 220 B'way (Pressed Flint)..B
Davison Bros., 12 Barclay (Art Decorated) .....B
Dorflinger & Sons' Co., 36 Murray (Cut) ....D
Durand, Paul, 41 Warren (Art) X
Dwenger, C. L., 35 Park Pl. (Decorated Art)....D
Eimer & Amend (Chemists') ... AA
Greiner, Emil, 78 John (Scientific) ....E
Hagerty Bros. & Co., 5 Platt (Pressed Flint)...A
Koscherak Bros., 33 Park Pl. (Bohemian) ......E
Lum & Son, Wm. H., 46 Murray (Cut) ....F
Lazarus, Rosenfeld & Lehmann, 62 Murray (Art Decorated) ....B
Straus & Sons, L., 42 Warren (Cut) ....AAAA

N. Y.—Port Jervis
Brox & Ryall (Blown; Pressed Flint) ....A

N. Y.—Niagara Falls
Co-operative Flint Glass Co. (Bar; Cut; Druggists'; Table) X

OHIO—Bellaire
Rodefer, T. A. (Blown; Novelties; Pressed Flint) ... A

OHIO—Bowling Green
Ohio Cut Glass Co. (Cut)..B

OHIO—Bridgeport
Crystal Glass Co. (Blown; Pressed Flint) ....A

OHIO—Cincinnati
Tatam Co., Samuel C. (Blown) ....B

OHIO—Newark
Heisey & Co., A. H. (Fancy Colored; Pressed Flint; Bar; Table) ....A

OHIO—Toledo
Libbey Glass Co. (Blown; Cut; Pressed Flint) ..AA

PA.—Beaver
Co-operative Flint Glass Co. (Blown; Fancy Colored; Novelties; Pressed Flint) ... A

GLASSWARE (Con.)

PA.—Beaver Falls
Merriman & Co., J. (Blown) ... A

PA.—Coraopolis
Consolidated Lamp & Glass Co. (Fancy Colored; Novelties) ....A

PA.—Grapeville
Westmoreland Specialty Co. (Pressed Flint; Blown; Novelties) ....A

PA.—Hawley
Maple City Glass Co. (Cut) ... B

PA.—Honesdale
Clark & Co., T. B. (Cut)..B
Kelly & Steinwan (Cut)...C
Krantz, Smith & Co., (Cut) ... D

PA.—Jeannette
McKee-Jeannette Glass Co. (Blown; Fancy Colored; Novelties; Pressed Flint) ... B

PA.—Philadelphia
Burgin & Sons Glass Co. (Pressed Flint) ....A
Fox & Sons, H. C. (Pressed Flint) ....AA
French & Co., Samuel H. (Cut) ....A
Fricke, Arthur (Fancy Colored) C
Gill & Co. (Inc.) (Blown).A
Gillinder & Sons (Inc.), 135 Oxford (Chemical; Druggists'; Car Lamp; Lantern; Blown; Novelties; Pressed Flint; Cut).....A
Murray & Co., James J. (Blown; Pressed Flint).A
Quaker City Cut Glass Co., 1819 N. 5th (Cut) ......A
Thomas Co., Arthur H. (Chemical) ....B
Whitall, Tatum & Co. (Blown; Pressed Flint; Chemists') ....AAAA

PA.—Pittsburg
Bryce Bros. Co. (Inc.) (Blown; Pressed Flint; Novelties) ....A
Flaccus Glass Co., C. L. (Blown; Pressed Flint) ... AA
Macbeth-Evans Glass Co. (Blown; Pressed Flint) ... AAAA
Oriental Glass Co. (Pressed Flint) C
Phoenix Glass Co. (Art; Blown; Cut; Fancy Colored; Novelties; Pressed Flint; Opalescent) .A
U. S. Glass Co. (Chemists'; Blown; Fancy Colored; Pressed Flint) ....AAAA

PA.—Pittston
Pittston Cut Glass Co. (Cut) ... D

PA.—Tarentum
Fidelity Glass Co. (Pressed Flint) ....D
Tarentum Glass Co. (Blown; Fancy Colored; Novelties; Pressed Flint) ....A

PA.—Uniontown
Uniontown Flint Glass Co. (Pressed Flint) ....D

PA.—Washington
Duncan & Miller Glass Co. (Fancy Colored; Novelties; Pressed Flint) ....A
Perfection Glass Company (Pressed Flint) ....A

PA.—White Mills
Dorflinger & Sons' Co. (Cut; Blown; Pressed Flint).AA

R. I.—Providence
Hope Glass Works (Cut)..E

W. VA.—Moundsville
Fostoria Glass Co. (Fancy Colored; Cut; Pressed Flint; Table) ....AAA

W. VA.—Wheeling
Central Glass Works (Inc.) (Blown; Cut; Fancy Colored; Novelties; Pressed Flint) ....A

GLASSWARE (Con.)

W. VA.—Wellsburg

Eagle Glass & Mfg. Co. (Cut; Fancy Colored; Novelties) ....A

George Co., S. (Cut) .....A

Riverside Glass Wks. (Cut; Blown; Fancy Colored; Novelties; Pressed Flint) C

GLOBES

See also Shades

CONN.—Meriden

Hall & Co., A. J. (Decorated Gas Light) ......B

ILL.—Chicago

Andrews Co., A. H., 300 Wabash Av. (Celestial; Terrestrial; Relief; School) ....AA

Baggott Co., E. (Electric Light; Glass; Cut Glass) ....B

Union School Furnishing Co., 211 E. Madison (School) C

IND.—Alexandria

Lippincott Glass Co. (Lantern; Lamp) ....A

IND.—Hartford City

Sneath Glass Co. (All Colors Lantern; Semaphors) ....B

MASS.—New Bedford

Smith Bros. (Cut Gas) X

N. Y.—Albany

Choate & Co., W. A. (School) ....F

N. Y.—Brooklyn

Gair Co., Robert (Celestial; Terrestial; Relief) ....D

Williamsburg Flint Glass Co., 260 Boerum (Lantern) ....E

New York City

Bryan-Marsh Co., 136 Liberty (Arc Lamp) ......B

Fensterer & Ruhe, 47 Murray (Gas Light) ......B

Gleason Mfg. Co., E. P. (Electric Light; Lamp; Gas) ....B

Gleason-Tiebout Glass Co., 37 Murray (Gas) X

Holophane Glass Co., 15 E. 32d (Compound Prism; for Increasing Illumination; Prismatic) ....D

Kirchberger & Co., M., 50 Warren (Incandescent Gas Light) C

Phoenix Glass Co., 15 Murray (Electric Light; Cut Gas) ....A

Schedler, Herman (Celestial; Relief; Toy) .....E

OHIO—Athens

Hudson School Furniture Co. (School) X

OHIO—Bellaire

Rodefer, T. A. (for Lantern Mfrs. & Jobbers)..A

OHIO—Fostoria

Fostoria Bulb & Bottle Co. (Arc Lamp) ....A

OHIO—Steubenville

Gill Bros. & Co. (Lantern) ....AA

OHIO—Toledo

Libbey Glass Co. (Lantern) ....AA

PA.—Beaver Falls

Co-operative Flint Glass Co. (Fish; Aquaria) ....A

PA.—Philadelphia

Gill & Co. (Inc.) (Electric Light; Gas; Lamp; Decorated Lamp) ....A

Gillinder & Sons (Electric Light; Fish; Aquaria; Cut Gas; Decorated Lamp)..A

Murray & Co., James J., Trenton Av., Willard & Collins (Lantern; Electric Light; Cut Gas; Lamp).A

Whitall, Tatum & Co. (Fish; Aquaria) ....AAAA

PA.—Pittsburg

McKee Glass Co., S., 13th & Carson (Lantern; Fish; Aquaria) ....D

GLOBES (Con.)

Macbeth-Evans Glass Co., 18th & Josephine (Lantern) ....AAAA

Wormser Glass Co., 2d & Sylvan Av. (Lantern; 871 A Globules) X

GLOBULES

N. Y.—Brooklyn

Bishoff, F. (Homoeopathic) ....B

GLOVES & MITTENS

CAL.—Napa

Raymond & Williams (Unlined; Lined) C

CAL.—Oakland

Hodkins Co., M. W. (Buck; Calf; Goat; Horsehide; Kid; Dog; Gloves; Mittens; Gauntlets) ......D

CAL.—San Francisco

Bloch, H. & L. (Pacific Glove Wks.) (Leather)..A

Blumenthal & Co., B. (of all descriptions) ....A

Busby, Fred H. (Gloves).C

Carson Glove Co. C

Conklin & Co., F. G. (Buck; Horse; Sheepskin Gloves) C

Croker & Laws (Gloves; Gauntlets) ....D

Heineman, H. M. (Gloves) ....B

Lewis & Co., E. (Standard Glove Works) (Gloves).D

Newman & Franklin (Glove Co.) (Gloves) ....D

CONN.—New Haven

Seamless Rubber Co. (Rubber) ....AA

ILL.—Chicago

Aeppli Glove Wks. (Heavy Work Gloves) ....D

American Glove Co. (Split; Chrome; Sheep; Napa, &c.) ....B

Chicago Sporting Goods Mfg. Co. (Boxing; Baseball) ....B

Connelly Bros. & Hall (Leather Gloves) .....B

Eisendrath Glove Co. ....A

Farwell Co., John V. (Gloves) ....AAAA

Friedlander, Brady & Co. (Knit Silk; Wool) ......A

Hoffman Bros. & Co. (Leather Work Gloves).D

Hutchins Bros. Glove Co...D

Lehman & Co., L. B. (Kid Gloves) ....B

Osborn Co., C. D. ....D

Price Co., Hy. W. (Knit).B

Simmons & Co., Francis T. (Womens' Kid Gloves)..B

ILL.—De Kalb

Brandt & Shipman (Gloves) ....A

ILL.—Kewanee

Boss Mfg. Co. (Canton Flannel; Corn Husking) ....B

ILL.—Rockford

Prince Co., Hy. W. (Knit).B

ILL.—Rock Island

Bennett, George (Leather; Fur) ....A

IND.—Bluffton

Zero Mitten Mfg. Co. (Canton Flannel) ....D

IND.—Ft. Wayne

Ft. Wayne Glove & Mitten Co. (Sheep; Calf; Horsehide; Napa Muleskin Gloves; Faced; Full; T-Back Mittens) ....B

IND.—Michigan City

Lakeside Knitting Co. (Knit) C

IND.—Winchester

Tecumseh Facing Mills (Leather) C

IOWA—Des Moines

Cownie Glove Co., J. H. (Leather) ....A

IOWA—Grinnell

Morrison, McIntosh & Co.

GLOVES (Con.)
(Womens'; Men's) .....B

IOWA—Iowa City
Iowa Glove Co. (Work;
Driving) ....D
Rate & Sons, E. F.
(Leather) ....D

MAINE—Penobscot
Condon & Co., A. C. (Hand
Knit Mittens) C

MD.—Frederick
Eissler, Daniel ....D

MD.—Hagerstown
Updegraff & Son, Geo. (Fur;
Kid; Leather; Buck;
Mocha Gloves) ....A

MASS.—Boston
Boston Belting Co. (Aid
Mittens) ....AAAA

MASS.—Everett
Bailey & Co., Oscar L.
Knit Wool; Golf; Silk)..C

MASS.—Florence
Nonotuck Silk Co. (Silk)
AAA

MASS.—Needham
Carter Co., William (Knit
Silk; Wool Mittens) ...B
Latham & Co., Frederick
(Knit; Worsted; Merino
Gloves) ....D
Moseley & Co. (Knit) ...D

MASS.—Peabody
Clark Glove Co. (Leather
Sporting) ....AA

MASS.—Westfield
Bay State Glove Co. C

MICH.—Clare
Woisey & Co., W. (Knit
Mitts) ....D

MICH.—Colon
Lamb Knit Goods Co. (Knit)
D

MICH.—Detroit
Detroit Alaska Knitting Co.
(Knit Mittens) ......D
Detroit Leather Specialties
Co. (Mechanics' Heavy
Leather) C
Forrester & Cheney Co.
(Golf) ....D
Maddocks Glove Co. (Gloves)
D
Progressive Knitting Co.
(Worsted; Silk) ......A
Ryan Bros. Knitting Co.
(Knit Gloves) C

MICH.—Lansing
Michigan Knitting Co. ...D

MICH.—Muskegon
Amazon Knitting Co. .....A

MICH.—Perry
Perry Glove & Mitten Co.
(Knit) ....D

MICH.—Pontiac
Pontiac Knitting Wks. Co.
(Knit) C

MICH.—Quincy
Quincy Knitting Co. (Knit)
D

MICH.—Rochester
Western Knitting Mills
(Knit) ....A

MINN.—Mankato
Mankato Mills Co. (Knit).A

MINN.—St. Paul
Gordon & Ferguson (Gloves)
AAA
Horne & Druck ....D
McKibbin, Driscoll & Dorsey
A

MO.—St. Louis
Ferguson, McKinney Dry
Goods Co. (Gloves).AAAA
Mueller, August C

N. H.—Littleton
Saranac Glove Co. ....B

N. H.—Plymouth
Draper & Maynard Co. (Box-
ing Gloves) ....B
Rollins, F. H. (Men's)....C

N. J.—Hoboken
Litchenheim, Louis (Golf
Gloves) ....B

N. J.—Jersey City
De Renzier & Co., S.
(Leather Gloves) ......D
Hall, H. S. (Silk) ....D

N. Y.—Amsterdam
Amsterdam Silk Mills (L.
Litchenhein) (Knit) ...B
Lovenheim, L. (Knit) ...D

GLOVES (Con.)
N. Y.—Auburn
Lemmon & Co., H. N. (Fur;
Lamb Wool) ....D

N. Y.—Binghamton
Parlor City Glove & Mitten
Co. ....D

N. Y.—Broadalbin
Dye & Robertson (Leather)
D

N. Y.—Brooklyn
Jennings Lace Works (Silk
Lace Mitts) ......AAAA

N. Y.—Buffalo
Am. Buffalo Robe Co.
(Cloth) ....A
Buffalo Glove & Whip Man-
ufactory C
D
Chisholm, H. L. (Leather)
D
Orr, George ....D

N. Y.—Candor
Wands Glove Co. (Men's &
Boys' Heavy Working
Gloves) ....A

N. Y.—Fonda
Behr, Isaac H. ....D

N. Y.—Fultonville
Starin Silk Fabric Co. (Knit
Silk) ....B

N. Y.—Gloversville
Adler & Co., Jacob (Gloves)
AAAA
Allen & Son, J. C. C
Bachner-Moses Co. (Suede;
Mocha; Kid Gloves) ..B
Batty, J. A. & Co........D
Brown, L. S. (Buckskin)..C
Clark, Easterly & Co.
(Men's Cape; Kid; Mocha;.
Suede Gloves) C
Dade, Frederick ....D
Danforth, J. H. (Men's
Kid; Mocha; Suede
Gloves) ....D
Dempster & Place ....A
Dye, C. H. (Suede; Kid).D
Fear & White (Men's;
Ladies' Kid Gloves) ...C
Fiske & Co., Edward W...C
Foerderer, Robert H. (Kid;
Suede; Mocha Gloves)
AAAA
Gloversville Knitting Co.
(Knit) ....B
Hall, Jesse (Gloves; Mit-
tens) C
Hays & Co., Daniel (Men's;
Womens' Buck; Mocha;.
Kid; Horsehide; Suede
Gloves) ....A
Hilts & Son, G. H. C
Ketcham, F. T. ....D
Kibbe, Chauncey S. (Kid;
Buck; Cape; Horse; Calf
Gloves) ....D
Kibbe & Radford (Leather)
B
Klein & Son, Albert .....D
Kraus, Julius (Kid Gloves)
D
Leak Fur Mfg. Co. (Fur
Gloves) ....D
Lefi-Straus Co. (Buckskin;
Reindeer Gloves; Automo-
bile Gauntlets) C
Lefi & Co., Wm. (Suede;
Kid; Mocha Gloves) C
Littauer Bros. (Gloves)
AAAA
McDougall, Wm. (Gloves;
Mittens) ....D
McDougall & Co., James A.
(Gloves; Mittens) C
McGraw, Loucks & Co.
(Gloves; Mittens) C
Mandrill, Geo. W. (Mocha;
Kid Gloves) ....B
Meyers & Son, Louis (all
kinds Gloves & Gauntlets)
AA
Mills, Frederick S. (Gloves;
Mittens) ....D
Mosher & Son, D. A. (Kid;
Suede Gloves) ....D
Peck, Frank L. (Leather
Gloves; Mittens) C
Phair & Co., J. S. (Mocha;
Kid; Suede Gloves & Mit-
tens) ....D
Quackenbush, J. A. & A. V.
(Leather; Fabric) .....D
Rea, White & Carter

GLOVES (Con.)

(Gloves; Mittens) C
Rose, Anna A. ....D
Schey & Co. (Gloves) C
Schlussel, Seymour C
Schwartz, Schiffer & Co.
  (Leather Gloves) ......A
Shaw, John M. ....D
Steele & Co., H. H. .....D
Steele Bros. (Fur; As-
  trachan) ....D
Tannert Co., Charles ....D
Van Dresser, Wm. C
Whitney, Warren E. C

N. Y.—Johnstown
Argersinger & Co., P. P...A
Chant Bros. (Kid) ......D
Cole, Geo. B. ....D
Colin Bros. ....D
Davies, McIntyre & Co.
  (Men's) ....D
Decker, Son & Co., John H.
  ....A
Evans & Sons, Richard (&
  Gauntlets) ....A
Foote, Wm. D. (Fur Gloves;
  Gauntlets) ....A
Hays & Gates C
Hewett & Hillock C
Hutchins & Potter (Gaunt-
  lets) ....A
Ireland Bros. (Kid; Mocha
  Gloves) ....A
Johnstown Glove Co.
  (Gloves) ....D
Karg, Tomlinson & Butler
  (Horse; Cow; Calf; Sheep-
  skin) ....D
Lucas & Kennedy (Wom-
  ens'; Men's; Mocha; Kid
  Gloves) C
McMartin's Sons, J. I. (&
  Buckskin Gauntlets) ...C
Mason, Campbell & Co. (&
  Gauntlets) C
Maylender Bros. ....D
Miller & Co., J. P. ....B
Northrup Glove Mfg. Co.
  (Mocha; Buck; Fine Kid
  Gloves) ....A
Pierson Bros. (Kid; Euede)
  ....D
Ricketts & Son, Thos. E.
  (Hogskin; Calf; Buck;
  Horsehide; Kid Gloves;
  Flesher & Military Gaunt-
  lets; Fencing; Boxing)..C
Riton Bros. (Kid; Castor
  Gloves) ....D
Rowles, Chas. W. (Gloves)
 C
Stewart & Briggs ....D
Streeter, Hackney & Co.
  (Heavy Leather) ......D
Van Sickler & Co., C. H.
  (Kid; Mocha; Suede
  Gloves) ....D
Wertheimer Glove Mfg. Co.
  (Leather Gloves) ......B
Young & Murphy C

N. Y.—Mayfield
Christie & Wilkins ....D
Kelly, Jas. E. (Kid; Suede;
  Astrachan) ....D
Mayfield Glove Co. (Gloves)
  ....B

New York City
Abercrombie & Fitch, 314
  B'way (Hunters'; Explor-
  ers') ....B
Cohen, Cassel (Fur Gloves)
  ....B
Dent, Allcroft & Co. (Im-
  porters) ....AAAA
Fisk, Clark & Flagg
  (Gloves) ....A
Goodyear's India Rubber
  Glove Mfg. Co., 503 B'way
  (Rubber) ....AAAA
Ingersoll & Bro., Robert H.,
  51 Maiden Lane (Boxing;
  Fencing) ....A
Johns-Manville Co., H. W.,
  100 William (Asbestos)
  ....AAAA
Lehman, J. & D. (Gloves)
  ....B
Silberfeld, S. (Kid; Mocha
  Gloves) ....D
Tannert Co., C. (Men's Kid;
  Mocha; Castor Gloves)..D

N. Y.—Northville
Hubbell, Ray & Co. (Cape;

GLOVES (Con.)

Kid; Suede; Jersey; As-
  trachan) ....B
Willard, James R. ......D
Wilson & Heath (Kid; As-
  trachan; Jersey Gloves)..C

N. Y.—Norwich
Barr, H. D. ....D

N. Y.—Ogdensburg
Phair, John T. ....D

N. Y.—Port Jervis
Chant, Charles (Jersey
  Cloth; Sheepskin; Horse-
  hide) ....D

N. Y.—Poughkeepsie
Hoag, C. F. (Knit) ......B

N. Y.—Pulaski
Pulaski Glove Co. (Gloves)
  ....D

N. Y.—Rochester
Lowenthal & Bro., Max
  (Knit Mittens) ....B

N. Y.—Sidney
Clark Textile Co. (Silk
  Gloves) ....A

N. Y.—Spencer
Spencer Glove Co. ......B

OHIO—Akron
Faultless Rubber Co. (Rub-
  ber Gloves) ....AA
Miller Rubber Mfg. Co.
  (Rubber) ....B

OHIO—Bucyrus
Blair, H. S. (Blair Husking
  Glove Co.) (Husking
  Gloves) C

OHIO—Cambridge
Addison & Co., J. E.
  (Gloves) ....D

OHIO—Cincinnati
Bacharach & Loeb (Knit
  Mittens) ....D
Dormer Bros. Co. (Knit
  Mittens) ....D
Goldsmiths' Sons, P. (Base-
  ball; Boxing) ....B
Roth & Co. ....B

OHIO—Cleveland
Bamber & Neuman (Knit).C
Diemer, Geo. C. (Knit Mit-
  tens) ....D
Friedman & Co., H. (Knit
  Mittens) ....B
Rich & Co., N. J. (Knit
  Mittens) C
Standard Glove Co. (Gloves)
  ....B

OHIO—Columbus
Armbruster, Wm. (Knit
  Mittens) ....B
Butler Glove Mfg. Co.
  (Working) ....D

OHIO—Delaware
Ohio Glove Co. ....A

OHIO—Eaton
Fox Bros. Mfg. Co. (Canvas
  Gloves; Tick Mittens)..D

OHIO—Toledo
Defiance Tick Mitten Co...D
Ohio Knitting Mills Co.
  (Knit Golf Gloves) ....D
Peerless Knitting Mills Co.
  (Knit Mittens) ....D
Roth & Co., Joseph (Silk;
  Wool) ....B

OHIO—Wash. Court House
Inskeep, Biber & Co. (Can-
  vas Gloves; Tick Mittens)
 C

PA.—Allegheny City
Lappe Tanning Co., J. C.
  ....A

PA.—Hanover
Hanover Glove Factory
  (Heavy Work Gloves)..D

PA.—Lewisburg
Musser & Sons, Joseph
  (Knit Mittens) ....D

PA.—Philadelphia
Foerderer, Robert H. (Kid;
  Suede; Mocha Gloves)
  ....AAA
Hall, Jr. & Co., L. C. (Knit)
  ....B
Hawkins & Co., Wm. (Knit)
  ....B
Reach & Co., Tulip & Pal-
  mer (Baseball; Boxing;
  Fencing) ....AA

PA.—Reading
Reading Glove & Mitten
  Mfg. Co. (Lisle; Cotton;
  Woolen; Cashmere; Taf-

GLOVES (Con.)
feta; Silk Gloves & Mittens) C
PA.—Woolrich
Rich & Bros., John (Knit Mitts) ....A
R. I.—Providence
Davol Rubber Co. (Rubber) AA
VA.—Winchester
Graichen, F. August (Buck; Kid Gloves) C
WASH.—Seattle
Eureka Glove & Suspender Co. (Leather Gauntlets).D
W. VA.—Wheeling
Wheat Glove Co. (Leather) B
WIS.—Beloit
Leonard Mfg. Co., H. J...D
WIS.—Berlin
Russell Glove Co., Frank (Hand Sewed) ....D
WIS.—Hartford
Uber Bros. (Buckskin; Fur) D
WIS.—Janesville
Howe Bros. (Rock River Cotton Co.) (Gloves) ..B
WIS.—La Crosse
Fox River Valley Knitting Co. (Knit Mittens) ......D
La Crosse Knitting Works (Knit Mittens) C
WIS.—Milwaukee
Braun Glove Co., P. J. (Leather; Faced Knit).D
Brown-Bouton Glove Co. (Leather) C
Ellsworth & Thayer Mfg. Co. (Fur) ....A
Friedlander, Morris (Knit) C
Great Western Knitting Co. (Knit Gloves) C
Hansen Mfg. Co., O. C. (Automobile Gauntlets; Working) ....A
Kalamazoo Knitting Co. (Knit; Leather) ......A
Milwaukee Glove & Mitten Co. (Heavy Gloves; Palm Mittens) ....D
Natl. Knitting Co. (Knit) AA
Nicolai-Plantke Co. .....D
Phoenix Knitting Works (Knit) ....B
Sauer, J. W. ....D
Tabor Glove Co. (Unlined; Leather Lined) ....B
Wisconsin Knitting Works (Knit) ....D
WIS.—Portage
Portage Hosiery Co. (Knit) C
WIS.—Ripon
Bouton & Germain Co. (Engineers' Gloves) C
Ripon Knitting Wks. (Leather) ....B
WIS.—Sheboygan
Ross, Sellinger Co. (Leather) ....A
Sheboygan Knitting Co. (Knit) C

GLUCOSE

ILL.—Chicago
Corn Products Co. ....AAA
Glucose Sugar Refining Co., The Rookery ......AAAA
ILL.—Waukegan
U. S. Sugar Refinery.AAAA
MD.—Baltimore
U. S. Sugar Refinery, 406 Exchange Pl. ....AAAA
Woods & Co., D. C., 110 S. Gay (Confec.) ....B
New York City
Corn Products Co., 25 Broad AAAA
New York Glucose Co., 26 B'way ....AA
Seelye, Thomas, 142 Front AA
PA.—Philadelphia
Perfection Jar Glucose Co., 514 Beach ....D
WIS.—Milwaukee
Stark, W. F., 306 E. Water C

GLUE

CAL.—San Francisco
California Glue Works, 106 Pine ....A
California Paint Co., 22 Jessie ....B
Challenge Glue Co., 17th Av. South, nr. G. C
DEL.—Wilmington
Delaware Glue Co. ......B
D. C.—Washington
Royal Glue Co. (Bottled)..C
ILL.—Chicago
American Glue Co., 150 Kinzie (Fish; Liquid).AAAA
Anglo-American Provision Co. ....AAAA
Armour Glue Works, 205 La Salle (Carriage; Family; Colored; Elastic).AAAA
Baeder, Adamson & Co., 172 Lake ....AAAA
Chicago Fireproof Covering Co. (Fireproof) ....E
Diamond Glue Co., 218 La Salle ....A
Lister, Joseph, 1158 Elston Av. ....A
Midland Glue Co., Monadnock Blk. ....D
Spiegel & Co., J., 218 La Salle ....A
Stein, Hirsh Co., 2597 Archer Av. ....AAA
Swift & Co. ....AAAA
Thurston & Co., F. W., 29 River (Liquid) ....A
Wisdom & Co., 205 E. Lake B
IND.—Indianapolis
Kingan & Co. ......AAAA
National Glue Co., 525 W. 14th ....B
IND.—New Albany
Conrad & Krammerer ...AA
MD.—Baltimore
Baker Bros. & Co., 36 S. Charles ....A
Baugh & Sons' Co., 36 South AAAA
Coulson, Edw. L., Jenkins Lane ....F
McCormick & Co., 106 W. Falls Av. (Iron) ......D
Wachter Mfg. Co., 509 W. Pratt ....D
MASS.—Boston
American Glue Co., 415 Atlantic Av. (Fish; Liquid) AAA
Baeder, Adamson & Co., 143 Milk ....AAAA
Carter's Ink Co. (Family; Fish; Liquid) ....A
Diamond Glue Co., 164 Federal ....A
Golding & Co. (Colored; Elastic) ....B
Hammond Glue Co., 417 Atlantic Av. ....A
International Glue Co., 421 Atlantic Av. ....D
Nash Co., E. W., 90 Pearl B
Whitten Co., J. O., 68 Western Av. ....A
MASS.—Cambridge
Whittemore Bros. & Co. (Liquid) ....AA
MASS.—Gloucester
Dodd & Co., A. W., 5 Wharf (Fish; Liquid)..B
Gloucester Isinglass Glue Co., Eastern Av. (Carriage) ....D
Improved Process Glue Co. (Liquid) ....B
Robinson Bros., Whittemore ....D
Russia Cement Co., off Essex Av. (Fish; Liquid; Family) ....A
MASS.—Peabody
American Glue Co. (Fish; Liquid) ....AAAA
MASS.—Salem
Atlantic Glue Co. C
MICH.—Detroit
Berry Bros., Wight & Lieb AAA
Michigan Carbon Co., 5 Front ....AAA

GLUE (Con.)
MO.—St. Joseph
Swift & Co., Stock Yards
.... AAAA
MO.—St. Louis
American Glue Co., 410 Elm
(Fish; Liquid) ....AAAA
Clarkson Glue Co., 214 N.
Commercial ....D
Mathiason Mfg. Co., P. B.,
5342 N. 2d ....A
Reardon Mfg. Co. ......A
Tamm Bros. Glue Co., Sarpy
Av., nr. Manchester Av.
.... AA
N. H.—Dover
Wiggins & Stevens .....AA
N. H.—Keene
Keene Glue Co. ....B
N. J.—Newark
Baeder, Adamson & Co.,
Lockwood ....AAAA
Lane, F. F. L............C
Listers' Agr'l. Chemical
Wks., (Lister Wks.)
.... AAAA
N. Y.—Buffalo
Blehdon, Victor R., Mooney
Bldg. ....A
Couch & Co., B. T., 166 S.
Park Av. ....B
N. Y.—Johnstown
Fulton County Glue Co....B
Knox, C. B., 217 Chestnut
.... A
New York City
American Glue Co., 14 Ferry
(Fish; Liquid) ...AAAA
Amour Glue Works, 211
Pearl (Carriage; Family;
Colored; Elastic) .AAAA
Arabol Mfg. Co., 100 Wil-
liam (Bookbinders') ...A
Baeder, Adamson & Co., 67
Beekman ....AAAA
Behr & Co., Herman, 75
Beekman ....AA
Cooper's Glue Factory,
Peter, 13 Burling Slip
.... A AA A
Davids Co., Thaddeus, Wil-
liam (Liquid) C
Delaware Glue Works, 61
Beekman ....A
Delaney & Co., 97 Beekman
.... AA
Diamond Glue Co., 101 Beek-
man ....A
Eagle Glue & Curled Hair
Co., 2 Dover ....B
Hewett & Bros., C. B., 98
Beekman ....A
Hoyt, Arthur S., 90 West
Broadway (Powder; Cold
Water) ....B
Isaacs & Co., S., 299 Pearl
.... AA
Lister's Agricultural Chem-
ical Works, 26 Broadway
.... AAAA
Milligan & Higgins Glue
Co., 222 Front ....A
National Gum & Mica Co.,
502 W. 45th (Liquid)...A
Putnam & Son, Thos. L., 170
Front ....D
Toch, J. L. & J., 85 Pearl
.... F
Tower & Lyon Co., 95 Cham-
bers (Liquid Fish) ....B
Townsend, Charles, 276
Pearl ....B
Waddell & Co., R. J., 52
Beekman ....AA
OHIO—Cincinnati
Bird Glue Co., 3d & Main..B
Stephens & Bro., Miami Ca-
nal & Marshall Av.....AA
Van Bibber Roller Co. (Tab-
let) ....D
OHIO—Cleveland
Masek, Charles, 43 Brook-
lyn ....E
PA.—Allegheny
Globe Glue Co., 164 Spring
Garden Av. ....D
PA.—Philadelphia
American Glue Co., 142 N.
Front (Fish; Liquid)
.... AAAA
Baeder, Adamson & Co., 730
Market ....AAAA
Baugh & Sons' Co. ....AAAA

GLUE (Con.)
Berg Glue Co., ., Ontario
below Richmond ......B
Continental Manufacturing
Co. (Liquid) ....D
Delany & Co., 209 N. 3d
.... AA
Dimond Glue Co., 420 Com-
merce ....A
Martin Co. (Inc.), D. B.,
Land Title Bldg. ..AAAA
Tunnell & Co., F. W., 15
N. 5th ....A
PA.—Pittsburg
Wilhelm, Hy., 4 Fountain
.... A
PA.—Warren
Keystone Glue Co. C
W. VA.—Wheeling
Gilleland Glue Co., R. M.
.... B
WIS.—Manitowoc
Manitowoc Glue Co.......C

GLYCERATES

MICH.—Detroit
Parke, Davis & Co. ..AAAA
New York City
Caswell, Massey & Co. ..AA

GLYCERINE

CAL.—San Francisco
Heuter, E. L. ....AA
San Francisco Candle Co...A
DEL.—Wilmington
Atlantic Dynimite Co.
(Nitro) ....AAA
ILL.—Aurora
Jobbins, Wm. F. ....A
Barrett & Co., M. L., 219
Lake ....A
Kirk & Co., J. S. ......AAA
Wrisley Co., Allen B., 477
5th Av. ....A
IND.—Evansville
Melzer Bros. ....A
MO.—St. Louis
Goodwin Mfg. Co. ......AA
NEB.—South Omaha
Cudahy Packing Co., AAAA
N. J.—Newark
Butterworth-Judson Co. ..B
N. Y.—Buffalo
Larkin Co. ....AAAA
N. Y.—Kingston
Nitro Powder Co. (Nitro), B
New York City
Bradford Glycerine Co., 55
Liberty C
Fuerst Bros. Co. ....D
Giese & Son, Aug., 2 Cedar
.... D
Grasselli Chem. Co. (For
Nitro) ....AAAA
Klipstein & Co., A. ....AA
Marx & Rowelle, 100 Wil-
liam (For Nitro) .....AA
N. Y. Quinine & Chem. Wks.
(Ltd.) ....A
Segaller, Phil. X
N. Y.—Syracuse
Will & Baumer Co. .....AA
OHIO—Cincinnati
Emery Candle Co. ......AA
Harkness & Cowing Co....A
Proctor & Gamble Co. (For
Nitro) ....AAAA
Werk Co., M. ....AA
OHIO—Cleveland
Grasselli Chemical Co. AAAA
Harshaw, Fuller & Goodwin
Co. ....AA
OHIO—Findlay
Findlay Glycerine Co. ....D
PA.—Philadelphia
Powers - Weightman-Rosen-
garten Co ....AAAA
PA.—Pittsburg
Walker, W. H. ....AAAA

GLYCERITES

MD.—Baltimore
Sharpe & Dohme ......AAA

GLYCOSINE

New York City
Fries Bros. ....A

GOATSKIN

See Leather

GOBLETS
See Glasses & Glassware

GO-CARTS
See Carriages; Baby

GOGGLES
See Also Optical Goods

MICH.—Detroit
Johnston Optical Co.......A
New York City
Spencer Optical Co. C

GOLD
COLO.—Denver
Boston & Colorado Smelting
Co. (Smelted) ....AAA
MASS.—Boston
Billings, Clapp & Co. (Chloride) ....B
MO.—St. Louis
Mallinckrodt Chem. Wks.
(Chloride) ....AAAA
PA.—Philadelphia
Phillips & Jacobs (Chloride)
.....................A
Powers - Weightman-Rosengarten Co. (Chloride)
.....................AAAA
R. I.—Providence
Coe Mfg. Co., W. H. (Ribbon) ....B
Wall & Co., A. T. (Sheet),C

GOLDFOIL
See Foil

GOLD GOODS
See Jewelry

GOLF
See Sporting Goods

GONGS
See Also Bells

CONN.—Bridgeport
Amer. Tube & Stamping Co.
.....................AAAA
CONN.—East Hampton
Bevin Bros. Mfg. Co.
(Street Car) ....A
Gong Bell Mfg. Co. (Signal)
.....................AAAA
Starr Bros. Bell Co.......B
ILL.—Chicago
Arams & Westlake Co., Ontario Cor. N. Franklin
(Locomotive Cab), AAAA
Wallace Supply Co. C
Western Electric Co. (Electric) ....AAAA
MASS.—Boston
Electric Gas Lighting Co.,
195 Devonshire (Electro-Mechanical) ....A
Marshall Electric Mfg. Co.,
301 Congress (Electro-Mechanical) ....B
MASS.—Brookline
Holtzer-Cabot Electric Co.
(Electro-Mechanical) ...A
MASS.—Worcester
Union Water Meter Co.
(Steam) ....B
N. J.—Jeresy City
Williams & Son, E. A. (Steel
Signal; Table Electric)
.....................AA
N. Y.—Binghamton
Star Electric Co. (Electro-Mechanical) ....D
New York City
Edwards & Co., 407 E. 144th
(Electro-Mechanical) ..B
Gamewell Fire Alarm Telegraph Co., 19 Barclay
(Electro-Mechanical) ..AA
Ostrander & Co., W. R., 22
Dey (Electro-Mechanical)
.....................A
Pearce, Frederick, 18 Rose
(Electro-Mechanical) ..B
OHIO—Cincinnati
Powell Co., Wm., 2529

GONGS (Con.)
Spring Grove Av. (Steam)
.....................A
PA.—Allegheny
Wall Mfg. Supply Co., P.
(Forged Steel) ....B
PA.—Cheswick
Cheswick Mfg. Co. X
PA.—Philadelphia
Partrick, Carter & Wilkins,
1231 Callowhill (Electro-Mechanical) ....B

GOODS: DRESS
See Cotton Goods; Woolen
Goods; Silk Goods

GOODS: SURGICAL
See Surgical Goods

GOODS: UPHOLSTERY
See Upholstery Goods; Trimmings; Gimps; Fringes;
&c.

GORING
MASS.—Chelsea
Boston Gore & Webb Mfg.
Co. (Shoe) ....D
Martin & Bro., Mfg. Co.
(Shoe) ....A
MASS.—E. Braintree
Hub Gore Makers (Shoe)..A
MASS.—Easthampton
Easthampton Elastic Webb
Co. (Shoe) ....E
Glendale Elastic Fabrice Co.
(Elastic) ....A
MASS;—Hudson
Taylor & Sons, Thos. (Shoe)
.....................F

GOUGES
CONN.—Seymour
Iwan Co., James ....A
CONN.—West Winsted
Winsted Edge Tool Works
.....................C
CONN.—Yelesville
Yale Mfg. Co. C
MASS.—Millbury
Buck, Charles (Socket;
Tanged) ....B
N. J.—Newark
Bernz, Otto, S. 13th Cor.
Orange Av. ....B
N. Y.—Buffalo
White & Co., L. & I. J.
(Socket; Tanged) ......A
New York City
Peck, Stow & Wilcox Co., 27
Murray (Socket; Tanged)
.....................AAAA
Russell & Erwin Mfg. Co.,
43 Chambers (Socket;
Tanged) ....AAAA
Tower & Lyon Co., 95 Chambers (Socket) ....B

GOVERNORS
See Also Regulators

CAL.—Oakland
Ford, A. (Gas) ....D
CAL.—San Francisco
Dow Pumping Engine Co.,
179 1st (Pump) ....AA
San Francisco Tool Works,
23 Stevenson (Pump) ...E
CONN.—Portland
Pickering Governor Co.
(Steam Engine) ....B
ILL.—Chicago
Chicago Engineer Supply
Co., 112 Lake (Pump) ..B
Davis Regulator Co., G. M.,
96 N. Clinton (Auto Condenser; Receiver Pump) C
Davis Co., Jno., 69 Michigan
(Pump) ....AA
ILL.—Moline
Moline Tool Co. (Steam; Automatic for Corliss Engines). ....E
ILL.—Quincy
Gardner Governor Co.

GOVERNORS (*Con.*)
(Pump; Steam Engine;
Speed; Pressure Com-
bined) ....AA
ILL.—Rockford
Woodward Governor Co.
(Water Wheel) C
IND.—Connersville
Roots Co., P. H. & F. M.
(Gas) ....AA
IND.—Indianapolis
Dean Bros. Steam Pump
Wks. (Pump) ....AA
Monarch Governor & Machine
Co., 740 E. Wash. (Steam
Engine; Horizontal;
Throttling; Gas; Gasoline
Engine; Air Compressor;
Elevator) ....B
Sensitive Governor Co., 140
S. Capitol Av. (Steam En-
gine) ....B
Sinker-Davis Co., 230 So.
Missouri (Steam Engine)
B
IOWA—Burlington ....
Murray Iron Wks. Co.
(Steam Engine) ....A'
IOWA—Marshalltown
Fisher Governor Co. (Grav-
ity; Pump; Steam Pump-
ing Engine) ....D
KY.—Owensboro
Gunther-Wright Mach. Co.
(Steam Engine) ....B
MD.—Baltimore
Bartlett, Hayward & Co.
(Gas) ....B
MASS.—Boston
Boston Steam Specialty Co.
(Feed Water) ....D
D'Este Co., Julian, 24 Canal
(Pump) ....B
Mason Regulator Co. (Pump;
Steam Engine; Tank) ..A
Waters Governor Co., 34
Oliver (Pump; Steam En-
gine) C
MASS.—Holyoke
Dean Steam Pump Co.
(Pump) ....AAAA
ter Wheel) ....AA
Holyoke Machine Co. (Wa-
MASS.—Lawrence
Watts Regulator Co. (Pump)
X
MASS.—Lowell
Middlesex Machine Co.
(Pump) ....E
MASS.—Orange
Hunt. Rodney Machine Co.
(Water Wheel) ....A
MASS.—Salem
Locke Regulator Co. (Fire
Pump) ....A
MASS.—Springfield
Electron Mfg. Co. (Pump) A
MICH.—Comstock
Comstock Mfg. Co. (Steam
Engine) ....B
MICH.—Detroit
Murray Automatic Boiler
Feed Co. (Pump) ....D
MICH.—Vicksburg
Eclipse Governor Co. (Steam
Engine) ....D
N. H.—Keene
Humphreys Machine Co.
(Water Wheel) C
N. J.—Newark
Foster Engineering Co., 107
Monroe (Pump; Speed;
Gas)................A
N. Y.—Albany
Albany Steam Trap Co.
(Pump; Steam Engine) D
N. Y.—Brooklyn
Acton, John, 116 John
(Pump; Receivers) ....D
Leffler & Co., Chas., 63 Cly-
mer (Gas) C
New York City
Baylis Co., 140 Wash. (Gas)
D
Connelly Iron Sponge & Gov-
ernor Co., 395 Bway. (Au-
tomatic; Balance; Service
Gas)................A
Creamer Steam Specialties
Co., 123 Liberty (Pump) B
Ford, Co., Thos. P., 81 Cen-
tre (Automatic Pump) ..D
Harlem Mfg. Co., 42 W. 67th
(Pump) ....F
Kieley & Mueller, 7 W. 13th

GOVERNORS (*Con.*)
(Pump) ....B
Leonard & McCoy (Steam
Engine) ....B
Monash-Younker Co., 43
Centre (Pump) ....B
Quimby, Wm. E. (Inc.) 141
Bway. (Pump) ....B
Roberts & Bros., Geo. J., 471
4th Av. (Pump) ....A
Standard Steam Specialty
Co., 111 5th Av. (Pump) D
Thorpe, Platt & Co. (Imps.)
99 Cedar (Marine Steam
Engine) ....F
Worthington Pumping En-
gine Co. (Pump) ...AAAA
N. Y.—Oswego
Kitts Mfg. Co. (Pump) ...D
N. Y.—Rochester
Judson Governor Co., Browns
Race & Furnace (Steam
Engines) ....B
N. Y.—Yonkers
Van Auken-Clevance Co.
(Pump) ....E
OHIO—Akron
Jones & Kuhlke (Steam En-
gine) ....F
Replogle Governor Wks.
(Water Wheel) ....A
OHIO—Cincinnati
Laidlaw-Dunn-Gordon Co.
(Pump) ....AAAA
OHIO—Cleveland
Strong, Carlisle & Hammond,
61 Frankfort (Pump) ..A
OHIO—Dayton
Dayton Globe Iron Wks. Co.
(Water Wheel) ....B
OHIO—Springfield
Leffel & Co., Jas. (Water
Wheel) ....AA
PA.—Chester
Vulcan Wks. (Marine Steam
Engine) ....E
PA.—Erie
Jerecki Mfg. Co. (Steam En-
gine) ....AAAA
Skinner Engine Co, (Steam
Engine) ....A
Stearns Mfg. Co. (Steam En-
gine) ....B
PA.—Philadelphia
Lovegrove & Co., 143 N. 3d.
(Engine) C
Wood Co., R. D., 400 Chest-
nut (Pump; Gas) ..AAAA
PA.—Pittsburg
Chaplin-Fulton Mfg. Co., 28
Penn Av. (Pump) .....A
Williams Guage Co., 543 4th
Av. (Pump) ....D
Wilson-Snyder Mfg. Co.,
Ross & Water (Pump) AA
PA.—Williamsport
Valley Iron Wks. (Pump) A
WIS.—Milwaukee
Filer & Stowell Mfg. Co.
(Ltd.) (Steam Engine)
AAA
Johnson-Service Co. (Pres-
sure for Steam Boilers;
Air Compressors; Water
Level; for closed or open
Tanks) ....AAA
Nordberg Mfg. Co., 476 Vir-
ginia (Automatic Cut-off
Steam Engine) .....AAA

GOWNS
See Clothing; Ladies

GRADERS
See also Scrapers & Agr.
Imps. for Road Graders

MASS.—Boston
Boston & Lockport Block
Co. (Coffee, Rice & Grain)
A
N. Y.—Silver Creek
Huntley Mfg. Co. (Coffee;
Peanut; Rice) ....A
N. C.—Salem
Salem Iron Wrks. (Coffee;
Rice; Grain) ....A

GRADOMETERS
IOWA—Dubuque
Adams Co. (Automobiles;

GRADOMETERS (Con.)
Bicycle; Measuring Grades
of Hills) ....A

GRADUATES

N. Y.—New York City
Hoehn Co., R. 80 Chambers
(Glass) ....B
Maris & Co., J. M., 219 Fulton ....B
Tagliabue, Guiseppe, 302
Pearl ....B
OHIO—Cambridge
Cambridge Glass Co. (Glass)
B

GRANARIES

ILL.—Joliet
Adam Steel & Wire Co. (Portable) ....D

GRANITE

MD.—Baltimore
Maryland Granite Co., 218
E. York (Building ....A
MO.—St. Louis
Schmeider Granite Co.
(Crushed) ....A
N. Y.—Albany
Flint Granite Co. (Building) ....A
PA.—Philadelphia
Giles, McMichael & Co.
(Building) ....D
VT.—Woodbury
Woodbury Granite Co.
(Building) ....AA
WIS.—Milwaukee
Milwaukee Monument Co.
(Building; Crushed) ...C

GRANU-LATORS

See also Machinery

LA.—New Orleans
Haubtman & Loeb Co. (Ltd.)
(Sugar) ....D
MD.—Baltimore
Adt, John B., (Tobacco) ..A
MASS.—Boston
Hersey Mfg. Co. (Sugar)
AA
MICH.—Detroit
Colton, Arthur, (Pharmaceutical) C
MINN.—Minneapolis
Schultz-O'Neil Co. (Roller)
C
N. Y.—Brooklyn
Gould & Garrison, ft. So.
10th. (Sugar) ....B
N. Y.—Buffalo
Squier Mfg. Co., Geo. L.
(Sugar) ....AAA
PENN.—Philadelphia
Morris, Henry G., (Sugar)
B
VA.—Richmond
Cardwell Machine Co. (Tobacco) ....A

GRANULES

ILL.—Chicago
Baker & Co., Chas. S.,.....C
MD.—Baltimore
Sharpe & Dohme......AAA
MASS.—Cambridge
Thayer & Co., Henry ....A
MICH.—Detroit
Parke, Davis & Co......AAAA
Stearns & Co., Fred'k., AAA
MICH.—Kalamazoo
Upjohn Co. ....AA
N. Y.—New York City
McKesson & Robbins, AAAA
Schieffelin & Co., W. H..AA
OHIO—Cincinnati
Merrell Chemical Co., Wm.
S. ....AAA

GRAPERIES

See Also Greenhouses

N. Y.—Irvington
Lord & Burnham Co.......A

GRAPHITE

MASS.—Springfield
Springfield Facing Co....C
MICH.—Saginaw
United States Graphite Co.
(Miners;' Refiners') ....A
N. J.—Jersey City
Dixon Crucible Co., Jos.
(Miners; Refiners; Brazing; Grease; Electric Appliances) ....AAA
N. Y.—New York City
Ilsley, Doubleday & Co.
(Lubricating; Paint;
Grease) ....A
Peabody & Co., H. W., 17
State ....AAA
Standard Graphite Co., 11
B'way (Miners; Refiners)
B
Swan & Finch Co. ....A
N. Y.—Niagara Falls
International Atcheson
Grabpite Co. (Electric
Furnace) ....B
N. Y.—Rochester
Hall & Co. (Inc.)........D
N. Y.—Ticonderoga
Ticonderoga Graphite Co.
(Miners; Refiners)......B
OHIO—Cincinnati
Hill & Griffith Co. (Foundry) ....D
Obermayer Co., S. (Foundry)
AA
OHIO—Cleveland
Smith Foundry Supply, J. D.
D
OHIO—Toledo
National Cement & Rubber
Mfg. Co. (Stick) C
PA.—Allegheny
Wisconsin Graphite Co.
(Miners; Refiners) X
PA.—Bethlehem
Pettinos Bros. (Miners; Refiners) ....A
PA.—Philadelphia
Eclipse Cement & Blacking
Co., 1238 Belmont Av.
C
Felton, Sibley & Co., 136 N.
4th ....AAA
Philadelphia Graphite Co.,
Stephen Girard Bldg. (Miners; Refiners) ....B
PA.—Pittsburg
Lawrence & Co., W. W., AA
McCullough-Dalzell Crucible
Co. (for all purposes) ..A
R. I.——Providence
Rhode Island Graphite Co.
X

GRAPHO-PHONES

N. Y.—New York City
American Graphone Co., 90
W. B'way............AAAA
Columbia Phonograph Co.
A
Edison Phonograph Agency
D

GRAPPLES

ILL.—Ottawa
Porter & Co., J. E. (Rafter)
A
MICH.—Evart
Champion Tool & Handle Co.
(Timber) ....AA
OHIO—Ashland
Myers & Bro., F. E. (Rafter) ....AAAA
OHIO—Canton
Ney Mfg. Co. (Rafter) ..B
PA—So. Bethlehem
Bethlehem Foundry & Machinery Co. (Rafter)....C
WIS.—So. Milwaukee
Stowell Mfg. & Foundry Co.
(Rafter) ....A

GRASS FURNITURE

See Furniture

GRATERS

CONN.—Bridgeport
Knapp & Cowles Mfg. Co.
(Vegetable) C
MD.—Baltimore
Mitchell Co., Jno. R. (Pine
Apples) ....F
Sinclair-Scott Co . (Vegetables; Pineapples).......E
MASS.—Boston
Ames Plow Co. (Cocoanut;
Horseradish) ......AAAA
New England Novelty Mfg.
Co. (Nutmeg) ....H
MASS.—Reading
Edgar Mfg. Co. (Chocolate;
Nutmeg) ....D
N. J.—Newark
National Saw Co. (Corn).B
N. Y.—Buffalo
Shepard & Co., Sidney,
(Box) ....AAAA
Smith's Sons Co., Jno. E.
(Horseradish) ....B
N. Y.—Malone
Hinds, Thos., (Starch) ..D
New York City
Crandell & Godley Co., (Cocoanut) ....AA
Houchin & Co., Thos. W.,
(Revolving) ....D
Hubbard Portable Oven Co.
(Horseradish; Yuca)....C
N. Y.—Rochester
Caldwell Mfg. Co. (Nutmeg)
C

OHIO.—Cincinnati
Day & Co., J. H. (Horseradish) ....A
PA.—Philadelphia
Anderson & Co., J. P. (Cocoanut) X
Disston & Sons, Henry,
(Corn) ....AAAA
Enterprise Mfg. Co., No. 3d
& Dauphin (Horseradish)
AAAA

GRATES

ILL.—Bradley
Bradley Mfg. Co., David
(Furnace) ....AAA
ILL.—Chicago
Green Engineering Co.,
Western Union Bldg.
(Traveling Link) ......D
IOWA—Dubuque
A d a m s C o. (Extension
Front) ....B
KY.—Louisville
Peerless Mfg. Co. (Fire
Place; Furnace; Stove;
Gas) ....AA
MASS.—Boston
Murdock Corporation (Mantel) X
MASS.—Lowell
Woods, Sherwood & Co.
(Wire; Pan) ....E
MASS.—Worcester
National Mfg. Co. (Wire
Pan) ....A
Wheeler Fdy. Co. (Stove)
D
Wire Goods Co. (Wire Pan)
A
MO.—St. Louis
Fritz, Geo. J. (Furnace)..B
Pleuger & Hengee Mfg. Co.
(Dumping) ....A
N. H.—Concord
Concord Fdy. & Mach. Co.
(Sewer) ....B
N. Y.—Corning
Allen Foundry Co., E. R.
(Shaking) ....E
New York City
Donegan & Swift, 6 Murray
(Shaking) C
Fee & Mason, 68 Beekman
(Fresh Air) ....F
Hubbard Portable Oven Co.
(Oven) C
Jackson & Bro., Edwin A.,
50 Beekman (Ventilating)
C
Jackson Co., Wm. H. (Fire
Place) ....A
Lalance & Grosjean Mfg.
Co. (Enamelled) ..AAAA
Manhattan Brass Co. (Fire
Place) ....A

GRATES (Con.)
Mott Iron Works J. L.
(Enamelled; Fire Place;
Furnace; Stove) ......AA
Treadwell & Co., M. H., 95
Liberty (Dumping) C
OHIO—Cleveland
Schneider & Trenkamp Co.,
479 Case Av. (Gas Parlor)
AAAA
Taylor & Boggis Foundry Co.
(Fire Place) ....AA
OHIO—Toledo
Auer Register & Mfg. Co.
(Warm Air) ....B
PA.—Allegheny
Rosedale Foundry & Mach.
Co. (Fire Place) .....,A
PA.—Beaver Falls
Knott, Harker & Co. (Fire
Place) ....AA
PA.—Oil City
Oil City Boiler Works (Furnace) ....AA
PA.—Philadelphia
Conroy, P. J. (Furnace)..X
Harrison's Sons, W. H.
(Fire Place) ....A
Miller & Co., Jos. S. (Gas)
E
Sharpless & Watts (Fire
Place) ....A
PA.—Scranton
McClave. Brooks & Co.
(Fire Place; Stove) ....A
PA.—Williamsport
Valley Iron Works (Fire
Place; Furnace; Power).A
TENN.—Chattanooga
Casey & Hedges Mfg. Co.
(Furnace) ....A
Chattanooga Roofing & Fdy.
Co. (Mantel) ....A
Chattanooga Stove Co.
(Stove) ....A
TENN.—Memphis
Wetter Mfg. Co., N. (Fire
Place) ....A
TENN.—Nashville
Phillips & Buttorff Mfg. Co.
(Enamelled; Fire Place)
AAAA
PA.—S. Pittsburg
Blacklock Foundry (Mantle)
C

GRATINGS

ILL.—Chicago
Barbee Wire & Iron Works
(Sidewalk) ....B
Braumoeller & Son, Henry
(Iron; Sidewalk; Office)
B
Globe Iron Works (Iron)..B
Illinois Malleable Iron Co.
(Foundation; Sewer, &c.)
AAAA
MO.—St. Louis
Kupferle, J. C. (Foundations; Sewer, &c.) ....AA
Pleuger & Henger Mfg. Co.
(Foundation; Sewer, &c.)
A
N. Y.—Cato
Dutton & Co., E. Q. (Window) ....E
New York City
Dimond, Thomas (Iron)...A
Fiske Iron Works, J. W.
(Iron) ....B
Steckenreiter Iron Works,
534 W. 58th (Iron)....D
OHIO—Cleveland
Van Dorn Iron Wks. (Iron)
AA
OHIO—Kenton
Champion Iron Co. · (Iron)
AA
PA.—Pittsburg
Pittsburg Lamp & Brass &
Glass Co. (Office)..AAAA
PA.—Elizabethtown
Buch's Sons. A. (Iron)....A
PA.—Harrisburg
Hickok Mfg. Co., W. O.
(Iron) ....AA
PA.—Wilkesbarre
Vulcan Iron Works (Iron;
Sidewalk) ....AAAA
TENN.—Memphis
Chickasaw Iron Wks. (Iron;

GRATINGS (Con.)
Sidewalk) ....A
WIS.—Milwaukee
Bayley & Sons' Co. (Foundation; Sewer, &c.) ..X

GRAVEL

ILL.—Chicago
Puhl-Webb Co., 119 West Randolph (Bird) C
N. J.—Hoboken
Vanderbilt & Son, J. (Bird) D
New York City
Barrett Mfg. Co. (Roofing) AAAA
OHIO—Piqua
Piqua Paint & Putty Co. (Bird) ....D

GREASE

See Also Oils

CONN.—Hartford
Tracy Oil & Varnish Co. (Axle) X
ILL.—Chicago
Frazer Lubricating Co., 31 Superior (Axle; Car; Machinery) ....AAAA
Hisgen Bros., 335 W. 43d (Axle) ....B
Stuart & Co., D. A. (Inc.), 447 Illinois (Axle) C
ILL.—Galena
Galena Axle Grease Co. (Axle) ....D
ILL.—Kishwaukee
Johnson, F. C. (Axle)....A
ILL.—Quincy
Richardson Lubricating Co. (Axle) C
ILL.—Rockford
Johnson, F. C. (Axle)....A
IND.—Jeffersonville
Pfau & Sons, George (Axle) A
IOWA—Council Bluffs
Monarch Mfg. Co. (Axle)..A
LA.—New Orleans
McWilliams, R. (Ltd.) (Axle; Belt; Cup; Machinery) X
MASS.—Chicopee Falls
Stevens Arms & Tool Co., J. (Gun) ....AAA
MASS.—New Bedford
Nye, Wm. F. (Axle; Gun) A
MO.—St. Louis
Broderick & Bascom Rope Co. (Wire Rope) .....AA
Frazer Lubricator Co. (Axle) AAAA
Leschen & Sons Rope Co., A. (Wire Rope) ......AAA
Waters - Pierce Oil Co. (Axle; Car) ....AA
N. J.—Jersey City
Dixon Crucible Co., Joseph (Axle; Gear; Graphite; Waterproof) ....AAA
N. J.—Newark
Lister's Agricultural Chemical Wks. (Bone) ..AAAA
N. Y.—Albany
Hisgen Bros. (Axle) ....B
N. Y.—Binghamton
Binghamton Oil Refining Co. (Cylinder; Machinery) A
N. Y.—Buffalo
Shining Light Mfg. Co. (Axle) C
New York City
Columbia Refining Co. (Machinery) ....B
Cook's Sons, Adam (Machinery) ....A
Fiske Bros. Refining Co. (Axle; Bicycle Chain; Car Cup; Gear; Machinery) ....B
Frazer Lubricator Co., 83 Murray (Axle) ....AAAA
Ilsley, Doubleday & Co., 229 Front (Axle; Belt; Car; Cup; Cylinder; Gear; Machinery, Graphite) ....A
Kellogg & Co., E. H. (Ma-

GREASE (Con.)
chinery) ....B
Klipstein & Co., A.....AA
Langman & Martinez (Axle; Belt; Car) ....AAA
Smith & Nichols, 145 Front (Axle; Belt; Cup; Cylinder; Gear) ....A
Standard Oil Co. of New York, 666 Hudson (Axle) AAAA
Swan & Finch Co., 151 Maiden Lane (Axle; Belt; Car; Cylinder; Gear; Cup; Graphite) ....A
Tide Water Oil Co. (Machinery) ....AAAA
N. Y.—Syracuse
Baum's Castorine Co. (Axle) D
OHIO—Akron
Akron Mining, Milling & Mfg. Co. (Axle) .....B
OHIO—Cincinnati
Obermayer Co., S. (Graphite) ....AA
Crystal Oil Co. (Axle)....E
Moore Oil Co., Chas. H. (Axle) ....A
Ogilvy, D. J. (Axle)......B
OHIO—Cleveland
Brooks Oil Co. (Axle)....A
Canfield Oil Co. (Axle)..B
Globe Oil Co. (Axle; Cup).A
Monitor Oil Co. (Axle; Cup) C
Reliance Oil & Grease Co. (Car; Cup; Cylinder; Gear) X
PA.—Freedom
Freedom Oil Works Co. (Axle; Belt; Cup; Gear) A
PA.—Philadelphia
Houghton & Co., E. P., 240 W. Somerset (Axle; Wire Drawing) ....AA
Smith & Co., C. K. (Axle) A
Stevenson Bros. & Co. (Car; Machinery; Printing Ink) B
PA.—Pittsburg
Atlas Paint Co. (Cable; Elevator Shaft) X
Turner, C. A. (Belt) ....B
R. I.—Providence
American Oil Co. (Machinery) ....B
WIS.—Milwaukee
Delaney Oil & Lubricant Co. (Axle; Belt; Car; Cup; Cylinder; Gear; Graphite) X
Wadhams Oil & Grease Co. (Axle) ....B

GREEN

See Also Colors

MASS.—Boston
Wright & Co., H. (Paris).C
New York City
Adler Color & Chemical Works (Paris) ....A
Ansbacher & Co., A. B. (Paris) ....AAA
F. W. Devoe & C. T. Reynolds Co. (Paris) .AAAA
Lavanburg, F. L., 100 William (Paris) ....A
Pfeiffer, I., 92 William (Paris) ....A
N. Y.—Penn Yan
Empire Chemical Co. (Paris) ....B
OHIO—Newark
Styron, Beggs & Co. (Paris) A

GREEN-HOUSES

MASS.—Boston
Stearns Lumber Co., A. T. (Builders') ....AA
MO.—St. Louis
Thomson, Kenedy & Co., 607 Pope Av. (Builders') H
N. J.—Jersey City
Pierson-Sefton Co., Westside

GREENHOUSES (Con.)

Av. (Builders') ....B
Plenty, Josephus, 215 Randolph Av. (Builders')...X

N. Y.—Brooklyn
Scollay, Jno. A. (Est. of), 74 Myrtle Av. (Builders')
　　C

N. Y.—Irvington
Lord & Burnham Co. (Builders') ....A

New York City
Hitchings & Co., 233 Mercer (Builders') ....B
Kay, Wm. H., 244 Fulton (Builders') ....D

GRENADES

ILL.—Chicago
Harden Hand Grenade Fire Ext. Co. (Hand) ....D
ILL.—Quincy
Stahl, Geo. H. (Hand) ...B
MO.—St. Louis
Meyrose Lantern Co., F. (Hand) X
New York City
Hayward & Co., S. F., 20 Warren (Hand) ....D

GRIDDLES

See Also Holloware; Wire Goods; Tinware; &c.

IOWA—Dubuque
Adams Co. (Cake) ....A
MO.—St. Louis
St. Louis Stamping Co. (Cake) ....AAAA
N. H.—Pike Station
Pike Mfg. Co. (Soapstone)
　　A
N. J.—Burlington
Stewart & Peterson Co. (Cake) ....A
N. Y.—Albany
Hoy & Co. (Cake).........A
N. Y.—Brooklyn
New York Stamping Co., 11th & Berry (Stamped).A
N. Y.—Manlius
Cheney & Son, S. (Cake)..A
New York City
Lalance & Grosjean Mfg. Co. (Cake) ....AAAA
OHIO—Cleveland
Avery Stamping Co. (Steel)
　　B
PA.—Philadelphia
Gaumer Co., Jno. L. (Brass; Bronze) C
PA.—Royersford
Royal Gas Stove & Fdry. Co. (Cake) C

GRIDIRONS

MO.—St. Louis
St. Louis Stamping Co.
　　AAAA
New York City
Central Stamping Co....AA
Lalance & Grosjean Mfg. Co. ....AAAA
Stoutenborough, X. ......D
OHIO—Hamilton
Kahn & Bro., F. L........X

GRILLES

CAL.—Los Angeles
Frey, J. W., 539 So. Bdway. (Wood; Fret; Lattice Work) ....B
Fruhling, Wm. A. (Brass; Bronze; Wrought Iron)..C
Smith, Jno. A., 456 So. Bway. (Wood; Fret; Lattice Work) ....G
CAL.—Pasadena
Pasadena Mfg. Co. (Wood; Fret; Lattice Work)..B
CAL.—San Francisco
Bush & Mallett Co., 328 Post (Wood; Fret; Lattice Work) ....B
Inlaid Floor Co., 422 Sutter (Wood; Fret; Lattice Work) ....D
Smith & Young, 723 Market

GRILLES (Con.)

(Wood; Fret; Lattice Work) ....D
West Coast Wire & Iron Wks. (Wrought Iron)..F
COLO.—Denver
Denver Iron & Wire Wks., 1401 Market (Brass; Bronze; Wrought Iron).D
Pioneer Iron & Wire Wks., 1437 Market (Brass; Bronze) ....D
Richter Iron Wks., P.. 1521 Stout (Brass; Bronze; Wrought Iron) X
CONN.—Essex
Essex Wood Turning Co. (Wood; Fret; Lattice Work) X
CONN.—Hartford
Buellesbach, W., 8 Spruce (Wrought Iron) X
Howard & Co., Jas. L. (Brass; Bronze)........A
CONN.—Meriden
Bradley-Hubbard Mfg. Co. (Brass; Bronze; Wrought Iron) ....AAAA
D. C.—Washington
Jorss, A. F., 315 13th N. W. (Wrought Iron) ....D
Simmons Grille Co. (J. Lee) 427 N. J. Av. N. W. (Wood; Fret; Lattice Work) ....H
GA.—Atlanta
Atlanta Wire & Iron Wks., 64 N. Broad (Brass; Bronze; Wrought Iron).F
ILL.—Chicago
Amer. Iron & Wire Wks., cor. Jefferson & W. Lake (Wrought Iron) ....E
Architectural Decorating Co. 204 Illinois C
Barbee Wire & Iron Wks. (Wrought Iron; Window; Door) ....B
Bertelsen Adjustable Grille Co., 306 So. Clinton (Wood; Fret; Grille; Lattice Work).........G
Booth, Jno., 114-116 E. Lake (Brass; Bronze; Wrought Iron) ....B
Boynton & Co., 67 W. Wash. (Wood; Fret; Grill; Lattice Work) ....B
Brown Bros. Mfg. Co., 22d & Campbell Av. (Wrought Iron) ....B
Chicago Ornamental Iron Co., 37th & Stewart Av. (Brass; Bronze; Wrought Iron) ....A
Dauchy Iron Wks., 88 Illinois (Wrought Iron)..B
Decorators Supply Co.. 209-219 So. Clinton (Wood; Fret; Lattice Work)..B
Halsted, Joseph, 390 W. Randolph (Wrought Iron)
　　D
Hickey Wire & Iron Wks., M. H., 54 Dearborn (Wrought Iron) ....B
Lorenzen & Co., Chas. F., 278 N. Ashland Av. (Wood; Fret; Lattice Work) C
Nelson, Chas.. 701 W. Lake (Wood; Fret; Lattice Work) ....G
Northern Grille Wks.. 1458 Milwaukee Av. (Wood; Fret; Lattice Work)...G
Schreiber, E. A., 158 W. Ohio (Wrought Iron)...X
Smith Wire & Iron Wks., F. P.. 100 Lake (Brass; Bronze; Wrought Iron)
　　AA
Standard Co., W. 15th & Laflin (Brass; Bronze).E
Streib & May. 211 E. Randolph (Brass; Bronze).H
Voss, Frederick, 617-621 Austin Av. (Wrought Iron) ....B
Winslow Bros. Co., 368 Carroll Av. (Brass; Bronze; Wrought Iron) ....AA

GRILLES (*Con.*)

ILL.—Peoria
Lucas & Sons, A., cor. Cedar & Washn. (Wrought Iron)

IND.—Goshen
I. X. L. & Goshen Pump Co. ....B

IOWA—Cedar Falls
Harris & Cole Bros. (Wood; Fret; Lattice Work).AA

KY.—Louisville
Snead Architectural Iron Wks.,, 710 14th (Brass; Bronze; Wrought Iron).B

MAINE—Portland
Megquier & Jones Co. (Brass; Bronze)........B

MD.—Baltimore
Balderston & Son, H., 119 Light (Brass; Bronze).A
Dietrich Bros., 344 North (Wrought Iron)........B
Stidman & Co., 16 N. Frederick (Brass; Bronze)..H

MD.—Westport
Lauer & Harper Co. (Inc.) (Wrought Iron) C

MASS.—Boston
Morss & Whyte, 75 Cornhill (Wrought Iron).AAA
Nelson Bros., 155 A (Wrought Iron) X
Stearns Lumber Co., A. T. (Wood; Fret; Lattice Work) ....AA
Whyte & Co., Oliver, 17 Cornhill (Brass; Bronze) C

MASS.—Medford
Boston Steel & Iron Co. (Wrought Iron) X

MASS.—Worcester
National Mfg. Co., 19 Union (Brass; Bronze)..A

MICH.—Detroit
Amos & Co., Chas., 94 W. Larned (Brass; Bronze).F
Barnum Wire & Iron Wks., E. T., 99-105 Shelby (Brass; Bronze; Wrought Iron) ....B
Keddy Grill Co. (Wood; Fret; Lattice Work)..H
Vulcan Co. (Brass; Bronze; Wrought Iron) ....F

MICH.—Grand Rapids
Dupree & Co., Jno., 329 Taylor (Wood; Fret; Lattice Work) ....D
Grand Rapids Carved Mould-Co. (Wood; Fret; Lattice Work) X
Ocker & Ford Mfg. Co. (Wood; Fret; Lattice Work) ....B

MICH.—Kalamazoo
Kalamazoo Grille Co. (Wood; Fret; Lattice Work) ....H

MINN.—Minneapolis
Flour City Ornamental Iron Wks., 27th Av. & 27 St. S. (Brass; Bronze; Wrought Iron) ....B

MINN.—St. Paul
Roberts-Goss Co. (Brass; Bronze) ....F

MO.—Kansas City
Kleeman, Trotter & Co., 1327 Main (Brass; Bronze) D

MO.—St. Louis
Aetna Iron Wks., 21st & Papin (Brass; Bronze; Wrought Iron) ....B
Globe Iron & Foundry Co., 901 Victor (Brass; Bronze; Wrought Iron) ....B
Herr Floor Co., Jno., 1203 Olive (Wood; Fret; Lattice Work) ....D
Koken Iron Wks., Koken Bldg. (Wrought Iron)..B
Lasar-Letzig Mfg. Co., 16th & O'Fallon (Brass; Bronze; Wrought Iron)..C
Ludlow-Saylor Wire Co., 4th & Elm Brass; Bronze).AA
Mesker & Bro., 421 S. 6th (Wrought Iron) ......AA
Pullis Iron & Steel Wks. Co. 816 Chestnut (Wrought Iron) ....A

GRILLES (*Con.*)

Nnion Iron Foundry Co., 1458 S. 2nd (Wrought Iron)..A

NEBR.—Omaha
Champion Iron & Wire Wks. 617 S. 16th (Brass; Bronze; Wrought Iron).F

N. J.—Boonton
Lincoln Iron Wks. (Iron).B

N. J.—Jersey City
Enead & Co. Iron Wks. (Brass; Bronze; Wrought Iron) ....A

N. Y.—Binghamton
Roberson & Son, A. (Wooden) ....AA

N. Y.—Brooklyn
Ajax Iron & Wire Co., 77 York (Brass; Bronze; Wrought Iron) ....F
Bossert & Son, Louis (Wood; Fret; Grille; Lattice Work) ....AAAA
Grossback & Co., Wm., 37 Maspeth Av. (Wrought Iron) C
Hecla Iron Wks., N. 11th & Berry (Brass; Bronze; Wrought Iron) ....AA

N. Y.—Buffalo
Buffalo Grille Co., 271 Court (Wood; Fret; Lattice Work) ....D
Cutting, Henry, 233 Mortimer Wood; Fret; Lattice Work) ....D
Feine, August, 152 Terrace (Wrought Iron) ....D
Sanford, Thos. F., •193 Seneca (Brass; Bronze).F

New York City
Anderson, Henry C., 414 Bleecker (Brass; Bronze; Wrought Iron) ....E
Cabaret, Paul E., 342 W. 14th (Brass; Bronze; Wrought Iron)..........D
Cornell Co., J. B. & J. M., 26th & 11th Av. (Wrought Iron) ....AA
Dimond, Thos., 128 W. 33d (Brass; Bronze; Wrought Iron) ....A
Fiske Iron Wks., J. W., 39 Park Pl. (Wrought Iron) B
Goulds' Son & Co., M., 83 Reade (Brass; Bronze)..A
Howard & Morse, 45 Fulton (Brass; Bronze; Wrought Iron) ....AAAA
Jackson Co., Wm. H., 29 E. 17th (Union Sq.) (Brass; Bronze; Wrought Iron).A
Janusch. F. G. (Est. of), 750 E. 134th (Brass; Bronze) C
Judd, H. L. ....AA
Koehn, Alfred, 157 W. 29th (Wrought Iron) ....E
Lobel, Andrews Co., 531 W. 55th (Brass; Bronze)...C
McMurray & Bro., Robt. T., 105 E. 22d (Bress; Bronze; Wrought Iron).C
Manhattan Brass Co., 338 E. 28th (Brass; Bronze).A
Mott Iron Wks., 84 Beekman (Brass; Bronze; Wrought Iron) ......AA
New York Carved Moulding Co., 771 1st Av. (Wood; Fret; Lattice Work) ....D
Pitt Composite Iron Wks., Wm. R., 111 5th Av. (Brass; Bronze; Wrought Iron) ....D
Prince Iron Wks., 553 W. 33d (Brass; Bronze; Wrought Iron) C
Terwilliger Mfg. Co., 23d & 5th Av. (Wood; Fret; Lattice Work) ....D
Thompson, Hervey, 176 E. 119th (Brass; Bronze; Wrought Iron) ....F
Union Equipment & Bronze Co., 514 W. 36th (Brass; Bronze) ....D
Uris, Harris H., 525 W. 24th (Wrought Iron)...C
Westervelt, A. B. & W. T.,

491

GRILLES (Con.)
102 Chambers (Wrought Iron) ....B
Williams, Jno., 544 W. 27th (Brass; Bronze; Wrought Iron) ....B

N. Y.—Rochester
Snow Wire Wks. C., 76 Exchange (Brass; Bronze; Wrought Iron) ....D

N. Y.—Syracuse
Syracuse Wire Wks. (Brass; Bronze) ....D

OHIO—Alliance
Weybrecht's Sons, J. T. (Wood; Fret; Lattice Work) ....B

OHIO—Cincinnati
Cincinnati Mfg. Co., 512 Main (Brass; Bronze; Wrought Iron) ....B
Schreiber & Sons Co., L., 8th 8th & Eggleston Av. (Brass; Bronze; Wrought Iron) ....AA
Stewart Iron Wks., 714 E. 3d (Wrought Iron).....A

OHIO—Cleveland
Forrest City Steel & Iron Co. (Wrought Iron) A
Tyler Co., W. S., 1150 St. Clair (Brass; Bronze; Wrought Iron)....AAAA
Van Dorn Iron Wks. Co. (Wrought Iron)......AA

OREGON—Portland
Tuereck, I. K., Davis & 9th (Brass)...........F

PA.—Allegheny
Albree Iron Wks., Chester B., 1115 Market (Wrought Iron) ....B
Baker Mfg. Co. (Brass; Bronze) ....F
Rieseck P., Allegheny Av. & Rebecca (Wrought Iron) C

PA.—Philadelphia
Darby & Sons, ˙Edw., 233 Arch (Brass; Bronze; Wrought Iron; Ornamental) ....A
Gaumer Co., J. L., 19th & Hamilton (Brass; Bronze; Wrought Iron) C
Hall & Garrison Mfg. Co. X
Heaton & Wood, 1706 Chestnut; (Wood Fret; Lattis Work) ....D
Merritt & Co., 1024 Ridge Av. (Wrought Iron)..B
Nacke & Son, A., 240 S. 9th (Brass; Bronze)....E
Strawbridge & Chase Co. 222 Arch Brass; Bronze) F
Wayne Iron Wks. (Inc.) Arcade Bldg. (Wrought Iron) ....B

PA.—Pittsburg
Phoenix Steel Construction Co., Penn Av. & 3d (Brass; Bronze; Wrought Iron) ....D
Pittsburg Brass Mfg. Co. (Brass) ....D
Taylor & Dean, 205 Market (Brass; Bronze; Wrought Iron) ....B
Vilsack Co., Martin (Wrought Iron) ....E

PA.—Reading
Remppis Co. Wm. F. (Wrought Iron) ....B

PA.—Ridgway
Hyde-Murphy Co. (Wood; Fret; Lattice Work)...A

WIS.—Milwaukee
Bayley & Sons Co., Wm., 732 Greenbush (Wrought Iron) X
Globe Wire & Iron Wks., 136 Reed (Brass; Bronze; Wrought Iron) ....G
Loeffelholz & Co., 170 Clinton (Wrought Iron)....A
Wisconsin Iron & Wire Wks. 186 E. Water (Wrought Iron) ....D

WIS.—Oshkosh
McMillen Co., R. (Wood;

GRILLES (Con.)
Fret; Lattice Work)...A

GRINDERS
See Also Machinery; Mills; Agricultural Implements

COLO.—Denver
Davis Iron Wrks. Co., F. M., 8th & Lorimer (Sample Ore) ....AA
Denver Engineering Wrks. Co., Blake & 30th (Sample Ore) ....A
Mine & Smelter Supply Co. (Sample Ore) ....AAAA

COLO.—Leadville
Engelbach Mach'y Mfg. Co. (Sample Ore) ....D

CONN.—Ansonia
Farrell Foundry & Machine Co. (Roll) ....AAAA

CONN.—Bridgeport
Bridgeport Safety Emery Wheel Co. (Bench; Car; Wheel; Cup; Cone; Hub; Emery; Plain Tool; Rotary Shear; Surface; Swing Frame; Wet Tool; Electrically Driven; Planer Knife; Surface; Tool; Plowshare; Swing Frame) F
Grant Mfg. & Machine Co. (Emery; Bench; Lathe Center; Surface) ......E
Springfield Mfg. Co. (Bench; Car Wheel; Cup; Cone & Hub; Emery; Plain Tool; Roll; Rotary Shear; Surface; Swing Frame; Die; Five Wheel; Floor; Knife; Pulley; Shafting; Shear; Special; Spindle; Universal Lathe; Lawn Mower; Punch & Die; Tool) ....B

CONN.—Derby
Birmingham Iron Foundry (Roll) ....A

CONN.—Hartford
Dwight Slate Machine Co. (Drill; Plain Tool; Reamer & Cutter; Center; Combination; Lathe Center).B
Pratt & Whitney Co. (Cock; Cone & Hub; Cup; Drill; Plain Tool; Reamer & Cutter; Bench; Cutter; Lathe Center) .....AAAA
Whitney Mfg. Co. (Plain Tool; Wet Tool) ....A

CONN.—Higganum
Cutaway Harrow Co. (Tool) X

CONN.—Naubuc
Williams Bros. Mfg. Co. (Mower; Knife; Sickle).A

CONN.—New Haven
Herrick & Cowell (Emery) C
Hill, Albert M. (Cinder & Ore) ....E

CONN.—Norwich
Rogers & Co., C. B. (Emery; Knife) ....AAAA

CONN.—Tolland
Clough, R. M. (Reamer; Cutter; Surface) ....D

CONN.—Waterbury
Blake & Johnson (Emery).A

DEL.—Wilmington
Lobdell Car Wheel Co. (Roll) ....AAAA
Pusey & Jones Co. (Wood Pulp) ....AAA
Trump Bros. Machine Co. (Lathe Center) ....A

ILL.—Chicago
Allis-Chalmers Co., Home Ins. Bldg. (Sample Ore) AAAA
Amer Can Co., 100 N. Clinton (Disc) ....AAAA
Besly & Co., Chas. H., 10 N. Canal (Plain Tool; Flat; Surface) .....AA
Chicago Flexible Shaft Co., La Salle Av. & Ontario (Portable; Lathe; Lathe Center) ....B
Chicago Wheel & Mfg. Co. (Sickle & Mower Knife; Cutter; Disc; Drill; Bench; Circular Saw; Elec-

GRINDERS (Con.)
(Knife, Planer Knife).AA

PA.—Lancaster
Lancaster Peerless Emery
Wheel Co. (Emery) ...D

PA.—Mechanicsburg
Comstock, Geo. S. (Lighten-
ing Sickle; Mower Knife)
..................................C

PA.—Muncy
Sprout, Waldron & Co. (Oil
Cake) ....A

PA.—Philadelphia
Atlantic Wrks. 23d
& Arch (Planer Knife).B
Bullock, C. K., 1357 Ridge
Av. (Mill Pick; Plain
Tool) C
Butterworth & Sons Co., H.
W. (Indigo) ....A
Challenge Machine Co., 3223
Turner (Bench; Disc;
Drill; Plain Tool; Reamer;
Cutter; Surface; Wet
Tool) ....D
Disston & Sons, Henry (Inc.)
(Reamer; Cutter) .AAAA
Dock, Herman, 905 N. Car-
lisle (Lathe Center) ....A
Harrington Son & Co., E.
15th & Penn. Av (Roll)
..........................AA
Johnson, Jr., & Co., Israel
H., 1422 Callowhill (Drill;
Plain Tool) ....A
Stow Flexible Shaft Co., N.
26th & Buttonwood (Em-
ery; Portable; Electrically
Driven; Lathe Center) ...B

PA.—Pittsburg
Mc Kenna Bros. Brass Co.
(Laboratory; Ore) ......A
Mesta Machine Co. (Roll)
..........................AAAA

PA.—Stroudsburg
Tanite Co., (Bench; Emery;
Plain Tool; Surface; Cor-
nish Roll; Car Box;
Knife) ....A

PA.—Waynesboro
Landis Tool Co. (Drill;
Face; Plain Tool; Reamer;
Cutter; Surface; Univer-
sal Metal; Flat; Univer-
sal) ....A

PA.—Weissport
Lehigh Valley Emery Wheel
Co. (Emery) ....E

R. I.—Providence
Amer Emery Wheel Wrks.
(Bench; Drill; Plain Tool;
Knife; Scissors) ....B
Brown & Sharpe Mfg. Co.
(Face; Plain Tool; Ream-
er; Cutter; Surface; Uni-
versal Metal; Bench-; Cut-
ter) ....AAAA
Builders Iron Foundry
Surface; Universal Met-
al; Bench; Tool) ....AA
Diamond Machine Co.
(Bench; Center; Cup;
Cone; Hub; Disk; Drill;
Emery; Plain Tool; Ream-
er; Cutter; Automatic
Hand Surface; Car Box;
Knife; Mill Pick; Cut-
ter; Lathe; Lathe Center;
Planer Knife; Reamer;
Portable; Surface; Swing
Frame; Tool) ....B
Iroquois Machine Co. (Disk;
Face; Plain Tool; Surface;
Universal Metal) ......A

VT.—Bennington
Scott, Olin (Wood Pulp)
..........................A

VT.—Springfield
Park & Woolson Machine
Co. (Shear) ....B

WIS.—Appleton
Valley Iron Wrks. Co.
(Wood Pulp) C

WIS.—Janesville
Rock River Machine Co.
(Bench) ....D

WIS.—Madison
Gisholt Machine Co. (Plain
Tool; Lathe; Lathe Cen-
ter; Universal ......AAA
Northern Electrical Mfg. Co.
(Electrically Driven)
..........................AAAA

GRINDERS (Con.)
WIS.—Manitowoc
Smalley Mfg. Co. (Cob;
Crushers ....B

WIS.—Milwaukee
Allis-Chalmers Co. (Oil
Cake) ....AAAA
Milwaukee Cock Grinder Co.
(Cock) X

WIS.—Oshkosh
Ransom Mfg. Co. (Plain
Tool, Belt; Motor Driven;
Wet Tool) ....D

WIS.—Port Washington
Western Implement Co.
(Sickle; Mower Knife).E

WIS.—Racine
Gorton Machine Co., Geo.
(Drill) ....B
Racine Malleable & Wrought
Iron Co. (Sickle; Mower
Knife) ....A

GRINDSTONES

CONN.—Hartford
Francis & Co., 859 Main..B

CONN.—New Haven
Bronson & Townsend Co.,
406 State ....B

ILL.—Aurora
Wilcox Mfg. Co. (Mounted;
Loose) ....B

MICH.—Port Austin
Wallace Co. ....B

MO.—St. Louis
Pleuger & Henger Mfg. Co.
(Family) ....A

N. Y.—Buffalo
Buffalo Foundry Supply Co.,
345 Babcock ....A
Smith Sons, Jno. E., 56
B'way ....B

New York City
Fairbanks Co., 416 Broome
(Family) ....AAAA
McCroden & Co., Jno., 33
West (Family) ....AA
Millers Falls Co., 28 Warren
(Family) ....AA
Niles-Bement-Pond Co., 136
Liberty (Mounted) AAAA
Peck, Stow & Wilcox Co.,
27 Murray (Family) ....
..........................AAAA
Pike Mfg. Co. 151 Cham-
bers (Family; Razor;
Unmounted) ....A

OHIO—Akron
Whitman & Barnes Mfg. Co.
mounted) ....AAAA

OHIO—Cincinnati
Morris & Co., E. K., 317
W. 2d................A
Obermayer Co., S. ......AA

OHIO—Cleveland
Cleveland Stone Co. Hickok
Bldg. (Mounted; Un-
mounted) ....AAAA
Independent Stone Co., Cu-
ayhog Bldg. (Mounted;
Unmounted) ....B
Ohio Quaries Co., 190
Euclid Av.............B

OHIO—Elyria
Grafton Stone Co. (also
Scythe Stones) ....B
Middleburg Stone Co....X

OHIO—Mariette
Mariette Stone Co. (Inc.)
(for Saw; Edge Tools) E

PA.—Philadelphia
Mitchell, Wilson, 312 N. 4th
..........................B

PA.—Reading
Penn Hardware Co. (Kit-
chen) ....AA
Reading Hardware Co. (Fa-
mily) ....AAAA

R. I.—Providence
Atlantic Grindstone Co.
(Mounted; Unmounted) B
Goff, Jas. C., 31 Point....B

VA.—Richmond
Gordon Metal Co........C

GRIPS

CONN.—Torrington
Union Hardware Co. (Bicy-
cle) ....AA

ILL.—Chicago
Klein & Son, M., 89 W. Van

GRIPS (Con.)
Buren (Wire).........B
ILL.—Litchfield
Litchfield Foundry & Machine Co. (Cable)......A
MASS.—Boston
Boston Belting Co. (Rubber Bicycle) ....AAAA
Brown & Wales Co. (Bicycle) ....A
Samson Cordage Wks (Cord; Line) ....A
Walworth Mfg. Co. (Rubber Bicycle) ....AAAA
MO.—St. Louis
Leschen & Sons Rope Co. (Cable) ....AAA
N. J.—Jersey City
New Jersey Car Spring & Rubber Co. (Rubber Bicycle) ....AA
N. J.—Newark
Walker Mfg. Co., D. (Stair Carpet) ....E
New York City
Gutta Percha & Rubber Mfg. Co. (Rubber Bicycle) ....AAAA
Leng's Sons & Co., J. S., 4 Fletcher (Bicycle)......B
Prentiss Vise Co., 44 Barclay (Pipe) C
OHIO—Ashtabula
Barber Mfg. Co. (Cable)..C
OHIO—Cleveland
Avery Stamping Co. (Wood; Malleable) ....B
Federal Mfg. Co. (Bicycle) ....AAAA
OHIO—Piqua.
Piqua Handle & Mfg. Co. (Bicycle) ....A
PA.—Brownsville
Herbertson's Sons, John (Cable) ....D
PA.—Philadelphia
Chester Steel Castings Co. (Railway Cable) AAAA
Morse, Williams & Co. (Elevator Hand Stop).AA AA
Wharton Jr. & Co., Wm. (Inc.) (Railway Cable) AAA
PA.—Pittsburg
Armstrong Cork Co. (Bicycle) ....AAAA
Marshall Bros. (Elevator Hand Stop).........AA
WIS.—Milwaukee
Kieckhefer Elevator Co., A. (Elevator Hand Stop) C

GRITS

DEL.—Wilmington
Lea Milling Co. (Hominy).C
IND.—Terre Houte
American Hominy Co. (Hominy) ....AAAA

GROMMETS

CONN.—Middletown
Wilcox, Crittenden & Co. (Metal) ....A
CONN.—Seymour
Rimmon Mfg. Co.........B
CONN.—Waterbury
Waterbury Brass Co. (Metallic) ....AAAA
N. J.—Newark
Jenkinson & Co., R. C. (Bur) ....AA
New York City
Foyle & Co., John, 112 Duane (Metal) ......AA
Metal Stamping Co., 468 W. B'way (Brass; Metal) B
Stimpson & Son, Edwin B. (Brass) ....B
OHIO—Dayton
Dayton Mfg. Co. (Metal).A

GROOVERS

See Also Machinery

CONN.—Southington

GROOVERS (Con.)
Peck, Stow & Wilcox Co. (Sheet Metal) ....AAAA
MASS.—Orange
Chase Turbine Mfg. Co. (Automatic) ....A
N. J.—Newark
Johnson, Wm. (Sheet Metal) ....D
N. Y.—Buffalo
Niagara Machine & Tool Wks. (Sheet Metal) ....A
OHIO—Ashtabula
Barber Mfg. Co. (Sheet Metal) C

GROS-GRAINS

See Silk Goods

GRUBBERS

See Agricultural Implements

GUANO

See Also Fertilizers

ALA.—Roanoke
Roanoke Guano Co........C
GA.—Albany
Pioneer Guano Co.........A
GA.—Atlanta
Old Dominion Guano Co...A
GA.—Savannah
Savannah Guano Co.......A
N. J.—Port Monmouth
New York & New Jersey Oil & Guano Co........D
N. C.—Wilmington
Navassa Guano Co....AAAA
VA.—Norfolk
Columbia Guano Co.......A

GUARDS:

See Also Hardware; Carriage for Wagon Box-Guards; For Watch Guards See Next Heading

COLO.—Denver
Brewer & Co., E. P., 1008 15th (Razor) ....G
CONN.—Easthampton
Bevin Bros. Mfg. Co. (Trouser) ....A
CONN.—Georgetown
Gilbert & Bennett Mfg. Co. (Wire; Window; Spark; Tree; Grate; Grave; Lamp Light ......AAA
CONN.—New Haven
Hendryx & Co., Andrew B. (and Cage Screens).....A
DEL.—Wilmington
Amer. Vulcanized Rubber Co. (Journal Box Dust) AAAA
ILL.—Chicago
Barbee Wire & Iron Wks. (Wire; Asylum; Wheel; Window; Skylight; Electric Light; Elevator; Bottle; Grave; Door; Lawn; Portable; Radiator; Spark; Store Front; Tree) B
Central Electric Co., 266 5th Av. (Electric Lamp; Wire) ....A
Fairbanks, Morse & Co., Franklin & Monroe (Cattle for Railway) ......AAAA
Harrington & King Perforating Co. (Radiator)...A
Railroad Supply Co., Old Colony Bldg. (Cattle for Railway) ....B
Sturges & Burn Mfg. Co. (Bicycle) ....A
Turner Brass Wks. (Bicycle Chain) ....A
ILL.—De Kalb
De Kalb Fence Co. (Tree) AA
ILL.—Freeport
Stover Mfg Co. (Bicycle) AA
IND.—Fort Wayne
Old's Wagon Wks. (Bicycle Chain; Bicycle Mud)...X

GUARDS (Con.)

IND.—Hammond

National Surface Guard Co. (Cattle for Railway)....C

IND.—Indianapolis

Atkins & Co., E. C. (Saw) ....AAAA

Lauter, H. (Bicycle Mud).B

KY.—Louisville

Dow Wire Works Co. (Window; Spark) ....D

MAINE—Portland

Burrows Co., E. T. (Wire) ....AA

MASS.—Boston

Folsom Snow Roof Guard Co., 116 South (Roof Snow) X

Murdock Corporation (Window Wire) X

MASS.—Clinton

Clinton Wire Cloth Co. (Wire; Elevator; Radiator; Window Wire).AAA

MASS.—Hopedale

Draper Co. (Belt Hole; Shuttle) ....AAAA

MASS.—Lowell

Mack & Co., W. A. (Oil for Engines) C

MASS.—Springfield

Applied Device Co. (Lamp) X

Bigelow-Cheney Wire Works (Wire; Asylum; Counter; Elevator; Nursery; Skylight; Window) ....A

Wagor Mfg. Co., P. R. (Electric Lamp Wire) ...G

MASS.—Woburn

Smith & Wallace (Car)...D

MASS.—Worcester

Crompton & Knowles Loom Wks. (Shuttle)....AAAA

Deane & Co., Henry E. (Window) C

Hamblin & Russell Mfg. Co. (Electric Lamp Wire).B

National Mfg. Co. (Electric Lamp Wire) ....A

Parker Wire Goods Co. Lamp; Light) ....D

Spencer Wire Co. (Lawn; Snow; Ice; Tree) .....A

Wire Goods Co. (Lamp; Light) ....D

Wright Wire Co. (Electric Lamp; Elevator; Lawn; Tree; Window Wire)..AA

MICH.—Detroit

Acme Fancy Wire Wks. (Incandescent Lamp) ...D

Amos & Co.. Chas., 94 W. Larned (Electric Lamp; Wire) ....F

Barnum Wire & Iron Wks., E. T. (Grave) ....A

Bolles Iron & Wire Wks., J. E. (Window) X

Burton, C. D., P. O. Box 746 (Razor) X

Inglis Wire & Iron Wks., Wm., 59 Woodbridge (Electric Lamp; Wire)..C

Scott Bros. Electric Co., 3 Farrar (Electric Lamp; Wire) ....H

MICH.—Grand Rapids

Baldwin, Tuthill & Bolton (Saw) ....B

MICH.—Kalamazoo

Kalamazoo Railway Supply Co. (Cattle, for Railway) ....B

Merrill-Stevens Mfg. Co. (Cattle, Steel, for Railways) ....D

MICH.—Three Rivers

Sheffield Car Co. (Cattle, for Railways) ....AA

MO.—Kansas City

Kansas City Wire & Iron Wks. (Window) ....A

MO.—St. Louis

Brownell Co. (Car) ..AAA

Handlan-Buck Mfg. Co., 212 N. 3rd (Cattle, Chain Surface for Railways) ...AA

Ludlow-Saylor Wire Co. (Window; Elevator; Grate; Grave; Lamp; Light; Tree) ....AA

GUARDS (Con.)

N. J.—Boonton

Lincoln Iron Wks. (Door; Window) ....B

N. J.—Hoboken

Woodman, Joel H. (Automobile Mud) ....A

N. J.—New Brunswick

India Rubber Co. (Bicycle Frame) ....AA

N. J.—New Orange

American Veneer Co. (Automobile Mud) ....D

N. Y.—Buffalo

Buffalo Wire Wks. Co. (Elevator; Grate; Window) ....A

Forsyth Mfg. Co., 308 Terrace (Bicycle Chain; Bicycle Mud; Bicycle Sprocket) C

Western Wire Goods Co. (Lamp; Light) ....D

New York City

Cabble Excelsior Wire Mfg. Co., Wm. (Wire; Window) ....B

Dewitt Wire Cloth Co. (Wire) ....A

Dimond, Thos. (Iron Folding; Tree) ....A

Estey Wire Wks. Co., 59 Fulton (Electric Lamp Wire; Grate; Grave; Tree; Window Wire)...D

Fiske Iron Wks., J. W. (Window; Door; Tree).B

Gleason Mfg. Co., E. P., 20 W. Houston (Electric Lamp; Wire) ....B

Gould-Mersereau Co. (Counter) ....B

Hartman Mfg. Co. (Tree) X

Howard & Morse (Wire; Asylum; Church Window; Elevator; Nursery; Cell Door; Spark; Tree; Grate; Lamp; Light; Window Wire) ....AAAA

Johns, H. W.-Manville Co. (Journal Box Dust).AAAA

Joseph, Sigmund, 245 B'way (Electric Lamp; Wire)..G

Maxwell Son, John (& Cage Screens) X

Pitt Composite Iron Wks., Wm. R., 111 5th Av. (Window; Folding; Stationery) ....D

Stimpson & Son, Edwin B. (Trouser) ....B

Tower & Lyon Co., 95 Chambers (Trouser) ..B

Westervelt, A. B. & W. T. (Tree) ....B

N. Y.—Unadilla

Tie Co. (Trouser) ....D

OHIO—Akron

Whitman & Barnes Mfg. Co. (Mower; Reaper) ..AAAA

OHIO—Canton

Diebold Safe & Lock Co. (Cell Door) ....AAA

Kohler & Co., F. E. (Tree) B

OHIO—Cincinnati

Bromwell Brush & Wire Goods Co. (Window; Spark) ....AA

Cellar Door Guard Co. (Door) ....D

Stewart Iron Wks. (Tree).A

OHIO—Cleveland

Cleveland Wire Spring Co. (Skylight; Snow; Ice)..A

Forest City Steel & Iron Co. (Elevator; Tree; Window Wire; Snow; Ice) ......A

Tyler, C. W. S. (Elevator) ....AAAA

Universal Skirt Guard Co. (Bicycle Dress) ......F

Van Dorn Iron Wks. Co. (Cell Door; Door; Window; Tree) ....AA

OHIO—Columbus

International Fence & Fireproofing Co. (Tree).....A

OHIO—Dayton

City Forge & Iron Wks. (Tree; Window Wire) ..D

GUARDS (Con.)

OHIO—Hamilton
Meyers Mfg. Co., Fred. J.
(Window; Spark; Tree;
Grate; Grave; Lamp;
Light; Window Wire)...B
OHIO—Kenton
Champion Iron Co. (Win-
dow; Tree) ....AA
OHIO—Toledo
Donovan Wire & Iron Co.
(Tree) C
Toledo Saw Co. (Circular
Saw) C
PA.—Allegheny
Carlin's Sons, Thos. (Door;
Window) ....A
Hipwell Mfg. Co. (Electric
Lamp; Wire) ....D
PA.—Elwood City
Glen Mfg. Co. (Grate;
Grave; Tree; Window
Wire) C
PA.—Philadelphia
Berger Bros. Co., 231 Arch
(Snow; Ice) ....A
Brill Co., J. G., 62nd &
Woodland Av. (Car)....
........................AAAA
Darby & Sons, Edw., 232
Arch (Electric Lamp
Wire; Elevator; Stall;
Spark; Tree; Grate;
Grave; Window Wire)..A
Gaumer Co., John L. (Win-
dow) C
Klemm & Co., 132 N. 5th
(Electric Lamp; Wire).C
Paxson Co., J. W. (Window
Wire) ....AA
PA.—Pittsburg
McDowell Mfg. Co., 541
Wood (Window, Expanded
Metal) ....D
PA.—So. Bethlehem
Bethlehem Foundry & Mach.
Co. (Lawn; Tree; Win-
dow Wire) C
R. I.—Providence
Clason Architectural Metal
Co. (Snow; Ice) ......B
VA.—Alexandria
Alexandria Iron Works
(Door) ....D
WIS.—Janesville
Automatic Machine Co.
(Adjustable Saw) .....F
WIS.—Two Rivers
Aluminum Mfg. Co. (Bicy-
cle Chain) ....A

GUARDS:
WATCH

See Also Jewelry

MASS.—Sandwich
Armstrong Braiding Co.
(Silk) ....D
MASS.—Springfield
Union Braiding Co. (Silk).C
New York City
Jonas & Co., Wm. (Silk)..C

GUDGEONS

MASS.—Worcester
Wire Goods Co. (Spool) ..A
New York City
Brown Co., A. & F. .....B
PA.—New Brighton
Townsend, C. C. & E. P...
........................AAA

GUIDEBOARDS

New York City
Hartman Mfg. Co. (Steel).X

GUIDES

ILL.—Decatur
Mueller Mfg. Co., H. (Hop-
per Cock) ....AAA
IND.—Indianapolis
Atkins & Co., E. C. (Saw)
........................AAAA
Barry Saw Co. (Saw) C
MASS.—Fitchburg
Simonds Mfg. Co. (Band ...
Saw) ....AAA
MASS.—Hopedale
Draper Co. (Spooler).AAAA

GUIDES (Con.)

MASS.—Springfield
Bigelow-Cheney Wire Wks.
(Felt; Wire) ....A
MICH.—Grand Rapids
Baldwin, Tuthill & Bolton
(Saw) ....B
New York City
Mitchell-Bissell Co., 38
Murray (Porcelain; Enam-
elled) X
Tiebout, W. & J., 118
Chambers (Sheet; Rope)B
OHIO—Dayton
Dayton Malleable Iron Co.
(Air Brake Lever) ...AA
OHIO—Hamilton
Black-Clawson Co. (Felt;
Wire) ....AAA
OHIO—Youngstown
Finished Steel Co. (Engine,
Shapes for) ....A
PA.—Beaver Falls
Standard Gauge Steel Co.
(Finished; Compressed
Steel Car; Cold Pressed
Steel Elevator) ......A
PA.—Danville
Curry & Co. (Elevator)...B
PA.—Philadelphia
Disston & Sons, Henry
(Band Saw) ......AAAA
VT.—Montpelier
Lane Mfg. Co. (Saw) ....A
WIS.—Milwaukee
Filer & Stowell Co. (Ltd.)
(Saw) ....AAA

GUIMPS

See Trimmings; Dress

GUITARS

See Musical Instruments

GUM

For Drug Gums, See Fol-
lowing Heading

CAL.—San Francisco
Amer Chicle Co. (Chewing)
........................AAAA
Newton Gum Co. (Chewing)
........................C
CONN.—New Haven
Century Chemical Co.
(Chewing) ....F
ILL.—Chicago
Amer. Chicle Co. (Chewing)
........................AAAA
Barrett & Co., M. L. (Ara-
bic; Tragacanth; &c.)..A
Brewer, Chas. A. (Chewing)
........................C
Ripe Fruit Gum Co. (Chew-
ing) C
Wheaton & Co., J. C.
(Chewing) ....B
Wrigley, Jr., & Co., Wm.
(Chewing) ....A
Zeno Mfg. Co. (Chewing).A
ILL.—Rock Island
West, L. E. (Chewing) ..C
IND.—Indianapolis
Fitch & Co., A. M. (Chew-
ing) C
IND.—Madison
Roberts & Co., W. B.
(Chewing) C
KY.—Louisville
Amer Chicle Co. (Chewing)
........................AAAA
Colgan Gum Co. (Chewing)
........................C
KY.—Paducah
Van Culin Mfg. Co. (Chew-
ing) ....D
MAINE—Portland
Curtis & Son Co. (Chewing;
Spruce) ....A
Rundlet Bros. (Chewing) .F
MD.—Baltimore
Baltimore Chewing Gum Co.
(Chewing) ....E
Faultless Chemical Co.
(Chewing) ....E
Lauer & Suter, (Chewing).A
MASS.—Boston
Davidson Rubber Co. (Den-
tal) ....A
MASS.—Malden
National Chicle Co. (Chew-

408

GUM (Con.)
ing) ....F
MICH.—Detroit
Schroder, V. (Chewing) ..C
MICH.—Niles
Noble Mfg. Co., K. W.
(Chewing) ....F
MICH.—Omo
Seng Chemical Co. (Chew-
ing ....F
MO.—Kansas City.
Lidwell Gum Co. (Chewing)
E
MO.—St. Louis
Amer Chewing Gum Co.
(Chewing) C
Chicola Mfg. Co. (Chewing)
A
Van Culin Mfg. Co. (Chew-
ing) ....E
N. J.—Newark
Amer. Pepsin Gum Co.
(Chewing) ....E
Columbia Gum Co. (Chew-
ing) ....D
N. J.—Trenton
Trenton Rubber Mfg. Co.
(Pure Sheet) ....A
N. Y.—Brooklyn
Amer. Chicle Co. (Chewing)
AAAA
Doherty, Eugene (Pure
Sheet) ....D
N. Y.—Buffalo
Buffalo Sour Pepsin Gum
Co. (Chewing) ....F
Medical Gum Co. (Chewing)
E
New York City
Amer. Chicle Co. (Chewing)
AAAA
Bishop Gutta Percha Co.
(Pure Sheet) ....B
Goodyear Rubber Co. (Pure
Sheet) ....AAAA
Green & Co., D. E., 1 Platt
(Arabic; Tragacanth) ..A
Gutta Percha & Rubber Mfg.
Co. (Dental; Pure Sheet)
AAAA
Hoople & Androvette, 218
Fulton (Gambier) ......A
Kleinert Rubber Co., I. B.
(Dental) ....A
Klipstein & Co., A., 122
Pearl (Gambier; Traga-
canth; Arabic) ....AA
Lamson & Bro., Jno. S., 77
Maiden La. (Varnish) ..A
Thurston & Braidich, 130
William (Arabic; Traga-
canth, etc.) ....AA
Traun Rubber Co. (Dental)
E
Winterbourne & Co., S.
(Varnish) ....B
N. Y.—Watertown
Stokes, F. A. (Chewing) ..F
OHIO—Akron
Akron Rubber Wks. (Pure
Sheet) ....AAAA
OHIO—Canton
Southern Gum Co. (Chewing)
D
OHIO—Cincinnati
Buhr, Pfaff Co. (Chewing)
B
Chusit Gum Co. (Chewing) E
Dental Chewing Gum Co.
(Chewing) ....F
Doscher Bros. (Chewing) B
Kenton Baking Powd. Co.
(Chewing) ....A
Smith Co., H. D. (Chewing)
B
Wehking, F. (Chewing) E
OHIO—Cleveland
Beeman Chemical Co.
(Chewing) ....B
Cuyahoga Chemical Co.
(Chewing) ....D
Heisel, G. L. (Chewing) ..F
Selleck-Fischer Mfg. Co.
(Chewing) ....E
White & Son, W. J.
(Chewing) ....B
OHIO—Dayton
Royal Remedy & Extract
Co. (Chewing) ....B
Ware Coffee Co., C. F.
(Chewing) ....A
OHIO—Findlay
Gobel, W. H. (Chewing) D

GUM (Con.)
OHIO—Lima
Banta & Son, F. J. (Chew-
ing) C
OHIO—Salem
Grove Co. (The) (Chewing)
E
OHIO—Toledo
National Chewing Gum Co.
(Chewing) ....D
Toledo Chewing Gum Co.
(Chewing) ....A
PA.—Erie
Erie Pepsin Gum Co.
(Chewing) ....D
PA.—Meadville
Garfield Gum Co. (Chew-
ing) ....D
PA.—Philadelphia
Amer. Chewing Gum Co.
(Chewing) C
Fleer & Co., Frank H.
(Chewing) ....AA
Green's Chemical Co., Dr.
(Chewing) C
Hance Bros. & White
(Chewing) ....AA
PA.—Pittsburg
Soda Mint Gum Co
(Chewing) ....D
PA.—Reading
Kola Chemical Co. (Chew-
ing) ....E
PA.—Warrior's Mark
Malena Co. (Chewing) ...C
R. I.—Providence
Davol Rubber Co. (Pure
Sheet) ....AA
TENN.—Knoxville
Biddle, W. D. (Chewing) E
TENN.—Memphis
Coleman, Solomon (Chew-
ing) ....A
TENN.—Nashville
Hoggins-Murkin Mfg. Co.
(Chewing) C
Valentino Mfg. Co. (Chew-
ing) ....A

GUMMERS

CAL.—San Francisco
California Saw Wks., 208
(Mission (Saw) ....A
GA.—Atlanta
Southern Saw Wks. (Saw) B
Wood Gummer & Filer Co.
(Saw) ....F
ILL.—Cairo
Reed, Jos. B. (Saw) ....B
ILL.—Chicago
Chicago Wheel & Mfg. Co.
(Saw) C
Covel Mfg. Co. (Saw; Emery
Wheel) C
IND.—Indianapolis
Atkins & Co., E. C. (Saw,
Emery Wheel) ....AAAA
LA.—Pool's Bluff
Pierce & Pounds (Cotton) D
MASS.—Fitchburg
Simonds Mfg. Co. (Saw)
AAA
MICH.—Detroit
Star Corundum Wheel Co.
(Ltd.) (Saw) ....E
MICH.—Grand Rapids
Austin & Son (Saw) ......B
MISS.—Corinth
Adams Machine Co., W. T.
(Saw) ....AA
N. Y.—Buffalo
Rogers & Co., S .C., 10 Lock
(Saw) C
N. Y.—Malone
Hinds, Thos. (Band Saw) D
New York City
Amer. Woodworking Machin-
ery Co., 136 Liberty (Saw)
AAAA
Hoe & Co., R. 504 Grand
(Saw) ....AAAA
OHIO—Cincinnati
Rowe & Trunnell, 123 W. 2d
(Saw) ....E
OHIO—Salem
Silver Mfg. Co. (Saw) ..AA
OHIO—Tiffin
Sterling Emery Wheel Mfg.
Co. (Saw) ....A
PA.—Allegheny
Ajax Mfg. Co. (Saw) ....D
PA.—Beaver Falls
Emerson, Smith & Co.

GUMMERS (Con.)
(Saw) ....A
PA.—Philadelphia
Atlantic Wks. (Inc.) 23d & Arch (Saw) ....B
Disston & Sons, Henry (Inc.) (Saw) ....AAAA
PA.—Pittsburg
Amer. Axe & Tool Co. (Saw) AAAA
PA.—Stroudsburg
Tanite Co. (Saw) ......A
PA.—Williamsport
Andrews & Sons, E. (Emery Saw) ....D
WIS.—Milwaukee
Filer & Stowell Co. (Ltd.) (Saw) ....AAA

GUMS: DRUG

MICH.—Detroit
Parke, Davis & Co. AAAA
New York City
Fuerst Bros. & Co. .....D
Hill's Sons Co., Edw. ...AA
Hopkins & Co., J. L. .....A
Klipstein & Co., A. ...AA
Lehn & Fink ....AAA
McKesson & Robbins..AAAA
Magnus & Lauer C
Parke, Davis & Co...AAAA
Patterson, Boardman & Co. AAA
Schieffelin & Co. ......AA
Thurston & Braidich (Arabic; Senegal; Tragacanth) ....AA
R. I.—Providence
Arnold, Hoffman & Co. AA

GUNPOWDER

DEL.—Wilmington
Dupont Co., E. I. ....AAAA
ILL.—Chicago
Aetna Powder Co., 143 Dearborn ....A
Amer. Powd. Mills, 188 Madison ....AA
MAINE—Portland
Oriental Powder Mills AAA
MD.—Baltimore
Hazard Powd. Co., (The) (Br.) 22 S. Calvert AAA
Laflin & Rand Powder Co. (Br.) 13 S. Charles AAAA
Oriental Powder Mills (Br.) 130 Hanover ....AAA
MICH.—Detroit
Austin Powder Co. ......AA
N. Y.—Kingston
Nitro Powder Co. C
New York City
Dupont Co., E. I. (Br.) AAAA
Hazard Powder Co., 46 Cedar ....AAA
Laflin & Rand Powder Co., 99 Cedar ....AAAA
Von Lengerke & Detmold, 318 B'way ....A
OHIO—Akron
Hardy & Co., O. B. .....B
OHIO—Cincinnati
King Powder Co., 5th & Main ....AAA
OHIO—Cleveland
Austin Powd. Co. ......AA
OHIO—Xenia
Miami Powder Co. .....AA
OHIO—Youngstown
Ohio Powder Co. ....AA
PA.—Allentown
Blue Ridge Powder Co. ...E
PA.—Shamokin
Shamokin Powder Co., Independence Av. & Franklin C

GUNS

See also **Fire-Arms**

MICH.—Grand Rapids
Brummeler & Sons, Wm. (Paris Green) C
Foster, Stevens & Co. (Paris Green) ....A
MICH.—Perry
Olcott & Son, R. S. (Paris Green) C
N. H.—Antrim

GUNS (Con.)
Goodell Co. (Insect Powder) A
N. Y.—Brooklyn
Kahnweiler's Sons, David (Line Carrying) ....B
N. Y.—Utica
Eureka Mower Co. (Paris Green) ....A
OHIO—Toledo
Union Fire Arms Co. (Shot) ....B
PA.—Philadelphia
Schoenhut & Co., A. (Rubber Ball; Toy) ....A
R. I.—Pawtucket
Bliss Mfg. Co., R. (Bow) AAAA

GUTTA PERCHA GOODS

New York City
Bishop Gutta Percha Co. B
Goodyear India Rubber Glove Mfg. Co. ...AAAA
Gutta Percha & Rubber Mfg. Co. ....AAAA
Mechanical Rubber Co. AAAA
OHIO—Akron
Akron Rubber Works AAAA

GUTTERS

ILL.—Chicago
Barbee Wire & Iron Wks. (Stable) ....B
ILL.—Desplaines
Garland Co., G. M. (Iron Greenhouse) ....D
LA.—New Orleans
New Orleans Roofing & Metal Wks. (Cornice) A
MAINE—Portland
Berlin Mills Co. (Wooden) AAAA
MASS.—Boston
Stearns Lumber Co., A. T. AA
MASS.—Lowell
Mack & Co., W. A. C
MO.—St. Louis
Harry Steel Wks., O. K. ..B
N. J.—Burlington
Steuart & Peterson Co. (Stable) ....A
N. Y.—Brooklyn
Wilson & Baillie Mfg. Co. (Steel) ....B
New York City
Fiske Iron Wks., J. W. (Stable) ....B
Mosley Iron Bridge & Roof Co. (Iron) ....B
Wheeling Corrugating Co. (Iron; Tin) ......AAAA
N. Y.—Oxford
Clark Blue Stone Co., F. G. (Stone) ....A
N. Y.—Syracuse
Stearns & Co., E. C. (Stable) ....AA
OHIO—Cleveland
Cleveland Stone Co. (Stone) AAAA
Garry Iron & Steel Co. (Eave) ....A
PA.—Philadelphia
Berger Bros. Co., 231 Arch (Galvanized) ....A
Gara, McGinley & Co. (Iron) ....A

HABITS

See also **Clothing; Ladies**
New York City
Krakauer, Jacques (Riding) ....A
Redfern (Ltd.) (Riding) A

HACKLES

MASS.—Lowell
Bagshaw, W. H. ....B
Dean, John M. ....F
N. J.—Newark
Crabb & Co., Wm. ....A

HAFTS

PA.—Bethlehem

HAFTS (Con.)
Strock & Co., L. W. (Pegging; Sewing Awl) ....D

HAIR

ILL.—Chicago
Armour Curled Hair Wks. (Curled) ....AAAA
Illinois Leather Co. (Cattle; Goat; Plastering) AA
MD.—Baltimore
Wilkens Co., Wm. (Curled) ....AA
MASS.—Boston
Sammet & Son, G. W. (Curled) ....D
Wheeler & Co., A. W. (Curled) ....B
Willcomb & Co., Geo. (Curled) ....AA
New York City
Baeder Adamson & Co., 67 Beekman (Curled; Saddlers'; Plastering) AAAA
Ritchie & Co., Geo. B., 57 Ferry (Curled) ....B
Rogers & Co., C. P. (Curled) ....A
Wilkens Bros., 440 Pearl (Curled) ....AA
Woll & Sons, Peter, 27 Howard (Curled) ..AAAA
OHIO—Cincinnati
Mitchell Co., P. R., 124 Pearl (Curled) ....AAA
PA.—Philadelphia
Baeder, Adamson & Co., 730 Market (Curled) ..AAAA
Coghlan & Co., Jos. T., E. Lehigh Av. & Edgemont (Curled) ....D
Cover & Drayton (Plastering) ....AAA
Delany & Co., 209 N. 3d (Curled) ....AA
Gordon Bros. (Curled) C
Grover & Son, Jno. D., 2800 Tulip (Curled) ....A
Tunnell & Co., W. F. (Curled) ....B
Woll & Sons Feather Co., Peter (Curled) ....A
VT.—Burlington
Whiting, E. B. & A. C. (Plastering) ....B
WIS.—Milwaukee
Gem Hammock & Fly Net Co. (Curled) ....A

HALTERS
See Harness

HAMES

IND.—New Albany
Todd Mfg. Co. (Steel) ..B
MO.—St. Louis
Nixdorff-Krein Mfg. Co. (Wooden) ....AA
N. H.—Andover
United States Hame Co. (Wood; Iron) ......AAA
N. J.—Newark
Grosner, F. W. (Wood; Iron; Scotch; Tubular) ......H
Peters Harness & Saddlery Co. (Wood) ....D
Sargeant Mfg. Co. ....A
N. Y.—Auburn
Auburn Hame Co. (Common; Scotch; Steel Clad) ....B
N. Y.—Buffalo
Pratt & Letchworth Co. AAA
United States Hame Co. AAA
N. Y.—Rome
Bingham Harness Co. (Wood) ....D
N. Y.—Syracuse
Fraser & Jones Co. (Iron; Wood) ....AA
OHIO—Canton
Elhel Co. (Dog; Goat) ...A
OHIO—Cleveland
Eberhard Mfg. Co. (Iron) AA
PA.—Jeddo
Wise, Geo. ....B
VA.—Rural Retreat
American Collar Hame Co. (Collar) ....F

HAMMERS
See also Machinery

HAMMERS (Con.)
CAL.—San Francisco
Doble Co., Abner (Bricklayers'; Masons') ......A
COLO.—Denver
Shaw Pneumatic Tool Co., C. H., 35th & Wazee (Pneumatic) ....F
CONN.—Bridgeport
Coulter & McKenzie (Drop) B
Knapp & Cowles Mfg. Co. (Tack; Masons') C
CONN.—Collinsville
Collins Co. (Blacksmiths') AAAA
CONN.—Cromwell
Warner & Son, M. R. (Blacksmiths'; Machinists'; Masons'; Riveting; Stone Cutters') ....E
CONN.—Hamden
Henry Mfg. Co., John T. (Tack; Nail) ....E
CONN.—Hartford
Billings & Spencer Co. (Drop Forged Blacksmiths'; Boilermakers'; Drop; Tack; Nail; Drop Forged Machinists'; Horse Shoers') ....AA
Pratt & Whitney Co. (Drop) AAAA
CONN.—Ivoryton
Comstock, Cheney & Co. (Piano) ....AA
CONN.—Meriden
Merriman, A. H. (Drop) ..C
CONN.—New Britain
Humason & Beckley Mfg. Co. (Carpenters' Claw; Masons'; Tack; Nail; Bricklayers') ....A
Landers, Frary & Clark (Tack; Nail) ......AAA
Stanley Rule & Level Co. (Tack; Nail; Magnetic; Upholsters') ....AAA
CONN.—New Haven
Brown & Co., R. H. (Steak) B
Kilborn & Bishop Co. (Bill Posters') C
Miner & Peck Mfg. Co. (Drop) X
Scranton & Co. (Power) ..C
CONN.—Southington
Peck, Stow & Wilcox Co. (Blacksmiths'; Machinists'; Riveting; Tack; Nail; Shoemakers') AAAA
CONN.—Waterbury
Waterbury Farrell Fdry. & Mach. Co. (Drop) .....AA
ILL.—Chicago
Chicago Pneumatic Tool Co., Fisher Bldg. (Calking; Pneumatic; Casting Scaling; Pneumatic Clipping; Riveting; Beading) AAAA
Elmes Engineering Wks., Chas. F., N. Morgan & Fulton (Power) ....A
Fairbanks, Morse & Co., Franklin & Monroe (Pneumatic) ....AAA
Higgins & Son, John C., 165 W. Kinzie (Bush) .....E
Murphy & Co., Christopher 204 Dearborn (Pneumatic) B
Nicol & Co. (Steak) ....D
Piano & Organ Supply Co., 125 Racine Av. (Piano) AA
Railway Appliances' Co., Old Colony Bldg. (Pneumatic) A
Vaughan & Bushnell Mfg. Co., 875 Carroll Av. (Machinists') ....A
Vulcan Iron Wks., 63 Milwaukee Av. (Pile Drivers'; Steam Pipe) ......AA
Whitman & Barnes Mfg. Co. (Machinists'; Riveting; Tack; Nail) .....AAAA
ILL.—Decatur
Tait Mfg. Co., F. B. (Lever) A
ILL.—Downers Grove
Dicke Tool Co. (Upholsters'; Bricklayers') C
ILL.—Freeport
Arcade Mfg. Co. (Cast Claw;

HAMMERS (Con.)
Tack; Nail; Foot Power)
.... A

Stover Mfg. Co. (Claw; Riveting; Cast Tack; Nail)
.... AA

ILL.—Moline
Williams, White & Co. (Drop; Justice; Power; Steam; Tack; Nail; Spring; Tire Welding) AA

IND.—Anderson
Wooley Fdry. & Machine Co. (Power) .... B

IND.—Evansville
Evansville Tool Wks. (Blacksmiths'; Boilermakers'; Bush; Farriers'; Macadamizing; Machinists'; Masons'; Napping; Pavers'; Stone Cutters'; Nail; Tack; Tinners') ......A

IND.—Indianapolis
Atkins & Co., E. C. (Pavers'; Saw) ...AAAA

IOWA—Dubuque
Davis, Geo. E. (Drop; Power) .... E

MASS.—Boston
Ames Plow Co. (Pavers'; Stone) ....AAAA
Beaudry & Co., 8 Oliver (Power) .... D
Harvey, H. H., 608 Atlantic Av. (Blacksmiths'; Boilermakers'; Masons'.; Pavers'; Riveting; Slaters'; Stone Cutters'; Bricklayers'; Shoemakers') ....D
Isele & Son, A. W., 51 Pitt. (Blacksmiths'; Boilermakers'; Masons'; Pavers'; Slaters'; Stone Cutters')
.... F
Lockwood Mfg. Co., E. B. (Inc.) (Steam) X
Robertson, Arthur R., 144 Oliver (Magnet; Bill Posters') ....F
Whitcher & Co., Frank W. (Shoemakers') ....A

MASS.—Cambridgeport
Tower Co., Sylvester (Piano)
.... A

MASS.—Fitchburg
Sawyer Tool Mfg. Co. (Machinists'; Blacksmiths'; Boilermakers'; Carriage Ironers'; Chipping; Engineers') C

MASS.—Kingston
Drew & Co., C. (Masons'; Bricklayers') C

MASS.—North Easton
New England Specialty Co. (Tack; Nail) ....F

MASS.—North Hadley
Dickinson & Son, E. P. (Broom Makers') ......D

MASS.—Quincy
Clark & Co., Alex. (Stone Cutters) ....G

MASS.—Springfield
Baush Mach. Tool Co. (Drop; Power) .... A

MASS.—Winchendon
Piper, Geo. M. (Tack; Nail)
.... X

MASS.—Worcester
Kidder, R. E., 35 Hermon (Power) .... E

MICH.—Alpena
Kline, Lewis T. (Steam) D

MICH.—Detroit
Anderson & Sons., W. H. (Blacksmiths'; Boilermakers'; Bush; Machinists'; Masons'; Napping; Pavers'; Slaters'; Stone Cutters'; Bricklayers') C

MINN.—Mankato
Mayer Bros. (Trip) ......F

MINN.—St. Paul
Amer. Hoist & Derrick Co. (Pile Drivers') ....AAA

MO.—Kansas City
Hauck, W. J., 20th & Southwest Boul. (Bush) ......F

MO.—St. Louis
Brecht Butchers' Supply Co., V. G., 1201 Cass Av. (Butchers'; Killing) AAA
Crescent Novelty Mfg. Co., 703 S. Bway. (Masons'

HAMMERS (Con.)
Brick; Pavers'; Stone Cutters') ....E
Schueddig & Son, Ferd., 525 So. Jefferson (Masons'; Pavers'; Stone Cutters') G
South St. Louis Foundry, 7516 So. Bway. (Pile Drivers') C
Standard Railway Equipment Co., Union Trust Bldg. (Calking; Pneumatic; Beading) ....G

N. J.—Newark
Atha Tool Co. (Blacksmiths'; Boilermakers'; Bush; Claw; Coopers'; Masons'; Macadamizing; Machinists'; Napping; Pavers'; Stone Cutters'; Tack; Nail; Tinners'; Upholsterers'; Magnetic; Bricklayers') ....A
Bernz, Otto, So. 13th cor. So. Orange Av. (Clipping; Machinists'; Plumbers') ...B
Heller Bros. Co. (Tack; Nail; Blacksmiths'; Chipping; Carriage Ironers'; Engineers') ....AA
Kraeuter & Co. (Upholsterers') X
Mundy, J. S., 22 Prospect (Pile Drivers') ....A
Osborne & Co.. C. S., 96 Mechanic (Nail; Tack; Upholsterers'; Saddlers') ..B

N. Y.—Albany
Troy Nickel Works, (Jno. E. Gaitley) (Solid Steel; full Nickel Plated Tack; Nail) C

N. Y.—Auburn
Crane Fdry. & Mach. Wks., W. W. (Drop; Trip) ..B

N. Y.—Brooklyn
Bliss Co., E. W., 15 Adams (Drop; Power) ....AAAA
Merrill Bros. 465 Kent Av. (Drop; Trip; Power; Spring; Air Cushion Trip)
.... A

N. Y.—Buffalo
Bell Engineering Wks., David (Steam) ....F
Contractors' Plant Mfg. Co., 125 Erie (Pile Drivers') B
Niagara Machine & Tool Wks., cor. Superior & Randall (Drop) ......A
Oliver Mfg. Co., W. W. (Fibre Faced Jewelers') C
White Co., L. & I. J., cor. Perry & Columbia (Coopers'; Masons'; Pavers'; Stone Cutters'; Bricklayers') ....A

N. Y.—Homer
Phoenix Hdw. Mfg. Co. (Tack; Nail) ....D

N. Y.—Little Falls
Cheney Hammer Co., Henry (Blacksmiths'; Carpenters'; Claw; Farriers'; Machinists'; Riveting; Tack; Nail; Tinners') ....D

N. Y.—Montour Falls
General Pneumatic Tool Co. (Pneumatic Riveting; Chipping) ....B

New York City
American Axe & Tool Co., 253 Bway. (Bricklayers')
.... AAAA
Dudgeon, Richard (Steam) A
Greene, Tweed & Co., 17 Murray (Interchangeable, with Rawhide, Wood or Copper Head) ....A
Hungerford Brass & Copper Co., U. T., 121 Worth (Copper) ....AA
Lidgerwood Mfg. Co., 96 Liberty (Pile Drivers')
.... AAA
McDougall & Potter Co., 606 W. 55th (Steam) ......D
Manning, Maxwell & Moore, 85 Liberty (Power; Drop; Steam) ....AA
Niles-Bement-Pond Co., 136 Liberty (Drop; Rubber Cushioned Pelve; Pneumatic; Power; Single;

HAMMERS (Con.)

Double & Open frame Steam) ....AAAA
Pfriemer, Chas., 229 E. 22d (Piano) C
Salem Nail Co., 279 Pearl (Slaters' best Steel) .A
Schmidt, David H., 1945 Park Av. (Piano) C
Strauch Bros., 30 10th Av. (Piano) ....A

N. Y.—Norwich
Maydole Hammer Co., David (Blacksmiths'; Boilermakers'; Crucible Steel Chipping; Nail; Engineers'; Farriers'; Machinists'; Claw; Coopers'; Masons; Riveting; Stone Cutters'; Tack; Tinners'; Magnetic)
.................B

N. Y.—Rochester
Streeter & Co., N. R. (Steak) ....A

OHIO—Alliance
Alliance Machine Co. (Drop; Steam) ....A
Morgan Engineering Co. (Drop; Power; Steam)
AAAA

OHIO—Canton
Elbel Co. (Tack; Setter & Lifter Combined) ......A

OHIO—Cleveland
Cady Machine Co. (Drop) X
Chisholm & Moore Mfg. Co. (Pneumatic) ....AA
Cleveland Pneumatic Tool Co. (Pneumatic; Steam)A
Lane Tool Co., 1196 Hamilton (Steam; Drop; Forge)
D
Strong, Carlisle & Hammond Co., 61 Frankfort (Machinists') ....A

OHIO—Columbus
Columbus Anvil & Forging Co. (Saw Makers') ....D

OHIO—Cuyhoga Falls
Turner, Vaughn & Taylor Co. (Power) ....B

OHIO—Hamilton
Long & Alistatter Co. (Drop; Helve; Power) ......AA
Niles Tool Wks. Co. (Steam)
AAAA

OHIO—Miamisburg
Kauffman, J. A. (Light Power) ....D

OHIO—Ravenna
Williams, A. C. (Tack; Nail) ....A

OHIO—Tiffin
National Machinery Co. (Power) ....AA

OHIO—Toledo
Toledo Fdry. & Machine Co., 202 Cherry (Pile Drivers')
B
Toledo Machine & Tool Co. (Power) ....A

OHIO—Warren
Denison Mfg. Co. (Tack) F

PA.—Allegheny
Carlins' Sons, Thos. (Pile Drivers') ....A

PA.—Bellefonte
Lingle, J. H. (Helve) ..D

PA.—Bethlehem
Strock & Co., L. W. (Sledge) ....D

PA.—Chambersburg
Chambersburg Engineering Co. (Drop; Power; Steam)
A

PA.—Chester
Black & Co. (Butchers' Killing) ....AA

PA.—Erie
Erie Specialty Co. (Confectioners' Candy) ....B

PA.—Glassport
American Axe & Tool Co. (Brick) ....AAAA

PA.—Harrisburg
Hickok Mfg. Co., W. O. (Bookbinders' Beating)AA

PA.—Ogontz
Hammond & Son, C. (Blacksmiths'; Masons'; Riveting; Tack; Nail; Bricklayers'; Saddlers'; Shoemakers') ....A

HAMMERS (Con.)

PA.—Philadelphia
Bement, Niles & Co. (Steam) ....AAAA
Dallett Co., Thos. H., 2303 York (Pneumatic) ......B
Dienelt & Eisenhardt, 1302 N. Howard (Power) .A
Disston & Sons, Henry (Inc.) (Tack; Nail)AAAA
Germantown Tool Wks., 518 Commerce (Brick) ....A
Justice & Co., Philip S., 14 N. 5th (Power) ....D
Nittinger, August (Hog Killing) ....A
Phila. Pneumatic Tool Co., 21st & Allegheny Av. (Calking; Pneumatic; Pneumatic Chipping) ..B
Phila. Steel & Iron Co. (Tack; Nail) X
Plumb, Fayette R. (Inc.) (Machinists'; Masons'; Napping; Pavers'; Riveting; Stone Cutters'; Shoemakers') ....AA
Sellers & Co., Wm. (Inc.) 1600 Hamilton (Steam)
AAAA
Stortz & Son, Jno., 210 Vine (Masons'; Pavers'; Slaters') ....E
Stow Flexible Shaft Co., 26th & Collowhill (Electric Claw) ....B
Stubbs Steel Co. (Bush) .E
U. S. Metallic Packing Co. . (Pneumatic) ....B

PA.—Pittsburg
Baird Machinery Co., V. (Steam) ....B
Hubbard & Co., Murtland Bldg. (Blacksmiths'; Stone Cutters') ......AA
Iron City Tool Wks., 32nd & Smallman (Blacksmiths'; Masons'; Napping) ....AA
Jones & Laughlins Steel Co. (Blacksmiths'; Machinists'; Masons'; Riveting)
AAAA
Klein-Logan Co., So. 13th & Breed (Blacksmiths'; Bush; Masons'; Napping; Stone Cutters') ......A
Pittsburg Tool & Drop Forge Co., Arrott Bldg. (Masons'; Napping) ....D
Scaife Fdry. & Mach. Co., 28th & Smallman (Drop) B
Tretheway & Co., Saml. (Ltd.) (Steam, especially for tool steel) ....F

PA.—Reading
Chantrell Tool Co. (Cast-Iron; Steel; Nail; Tack) B
Franklin Specialty Co. (Nickel Plated Claw; Tack; Nail) ....G

PA.—South Bethlehem
Bethlehem Fdry. & Mach. Co. (Pile Drivers'; Steam)
C

PA.—Wrightsville
Wrightsville Hdw. Co. (Tack; Nail; Upholsterers'; Steak; Toy) .....B

R. I.—Providence
Iroquois Machine Co. (Plain; Automatic Drop) ....A

VT.—Barre
Trow & Holden (Stone Cutters') ....A

VT.—St. Johnsbury
Fairbanks & Co., E. & T. (Power) ....AAAA

W. VA.—Wheeling
Warwood Tool Co. (Heavy)
B

WIS.—Racine
Dickey Mfg. Co., A. P. (Drop) ....F

HAMMOCKS

CAL.—San Francisco
Neville & Co. (Inc.) .....A

CONN.—Middletown
Palmer, I. E. (Arawana Mills) Double; Patent; Willow) ....AAA

ILL.—Chicago
Ericksen Mfg. Co. ....E

HAMMOCKS (Con.)

MASS.—Boston
Amer. Net & Twine Co... AAA

MASS.—North Weymouth
Brayshaw, James ....F

MASS.—Quincy
Thomas & Co., T. B. .....F

MINN.—Minneapolis
Lloyd Mfg. Co. (Woven Wire) ....A

MO.—St. Louis
Missouri Tent & Awning Co. ....B

N. J.—Mt. Holly
Standard Hicks Hammock Co. C

New York City
Boyle & Co., John 112 Duane (Canvas) ....AA
Hoffman-Corr Mfg. Co., 107 Duane ....AA
Travers Bros. Co., 41 Worth AA

OHIO—Columbus
Sun Mfg. Co. (Automatic; Swinging) ....A

OHIO—Dayton
Ohio Rake Co. (Lawn)..AA

PA.—Philadelphia
Fowler Net & Twine Co., 200 Market C
Masland Co., Joseph H. 4819 Germantown Av...E
Patterson, Jos. B., 8th & Dauphin ....A
Shoyer & Co., D. W., 18th & Bristol C
Weston & Wells Mfg. Co., 1110 Noble ....B
Woodcock Bros. C

WIS.—Fond du Lac
Fond du Lac Awning & Tent Co. ....B

WIS.—La Crosse
La Crosse Hammock Co...D
Western Hammock Co...E

WIS.—Milwaukee
Gem Hammock & Fly Net Co. (Woven Cotton; Knot; Mexican Grass) ....A
Meinecke & Son, A. (Woven Cotton; Knotted; Mexican Grass) ....AA

HAMPERS

ALA.—Bridgeport
Bridgeport Woodenware Mfg. Co. (Bean).......B

ILL.—Chicago
Chicago Willow & Rattan Wks., 424 Blue Island Av. (Automobile) C
Wilt, Chas. T............B

IND.—Peru
Peru Basket Co. (Square Clothes) ....B

MASS.—Gardner
Heywood Bros. & Wakefield Co. (Willow) .....AAAA

MICH.—Belding
Ballou Basket Wks. (Candy Shipping) ....B

MO.—St. Louis
Huke Rattan & Willow Ware Mfg. Co., Wm. (Reed; Rattan) ....D

New York City
Leipzig, Abraham (Laundry Shipping) ....A

N. Y.—Poughkeepsie
Lane & Bro., W. T. (Canvas Shipping) C
Poughkeepsie Art Pulp Co. (Automobile) ....F

WIS.—Milwaukee
Meinecke & Son, A. (Laundry Shipping) ....AA

HAMS

See Meat Packers

HANDCUFFS

CONN.—New Haven
Marlin Fire Arms Co. ..AA

N. Y.—Binghamton
Wilkinson Mfg. Co. .....A

New York City
Tower & Lyon Co., 95 Chambers ....B

HAND-KERCHIEFS

CONN.—South Manchester
Cheney Bros. (Inc.) (Crêpe; Silk) ....AAAA

N. J.—Camden
Loeb & Schoenfeld Co....AAAA

N. J.—Paterson
Anderson Bros. (Silk) ...X
Ashley & Bailey Co. (Silk) AAA
Ball, Wm. H. (Silk) C
Dexter, Lambert & Co. (Crêpe; Silk) ....AAAA
Doherty & Wadsworth Co. (Silk) ....AA
Holmes Silk Co. (Silk)...A
Phoenix Silk Mfg. Co. (Silk) ....AAAA
Taylor Silk Mfg. Co. (Silk) C

New York City
Herrmann, Aukam & Co. (Cotton) ....AAAA
Schwab & Co., S. M., Jr. (Cotton) ....A
Stearns & Co., John N. (Silk) ....AAAA
Horlikoshi & Co., Z. (Silk) B

PA.—Columbia
Ashley & Bailey Co. (Silk) AAA

R. I.—Providence
Grosvenor-Dale Co. (Cotton) ....AAAA

HANDLES

See also Heads; Hardware; Carriage.

ALA.—Huntsville
Henderson, Murphree & Henderson (Wood) ...AA
Southern Handle Mfg. Co. (Wood) C

ALA.—Mobile
Zelnecke Supply Co., Walter A. (Axe; Maul; Hickory, etc.) ....B

ALA.—Union Springs
Caldwell & Ramsey (Wood) D

ARK.—Little Rock
Little Rock Hoop Co. (Wood) ....D

ARK.—Paragould
Rogers-Meiser Handle Co. (Axe; Pick; Hammer. etc.) ....E

CONN.—Bridgeport
Burns-Silver & Co. (Ratchet Brake) ......A
Knapp & Cowles Mfg. Co. (Awl; Iron) ....D
Krouse, A. & A. L. (Cane; Parasol; Umbrella; Whip) E

CONN.—Clinton
Kelsey, Horatio (Axe; Hammer; Hatchet; Pick; Soldering Iron; Stave Cutter) E

CONN.—Deep River
Williams & Marvin Co. (Wood; Auger; Awl; Chisel; File; Wrench; Ice Pick) ....D

CONN.—Hartford
Billings & Spencer Co. (Drop Forged Brake; Machine; Ratchet Brake) . AA

CONN.—Meriden
Foster, Merriam & Co. (Drop) ....AA

CONN.—Middletown
Rogers & Hubbard Co. (Cutlery) ....A

CONN.—Mount Carmel
Woodruff & Sons, Walter W. (Drop; Vehicle Seat) A

CONN.—New Britain
Corbin. P. & J. (Bronze; Door) ....AAAA
North & Judd Mfg. Co. (Shawl Strap) ....AA

Stanley Rule & Level Co.
(Awl; Plane; Saw; Chest;
Screwdriver) ....AAA

CONN.—New Haven
Mallory, Wheeler Co. (Bar;
Bronze; Store Door)..AA

CONN.—Pine Meadow
Chapin-Stevens Co. (Plane;
Saw; Chisel; File; Awl;
Carving Tool, Wood)....A

CONN.—Salisbury
Salisbury Cutlery Handle
Co. (Wooden; Cutlery).C

CONN.—Saugatuck
Doscher Plane & Tool Co.
(Leather Head Wooden
Chisel) ....E

CONN.—Seymour
Swan Co., Jas. (Auger;
Chisel) ....A

CONN.—Southington
Peck, Stow & Wilcox Co.
(Auger; File; Soldering
Iron; Chest) ......AAAA

CONN.—Stamford
Yale & Towne Mfg. Co.
(Store Door) ......AAAA

CONN.—Torrington
Union Hdw. Co. (Electric
Switch; Knife; Mop; Awl;
Chisel; File; Screw-
driver) ....AA

CONN.—Waterbury
Amer. Ring Co. (Drop)...A
Benedict & Burnham Mfg.
Co. (Drop) ....AAAA
Plume & Atwood Mfg. Co.
(Drop) ....AAA

GA.—Atlanta
Atlanta Woodenware Co.
(Wooden Axe) ....B

GA.—Rome
Towers & Sullivan Mfg.
Co. (Plow) ....B

ILL.—Chicago
Adams & Westlake Co., On-
tario & N. Franklin
(Ratchet Brake) ..AAAA
Ehnborn & Co., C., 214 S.
Clinton (Electric Switch)
..............G
Geisen & Co., N. (Wooden
Hammer) ....B
Hubbard & Co., 125 Kinzie
(Mop; Broom) '.......X
McGuire - Cummings Mfg.
Co., 122 N. Sangamon
(Brake) ....AA
Simons Bros. & Co., 103
State (Cane; Umbrella).A

ILL.—Chicago Heights
Hartwell Bros. (Hammer)
..............D

ILL.—Flora
Meyer Bros. (Wooden Axe,
etc.) ....B

ILL.—Freeport
Arcade Mfg. Co. (Boiler).A
Stover Mfg. Co. (Chest;
Mop; Door; Store Door;
Broom; Boiler) ......AA

ILL.—Shelbyville
Shelbyville Handle & Milling Co. ....D

IND.—Auburn
Cherry & Co., J. M.
(Wooden) ....D

IND.—Bluffton
Buck, J. M. (Wooden) ...C

IND.—Columbus
Columbus Handle & Tool
Co. (Wood Shovel, etc.)
..............B

IND.—Frankfort
Cleveland & Palmer
(Wooden) ....D
Frankfort Handle Mfg. Co.
(Wooden; Adze; Axe;
Blacksmiths'; Hammer;
Hatchet; Hickory; Maul;
Pick; Sledge) ....E

IND.—Huntingburg
Hartwell Mfg. Co. (Adze;
Axe; Chisel; File; Ham-
mer; Hatchet; Pick;
Sledge) ....F

IND.—Indianapolis
Atkins & Co., E. C. (Saw)
..............AAAA

IND.—Logansport
Hillock & Pitman (All
Kinds Wooden) ....E

Howe, Saml. E. (Wooden)
..............A

IND.—Marion
Marion Handle & Mfg. Co.
(Shovel; Spade) X

IND.—Montpelier
Jackson Shovel & Tool Co.
(Wooden Shovel; Spade,
etc.) ....B

IND.—New Albany
Force Handle Co., I. F.
(Wooden) C

IND.—New Castle
Jennings, S. P. (Wooden).C

IND.—New Haven
Schnitker & Fisher
(Wooden) ....E
Sperry Mfg. Co. (Wooden)
..............E

IND.—Vincennes
Hartwell Bros. (Wooden;
Adze; Axe; Hammer;
Hatchet; Hickory; Maul;
Pick; Sledge) ....B
Indiana Handle Co.
(Wooden) ....D

IND.—Warsaw
Lesh Mfg. Co., G. B.
(Farming Tool) ....D

IOWA—Dubuque
Adams Co. (Boiler) .....A

IOWA—Fort Madison
Iowa Farming Tool Co.
(Farming Tool) ....A

KY.—Louisville
Turner, Day & Woolworth
Handle Co., 1818 7th
(Wooden Adze; Axe;
Blacksmiths'; Farming
Tool; Hammer; Hatchet;
Ice Pick; Maul; Pick;
Hickory; Sledge; Straight
Taper) ....AA

MAINE—Augusta
Harvey Handle Co., H. H.
(Wooden Hammer; Pick;
Sledge) ....D

MAINE—East Hiram
Flint, Nathan Ripley
(Axe) ....G

MAINE—Gardiner
Oakland Mfg. Co. (Wooden
Broom) ....B

MASS.—Boston
Sewing Machine Supplies
Co. (Shoe Knife) .....B
Standard Turning Wks., 53
State (Wooden) C

MASS.—Fitchburg
Novelty Turning Co. (Cir-
cuit Breaker; Electric
Switch; Wooden Hand
Tool; Switch. etc.).....E
Sawyer Tool Mfg. Co.
(Wire Valve) C

MASS.—Greenfield
Bugg Mfg. Co. (Rake) ...F

MASS.—Harvard
Murphy & Sons, Robert....F

MASS.—Leominster
Goodhue & Phillips (Horn)
..............E

MASS.—Northampton
Smith, Chas. O. (Wooden
Broom) ....E

MASS.—Sharon
Lothrop Mfg. Co., H. A.
(Awl) X

MASS.—Westboro
Hunt Leather Goods Co.
(Leather Bag) ....B

MASS.—Worcester
Warren Leather Goods Co.
(Leather Trunk) ......B

MICH.—Birmingham
Zimmerman, J. N.
(Wooden) ....E

MICH.—Cadillac
Cadillac Handle Co.
(Broom; Torch) C

MICH.—Coldwater
Hellenberg & Son, J. B.
(Wooden) ....E

MICH.—Escanaba
Escanaba Wooden Ware Co.
(Mop; Broom) ....AA

MICH.—Evart
Champion Tool & Handle
Wks. (Wooden) ......AA

MICH.—Freeport
Cheesebrough, Job (Wooden
Rake) ....D

HANDLES (Con.)

MICH.—Galien
Montrose, Richard W.
(Farming Tool) ....B
MICH.—Grand Rapids
Grand Rapids Brass Co.
(Drop) ....A
MICH.—Jackson
Withington & Cooley Mfg.
Co. (Wooden Farming
Tool; Fork; Hoe; Rake;
Scoop; Shovel; Spade).AA
MICH.—Mancelona
Mancelona Handle Co.
(Wooden) ....B
MICH.—Vanderbilt
Olds & Hudson (Broom)..A
MINN.—St. Paul
Rauscher, Jno., 98 W. 3rd
(Circuit Breaker; Electric
Switch) ....H
MISS.—Jackson
Burleigh's Sons, R. G.
(Wooden) ....B
MO.—Dexter
I. X. L. Handle Mfg. Co.
(Wooden) ....D
MO.—Kirksville
Storm, Jno. (Wooden) ..D
MO.—Memphis
Rees Bros. Mfg. Co.
(Wooden) ....E
MO.—Puxico
Fulkerson Bros. Handle Co.
(Wooden) ....D
MO.—St. Louis
Beck & Corbitt Iron Co.
(Plow) ....D
Central Union Brass Co.
(Brake) ....E
Handlan-Buck Mfg. Co., 212
N. 3rd (Car Coupling;
Iron Shovel) ....AA
Western Electric Supply Co.
(Brake) X
N. H.—Concord
Page Belting Co. (Trunk)
AA
N. H.—Keene
Ellis, Austin A. (Wooden
Brush) ....D
Pierce & Co., F. B.
(Wooden Brush) ......B
N. H.—Manchester
Piper, B. H. (Wooden Axe,
etc.) ....D
N. H.—Milford
Pierce & Co., W. E.
(Wooden) ....D
N. H.—North Weare
Flanders Hardware Co.
(Butcher's Knife) .....G
N. H.—Sunapee
Alexander & Perkins (Fork;
Hoe) ....F
N. H.—Wolfboro Falls
Berry Co., O. B. (Wooden)
D
N. J.—Newark
Bannister & Co., A. F.
(Ivory; Pearl; Iron; Cel-
luloid Umbrella) .....A
Celluloid Co. (Celluloid Um-
brella) ....B
Cross Mfg. Co., C. E., 67
Hamilton (Leather Dress
Suit Case; Bag) ......F
Duranoid Mfg. Co., 28 Pros-
pect (Circuit Breaker).B
Gould's Son & Co., M.
(Leather Trunk) .....A
Jenkinson & Co., R. C.
(Leather Bag) ......AA
National Saw Co. (Plane;
Saw; Cross-Cut Saw)..B
Sterling-Meaker Co., 420 Og-
den (Electric Car Brake)
D
Unger Bros. (Cane; Um-
brella) ....A
N. Y.—Addison
Harrison, Jas. S. (Plow;
Wooden) ....D
N. Y.—Albany
Troy Nickel Wks. (Gaitley,
Jno. E.) (Boiler; Valve;
Soldering Iron; Drop.
etc.) C
N. Y.—Amsterdam
Amsterdam Broom Co.
(Mop; Broom) ....A
N. Y.—Brooklyn
Columbia Machine Wks. &

HANDLES (Con.)

Malleable Iron Co., 167
Chestnut (Adjustable;
Ratchet Brake) ....A
Electrose Mfg. Co., 127 N.
10th (Electric Switch).B
Williams & Co., J. H., 9
Richards (Machine;
Crank) ....AA
N. Y.—Buffalo
Buffalo Specialty Mfg. Co.,
375 Ellicott (Rawhide
Tool; Leather Tool) ...B
Elias & Bros., G. (Ash)..
AA
Union Mfg. Co. (Mop;
Wooden) C
N. Y.—Horseheads
Weller Hdw. & Fdry. Co.
(Boiler) ....D
New York City
Barron & Co., Jas. S., 202
W. B'way (Broom) ....A
Basch Bros., 67 Spring
(Cane; Umbrella) ......B
Bogert & Hopper, 162 Wil-
liam (Electric Switch)..B
Carpenter & Bayles, 91
Chambers (Wooden) ...D
De Muth & Co., Wm., 507
B'way (Cane; Umbrella)
AAA
Estes & Sons, E. B., 45
John (Electric Switch;
Cutlery; Knife; Awl;
Farming Tool; Hammer;
Hathet; Ice Pick; Saw;
Screwdriver; Shoeknife)
AA
Fradley & Co., J. F., 114 E.
14th (Cane; Umbrella)..E
Friedman & Co., M. (Para-
sol; Umbrella) ....D
Grote & Co. F., E. 14th St.
(Ivory) ....D
Harrison, W. W., 1149
B'way (Cane; Umbrella)
D
Gutta Percha & Rubber
Mfg. Co. (Electric
Switch) ....AAAA
Houchin Co., Thos. W.
(Feather Duster; Exten-
sion Torch) ....D
Jennings & Co., C. E.
(Auger) ....B
Locklin & Sons, P. H., 142
Fulton (Cane; Umbrella)
G
Lott & Schmitt, 116 Walker
(Cane; Umbrella) C
Ludwig, A., 75 Spring
(Box) ....D
Luxenberg & Haskell, 177
Grand (Silver, Gold, etc.,
Umbrella) ....B
Marx & Co., A., 210 Canal
(Cane; Umbrella) .....A
Metal Stamping Co. (Door;
Vehicle Seat) ....A
Millers Falls Co., 28 Warren
(Auger) ....AA
Morgenstern & Goldsmith
(Umbrella) C
Rest, Fenner, Smith Co.,
(Umbrella) C
Shardlow, Joseph, 116 Ful-
ton (Ivory Cane) ......D
Simons, Bro. & Co., 170
B'way (Cane; Umbrella)
C
Stokes & Co., Wm. A., 30
Warren (Umbrella) C
N. Y.—Rochester
Sargent & Greenleaf Co.
(Store Door) ....AA
N. Y.—Syracuse
New Process Rawhide Co.
(Rawhide Tool) ....B
Stearns & Co., E. C. (Chisel;
Bar Door) ....AA
N. Y.—Troy
Hart Specialty Co. (Mop).X
Parks & Parks (Mop) ....D
N. Y.—Unadilla
Tie Co. (Labelled Parcel).D
N. Y.—Yonkers
India Rubber & Gutta
Percha Insulating Co.
(Electric Switch) ......B
N. C.—Greensboro
Merrimon, B. H. (Woolen).A

N. C.—McLeanville
Forbes Mfg. Co. (Wooden Broom) ....D

OHIO—Akron
Baker - McMillen Co. (Wooden Coffee Pot; Enamelled Wood; Pail; Tool; Rubber Stamp)...B
Goodrich Co., B. F. (Electric Switch) ......AAAA
Whitman & Barnes Mfg. Co. (Machine) ....AAAA

OHIO—Alliance
Transue & Williams Co. (Machine) ....A

OHIO—Canton
Kohler & Co., F. E. (Mop; Broom) C

OHIO—Chagrin Falls
Ober Mfg. Co. (Sad Iron).C

OHIO—Cincinnati
Knecht Co., Victor (Leather Trunk) .....B

OHIO—Cleveland
Federal Mfg. Co., Amer. Trust Bldg. (File).AAAA

OHIO—Columbus
Brown, Hinman & Huntington Co. (Farming Tool).A
Ohio Tool Co. (Special; Auger; Awl; Chisel; File; Plane) ....AA

OHIO—Dayton
Dayton Mfg. Co. (Brake; Street Car Brake) .....A

OHIO—Edon
Sheline, E. R. (Wooden)..B

OHIO—Hicksville
Kerr Bros. Mfg. Oo. (Brush; Mop; Special; Farming Tool; Fork; Ice Hook; Shovel) C

OHIO—Lima
Selfridge Co., O. B. (D.).X

OHIO—Mansfield
Ohio Brass Co. (Brake; Ratchet Brake) ......AA

OHIO—Monroeville
Yingling Bros. & Co. (Wooden) ....B

OHIO—Piqua
Piqua Handle & Mfg. Co. (Brush; Carpet Sweeper; Crank; Feather Duster; Knife; Mop; Sad Iron; Torch; Awl; Brace; Cant Hook; Chisel; Cleaver; "D."; Farming Tool; File; Fork; Garden Set; Hammer; Hatchet; Hoe; Ice Hook; Ice Pick; Machine; Rake; Cross-cut Saw; Scoop; Screwdriver; Shoe Knife; Shovel; Spade; Trowel; Straight Taper; Wrench; Valve).A

OHIO—Spencerville
Raynolds, W. A. (Wooden) C

OHIO—Sandusky
Sandusky Tool Co. (Wooden Saw; Plane; File; Chisel; Awl; Auger. etc.) .....A

OHIO—Sidney
Benjamin & Son, C. R. (Forbes) C

OHIO—Wapakoneta
Standard Churn Co. (Wooden) ....B

PA.—Bedford
McLaughlin & Son, J. L. (Wooden Axe) ....E

PA.—Chester
Keystone Drop Forge Wks. (Machine) ....B

PA.—Eldred
Prouty & Co., C. (Wooden Cross-Cut Saw; Cant Hook, etc.) ....B

PA.—Kane
Holgate Bros. Co. (Wooden Artists' Brush, etc.) ..B

PA.—Lancaster
Lancaster Silver Plate Co. (Umbrella) C

PA.—Lebanon
Amer. Iron & Steel Mfg. Co. (Brake) ....AAAA

PA.—Mechanicsburg
Wilcox Mfg. Co., D. (Machine) ....A

PA.—Philadelphia
Brill Co., J. G., 62nd & Woodland Av. (Brass; Malleable Iron Brake; Ratchet Brake) ...AAAA
Harvey & Watts Co., 1804 E. Venango (Ivory; Horn; Bone; Wood Umbrella)..A
Haslet, Flanagan & Co. (Wash Boiler) ....B
Randolph, Wm. C., 243 Arch (Bone; Whisk Broom) ....E

PA.—Pittsburg
Armstrong Cork Co. (Cork Fishing Rod) .....AAAA

PA.—Reading
Chantrell Tool Co. (Hollow Tool) ....B
Penn. Hdw. Co. (Chest).AA

PA.—Scranton
Scranton Button Co. (Electric Switch) ......A

PA.—Union City
Novelty Wood Wks. Co. (Wooden Awl; File; Ice Pick; Wrench) ....B

PA.—Warren
Peterson, Samuel (Wooden Pick; Mining, etc.) ...A

PA.—Wrightsville
Wrightsville Hdw. Co. (Boiler; Surface Chest).B

R. I.—Pawtucket
Bliss Mfg. Co., R. (Auger; Awl; Chisel) ......AAAA

R. I.—Providence
Amer. Enamel Co. (Circuit Breaker; Electric Switch) B
Braitsch & Co., W. J. (Umbrella) C

TENN.—Knoxville
Amer. Handle Co. (Ash; Hickory) ....AA
Standard Handle Co. (Axe; Hammer; Hickory; Pick; Sledge) C

TENN.—Nashville
Nashville Spoke & Handle Co. (Axe; Chisel; Farming Tool; Hammer; Hatchet; Hoe; Pick; Ice Pick; Rake; Screwdriver; Sledge; Shoe Knife) ....AA
Parkes & Co., Geo. S. (Wooden) ....B

TENN.—Sequatchie
Sequatchie Handle Wks. (Wooden) ....D

TENN.—Tullahoma
Campbell & Dann Mfg. Co. (Wooden File; Chisel, in the white) ....B

VT.—Bellows Falls
Derby & Ball (Farming Tool; Fork) ....B

VT.—Burlington
Vermont Shade Roller Co. (Mon) ....A

VT.—East Arlington
Judson, J. R. (Wooden Kitchen Knife; Brush, etc.) ....B

VT.—Hyde Park
Page, Carroll S. (Bone Knife) ....A

VT.—Marion
Look & Lincoln (Plow)...A

WIS.—Racine
Racine Malleable & Wrought Iron Co. (Vehicle Seat) ....A

HANDS

MASS.—Winchester
Winn & Son, J. H. (Clock; Watch) ....B

New York City
Condell. A.. 852 B'way (Artificial) ....D
Frees, C. A., 853 B'way (Artificial) X

OREGON—Portland
Portland Artificial Limb Co. (Artificial) ....F

HANGERS

ALA.—Huntsville

HANGERS (Con.)

Huntsville Fdry. & Mach. Wks. (Nolan & Jones, Prop.) (Shaft; Post; Bracket) ....B

COLO.—Denver
Davis Iron Wks., F. M., 8th & Larimer (Shaft; Post; Bracket) ....AA

CONN.—Bridgeport
Bridgeport Brass Co. (Chain Lamp) ....AAA

CONN.—Meriden
Bradley & Hubbard Mfg. Co. (Chain Lamp).AAAA
Miller & Co., Edward (Chain Lamp) ....AAAA

CONN.—New Britain
Corbin, P. & F. (Sliding Door) ....AAAA
Union Mfg. Co. (Barn Door) ....AA

CONN.—New Haven
Peck Bros. & Co. (Pipe)..
...............AA

CONN.—Norwalk
Arnold Co. (Barn Door)..C

CONN.—Southington
Beaton & Corbin Mfg. Co. (Pipe) ....D

CONN.—Stamford
Yale & Towne Mfg. Co. (Sliding Door) ...AAAA

CONN.—Waterbury
Plume & Atwood Mfg. Co. (Sliding Door) ....AAAA
Waterbury-Farrell Fdry. & Machine Co. (Shaft; Post; Bracket) ....AA

DEL.—Wilmington
Diamond State Steel Co. (Stirrup) X

GA.—Atlanta
Conklin Tin Plate & Metal Co. (Eave Trough) ...A

GA.—Columbus
Golden Fdry. & Mach Co. (Shaft; Post; Bracket).A

ILL.—Aurora
Wilcox Mfg. Co. (Barn; Sliding Door) ....B

ILL.—Chicago
Barbee Wire & Iron Wks. (Clothes; Trousers) ...B
Central Electric Co., 264 5th Av. (Straight Line Trolley Wire) ....A
Chicago Nut Co., 207 S. Canal (Cable) ....E
Continental Bolt & Iron Wks., 22nd & Union (Stirrup) ....A
Crane Co. (Pipe) ...AAAA
Cutter Co., Geo., 127 Fulton (Arc Lamp) C
Davis Co., Jno., 69 Michigan (Pipe) ....AA
Excelsior Steel Furnace Co. 40 W. Monroe (Eave Trough) ....A
Illinois Malleable Iron Co., 30 W. Monroe (Pipe)...
..............AAAA
Jones Fdry. & Mach. Co. W. A., 143 W. North Av. (Shaft; Post; Bracket) ....A
Kaestner & Co. (Inc.) 241 S. Jefferson (Shaft; Post; Bracket) ....A
Melchior Bros. Furn. Co. 6 Dayton (Garment) ...C
Peirce, Jr., C. L., 14 S. Jefferson (Cable) X
Plamondon Mfg. Co., A., 57 S. Clinton (Shaft; Post; Bracket) ....A
Republic Iron & Steel Co. (Stirrup) ....AAAA
Skillin & Richards Mfg. Co., 147 Fulton (Shaft; Post; Bracket) C
Smith Wire & Iron Wks., F. P., 100 Lake (Joist) ....AA
Street & Kent Mfg. Co., 109 S. Jefferson (Pipe) ...B
Variety Mfg. Co., 54 N. Clinton (Joist; Shaft Post; Bracket) ....D
Walker & Ehrman Mfg. Co. (Bicycle Crank) ....A

HANGERS (Con.)

Webster Mfg. Co., 1075 W. 15th (Shaft; Post; Bracket) ....AA

ILL.—Galva
Hayes Pump & Planter Co. (Pipe) ....A

ILL.—Harvard
Hunt, Helm, Ferris & Co. (Barn; Sliding Door)..AA

ILL.—Joliet
Bates Machine Co. (Shaft; Post; Bracket) ....AA
Joliet Mfg. Co. (Eaves Trough) ....A

ILL.—Kewanee
Western Tube Co. (Expension Pipe) ....AAA

ILL.—Marseilles
Moore, Joshua (Pipe) ....F

ILL.—Moline
Barnard & Leas Mfg. Co. (Shaft; Post; Bracket)
..............AA

ILL.—Ottawa
Amer. Hdw. Mfg. Co (Pipe)
..............C

ILL.—Peoria
Clark, Quien & Morse (Eaves Trough) ....A

ILL.—Quincy
Modern Iron Wks. (Expansion or Ring Hooks Pipe)
..............B

ILL.—St. Charles
Glenn Mfg. Co. (Pipe)....D

ILL.—Sterling
Lawrence Bros. (Sliding Door) ....AAA

ILL.—Streator
Iwan Bros. (Wire Conductor; Pipe; Eaves Trough)
..............C

IND.—Indianapolis
Tucker & Dorsey Mfg. Co. (Garment) ....A

IND.—Mishawaka
Dodge Mfg. Co. (Self-Oiling; Shaft; Post; Bracket) ....AAA

IND.—New Albany
Goetz Box Anchor Co. (Joist) C

KANS.—Leavenworth
Great Western Mfg. Co. (Self-Oiling; Post) ..AA

KY.—Louisville
Ahrens & Ott Mfg. Co. (Pipe) ....AAAA
Horan Stay Hanger Co. (Eave Trough) ....F

MD.—Baltimore
Dietrich Bros., 344 North (Stirrup) ....B
Ellicott Machine Co., Bush, cor Severn (Shaft; Post; Bracket) C
National Supply Co., 7 W. Lombard (Stirrup; Pipe)
..............B
Poole Engineering & Machine Co. (Shaft; Post; Bracket; Parting) ...AA
Register's Sons Co., J., 49 W. Holliday (Pipe) ...A

MASS.—Boston
Amer. Tool & Machine Co., 109 Beach (Self-Oiling; Shaft; Post; Bracket).AA
Anderson Mfg. Co., Albert & J. M., (Arc Lamp)...A
Barrett Mfg. Co., Jas., 215 Franklin (Pipe) C
Billings Co., D. L., 780 Dudley (Pipe) ....F
Boston Bolt Co., 31 Purchase (Pipe) C
Crawford Specialty Co., 311 Warren (Pipe) ....
Grundy & Co., J. E., 50 Sudbury (Pipe) ......F
Hodgdon Brass Wks. (Brass Pipe) ....E
Macallen Co., W. T. C., 338 Congress (Arc Lamp).AA
Walworth Mfg. Co., 132 Federal (Pipe) ...AAAA
Webb Mfg. Co., F. W., 50 Elm (Pipe) ....A
Young, Jos. H., 224 Franklin (Pipe) ....D

MASS.—Haydenville
Haydenville Co. ((Pipe)...A

HANGERS (Con.)

Knecht Co., Victor (Post) B
Lane & Bodley Co., Cor.
John & Water (Shaft;
Post; Bracket) ....B
Post-Glover Electric Co., 314
W. 4th (Trolley Wire)..A
Schrieber & Sons Co., L., 8th
& Eggleston Av. (Joist;
Stirrup) ....AA

OHIO—Cleveland

Adams-Bagnall Electric Co.,
Stanton & C. P. Crossing
(Arc Lamp) ....B
Avery Stamping Co. (Pipe)
A

Bartlett & Snow Co., C. O.,
French near Columbus
(Shaft; Post; Bracket)..A
Chisholm & Moore Mfg. Co.
(Door) ....AA
Duplex Hanger Co. (Joist;
Wall I. Beam) ....D
Hill Clutch Co., ft. Waverly
Av. (Shaft; Post; Brack-
et) ....B
National Iron & Wire Co.
(Steel Joist) ....B
Taylor & Boggis Fdy. Co.
(Barn Door) ....AA
Van Dorn Iron Wks., Co.
1793 E. Madison Av.
(Steel Joist; Shaft; Post;
Bracket) ....AA

OHIO—Columbus

Case Mfg. Co. (Shaft; Post;
Bracket) ....A
Schroth & Potter (Extension
Shade) ....B

OHIO—Coshocton

Keagy & Lear Machine Co.
(Shaft; Post; Bracket), C

OHIO—Cuyahoga Falls

Falls Rivet & Machine Co.
(Self-Oiling; Shaft; Post;
Bracket) ....A

OHIO—Dayton

Dayton Globe Iron Wks. Co.
(Shaft; Post; Bracket), B
Fletcher Mfg. Co. (Arc
Lamp) ....D

OHIO—Defiance

Defiance Machine Wks.
(Post). ....A

OHIO—Kenton

Champion Iron Co. (Stirrup)
AA

OHIO—Mansfield

Ohio Brass Co. (Arc Lamp;
Trolley Wire) ....AA

OHIO—Massillon

Hess, Snyder & Co. (Post)
AA

OHIO—Middletown

Amer. Steel Roofing Co.
(Eave-Trough) ....AA

OHIO—Niles

Bostwick Steel Lath Co.
(Eave-Trough) C

OHIO—Salem

Clark Co., W. J. (Joist)..A

OHIO—Springfield

Victor Supply Co. (Pipe)..B

OHIO—Toledo

Bissel & Co., F. (M. & P. In-
sulated Arc Lamp;Cabel)
A
Heartley, Geo. W. (Eave-
Through) ....D

OHIO—West Lafayette

West Lafayette Mfg. Co.
(Coat) ....E

OHIO—West Park

Norton Tool Co. (Cable) ..C

PA.—Allegheny

Rieseck, P., Allegheny Av.
& Rebecca (Wrought Steel
Joist). ....D

PA.—Allentown

Allentown Fdry. & Mach.
Wks. Co. (Shaft; Post;
Bracket) ....A

PA.—Chambersburg

Woods Sons. T. B. (Shaft;
Post; Bracket) ....A

PA.—Chester

Keystone Drop Forge Wks.
(Step. for Cars) ....B

PA.—Erie

Jarecki Mfg. Co. (Pipe)
AAAA
Reed Mfg. Co. (Adjustable
Pipe) ....A
Taper Sleeve Pulley Wks.

HANGERS (Con.)

(Self-Oiling) C

PA.—Hazelton

Koenig, M. F. (Wire Gar-
ment) X

PA.—Lebanon

Amer. Iron & Steel Mfg. Co.
(Stirrup) ....AAAA

PA.—Mechanicsburg

Wilcox Mfg. Co., D. (Bicycle
Crank) ....A

PA.—Muncy

Sprout, Waldron & Co.
(Shaft; Post; Bracket;
Self-Oiling) ....A

PA.—Philadelphia

Belfield & Co., H., 435 N.
Broad (Pipe) ....A
Berger Bros. Co., 237 Arch.
(Eave-Trough; Pipe)....A
Berger, L. D., 59 N. 2d
(Eave-Trough) C
Cresson Co., Geo. V., 18th &
Allegheny Av. (Shaft;
Post; Bracket; Parting;
Self-Oiling) ....AA
Devlin Mfg. Co., Thos., 3d
& Lehigh Av. (Pipe) ..AA
Flagg & Co., Stanley G.,
19th & Penn Av, (Malle-
able Iron; Pipe) ....AAA
Hall & Carpenter, 518 Race
(Garment) ....AA
Hoopes & Townsend Co.,
1330 Buttonwood (Stirrup;
Pipe) ....AA
Kriebel & Co., 826 Spring
Garden (Pipe) ....D
Link Belt Engineering Co.
(Shaft; Post; Bracket) AA
Mayer & Englund Co., 1026
Filbert (Cable) ....A
Merritt & Co., 1024 Ridge
Av. (Joist) ....B
Pennsylvania Engineering
Co., 312 Cherry (Ball Joint
Pipe) ....E
Pressed Steel Mfg. Co.,
Ridge Av. & Willow
(Ball Bearing) ....D
Sellers & Co., Wm., 1600
1600 Hamilton (Shaft;
Post; Bracket) ....AAAA
Standard Roller Bearing Co.,
48th & Girard Av. (Roller
Bearing) ....AA
Steward & Romaine Mfg.
Co., 124 N. 6th (Stirrup)
B
Yocum & Son, Jas., 145 N.
2nd (Adjustable Shaft;
Post; Bracket) ....B

PA.—Pittsburg

Bailey-Farrell Mfg. Co., 619
Smithfield (Pipe) .....AA
Collins Mfg. Co., 104 1st Av.
(Pipe) X
Hubbard & Co., Murtland
Bldg. (Cable) ....AA
Jones & Laughlin Steel Co.
(Shaft; Post; Bracket;
Self-Oiling) ....AAAA
Kelly & Jones Co., 135
Water (Pipe) ....AA
Oliver Iron & Steel Co.
(Stirrup) ....AAAA
Standard Underground Cable
Co. (Electric Cable) AAAA

PA.—Pittston

Exeter Machine Wks.
(Shaft; Post; Bracket) AA

PA.—Reading

Penn Hardware Co.
(Barn-Door) ....AA
Reading Hdw. Co. (Barn-
Door) ....AAAA

PA.—So. Bethlehem

Bethlehem Fdry. & Mach.
Co. (Stirrup) C

PA.—Waynesboro

Frick Co. (Shaft; Post;
Bracket) ....AAAA

PA.—Williamsport

Valley Iron Wks. (Post)..A

PA.—Wrightsville

Wrightsville Hardw. Co.
(Barn-Door) ....B

R. I.—Pawtucket

Haskell Mfg. Co., Wm. H
(Stirrup) ....AA
Pawtucket Mfg. Co. (Stir-
rup) ....A

R. I.—Providence

Brown & Sharpe Mfg. Co.

HANGERS (Con.)

(Counter Shaft) ...AAAA
Iroquois Machine Co. (Roller
Bearing) ....A
New England Butt Co.
(Barn-Door) ....AA
Rhode Island Telephone &
Electric Co. (Cable) ....D
R. I.—Woonsocket
Woonsocket Mach. & Press
Co. (Shaft; Post; Bracket;
Parting; Self-Oiling)..AA
TENN.—Memphis
Chickasaw Iron Wks.
(Shaft; Post; Bracket), A
VT.—Montpelier
Lane Mfg. Co. (Post) ....A
VA.—Richmond
Old Dominion Iron & Nail
Wks. Co. (Stirrup) ...AA
W. VA.—Charlestown
Powhatan Brass & Iron Wks.
(Pipe) ....B
W. VA.—Wheeling
Wheeling Corrugating Co.
(Eaves-Trough) ...AAAA
WIS.—La Crosse
Vought-Berger Co. (Cable) C
WIS.—Kenosha
Badger Brass Mfg. Co.
(Pipe) C
WIS.—Milwaukee
Filer & Stowell Co. (Shaft;
Post; Bracket) ......AAA
Hoffman & Billings Mfg. Co.
(Pipe) ....AA
League Cycle Wks. (Bicycle;
Bicycle Crank) ....D
Milwaukee Corrugating Co.
(Eaves-Trough) ....A
Willer Mfg. Co., 313 Cedar
(Storm Sash) ....A
WIS.—Racine
Racine Malleable & Wrought
Iron Co. (Bicycle Crank;
Farm Gate) ....A

HANSOMS

See also Carriages; Wagons.

New York City
Stivers, R. M. ....B

HARDENERS

CONN.—Ansonia
Farrel Foundry & Mach. Co.
(Felt) ....AAAA

HARDIES

IND.—Evansville
Evansville Tool Wks.
(Straight; Circular Cut) A
N. J.—Newark
Heller Bros Co. ....AA

HARDWARE: CARRIAGE, WAGON, ETC.

ARK.—Little Rock
Dickinson Ball Bearing
Wheel & Vehicle Co.
(Anti - Friction Axle;
Boxes; Ball Bearing)....C
CONN.—Bantam
Bantam Mfg. Co. (Wire
Wheels, Fifth Wheels)..F
CONN.—Bridgeport
Amer. Tube & Stamping Co.
(Steel Tires; Spring Steel;
Steel Rims; Tubing)
AAAA
Bridgeport Malleable Iron
Co. (Malleable Iron Work) .
A
Fletcher, Thomas (Top Prop.
Puts; Handles; Moulding)
F
Miller Wire Spring Co.
(Seat; Cushion Springs), A
Spring Perch Co. (Plated
Carriage Trimmings) ...B
White Mfg. Co. (Carriage;
Hearse Mountings) C
CONN.—Bristol
Barnes, Wallace Co., (Anti-
Ratlers) ....B
Dunbar Bros. (Anti-Rattlers;
Trace Fasteners) ....B
Sessions & Son, J. H. Telloe

HARDWARE (Con.)

Plates; Steel Washers;
Trunk) ....A
CONN.—Danielson
Scott, E. W. (Whip Sock-
ets; Fasteners) C
CONN.—Derby
Bassett, D. M. (Bolts; Axle
Clips) C
Shelton Co. (Bolts; Lining
Nails, etc.) ....O
CONN.—Hartford
Billings & Spencer Co. (Drop
Forgings) ....A
Hartford Ruber Wks. (Rub-
ber Anti-Rattlers)..AAAA
Premise Mfg. Co. (Fifth
Wheels; Shaft Attach-
ments; Steel Rims; Axles)
B
CONN.—Marion
Frost, L. D., (Est. of)
(Bolts; Nuts) C
CONN.—Milldale
Clark Bros. Bolt Co. (Bolt;
Nuts). ....B
CONN.—Mt. Carmel
Miller, Willis P. (Axles)..A
Mt. Carmel Bolt Co. (Tires;
Bolts; Nuts) ....B
Woodruff & Sons Co., Wal-
ter W. (Mountings; Locks;
Hinges) ....B
CONN.—Naugatuck
Naugatuck Malleable Iron
Co. (Malleable; Hub
Bands) ....A
CONN.—New Britain
Brady, T. H. (Roller Chafe
Iron) ....D
Corbin Screw Corp. (Bolts)
AAA
CONN.—New Haven
Cowles & Co., C. (Curtain
Fasteners; Corner Irons;
Silver Mouldings; Step
Cover; Lamps) C
Bruen, B. D. (Steps;Whiffle-
trees; Couplings; Pole
Crabs) ....F
English Mersick Co.
(Hinges; Corner Irons;
Anti-Candles, etc.) .....D
Kilbourn & Bishop Co. (Forg-
ings) ....D
Ochsner & Son, A. (Tacks;
Hinges) ....E
Perpente Mfg. Co. (Coach
Inside Mountings) ......F
Seward & Son Co., M. (Fifth
Wheels; Forgings; Dashes)
F
Vulcan Iron Wks. (Malleable
Iron Wks.) ....A
CONN.—Newtown
Beers & Co., D. G. (Seat
Locks) ....E
CONN.—Norwich
Conn. Safety Whiffletree Co.
(Whiffletree Attach-
ments) ....F
CONN.—Plantsville
Atwater Mfg. Co. (Forg-
ings) ....B
Blakester Forging Co. (Forg-
ings) C
Smith & Co., H. D. (Forg-
ings) C
Thompson Drop. Forging Co.
(Forgings) ....F
CONN.—Seymour
Matthews Mfg. Co., H. A.
(Sheet Steel Stampings) B
CONN.—Southington
Peck, Stow & Wilcox Co.
(Bolts; Nuts, etc.), AAAA
Southington Cutlery Co.
(Tire Bolts) ....A
CONN.—Unionville
Upson Nut Co. (Bolts; Nuts,
etc.) ....AAA
CONN.—Waterbury
Scovill Mfg. (Brass Hub;
Bands) ....AAAA
CONN.—Winsted
Moore Co., Franklin (Bolts;
Axle; Clips, etc.) ......B
D. C.—Washington
Kendall, J. B. (Brake Block)
A
ILL.—Ashkum
Comstock, C. H. (End Gate
Irons) ....B
ILL.—Carpentersville

512

N. Y.—Utica

Empire State Shaft Coupler Co. (Anti Rattlers; Chafe Iron) ....D

Gibbin & Co. (Whiffletree Hooks) C

Weston-Mott Co. (Steel Rims for Pneumatic Wheels; Ball Bearing Axles). ....B

N. Y.—Wellsville

Freeland & Son (Pole; Single & Doublefree Iron) ...F

N. Y.—Westmoreland

Westmoreland Malleable Iron Co. (Malleable Work) C

OHIO—Akron

Diamond Rubber Co. (Rubber Anti-Rattler) ...AAA

Goodrich Co., B. F. (Rubber Anti-Ratlers) .....AAAA

OHIO—Ashtabula

Ashtabula Carriage Bow Co. (Top Bow Sockets; Steel Washers) ....D

OHIO—Bellville

Perfection Spring Nut Co. (Spring Nuts) ....:.F

OHIO—Canton

Cleveland Axle Mfg. Co. (Steel Axles) ....A

Cleveland Canton Spring Co. (Springs) ....B

Timken Roller Bearing Axle Co. (Roller Bearing Axles) ....B

OHIO—Carthage

Hess Spring & Axle Co. (Springs; Axles) .....AA

OHIO—Cincinnati

Albrecht Co., Chas. H. (Prop Rests; Knobs; Curtain Fasteners) ....B

Cinn. Bow Socket Co. (Bow Sockets) ....E

Cinn. Carriage Goods Co. (Shaft Couplers) ......D

Cinn. & Hammond Spring Co. (Springs) ....A

Corcoran Sons, T. H. (Dash Rails; Mountings, Lamps) ....B

Crane & Breed Mfg. Co. (Hearse Mountings) ..AA

Enterprise Brass & Plating Wks. (Mountings; Dash & Seat Rails) ....D

Greno, C. L. (Cushion Springs) ....A

Kinsley, J. R. (Mountings; Rails) C

Lounsberry & Sons, G. H. (Cushion Seat; Back Springs) C

Martin Singletree Clip Co. ....E

Monarch Carriage Goods Co. (Prop Nuts; Rests; Knobs; Anti-Rattlers, etc.) ....D

Murdock, Jas. R. (Rails; Bands; Tips, etc.) C

Murray, Wm. A. (Cushion Seats; Back Springs)....E

Queen City Forging Co. (Forgings) ....B

Schacht Mfg. Co. (Wire Wheels; Gears) C

Tower Mfg. Co. (Tacks) ..C

OHIO—Cleveland

Bettcher Mfg Co. (Washers; Burrs) ....E

Bourne & Knowles Mfg. Co. (Nuts; Washers; Felloe Plates) ....A

Cleveland Bolt & Mfg. Co. (Bolts) C

Cleveland Hardware Co. (Steel Carriages) ...AA

Cleveland Wire Spring Co. (Cushion Seat; Back Springs) ....B

Eberhard Mfg. Co. (Malleables) ....AA

Federal Mfg. Co. (Tubular Gears) ....AAAA

Kirk Latty Mfg. Co. (Tire Bolts; Rivets; Tacks) ..B

Lamson & Sessions Co. (Bolts) ....A

Nat. Screw & Tack Co. (Tire Bolts; Rivets)...AA

Topliff Mfg. Co.. I. N. (Bow

Sockets; Steel Washers) ....AA

Upson Nut Co. (Bolts) ....AAAA

OHIO—Columbus

Brown Mfg. Co., Jno. W. (Lamps; M't'gs.) ....B

Columbus Bolt Wrks. (Bolts; Nuts; Fifth Wheels) ....A

Columbus Brass Co. (Hearse Trimmings) C

Columbus Skein & Iron Wrks. (Skeins) C

Lamnan Co., E. B. (Corner Screws; Felloe Plates; Clip Yokes) C

Midgley Mfg. Co. (Steel Wheels) ....A

Peters & Heron Dash Co. (Dashes) C

Schreyer, G. (Steel Skeins) C

OHIO—Coshocton

Houston-Hay Axle Co. (Axles) X

Keagy & Lear Mach. Co. (Steel Axles) C

OHIO—Dayton

Corbin Screw Corp. (Bolts) ....AAA

Dayton Malleable Iron Co. (Malleable Work) ..AAA

Meeker Mfg. Co. (Ball Bearing Steel Axles) ......D

OHIO—Elyria

Topliff & Ely Co. (Bow Socket; Equalizer) ...A

OHIO—Fremont

Herbrand Co. (Drop Forgings; Fifth Wheels).....C

OHIO—Geneva

Geneva Metal Wheel Co. (Steel Wheels) ....B

OHIO—Mansfield

Union Fdry. & Mach. Wrks. (Thimble Skeins; Wood Axles) ....D

OHIO—Springfield

Bettendorf Metal Wheel Co. (Steel Wheels) ....AAA

Springfield Malleable Iron Co. (Malleable) ....B

OHIO—Struthers

Cooper Co., J. A. & D. P. (Reaches & Gear Irons).D

OHIO—Sunbury

Wheaton & Cockrell (Buggy Runner Attachments) ..D

OHIO—Toledo

Am. Tubular Axle Co. (Axles) C

Foster Co., G. H. (Wagon Skeins; Axles Boxes) C

Kroh Co., E. Z. (Dashes)..E

OHIO—Troy

McKinnon Dash Co. (Dashes) ....A

OHIO—Youngstown

Fredonia Mfg. Co. (Gear; Iron; Couplings) .....D

PA.—Allegheny

Liggett Spring & Axle Co. (Springs; Axles) .....AA

PA.—Carlisle

Gardner's Sons, F. (Axles) ....A

PA.—Corry

Raymond Mfg. Co. (Top Prop Washers; Anti-Rattlers; Coil Springs) C

PA.—Elizabethtown

Dauphin Axle Co. (Axles) X

PA.—Elwood City

Baker Forge Co. (Forgings) X

PA.—Emigsville

Nat. Tubular Axle Co. (Self Oiling Axles) C

PA.—Erie

Erie Malleable Iron Co. (Rim; Hub Bands) ....A

Erie Torsion Spring Co. (Pole; Seat; Bolster Springs) ....B

Reno Mfg. Co. (Safety Pole Tips) ....F

PA.—Girard

Ely Mfg. Co., Theo. J. (Anti-Rattlers) C

HARDWARE (Con.)

PA.—Lancaster
Nat. Mfg. Co. (Fifth Wheels) ....D
Stand Ball Axle Wrks. (Axles-Ball) ....B
Star Ball Retainer Co. (Ball Bearing Retainers) .....B

PA.—Lebanon
Am. Iron & Steel Mfg. Co. (Iron Tires) ......AAAA

PA.—Mercer
Bell & Co., Jno. W. (Anti-Rattlers; Shafts Couplers) E

PA.—Millersburg
Miliersburg Fifth Wheel Co. (Fifth Wheel) ....B

PA.—Milton
Milton Mfg. Co. (Nuts; Iron Washers) ....A

PA.—New Brighton
Townsend, C. C. & E. P. (Tire Bolts; Rivets)..AA

PA.—No. East
Fernald Mfg. Co. (Anti-Rattlers; Shaft-Couplers) F

PA.—Northumberland
Keystone Forging Co. (Fifth Wheel; Forging) ....B

PA.—Philadelphia
Am. Axle Wrks. (Axles)..X
Devlin Mfg. Co., Thomas (Castings) ....AAA
Excelsior Brass Wrks (Hub Bands; Handles; Whips; Sockets) ....F
Hindermyer & Son, Jos. (Hub Bands; Oil Cup) ..F
King Fifth Wheel & Gear Co. (Roller Bearing Fifth Wheel) ....D
Modern Mfg. & Plating Co. (Mountings) ....F
Philadelphia Hdw. & Malleable Iron Wrks. (Castings)..................E
Pressed Steel Mfg. Co. (Ball Bearing Axles) ....E
Skelly & Co., Thos. P. (Bolts) ....D
Standard Roller Bearing Co. (Roller Bearings; Steel Balls) ....B
Weston & Wells Mfg. Co. (Torison Springs for Cushions) C

PA.—Pittsburg
Ahlborn & Neckermann
Baker Mfg. Co., Jas. H. (Drop Forgings; Wagon Irons) ....A
(Axles) X
Crucible Steel Co. of Am. (Axles) ....AAAA
Jarvis Co., Adam S. (Axle Boxes) ....A
Jones & Laughlin, (Ltd.) (Steel Tires) ......AAAA
Keystone Axle Wrks. (Axles) ....B
McLean & McGinniss (Dashes) ....A
Oliver Iron & Steel Co. (Bolts; Steel Tires; Wagon Hdw.) ......AAAA
Pittsburg Tubular Steel Whiffletree Co. (Steel Whiffletrees; Neck Yokes) B
Standard Chain Co. (Wagon Chains) ....AAAA

PA.—Pittston
Rommel & Co., G. B. (Axles) X

PA.—Rankin
Duquesne Forge Co. (Nickle Steel Axles)..A

PA.—Scranton
Scranton Axle Wrks. (Axles) ....A
Scranton Forging Co. (Drop Forgings) ....A

PA.—Waverly
Stone Mfg. Co., P. B. (Wagon Tongue Support Spgs.) X

PA.—Wilkesbarre
Sheldon Axle Co. (Axles) AA

R. I.—Pawtucket
Haskell Mfg. Co., Wm. H.

HARDWARE (Con.)
(Spgs.; Bolts ; Screws) A

R. I—Providence
Am. Ball Co. (Steel Balls) D
Am. Screw Co. (Tire Bolts; Screws) ....AAAA

VT.—Montpelier
Sabin Machine Co. (Anti-Rattlers; Couplers) ....E

W. VA.—Wheeling
Spears Axle Co. (Axles) ..B
Wheeling Hinge Co. (Bolts; Washers; &c.) ......AA

WIS.—Boscobel
Ruka Bros. Mfg. Co. .....B

WIS.—Milwaukee
Am. Mfg. Co. (Pole Tips) H
Milwaukee Wagon Iron Wrks. (Neck Yokes; Singletree Brake Locks)..AA
Wis. Malleable Iron Co. (Wagon Malleables) ...A
Wrought Washer Mfg. Co. (Plate Washers; Felloe Plates).......... .....A

WIS.—Racine
Adams & Son, E. B. (Bolster Springs) C
Belle City Malleable Iron Co. (Malleable) ....B
Harvey Spring Co. (Truck Platform; Bolster Springs) D
Higgins Spring & Axle Co. (Axles; Bolsters; Seat; Vehicles Springs) ....B
Imperial Bit & Snap Co. (Whip Sockets; Rim Holders) ....B
Racine Economy Spg. Co. (Bolster Springs) ......D
Racine General Mfg. Co. (Wagon Hdw.) ....E
Racine Malleable & Wrought Iron Co. (Whip Sockets; Wagon Brakes) ....B
Racine Metal Stamping Co. (Shaft Iron) ....H
Racine Pole & Spring Co. (Bolster Spgs.) ....E
Racine Steel & Iron Mfg. Co. (Wagon Skeins) X
Tecktonius, E. C. (Bolster Springs; Pole Supports) F

WIS.—So. Milwaukee
Stowell Mfg. & Fdry. Co. (Carriage; Wagon Malleables) ....A

HARDWARE: TRUNK

CONN.—Bristol
Sessions & Son, J. H. (Trunk) ....AA

MICH.—Detroit
Michigan Stamping Co. ..F
Premier Mfg. Co., 58 Shelby (Trunk Suit Case) X

MO.—St. Louis
St Louis Trunk Hdw. Mfg. Co., 208 S. 17th (Trunk) D

N. J.—Newark
Goldsmith & Son, L. ....A
Gould Sons Co., M. ......A
Newman Hdw. Co., R. ..B

N. Y.—Buffalo
Keim, John R. ....AA

WIS.—Milwaukee
Milwaukee Stamping Co. (Trunk) ....E

HARDWOOD
See Lumber

HARNESS
See also Saddlery & Harness

CONN.—Middletown
Russell Mfg. Co. (Halters; Surcingles) ......AAAA

CONN.—Waterbury
Novelty Mfg. Co. (Dog) A

DEL.—Middletown
Parker Son Co., J. C. (Halters) ....B

HARNESS (Con.)

ILL.—Aurora
Frazier & Co., W. S.
(Breaking) ....A

ILL.—Bloomington
Green Co., B. C. (Buggy) B

ILL.—Chicago
Bressman & Co., F. 142
Monroe (Halters) .....E

KY.—Louisville
Harbison & Gathright
(Buggy; Carriage) ..AA

MASS.—Holyoke
Holyoke Halter Mfg. Co.
(Halters) ....F

MASS.—Westfield
Planet Mfg. Co. (Halters)
D

MINN.—Winona
Minnesota Harness Factory
(Halters) C

MO.—St. Louis
Copeland Halter Co. (Halters) X
Meyer, Bannerman & Co.,
618 N. 6th (Contractors';
Supplies) ....AAA
Sickles Saddlery Co., J. B.
21st & Washn. Av. (Contractors'; Supplies) ...A

N. H.—Concord
Page Belting Co. (Halters)
AA

N. J.—Newark
Harness Mfg. Co. ......E

N. Y.—Buffalo
Buffalo Weaving & Belting
Co. (Web) ....A

New York City
Abercrombie & Fitch, 314
Bway. (Pack) ....B
Medford Fancy Goods Co.
(Dog) ....E
Smith-Worthington Co., 40
Warren (Bridles) ...B

N. Y.—Utica
Adams Bros. & Co.
(Halters) C

OHIO—Cincinnati
Eagle Harness Co. (Pony)F
Engelke Saddlery Co.
(Bridles) C
Perkins-Campbell Co.
(Halters) ....AA

OHIO—Columbus
Hayden Saddlery Hdw.
Co., P. (Contractors';
Supplies) ....A

TENN.—Nashville
Nashville Saddlery Co.
(Halters) ....AA

WIS.—Milwaukee
Western Rawhide & Belting Co. (Halters) .....B

HARNESSES

ILL.—Chicago
Street & Co., R. R., 184
Washington (Loom) ...A

MASS.—Clinton
Gibbs, Loom, Harness &
Reed Co. (Loom) .....B

MASS.—Fall River
Webster Loom Harness Co.
(Loom) ....D
Williams Co., J. H. (Loom)
A

MASS.—Lawrence
Clegg, Thos. W. (Loom) F
Emmone Loom Harness Co.
(Loom) ....A

MASS.—Lowell
Carruthers, Robt. (Loom) B
Harris, Geo. W., 199 Perkins (Loom) ....B

MASS.—New Bedford
Fowler, Henry C. (Loom) E

N. J.—Newark
Crabb & Co., Wm. (Loom)
A

N. J.—Paterson
Hall & Co., I. A., 30 Hamilton Av. (Loom; Fancy
Loom) ....A
Paterson Reed & Harness
Co. (Loom; Fancy Loom;
Weaving) ....B
Ulrich & Co. (Loom) C
Walder, J. (Loom) ....AA

PA.—Philadelphia
Schaum & Uhlinger, N. 2nd
& Glenwood Av. (Loom;
Fancy Loom) ......AAA

HARNESSES (Con.)

R. I.—Pawtucket
Blackstone Reed & Harness
Co. (Loom) ....F
Excelsior Loom Reed Wks.
(Loom) ....E

R. I.—Providence
Amer. Supply Co., 11
Eddy (Loom) ....AA

S. C.—Spartanburg
Andrews Loom, Reed &
Harness Co. (Loom) ..C

HARPOONS

New York City
Tiebout, W. & J., 118 Chambers ....B

HARPS

See also Musical Instruments

CONN.—Bridgeport
Bridgeport Brass Co.
(Lamp) ....AAA

CONN.—Meriden
Bradley & Hubbard Mfg.
Co. (Lamp) ......AAAA
Miller & Co., Edward
(Lamp) ....AAAA
Holmes, Booth & Haydens
(Inc.) (Lamp) ...AAAA

MICH.—Kalamazoo
Star Brass Works (Trolley)
C

HARROWS

See Agr. Implements

HARVESTERS

See Agr. Implements

HASPS

CONN.—New Britain
Humason & Beckley Mfg.
Co. ....A
Stanley Wks. ....AAA

ILL.—Aurora
Wilcox Mfg. Co. ....B

ILL.—Chicago
Vaughn & Bushnell Mfg.
Co. ....A

ILL.—Sterling
Lawrence Bros. (Hinge;
Wrought Iron) ....AAA

N. Y.—Elmira
Cronk & Carrier Mfg. Co. B

New York City
Cary Mfg. Co., 19 Roosevelt (Crate) ....B
Sargent & Co., 151 Leonard
(Hinge) ....AAAA

OHIO—Canton
Ney Mfg. Co. ....B

PA.—Allegheny
McKinney Mfg. Co.
(Hinge) ....AAA

PA.—Erie
Griffing Mfg. Co. (Hinge)
A

PA.—Philadelphia
Conroy, P. J. X
White Dental Mfg. Co., S.
S. ....AAAA

PA.—Pittsburg
Lanz & Sons, M. ....AA

PA.—Reading
Reading Hdw. Co. (Hinge;
Wrought Iron) ...AAAA

W. VA.—Wheeling
Wheeling Hinge Co. ...AA

WIS.—Racine
Racine General Mfg. Co. E

HASSOCKS

See Furniture

HATCHES

MASS.—Florence
Norwood Engineering Co.
(Elevator; Safety) ....B

MASS.—Holyoke
Holyoke Machine Co. (Elevator Safety) ....AA

WIS.—Milwaukee
Kieckhefer Elevator Co., A.
(Elevator Safety) C

HATCHETS

CONN.—Collinsville
Collins Co. ....AAAA
CONN.—Southington
Peck, Stow & Wilcox Co.
........AAAA
CONN.—Westport
Bradley's Sons, G. W. ...D
ILL.—Freeport
Arcade Mfg. Co., (Boys,
Lay) ....A
ILL.—Streator
Iwan Bros. C
IND.—Evansville
Evansville Tool Wks. (All
Kinds) ....A
MAINE—Hallowell
North Wayne Tool Co.
(Tobacco) C
MAINE—Skowhegan
Williams & Co., C. A. ...D
MASS.—Winchendon
Mason & Parker .....AAA
N. J.—Newark
Atha Tool Co. ....A
Harding Edge Tool Co.,
cor. McWhorter & Oliver
...................F
N. Y.—Buffalo
White Co., L. & I. J., cor.
Perry & Columbia .....A
N. Y.—Cattaraugus
U. S. Edge Tool Co. .....D
N. Y.—Cohoes
Peck Edge Tool Co. (All
Kinds) X
N. Y.—Dunkirk
Romer Axe Co. ....B
N. Y.—Homer
Phoenix Hdw. Mfg. Co. .D
New York City
Amer. Axe & Tool Co., 253
Bway ....AAAA
Wiebusch & Hilger (Ltd.)
13 Murray ....A
OHIO—Findlay
Findlay Axe & Tool Co. .A
OHIO—Ravenna
Williams, A. C. ....A
OHIO—West Park
Norton Tool Co. (Axe Pat-
tern) C
PA.—Chester
Black & Co., H. B. ...AA
PA.—Glassport
Amerisan Axe & Tool Co.
(Bench) ....AAAA
PA.—Ogontz
Hammond & Son, C. (All
Kinds) ....A
PA.—Philadelphia
Germantown Tool Wks.,
518 Commerce ....A
Phila. Steel & Iron Co.
(Carpenters') X
Plumb, Fayette R., cor.
Tucker & Trenton Av. AA
PA.—Reading
Chantrell Tool Co. (Cast
Iron; Steel) ....B
Franklin Specialty Co.
(Nickel Plated) ....G
PA.—Wrightsville
Wrightsville Hdw. Co. ...B

HATS & CAPS

CAL.—San Francisco
Fleisher, Wolf (Cloth
Caps) ....A
CONN.—Bethel
Baird-Untiedt Co. (Fur
Hats ....B
CONN.—Danbury
Green & Sons, John W.
(Inc.) (Fur Hats).....B
Hawes, Von Gal Co. (Inc.)
(Fur Hats) ....A
Holley & Co., L. C. (Fur
Hats) ....A
Loewe & Co., D. E. (Felt
(Hats) ....B
Mc Lachlan & Co., H. (Fur
Hats) ....B
Mallory & Sons, E. A.
(Felt Hats) ....AA
Meeker Bros. & Co. (Fur
Hats) ....B
Merritt & Son, C. H. (Fur;
Felt Hats) ....A
National Hat Co. (Fur Hats)
B

HATS & CAPS (Con.)
CONN.—Milford
Mitchell, W. G. (Straw) C
CONN.—New Milford
New Milford Hat Co. (Fur
Hats) ....A
CONN.—South Norwalk
Dennis & Blanchard
(Straw) C
Hubbell, Wm. B. (Fur Hats)
B
Wilson & Co., Jno. C. (Fur
Hats) ....A
Volk Hat Co. (Coach
Hats) ....D
GA.—Atlanta
National Straw Hat Wks.
(Childrens' Straw Hats)
C
Piedmont Hat Mfg. Co.
(Childrens' Felt Hats)..E
Wiseberg Bros. (Cloth
Caps) ....D
ILL.—Chicago
Armstrong Mfg. Co., E. A.
(Cloth Caps) ....D
Elger & Bro., E., 1249 Wa-
bash Av. (Ladies' Felt
Hats) ....AA
Forster, G. F. Son & Co.
(Cloth Caps) ....D
Hackner Bros. & Bruski D
Kaatz, Marcus (Cloth Caps)
C
Schetnitz, S. & Co. (Cloth
Caps) C
Shoninger Bros. Mfg. Co.
(Childrens') C
Taylor & Parrott (Cloth
Caps) ....B
ILL.—Decatur
Home Mfg. Co. (Ladies'
Sun Bonnets) ....D
ILL.—Mattoon
Buck Mfg. Co., Geo. N.
(Sun Bonnets) ....B
IND.—Wabash
Pioneer Hat Wks. (Nathan
Meyer & Co.) (Fur Hats)
A
MAINE—Portland
Ayer, Houston & Co. (Fur;
Wool Hats) ....A
Somers & Co., Robert F.
(Silk and Stiff Hats)
D
MD.—Baltimore
Brigham-Hopkins Co.
(Silk and Straw) ..AA
Duke, Montague & Gillet
Co. (Straw) ....B
Gehrman & Co. P. F.
(Childrens') C
Howser & Co., G. S.
(Cloth Caps) ....B
Strouse & Co., J. S. (Felt
Hats) ....D
Townsend & Grace Co.
(Straw) ....B
MASS.—Amesbury
Merrimac Hat Co.
(Boys Soft Wool Hats)
A
MASS.—Amherst
Hills Co. (Straw).......B
MASS.—Athol
Powers & Sons, O. J.
(Panama Hats) C
MASS.—Attleboro
Wilmarth & Co., W. D.
(Felt) ....D
MASS.—Boston
Brodersen & Day. (Straw)
B
Dinner, I. H. (Cloth)...D
Guyer Hat Co. (Felt Hats)
A
Lamson & Hubbard, 92 Bed-
ford (Silk; Fur Hats)..A
Rosnosky & Co., Wm.
(Cloth Caps) ....D
Smith & Cheney Co.
(Straw) X
Stoughton Rubber Co.
(Rubber) ....AA
Tower & Co., A. T., 18 Sim-
mons (Oiled Hats)..AA
Wliamson & Sleeper
(Straw; Womens' Felt)..B
MASS.—Fall River
Bristol County Hat Wks.
(Fur and Wool Hats)..A
Old Colony Hat Co. (Fur
Hats) ....B

HATS & CAPS (Con.)

MASS.—Franklin
Franklin Hat Co. (Ladies; Straw) X

MASS.—Haverhill
Thorn & Co., W. B. (Felt Hats) ....A

MASS.—North Dana
Goodman Co., H. W. (Straw) C

MASS.—So. Framingham
Barber & Co., T. L. (Felt Hats) ....A

MICH.—Detroit
Armstrong Regalia Co. (Military; Police; Firemen's; Yachting Caps) C

Crown Hat Mfg. Co. (Black Hats) ....D

Detroit Cap Mfg. Co. (Cloth Caps) C

MICH.—Kalamazoo
Henderson Ames Co. (Band; Police; Firemens') A

MINN.—St. Paul
Marks & Co., A. S. (Cloth Caps) ....D

MO.—St. Joseph
Johnston-Woodbury Hat Co. (Cloth) ....B

MO.—St. Louis
Gram & Glass (Cloth Caps) D

N. J.—Hoboken
Brittain, Horace (Straw) A

Heath, Joseph A. (Cloth Caps) ....D

N. J.—Newark
Connett & Co., E. V. (Fur Hats) ....AA

Excelsior Hat Works (Beaver Hats) ....B

Ferry, Weber & Co., 325 5th Av. (Fur Hats) ......AA

Fisch, Jos., 24 Arch (Fur Hats) ....A

Fulcher, R. & A. (Fur Hats) A

Hedden Co., C. M. (Fur Hats) X

Henegan, John H. (Straw) X

Parmelee & Co., H. D. (Fur Hats) ....B

Seitz & Son, Albert (Fur Hats) ....A

Rummel Co., J. (Felt) ....A

N. J.—New Brunswick
Barkelew & Co., J. M. (Maids' Caps) ....D

N. J.—Orange
Austin, Drew & Co. (Fur Hats) ....B

Berg & Co., (Felt; Fur).A

Brennan, Carr & Co. (Felt Hats) ....A

Cummings Son & Co., F. (Felt) ....A

Harrop, Gist & Co.........A

No Name Hat Mfg. Co. (Felt) ....A

N. J.—Woodbine
Quaker City Knitting Mills (Toques; Tams) ....A

N. Y.—Albany
Lashever & Co., H. (Cloth Caps) ....D

N. Y.—Augusta
Cunningham & Son, James (Scotch Caps) ....D

N. Y.—Brooklyn
Mundheim Co., Samuel (Straw; Fur) ....AA

Spear & Co. (Cloth Caps) C

N. Y.—Buffalo
Miller, John (Cloth Caps) D

N. Y.—Fishkill on Hudson ..
Dutchess Hat Wks. (Fur; Wool Hats) ....AA

N. Y.—Matteawan
Matteawan Mfg. Co. (Wool Hats) ....A

N. Y.—Middletown
Union Hat Co. (Straw)..C

N. Y.—New York City
Alland Bros., 661 Broadway, (Straw; Ladies').A

Alley & Allen, 606 Broad-

HATS & CAPS (Con.)
way, (Ladies' Hats)..D

American Railway Supply Co. (Uniform Caps) ...C

Apple & Co., 621 Broadway, (Imitation- Panama) ....D

Bamberger & Son, 4 East 11th (Infants') ....B

Berg Bros., 225 Wooster (Duck; Felt; Ladies' Hats) ....A

Blom & Mayer (Ladies').A

Blum & Koch (Straw)....A

Boretti, R., 70 W. 3d (Wool Hats) C

Brower, Alex. R. (Silk; Opera; Ladies' Riding Hats) C

Brown, Alex. R. (Straw) C

Burgesser & Co., A. D. 106 West 11th (Ladies' Hats) ....D

Cairns & Bro. (Firemen).D

Carpenter, Wm. H., 621 B'Way (Ladies' Hats).D

Carroll & Co., Wm. (Straw) ....AAAA

Cohen, Cassel (Fur Caps) B

Cornell & Co., M. S., W. B'way & Prince (Silk; Fur Hats) ....B

Cotton, H. L. & Co. (Infants') C

Crieger & Meyer, 621 B'way (Ladies' Felt Hats).....E

Davis Mark, Sons & Co. (Cloth) ....A

Demmerle & Co. (Cloth Caps) C

Dunlap & Co. (Felt; Silk) AA

Eaves Costume Co., 586 7th Av. (Theatrical Hats) ....D

Feltenstein & Joffe, 596 B'way (Ladies' Hats)..B

Fox, Lederer & Co. (Cloth Caps) ....B

Frankfeldt, L. & Sons (Cloth Caps) .....AAAA

George, A. E. (Straw)..D

Goodyear Rubber Co., 787 B'way (Rubber) .AAAA

Goodyears Ind. Rubber Glove Mfg. Co., 503 B'way (Rubber) ....AAAA

Heiliger, I. (Infants').....D

Heimann & Leichten, 602 B'way (Ladies' Hats).AA

Herzig, L. & Co. (Infants) B

Hildesheimer & Schlesinger (Infants') ....B

Hirschberg & Co., 15 Waverly Pl. (Cloth)....C

Hodgman Rubber Co., 806 B'way (Rubber) .....AA

Hofhenheimer, Alex. & Co., Infants; Lace; Silk)...C

Knox, E. M. (Felt; Silk) AAA

Liberman & Co., S. N., 710 B'way ....D

Love, Scott & Jaursch (Boys'; Childrens' Cloth) C

Lustig Bros. (Cloth Caps) A

Marty & Son, 42 East Houston (Straw) ......D

Maxim & Goldsmith, 621 Broadway (Straw) ....D

Mindheim, Max, 67 Prince Straw ....A

Mork Co., M. S. (Straw) A

Olson, John, 138 Grand Aluminum Firemens' Hats) X

Phipps & Atchison, 145 5th Av. (Ladies'; Cloth)...C

Rosenbluth, A. & H. (Advertising Caps) ...C

Rosenthal-Samstag Co., 598 B'way (Ladies' Hats)..C

Richman, Wm. 98 F'klin (Tam; Toques) ....B

Schaniro & Anderson (Straw) ....D

Schiller, S., 604 B'way (Ladies' Hats) C

Schultz & Co., Jos. (Ladies'

HATS & CAPS (Con.)
Felt; Straw) ....A
Seybel Co., F. M. (Ladies')
..........D
Shields & Co., J. S., 596
B'way (Silk) ....B
Simonson, Lichtenstein
Pachner Co., (Cloth Caps)
..........A
Standard Oiled Clothing
Co., 152d & Union Av.
(Oiled Made) ......B
Stern, B. & Co. (Silk;
Lace; Infants') C
Stiehl, G. H. & Co.
Childrens' Caps) .....D
Ury & Mendelson Bros.
(Ladies' Hats) C
Velleman & Co. (Straw..D
Wallner, Henry & Son
(Cloth & Plush Hats)..D
Young & Staples (Straw)
..........D
N. Y.—Peekskill
Peekskill Hat Mfg. Co.
(Fur Hats) ....B
N. Y.—Prospect
Hoag, C. F. (Toques)..B
Wolf Mfg. Co. (Childrens'
Headwear) C
N. Y.—Richfield Springs
Richfield Springs Cloth
Cap Co. ....B
N. Y.—Utica
Balch Bros. & West Co.
(Felt) ....D
Mohawk Valley Cap Fac-
tory (Cloth; Knit Caps)
..........B
Northrup, D. W. (Scotch
Caps) ....A
N. Y.—Yonkers
Waring Hat Mfg. Co. (Fur
Hats) ....AA
OHIO—Cincinnati
Cincinnati Cap Co. (Caps)
..........D
Tobias Bro. & Co., Chas.
(Cloth; Military; Band
Caps) ....B
OHIO—Cleveland
Bamber & Neumann
(Toques) C
PA.—Adamstown
Ficthorn, Redcay & Co.
(Wool) ....A
PA.—Harrisburg
Blough Mfg. Co. (Sun-
bonnets) ....B
PA. Mohns Store
Kessler & Co., Jacob C.
(Wool Hats) X
Spratz & Co., J. H.
(Straw) ....B
PA.—Philadelphia
Fenton, J. H. (Silk Hats).B
Branson & Co., Howard I.
(Infants') C
Heid & Co., Frank P.
(Cloth; Ladies') C
Miller & Co., Geo. P.
(Straw) C
Price & Vogt, Cor. Berks &
Hancock (Fur Hats)....B
Roelofs & Co., Henry H.
(Felt Hats) ....AA
Rothschild & Co., S. (In-
fants) C
Schoble & Co., Frank (Felt
Hats) X
Schoenfeld, Tuch & Co. (In-
fants' Caps) ....B
Smith & Co., W. H. V.
(Straw) ....D
Stetson & Co., Jno. B.
(Felt Hats) ....AAAA
Weiberger, Louis H.
(Silk; Children's)......D
PA.—Reading
Alexander & Co., Geo. W.
(Fur Hats) ....A
Hendel Co., C. W. (Fur
Hats) ....A
Hendel & Sons, Geo. (Fur;
Wool Hats) ....AA
Kessler & Sons, C. F. (Wool
Hats) ....A
Miller & Co., John R. (Wool
Hats) ....AA
Mohn & Bros. (Wool)..AA
R. I.—Providence
Feiner Cap Co. (Cloth Caps)
..........C

HATS & CAPS (Con.)
WIS.—Milwaukee
Middleton Mfg. Co. (Cloth
Caps) ....B

HAULS

ILL.—Chicago
Allis-Chalmers Co. (Log)
..........AAAA
IND.—Indianapolis
Chandler & Taylor Co.
(Log) ....AA
MICH.—Detroit
Buhl Malleable Co. (Log)
..........A
MICH.—Saginaw
Wickes Bros. (Log)....AAA
N. J.—High Bridge
Taylor Iron & Steel Co.
(Log) ....AAAA
N. C.—Charlotte
Mecklenberg Iron Wks.
(Log) X
OHIO—Columbus
Jeffrey Mfg. Co. (Car)
..........AAAA
TENN.—Jackson
Southern Engine & Boiler
Wks. (Log) ....AA
VT.—Montpelier
Lane Mfg. Co. (Log)....A
WIS.—Milwaukee
Allis-Chalmers Co. (Log)
..........AAAA

HAVERSACKS

CONN.—Hartford
Wiley & Son Co., Wm. H.
..........A
New York City
Boyle & Co., John, 112
Duane ....AA
Goodyear's Ind. Rub. Glove
Mfg. Co. ....AAAA
Hodgman Rubber Co...AA
McHugh, John F..........C

HAZEL, WITCH
See Witchhazel

HEADERS
See also Machy

CAL.—Stockton
Shaw Co., H. C. ....A
CONN.—Bridgeport
Automatic Machine Co.
(Rod) ....B
CONN.—Hartford
Cook Co., Asa S. (Rivet;
Wooden Screw) ......B
Pratt & Whitney Co. (Bolt)
..........AAAA
CONN.—Waterbury
Blake & Johnson (Wire)..A
Manville Machine Co., E. J.
(Bicycle) C
Waterbury-Farrell Fdy. &
Machine Co. (Bolt)....AA
ILL.—Chicago
Pfeiffer Boiler Co., Chris.,
66 Mich. (Steam)......C
ILL.—Pekin
Acme Harvester Co. (Bolt)
..........X
ILL.—Peoria
Acme Harvester Co. (Grain)
..........X
MASS.—Fitchburg
Putnam Machine Co. (Bolt)
..........A
MASS.—Greenfield
Wells Bros. Co. (Bolt)....A
MASS.—Springfield
Bausch Mach. Tool Co
(Bolt) ....A
N. J.—Salem
Ayars' Machine Co. (Fruit
Can) ....B
N.Y.—Batavia
Johnston Harvester Co.
(Reaper) ....AAAA
N. Y.—Brooklyn
Upham & Bros. V. B., 30
Hudson Av. (Rivet)...X
N. Y.—Buffalo
Howard Iron Works (Bolt)
..........A
Niagara Mach. & Tool Wks
(Fruit Can; Rivet)....A

HEADERS (Con.)
Sherwood Mfg. Co. (Steam)
B
OHIO—Cleveland
Acme Machinery Co. (Bolt)
AA
Ajax Mfg. Co., cor. Lake &
Wason (Rivet) ......AA
McMyler, John, 182 Columbus (Rivet; Bolt)...AA
OHIO—Hamilton
Niles Tool Wks. (Bolt)
AAAA
OHIO—Tiffin
National Mchy. Co. (Rivet;
Rod; Bolt; Stove Rod)
AA

HEADINGS

See Heads; Cooperage

HEADLIGHTS

CAL.—San Francisco
Boesch Lamp Co., 585 Mission (Electric; Locomotive) C
ILL.—Chicago
Adams & Westlake Co. Ontario, cor. N. Franklin
(Acetylene Gas; Arc; Locomotive; Street; Interurban Oil).......AAAA
Pyle National Elec. Headlight Co., Monadnock
Bldg. (Electric; Locomotive) ....D
Wilson & Co., F. Cortez,
239 Lake (Acetylene; Locomotive) ....B
IND.—Evansville
Schroeder Headlight Co.
(Locomotive) ....D
IND.—Fort Wayne
Fort Wayne Electric Corporation (Electric; Locomotive; ....AAAA
MASS.—Boston
Dewey Co., F. O., 28 Canal
(Electric; Locomotive)..D
Sherbourne & Co., 53 Oliver
(Locomotive) ....A
Wheeler Reflector Co., 156
Pearl (Electric; Locomotive) C
MICH.—Detroit
Buhl Stamping Co. (Locomotive) ....AA
MO.—St Louis
Eagle Generator Co., 1530
Pine (Acetylene Gas)..A
Handlan-Buck Mfg. Co.,
210 N. 3d (Locomotive)
AA
Kraushaar Brass Mfg. Co.,
510 Elm (Locomotive).A
St. Louis Car Co., 8000
No. B'way (Arc) ..A'AAA
Western Electric Supply
Co. (Electric Locomotive)
X
N. Y.—Buffalo
Russell & Watson, 145
Main (Locomotive)....D
U. S. Headlight Co.,
(Locomotive) ....B
New York City
Dietz Co., R. E. (Locomotive) ....A
Dressel Railway Lamp Wks
3878 Park Av. (Locomotive) ....D
Morris, E. P., 15 Cortlandt
(Electric) ....D
N. Y.—Rochester
Glazier Head Light Co., 7
Griffith (Locomotive)..E
Ham Mfg. Co., C. T., 731
Oak (Locomotive; Traction Engine) ....AA
Rochester Head Light Wks.
(Locomotive) ....D
Star Head Light Co., 13
Allen (Electric; Locomotive) X
N. Y.—Schenectady
General Electric Co. (Electric; Locomotive).AAAA
N. Y.—Syracuse
Crouse-Hinds Co. (Electric;
Locomotive) ....A
OHIO—Cincinnati
Cinn. Railway Supply Co.

HEADLIGHTS (Con.)
(Locomotive) ....A
OHIO—Dayton
Dayton Mfg. Co. (Arc; Incandescent; Locomotive)
A
OHIO—Mansfield
Ohio Brass Co. (Electric;
Locomotive) ....AA
PA.—Philadelphia
Brill Co., J. G., 62nd &
Woodland Av. (Electric
Car; Locomotive).AAAA

HEADS

See also Cooperage

CONN.—Bridgeport
Braitling, F. K. (Doll)....F
CONN.—Elmwood
Whitlock Coil Pipe Co. (Exhaust) ....AA
CONN.—Hartford
Pratt & Whitney Co.
(Emery Wheel Grinding;
Index; Dividing; Screw
Cutting Die) ......AAAA
Sterling Blower & Pipe Mfg.
Co. (Exhaust) ....A
CONN.—New Haven
Geometric Drill Co. (Screw
Cutting Die) C
CONN.—Norwich
Rogers & Co., C. B. (Lathe)
'AAAA
ILL.—Chicago
American Spiral Pipe Wks.,
1173 S. Paulina (Exhaust) ....B
Chicago Rawhide Mfg. Co.
(Drum) ....A
Curtis-Leger Fixture Co.,
126 Franklin (Wax) ...B
Diamond Whip Co., 85 W.
North Av. (Drum) ....E
Lyman, W. C., 49 Michigan
(Exhaust) ....D
Prentice Co., L. H., 34 Sherman (Exhaust) ....A
Ryerson & Son, Jos. T., 22
Milwaukee Av. (Flanged
Boiler) ....AAAA
Warren, James P., 134 N.
Jefferson (Exhaust) ...X
ILL.—Quincy
Gardner Governor Co. (Exhaust) ....AA
ILL.—Springfield
Springfield Boiler & Mfg.
Co. (Flanged Boiler)....A
IND.—Indianapolis
Atkins & Co., E. C. (Dado)
AAAA
IOWA—Dubuque
Adams Co. (Cylinder) ....A
MASS.—Boston
Chandler & Farquhar Co.
(Polishing) ....B
Sturtevant Co., B. F. (Exhaust) ....AAA
Woods Machine Co., S. A.
(Matcher) ....AA
MASS.—Fall River
Fall River Fdy. & Mach. Co.
(Railway) ....F
MASS.—Greenfield •
Goodell-Pratt Co. (Polishing) ....B
MASS.—Hopedale
Draper Co. (Railway).AAAA
MASS.—Leominster
Tilton & Cook (Cane) ...A
MASS.—Lowell
Lowell Machine Shop (Railway) ....AAAA
MASS.—Newton Upper Falls
Saco & Pettee Mach. Shops
(Railway) ....AAA
MASS.—Taunton
Mason Mach. Wks. (Railway; Cotton Railway).AA
MASS.—Whitinsville
Whitin Machine Wks. (Railway) ....AAAA
MICH.—Detroit
Young Bros. Co., 263 Franklin (Exhaust) ....E
MICH.—Grand Rapids
Fox Machine Co., 127 N.
Front (Dado) ....A
Waddell Mfg. Co. (Carved
Grotesque) ....B

HEARSES (Con.)
N. J.—Newark
Quimby & Co., J. M......A
N. Y.—Albany
Goold Co., James ....B
N. Y.—Rochester
Cunningham, Son & Co., Jas.
                        AAAA
OHIO—Cincinnati
Crane & Breed Mfg. Co.
                        AA
Sayers & Scovill ....AA
OHIO—Ravenna
Riddle Coach & Hearse Co.
                        AA

HEARTHS

N. Y.—Long Island City
Leininger, Peter H. ......D
N. Y.—Oxford
Clark Bluestone Co., F. G.
(Stone) ....A
PA.—East Bangor
East Bangor Consolidated
Slate Co. (Slate) ....AA
PA.—Philadelphia
Philadelphia Roll & Machine
Co. (Open) ....A
PA.—Pittsburg
Aiken & Co. (Tile) ......B
Star Encaustic Tile Co.
(Tile) ....B
PA.—Tunkhannock
Hawke Stone Co. ....D
VT.—Fairhaven
Fairhaven Marble & Marble-
ized Slate Works ......B
WIS.—Milwaukee
Allis-Chalmers Co. (Fore)
                        AAAA

HEATERS

**See also Furnaces; Boilers;
Super Heaters**

CAL.—San Francisco
Ribbons Water Heating Co.
(Water; Bath; Tank)..G
Tay Co., Geo. H., 49 1st
(Hot Water) ....AA
Wilson Co., Wm. F. (Hot
Water) ....A
CONN.—Bridgeport
Coulter & McKenzie Machine
Co. (Feed Water) .....B
CONN.—Derby
Birmingham Iron Foundry
(Stationary) ....AA
CONN.—Elmwood
Whitlock Coil Pipe Co.
(Feed Water) ....AA
CONN.—Hartford
Davis & Son, I. B. (Feed
Water; Steam) ....A
CONN.—Meriden
Bradley & Hubbard Mfg. Co.
(Oil) ....AAAA
CONN.—New Haven
Foskett & Bishop Co., Grand
& Railroad Av. (Feed
Water; Greenhouse;
Steam; Hot Water) ....B
National Pipe Bending Co.
(Feed Water; Combina-
tion Hot Water; Air;
Stationary; Hot Water)
                        B
CONN.—New London
Hopson & Chapin Mfg. Co.
(Hot Water) ....B
CONN.—Putnam
Putnam Fdy. & Machine Co.
(Steam; Hot Water)....B
CONN.—Stamford
Stamford Fdy. Co. (Hot Air;
Hot Water Combination)
                        A
Stamford Gas Stove Co.
(Gas; Gas Water; Bath;
Tank) ....B
CONN.—Thompsonville
Bushnell Press Co., G. H.
(Oil Seed Meal) ....A
CONN.—Waterbury
Plume & Atwood Mfg. Co.
(Gas; Oil) ....AAA
DEL.—Wilmington
Remington Machine Co.
(Steam; Hot Water) ..A
ILL.—Chicago
Allis-Chalmers Co., Home

HEATERS (Con.)
Ins. Bldg. (Feed Water)
                        AAAA
American Radiator Co.,
Lake & Dearborn (Water
Tank; Laundry; Steam;
Hot Water) .....AAAA
Baragwanath & Son, Wm.,
52 W. Division (Feed
Water) C
Barler Mfg. Co., A. C., 104
Lake (Oil) ....B
Chicago Flexible Shaft Co.
(Carriage) ....B
Chicago Heater & Supply
Co., 54 Dearborn (Combi-
nation) ....E
Colles & Co., E. G. T., 42
S. Clinton (Feed Water)
                        B
Excelsior Steel Furnace Co.,
38 W. Monroe (Combina-
tion) ....A
Fairbanks, Morse & Co.,
cor. Franklin & Monroe
(Galvanized Steel Tank)
                        AAAA
Fuller-Warren Co., 147 Lake
(Steam; Hot Water) ...B
Illinois Malleable Iron Co.,
30 W. Monroe (Water
Tank; Steam; Hot Water)
                        AAAA
Instantaneous Water Heat-
ing Co., 90 Ohio (Instan-
taneous; Bath; Water;
Tank) ....D
Kellogg, Mackey, Cameron
Co., 222 Lake (Steam;
Hot Water) ....AAA
Kimbark, S. D., 80 Michigan
Av. (Tire) X
Kost Mfg. Co., 152 E. Lake
(Gas Jet) X
Kroeschell Bros. Co., 29
Erie (Feed Water; Green-
house) ....A
Lyman, W. C., 49 Michigan
(Asphalt; Tar) ....D
McGuire-Cummings Mfg.
Co., 122 N. Sangamon
(Car; Curling Iron) ..AA
National Boiler Works, 60
Fulton (Feed Water)..B
Nicol & Co. (Curling Iron)
                        D
Prentice & Co., L. H., 34
Sherman (Greenhouse)..A
Rubel & Co., 82 Lake
(Steam; Hot Water)....B
Smith Co., Charles, 122 Lake
(Hot Air; Water; Gas;
Bath; Tank) ....D
Wilson & Co., F. Cortez
(Portable) ....B
Wolf Co., Fred W., 139
Rees (Juice) ....AAA
ILL.—Decatur
Oakes, Wm. L. (Feed
Water) ....D
ILL.—Galva
Hayes Pump & Planter Co.
(Hot Water) ....A
ILL.—Harvard
Hunt, Helm, Ferris & Co.
(Tank) ....AA
ILL.—Joliet
Adams Steel & Wire Co.
(Instantaneous Water;
Bath; Tank) ....D
ILL.—Kewanee
Kewanee Boiler Co. (Steam;
Hot Water) ....AA
Peters Pump Co. (Steam;
Hot Water) ....A
ILL.—Moline
Barnard & Leas Mfg. Co.
(Wheat; Hot Water;
Steam) ....AA
ILL.—Peoria
McAleeman Boiler Co. (Hot
Water; Steam) ....A
O'Neill Water Heater Mfg.
Co. (Water; Bath; Tank)
                        E
ILL.—Rockford
Eclipse Gas Stove Co. (Gas;
Gas Water; Tank; Bath)
                        B
IND.—Anderson
Anderson Fdy. & Machine
Wks. (Steam; Hot Water)
                        B

IND.—Butler
Butler Co. (Tank) ......B
IND.—Evansville
Carmody, J. D. (Green-
house) ....B
IND.—Goshen
Kelly Fdy. & Mach. Co.
(Tank) ....A
IND.—Indianapolis
Knight & Jillson Co. (Bath;
Steam; Hot Water; Tank;
Coal; Gas) ....AAA
Nordyke & Marmon Co.
(Wheat) ....AAA
IND.—Kendallville
Flint & Walling Mfg. Co.
(Tank) ....AA
IND.—Logansport
Dorner Truck & Fdy. Co.
(Electric Car) X
IND.—Terre Haute
Prox & Brinkman Mfg. Co.
(Steam; Hot Water)....A
IOWA—Burlington
Murray Iron Works Co.
(Feed Water) ....A
IOWA—Des Moines
Des Moines Mfg. & Supply
Co., 121 Court Av. (Hot
Water; Steam) ....A
IOWA—Waterloo
Kelly & Tannyhill Co.
(Tank) C
KY.—Newport
Higgin Mfg. Co. (Vehicle)
A
LA.—New Orleans
Haubtman & Loeb Co.
(Ltd.) 217 Gravier (Juice)
B
Murphy, Jno. H., 643 Maga-
zine (Juice) ....AA
Payne & Joubert, 423 Ca-
rondelet (Juice) ....A
MAINE—Portland
Portland Stove Foundry Co.
(Combination; Hot Wa-
ter) ....B
MD.—Baltimore
Bibb Stove Co., B. C., 107
Light (Baltimore; Fire
Place) ....A
Flynn & Emrich, 222 N.
Holliday (Steam; Hot
Water) ....B
Sheppard & Co., Isaac A.,
cor. Eastern Av. & Ches-
ter (Steam; Hot Water)
AAA
Weisskittle & Son, G., Alice-
anna & Washn. (Gas Ra-
diator; Oil) ....A
Wood Co., W. S., 18 N.
Howard (Steam; Hot
Water) ....B
MASS.—Boston
Bernstein Electric Mfg. Co.,
286 Roxbury (Electric
Fan) ....B
Empire Laundry Machy. Co.
(Gas) C
Gurney Heater Mfg. Co., 74
Franklin (Water; Bath;
Tank; Laundry; Steam).B
Highland Foundry Co. (Hot
Water; Steam) ....B
Magee Furnace Co., 38 Un-
ion (Hot Water; Steam;
Combination) ....AA
Page Bros. & Co., 227 Cam-
bridge (Oil) ....B
Simplex Electric Heating
Co. (Electric Car; Fan).B
Smith & Anthony Co., 48
Union (Hot Water;
Steam) ....AA
Walker & Pratt Mfg. Co.,
33 Union (Combination
Water; Bath; Tank; Hot
Water; Steam) .....AA
Walworth Construction &
Supply Co., 100 Pearl
(Greenhouse) ....B
Walworth Mfg. Co. (Feed
Water) ....AAAA
MASS.—Springfield
Giant Heater Co., 82 Mon-
mouth (Gas Jet) ......D
MASS.—Taunton
Taunton Locomotive Mfg.
Co. (Feed Water) .....A
Weir Stove Co. (Hot Water;

Steam) ....A
White-Warner Co. (Hot
Water; Steam) ....B
MASS.—Westfield
Smith Co., H. B. (Steam;
Hot Water; Steam Port-
able) ....AA
MASS.—Worcester
Stewart Boiler Works, Al-
bany & Muskeego (Steam;
Hot Water) ....B
MICH.—Ann Arbor
Schneider Closet & Heater
Co. (Bath; Water) ....F
MICH.—Detroit
American Electric Heater
Co. (Electric; Sad Iron;
Curling Iron; Sterilizing)
B
Day Metallic Mfg. Co., 6th
above Michigan (Water;
Bath; Tank) ....B
Detroit Electric Co., 47
State (Electric) ....F
Detroit Heating & Lighting
Co. (Hot Water; Steam)
B
Detroit Stove Works (Gas;
Oil; Instantaneous Water;
Water; Bath; Tank)
AAAA
Ideal Mfg. Co., 546 Frank-
lin (Fire Place; Water;
Bath; Tank) ....A
Peninsular Stove Co. (Hot
Water; Steam) ......AA
MICH.—Grand Rapids
Weatherly & Pulte (Steam
Glue) C
MICH.—Jackson
Novelty Mfg. Co. (Tank;
Aluminum Oil) ......A
MICH.—Kalamazoo
Humphrey Co. (Gas; In-
stantaneous Water; Bath;
Tank; Domestic Circulat-
ing) C
MICH.—Monroe
Monroe Fdy. & Furnace Co.
(Combination) ....B
MICH.—Saginaw
Wickes Bros. (Feed Water;
Steam; Hot Water).AAA
MINN.—Minneapolis
Howell & Co., R. R. (Tank)
B
Kinne Mfg. Co., 213 S. 2d
(Oil) ....E
MINN.—St. Paul
South Park Fdy. & Mach.
Co. (Hot Water) ......B
MISS.—Corinth
Adams Machine Co., W. T.
(Feed Water) ....AA
MO.—Kansas City
Cotter, James, 923 E. 12th
(Steam; Hot Water)....B
MO.—St. Louis
American Stove Co., 414 N.
6th (Gas; Instantaneous
Water; Bath; Tank)
AAAA
Front Rank Steel Furnace
Co., 2301 Lucas Av. (Hot
Water; Steam) ....B
Handlan-Buck Mfg. Co., 212
N. 3d (Sand) ....AA
Schifferle, Fredolin, 1224 S.
B'way (Water; Bath;
Tank) C
N. H.—Exeter
Exeter Machine Works (Hot
Water; Steam) ....B
N. J.—Burlington
Stuart & Peterson Co.
(Steam Glue) ....A
N. J.—Camden
Webster, Warren & Co.
(Feed Water) ....AA
N. J.—Jersey City
Flynn, W. S., 74 Hudson
(Feed Water) C
Griffing Iron Co., A. A.
(Car; Feed Water; Ex-
haust Steam; Steam; Hot
Water) ....AA
Phillips Mfg. Co., West
Side Av. (Greenhouse)..X
N. J.—Passaic
De Vries Bros. (Feed Wa-
ter) ....E

HEATERS (Con.)

N. Y.—Albany

Albany Steam Trap Co. (Feed Water) ....D

Weller, Anton (Steam; Hot Water) ....B

N. Y.—Binghamton

Gaylord & Eitapence Co. (Steam; Hot Water) ...B

N. Y.—Brooklyn

Pioneer Iron Works, 151 William (Juice) ....A

Scollay, John A. (Est. of) (Greenhouse) C

N. Y.—Buffalo

American Radiator Co., 1741 Elmwood Av. (Steam; Hot Water) .....AAAA

Buffalo Dental Mfg. Co. (Gas) ....B

Dopp Co., H. W., 522 Ellicott (Steam Jacketed Glue) ....B

Iroquois Iron Works, 178 Walden Av. (Asphalt) ..A

Learmouth, Robert, White Bldg. (Feed Water) ....E

Niagara Machine & Tool Works (Soldering Iron) .A

Seamans, Irving M., 377 Maryland Av. (Automatic Gas; Cold Water, for Kitchen Boilers; Instantaneous Water) ....F

Squier Mfg. Co., Geo. L., 420 Niagara (Juice) .AAA

Stewart Heater Co. (Feed; Steam Water; also Combination) ....D

N. Y.—Geneva

Herendeen Mfg. Co. (Steam; Hot Water; Stationary) AA

New York Central Iron Works Co. (Hot Water; Steam) ....B

N. Y.—Irvington

Lord & Burnham Co. (Hot Water; Steam; Greenhouse) ....A

N. Y.—Ithaca

Williams Bros. (Steam) ..AA

N. Y.—Lockport

American District Steam Co. (Automatic Water, for heating water direct from steam lines) ....AAA

N. Y.—Long Island City

Stuebner Iron Works, G. L. (Asphalt; Tar; Gravel) .B

N. Y.—Medina

Swett Iron Works, A. L. (Hot Water) ....A

N. Y.—Newburg

Coldwell-Wilcox Co. (Juice; Greenhouse; Steam; Hot Water) ....B

New York City

Abendroth Bros., 109 Beekman (Fire Place; Water; Bath; Tank; Steam)....A

American Gas Furnace Co. (Gas) ....A

Baker, Smith & Co., 83 W. Houston (Car; Steam; Hot Water) ....AA

Baker, Wm. C. (firm of), 143 Liberty (Automatic Car; Freight Car) ......B

Barstow Stove Co., 228 Water (Fire Place; Hot Water; Combination) .AA

Bernstein Co., S., 86 W. B'way (Water; Bath; Tank) ....D

Boynton Furnace Co., 207 Water (Fire Place; Hot Water; Stationary; Combination; Steam) ......A

Cornell Co., J. B. & J. M., 26th & 11th Av. (Juice) AA

Crane Co., Wm. M., 1131 B'way (Gas; Glue; Instantaneous Water; Bath; Tank) ....A

Creamer & Co., W. G., 96 John (Car) ....A

Criterion Gas Stove Mfg. Co. (Inc.), 445 G'wich (Gas) X

Dame & Townsend Co., 76 John (Glue) ....B

HEATERS (Con.)

Deeley & Co., Robert, 507 W. 32d (Juice) ......AA

Fuller & Warren Co. (of Troy, N. Y.) 256 Water (Steam; Hot Water)..AA

Gilbert & Barker Mfg. Co., 82 John (Gas; Coil Gas Water; Bath; Tank; Instantaneous Water) ....A

Gold Car Heating & Lighting Co. (Car; Steam; Hot Water) ....B

Goldstein, Joseph, 323 Pearl (Gas; Oil) ....D

Gorton & Lidgerwood Co., 96 Liberty (Steam; Hot Water) ....B

Goubert Mfg. Co., 85 Liberty (Feed Water) ....B

Graff Furnace Co., 208 Water (Steam; Hot Water) ....B

Griffing Iron Co., A. A. (of Jersey City, N. J.) (Hot Water; Steam) ......AA

Hadaway Electric Heating & Engineering Co., 228 W. B'way (Electric) ...D

Hammacher, Schlemmer & Co., 209 Bowery (Glue) AAA

Harrisburg Mfg. & Boiler Co., 95 Liberty (Steam; Hot Water) ....B

Heipershausen Bros. (Hot Water) ....D

Herendeen Mfg. Co. (of Geneva, N. Y.), 39 Cortlandt (Steam; Hot Water) A

Hitchings & Co., 233 Mercer (Water; Bath; Tank; Hot Water; Greenhouse) ...B

Houchin Co., Thos. W. (Curling Iron) ....D

Huber Co., Henry, 244 5th Av. (Water; Bath; Tank) X

Hydrocarbon Burner Co. (Oil) X

International Heater Co. (of Utica, N. Y.) (Steam; Hot Water) ....AAAA

Johns-Manville Co., H. W., 100 William (Car; Electric Car) ....AAAA

Kay Co., W. H., 244 Fulton (Greenhouse) ....D

Kelley & Son, B. F., 191 Liberty (Feed Water) . B

Koven & Bro., L. O., 50 Cliff (Asphalt; Feed Water) ....A

Lawler Water, Feed & Damper Regulator Co., 189 Mercer (Water; Bath; Tank) ....F

Lord & Burnham Co., 1133 B'way (Hot Water) ...A

Manhattan Brass Co., 338 E. 28th (Oil) ....A

Manhattan Gas Heating Co., 903 7th Av. (Gas; Gas Jet) X

Miller & Co., Edward, 28 W. B'way (Oil) ...AAAA

Mott Iron Works, J. L., 84 Beekman (Bath; Tank; Water; Sad Iron; Steam; Hot Water; Combination) AA

Munsell & Co., Eugene, 218 Water (Gas) ....B

Nason Mfg. Co., 71 Beekman (Glue; Hot Water; Steam) ....B

New York Central Iron Works Co. (of Geneva, N. Y.), 150 Nassau (Steam; Hot Water) ....B

Niles-Bement-Pond Co., 136 Liberty (Steam Glue) AAAA

Patterson & Co., Frank L., 26 Cortlandt (Feed Water) E

Pierce, Butler & Pierce Mfg. Co. (of Syracuse, N. Y.), 16 E. 29th (Steam; Hot Water) ....AAA

Prometheus Electric Co., 60 Reade (Electric Car) ...F

Raymond Mfg. Co. (of Mid-

HEATERS (Con.)

PA.—Erie
Erie City Iron Works (Feed Water) ....AAAA
Erie Machine Shops (Feed Water) ....B
Erie Mfg. & Supply Co. (Feed Water) ....B
Hollands Mfg. Co. (Water; Bath; Tank) ....B
Odin Stove Mfg. Co. (Gas Water; Bath; Tank) ...B
Sims Co. (Feed Water) ...D

PA.—Harrisburg
Harrisburg Mfg. & Boiler Co. (Steam; Hot Water) ....B
Harrisburg Pipe & Pipe Bending Co. (Feed Water) ....AAA
Hickok Mfg. Co., W. O. (Gas; Glue) ....AA

PA.—Homestead
Lawson Mfg. Co., L. S. (Instantaneous Gas; Water; Bath; Tank) ....D

PA.—Huntingdon
Keystone Boiler & Radiator Co. (Hot Water) ....B

PA.—Lansdale
Heebner & Sons (Steam; Hot Water) ....B

PA.—Meadville
Phoenix Iron Works Co. (Feed Water) ....A

PA.—Middletown
Raymond Mfg. Co. (Steam; Hot Water) ....B

PA.—New Castle
Stevenson Bros. (Water; Bath; Tank) ....B

PA.—Philadelphia
American Radiator Co., 622 Arch (Steam; Hot Water) ....AAAA
Atlantic Works (Inc.), 23d & Arch (Steam Glue) ...B
Brill Co., J. G., 62d & Woodland Av. (Car) ....AAAA
Cox Stove Co., Abram, Amer. & Dauphin (Fire Place; Laundry; Combination) ....AAA
Cox & Sons' Co., 215 Race (Feed Water; Steam; Hot Water) ....B
Coatesville Boiler Works, Fidelity Bldg. (Steam; Hot Water) ....A
Enterprise Mfg. Co. of Pa. (Sad Iron) ....AAAA
Eynon - Evans Mfg. Co. (Water; Bath; Tank)...A
Harrison Safety Boiler Wks., 17th & Allegheny Av. (Feed Water) .....A
Kensington Engine Works (Ltd.) Beach & Vienna (Feed Water; Hot Water) ....A
Model Heating Co., Amer & Dauphin (Hot Water; Steam) ....AAA
Morris, Henry G., Phila. Bourse (Juice) ....B
Pancoast & Co., Henry B., 243 S. 3d (Glue) ......B
Paxson Co., J. W., 1021 N. Delaware Av. (Glue)..AA
Pennsylvania Range Boiler Co., 2010 N. 10th (Feed Water) ....B
Phila. Engineering Wks. (Feed Water) .....AAAA
Sheppard & Co., Isaac A., 1801 N. 4th (Steam; Hot Water; Combination).AAA
Spear Stove & Heating Co., James, 1014 Market (Elec. Car Heating; Ventilating Combined) ....A

PA.—Pittsburg
Bonar & Co., James (Feed Water) ....B
Gabel Mfg. Co., 103 Market (Water; Bath; Tank; Instantaneous Water)...D
Klingelhoffer & Co., Wm., 1428 5th Av. (Gas) ....E
Monarch Water Heater Co., 306 Wood (Water; Bath; Tank; Instantaneous)...D
Pittsburg Feed Water Heat-

HEATERS (Con.)

er Co. (Feed Water) ...D
Scaife & Sons' Co., Wm. B., 221 1st Av. (Asphalt; Hot Water; Feed Water; Steam) ....AAA
Taylor Burner & Electroplating Co., 804 Duquesneway (Water; Bath; Tank) ....D
Woodworth & Sons, A. M., 112 Wood (Water; Bath; Tank) X

PA.—Pottstown
March-Brownback Stove Co. (Steam; Hot Water; Combination) ....A
Sotter Bros. (Feed Water; Steam; Hot Water) ....B

PA.—Reading
Orr, Painter & Co. (Fire Place; Steam; Hot Air; Hot Water; Combination) ....AA
Prizer-Painter Stove & Heater Co. (Hot Water; Steam) ....A

PA.—Scranton
Union Steam Specialty Co. (Feed Water) ....A

PA.—Uniontown
Johnson Machine Co. (Gas) C

PA.—Washington
Petroleum Iron Wks. Co. (Feed Water) ....A

PA.—Waynesboro
Frick Co. (Feed Water) ....AAAA

PA.—Wilkesbarre
Vulcan Iron Works (Hot Water) ....AAAA

PA.—Williamsport
Steel & Robinson Co. (Hot Water; Steam) ....B

PA.—York
Broomell, Schmidt, Steacy & Co. (Inc.) (Steam; Hot Water) ....A
Motter & Sons, Geo. F. (Steam; Portable) C

R. I.—Providence
Allen Fire Dept. Supply Co., Edy, cor. Friendship (Hot Water; Steam) ....B
Barstow Stove Co. (Hot Water) ....AA
Brown & Sharpe Mfg. Co. (Gas, for tool tempering) ....AAAA

TENN.—Chattanooga
Casey & Hedges Mfg. Co. (Feed Water) ....A

TENN.—Jackson
Southern Engine & Boiler Wks. (Hot Water; Steam) ....AA

WIS.—Beloit
Thompson & Sons Mfg. Co., J. (Tank) ....AA

WIS.—Cudahy
Power & Mining Machinery Co. (Asphalt) ......AAA

WIS.—La Crosse
Funk Boiler Works Co., M. (Feed Water) C

WIS.—Milwaukee
Allis-Chalmers Co. (Feed Water) ....AAAA
Fuller-Warren Co. (Car; Hot Water; Steam; Combination) ....AAA
Milwaukee Gas Works Co., 139 Burrell (Open Grate; Gas; Gas Water; Bath; Tank) ....D
Mooers Co., H., 112 2d (Hot Water; Steam) ....B
Mueller Furnace Co., L. J. (Combination) ....A
Nordberg Mfg. Co., 476 Virginia (Feed Water) .AAA
Schwab & Sons' Co., R. J., 271 Clinton (Steam; Hot Water) ....AAA
Western Malleable & Grey Iron Mfg. Co. (Water Tank) ....B

WIS.—Wausau
Murray Mfg. Co., D. J. (Feed Water) ....A

HEDDLES

MASS.—Leicester
Watson Mfg. Co., L. S.
(Wire) ....B
MASS.—Lowell
Carruthers, Robert ......B
Harris, Geo. W., 199 Perkins ....B
MASS.—Worcester
Howard Bros. Mfg. Co., 42
Vine (Wire) ....A
N. J.—Paterson
Ferrary & Schauble Co.
(Horse Hair) ....D
Hall & Co., I. A., 30 Hamilton Av. (Braided) ...A
Walder, J. ....AA
N. Y.—Utica
Williams Co., J. H. ......A
PA.—Darby
Benazet, Heddle Co. (Ltd.)
B
PA.—Philadelphia
Billington Co., Jos. H., 113
Chestnut (Wire) ....A
Schaum & Uhlinger, N. 2d
& Glenwood Av.....AAA
Steel Heddle Mfg. Co., 1840
G'tn. (Steel) ....D
R. I.—Pawtucket
Excelsior Loom Reed Wks.
(Steel) ....E
R. I.—Providence
American Supply Co. (Jacquard) ....AA

HEELS

ILL.—Chicago
Chicago Tire & Rubber Co.
(Rubber) ....D
Farnsworth, Hoyt & Co.
(Rubber) ....B
First Rubber Co., 156 Lake
(Rubber) ....D
Morgan & Wright (Rubber)
AA
Salomon, Carl J. (Rubber)
D
MASS.—Boston
Pneumatic Cushion Rubber
Heel Co., 19 Lincoln (Rubber) ....F
Whitcher & Co., Frank W.
(Rubber) ....A
MASS.—Brockton
Shaw & Son, F. M.........B
MASS.—Cambridge
Boston Woven Hose & Rubber Co. (Rubber)..AAAA
MASS.—Chelsea
Dandy Rubber Heel Co.
(Rubber) ....F
MASS.—Haverhill
Fox Heel Co., Chas. K.
(Wood) ....A
Slipper City Wood Heel Co.
(Wood) ....F
MASS.—Lowell
O'Sullivan Rubber Co. (Rubber) ....B
MASS.—Lynn
Houghton Heel & Leather
Co. X
Tebbets, C. B. (Rubber)..H
MASS.—Milford
Greene Bros. C
MASS.—South Easton
Ross Heel Co. (Wood)....C
MASS.—Spencer
Barr & Son, W. A........D
N. J.—Newark
Shaw, W. & J. H. (Cast
Iron) ....F
New York City
New York Wood Heel Co.,
390 3d (Wood) ....E

HEKTOGRAPHS

MO.—St. Louis
Leveson & Blythe Mfg. Co.,
209 Locust ....D
New York City
Hektograph Mfg. Co. ....D

HELIOGRAPHS

MD.—Baltimore
Friez. Julian P., 1320 E.
Baltimore ....E

HELIOTYPES

MASS.—Boston
Heliotype Printing Co. ....E
New York City
Behr & Co., Herman ....AA

HELMETS

CONN.—South Norwalk
Volk Hat Co. ....D
ILL.—Chicago
Stumps, P., 6416 Ingleside
Av. (Firemen's) X
IND.—Indianapolis
Vajen-Bader Co. (Firemen's)
X
N. J.—Newark
Rummell Co., J. ....A
New York City
Berkson, M., 50 W. Houston ....F
Knox, E. M., B'way & Fulton (Police; Letter Carriers') C
Warnock Uniform Co., 19
W. 13th C
Witt, Isaac M., 5 2d.....F
PA.—Philadelphia
Horstmann & Co., Wm. H.
AAAA
Schoenhut & Co., A. (Toy)
A

HEMLOCK
See Lumber

HEMP

KY.—Lexington
American Hemp Co. ......B
Logan Bros. & Haggin
(Dressers) ....D
Longbridge, W. J. (Single;
Double Dressed) ....B
Morgan & Co., R. C. (Undressed; Dressed) .....D
KY.—Nicholasville
Brown & Bro. (Hackled;
Undressed) C
MASS.—Boston
Ludlow Mfg. Associates
AAAA
MICH.—Yale
Livingston Flax Co., Jas...C
MINN.—Jackson
Wallace, J. S. (Upholsters)
E

HENBANE

New York City
Hopkins & Co., J. L., 100
William ....A

HERBS:
PRESSED

See also Drugs; Crude
MD.—Balto
Sharpe & Dohme......AAA
MICH.—Detroit
Parke Davis & Co...AAAA
MINN.—Minn
McMillan Fur & Wool Co..X
New York City
Adams & Co., Walter....H
VT.—Burlington
Wells & Richardson Co..AA
WIS.—Fon-du-lac
Huber & Fuhrman Drug
Mills ....B

HERRING
See Fish

HIDE: RAW
See Rawhide

HIDES

ALA.—Birmingham
Adler, I. ....B
CAL.—San Francisco
Bissinger & Co. ....A
Frank & Co., S. H......AAA
Sumner & Co., W. B......A
Western Meat Co. .....AAA

COLO.—Denver
McLean & Co., E. J......B
Watkins Mdse. Co., L. A.
A
CONN.—Bridgeport
McElroy Bros. ....B
Plumb & Winton Co. .....B
FLA.—Jacksonville
Sabel Bros. ....B
GA.—Atlanta
Schoen Bros. C
ILL.—Chicago
Adler & Oberndorf ......A
Bolles & Rogers ....A
Darling & Co. ....A
Elkan & Co., H. ....A
Miller & Co., John.......A
ILL.—Decatur
Starr & Son, J. G........B
ILL.—Lincoln
Atlass, Frank ....B
ILL.—Mattoon
Duncan & Kingsolver ....B
IND.—Evansville
Evansville Abattoir Co.....B
IND.—Ft. Wayne
Weil Bros. & Co. ....A
IND.—Hammond
Hammond Co., Geo. H.
AAAA
IND.—Indianapolis
Indianapolis Abattoir Co..A
Kingan & Co. ....AAAA
Rauh & Sons, E. ....B
IND.—Logansport
Heppe & Sons, Wm. .....B
IOWA—Mason City
Decker & Sons, J. E.....B
IOWA—Sioux City
Strange Bros. Hide Co.....C
KANS.—Ft. Scott
Glunz, John ....B
KY.—Lexington
Speyer & Son C
KY.—Louisville
Davis & Son, D. G........B
Isenberg & Co., G.......C
Rosenbaum & Sons, I.....A
Sabel & Sons, M.........A
White & Co., Jno. ......AA
LA.—New Orleans
Chapman, W. W..........C
McShane, A. J...........B
MD.—Baltimore
Baer & Co., Lewis.......A
MD.—Cumberland
Hirsch Bros. ....B
Rosenthal Bros. C
MASS.—Boston
Allen & Son, Wm. H.....B
Boston Hide & Skin Assn..C
Brackett & Co., Geo. A...C
Buck & Son, Chas. (Sheep)
B
Chubb, W. B. (Sheep)....B
Howard, Harry M. (Pickled
Sheep; Lamb) ....B
Nyman, Franklin A.......B
MICH.—Detroit
Millenbach Bros. C
Schmidt, Carl E. ....A
Schmidt, Traugott & Sons
AA
MICH.—Eaton Rapids
Vaughn & Son, W. ......B
MICH.—Grand Rapids
Perkins & Hess C
Welden & Son, H. C
MICH.—Howell
McPherson, Jr., Wm......B
MICH.—Hudson
Frensdorf & Son, L. C
MICH.—Ionia
Page & Co., W. C........C
MICH.—Saginaw
Carlisle, F. W. & F.......A
MINN.—Duluth
Halford & Co., Thos. E...D
MINN.—Mankato
Henline & Son, F........D
Mankato Hide & Fur Co...D
MINN.—Minneapolis
Hudresch Bros. C
N. W. Hide & Fur Co.....C
MINN.—Rochester
Thompson, J. C. C
MO.—Kansas City
Biggs & Koch ....B
Lyon & Co., M..........A
Nelson, Jno. C
MO.—Marshall
Lowenstein & Co., A. C

MO.—Neosho
Haas, E. C
MO.—St. Louis
Byrne & Co., Jos. ......B
Crowdus & Co., J. C.....A
Landau & Co., A. ....A
St. Louis Hide & Tallow Co.
C
Wolfheim, Moses C
MO.—Trenton
Stein & Son, H..........C
MONT.—Billings
Yegen Bros. ....B
MONT.—Butte
Hample, J. E. ....B
MONT.—Ft. Benton
Power & Bro., T. C.....AA
N. Y.—Balston Spa
Schwartz, Magnus C
N. Y.—Buffalo
Hoffeld & Co. ....A
Krauss & Co., A. ......B
Wolff, Nathan ...... .A
N. Y.—Elmira
Sheely, E. & J..........B
N. Y.—Keeseville
Callanan Bros. C
New York City
Froivenfeld, J., 76 Gold
(Hides; Goat; Calf Skins)
AA
Goat & Sheep Skin Import
Co., 28 Spruce ....B
Harburger & Stack, 55
Frankfort C
Hecht, Joseph, 6 Jacob
(Deer Skins) ....AAA
Kubie & Co., Isaac, 96
Maiden Lane ....B
N. Y. Butchers' Calfskin
Assn., 407 E. 47th C
Plum & Gale, Jas. R., 76
Gold ....AA
Robertson & Sons, L. F., 39
Spruce ....B
Stein Co., Abe, 97 Gold
(Goat Skins; Hides) ..AA
Weil & Bros., Alphonse, 70
Gold ....AA
Wertheim & Son, B., 101
Gold ....A
N. Y.—Niagara Falls
Rose, H. V. C
N. Y.—Palmyra
Knowles, H. P. C
N. Y.—Rochester
Aikenhead, Wm. ....B
Fritsche & Son, F. C
Hale & Son, Wm. S......C
N. Y.—Syracuse
Marschall & Son, Jacob...B
OHIO—Akron
Christy Co., Jas. J.......A
OHIO—Cincinnati
Barth & Co., E. J ......B
Butchers' Hide Assn. ....D
Cincinnati Abattoir Co....A
Marienthal & Son........C
Martin & Riedle C
Wise & Bros., L. ....B
OHIO—Cleveland
Cleveland Provision Co.AAA
Hill & Co., H. E. C
Mittleberger & Son, M....C
OHIO—Dayton
Rauh & Sons' Co., E.....B
OHIO—Defiance
Miller Co., H. P........C
OHIO—Kensington
McAllister, J. A. C
OHIO—Lima
Schulthies Bros. ....B
OHIO—Marietta
Streecker Bros. ....A
OHIO—Norwalk
Richardson & Co., J. W...C
OHIO—Toledo
Mack, Julius ....B
OHIO—Zanesville
Frank & Sons, L.........C
OREGON—Portland
Bernheim & Co., Theo....D
Silverfield, Saul C
OREGON—Salem
Brown & Co., Wm. C
PA.—Bethlehem
Hill, Alvin C
PA.—Cannonsburg
Paxton Bros. C
PA.—Elizabethville
Romberger & Sons, S. B..A

HIDES (Con.)
PA.—Philadelphia
Cover, Drayton & Leonard
............................AAA
Janney & Son, E. K...AAA
Lindauer & Strauss, 422 No.
3d C
Ludy's Sons, C., 1507
Mascher C
Pierson's Sons, C. C., 426
No. 3d ....
Speier, A. G., 349 No. 3d
............................B
Sternfield & Co., Henry, 402
No. 3d ....B
West Phila. Stock Yard Co.
............................A
PA.—Troy
Bowen & Co. C
PA.—West Earl
Carpenter, S. L. ....B
PA.—Wilkesbarre
Lackawanna Fertilizer &
Chem. Co. ....A
TENN.—Memphis
Scheibler & Co. ....B
TENN.—Nashville
Lefkovitz & Co., J......B
TEXAS—Brownsville
Yturria, F. ....B
TEXAS—Culro
Buchel & Co., Otto ....A
Runge & Co., H........AA
TEXAS—Fort Worth
Crowdus Bros. C
TEXAS—Hearne
Crenan, W. ....B
TEXAS—Houston
Finnigan Co., Jno. ......A
UTAH—Ogden
Kuhn & Bro., A. ....A
VT.—Hyde Park
Page, Carroll S. ....A
VT.—Waterbury
Warren, Chas. C. ....B
VA.—Clarksburg
Ruhl, Koblegard Co.......A
WASH.—Spokane
Fisher & Son, Theo.......C
WASH.—Tacoma
Sheard, Wm. F...........B
WIS.—Edgerton
Child, H. W.............B
WIS.—Fond du Lac
Rueping Bros. ....A
WIS.—Merrill
Thielman, Jul. ....B
WIS.—Milwaukee
Plankington Packing Co.AA
Rosenberg & Lieberman..B
Schram & Co., W. J......C
WIS.—Oshkosh
Metz & Schloert..........C
Roenitz, H. C............C
WIS.—Platteville
Shepherd, Thos. C

HINGES

See also Hardware; Carriage

CONN.—Ansonia
Gardner's Sons, J. B.
(Butt) ....F
CONN.—Beacon Falls
Bronson, Homer Co. (Butt)
............................C
CONN.—Bridgeport
Amer. Tube & Stamping Co.
............................AAAA
Bridgeport Brass Co.
(Double Acting Spring)
............................AAA
Knapp & Cowles Mfg. Co.
("T") C
Smith & Egge Mfg. Co.
(Door) ....A
Spring Perch Co. (Con-
cealed) ....B
CONN.—Bristol
Root, C. J. (Wrought Brass;
Butt; Piano) ....B
Sessions & Son, J. H.
(Trunk) ....AA
CONN.—Meriden
Parker Co., Chas. (Blind;
Shutter; Gate) ......AAA
CONN.—Middletown
Wilcox, Crittendon & Co.
(Awning) ....A
CONN.—Mount Carmel
Woodruff & Sons Co., W.

HINGES (Con.)
W. (Carriage Door "T")
............................A
CONN.—New Britain
Corbin, P. & F. (Butt;
Door) ....AAAA
Stanley Wks. (Ball Bear-
ing Wrought Steel; Butt;
Blind; Shutter; Strap;
"T"; Bed Lounge;
Wrought Brass; Corru-
gated; Cigar Box; Door;
Trunk; Refrigerator Door)
............................AAA
Union Mfg. Co. (Door;
Spring; Gate; String
Double Acting).......AA
CONN.—New Haven
Cowles & Co., C. (Inc.)
(Carriage) ....A
English & Mersick Co.
(Carriage) ....B
Sargent & Co. (Blind; Shut-
ter; Butt; Gate; Strap;
"T") ....AAAA
CONN.—Southington
Aetna Nut Co. (Door)....A
Peck, Stow & Wilcox Co.
(Butt; Gate; Spring Door;
Ratchet Spring) ..AAAA
CONN.—So. Norwalk
Lockwood Mfg. Co. (Butt)
............................X
Norwalk Lock Co. (Butt)
............................A
CONN.—Stamford
Yale & Towne Mfg. Co.
(Butt) ....AAAA
CONN.—Terryville
Eagle Lock Co. (Brass;
Coffin) ....AAA
CONN.—Waterbury
Amer. Ring Co..........A
Benedict & Burnham Mfg.
Co. (Butt; Brass; Piano)
............................AAAA
ILL.—Aurora
Wilcox Mfg. Co. (Double
Acting Spring Gate)....B
ILL.—Chicago
Acme Flexible Clasp Co.,
17th & Clark (Strap;
Wire; "T")...........A
Chicago Hdw. Co., 132 Lake
(Butt) ....D
Chicago Spring Butt Co.,
493 Carroll Av. (Engine
House; Floor; Screen
Door; Spring Bank; Office
Railing; Spring Butt;
Spring Door) ....B
Coleman Hdw. Co. 59 Dear-
born (Spring; Floor)....A
Lawson Mfg. Co., 115 Lake
(Pivot; Double Acting;
Ball-Bearing; Spring
Floor) ....E
Niles Mfg. Co., 16. N. Canal
(Double Acting Spring).B
Orr & Lockett Hdw. Co.,
50 State (Spring Bank;
Office Railing; Buut;
Door) ....A
Payson Mfg. Co., 1319 W.
Jackson Boul. (Spring
Door) ....D
ILL.—Downers Grove
Dicke Tool Co. (Gate)....C
ILL.—Edwardsville
Edwardsville Brass Co.
(Brass Closet Door; Closet
Seat) ....B
ILL.—Freeport
Arcade Mfg. Co. (Screen
Door; Spring) ....A
Stover Mfg. Co. (Blind;
Shutter; Butt; Double
Acting Spring.. Screen
Door; Spring Door; Brass)
............................AA
ILL.—Harvard
Hunt, Helm, Ferris & Co.
(Spring) ....AA
ILL.—Joliet
Joliet Spring Hinge Co.
(Spring Door) ....G
ILL.—Lockport
Barrows Lock Co. (Butt).A
ILL.—Sterling
Lawrence Bros. (Steel
Strap; "T"; Wrought
Steel Butt) ....AAA

IND.—Evansville
Carmody, J. D. (Indestructible Green House Sash)
................................B

IND.—Fort Wayne
Knott & Van Arnam Mfg.
Co. (Closet Seat).......B

MD.—Baltimore
Maryland Hinge Co. (Strap;
"T") X

MASS.—Boston
Austin & Eddy, 117 Broad
(Blind; Shutter).......C

MASS.—Greenfield
Hale & Benjamin (Blind;
Shutter) ....F

MASS.—Springfield
Whipple & Co., R. P. (Automatic Blind; Shutter).H

MASS.—Winchendon
New England Lock & Hinge
Co. (Brass Finish; Tin).A

MASS.—Worcester
Wire Goods Co. (Blind;
Shutter; Wire) ....A

MICH.—Detroit
Detroit Shipbuilding Co.
(Brass Dept.; Butt)
.......................AAAA
Ireland & Matthews Mfg.
Co. (Closet Seat).......A

MO.—St. Louis
Baitinger & Berkley Patent
Hinge Mfg. Co., 122 N. 7th
(Blind; Shutter) .....F
Hager. & Sons Hinge Mfg.
Co., C., 2427 De Kalb
(Strap; "T..; Wraught
Steel Butt) ....AA
Kupferle, John C., 2d &
Mound (Self-Closing Gate)
.........................AA
Pleuger & Henger Mfg. Co.,
11th & Hebert (Blind;
Shutter; Gate) ....A
United States Box Lock Co.,
154 Blair Av. (Wooden
Box) X

N. J.—Newark
Goulds' Son & Co., M.
(Trunk) ....A

N. Y.—Albany
Fiset, Michl., 253 So. Pearl
(Blind; Shutter).......F

N. Y.—Brooklyn
Bommer Bros., 257-271 Classon Av. (Double Acting
Spring; Spring Butt;
Closet Seat; Office Gate;
Screen Door; Bank; Office Railing; for Hardwood Doors; for Interior
Marble Work; for Iron
Metal Railing Makers';
Safe Makers'; Wrought
Brass; Bronze Door;
Wrought Steel; Slef-Closing) ....A

N. Y.—Buffalo
Pratt & Letchworth Co.
(Tail Board) ....AAA

N. Y.—Medina
Swett Iron Wks., A. L.
(Automatic Gate)......A

New York City
Bardsley, Joseph, 147 Baxter (Spring Door)......B
Bayer, Gardner Hinge Co.,
157 W. 29th (Wrought
Steel Butt) X
Hungerford Brass & Copper
Co., U. T., 497 Pearl
(Butt) ....AA
Ludwig, A., 75 Spring
(Box) ....B
Plume & Atwood Mfg. Co.,
29 Murray (Butt; Closet
Seat; Brass) ....AAA
Russell & Erwin Mfg. Co.,
45 Chambers (Blind; Shutters; Butt; "T"; Spring
Door) ....AAAA
Scovill Mfg. Co., 423 Broome
(Butt; Spring Door;
Brass) ....AAAA
Tiebout. W. & J., 118
Chambers ....B

N. Y.—Rochester
Enterprise Fdry. Co., 48
Olean (Blind; Shutter)..B
National Casket Co. (Coffin)
.......................AAA

Pullman Mfg. Co. (Flexible
Steel) ....B
Streeter & Co., N. R.
(Blind) ....A

N. Y.—Syracuse
Stearns & Co., E. C., 100
Oneida (Spring Double
Acting) ....AA

N. Y.—Troy
Paimer Hdw. Mfg. Co.
(Blind Shutter) ....D

N. Y.—Watertown
Wise, J. B. (Sewing Machine; Closet; Organ).AA

OHIO—Canton
Kohler & Co., F. E. (Strap;
"T"; Spring)..........B

OHIO—Cleveland
Clevland Lock Co., Wason,
cor. Hamilton (Screen
Door; "T"; Strap).....D
Columbian Hdw. Co., Coe &
Hamilton (Spring Butt;
Door; Closet Seat; Office
Railing; Screen Door;
Spring for Hardwood
Doors; Spring for Interior
Marble Work; for Iron;
Metal Railing Makers;
Spring Safe Makers';
Spring Wrought Brass;
Bronze Door; Spring
Wrought Steel) .....AA
Hoffman Hinge & Fdy. Co.,
Hubbard, Porter & Burlington Sts. (Screen Door;
Spring Butt) ....B
Taylor & Boggis Fdry. Co.,
521 Seneca ....AA
Van Wagoner Co., 27 Perkins Pl. (Ball-Bearing
Wrought Steel Spring
Butt; Double Acting
Spring; Screen Door;
Spring Door; Brass;
Bronze; Ratchet Spring)
.........................X

OHIO—Columbus
Ohio Pump & Brass Co.
(Brass Closet) C

OHIO—Dayton
Dayton Malleable Iron Co.
(Factory Door) ......AAA
Dayton Mfg. Co. (Door)..A

OHIO—Shelby
Shelby Spring Hinge Co.
(Double Acting Spring
Floor) ....B

OHIO—Springfield
Springfield Brass Co.
(Brass; Nickel Closet
Seat; Wire) ....E

OHIO—Toledo
Church. Isaac (Expansion
Awning) ....F

PA.—Allegheny
McKinney Mfg. Co., Locust
& Market (Wrought Steel
Butt; Strap; "T")..AAA

PA.—Allentown
Grammes & Sons, L. F.
(Cigar Box) ....A

PA.—Erie
Griffin Mfg. Co. (End
Gate; Strap; "T";
Wrought Steel Butt)...A

PA.—Philadelphia
Conroy, P. J. (Brass; Refrigerator Door) X
Devlin Mfg. Co., Thos., 3d
& Lehigh Av. ....AA
Hoag & Co., R. C., 11th &
Catharine (Circular Door;
Window) X
Schoenhut Co., A., 2215
Adams (Cigar Box) .....A
Shannon & Sons. J. B., 1020
Market ....A

PA.—Pittsburg
Lanz & Sons, M., 101 So.
29th (Gate; Screw Hook)
.........................AA
Oliver Iron & Steel Co.
(Screw Hook; Eye).AAAA
Stiner & Voegtly, 310 Wood
(Elevating Casement Window) ....A

PA.—Reading
Penn. Hdw. Co. (Blind;
Shutter; Bronze Cast
Butt; Gate; Refrigerator)
.........................AA

HINGES (Con.)

Reading Hdw. Co. (Blind; Shutter; Wrought Steel Butt; Closet Seat; Gate; Spring Door; Wire).AAAA
PA.—Sharon Hill
Pickering, R. S. (Closet Seat; Wire) ....E
PA.—Titusville
Schatt & Morgan Cutlery Co. (Screen Door) .....B
PA.—Wrightsville
Susquehanna Casting Co. (Blind; Shutter; Gate)
.......................AA
Wrightsville Hdw. Co. (Shutter! Blind; Gate; Reversible; Self-Closing)
.......................B
R. I.—Providence
New England Butt Co. (Door; Self-Closing Gate)
.......................AA
VT.—Montpelier
Sabin Machine Co. (Spring; Spring Double Acting)..E
WIS.—Racine
Racine General Mfg. Co. (Gate) ....E

HIVES

CAL.—Petaluma
Petaluma Incubator Co. (Bee) ....B
ILL.—Hamilton
Dadant & Son, Chas. (Bee)
.......................B
IOWA—Red Oak
Kretchmer Mfg. Co. (Bee)
.......................C
MINN.—Minneapolis
Minnesota Beekeepers' Supply Mfg. Co. (Bee)....G
N. Y.—Jamestown...
Falconer Mfg. Co., W. T. (Bee) ....A
OHIO—Berlin Heights
Berlin Fruit Box Co. (Bee)
.......................D
OHIO—Medina
Root Co., A. I. (Bee)..AA
VT.—Bristol
Drake, Smith & Co. (Bee)
.......................B

HOBS

MASS.—Athol
Gay & Ward (Worm)....A
Starrett Co., L. S. (Worm)
.......................A
MASS.—Fitchburg
Putnam Machine Co. (Bolt Cutter) ....A
MASS.—Greenfield
Wells Bros. Co. (Bolt Cutter) ....A
MASS.—Mansfield
Card Mfg. Co., S. W. (Bolt Cutter) ....B
MINN.—St Paul
Helwig Mfg. Co. (Bolt Cutter) ....D
New York City
Niles-Bement-Pond Co. (Worm) ....AAAA
R. I.—Providence
Brown & Sharpe Mfg. Co. (Worm) ....AAAA

HODS

CONN.—Meriden
Bradley & Hubbard Mfg. Co. (Brass; Coal) AAAA
ILL.—Quincy
Quincy Stamping Co. (Coal)
.......................C
MICH.—Detroit
Anderson & Sons, W. H. (Mortar; Brick Beet; Grub) C
Buhl Stamping Co. (Coal).A
MICH.—Lansing
Lansing Wheelbarrow Co. (Mortar; Brick; Coal)
.......................AAA
N. Y.—Buffalo
Aldrich Mfg. Co. (Brass; Coal) ....B
Heinz & Munschauer (Brass; Coal) ....A

HODS (Con.)

Jewett Mfg. Co., John C. (Brass; Coal) ....AA
Shepard & Co., Sidney (Brass; Iron; Coal)
.......................AAAA
New York City
Jackson Co., Wm. H. (Iron; Coal) ....A
Judd & Co., H. L. (Brass; Coal) ....AA
Troy Stamping Wks. (Iron; Coal) ....AAAA
OHIO—Cincinnati
Knecht Co., Victor (Iron) Corrugated Steel; Coal)..B
.......................B
OHIO—Cleveland
Cleveland Wire Spring Co. (Steel; Mortar; Brick).A
Duplex Hanger Co. (Mortar)
.......................D
OHIO—Salem
Clark Co., W. J. (Coal) A
OHIO—Warren
Warren Sheet Metal Co. (Coal) ....B
PA.—Philadelphia
Pfeifer & Co., John (Ltd) 222 Race (Iron; Coal) A
Storz & Son, John, 210 Vine (Mortar; Brick) ....E
PA.—Pittsburg
Pittsburg Brass Mfg. Co. (Brass; Coal) ....D

HOES

See also Agr. Imps.

CONN.—Bridgeport
Bridgeport Hdw. Mfg. Co. (Hand; Scuffle)........C
CONN.—Collinsville
Collins Co. (Hand; Corn; Double Edge; Eye Mattock; Nurserymans'; Planters') ....AAAA
CONN.—Higganum
Scovill, D. & H. (Iron; Hand; Cotton; Eye; Field; Garden; Tobacco; Planters') ....A
CONN.—Southport
Jelliff & Co., C. O. (Hand; Wheel) ....D
CONN.—Westport..
Bradley's Sons, G. W. (Cranberry) ....D
ILL.—Bradley
Bradley Mfg. Co., David (Horse) ....AAA
ILL.—Moline
Moline Plow Co. (Wheel)
.......................AAAA
ILL.—Monmouth
Milne Mfg. Co. (Iron; Grub)
.......................C
IND.—Terre Haute
Terre Haute Shovel & Tool Co. (Iron; Hand; Corn; Double Edge; Eye; Mortar; Nurserymens')....A
IOWA—Fort Madison
Am. Hoe & Fork Co. (Iron; Hand; Field; Garden; Mattock; Planters'; Scuffle; Mortar) ..AAAA
IOWA—Lone Tree
Monarch Grubber Mfg. Co. (Iron; Grub) ....B
MAINE—Hollowell
North Wayne Tool Co. (C. C. Brooke Prop.)...A
MAINE—North Berwick
Hussey Plow Co. (Wheel)
.......................E
MASS.—Boston
Ames Plow Co. (Horse; Wheel) ....AAAA
MASS.—Chicopee Falls
Belcher & Taylor Agricultural Tool Co. (Horse; Hand; Ridgers; Potato Coverers') ....A
MASS.—Northampton
Maynard, C. A. (Hand) X
MICH.—Jackson
Am. Hoe & Fork Co. (Iron; Hand; Corn; Cotton; Field; Garden; Grub; Meadow; Planters'; Riveted; Scuffle; Socket; Shank; Tobacco; Weed-

HOES (Con.)

ing) ....AAAA
MICH.—Lansing
Bement's Son, E. (Horse)
X

MICH.—Pontiac
Bacon Mfg. Co. (Wheel) X
N. H.—Concord
Ford & Co., Wm. P. ,Horse)
B

N. J.—Grenloch
Bateman Mfg. Co. (Horse; Wheel; Hand; Ridgers)
A

N. Y.—Frankfort
Continental Tool Co. (Field; Garden; Mortar; Mixing; Planter; Cotton;Chopper; Sugar-Cane; Shuffle)...A
N. Y.—Greenwich
Eddy Plow Co., W. (Horse; Potato Coverers').....B
New York City
Amer. Axe & Tool Co., 253 B'way (Hand; Grub; Planters') ....AAAA
N. Y.—Rome
Adams & Son, S. (Horse)
C

N. Y.—Troy
Lane & Gale (Iron; Hand; Eye) ....B
Planters' Hoe Co. (Hand; Eye) ....B
OHIO—Canton
Kohler & Co., F. E. (Mortar; Weeding) ......B
OHIO—Cleveland
Amer. Fork & Hoe Co. (Iron; Hand).....AAAA
Columbian Hdw. Co., Coe & Hamilton ....AA
Gerlach & Co., Peter, 28 Columbus ....A
OHIO—Columbus
Am. Hoe & Fork Co. (Iron; Hand; Cotton; Field; Garden; Grub; Meadow; Planters'; Socket; Shank; Tobacco; Weeding; Mortar) ....AAAA
United State Hoe & Tool Co. (Hand; Garden, etc)
A

OHIO—Findley
Findley Axe & Tool Co. (Grub) ....A
OHIO—Sandusky
Sandusky Tool Co. (Hand; Grub; Planters'; Tobacco)
A

PA.——Ogontz
Hammond & Son, C. (Iron; Grub) ....A
PA.—Philadelphia
Allen & Co., S. L., 1107 Market (Horse; Cultivators'; Wheel; Combination Wheel) ....AA
Myers & Ervien Co. (Iron; Hand) ....B
Plumb, Fayette R. (Iron; Grub) ....AA
PA.—Pittsburg
Iron City Tool Wks., 32d & Smallman (Palmetto Grub) ....A
Klein, Logan Co., So. 13th (Palmetto Grub) ......A
PA.—Reading
Chantrell Tool Co. (Garden)
B

PA.—York..
Farquhar Co., A. B. (Horse)
AAA

TENN.—Harriman
Harriman Hoe & Tool Co. (Iron; Hand) ....A
VT.—Bellows Falls
Derby & Ball (Hand; Field; Garden; Planters') .....B
VT.—Brookfield
Peck, Clark & Co. (Iron; Hand) ....B
VT.—Hartford
French, Watson & Co. (Iron; Hand) C
VT.—St. Johnsbury
Ely Hoe & Fork Co. (Iron; Hand; Socket; Shank) B
VT.—Wallingford
Batcheller & Sons Co. (Iron; Hand) ....A

HOES (Con.)

WIS.—Fort Atkinson
Hager, E. (Iron; Hand)..D

HOGSKINS

See Leather

HOISTS

CAL.—San Francisco
Risdon Iron & Locomotive Wks., cor. Stewart & Falsom (Steam) ...AAAA
Rix Compressed Air & Drill Co., 396 Mission (Pneumatic Mine) ....D
Union Iron Wrks., 222 Market (Steam; Dock; Deck)
X

COLO.—Colorado Springs
Hassell Iron Wrks. Co. (Hand) ....B
COLO.—Denver
Davis Iron Wrks. Co., F. M. 8th & Larimer (Hand; Mining) ....AA
Denver Engineering Wrks. Co., Blake & 30th (Electric; Mining) ....A
Hendrie & Bolthoff Mfg. & Supply Co., 1625 17th (Steam) ....AA
Mine & Smelter Supply Co. (Electric; Hand Mining)
AAA

Stearns-Rogers Mfg. Co. (Electric) ....A
CONN.—Derby
Shelton Co. (Sail) ......A
CONN.—Stamford
Yale & Towne Mfg. Co. (Hand; Outrigger; Safety Double Lifts) .....AAAA
ILL.—Chicago
Allis-Chalmers Co., Home Ins. Bldg. (Steam; Drum; Reel) ....AAAA
Chicago Pneumatic Tool Co., Fisher Bldg. (Pneumatic Chain; Cylindrical Air; Pneumatic; Geared; Trolley Combined) ....AAAA
Fairbanks, Morse & Co., Franklin & Monroe (Gasoline; Steam Geared)
AAAA

Goodman Mfg. Co., S. Halsted & 48th Pl. (Electric Mining) ....AA
Jeffry Mfg. Co. (Beer Barrel) X
Kaestner & Co. (Beer Barrel) ....A
Railway Appliances Co.. Old Colony Bldg. (Pneumatic)
A

Shaw, Willis, N. Y. Life Bldg. (Hand; Steam) ..E
Webster Mfg. Co. (Hog).AA
Wolf Co., Fred. W. (Pneumatic) ....AAA
ILL.—Harvey
Whiting Fdry. Equipment Co. (Pneumatic) ......AA
ILL.—Litchfield
Litchfield Fdry. & Mach. Co. (Electric) ....A
ILL.—Sterling
Charter Gas Engine Co. (Gas; Gasoline) ....A
IND.—Brazil
Crawford & McCrimmon Co. (Horse Power Mining).A
IND.—Mishawaka
Dodge Mfg. Co. (Pneumatic)
AAA

IND.—New Albany
New Albany Mfg. Co. (Steam) C
IA.—Ottumwa
Ottumwa Iron Wrks. (Quarry; Steam) ....B
KANS.—Fort Scott
Ft. Scott Fdry. & Machine Co. (Horse Power) ....H
ME.—Portland
Maine Electric Co. (Electric)
E

MASS.—Boston
Boston & Lockport Block Co. 160 Commercial (Chain; Hand) ....A
Hersey Mfg. Co. (Friction; Rope) ....AA

Steel Cable Engineering Co.,
92 State (Steam Shovel)
　　　　　　　　　　B

MASS.—Cambridge
Rawson & Morrison Mfg. Co.
(Gearless Electric; Steam)
　　　　　　　　　　A

MASS.—Orange
Chase Turbine Mfg. Co.
(Gate) ....A

MASS.—Springfield
Elektron Mfg. Co (Electric)
　　　　　　　　　　A

MICH.—Bay City
Marine Iron Co. (Steam).C

MICH.—Detroit
Byram & Co., (Elevator;
Furnace) ....D
Northern Engineering Wrks.
(Electric; Gasoline; Pneu-
matic; Trolley) ....A

MICH.—Hancock
Portage Lake Fdry. & Ma-
chinery Co. (Steam).....D

MICH.—Port Huron
Jenks Shipbuilding Co.
(Dock; Deck) ....A

MICH.—Saginaw
Bartlett & Co., A. F.
(Dock; Deck) ....A
Jackson & Church Co.
(Dock; Deck; Steam))..A
Wickes Bros. (Pneumatic)
　　　　　　　　　　AAA

MINN.—St. Paul
Amer. Hoist & Derrick Co.
(Electric; Hand; Belt;
Steam) ....AAA

MO.—Joplin
Freeman, J. W. (Steam)..A

MO.—Kansas City
Weber Gas & Gasoline En-
gine Co. (Gasoline; Por-
table) ....A
Witte Iron Wrks. Co. (Gasoline) ....B

MO.—St. Louis
Brecht-Butcher Supply Co.,
G. V., 1201 Cass Av.
(Friction) ....AAA
Curtis & Co. Mfg. Co., 2201
Wash'n Av. (Pneumatic)
　　　　　　　　　　A
Standard Railway Equip-
ment Co., Union Trust
Bldg. (Pneumatic) ....G

N. J.—Dover
Morris County Machine &
Iron Co. ....B

N. J.—Newark
Lambert Hoisting Engine
Co., 115-121 Pionier (Elec-
tric Mining; Hand;
Steam) ....A
Mundy, J. L., 22 Prospect
(Hand; Steam) ....A
Storm Mfg. Co. (Ash; Side-
walk) ....B

N. Y.—Albany
Dedrick's Sons, P. K.
(Hand; Horse; Horse Pow-
er) ....A

N. Y.—Buffalo
Contractors' Plant Mfg. Co.,
129 Erie (Chain; Dock;
Deck; Hand; Steam;
French; Quarry; Horse
Power Mining) ....A
Howard Iron Wrks. (Side-
walk) ....A

N. Y.—Long Island City
Steubner Iron Wrks., Geo L.
(Chain) ....B

N. Y.—Montour Falls
General Pneumatic Tool Co.
(Pneumatic) ....B

New York City
Amer. Air Compressor Wrks.
26 Courtlandt (Pneumatic)
　　　　　　　　　　F
Arthur Co., 188 Front (Grip,
for Hand Elevator) ....A
Eckstein, Chas G., 249 Cen-
ter (Chain) ....D
Hunt Co., C. W., 45 B'way.
(Electric; Steam) ....AA
Lidgerwood Mfg. Co., 96
Liberty, (Dock; Deck;
Electric; Steam; Mine)
　　　　　　　　　　AAA
McCoy Co., Jos. F., 157
Chambers (Chain) .....B
Nason Mfg. Co., 71 Beek-
man (Pneumatic) .....B

N. J. Fdry. & Machine Co.,
9 Murray (Trolley; Hand;
Portable; Sidewalk) ....D
Niles-Bement-Pond Co., 136
Liberty (Chain; Pneumat-
ic; Hand; Trolley).AAAA
Rand Drill Co., 128 B'way
(Pneumatic) ......AAAA
Sprague Electric Co., 529 W.
34th (Electric Traveling;
Trolley) ....AAAA
Watson Stillman Co. (Porta-
ble) ....A

N. Y.—Niagara Falls
Dobbie Fdry. & Mach. Co.
(Chain; Dock; Deck; Elec-
tric; Hand Power; Steam;
Trolley; Friction Drum
Belt) ....D

N. Y.—Orangeburg
Empire Engine & Motor Co.
(Pneumatic Motor; Chain)
　　　　　　　　　　B

N. Y.—Poughkeepsie
Lane Bros. Co. (Chain) ..A
Sedgwick Machine Wrks.
(Hand) ....D

N. Y.—Schenectady
General Electric Co. (Electric Mining) ......AAAA

N. Y.—Warsaw
Warsaw Elevator Co. (Hand;
Sidewalk) ....B

N. C.—Charlotte
Mecklenburg Iron Wrks.
(Chain) X

OHIO—Akron
Webster, Camp & Lane
Mach. Co. (Elec. Min-
ing; Steam) ......AAAA

OHIO—Canton
Ney Mfg. Co. (Rope Chain;
Hand) ....B

OHIO—Cincinnati
Warner Elevator Mfg. Co.
(Carriage; Sidewalk) .AA

OHIO—Cleveland
Brown Hoisting M'ch'ry
Co., 1345 St. Clair (Elec-
tric; Portable; Trolley)
　　　　　　　　　　AAAA
Chase Machine Co., 111 Elm
(Dock; Deck; Steam) ..B
Chrisholm & Moore Mfg. Co.,
cor. Lake & Kirkland
(Chain; Hand with Lock
Brake; Pneumatic; Trol-
ley; Electric; Portable;
Screw; Combined Geared;
Plain Yoke) ....AA
Cleveland Punch & Shear
Wrks. (Electric) ......A
Dunn, Jas. P., 207 Dunham
Av. (Chain; Portable) ..H
Garry Iron & Steel Co. (Hy-
draulic; Pneumatic; Trol-
ley) ....A
Lord, Bowler &Co., 41 Cen-
ter (Hand; Steam) C
McMyler, John, 182 Colum-
bus Av. (Electric) ....AA
Round & Son, D., 2287 B'way
(Chain) ....A
Wellman-Seaver-Morgan Co.
(Trolley) ....AAAA

OHIO—Columbus
Case Mfg. Co. (Hand Power;
Pneumatic; Trolley) ....A
Jeffrey Mfg. Co. (Beer Bar-
rell) ....A

OHIO—Mansfield
Phoenix Electric Mfg. Co.
(Electric Mining) ......B

OHIO—Ravenna
Byers Machine Co., Jno. F.
(Steam) ....B

PA.—Allegheny
Carlin's Sons Co., Thos.
(Hand; Steam; Ammuni-
tion; Portable) ....A

PA.—Bangor
Flory Mfg. Co., S. (Elec-
tric; Hand; Steam) ....A

PA.—Coatesville
Ridgeway Craig & Son Co.
(Pneumatic; Portable) .A

PA.—Franklin
Franklin Portable Crane &
Hoist Co. (Hand; Port-
able) ....B

PA.—Philadelphia
Box & Co., 813 N. Front
(Chain; Electric; Steam;
Hand; Screw; Pulley; Por-

HOISTS (Con.)

table) ....B
Dallett Co., Thos. (Electric)
......................B
Energy Elevator Co. (Side-
walk) ....D
Harrington Son & Co., Ed-
win, (Inc.) 15th & Penn.
Av. (Chain; Hand; Port-
able; Screw; Pulley; Elec-
tric) ....AA
Maris Bros., 56th, cor.
Gray's Av. (Dock; Deck)
......................D
Olsen, Tinius & Co., 500 N.
12th (Chain; Portable;
Hand) ....A
Pedrick & Ayer Co., 1001
Hamilton (Pneumatic;
Portable) ....A
Pennsylvania Iron Wrks.
Co., 50th & Lancaster Av.
(Hydraulic) ....AAA
Philadelphia Pneumatic
Tool Co., 21st & Allegheny
Av. (Pneumatic) ....B
Sellers & Co., Wm., (Inc.)
1600 Hamilton (Hydraul-
ic; Riveters) .....AAAA
Stokes & Parrish Elevator
Co. (Furnace; Mining) ..A
Stow Flexible Shaft Co.
(Pneumatic; Portable) ..B
Williamson Bros. Co., Cum-
berland & Aramingo
(Dock; Deck; Steam).AA
PA.—Pittsburg
Carron & Co., A. M. (Pneu-
matic) ....D
Jones & Laughlin Steel Co.
(Worm) ....AAAA
PA.—Reading
Reading Crane & Hoist Wks.
(Chain) ....A
Speidel, J. G., cor. Button-
wood & Gordon (Chain;
Hand Power; Trolley; Por-
table; Sidewalk) .....B
PA.—So. Bethlehem
Bethlehem Fdry. & Mach
Co. (Hand; Sidewalk) ..C
PA.—Wilkesbarre
Vulcan Iron Wrks. (Fric-
tion; Mining; Horse Pow-
er Mining) ....AAAA
R. I.—Providence
Mason & Co., Volney W.
(Hand) ....D
VT.—Barre
Whitcomb Bros. (Steam for
Granite Quarries) X
W. VA.—Fairmont
Wagner-Palmros Mfg. Co.
(Chain) ....A
WIS.—Cudahy
Power & Mining Machry. Co.
(Gasoline) ....AAA
WIS.—Milwaukee
Pawling & Harnischfeger
(Chain; Electric; Hand;
Beer Barrel) ....AAA

HOLDBACKS

See also Hardware; Carriage

N. J.—Newark
Searls Mfg. Co. (Vehicle;
Pole; Shaft) ....B
N. Y.—Buffalo
Pratt & Letchworth Co.
(Vehicle; Pole; Shaft)
......................AAA
New York City
Metal Stamping Co. (Vehi-
cle; Pole; Shaft) .....A
OHIO—Cleveland
Cleveland Hdw. Co. (Vehi-
cle; Pole; Shaft) ....AA

HOLDERS

CONN.—Bridgeport
Armstrong Mfg. Co. (Pipe
Nipple) ....A
Bryant Electric Co. (Elec-
tric Shade) ....A
Curtis & Curtis Co. (Pipe
Nipple) ....AA
Knapp & Cowles Mfg. Co.
(Broom) C
Smith & Egge Mfg. Co.
(Key) ....A
Wheel & Wood Bending Co.

HOLDERS (Con.)

(Rein) ....B
CONN.—Derby
O. K. Tool Holder Co.
(Machine Tool) ....F
CONN.—East River
Munger & Son (Crayon &
Pencil) C
CONN.—Hartford
Billings & Spencer Co.
(Tool; Chucking Reamer;
Reamer) ....AA
Hartford Mach. Screw Co.
(Die; Tool) ....AAAA
Ideal Machine Co. (Tap) ..X
Pratt & Whitney Co. (Die;
Tool; Bit; Brace; Drill;
Tap; Reamer) ....AAAA
Quint, A. D. (Tool; Drill;
Tap) ....B
CONN.—Meriden
Bradley & Hubbard Mfg. Co.
(Roll Paper) .....AAAA
Manning, Bowman & Co.
......................AA
Meriden Britannia Co.
(Cracker; Chase) .AAAA
Meriden Curtain Fixture Co.
(Cord) ....B
CONN.—New Britain
Brady, T. H. (Electric
Lamp) ....B
Corbin, P. & F. (Mop)
......................AAAA
Landers, Frary & Clark
(Currency) ....AAA
Stanley Wrks. (Card; Stake;
Wagon) ....AAA
Taplin Mfg. Co. (Match;
Match Box) ....D
CONN.—New Haven
English & Mersick Co.
(Rein) ....B
Hoggson & Pettis Mfg. Co.
(Combination Tool) ...A
Scranton & Co. (Copy) ..C
CONN.—Seymour
Little River Mfg. Co. (Cuff;
Letter; Plate; Cup; Sau-
cer) ....E
CONN.—Southington
Peck, Stow & Wilcox Co.
(Paper Bag) ......AAAA
CONN.—So. Norwalk
Le Count, Wm. G. (Chuck
Drill; Drill; Tap) .....D
CONN.—Waterbury
Amer. Pin Co. (Brass Pipe
Nipple) ....AA
Am. Ring Co. (Cuff; Eye
Glass; Pen; Pencil; Scarf)
......................A
Novelty Mfg. Co. (Label;
Towel) ....A
Plume & Atwood Mfg. Co.
(Shade) ....AAA
Steele & Johnson Mfg. Co.
(Shade; Globe) ....A
Waterbury Mfg. Co. (Shade)
......................AAAA

ILL.—Aurora
Wilcox Mfg. Co. (Door
Clothes Line) ....B
ILL.—Chicago
Armstrong Bros. Tool Co.,
617 Austin Av. (Tool;
Drill; Tap) ....B
Baird Mfg. Co. (Telephone)
......................C
Barbee Wire & Iron Wrks.
(Broom; Globe; Shade;
Iron Bouquet; Wire Fruit;
Nut) ....B
Central Electric Co., 266 5th
Av. (Electric Lamp) ...A
Evans Co., R. O., 210 Madi-
son (Dictionary) .....A
Hamler Boiler & Tank Co.,
3906 So. Halsted (Gas).B
Illinois Malleable Iron Co.,
30 W. Monroe (Hose)
......................AAAA
Nicol & Co. (Broom; Mop;
Flag Pole; Cigar; Paper-
Bag) ....D
Reed & Crockett, 137 E.
Kenzie (Can) X
Skillen-Richards Mfg. Co.
(Bag) C
Spinks & Co., Wm. A., 93
Erie (Billiard Chalk) ..C
Swisher Mfg. Co., R. D.,
152 5th Av. (Type) ...D
Turner Brass Wks., Cor.

HOLDERS *(Con.)*

Franklin & Michigan (Carbon) ....B

Warren Mfg. Co., J. D. (Rope & Sample) .....B

Webster Mfg. Co. (Bag) . .AA

ILL.—Decatur

Faries Mfg. Co. (Adjustable Electric Lamp) ....A

ILL.—Freeport

Arcade Mfg. Co. (Mop) . .A

Stover Mfg. Co. (Dictionary) ..AA

ILL.—Sterling

Lawrence Bros. (Sash) .AAA

National Mfg. Co. (Door).C

IND.—Anderson

Hill Tool Co. (Tool) ....E

IND.—Evansville

Mingst, C. P. (Lathe; Plainer) ....F

IND.—Fort Wayne

Kerr-Murray Mfg. Co. (Gas) ..A

IND.—Indianapolis

Amer. Buncher Mfg. Co. (Bag) ....B

Nordyke & Marmon Co. (Bag) ....AAA

IND.—South Bend

Bowsher Co., N. P. (Bag) ..B

South Bend Sparker Arrester Co. (Bag) C

IOWA—Fairfield

Louden Mchry. Co. (Stake; Wagon) C

MD.—Baltimore

Bartlett, Hayward & Co., Continental Trust Bldg. (Gas) ....B

Berger & Co., F. (Whisk Broom) ....B

Brinkmann & Co., A. H., 109 Hanover (Asparagus) ..X

MASS.—Attleboro

Eden Co., C. H. (Scarf) .A

MASS.—Boston

Boston & Lockport Block Co. (Bicycle) ....A

Chandler & Farquhar (Drill; Tap) ....B

Cutter-Tower Co. (Coin; Pencil) ....B

Davidson Rubber Co. (Pencil) ....A

Dennison Mfg. Co. (Coin; Currency) ....AAAA

Frost & Co., Geo. (Cuff; Hose, etc.) ....A

Jones & Co., Melville D. (Iron Bouquet) ....G

Lamson Consolidated Store Service Co. (Coin) .AAAA

Mason Regulator Co. (Belt; Shifters) ....A

New England Novelty Mfg. Co. (Mop; Cuff; Tidy).H

Sturtevant Co., B. F. (Rein) ..AAA

Walworth Mfg. Co., 132 Federal (Pipe Nipple) .AAAA

Welch & Co., T. F., 65 Sudbury (Die) ....D

Whitcher & Co., Frank W. (Bicycle) ....A

MASS.—Cambridge

Place Box Co. (Whisk Broom) X

MASS.—Chicopee

Ames Sword Co. (Key) ..B

MASS.—Chicopee Falls

Belcher & Taylor Agricultural Tool Co. (Bag) ..A

MASS.—Fitchburg

Dillon, D. M. (Gas) ....A

MASS.—Gardner

Heywood Bros. & Wakefield Co. (Wood; Rattan) ..AAAA

MASS.—Greenfield

Goodell-Pratt Co. (Tool) ..B

Reece Co., E. F. (Die; Tool; Bit; Brace) ....D

Wells Bros. Co. (Die; Tool; Chuck Drill; Drill; Tap) ..A

Wiley & Russell Mfg. Co. (Die; Nipple; Tire Bolt) ..AA

MASS.—Hopedale

Draper Co. (Bobbin) . .AAAA

HOLDERS *(Con.)*

MASS.—Lowell

Woods, Sherwood & Co. (Whisk Broom; Wire; Dish Cloth) ....E

MASS.—Mansfield

Card Mfg. Co., S. W. (Die; Lathe Die) ....B

MASS.—New Bedford

Morse Twist Drill & Mach. Co. (Die) ....AAA

MASS.—Salem

Locke-Regulator Co. (Flag Pole) ....A

MASS.—Springfield

Bemis & Call Hdw. & Tool Co. (Divider Pencil) ..A

Wagor Mfg. Co., Philo R. (Shade) ....G

MASS.—Waltham

Davis & Farnum Mfg Co. (Gas) ....A

MASS.—Winthrop

Winthrop Wire Goods Co. (Paint Brush) X

MASS.—Worcester

Hamblin & Russell Mfg. Co. (Bicycle) ....B

Heald Machine Co. (Tool) ..B

National Mfg. Co. (Dish Cloth; Wire) ....A

Parker Wire Goods Co. (Plate; Cup; Saucer) ..D

Warren Leather Goods Co. (Banner) ....B

Wire Goods Co. (Card; Door; Photograph; Plate; Cup; Saucer) ....A

Worcester Envelope Co. (Ferrotype) ....B

MICH.—Ann Arbor

Goodspeed Mfg. Co. (Skirt; Waist) ....D

Amer. Electric Heater Co. (Shade) ....B

Detroit Twist Drill Co. (Drill; Tap) C

Laughlin Mfg. Co., 133 Griswold (Pen) ....D

MICH.—Fenton

Phillips Co., A. J. (Door; Bicycle) ....A

MICH.—Grand Rapids

Amer. Machinery Co. (Oil Stove) ....B

Davenport Co. (Typewriter Copy) ....F

MINN.—Minneapolis

Howell & Co., R. R. (Bag) ..B

MO.—St. Louis

Amer. Roll Paper Co. (Roll Paper) ....B

Kufferle, Jno. C., 2d & Mound (Hose) ....A

Pleuger & Henger Mfg. Co., 1015 Herbert (Hose) ..A

NEBR.—Beatrice

Kees, F. B. (Copy ....D

N.H.—Pike

Pike Mfg. Co. (Oil Stove).A

N. J.—Camden

Estabrook Steel Pen Mfg. Co. (Pen) ....AA

Hunt Pen Co., C. H. (Pen) ..A

N. J.—Elizabeth

Braunsdorf-Mueller Co. (Die) ....D

N. J.—Montclair

Heller & Co., W. C. (Sample) ....F

N. J.—Newark

Bernz, Otto, So. 13th cor. So. Orange Av. (Plumbers' Candle) ....B

Durand & Co. (Inc.) (Scarf) ..AA

Gould & Eberhard (Tool).A

Searle Mfg. Co. (Brush; Comb; Match; Soap; Cup; Whisk Broom; Sponge) ..B

Williamson Wire Novelty Co., C. T. (Swab; Rubber Stamp) ....B

N. J.—Vineland

Gage Tool Co. (Blotting Pad) ....A

N. Y.—Albany

Tibany Perforated Wrapping Paper Co. (Roll Paper) ....A

HOLDERS (Con.)
. (Boring Tool; Tool) ....A
OHIO—Hamilton
Meyers Mfg. Co., F. J.
 (Sample) ....B
OHIO—Mansfield
Ohio Brass Co. (Adjusta-
ble Track; Brush; Carbon)
                        AA
OHIO—Medina
Root Co., A. I. (Cuff; Hose,
 etc.) ....AA
OHIO—Piqua
Champion Paper Cutter Co.
 (Roll Wrapping Paper).F
OHIO—Ravenna
Williams, A. C. (Broom)
                         A
OHIO—Salem
Clark Co., W. J. (Mop)...A
OHIO—Springfield
Western Mfg. Co. (Tool)..D
OHIO—Toledo
Merrell Mfg. Co. (Pipe Nip-
ple) ....B
OHIO—Troy
Ohio Electric Specialty Mfg.
 Co. (Electric Lamp) ....G
OHIO—Wellington
Phelps Bros. & Co. (Belt)..F
PA.—Allentown
Grammes & Sons, L. F.
 (Label) ....A
Heilman Boiler Wks. (Gas)
                        AA
PA.—Corry
Raymond Mfg. Co. (Ltd.)
 (Broom) ....B
PA.—Erie
Erie Specialty Co. (Toilet
 Paper) ....B
Modern Tool Co. (Die;
 Tap) ....E
PA.—Hazleton
Koenig, M. T. (Broom) ...X
PA.—Philadelphia
Darby & Sons, Edward
 (Card) ....A
Deily & Fowler, 39 Laurel
 (Gas) ....A
Enterprise Mfg. Co., 3rd &
 Dauphin (Flag Pole)....
                      AAAA
Gillinder & Son (Match)..A
North Bros. Mfg. Co., Le-
 high Av. & Amer. (Christ-
 mas Tree) ....AA
Phila. Electrical & Mfg. Co.,
 2011 Market (Carbon)...E
Phila. Novelty Mfg. Co.
 (Postage Stamp) ......D
Warner, Frank D., 927
 Arch (Price Card) X
White Dental Mfg. Co. S.
 S. (Rubber Dam)..AAAA
Wood & Co.. R. D., 400
 Chestnut (Gas) ....AAAA
PA.—Pittsburg
Pittsburg Brass Mfg. Co.
 (Globe; Shade; Brass;
 Wood) ....D
Riter-Conley Mfg. Co. (Gas)
                       AAA
Standard Scale & Supply Co.
 (Ltd.) (Bag) X
Supply Mfg. Co., 32nd &
 Smallman (Brush) X
PA.—Reading
Pennsylvania Hdw. Co.
 (Christmas Tree) ....AA
Reading Hdw. Co. (Door)
                      AAAA
Reading Mach. & Tool Co.
 (Tool) ....B
PA.—Washington
Petroleum Iron Wks. Co
 (Gas) ....A
PA.—Wrightsville
Wrightsville Hdw. Co.
 (Blacking Box) ....B
R. I.—Pawtucket
Carpenter Tap & Die Co., J.
 M. (Die) C
R. I.—Providence
Amer. Ship Windlass Co.
 (Capstan Sheet) .....AA
Ballou & Co., B. A., 61
 Peck (Scarf; Eye Glass)
                        AA
Barstow & Williams
 (Scarf) C
Beaman & Smith Co. (Safe-
 ty Drill; Tap) ....A

HOLDERS (Con.)
Brown & Sharpe Mfg. Co.
 (Die for Screw Mach.)..
                      AAAA
Cory & Reynolds (Scarf)..C
Lind Co., Thos. W.
 (Cuff) ....D
Nicholson File Co. (File)..
                      AAAA
Providence Stock Co.
 (Scarf) ....D
Waite, Mathewson & Co.
 (Eye Glass) ....B
R. I.—Woonsocket
Roney & Rae Co. (Bobbin)
                         F
VT.—Derby Line
Butterfield & Co. (Die;
 Bit; Brace) ....A
VT.—Montpelier
U. S. Clothes Pin Co.
 (Test Tube) ....D
VT.—St. Albans
St. Albans Fdry. & Imple-
 ment Co. (Bag) ....D
W. VA.—Wheeling
Wheeling Mold & Fdry. Co.
 (Work) ....A
WIS.—Racine
Racine Malleable & Wrought
 Iron Co. (Rein) ....A
WIS.—Two Rivers
Hamilton Mfg. Co. (Label)
                        AA

HOLLANDS: WINDOW SHADE

See Cotton Goods

HOLLOWARE: IRON; COOK-ING, ETC.

See also Enamelled Ware

ALA.—Mobile
Mobile Stove & Pulley Mfg.
 Co. ....B
GA.—Atlanta
Atlanta Stove Wks. ......A
IND.—Jeffersonville
Indiana Mfg. Co. ....A
MO.—St. Louis
Mound City Enamelling &
 Mfg. Co. (Steel) ....D
N. Y.—Brooklyn
N. Y. Stamping Co. (Steel)
                         A
New York City
Iron Clad Mfg. Co....AAA
OHIO—Cleveland
Avery Stamping Co. (Cook-
 ing) ....B
Cleveland Stamping & Tool
 Co. (Steel)...........A
Fanner Mfg. Co. (Steel)..A
OHIO—Sidney
Wagner Mfg. Co. (Cast
 Iron) ....A
PA.—Cheswick
Cheswick Mfg. Co. (Steel)
                         X
PA.—Marietta
Marietta Casting Co......B
Marietta Holloware &
 Enamelling Co. ....B
TENN.—Nashville
Phillips & Buttorff Mfg.
 Co. ....AAAA
TENN.—South Pittsburg
Blacklock Foundry Co.
 (Cooking) C

HOLSTERS

ILL.—Chicago
Cook & Bro., E. C. (Pistol)
                         A
MASS.—Worcester
Warren Leather Goods Co.
 (Pistol) ....B
MO.—St. Joseph
Wyeth Hdw. & Mfg. Co.
 (Pistol) ....AAA
MO.—St. Louis
Brauer Bros. Mfg. Co.
 (Gun) ....E
Straus Saddlery Co., Jacob

HOLSTERS (*Con.*)
(Pistol) ....A
New York City
Abercrombie & Fitch, 314
B'way (Pistol) ....B
OHIO—Akron
Goodrich Co., B. F. (Rubber; Pistol) ....AAAA

HOMINY

See Cereals

HONES

See also Oil Stones & Whet-Stones

ILL.—Chicago
Chicago Wheel & Mfg. Co.
(Emery; Carundum; Razor) C
Goodrich, A., 541 Madison
(Razor) C
KY.—Louisville
Caron Stone Co. (Stone
Polishing) ....D
MINN.—St. Paul
Lukins Co. F. M., Ger. Life
Bldg. (Razor) X
N. H.—Pike Station
Pike Mfg. Co. ....A
N. Y.—Little Valley
Cattaraugus Cutlery Co.
(Razor) ....A
New York City
Silberstein, A. L., 459
B'way (Razor) ....A
N. Y.—Niagara Falls
Carborundum Co. ....A
N. Y.—Rochester
Robeson Cutlery Co. (Razor)
A
OHIO—Cleveland
Cleveland Stone Co...AAAA
OHIO—Tiffin
Sterling Emery Wheel Mfg.
Co. (Emery; Carundum).A

HONEY

CAL.—Los Angeles
German Fruit Co. (Inc.) ..A
Simpson & Hack. Fruit Co.
C
CAL.—San Francisco
Balfour, Guthrie & Co., 316
Calif. ....AAAA
Dennison, Fieweger & Co.,
117 Sacramento ....B
Guggenhime & Co., 118
Davis ....A
Rosenberg Bros. & Co., 211
Calif. ....A
Russ, Early & Harville, 125
Davis ....A
CAL.—Yuba City
Rosenberg Bros. (Br. San
Francisco) ....A
ILL.—Chicago
Armsby Co., J. K. ......A
Weaver & Co., C. H......A
MAINE—Portland
Pettingill Co., E. H. ....B
MD.—Baltimore
Orem & Co., O. C., McElderrys Wharf C
MASS.—Somerville
Lamb, W. J. C
MASS.—South Easton
Simpson Spring Co. ....B
N. MEX.—Farmington
San Juan Stores Co. C
N. Y.—Albany
MacDougal & Co. ....A
N. Y.—Buffalo
Gleason & Lansing, 150
Michigan ....A
New York City
Ams, Max., 372 Greenwich..
AA
Falcon Packing Co., 158
Franklin C
Hildreth & Segelken, 265
Greenwich C
Israel & Bros., 490 Canal..B
Wickes, W. W., 10 Gouverneur C
Williams & Co., R. C., 56
Hudson ....AA
OHIO—Bellefontaine
Johnson Co., F. N. ......A

HONEY (*Con.*)
OHIO—Medina
Root Co., A. I. ....AA
PA.—Philadelphia
Ritter Conserve Co., P. J..A
UTAH—Ogden
Blackman & Griffin C
W. VA.—Wheeling
McMechan & Son Co., Geo.
K. ....B
WIS.—Reedsburg
Stolte, Dengel & Foss Co..B
Webb & Schweke ....B

HOODS

See also Hats & Caps

CONN.—New Britain
Brady, T. H. (Electric
Light) ....B
IND.—Fort Wayne
Ft. Wayne Electric Corporation (Electric Light)....
AAAA
MD.—Baltimore
Hutchinson Bros., 116 N.
Howard (Canopy) ......D
N. H.—Manchester
Campbell, John (Horse)..H
N. J.—Newark
Peters Harness & Saddlery
Co. (Horse) C
N. Y.—Buffalo
Buffalo Forge Co. (Emery
Wheel) ....AAA
New York City
Goodyear Rubber Co.
(Horse) ....AAAA
PA.—Erie
Erie City Iron Wks. (Manhole) ....AAAA
PA.—Philadelphia
Klemm & Co., 132 N. 5th
(Electric Light) C

HOOKS

See also Canthooks & Hardware; Carriage.

CONN.—Bradford
New York Lock Co. (Coat
Hat) ....B
CONN.—Bridgeport
Armstrong Mfg. Co. (Paint
Pot; Snap; Shoe Button;
Adjustable Ladder) ....A
Bridgeport Chain Co. (S.;
S.) ....A
Hurwood Mfg. Co. (Box;
Cotton; Hay; Meat) ...B
Jennings Bros. Mfg. Co.
(Shoe; Glove Buttoning)
AA
Knapp & Cowles Mfg. Co.
Bale; Meat, etc.; Grass;
Box; Weeding) ....A
Smith & Egge Mfg. Co.
(Coat; Hat; S. & S.)..A
CONN.—Chester
Brooks & Sons, M. S. (Brass
Cup; Shoulder; Hammock;
Awning; Harness; Drapery; Jack; Meat; Picture;
Lambrequin; "S." or
"Eight"; Strap Screw;
Gate; Shutter; Wire; Tassel) ....B
CONN.—Collinsville
Collins Co. (Bush; Grass)..
AAAA
CONN.—Deep River
Potter & Snell (Shoe; Glove
Buttoning) ....D
CONN.—Derby
Shelton Co. (Boat) ......A
CONN.—Essex
Dickinson & Co., E. E.
(Boat) ....A
Tiley-Pratt Co. (Shoe; Glove
Buttoning) ....D
CONN.—Hartford
Billings & Spencer Co.
(Snap; Belt; Harness).AA
Jewell Belt Hook Co. (Belt)
AAA
CONN.—Meriden
Bradley & Hubbard Mfg.
Co. (Chandelier) ..AAAA
Foster, Merriam & Co.
(Coat; Hat) ....A

HOOKS (Con.)

CONN.—Middletown
Palmer, I. E. (Adjustable Hammock; Patent Hitching) ....AAA
Wilcox, Crittenden & Co. (Hammock; Boat) .....A

CONN.—Mount Carmel
Woodruff & Sons, Walter W. (Apron; Rein) .....A

CONN.—New Britain
Corbin, P. & F. (Hammock; Clothes Line; Cornice)... AAAA
Humason & Beckley Mfg. Co. (Hammock; Bale; Awning; Meat; Screw; Box; Cotton; Hay) .....A
Judd, Oliver S. (Picture)..A
Landers, Frary & Clark (Hammock; Bird Cage; Ceiling; Chandelier; Coat; Hat; Cornice; Desk; Meat; Screw; Strap; Clothes Line; Gate; Door) ....AAA
North & Judd Mfg. Co. (Harness; Breeching; Ox Tug; Trace; Harness)..AA
Taplin Mfg. Co. (Painters' Ladder) ....D

CONN.—New Haven
Atlas Mfg. Co. (Coat; Hat) F
Cowles & Co., C. (Inc.) (Apron) ....A
Fitch Co., W. & E. T. (Express) ....AA
Hendryx Co., Andrew B. (Bird Cage) ....A
Mallory-Wheeler Co. (Hat; Coat) ....AA
North & Co., O. B. (Harness; Bolt; Breeching; Check; Express; Post; Snap; Tug) ....AA
Sargent & Co. (Pipe; Harness; Awning; Hitching; Beet; Meat; Picture; Bird Cage; Hammock; Malleable; Box; Cotton; Hay; Cabin Door; Brine; Chandelier; Lamp; Clothes Line; Coat; Hat; Conductor; Cup; Shoulder; Desk; Drive; "S. & S."; Fire Pail; Floor Pulley; Gate; Door) ....AAAA

CONN.—Norwich
Ossowan Mills Co. (Coat; Hat; Gate; Shutter; Screw; Picture) ....B
Turner Mfg. Co., Emerson P. (Picture) X

CONN.—Oakville
Smith & Son, S. (Pruning)D

CONN.—Plainville
Hills, Edwin (Awning; Hammock, etc.) ....A

CONN.—Southington
Peck, Stow & Wilcox Co. (Brush; Coat; Hat; Harness; Awning; Bird Cage; Box; Cotton; Hay; Cabin Door; Chandelier; Lamp; Clothes Line; Corn; Tobacco; Cup; Shoulder; Gate; Door; Hammock; Jamb; Picture) ....AAAA

CONN.—Stamford
Yale & Towne Mfg. Co. (Coat; Hat; Grapple)... AAAA

CONN.—Torrington
Turner & Seymour Mfg. Co. (Bird Cage; Cup; Drapery; Picture; Tassel) ..A

CONN.—Unionville
Upson Nut Co. (Belt)..AAA

CONN.—Wallingford
Wallace & Sons Mfg. Co., R. (Shoe Button) ..AAAA

CONN.—Waterbury
Amer. Pin Co. (Chandelier; Wardrobe) ....A
Amer. Ring Co. (Hat; Coat) A
Bristol Co. (Belt) ....D
Novelty Mfg. Co. (Moulding) ....A
Plume & Atwood Mfg. Co. (Picture; "S. & S.") ... AAA

HOOKS (Con.)

CONN.—Westport
Bradley's Sons, G. W. (Cotton; Box) ....D

ILL.—Chicago
Allis, Chalmers & Co. (Safety; Quarry) ..AAAA
Amer. Steel & Wire Co., "The Rookery" (Awning) AAAA
Barbee Wire & Iron Wks. (Coat; Hat; Lantern; Oiling; Bill File; Harness) ....B
Crane Co., 10 N. Jefferson (Pipe) ....AAAA
Edwards Mfg. Co., W. S., 21 Lake (Chandelier)...B
Illinois Malleable Iron Co., 30 W. Monroe (Soil; Gas Pipe; Beam; Lamp; Chandelier) ....A AA
Klein & Son, Mathias, 87 Van Buren (Carrying)..A
Manasse Co., L. (Eye Glass) C
Nicol & Co., 55 W. Washington (Bale; Meat, etc.; Glove Buttoning; Box; Shoe Buttoning) ....D
Solid Steel Tool Co., 11 S. Jefferson (Dolly Bar)...F
Vaughan & Bushnell Mfg. Co., 877 Carroll Av. (Bench; Ceiling; Meat; Box; Cotton; Car; Grapple; Hay; Meat Selecting) B

ILL.—Decatur
U. S. Wire Mat Co. (Clinker) ....D

ILL.—Downers Grove.
Dicke Tool Co. (Bench; Cant) C

ILL.—Freeport
Arcade Mfg. Co. (Hammock; Awning; Weeding; Chandelier; Lamp; Harness).B
Stover Mfg. Co. (Bench; Bird Cage; Ceiling; Harness; Chandelier; Lamp) AA

ILL.—Harvey
Whiting Fdry. Equipment Co. (Foundry Draw)..AA

ILL.—Kewanee
Western Tube Co. (Pipe).. AAA

ILL.—Ottawa
Porter Co., J. E. (Floor Pulley) ....A

ILL.—Peoria
Clark, Queen & Morse (Conductor) ....A

ILL.—Rockford
Sovereign, C. E. (Harness) C

ILL.—Streator
Iwan Bros. (Bush; Conductor) ....D

IND.—Columbus
Keeves & Co. (Inc.) (Cant) ....AA

IND.—Evansville
Evansville Tool Wks. (Bush) ....A

IND.—Indianapolis
Atkins & Co., E. C., 402 S. Illinois (Cant) ....AAAA
Tucker & Dorsey Mfg. Co., State Ave. & Bates (Bench) ....A

IND.—Jeffersonville
Indiana Chain Wks. (Grab, for Log Chains) C

IND.—Montpelier
Jackson Shovel & Tool Co. (Log; Timber Carriers').B

IND.—South Bend
Studebaker Bros. Mfg. Co. (Check) ....AAAA

IOWA—Cedar Rapids
Adams Mfg. Co., A. L. (Hammock) ....F

IOWA—Fairfield
Louden Machry. Co. (Floor Pulley) ....D

IOWA—Fort Madison
Iowa Farming Tool Co. (Chain; Corn; Tobacco).A

IOWA—Iowa City
Berry Flush Tank Co. (Sewer Pipe) ....H

MAINE—Hollowell
North Wayne Tool Co.
(Corn; Grass) ....D
MAINE—Portland
Frye, John J. (Snap) ...C
Laughlin Co., Thos. (Screw;
Barrel; Box; Cotton) ..A
MAINE—Skowhegan
Nolin Mfg. Co. (Grass) ..B
MD.—Baltimore
Levy & Sons, M. S. (Pic-
ture Hanging) ....A
Marden, Jesse (Est.) (Bale;
Box; Meat, etc.) X
MASS.—Arlington
Wood & Co., Wm. T.
(Barrel) ....A
MASS.—Attleboro
Bliss Bros. Co. (Belt) ....A
MASS.—Boston
Boston Bolt Co., 33 Pur-
chase (Pipe) ....B
Boston & Lockport Block
Co., 160 Commercial
(Cant) ....B
Harvey, H. H., 606 Atlantic
Av. (Box; Cotton; Hay) .B
New England Bolt & Nut
Co., 253 Atlantic (Pipe)
...........................C
New England Novelty Mfg.
Co. (Skirt Supporting) ..H
Sewing Machine Supplies
Co. (Belt) ....B
Tubular Rivet & Stud Co.,
87 Lincoln (Eyelet Lac-
ing) ....AA
MASS.—Chelsea
Low Tile Co. (Bill File) ..F
MASS.—Kingston
Drew & Co., C. (Box; Cot-
ton; Hay) C
MASS.—Mansfield
Spaulding, D. S. (Shoe;
Glove Buttoning) ......B
MASS.—North Attleboro
Codding & Heilborn Co.
(Shoe; Glove Buttoning).A
Whiting Co., F. M. (Shoe
Button) ....A
MASS.—Springfield
Whipple & Co., R. P. (Car-
penters' Bench) ....H
MASS.—West Medway
United Awl & Needle Co.
(Shoe Button) C
MASS.—Worcester
Parker Wire Goods Co.
(Belt; Chandelier; Lamp;
Clothes Line; Coat; Hat;
Cup; Shoulder; "S. & S.";
Floor Pulley; Gate; Door;
Hammock; Meat; Mould-
ing; Picture) ....E
Spencer Wire Co. (Cup;
Shoulder) ....A
Wire Goods Co. (Hammock;
Bird Cage; Belt; Chande-
lier; Coat; Hat; Cup;
Desk; Meat; Picture;
Screw; Tassel; Wardrobe;
Wire; Regalia; Shoe But-
ton; Harness; Bicycle
Store; Brine; Clothes
Line; "S. & S."; Fire
Paul; Floor Pulley; Gate;
Door) ....A
MICH.—Detroit
Anderson & Son, W. H., St.
Cuburn & Guoin (Hoist;
Engineers' Packing) ...C
Detroit Bronze & Plating
Wks., 44 Jefferson
(Nickel; Bronze Hat;
Coat) ....G
Michigan Bolt & Nut Wks.,
Meldrum Av. (Floor;
Hanger) ....A
MICH.—Evart
Champion Tool & Handle
Wks. (Grab; Lumber-
mans' Lug; Grappling;
Swamp, etc.) ....A
MICH.—Fenton
Phillips Co., A. J. (Ward-
robe) ....A
MICH.—Grand Rapids
Grand Rapids Brass Co.
(Wardrobe) ....A
Hardware Supply Co.
(Wardrobe) X

MICH.—Jackson
Withington & Cooley Mfg.
Co. (Potato; Manure;
Corn; Hop; Stone; Clam)
...........................AAA
MICH.—Lansing
Lansing Wheelbarrow Co.
(Barrel) ....AAA
MICH.—Saginaw
Morley Bros. (Cant; Chain;
Lug; Timber; Timber
Carrying) ....AA
MISS.—Meridian
Soule Steam Feed Wks.
(Cant) C
MO.—St. Louis
Leschen & Sons Rope Co.,
920 N. Main (Overhead
Carrying Track) ......AAA
Pleuger & Henger Mfg. Co.,
1015 Herbert (Bird Cage;
Clothes Line; Harness) .A
N. H.—Exeter
Exeter Machine Wks. (Pipe)
...........................B
N. H.—Tilton
Lord Optical Co., L. C. (Eye
Glass) ....B
N. J.—Elizabeth
Braumdorf-Mueller Co.
(Box; Cotton; Hay) ....D
N. J.—Greenloch
Bateman Mfg. Co. (Potato)
...........................A
N. J.—High Bridge
Taylor Iron & Steel Co.
(Car) ....AAAA
N. J.—Montclair
Heller & Co., W. C. (Grass)
...........................F
N. J.—Newark
Bernz, Otto, S. 13th &
S. Orange Av. (Cotton;
Box) ....B
Celluloid Co. (Shoe Button)
...........................B
Grossner, F. W., 392 Bank
(Check) ....G
Johnson, Wm., 249 Plane
(Cotton; Box) ....D
National Saw Co., 15 River
(Corn; Tobacco) ....B
Osborne & Co., C. S., 96
Mechanic (Cotton) .....B
Rubber & Celluloid Harness
Trimming Co. (Check).AA
Sacks Iron Fdry., Louis,
Hamburg Pl. & Av. L.
(Button) ....A
Searls Mfg. Co. (Robe) ...B
Williamson Wire Novelty
Co., C. T., 369 Mulberry
(Cart; Ceiling; Coat; Hat;
Cornice; Picture; Wire).B
N. Y.—Auburn
Wadsworth & Son, David
((Bush; Grass) ....A
N. Y.—Binghamton
Crandal, Stone & Co.
(Apron; Carpet) ....A
N. Y.—Brooklyn
De Haven Mfg. Co., 50 Co-
lumbia Heights (Pail)).A
Hay-Budden Mfg. Co., 254
Henry (Awning) ....B
Williams & Co., J. H., 9
Richards (Chain; Hoist;
Crane) ....AA
N. Y.—Buffalo
Buffalo Specialty Mfg. Co.,
375 Ellicot (Belt) ....B
Contractors' Plant Mfg. Co.,
129 Erie (Grab) ....B
Pratt & Letchworth, 189
Tonawanda (Bolt; Check;
Express Pad; Whiffle-
tree) ....AAA
Shepard & Co., Sidney, 145
Seneca (Conductor).....
...........................AAAA
Western Wire Goods Co.
(Coat; Hay; Cup; Shoul-
der; "S. & S."; Floor
Pulley; Gate; Door; Ham-
mock; Mirror) ....E
White Co., L. & I. J., Perry
& Columbia (Meat Select-
ing) ....A
N. Y.—East Syracuse
Benedict Mfg. Co., M. S.

HOOKS (Con.)

(Shoe; Glove Buttoning)

N. Y.—Elmira AA
Cronk & Carrier Mfg. Co.
(Grass) ....B
N. Y.—Frankfort
Continental Tool Co. (Clam;
Potato; Manure) ....A
N. Y.—Homer
Phoenix Hdw. Mfg. Co.
(Bench) ....D
N. Y.—Manlius
Cheney & Son, S. (Harness)
A

N. Y.—Monroe
Newbury Mfg. Co. (Pipe).D
N. Y.—Munnsville
Munnsville Plow Co.
(Hop) C
New York City
Amer. Axe & Tool Co., 253
B'way (Bush; Bill; Grass)
AAAA
Amer. Railway Supply Co.,
24 Park Pl. (Whistle
Cord) ....B
Chatillon & Sons, John, 85
Cliff (Hog) ....A
Collins & Co., 212 Water
(Bush) ....A
De Graw, Aymar & Co., 34
South (Boat) ....AA
Fiske Iron Wks., J. W., 39
Park Pl. (Harness) .....B
Graham & Co., J. H., 113
Chambers (Belt; Coat;
Hat) ....AA
Grote & Co., F. (Shoe Button) ....D
Judd & Co., H. L., 87
Chambers (Bird Cage;
Chandelier; Drapery;
Picture; Screw; Tassel;
Bill File) ....AA
Krieg & Co., J. K., 39 Warren (Shoe Button) .....A
Kroder, Jno. & Reubel, Hy.,
Co., 31 E. 17th (Tassel)
B
Lalance & Grosjean Mfg.
Co., 19 Cliff (Pipe; Meat;
Pot) ....AAAA
Lange, August, 606 E. 15th
(Pipe) ....H
Manhattan Brass Co., 332 E.
28th (Picture) ....A
Metal Stamping Co., 468 W.
B'way (Apron; Rein;
Whiffletree) ....B
Palmenbergs' Sons, J. R.,
710 B'way (Coat; Hat).X
Reilley Bros. (Ladder;
Paint Pot) ....D
Russell & Erwin Mfg. Co.,
43 Chambers (Bird Cage;
Box; Cotton; Hay; Cabin
Door; Chandelier; Lamp;
Clothes Line; Coat; Hat;
Gate; Door; Hammock;
Harness; Jamb) ...AAAA
Sargent & Co., 151 Leonard
(Brine) ....AAAA
Spencer Optical Co. (Eye
Glass) C
Stimpson & Son. Edwin B.,
31 Spruce (Shoe Eyelet
Lacing) ....A
Tiebout. W. & J., 118
Chambers (Awning; Bale;
Box; Hogshead; Boat;
Clothes Line; Coat; Hat;
Cup; Shoulder; "S. & S.";
Gaff Topsail; Hammock)
B
N. Y.—Niagara Falls
Dobbie Fdry. & Machine Co.
(Grab; Hoist) ....D
N. Y.—Seneca Falls
Climax Specialty Co. (Pipe)
B
N. Y.—Syracuse
Stearns & So., E. C. (Harness; Awning; Bench;
Hammock; Pulley; Hay).
AA
Whitman & Barnes Mfg. Co.
(Grass) ....AAAA
N. Y.—Utica
Giblin & Co. (Whiffletree)
B
OHIO—Ashland
Myers & Bro., F. E. (Floor

HOOKS (Con.)

Cleveland Faucet Co., 21
Pulley; Overhead Carrying
Track) ....AAAA
OHIO—Canton
Berger Mfg. Co. (Conductor)
AA
Elbel & Co. (Check; Strap;
Tug; Harness) ....B
Gibbs Mfg. Co. (Potato;
Weeding) ....A
Knight Mfg. Co. (Cant)...E
Kohler & Co., F. E. (Weeding) C
Ney Mfg. Co. (Floor Pulley; Harness) ....B
OHIO—Cincinnati
Cincinnati Tool Co. (Bench)
B
Lane & Bodley Co., cor.
John & Water (Cant)...A
Obermayer Co., S., Evans &
8th (Foundry; Draw).AA
Tatum Co., Samuel C., 414
W. Water (Bench; Harness) ....B
OHIO—Cleveland
Amer. Fork & Hoe Co.
(Clam; Corn; Tobacco;
Hop; Potato; Manure,
etc.) ....AAAA
Avery Stamping Co., Lake
& Coe (Pipe; Pot) .....A
Columbian Hdw. Co., Coe &
Hamilton (Coat; Hat).AA
Federal Mfg. Co., Amer.
Trust Bldg. (Button)....
AAAA
Garry Iron & Steel Co., Coe
& Lake (Conductor) ...A
Gerlach & Co., Peter, 28 Col.
Av. (Cant; Timber Carrying) ....B
Smith Fdry. Supply Co., J.
D., 40 S. Water (Foundry;
Draw) ....D
Taylor & Boggis Fdry. Co.,
521 Seneca (Harness;
Coat; Hay) ....AA
OHIO—Columbus
Brown, Hinman & Huntington Co. (Potato; Manure,
etc.) ....A
Case Mfg. Co. (Chain;
Hoist; Crane; Overhead
Carrying Track) ....A
Hayden-Corbett Chain Co.
(Grab, for Log Chain)..A
Ohio Tool Co. (Bench) ...A
OHIO—Dayton
Dayton Malleable Iron Co.
(Chain) ....AA
OHIO—Geneva
Geneva Tool Co. (Manure;
Potato) ....AA
OHIO—Hamilton
Meyers Mfg. Co., Fred. J.
(Coat; Hat; Bird Cage).B
OHIO—Hicksville
Kerr Bros. Mfg. Co. (Cart)
C
OHIO—Ravenna
Williams. A. C. (Box; Cotton; Hay; Chandelier;
Lamp; Clothes Line; Coat;
Hat; Harness) ....A
OHIO—Toledo
Donovan Wire & Iron Co.
(Harness) C
PA.—Chester
Keystone Drop Forge Wks.
(Shackle; Hoist) ....B
PA.—Cheswick
Cheswick Mfg. Co. (Bill).X
PA.—Erie
Griswold Mfg. Co. (Pot)..A
Jarecki Mfg. Co. (Pipe)...
AAAA
Standard Saw Mill Machry.
Co. (Cant) C
Stearns Mfg. Co. (Grapple)
AA
PA.—Freemansburg
Shimer Son Co., Wm. (Ceiling) ....B
PA.—Howard
Howard Iron & Tool Co.
(Log Chain; Grab, for R.
R.; Switch or Wrecking
Train) ....B
PA.—Mount Joy
Gray Iron Casting Co. (Bill;
Coat; Hat) ....AAAA

HOOKS (Con.)

PA.—New Castle
New Castle Forge & Bolt
Co. (Chain) ....A

PA.—Philadelphia
Berger Bros. Co., 237 Arch
(Conductor; Soil; Gas
Pipe) ....
Darby & Sons, Ed., 233
Arch (Bird Cage) ......A
Devlin Mfg. Co., Thos., 3rd
& Lehigh Av. (Pipe) .AAA
Disston & Sons, Henry
(Pruning) ....AAAA
Enterprise Mfg. Co., N. 3rd
& Dauphin (Meat)..AAAA
Keystone Drop Forge Co.,
20th & Clearfield (Ham-
mock; Drop Forged Hoist)
B
Nittinger, August, 828 N.
4th (Meat) ....A
Phila. Novelty Mfg. Co., N.
13th & Noble (Bill File).B
Plumb, Fayette R., James
& P. R. R. (Bush).....AA
Stortz & Son, Jno., 210 Vine
(Ice) ....F

PA.—Pittsburg
Lanz & Sons, M., cor. Car-
son & 29th ....B
McKay & Co., James
(Chain) ....AAA
Standard Chain Co., 255 5th
Av. (Chain; Log; Switch
Chain) ....AAAA

PA.—Reading
Franklin Specialty Co.
(Clothes Line) ....F
Penn. Hdw. Co. (Ceiling;
Clothes Line; Coat; Hat;
Hammock; Harness)..AA
Reading Hdw. Co. (Sash
Pull; Bird Cage; Cabin
Door; Lamp; Chandelier;
Clothes Line; Coat; Hat;
Cup; Shoulder; Fire Pail;
Gate; Door; Harness;
Store Rack; Toilet;
Towel; Well Wheel) ....
AAAA

PA.—Scranton
Scranton Bolt & Nut Co.
(Log) ....B

PA.—Wrightsville
Susquehanna Castings Co.
(Clothes Line; Coat; Hat;
Harness) ....AA
Wrightsville Hdw. Co.
(Coat; Hat; Bird Cage;
Harness; Clothes Line).B

R. I.—Pawtucket
Fuller & Son, Geo. H. (Jew-
elers' Chain) ....A
Haskell Mfg. Co., Wm. H.
(Pipe) ....A
Jenckes Mfg. Co., E. (Coat;
Hat; Belt; Strap; Cup;
Shoulder) ....AA

R. I.—Providence
Brown Bros. & Co., 62
Exch. Pl. (Belt) ......A
Budlong & Co., S. E. (Belt)
F
Chase & Co., F. A., 253 W.
Exch. (Belt) ....B
Halkyard Mfg. Co. (Eyelet
Lacing) ....B
Lind Co., Thos. W. (Jewel-
ers' Chain) ....B
National Ring Traveler Co.,
257 W. Exch. (Belt).AA
Talcott, W. O., 91 Sabin
(Belt) ....B
Waite, Mathewson & Co.
(Eye Glass) ....B
Wall & Co., A. T. (Shoe
Button) C

TENN.—Jackson
Southern Engine & Boiler
Wks. (Cant) ....A

VT.—Barre
Trow & Holden (Chain)..B

VT.—Bellows Falls
Derby & Ball (Manure;
Potato) ....B

W. VA.—Wheeling
Wheeling Corrugating Co.
(Conductor) ......AAAA

WIS.—Eau Claire
Eau Claire Mill Supply Co.
(Chain) ....D

HOOKS (Con.)

WIS.—Milwaukee
Filer & Stowell Co., Becher
& Zeimas (Cant)....AAA

WIS.—Oshkosh
Oshkosh Logging Tool Co.
(Lumbermans' Lug; Grap-
pling; Swamp, etc.).....C

WIS.—So. Milwaukee
Stowell Mfg. & Fdry. Co.
(Beam; Bird Cage;
Clothes Line; Coat; Hat;
Floor Pulley; Harness)..A

HOOKS & EYES

CONN.—Derby
Star Pin Co. ....A
Sterling Pin Co..........D

CONN.—New Britain
Humason & Beckley Mfg.
Co. (Gate) ....A

CONN.—New Haven
Sargent & Co. ....AAAA

CONN.—Torrington
Turner & Seymour Mfg. Co.
A

CONN.—Waterbury
American Pin Co.........A

ILL.—Chicago
Illinois Malleable Iron Co.,
30 W. Monroe ....AAAA
Reid & Co., 47 S. Canal..E

ILL.—Freeport
Arcade Mfg. Co..........B

MASS.—Worcester
Wire Goods Co. ....A

N. Y.—Buffalo
Western Wire Goods Co.
(Malleable) ....E

New York City
Judd & Co., H. L., 87
Chambers (Gate) ....AA

N. Y.—Niagara Falls
Francis Hook & Eye &
Fastener Co. ....A

HOOKS & STAPLES

CONN.—New Britain
Humason & Beckley Mfg.
Co. ....A

HOOPS

See also Cooperage

COLO.—Denver
Colorado Fuel & Iron Co.
(Iron; Steel) ....B
Sheffield Rolling Mill Co.
(Iron; Steel) ....A

CONN.—Bridgeport
American Tube & Stamping
Co. (Steel) ......AAAA
Taylor, Thos. P. (Em-
broidery) ....A

CONN.—Scotland
Moffitt, J. D. (Mast)....F

GA.—Atlanta
Atlanta Steel Hoop Co.
(Steel) ....A

ILL.—Chicago
American Steel & Wire Co.
(Iron) ....AAAA
Sturges & Brown Mfg. Co.
(Seamless Cheese)......A

IND.—Anderson
Globe Mfg. Co. (Embroid-
ery) ....F

MICH.—Northville
Dubuar Mfg. Co., J. A.
(Mast) X

MO.—Sawyer
Implement Woodstock Mfg.
Co. (Fish Net) X

N. H.—Keene
Wilkins Toy Co. (Iron;
Toy) ....AAA

N. Y.—Brooklyn
De Haven Mfg. Co., 50
Columbia Heights) (Steel;
Shaft) ....A

N. Y.—Cattaraugus
Oakes & Burger (Cheese)..B

New York City
American Steel & Wire Co.,
71 B'way (Steel)..AAAA
Hunt Co., C. W. (Mast)..AA
Mace & Co., L. H. (Toy)..B
New York Boat Oar Co.

542

HOOPS (Con.)

(Mast) ....A
Richards & Co., E. Ira
  (Rolled Plate) ....AAA
Tiebout, W. & J., 118
  Chambers (Mast) ......B
N. Y.—Utica
Jones, Frank L. (Cheese).C
OHIO—Canton
Gibbs Mfg. Co. (Embroid-
  ery) ....A

OHIO—Cincinnati
Cincinnati Truss Hoop Co.
  (Truss; Barrel) ....B
Nunning & Son, Frank
  (Iron; Steel Truss).....X
OHIO—East Liverpool
Milligan Hdw. Supply Co.
  (Lawn) ....B
PA.—Pittsburg
Jones & Laughlin Steel Co.
  AAAA
Pittsburg Steel Co...AAAA
PA.—Sharon
Sharon Steel Hoop Co.
  (Steel) ....AA
R. I.—Pawtucket
Haskell Mfg. Co., Wm. H.
  (Tub) ....AA
R. I.—Providence
Cooke Co., C. H. (Rolled
  Plate) ....D
VT.—Bellows Falls
Vermont Farm Machine Co.
  (Cheese) ....A
VT.—Rutland
Stoddard Mfg. Co. (Cheese)
  B
WIS.—Fort Atkinson
Cornish, Curtis & Greene
  Mfg. Co. (Cheese)......A

HOPPERS

MD.—Baltimore
Jones Holloware Co. (Water
  Closet) ....D
MO.—St. Louis
Kay-Pim Mfg. Co. (Bin)...X
N. J.—Trenton
Maddock & Sons, Thos.
  (Slop) ....AA
N. Y.—Buffalo
Squier Mfg. Co., Geo. L.
  (Coffee Mill) ......AAA
N. Y.—Manlius
Cheney & Son, S. (Shop)..A
New York City
Haydenville Mfg. Co.
  (Water Closet) ....A
Hunt Co., C. W. (Coal
  Weighing) ....AA
Steeger, Henry (Water
  Closet) ....A
N. Y.—Syracuse
Stearns & Co., E. C.
  (Slop) ....AA
OHIO—Cleveland
Taylor & Boggis Fdy. Co.
  (Slop) ....AA
OHIO—Mansfield
Humphreys Mfg. Co.
  (Slop; Water Closet)..B
PA.—Philadelphia
McCambridge & Co. (Ltd.)
  (Slop; Water Closet)..B
PA.—Pittsburg
Amer. Furnace & Mach. Co.
  (Coal; Gas Producer)..D
Standard Mfg. Co. (Slop;
  Water Closet) ....AA

HOPS

CAL.—Sacramento
Mebius & Drescher Co...AA
CAL.—San Francisco
Bauer-Schweitzer Hop &
  Malt Co., 632 Sac.....AA
Dennison, Fieweger & Co.,
  117 Sac. ....B
Horst, Clemens E., 122
  Battery ....AA
Lillienthal & Co., Mission &
  Beale ....AAA
Uhlman & Co., W., 120
  Battery ....B
Wolf & Co., P., 419 Bat-
  tery ....A
ILL.—Chicago
Falk, Wormser & Co.,....A
Goldman & Co., E.......A
Magnus Sons Co., A.......B

HOPS (Con.)

Watkins, Fretts & Vincent,
  169 Jackson Boul.......A
MICH.—Detroit
Weidner, P. ....B
MINN.—St. Paul
Hauser & Sons Malting Co.
  B
N. Y.—Albany
May & Co., C. S.........C
N. Y.—Clinton
Kennedy & Co., O. W.....A
N. Y.—Cobbleskill
France Milling Co.........C
France, Shaver & Co......C
Tator, J. H. ....A
N. Y.—Cooperstown
Brady, H. J..............C
Lane & Co., A............D
Quaif, R. ....D
Stocker & Son, M. R.....D
N. Y.—Kenwood
Snell, I. ....D
N. Y.—Lowville
Richardson & Co., R. J...C
New York City
Brand, G. W., 19 Whitehall
  C
Dole, W. H., 44 Pearl....A
Fox. H. F., 12 Coenties
  Slip C
Gottlieb, W. B., 44 Pearl
  C
Horst, R. R. G., 28 White-
  hall ....AA
Kegeler, H. C., 326 E. 27th
  D
La Vie, G. A., 28 Whitehall
  B
Lillienthal Bros., 116 Broad
  AA
Loewi, V., 37 Pearl.....AA
McGowan, Jr., T. W., 36
  Whitehall ....B
Mugford, J. H., 19 White-
  hall ....D
Reinermann, P., 3 So. Wil-
  liam C
Reisinger, Hugo, 11B'way
  AA
Rosenwald & Co., T., 116
  Broad ....B
Rothbarth & Co., M., 26
  Whitehall C
Schwartz, F., 41 S. Wil-
  liam ....A
Schwartz & Sons, B., 25
  Pearl C
Uhlman, S. & F., 69 Broad
  B
Ullmann & Co., C., 17
  B'way C
N. Y.—Oneida
Luce Hop Co., A. J.......D
N. Y.—Oneonta
Kenyon & Saxton.........D
Miller, F. D.............B
Smith Bros. C
N. Y.—Waterville
Conger, D. ....B
Green & Son. C...........A
OREGON—Gervais
Mitchell & McKinley.....D
OREGON—Salem
Horst Bros. ....AA
WASH.—North Yakima
Horst & Lachmund Co...AA
WASH.—Seattle
Ramsey & Co., S..........B
WASH.—Tacoma
Klaber & Co., Herman..C
WIS.—Fort Atkinson
Klein, Geo. ....B
WIS.—Kewaskum
Beckhaus, A. F...........D
WIS.—Milwaukee
Kiewert Co., Chas. L.....A
Koss & Bros. Co., Chas...A
WIS.—Portage
Mohr & Bro., C..........D

HORNS

See also Mus. Instruments
CONN.—Essex
Tiley, Pratt & Co. (Shoe).D
CONN.—Meriden
Meriden Britannia Co.
  (Shoe) ....AAAA
CONN.—Wallingford
Wallace & Sons Mfg. Co.,
  R. (Shoe) ....AAAA

HORNS (Con.)

IOWA—Council Bluffs
Henderson Mfg. Co., J. T.
(Carnival) X

MASS.—Boston
Edson Mfg. Co. (Fog)....B

MASS.—Leominster
Blodgett & Co., B. F. (Toy)
...........................B
Earl & Co., W. D. (Toy).C
Forbes, Geo. (Toy) ....F
Leominster Comb Co.
(Pressed) ....D

MASS.—Westfield
Crane Bros. (Phonograph)
........................AAA

N. J.—Newark
Celluloid Co. (Shoe).....B
Jenkinson & Co., R. C.
(Shoe) ....A

New York City
Grote & Co., F., E. 14th
(Shoe) ....D
Helvig, H. A. J., 228 Pearl
(Fog) ....F
International Silver Co.,
Maiden Lane (Shoe)....
.......................AAAA
Schlesinger & Co., Leo., 372
South (Tin) ....AB

PA.—Irwin
Forman Can Co. (Shoe)...X

PA.—Philadelphia
Hawthorne & Sheble Mfg.
Co. (Phonograph).......B

HORSEHIDE
See Leather

HORSE RADISH
See Condiments and Sauces

HORSES

MASS.—Boston
Prescott, Edwin (Clothes)
...........................E

MASS.—Leominster
Whitney Reed Chair Co.
(Galloping; Hobby; Toy;
Swinging; Rocking)
.......................AAAA

MICH.—Fenton
Phillips Co., A. J.
(Clothes) ....A

MO.—St. Louis
Great Western Planing
Mill Co. (Hobby) ......B

N. H.—Nashua
Fletcher & Webster Furni-
ture Co. (Rocking; Toy)
...........................C
Nashua Novelty Wks.
(Clothes; Rocking Toy) B

N. J.—Vineland
Gage Tool Co. (Clothes)..A

N. Y.—Brooklyn
Cooper & McKee, 119 Gwin-
nett (Clothes)...........A

New York City
Crandall Carriage Co.
(Rocking; Toy)..........X
Mace & Co., L. H., 117 E.
Houston (Clothes; Rock-
ing; Toy) ....B

OHIO—Cincinnati
Queen City Carousel Co.
(Carousel; Galloping Toy)
...........................H
Randall & Co. (Saddlers';
Stitching) ....B

OHIO—Toledo
Toledo Display Horse Co.
(Display) ....A

VT.—Brattleboro
Smith Co., S. A. (Hobby;
Rocking; Toy).......AAA

WIS.—Milwaukee
Meinecke & Son, A. (Car-
rousel; Hobby; Rocking;
Swinging; Toy).......AA

HORSE-SHOES -

CONN.—Mt. Carmel
Woodruff & Sons Co., W.
W. ....A

DEL.—Wilmington
Diamond State Steel Co...X

ILL.—Joliet

HORSE-SHOES (Con.)
Phoenix Horse Shoe Co.
.......................AAA

MASS.—Boston
Ames Plow Co. ....AA
Neverslip Horseshoe Co...D

N. J.—Bloomfield
Combination Rubber Mfg.
Co. (Rubber) ....B

N. J.—Phillipsburg
American Horse Shoe Co..B

New York City
Am. Steel & Wire Co., 71
B'way ....AAAA
Hahn Mfg. Co., 360 Grand
(Rubber) ....D

N. Y.—Poughkeepsie
Phoenix Horseshoe Co. of
Illinois ....AAA

N. Y.—Troy
Burden Iron Co......AAAA

OHIO—Akron
Goodrich Co., B. F. (Rub-
ber) ....AAAA

PA.—Catasauqua
Bryden Horseshoe Co...AA

R. I.—Providence
Rhode Island Perkins Horseshoe Co. ....AAAA

VA.—Richmond
Old Dominion Iron & Nail
Wks. Co. ....AA

HOSE
See also Rubber Goods; also Hosiery

CAL.—San Francisco
Neville & Co. (Inc.) (Air;
Fire) ....A

CONN.—Hartford
Jewell Belting Co. (Fire)
.......................AAA

CONN.—Middletown
Russell Mfg. Co. (Linen;
Fire) ....AAAA

ILL.—Chicago
Allen Mfg. Co., W. D., 151
Lake (Steel Armour Gar-
den; Mill; Steam).....D
Chicago Fire Apparatus Co.,
54 La Salle (Cotton Rubber
Lined Fire) ....D
Chicago Rubber Brokerage
Co., 312 Dearborn (Air
Brake; Breewers' Fire;
Oil; Rubber; Steam; Suc-
tion; Tanners) ....E
Crane Co., 10 N. Jefferson
(Cotton) ....AAAA

MASS.—Boston
Boston Belting Co., 256 De-
vonshire (Air Brake; Cor-
rugated Tender; Cotton;
Fire; Garden; Mill;
Steam; Linen; Rubber for
Steam Drills; Acid; Air;
Brewers'; Chemical; Div-
ers'; Gas; Hydraulic;
Leather; Oil; Locomotive;
Suction; Tank; Tanners';
Wire Bound).......AAAA
Boston Woven Hose &
Rubber Co. (Knit; Spiral;
Rubber) ....AAAA
Callahan Co., Cornelius, 127
Purchase (Fire) ....D
Knoltown Rubber Co., Geo.
W., 72 Broad (Garden;
Mill; Steam) ....F
Pevear & Co. (Leather) AA
Revere Rubber Co., 63
Franklin (Air Brake;
Cotton; Fire; Garden;
Mill; Steam; Linen; Rub-
ber ....AAAA

MASS.—Cambridge
Boston Woven Hose & Rub-
ber Co. (Air Brake; Fire;
Linen; Cotton; Garden;
Cotton; Rubber Lined;
Rubber; Steam; Suction
.......................AAAA

MASS.—Canton Junction
Callahan, C. (Linen)....X

MASS.—Fitchburg
Fitchburg Duck Mills
(Duck) ....AA

MASS.—Malden
Clark Hose Co. (Cotton;
Fire; Linen) X
Niedner, Chas. H. (Mill;
Steam; Linen Fire; Gar-

HOSE (*Con.*)

den) ....D

MO.—St. Louis

Cooney Mfg. Co., P. J., 900 Cass Av. (Carriage Fire) C

Nelson Mfg. Co., N. O. (Wire Bound)......AAA

N. J.—Bloomfield

Comb. Rubber & Belting Co. (Rubber) ....A

N. J.—Jersey City

New Jersey Car Spring & Rubber Co. (Air Brake; Cotton; Cotton Rubber Lined; Fire; Garden; Mill; Steam; Linen; Acid; Air; Brewers'; Rubber; Divers'; Gas; Oil; Suction; Tanners'; Wire Bound ....A

Voorhees Rubber Mfg. Co., 18 Bostwick Av. (Cotton; Rubber Lined; Fire; Garden; Mill; Steam; Linen) ....A

N. J.—Newark

Rossendale-Reddaway Belting & Hose Co. (Fire; Linen) ....A

N. J.—New Brunswick

India Rubber Co. (Acid) ....AA

N. J.—Trenton

Consolidated Rubber Co. Air Brake; Cotton; Fire; Garden; Mill; Steam)..B

Crescent Belting & Packing Co. (Air Brake; Cotton; Garden; Mill; Steam; Rubber; Suction) ......A

Hamilton Rubber Mfg. Co. (Air Brake; Cotton; Fire) ....A

Home Rubber Co. (Air Brake; Cotton; Fire; Rubber Garden; Mill; Steam; Air; Brewers'; Loomotive; Suction; Tank) ....AA

Mercer Rubber Co. (Fire; Brewers'; Locomotive; Rubber; Steam; Suction; Tank; Air Brake)......A

Stokes Rubber Co., Joseph (Cotton; Garden; Fire; Mill; Steam)..........A

Trenton Rubber Mfg. Co. (Air Brake; Garden; Mill; Steam; Brewers'; Rubber; Steam; Suction) ....A

United & Globe Rubber Mfg. Co. (of Trenton, N. J.) Air Brake; Cotton; Fire; Garden; Mill; Steam; Rubber) ....AAA

Whitehead Bros. Rubber Co. (Air Brake; Cotton; Fire; Garden; Mill; Steam) ....A

N. Y.—Buffalo

Bickford & Francis Belting Co. (Leather) ....A

Buffalo Weaving & Belting Co. (Insulating Cotton) ....A

Hollfeld & Co., R., 61 Carroll (Leather) ....AA

N. J.—Lockport

Empire Mfg. Co. (Rubberlined Cotton; Fire; Garden; Mill; Steam; Linen) ....B

New York City

Buckley Rubber Co., J. W., 69 Warren (Garden; Mill; Steam, wound with Steel Wire) ....B

Empire Rubber Mfg. Co., 88 Reade (Air Brake; Cotton; Rubber; Rubberlined Cotton; Fire; Garden; Mill; Steam; Unlined Linen; Brewers'; Engine; Suction; Wire Wound) ....AA

Eureka Fire Hose Co., 13 Barclay (Cotton; Linen; Fire; Garden; Mill; Steam; Linen; Rubber Lined) ....AAA

Fabric Fire Hose Co., 68

HOSE (*Con.*)

Murray (Fire; Linen; Suction) C

Goodyear Rubber Co. (Rubber; Suction) ....AAAA

Gutta Percha & Rubber Mfg. Co., 126 Duane (Air Brake; Cotton; Fire; Garden; Mill; Steam; Brewers'; Linen; Oil; Rubber; Steam; Suction) ....AAAA

Manhattan Rubber Mfg. Co., 18 Vesey (Cotton; Fire; Garden; Mill; Steam; Linen) ......AA

Mineralized Rubber Co., 18 Cliff (Cotton; Fire; Linen; Rubber Lined)..A

Neumann & Co., R. (Leather) ....A

New York Belting & Packing Co. (Ltd.), 23 Park Pl. (Air Brake; Cotton; Fire; Garden; Mill; Steam; Antiseptic Cable; Linen; Rubber; Suction; Test) ...AAAA

New York Rubber Co. 84 Reade (Air Brake; Garden; Mill; Steam) ..AA

Pedrick & Ayer Co. (Air Tool) ....A

Peerless Rubber Mfg. Co., 16 Warren (Air Brake) ....AA

Rand Drill Co. (Air Tool; Steam) ....AAAA

Rees' Sons, Hans (Leather) ....AA

Schrader & Son, 32 Rose .. (Divers) ....A

United States Leather Co. (Leather) ....AAAA

Waterbury Rubber Mfg. Co., 49 Warren (Wire Bound; Air Brake; Corrugated Tender; Grip Steel Armored; Rubber Lined Cotton; Fire; Garden; Mill Steam) ....D

Young Co., Richard (Leather) ....AA

OHIO—Akron

Diamond Rubber Co. (Air Brake; Corrugated Tender; Fire; Garden; Mill; Steam) ....AA

Goodrich Co., B. F. (Air Brake; Corrugated Tender; Fire; Garden; Mill; Steam; Rubber for Steam Drills) ....AAAA

Whitman & Barnes Mfg. Co. (Air Brake; Rubber for Steam Drills) .....AAAA

OHIO—Cincinnati

Nuhring, Chas., 907 Walnut (Fire) ....H

Trautman & Co., C. (Leather) ....A

OHIO—Cleveland

Mechanical Rubber Co. (Air Brake; Fire; Garden; Mill; Steam; Acid; Cotton; Rubber) ......AAAA

OHIO—Youngstown

Republic Rubber Co. (Fire; Garden; Mill; Steam) AA

PA.—Erie

Continental Rubber Wks. (Garden; Mill; Steam; Rubber for Steam Drills) ....A

PA.—Jeannette

Pennsylvania Rubber Co. (Air Brake; Fire; Rubber Garden; Mill; Steam) AA

R. I.—Bristol

National India Rubber Co. (Rubber) ....AAAA

R. I.—Providence

Amer. Multiple Fabric Co. (Fire; Hydraulic) .....A

HOSE SUP-PORTERS

See Suspenders

HOSIERY

ALA.—Sylacauga

HOSIERY (Con.)

Mathews, T. J. (Marble City Hosiery Mill) (Cotton Hose; Half Hose) C

ALA.—Talladega
Talladega Hosiery Mills (Cotton Hose; Half Hose) C

ALA.—Tuscaloosa
Rosman Hosiery Mills C

CONN.—Bridgeport
Cenfield Rubber Co. (Stockinets) ....A

CONN.—Bristol
Birge Sons Co., N. L. (Cotton; Wool; Merino) ....B

CONN.—Derby
Allig. A. H. & C. B. (Worsted Half Hose) .....AA

CONN.—Hartford
Plaisted & Co., C. C. (Bicycle; Golf) ....F

CONN.—New Britain
Amer. Hosiery Co. (Cotton; Woolen; Merino; Silk Full Fashioned) ....AAAA
New Britain Knitting Co. A

GA.—Athens
Stand. Mfg. Co. (Cotton) D

GA.—Columbus
Georgia Mfg. Co. (Cotton) B

GA.—Graniteville
Graniteville Hosiery Mills (Cotton) ....D

GA.—Lafayette
Elizabeth Hosiery Mills (Women's Cotton) .....D

GA.—Macon
Bibb Mfg. Co. ......AAAA
Macon Knitting Co. (Cotton) ....AAAA

GA.—Marietta
Marietta Knitting Co. ....B

GA.—Penfield
Penfield Hosiery Mills ...D

GA.—Rossville
Richmond Hosiery Mills (Cotton; Fancy; Lisle) D

GA.—Union Point
Union Mfg. Co. ....D

ILL.—Chicago
Bliss, Fabyan & Co. (Com.) AAAA
Common Sense Truss Co. (Surgical Elastic) ....D
Dornbaum, Albert (Golf; Bicycle) ....F
Lorenz, Rich. (Bicycle) ..D
Paramount Knitting Co. (Cotton Seamless) .....B
Sharp & Smith (Cotton; Silk Elastic) ....B
Shaw & Co., T. A. (Com.) AAA
Strauss-Cahn Knitting Co. (Worsted; Silk; Merino; Cotton) C
Truax Greene & Co., 42 Wab. Av. (Elastic Stockings) ....A

ILL.—Rockford
Burson Knitting Co. (Cotton) ....A
Forest City Knitting Co. (Cotton) ....B
Nelson Knitting Co. (Cotton) ....A
Rockford Mitten & Hosiery Co. ....B

IND.—Fort Wayne
Wayne Knitting Mills (Cotton; Lisle Thread) .....A

IND.—Michigan City
Lakeside Knitting Co. (Men's) C

IND.—New Albany
New Albany Hosiery Mills B

KY.—Paducah
Alden Knitting Mills .....B

MD.—Frederick
Union Mfg. Co. (Knit Cotton; Lisle; Wool; Merino) A

MD.—Hagerstown
Blue Ridge Knitting Co. (Cotton Seamless Hosiery; Half Hose) C
Windsor Knitting Mills (Seamless) C

MASS.—Boston
Bliss, Fabyan & Co. (Com.) AAAA
Hub Hosiery Mills (Infants' Cashmere) ....E

HOSIERY (Con.)

Joy, Langdon & Co. (Com.) AAAA

MASS.—Kingston
Kingston Knitting Co. ..C
White & Co., C. W. (Rubber Elastic) ....A

MASS.—Florence
Nonotuck Silk Co. (Silk) AAA

MASS.—Highlandville
Moseley, Wm. (Surg. Elastic) ....E

MASS.—Ipswich
Ipswich Mill ....AA

MASS.—Lowell
Appleton Co. (Cotton) AA
Brown Hosiery Co. (Children's Cashmere; Cotton Hose) ....E
Greenwood & Payton Co. B
Hooper Knitting Co. (Cotton; Woolen Seamless) B
Lawrence Mfg. Co. (Knit Cotton) ....AAAA
Lowell Hosiery Co. (Plain; Fancy) ....A
Shaw Stocking Co. (Cotton; Woolen; Merino) C

MASS.—New Bedford
Cornell Stocking Corp. ..C

MASS.—Northampton
McCallum Hosiery Co. (Silk) C

MASS.—Worcester
Aetna Knitting Co. (Woolen; Merino) ....E
Scott, L. H. (Elastic Silk Stockings) ....F

MICH.—Belding
Belding Bros. & Co. (Silk) AAAA

MICH.—Clare
Wolsey, W. (Merino) ...D

MICH.—Detroit
Angora Knitting Co. .....E
Chicago Hosiery Co. (Lumbermans Socks) ....B
Detroit Alaska Knitting Mills (Plush Cushion Lined Socks) C
Ryan Bros. Knitting Co. (Cotton; Woolen) C

MICH.—Muskegon
Amazon Knitting Co. .....A

MICH.—Pontiac
Pontiac Knitting Co. C

MICH.—Rochester
Western Knitting Mills (Lumbermen's Socks) A

MICH.—St. Joseph
Cooper, Wells & Co. (Cotton; Wool; Merino) ...A

MINN.—Duluth
Neilson Bros. C

MINN.—Mankato
Mankato Mills Co. ....A

MINN.—Minneapolis
Minneapolis Knitting Wks. B

MINN.—Rushford
Rushford Knitting Mills (Wool) ....E

MISS.—Columbus
Columbus Hosiery Mills ..B

MO.—St. Louis
Posnausky Hosiery Co., M. (Woolen) ....D
Premier Hosiery Mills ....D
Willbrandt Surg. Mfg. Co. (Elastic) ....B

N. H.—Ashland
Ashland Knitting Co. ...D

N. H.—Belmont
Gilmanton Mills.... ....B

N. H.—Canterbury
Shaker Knitting Co. (Bicycle) C

N. H.—Franklin Falls
Sulloway Mills (Seamless Cotton; Woolen) .....A

N. H.—Hillsborough Bridge
Contoocook Mills Co. .....A

N. H.—Laconia
Busiel & Co., J. W. ....AA
Pitman Mfg. Co. (Cotton; Worsted) ....B
Rowe Co., F. B. ....D
Union Hosiery Co. ....D

N. H.—Lakeport
Clow & Son, Wm. ....B
Wood & Co., H. H. (Woolen) ....B

N. H.—Manchester
Bicycle Hosiery Co.

HOSIERY (Con.)

(Bicycle) ....D
N. H.—Tilton
Tilton, G. H. ....A
N. J.—Riverside
Dick, Christian (Cotton;
  Wool Seamless) C
Taubel, Wm. F. (Cotton;
  Wool; Lisle Seamless) .B
N. J.—Salem
Sheppard, Jno. P. (Lisle) C
N. Y.—Brooklyn
Standard Knitting Mills
  (Golf) ....D
New York City
Abegg & Rusch (Import.)
                    AAAA
Amer. Hosiery Co. ...AAAA
Auffmordt & Co., C. A.
  (Com.; Import.) ...AAAA
Bliss, Fabyan & Co. (Com.
  Cotton) ....AAAA
Boessneck, Broesel & Co.
  (Com.) ....AAAA
Caeser & Co., H. A. (Com.)
                    AAA
Chaffee, Moorehouse & Co.
  (Com.) ....B
Columbia Hosiery Co. (Cot-
  ton; Wool; Silk) C
Conover Co., C. E. (Com.) D
Eldredge, Lewis & Co.
  (Com.) ....AAAA
Farber & Co., Fred. M.
  (Com.) C
Farber, Drewry & Co., H. J.
  (Com.) C
Goodman Bros. (Import) B
Gutman Bros. (Import) AA
Haydock, Jno. (Import) ..A
Heinze & Co., Otto (Import)
                    AAAA
Hinchman, Vezin & Co.
  (Mfrs. Agts.) ....B
Joy, Langdon & Co. (Com.)
                    AAAA
Kahn & Frank (Import.) .A
Lamson, Roger & Co. (Com.)
                    A
Lawrence & Co. (Com.)
                    AAAA
Levin, Wm., 161 Bowery
  (Baseball; Bicycle; Foot-
  ball) ....F
Lippman, Israel (Bicycle;
  Golf) ....D
Mayer, M. & C. (Import.) A
Oelberman, Dommerich &
  Co. (Com.) ......AAAA
Richardson Silk Co. (Silk) A
Robertson & Bruhn (Mfrs.
  Agts.) ....B
Schachne & Bro., L. (Im-
  port.) ....B
Scheitlin & Co., Edw. (Im-
  port.) ....A
Schiff & Co., E. (Import.)
                    A
Semel & Co., J. H. (Import.)
                    A
Schreve & Adams (Import.)
                    A
Stokes, Cromie & Co. (Com.)
                    B
Sudbury & Co., E. B.
  (Import.) ....A
Townsend & Co., E. M.
  (Com.) ....A
Verdier & Hardy (Com.; Im-
  port) ....A
Watson, Porter, Giles &
  Co. (Com.) ....A
Weld, Colburn & Wilckens
  (Import.) ....A
Wesendonck, Lorentz & Co.
  (Com.) ....A
Wilmerding & Bisset (Com.)
                    AA
N. Y.—Oneida
Oneida Hosiery Co. (Wom-
  en's; Children's Seam-
  less) ....D
N. Y.—Troy
Rob Roy Hosiery Co. ....D
N. Y.—Utica
Albin Knit Goods Co. (Golf)
                    D
Argo Knitting Mill (Infants)
                    C
Olympian Knit Goods Co.
  (Bicycle) C
Weaver, Van R. (Golf) ..D
N. C.—Albermarle
Windmere Knitting Mills
  (Cotton) C

HOSIERY (Con.)

N. C.—Burlington
Burlington Hosiery Mills D
N. C.—Chapel Hill
Blanch Hosiery Mills Co. D
N. C.—Durham
Durham Hosiery Mills
  (Seamless Fleeced Cotton)
                    B
N. C.—Elizabeth City
Elizabeth City Hosiery Co.
  (Cotton Seamless) .....D
N. C.—Greenville
Greenville Knitting Mills D
N. C.—Kernersville
Davis-Crews Knitting Mill C
Lowrey Son. & Co. ....D
Victory Hosiery Mills ..D
N. C.—Kinston
Orion Knitting Mills (Cotton
  Seamless) C
N. C.—Littleton
Littleton Hosiery Mills ..D
N. C.—Newton
Newton Hosiery Mills
  (Needle Ribbed Blue;
  Red; Tan) ....D
N. C.—Raleigh
Martin Hosiery Mill C
Raleigh Hosiery Co. C
N. C.—Randleman
Randleman Hosiery Mills
  (Misses'; Children's
  Ribbed) C
N. C.—Scotland Neck
Crescent Hosiery Co. ....D
Scotland Neck Cotton Mills
  (Knit Cotton) ....B
N. C.—Tarboro
Runnymede Hosiery Mills
  (Cotton) ....D
N. C.—Valdese
Waldensian Hosiery Mills
  (Cotton) ....D
N. C.—Winston-Salem
Hanes, J. W. (Fine; Fancy)
                    B
OHIO—Cincinnati
Bacarach & Loeb (Seamless)
                    C
Dormer Bros. Co. (Seam-
  less Woolen) C
Fairmount Woolen Mills ..A
Hutzier, Hy. (Woolen) ...C
OHIO—Clark
Wuest, Edw. (All Wool) D
OHIO—Cleveland
Friedman & Co., H. .....B
Hessler Truss Co., E. M.
  (Elastic) ....D
OHIO—Columbus
Armbruster, Wm. (Cotton;
  Woolen Seamless) .....B
OHIO—Dresden
Kapner Bros. & Duga Ho-
  siery Co. (Cotton; Wool-
  en) ....B
OHIO—Elyria
Fay Stocking Co. (Cotton;
  Merino) C
OHIO—New Richmond
Dormer Bros. Co. (Woolen)
                    B
OHIO—Toledo
Roth & Co., Jos. ....B
PA.—Allentown
Gabriel's Sons, Hy. (Seam-
  less) ....D
Novelty Hosiery Co. C
PA.—Bath
Odenwelder & Co. (Seam-
  less; Ribbed; Flat) ....D
PA.—Bethlehem
Halcyon Knitting Mills Co.
  (Cotton) C
PA.—Chambersburg
Chambersburg Hosiery Co.
  (Men's Black; Fancy) D
PA.—Clifton Heights
Columbus Knitting Mills
  (Fine Gauze) C
PA.—Collegeville
Todd & Spooner (Cotton
  Seamless) ....D
PA.—Coopersburg
Bergey & Co., M. B.
  (Cotton) ....D
PA.—Danville
Danville Knitting Mills Co.
  (Cotton Knit) ....A
PA.—Easton
Chipman's Sons, Chas. (Cot-
  ton Seamless; Cut) C

PA.—Elizabethville
Enterprise Hosiery Mills
(Women's Cotton) ....D
PA.—Fleetwood
Kelehner, D. F. C
Kutz Bros. (Cotton) ....D
Medeira & Wanner C
PA.—Grill
Yocom, Harry Y. (Cotton) D
PA.—Harrisburg
Harrisburg Knitting Mill
(Cotton) ....B
PA.—Hawley
U. S. Knitting Mill Co.
(Golf) ....D
PA.—Highspire
Good, Martin ....B
PA.—Lewisburg
Musser & Sons, Joseph
(Knit Wool) ....D
PA.—Lewiston
Lewiston Knitting Mill
(Seamless Worsted) ...B
PA.—Lykens
Duncan & Co., Walter C
Fisher & Jones (Plain;
Fancy) C
Keen & Kniley (Cotton) ..D
PA.—Mechanicsburg
Black Rock Knitting Co. D
PA.—Middletown
Romberger, H. A. (Cotton)
A
PA.—Mifflintown
Karl & Schott (Women's) C
PA.—Milroy
Thompson Bros. (Seamless)
B
PA.—Milton
West Branch Hosiery Co.
(Full Fashioned; Seamless) ....D
PA.—Mohnsville
Wyomissing Hosiery Co.
(Men's; Women's) ......B
PA.—Nanticoke
Black Diamond Knitting
Mills ....D
PA.—Nazareth
Kraemer, Hy. (Cotton Full
Fashioned; Seamless) ..B
PA.—New Cumberland
New Cumberland Knitting
Co. (Cotton Seamless) C
PA.—Newport
Romberger, H. A. (Cotton)
A
PA.—Newville
Newville Knitting Co. (Cotton; Lisle) C
PA.—Norristown
Keystone Knitting Mills Co.
(Cotton Seamless) ......D
Norristown Hosiery Co.
(Cotton Seamless) .....A
Rambo & Reger (Cotton;
Lisle Thread) ....A
Roop & Baker ....D
Taubel, Louis E. (Seamless Cotton) ....B
PA.—Philadelphia
Aberle & Co., Hy. C. ....A
Allen, J. & B. (Cut; Seamless Woolen) ....AA
Ballantyne & Sons, Jno.
(Cotton) ....B
Bennett, Wm. (Cotton Seamless; Cut) ....B
Berlizheimer, I. & D. T.
(Children's Seamless Cotton Ribbed) ....B
Beswick, Samuel (Wool;
Merino) C
Blood & Co., Jno. (Cotton
Seamless; Cut) ....A
Boyle & Bro., A. (Children's; Women's; Men's
Seamless) C
Braun, H. ....B
Brown & Hunt (Women's;
Misses' Fine Seamless) C
Brown-Aberle Co. ......AA
Brown & Son, Thos. E.
(Seamless) ....B
Brown Knitting Co. (Full
Fashioned) ....B
Buck Hosiery Co., Thos.
(Cotton) ....A
Charter-Hosiery Co. (Fancy
Seamless; Cut) ....D
Chester Hosiery Co., E. G.
(Fine Gauze Cotton) ...A
Credential Mfg. Co. (Cotton
Seamless; Cut) ....A

Crown Knitting Co. (Seamless Cotton) C
Dalzell, Isaac C
Ellis & Co., W. G. (Cotton;
Woolen; Worsted Seamless) C
Feld & Co. (Golf; Bicycle,
etc.) C
Ferguson & Co., S. B. (Misses'; Children's Cotton
Seamless) C
Flavell & Bro., G. W., 1005
Spring Garden (Surg. Elastic) ....A
Frankford Hosiery Mills
(Seamless Cotton) .....B
German-Amer. Hosiery Co.
(Cotton) ....B
Gutsche, R. (Bicycle) C
Hanifen & Co., J. E. .....A
Harold Hosiery Co. C
Holmes, Jno. G., 111 So.
8th (Elastic Stockings) C
Holmes, Saml. M. (Elastic)F
Horn & Bro., W. H., 451
No. 3rd (Surgical Elastic)
B
Hygienic Fleeced Underwear Co. (Plain; Fancy)A
Isaac, Dalzell C
Kendrick, Jas. R. (Elastic)
E
Koch & Co., Justus ......B
Lanbach, Milton B. (Children's Seamless) C
Lee Hosiery Mills (Men's;
Infants' Cotton) C
Marion Hosiery Mills (Cotton Seamless) ....B
Mascot Hosiery Co. (Women's Seamless) ....B
Osborne, Owen (Woolen) A
Osborne, Wm. (Athletic) D
Palmyra Hosiery Mill C
Peberdy & Sons, Geo. (Cotton; Woolen Seamless;
Cut) ....B
Philadelphia Knitting Mills
Co. (Silk; Lisle Thread;
Cotton) ....A
Pilling & Madeley (Men's;
Boys' Seamless) ....B
Powell & Bro. (Cotton;
Woolen; Worsted) ...AAA
Rosenau & Loeb (Seamless)
B
Saxony Hosiery Co. (Plain;
Fancy) C
Saxony Knitting Mills ...B
Short, W. F. (Cotton; Woolen) C
Smalley, H. R. ....B
Sullivan & Co., Wm. (Cotton; Woolen) ....B
Sutro & Son. E. (Infants';
Women's; Men's) ......B
Thompson, Foust & Co.
(Com.) ....B
Threapelton, Wm. B. (Seamless Cotton) C
Townsend & Co., E. M.
(Com.) ....A
Weber, Chas. (Ladies' Seamless) C
Weber & Co., Louis (Seamless Cotton; Lace) C
Wilson, Wallace (Cotton;
Cashmere; Silk Infants')C
Wilson & Co., J. Scott ...C
Worster & Sons, Jno. H. .D
PA.—Plymouth
West, Ambrose (Fancy) ..B
PA.—Pottstown
Searles Knitting Co. (Cotton; Wool) ....D
PA.—Pottsville
Adcock & Bro., J. C. (Men's;
Women's Cotton) C
Reber, Jno. (Cotton) C
PA.—Reading
Bobst & Son, W. J. (Full
Seamless Cotton) ......D
East Penn. Hosiery Co.
(Men's Seamless) C
Guenther, Geo. G. (Women's; Children's; Men's)
D
Hahn & Wilson ....D
Hampden Knitting Mills Co.
(Knit) C
Hawk Knitting Co. (Cotton
Seamless) C
Hendel, W. B. (Seamless
Cotton) C

HOSIERY (Con.)

Kauffman, Jas. K. (Men's Cotton) ....B
Knersten & Rick (Mfg. Seamless) ....D
Nolde & Horst Co. (Cotton) A

Penn Knitting Mills of Reading (Men's; Women's) C
Reading Hosiery Co. (Men's; Women's Cotton) C
Reading Knitting Mills (Cotton Seamless) C
Shantz Knitting Co., W. C. (Seamless) ....D
Weber, Albert (Cotton Seamless) ....D

PA.—Ringtown
Ringtown Knitting Co. (Men's) ....B

PA.—Royersford
Emmers & Co., E. (Seamless Cotton) ....AA
Urner & Co., W. C. (Full Fashioned; Seamless) ..B

PA.—Shamokin
Forrey & Son, I. W. (Cotton Seamless) C

PA.—Shippensburg
Shippensburg Hosiery Co. C

PA.—Souderton
Bergey & Co., M. B. (Cotton Seamless) ....D

PA.—South Bethlehem
Excelsior Knitting Mills .D

PA.—Towanda
Young, W. J. (Women's Laced) ....D

PA.—Watsontown
Watsontown Knitting Co. (Cotton) ....D

PA.—Wisconisco
Mossop & Co., Isaac (Cotton Seamless) ....B

PA.—Wilkesbarre
Kingston Knitting Mills (Cotton) ....A
Wilkesbarre Knitting Mills Co. (Women's; Men's; Misses'; Infants') .....B

PA.—Williamstown
Durbin & Sons, J. W. ....B

PA.—York
Black & Sons Co., Jos. (Seamless) ....A
York Knitting Mills Co. (Cotton) C

R. I.—Pawtucket
Blackstone Stocking Co. (Men's; Women's; Children's) ....A
Boyden & Son, Geo. E. (Seamless Cashmere) ..B

R. I.—Thornton
British Hosiery Co. (Cotton; Cashmere) ....A

S. C.—Columbia
Columbia Hosiery Mills (Cotton Knit) ....B

S. C.—Cross Hill
Cross Hill Oil & Hosiery Co. C

S. C.—Jonesville
Jonesville Knitting Mills (Cotton Knit) ....A

S. C.—Landrum
Blue Ridge Hosiery Mills (Cotton Knit).........D

S. C.—Newberry
Newberry Knitting Mill ..C

S. C.—Pelham
Pelham Mills (Knit Cotton) A

S. C.—Union
Excelsior Knitting Mills (Cotton Seamless Knit) C

S. C.—Williston
Rosemary Knitting Mills D

TENN.—Nashville
Nashville Hosiery Mills (Children's Ribbed Cotton) B
Rock City Hosiery Mills Misses' Cotton; Worsted Hose) ....A

TENN.—Sweetwater
Mascot Knitting Mills (Cotton) ....D

VT.—Bennington
Scott Stocking Mills (Cotton; Wool; Merino Half Hose) ....B

VT.—Pownal
Wright's Health Underwear

HOSIERY (Con.)

Co. (Woolen Knit Stockinets) ....B

WIS.—Berlin
Russell Frank Glove Co. (Sheepskin Socks) ....D

WIS.—Kenosha
Chicago - Rockford Hosiery Co. (Pure Wool; Worsted; Cotton Seamless) ....AA

WIS.—La Crosse
La Crosse Knitting Wks. (Knit Seamless Socks) ..C

WIS.—Milwaukee
Kalamazoo Knitting Co. (Knit Woolen; Merino Seamless) ....A

WIS.—Ripton
Ripton Knitting Wks. (Knit) ....B

HOSPITAL FURNITURE
See Furniture

HOUNDS; GEAR
See Woodwork; Carriage.

HOUSES
See also Greenhouses

ILL.—Chicago
Barbee Wire & Iron Wks. (Summer; Poultry) .....B
Saladin Pneumatic Malting Const. Co. (Malt) ......A

MICH.—Detroit
Amos & Co., Chas., 94 W. Larned (Portable) .....F

MICH.—Grand Rapids
Iron Cottage Co. (Portable) X

MICH.—Saginaw
Mershon & Morley Co. (Portable) ....D

MO.—St. Louis
Ludlow-Saylor Wire Co. (Wire Summer) ......AA

New York City
Abercrombie & Fitch, 314 Bway. (Portable) .....B
Deeley & Co., Robert (Light) ....AA
Ducker Co., 277 Bway. (Portable) X
Estey Wire Wks. Co. (Wire Summer) ....D
Howard & Morse (Summer) D
Squires & Son, Henry C., 20 Cortlandt (Portable) ..B
Staubach, B. (Portable Smoke) ....A
Westervelt, A. B. & W. T. (Summer) ....B

OHIO—Hamilton
Meyers Mfg. Co., Fred. J. (Summer) ....B

PA.—Pittsburg
Riter-Conly Mfg. Co. (Iron Engine) ....AAA

WIS.—Milwaukee
Gallant-Henning Pneumatic Malt Drum Mfg. Co. (Malt)

Phoenix Mfg. Co. (Portable) F

HOUSINGS

DEL.—Wilmington
Lobdell Car Wheel Co. (Roll) ....AAAA

ILL.—Chicago
Ortmayer & Son, A. (Horse Harness) ....AA

IND.—South Bend
Studebaker Bros. Mfg. Co. (Horse Harness) ..AAAA

N. J.—Newark
Peters Harness & Saddlery Co. (Horse Harness) C
Rubber & Celluloid Harness Trimmings Co. (Horse Harness) ....AA

OHIO—Canton
Gilliam Mfg. Co. (Horse Harness) ....A

OHIO—New Berlin
Hoover, W. H. (Horse Harness) ....A

HOUSINGS (*Con.*)
PA.—Pittsburg
Mesta Machine Co. (Roll)
AAAA

HUBS

See also Woodwork; Carriage

ILL.—Chicago
Sturges & Brown Mfg. Co.
(Bicycle) ....A
OHIO—Cleveland
Federal Mfg. Co. (Bicycle;
Wire Wheel) ......AAAA

HULLERS

**See also Agr. Implements &
Machinery**

CONN.—Thompsonville
Bushnell Press Co., G. H.
(Cotton Seed) ....A
GA.—Atlanta
Van Winkle Gin & Machine
Wks., E. (Cotton Seed)
AAA
GA.—Dalton
Sanders Mfg. Co. (Pea;
Bean) X
ILL.—Moline
Barnard & Leas Mfg. Co.
(Rice) ....AA
IND.—Columbus
Reeves & Co. (Clover Feed-
er; Blower) ......AAAA
IND.—Indianapolis
Nordyke & Marmon Co.
(Corn) ....AAA
IND.—Richmond
Gaar, Scott & Co. (Clover)
AAAA
Robinson & Co. (Clover) AA
IND.—South Bend
Birdsall Mfg. Co. (Clover)
AA
MICH.—Battle Creek
Advance Thresher Co.
(Clover) ....AAAA
Nichols & Shepard Co.
(Clover) ....AAAA
MICH.—Port Huron
Port Huron Engine &
Thresher Co. (Clover)AAA
MO.—St. Louis
Fritz, Geo. J. (Cotton Seed)
B
N. J.—Hackettstown
Bowers & Son, R. Q. (Clover)
D

N. Y.—Buffalo
Buffalo-Pitts Co. (Clover)
AAAA
Noye Mfg. Co., John T.
(Buckwheat) X
Squier Mfg. Co., Geo. L.
(Coffee; Rice) ......AAA
N. Y.—Central Bridge
Campbell Co., S. K.
(Clover) ....D
N. Y.—Cobleskill
Harder Mfg. Co. (Clover)
B
N. Y.—Groton
Groton Bridge Co. (Clover)
A
N. Y.—Lockport
McLean, John (Peanut) ..D
N. Y.—Niagara Falls
Chisholm Co., Scott (Pea;
Bean) ....A
N. Y.—Schenectady
Westinghouse Co. (Clover)
AA
N. Y.—Syracuse
Boomer & Boschert Press
Co. (Cotton Seed) ......A
Engelberg Huller Co. (Cof-
fee; Rice) ....D
N. C.—Winston Salem
Salem Iron Wks. (Coffee) .A
OHIO—Canton
Aultman Co. (Clover) ......
AAAA
OHIO—Cincinnati
Blymer Iron Wks. Co.
(Coffee; Rice) ....B
OHIO—Mansfield
Aultman & Taylor Mach Co.
(Clover) ....AAAA
OHIO—Marion
Huber Mfg. Co. (Pea; Bean)
AAA

HULLERS (*Con.*)
OHIO—Newark
Newark Machine Co.
(Clover) ....B
OHIO—Springfield
Foos Mfg. Co. (Cotton Seed)
A

PA.—Waynesboro
Geiser Mfg. Co. (Clover)..
AAAA
TENN.—Chattanooga
Chattanooga Implement &
Mfg. Co. (Pea) ......B
TENN.—Memphis
Livermore Fdry. & Machine
Co. (Cotton Seed) ......A
VA.—Richmond
Cardwell Machine Co. (Cot-
ton Seed)..............A

HULLS

ALA.—Jacksonville
Jacksonville Oil Mill Co.
(Cotton Seed) ....B
GA.—Columbus
Mutual Cotton Oil Co. (Cot-
ton Seed) ....AAAA
N. J.—Janesville
Janesville Mfg. Co. (Bicy-
cle) ....D
N. Y.—Buffalo
Keim, John R. (Bicycle).AA
New York City
American Bridge Co. (Steel)
A
American Cotton Oil Co.
(Cotton Seed) .....AAAA
N. Y.—Utica
Weston-Mott Co. (Bicycle)
A

OHIO—Marion
Marion Steam Shovel Co.
(Dredge) ....AAA
TEXAS—Taylor
Taylor Cotton Oil Wks.
(Cotton Seed) ....B

HUMIDORS

ILL.—Chicago
Brown Specialty Machry.
Co., Jackson Boul. & Clin-
ton (for Radiators) .....E

HUSKERS

**See also Pins; Husking Agr.
Implements**

ILL.—Batavia
Appleton Mfg. Co. (Corn).A
ILL.—Bradley
Bradley Mfg. Co., David
(Corn) ....AAA
ILL.—Harvard
Hunt, Helm, Ferris & Co.
(Corn) ....AA
ILL.—Moline
Deere & Mansur Co. (Corn;
& Cornstalk Shredders
Combined) ....AAAA
ILL.—Sterling
Keystone Co. (Corn) ....AA
IND.—New Castle
Safety Thredder Co. (Corn)
A
MD.—Baltimore
Sinclair-Scott Co. (Canned
Corn) ....E
MICH.—Battle Creek
Advance Thresher Co.
(Corn) ....AAAA
N. Y.—Auburn
New Birdsall Co. (Corn).AA
New York City
Graham & Co., John H., 113
Chambers ....AA
OHIO—Cleveland
Cleveland Lock Co........D
VT.—Wallingford
Wallingford Mfg. Co. (Corn)
X
WIS.—Marinette
Stevens Co., A. W. (Corn)
AA
WIS.—Milwaukee
Milwaukee Hay Tool Co.
(Corn) ....A

HYDROGEN

See also Gas

HYDROGEN (Con.) ..
New York City
Williamson & Co., D. D., 14
  Dey (Peroxide of) ....B

HYDRANTS

ALA.—Birmingham
Dimmick Pipe Co. (Fire)
  AA
CAL.—Los Angeles
Lacy Mfg. Co. ....AA
CAL.—San Francisco
Garratt & Co., W. T. (Inc.)
  Fremont & Natoma (Fire)
  AA
CONN.—Hartford
Pratt & Cady Co. (Fire)
  AAA
ILL.—Chicago
Illinois Malleable Iron Co.,
  30 W Monroe (Yard)
  AAAA
ILL.—Edwardsville
Edwardsville Brass Co.
  (Yard; Fire) ....B
ILL.—Kankakee
Beaumont, Richard (Fire).D
IND.—Indianapolis
Dean Bros. Steam Pump
  Works (Fire) ....AA
IND.—Kendallville
Flint & Walling Mfg. Co.
  (Yard) ....AA
MASS.—Boston
Coffin Valve Co. (Fire) ..D
Walworth Mfg. Co., 132
  Federal (Fire) ....AAAA
MASS.—Florence
Norwood Engineering Co.
  (Fire) ....B
MASS.—Holyoke
Holyoke Valve & Hydrant
  Co. ....B
MASS.—Indian Orchard
Chapman Valve Mfg. Co.
  (Fire) ....AAA
MICH.—Detroit
Stephens - Roe Mfg. Co.
  (Fire) ....A
MINN.—St. Paul
South Park Fdy. & Mach.
  Co. (Fire) ....B
Waterous Engine Works Co.
  (Fire) ....B
MO.—St. Louis
Kupferle, Jno. C. (Fire).AA
Nelson Mfg. Co., N. O., 424
  N. 8th (Yard; Fire).AAA
Pleuger & Henger Mfg. Co.,
  11th cor. Hebert (Yard;
  Street; Fire) ....A
N. H.—Keene
Humphrey Machine Co. ..C
N. J.—Camden
Camden Iron Wks. (Fire).A
N. J.—Trenton
Consolidated Rubber Co.
  (Fire) ....B
N. Y.—Coxsackie
American Valve Co. (Fire)
  D
New York City
Barr Co., Edward (Water-
  works) X
Colwell Lead Co., 51 Centre
  AA
Douglas, W. & B., 83 John
  (Yard) ....A
Drummond & Co., M. J., 192
  B'way (Fire) ....A
Fairbanks Co., 416 Broome
  AAAA
Fox & Co., John, 253 B'way
  (Fire) ....B
Goulds Mfg. Co., 16 Murray
  AAA
Haydenville Co., 150 Nas-
  sau ....A
International Steam Pump
  Co., 114 Liberty ...AAAA
Kennedy Valve Mfg. Co., 57
  Beekman (Fire; Water-
  works) ....AAA
McNab & Harlin Mfg. Co.
  AAA
N. Y.—Seneca Falls
Rumsey & Co., Ltd. (Inc.)
  (Fire; Yard) ....A
N. Y.—Troy
Ludlow Valve Mfg. Co.
  (Fire; Yard) ......AAA

HYDRANTS (Con.)
Rensselaer Mfg. Co. (Fire)
  C
N. Y.—Waterford
Eddy Valve Co. (Fire)..AA
OHIO—Ashland
Myers & Bro., F. E...AAAA
OHIO—Cincinnati
Bourbon Copper & Brass
  Wks., 618 E. Front (Fire)
  A
OHIO—Salem
Deming Co. ....AA
PA.—Erie
Hays Mfg. Co. (Yard)....A
PA.—Philadelphia
Thompson & Co., J., cor.
  Van Dorn & Sophia (Fire)
  A
Wood & Co., R. D., 400
  Chestnut (Fire) ...AAAA
PA.—Reading
Reading Fdy. Co. (Ltd.)
  (Fire) X
PA.—St. Clair
Quirin & Bro., John (Non-
  Freezing Street) .....F
PA.—Sayre
Cayuta Wheel & Fdy. Co.
  (Fire) ....B
PA.—Tamaqua
Tamaqua Mfg. Co. (Fire;
  Yard) ....B
PA.—Towanda
Frosts' Sons Mfg. Co., J.
  O. (Fire) ....B
Loetzer Valve & Mfg. Co.
  (Fire) X
PA.—Williamsport
Darling Pump & Mfg. Co.
  (Ltd.) (Fire) ....B
R. I.—Pawtucket
Fales & Jenks Machine Co.
  AAA
VA.—Lynchburg
Glamorgan Pipe & Fdy. Co.
  (Fire) ....AA

HYDROM-
ETERS

ILL.—Chicago
Weiskopf, A. ....E
MASS.—Boston
American Steam Gauge &
  Valve Mfg. Co. ......A
Huddleston, John S. .....F
New York City
Bunnell & Co., 20 Park Pl.
  B
Hoehn Co., R., 80 Chambers
  B
Tagliabue Mfg. Co., Chas.
  J. ....A
Tagliabue, Guiseppe, 302
  Pearl ....B
Weinhagen, Henry, 22 N.
  William ....B
N. Y.—Rochester
Hohman & Maurer Mfg. Co.
  B
Taylor Bros. Co. .....AA
N. Y.—Watertown
Watertown Thermometer Co.
  C
PA.—Philadelphia
Riggs & Bros. ....B
Whitall, Tatum & Co.
  AAAA

ICE BOXES
See Refrigerators

IGNITERS

IND.—Anderson
Remy Electric Co. (Gas;
  Gasoline Engine) .....D
IND.—Indianapolis
Hendricks Novelty Co. (Gas;
  Gasoline Engine) .....D
Hercules Electric & Mfg. Co.
  (Gas; Gasoline Engine)..D
IND.—Pendleton
Motsinger Device Mfg. Co.
  (Gas; Gasoline Engine).D
IND.—South Bend
Knoblock-Heiderman Mfg.
  Co. (Gas; Gasoline En-
  gine) ....D
MASS.—Brookline
Holtzer-Cabot Electric Co.

IGNITERS (Con.)
(Gas; Gasoline Engine).A
MASS.—Somerville
American Coil Co. (Gas;
Gasoline Engine) ......D
N. H.—Lebanon
Kendrick & Davis (Gas;
Gasoline Engine) ......A
N. Y.—Elbridge
Elbridge Electrical Mfg. Co.
(Gas; Gasoline Engine).D
New York City
Auto-Igniter Co., 24 West
(Gas; Gasoline Engine).B
Caesar Bros. (Enameled
Match) ....D
Roche, Wm.. 42 Vesey (Gas;
Gasoline Engine) ......D
Splitdorf, C. F.. 17 Vande-
water (Gas; Gasoline En-
gine) ....E
OHIO—Cincinnati
Carlisle & Finch Co., 229 E.
Clifton Av. (Gas; Gasoline
Engine) ....B
OHIO—Cleveland
Ohio Electric Works, 76 El-
len (Gas; Gasoline En-
gine) ....D
OHIO—Columbus
Columbus Storage Battery
Co. (Gas; Gasoline En-
gine) ....F
OHIO—Dayton
Dayton Electrical Mfg. Co.
(Gas; Gasoline Engine).B
OHIO—Troy
Hobart Electric Mfg. Co.
(Gas; Gasoline Engine).B
WIS.—La Crosse
Benton & Son, Thos. P.
(Dynamo) ....E

INCINER-
ATORS
MINN.—Minneapolis
Decarle Mfg. Co. ....B

INCLINOM-
ETERS
MASS.—Athol
Starrett Co.. L. S. ....A
New York City
Keuffel & Esser Co., 127
Fulton ....AA

INCUBATORS
& BROODERS
CAL.—Petaluma
Petaluma Incubator Co....B
ILL.—Freeport
Shoemaker, C. C. ....D
ILL.—Quincy
Ertel Co.. Geo. ....A
Reliable Incubator & Brood-
er Co. ....B
Stahl. Geo. H. ....B
IOWA—Allerton
Allerton Caponizer Mfg. Co.
H
IOWA—Des Moines
Des Moines Incubator Co...D
N. J.—Bound Brook
Star Incubator & Brooder
Co. ....D
N. Y.—Buffalo
Cyphers Incubator Co. ...A
N. Y.—Ithaca
Cornell Incubator & Mfg.
Co. ....B
OHIO—Springfield
Buckeye Incubator Co. ...B
PA.—Homer City
Prairie State Incubator Co.
A
PA.—Philadelphia
Boekel & Co., Wm. (Bacteri-
ological) X
PA.—West Elizabeth
Campbell, J. L. ....F

INDEXES
See also Cases; Furniture.

CONN.—Hartford
Burr Index Co. (Book)....B

INDEXES (Con.)
ILL.—Chicago
Amberg File & Index Co.
(Book) ....A
MASS.—Boston
Crosby Steam Gauge &
Valve Co., 95 Oliver
(Crank) ....AA
Library Bureau (Card)..AA
New York City
Lusk & Son, Richard E.
(Book) ....B
N. Y.—Rochester
Yawman & Erbe Mfg. Co.
(Book) ....AA
OHIO—Columbus
National Index Co. (Book)
D

INDICATORS
CONN.—Hartford
Veeder Mfg. Co. (Speed)..A
CONN.—New Haven
Bradley Mfg. Co. (Polarity)
D
ILL.—Chicago
Allis-Chalmers Co., Home
Ins. Bldg. (Steam En-
gine) ....AAAA
Burdett-Rountree Mfg. Co.,
85 W. Jackson Boul.
(Elevator) ....B
Chicago Wheel & Mfg. Co.,
39 W. Randolph (Speed)
C
Crane Co. (Combination, for
testing hole or shaft)
AAAA
Manning, Maxwell & Moore,
22 S. Canal (Steam En-
gine; Speed) ....AA
IND.—South Bend
Bowsher Co.. N. P. (Speed,
or Motion for Water Pow-
er) ....B
IOWA—Dubuque
Dubuque Turbine & Roller
Mill Co. (Motion) ......B
MASS.—Athol
Starrett Co., L. S. (Lathe;
Speed; Test) ....A
MASS.—Boston
American Steam Gauge &
Valve Mfg. Co. (Speed;
Steam Engine) ....A
Ashton Valve Co. (Steam
Engine) ....A
Beckwith Elevator Co., 123
Pearl (Elevator) ......H
Brainerd Steam Trap Co.,
Chamber of Commerce
(Water) ....H
Crosby Steam Gauge &
Valve Co., 95 Oliver
(Speed; Steam Engine)
AA
Star Brass Mfg. Co.. 103
E. Dedham (Speed; Steam
Engine) ....A
Walworth Mfg. Co., 132 Fed-
eral (Valve) ....AAAA
Whittier Machine Co. (Ele-
vator) ....A
Woodman Mfg. & Supply
Co., R., 63 Oliver (Speed)
F
MASS.—Chicopee Falls
Stevens Arms & Tool Co., J.
(Center) ....AAA
MASS.—Fitchburg
Sawyer Tool Mfg. Co.
(Angle) C
Simonds Mfg. Co. (Speed)
AAA
MICH.—Detroit
Detroit Lubricator Co. (Low
Water) ....AA
Wing & Co.. J. T., Wood-
ward Av. (Speed) C
MO.—St. Louis
Bajohr. Carl, 4055 Meramec
(Lighting) ....D
N. J.—Elizabeth
Braunsdorf - Mueller Co.
(Speed) ....D
N. J.—Newark
Weston Electrical Instru-
ment Co. (Polarity) ....A
N. Y.—Auburn
New Burdsall Co. (Log Set-
ting) ....AA
N. Y.—Brooklyn
Schaffer & Budenberg Mfg.

INGOTS (*Con.*)

Farmers' Bank Bldg.
(Brass; Copper) ......A
Hussey & Co., C. G., 2850
2d Av. (Brass; Copper)
............................AAA
Pittsburg Reduction Co.,
Park Bldg. (Aluminum)
..........................AAAA
Pittsburg Steel Fdy. Co.
(Steel, up to 70,000)..AA

INHALANTS

MICH.—Detroit
Parke, Davis & Co. ...AAAA

INHALERS

IND.—Indianapolis
Armstrong & Co., W. H...B
IND.—Vincennes
Cushman Drug Co. (Pocket)
..................................C
N. Y.—Brooklyn
Gold-Burkam Co., 55 Bart-
lett ....E
New York City
Maris & Co., Jno. M., 219
Fulton ....B
Wetmore Co., S. H., 242
Pearl (Pocket) ......D
OHIO—Cincinnati
Altenheim Medical Dispen-
sary ....D
PA.—Bradford
Penn Glass Tube Co. (Glass)
..................................D
PA.—Philadelphia
Boekel & Co., Wm., 578
Vine X

INITIALS

N. J.—Newark
Reynolds & Zahn (Harness;
Ladies' Hand Bag) ....B
New York City
Dunn & Co., Thos. J., 101
Chambers (Jewelry) ..D
Rice's Sons, Bernard, 542
B'way (Leather Goods).A

INJECTORS

ILL.—Chicago
Crane Co. (Boiler; Locomo-
tive) ....AAAA
MD.—Baltimore
Register's & Sons Co., 49
W. Halliday (Boiler)...A
MASS.—Peabody
Little, Geo. H. (Boiler)..X
MICH.—Detroit
American Injector Co., Con-
gress & Brooklyn Av. (Au-
tomatic Boiler; Locomo-
tive) ....D
Detroit Lubricator Co.,
Hodges Bldg. (Boiler;
Kerosene Oil) ....AA
Michigan Lubricator Co.
(Boiler Oil) ....A
Pemberthy Injector Co., 346
Holden Av. (Boiler; Auto-
matic Locomotive) ....A
Stephens, Roe Mfg. Co.
(Boiler) ....A
MO.—St. Louis
Handlan-Buck Mfg. Co., 212
N. 3d (Boiler; Locomo-
tive) ....AA
N. Y.—Brooklyn
Schaffer & Budenberg Mfg.
Co., 10 Division (Boiler)
..................................D
N. Y.—Buffalo
Sherwood Mfg. Co., 34
Washn. (Boiler; Locomo-
tive) ....B
N. Y.—Jamestown
Engineering & Power Co.
(Boiler) ....AA
New York City
Fairbanks Co., 186 Elm
(Boiler; Locomotive)
..........................AAAA
Jenkins Bros. (Boiler)....A
Manning, Maxwell & Moore,
85 Liberty (Boiler)....AA
Nathan Mfg. Co., 92 Liberty
(Boiler; Locomotive) ...A

INJECTORS (*Con.*)

OHIO—Cincinnati
Automatic Injector Co., 12
E. 3d (Boiler) C
Lunkenheimer Co. (Boiler;
Locomotive; Boiler Oil)
..................................AA
Powell Co., Wm., 2525 Spg.
Grove Av. (Stationary;
Marine Boiler; Locomo-
tive) ....A
OHIO—Urbana
Desmond-Stephan Mfg. Co.
(Steam) ....D
OHIO—Wadsworth
Ohio Injector Co. (Boiler;
Locomotive) ....A
PA.—Erie
Sims Co. (Kerosene Oil)...D
Watson, N. A. (Boiler)...A
PA.—New Castle
Douds & Co., F. C. (Boiler)
..................................B
PA.—Philadelphia
Belfield & Co., H., 435 N.
Broad (Boiler; Locomo-
tive) ....AA
Eynon-Evans Mfg. Co. (Boil-
er) ....A
Griffiths, Jas. A., 500 N.
12th (Boiler; Locomotive)
..................................D
Lonergan & Co., J. E., 211
Race (Locomotive) ...AA
Rue Mfg. Co., 215 Race
(Boiler) C
Schutte & Koerting Co.,
1253 N. 12th (Boiler; Lo-
comotive) ....A
Sellers & Co., Wm. (Inc.),
1600 Hamilton (Oil Boiler;
Locomotive) ....AAAA
PA.—York
Motter & Sons, Geo. F.
(Exhaust Steam) C

INKOLEUM

MINN.—St. Paul
Electrine Mfg. Co. ......F

INKS

CAL.—San Francisco
Shattuck & Co., E. J.
(Printing) ....B
COLO.—Denver
Cannon, W. F. (Writing).D
CONN.—Hartford
Barber Ink Co. (Writing).D
ILL.—Chicago
American Printing Ink Co.
(Wood Printing) ......D
Applegate Chemical Co.,
6322 Ellis Av. (Indelible
Marking) ....F
Central Commercial Co.
(Printing) C
Dietzgen Co., Eugene
(Draughting; Gold; Sil-
ver) ....A
Kane & Co., G. B., 108 5th
Av. (Printing) ....B
Kirk, H. D. (Writing)....F
Landell, J. E. (Writing)..D
Post Co., Frederick, 218 S.
Clark (Draughting)....D
Sanford Mfg. Co. (Writing;
Indelible) ....A
Thomas Co., L. H. (Writ-
ing; Safety) C
MD.—Baltimore
Dorman Co., J. F. W.
(Stamp Pad) ....F
S.—Boston
Carter's Ink Co., 164 Co-
lumbus Av. (Draughting;
Writing; Carmine; Col-
ored; Copying; Indelible;
Marking; Rubber Stamp;
Ruling; Safety; Stylo-
graphic; Liquid India)..A
Davis Co., Wm. A. (Car-
mine; Colored; Copying;
Marking; Safety; Stylo-
graphic) X
Golding & Co. (Printing)..B
Morrill & Co., Geo. H., 146
Congress (Printing; Lith-
ographing) ....AA
Webster Co., F. S. (Copy-
ing; Rubber Stamp;
Printing) ....AA

INKS (Con.)

—Cambridge
Whittemore Bros. & Co. (Burnishing) ....AA

MASS.—Northampton
Williston, A. L. (Indelible) A

MASS.—Springfield
Smith Mfg. Co., R. H. (Rubber Stamp) C

MASS.—Warren
Moore, J. & J. E. (Writing; Safety; Stylographic)..E

MICH.—Detroit
Detroit Rubber Stamp Co. (Rubber Stamp) ....E
Keller Ink Co., Robt. (Writing) ....F
Phelps, Brace & Co. (Writing) ....AA
Williams, Davis, Brooks & Hinchmann Sons (Writing) ....AA

MO.—St. Louis
Aloe Instrument Co., A. S., 414 N. B'way (Draughting) ....A
Donnell Mfg. Co. (Writing) B
Levison & Blyth Mfg. Co. (Writing; Copying) ....E
Thalmann Printing Ink Co., B. (Printing; Lithographing) ....B

N. J.—Jersey City
Safety Bottle & Ink Co. (Writing) C

N. J.—Newark
Dovell Son Mfg. Co., R. B. (Writing) ....D
Pomeroy Co., I. (Writing; Carmine; Colored; Copying; Indelible; Liquid India) ....G

N. Y.—Brooklyn
Higgins & Co., Chas. M., 271 9th (Draughting; Writing) ....A

N. Y.—Buffalo
Amer. Blueing Co. (Writing) ....D
Buffalo Printing Ink Works (Printing; Lithographing; Copyable Printing) ....E
Favorite Mfg. Co. (The) (Writing) ....D

New York City
Binney & Smith Co. (Marking) ....AA
Carragan & Tilison (Indelible; Stencil; Marking).D
Caws Pen & Ink Co. (Carmine; Copying; Safety).D
Davids Co., T. (Writing; Carmine; Colored; Copying; Indelible; Marking) C
Devoe, F. W. & C. T. Reynolds Co. (Liquid India; Gold; Silver) ....AAAA
Faber, Eberhard (Copying) AAA
Fuchs & Lang Mfg. Co. (Lithographing) .....AA
Fulton Rubber Type, Ink & Pad Mfg. Co., 31 Frankfort (Stamp Pad).....D
Gerstendorfer Bros. (Gold) B
Haley Ink Co. (Carmine; Colored; Safety) .....G
Keuffel & Esser Co., 127 Fulton (Draughting)..AA
Kolesch & Co., 138 Fulton (Draughting) ....E
Levey Co., Fred H. (Printing) ....AA
Miller Co. Frank, 349 W. 26th (Burnishing) .....A
New York Stencil Works (Marking; Rubber Stamp) X
Soltmann, E. G., 125 E. 42d (Draughting) .....D
Stafford, S. S. (Carmine; Colored; Copying; Safety; Drawing; Indelible; Rubber Stamp; Stylographic) B
Ullman Co., Sigmund (Lithographing; Printing) ...A
Underwood & Co., John. 30 Vesey (Machine Copying;

INKS (Con.)

Safety; Printing; Marking; Stencil; Copyable).B
Wade & Co., H. D., 28 Reade (Lithographic) ..X
Wilson Printing Ink Co., W. D. (Ltd.) (Printing; Lithographing) ....B

N. Y.—Rochester
American Ribbon & Carbon Co. (Stamp Pad) .....D

OHIO—Cincinnati
Ault & Wiborg Co. (Printing; Lithographing). AAAA
Queen City Printing Ink Co. (Printing; Lithographing) F
Standard Printing Ink Co. (Printing; Lithographing) A
Woodmansee, F. A. (Writing) ....D

OHIO—Cleveland
Taylor Bros. Co., 82 Superior (Draughting; Quick Drying Waterproof for Tracing Cloths).........G

PA.—Harrisburg
Hickok Mfg. Co., W. O. (The) (Paging; Ruling; Powder) ....AA

PA.—Philadelphia
Continental Mfg. Co. (Carmine; Copying; Rubber Stamp; Safety) ....D
Diamond & Onyx (Writing) B
Johnson & Co., Chas. E. (Printing; Lithographing) AA
Mann Co., Wm. (Stylographic) ....AA
Queen & Co., 1010 Chestnut (Draughting) ....A
Quint & Son, S. H., 15 S. 4th (Indelible) C
Williams, Brown & Earle, 918 Chestnut (Draughting) ....B
Wright Printing Ink Co., J. K. (Lithographing)..X

PA.—Pittsburg
Elliott Electric Blue Print Co., 723 Liberty Av. (Draughting) ....D
Kopp & Co., Geo. L., 538 Smithfield (Draughting) D
Swearingen Ink Co., J. C. (Writing) ....D

PA.—Scranton
Reynolds Bros. (Writing).D

WIS.—Milwaukee
Diamond Ink Co. (Writing) D
Ritz, A. N. (Safety) C

INKSTANDS

CONN.—Meriden
Bradley & Hubbard Mfg. Co. (Brass; Iron) .AAAA
Meriden Britannia Co. (Plated) ....AAAA

CONN.—New Britain
Landers, Frary & Clark (Iron) ....AAA

CONN.—Southington
Peck, Stow & Wilcox Co. (Brass; Iron) .....AAAA

CONN.—Wallingford
Wallace & Sons Mfg. Co., R. Glass ....AAAA

ILL.—Chicago
Nicol & Co. ....D
Sherwood Co. (School Desk) D

MASS.—Boston
Carter's Ink Co. (Automatic) ....A
Cutter-Tower Co. (Pocket; School Desk) ....B

MASS.—Chelsea
Low Tile Co. (Tile) ......F

N. H.—Keene
Mason & Co., W. L. X

N. J.—Newark
Riley-Koltz Mfg. Co. (Pocket) ....A

N. Y.—Brooklyn
Prahar, Louis B. (Pocket Safety) C

INKSTANDS (Con.)

New York City
Davis, Emry, 298 Bway.
(Automatic) ....B
Goodyear's India Rubber
Glove Mfg. Co. (Pocket)
AAAA
Gould-Mersereau Co. (Brass;
Call Bell) ....B
Judd & Co., H. L. (Brass)
AA
N. Y.—Seneca Falls
Westcott-Jewell Co. (Auto-
matic) ....D
OHIO—Akron
Akron Rubber Wk. (Good-
rich Co.) (Pocket), AAAA
OHIO—Cincinnati
Tatum Co., Samuel C.
(School Desk) ....B
PA.—Philadelphia
Gillinder & Son (Glass) ..A
W. VA.—Moundsville
Fostoria Glass Co. (Glass)
AAA

INLETS

CONN.—Bristol
Sessions Fdy. Co. (Sewer)
AAA
IND.—South Bend
South Bend Fdy. Co.
(Sewer) ....B
MASS.—Worcester
Desper, Henry A. (Fresh
Air) ....F
N. H.—Concord
Ford & Kimball (Sewer), B
N. Y.—Brooklyn
Hart-Ayres Plumbing Co.,
182 4th Av. (Fresh Air), D
N. Y.—Buffalo
Zero Valve & Brass Mfg.
Co., 296 Seneca (Fresh
Air) ....F
New York City
Du Bois & Co., Frederick N.,
247 9th Av. (Fresh Air)
AAA
Fee & Mason, 66 Beekman
(Fresh Air) ....F
Mott Iron Wks., J. L., 88
Beekman (Fresh Air), AA
Phillips Mfg. Co., 215 E.
34th (Fresh Air) ......D
OHIO—Cincinnati
Buckeye Fdy. Co. (Sewer) A
OHIO—Springfield
Rogers Iron Wks. (Sewer)
B

INSOLES

CONN.—Hartford
Wiley & Son Co., Wm. H.
(Wool; Leather; Silk
Quilted) ....A
KANS.—Burlington
Electric Appliance Co.
(Inc.) (Magnetic) ......D
MASS.—Boston
Fuller, F. T., 16 Lincoln
(Leather) C
MASS.—Worcester
Graton & Knight Mfg. Co.
(Cut) ....AAAA
MASS.—Lynn
Hillard & Merrill (Leather)
A
N. Y.—Middletown
Howell-Hinchman Co. (Cut)
A
New York City
Pall Mall Electric Associa-
tion, 870 Bway. (Electric)
F
OHIO—Cleveland
Ohio Electric Wks.
(Leather) ....A
PA.—Ludlow
Martin Co., Edw. P.
(Leather) ....AA
PA.—Pittsburg
Armstrong Cork Co. (Cork)
AAAA
TENN.—Harriman
Harriman Leather Co.
(Flexible) ....A

INSPECTION

PA.—Pittsburg
Pittsburg Testing Labora-
tory (Steel) ....D

INSTRU-MENTS

See also Specific Headings;
also Musical Instruments

CAL.—Los Angeles
Sweeney Surgical Mfg. Co.
(Surgical) ....B
CAL.—San Francisco
Crocker Co. H. S., 217 Bush
(Architect's; Engineer's)
AA
Payot Upham & Co., 204
Pine (Architect's; Engin-
eer's) ....A
COLO.—Denver.
Ainsworth & Sons, Wm.
(Mathematical) ....B
CONN.—Manchester
Norton Electric Instrument
Co. (Electrical) ....D
CONN.—Westport
Embalmers' Supply Co.
(Embalming) C
D. C.—Washington
Saegmuller, G. N., 108 2d
S. W. (Architect's; Engin-
eer's) ....H
Schmidt, Fred. A., 516 9th
(Architect's ; Engineer's)
F
GA.—Savanah
Fretwell, John W. (Archi-
tect's; Engineer's)......D
ILL.—Chicago
Abbott & Co., A. H., 50
Madison (Architect's; En-
gineer's) ....B
Betz Co., Frank S. (Surgi-
cal) ....A
Central Scientific Co., 14
Mich. (Meterological)...D
Electric Appliance Co., 92
W. Van Buren (Electric)
F
Gaertner &Co., Wm., (As-
tronomical) ....E
Haussmann & Dunn (Ortho-
paedical; Veterinary; Sur-
gical) C
McDonnell Odometer Co.
(Intricate Mechanical), X
McIntosh Battery & Optical
Co. (Nasal Cautery) ...D
Manasee Co., L., 107 Madison
(Architect's; Engineer's)
A
Martin Co., Edw. P. (Elec-
trical Testing) C
Nafis, Louis F., 120 Ran-
dolph (Architect's; Engin-
eer's) ....G
Post Co., Fredk., 218 So.
Clark (Architect's; Engin-
eer's) ....D
Seelig, Roman, 122 Clark
(Architect's; Engineer's)
D
Sharp & Smith (Dental;
Surgical) ....A
Truax, Green Co. (Surgical)
A
Wadsworth-Howland Co.,
Ind & 13th (Architect's;
Engineer's) ....A
Western Electric Co., 259
So. Clinton (Telegraph;
Electrical; Electric Test-
ing) ....AAAA
IND.—Fort Wayne
Ft. Wayne Electric Corpora-
tion (Electrical) ..AAAA
IND.—Indianapolis
Armstrong & Co., Wm. H.
(Surgical) ....B
IND.—Lafayette .
Duncan Elect. Mfg. Co.
(Electric)............B
MASS.—Athol
Athol Machine Co. (Level-
ing) ....B
Starrett Co., L. S. (Level-
ing; Surveying; Drawing)
A
MASS.—Boston
Berger & Son, C. L., 9
Province Ct. (Astronomi-
cal; Architect's; Engin-
eer's) ....B
Buff & Buff Mfg. Co., Ja-
maica Plain (Architect's;
Engineer's; Astronomical;
Surveying) ....B

INSTRUMENTS (Con.)

Codman & Shurtleff (Dental; Orthopaedical; Veterinary; Surgical) C

Frost & Adams Co., 37 Cornhill (Architect's; Engineer's) C

Gleeson, Thos. W. (Electrical) ....F

Leach & Greene (Surgical) ....F

Spaulding Print Paper Co., 44 Federal (Architect's; Engineer's) ....E

Swan, C. Irving (Architect's; Engineer's) ....H

Thaxter & Son, S. (Nautical) ....B

Wadsworth, Howland & Co., 84 Wash. (Architect's; Engineer's) ....A

MASS.—Cambridge

Clark & Sons, Alvan (Astronomical; Optical) .....F

MASS.—Lynn

Flego, Alex J. R. (Precision) ....F

MICH.—Grand Rapids

Durfee Embalming Fluid Co. (Embalming) ....B

Mills & Lacy Mfg. Co. (Embalming) ....D

MINN.—St. Paul

Brown, Treacy & Sperry Co. (Architect's; Engineer's) ....B

Kuhlo, Arnold, 320 Robert (Architect's; Engineer's) ....E

MO.—St. Louis

Aloe Co., A. S., 414 N. Bwa.y. (Architect's; Engineer's; Scientific; Drawing; Surveying; Surgical) ....A

Buxton & Skinner Stationery Co., 306 N. 4th (Architect's; Engineer's) ......A

Erker Bros. Optical Co., 608 Olive (Architect's; Engineer's) ....B

Mahn & Co., 302 Olive (Architect's; Engineer's) ..F

Ruckert, Louis, Laclede Bldg. (Architect's; Engineer's) ....E

Wissler, A., 613 Pine (Architect's; Engineer's; Scientific) ....D

N. J.—Newark

Plumb, D. S. (Intricate Mechanical) ....D

Sloan & Chace Mfg. Co. (Ltd.) (Intricate Mechanical) X

N. Y.—Brooklyn

Brandis Sons, & Co., F. E., 814 Gates Av. (Architect's; Engineer's; Nautical) C

Schaffer & Budenberg Mfg. Co., 10 Division (Scientific; Engineering) ......D

N. Y.—Buffalo

Adams & White, 209 Main (Architect's; Engineer's) C

Buffalo Dental Mfg. Co. (Dental) ....D

Lockwood, M., 207 Ellicott Sq. (Architect's; Engineer's) ....D

N. Y.—Little Falls

Burrell & Co., D. H. (Testing) ....AAAA

New York City

Albrecht, Chas. R. (Nautical) ....F

Akouphone Mfg. Co., 36 E. 20th (Deaf Mutes) X

Bliss & Co., John (Nautical) D

Bunnell & Co., J. H., 20 Park Pl. (Telegraph; Electrical) ....B

Consolidated Dental Mfg. Co. (Dental) C

Devoe, F. W. & C. T. Reynold's Co. (Surveying; Mathematical) ....AAAA

Dietzgen Co., Eugene, 149 5th Av. (Architect's; Engineer's) ....B

Draper Mfg. Co., 152 Front (Meteorological) ......E

INSTRUMENTS (Con.)

Favor, Ruhl & Co., 49 Barclay (Architect's).....B

Foote, Pierson & Co., 84 Fulton (Telegraph; Measuring; Testing of Precision) C

Gardam & Son, Wm. (Astronomical; Philosophical; Surveying; Mathematical; Engineering) ....D

Gesswein Co., F. W. (Dental) ....A

International Brass & Electric Co., 76 Beekman (Telegraph) ....D

Keuffel & Esser Co., 127 Fulton (Arhitect's; Engineer's; Leveling; Precision; Scientific; Nautical; Surveying; Mathematical; Drawing) ....AA

Knauth Bros., 222 4th Av. (Surgical) ....D

Kny-Scherer Co., 225 4th Av. (Surgical) C

Manhattan Electrical Supply Co., 32 Cortlandt (Telegraph) ....AA

Merrill's Sons, Robt. (Nautical; Philosophical; Mathematisal) ....B

Meyrowitz, E. B. (Surgical) A

N. Y. Blue Print Paper Co., 58 Reade (Architect's; Engineer's) ....F

Parsell & Weed, 129 W. 31st (Technical) ......D

Pearce, Fredk., 18 Rose (Telegraph) ....B

Pomeroy Co., 17 Union Sq. (Orthopaedical) ....B

Reichardt & Co., F. A., 391 Bway. (Surgical) ......B

Riker, Chas. E. (Surgical) B

Robertson & Sons, Jas. L. (Engineering) ....D

Rupp & Co., Michael, 39 South (Nautical) ......B

Sartorius & Co., A., 46 W. Bway. (Architect's; Engineer's) ....B

Schneider Bros., 265 Greene (Meteorological) ....D

Schivencke, Kirk & Co., 26 Church (Architect's; Engineer's) ....D

Soltmann, E. G., 125 E. 42d (Architect's; Engineer's; Scientific) ....D

Stackpole & Bros., 41 Fulton (Nautical; Philosophical; Mathematical) ....F

Tagliabue, G., 302 Pearl (Nautical; Philosophical; Testing; Mathematical) B

Taylor & Co., H. E., 510 E. 72d (Embalming) ......A

Tiemann & Co., Geo. (Dental; Surgical) ....A

Tutsche, K. F., 209 Centre (Hearing) ....F

Wittemann Bros. (Veterinarc) ....A

N. Y.—Rochester

Amer. Drafting Furn. Co., 223 Mill (Architect's; Engineer's) ....D

Bausch & Lomb Optical Co. (Optical) ....AAA

Gundlach Optical Co. (Optical) ....A

Ritter Dental Mfg. Co. (Dental) ....B

N. Y.—Schenectady

General Electric Co. (Electrical) ....AAAA

N. Y.—Troy

Gurley, W. & L. E. (Architect's; Engineer's; Surveying; Drawing) ....A

OHO—Cincinnati

Pfister, Herman, 428 Plum (Architect's; Engineer's) F

Prince & Bro., L. M., 108 W. 4th (Architect's; Engineer's) C

Randolph Co., T. F., 232 E. 5th (Architect's; Engineer's) ....E

OHIO—Cleveland

Cleveland Dental Mfg. Co.

INSTRUMENTS (Con.)
(Dental) ....B
Osborn Co., A. T., 22 Seneca
(Architect's; Engineer's)
...........................D
Ullmer & Co., J. C., 225
Champlain (Architect's;
Engineer's) ....D
U. S. Dental Mfg. Co. (Dental) ....D
Warner & Swasey Co. (Astronomical; Precision)..A
OHIO—Columbus
Cole Co., H., 82 N. High
(Architect's; Engineer's)
...........................D
OHIO—Middleton
Miles Steel & Tool Co.
(Dental) ....B
OHIO—Springfield
Champion Chemical Co.
(Embalming) C
OHIO—Toledo
Beckmann Co., L., 318 Adams
(Surveying) ....D
DeVilbiss Mfg. Co. (Surgical) C
PA.—Philadelphia
Alteneder & Sons, Theo., 945
Ridge Av. (Architect's;
Engineer's; Precision;
Calculating; Nautical;
Philosophical; Drawing) D
Climax Dental Mfg. Co.,
409 S. 8th (Dental) ....D
Gemrig & Son,J.H. (Surgical) ....D
Heller & Brightly, Spring
Garden & Ridge Avs.
(Optical; Surveying; Engineer's) ....A
Horn & Bro., Wm. H. (Veterinary) ....B
Johnson & Lund (Dental)
...........................AA
Justi & Sons, H. D. (Dental) ....AA
Keystone Electrical Instrument Co. (Electrical) ..B
Knight & Co., F. C., 400 Locust (Architect's; Engineer's) ....D
Kolbe Co., D. W. (Veterinary) X
Lentz & Sons, Chas. (Surgical) ....A
Lukens & Whittington, 624
Race (Dental) ....D
McCollin & Co., Thos. H., 54
N. 9th (Architect's; Engineer's) ....H
Olsen & Co., T. (Measuring)
...........................A
Partrick, Carter & Wilkins,
1231 Callowhill (Telegraph; Electrical) ......B
Pennsylvania Dental Mfg.
Co. (Dental) ....D
Penn. Surgical Mfg. Co., 104
S. 8th (Dental) ....D
Pilling & Son, Geo. P.
(Dental & Surgical) C
Queen & Co., 1010 Chestnut
(Architect's; Engineer's;
Testing; Scientific; Surveying; Mathematical)..A
Riggs & Bro., 310 Market
(Nautical) ....B
Ripka Co., Chas., 1539
Chestnut (Architect's;
Engineer's) ....E
Sibley, Gideon (Dental), AA
Taws, Henry M., 929 Arch
(Architect's; Engineer's)
...........................F
Teufel & Bros., Jacob J.,
114 So. 10th (Surgical)..F
Thomas Co., Arthur H.
(Laboratory; Scientific).B
Weber & Co., F., 1125
Chestnut (Architect's; Engineer's) ....B
Weil, J. H., 1303 Market
(Architect's; Engineer's)
...........................F
White Dental Mfg. Co., S.
S., Chestnut & 12th (Dental) ....AAAA
Williams, Brown & Earle
(Architect's; Engineer's;
Philosophical; Mathematical) ....B
Young & Sons, 43 N. 7th
(Architect's Engineer's;
Surveying, ...C

INSTRUMENTS (Con.)
PA.—Pittsburg
Elliott Electric Blue Print
Co., 723 Liberty Av.
(Architect's Engineer's)
...........................C
Kopp & Co., Geo. L., 538
Smithfield (Architect's;
Engineer's) ....H
Kurtz, Langbein & Swatz,
435 Wood (Architect's;
Engineer's) ....E
Pittsburg Blue Print Co.,
Park Bldg. (Architect's;
Engineer's) C
Steiren Co., Wm., E., 544
Smithfield (Architect's;
Engineer's) ....B
PA.—West Chester
Sharples, P. M. (Testing)
...........................AA
R. I.—Providence
Brown & Sharpe Mfg. Co.
(Drawing) ....AAAA
Slocomb Co., J. T. (Surveying) ....D
TEXAS—Galveston
Clarke & Courts (Architect's; Engineer's)....A
WASH.—Spokane
Graham & Co., J. W.
(Architect's; Engineer's)
...........................A

INSULATORS

CONN.—Hartford
Billings & Spencer Co. (Drop
Forged; Strain; Trolley)
...........................AA
Hartford Faience Co. (Porcelain) ....B
Johns-Pratt Co. (Moulded
Mica) ....A
ILL.—Chicago
Central Electric Co., 266 5th
Av. (All Kinds) ....A
Cutter Co., Geo., Union &
Fulton (Arc; Tree) C
Sells-Eddy Mica Co., 34
Clark (Mica) X
Western Electric Co., 259 S.
Clinton ....AAAA
IND.—Peru
Peru Electric Mfg. Co. (Porcelain) ....A
KY.—Covington
Hemingray Glass Co.
(Glass) ....AA
MAINE—Kennebunk
Leatheroid Mfg. Co. (Rail)
...........................A
MASS.—Boston
Anderson Mfg. Co., Albert
& J. M. (Tree) ....A
Knowles, C. S., 9 Arch
(Glass; Porcelain) ....B
Macallen Co., W. T. C., 338
Congress (Overhead) ..AA
Renim Specialty Co., 176
Federal (Porcelain Wiring
Tubes) ....B
MINN.—Winona
Union Fibre Co. (Lith
Board; Flax Fibre) ....B
N. H.—Manchester
Brodie Electric Co. (Tree) F
N. J.—Trenton
Brian Pottery Co. (Porcelain) ....D
Diamond Porcelain Co.
(Porcelain) X
Electric Porcelain & Mfg.
Co. (All Kinds) ....D
Greenwood Pottery Co.
(Porcelain) ....A
Imperial Porcelain Wks.
(Porcelain; Transmission)
...........................AA
N. Y.—Brooklyn
Krantz Mfg. Co...........B
Union Porcelain Wks., 300
Eckford (Porcelain) ....B
New York City
Brookfield Glass Co., 220
Bway. (Glass) ....B
Federal Clay Mfg. Co., 170
Bway. (Vitrified Clay;
Third Rail) ....B
Johns, Manville Co., H. W.,
100 William (Third Rail;
Tree) ....AAAA
Mica Insulator Co., 218
Water (Mica) ....B
Reconstructed Granite Co.

INSULATORS *(Con.)*
(Granite; Third Rail) ..D
N. Y.—Schenectady
General Electric Co .(Porcelain; Wall; Floor; Pole;
Trolley) ....AAAA
N. Y.—Syracuse
Pass & Seymour ....A
N. Y.—Utica....
Bossert Electric Construction Co. (Conduit Outlet)
..............................B
N. Y.—Victor
Locke Insulator Mfg. Co.
(High Voltage; Porcelain;
China) ....A
OHIO—Akron
Amer. Marble & Toy Mfg.
Co. (Clay; Porcelain) ..X
OHIO—Cincinnati
Creaghead Engineering Co.,
313 Walnut (Strain)....D
OHIO—Cleveland
Homer Commutator Co., 108
Mason (Mica).........D
OHIO—East Liverpool
Brunt Porcelain Wks., G. F.
(Porcelain) ....B
Thomas & Sons Co., R.
(Porcelain) ....A
OHIO—Mansfield
Ohio Brass Co. (Tree)..AA
OHIO—Mogadore
Bowers Mfg. Co. (Clay) ..F
PA.—Erie
Erie City Iron Wks. (Third
Rail) ....AAAA
PA.—Philadelphia
Flagg & Co., Stanley G.
(Lava; Electric) ....AAA
PA.—Pittsburg
Wormser Glass Co., 2d &
Sylvan Av. (Glass) X
TENN.—Chattanooga
Crescent Novelty Mfg. Co.
(Electrical) ....E
Steward Mfg. Co., D. M.
(Lava) ....B

INTERMEDI-ATES

See also Gears

MASS.—Lowell
Lowell Machine Shop, AAAA
MASS.—Newton Upper Falls
Saco & Pettee Machine
Shops ....AAA
MASS.—Whitinsville
Whitinsville Machine Wks.
...................AAAA

IODINE

MD.—Baltimore
Thomson Chemical Wks...B
MASS.—Boston
Billings, Clapp & Co. ....B
Burnham Soluble Iodine Co.
...................G
MO.—St. Louis
Herf & Frerichs Chemical
Co. (Resublimed) ......A
Larkin & Scheffer Chemical
Co. ....A
Mallinckrodt Chemical Wks.
...................AAAA
New York City
Cooper & Co., Chas. ...AA
PA.—Allegheny
Beck & Co., John A. .....A
PA.—Easton
Baker & Adamson Chemical
Co. ....A
PA.—Philadelphia
Powers - Weightman-Rosengarten Co. ....AAAA

IODOFORM

MASS.—Boston
Billings, Clapp & Co. ....B
MO.—St. Louis
Herf & Frerichs Chemical
Co. ....A
Larkin & Scheffer Chem.
Co. ....A
Mallinckrodt Chemical Wks.
...................AA
New York City
New York Quinine & Chemical Wks. (Ltd.)........A

IODOFORM
PA.—Philadelphia
Powers - Weightman-Rosengarten Co. ....AAAA

IRON & STEEL

ALA.—Anniston
Woodstock Iron Wks. (Car
Wheel; Pig) ....A
ALA.—Birmingham
Alabama Consolidated Coal
& Iron Co. (Foundry; Pig)
...................AAAA
Birmingham Rolling Mill
Co. (Bar; Rolled; Bridge)
...................AAA
Pioneer Mining & Mfg. Co.
Pig) ....AAAA
Sloss Sheffield Steel & Iron
Co. (Foundry; Pig; Merchant Steel) ......AAAA
Tennessee Coal Iron & Railroad Co. (Bastic; Foundry
Pig; I. & S. Angles;
Blooms; Billets)...AAAA
Williamson Iron Co. (Pig) X
ALA.—Huntsville
Nolan & Jones (Architectural; Ornamental) ....B
ALA.—Mobile
Alabama Iron Works (Architectural; Ornamental) ..B
ALA.—Montgomery
Janney & Co. (Architectural; Ornamental) ....A
ALA.—Sheffield
Sheffield Coal & Iron Co.
(Pig) ....AAAA
Sheffield Rolling Mill Co.
(Bar) ....A
ALA.—Shelby
Shelby Iron Co. (Car Wheel)
...................AAAA
ALA.—Woodward
Woodward Iron Co. (Pig)
...................AAAA
ARK.—Little Rock
Thomas Fordyce Mfg. Co.
Architectural; Ornamental) ....A
ARK.—Pine Bluff
Dilley, Foundry Co. (Architectural; Ornamental) ..A
CAL.—Fresno
Fresno Agricultural Wks.
(Architectural; Ornamental) ....B
CAL.—Los Angeles
Baker Iron Works, 950
Buena Vista (Architectural; Ornamental) ...AA
Fulton Engine Wks. (Architectural; Ornamental) ..A
Llewellyn Iron Wks., Main
& San Fernando (Architetural; Ornamental)...AA
...................AA
Union Iron Wks., 406 1st
(Architectural; Ornamental) ....B
CAL.—Sacramento
Root, Neilson & Co. (Architectural; Ornamental) ..B
CAL.—San Francisco
Burnstone Bros., 543 Brannon (& Steel Scraps) ...A
Harley Co., Chas., 844 Harrison (& Steel Scraps)..A
Hendy Machine Wks., 38
Fremont.. (Architectural;
Ornamental) ....AA
San Francisco Novelty &
Plating Wks., 68 1st
(Architectural; Ornamental) ....B
Vulcan Iron Wks., 505 Mission (Architectural; Ornamental) ....AAAA
Western Iron Wks., 123
Beale (Architectural;
Ornamental) ....B
CAL.—Stockton
Globe Iron Wks. (Architectural; Ornamental) .....B
Stockton Iron Wks. (Architectural; Ornamental) ..A
COLO.—Colorado Springs
Hassell Iron Wks. (Architectural; Ornamental) ..B
COLO.—Denver
Colorado Fuel & Iron Co.
(Pig; Bar; Angles;
Blooms; Billets; Sheet

IRON & STEEL (Con.)
Steel) ....AAAA
Colorado Iron Wks., 33d & Wynkoop (Architectural; Ornamental) ....AA
Davis Iron Wks. Co., 723 Larimer (Architectural; Ornamental) ....A
CONN.—Bridgeport
Bridgeport Malleable Iron Co. (Malleable) .....AAA
Am. Tube & Stamping Co. (Cold; Hot Rolled Strip; Sheet; Spring; Tool; Corset; Bar Steel) .....AAA
Farist Steel Co. (Bar; Die; Block; Tool; Steel)..AAA

Brewer 543 Register 422—

Taylor, Thos. P. (Corset Steel) ....B
CONN.—Bristol
Warner Bros. Co. (Corset Steel) ....AAAA
Sessions Foundry Co. (Architectural; Ornamental) AAA
CONN.—East Berlin
American Bridge Co. (Corrugated) ....AAAA
CONN.—Hartford
Hartford Foundry Corpn. (Architectural; Ornamental) ....B
CONN.—Lime Rock
Barnum-Richardson Co. (Salisbury Charcoal Pig) AAA
CONN.—Meriden
Bradley & Hubbard Mfg. Co. (Architectural; Ornamental) ....AAAA
CONN.—New Haven
Nat. Steel & Wire Co. (Steel Blooms; Billets; Special Shapes; Cold Drawn) ....AAAA
Omega Steel Co. (Tool Steel) X
CONN.—Waterbury
Fry & Co., B. H., Porter & S. Leonard (Architectural; Ornamental) ....A
Waterbury Scrap Iron Co. (& Steel Scrap) C
DEL.—Marshalltown
Marshalltown Iron & Steel Co. (Sheet Steel) ....D
DEL.—Newport
Marshall Iron Co. (Sheet Iron) ....B
DEL.—Wilmington
Diamond State Steel Co. (Architectural; Ornamental Bar; Steel Blooms; Billets) ....AAAA
Edge Moor Bridge Wrks. (Bridge) ....AAAA
Johnson Forge Co. (Bar)..B
McCullough Iron Co. (Corrugated; Black S. & I. Sheets; Galvanized) ..AA
Stoileth Bros. (Steel Scrap) B
D. C.—Washington
Allegheny Co. (Pig) .....D
Barber & Ross, 614 11th N. W. (Architectural; Ornamental) ....A
McGill, James H., McGill Bldg. (Architectural; Ornamental) ....A
FLA.—St. Augustine
Hamblen, C. F. (Architectural; Ornamental) ....B
GA.—Atlanta
Atlanta Machine Wrks Co. (Architectural; Ornamental) ....B
GA.—Augusta
Lombard Iron Wrks. & Supply Co. (Architectural; Ornamental) ....A
GA.—Savannah
Kehoe & Sons, Wm. (Architectural; Ornamental) ..A
Rourke Iron Wrks. (Architectural; Ornamental) ..B
ILL.—Aurora
Love Bros. (Architectural; Ornamental) ....A
ILL.—Bloomington
Amer. Fdry. & Furnace Co.

IRON & STEEL (Con.)
(Architectural; Ornamental) ....A
ILL.—Chicago
Barbee Wire & Iron Wrks. 44 Dearborn (Architectural; Ornamental) ....B
Am. Steel & Wire Co. (Steel Billets; Blooms; Angles; Cold Rolled Spring; Strip; Swedish) ....AAAA
Armstrong Bros. Tool Co. (Self Hardening Steel).C
Block-Pollock Iron Co., Marquette Bldg. (& Steel Scrap) ....AA
Bolter & Sons, A., 84 La Salle (Architectural; Ornamental) ....B
Booth, John, 114 E. Lake (Architectural; Ornamental) ....B
Branmoeller & Son, Henry, 90 W. Van Buren (Architectural; Ornamental)..B
Butler Street Fdy. & Iron Co., 3422 Butler (Architectural; Ornamental) .B
Chicago Bridge & Iron Co., 105th & Throop (Architectural; Ornamental) ..A
Crerar-Clinch & Co., Rookery Bldg. (Pig) .....AA
Dauchy Iron Wrks., 88 Illinois (Cast; Wrought; Ornamental) ....B
Dearborn Foundry Co., 1525 Dearborn (Cast; Wrought; Arch'l; Ornamental) ..A
Hansell-Elcock Fdy. Co., 251 23d Pl. (Architectural; Ornamental) ....A
Hirsch Co., L. K., Rookery Bldg. (& Steel Scrap).B
Holmes, Pyott Co., 13 N. Jeff (Architectural; Ornamental) ....AA
Illinois Steel Co., The Rookery (Pig; Steel Angles, Blooms; Billets) ..AAAA
Inland Steel Co. (Steel Blooms; Billets; Angles; Bar) ....AAAA
Lieberman Iron Co., A. W., 22d & S. Jefferson (& Steel Scrap) C
Kenwood Bridge Co., 1st Nat. Bank (Architectural; Ornamental) ....B
McVoy & Co., John (Galvanized) ....B
Morris & Co., S., 462 S. Canal (& Steel Scrap)....A
Ohio Iron & Metal Co., 108 La Salle (& Steel Scrap) AAA
Pickands, Brown & Co., Rookery Bldg. (Pig) AAAA
Republic Iron & Steel Co., Stock Exch. Bldg. (Staybolt; Bessemer Foundry; Mill Pig Bar; Steel Angles; Blooms; Billets; Bars) ....AAAA
Rogers, Brown & Co., Stock Exch. Bldg. (Bessemer; also Coke Pig) ....AAAA
Ryerson & Son, Jos. T. (Staybolt; Bar Implement) ....AAAA
Smith Iron & Wire Wks., 100 Lake (Wrought; Cast; Ornamental) ....B
South Chicago Furnace Co., The Rookery (Malleable Bessemer Pig) ......AAA
South Halsted Street Iron Wrks., 2611 S. Halsted (Architectural; Ornamental) ....B
Stern, Harris, 272 S. Clinton (& Steel Scrap) ...C
Stevens & Co., Chas. G. (Self Hardening Steel).C
Stevenson Pig Iron & Coke Co., Fisher Bldg. (Coke; Pig) ....A
Streeter, H. A., 35 Indiana (Architectural; Ornamental) ....A
Stroud & Co., E. H., 36 La Salle (Pig) ....D
Vierling, McDowell & Co.,

IRON & STEEL (Con.)

23d & Stewart Av. (Architectural; Ornamental) ....A

Voss, Frederick, 617 Austin Av. (Architectural; Ornamental) ....B

Western Iron & Steel Co., 39th & Emerald Av. (& Steel Scrap) ....B

Williams, Jacob, 403 S. Canal (& Steel Scrap) ..A

ILL.—Elgin

Woodruff & Edwards Co. (Architectural; Ornamental) ....B

ILL.—Galesburg

Frost Mfg. Co. (Architectural; Ornamental).......A

ILL.—Joliet

Bates Machine Co. (Architectural; Ornamental)..A

ILL.—Macomb

Fisher Arch Fdy. & Machine Shop (Architectural; Ornamental) ....B

ILL.—Peru

Brumer, Charles (Architectural; Ornamental) ....A

ILL.—Quincy

Central Iron Wrks. (Architectural; Ornamental)..B

Rupp & Bros. Co., Geo., (& Scrap Steel) .....B

ILL.—Peoria

Lanski & Son Scrap Iron Co. I. (& Steel Scrap) C

ILL.—Rockford

Love Mfg. Co. (Architectural; Ornamental) ......B

IND.—Evansville

Mesker & Co., Geo. L., 100 L. 1st (Arch.............X

IND.—Fort Wayne

Fort Wayne Iron & Steel Co. (Bar) ....A

Kerr Murray Mfg. Co. (Architectural; Ornamental) ....A

IND.—Goshen

Kelly Fdy. & Machine Co. (Architectural; Ornamental) ....A

Thomas Albright Co. (Architectural; Ornamental)..A

IND.—Indianapolis

Brown-Ketcham Iron Wrks., 2549 W. Michigan (Architectural; Ornamental) ....AAA

Hetherington & Berner Co., 27 W. South (Architectural; Ornamental) ......A

Moelke-Richards Iron Wrks. (Architectural; Ornamental) ....A

IND.—New Albany

Ohio Falls Iron Co. (Staybolt; Bar) ....A

IND.—South Bend

Sibley & Ware (Architectural; Ornamental) ......A

South Bend Foundry Co. (Architectural; Ornamental) ....B

IND.—Terre Haute

Highland Iron & Steel Co. (Bar) ....AA

Prox & Brinkman Mfg. Co. (Architectural ; Ornamental) ....A

IOWA—Burlington

Murray Iron Wrks Co. (Architectural; Ornamental) ....A

IOWA—Clinton

Clinton Bridge & Iron Wrks. (Architectural; Ornamental) ....AA

IOWA—Davenport

Davenport Fdy. & Machine Co. (Architectural; Ornamental) ....B

IOWA—Des Moines

American Iron Wrks. (Architectural; Ornamental) ....B

Des Moines Bridge & Iron Wrks. (Architectural; Ornamental) ....A

Des Moines Mfg. & Supply Co. (Architectural; Ornamental) ....A

Eagle Iron Wrks. (Architectural; Ornamental) ..B

IRON & STEEL (Con.)

IOWA—Ottumwa

Fair-Williams Bridge & Mfg. Co. (Architectural; Ornamental) ....B

KANS.—Atchison

Seaton, John (Architectural; Ornamental) ....AA

KANS.—Kansas City

Riverside Iron Wrks. Co., Central Av. & 4th (Architectural; Ornamental) ....A

KANS.—Leavenworth

Missouri Valley Bridge & Iron Wrks. (Architectural; Ornamental) ......A

KANS.—Parsons

Steele Hdw. Co. (Architectural; Ornamental) ....B

KANS.—Topeka

Cofran, R. L. (Architectural; Ornamental) ......B

KY.—Ashland

Ashland Steel Co. (Bessemer Pig; Steel Billets; Sheets) ....AAA

Ashland Sheet Mill Co. (Sheet Steel) ....AAA

Norton Iron Wrks. (Pig) ....AA

KY.—Covington

Licking Rolling Mill Co. (Iron; Steel Angles; Sheets) ....B

KY.—Louisville

Hickman, Williams & Co. (Pig) ....AA

O'Brien, P. (& Steel Scrap) ....B

Weber & Son, Simon (& Steel Scrap) ....B

KY.—Newport

Newport Rolling Mill Co. (Sheet Steel) ....AA

LA.—New Orleans

Hinderer's Iron Fence Wrks. 1116 Camp (Architectural; Ornamental) ......B

Marx, Alphonse (& Steel Scrap) ....B

Swoop, Julian M., 913 Girod (Architectural; Ornamental) ....A

LA.—Shreveport

Hendersen Iron Wks (Architectural; Ornamental)..A

MAINE—Portland

Megquier & Jones, 33 Pearl (Architectural; Ornamental) ....B

MD.—Baltimore

Baltimore Bridge Co. (Architectural; Ornamental) ....AA

Bartlett, Hayward & Co., Continental (Architectural; Ornamental) ..AAA

Dufur & Co., 311 N. Howard (Architectural; Ornamental) ....B

Hoopes & Radford, 1018 Ashland Av. (& Steel Scrap) ....B

Smyser's Sons, E. G., 4 Light (Architectural; Ornamental) ....A

Wehr & Co., Pratt & President (& Steel Scrap) ..A

Winternitz, Hiram, 221 S. Howard (& Steel Scrap) ....A

Woolford, N. B., 914 S. B'way (& Steel Scraps) ....A

MD.—Cumberland

Cumberland Steel & Tin Plate Co. (Bessemer Machinery; Plow; Tool Steel) ....A

MD.—Muirkirk

Coffin, Chas. E. (Charcoal Pig) ....B

MASS.—Boston

Boston Bridge Wrks., 70 Kilby (Architectural; Ornamental) ....A

Boston Steel & Iron Co., 101 Tremont (Architectural; Ornamental) ....B

Brown, Wales Co. (Swedish Steel) ....A

Dodge, Haley & Co. (Swedish Steel) ......AA

Fitz, Dana & Co. (Swed-

561

562

IRON & STEEL (Con.)

Koken Iron Wrks., Koken Bldg. (Architectural; Ornamental) ....AA

Ludlow-Saylor Wire Co., 4th & Elm (Architectural; Ornamental) ....AA

Mesker & Bro., 423 S. 6th (Architectural; Ornamental) ....AA

St. Louis Blast & Furnace Co., Union Tr. Bldg. (Pig) ....AA

Souther Iron Co., E. E. (Corrugated I. & S.) ....A

Spuck Iron & Fdry. Co., 1013 N. 11th (Architectural; Ornamental) ....B

Stupp Bros. Bridge & Iron Co., 7th & Shenandoah Av. (Architectural; Ornamental) ....B

Union Iron & Fdry. Co., 1458 S. 2nd (Architectural; Ornamental) ....B

MONT—Anaconda

Anaconda Copper Mining Co. (Architectural; Ornamental) ....AAAA

MONT.—Helena

Cavid & Hawksworth (Architectural; Ornamental)..B

MONT.—Great Falls

Great Falls Iron Wks. (Architectural Ornamental) ....B

NEBR.—Omaha

Paxton & Vierling Iron Wks. S. 17th (Architectural; Ornamental) ....A

N. H.—Concord

Concord Foundry Co. (Architectural; Ornamental)..B

N. J.—Bayonne

Clark Iron Foundry (Architectural; Ornamental).AA

N. J.—Boonton

Lincoln Iron Works (Pig).B

N. J.—Dover

Ulster Iron Wks. (Staybolt; Bar) ....AA

N. J.—Elizabeth

Moore & Sons Co., S. L. (Architectural; Ornamental) ....A

N. J.—Harrison

Crucible Steel Co. of America; Blooms; Tool; Bar; Cast; Drill Steel)..AAAA

N. J.—High Bridge

Taylor Iron & Steel Co. (Manganese Steel).AAAA

N. J.—Hoboken

Fagan Iron Wks., 309 Jeff (Architectural; Ornamental) ....A

N. J.—Jersey City

Jersey City Galv. Wks. (Galv. I. & S. Sheets)..B

Natl. Sheet Metal Roofing Co., 339 Grand (Architectural; Ornamental) ......B

Snead & Co. Iron Wks., ft. Pine (Architectural; Ornamental) ....A

Spauldings & Jennings Co. (Tool Steel) ....AAAA

N. J.—Newark

Benisch & Son, Chas. (Steel Scrap) ....B

Burns Iron Wks., 201 Commerce (Architectural; Ornamental) ....B

Hay Fdry. & Iron Wks. (Architectural; Ornamental) ....B

Heller Bros. Co. (Self-Hardening Tool Steel) AA

N. J.—Orange

Orange Iron Wks., Alden (Architectural; Ornamental) ....B

N. J.—Oxford

Janson Steel & Iron Co. (Bar) ....B

N. J.—Paterson

Eastwood Co., Benj. (Architectural; Ornamental)..A

Passaic Steel Co. (I. & S. Angles) ....A

Passaic Rolling Mill Co. (I. & S. Angles).......A

IRON & STEEL (Con.)

N. J.—Perth Amboy

Pardee Wks. Co. (Cold Drawn; Bar Steel)...AAA

N. J.—Phillipsburg

Amer. Sheet Iron Co. (Block Sheets) ....AA

N. J.—Trenton

MacKenzie & Duncan (Architectural; Ornamental).A

Trenton Iron Co. (Merchant; L. T. & Z.)............A

N. J.—Wharton

Wharton, Joseph (Pig)
AAAA

N. Y.—Albany

McKinney & Son, J., 925 B'way (Architectural; Ornamental) ....A

N. Y.—Auburn

Tuttle & Co., C. W. (Bar)
A

N. Y.—Binghamton

Shapley & Wells, 118 Wash. (Architectural; Ornamental) ....A

N. Y.—Brooklyn

Hecla Iron Wks. (Architectural; Ornamental).AA

Chrome Steel Wks. (Bar; Cast; Chrome; Safe; Vault Steel) ....AAA

Miller & Van Winkle (Cold Rolled Strip; Corset Steel) ....A

Samuel's Sons, Kent Av. & N. 2d (Steel Scrap) ....A

N. Y.—Buffalo

Brinker Coal Co., J. M., Mooney Bldg. (Pig)....X

Buffalo Structural Steel Wks. (Architectural; Ornamental) ....B

Ernst, Chas. F., 311 Walnut (Architectural; Ornamental) ....A

Ginsburg & Sons, R. L. (Steel Scrap) ....A

Ginther's Sons, J., 419 B'way (Architectural; Ornamental) ....A

Harrower, H. C., 35 Court (Architectural; Ornamental) ....B

Hofeller & Son, Theo. 98 Terrace (Steel Scrap)..B

Jones Iron Wks., 308 Terrace (Architectural; Ornamental) ....B

Lackawanna Steel Co. (Bar)
AAAA

Pratt & Letchworth Co. (Malleable) ....AAA

Shepard. Chas. G., 40 Ellicott Sq. (Domestic; Foreign Pig; Bar) ....E

Tonawanda Iron & Steel Co., Erie Co. Bank Bldg. (Pig)
AAAA

Ullman's Sons, D., 229 Van Rensselaer (Steel Scrap)
A

N. Y.—Cohoes

Cohoes Iron Fdy. & Machine Co. (Architectural; Ornamental) ....A

Cohoes Rolling Mill Co. (Bar) ....AA

N. Y.—Elmira

Elmira Rolling Mill Co. (Bar) ....B

N. Y.—Long Island City

Daly, Jno. J., (Steel Scrap)
C

Richey, Browne & Donald (Architectural; Ornamental) ....A

N. Y.—Newburgh

Coldwell-Wilcox Co. (Architectural; Ornamental)..B

Hart, Patrick (Steel Scrap)
A

New York City

Abendroth & Root Mfg. Co. (Galvanized) ....A

Allen Co.. Edgar (Manganese Steel) ....B

Am. Sheet Steel Co. (Cold Rolled; Bessemer; Open Hearth; Galvanized Steel Sheets) ....AAAA

Blake, M. J. & M., 10th Av.

IRON & STEEL (Con.)
& 15th (Steel Scrap) ...A
Bowes, Jno. J., 227 W. 29th
(Architectural; Orna-
mental) ....B
Braun, J. G. (Architectural;
Ornamental) ....B
Cary Spring Works (Corset;
Clock; Watch Spring
Steel) ....D
Continental Iron & Steel Co.
25 Broad (Steel Scrap).B
Cooper, Hewitt & Co., (Pig;
Anthracite; Bessemer
Pig) ....AAAA
Cornell Co., J. B. & J. M.,
26th & 11th Av. (Archi-
tectural; Structural)..AA
Crocker Bros., 99 John (Pig)
AAA
Dana & Co., 32 Bdway.
Swedish Steel) ......AA
Dimond, Thos., 128 W. 33d
(Architectural; Orna-
mental) ....B
Dominion Iron & Steel Co.,
100 Bdway. (Steel Bil-
lets; Blooms) ......AAAA
Fuller Bros. & Co., 139
Greenwich (Staybolt)..D
Hobson, Houghton & Co.,
Ltd., 98 John (Crucible
Cast; Saw; Tool; Self-
Hardening Steel).......A
Illingworth Steel Co., Jno.,
25 Cliff (Cold Drawn
Steel) ....B
Happel, Adam, 1801 1st
Av. (Architectural; Or-
namental) ....B
Jackson Arch'l Iron Wks.,
815 E. 28th (Architec-
tural; Ornamental)....AA
Jackson Co., Wm. H., 29
E. 17th (Architectural;
Ornamental) ....A
Jessup & Sons, Ltd., Wm.,
91 John (Cold Rolled; Cru-
cible; Cast; Die; Shear;
Saw; Tool Steel)....AAA
Hahn Bros., 525 E. 19th
(Steel Scrap) ....AA
Lefferts Galvanizing Wks.
(Galvanized) C
Leonard & Co., Jno., 220
B'way (Steel Scrap)..AA
Levering & Garrigues, 552
W. 23d (Architectural;
Ornamental) ....B
Lewinson & Just, 128 W.
42d (Architectural; Orna-
mental) ....B
Milne & Co., A., 1 Bdway.
(Norway Steel) ......AA
Moseley Iron Bridge & Roof
Co. (Corrugated; Galvan-
ized; Painted) ....B
Mott Iron Wks., J. L., 88
Beekman (Architectural;
Ornamental) ....AA
Nicoll & Co., B., 59 Wall
(Bastic; Bessemer; Forge;
Foundry Pig).......AAA
Ogden & Wallace (Dirs. in
Bar; Carriage; Car Wheel;
Cylinder; Hammered;
Hoop; Horse Shoe; Mer-
chant Iron; Steel).....A
Pierson & Co., 29 B'way
(Architectural; Orna-
mental; Bar; Swedish;
I. & S.) ....AAA
Radley & Co., 624 E. 19th
(Architectural; Orna-
mental) ....A
Railway Steel Spring Co.
(Spring Steel) ......AAA
Schnatz & Massoth, 127 E.
76th (Architectural; Or-
namental) ....B
Shriver & Co., T., 336 E.
56th (Architectural; Or-
namental) ....A
Smith Co., Morton B., 243
Front (Steel Scrap) ...A
Todd, J. H. L., 11 William
(Swedish Steel) ....D
U. S. Metal & Mfg. Co., 25
Broad (Steel Scrap)....A
U. S. Steel Corp. (Angles;
Blooms; Bars; Billets)...
AAAA
Vreeland, G. A., 229 W.

IRON & STEEL (Con.)
36th (Architectural; Orna-
mental) ....B
Wardlow, S. & Co., 95 John
(Cold Rolled Strip; Cast;
Crucible; Cutting; Die;
Tool; Spring Steel)..AA
Westervelt, A. B. & W. T.,
102 Chambers (Architec-
tural; Ornamental).....B
Wheelock, Lovejoy & Co.
(Swedish Steel) ....A
Williams, John, 556 W. 27th
(Architectural; Orna-
mental) ....B
N. Y.—Poughkeepsie
Poughkeepsie Iron Co., (Pig)
A
N. Y.—Rochester
Genessee Metal Wks. (Arch-
itectural; Ornamental) AA
Hughes & Co., F. L., 190
South Av. (Architectural;
(Ornamental) ....B
Hey & Co. (Steel Scrap)..B
N. Y.—Rome
Rome Merchant Iron Mill
(Staybolt; Bar).......AA
N. Y.—Syracuse
Ames Iron Wks., The Mas-
stable (Architectural; Or-
namental) ....AA
Eckels-Nye Steel Co. (Bar)
B
Economy F'dy. & Machine
Co., W. Belden Av. (Arch-
itectural; Ornamental)..B
Sanderson Bros. Steel Co.
(Tool; Axe; Crucible; Cut-
lery; Drill; Machinery
Steel) ....AAAA
Syracuse Arch'l Iron Wks.,
107 N. Franklin (Archi-
tectural; Ornamental)..B
Sweets Steel Co. (Imple-
ment; Spring; Axe; File;
Tool; Bar Steel).......A
Syracuse Malleable Iron
Wks. (Malleable) .....A
N. Y.—Tonawanda
Buffalo Steel Co. (Angles;
Bars; Implement Steel)
AA
N. Y.—Troy
Burden Iron Co. (Bar; Pig)
AAAA
Mahony Mfg. Co., 5th Av.
(Architectural; Orna-
mental) ....B
Troy Malleable Iron Co.
(Malleable) ....A
West Side Foundry Co., 3d
Av. (Architectural; Orna-
mental) ....A
OHIO—Cambridge
Cambridge Rolling Mill Co.
(S. & I. Angles; Billets;
Implement) ....A
OHIO—Canton
Bergen Mfg. Co. (Galvan-
ized; Corrugated; I. & S.)
AA
Canton Bridge Co. (Archi-
tectural; Ornamental) ...
AAAA
Canton Iron Co. (Drill
Steel) ....A
Canton Iron & Metal Co.
(Steel Scrap) ....A
Canton Steel Co. (Cast;
Spring; Tool Steel)...AA
Carnahan Tin Plate & Sheet
Steel Co. ....AA
Stark Rolling Mill Co.
(Sheet Iron) ....B
OHIO—Cincinnati
Amer. Galvanizing Co. (Gal-
vanized) ....E
Brackett Bridge Co., Atlas
Bank Bldg. (Architec-
tural; Ornamental)....B
Dayton Coal & Iron Co.,
Johnston Bldg. (Pig)...
AAAA
Domhoff & Joyce Co., Raw-
son Bldg. (Pig) ......B
Globe Rolling Mill Co. (Bar;
Carriage; Hoop; Horse
Shoe; Pig; Staybolt; Im-
plement) ....A
Hoefinghoff & Lane Mfg.
Co., 500 E. Front (Archi-
tectural; Ornamental)..A

IRON & STEEL (Con.)
Hyndman Steel Roofing Co.
(Corrugated) C
Joseph Iron Co., Isaac, 525
Hunt (Steel Scrap)....B
Klein & Cohn, 830 Wade
(Steel Scrap) ....B
Schreiber & Sons Co., 8th &
Eggleston Av. (Architec-
tural; Ornamental) ...AA
Stacy Mfg. Co., 239 Mill
(Architectural; Orna-
mental) ....A
Stewart Iron Wks., 714 E.
3d (Architectural; Orna-
mental) ....A

OHIO—Cleveland
Bassett-Presley Co. (Stay-
bolt) ....AA
Bourne-Fuller Co., Perry-
Payne Bldg. (Bessemer;
Foundry Pig) ....AA
Brooks & Co., T. H., 960
Lake (Architectural; Or-
namental) ....A
Brown & Co., Harvey H.,
Perry-Payne Bldg. (Pig)
.................AAAA
Cleveland City Forge &
Iron Co. (Hammered; I. &
S.) ....AA
Cleveland Cliff Iron Co.,
Mercantile Bank (Pig)..
.................AAAA
Cleveland Rolling Mill Co.
(Billets; Bars; Machinery;
Spring Steel) ......AAAA
Cohen, Magusky & Co., 184
Wilson Av. (Steel Scrap)
.......................B
Empire Rolling Mill Co.
(Bar) ....A
Federal Mfg. Co. (Cold
Rolled Steel) ......AAAA
Forest City Steel & Iron
Co., Ramsey (Architec-
tural; Ornamental) ....A
Garry Iron & Steel Roofing
Co. (Corrugated) ......A
Hanna & Co., M. A., Perry-
Payne Bldg. (Bessemer;
Foundry; Charcoal Pig)..
.................AAAA
King Bridge Co., St. Clair
(Architectural; Orna-
mental) ....AAA
Lake Erie Iron Co. (Bar;
Hoop) ....AAA
Otis Steel Co. (Bar; Bil-
lets) ....A
Pickands, Mather & Co.
(Pig; Bar) ......AAAA
Runyon, Stubbs & Co. (Pig)
.....................AA
Schwarzenberg, Henry H.,
Cuyahoga Bldg. (Steel
Scrap) C
Shimer & Co., Saml. M.
(Steel Scrap) C
Stewart Iron Co., Perry-
Payne Bldg. (Pig; Bil-
lets) ....AAA
Struthers Furnace Co.,
Perry-Payne Bldg. (Pig)
.................AAA
Tod, Stambaugh & Co.,
Perry-Payne Bldg. (Pig)
.....................AA
Tyler Co., W. S., 1150 St.
Clair (Architectural; Or-
namental) ....AA
Union Rolling Mill Co.
(Staybolt; Merchant; Bar;
Rivet; I. & S.).......AA
Van Dorn Iron Wks., 1793
E. Madison (Architec-
tural; Ornamental)...AA

THE VAN DORN IRON
WORKS COMPANY,
CLEVELAND, OHIO,
MANUFACTURERS OF
IRON AND STEEL
PRODUCTS.
Our Specialties are:
The Celebrated Van
Dorn Iron Fences, ac-
knowledged by experts
the best constructed in
the world.
Our Cell Work for Pen-
itentiaries, County Pris-

IRON & STEEL (Con.)
ons, City Station Houses,
Village Lock-ups and
Burglar-Proof Gratings,
have a national reputa-
tion.
Structural Steel, Orna-
mental Iron Work, Stairs
and Railings.
Office Equipments in
Steel, consisting of Doc-
ument Files, Cases, Book
Stacks, Desks, Steel Lock-
ers and Railings.
Steel Joist Hangers,
Post Caps and Bases, the
strongest made.
Vault Doors, Folding
Gates, Steel Lawn Seats,
and Vases.
Japan Ovens for Fac-
tories.
Fittings for Stables,
etc.
Catalogs upon appli-

Variety Iron Wks. Co., Case
Av. (Architectural; Orna-
mental) ....B
Wellman-Seaver-Morgan Co.
(Machy. Steel) ..AAAA

OHIO—Columbus
Columbus Iron & Steel Co.
(Foundry; Bessemer; Mal-
leable Pig) ......AAAA
Hayden Saddlery Hdw. Co.
(Architectural; Orna-
mental) ....AAAA
Morris & Co., C. E. (Archi-
tectural; Ornamental)..B
Rarig Engineering Co., A.
K., 5th Av. (Architec-
tural; Ornamental).....A

OHIO—Cuyahoga Falls
Falls Hollow Staybolt Co.
(Hollow; Solid Boiler
Staybolt) ....A

OHIO—Dayton
Dayton Malleable Iron Co.
(Malleable) ....AAA

OHIO—Dennison
Dominion Rolling Mills
(Sheet Steel) ....F

OHIO—Elyria
June & Co., D. (Architec-
Columbia Steel Wks. (Cold
Rolled; Sheet; Strip;
Spring Steel) ......AAA

OHIO—Fremont
tural; Ornamental)...AA
Lehr Agricultural Co. (Architectural; Onamental)..B

OHIO—Girard
Girard Iron Co. (Bessemer;
Foundry; Grey Forge Pig)
.......................A

OHIO—Ironton
Belfont Iron Wks. Co.
(Pig) ....AAA
Kelly Nail & Iron Co.
(Pig) ....AA

OHIO—Jackson
Globe Iron Co. (Pig)...AA
Star Furnace Co. (Pig)...A

OHIO—Kenton
Champion Iron Co. (Archi-
tectural; Ornamental).AA

OHIO—Leetonia
McKeefrey & Co. (Pig).AA
Salem Iron Co. (Pig)..AAA

OHIO—Lisbon
Beaver Tin Plate Co. (Cold
Rolled & Sheet Steel)
.................AAAA

OHIO—Lowellville
Ohio Iron & Steel Co. (Foundry & Bessemer) .....AA

OHIO—Marietta
Pattin Bros. Co. (Architectural; Ornamental) .....B

OHIO—Middletown
American Rolling Mill Co.
(Sheet; Galvanized Steel)
.....................AA

OHIO—New Comerstown
Tuscarora Steel Co. (Sheet
Steel) ....A

OHIO—Niles
Empire Iron & Steel Co.
(Sheet; Galvanized; Bar)
.......................A

IRON & STEEL (Con.)

Niles Iron & Steel Co. (Sheet; Galvanized Steel) B

Ohio Galvanized & Mfg. Co. (Galvanized Sheet) .....B

OHIO—Norwalk
Norwalk Iron & Steel Co. (Implement Plow; Crucible Steel) ....AA

OHIO—Sandusky
Klotz Machine Co. (Architectural; Ornamental)..B

OHIO—Springfield
Springfield Malleable Iron Co. (Malleable) ....A

OHIO—Steubenville
La Belle Iron Works (Billets; Bloom; Basic; Merchant; Shovel) ....AAAA

OHIO—Toledo
Toledo Fdy. & Machine Co. (Architectural; Ornamental) ....B
Toledo Furnace Co. (Scotch Fdy.; Malleable Pig) AAAA

OHIO—Youngstown
Andrews & Hitchcock Iron Co. (Bar; Hoop; Pig; Bessemer Pig) ......AA
Baier, Hill Iron & Coal Co. (Bessemer Pig) .....AA
Finished Steel Co. (Cold Drawn Steel) ....B
Youngstown Bolt Co. (Bar) A
Youngstown Iron Sheet & Tube Co. (Pig; Skelp; Sheet; Bar) ....AAAA
Youngstown Iron & Steel Roofing Co. (Galvanized Sheets) ....B
Youngstown Steel Co. (Bessemer; Basic; Billets; Forge Pig) ....AA

OHIO—Zanesville
Muskingum Valley Steel Co. (Sheet Steel) ....A

OREGON—Portland
Pacific Bridge Co. (Architectural; Ornamental)..B
Portland Iron Works, 495 Northrup (Architectural; Ornamental) ....A
Smith & Watson Iron Wks., foot Hall (Architectural; Ornamental) ....B
Willamette Boiler Works, 123 3d N. (Architectural; Ornamental) ....B

PA.—Aliquippa
Vulcan Crucible Steel Co. (Steel Billets; Tool; Axe; Ball; Die; Shear; File; Fork; Knife; Drill; Spring Steel) ....B

PA.—Allegheny
Albree, Chester B., 1129 Market (Architectural; Ornamental) ....A
Jones & Co., J. B. (& Steel Scrap) ....B
Rosedale Fdy. Co., cor. Washn. & Preble Av. (Ornamental; Architectural) B
Solomon, Julius, 2030 Knox (& Steel Scrap) ....A

PA.—Allentown
Allentown Fdy. & Machine Works Co. (Architectural; Ornamental) ....A
Allentown Rolling Mills (Pig; Bar) ......AAAA

PA.—Altoona
Altoona Iron Co. (Bar)...A

PA.—Beaver Falls
Standard Gauge Steel Co. (Squares; Rounds; Angles; Special Shapes) ....B
Union Drawn Steel Co. (Cold Drawn; Rolled; Bar Steel) AA

PA.—Bellefonte
Bellefonte Furnace Co. (Pig) A

PA.—Birdsboro
Brooke Iron Co., E. & G. (Pig) ....AAA

PA.—Bloomsburg
Harman & Hassert (Archi-

IRON & STEEL (Con.)

tectural; Ornamental)..A

PA.—Braeburn
Braeburn Steel Co. (Spring; Tool; Machinery; Hammer; Clock; Drill; Bar Steel) ....A

PA.—Bradford
Caldwell & Co., E. R. (Architectural; Ornamental) ....B

PA.—Burnham
Logan Iron & Steel Co. (Angles, &c.) ....AA

PA.—Catasauqua
Empire Steel & Iron Co. (Bessemer; Foundry Pig) AAAA

PA.—Carnegie
Superior Steel Co. (Hot; Cold Rolled Strip Steel).B

PA.—Chiswick
Chiswick Mfg. Co. (Implement Steel) ....D

PA.—Clearfield
Clearfield Steel & Iron Co. (Skelp) ....AA

PA.—Chester
Tidewater Steel Co. (Billets; Blooms) ....AAAA

PA.—Danville
Curry & Vannam (Architectural; Ornamental) ....A

PA.—Coatesville
Lukens Iron & Steel Co. (Billets; Blooms; Boiler Plate) ....AAAA

PA.—Connellsville
Sligo Iron & Steel Co. (Bar) B

PA.—Conshohocken
Longmead Iron Co. (Skelp) AA
Wood Bros. Co., J. (Sheet Steel) ....AA

PA.—Corry
McInnes Steel Co. (Self-Hardening Tool; Bar)...C

PA.—Demmler
Firth-Sterling Steel Co. (Tool) ....AAA

PA.—Dubois
Dubois Iron Wks. (Architectural Ornamental) AAAA

PA.—Easton
Thomas Iron Co. (Pig) AAAA

PA.—Emporium
Emporium Iron Co. (Foundry Pig) X

PA.—Erie
Ball Engine Foundry Co. (Architectural; Ornamental) ....AA
Erie Malleable Iron Co. (Malleable) ....AA
Griffin Mfg. Co. (Cold Rolled Strip Steel) .....A

PA.—Harrisburg
Central Iron & Steel Co. (Malleable) ......AAAA

PA.—Hollidaysburg
Eleanor Iron Co. (Skelp)..B
Hollidaysburg Iron & Nail Co. (Steel Angles)...A
McLanahan Stone Machine Co. (Architectural; Ornamental) ....A

PA.—Johnstown
Cambria Steel Co. (Blooms; Billets; Implement; Cold Rolled; Spring; Bar) AAAA

PA.—Lancaster
Pennsylvania Iron Co. (Bar) A

PA.—Lebanon
American Iron & Steel Mfg. Co. (Stay Bolt; Bar) AAAA
West End Rolling Mill Co. & Chain Works (Bar; Stay Bolt; U-Bar) ....A
Wiemer Machine Wks. Co. (Architectural; Ornamental) ....AA

PA.—Leechburg
West Leechburg Steel & Tin Plate Co. (Strip Steel)..B

PA.—McKees Rocks
Kidd Bros. & Burgher Steel & Wire Co. (Bar; Cold Rolled; Crucible; Tool;

566

IRON & STEEL (Con.)
Die, &c., Steel) ....B
Lockhart Iron & Steel Co.
(Staybolt; Borter Brace;
1. & S. Angles) ....AA
PA.—Mauch Chunk
Carbon Iron & Steel Co.
(Pig) ....AA
Stroh & Son, Wm. H. (Arch-
itectural; Ornamental)..B
PA.—Monaca
Pittsburg Tool Steel Wire
Co. (Cold Drawn Shapes)
C
PA.—New Castle
Atlantic Iron & Steel Co.
(Bessemer Pig; Skelp)..B
Elliott, Blair Steel Co. (Cold
Rolled Spring & Strip
Steel) ....B
PA.—Pencoyd
Roberts Co., A. & P. (Bar;
Ship) ....AAAA
PA.—Philadelphia
Adams & Co., Wm., 960 N.
9th (Architectural; Orna-
mental) ....B
Baizley Iron Works, 514 S.
Del. Av. (Architectural;
Ornamental) ....AA
Belmont Iron Works, 22d &
Washn. Av. (Architec-
tural; Ornamental) ....A
Cabeen & Co., R. E., Trust
Bldg. (Bar) ....B
Cambria Steel Co. (Bars;
Angles; Blooms) ..AAAA
Camden Iron Works (Bar).A
PA.—Philadelphia
Cox. Jr., Justus, 133 S. 4th
(Bessemer; Forge; Foun-
dry; Low Phos. Pig)....X
Creswell Iron Works, Saml.
J., 23d & Cherry (Archi-
tectural; Ornamental)..B
Cunliffe, Robert M., 140
Washn. Av. (& Steel
Scrap) ....B
Damascus Nickel Steel Co.
(Tool; Machy.; Bar; Nick-
el Steel) ....D
Darby & Sons, E., 233 Arch
(Architectural; Ornamen-
tal) ....A
De Cou, Richard, 12th &
Noble (& Steel Scrap)..B
Devlin Mfg. Co., Thos. (Mal-
leable) ....AA
Dimmick & Co., J. K. (Pig)
A
Disston & Sons, Hy. (Steel;
Squares; Flats; Strip;
Tool; Saw; Cutlery; Ma-
chinery) ....AAAA
Dreifus, Trimble & Co., E.,
Arcade Bldg. (& Steel
Scrap) ....B
Duncannon Iron Co. (Bar;
Horseshoe) ....AA
Flagg & Co., Stanley G.
(Malleable) ....AAA
Foster & Co., Alex., 2325
Spg. Garden (Tool Steel)
D
Gaulbert & Caskey, York &
American (Bar) ....B
Girard Iron & Metal Co.,
E. York & Aramingo (&
Steel Scrap) ....B
Gillingham & Co., H. F.,
1013 N. Front (& Steel
Scrap) ....B
Hitner's Sons, Hy. A., 2239
Vine (& Steel Scrap)..B
Houston & Co., C. B., Girard
Bldg. (& Steel Scrap)..A
Hughes & Patterson, 800
Richmond (Stay Bolt).AA
Johnson & Co., Geo. T.,
Drexel Bldg. (Pig) ....B
Kaiser & Co., A. V., 222 S.
3d (& Steel Scrap) .....B
Law & Co., Ernest, Harrison
Bldg. (& Steel Scrap;
Bar) ....A
Leaf & Co., E. B., R. E.
Trust Bldg. (Bar) ....A
McInnes & Co., Chas. E.
(Bar) C
Logan Iron & Steel Co., Har-
rison Bldg. (Charcoal Pig;
Angles; Stay Bolt)....AA
Marshall Bros. & Co. (Gal-

IRON & STEEL (Con.)
vanized Sheets) ......AA
Midvale Steel Co. (Blooms;
Billets; Spring; Tool;
Bar Steel) ....AAAA
Mohr, J. J., Bullitt Bldg.
(Foundry; Forge; Char-
coal; Bessemer Pig)....B
Morris, Wheeler & Co. (Mer-
chant Pig; Bar Iron &
Steel) ....AAA
Newkirk & Co., Jno. B.,
Harrison Bldg. (& Steel
Scrap; Bar) ....B
Penna. Steel Co. (Pig; Ship;
Blooms; Billets; Spring;
Bar; Machinery; Tire
Steel) ....AAAA
Perry Co., W. H., Real Es-
tate Trust Bldg. (& Steel
Scrap) ....A
Phila. Hdw. & Malleable
Iron Works (Malleable).A
Phillips & Sons' Co., F. R.,
Penna. Bldg. (& Steel
Scrap) C
Phoenix Bridge Co. (Bridge
& L. T. & Z.) ....A
Phoenix Iron Co. (Iron;
Steel; Bulb Angles).AAAA
Pilling & Crane (Pig)...AA
Potts & Co., Horace T.
(Swedish Iron; Steel)..A
Pulaski Iron Co., 330 Wal-
nut (Foundry Pig).AAA
Purves Mchry. & Iron Co.,
S. Water (& Steel Scrap)
B
Roberts & Co., A. & P.
(Bars; Beam, &c.)....AA
Rowland, Wm. & Harvey
(Norway; Iron; Steel
Billets; Implement; Bar;
Shovel; Spring; Tire)..B
Samuel, Frank, 1502 Market
(Importers & Exporters
Pig) ....A
Steward & Stevens Iron
Works, 9th (Architec-
tural; Ornamental) ....B
Tacony Iron & Metal Co.
(Architectural; Ornamen-
tal) ....A
Taylor & Co., N. & G.
(Sheet Steel) ......AAAA
Thompson & Co., J., cor.
Van Horn (Architectural;
Ornamental) ....B
Thompson & Co., W. H.,
Broad & Chestnut (Bar)
B
Warwick Iron & Steel Co.,
Girard Trust Bldg. (Fdy.;
Mill Pig) ....AAAA
Wheeler, Mifflin & Co., The
Arcade (Muck Bars; Pig)
D
Wilson & Co., E. H., Fi-
delity Bldg. (Pig) ....A
Wister & Co., L. & R.,
Bullitt Building (Basic;
Forge; Foundry Pig)..AA
Wood Iron & Steel Co., Alan
(Corrugated Iron; Open
Hearth; Billets; Cold
Rolled; Galv. Sheets)
AAAA
PA.—Pittsburg
Allegheny Steel & Iron Co.
(Sheets; Open Hearth
Steel Billets) ....AA
Bole, Ross & Co., Park
Bldg. (Pig) ....B
Banning, Cooper & Co.
(Steel Blooms; Billets).B
American Steel Hoop Co.
(Shapes; Hoop Saw; Tire;
Bar) ....AAAA
Anderson, De Puy & Co.
(Implement; Cutlery; Die;
Drill; Safe; Sheet, &c.,
Steel) ....AAAA
Brown & Co. (Pig Iron;
Tool; Crucible; Machy.;
Safe; Bar, &c., Steel).AA
Carbon Steel Co. (Steel
Blooms; Billets) .....A
Cannonsburg Iron & Steel
Co. (Sheet Steel) ....AAA
Carnegie Steel Co. (Pig;
Bar; Angles; Billets; Cor-
rugated; L. T. & Z.;

IRON & STEEL (Con.)
Ship Steel of all Kinds)
................................AAAA

Canton Steel Co. (Spring;
Lathe; Tool Steel)....AA

Carroll-Porter Boiler & Tank
Co. (Corrugated) ....AA

Central Plow Co. (Plow
Steel) ....B

Cherry Valley Iron Co., Peoples' Savings Bank Bldg.
(Pig) ....A

Clinton Iron & Steel Co.
(Foundry; Bessemer Grey;
Forge Pig) ....AA

Colonial Steel Co. (Plow;
S a w; B a r s; S h e e t s;
Plates; Shovel; Axe, &c.,
Steel) ....AAAA

Columbia Bridge Co. (Hek;
Square; Flat; Tool, &c.,
Steel) C

Crescent Steel Co. (Tool;
Die; Drill; Sheet; Spring;
Saw, &c., Steel) ..AAAA

Crucible Steel Co. of America (Blooms; Billets;
Rolled; Strip; Spring;
Tool; Bar Steel) ..AAAA

Dreifus & Co., Chas., Frick
Bldg. (& Steel Scrap)..B

Dreifus, Charles, Farmers'
Bank (& Steel Scrap)..A

Duquesne Co. (Sheet Steel)
................................C

Follansbee Bros. Co. (Sheet
Steel; Iron) ....AA

Goff, Horner & Co., Frick
Bldg. (Bessemer; Pig;
Cold Rolled Sheet Steel)
................................A

Hillman & Son, J. H., Frick
Bldg. (Basic; Bessemer
Pig; Bar) ....A

Humphreys, Stewart & Co.,
Lewis Blk. (Pig) ...AAA

Jones & Laughlin's Steel
Co. (Pig; Bar; Angle;
Billets; Shapes) ..AAAA

McLean & Co., Geo. A. (&
Steel Scrap) ....A

Monongahela Iron & Steel
Co. (Stay Bolt; Bar)....A

Morris & Bailey Co. (Rolled
Sheet; Strip Steel) ....B

National Steel Co. (Steel
Blooms; Billets) ..AAAA

National Tube Co. (Bessemer; Forge; Foundry Pig;
Galvanized) ....AAAA

Oliver Iron & Steel Co.
(Angles; Agricultural;
Bar) ....AAAA

Pittsburg Forge & Iron Co.
(Stay Bolt; Bar; Pig)..A

Park Steel Co. (Tool Steel)
................................AAAA

Pittsburg Crushed Steel Co.
(Crushed Steel) C

Riter-Conley Mfg. Co., 55
Water (Architectural; Ornamental) ....AAA

Republic Iron Works (Sheet;
Corrugated) ....B

Scaife & Sons' Co., Wm. B.,
221 1st (Architectural;
Ornamental; Bar) ...AAA

Sheet Steel Co. (Sheets;
Galvanized Sheets) C

Shenango Furnace Co.,
Frick Bldg. (Machine
Cast & Sand Cast Pig)..A

Snyder & Co., W. P. (Steel
Blooms; Billets) .....AA

Spang-Chalfant Co. (Pig;
Blooms; Machy.; Merchant Steel) ......AAAA

Taylor & Dean, 201 Market (Architectural; Ornamental) ....B

Westmoreland Steel Co.
(Strip; Crucible; Tool)..B

Zug & Co. (Ltd.) (Stay
Bolt; Bar; Galvanized
Sheets) ....AAAA

PA.—Pottsville
Eastern Steel Co. (Angles)
................................B

PA.—Pottstown
Potts Bros. Iron Co. (Skelp;
Open Hearth; Soft Iron;
Steel) ....A

IRON & STEEL (Con.)
PA.—Punxsutawney
Punxsutawney Iron Co.
(Pig) ....AA

PA.—Reading
Carpenter Steel Co. (Strips;
Tool; Die Steel) ..AAAA

Johnson Foundry Machine
Co. (Architectural; Ornamental) ....B

Reading Foundry Co. (Architectural; Ornamental) .B

Reading Iron Co. (Pig; Bar;
Staybolt; Muck) .AAAA

Seyfert, Simon (Iron; Steel
Angles) ....AA

PA.—Royersford
Keystone Structural Co.
(Architectural; Ornamental) ....B

PA.—Scranton
Finch Mfg. Co. (Structural;
Ornamental) ....AA

PA.—Sharon
Sharon Steel Hoop Co. (Billets) ....A

Stewart Iron Co. (Muck)
................................AAAA

Wilkes Rolling Mills Co.
(Sheet Steel) ....B

PA.—Sharpsville
Claire Furnace Co. (Pig)
................................AA

Perkins & Co. (Pig) .....A

Sharpesville Furnace Co.
(Pig) ....AAAA

PA.—Shenango
Shenango Iron Works Co.
(Skelp) ....A

PA.—Slatington
Slatington Rolling Mill Co.
(Bar) ....B

PA.—South Bethlehem
Bethlehem Steel Co. (Tool;
Blooms; Billets; Spring)
................................AAAA

PA.—Steelton
Penna. Steel Co. (Iron;
Steel) ....AAAA

PA.—Titusville
Burgess Cyclops Steel Wks.
(Crucible Tool; Bar Steel)
................................A

PA.—Waynesburg
Waynesburg Forge; Sheet &
Tin Mills (Soft Sheets).A

R. I.—Pawtucket
White Co., J. S. (Architectural; Ornamental) ....B

Washburn Wire Co. (Flat;
Round; Square; Cold
Rolled Steel) ...AAAA

R. I.—Providence
Bishop Co., J. W., Butler
Exch. (Architectural; Ornamental) ....A

Builders' Iron Foundry, 22
Codding (Architectural;
Ornamental) ....AA

Colvin Foundry Co., 191
Globe (Architectural; Ornamental) ....A

Carpenter & Sons Fdy. Co.
272 W. Exchange, (Architectural; Ornamental)...B

Perry Co., Wm. H. (& Steel
Scrap) ....B

Tower, James H., 48 Borden (Architectural; Ornamental) ....B

S. C.—Charleston
Valk & Murdoch Iron Wks.
(Architectural; Ornamental) ....B

TENN.—Bristol
Virginia Iron, Coal & Coke
Co. (Foundry; Forge; Billets; Blooms; Malleable;
Charcoal Pig) ....A

TENN.—Chattanooga
Cahill Iron Works, 102
Boyce (Architectural, Ornamental) ....B

Chattanooga Car & Fdy. Co.,
401 Boyce (Architectural;
Ornamental) ....B

Chattanooga Roofing & Fdy.
Co., 720 E. Montgomery
Av. (Architectural; Ornamental) ....B

Citico Furnace Co. (Pig).A

Roane Iron Co. (Pig)....A

Rome Furnace Co. (Pig)..B

IRON & STEEL (*Con.*)

Sale Creek Coal & Coke Co. (Pig) C

Southern Malleable Iron Wks. (Architectural; Ornamental) ....A

TENN.—Jackson

Southern Engine & Boiler Wks. (Architectural; Boiler Works) ....A

TENN.—Knoxville

Jellico Coal Mining Co. (Pig) ....AA

Knoxville Fdy. & Machine Co. (Architectural; Ornamental) ....A

Knoxville Iron Co. (Bar; Refined Bar; Horseshoe; Pig) ....AA

Tennessee Coal Co. (Pig) .A

TENN.—Memphis

Chickasaw Iron Works, 98 2d (Architectural; Ornamental) ....A

Livermore Fdy. & Machine Co., 160 Adams (Architectural; Ornamental) ....A

Manogue, Pidgeon Iron Co., 226 2d (Architectural; Ornamental) ....B

TENN.—Nashville

Bon Air Coal & Iron Co. (Pig) ....AAAA

TEXAS—Austin

Teps Foundry, Walter (Architectural; Ornamental) ....AA

TEXAS—Dallas

Harry Steel Wks., O. K. (Architectural; Ornamental) ....B

TEXAS—Fort Worth

Ft. Worth Machine & Fdy. Co. (Architectural; Ornamental) ....B

TEXAS—Houston

Dickson Car Wheel Co. (Architectural; Ornamental) ....A

UTAH—Salt Lake City

Utah Foundry & Mach. Co. (Architectural; Ornamental) ....A

VA.—Richmond

Old Dominion Iron & Nail Wks. Co. (Staybolt; Bar; Horse Shoe; Merchant; Muck; Refined; Rolled) ....AA

Tredegar Iron Wks. (Architectural; Ornamental; Bar) ....AAA

VA.—Roanoke

Virginia Bridge & Iron Co. (Architectural; Ornamental) ....AA

WASH.—Seattle

Hofius & Co., W. D. (Pig) ....A

WASH.—Tacoma

Puget Sound Iron & Steel Wks. (Architectural; Ornamental) ....B

W. VA.—Parkersburg

Parkersburg Iron & Steel Co. (Sheet; Bar)......AA

W. VA.—Wheeling

Laughlin Nail Co. (Blooms; Galv. Sheets)......AA

Portsmouth Steel Co. (Steel Billets) ....A

Wheeling Corrugating Co. (Galv.; Corrugated Sheets) ....AAAA

Wheeling Mold & Foundry Co. (Architectural; Ornamental) ....A

Wheeling Steel & Iron Co. (Pig; Billets; Sheet; Skelp) ....AAAA

Whittaker Iron Co. (Sheets) ....AA

WIS.—Ashland

Ashland Iron & Steel Co. (Pig) ....AAAA

WIS.—Eau Claire

Phoenix Mfg. Co. (Architectural; Ornamental)..A

WIS.—La Crosse

Smith Mfg. Co. (Architectural; Ornamental) ....B

WIS.—Madison

King & Walker Co. (Archi-

IRON & STEEL (*Con.*)

tectural; Ornamental)...B

WIS.—Milwaukee

Bayley & Sons Co., Wm., 732 Greenbush (Architectural; Ornamental) .....A

Greenslade Fdy. Co. (Architectural; Ornamental)..B

Pietsch, Ferd., 619 Cedar (Architectural; Ornamental) ....B

Skobes Bros., 955 30th (Architectural; Ornamental) ....B

Thomas Furnace Co. (Foundry Pig) ....AA

Western Malleable & Grey Iron Mfg. Co. (Malleable) ....B

Wisconsin Bridge & Iron Co. Pabst Bldg. (Architectural; Ornamental)...AA

Worden-Allen Co., P. Wash. Rd. (Architectural; Ornamental) ....A

WIS.—Waukesha

Waukesha Sheet Steel Co. (Galv. Sheet) ....A

IRONERS

See also **Machinery; Laundry**

ILL.—Chicago

Sinclair Laundry Co., 60 N. Clinton (Collar)....X

Steel Roll Machine Co., 830 Canal (Collar; Cuff; Shirt) ....F

MASS.—Boston

Empire Laundry Machinery Co. (Collar; Cuff; Shirt) C

N. Y.—Rochester

Hagen Co., A. T. (Collar; Cuff) ....AA

N. Y.—Troy

Adams Laundry Machinery Co. (Collar; Cuffs; Shirt) ....B

Troy Laundry Machine Co. (Cape; Collar; Cuff; Shirt) ....AA

OHIO—Cincinnati

Amer. Laundry Machinery Co. (Cape Collar; Collar; Cuff; Shirt) ....AA

PA.—Columbia

Wilson Laundry Machinery Co. (Collar; Cuff) ......A

IRONS

See also **Hardware; Carriage.**

CONN.—Derby

Howe Mfg. Co. (Curling).A

CONN.—Middletown

Wilcox, Crittenden & Co. (Calking) ....A

CONN.—Mt. Carmel

Woodruff & Sons, Walter W. ((Carriage; Wagon; also Whiffletree)......A

CONN.—New Britain

Russell & Erwin Mfg. Co. (Sash Cord) ......AAAA

Stanley, Rule & Level Co. (Plane; Sash Cord).AAA

Stanley Wks. (Corner; Brace) ....AAA

Union Mfg. Co. (Sash Cord) ....AA

CONN.—New Haven

Cowles & Co., C. (Vehicle Corner; Whiffletree) ...A

English & Mersich Co., 70 Crown (Corner; Brace; Carriage; Wagon Whiffletree) ....B

Sargent & Co. (Corner; Brace; Sash Cord) .AAAA

Seward & Son, M. (Vehicle Gear) ....A

CONN.—Pine Meadow

Chapin-Stevens Co. (Plane) ....A

CONN.—Southington

Peck, Stow & Wilcox Co. (Sash Cord) ......AAAA

CONN.—Stamford

Stamford Foundry Co.

IRONS (Con.)
(Hawsing) ....A
CONN.—Wallingford
Wallace & Sons Mfg. Co.,
R. (Curling) ......AAAA
GA.—Columbus
Southern Plow Co. (Dog)
AA
ILL.—Aurora
Amer. Well Wks. (Rig) AA
Richards Mfg. Co. (Corner;
Brace) ....B
Richard & Sencenbaugh
Mfg. Co. (Corner; Brace)
B
Wilcox Mfg. Co. (Corner;
Brace) ....B
ILL.—Carpentersville
Illinois Iron & Bolt Co.
(Tuyere; Sad; Tailors)
AA
ILL.—Chicago
Braumoeller & Son, H. V.
(Sash Cord) ....B
Cassaday-Fairbank Mfg. Co.
(Curling) C
Illinois Malleable Iron Co.
(Sad; Laundry; etc.)
AAAA
Nicol & Co. (Crimping;
Curling; Pinching) ....D
ILL.—Decatur
Mueller Mfg. Co. (Calking)
AAA
ILL.—Downer's Grove
Dicke Tool Co. (Croner) .C
ILL.—Freeport
Arcade Mfg. Co. (Curling;
Pinching; Tuyere) .....A
Stover Mfg. Go. (Sad;
Laundry, etc) ....AA
ILL.—Geneva
Howell Co., W. H. (Pol-
ishing Sad).............B
ILL.—Harvey
Austin Mfg. Co., F. C.
(Rig) ....AAA
ILL.—Ottawa
Amer. Hdw. Mfg. Co.
(Corner; Brace) C
ILL.—Rockford
Sovereign Co., C. E.
(End Gate) C
Weyburn Co. (Tuyere) ...C
ILL.—Sterling
National Mfg. Co. (Corner;
Brace) C
IOWA—Fairfield
Louden Machinery Co.
(Hay Rack) C
KANS.—Fort Scott
Fort Scott Fdry. & Machine
Co. (Rig) ....H
KY.—Newport
Higgin Mfg. Co. (Carriage;
Wagon) ....A
MAINE—Portland
Lang Co., E. M. (Capping)
C
MD.—Baltimore
Nat'l Supply Co., 7 W.
Lombard (Corner; Brace;
Dog; Hanger; Wall) ...B
MASS.—Boston
Boston Bolt Co., 33 Pur-
case (Wall) C
Dame, Stoddard Co. (Bur-
nishing; Pinking) ....A
Jones & Co., Melville D.
(Rubber Horse Mender) .G
MASS.—Brocton
Snell & Atherton (Edge
Setter) C
MASS.—Fiskdale
Snell Mfg. Co. (Plane) ..B
Drew & Co., C. (Clakings;
Hawsing) C
MASS.—Lowell
New England Shuttle Co.,
64 Leverett, (Shuttle) ..X
MASS.—Millbury
Buck, Charles (Plane) ....B
Buck Bros. (Plane) ....A
MASS.—North Easton
New England Specialty Co.
(Plane) ....F
MASS.—West Mansfield
Richardson & Bottomley
(Shuttle) ....D
MASS.—Wilkinsville
Marble & Co., E. W.
(Shuttle) X

IRONS (Con.)
MASS.—Worcester
Smith & Co., Thos. (Dog) .C
Wire Goods Co. (Sash
Cord) ....A
MICH.—Detroit
Amer. Electric Heater Co.
(Elec.; Hat; Heating
Soldering) ....B
Anderson & Sons, W. H.
(Calking; Branding) ...C
Bolles Iron & Wire Wks.
(Bridle) X
Michigan Bolt & Nut Works
(Pole Step) ....AA
Wilson Carriage Co., C. R.
(Vehicle Gear).........F
MICH.—Dowagiac
Farr, Willie M. (Carriage;
Wagon) C
MICH.—Jackson
Hovey, A. N. (Store
Shelving) ....D
MINN.—Minneapolis
Fawkes Mfg. Co. (Sad;
Laundry, etc.).........E
MO.—Macon
Patton, J| W. (Store
Shelving) ....B
MO.—St. Louis
Kupferele, Jno. C. (Rub;
Sad; Laundry; Tuyere)
AA
Pleuger & Henger Mfg. Co.
(Dog; Sad; Laundry;
Tuyere) ....A
N. J.—Boonton
Lincoln Iron Wks. (Bridle)
B
N. J.—Elizabeth
Braunsdorf-Mueller Co.
(Calking; Binding)....D
N. J.—Newark
Bliss & Drake (Sad; Cold
Hand Sad; Laundry; Pol-
ishing; Tailors')........A
Johnson, William (Pinking)
D
Kraeuter & Co. (Pinking)
X
Osborne & Co., C. S.
(Pinching; Pinking)....B
Strieby & Foote Co.
(Carriage; Wagon).....B
N. Y.—Auburn
Clapp Mfg. Co., E. D.
(Carriage; Wagon also
Gear) ....B
N. Y.—Brooklyn
Hauck & Son, Chas. J.
(Curling) ....B
Williams & Co., J. H.
(Golf) ....AA
N. Y.—Buffalo
Forsyth Mfg. Co. (Carriage;
Wagon) C
Howard Iron Wks.
(Forming) ....A
Niagara Machine & Tool
Wks. (Capping) ....A
Pratt & Letchworth Co.
(Corner; Brace; Carriage;
Wagon; Lamp; Whiffle-
tree) ....AAA
Shepard & Co., Sidney
(Fluting) ....AAAA
White & Co., L. & I. J.
(Calking; Plane).......A
N. Y.—Ithaca
Williams Bros. (Rig) .AA
N. Y.—Manlius
Chaney & Son, S.
(Stanchion) ....A
N. Y.—Medina
Swett Iron Wks., A. L.
(Tuyere) ....A
N. Y.—Mount Morris
Genesee Valley Mfg Co.
(Sad; Tailors')........B
New York City
Diamond, Thomas,
(Bridle) ....A
Fulton Rubber Type, Ink,
& Pad Mfg. Co., 31
Frankfort (Branding)...D
Hadaway Electric Heating
Co., 136 Liberty (Elec-
tric Laundry)..........D
Ness, Jr., Geo. M.
(Branding) ....H
Tiebout, W. & J., 118
Chambers (Calking; Cor-
ner; Brace; Grappling) .B

IRONS (Con.)

Tower & Lyon Co. (Pinking; Sash Cord).........B

Troy Laundry Machinery Co. (Sad)............AA

N. Y.—Rochester

Puttman Mfg. Co. (Sash Cord; Sash Ribbon; Wire) ....B

Streeter & Co., N. R. (Sad; Cold Handle Polishing; Tailors'; Flating ....A

N. Y.—Seneca Falls

Knight & Son, H. W. (Branding) C

Rumsey & Co., Ltd. (Revolving Clothes Dryer) . A

N. Y.—Syracuse

Syracuse Malleable Iron Wks. (Carriage; Wagon) ....A

N. Y.—Troy

Empire Forge Co. (Sash Cord) ....F

N. Y.—Watervliet

Covert Mfg. Co. (Balling) . A

OHIO—Akron

Akron-Selle Co. (Carriages; Wagon, also End Gate..A

OHIO—Ashtabula

Barber Mfg. Co. (Tuyere) C

OHIO—Cincinnati

Tatum Co., Sam'l C. (Sad) ....B

OHIO—Cleveland

Cleveland Hardware Co. (Carriages; Wagon)...AA

Eberhard Mfg. Co. (Vehicle Gear) ....AA

Federal Mfg. Co. (Curling) ....AAAA

OHIO—Columbus

Ohio Tool Co. (Plane)...AA

OHIO—Hamilton

Kahn & Bros., F. & L. (Waffle) ....A

OHIO—Indiana

Indiana Foundry Co. (Blacksmith's Tuyere) . . D

OHIO—New Lexington

Star Mfg. Co. (Car).....B

OHIO—Plymouth

Root Brost Co. (Tuyere) . B

OHIO—Ravenna

Williams, A. C. (Sad; Laundry, etc.).........A

OHIO—Salem

Silver Mfg. Co. (Tuyere) ....AA

OHIO—Sandusky ..

Sandusky Tool Co. (Plane) ....A

OHIO—Sidney

Wagner Mfg. Co. (Tuyere) ....A

OHIO—Toledo

Nagel Electric Co., W. G. (Cable) ....B

PA—Allegheny

McKinney Mfg. Co. (Corner; Brace).........AAA

PA.—Atglen

Chalfant Hdw. Co. (Druggists; Cold Handle; Gas Heating Sad; Laundry; Polishing Sad; Tailors'; Hat Brim)...........X

PA.—Erie

Erie Malleable Iron Co. (Carriages; Wagon)...AA

Griswold Mfg. Co. (Waffle) ....A

PA.—Harrisburg

Hicox Mfg. Co., W. C. (Forming) ....AA

PA.—Lebanon

Amer. Iron & Steel Mfg. Co. (Dog; Hanger; Wall) ....AAAA

PA.—Philadelphia

Berger Bros. Co. (Snow Shoe) ....A

Enterprise Mfg. Co. (Cold Handle Sad) ......AAAA

Hill Mfg. Co., B. B. (Branding) ....B

Merritt & Co., 1024 Ridge Ave (Hanger).........B

Paxson Co., J. W. (Tuyere) ....AA

Quint's Sons, S. H. (Branding) ....B

IRONS (Con.)

Stortz & Son, Jno., 210 Vine (Calking; Burling) ....E

Woodason, Thomas (Rubber Hose Mender) ....F

PA.—Pittsburg

Oliver Iron & Steel Co. (Dog; Hanger; Well) ....AAA

Riter-Conley Mfg. Co (Tuyere) ....AAA

PA.—Reading

Penn Hdw. Co., (Porch Post Sash Cord) ....AA

Reading Hdw. Co. (Sash Cord; Sad; Waffle) AAAA

PA.—Sharon

Sharon Boiler Wks., Ltd (Car) ....A

PA.—Wilkesbarre

Vulcan Iron Wks. (Car) ....AAAA

PA.—Wrightsville

Wrightsville Hdw. Co (Polishing; Porch; Post; Sad) ....B

R. I—Pawtucket

Luther & Co., C. A. (Curling; Pinching).....C

R. I—Providence

Amer. Supply Co. (Burling) ....AA

New England Butt. Co. (Sad; Laundry; Polishing Sad) ....AA

TENN.—South Pittsburg ..

Blacklock Foundry (Sad; Laundry, etc.; Waffle) . . C

VA.—Norfolk

Whitehurst & Co., R. W. (Dog) ....B

VA.—Richmond

Old Dominion Iron & Nail Wks. (Corner; Brace; Wall) ....AA

WIS.—Milwaukee

Western Malleable & Grey Iron. Mfg. Co. (Chair; Stool) ....B

WIS.—Racine

Racine Malleable & Wrought Iron Co (Whiffletree) . . A

WIS.—Sheboygan

Globe Foundry & Machine Co. (Chair) C

WIS.—South Milwaukee

Stowell Mfg. & Fdy. Co. (Chair; Stool)..........A

WIS.—Waukeska

Ladewig W. E. (Blind) . . E

ISINGLASS

ILL.—Chicago

Armour Glue Wks . .AAAA

MASS.—Boston

Haskins, Leander M., 10 Long Whf. (for Brewers) ....A

Howe & French Isinglass Co., 147 High ....A

MASS.—Gloucester

Dodd & Co., Andrews W. ....B

Gloucester Isinglass & Glue Glue Co. ....D

MASS.—Ipswich

Norwood, C. J...........H

MASS.—Rockport

Cape Ann Isinglass Co. ....AAAA

N. Y.—New York City

Cooper's Glue Factory, Peter ....AA

Heyman & Fischer C

Schwenker, W. M........B

Zinsser & Co., W. 197 William .:..........A

WIS.—Milwaukee

Kiewert Co., Chas. L.....A

IVORY GOODS

CONN.—Chester

Bates, C. J..............D

CONN.—Ivoryton

Comstock, Cheney & Co., (Cut Ivory)..........AA

N. Y.—New York City

Baumann, A. O., 112 University Pl...........D

Deitsch Bros., 7 E. 17th . X

Kapps' Sons Ivory Co., A.

IVORY GOODS (Con.)

J., 255 4th Av.........G
Seiwyn Importing Co., 18 E.
  17th ....H
Shardlow, Joseph, 116 Ful-
  ton (Boxes)...........D
Willenert, M., 206 Centre
  H

PA.—Philadelphia
Harvey & Watts Co......A
Randolph, Wm. E., 243
  Arch ....E

JACKERS

LA.—Shreveport
Henderson Iron Wks., W.
  R. (Log)...........AA
MICH.—Bay City
Garland Co., M. (Log)...C
MICH. Detroit
Buhl Malleable Co. (Log)
  A
MICH.—Menominee
Prescott Co. (Log).......A
MICH.—Saginaw
Wickes Bros. (Log)...AAA
TENN.—Chattanooga
Wheland Machine Wks.
  (Log) ....A
VT.—Montpelier
Lane Mfg. Co. (Log).....A

JACKETS

See also Clothing; Mens.

MICH—Detroit
Ryan Bros. Knitting Co.
  (Cardigan) C
MICH.—Grand Rapids
Mich. Barrel Co. (Can)..A'
N. Y.—Brooklyn
Shimdelman, Samuel
  (Cardigan) C
Standard Knitting Mills..D
N. Y.—Little Falls
Burrell & Co., D. H.
  (Milk Can) ....AAAA
N. Y.—Long Island City
Lane & De Groot Co.
  (Cork) ....D
New York City.
Goodyear's India Rubber
  Mfg. Co. (Surf)..AAAA
Gutta Percha & Rubber Mfg.
  Co. (Hose)......AAAA
Hatch & Co., 92 Murray
  (Can) ....F
Levy-Stiefel Co. (Cardigan)
  C
Wertheimer & Hollander,
  159 Greene, ((Cardigan)
  B
N. Y.—Utica
Albin Knit Goods Co.
  (Cardigan) ....D
Olimpian Knit Goods Co.
  (Cardigan) C
OHIO—Clark
Wuest, Edw. (Cardigan) D
PA.—Hawley
U. S. Knitting Mills Co.
  (Cardigan) ....D
PA.—Honesdale
American Knitting Co.
  (Cardigan) ....D
Maple City Knitting Mills
  (Cardigan) ....D
PA.—Philadelphia
Blickle's Sons, Jno.
  (Cardigan) ....D
Braun, H. (Knit).......B
Feld & Co. (Cardigan)...B
Greaves, Thomas (Cardi-
  gan) ....B
Gutsche, R. (Cardigan)...C
Koch, Justus (Cardigan).B
Mottram, Thos.' (Cardigan)
  D
Peberdy & Sons, Geo.
  (Cardigan) ....B
Riter & Conley Mfg. Co.
  (Furnace Shell) ...AAA
PA.—Pittsburg
Armstrong Cork Co. (Cork)
  AAAA
R. I—Providence
Allen Fire Dept. Supply Co.
  (Hose) ....D
WIS.—Keil
Keil Woodenware Co
  (Oil Can).............B

JACKS

CAL.—San Francisco
Garratt & Co., W. T.
  (Log) ....AA
CONN.—Higganum
Cutaway Harrow Co. (Car-
  riage; Wagon).........X
CONN.—Mt. Carmel
Woodruff & Sons, Walter
  W. (Wagon)..........A
CONN.—New Haven
Mc Lagon Foundry Co.
  (Screw) C
CONN.—New London
New London Vise Wks.
  (Lifting; Screw).......E
CONN.—Southington
Peck, Stow & Wilcox Co.
  (Screw; Boot) ....AAAA
DEL.—Wilmington
Henderers Sons, A. L.
  (Hydraulic; Lifting;
  Track) ....E
GA.—Augusta
Lombard Iron Wks. & Sup-
  ply Co. (Screw).......A
ILL.—Batavia
Appleton Mfg. Co. (Power;
  Speed) ....A
Challenge Wind Mill &
  Feed Mill Co .....AAA
U. S. Wind Engine & Pump
  Co. (Horse Power & Pow-
  er ....AA
ILL.—Belleville ....
Belleville Pump & Skein
  Wks. (House Moving;
  Locomotive; Rachet;
  Screw; Track).......AA
ILL.—Carpentersville
Ill. Iron & Bolt Co. (House
  Moving; Locomotive;
  Screw; Track; Car; Car-
  rying; Tripod; Wagon)
  AA
ILL.—Chicago
Armstrong Bros. Tool Co.
  (Planer) ....B
Barbee Wire & Iron Wks.
  (Wagon) ....B
Brown Bros. Mfg. Co., cor
  Jackson (Screw; House
  Moving) ....B
Brunner & Lay, 133 W.
  Polk, (Stone).........C
Chicago Pneumatic Tool
  Co., Fischer Bldg. (Pneu-
  matic) ....AAAA
Fairbanks , Morse & Co.
  (Hydraulic & Track)
  AAAA
Klemm, E. R., 103 W.
  Monroe (Lifting; Stone).E
Lovejoy, T. H., 90 Ohio
  (Screw) ....D
Morden Frog & Crossing
  Wks., The Rookery
  (Track) ....A
Nicol & Co. (Boot).....D
O'Leary & Son Co.,A. J.,
  130 Lake (Stone)......B
Pettibone, Milliken & Co.,
  204 Dearborn (Track)
  AAAA
Railway Appliances Co.
  (Railway Track).......A
Schomer Henry (Wagon) D
Templeton Kenley & Co.,
  The Rookery (Car)...D
Wallace Supply Co., 169
  Jackson Boul. (Hyraulic)
  C
ILL.—Freeport
Arcade Mfg. Co. (Wagon
  Lever) ....A
ILL.—Harvey
Buda Fdy. & Mfg. Co.
  (Track; Screw) .....AA
ILL.—Joliet
Joliet Mfg. Co. (Power) A
ILL.—Ottawa
Porter Co., J. E. (Carriage;
  Wagon) ....A
ILL.—Sandwich
Sandwich Mfg. Co. (Power;
  Speed) ....AA
IND.—Anderson
Anderson Pole & Shaft Co.
  (Lever) ....E
Buckeye Mfg. Co. (Wagon)
  AA
Wooley Fdy & Machine Co.
  (House Moving) .....B

JACKS (Con.)

IND.—Columbus
Rewes & Co. (Lifting)
.................AAAA

IND.—Elkhart
Elkhart Frog & Crossing
Wks. (Track) C

IND.—Kendallville
Flint & Walling Mfg. Co.
(Horse Power Pumping)
.....................AA

IND.—South Bend
Gilchrist Bros. (Log)..,..X

KANS.—Fort Scott
Fort Scott Fdy & Machine
Co. (Horse Power Pump-
ing) ....H

MAINE—Gardiner
Newell & Co., J. F. (Lifting; Screw) ....H

MD.—Hagerstown
Hagerstown Fdy Co. (Lift-
ing) ....H

MASS.—Athol
Starrett Co., L. S. (Screw)
.......................A

MASS.—Barre
Allen & Co., C. G. (Wagon)
.......................D

MASS.—Boston
Ames Plow Co. (Wagon)
.....................AAAA
Boston & Lockport Block
Co. (Wagon; Lever) A
Fifield Shoe Machinery Co.
(Pegging) ....D
Harvey, H. H., 608 Atlan-
tic Av. (House Moving;
Lifting; Screw; Stone)
.......................D
Norton, A. O., 167 Oliver
(Ball Bearing Car; Re-
placing; Ball Bearing
Screw Lifting; Screw
Ratchet; Sure Drop
Track; Carrying; Loco-
motive Traversing; Le-
ver; Track; Carriage;
Wagon) ....AA
Prescott, Edwin (Wagon)
.......................E
Whitcher & Co., Frank W.
(Boot) ....A

MASS.—Canton
Kinsley Iron & Machine Co.
(House Moving; Screw)
.....................AA

MASS.—Chicopee Falls
Belcher & Taylor Agricul-
tural Tool Co. (Wagon)
.......................A

MASS.—Lowell...
Turner, Jno. D. (Locomo-
tive; Log; Railroad Rat-
chet; Screw; Traveling)

MASS.—Millers Falls
Millers Falls Co. (Screw;
Carriage; Wagon) ...AA

MASS.—Springfield
Springfield Foundry Co.
(Car; Screw; Level)..A

MICH.—Bay City
Garland Co., M. (Log)..C

MICH.—Detroit
Anderson & Sons, W. H.
(Hydraulic; Lifting;
Stone) C
Buhl Malleable Co., Wight
& Adair (Log) ....A
Northern Engineering Wks.
(Pneumatic) ....A

MICH.—Galien
Montross, Richard W. (Wa-
gon) ....B

MICH.—Kalamazoo
Hill & Co., W. E. (Log) B
Kalamazoo Railway Supply
Co. (Hydraulic; Lifting;
Track) ....B
Merrill-Stevens Mfg. Co.
(Automobile; Car) ....D

MICH.—Lansing
Lansing Wheelbarrow Co.
(Wagon) ....AAA

MICH.—Monroe
Wilder Strong Implement
Co. (Speed) ....B

MICH.—Petoskey
Burnett Fdy. & Machine
Wks. (Log) X

MICH.—Saginaw
Wickes Bros. (Log)...AAA

JACKS (Con.)

MICH.—Vicksburg
Vicksburg Mfg. Co. (Car
Lifting) ....D

MINN.—Minneapolis
Howell & Co., R. R. (Lift-
ing; Screw; Horse Power)
.......................B
Minneapolis Steel & Mchy.
Co. (Log) ....AAA

MO.—St. Louis
Pieuger & Henger Mfg. Co.
(Boot) ....A

N. J.—Hightstown
Peppler, Thomas (Wagon)
.......................D
Shangle, Jno. R. (Wagon)
.......................C

N. J.—Newark
Bray Mfg. Co. (Adjustable
Lifting) X
Borroughs, Chas. Co., 141
Commerce (Hydraulic) X
Currier & Sons, Cyrus (Hy-
draulic) ....AA
Jersey Brake Co. (Carriage)
.......................X
Sacks Louis (Boot)......A
Standard Machine Wks.
(Lifting) X

N. Y.—Albany
Kelly Mfg. Co., L. J.
(Stone) ....F

N. Y.—Brooklyn
Taylor & Co., 415 Dreggs
Av. (Screw; Lever)....D

N. Y.—Buffalo..
Buffalo Last Wks. (Nailing
Pegging; Boot) ....B
Contractors Plant Mfg. Co.
(Lifting; Screw) .....B
Lazier, A. A. (Combination
Pumping) ....E

N. Y.—Medina
Swett Iron Wks., A. L.
(Screw) ....A

N. Y.—Munnsville
Munnsville Plow Co.
(Screw) ....B

New York City
Dudgeon, Richard (Hydrau-
lic; Screw)...........A
Fairbanks Co., 416 Broome
(Hydraulic; Screw) AAAA
Krieg & Co., J. K. (Nail-
ing; Heeling) ....B
McCoy & Co., Jos. F., 157
Chambers (Hydraulic;
Lifting; Screw).......B
Niles-Bement-Pond Co., 136
Liberty (Screw)...AAAA
Reilley Bros. (Painters)..D
Russell & Erwin Mfg. Co.,
3 Chambers ...AAAA
Sargent & Co., 151 Leonard
(Boot; Screw) ...AAAA
Smith & Hemenway Co.,
296 B'way (Ball Bearing)
.......................B
Urquhart's Son Co., John
S., 46 Cortlandt (Screw)
.......................B
Watson-Stillman Co., 210 E.
43d (Hydraulic; Hydro-
static; Lever; Palling;
Screw) ....A

N. Y.—Norwich
Wheeler, George (Wagon)
.......................G

N. Y.—Palmyra..
Allen, Joseph (Wagon)..D

N. Y.—Poughkeepsie
Lane Bros. Co. (Steel;
Automatic Wagon) ....A

N. Y.—Seneca Falls
Goulds Mfg. Co. (Screw)
.....................AAA
Rumsey & Co., Ltd (Screw;
Horse Power Pumping) A

N. Y.—Syracuse
Stearns & Co., E. C.
(Screw) ....AA

N. Y.—Utica
Eureka Mower Co. (Steel;
Malleable Iron Wagon) A

N. Y.—Watertown
Bagley & Sewell Co. (Le-
ver) ....AA

N. Y.—Watervliet
Covert Mfg. Co. (Wagon;
Steel Wagon) ....A
Tilley, John S. (Scaffold-
ing) ....F

JACKS (Con.)

OHIO—Ashland
Myers & Bros., F. E. (Combination Pumping)
................AAAA

OHIO—Ashtabula
Barber Mfg. Co. (Screw; Wagon)................C

OHIO—Chillicothe
Deweese, F. M. (Lifting)
................X
Schwartz & Son, M. (Lifting)................F

OHIO—Cincinnati
Blymer Iron Works Co. (Speed)................B
Hauser, Brenner & Fath Co. (Hop)................B
Lane & Bradley Co. (Log)
................B
McKeown, H. J., 612 N. Front (Stone)................E

OHIO—Cleveland
City Machine Co. (Hydraulic)................B
Cleveland City Forge & Iron Co. (Screw)....AA
Garry Iron & Steel Co. (Pneumatic Car)......A

OHIO—Columbus
Jeffrey Mfg. Co. (Log)
................AAAA

OHIO—Dayton
Boyer & Railroad Mfg. Co. (Lifting; Lever; Ratchet Screw; Track)........C
Dayton Malleable Iron Co. (Lever)............AAA
Joyce-Cridland Co. (House Moving; Hydraulic; Gear Levered Lifting; Log; Ratchet; Screw; Stone; Track; Traveling; Car; Locomotive; Traversing Lever; Pulling)........B

OHIO—Defiance
Defiance Machine Wks. (Screw)................A

OHIO—Fremont
Lehr Agricultural Co. (Horse Power Pumping)
....

OHIO—Galena
Hughes & Smythe (Wagon)
................C

OHIO—Louisville
Buckeye Jack Mfg. Co. (Hoisting)............D

OHIO—Plymouth
Root Bros. Co. (Boot)....B

OHIO—Salem
Deming Co. (Horse Power Pumping)............AA
Silver Mfg. Co. (Horse Power; Wagon)......AA

OHIO—Toledo
Milburn Wagon Co. (Wagon)................AAA

PA.—Allegheny
Duff Mfg. Co., 405 Marion Av. (Lifting; Log; Differential Screw Stone Track; Power)........A

PA.—Atglen
Chalfont Hdw. Co. (Boot)
................X

PA.—Bellefonte
Howard Iron & Tool Co. (Wagon)................B

PA.—Butler
Masseth & Black (Gas Pumping)............B

PA.—Elizabethtown
Brick's Sons, A. (Wagon)
................A

PA.—Emigsville
Nat'l Tubular Axle Co. (Wagon)................D

PA.—Erie
Stearns Mfg. Co. (Log) B

PA.—Glen Rock
Sheffer, B. F. (Lifting)..D

PA.—Philadelphia
Bonney Vise & Tool Wks.. 3015 Chestnut (Lever) C
Brell Co., J. G. (Hydraulic)
................AAAA
Dienelt & Eisenhardt. 1308 N. Howard (Hydraulic)
................A
Hall Son & Co.. Amos H. (Hop)................C

JACKS (Con.)

Justice & Co., Philip S., 14 N. 5th (Hydraulic; Ratchet; Screw; Track)...D
Link-Belt Engineering Co. (Log)................AA
Pedrick & Ayer Co., 1001 Hamilton (Screw)....A
Riehle Bros. Testing Mach. Co. 1424 N. 9th (Robie; Ball Bearing; Screw; Stone)................B

PA.—Pittsburg
Pittsburg Tool & Drop Forge Co., Arrott Bldg. (Track)................D
Standard Scale & Supply Co. (Log)................X
Verona Tool Wks. (Track; Power)................A

PA.—Reading
Reading Hdw. Co. (Boot)
................AAAA

PA.—South Bethlehem
Bethlehem Fdy. & Mach. Co. (Hydraulic; Machinist)................C
Bethlehem Steel Co. (Hydraulic)........AAAA

PA.—Williamsport
Moliz, Jacob J. (Log)....C

PA.—Wrightsville
Wrightsville Hdw. Co. (Boot)................B

TENN.—Jackson
Southern Engine & Boiler Wks. (Log)........AA

TEXAS—San Antonio
Collins Mfg. Co., F. F. (Horse Power Pumping)
................AA

VT.—Fairhaven
Pelky, W. H. (Lifting; Stone)................E

VT.—Montpelier
Lane Mfg. Co. (Log) ....A

VT.—St. Albans
St. Albans Fdy. & Implement Co. (Wagon).....D

VA.—Norfolk
Whitehouse Co., R. W. (Carriage; Wagon)....B

W. VA.—Huntington
Maxon-Miller Jack Co. (Improved Lever Car; Lever House Moving; Lifting; Lever Locomotive; Log; Track)................F

WIS.—Eau Claire
Phoenix Mfg. Co. (Log) A

WIS.—Evansville
Baker Mfg. Co. (Screw)
................AA

WIS.—Kenosha
Badger Brass Mfg. Co. (Automobile)..........C

WIS.—Milwaukee
Barth Mfg. Co. (Lifting; Screw; Stone; Track; Steel; Wagon)........C
Filer & Stowell Co. (Log)
................AAA

WIS.—Racine
Foster & Williams Mfg. Co. (Wagon)................B
Freeman & Sons Mfg. Co., S. (Horse Power)......A
Racine Malleable & Wrought Iron Co. (Wagon)................A

WIS.—Wausau
Murray Mfg. Co.. D. J. (Iron Frame Log)......A

JACKONETS

See Cotton Goods

JAMS: JELLIES: MARMALADES & PRESERVES

CAL.—Los Angeles
Baker-Heron Mfg.Co. (Preserves), 125 W. 14th..A
Bishop & Co. (Preserves AA
Keppler & Tamm (Preserves)................B
Shaw Preserve Co. (Preserves)................B

CAL.—Redland
Kingsbury, H. P. D. (Pre-

JAMS, JELLIES, ETC.

serves) C
CAL.—San Francisco
Calif. Pack'g. Co., 126 Davis ....A
Loeffler, Jno. (Preserves), 422 5th C
Pacific Coast Syrup Co. (Fr. Butter Jellies), 713 Sansome ....B
Sherwood & Sherwood (Preserves) ....AAA
CAL.—San Jose
Costa Orchard Can Co., L. D. ....A
COLO.—Denver
Beebe-Crauel Pickle Co., 11th & Bayard C
CONN.—Hartford
Fitzgerald, R. M., 44 Mk't B
DEL.—Rising Sun
Farmers' Pres. Co. (Preserves) C
FLA.—Key West
Granday & Co., A. (Guava Jelly) C
ILL.—Chicago
Berry-Maybrum Co., 59 Larrabee C
Curtice Bros. Co. (Preserves) ....AA
Durand & Casper Co., 153 W. Lake ....AAA
Heinz Co., H. J. (Preserves) AAAA
Heuss-Edler Pres. Co. (Preserves) ....B
Manierre-Yoe Syrup Co. 30 River (Preserves)...B
Reber Preserving Co.....C
Reid Murdoch & Co. (Preserves), Lake & Mk't AAAA
Sherman Bros. & Co. (Preserves) ....A
Snider Pres. Co., T. A. (Br. Cinn. O.) (Preserves)..A
IND.—Brookville
Brookville Mfg. Co. (Preserves) ....B
Ind. Crescent Preserving Co. (Schnull & Co. Prop.) (Pres.) ....AAAA
IND.—Lafayette
Heinz Co. (Preserves)....A
IOWA—Davenport
Glucose Sugar Ref'g Co. AAAA
IOWA—Glenwood
New Glenwood Can Co. (Preserves) C
KANS.—Topeka
Kuehne Pres. Co., O. (Preserves) ....B
KY.—Louisville
Goodwin Preserving Co. (Preserves), 307 9th...A
KY.—Milldale..
Weiler Co., J. (Preserves) A
KY.—Owensboro
Blue Grass Canning Co. (Preserves) ....B
LA.—New Orleans
Barataria Can. Co. (Preserves) 610 St. Peters ..A
Dunbar's Sons, G. W., (Preserves) ....G
MAINE—Portland
Pettengill Co., E. D. (Preserves) ....B
MD.—Baltimore
Fruit Puddine Co., 13 Balderston ....A
Gibbs Preserving Co. (Jellies) Apple; Butter; Preserves) ....AA
Numsen & Sons, W. (Pres.) 18 Light ....A
Van Lil Preserving Co. (Pres.) 108 Concord ....B
N. Y.—Rochester
Curtice Bros. Co. (Preserves) ....AA
N. Y.—Webster
Webster Preserving Co...B
OHIO—Cincinnati
Heinz Co., H. J. (Pres.) 918 Sycamore ......AAAA
Ritter Conserve Co., P. J. (Pres.) 32 W. Court ...A
Snider Preserve Co., T. A.

JAMS, JELLIES, ETC.

(Pres.), 324 E. 2d....A
Waller Co., J. (Pres.)....A
—Cleveland
Jankowsky, Frank (M. Jellies) 1284 B'way ...B
OHIO—Creston
Lutz & Schramm Co. ....AA
OHIO—Marietta
Crystal Ice & Pres. Co. (Preserves) C
OHIO—Wooster
Wooster Preserving Co. (Preserves) ....B
PA.—Allegheny
Criukshank Bros. Co (Pres.) ....B
Lutz & Schramm Co. (Preserves) ....AA
Vogel Co., Frank (Preserves) C
PA.—Erie..
Werner Vin. & Pickl'g Co. (Preserves) C
PA.—Fairview
Hauck, Jos. H. (Fairview Creamery) C
PA.—McKean
Hauck, Jos. H. (McKean Creamery) C
PA.—North East
North East Pres. Wks. (Fink & McLaughlin) (Pres.) ....A
PA.—Philadelphia
Amer. Pres. Co. (Preserves) 946 Beach ....A
Ritter Conserve Co., P. J. (Pres.), 2156 E. Dauphin A
PA.—Scranton
Reliable Pres. Co. (Preserves) C
Schroeder, Jno. L. (Preserves) C
PA.—Sterrettania
Hauck, J. H. (Jelly)....C
MASS.—Boston
Johnson & Co., H. A. (Pres.), 222 State.....A
Knights & Son, A. A. (Pres.), 87 Commercial B
Logan, Johnson & Co. (Confec. Sup.)..........A
Middeby Jr., Jos. (Pres.), 201 State ....A
Sherman Mfg. Co., R. I. (Pres.) C
MASS.—Worcester
Blodgett Co., W. H. (Pres.) ....B
MICH.—Detroit
Vaughn Co., Wm. W. (Pres.), 316 River.....B
William Bros. Co. (Pres.) A
MICH.—Grand Rapids
Fallas, Edwin (Pres.)....C
MICH.—Mill Grove..
Williams Bros. Co. (Br. Detroit) (Pres.) ......A
MICH.—Shelby
Mikesell Co., J..........B
MICH.—West Bay City
Bentel Co., R. (Pres.)..A
MINN.—Lake City
Minn. Pickl'g & Preserving Co. (Pres.) ....A
Minn. Bonk Syrup Co. (Pres.) ....B
MO.—Kansas City
Bliss Syrup Ref'g. Co. (Pres.) ....B
MO.—Erie
Erie Preserving Co. (Preserves) ....AA
MO.—St. Louis
Dodson-Braun Mfg. Co. (Pres.) 3d & Cedar..AA
St. Louis Syrup & Pres. Co. (Pres.) Collins & Dickson ....AA
NEB.—Nebraska City
Otoi Pres. Co. (Pres.)....B
NEB.—Omaha
Farrell & Co. (Preserves), 223 S. 8th...........A
N. J.—Camden
Campbell Pres. Co., Jos. (Pres.) ....AA
N. J.—Greenwich
Brady Co., J. F..........C

JAMS, JELLIES, ETC.

N. Y.—Buffalo
Buffalo Pres. Co. (Preserves) ....A
Erie Pres. Co. (Pres.)...941
  W. Ferry........AAAA
Heinz Co., H. J. (Pres.
  Butter) ....AAAA
United States Canning Co.
  (Preserves) ....AA

N. Y.—Kenwood
Oneida Community (Ltd.)
  ....AAA

N. Y.—Le Roy
Genesee Pure Food Co.
  (Jelly Powder)........A

N. Y.—Lockport
Niagara Mfg. & Merc. Co.
  (Pres.)...............C
Niagara Pres'g Co. (Pres.)
  ....AA

New York City
Ams, Max, 372 Greenwich
  (Pres.) ....AA
Anthony Co., H. M. (Pres.)
  ....AA
Booth & Co., A. (Br.)
  (Pres.) ....AAAA
Cobb Preserving Co. (Pres.)
 C
Cohen & Co., W. H. (Pres.)
 C
Cudahy Pack'g. Co. (Pres.)
  ....AAAA
Curtice Bros. Co. (Pres.)
  ....AA
Erie Pres. Co. (Br.) (Fr.
  Butter), 107 Hudson AA
Gordon & Dilworth (Pres.),
  563 Greenwich ....A
Heartwig & Bennett (Pres.)
  ....A
Heinz Co., H. J. (Br.)
  Allegheny, Pa.) (Pres.)
  206 Spring.......AAAA
Israel & Bros., C. (Pres.),
  490 Canal ....B
Kemp, Day & Co., (Pres.),
  73 Hudson ....AA
Kress & Co., A. (Pres.) B
Oneida Community (Ltd.).
  413 B'way.........AAA
Ritter Conserve Co., P. J.
  (Br.) 448 Washn......A
Seeman Bros. (Pres.) ....A
Seville Pack'g Co. (Pres.)
  202 Franklin ....A
Waeber & Lea (Pres.)..B
Williams Bros. Co. (Pres.)
  105 Hudson ....A

R. I.—Central Falls
Fournier & Schiller Co.
  (Pres.) C

TEXAS—Dallas
Hughes Bros. Mfg. Co...A
Kemper & Dodson (Pres.)
 C

VT.—Brattleboro
Brattlebero Jelly Co. (A.
  & C. Jelly) ....B

VT.—Newport
Vermont Pres. Wks. (Preserves) ....A

VA.—Craig City
Penna. Canning Co.
  (Pres.) C

VA.—Springwood
Penna. Canning Co. (Pres.)
 C

W. VA.—Wheeling
Exley, Watkins & Co., 84
  19th (Fr. Butter; Pres,
  &c.) ....B
Flaccus Bros. (Pres.)....A
Flaccus Co., E. C. (Pres.)
 C
McMechen & Son Co., G. K.
  (Pres.) ....A

JAPANS

See also Paints

CAL.—Bakersfield
Jewett-Blodgett Oil Co.
  (Asphalt) X

CAL.—Los Angeles
Densmore-Stabler Refining
  Co. (Asphalt) ....B
Southern Refining Co.
  (Asphalt) ....A

CAL.—San Francisco
Union Oil Co. of California,

JAPANS (Con.)
Mills Mldg. (Asphalt)
  ....AAAA

GA.—Atlanta
Southern Roofing Co.
  (Asphalt) ....D

ILL.—Chicago
Chicago Varnish Co. (Baking) ....AA
Chicago Wood Finishing Co.
  (Asphalt) ....A
Elliott Varnish Co., 155
  Fulton ....F
Ford Mfg. Co., 71 S. Ashland Av. (Asphalt).....B

IND.—South Bend
O'Brien Varnish Co.......A

MD.—Baltimore
MacNeal & Co., Jas. B.,
  34 S. Calvert........B

MICH.—Detroit
Acme White Lead & Color
  Wks. ....AAA

MO.—St. Louis
Asphalt Roofing Co., 808
  Theresa Av. (Asphalt...X
Trinidad Asphalt Mfg. Co.
  (Asphalt) ....A

N. J.—Newark
Anglo-American Varnish
  Co., 55 Johnson ......B
Armitage & Co., Jno. L..X

N. Y.—Brooklyn
Moller & Schumann Co.,
  Marcy & Flushing Avs.
  (Baking) ....A

N. Y.—Buffalo
Buffalo Enamel & Stain Co.,
  Ellicott Sq. ....F
McLennan Paint Co., Ltd.,
  175 Rano (Baking)....AA

New York City
Smith & Co., Edward, 46
  B'way (Asphalt).......A
Standard Varnish Wks., 29
  B'way ....AA

OHIO—Akron
Akron Varnish Co. (Baking)
 X

OHIO—Cleveland
Forest City Paint & Varnish
  Co., Hamilton & Kirkland
  (Baking) ....B
Glidden Varnish Co., Williamson Bldg. ....AA
Star Varnish Co..........E

PA.—Franklin
Riesenman Mfg. Co........B

PA.—Jamestown
Jamestown Paint & Varnish
  Co. ....A

PA.—Philadelphia
Atlantic Drier & Varnish
  Co., S. Swanson & McKean ....B
Barrett Mfg. Co., Land
  Title Bldg. (Asphalt)...
  ....AAAA
French & Co., Saml. H.,
  4th & Callowhill (Asphalt;
  Baking) ....A
Woodhouse, Saml. F......D

PA.—Pittsburg
Globe Asphalt Co. (Asphalt)
 X
Suvdam Co., M. B., 4th &
  Wood (Baking; Asphalt)
  ....A

PA.—Reading
Wilhelm Co., A..........AA

R. I.—Providence
Amer. Enamel Co. (Baking)
  ....B

JARDINIERES

See also Chinaware; Pottery; Glassware.

CONN.—Meriden
Bradley & Hubbard Mfg.
  Co. ....AAAA
Manning, Bowman & Co.
  ....AA

IND.—Evansville
Bockstege Furniture Co...B

MD.—Baltimore
Bennett Pottery Co., Edwin, Central Av. &Canton
  ....A

MASS.—Cambridge
Hews & Co., A. H........A

MASS.—Gardner
Heywood Bros. & Wakefield

JARDINIERES (Con.)

Co. (Rattan) ......AAAA
MASS.—Taunton
Reed & Barton Corpn..AAA
N. J.—Jersey City
American Staturary Co...C
N. J.—Trenton
Maddock & Sons, Thos..AA
Trenton Potteries Co..AAA
OHIO—Sebring
Sebring Pottery Co ....AA
PA.—Allegheny
Pittsburg Lamp, Glass &
Brass Co. ....AAAA
PA.—Philadelphia
Brannen Mfg. Co.......AA
PA.—Reading
Natl. Brass & Iron Wks..A

JARS

See also Glassware; Earthenware; Chinaware; Pottery.

CAL.—San Francisco
Hermetical Closure Co.
(Glass Fruit) ....D
Landsberger Co., J. A.
(Glass Fruit) ....D
Vacuum Jar & Fruit Package Co. (Glass Fruit)..D
CONN.—Meriden
Manning, Bowman & Co.
(Euameled Slop) .....AA
ILL.—Alton
Illinois Glass Co. (Glass
Fruit).............AAAA
ILL.—Bellville
Port Glass Wrks. (Glass
Fruit) ....B
ILL.—Chicago
Chicago Pottery Co. (Earthenware Fruit) C
Morgan & Wright, 333 W.
Lake (Battery Rubber)
AA
Safe Glass Co. (Glass Fruit)
B
ILL.—Monmouth
Weir Pottery Co. (Acid
Proof) ....A
IND.—Anderson
Penna Glass Co. (Glass
Fruit) ....A
IND.—Eaton
Western Flint Glass Co.
(Glass Fruit) C
IND.—Evansville
Sargent Glass Co. (Candy)
B
IND.—Greenfield
Greenfield Fruit Jar & Bottle Co. (Glass Fruit).AAA
IND.—Hartford City
Sneath Glass Co. (Glass
Fruit) ....B
IND.—Indianapolis
Hollweg, Louis (Glass
Fruit) ....AAA
IND.—Marion
Canton Glass Co. (Battery)
AAAA
Marion Fruit Jar & Bottle
Co. (Glass Fruit) ......A
IND.—Muncie
Ball Bros. Glass Mfg. Co.
(Glass Fruit) ....AAAA
IND.—Peru
Peru Electric Mfg. Co.
(Battery) ....A
IND.—Red Key
Red Key Glass Co. (Glass
Fruit) ....B
IND.—Swayzee
Swayzee Glass Co. (Glass
Fruit) ....B
IND.—Terre Haute
Terre Haute Glass Mfg. Co.
(Glass Fruit) ....B
IND.—Upland
Safe Glass Co. (Glass Fruit)
B
Upland Co-Operative Glass
Co. (Glass Fruit) C
IND.—Yorktown
Skillin-Goodin Glass Co.
(Glass).............D
IOWA—Fort Dodge
Fort Dodge Stoneware Co.
(Butter) C
KANS.—Coffeyville
Pionier Flint Glass Co.
(Battery; Glass) C

JARS (Con.)

KY.—Covington
Hemingway Glass Co.
(Battery; Glass; Glass
Fruit) ....A
MASS.—Boston
Smalley & Co., A. G. (Glass
Fruit) C
Swett & Lewis Co. (Leyden)
E
MICH.—Detroit
Victor Jar Co. (Glass) ....E
MO.—St. Louis
Illinois Glass Co. (Battery)
AAAA
St. Louis Stamping Co.
Fibre & Hotel Slop)
AAAA
N. J.—Bridgeton
Cumberland Glass Mfg. Co.
(Battery; Glass Fruit;
Glass Milk) ....A
N. J.—Clayton
Moore Bros. Glass Co.
(Glass Fruit) ......AAA
N. J.—Elmer
Gilchrist Improved Jar Co.
(Glass Fruit) ....D
N. J.—Hoboken
Schimper & Co., Wm. (Cigar; Cigarette) ......AA
N. J.—New Brunswick
Consolidated Fruit Jar Co.
(Glass Fruit; Battery)
AAA
N. J.—Salem
Gayner Glass Wrks. (Battery) ....D
N. J.—Trenton
Egyptian Pottery Co. (Battery) C
N. J.—Woodbury
Woodbury Bottle Wrks.
(Glass Fruit) ....D
N. Y.—Brooklyn
Palmer, F. H., 186 6th Av.
(Glass Fruit) X
N.Y.—Buffalo
Jewitt Mfg. Co., Jno. C.
(Tin Slop) ....AA
Shepard & Co., Sidney (Tin
Slop) ....AAAA
Wright & Co., R. G. (Glass
Fruit) ....AA
N. Y.—Lockport
Mansfield Glass Works.
(Glass Fruit) ....A
New York City
Amer. Hard Rubber Co., 11
Mercer (Battery) ..AAAA
Brookfield Glass Co., 220
B'way (Battery) ......A
Central Stamping Co. (Tin
Slop) ....AA
Consolidated Fruit Jar Co.
(Glass Fruit; Battery)
AAA
Cordley & Hayes (Fibre
Slop) ....A
Lalance & Grosjean Mfg.
Co. (Enameled Slop)
AAAA
Stoutenborough, X. (Tin
Slop) ....A
Vulcanized Rubber Co. (Battery Rubber) ....A
Whitall Tatum Co., 46 Barclay (Battery) ....AAAA
Whitman, A. V. (Glass
Milk) ....B
N. Y.—Poughkeepsie
Poughkeepsie Glass Wrks.
(Glass Fruit) ....A
N. Y.—Syracuse
Syracuse Stoneware Co.
(Laundry Bleach) X
OHIO.—Akron
Weeks, Arthur J. (Acid).B
OHIO—Bridgeport
Crystal Glass Co. (Glass
Fruit) ....A
OHIO—Cincinnati
Glenny Glass Co., W. (Glass
Fruit) ....A
OHIO—Cleveland
National Carbon Co. (Battery) ....AAAA
OHIO—Zanesville
Kearns-Gorsuch Bottle Co.
(Glass Fruit) ....B
PA.—Beaver Falls
Co-operative Flint Glass
Co. (Ltd.) (Glass; Glass
Candy) ....A

JARS (Con.)

PA.—Philadelphia
Burgin & Sons Glass Co.
(Glass Milk) ....A
Gilchrist Improved Jar Co.
(Glass Fruit) ....D
Gillinder & Sons, 135 Oxford (Battery; Glass) ..A
Hero Fruit Jar Co. (Glass Fruit) ....AAA
Murray & Co., Jas. J., Trenton Av. (Battery) ....A
Whitney Glass Wrks., 227 S.
Front (Battery) ....AAA

PA.—Pittsburg
Cunningham Glass Co., D.
O. (Glass Fruit) .....AA
Hamilton Co., W. H. (Glass Milk) ....AA
McBeth-Evans Glass Co.
(Glass Candy) ......AAAA
National Glass Co. (Glass Candy; Glass Fruit) ..X
U. S. Glass Co. (Glass; Druggists' Show) ..AAAA
Weightman Glass Co. (Glass Fruit) ....A
Wormser Glass Co. (Glass Fruit) X

PA.—Washington
Hazel-Atlas Glass Co. (Glass Fruit) ....AAAA

TEXAS—Athens
Athens Pottery Co. (Butter) ....D

W. VA.—Wellsburg
Eagle Glass & Mfg. Co.
(Beef Extract) ....A
George Co., S. (Glass Fruit) ....A

W. VA.—Weston
Weston Glass Co. (Glass Fruit, &c.) X

W. VA.—Wheeling
Hazel-Atlas Glass Co. (Glass Fruit) ....AAAA

JAWS

ALA.—Selma
Peacock's Iron Wrks.
(Brake) X

CONN.—Bridgeport
Armstrong Mfg. Co. (Pipe Vise) ....A

CONN.—Hartford
Cushman Chuck Co. (Face Plate) ....AA

CONN.—New Britain
Skinner Chuck Co. (Face Plate) ....B
Union Mfg. Co. (Face Plate) ....AA

CONN.—New Haven
Hoggson & Pettis Mfg. Co.
(Face Plate) ....A

MICH.—Detroit
Detroit Twist Drill Co.
(Drill; Brace) C

MO.—Kansas City
Kansas City Bolt & Nut Co. (Brake) ....A

New York City
Garwin Machine Co. (Face Plate) ....AA
Prentiss Vise Co., 44 Barclay (Vise) C

OHIO—Cleveland
Cleveland City Forge & Iron Co. (Brake) .....AA

ILL.—Chicago
Strong & Co., C. H. 218
Washington St. (Arnica; Toilet) ....D

MD.—Baltimore
McCormick & Co., 106 W.
Falls Av. (Petroleum).D

N. Y.—Binghamton
Harris, F. E. (Petroleum) C

PA.—Petrolia
Dougherty & Son, W. H.
(Petroleum) ....A

PA.—Philadelphia
Wilbert Drug Co., 2324 Market(Petroleum) .....F

JEANS

See Clothing; Mens; Cotton Goods; Woolen Goods.

JELLY

See Jams; Jellies; Marmalades.

JEWELRY

CAL.—Los Angeles
Field & Cole (Mexican Filignee) ....B
Trapton Co., P. J. (Native) ....A

CAL.—San Francisco ..
Judis Co.. A. (Precious Stones; Diamonds) ....B
Rothschild & Hadenfeldt (Electro Plate; Gold Quartz; Diamonds) ...B
Shreve & Co. (Electro Plate) ....AA

COLO.—Denver
Rell Co.. George (Pyrites; Native) ....D
Waltham, Chas. (Gold Pyrites) ....B

CONN.—Meriden
Bliss & Co.. E. A. (Electro Plated) ....B

CONN.—No. Winham
Harris, Chas. R. (Gold Plated Chains) C

CONN.—South Manchester
Cheney Bros. (Armures; Broches) ....AAAA

CONN.—Williamantic
Kirby Co., G. J. (Chains) ....D

ILL.——Chicago
Adams & Co.. F. W., (Gold) C
Allen, Herbert W. (Diamonds) C
Burnham, E. (Hair) ....B
Brischbaum & Co.. S. (Settings) ....B
Campbell, M., Mason & Temple (Hair Chains) .G
Feiley Co.. Wm J.. 6 E.
Monroe (Eclesiastical) ..B
Hancock Co.. Chac. E. 103
State (Diamond Mountings Gold) ....B
Hillinger & Co.. R. J., 131
Wabash Av. (Silk; Gold Chains) ....F
Hirsh & Oppenheimer, Mason & Temple (Gem Set) ....B
Juergens & Anderson Co..
126 State (Emblems; Badges; Medals; Gem Set; Gold; Precious Stones; Settings; Diamonds) ..AA
Klein & Bro. F. C.. 126
State (Imitation; Precious Stones) ....B
Logee & Co.. F. L., 103
State (Emblem Badges; Medals) ....B
Morse Co.. F. E. 161 State
(Gem Set; Precious Stones; Diamonds) ....B
Noble & Co.. F. H.. 103
State (Medal Badges) ..A
Ostby & Barton Co.. 103
State (Diamonds Mtgs.; Gold) ....AAA
Schrader & Wittstein Co..
103 State (Diamond Mtgs.; Gem Set; Gold Rings; Settings) .....B
Simmons Bros. & Co.. 103
State (Emblems; Badges; Medals; Gold) ....A
Smith & Co.. Alf. H.. 103
State (Precious Stones; Diamonds) ....AA
Smith & Co.. T. J.. 103
State (Silver) ....A
Stern Bros. & Co. (Gem)))
Set; Gold; Diamonds) .AA
Street & Sons, Geo. O.. 103
State (Gold) ....B
Van Gilder Kahn & Co.. 67
Wabash (Diamonds) .AA
Wendell & Co.. 57 Washington (Diamond Mtgs.) ..B
Wilcox & Co.. D.. 103
State (Diamonds Mtgs.) ....AA

ILL.—Freeport
Dirkin Silver Filignee Co.
(Filignee) ....E

JEWELRY (Con.)

IOWA—Cedar Rapids

Wittstein, Geo. (Emblems; Badges; Medals) ......D

MD.—Baltimore

Feetting, A. H., 14 St. Paul (Gem Setting; Gold) ..C

Limerick, J. Arthur, 12 S. Calvert (Emblems; Badges; Medals) ....D

MASS.—Attleboro

Allen & Co., C. H. (Electro Plated) ....B

Anthony, Jno. (Chains) ...E

Attleboro Mfg. Co. (Rolled Gold Plate Electro Plated; ....A

Bates & Bacon (Bangles; Bracelets; Plated Chains) ....AAA

Bigney & Co., (Gold Plated; Filled Chains) ....A

Blake Co., James E. (Silver; Chatelaines) ....A

Bliss Bros. & Co. (Chains; etc.) ....A

Briggs Co., D. F. (Gold Plated Chains; Rings; etc.) ....AA

Bristol Mfg. Co. (Silver) C

Brown & Co., Geo. L. (Gold; Plated Chains)..B

Bushee & Co., A. (Rolled Plate Gold; Electro Plate) Collar; Cuff; Gold Plated; Ladies Collar; Lever Collar and Cuff; Separable Collar and Cuff Buttons) ....B

Carter, Guarnstrown & Remington (Rolled Gold Plate) ....B

Chapman & Barden (Gold) C

Cummings Co., P. J. (Gold Plated Chains) ....B

Daggett & Clapp Co. (Charms; Drops; Earrings; Chains; Rolled Gold Plate; Silver; Bracelets; Brooches; Necklaces; Medals) ....A

Eden & Co. (Electro Plate; Pearl Buckles; Gold Plated Bead; Leather Fob Chains) ....A

Fargo Co., E. A. (Earrings; Ear; Children's Ear; White Stone Drops ....A

Fisher & Co., J. M. (Chains; Lockets; Rolled Gold Plate) ....A

Fouineau & Cook Co. (Nickle Chains; Gold Charms) ....B

Gilmore & Co., E. D. (Gold) B

Hayward, Walter E. (Ladies' Chain; Pin; Lever Collar; Cuff; Linked Cuff; Separable Collar; Cuff Buttons; Ribbon Chains; Rolled Gold Plated C

Horton-Angel Co. (Rolled Gold; Plated Buttons; Studs; etc.) ....A

McRae & Keeler (Chains; etc. Electro and Gold Plated; Chatelaines) A

McDonald & Co. (Buckles; Silver Bracelete) .....D

Marble, Forrester & Co. (Chatelains) C

Marsh & Co., C. A. (Gold Plated Chains Goldfilled; Necklace; Vest Chains) A

Mason Co., Howard (Bracelets; Emblems; Badges; Medals; Rolled Gold Plate) ....D

Regnell, Bigney & Co. (Imitation Diamonds; Bracelets; Rolled Gold Plated; Electro Plated) ....B

Robbins Co., Chas. M. Emblems; Badges; Medals; Souvenirs) C

Sadler & Co., F. H. (Imitation Diamonds; Gold; Silver) ....B

Simmons Co., R. F. (Gold Plated Chains, etc; Fob

JEWELRY (Con.)

Safety Device) .....AAA

Smith & Crosby (Rolled Gold Plate) ....B

Smith & Richardson (Chains) ....D

Sturdy & Sons, F. (Plated Chains) ....A

Torrey Jewelry Co. (Buttons; Gun Metal Collar; Cuff) ....F

Union Braiding Co. (Chains) D

Watson & Newell Co. (Electro Plated) ......AA

Weaver & Co., F. W. (Rolled Gold Plate; Electro Plated) C

Wilmarth & Co., W. H. (Ladies' Cuff; Rolled Gold Plate; Electro Plated) ....B

MASS.—Attleboro Falls

Bell & Co., W. H. (Chains) C

Blankington & Co., V. M. (Emblems; Badges; Medals) C

Freeman & Co., B. S. (Chains; Rolled Gold Plate) ....D

Hall & Co., W. H. (Chains) H

Sturdy & Sons, J. F. (Gold Plated Chains) ....A

MASS.—Boston

Cain, Eben H. (Emblems; Badges; Medals) X

Gilchrist & Co., C. A., 43 Haverhill (Electro Plated) B

Harnott, Jno. (Emblems; Badges; Medals) ......G

Hirschburg, A. S. (Diamond Settgs.) C

Humphrey, John B. (Diamonds) ....B

Jepson, Godfrey (Badges; Emblems; Medals) .....G

Passmore Gem Co., 373 Washington (Stones)...F

Ripley-Howland Mfg. Co. (Collar; Cuff Buttons; Diamond Settgs.; Rings) A

Spencer Mfg. Co., S. M. (Emblems; Badges; Medals) ....E

MASS.—Chartley

Freeman, Daughaday & Co. (Ear Drops; Watch Chains; Onyx; Rolled Gold Plate; Elec. Plated) C

Sturdy Bros. (Gold Plated Chains) ....E

Sturdy Mfg. Co., W. A. (Rolled Gold Plate; Elec. Plated) ....B

MASS.—Chicopee

Ames Sword Co. (Regalia; Society) ....B

MASS.—Florence

Florence Mfg. Co. (Aluminum) ....A

MASS.—Mansfield

Cobb, F. M. & J. L. (Chains; Rolled Gold Plate; Elec. plate Silver) ....A

Spaulding, D. S. (Chains; Gold; Silver) ....B

MASS.—N. Attleboro

Barrows & Co., H. F. (Eyeglass; Necklace; Vest Chains Glove; Collar; Cuff; Sterling Silver Cuff Buttons; Bangles; Bracelets; Garter Buckles; Plated Chains) ....A

Blankington & Co., R. (Rolled Gold; Plated; Silver; Gold Plated; Silver Buttons; Buckles; Silver Chatelaines) ....A

Blankington & Co., W. S. (Chains) ....A

Bliss & Co., A. H. (Brass; Gold; Silver Chains)..B

Bugbee & Niles Co. (White Stone; Collar; Cuff Buttons; Imt. Diamonds; Gold) ....B

Burrows & Co., H. F.

579

JEWELRY (Con.)
(Nickel) ....A
Cheever, Tweedy & Co.
(Nickel; Fire Gilt; Watch
Chains; Broaches; Watch
Charms; Rolled Gold
Plated; Silver) ......AAA
Clark & Co., W. G. (Rolled
Gold Plated) C
Codding & Hulborn Co.
(Silver Buckles; Brace-
lets; Ladies' Necklace
Chains; Rolled Gold
Plated; Ear Drops; Elec-
tro Plate; Silver) ......A
Cutter & Co., F. H. (Rolled
Gold Plated) ....B
Doran, Bagnall & Co. (Gold;
Silver Plated Chains)...B
Draper, O. M., (Est. of)
(Fire Gilt Watch Chains;
Watch Charms; Plated
Fire Gilt; Nickel Chains,
etc.) ....B
Franklin & Co., E. I.
(Broaches; Ear Drops;
Bangles; Bracelets; Imt.
Diamonds; Rolled Gold
Pated; Electro Plate)..C
Frothingham & Co., T. G.
(Imt. Diamonds; Gold).C
Hudson & Co., G. C.
(Chains) C
Merritt & Co., H. D.
(Plated; Silver Necklaces;
Vest. etc.; Chains; Brace-
lets) ....A
Richards & Co.. E. Ira
(Rolled Gold Plated)...A
Riley, French & Hefron
(Gold; Rolled Plated);
Silver) ....AA
Sheppardson & Co., F. L.
(Gold Plated Chains)...D
Smith & Co., T. I. (Rolled
Gold Plated; Silver)...A
Sommer & Co., J. J. (Gold;
Gold Plated; Silver)...C
Sturtevant Whiting & Bige-
low (Rolled Gold Plated;
Silver) ....B
Webster & Co. (Silver)...A
Whiting Co., F. M. (Ear
Drops; Bracelets; Ear-
rings; Old Coin; Silver).B
MASS.—Plainville
Plainville Stock Co. (Hoop
Earrings; Broaches; Ear
Drops; Imt. Diamonds;
Gold; Gold Plated; Silver)
                      A
Scofield Melcher & Scofield
(Gold; Gold Plated; Sil-
ver) ....B
Whiting & Davis (Silver).
                      A
MASS.—Sandwich
Armstrong Braiding Co.
(Br. Boston) (Chains)..X
MASS.—So. Attleboro
Sadler Bros. & Co. (Imt.
Diamonds; Rolled Gold
Plated; Electro-Plated)B
MASS.—Springfield
Fletcher Aluminum Co.
(Aluminum) X
MASS.—Taunton
Fargo Co., E. A.
(Aluminum) ....D
MASS.—West Sanerville
Can & Co.. M. W. (Electro-
Plated) ....AA
MICH.—Detroit
Wright. Kay & Co. 140
Woodward Av. (College
Badges) ....A
MO.—Kansas City
Edwards & Sloan Jewelry
Co. (Gold) ....A
MO.—St. Louis
Bauman-Frey Mfg. Co.,
Com. Bldg. (Diamond
Mountings) ....A
Eisenstadt Mfg. Co.
(Badges; Medals; Em-
blems; Gold; Diamond)AA
N. J.—Hoboken
Schimner & Co., Wm.
Buckles. Silver) .....AA
N. J.—Newark
Abrecht. Oliver. 46 Oliver
(Chains) ....F
Adams & Co., Thos. W.

JEWELRY (Con.)
(Linked Cuff Buttons;
Brooches; Bangles; Brace-
lets) ....B
Alling & Co. (Collar; Cuff
Buttons; Bangles;
Brooches; Charms) ..AA
Alsop Bros. (Rings) ......B
Battlin & Co. (Gold Novel-
ties) ....B
Bippart, Griscom & Osborn
(Gold; Brooch, Safety De-
vice) ....A
Block & Bergfels (Link Cuff
Buttons; Brooches; Ear-
rings) ....B
Celluloid Co. (Celluloid
Charms; Celluloid)....B
Champenois & Co. (Gold).B
Cory Bros. W. F. (Gold)..B
Day, Clark & Co. (Bangles;
Bracelets; Necklaces)..B
Dodd, D. C., Jr. (Gold)...C
Durand & Co., 49 Franklin
(Chatelaine; Gold-filled;
Necklace Chains; Ear
Drops; Gold; Society;
Watch Charms; Belt;
Hoop Earrings; Brooches;
Hoop Earrings; Brooches)
Diamond Mountings; Gold
Novelties; Gold Jewelry;
Bangles; Bracelets; Col-
lar; Cuff; Dress; Cloak
Buttons; Necklaces; Med-
als) ....AA
Eastwood & Park Co.
(Gold) C
Eckfield & Ackley (Gold).C
Edge Co.. W. C.. 46 Green
(Gold; Silver Plated; Fox-
tail Chains) X
Hayden, Wm. W. (Gold
Novelties) ....B
Hayes Bros. & Co. (Badges;
Medals; Emblems; Gold)C
Hedges & Co.. A. J. (Gar-
ter Buckles; Brooches;
Bracelets; Ear Drops;
Gold Watch Charms;
Chatelaine; Necklace
Chains; Earrings) ......A
Hendrick & Co. (Gold) ...B
Huebner & Sons. E. (Pearl
Shell Brooch, Safety De-
vice) C
Jones & Woodland (Gold).B
Kiefer, Andrew O. (Rings)
                      B
Krementz & Co. (Gold;
Brooches) ....AAA
Kursch & Son Co., Frank
(Gold) ....B
Link & Angel (Silver) ....A
Mandeville. Carrow &
Crane (Rings) ....A
Mertz Bros. (Gold; Rings)
                      B
Moore & Son (Rings).....B
Nesler & Co., 38 Crawford
(Rope Chains) ....D
N. Jersey Aluminum Co.
(Aluminum) ....B
N. Y. Aluminum Co.
(Aluminum) X
Nobs & Son. Chas. H. (Pin;
Brooch, Safety Device).B
Reeves & Brown (Ear
Drops; Bracelet Chains;
Earrings; Bangles; Wire
Bracelets; Gold; Brooches)
                      B
Rich & Son Co. (Chains)..F
Riker Bros. (Emblems;
Badges; Medals; Gold)..
                      AA
Schappel. Schambacher &
Brod, (Gold) C
Schappel. Theo., 211 Mul-
bury (Chains) ....F
Schlosstein & Co.. F. A.
(Chains) ....B
Schuetz & Sons Co. (Gold).B
Schwarzkopf & Dover
(Gold; Silver) ....B
Schafer & Douglas (Chains)
                      A
Spanberg. J. A. & S. W.
(Gold) ....B
Strobel & Crane (Gold) ...A
Unger Bros. (Silver) .....A
Van Houten Bros. Jewelry
Co. (Gold) C

JEWELRY (Con.)

Lane (Imt.; Prec. Stones) .... A

Goodman Bros., 27 Maiden Lane (Prec. Stones) ...AA

Goodman & Byck, 23 Duane (Coral) .... F

Goodyear's India Rubber Glove Mfg. Co. (Rubber) .... AAAA

Gorham Mfg. Co., 19th & Broadway (Ecclesiastical) .... AAAA

Granberry, G. P., 114 E. 14th (Onyx; Pearl; Bead; Black; Lorgnette Chains; Gold Jewelry) ....F

Greaser & Son, J. R., 182 Broadway (Gem Set; Gold) ....B

Griffith & Son Co., R. L., 194 Broadway (Gold) ..B

Green & Bro., 51 Maiden Lane (Diamonds) ......A

Grenberg & Sons, A. I. (Gem Set; Am. Pearl; Diamonds) ....B

Hahn & Co., Reid C. (Agates; Diamonds) ....B

Hancock & Co., Chas E. (Diamond Mtgs.; Gold Jewelry) ....B

Hartman, Peter (Filigree; Pearl) ....D

Hedges & Co., A. J (Gold) ....A

Hedges & Co., Wm. S. (Gem Set; Prec. Stones; Diamonds) ....AA

Heller & Son, L., 51 Maiden Lane (Prec. Stones) ...B

Hellinger & Co., R. J., 194 B'way (Silk; Gold Chains) X

Hirsch & Flaschner, 29 Gold (Rings) ....B

Hirsch & Hyman, 2 Maiden Lane (Diamonds) ......B

Hirschberg, Sig, 65 Nassau (Prec. Stones) ....A

Hodenpyl & Sons, 170 Bway (Gold; Gold Chains; Prec. Stones) ....B

Howard & Hockshaw, 220 4th Av. (Gold) ....B

Hutchison & Huestis, 3 Maiden Lane (Rings) ......A

Irons & Russell, 9 Maiden Lane (Emblems; Badges; Medals) ....A

Jonassohn, Oscar F., 65 Nassau (Imt.; Prec. Stones; Diamonds) ....B

Jonest, Victor, 33 Union Sq. (Imt. Diamonds) ......B

Jung. Staiger & Klitz, 1 Maiden Lane (Gold) ....B

Kahn, L. & M., 170 Broadway (Diamonds) ....AAA

Kaiser & Co., David (Diamond Mtgs.; Gem Set) ..B

Kameras, Max, 215 Grand (Gold Chains) ....F

Kaufman & Co., Lewis, 84 Fulton (Rings) ....A

Klein, Jno. R., 246 5th Av. (Gem Set) ....AA

Keller & Co., Chas., 192 B'way (Gold) ....AA

Kinder, Julius, 29 Gold (Gold Chains) X

King Collar Button Co., 530 B'way (Rolled Plate Collar Buttons) C

Kinscherf, Wm., 63 Maiden Lane (Gem Set) ......A

Kirby, Hy. A., 9 Maiden Lane (Gold) ....AAA

Kleinschmidt, Howland Co., 170 B'way (Diamonds) ..A

Kohn & Co., Alois, 16 Maiden Lane (Filled; Gold Chains) ....A

Kollender, M., 37 Maiden Lane (Prec. Stones) ....B

Krementz & Co., 170 B'way (Gold) ....AAA

Larter & Sons, 21 Maiden Lane (Link Collar, Cuff. etc.. Buttons; Onyx; Watch Charms) ....A

Lawson, Samuel, 19 John (Agate; Chains; Onyx;

JEWELRY (Con.)

Bead) ....F

Leimbach, F. E., 65 Nassau (Am. Pearls) C

Levy, Chas. M., 90 William (Gold; Rings) C

Levy, Herman, 65 Nassau (Diamonds) ....B

Lewis & Co., Fred W., 1 Maiden Lane (Precious Stones; Diamonds) ...AA

Leys, Christie & Co., 65 Nassau (Gold) ....B

Lessauer & Co., 12 Maiden Lane (Gold) ....AA

Lorsch & Co., Albert, 37 Maiden Lane (Imt.; Prec. Stones; Diamonds) ...AAA

Lott & Schmitt, 116 Walker (Gold Novelties) C

Lounsberg & Son, A., 9 Maiden Lane (Gem Set) .C

Lowe & Co., Edwin, 180 B'way (Rings) ....A

Maas & Co., Wm. (Amber; Diamond; Imitation; Electro-Plate; Hair; Horn) .... AA

Malliet & Maxwell, 14 Maiden Lane (Diamonds) ...B

Marchand Freres, 12 John (Diamonds) ....AA

Marsellus & Pitt, 2 Maiden Lane (Prec. Stones) ..B

Martin, Copeland & Co. (Neck laces) ....AA

Mauran Mfg. Co., Jno. T., 3 Maiden Lane (Gold) ....A

Mayer, David, 14 Maiden Lane (Diamonds) ......B

Metropolitan Aluminum Mfg. Co., 182 Houston (Aluminum) ....F

Moore & Son, 3 Maiden Lane (Rings) ....B

Mount & Woodhull, 26 Maiden Lane (Precious Stones; Diamonds) .....B

Myers & Co., S. F. (Brooches; Bracelets; Earrings) ....A

Nissen & Co., Ludwig, 182 B'way (Gem Set; Prec. Stones; Diamonds) ...AA

Nordlinger & Mamluck, 24 John (Imt. Stones) ....A

Oppenheimer & Co., E., 3 Maiden Lane (Prec. Stones) ....A

Oppenheimer Bros. & Veitch, 65 Nassau (Diamonds) ..
.... AAA

Ostby & Barton Co., 9 Maiden Lane (Diamond Mtgs.; Gold) ......AAA

Peckham & Co., J. H., 9 Maiden Lane (Rolled Gold Plate) C

Peckham Seamless Ring Mfg. Co., 45 Maiden Lane (Gold Rings) C

Pierce, Clarence F., 170 B'way (Gold Chains) ...E

Potter & Buffington Co., 65 Nassau (Gold) ......A

Power & Co., Chas. L., 2 Maiden Lane (Precious Stones) ....E

Prager & Co., Morris, 14 Maiden Lane (Precious Stones; Diamonds) ...AA

Provenzano, J. N., 114 E. 14th. (Gun Metal) ......D

Purpur, Aug., 12 John (Prec. Stones) ....B

Quayle & Co., T., 9 Maiden Lane (Gold) C

Richards & Co., E. Ira (Bracelet Chains; Enamelled; Gold; Silver:; Sterling Bangles; Charms; Ear Drops; Collar; Cuff Buttons; Buckles; Brooches; Earrings) ....AAA

Richardson & Co., Enos. 23 Maiden Lane (Gold Chains) ....AAA

Riley, French & Heffron, 14 Maiden Lane (Gold) ..AA

Ripley, Howland Mfg. Co., 3 Maiden Lane (Diamond Mtgs.) ....A

Roe & Hordemaker Co., 36

JEWELRY (Con.)

Maiden Lane (Precious Stones) ....B
Rothschild Bros., 51 Maiden Lane (Gold Lockets; Brooches; Collar; Cuff Button; Links) C
Sachs, Leo. M.. 7 Maiden Lane (Prec. Stones) ..B
Saunders, Jno. F., 68 Nassau (Prec. Stones) ....B
Scherr. Wm., 542 5th Av. (Gem Set) ....AA
Schenken & Sons, H., 130 Fulton (Diamonds) .....A
Seckels, Wm., 65 Nassau (Precious Stones) ......B
Sexton & Co., Wm. L., 7 Maiden Lane (Brooches; Pearl Necklaces; Gem Set; Gold; Diamond) ..C
Shiebler & Co., Geo. W., 5 Maiden Lane (Silver) ..A
Shuman Bros., 12 John (Gem Set) ....A
Simmons Bros. & Co., 170 B'way (Gold) ....A
Simmock & Serrill, 21 Maiden Lane (Rings; Onyx; Society Charms; Onyx; Society Charms) ..B
Sloan & Co., 21 Maiden Lane (Emerald; Horn; Silver; Earrings; Necklaces; Bracelets; Rosaries; Collar; Cuff; Linked Cuff Medals; Gold Watch Charms; Ear Drops; Bracelet Chains; Miniature Brooches; Garter Buckles; Buttons) ......B
Smith & Co.. Alf. H.. 170 B'way (Prec. Stones; Diamonds) ....AA
Snow & Westcott, 21 Maiden Lane (Gold) ....A
Sommer & Co., J. J., 180 B'way (Gold; Silver) ..C
Spencer Co.. E. L., 9 Maiden Lane (Gold) ....B
Stafford Co.. N. (Medals).F
Stern Bros. & Co. 68 Nassau (Gem Set; Gold Diamonds) ....AAAA
Strassburger & Co., Byron L.. 17 Maiden Lane (Gem Set; Prec. Stones; Diamond) ....AA
Strassburger Son & Co., Louis. 170 B'way (Diamonds) ....AA
Strauss & Sons, Jacob, 14 Maiden Lane (Diamonds) ....A
Street & Sons. Geo. O., 24 John (Plated Chains; Gold; Collar; Cuff Buttons) ....B
Sturtevant Whiting & Bigelow. 12 John (Silver) ..B
Tannenbaum & Co., L.. 52 Nassau (Prec. Stones; Diamonds) ....AA
Terrace & Strausman, 101 Canal (Chains) X
Toltec Gem Mining Co.. 1 Maiden Lane (Prec. Stones) ....B
Townsend & Co.. D. C.. 170 B'way (Diamonds) ....AA
Treihs Bros.. 68 Nassau (Pearls) ....B
Trenkmann. August (Tortoise Shell; Bracelets) ...
..............AAA
Van Dam. Edward, 101 Beekman (Diamonds) ..B
Van Gilder. Kahn & Co., 170 Broadway (Diamonds).AA
Wahrman, Adolph (Chains) ....G
Wallach & Co.. A.. 37 Maiden Lane (Necklace Chains; Gold Chains; Bracelets).A
Wallach & Schiele, 65 Nassau (Diamonds) ......AA
Weller & Co., 34 E. 29th (Gem Set) ....A
Wheeler & Co.. Hayden W.. 2 Maiden Lane (Gold Chains) ....AA
White & Co.. J. J.. 37 Maiden Lane (Gold) ....B

JEWELRY (Con.)

Whiting Mfg. Co.. 18th & Broadway (Gold Novelties; Gun Metal) ....AA
Wightman & Hough Co., 3 Maiden Lane (Badges; Emblems; Gold Medals).A
Wilcox & Co.. D., 40 Maiden Lane (Diamond Mtgs.; Gem Set; Gold) ......AA
Wood & Co., Chas. F.. 1 Maiden Lane (Necklaces; Diamonds) ....A
Wood & Sons. J. R., 170 B'way (Rings; Diamonds) AAA
Ziruth-Kaiser Co., 2 Maiden Lane (Gold Chains) ....B

N. Y.—Syracuse

Hoveth. Geo. H. (Gold Rings) C

OHIO—Cincinnati

Fox Co., Gustave . .... (Gold) ....B
Fox Bros. & Co. (Gem Set; Diamonds) ....AA
Gebhardt Bros., Lion Bldg. (Emblems; Badges; Medals; Brooch, Safety Device) C
Keck Mfg. Co.. Herrman (Gem Set; Gold; Diamonds) ....AA
Naterman & Co., Jos. (Gold) ....B
Peck, Selmier & Peck (Gold) C

OHIO—Cleveland

Amestine Bros. & Mier (Gold) ....A

PA.—Philadelphia

Bedichimer & Co., I., 11th & Sansom (Emblems; Badges; Medals) ......B
Bennett & Son, Jacob, 1024 Chestnut (Gem Set) ....B
Deschamps, Jos. H.. 701 Chestnut (Diamond Mtgs.; Gold; Jewerly) C
Diehl, J. H. (Medals) ...F
Krider Co.. Peter L. (Socety Medals) ....D
Pearce & Feraile, 103 18th (Gold; Bangles) ......B
Sickles & Sons.. 726 Chestnut (Diamonds) ..A
Simmons Bros. & Co.. 611 Sansome (Emblems; Badges; Jewelry; Electro-Plate; Gold; Silver).A

PA.—Pittsburg

Heeren Bros. & Co (Gold; Diamonds) ....AA

PA.—Reading

Anderson Jewelry Co.. L. D. (Pyrites; Alligators; Teeth) ....D

R. I.—Pawtucket

Cobb & Co.. W. R. (Settings) ....B
Fuller & Son Co., Geo. H. (Linked Cuff Buttons; Settings) ....A

R. I.—Providence

Adams, D. F. (Old Chains; Onyx; Mourning) C
Allen. Jno. F. (Imt.; Prec. Stones; Diamonds) .....B
Arnold & Steeve (Gold; Rings) ....B
Ballou & Co.. B. A. (Collar; Cuff Buttons; Silver; Ear Drops; Gold; Plated Chains) ....AA
Barstow & Williams (Bangles) C
Bassett Jewelry Co. (Plated; Silver Chains; Gold).....B
Pecker & Co., Geo. (Gold).C
Bennett & Co.. E. A. (Rolled Gold Plate; Electro-Plate) C
Breidenbach. R. A. (Imt. Stone; Diamonds) ....AA
Bruhl Bros. & Co. (Imt. Stones; Diamonds) .....A
Cahoon & Co.. Geo. H. (Imt. Diamonds; Gold; Silver; Rings) ....A
Canron & Co. (Rolled Gold Plated) C
Champlin. S. B. (Plated; Filled Chains; Gold)....B

Chapin & Hollister Co.
(Gold Plated Chains) ..B

Clark & Coombs Co.
(Rolled Gold; Plated
Rings) ....A

Cook Co., C. H. (Neck-
laces) ....D

Cory & Reynolds Co.
(Plated Watch Charms;
Ear Drops; Collar; Cuff
Buttons; Coral; Rolled
Gold Plated Scarf Pins).C

Darling & Co., Chas. C.
(Emblems; Badges; Med-
als) ....B

Devereux & Co., O. C.
(Watch Charms; Gold
Plated Collar; Cuff But-
ton; Imt. Diamonds;
Mourning) ....D

Dunn & Co., M. J. (Chains)
...............E

Eichenberg, Julius (Imt.
Stone; Rolled Gold Plate;
Electro-Plate; Precious
Stones; Buckles; Gold
Plate) C

Esser & Co. (Imt. Diamonds;
Rolled Gold Plate; Elec-
tro-Plate) C

Ettlinger, E. J. (Imt. Diamonds) C

Feeley Co., W. J. (Medals)
...............B

Fitzgerald & Co., M.
(Gold) ....A

Fletcher, Burrows & Co.
(Imt. Diamonds; Rolled
Gold Plate) C

Ford & Carpenter (Rolled
Gold Plate) ....B

Foster & Bro. Co., Theo. W.
(Earrings; Watch Charms;
Ear Drops; Band Brace-
lets; Chains, etc.; Gold;
Gold Plated; Buckles; Sil-
ver) ....AA

Fowler Bros. (Mourning) .C

Fuller Mfg. Co., J. G. (Gold
Plated Chains) ....B

Goldsmith & Harzberg
(Electro-Plate) ....B

Goodfriend Bros. (Imt.
Diamonds) ....A

Gorham Mfg. Co. (Ivory).
...............AAAA

Graham & Williams (Elec-
tro-Plate) C

Green Co., A. A. (Plated;
Filled Chains) ....A

Griffith & Sons Co., R. L.
(Plated Chains; Imt. Dia-
monds; Gold; Gold Plated;
Coral) ....B

Hamilton & Hamilton, Jr.
(Plated Chains, etc.)...A

Hancock Co., Chas. E.
(Hoop Earrings; Collar;
Cuff; Ladies' Collar;
Linked Cuff; Ear Drops;
Band Bracelets; Imt. Dia-
monds Gold) C

Harvey & Otis (Emblems;
Badges; Medals) C

Hutchinson & Heustes
(Gold Rings) ....A

Irons & Russell (Charms;
Emblems; Badges; Med-
als) ....A

Kirby, Hy. A. (Gold) ..AAA

Lederer & Bro. (Plated
Chains, etc.) ....D

Lederer Co., S. & B.
(Plated; Shell; Society;
Watch Charm; Plated;
Gilt; Hair; Silk Chains;
Emblems; Badges; Med-
als; Imt. Diamonds; Elec-
tro-Plated; Silver; Neck-
laces; Band Bracelets;
Brooches; Bangles) C

Leider & Bernkopf (Prec.
Stones) ....B

Lewis & Co., S. M. (Silver)
...............A

Lindol & Co., H. C. (Imt.
Diamonds; Gold) C

Linton Co., P. & A. (Hoop
Earrings; Ear Drops;
Electro - Plate; Rolled
Gold Plated) ....B

Loeb & Co., Wm. (Collar;
Cuff Buttons; Imt. Dia-

monds; Rolled Gold
Plated; Electro-Plated).A

Lorsch & Co., Albert (Imt.
Diamonds) ....AAA

Luther & Son, Wm. H. (Ear
Drops; Charms; Collar;
Cuff Buttons; Bracelets;
Brooches; Electro-Plated;
Silver) ....B

Marders & Kettlety (Elec-
tro-Plated) C

Martin. Copeland & Co.
(Gold Chains; Rings; Eye-
glass; Necklace; Chate-
laine; Silver Watch
Chains) ....AA

Mauran Mfg. Co., Jno. T.
(Gold) ....A

Merrill & Co., S. K.
(Rolled Gold Plated)..B

Messier, A. C. (Rolled Gold
Plated) ....B

Moorhead & Co., R. L.
Brooches; Collar; Cuff;
Linked Buttons; Brace-
lets; & Silver; Ear Drops;
Imt. Diamond; Rolled
Gold Plated) ....B

Ostby & Barton Co. (Gold
Rings) ....AAA

Palmer & Caprove (Rings).
...............AA

Parks Bros. & Rogers
(Rolled Gold Plate) ...A

Payton & Kelly Co. (Chains;
Gold) C

Pollard & Co., A. (Chate-
laines; Brooches) ......E

Potter & Co., E. A. (Ear
Drops; Gold; Gold Plated)
...............C

Potter & Buffington Co.
(Collar; Cuff; Linked
Buttons; Brooches; Neck-
laces; Amber; Diamond;
Gold; Bracelets) ....A

Providence Stock Co. (Plated
Chains; Gold; Silver
Buckles) ....D

Quale & Co., Thos. (Gold).C

Rodenberg, Smith Co.
(Plated Chains, etc.; Wire
Gilt Chains) ....B

Roy & Co., L. J. (Chains).F

Schofield, Batty & Co.
(Electro-Plated) C

Schwarzkopf & Co., J.
(Rolled Gold Plated) ...C

Seamless Wire Mfg. Co.
(Gold; Plated; Watch
Charms; Chains) X

Smith Co., C. Sydney
(Gold Chains) ....A

Smith & Co., Geo. J. (Imt.
Diamond; Rolled Gold
Plated; Chatelaines;
Buckles) C

Smith & Co., Wm. (Brace-
lets; Gold; Silver Chains)
...............A

Smith & Blankington
(Chains) X

Smith Bros. (Electro-
Plated) ....B

Snow & Westcott (Black;
Onyx Chains; Charms;
Diamond; Gold; Onyx
Bangles; Bracelets;
Brooches; Collar; Cuff
Buttons; Ear Drops; Ear-
rings; Hair Brooches).A

Solinger & Co., J. (Rolled
Gold Plated; Electro-
Plated; Rings) C

Spencer Co., E. L. (Gold).B

Stern & Co., Louis
(Chains) ....B

Thornton Bros. (Badges;
Medals; Emblems; Rolled
Gold Plated) ....A

Tuttle & Stark (Chate-
laines) ....E

Vose Mfg. Co., Geo. L. (Collar; Cuff; Linked But-
tons; Necklaces) ......B

Waite. Matthewson & Co.
(Collar; Cuff Button;
Electro-Plate; Gold; Gold
Plated; Bangles) ......B

Waite-Thresher Co. (Ear
Drops; Watch Charms;
Chains; Imt. Diamonds;

JEWELRY (Con.)
Gold; Gold Plated; Silver)
..............................A
Warren & Williams (Gold;
Stone Rings) C
White & Co., J. J. (Gold;
Gold Plated; Silver)...B
Wightman & Hough Co.
(Gold; Gold Plated) ...A
Wilcox & Co., D. (Gold;
Diamond) ....AA
Wildprett & Saacke (Gold
Rings) ....B
Williams & Co., M. F.
(Imt. Diamonds; Rolled
Gold Plate) C
Williams & Anderson
(Badges; Medals; Em-
blems) ....A
Williams & Son, Hy.
(Chains, etc.; Pyrites).D
Williams & Payton (Mourn-
ing; Buckles; Gold
Plated;; Buttons; Pearl
Collar; Cuff) ....D
WIS.—Manitowoc
Manitowoc Aluminum Nov.
Co. (Aluminum) ......B
WIS.—Milwaukee
Bunde & Upmeyer Co. (Dia-
mond; Pearl) ....AA
Schwaab Stamp & Seal Co.
(Medals) C
WIS.—Two Rivers
Aluminum Mfg. Co. (Alum-
inum; Medals) ....A

JEWELS
ILL.—Elgin
Gustason Jewel Co., O.
(Balance) ....G
ILL.—Evanston
Wehrstedt, C. H. (Watch)
..............................B

JIGGERS
CONN.—Danbury
Morlock & Heusk (Leather)
..............................E
N. J.—Paterson
Terhune Machine Wks., J.
S. ....E
Watson Machine Co. .....A
N. J.—Trenton
Crossley Mfg. Co. (Cruci-
ble) ....A
MacKenzie Sons Co., Dun-
can ....A
PA.—Philadelphia
Butterworth & Sons Co.,
H. W. ....A
R. I.—Providence
Textile Finishing Mchry.
Co. ....AAA

JIGS
CONN.—Hartford
Sigourney Tool Co. (Drill)
..............................A
ILL.—Chicago
Allis-Chalmers Co. (Ore)..
..............................AAAA
MASS.—Lynn
Dwyer Machine Co. ......F
MICH.—Detroit
Anderson & Sons, W. H.
(Concentrating) ....A
MICH.—Menominee
Dudley Mfg. Co., A. (Bicy-
cle Construction Frame).F
PA.—Hazleton
Hazleton Iron Wks. (Coal)
..............................B
PA.—Mauch Chunk
Stroh, W. H. (Coal) C
PA.—Tamaqua
Tamaqua Mfg. Co. (Coal).B
PA.—White Haven
Wallace, Samuel (Coal)..D

JOGGERS
MICH.—Battle Creek
Hart, R. A. (Paper) ....E

JOINTERS
See also Machinery

CONN.—New Haven
Sargent & Co. .....AAAA

JOINTERS (Con.)
CONN.—Norwich
Rogers & Co., C. B...AAAA
CONN.—Pine Meadow
Chapin-Stevens Co. ......A
ILL.—Decatur
Mueller Mfg. Co., H. (Pipe)
..............................AAA
MASS.—Boston
Woods Machine Co., S. A.
..............................AA
MASS.—Kingston
Drew & Co., C. (Bricklay-
ers') C
MICH.—Jackson
Dennis Machine Co.
(Hand) ....D
N. H.—Pike Station
Pike Mfg. Co. (Saw) ....A
N. J.—Smithville
Smith Mach. Co., H. B...A
N. Y.—Buffalo
Frank Machinery Co.
(Glue) C
N. Y.—Lockport
Trevor Mfg. Co. (Shingle).B
New York City
American Wood Working
Mach. Co. ....AAAA
N. Y.—Rome
Adams & Son, T. (Box
Board; Shingle) C
OHIO—Cincinnati
Fay, J. A. & Egan Co.
(Glue) ....AAAA
OHIO—Cleveland
Gerlach Co., Peter
(Shingle) ....A
Oram, Jno. S., 160 Coe
(Heading; Nail Keg) ..A
OHIO—Columbus
Ohio Tool Co. ....AA
OHIO—Hamilton
Bentel & Margsdant Co.
(Masons') ....A
OHIO—Sandusky
Sandusky Tool Co. ....A
PA.—Philadelphia
Colladay, Jos. O. ....B
Power & Co., L. ....A
VT.—Montpelier
Lane Mfg. Co. (Shingle)..A
WIS.—Beloit
Berlin Machine Wks.
(Glue) ....AAAA
WIS.—Milwaukee
Filer & Stowell Co. (Ltd.)
(Shingle) ....AAA
WIS.—Sheboygan Falls
Falls Machine Co. (Auto-
matic Glue)............D

JOINTS
See also Knuckles
See also Hardware; Car-
riage; etc.

CONN.—Hartford
Gray & Prior Machine Co.,
302 Asylum (Ball; Univer-
sal) ....F
Vanderbeck Tool Wks.
(Knuckle; Universal) ..B
CONN.—Mt. Carmel
Woodruff & Sons, Walter
W. (Concealed) ....A
CONN.—New Britain
Stanley Works (Step
Ladder) ....AAA
CONN.—New Haven
Cowles & Co., C. (Stump) A
CONN.—Plantsville
Atwater Mfg. Co. (Stump)
..............................A
Blakeslee Forging Co.
(Stump) ....B
Smith & Co., H. D.
(Stump) ....A
ILL.—Batavia
Challenge Wind Mill &
Feed Mill Co. (Expansion)
..............................AAA
ILL.—Chicago
Chicago Gas & Elect. Fix-
ture Co., 212 Wabash Av.
(Insulating) ....B
Clow & Sons, Jas. B., 344
Franklin (Flexible Ball)
..............................AAA
Crane Co. (Expansion)
..............................AAAA
Railway Appliance Co. (Ex-
pansion) ....A

586

JUICES: FRUIT, ETC.

Evans & Sons (Ltd.), 133
William (Lime) ......A
McKesson & Robbins (Fruit)
............................AAAA
Peloubet Mfg. Co., A. H.,
309 E. 43d (Fruit) ....D
Matthews, John (firm of)
(Fruit) ....AA
Ross & Bro., W. A., 11 S.
William (Lime) ....B
Rath & Co., Nicholas (Fruit;
Prune) ....AA
Rudkins' Sons, W., 427 4th
Av. ....A
Sarsaferine Co., 528 E. 43d
(Fruit) ....D
Schieffelin & Co., W. H.
(Fruit) ....AA
Shafer Co., I. C., 268 W.
B'way (Fruit) ....A
Soloman & Co., A. A., 37
Beaver (Peach; Prune).E
Waterman Condensing Co.,
48 Vesey (Liquid Fr.).C
Welch Grape Juice Co., 78
Park Pl. ....B
Wood & Selick (Fruit)....A

N. Y.—Penn Yan
Gray Rock Vineyard Co.
(Grape) ....B
Snow Grape Juice Co.....D

N. Y.—Portland
Taylor & Fuller (Grape)..A

N. Y.—Ripley
Chantauqua Fruit Company
(Grape) ....D
Gleason Grape Juice Co...D

N. Y.—Silver Creek
Silver Creek Pres. Co....D

N. Y.—Westfield
Chautauqua Fruit & Grape
Juice Co. ....B
Holland Wine Co. (Grape).D
Welch Grape Juice Co.....B

OHIO—Cleveland
Benton, Hall & Co.......AA

OHIO—Cincinnati
Mihalovitch - Fletcher Co.
(Fruit) ....AAA

OHIO—Fremont
Fremont Grape Juice Co...D

OHIO—Unionville
Cleveland Cider Co. (Fruit)
............................D

PA.—Erie
Werner Vin. & Pickling Co.
(Grape) ....A

PA.—Philadelphia
Ritter Conserve Co., P. J.,
2156 E. Dauphin (Grape)
............................A
Hance Bros. & White
(Fruit) ....AA

R. I.—East Providence
Huntington Maple Syrup &
Sugar Co. (Lime) ......D

JUMPERS
See Clothing; Mens.

JUNKET
See Rennet

KALAMEIN

New York City
Howell & Lawrence, 402 E.
93d (for Fire Proofing
Doors; Windows; Shut-
ters) ....D

KALSOMINE

ILL.—Chicago
Rubber Paint Co. ....A

MASS.—Boston
Bird & Co., J. A. & W.,
34 India ....AA

MICH.—Hudson
Hook, Hardis Co. ....D

MO.—St. Louis
Mound City Paint & Color
Co. ....AA

N. J.—Jersey City
Woolsey Paint & Color Co.,
C. A. ....A

N. Y.—Buffalo
Mets Paint Co., P. A., 326
Washn. (Cold Water) ..D

N. Y.—New Brighton
Murralo Co. ....A

KALSOMINE (Con.)

New York City
Fox & Co., M. E., 136th &
Rider Av. (Prepared) .D
Longman & Martinez ..AAA
Tieman & Co., Daniel F. A
Valentine & Co. .....AAAA
Whittaker, W. H., 245
Front ....E

N. Y.—Troy
Connors Paint Mfg. Co. A
Troy Cold Water Kalsomine
Co. (Cold Water) .....E

PA.—Philadelphia
French & Co., S. H. ....A
Lucas & Co., Jno., 4th &
Race ....AAA

R. I.—Providence
Hainbach, Bernan ....D

VT.—Saxton's River
Edson Starks & Co. .....D

VA.—Richmond
Atlantic Varnish Wks....D

KANGAROO
See Leather

KAOLIN
See also Clay

DEL.—Wilmington
Golding Sons' Co. ......AA

N. J.—Metuchen
Bloomfield Clay Co. X

N. J.—Woodbridge
Valentine & Bro. Co., M. D.
............................AA

N. Y.—Troy
Ostrander Fire Brick Co. A

PA.—Philadelphia
Paxson Co., J. W. .....AA

S. C.—Langley
Immaniate Kaolin Co......C
Lamar Kaolin Co., T. G. B
Peerless Clay Co. ....D

KEELERS

New York City
Cordley & Hayes (Fibre) A

N. C.—Fayetteville
Fayetteville Woodenware
Co. (White Cedar) C

VA.—Richmond
Richmond Cedar Wks.
(Ltd.) (Cedar)·....AAAA

KEGS
See also Cooperage; Woodenware.

CAL.—San Francisco
Cal. Barrel Co. (Nail;
Syrup; White Lead) AA

CONN.—Hazardville
Bridge, A. D. (Powder) ..A

MASS.—Boston
Lang & Jacobs Co. (Nail) F

MASS.—Lunenberg
Taylor, Agustus (Syrup) D

N. H.—Keene
Impervious Package Co.
(Nail; Powder; Syrup;
White Lead) ....B

N. Y.—Brooklyn
Brooklyn Cooperage Co.
(Nail; Syrup) ....A

New York City
Schwarzwalder & Sons, J.
(Nail) ....AAAA

OHIO—Cincinnati
Cincinnati Cooperage Co.
(Nail; White Lead) AAA
Hauser, Brennan & Fath Co.
(Nail) ....B

OHIO—Circleville
Eagle Cooperage Wks.
(Nail; Bolt; Nut, etc.) G

OHIO—Cleveland
Cleveland Wire Spring Co.
(Steel Shop; Factory) A

OHIO—Niles
Ohio Galvanizing & Mfg. Co.
(Steel) ....B

OHIO—Salem
Clark Co.. W. J. (Metallic;
Steel; Factory; Nail; Nut;
Bolt, etc.) ....A

OHIO—Sandusky
Kilbourn & Co. (Nail;
Pickle) C

KEGS *(Con.)*

PA.—Pittsburg
Badke Mfg. Co. (Powder) B
Bell Co., Edwin (Nail;
  Bolt; Nut, etc.) ....A
R. I.—Pawtucket
Jenckes Mfg. Co., E. (Nail)
                          A
VA.—Richmond
Richmond Cedar Wks.
  (Oak) ....AAAA

KERSEYS

See Woolen Goods

KETTLES

**See also Caldrons; Tinware;
Aluminum Ware; Hollo-
ware; Woodenware; En-
amelled Ware.**

CONN.—Meriden
Manning, Bowman & Co.
  (Enameled; Swing; Tin
  Tea) ....AA
Meriden Britannia Co.
  (Covered) ....AAAA
Miller & Co., Edw. (Brass)
                       AAAA
CONN.—Waterbury
Randolph-Clowes Co.
  (Brass) ....AAA
Waterbury Brass Co.
  (Brass) ....AAAA
CONN.—Winsted
Goodwin & Kintz Co.
  (Five O'Clock Tea) ....B
GA.—Columbus
Columbus Iron Wks. Co.
  (Iron) ....AA
ILL.—Batavia
Sperry & Co., D. R. (Steam
  Jacket; Sugar) ....B
ILL.—Chicago
Harris & Bro., Geo. P., 64
  W. Lake (Steam Jacket)
                          B
Kaestner & Co. (Steam
  Jacket) ....A
Perrin & Co., W. R. (Lard)
                       A
Vulcan Iron Wks. (Foundry)
                       AA
ILL.—Clyde
Coonley Mfg. Co. (Tea) ..B
ILL.—Hoopeston
Sprague Cahning Machy.
  Co. (Steam Jacket) ...A
ILL.—Lemont
Illinois Pure Aluminum Co.
  (Aluminum Steam Jack-
  eted) ....A
IND.—Indianapolis
Langsenkamp, Wm. (Steam
  Jacket; Copper) ....B
Over, Ewald, 426 S. Penn
  (Sugar) ....B
IND.—Jeffersonville
Indiana Mfg. Co. (Sugar) A
IND.—Terre Haute
Columbian Enameling &
  Stamping Co. (Tea) AAA
IOWA—Burlington
Murray Iron Wks. Co.
  (Steam Jacket) ....A
IOWA—Keokuk
McElroy Iron Wks. Co.
  (Steam Jacket) ....F
KANS.—Leavenworth
Great Western Mfg. Co.
  (Plaster) ....AA
MD.—Baltimore
Poole Engineering & Mach.
  Co. (for Melting Lead) AA
MASS.—Boston
Badger & Sons Co., E. B.,
  63 Pitts (Steam Jacket;
  Mixing) ....A
Braman, Dow & Co., 239
  Causeway (Steam Jacket)
                       AAA
Strater & Sons, Herman
  (Copper; Steam Jacket) A
Walker & Pratt Mfg. Co.,
  33 Union (Steam Jacket;
  Glue; Tar, etc.) .....AA
Walworth Mfg. Co., 132
  Federal (Steam Jacket)
                       AAAA
MASS.—Cambridge
Campbell Iron Wks. (Tar) X

KETTLES *(Con.)*

MASS.—Lowell
Lowell Machine Shop (Size)
                       AAAA
MICH.—Grand Rapids
Buterworth & Lowe
  (Stucco) ....A
MICH.—Kalamazoo
Clark Engine & Boiler Co.,
  Geo. (Steam Jacket) ..B
MICH.—Lansing
Bement & Sons, E. (Sugar)
                       X
MO.—St.Louis
Brecht Butchers' Supply
  Co., G. V., 1201 Cass Av.
  (Lard) ....AAA
O'Brien Boiler Wks. Co.,
  Jno. (Soup) ....AA
St. Louis Stamping Co.
  (Brass; Enameled; Pre-
  serving; Stove; Covered;
  Fish; Enameled Tea)
                       AAAA
N. J.—Burlington
Stuart & Peterson Co.
  (Sugar; Steam Jacket;
  Preserving Plain or Por-
  celain Lined) ....A
N. Y.—Albany
Hoy & Co. (Tin Tea) ..A
Townsend Furnace & Ma-
  chine Shop Co. (Aniline
  Size) ....B
N. Y.—Brooklyn
Burkhard, Thomas, 494
  Flushing Av. (Steam Jack-
  et; Copper Jacketed) ...C
Houchin & Huber (Soap) D
New York Stamping Co.
  (Five O'Clock Tea) ....A
Pioneer Iron Wks., William
  & King (Steam Jacket;
  Tar) ....A
Sweeney Mfg. Co., W. H.
  (Brass; Butter; Copper;
  Copper Range; Stove;
  Punch; Brass Range; Tin
  Range; Tea; Tin, Copper
  Tea) ....A
N. Y.—Buffalo
Aldrich Mfg. Co. (Copper;
  Tea; Copper Sugar;
  Sugar) ....A
Dopp Co., H. W., 522 Elliot
  (Steam Jacket Hotel;
  Sugar; Soap) ....D
Jewett Mfg. Co., Jno. C.
  (Swing; Tin Tea) .....A
Pierce Co., Geo. N. (Cop-
  per; Tin Tea) ....AA
Shepard & Co., Sidney (Tin
  Tea; Brass; Copper) AAAA
Smith's Sons Co., John E.
  (Lard; Tanners') ......B
Squier Mfg. Co., Geo. L.
  (Copper; Iron; Sugar) AAA
N. Y.—Manlius
Cheney & Son, S. (Caldron)
                       A
New York City
Ansonia Brass & Copper Co.
  (Brass) ....AAAA
Bramhall-Deane Co. (Jacket
  Hotel Steam; Iron)....B
Cottrell & Sons Co., C. B.
  (Wax) ....AAA
Crandall & Godley Co.
  (Copper) ....AA
Dame & Townsend Co., 76
  John (Steam Jacket) D
Deeley & Co., Robert (Tar;
  Glue; Soap; Sugar) ..AA
Joachum, Andrew, 148 E.
  50th (Steam Copper Jack-
  eted) ....E
Koven & Bro., L. O., 50
  Cliff (Tar) ....A
Lalance & Grosjean Mfg.
  Co. (Brass; Butter; Enam-
  eled; Fish; Preserving;
  Enameled Tea) ....AAAA
Lovejoy Co. (Wax) ......B
Mott Iron Wks., J. L., 88
  Beekman (Steam Jacket)
                       AA
Pollock Co., Alex., 203 West
  (Tar) ....D
N. Y.—Rome
Rome Mfg. Co. (Tea; Brass;
  Copper; Range) ......B
N. Y.—Troy
Brewer, Wm. W., 2787 6th
  Av. (Steam Jacket) ..F

KETTLES (Con.)

Troy Stamping Wks. (Milk; Preserving; Tin Tea) .... **AAAA**

N. Y.—Utica
International Heater Co. (Caldron; Glue; Tar, etc.) .... **AAA**

N. Y.—Watkins
Frost, C. S. & Chas. H. (Iron) ....**F**

N. C.—Charlotte
Tompkins Co., D. A. (Size) .... **AA**

OHIO—Bucyrus
Geiger & Bush (Copper) **D**
Picking & Co., D. (Copper; Copper Jacket; Brass) ..**C**

OHIO—Cincinnati
Amer. Copper & Brass Wks. 427 E. Front (Brass; Copper) ....**A**
Blymyer Iron Wks. Co. (Iron; Sugar) ....**B**
Ellerhorst & Co., J. G. (Steam Jacketed; Copper) **A**
Day Co., J. H., 1144 Harrison Av. (Steam Jacket) **A**
Honhorst & Co., Jos., 525 E. Pearl (Tar) ....**E**
Littleford Bros., 453 E. Pearl (Steam Jacket; Tar) ....**B**
Van Range Co., John (Jacketed Steam Hotel; Copper Jacket) ....**A**

OHIO—Cleveland
Cleveland Stamping & Tool Co. (Tea; Range) .....**A**

OHIO—Defiance
Defiance Machine Wks. (Iron) ....**A**

OHIO—Hamilton
Kahn & Bros., F. & L. (Iron) ....**A**

OHIO—Massillon
Hess Snyder & Co., (Sugar; Soda) ....**AA**

OHIO—Salem
Silver Mfg. Co. (Lard) **AA**

OHIO—Sidney
Wagner Mfg. Co. (Iron) ..**A**

OHIO—Springfield
Long, W. Z. (Copper) ....**D**

PA.—Allegheny
Carlin's Sons Co., Thos. (Tar) ....**A**

PA.—Belleville
Hertzler & Zook (Iron) ..**E**

PA.—Elizabethport
Buch's Sons Co., A. (Caldron) ....**A**

PA.—Marietta
Marietta Hollow Ware & Enameling Co. (Preserving) ....**B**

PA.—New Castle
Penna. Engineering Wks. (Soda) ....**AA**

PA.—Philadelphia
Butterworth & Sons Co., H. W. (Color) ....**A**
Hibbs, E. A., 209 Quarry (Tar) ....**B**
Nittinger, August (Lard) **A**
Wilfong Bros. (Galvanizing; Lead Melting) ....**B**

PA.—Pittsburg
Riter-Conley Mfg. Co. (Tar; Glue) .·.............**AAA**
Scaife & Sons Co., Wm. B., 221 1st Av. (Steam Jacket) ....**AAA**
Standard Mfg. Co.(Acid) **AA**

PA.—Reading
Mt. Penn Stove Wks. (Soap; Sugar) ....**A**

PA.—South Pittsburg
Blacklock Foundry (Sugar; Tea; Range) ....**C**

PA.—Washington
Petroleum Iron Wks. Co. (Steam Jacket) ....**A**

PA.—Williamsport
Keeler Co.. E. (Steam Jacket; Tar) ....**A**

PA.—York
Motter & Sons, Geo. F. (Steam Jacket) ....**C**

R. I.—Providence
Brown & Sharpe Mfg. Co. (Soda; Tool Cleaning) .... **AAAA**

KETTLES (Con.)

Franklin Machine Co. (Size) ....**A**

TENN.—Chattanooga
Chattanooga Plow Co (Sugar) ....**AA**

WIS.—Milwaukee
Allis-Chalmers Co. (Lead Melting) ....**AAAA**
Toepfer & Sons, W. (Brewing) ....**B**

WIS.—Racine
Freeman's Sons Mfg. Co., S. (Steam Jacket) ....**A**

KEYS

CONN.—Chester
Brooks & Sons, M. S. (Flat Riveted; Flat Spring) ..**B**

CONN.—Deep River
Pratt, Reed & Co. (Piano; Organ) ....**AA**

CONN.—Hartford
Billings & Spencer Co. (Machine) ....**AA**
Hartford Machine Screw Co. (Bicycle) ......**AAAA**
Whitney Mfg. Co. (Machine) ....**A**

CONN.—Ivoryton
Comstock, Cheney & Co. (Organ; Piano) ......**AA**

CONN.—Plainville
Clark & Son, A. N. (Watch) **B**

ILL.—Chicago
Illinois Malleable Iron Co. (Street Washer) ..**AAAA**
Piano & Organ Supply Co., 125 Racine Av. (Piano)**AA**
Railway Appliance Co. (Brakeshoe) ....**A**
Whitman & Barnes Mfg. Co. (Machine; Rivetd) **AAAA**

ILL.—Kewanee
Western Tube Co. (Street Washer) ....**AAA**

ILL.—Sandwich
Sandwich Mfg. Co. (Machine) ....**AA**

MASS.—Cambridge
Tower, Sylvester (Organ; Piano) ....**AA**

MASS.—Plymouth
Cobb & Drew (Flat Spring) **AA**

MASS.—Springfield
Bullock Mfg. Co. (Watch) **A**

MASS.—Worcester
Wilson & Smith (Flat Spring) ....**E**
Wire Goods Co. (Flat Spring) ....**A**

MICH.—Muskegon
Morton Mfg. Co. (Machine) **B**

N. H.—Lebanon
Kendrick & Davis (Dust Proof Watch; Self Adjusting Watch) ....**A**

N. Y.—Auburn
Henry & Allen (Machine)**A**
Meyer & Co. (Gib Head Machine) ....**D**

N. Y.—Brooklyn
Williams & Co., J. H. (Machine) ....**AA**

New York City
Houchin Co., Thos. W. (Gas Turning) ....**D**
Mitchell-Vance Co. (Gas Turning) ....**AA**
Olney & Warren, 35 Dey (Finished Gib; Plain Head Machine) ....**D**
Russell & Erwin Mfg. Co. (Door) ....**AAAA**
Sargent & Co., 151 Leonard (Bed) ....**AAAA**
Shrauch Bros. (Piano) ..**A**
Yale & Towne Mfg. Co. **AAAA**

N. Y.—Throopsville
Meyr & Co. (Spring; Machine) ....**D**

OHIO—Akron
Whitman & Barnes Mfg. Co. (Spring; Machine) **AAAA**

OHIO—Canton
Buckeye Mfg. Co. (Machine) **D**

KEYS (Con.)

OHIO—Cleveland
Standard Tool Co. (Flat
Spring; Machine) ....AA
OHIO—Dayton
Climax Tag Co. (Flat
Riveted) X
OHIO—Youngstown
Finished Steel Co. ....A
PA.—Beaver Falls
Standard Gauge Steel Co.
(Finished Steel Machine)
A
PA.—Chester
Keystone Drop Forge Wks.
(Shafting Machine) ....B
PA.—McKees Rocks
Kidd Bros. & Burgher Steel
Wire Co. ....B
PA.—Philadelphia
Hoopes & Townsend Co.,
1330 Buttonwood (Ma-
chine) ....AAA
PA.—Reading
Reading Hdw. Co. ..AAAA
R. I.—Pawtucket
Haskell Mfg. Co., W. H.
(Riveted) ....AA
Janckes Mfg. Co., E.
(Spring) ....A
R. I.—Valley Falls
Hindley Mfg. Co. (Flat
Spring; Riveted Machine)
D

KID

See Leather

KILLERS

CONN.—Bridgeport
Hotchkiss. Edw. S. (Rat) A
MASS.—Worcester
Bigelow, J. F. (Fly) .....F
Parker Wire Goods Co.
(Fly) ....D
Wire Goods Co. (Fly) ....A
MICH.—Fenton
Phillips Co., A. J. (Fly) A
N. Y.—Buffalo
Western Wire Goods Co.
(Fly) ....D
OHIO—Cleveland
Osborn Mfg. Co. (Fly) ...B

KILNS

See also Dryers

ALA.—Birmingham
Milner & Kettig Co. (Dry)
AA
ILL.—Chicago
Aitchison Perforated Metal
Co. (Malt) ....B
Allis-Chalmers Co., Home
Ins. Bldg. (Rotary)AAAA
Andrews & Johnson Co., 256
Washn. Boul. (Dry) ..B
Andrews Co., A. H. (Lum-
ber Drying) ....AA
Dorrance, Chas. J. (Brick)
B
Garden City Fan Co., 43 S.
Clinton (Hot Blast Dry)B
Goetz & Flodin Mfg. Co.
(Malt) ....A
Laubenheimer Co., Geo. H.
(Malt) ....D
Stier Mfg. Co., Herman
(Malt) ....D
Wolf Co., Fred. W., 139
Rees (Lime; Malt; Ice)
AAA
Trenkhorst, Frank (Malt) F
IND.—Indianapolis
Natl. Dry Kiln Co. (Dry) A
Standard Dry Kiln Co.
(Lumber Drying; Brick)A
LA.—New Orleans
Haubtman & Loeb Co., 217
Gravier (Lime) ......B
MD.—Baltimore
Emerson Co., Fidelity Bldg.
(Dry) C
MASS.—Boston
Sturtevant Co., B. F. (Dry)
AAA
MASS.—Hyde Park
Boston Blower Co. (Dry;
Lumber) ....B
MICH.—Detroit
Amer. Blower Co. (Dry;
Lumber; Brick) ......AA

KILNS (Con.)

N. J.—Jersey City
Krom Machine Wks., 10
Essex (Dry) X
N. Y.—Buffalo
Buffalo Forge Co. (Dry)
AAA
Squier Mfg. Co., G. L.
(Bone Coal) ....AAA
New York City
Bartlett, Hayward & Co.,
100 Bway. (Lime) .....B
Deeley & Co. (Bone Black)
AA
Howard & Morse, 45 Fulton
(Dry) ....D
Koven & Bro., L. O., 50
Cliff (Dry) ....A
OHIO—Bucyrus
New York Blower Co. (Dry)
A
OHIO—Canton
Bonnot Co. (Dry; Rotary) A
OHIO—Cleveland
Cummer & Son Co., F. D.
(Dry) ....AA
Dyer & Co., E. H., New
England Bldg. (Lime)
AAA
OHIO—Youngstown
Pollock Co., Wm. B. (Ce-
ment; Dry; Lime) ....AA
PA.—Allentown
McDermott Bros. (Rotary)
E
Mosser & Son, W. F.
(Rotary) ....A
PA.—Erie
Link Machinery Co., E. M.
(Dry) C
PA.—Philadelphia
Carnell. Geo. (Dry) ......B
Phila. Textile Mchry. Co.
(Veneer Drying) ....AA
PA.—Pittsburg
Amer. Furnace & Mach. Co.
(Cement) ....D
Riter-Conley Co. (Lime)
AAA
PA.—South Bethlehem
Bethlehem Fdry. & Machine
Co. (Rotary) C
PA.—Wilkesbarre
Vulcan Iron Wks. (Rotary)
AAAA
PA.—York
Broomell Schmidt & Steacy
Co. (Continuous Lime
Burning; Dry) ....A
WIS.—Milwaukee
Bayley & Sons Co., Wm.,
732 Greenbush (Dry) ..X
Galland-Henning Pneumatic
Malt Drum Mfg. Co.
(Malt) ....D
Natl. Blower Wks. (Dry) A

KINET-
OPHONES

New York City
Stevens & Co., C. E. .....F

KIPS

See also Leather

MICH.—Holland
Cappon & Bertoch Leather
Co. ....AA
N. J.—Newark
Kaufherr & Co. ....A
New York City
Neumann & Co., R. .....A
U. S. Leather Co. ....AAAA
PA.—Allegheny
Lappe & Sons, J. C. ....AA
WIS.—Milwaukee
Gallun & Sons, A. F..AAAA
Pfister & Vogel Leather Co.
AAAA
Zohrlaut Leather Co.,
Herman ....AA

KITES

New York City
Horsman Co., E. I.........C

KITS

See also Cooperage

CAL.—San Francisco

KITS (Con.)
California Barrel Co. ....**AA**
MICH.—Grand Haven
Kilbowm & Kilbourn (Fish)
       D
N. H.—Keene
Impervious Package Co.
 (Paint) ....**B**
New York City
Wilkens Bros., 440 Pearl
 (Tool) ....**A**
N. Y.—Poughkeepsie
Poughkeepsie Art Pulp Co.
 (Fishing Tackle) ......**F**
OHIO—Middlefield
Ohio Pail Co. (Paint) ....**B**
OHIO—Sandusky
Kilbourne & Co ....**C**
VA.—Richmond
Richmond Cedar Works
 (Wooden Pickle)...**AAAA**

KNAPSACKS

N. J.—Newark
Peddie & Co., T. B. .....**AA**
New York City
Boyle & Co., John, 112
 Duane ....**AA**
McHugh, John F. ....**C**
OHIO—Cincinnati
Pettibone Bros. Mfg. Co., **A**

KNEES

MICH.Allegan
Allegan Fdy. & Machine Co.
 (Oscillating Bob) .....**H**
N. Y.—Manlius
Cheney & Son, S. (Iron;
 Bob) ....**A**
WIS.—Menominee
Oscillating Sleigh Co. (Oscil-
 lating Sleigh) ....**D**
WIS.—Milwaukee
Milwaukee Wagon Iron Wks.
 (Sleigh) ....**AA**

KNITTERS

See also Machinery

VT.—Bennington
Tiffany Bros. (Cord) .....**A**

KNIVES

See also Silverware; Cutlery.

CAL.—San Francisco
California Saw Works (Ma-
 chine) ....**A**
Simonds Saw Co., 33 Market
 (Machine) ....**C**
CONN.—Bridgeport
Bridgeport Hdw. Mfg. Co.
 (Putty) ....**B**
Challenge Cutlery Corpora-
 tion (Farrier) ....**A**
Hubbell Harvey (Saw)....**C**
Hurwood Mfg. Co. (Oyster;
 Clam) ....**C**
Knapp & Cowles Mfg. Co.
 (Mincing; Lawn Border;
 Pruning) ....**C**
CONN.—Collinsville
Collins Co. (Cane)....**AAAA**
CONN.—Danielson
Parkhurst, L. D. (Butcher;
 Slicing; Bread.. Shoe;
 Kitchen; Oyster; Paper;
 Oil Cloth; Banana; Cigar;
 Rubber; Cork; Leather;
 Putty, etc.) ....**G**
CONN.—Derby
Derby Razor Co. (Pattern
 Cutting) ....**F**
Silver Plate Cutlery Wks.
 (Carving; Plated Table) **B**
CONN.—East Haddam
Boardman & Son, L. (Plated
 Table) ....**AA**
CONN.—Essex
Tiley Pratt Co. (Paper) ..**D**
CONN.—Hamden
Henry Mfg. Co., Jno. T.
 (Pruning) ....**E**
CONN.—Hartford
Billings & Spencer Co. (Com-
 bination; Paper Cutter;
 Leather; Oil Cloth; Cigar;
 Banana; Rubber; Cork;
 Sporting) ....**AA**
CONN.—Lakeville
Holley Mfg. Co. (Budding;

KNIVES (Con.)
Grafting; Cloth Cutter's;
 Pruning) ....**B**
CONN.—Meriden
Meriden Britannia Co. (Sar-
 dine; Fish; Plated Table)
       AAAA
Meriden Cutlery Co. (Putty;
 Bread; Palette; Carving;
 Cheese; Fruit; Hunting;
 Kitchen; **Lemon; Orange;**
 One Armed Men's; **Slicer;**
 Table; Butchers; Shoe;
 Skinning) ....**AA**
Miller Bros. Cutlery Co.
 (Hunting; Pocket) .....**A**
Rogers & Bros;, C. (Tinned)
       AAAA
CONN.—Naubuc
Williams Bros. Mfg. Co.
 (Bread; Hunting; Kitch-
 en: Table; Butcher;Plate
 Table) ....**A**
CONN.—New Britain
Humason & Beckley Mfg.
 Co. (Hunting) ....**A**
Landers, Frary & Clark
 (Putty; Oyster; Palette;
 Banana; Carving; Bread;
 Cheese; Fish Scaling;
 Fruit; Kitchen; Mincing;
 Sheath; Butcher's; Paint-
 er's; Beet; Cigar; Corn;
 Paper; Oil Cloth; Cork;
 Leather; Tobacco) .**AAAA**
CONN.—New Haven
Henn & Co., A. S. (Mincing)
       F
Sargent & Co. (Clam; Cigar)
       AAAA
Schollhorn Co., Wm. (Cigar)
       A
CONN.—Norwich.
Rogers & Co., C. B. (Planer;
 Tenoning) ....**A.AAA**
CONN.—Seymour
Swan Co., Jas. (Drawing) **A**
CONN.—Southington
Peck-Stow & Wilcox Co.
 (Drawing) ....**AAAA**
CONN.—Unionville
Humphrey, H. W. (Mincing)
       D
CONN.—Wallingford
Simpson, Hall, Miller & Co.
 (Fruit; Plated Table) **AAAA**
Wallace Sons Mfg. Co., R.
 (Carving; Fish; Fruit;
 Kitchen; Lemon; Orange;
 Pocket; Table; Plated
 Table) ....**AAAA**
CONN.—Waterbury
Rogers & Bros. (Plated Ta-
 ble) ....**AAAA**
Rogers & Hamilton (Fish;
 Plated Table) .....**AAAA**
CONN.—Westport
Bradley's Sons, G. W.
 (Drawing) ....**D**
CONN.—Winsted
Empire Knife Co. (Pocket)
       B
Winsted Edge Tool Co.
 (Drawing; Corn) ....**B**
Winsted Mfg. Co. (Hay;
 Corn Cutter) ....**AAA**
GA.—Atlanta
Southern Saw Wks. (Ma-
 chine) ....**B**
ILL.—Chicago
Amer. Cutlery Co., 193 Ma-
 ther (Putty; Carving;
 Butcher's; Slicing; Paper
 Hanger's; Tobacco; Cigar;
 Cotton Sampling; Fish;
 Table; Bread; Cake;
 Fruit; Cheese; Shoe;
 Crumb; Paper; Oil Cloth;
 Banana; Rubber; Cork;
 Leather, etc.) ....**AA**
Dunne & Co., Geo. W., 687
 Carroll Av. (Brick)....**B**
Latham Machinery Co.
 (Bookbinder's; Paper Cut-
 ter) ....**C**
Nicol & Co. (Paper) ......**D**
ILL.—Freeport
Arcade Mfg. Co. (Mincing)
       A
ILL.—Peoria
Herschel Mfg. Co.
 (**Mower; Reaper**) ......**A**
ILL.—Rock Island
Donaldson Bros. (Planer), **C**

KNIVES (Con.)

ILL.—Streator
Iwan Bros. (Both Handles Adjustable Hay; Corn Cutter, also Hedge) C

IND.—Anderson
Anderson Knife & Bar Co. (Machine) C

IND.—Evansville
Evansville Tool Wks. (Axle Handle Hedge: Root) ..A

IND.—Indianapolis
Alkins & Co., E. C. (Machine; Cane; Hedge; Corn; Planer; Striking; Tobacco; Veneer; Beet; Saw) AAAA
Barry Saw Co. (Planer) ..C

IND.—Lawrenceburg
Bishop & Co., Geo. H. (Cane; Corn) ....A

IOWA—Ft. Madison
Iowa Farming Tool Co. (Corn) ....A

MAINE—East Wilton
Clark & Parsons Co. (Corn; Sugar Cane) ....B

MAINE—Hallowell
North Wayne Tool Co. (Hay; Corn Cutter; Bread; Cake; Carving; Straw) C

MAINE—Skowhegan
Nolin Mfg. Co. (Hay; Rag)
...............E

MD.—Baltimore
Toland & Son (Machine) ..C

MASS.—Attleboro
Blake Co., Jas. E. (Silver; Cuticle) ....A

MASS.—Boston
Amer. Tool & Machine Co., 109 Beach (Belt) .....AA
Dame, Stoddard & Co. (Butcher; Slicing; Bread; Shoe; Cigar; Oyster; Paper; Oil Cloth; Banana; Rubber; Cork; Cloth; Leather, etc.) ....A
Stanley Mfg. Co. (Shoe) ..B
Stubbs, Simeon K., 32 Kemble (Machine) ....D
Wilkinson & Co., A. J. (Drawing) ....B
Woods Machine Co., S. A. (Matcher) ....AA

MASS.—Brocton
Snell & Atherton (Machine; Shoe) C
Tuck Mfg. Co. (Oil Cloth; Oyster; Banana; Butchers; Cigar; Shoe; Paper Hange'rs; Pruning; Slicing; Bread; Leather; Tobacco)
...............E

MASS.—Fitchburg
Simonds Mfg. Co. (Drawing; Machine; Planer; Rag Cutter; Tobacco; Paper; Matcher; Leather; Angle; Cane; Rotary Slitting; Saw; Wood Pulp) ..AAA

MASS.—Greenfield
Nichols Bros. (Boning; Bread; Carving; Cheese; Fish; Hunting; Slicer; Butter; Fruit; Splitting; Steak; Butchers'; Skinning; Sticking) C

MASS.—Holyoke
Holyoke Bar Co. (Machine; Lumber Machine) ......E

MASS.—Lawrence
Horne & Sons Co., J. H. (Planing Machine; Paper Machine) ....A

MASS.—Lowell
Lovejoy & Son. D., 1 Cushing (Machine; Leather Splitting; Guillotine) ....B

MASS.—Millbury
Buck, Chas. (Drawing) ..B

MASS.—New Bedford
Pairpoint Corpn. (Plated Table) ....AA

MASS.—Newburyport
Towle Mfg. Co. (Plated Table) ....AA

MASS.—Northampton
Northampton Cutlery Co. (Paper Hanger's; Putty; Scraping; Bread; Fruit; Hunting; Kitchen; Slicer; Table; Butcher's; Skinning; Sticking; Plated; Table; Tobacco) ....A

KNIVES (Con.)

MASS.—North Easton
New England Specialty Co. (Shoe; Butcher's; Slicing; Bread; Kitchen; Mincing)
...............F

MASS.—Rockdale
Hankey & Co., A. (Machine; Bookbinder's; Rag Cutter; Lumber Machine; Planer)
...............A

MASS.—Sharon
Lothrop Mfg. Co., H. A. (Bread; Cheese; Fish; Kitchen; Mincing; Butchers'; Cigar; Shoe) X

MASS.—Shelburne Falls
Lamson & Goodnow Mfg. Co. (Butcher's; Painter's; Carving; Slicing; Bread; Shoe; Butter; Corn; Fish; Fruit; Hacking; Hunting; Kitchen; Mixing; Palette; Paper; Oil Cloth; Banana; Cigar; Rubber; Cork; Leather; Pie; Printer's Ink; Putty) ....A

MASS.—Southbridge
Harrington Cutlery Co. (Cloth Cutters; Feather Curler's; Butcher's; Cigar) C

MASS.—Springfield
Bullock Mfg. Co. (Printer's)
...............A

MASS.—Turners Falls
Russell Cutlery Co., Jno. (Clam; Druggist's; Oyster; Palette; Cigar; Shoe; Sticking; Plated Table; Boning; Bread; Carving; Cheese; Fish; Fish Scaling; Fruit; Hunting; Kitchen; Lemon; Orange; One Armed Men's; Pocket; Sheath; Slicer; Steak; Table) ....AA

MASS.—Worcester
Coes, Loring & Co. (of Every Description) ....A
Hardy Co., L. (Machine), C

MICH.—Detroit
Detroit Edge Tool Wks. (Machine; Tanner's Veneer Cutting) ....D

MICH.—Grand Rapids
Amer. Machinery Co. (Machine) ....B
Fox Machine Co., 127 N. Front (Machine)........A
Munson Co. (Machine) ....E

MICH.—Jackson
Withington & Cooley Mfg. Co. (Hay; Straw) .....AA

MICH.—Kalamazoo
Harrow Spring Co. (Lawn Mower) ....B

MICH.—Port Huron
Port Huron Saw Co., Ltd. (Machine) C

MO.—St. Louis
Curtis & Co. Mfg. Co., 2201 Wash. Av. (Machine) ..A

N. H.—Antrim
Goodell Co. (Putty; Boning; Bread; Hunting; Kitchen; Table; Carving; Cheese; Butcher's; Cigar; Shoe; Skinning; Sticking; Asparagus; Trimming; Corn; Fruit; Sportsmen's; Tomato) ....A

N. H.—Bennington
Kimball Co., C. J. (Draw; Fish; Tanner's; Butcher's; Shoe; Slicing; Bread; Oyster; Paper; Oil Cloth; Banana; Cigar; Rubber; Cloth; Leather; Putty), D

N. H.—Dover
Flagg & Son, Joshua G. (Leather Splitting, Machine) ....F

N. H.—Nashua
Grover File Co., Jno. B. (Machine) ....F

N. J.—Grenloch
Bateman Mfg. Co. (Hay; Corn Cutter; Asparagus) A

N. J.—Newark
Banister & Co., A. F. (Clam; Corn) ....A
Heller Bros. Co. (Farrier)
...............AA

KNIVES (Con.)

OHIO—Toledo
Toledo Saw Co. (Machine), C
PA.—Atglen
Chalfant Hdw. Mfg. Co.
  (Fish Scaling) X
PA.—Beaver Falls
Emerson, Smith & Co. (Machine; Lumber Machine) A
PA.—Philadelphia
Disston & Sons, Henry (Machine; Cork; Corn; Beet; Cane; Drawing; Hedge; Paper; Oil Cloth; Cigar; Rubber; Leather; Saw)
  AAAA
Enterprise Mfg. Co., of Phila. (Self Gauging; Cheese; Tobacco) ..AAAA
Hessenbruch H. (Pocket) ..A
McNiece & Son, Wm., 515 Cherry (Machine) C
Natl. Cutlery Co. (Serrated)
  C
Nittinger, Aug., 826 N. 4th (Butcher's) ....A
Phila. Novelty Mfg. Co. (Mincing) ....D
Phillips & Sons Co., F. R. (Machine) ....D
Stortz & Son, Jno., 210 Vine (Chipper; Machine; Paper Hanger's; Putty; Oyster; Butcher's; Paper) .....E
PA.—Pittsburg
Amer. Axe & Tool Co. (Hay; Rag; Planer; Tobacco)
  AAAA
Crucible Steel Co., of Amer. (Solid Steel Shear) AAAA
Heppenstall Forge & Knife Co. (Machine) ....B
Lippert, E. T. (Paper) X
Tretheway & Co., Samuel (Solid Steel Shear; Circular; Slitting; Wood Pulp)
  F
PA.—Titusville
Schott & Morgan Cutlery Co. (Sportsmen's) ....B
PA.—Wilkesbarre
Wyoming Cutlery Co. (Butcher's) ....AA
PA.—Williamsport
Foucart, J. E. (Machine; Moulding Machine) .....F
PA.—Wrightsville
Wrightsville Hdw. Co. (Fish Scaling) ....B
R. I.—Providence
Bens, Wm. (Silver; Cuticle)
  C
TENN.—Chattanooga
Chattanooga Saw Wks. (Machine) ....D
VT.—Bellows Falls
Derby & Ball (Corn) ......B
VT.—Wallingford
Wallingford Mfg. Co. (Hay; Corn Cutter) X
WIS.—Beloit
Beloit Iron Works (Machine)
  A
Dowd, R. J. (Machine)....C
WIS.—Janesville
Kent, A. C. (Corn) C
WIS.—Manitowoc
Willott & Sons, J. (Machine)
  E

KNOBS

See also Hardware; Carriage.

CONN.—Collinsville
Hartigan, Wm. R. (Base) H
CONN.—Meriden
Foster, Merriam & Co. (Desk; Drawer) .....AA
CONN.—Mt. Carmel
Woodruff & Sons Co., W. W. (Carriage) ....A
CONN.—New Britain
Corbin P. & F. (Desk; Door)
  AAAA
Judd, Oliver S. (Picture), B
CONN.—New Haven
Cowles & Co., C. (Carriage)
  A
Hoggson & Pettis Mfg. (Organ Stop) ....A
Mallory, Wheeler Co. (Door)
  AA
Sargent & Co. (Car Door; Screwless; Base; Floor;

KNOBS (Con.)

Carriage; Draw; Shutter; Picture) ....AAAA
CONN.—Norwich
Ossawan Mills Co. (Picture)
  B
CONN.—Stamford
Yale & Towne Mfg. Co. (Desk; Door; Drawer; Picture; Shutter) .....AAAA
CONN.—Torrington
Union Hdw. Co. (Wooden; Base; Floor) ....AA
CONN.—Waterbury
American Ring Co. (Desk; Cabinet) ....A
Plume & Atwood Mfg. Co. (Desk) ....AAA
CONN.—Winsted
Richards Hdw. Co., T. C. (Porcelain) ....A
ILL.—Freeport
Stover Mfg. Co. (Door; Shutter) ....AA
ILL.—Paxton
Paxton Hdw. Mfg. Co. (Tea; Coffee Pot)............X
ILL.—Rockford
Clark Co., J. L. (Enameled)
  D
ILL.—Waukegan
Alden & Sons, R. (Organ Stop) ....F
KY.—Newport
Higgins Mfg. Co. (Carriage)
  A
MASS.—Worcester
Parker & Co., Jno. L. (Stove) ....B
MICH.—Grand Rapids
Grand Rapids Brass Co. (Door; Drawers; Picture)
  A
Hardware Supply Co. (Drawer; Shutter)......X
N. J.—Newark
Sommer's Son John (Wooden) ....A
N. J.—Trenton
Artistic Porcelain Co. (Porcelain) X
Greenwood Pottery Co. (Porcelain) ....A
Morris & Wilmore (Porcelain) X
Standard China Works (Porcelain) ....D
N. Y.—Albany
Troy Nickel Wks. (Stove) C
N. Y.—Binghamton
Crandall, Stone & Co. (Carriage) ....A
New York City
Bardsley, Jos., 147 Baxter (Base; Floor; Door; Drawer; Shutter)......B
Estes & Sons, E. B. (Door)
  AA
Gutta Percha & Rubber Mfg. Co. (Key) ....AAAA
Judd & Co., H. L. (Drawer; Shutter; Picture) .....AA
Metal Stamping Co. (Door; Shutter; Carriage) .....A
N. Y. Nickel Plating & Mfg. Co. (Stove) ....D
Peck, Stow & Wilcox Co. (Carriage; Door; Drawer; Shutter) ....AAAA
Russell & Erwin Mfg. Co. (Car Door; Screwless; Drawer; Shutter) ..AAAA
N. Y.—Yonkers
India Rubber & Gutta Percha Insulating Co. (Key)B
OHIO—Akron
Baker, McMillen Co. (Enameled; Picture; Wood, for Covers) ....B
Goodrich Co., B. F. (Key)
  AAAA
OHIO—Cincinnati
Monarch Carriage Goods Co. (Carriage) ....B
OHIO—Cleveland
Taylor & Boggis Fdy. Co. (Door) ....AA
OHIO—East Liverpool
Brunt Porcelain Wks., G. F. (Porcelain) ....B
Thomas & Sons Co., R. (Door; Porcelain) ......A
OHIO—Piqua
Piqua Handle & Mfg. Co. (Closet; Wooden; Door) A

KNOBS (Con.)

PA.—Philadelphia
Hall & Carpenter , 518 Race
(Cabinet) ....AA
PA.—Reading
Reading Hdw. Co. (Door;
Drawer; Shutter) ..AAAA
R. I.—Providence
New England Butt Co.
(Door) ....AA

KNOCKERS

CONN.—Branford
New York Lock Co. (Door)
X
CONN.—New Haven
Sargent & Co. (Door) AAAA
NEW York City
Jackson Co., Wm. H., 29
E. 17th (Colonial Dooor)
A
Janusch, F.G., 752 E. 134th
(Door) C
Russell & Erwin Mfg. Co.,
43 Chambers (Door)
AAAA
Sargent & Co., 151 Leonard
(Door) ....AAAA
PA.—Reading
Reading Hdw. Co. (Door)
AAAA

KNOTS

PA.—Philadelphia
Horstmann Co., Wm. H.
(Regalia; Uniform also
Shoulder) ....AAAA

KNUCKLES

See also Joints

ILL.—Chicago
Nicol & Co. (Brass) ......D
Railway Appliances Co.,
Old Colony Bldg (Steel)
A
ILL.—Sterling
Novelty Iron Wks. (Pump
Rod) ....E
IND.—Indianapolis
Insert Knuckle Co. (Steel
Insert) ....D
N. J.—High Bridge
Taylor Iron & Steel Co.
(Steel) ....AAAA
New York City
Gould Coupler Co., 20 W.
34th (Steel) ....AAAA
PA.—Chester
Chester Steel Castings Co.
(Steel & Car Coupler)
AAAA

KNURLS

N. J.—Elizabeth
Braunsdorf-Mueller Co. ...D
N. Y.—Brooklyn
Crowell, Gilmer, 294 Gra-
ham ....E

KRUSHITE

VT.—Rutland
Fremier, J. H., Cleveland
Av. (for Sawing Stone)
D

LABELS

CAL.—San Francisco
Crocker Co., H. S., 215
Bush (Paper) ....AA
Galloway Lithographing Co.,
410 Sansome (Paper) ..B
Mutual Label & Litho Co.,
23 Main (Paper) ....AAA
Pacific Lithographic Co.,
615 Sansome (Paper) ....D
Roesch Co., Louis, 321 San-
some (Paper) C
COLO.—Denver
Union Photo Engraving Co.,
523 Market (Paper) ....D
CONN.—Bridgeport
Schwerdle Stamp Co.,
(Brass) ....F
CONN.—Waterbury
Steele & Johnson Mfg. Co.
(Brass) ....A
ILL.—Chicago
American Label Co., 34
Wabash Av. (Paper) ...A
Crowe Metal Mfg. Co., 71

LABELS (Con.)

W. Jack Boul. (Brass).E
Glaser & Co., B. Z., 156
Market (Paper).......C
Merchants Publishing Co.,
33 Clark (Paper) ......B
Randolph Box & Label Co..
35 So. Clark (Paper)...B
Redlich Mfg. Co., 2 Oak
(Pickles; Preserves) ...B
Riverside Ptg. Co., Schiller
Bldg. (Paper) ....A
IND.—South Bend
Pershing & Co. (Gummed).D
MD.—Baltimore
American Label Co.
(Canners) ....A
Bartgis & Bros., C. C., 206
Water (Canners') .....A
Maryland Color Ptg. Co.,
Holliday & Hillen (Can-
ners) ....D
Salisbury Mfg. Co., 5 S.
Liberty (Paper) ....A
Simpson & Doeller Co., Mil-
ton Av. & Lanvale (Can-
ners) C
MASS.—Boston
American Label Mfg. Co.,
120 Milk (Paper) ......A
Boston & Lockport Block
Co. (Plant; Tree) .....A
Dennison Mfg. Co. (Bottle;
Pasteboard) ......AAAA
Forbes Litho Mfg. Co., 185
Summer (Paper) ......AA
MICH.—Detroit
Calvert Litho Co. (Canners)
B
MICH.—Ypsilanti
Scarf Tag, Label & Box Co.
(Paper) ....B
MINN.—St. Paul
Collins Co., H. L. (Can-
ners') C
MO.—St. Louis
Central Label Co., 218 Wal-
nut (Paper) C
Igelstroem Sign & Label
Co., Jno., 19 S. B'way
(Paper) ....D
St. Louis Label Works, 306
Morgan (Paper) C
Woodward & Tiernan Ptg.
Co., 309 No. 3rd (Paper)
AAA
N. J.—Bloomfield
National Label Press
(Paper) ....B
N. J.—Pompton Lakes
German Artistic Weaving
Co. (Woven Silk) .....B
N. Y.—Binghamton
Binghamton Litho. Mfg.
Co. (Paper) ....D
N. Y.—Brooklyn
Brass Goods Mfg. Co., 92
3d (Aluminum) ....B
Schwencke Lithographic
Co., O. L. (Liquor Bottle)
A
N. Y.—Buffalo
Buffalo Woven Label Works
D
Burt, F. W., Seneca & Ham-
burg (Paper)..........D
Courier Co., 197 Main
(Paper) ....AA
Dunston, G. H., West Sen-
eca & Terrace (Canners')
A
Fox & Fox, 127 Erie
(Paper) ....D
N. Y.—Geneva
Geneva Woven Label Works
(Silk) C
New York City
American Label Mfg. Co.,
260 W. B'way (Paper).B
American Litho. Co., 4th
Av. & 19th (Paper).AAAA
American Silk Label Mfg.
Co. (Sila)............B
Hagerty Bros. & Co.
(Glass) ....A
Keller Printing Co., 722
B'way (Bakers').......C
Manhattan Tip Label Co.,
713 Broadway (Paper).D
Marris & Co., Jno. M.,
219 Fulton (Gummed)..B
Ness, Geo. M., Jr., 61 Ful-
ton (Brass)...........H
Nevins-Church Press, 141

LABELS (Con.)

B'way (Paper).........A
New York Woven Label
  Mfg. Co.............D
Price Bros. & Co., 65 Duane
  (Paper) C
Sperlings' Sons, E. M., 713
  B'way (Paper; Woven
  Silk) ....D
Stafford Co., N. (Brass).F
Tablet & Ticket Co., 381
  B'way (Gummed).....B
Wagner & Co., L. C, 43
  E. 20th (Paper).......B
Wicke Ribbon Co. (Cigar
  Box) ....A
Witteman Bros. (Bottle;
  Cigar Box)............

N. Y.—Rochester
Karle Lithographic Co.
  (Canners') ....A
Rochester Folding Box Co.
  (Paper) ....B
Stecher Litho. Co.
  (Canners') ....AA

OHIO—Cincinnati
Eagle Litho. Co (Paper).D
Henderson Litho. Co.
  (Liquor; Paper).......B
United States Ptg. Co.
  (Paper) ....AAAA

OHIO—Cleveland
K. D. Box & Label Co., 84
  Sterling Av. (Paper)...B

OHIO—Salem
Harris & Co. (Drug; Gum-
  med) ....D
Walton, Thos. J.........E

PA.—Beaver Falls
Ingram-Richardson Mfg. Co.
  (Tree; Plant)..........D

PA.—Bradford
Mc Cord Patent Label Co.,
  N. W. (Drug)........X

PA.—Philadelphia
American Label Mfg. Co.
  Bourse Bldg. (Paper)..A
Beck Paper Co., Chas....B
Fenton Label Co. (Gummed)
  ....F
Gillams' Sons' Co. (Drug).C
Hofstetter Bros...........C
Ketterlinus Litho. Mfg. Co.
  (Paper) ....AA
Keystone Silk Weaving Co.
  (Silk) ....D
National Decalcomania Co.
  ....F
Quaker City Label Works
  (Jno. Reilly), Powers'
  La. & S. 72d (Paper)..B
Whitall, Tatum & Co.
  (Glass) ....AAAA

PA.—Pittsburg
Fuller, Wm. H., 3117 Penn
  Av. (Paper)...........D

R. I.—Pawtucket
Salisbury Mfg. Co........A
Sutcliffe & Co., Adam
  (Paper) ....B

R. I.—Providence
Talcott. F. (Paper) .....B

VA.—Glen Allen
Cussons, May & Co. (Drug)
  ....B

WASH.—Seattle
Tucker-Hanford Co., 229
  Jackson (Salmon).......C

LACERS

N. J.—Paterson
Royle & Sons, Jno. (Auto-
  matic Lock; Shoe Stitch)
  ....A

LACES

See also Lacing

CONN.—Bridgeport
Bridgeport Coach Lace Co.
  (Coach) C

CONN.—Ansonia
Ansonia O. & C. Co. (Cot-
  ton Shoe; Corsets)....AA

ILL.—Chicago
Chicago Porpoise Lace Co.
  (Leather Shoe) X
Nelson Porpoise Lace Co.
  (Leather Shoe).......X

ILL.—Zion City
Zion Lace Industries (Point;

LACES (Con.)

Normandy; Nottingham)
  ....AAA

MASS.—Boston
Boston Excelsior Co., 26
  Canal (Bed)...........A
Jenkins Mfg. Co. (Corset;
  Shoe) ....B
Miller, Geo. A., (Shoe)....C

MASS.—East Braintree
Jenkins Mfg. Co. (Cotton
  Corset; Shoe)........B

MASS.—Easthampton
Colton, Geo. S. (Corset)...C

MASS.—Fall River
Heywood Narrow Fabric Co.
  ....D

MASS.—Springfield
Hutchins Narrow Fabric
  Co. (Bed).............C

MASS.—Worcester
Witter & Co., H. M. (Bed)
  ....B

N. J.—Camden
Loeb & Schoenfeld Co.
  (Dress; Curtain, etc.)
  ....AAAA

N. J.—Jersey City
Hall, H. S. (Silk Dress)..D

N. J.—Paterson
Gregory, Wm. (Silk Corset;
  Shoe) ....F

N. Y.—Brooklyn
Barthels Mfg. Co. (Shoe;
  Corset) ....A
Jennings' Lace W'ks..AAAA

New York City
Dusenbury, Louis, 398 B'way
  (Carriage) ....A
Fine Woolen Co., 339 B'way
  B'way (Carriage).....C
Locke & Altherr (Com)...B
Siegman & Weil, 110 Greene
  (Church) ....A
Stewart & Sparry, 438
  Broome (Baby Carriage)
  ....B
Schiess, Theodore.........C

N. Y.—Rochester
Rochester Textile Wks.
  (Dress Silk)..........E
Shaefer & Klein (Coach)..A
Schlegel Mfg. Co. (Coach)
  ....B
Union Textile Mfg. Co.
  (Coach) ....B
Vogt Mfg. & Coach Lace
  Co. (Coach)..........A

N. Y.—Unadilla
Tie Co. (Corset; Shoe)....D

PA.—Nazareth
Schneebeli & Co., G. A.
  (Edgings for Ribbed Un-
  derwear) C

PA.—Philadelphia
Byram, F. A. (for Under-
  wear) ....D
Friedberger Mfg. Co. (Silk;
  Cotton; Worsted)......A
Horstmann Co., Wm. H.
  (Coach) ....AAAA
Sibson & Stern (Trimming)
  ....A

PA.—Reading
Nat. Shoe & Corset Lace Co.
  (Silk Shoe; Corset).....X

PA.—Scranton
Scranton Lace Curtain Co.
  ....A

R. I—Pawtucket
Amer. Textile Co........B
Kenyon Mfg. Co., Jno. J.
  (Shoe) ....B

R. I.—Providence
Amer. Shoe Lace Co. (Shoe)
  ....D
Elmwood Mills (Shoe)....C
Fletcher Mfg. Co. (Boot;
  Shoe; Corset).......AAA
Hope Webbing Co. (Bed)
  ....AAA
Joslin Mfg. Co. (Shoe;
  Corset) ....B

LACING

See also Laces

CONN.—Hartford
Jewell Belting Co. (Belt;
  Metallic Tipped) ....AAA

CONN.—Norwich
Norwich Leather Belt Mfg.

LACING (Con.)

Co. (Belt Leather).....D
Ossawan Mills Co. (Bicycle Guard) ....B
CONN.—Unionville
Upson Nut Co. (Belt, Metallic) ....AAA
CONN.—Waterbury
Bristol Co. (Belt, Steel)..D
ILL.—Chicago
Allen Mfg. Co., W. D., 151 Lake (Belt, McCauley Wire) ....B
Chicago Rawhide Mfg. Co., 75 E. Ohio (Belt, Rawhide) ....A
Curtis & Co. Mfg. Co., 42 S. Canal (Belt, Wire)..C
Hercules Mfg. Co., 69 Dearborn (Belt) ....D
MASS.—Boston
Bay State Belting Co., 119 Franklin (Belt, Leather) ....A
Whitcher & Co. (Shoe)..A
MASS.—Easthampton
Colton, Geo. S. (Corset)..A
Dibble & Warner (Shoe)..B
MASS.—Salem
Kelton & Bruce Mfg. Co. (Belt, Rawhide) C
MASS.—South Attleboro
Coupe & Co., Wm. (Rawhide) X
MASS.—Worcester
Graton & Knight Mfg. Co. (Belt) ....AAA
MICH.—Grand Rapids
Hayden & Co., J. M. (Belt, Wire) ....D
MO.—St. Louis
Hartman Hide & Leather Co. (Belt) ....B
Missouri Belting Co. (Rawhide) C
Shultz Belting Co., 402 Barton (Belt, Leather)...AA
N. H.—Concord
Page Belting Co. (Belt, Rawhide) ....AA

Crown Lacing—genuine Raw Hide Lacing—guaranteed for quality and measurement. Will stand warm, moist climate and far more enduring than the ordinary Lacing sold on the market. The ordinary white lacing almost always seen, although called a rawhide, is not a genuine rawhide.

Hercules lacing—this is the best of the ordinary white so-caller raw-hides and is very carefully selected. It is surpassed only by the Crown process.

Crown Tanned Lacing—a choice tanned lacing.

N. H.—Dover
Williams & Sons, I. B. (Belt) ....AA
N. J.—Newark
American Porpoise Lace Co. (Shoe) ....B
N. J.—Paterson
Dempwolf, Charles (Belt).X
N. Y.—Brooklyn
Moll Mfg. Co., Aug. (Silk) ....B
New York City
New York Leather Belting Company, 8 Ferry (Belt Leather; Rawhide).....A
Schieren & Co., Chas. A., 15 Ferry (Belt; Tipped) ....AAAA
Southwick Co., Geo. W., 149 Centre (Belt Wire).D
Stine & Co., J. R. (Belt)..A
OHIO—Akron
Akron Belting Co. (Belt Wire; Rawhide) ......B
Whitman & Barnes Mfg. Co. (Rawhide) ....AAAA
OHIO—Cleveland
Malin & Co., 24 Long (Belt

LACING (Con.)

Composition Wire; Steel Belt; Metallic Belt)...D
OHIO—Youngstown
American Belting Co. (Belt; Wire) C
PA.—Philadelphia
Rhoads & Son, J. E., 241 Market (Leather Belt)..B
R. I.—Pawtucket
Kenyon Mfg. Co. (Corset; Shoe) ....B
Weatherhead, Thompson & Co. (Rawhide) ....A
R. I.—Providence
Brown Bros. Co., 62 Exch. Pl. (Belt; Rawhide)...A
Burgess & Son, A. (Rawhide) X
Fletcher Mfg. Co. (Tipped; Corset; Shoe) ......AAA
WIS.—Milwaukee
Anstedt Leather Co., C., 552 Commerce (Belt) ......A

LACQUERS

CONN.—Bridgeport
American Lacquer Company (Brass) ....F
CONN.—New Haven
New Era Lustre Co. (Canners') ....F
ILL.—Chicago
Barrett & Co., M. L. (Canners') ....A
Devoe & Raynolds Co., 176 Randolph ....AAAA
MICH.—Detroit
Detroit White Lead Works ....AAA
N. J.—Newark
Hanson & Van Winkle Co. ....AA
N. J.—Rahway
Egyptian Lacquer Mfg. Co. ....B
N. Y.—Brooklyn
Moller & Schumann Co.....A
New York City
Marx & Rawolle ....AA
Standard Varnish Wks...AA
Zinsser & Co., W ....A
Zucker & Levett & Loeb Co., 526 W. 25th ....A
OHIO—Cincinnati
British-American Co. ....E
OHIO—Cleveland
Glidden Varnish Co. ...AA
PA.—Pittsburg
Atlas Paint Co., 2638 Liberty Av. (Anti-Rust)...X

LADDERS

CAL.—San Francisco
California Barrel Co. (Step) ....AA
CONN.—New Haven
Flint, A. W. (Wooden)....E
ILL.—Aurora
Richards Mfg. Co. (Rolling Store) ....B
Wilcox Mfg. Co. (Rolling; Trolley) ....B
ILL.—Chicago
Bicycle Step Ladder Co., 50 State (Rolling; Trolley) ....B
Chicago Woodenware Co., 21st & Sagamon (Extension) ....D
Schomer, Henry (Step) ..D
Warren Mfg. Co., J. D., Masonic Temple (Rolling; Trolley) ....B
ILL.—Plano
Earl Mfg. Co., F. H. (Extension) C
IND.—Ft. Wayne
Bowser & Co., S. F. (Step) ....A
IND.—Goshen
I. X. L. & Goshen Pump Co. (Step) ....B
IND.—Indianapolis
Udell Works (Extension; Step) ....A
MAINE—South Paris
Paris Mfg. Co. (Step)....A
MASS.—Boston
Ames Plow Co. (Step) ....AAAA
MASS.—Holyoke
Coburn Trolley Track Mfg.

LADDERS (Con.)

Co. (Rolling; Trolley)..A

MASS.—Worcester
Hill Dryer Co. (Step) ...D

MICH.—Detroit
Barnum Wire & Iron Wks.,
103 Shelby (Steel).....B

MICH.—Saginaw
Morley Bros. (Inc.) (Rolling) ....AA

MINN.—St. Paul
Calander, Jno., 148 8th
(Rolling; Trolley) ...D

MO.—St. Louis
Ludlow-Saylor Wire Co.
(Steel) ....AA
Milbradt & Co., G. A., 1924
N. B'way (Rolling; Trolley) C

N. Y.—Albion
Mallory, C. M. (Step) ...F

N. Y.—Brooklyn
Cooper & McKee (Folding;
Shelf; Step) C

N. Y.—Forrestville
Pierce & Jewett (Step)...C

New York City
Cornell Co., J. B. & J. M.,
26th & 11th Av. (Steel)
AA
Fellows & Lathrop Co., 104
Reade (Step) ....D
M'Cabe Hanger Mfg. Co.,
425 W. 25th (Tubular
Rolling; Trolley) ......B
Mace & Co., L. H. (Folding; Step) ....B
Reilley Bros., 322 W. 41st
(Painters') ....D
Stokes & Co., Wm. A., 30
Warren (Step) ....D

N. Y.—Poughkeepsie
Lane Bros. Co. (Rolling;
Trolley) ....A

N. Y.—Rochester
Pease, F. B. (Extension).D

N. Y.—Watervliet
Tilley, John S. (Extension)
E

OHIO—Ashland
Myers & Bro., F. E. (Rolling; Trolley; Steel)
AAAA

OHIO—Canton
Balm, Julius C. (Extension
Step) ....F

PA.—Indiana
Indiana Bent Rung Ladder
Co. (Step) ....B

PA.—Philadelphia
Berger Bros. Co., 231 Arch
(Sectional; Extension;
Single) ....A
Hall Bros., 902 Master
(Rolling; Trolley) X

PA.—Pittsburg
Phoenix Steel Construction
Co., Penn. Av. & 3d
(Steel) ....D

VA.—Norfolk
Whitehurst Co., R. W.
(Step) ....B

LADLES

See also Silverware; Tinware; Glassware; etc.

CONN.—Meriden
Manning, Bowman & Co.
(Enamelled; Soup) ..AA
Meriden Britannia Co. (Ice
Cream; Soup) .....AAAA

CONN.—Southington
Peck, Stow & Wilcox Co.
(Melting; Plumbers')
AAAA

ILL.—Chicago
Holland, Wm., 60 S. Canal
(Melting; Plumbers')...E

ILL.—Clyde
Coonley Mfg. Co. (Soup)..B

ILL.—Downers' Grove
Dicke Tool Co. (Melting;
Plumbers') ...!.......C

ILL.—Evanston
Mark Mfg. Co. (Foundry)
AA

ILL.—Harvey
Whiting Fdy. Equipment
Co. (Crane; Truck; Foundry) ....AA

MD.—Baltimore
Poole Engineering & Ma-

LADLES (Con.)

chine Co. (Foundry)..AA
Sinclair-Scott Co. (Melting)
E

MASS.—Boston
Sturtevant Co., B. F. (Foundry) ....AAA

MASS.—Lowell
Scannell Boiler Wks. (Foundry) ....B

MASS.—Worcester
Stewart Boiler Wks. (Foundry) ....B

MICH.—Detroit
Byram & Co. (Inc.) (35 to
35,000 lbs. Foundry Steel;
Babbitt) ....D
Northern Engineering Wks.
(Foundry) ....A
Richardi & Bechtold (Batter) ....B
Union Heater Supply Co.
(Melting; Plumbers')..G

MICH.—Kalkaska
Freeman Mfg. Co. (Butter)
B

MO.—St. Louis
Pleuger & Henger Mfg. Co.
(Melting) ....A
St. Louis Stamping Co.
(Enamelled; Soup).AAAA

N. J.—Newark
Atha Tool Co. (Foundry)..A
Bernz, Otto S., 13th & S.
Orange Av. (Melting;
Plumbers') ....B
Johnson, Wm., 249 Plane
(Melting; Plumbers')...D
Osborne & Co., C. S. (Steel)
B

N. Y.—Buffalo
Aldrich Mfg. Co. (Brass).A
Pratt & Letchworth Co.
(Melting) ....AAA
Shepard & Co., Sidney (Tin)
AAAA

New York City
Cottrell & Sons' Co., C. B.
(Stereotypers') .....AAA
Crandall & Godley Co. (Ice
Cream) ....AA
Lalance & Grosjean Mfg.
Co., 19 Cliff (Wrought
Steel Melting; Plumbers';
Enamelled; Soup).AAAA
Ogden Co., J. Edward, 147
Cedar (Foundry) ......B
Sargent & Co. (Melting)
AAAA

OHIO—Cincinnati
Obermayer Co., S., 647
Evans (Foundry) .....AA

OHIO—Cleveland
Smith Foundry Supply Co.,
J. D., 40 S. Water.....D

OHIO—Columbiana
Columbiana Boiler Co.
(Open Hearth; Bessemer
Plant) C

OHIO—Girard
Girard Boiler & Mfg. Co.
(Cinder) ....D

OHIO—Lowellville
Meehan Boiler & Construction Co. (Foundry; Melting) ....B

OHIO—Massillon
Hess, Snyder Co. (Wax).AA

OHIO—Niles
Niles Boiler Co. (Foundry)
B

OHIO—Salem
Clark Co., W. J. (Melting;
Plumbers'; Foundry Steel)
A

OHIO—Warren
Warren City Boiler Works
(Foundry) ....A

OHIO—Youngstown
Pollock Co., Wm. B. (Foundry; Melting) ....AA

PA.—Allegheny
Carlins' Sons, Thos. (Foundry) ....A

PA.—Brownsville
Herbertson's Sons, J. (Glass
House) ....D

PA.—Chester
Vulcan Wks. (Open Hearth;
Bessemer Plant) ......B

PA.—Erie
Holland's Mfg. Co. (Melting; Plumbers') ....B

LADLES (Con.)

PA.—New Castle
Penna. Engineering Works (Open Hearth; Bessemer Plant; Foundry; Melting) ...... AA

PA.—Philadelphia
Mills & Bro., Thomas (Ice Cream) .... A
Paxson Co., J. W., 1021 N. Del. Av. (Foundry; Melting) .... AA
Wilfong Bros., 52d & P. W. & B. R. R. (Foundry) .. B

PA.—Pittsburg
Carroll-Porter Boiler & Tank Co. (Foundry; Bessemer Plant; Open Hearth) ... B
Munroe & Son Mfg. Co., 23d & Smallman (Bessemer Plant; Open Hearth). AA
Riter- Conley Mfg. Co. (Foundry; Melting). AAA
Standard Mfg. Co. (Plumbers') .... AA
Union Foundry & Machine Co. (Foundry) .... B

PA.—Reading
Reading Hdw. Co. (Melting; Plumbers') ..AAAA

PA.—Towanda
Loetzer Valve & Mfg. Co. (Seamless Plate Steel Melting; Plumbers') ...X

PA.—Washington
Petroleum Iron Works Co. (Foundry; Open Hearth; Bessemer Plant) ...... A

PA.—Wilkesbarre
Vulcan Iron Wks. (Foundry) .... AAAA

WIS.—Racine
Racine Malleable & Wrought Iron Co. (Foundry; Melting; Plumbers') .... A

LAGGING

IND.—Mishawaka
Dodge Mfg. Co. (Hardwood) AAA

MASS.—Boston
Trainer Mfg. Co., C. W., 89 Pearl (Locomotive) ....E

MINN.—Winona
Union Fibre Co. (Locomotive) .... B

New York City
Johns-Manville Co., H. W., 100 William (Locomotive) AAAA
United States Mineral Wool Co., 143 Liberty (Locomotive) ....D

OHIO—Alliance
Alliance Asbestos Mfg. Co. (Locomotive) .... B

OHIO—Lockland
Carey Mfg. Co., Philip (Locomotive) .... AAA

PA.—Ambler
Keasbey & Mattison Co. (Magnesia Locomotive) AAAA

PA.—Erie
Watson Co., H. F. (Locomotive) .... AAA

PA.—Franklin
Franklin Mfg. Co. (Locomotive) .... AA

LAMBREQUINS

See Draperies; Curtains.

PA.—Philadelphia
Derk & Co., J., 1310 Lawrence .... D
Lewis, Robert, Bridesburg (R. R. Car) .... B

LAMPS

See also Hardware; Carriage; see also Lights.

CAL.—San Francisco
Boesch Lamp Co., 585 Mission (Station) C
California Incandescent Lamp Co. (Incandescent Electric) C

LAMPS (Con.)

COLO.—Denver
Capitol Electric Co. (Incandescent Electric) C

CONN.—Bridgeport
American Tube & Stamping Co. (Miners' Safety; Steel; Millyard) ..AAAA
Bridgeport Brass Co. (Bicycle; Brass; Brass Hand; Car; Acetylene; Carriage; Automobile; Hand; Table; Piano; Banquet Hanging) AAA
Bridgeport Gun Implement Co. (Bicycle) ....AA
Perkins' Electric Switch Mfg. Co. (Direct; Alternating Enclosed Arc; Electric Arc) ....A

CONN.—Bristol
Bristol Brass Co. (Clock; Hanging) ....AAA
New Departure Mfg. Co. (Bicycle) ....AAAA

CONN.—Danbury
Handel Co. (Art) X

CONN.—Hartford
Franklin Electric Mfg. Co. (Incandescent Electric; Incandescent Electric Car) C
Green & Bauer (Incandescent Electric; Incandescent Miniature) X
Howard & Co., Jas. L. (Car) ....A

CONN.—Meriden
Bradley & Hubbard Mfg. Co. (Artistic Iron; Banquet Brass; Banquet Iron; Bracket; Brass; Bronzed Iron; Central Draught; Chandelier; Decorated; Extension; Hall; Hanging;.Harp; Library Extension; Metal; Newell Post; Nickel; Piano; Table; Vase; Marine; Pulpit) AAAA
Meriden Britannia Co. (Decorated) ....AAAA
Miller & Co., Edw. (Brass; Student; Portable Table; Kerosene Oil Street; Bicycle; Bracket; Chandelier; Decorated; Hall; Hall Extension; Hand Brass; Hanging; Harp; Jacket; Jewelled; Library Extension; Night; Brass Piano; Table; Marine; Miners') ....AAAA
Parker Co., Chas. (Banquet Brass; Brass; Banquet Iron; Chandelier; Extension Hall; Bracket; Extension; Library Extension; Vase; Pulpit; Newell Post; Brass Piano) AAA
Wilcox Silver Plate Co. (Silver Plated) ..AAAA

CONN.—New Haven
Cowles & Co. (Inc.), C. (Carriage) ....A
English & Mersick Co. (Carriage) ....B
Scoville & Peck Co. (Automobile) X

CONN.—Stamford
Stamford Gas Stove Co. (Incandescent Gas) ......B

CONN.—Wallingford
Simpson - Hall - Miller Co. (Silver Plated) ..AAAA

CONN.—Waterbury
Benedict & Burnham Mfg. Co. (Bicycle) .....AAAA
Holmes, Booth & Haydens Co. (Inc.) (Hall; Hanging;. Banquet Brass; Library Extension; Brass Piano; Metal Stand; Table) ....AAAA
Noera Mfg. Co. (Boiler Makers') ....B
Plume & Atwood Mfg. Co. (Bicycle; Brass; Hall; Extension; Brass Hand; Library. Extension; Night; Table) ....AAA

Scovill Mfg. Co. (Brass; Bicycle; Table; Banquet Hanging) ....AAAA

ILL.—Chicago

Acorn Brass Mfg. Co., 192 Fulton; (Arc Gas; Arc; Gasoline) ....D

Adams & Westlake Co., Ontario, cor. N. Franklin (Tubular Station; Electric Arc; Bicycle; Carriage; Alternating & Direct Incandescent Arc; Candle; Car; Semaphore Signal; Signal; Switch) ...AAAA

American Lighting Co., 112 Michigan (Incandescent Gasoline; Regenerative Gas) ....D

Beckley-Ralston Co. (Gas; Bicycle) C

Brilliant Gas Lamp Co., 42 State (Gasoline) X

Central Electric Co. (Arc; Incandescent) ....A

Chicago Edison Co. (Incandescent) ....AAAA

Clow & Sons, Jas. B., 344 Franklin (Street) .AAA

Cosmopolitan Electric Co., 41 State (Incandescent Gas) ....B

De Tray & Weyler Mfg. Co., 301 W. Lake (Gasoline; Street) ....F

Electric Appliance Co. (Arc; Incandescent) ....B

Globe Light & Heat Co., ft. of Orleans (Street) ....B

Hine-Watt Mfg. Co. (Acetylene Gas) ....D

Illinois Electric Co., 239 Madison (Incandescent Electric) ....B

Lindsay Light Co. (Incandescent Gas) ....D

National Stamping & Electric Works, La Salle & Michigan (Arc; Gas) ..C

Plew, James E. (Acetylene Bicycle) ....B

Sanitary Specialty Mfg. Co., 55 N. Clinton (Arc; Gas)

Standard Gas Lamp Co. (Acetylene Gas) C

Standard Carriage Lamp Co., 43 S. Canal (Carriage) ....D

Sunbeam Incandescent Lamp Co., 259 S. Clinton (Incandescent Electric) ...B

Turner Brass Works, Franklin & Michigan (Arc; Gas; Vapor Gasoline; Incandescent Gas) ....A

Western Electric Co., 259 S. Clinton (Petite, Alternating Enclosed Arc; Incandescent Electric; Focussing) ....AAAA

White Mfg. Co., 158 Indiana (Bicycle; Automobile; Acetylene Gas; Carriage) X

Wilson, T. Cortez & Co., 239 Lake (Portable Table) B

IND.—Bloomington

Oakes Mfg. Co. (Incubator) D

IND.—Ft. Wayne

Fort Wayne Electric Works (Inc.) (Alternating & Direct Incandescent Arc; Incandescent Electric; Arc, Enclosed) ....AAAA

IND.—Kendallville

Baker & Son Co., Jas. R. (Fishing) C

IND.—Muncie

Warner Arc Lamp Co. (Enclosed Arc) ....D

IND.—Richmond

Richmond Indiana Mfg. Co. (Automobile; Carriage) .A

IOWA—Ottumwa

Hardsocg Mfg. Co. (Coal Miners') ....B

KANS.—Coffeyville

Pioneer Flint Glass Co. (Glass) C

KY.—Covington

Hemingray Glass Company (Glass) ....AA

KY.—Owensboro

Kentucky Electrical Co. (Incandescent Electric; Incandescent Gas) ....B

MASS.—Amesbury

Atwood Mfg. Co. (Carriage) C

Gray & Davis (Automobile; Carriage) C

MASS.—Boston

Anderson Mfg. Co., Albert & J. M. (Direct Enclosed Incan. Arc) ....A

Bernstein Electrical Mfg. Co., 286 Roxbury (Incan. Electric; Incan. Series).B

Dewey Co., F. O., 28 Canal (Railway Switch) ......D

Gilmore Electric Co., 625 E. 1st (Incan. Electric; Incan. Miniature; Incan. Renewed; Incan. Series) AA

Globe Gas Light Co., 79 Union (Street) ....D

Gray & Sons, Peter, 12 Marshall (Station Switch) ..C

Hollings & Co., Richard (Banquet Brass; Brass Piano; Iron Piano) X

Page Bros. & Co., 349 Cambridge (Car; Railway; Marine; Street Car) ....B

Re-New Lamp Co., 134 State (Incan. Renewed) C

Sherbourne & Co. (Car; Locomotive Cab) ....A

Thompson & Co., A. T., 26 Bloomfield (Focussing) ..X

Wheeler Reflector Co., 156 Pearl (Street Gas; Bracket; Harp; Reflecting Street) C

Zeigler Apparatus Co., 200 Summer (Arc; Photo-Engraving) X

MASS.—Danvers

Consolidated Electric Lamp Co. (Incan. Electric; Incan. Renewed) ....E

MASS.—Marlboro

Marlboro Electric Machine & Lamp Co. (Incan. Electric) ....B

MASS.—Middleton

Eagle Lamp Co. (Incan. Renewed) ....F

New England Electrical Works (Incan. Renewed) X

MASS.—New Bedford

Smith Bros. (Decorated)..X

Pairpoint Mfg. Co. (Art; Silver Plated) ....AA

MASS.—Pittsfield

Stanley Electric Mfg. Co. (Alt. & Direct Arc).AAAA

MASS.—Springfield

Munder Electric Co. (Incan. Electric) C

MASS.—Worcester

White Co., O. C. (Portable Incan. Electric) ....F

MICH.—Ann Arbor

Superior Mfg. Co. (Gasoline) ....E

MICH.—Detroit

Buhl Stamping Co. (Foundry; Station) ....AA

Ireland & Matthews Mfg. Co. (Gasoline, for gravity & pressure for out or indoor) ....A

Phelps Co. 33 State (Arc, Gas; Hylo Turn-down Incandescent Electric)....D

MICH.—Grand Rapids

Wheelr Electric Co., M. B. (Portable Table) ......D

MICH.—Kalamazoo

General Gas Light Co. (Arc, Gas) ....A

MINN.—Dassel

Wreisner Bros. (Portable Table) ....G

MO.—St. Louis

Columbia Incan. Lamp Co., 2115 Locust (Incan. Electric; Incan. Gas) ....B

LAMPS (Con.)

Eagle Generator Co. (Acetylene; Gas) ....A

Franke, H. E., 1119 Pine (Incandescent Gas)....E

Handlan-Buck Mfg. Co., 212 3d (Railway; Signal; also Engine & Tail; Target Switch) ....AA

Merkel, Herman, 511 Elm (Gasoline) X

Meyrose Lantern Co., F., 731 S. 4th (Street; Bicycle; Bracket; Central Draught; Tin Hand; Student; Hanging; Gas Street) X

Western Electrical Supply Co. (Enclosed Arc; Incan. Electric) X

N. J.—Elizabeth

Diehl Mfg. Co. (Arc; Enclosed Arc) ....B

N. J.—Harrison

Germania Electric Lamp Co. (Incan. Electric) X

N. J.—Newark

Lockwood Mfg. Co., C. N. (Carriage; Dash) .....B

Romer & Co. (Inc.) (Dash)
..............................C

Sacks Iron Foundry, Louis (Shoemakers' Kit) .....A

N. J.—New Brunswick ..

N. J. Lamp & Bronze Wks. (Central Draught; Decorated Metal; Brass Piano) ....AA

N. J.—Trenton

American Lamp & Brass Co. (Brass) X

N. Y.—Albany

Consolidated Car Heating Co. (Street Car) ......A

N. Y.—Brooklyn

Brooklyn Electric Lamp & Novelty Co., 278 Fulton (Incan. Miniature) ....F

Fox, Arthur W. 83 Schermerhorn (Focussing Arc; Arc, Photo-Engraving) ....F

Incandescent Burner Co., 633 Fulton (Arc, Gas) ....F

New York Stamping Co. (Five O'Clock Tea) ....A

Sweeney Mfg. Co., W. H. (Table) ....A

N. Y.—Buffalo

Shepard & Co., Sidney (Miners' Safety) ..AAAA

N. Y.—Glens Falls

Glens Falls Lantern Co. (Safety Hand) ....D

New York City

American-Belgian Lamp Co. (Banquet Iron; Bracket; Brass; Decorated; Extension; Hanging; Harp; Brass Piano; Iron Piano; Vase; Marine) ....D

Amer. Incandescent Lamp Co., 351 E. 61st (Incan. Gas) C

Amer. Miniature & Decorative Lamp Co. 320 Hudson (Incan. Miniature).B

Anchor Lamp Co., 258 B'way (Incan. Electric; Incan. Renewed) ....B

Angle Lamp Co., 76 Park Pl. (Marine) ....E

Ansonia Brass & Copper Co. (Hall) ....AAAA

Armspear Mfg. Co., 447 W. 53d (Signal) ....

Block Light Co., 17 Park Pl. (Incan. Gas) .....A

Bogue, Chas. J., 213 Centre (Arc, Photo-Engraving).C

Britelite Lamp Co., 45 B'way (Acetylene) ...B

Bryan-Marsh Co., 136 Liberty (Incan. Electric; Incan. Car; Incan. Miniature) ....B

Bunnell & Co., J. H. (Incandescent) ....B

Cluster Gas Light Co., 64 Bowery (Incan. Gas)..D

Colt Co., J. B. (Acetylene Gas; Focussing; Gas Bicycle; Arc Projecting).B

Consolidated Fruit Jar Co.

LAMPS (Con.)

290 B'way (Brass; Miners') ....AA

Crane Co., Wm. M., 1133 B'way (Arc, Gas) ....A

Cremo Incandescent Light Co., 110 E. 129th (Incandescent Gas) ....D

Dietz Co., R. E., 60 Laight (Automobile; Tubular; Carriage; Locomotive Danger, Car; Inspectors', Conductors', Railway; Red Signal; Station; Bicycle; Streeet; Switch; Dash; Side; Socket; Marine; Hanging; Night; Miners'; Photographers' Dark Room; Hunting; Locomotive Cab; Warehouse) ....A

Electric Arc Light Co., 120 Liberty (Electric Arc).X

Fiske Iron Works, J. W. (Street) ....B

Folmer & Schwing Mfg. Co. (Photographic Flash)...B

Fondeville & Van Iderstine, 37 Warren (Art) C

Frink, I. P. (Vestibule; Orchestra) ....AA

Funke, A. H., 325 B'way (Imported Automobile).B

General Incan. Arc Light Co., 570 1st Av. (Enclosed & Open Arc; Incan. Electric; Incan. Miniature)..A

Gilbert & Barker Mfg. Co., 82 John (Gasoline) ....A

Gleason Mfg. Co., E. P., 20 W. Houston (Arc, Gas; Street; Jewelled) ......B

Hicks & Schmidt, 587 G'wich (Car; Marine)..X

Hollis, H. B., 64 Murray (Art) X

Houchin Co., Thos. W. (Night, Wax; Alcohol).D

Howard & Morse, 45 Fulton (Miners' Safety) ......D

Ingersoll & Bro., Robert H., 51 Maiden Lane (Bicycle; Automobile) ....A

Ingersoll-Sergeant Drill Co., 26 Cortlandt (Mine Acetylene) ....AAAA

Jaeger Miniature Lamp Mfg. Co., Bible House (Incan. Miniature) ....D

Judd & Co., H. L. (Banquet Iron; Brass; Brass Piano)
..............................AA

Keuffel & Esser Co., 127 Fulton (Miners') ......AA

Kinsman Electric & Railway Supply Co., 91 Liberty (Desk Electric; Incan. Electric; Incan. Gas)
..............................E

Knickerbocker Light & Heat Co., 25 W. B'way (Incandescent Gas) X

Lamb, J. & R. (Pulpit) ...D

La Roche Co., F. A., 656 Hudson (Arc, Photo-Engraving) ....A

Lowell & Co., F. H., 92 William (Electric; Brass)
..............................A

McCandless & Co., H. W. 67 Park Pl. (Incan. Miniature) ....D

McLeod, Ward & Co., 27 Thames (Desk Electric; Dash; Orchestra) .....E

Manhattan Brass Co. (Bicycle; Incan.; Bracket; Brass Hand; Hanging Student) ....A

Manhattan Electrical Supply Co. (Incan.) ....AA

Manhattan General Construction Co., 20 B'way (Enclosed Arc) X

Manhattan Silver Plate Co. (Silver Plated) ..AAAA

Mannello, Angelo, 676 Eagle Av. (Carriage) C

Matchless Mfg. Co., 35 Warren (Arc Gas) X

Miner, Thos. T. W., 823 Eagle Av. (Street) .....F

Mitchell-Vance Co. (Brass

LAMPS (Con.)

PA.—Allegheny
Hipwell Mfg. Co. (Central Draft) ....D
Keystone Electric & Mfg. Co. (Arc) ....D
Pittsburg Lamp, Brass & Glass Co. (Banquet Iron; Brass; Central Draught; Library, Extension; Metal; Brass Piano; Silver Plated; Vase) .AAAA

PA.—Braddock
Pittsburgh Electric Lamp Co. (Incan. Electric)...X

PA.—Coraopolis
Consolidated Lamp & Glass Co. (Bracket;. Cut Glass; Glass; Glass Hand; Glass Stand) ....A

PA.—Corry
Climax Mfg. Co. (Incandescent Electric) ....A

PA.—Ellwood City
Glen Mfg. Co. (Vestibule: Porte Cochere), &c.)....C

PA.—Monongahela
Anton, George (Miners' Safety) ....D
Anton & Son, Jno. (Miners' Safety) ....D

PA.—Philadelphia
American Electrical Mfg. Co., 931 Chestnut (Alternating Arc) ....D
Automatic Incan. Light Co., Phila. Bourse (Incandescent Gas) ....D
Brill Co., J. G., 62d & Woodland Av. (Car) ......AAAA
Carey & Co., 304 Race (Carriage) ....D
Gaumer Co., Jno. L., 19th & Hamilton (Street; Pulpit) C
Gillinder & Sons (Decorated; Glass Hand; Night; Glass Stand) ....A
Helios Mfg. Co., 1229 Callowhill (Alt. & Direct Incan. Arc; Arc; Photo-Engraving) ....A
Kitson Hydro-Carbon Heating & Incan. Lighting Co., 8th & Willow (Incandescent Gas; Incan. Vapor Gas; Signal; Street) ....A
Klemm & Co. 132 N. 5th (Arc Gas; Oil Car) C
McCollin & Co., Thos. H. (Flash) ....H
Murray & Co., James J. (Fairy; Glass; Glass Hand) ....A
Paxson Co., J. W., 1021 N. Del. Av. (Foundry; Flask) ......AA
Penna. Globe Gas Light Co., Broad & Arch (Street)..A
Philadelphia Electrical & Mfg. Co.. 2011 Market (Open & Enclosed Arc).E
Rath Light Co., 903 Walnut (Incan. Gas) ....B
Rose Mfg. Co., 910 Arch (Carriage; Bicycle) C
Stewart Electric Co. Frank H. (Incan. Electric) ..B
Toerring Co.. 19th & Allegheny (Alt. & Direct Enclosed Incan. Arc) .....D
United Electric Improvement Co. (Arc; High Resistance) ....A
Welsbach Co., 1530 Chestnut (Incan. Gas) ....A

PA.—Pittsburg
Hamilton Lighting Co. (Arc Gas; Incan. Gas) ......F
Liberty Electric Mfg. Co.. 543 4th Av. (Incan. Electric) ....B
McKee Glass Co., S. (Glass; Glass Hand; Metal Stand) ....D
Phoenix Glass Co. (Cut Glass; Glass) ....A
Pittsburg Blue Print Co., Park Bldg. (Arc, Photo-Engraving) X
Pittsburg Brass Mfg. Co.

LAMPS (Con.)
(Bracket; Brass; Central Draught; Decorated; Extension Hall; Brass Hand; Hanging; Harp; Nickel; Metal Stand; Table; Vase) ....D
Pittsburg Electrical & Machine Works (Alt. & Direct Current Arc) ....E
Supply Mfg. Co. (Enclosed Arc) X
U. S. Glass Co. (Glass) ......AAAA
Westinghouse Electric & Mfg. Co. (Alt. & Direct Enclosed Arc; Incandescent Electric) ....AAAA

PA.—Reading
Arrowsmith Electric Co. (Incan. Electric) ......A
National Brass & Iron Wks. (Artistic Iron; Banquet Iron; Cut Glass; Decorated; Glass; Hanging; Library; Brass Piano)..A

PA.—Scranton
American Safety Lamp & Mine Supply Co. (Miners' Safety) ....F
Dodson Signal Lamp & Lantern Co. (Signal) ......D
Everhart Brass Works (Miners' Safety) ....A
Hughes Bros. (Miners' Safety) ....F
Hunt, Alex E. (Miners' Safety) ....B

PA.—White Mills
Doerflinger & Sons. C. (Cut Glass) ....AA

R. I.—Pawtucket
Tenny Mfg. Co., A. E. (Direct) X

R. I.—Providence
American Endoscopic Co.. Fletcher Bldg. (Incandescent Miniature) X
Hamblin Co.. Jno. A., 12 Beverly (Direct Arc) ..X
Hill Mfg. Co.. James (Brass Hand; Galvanized Hand) ....B

TENN.—Memphis
Irby & Gilliland Co. (Arc Gas) ....B

W. VA.—Bluefield
Superior Supply Co. (Coke) ....B

W. VA.—Moundsville
Fostoria Glass Co. (Glass; Glass Hand; Glass Stand; Vase) ....AAA

W. VA.—Wellsburg
Eagle Glass & Mfg. Co. (Night) ....A
Riverside Glass Wks. (Inc.) (Glass Hand; Night) ...C

W. VA.—Wheeling
Central Glass Works (Inc.) (Glass; Glass Hand; Glass Stand) ....A
Mutual Electric & Machine Co. (Direct Arc; Arc. Photo-Engraving) C

WIS.—Kenosha
Badger Brass Mfg. Co. (Headlights. Automobile; Acetylene Gas; Acetylene Bicycle; Acetylene Carriage; Brass; Chandelier; Extension) C

WIS.—La Crosse
Pacific Electric Co. (Electric Desk) X

LANDAUS

See also Carriages; Wagons.

CONN.—Bridgeport
Hinckes & Johnson .....AA
CONN.—New Haven
Goodrich & Co., J. F......AAA
ILL.—Sterling
Rock Falls Mfg. Co. .....A
IOWA—Dubuque
Connolly. Tom ....A
MASS.—Amesbury
Biddle & Smart Co.......B
MASS.—Boston
French & Co.. Ferd. F...D

LANDAUS (Con.)

N. J.—Newark
Quimby & Co., J. M......A
N. Y.—Albany
Goold Co., James ....B
New York City
Brewster & Co., J. B....B
Demarest & Co., A. T....A
N. Y.—Troy
Troy Carriage Works ...B
N. Y.—Watertown
Babcock Co., H. H.....AA
OHIO—Youngstown
Youngstown Carriage & Wagon Co. ....A

LANOLINE

New York City
Evans & Evans, 133 William ....A
Koechl & Co., Victor.....E

LANTERNS

CAL.—San Francisco
Boesch Lamp Co., 585 Mission (Railway) C
COLO.—Denver
Richter Iron Works, P., 1521 Stout (Artistic Wrought) X
CONN.—Bridgeport
Bridgeport Brass Company (Brass) ....AAA
Hurwood Mfg. Co. (Tubular; Kerosene, &c.; Police)..C
CONN.—Meriden
Miller & Co., Edward (Bulkhead; Brass; Bulls' Eye; Hanging Hall) ....AAAA
Parker Co., Charles (Hanging Hall) ....AAA
CONN.—Waterbury
Holmes, Booth & Haydens Co. (Inc.) (Brass)..AAAA
Scovill Mfg. Co. (Dry Paste) AAAA
ILL.—Chicago
Adams & Westlake Co., Ontario & N. Franklin (Railway) ....AAAA
Comstock, J. J., 46 Lake..E
McIntosh Stereopticon Co., 35 Randolph (Magic)...E
Martin Co., Edw. P. (Acetylene; Electrical; Solar).C
Nicol & Co. (Candle) ....D
Wilson & Co., F. Cortez (Candle) ....A
ILL.—Chicago Heights
Parish & Co., Chas. P. (Special Tin) ....B
MD.—Baltimore
National Lantern & Lamp Co., 19 N. Liberty .AAAA
MASS.—Boston
Gray & Sons, Peter, 12 Marshall (Signal; Switch; Railway) C
Thompson & Co., A. T., 26 Bromfield (Magic).....X
Tufts Meter Co., Nathaniel (Railway; Street; Ship) A
Wheeler Reflector Co., 156 Pearl (Railway; Street).C
MASS.—New Bedford
Weeden Mfg. Co. (Magic) D
MICH.—Detroit
Buhl Stamping Co. (Tubular) ....AA
MO.—St. Louis
Handlan, Buck Mfg. Co., 210 N. 3d (Railway)..AA
Meyrose Lantern Co., F. (Railway; Tubular; Bulls' Eye; Conductors'; Tubular) X
Zelnicker Supply Co., Walter A. (Railway) X
N. Y.—Glens Falls
Glens Falls Lantern Co. (Railway; Driving; Tubular; Tubular Safety)..D
New York City
Abercrombie & Fitch, 314 B'way (Folding).......B
American-Belgian Lamp Co. (Street) ....D
Amer. Flag Co. (Paper;

LANTERNS (Con.)
Chinese) ....A
Amer. Railway Supply Co., 24 Park Pl. (Railway)..X
Armspear Mfg. Co., 447 W. 53d (Railway) ....B
Cairns & Bros. (Fireman's) D
Colt Co., J. B., 21 Barclay (Magic) ....A
Cornell Co., J. B. & J. M. (Street) ....AA
Dietz Co., R. E., 60 Laight (Tubular; Brass; Bulls' Eye; Conductors'; Fireman's; Globe; Pocket; Police; Railway; Street; Tubular; Pocket, Red)..A
Dressel Railway Lamp Wks. 3875 Park Av. (Railway) D
Folmer & Schwing Mfg. Co. (Dry Plate; Magic)....B
Gennert, G. (Pocket, Red; Dry Plate) ....B
Howard & Morse (Bulls' Eye) ....D
Jackson Co., Wm. H., 29 E. 17th (Union Sq.) (Artistic Wrought)........A
Lovell & Co., F. H. (Ship) A
Pitt Composite Iron Wks., Wm. R., 111 5th Av. (Artistic Wrought).........D
Prosch Mfg. Co. (Dry Plate) ....F
Ramsperger & Co., H. G. (Dry Plate) ....B
Smith of New York Co., 352 Pearl (Railway; Street; Conductors'; Globe) ....F
Tower & Lyon Co., 95 Chambers (Police).......B
Wellington Mfg. Co. (Street) X
N. Y.—Port Jervis
Orange County Flint Glass Wks. ....A
N. Y.—Rochester
Ham Mfg. Co., C. T. (Railway; Bulkhead; Buoy; Conductors'; Reflector; Tubular) ....AA
Rochester Head Light Wks. (Railway) ....D
Rochester Optical Co. (Dry Plate) ....A
Star Head Light Co. (Conductors') X
OHIO—Canton
Berger Mfg. Co. (Railway; Tubular; Kerosene, &c.) AA
OHIO—Cincinnati
Macleod & Co., Walter, 463 E. Front (Railway).....B
OHIO—Cleveland
Ohio Electric Wks. (Electrical) ....D
OHIO—Columbus
Ohio Pump & Brass Co., 18th & Oak (Railway).......C
OHIO—Tiffin
Ohio Lantern Co. (Dash Board; Railway; Tubular) B
OHIO—Warren
Winfield Mfg. Co. (Tubular) ....A
PA.—Philadelphia
Gaumer Co., Jno. L. (Hanging Hall) C
Keystone Lantern Co., Real Est. Bldg. (Railway)..D
Klemm & Co., 132 N. 5th (Gas) C
Roberts Mfg. Co., 3011 Chestnut (Railway) ...C
W. VA.—Wheeling
Wheeling Stamping Co. (Tubular) ....A
WIS.—Kenosha
Badger Brass Mfg. Co. (Dark; Magic) C
WIS.—Milwaukee
Loeffelholz & Co., 170 Clinton (Railway)..........A

LAPBOARDS

See Boards

LAPPERS

See also Machinery

MASS.—Boston
Leigh, Evan A., Mason Bldg. (Cotton) ....B
MASS.—Lowell
Kitson Machine Co. (Cotton) ....AAA
MASS.—Taunton
Mason Machine Wks. (Cotton) ....AA
MASS.—Whitinsville
Whitin Machine Wks. (Cotton) ....AAAA
PA.—Philadelphia
Philadelphia Textile Machy. Co., Hancock & Somerset (Cotton) ....AA
R. I.—Pawtucket
Atherton Machine Co., A. T. (Cotton) ....B
Howard & Bullough American Machine Co. (Cotton) AAA

LAPS

N. J.—Jersey City
Williams & Son, E. A. (Jewelers'; Metal) ...AA

LARD

CAL.—San Francisco
Armour Packing Co., 211 Clay ....AAAA
Cudahy Packing Co., 513 Front ....AAAA
Dodge, Sweeney & Co., 114 Market ....AAA
Western Meat Co., 6th and Townsend ....AAAA
COLO.—Pueblo
Nuckols' Packing Co......A
GA.—Macon
Mc Caw Mfg. Co......AAA
ILL.—Alton
Alton Packing Co........A
ILL.—Chicago
Anglo-Am. Prov. Co., B. of T. Bldg. ....A
Armour & Co., 205 La Salle AAAA
Fairbank Co., N. K..AAAA
Friedman Mfg. Co., Union Stock Yards..........A
Jenkins & Co., G. R., 12 Franklin (Oil) ....A
Nelson Morris & Co...AAAA
Swift & Co., Union Stock Yards ....AAAA
IND.—Hammond
Hammond Co., G. H..AAAA
Kingan & Co. ......AAAA
IND.—Jeffersonville
Pfau & Son, G............A
IOWA—Cedar Rapids
Sinclair & Co., T. M.AAAA
IOWA—Ottumwa
Morrell & Co., Jno....AAAA
KY.—Louisville
Louisville Packing Co., 1318 Story Av. ....AAA
MD.—Baltimore
Kingan Prov. Co., 355 North ....AAAA
MASS.—Boston
North Pack. & Prov. Co., 33 N. Mk't ....AAAA
Squire & Co., Jno. P., 39 N. Mk't ....AAAA
MASS.—Lowell
Dexter, S. K............A
MASS.—Springfield
Springfield Prov. Co. (Brightwood) ....AA
MINN.—Minneapolis
Swift & Co., 215 N. 5th AAAA
MO.—Kansas City
Dold Packing Co., Jacob AAAA
MO.—St. Joseph
Krug Packing Co., H..AA
Nelson Morris & Co...AAAA
Swift & Co. (Br.)....AAAA
MO.—St. Louis
Fairbank Co., N. K., 3d &

LARD (Con.)
Convent ....AAAA
Sayers & Co., Hy. Cham. of Com...........A
NEBR.—South Omaha
Cudahy Packing Co.AAAA
Union Rend. & Ref. Co. (Ltd.) ....A
N. J.—Jersey City
Central Lard (Br. N. Y. City) ....AA
N. Y.—Brooklyn
Stutz & Sons, L., 817 B'way C
N. Y.—Buffalo
Danahy Packing Co., Metcalf & Clinton ....A
Kamman Bros., 759 Seneca B
Klinck Bros., 588 Howard B
Klinck, C., 101 E. Market AA
Weppners' Sons, A., La. & Elk ....B
New York City
Central Lard Co., Produce Exchange ....AA
Cooke Bros., 138 Front..B
Fairbank Co., N. K., 27 Beaver ....AAAA
Nelson Morris & Co., 23 13th Av. ....AAAA
North Pack & Prov. Co. (Br.) Produce Exchange AAAA
Rohe & Bro., Produce Exchange ....AAA
Wilcox Lard & Ref. Co., W. J., 27 Beaver........AA
N. Y.—Syracuse
Nelson Morris & Co., (Br.) AAAA
OHIO—Cincinnati
Burckhardt & Co., 323 Sycamore ....AA
Morrison & Co., Thos., Bk. & Winchell Av.......AA
Perin Bros., 14 E. Front..C
PA.—Philadelphia
Burk & Bro., Wm., 1210 N. 3d ....A
Fairbank Co., N. K., Bourse Bldg......AAAA
Michener & Co., J. H....AA
Warthman & Co., 705 Callowhill ....A
PA.—Pittsburg
Dalzell Son & Co., J......C
PA.—Pottsville
Ulmer Packing Co., Jacob A
TEXAS—Ft. Worth
Ft. Worth Packing & Prov. Co. ....AA

LARIATS

See Saddlery & Harness

ILL.—Chicago
Chicago Rawhide Mfg. Co. (Rawhide) ....A
KY.—Louisville
Louisville Girth & Blanket Co. (Hair) C
MASS.—Boston
Samson Cordage Wks. (Cotton; Linen)........A
Silver Lake Co............A
MO.—St. Louis
Leschen & Sons Rope Co., A. AAA
New York City
Abercrombie & Fitch Co., 314 B'way.............B
N. Y.—Watervliet
Covert Mfg. Co. ....A

LARRIES

PA.—Connellsville
Connellsville Machine & Car Co. ....A
W. VA.—Fairmont
Helmick Fdy. & Machine Co. (Charging)........D

LARYNGOSCOPES

PA.—Philadelphia
Boekel & Co., Wm., 578

LATCHES (Con.)
tor Door; Gate; **Night**;
Refrigerator; Thumb;
Water Closet).....AAAA
PA.—Wrightsville
Susquehanna Castings Co.
(Gate) ....AA
Wrightsville Hdw. Co. (Reversible and Self Closing
Barn Door; Fire Door;
Gate; Thumb).........B
R. I.—Providence
New England Butt. Co.
(Gate) ....AA
WIS.—Albany
Albany Hdw. Specialty
Mfg. Co. (Steel)......F
WIS.—Racine
Racine General Mfg. Co.
(Gate) ....E
WIS.—South Milwaukee ..
Stowell Mfg. & Fdy. Co.
(Elevator Door; Thumb)A

LATH

See also Lumber; Lathing.

ILL.—Chicago
Barbee Wire & Iron Wks.,
44 Dearborn (Wire).....B
Imperial Expanded Metal
Co., Monadnock Blk. (Expanded Metal).........D
Northwestern Expanded
Metal Co., Old Colony
Bldg. (Expanded Metal;
Steel Metal)...........B
Smith Wire & Iron Wks.,
F. P., 100 Lake (Wire)
AA
Voss, Frederik, 617 to 621
Austin Av. (Wire).....B
MASS.—Boston
Eastern Expanded Metal
Co., 101 Tremont (Expande Metal)..............A
MASS.—Clinton
Clinton Wire Cloth Co.,
(Wire) ....AAA
MASS.—Worcester
Wright Wire Co., (Wire)
AA
MICH.—Detroit
Michigan Wire Cloth Co.,
900 Howard (Wire)...AA
MO.—St. Louis
Leschen & Sons Rope Co., A
(Yarn) ....AAA
St. Louis Expanded Metal
Fireproofing Co., Century
Bldg. (Expanded Metal)
B
Stockhoff Supply Co., 432
S. 12th (Metal).........E
New York City
De Witt Wire Cloth Co., 17
Warren (Wire)........A
Gilbert & Bennett Mfg. Co,
42 Cliff (Wire)....AAA
Hayes Co., 71 8th Av.
(Metal) ....B
Howard & Morse (Wire)..D
Roebling Construction Co.,
121 Liberty (Metal; Wire)
B
OHIO—Cambridge
Cambridge Roofing Co.
(Metal) ....B
OHIO—Canton
Berger Mfg. Co (Metal).AA
OHIO—Cleveland
National Concrete Fireproofing Co.. New England
Bldg. (Expanded Metal)
C
Tyler Co.. W. S., 1150 St.
Clair (Wire).....AAAA
OHIO—Niles
Bostwick Steel Lath Co.
(Metal) C
Sykes Metal Lath & Roofing
Co.. (Metal)..........B
OHIO—Xenia
Kelly Co., R. A. (Tarred
Sisal) ....A
OHIO—Youngstown
General Fireproofing Co.,
(Herringbone Metal)..AA
Youngstown Iron & Steel
Roofing Co.. (Sheet Metal;
Expanded Metal).....AA

LATH (Con.)
PA.—Philadelphia
Derby & Sons, Edw. (Wire)
A
Gara, Mc Ginley & Co.
(Metal) ....A
Merritt & Co.,. 1024 Ridge
Av. (Expended Metal)..B
PA.—Pittsburg
Amer. Sheet & Tin Plate
Co., (Corrugated Expanded Metal; Sheet Metal)
AAAA
Budke Mfg. Co. (Sheet
Metal) ....B
Canonsburg Iron & Steel
Co., 421 Wood (Metal).B
VT.—Burlington
Burlington Venetian Blind
(Venetian Blind).......A
W. VA.—Wheeling
Wheeling Corrugating Co.
(Metal) ....AAAA

LATHES

See also Machinery; Tools.

CAL.—San Francisco
Pacific Tank Co. (Zinc, for
Cutting Zinc Shavings).A
San Francisco Tool Wks.
(Engine) ....E
CONN.—Bridgeport
Armstrong Mfg. Co. (Axle)
A
Automatic Machine Co.,
(Screw Cutting. for
Worms and Screws;
Speed) ....B
Bridgeport Safety Emery
Wheel Co.. (Strapping).F
Bullard Machine Tool Co.
(Engine; Screw Cutting;
Turret; Brass Finishing;
Chucking; Special)....AA
Springfield Mfg. Co. (Grinding; Strapping; Buffing)
B
CONN.—Danbury
Turner Machine Co. (Hat
Velouring) ....A
CONN.—East Hampton
Brown & Co., H. B. (Nut
Tapping) ....E
CONN.—Hartford
Dwight State Machine Co.
(Bench; Special) .....B
Fenn-Sadler Machine Co.
(Bench) ....E
Pratt & Whitney Co.
(Bench; Brass Finished;
Chucking; Cutting-Off;
Engine; Grinding; Gun
Turning; Boring; Hand;
Turret; Combination; Pulley Turning; Special;
Spinning; Patternmakers)
AAAA
Sigourney Tool Co. (Hand)
A
CONN.—Meriden
Meriden Machine Tool Co.
(Spinning; Turret; Gauge)
X
Merriman, A. H., (Spinning) C
CONN.—New Haven
New Haven Mfg. Co.
(Chucking; Engine; Patternmakers'; Pulley Turning; Screw Cutting; Turret; Wood Working; Axle
Foot Power; Hand; Pulley Boring; Special;
Wood Turning) ......AA
CONN.—Norwich
Rogers & Co.. C. B. (Patternmakers'; Wood Turning; Gauge; Bedding)
AAAA
CONN.—Torrington
Hendey Machine Co. (Engine; Screw Cutting; Turret; Bench; Brass Finishing; Cutting-Off; Hand)
AA
CONN.—Waterbury
Cross & Speirs Machine Co.
(Brass Finishers; Hand;
Spinning; Trimming; Turret. for Small Screws;
Tapping Nuts, &c.)....X

LATHES (Con.)

Manville Machine Co., E. J. (Spinning; Trimming)..C

Waterbury Farrell Fdy. & Machine Co. (Knurling; Spinning; Burnishing; Buffing) ....AA

DEL.—Wilmington

Betts Machine Co. (Car; Driving Wheei; Axle; Special) ....AA

ILL.—Cairo

Reed, Jas. B. (Screw Cutting Engine) ....B

ILL.—Chicago

Hardinge Bros., 1036 Lincoln Av. (Watchmakers') ....B

Marshall & Huschart Mchy. Co., 62 S. Canal (Mfrs. Agts.; Engines) ....A

Pringle & Brodie Mchry. Co., 277 S. Canal (Handle Turning; Variety Turning; Back Knife Woodworking) D

ILL.—Elgin

Moseley Lathe Co. (Jewelers'; Watchmakers')...D

ILL.—Moline

Moline Tool Co. (Speed)..E

ILL.—Rockford

Barnes Co., B. F. (Engine; Foot Power; Screw Cutting) ....B

Barnes Co., W. F. & Jno. (Engine; Foot Power; Foot; Power Hand; Screw Cutting; Wood Working; Amateur; Irregular Forms Turning) ....AA

IOWA—Dubuque

Davis, Geo. E. (Gauge) E

KY.—Covington

Sebastian Lathe Co. (Engine; Foot Power; Foot Screw Cutting; Speed; Turret; Wood Working; Wood Turning) ....B

MAINE—Dexter

Fay & Scott (Engine; Gauge; Patternmakers'; Screw Cutting; Speed; Turret; Wood Working; Drill; Wood Turning)..C

MD.—Baltimore

Detrick & Harvey Machine Co., 508 E. Preston (Engine; Screw Cutting) ....AA

MASS.—Athol

Richardson - Oliver Co. (Hand, for Light Work) E

MASS.—Boston

Amer. Tool & Machine Co., 109 Beach (Brass Finishers' Turret; Drill)....AA

Cutter-Tower Co., 68 Pearl (Strapping) ....B

Faneuil Watch Tool Co., 1 Brooks (Bench; Precision; Watchmakers'; Jewelers') B

Hill, Clarke & Co. Engine; Hand; Speed) ....A

Holtzer-Cabot Electric Co. (Jewelers) ....A

Welch & Co., T. F., 65 Sudbury (Bench) ......D

MASS.—Brockton

Kimball Bros. & Sprague (Block; Turning Last; Irregular Forms Turning; Golf Club Turning)....B

MASS.—Everett

Blount & Co.,J. G. (Speed) D

MASS.—Fitchburg

Cowdry Machine Wks., C. H. (Variety Turning)..D

Fitchburg Machine Works (Chucking : Engine; Hand; Patternmakers'; Screw Cutting; Shaft Turning; Speed; Axle; Drill; Gap; Special)...B

Putnam Machine Co. (Axle Turning; Car; Driving Wheel; Cutting-Off; Engine; Marble Turning; Patternmakers'; Pulley Turning; Gap; Grinding;

LATHES (Con.)

Variety) ....A

Waymouth & Co., A. D. Handle Turning; Variety Turning; Wood Working) X

Wilder, Chas. W. Auger; Paint Brush File Handle Turning; Variety Turning) E

MASS.—Greenfield

Automatic Machine Co. (Screw Cutting; Speed) C

Massachusetts Tool Co. (Bench; Precision) C

Wells Bros. Co. (Foot Power; Speed; Screw Cutting) ....A

MASS.—Holyoke

Goddard Machine Co. (Engine; Screw Cutting)...X

MASS.—Lowell

Carey, W. W. (Wood Working) ....B

Fifield, Geo. W. (Engine, 17 to 84 inch Swing)..AA

Perkins Co., F. S. (Screw Cutting) ....B

MASS.—Millers' Falls

Millers' Falls Co. (Amateur) AA

MASS.—South Sudbury

Hulburt-Rogers Mach. Co. (Cutting-Off) C

MASS.—Springfield

Bausch Machine Tool Co. (Speed) ....A

Bullock Mfg. Co. (Watchmakers') ....A

Waltham Watch Tool Co. (Bench; Watchmakers') B

MASS.—Waltham

Amer. Watch Tool Co. (Bench; Screw Cutting) D

Stark Tool Co. (Bench)...B

MASS.—Winchendon

Goodspeed Machine Co., G. N. (Gauge; Bobbin; Warp Spool) ....E

Whitney & Son, Baxter D. (Pattern) ....AA

MASS.—Worcester

Blaisdell & Co., P. Chucking; Engine; Hand; Patternmakers'; Screw Cutting; Speed; Drill; Special) A

Chickering, W. F. (Speed) H

Draner Machine Tool Co. (Chucking; Engine; Hand; Screw Cutting; Special) B

Fish Machine Wks., H. C. (Screw Cutting; Crank Pin) ....D

Kidder. R. E. (Bench; Speed) ....E

McMahon & Co. (Screw Cutting; Special) .....E

Morgan Construction Co. (Roll Turning) ....A

Prentice Bros. Co. (Engine, 12-26 inch Swing; Foot Power; Hand; Pulley Turning) ....A

Reed Co., Francis (Bolt; Stud; Turret Head Chucking; Engine; Facing; Plain Foot Power; Forming; Hand; Wood Working; Brass Finishing; Screw Cutting; Amateur Screw Cutting; Manuel Training) ....A

Robbins, L. (Engine; Patternmakers'; Speed)....X

Young Mfg. Co., W. C. (Engine; Foot Power; Hand; Speed; Screw Cutting; Amateur) X

MICH.—Alpena

Kline, Lewis T. (Broom Handle Turning; Variety Turning) ....D

MICH.—Grand Rapids

Amer. Mchry. Co. (J. W. Oliver, Prop.) Patternmakers'; Wood Working) B

Porter. C. O. & A. D. Wood

LATHES (Con.)

Working) C

MICH.—Jackson

Wolcott & Son, Geo. D. (Engine) C

MICH.—Owosso

Steggall, A. (Wood Working) X

MICH.—Saginaw

Wickes Bros. (Engine) AAA

MICH.—St. Joseph

St. Joseph Iron Wks. (Veneer) C

N. H.—Dover

White Co., Jno. A. (Wood Working) C

N. H.—Keene

Humphrey Machine Co. (Spoke; Axe Helve)...C

N. H.—Nashua

Flather & Co. (Chucking; Screw Cutting; Engine; Turret; Drill; Hand; Special; Speed; Spinning)..A

N. J.—Belleville

Atlas Fdy. & Machine Co. (Trimming) ....D

N. J.—Bridgeton

Ferracute Machine Co. (Spinning) ....A

N. J.—Newark

Gould & Eberhardt (Engine; Roll Engraving; Roll Polishing; Roll Turning; Spinning; Special).....A

Seymour & Whitlock (Handle Turning) ......B

N. J.—Paterson

Royle & Sons (Inc.), Jno. (Photo-Engravers'; Facing) ....A

N. J.—Plainfield

Pond Machine Tool Co. (Axle; Cutting-Off; Driving Wheel; Engine; Hand) ....AAAA

N. J.—Smithville

Smith Machine Co., H. B. (Automatic Gauge; Handle Turning; Wood Working; Wood Turning; Bedding) A

N. Y.—Brooklyn

Bliss Co., E. W., 19 Adams (Engine; Spinning) AAAA

Hibbard Mfg. Co., Wm. H., 79 Washington (Spinning; Trimming) C

Houchin & Huber, 35 53rd (Handle Turning) ....D

Leffler & Co., Chas., 63 Clymer (Trimming)....C

N. Y.—Buffalo

Buffalo Dental Mfg. Co. (Dental) ....B

Frank Mchy. Co., 50 Mechanic Patternmakers'; Wood Working; Wood Turning) B

Holmes Mchy. Co., E. & B. (Wood Working; Wood Turning Gauge; Variety)

Niagara Machine & Tool Wks., Superior & Randall (Spinning) ....A

Oliver Mfg. Co., W.W., 1483 Niagara (Foot; Power Hand; Jewelers' Speed; Speed; Bench) C

N. Y.—Herkimer

Quackenbush, H. M. (Foot Power; Amateur)......A

N. Y.—Lockport

Merritt Mfg. Co., I. E. (Pulley Boring; Pulley Turning; Gauge) ....D

Trevor Mfg. Co. (Gauge; Handle Turning; Spoke; Axe Helve; Treenail; Wood Working; Wood Turning) ....B

N. Y.—Malone

Hinds, Thomas (Marble Turning) ....D

N. Y.—Mt. Morris

Empire Machine Wks. (Handle Turning)......E

New York City

Amer. Woodworking Mach. Co., 136 Liberty (Gauge;

LATHES (Con.)

Handle Turning; Patternmakers'; Wood Working; Wood Turning) ..AAAA

Consolidated Dental Mfg. Co. (Dental) ....B

Fairbanks Co., 186 Elm (Engine; Hand) ....AAAA

Frasse & Co., Peter A., 94 Fulton (Screw Cutting) B

Garvin Machine Co., cor. Varick & Spring (Bench; Chucking; Engine; Foot Power; Hand; Handle Turning; Speed; Spinning; Turret; Wood Working; Ale; Drill; Screw Cutting; Wood Turning; Jewelers') ....AA

McCabe, J. J., 14 Dey (Engine; Screw Cutting)..B

Manning, Maxwell & Moore, 85 Liberty (Engine; Lever; Screw Feed Speed; Turret) ....AA

Niles-Bement-Pond Co., 136 Liberty (Axle Turning; Bench; Bolt; Stud; Brass Finishers'; Car; Driving Wheel; Chucking; Cutting-Off; Engine; Foot Power; Forming; Gun Turning; Boring; Hand; Pulley Turning; Screw Cutting; Shaft Turning; Speed; Turret Spinning) AAAA

Prentiss Tool & Supply Co., 115 Liberty (Mfrs.-Agts.) (Car; Driving Wheel; Engine; Turret) ....A

Prybil, P.- (Est. of) 510 W. 41st (Brass Finishers'; Spinning; Wood Working; Wood Turning; Buffing) ....AA

Watson-Stillman Co. (Buffing) ....AA

N. Y.—Rochester

Bridgeford, Chas. (Screw Cutting) C

Davis Machine Co., W. P. (Bench; Bolt; Stud; Engine; Foot Power; Screw Cutting) ....A

Gleason Wks., 10 Browns' Race (Engine) ....A

N. Y.—Seneca Falls

Seneca Falls Mfg. Co. (Engine; Foot; Power Screw Cutting; Foot Power; Foot; Power Hand; Foot Screw Cutting; Speed; Wood Working; Wood Turning; Bedding)....B

N. Y.—Waterford

Snyder & Metcalf (Engine; Speed; Turret).........X

OHIO—Chagrin Falls

Ober Mfg. Co. (Handle Turning; Spoke; Axe Helve; Variety Turning; Wood Working; Wood Turning) C

OHIO—Cincinnati

Amer. Tool Wks. Co., 6th & Eggleston Av. (Brass Finishers'; Chucking; Engine; Hand; Pulley Turning; Screw Cutting; Shaft Turning; Speed; Turret) AA

Barker & Co., Wm. Pioneer & Calvert (Chucking; Engine; Screw Cutting)...E

Bradford Machine Tool Co. (Engine, 14 to 36 inch Swing; Screw Cutting; Turret) ....A

Cordesman Machine Co., 25 Butler (Wood Working; Wood Turning) X

Cordesman, Meyer & Co., 53 Central Av. (Wood Working; Wood Turning)....B

Dietz Machine Tool Co., Garrard Av. & Elam (Engine; Motor) C

Dreses Machine Tool Co. (Brass Finishers'; Forming; Hand; Turret)...AA

Fay, J. A. Egan Co., cor. Front & John (Gauge;

LATHES *(Con.)*

Handle Turning; Spoke; Axe Helve; Wood Working; Wood Turning; Patternmakers'; Variety)
......AAAA

Gray Co., G. A., Gest & Depot (Engine) ....AA

Greaves, Klusman & Co., Cor. Cook & Alfred (Engine; Patternmakers'; Screw Cutting; Spinning; Wood Working) ......B

Le Blond Machine Tool Co., R. K., 4609 Eastern Av. (Engine; Screw Cutting)
......A

Lodge & Shipley Machine Tool Co., 3055 Colerain Av. (Chucking; Engine; Screw Cutting; Turret; Axle; Brass Finishing; Pulley Boring; Speed; Pulley Turning; Foot Power; Wood Turning)
......AA

Rahn-Mayer-Carpenter Co., Sprg. Grove & Garrard Av. (Engine; Turret) ......B

Schumacher & Boye, Buck & Queen City Av. (Engine; Roughing; Turret)
......A

Shepard Lathe Co., 129 W. 2nd (Engine; Foot; Power; Turret Foot Power) ......F

Silk Machine Tool Co., 419 E. 2nd (Engine; Turret)
......X

Streit Machine Co., A. (Engine; Pulley Turning; Turret) ......D

OHIO—Cleveland

Bardons & Oliver, Case Av. & Hamilton (Brass Finishers' Turret) ......B

Cieveland Automatic Mach. Co., 131 2nd Av. (Brass Finishers') ......AAA

Grant, Peter (Hand)....H

Lane Tool Co., 1196 Hamilton (Engine) ......D

Warner & Swasey Co., 57 E. Prospect (Brass Finishers'; Hand; Speed; Turret, all kinds) ......A

OHIO—Dayton

Miami Valley Machine Tool Co. (Engine, 13½ inch) A

OHIO—Defiance

Defiance Machine Wks. (Axle Turning; Handle Turning, also Automatic; Spoke; Axe Helve; Wood Working; Neck Yoke; Variety; Hub) ......A

OHIO—Ghent

Purdy Machine Co. (Foot Power, 9 to 10 Swing; Patternmakers'; Wood Working) X

OHIO—Hamilton

Bentel & Mergedant Co. (Handle Turning; Spoke; Axe Helve; Spokes; Handles Wood Working)
......A

Hamilton Machine Tool Co. (Engine; Screw Cutting)
......A

Niles Tool Wks. Co. (Axle Car Wheel; Driving Wheel; Engine; Pulley Turning; Screw Cutting; Shafting; Special) AAAA

OHIO—Salem

Silver Mfg. Co. (Handle Turning) ......AA
--Sandusky

Klotz Machine Co. (Handle Turning; Spoke; Axe Helve) C

OHIO—Shelby

Brightman Mfg. Co. (Shaft Turning) ......AA

OHIO—Springfield

Springfield Machine Tool Co. (Brass Finishers'; Chucking; Engine, 14, 18 & 24 inches; Shaft Turning; Strapping Turret) ....A

LATHES *(Con.)*

PA.—Allegheny

Pittsburg Machine Tool Co. (Engine; Screw Cutting; Winding) ......A

PA.—Chambersburg

Woods' Sons, T. B. (Pulley Turning) ......A

PA.—Monroeton

Booth & Co., O. N. (Variety and Turning; Hand; Broom Handle) ......D

PA.—Philadelphia

Atlantic Wks. (Inc.). 23rd & Arch (Patternmakers'; Wood Working) ......B

Bagshaw & Field, 317 Cherry (Engine; Foot Power)...E

Bement, Niles & Co. Axle; Cutting - Off ; Driving Wheel; Engine Carwheel; Pulley Turning; Roll Turning; Screw Cutting; Special) ......AAAA

Ellison Bros., 2213 Bridge (Marble Turning) ......D

Harrington & Son Co., Edwin, 15th & Penn. Engine; Screw Cutting) AA

Johnson, Jr. & Co., Israel H., 1434 Callowhill (Axle Edwin, 15th & Penn. (Engine; Gun Turning; Boring; Hand; Screw Cutting; Shaft Turning; Turret) ......A

Johnson & Lund (Dental)
......AA

Phila. Roll & Machine Co., S. 23d & Washington Av. (Gun Turning; Boring; Roll Turning) ......A

Power & Co., L., 20 S. 23d (Wood Working) .....A

Sellers & Co., W. (Inc.), 1600 Hamilton (Axle Turning; Double Head; Car; Driving Wheel; Engine; Gun Turning; Pulley Turning; Shaft Turning; Gap; Screw Cutting; Special; Turret) ......AAAA
ing; Pulley Turning; Shaft Turning; Gap; Screw Cutting; Special; Turret) ......AAAA

White Dental Mfg. Co.. S. S. (Dental) ......AAAA

PA.—Pittsburg

Baird Mchy. Co., U. (Mfrs. Agts., Turret) ......B

Hogg Iron & Steel Fdy. Co., Geo. A., 24th & R. R. (Roll Turning)......A

Lewis Fdy. & Machine Co. (Rolling Turning) ....A

Mesta Machine Co., Lewis Blk. (Roll Turning)
......AAAA

Phillips & McLaren, 24th & Smallman (Roll Turning)
......B

Scaife Fdy. & Machine Co. (Roll Turning) ......B

Sommerfeld Mach. & Mfg. Co., 224 3d Av. (Winding)
......B

Tretheway & Co., Samuel (Roll Turning) ......F

United Engineering & Fdy. Co., 58th & A. V. R. R. (Roll Turning; Roughing)
......AAAA

PA.—Ridgeway

Ridgeway Machine Tool Co. (Engine) ......A

PA.—Williamsport

United States Machine Co. (Wood Working) ......D

R. I.—Pawtucket

Potter & Johnston Machine Co. (Double Turret Mfg.)
......A

R. I.—Providence

Brown & Sharpe Mfg. Co. (Hand;. Engine; Special)
......AAA

Diamond Machine Co. Bench; Engine; Hand; Special; Drill; Spinning) B

Mann, Chas. A.. 166 Doyle Av. (Engine; Foot Power; Hand; Screw Cutting)..D

LATHES (*Con.*)

Narragansett Machine Co.
(Foot Power) ....A
VT.—Barre
Whitcomb Bros. (Granite
Column) X
VT.—Rutland
Lincoln Iron Wks. (Marble
Turning) ....A
Patch Mfg. Co., F. R.
(Marble Turning).....B
Steam Stonecutter Co.
(Marble) ....A
VT.—Springfield
Gilman & Son (Last; Boot-
Tree; Gumstock; Hat
Block) ....D
Jones & Lamson Machine Co.
(Chucking; Special; Tur-
ret) ....AA
VT.—Windsor
Windsor Machine Co. (Brass
Finishers'; Plain Monitors;
Chucking; Turret)......X
W. VA.—Wheeling
Spears & Riddle (Axle Turn-
ing) ....D
WIS.—Madison
Gisholt Machine Co. (Turret)
AAA
WIS.—Milwaukee
National Machine Co. (Brass
Finishers'; Pattern-
makers'; Speed Wood
Working) ....F

LATHING

MASS.—Clinton
Clinton Wire Cloth Co.
(Metallic; Wire) ....AAA
MASS.—Worcester
Wright Wire Co. (Wire) AA
MO.—St. Louis
Ludlow-Saylor Wire Co.
(Wire) ....AA
N. J.—Trenton
New Jersey Wire Cloth Co.
(Metallic; Wire) ......A
N. Y.—Buffalo
Buffalo Wire Wks. Co.
(Wire) ....A
New York City
Gilbert & Bennett Mfg. Co.,
277 Bway. (Wire) ...AAA
Hayes Co., Geo., 71 8th Av.
(Metallic) ....B
Howard & Morse, 45 Fulton
(Metallic) ....D
OHIO—Cambridge
Cambridge Roofing Co. (Me-
tallic) ....B
OHIO—Cleveland
Tyler Co., W. S. (Wire)
AAAA
PA.—Pittsburg
Canonsburg Iron & Steel Co.
(Metallic) ....B

LATTICES

See Grilles

LAUNCHES

See also Boats

CAL.—San Francisco
Union Iron Wks. (Steam) X
CONN.—Coscob
Palmer Bros. (Gasoline) ..C
CONN.—Stamford
Stamford Motor Co. (Gaso-
line) ....D
ILL.—Chicago
Marine Iron Wks. (Steam) B
Willard & Co., Chas. P.
(Steam) ....D
IND.—Mishawaka
Dodge Mfg. Co. ....AAA
MAINE—Portland
Stickney, Henry R. (Steam)
D
MD.—Baltimore
Nilson Yacht Building Co.
(Steam) ....D
MASS.—Boston
Clark, Edward S. (Steam) X
Sheldon Co., Orim (Steam)
D
MASS.—Quincy
Stuart & Co., Jno. (Vapor)
X

LAUNCHES (*Con.*)

MICH.—Grand Rapids
Wolverine Motor Wks. (Gas;
Gasoline) ....B
MICH.—Montague
Montague Iron Wks. Co. ..C
MICH.—St. Joseph
Truscott Boat Mfg. Co.
(Steam) ....A
MINN.—Duluth
Pearson Boat Construction
Co. ....B
N. J.—Bayonne
Electric Launch Co. (Elec-
tric) ....D
N. J.—Gloucester City
Rogers' Boat, Gauge & Drill
Wks., Jno. M..........A
N. Y.—Canton
Rushton, J. H. (Gasoline) F
N. Y.—Long Island City
Daimler Mfg. Co., 939 Stein-
way Av. (Electric) .....D
New York City
Gas Engine & Power Co. &
C. L. Seabury & Co.
(Naphtha) ....AAA
Marine Engine & Machine
Co., 1123 B'way ......B
N. Y. Safety Steam Power
Co. (Steam) ....B
N. Y. Yacht, Launch & En-
gine Co. (Naphtha;
Steam) ....B
Smith, Jno. T. (Naphtha) E
R. I.—Bristol
Herreshoff Mfg. Co. (Elec-
tric; Steam) ....A
WIS.—Gren Bay
Conley, Horace J. (Naphtha)
F
WIS.—Racine
Pierce Engine Co. (Naphtha;
Steam) ....B

LAVATORIES

CONN.—New Haven
Peck Bros. & Co. (Open)
AA
ILL.—Chicago
Adams & Westlake Co.
AAAA
ILL.—Edwardsville
Illinois Marble Co. (Marble)
C
MD.—Baltimore
Weiskittel & Son, A. (Enam-
elled Iron, Open) ......A
MASS.—Boston
Dalton-Ingersoll Co. X
MO.—St. Louis
Nelson Mfg. Co., N. O.
(Open) ....AAA
New York City
Bishop Sons, Wm., 205 South
(Ship) ....D
Mott Iron Wrks., J. L.
(Open) ....AA
OHIO—Mansfield
Barnes Mfg. Co. (White
Enameled Iron) ....A
PA.—Philadelphia
Cooper Brass Wrks., 437 N.
12th ....B
McCambridge & Co. (Ltd.)
525 Cherry (Open) .....B
Owen & Salter, 12th & But-
tonwood Sts. (Open) ..A
PA.—Pittsburg
Standard Mfg. Co. (Open;
(Enamelled Iron. Open)
AA
TENN.—Chattanooga
Cahill Iron Wrks. (Enamell-
ed Iron) ....B
WIS.—Milwaukee
Rundle Mfg. Co. (Enamell-
ed Iron) C

LAWNS

See Cotton Goods

LAY BOYS

PA.—Harrisburg
Hickok Mfg. Co., W. O...AA

LAYERS

MAINE—Portland
Androscoggin Pulp Co. (Box;
Barrel) ....AA

LAYERS (Con.)
MASS.—Boston
Haskell-Dawes Machine Co.,
176 Federal C
N. Y.—Tonawanda
Tonawanda Board & Paper
Co. (Barrel) ....AA

LEAD

See also Plumbago; Paints

CAL.—San Francisco
Fuller & Co., W. P. (Red;
White) ....AAAA
Pacific Oil & Lead Wrks.
(Tinted) ....B
Selby Smelting & Lead Co.,
416 Montgomery (Pipe;
Sheet; Pig; Antimonial;
Bar; Damper; Key; Shot)
AAA
COLO.—Denver
Bogue Lead Co., 1810 Blake
(Pipe; Sheet; Pig) C
Denver Fire Clay Co. (Gran-
ulated) ....A
James Mercantile & Mfg Co.,
B. L. (Tinted) ....A
ILL.—Chicago
Alston Mfg. Co. (Tinted) .A
Blatchford & Co., E. W. 70
N. Clinton (Pipe; Sheet;
Pig; Damper; Keg; Gla-
ziers') ....AAAA
Carter White Lead Co., W.
21st cor. S. Peoria (White;
Red; Tinted) ....AAA
Great Western Smelting &
Refining Co., 175 W. Kin-
zie (Pipe; Sheet; Pig) .A
Harrington & King Perfo-
ting Co., (Perforated
Sheet) ....A
Heath & Milligan Mfg. Co.
(Tinted; White) ....AAA
Picher Lead Co. (Pig) ...AA
Raymond Lead Co., 57 W.
Lake (Pipe; Sheet; Pig)
AA
Ryan & Co., J. J., 68 Mon-
roe C
LA.—New Orleans
McWilliams (Ltd.), R.
(White) X
Maine—Portland
Lang Co., E. M. (Pipe;
Sheet; Pig) C
MD.—Baltimore
Robertson Mfg. Co., Jas., 30
Hanover (Pipe; Sheet;
Pig; Bar) ....A
Thomsen Chem. Co. (Ace-
tate) ....B
MASS.—Boston
Chadwick-Boston Lead Co.,
162 Congress (Pipe; Sheet;
Pig; White; Red; Wedge;
Tinted) ....AAA
Cochrane Chemical Co.,
(Acetate) ....AA
Merrimac Chemical Co.
(Acetate) ....AA
MASS.—Holyoke
Holyoke Lead Pipe Co.
(Pipe; Sheet; Pig) ....D
MASS.—South Hanover
Phillips & Sons, E. (Sheet)
A
MASS.—Worcester
Baker Lead Mfg. Co. (Pipe;
Sheet; Pig) C
MICH.—Detroit
Acme White Lead & Color
Wrks. (White; Tinted)
AAA
Detroit Lead Pipe & Sheet
Lead Wrks. (Pipe; Sheet;
Pig) ....A
Detroit White Lead Wrks.
(Red; Tinted; White)
AAA
MO.—Joplin
Picher Lead Co. (Red;
White) ....AA
MO.—St. Louis
Collier Shot Tower Wrks.,
319 N. 4th (Pipe; Sheet)
Pig) ....AAAA
Hammar Bros. White Lead
Co. (White) ....AAAA
Hiertz Metal Co., Theo. ..D
Mound City Paint & Color
Co. (White) ....AA
Nelson Mfg. Co., N. O., 8th

LEAD (Con.)
& St. Charles (Pipe;
Sheet; Pig) ....AAA
Platt & Thornburgh Paint
Co. (White) ....AA
Rumsey Mfg. Co., L. M.,
812 N. 2d (Pipe; Sheet;
Pig) ....AAA
NEBR.—Lincoln
Lincoln Paint & Color Co.
(Tinted) ....A
NEBR.—Omaha
National Lead Co., 1415
Dodge (White; Red;
Glassmakers') .....AAAA
N. J.—Jersey City
Dixon Crucible Co., Jos.
(Black) ....AAA
Williams & Son, E. A. (Bar;
Pig) ....AA
Woolsey Paint & Color Co.,
C. A. (Tinted) ....A
N. J.—Newark
Cawley, Clark & Co. (White;
Red) ....AA
N. Y.—Brooklyn
Brooklyn Metal Wrks. (Inc.)
4th Av. & Degraw (Pipe;
Sheet; Pig) ....D
Moore & Co., Benj. (White)
AA
Phillips, Jno. B., 78 9th
(White; Red) X
Wiarda & Co., Jno. C.
(Glassmakers') ....AA
N. Y.—Buffalo
Cornell Lead Co. (White)
AAAA
Kellogg & McDougall Lin-
seed Oil Wrks. (White)
AAAA
Shepard & Co., Sidney
(Shot) ....AAAA
New York City
Amer. Metal Co., 52 B'way
AAAA
Bruce & Cook, 190 Water
(Pipe; Sheet; Pig) ..AAA
Columbia Smelting & Refin-
ing Wrks., 307 Water
(Pipe; Steel; Pig) ..AA
Coldwell Lead Co., 63 Centre
(Pipe; Sheet; Pig; Shot)
AA
Conley Foil Co., 521 W. 25th
(Tea) ....AAA
Cooper & Co., Chas., 194
Worth (Black) ....A
Davol & Sons, Jno., 100
John ....AA
Devoe, F. W. & C. T. Ray-
nolds Co. (Red; Tinted)
AAAA
Du Bois & Co., Fred'k N.,
243 9th Av. (Pipe; Sheet;
Pig) ....AAA
Hendricks Bros., 49 Cliff
AAAA
Kelly & Co., T. P., 544 W.
22d (Black) C
Lalance & Grosjean Mfg.
Co., 19 Cliff (Bar) .AAAA
Lissberger, Marks & Son,
397 W. 12th (Pipe; Sheet;
Pig) ....B
Longman & Martinez (Red)
AAA
Matheson & Co. (Ltd.), Wm.
J., 182 Front (White) ..A
Mayor, Lane & Co., 128
White (Pipe; Sheet; Pig)
A
Mundt & Sons, Chas., 441
Pearl (Perforated Sheet)
B
National Lead Co., 100 Wil-
liam (Pipe; Sheet; Pig;
White; Red) ......AAAA
New Jersey Zinc Co., 11
B'way (White; Red) ..A
Pierce Well Engineering &
Supply Co. (Damper; Key)
D
Read Lead Wrks., H. P.,
645 Lexington Av. (Pipe;
Sheet; Pig) C
Ronalds & Johnson Co., 54
Cliff (Pipe; Sheet; Pig)
AA
Rutter & Co., Arthur T.,
256 B'way ....D
Smith & Co., J. Lee, 59
Frankfort (English White)
AA

LEAD (Con.)

Standard Graphite Co., 11
B'way (Black) ....E
United Lead Co. (White)
..................AAAA
N. Y.—Rochester
Rochester Lead Wrks.
(Pipe; Sheet; Pig) ....B
N. Y.—Syracuse
Pierce, Butler & Pierce Mfg.
Co. (Pipe; Sheet; Pig)
..................AAA
Syracuse Smelting Wrks.
(Pig) X
N. Y.—Utica
Miller & Son Co., Chas.
(Pipe; Sheet; Pig) ..AA
OHIO—Cincinnati
Crane-Hawley Co. (Pipe;
Sheet; Pig) ....A
Eagle White Lead Co. (Red)
..................AAAA
Moser & Co., Chas. (White)
..................AA
Obermayer Co., S.. 647
Evans (Black; India Sil-
ver) ....A
OHIO—Cleveland
Gibson & Price Co., 375 St.
Clair (Pipe; Sheet; Pig)
..................A
Grasselli Chemical Co., (Ace-
late) ....AAAA
Harkshaw, Fuller & Good-
win Co. (Acetate) ....AA
PA.—Allegheny
Gerdes & Bro., F. W. Grand
& N. South Avs. (Pipe;
Sheet; Pig; White; Red)
..................A
Nevin Co.. T. H., cor. Is-
land & Preble Avs.
(White; Red; Tinted)..A
PA.—Philadelphia
Fleck Bros. Co., 44 N. 5th
(Pipe; Sheet; Pig) ....A
French & Co.. Saml. H.. 4th
& Callowhill (White;
Red) ....A
Harrison Bros. & Co.. 35th,
cor. Gray's Ferry Rd.
(White; Red; Tinted)
..................AAAA
Lewis & Bros. Co., John T.,
231 S. Front (Pipe; Sheet;
Pig; White; Red) ..AAAA
Lucas & Co., Jno. (Red)
..................AAA
Merchant & Co. ....AA
North Amer. Smelting Co.,
9th & Thompson (Pipe;
Sheet; Pig) ....AA
Wetherill & Bro., 126 S. 30th
(White; Red) ....AAA
Wetherill & Co., Geo. D.
(White) ....A
PA.—Pittsburg
Bailey-Farrel Mfg. Co.. 619
Smithfield (Pipe; Sheet;
Pig) ....AA
Davis Lead Co.. Park Bldg.
(White; Red; Oxide of)
..................A
Hussey & Co., C. G. (Bar)
..................AAA
National Lead & Oil Co.,
Second Nat'l Bank Bldg.
(White; Red; Coachmak-
ers'; Glassmakers'; Var-
nishmakers') .....AAAA
Penna Smelting Co., 331 4th
Av. (Pipe; Sheet; Pig)
..................C
Standard Sanitary Mfg. Co..
Arrott Bldg. (Pipe; Sheet;
Pig) ....AAAA
Suydam Co., M. B. (Red).A
PA.—Reading
Wilhelm & Co., A. (Red;
Tinted) ....AA
PA.—Sharpsburg
Bender & Alldred (White;
Red) ....B
PA.—Williamsport
National Paint Wrks. (Red)
..................B
R. I.—Providence
Phillips Lead & Supply Co.
(Pipe; Sheet; Pig) C
Tillinghast Supply Co.. L.
H. (Pipe; Sheet; Pig)..C
U. S. Gutta Percha Paint
Co. (White) ....A

LEAD (Con.)

S. C.—Charleston
Cherleston Lead Wrks.
(Pipe; Sheet; Pig) ....B
TEXAS—San Antonio
Collins Mfg. Co.. F. F.
(Pipe; Sheet; Pig) ..AA

LEADERS

See also Leads

CONN.—New Britain
Humason & Beckley Mfg.
Co.. (Cattle) ....A
CONN.—Oakville
Smith, Seymour & Son (Cat-
tle) ....D
N. Y.—Kenwood
Oneida Community (Cattle)
..................AAA
New York City
Abbey & Imbrie (Fishing)
..................A
Peck, Stow & Wilcox Co.,
27 Murray (Cattle).AAAA
Plath & Son, Chas. (Fish-
ing) ....F
Sargent & Co., 151 Leonard
(Cattle) ....AAAA
N. Y.—Watervliet
Covert Mfg. Co. (Cattle)
..................A
OHIO—Akron
Enterprise Mfg. Co (Gut)
..................A

LEADS

See also Leaders

CONN.—Bridgeport
Smith & Egge Mfg. Co.
(Dog) ....A
CONN.—Torrington
Union Hdw. Co. (Dog)..AA
ILL.—Chicago
Barnhart Bros. & Spindler
(Printers) ....AA
MASS.—Boston
Hansen, H. C. (Brass; Prin-
ters') ....B
N. J.—Jersey City
Dixon Crucible Co.. Jos.
(Pencil; Lumber Marking)
..................AAA
Williams & Son, E. A. (Fish
Net; Piano) ....AA
N. Y.—Brooklyn
Wesel Mfg. Co., F. (Brass;
Printers') X
N. Y.—New York City
Amer. Type Founders' Co.
(Printers') ....AAAA
Eagle Pencil Co. (Pencil)
..................AAA
Faber Eberhard (Pencil)
..................AAA
Farmer & Son Type Foundry
Co.. A. D. (Brass) ....B
Lindsay Type F'dry (Brass)
..................B
Medford Fancy Goods Co.
(Dog) ....E
Sands & Son, Alfred B.
(Deep Sea Sounding) ..D
Sargent & Co. (Halter)
..................AAAA
Tiebout, W. & J. (Sounding)
..................B

LEAF

CONN.—Hartford
Ney & Co., Jno. M. (Gold)
..................C
N. Y.—Brooklyn
Grempler & Son, F. W., 113
Hopkins (Metal) ....D
New York City
Conley Foil Co.. 521 W. 25th
(Composition) ......AAA
Henry, T. J. (Gold) .....F
Kemp Co.. W. H.. 165
Spring (Gold) ....B
Schultz & Co. (Gold; Sil-
ver) X
Valleau Mfg. Co. (Gold)..B
PA.—Philadelphia
Hastings & Co. (Gold)..AA
Nelms & Son, Henry (Gold)
..................B
R. I.—Providence
Coe Mfg. Co.. W. H.
(Aluminum; Composition;
Silver) ....B

LEATHER

Sawyer Tanning Co. (Deer-
CAL.—Napa
skin) ....A
CAL.—San Francisco
Brown & Adams (Upper;
Sole; Harness) ....A
Frank & Co., S. H. ....AAA
Kron Tanning Co., (Sole).A
Kreig Tanning Co., A.
(Sole) ....A
Kullman, Salz & Co. (Oak;
Sole; Harness; Shirting)
..........................AAA
Norton Tanning Co. (Goat;
Sheep) ....B
Sawyer Tanning Co. (Sheep;
(Goat) ....A
Windt, Morris (Sole; Har-
ness; Skirting) ....A
CAL.—Santa Rosa
Santa Rosa Tanning Co. ..B
CONN.—Bridgeport
Bridgeport Patent Leather
Mfg. Co. ....B
CONN.—Danielson
Jacobs Mfg. Co., E. H.
(Picker) ....B
CONN.—Norwich
Norwich Belt Mfg. Co.
(Lace; Pump; Picker) .A
Ulmer Leather Co. (Lace;
Pump; Valve) ....B
DEL.— Wilmington
Beadenkopf., Chas. (Glazed
Kid; Colors) ....B
Beadenkopf, Martin ......B
Beadenkopf, Wm. (Glazed
Kid) ....A
Fritz & Co., Chas. E.
(Glazed Kid) ....B
Garrett & Bar (Glazed Kid)
..........................A
Mitchell & Thomas (Glazed
Kid; Colors) ....A
Pyle & Co., The C. & J.
(Patent Leather) ......A
Weldin, C. Wesley ......B
Wilmington & Brandywine
Leather Co. (Chrome
Glazed Kid) ....B
GA.—Buford
Allen Rotary Suspension
Tannery (Harness) ....A
GA.—Newnan
Burpee. T. G. ....B
ILL.—Chicago
Chicago Rawhide Mfg. Co.,
75 E. Ohio (Rawhide Pick-
er) ....A
Eagle Tanning Wrks. (Fan-
cy; Harness) ....A
Eisendrath Tanning Co., B.
D. ....B
Gane Bros. & Co. (Sheep;
Bookbinders) ....B
Grey, Clark & Engle ,Calf;
Kip; Glace) ....AAA
Illinois Leather Co. ......A
Weil & Eisendrath (Sheep)
..........................B
Wilder-Manning Tanning Co.
(Ebony; Seal; Kangaroo)
..........................C
Woelfel Leather Co. (Grain;
Collar; Strap; Colored
Side; Yard; Welting) ..A
IND.—New Albany
Day Leather Co. (Oak Har-
ness) ....B
Moser & Co., Geo. (Hem-
lock Collar) ....B
MAINE—Portland
Casco Tanning Co. (Calf;
Satin Finish; Upper) ..B
MD.—Baltimore
Deford Co. (Oak Sole;
Butts) ....AAA
Rosenberg, Happ & Siegel
(Sheep; Calf Kid) .....A
MD.—Cumberland
Hirsch Bros. (Sheepskin) ..B
MD.—Frederick
Birely & Sons, Geo. K.
(Calf; Harness; Upper;
Rough) C
MD.—Williamsport
Byron & Son, W. D. (Bag;
Case; Collar) ....A
MASS.—Boston
Beebe & Son. Lucius..AAAA
Beggs & Cobb (Split;
(Glove) ....AAA

LEATHER (Con.)
Boyle & Co. T. F. ......A
Bullivant & Co., Wm. M.
(Upper; Grain; Satin;
Splits) ....A
Chadbourne & Moore .....A
Corona Kid Co. ....A
Cottle Leather Co.. ......A
Dungan & Hood Co. ....AA
Dunn, Greene & Co. .....A
Foster & Co., A. J. (Kid;
Goat; Grain; Split) ....B
Hale, Gallup & Co. .....A
Hunt, Frank W. ....AA
Kistler, Leash & Co.
..........................AAAA
Lawrence Leather Co., A. C.
..........................AA
Leviseur Bros & Co. .....A
Moffat & Son, David (Har-
ness) ....AA
Morrill Leather Co. ......A
Mosser & Co., W. F.....AAAA
Morse & Co., J. C. ......A
National Calfskin Co. ....A
Pevear & Co. ....A
Pierce Leather Co., Jas.
(Split; Satin) ....A
Pope & Co., Arthur W.
..........................AAA
Proctor, Ellison & Co. (Hem-
lock; Oak; Union) ...AA
Stetson & Co., Wm. A.
(Sheepskin; Dongola) ..A
Stoddard, Haserick, Rich-
ards & Co., 152 Congress
(Picker) ....B
Wadleigh & Co., H. W.
..........................AA
Webster & Co. (Grain;
Split; Buff; Goat) ..AAA
Winslow Bros. & Smith Co.
..........................AA
Wyman, F. A. (Sheep)..B
MASS.—Lynn
Kelly & Co., Thos. A...A
Lennox & Co., P. ....AAA
MASS.—Peabody
Clark & Co., A. B. ...AA
O'Shea. Thos. H. (Goat)..B
Southwick & Co., L. B.
(Sheepskins) ....A
MASS.—Woburn
Robertson. Jas. (Patent
Leather) ....D
MICH.—Alpena
Alpena Hide & Leather Co.
(Hemlock Sole) ....B
MICH.—Battle Creek
Sherman Mfg. Co., H. B.
(Pump) ....A
MICH.—Detroit
Schmidt. Carl E. (Calf; Kan-
garoo; Sheepskin) .....A
Schmidt. Traugott & Sons
(Sheepskin) ....AA
MICH.—Grand Rapids
Mich. Leather Co. (Sole)..A
Wallin & Sons, C. (Hem-
lock Sole) ....B
MICH—Fremont
Gerber's Sons, D. (Hemlock
Sole) C
MICH.—Holland
Cappan & Bertsch Leather
Co. (Hemlock; Sole; Sad-
dle; Harness; Skirting;
Net; Straps) ....A
MICH.—Mill Creek
Michigan Leather Co.
(Slaughter Sole) ....B
MICH.—Petoskey
Rice Leather Co.. W. W.
(Hemlock Sole) ....A
MINN.—Red Wing
Foot & Co., Silas B. ....A
MO.—St. Louis
Hartman Hide & Leather
Co., (Harness; Lace) ..A
Hermann Leather Co. (Har-
ness) ....A
Kayser & Nies Raw Hide Co.
(Raw Hide; Lace & Hal-
ter) ....E
Kessler & Sons, Anthony
(Harness) ....A
Shultz Belting Co. (Picker)
..........................AA
N. H.—Concord
Page Belting Co. (Picker;
Rigging; Curried) ...AA

LEATHER (Con.)

N. H.—Littleton
Parker Bros. & Co. (Glove)
.....................................C

N. H.—Manchester
Gerrish Wool & Leather Co.
.....................................A
Kimball & Brown ....B

N. H.—Rochester
Wallace, E. G. & E. (Buff;
Grain; Split) ...AAAA

N. J.—Camden
Quaker City Morocco Co.
(Colored; Patent; Glazed
Kid) ....B

N. J.—Harrison
Hahn & Stumpf, H. ......A

N. J.—Hoboken
Lehman & Randwitz.....B

N. J.—Merchantville
Paschall Leather Co. (Glazed Kid) C

N. J.—Newark
American Hat Leather Co.
(Skivers) C
Am. Patent Leather Co.
(Patent) ....B
Atlantic Leather Co. (Furn;
Shoe; Carriage; Saddlery)
.....................................C
Blanchard Bro. & Lane (Pa-
tent) ....A
Caffrey, Matthew (Patent)
.....................................C
Cummings Leather Mfg. Co.,
M. M. (Dyed; Embossed)
.....................................D
Dawson Co., I. W. (Alliga-
tor) ....F
Good, R. & H. B. (Thong;
Collar Splits) C
Halsey, J. H. & Smith (Pa-
tents; Enamelled) ....AA
Halsey & Son, S. (Patent;
Enamelled) ....AAA
Hestz, Max (Rough) ......B
Hamburg, Cordovan Leather
Co. (Colored Kid; Patent
Calf; Cordovan; Kanga-
roo; Porpoise) ......AAA
Howell & Co., T. P. (Pat-
ent; Enamelled) ....AA
Kaufherr & Co. (Alligator;
Lizard; Fancy Grain)..B
Lang & Co., Henry (Pat-
ent; Enamelled) ......A
Loehnberg & Co., A. (Hides;
Rough Splits) ....B
McCormick, E. H. (Patent;
Enamelled) C
Mahon Leather Co., Mark
W. (Pocket Book) C
Rielly, Jno. (Patent; Enam-
elled) ....A
Smith, C. L. & R. E. (Rus-
set; Colored Grain; Pat-
ent) ....B
Smith, Hugh, Corporation
(Shoe; Tipping; Carriage;
Enamelled) ....B
Smyth Leather Mfg. Co...B
Straus & Sons, M. (Patent;
Enamelled) ....A
Steinhardt Co., G. (Fancy)
.....................................D
Stengel & Rothschild (Pat-
ent; Enamelled ......AA
Ward & Co., E. S. ......A
Ziegel, Eisman & Co. (Kan-
garoo; Dongola; Goat)..B

N. Y.—Auburn
Leather & Brass Mfg. Co.
(Pump) ....F

N. Y.—Binghamton
American Hide & Leather
Co. (Grain Splits)..AAAA

N. Y.—Bressport
Kinley & Son, A. (Hemlock)
.....................................B

N. Y.—Brooklyn
Mills-Platt Co., 44 Clinton
(Decorative Art) ......A

N. Y.—Buffalo
Laub & Sons, Geo. (Har-
ness; Skirting) ....B
Schoellkopf & Co. (Sheep)
.....................................AA
Schoellkopf's Sons, J. F.
(Hemlock Sole) ......A
Steffan's Sons, M. ......A
Zeller & Sons, G. F. (Har-
ness) ....A

N. Y.—Gloversville
Levor & New (Kangaroo;

LEATHER (Con.)

Glove) ....B

N. Y.—Hornellsville
Prindle & Son, A. T.
(Slaughter Sole) C

N. Y.—Middletown
Howell-Hinchman Co. (Rus-
sia; Fancy) ....B
West Mill Leather Co.
(Buckskin) X

New York City
Am. Hide & Leather Co.
.....................................AAAA
Baldwin Bros., 432 5th Av.
(Decorative Art) ......D
Barnett Leather Co. (Calf-
skins) ....A
Bittel, Tepel & Co., (Whol.
Glazed Kid) ....A
Booth & Co., 88 Gold (Whol.
Glazed Kid; Picker)
.....................................AAAA
Boston Artificial Leather
Co., 12 E. 18th (Artificial;
Decorative) C
Bulkley, J. L. (Dlrs. Sole)
.....................................A
Chapman & Burt (Dlrs.
Sole; Harness) ....A
Frank & Co., S. H. (Whol.
Sole) ....AAA
Gardnar & Co., Thos. (Book-
binders) ....B
Griffin & Sons, H. (Sheep)
.....................................A
Hahn, Berthold (Whol. Pat-
ent) ....B
Hess & Harburger (Whol.
Fancy; Furniture) ....B
Keck, Mosser & Co. (Dlrs.
Sole) ....AAA
Lenhart, P. F. (Hat) ...A
McDermott & Howard
(Glazed Kid) ....AA
Moffat & Co., David (Har-
ness) ....AA
Musliner & Co., Jos. (Whol.)
.....................................A
Neumann & Co., R., 76
Duane (Artificial) ....A
Pantasote Leather Co., 11
B'way (Artificial) ..AA
Paskusz & Son (Sheepskins;
Bag; Strap) ....AAAA
Rahmann & Co., Geo.
(Pump) C
Rees & Sons, Hans (Oak;
Rough) ....A
Righter & Kolb, 156 5th Av.
(Decorative) ....E
Scherer & Bro., Oscar (Col-
ored; Black Kid) ....AA
Soloman & Phillips ....AA
U. S. Leather Co. (Hemlock;
Union; Oak; Deerskin;
Buckskin) ....AAAA
Wallerstein, D. (Goat; Kid)
.....................................AA
Williams, H. E. & C. D.
(Dlrs. Fancy Colored)..B
Windmuller & Roelker,
.....................................L.A
Winter & Goetz ....A
Young Co., Rich. (Goat;
Sheep; Kangaroo; Buck-
skin) ....A

N. Y.—Olean
Quirin, W. C. A. (Glove;
Dongola) ....A
Tanners' Shoe Stock Co. (In-
nersole) ....A

N. Y.—West Winfield
Beckwith & Hiteman Bros.
(Chromo Calf; Black Col-
ored) ....B

N. C.—Andrews
Cover & Son, F. P. ......B

OHIO—Ashtabula
Raser Tanning Co. (Patent;
Enamelled; Russia) ..D

OHIO—Cincinnati
American Oak Leather Co.
(Oak Sole; Belting; Butts;
Upholstery; Patents; Car-
riage) ....AAAA
Bardis Sons, Christian (Har-
ness; Collar) C
Hulsemann Bros. (Harness;
Hogskins) ....A
Rasche Bros. (Harness; Col-
lar) C
Suhr, Rudolph (Harness)..B

OHIO—Cleveland
Cleveland Tanning Co. ..C

LEATHER (Con.)

OHIO—Columbus
Peters & Herron Dash Co.
(Shaft) C
OHIO—Ironton
Dupuy, R. S. (Oak Skirting)
C
OHIO—Lima
Schulther's Bros. (Harness)
B
OHIO—Mansfield
Barnes Mfg. Co. (Pump).A
Humphreys Mfg. Co.
(Pump) ....B
OHIO—Springfield
Bretney & Co., H. V. (Oak;
Welt; Skirting; Strap)
B
OHIO—Zanesville
Findeiss & Heckel Oak
Leather Co. (Oak Harness) C
OREGON—Eugene
Haines & Co., W. W.
W. (Skirting; Collar) ..C
PA.—Ambler
Faust's Sons, A. D. (Harness) ....B
PA.—Bernville
Renschler, C. F. (Calf
Skins) ....B
PA.—Big Run P. O.
Irvin, Wm. & Son (Union
Sole) ....A
PA.—Cambridge Springs
Bolard, Jacob (Rough) ..B
PA.—Cheswick
Standard Leather Co. (Patent; Enamelled) ....B
PA.—Conneaut Lake
Howard & Co., J. W. & A. P.
(Hemlock; Slaughter Sole)
A
PA.—Corry
Raymond Mfg. Co. (Ltd.)
(Flat; Crimped Pump)..B
PA.—Eldred
Duffy Leather Co., Jas. N.
(Patent; Enamelled) ..A
PA.—Erie
Gunnison & Co., Chas.
(Rough; Harness) .....B
Streuber, Emil (Calf; Kip;
Rough; Slaughter Sole).C
PA.—Lancaster
Hollinger, Amos (Est. of)
A
Helvetia Leather Co. (Picker; Lace) ....D
Park Run Tanning Co. (Harness) ....B
PA.—Laporte
Union Tanning Co. (Sole)
AAA
PA.—Lock Haven
Kistler, Wilson .....AAA
Curtis Leather Co., J. G.
(Bag; Strap; Case; Colored Shoe) ....A
PA.—Noxen
Mosser Tanning Co. (Sole)
A
PA.—Philadelphia
Baum Leather Co. ....A
Bockius, Chas. (Glazed Kid)
B
Behal & Sons, S. ......A
Berger Bros. Co., 231 Arch
(Pump) ....A
Braun, Chas. J. (Oak; Calf;
Welt) ....B
Burk Bros. (Glazed Kid)
AAA
Callery & Co., Jas. .....AA
Costello, Cooey & Co. (Glazed; Enamelled Kid) ..B
De Long Bros. (Rough; Oak;
Calf; Harness) ....A
England & Bryan (Oak
Backs; Bends; Butts;
Belting; Fly Net).AAA
Evans, Jno. R. & Co.
(Dlrs. in Sheepskins)..B
Foerderer, Robt. H. (vici
Glazed; Patent Kid; Colors) ....B
Hawkins & Co., W. W.
(Sheepskins) ....B
Holmes, Hy. (Sheepskins)
B
Keystone Leather Co. ...AA
Klauder, Chas. L. ....A
Lyon, Litchen & Co. (Kid)
A

LEATHER (Con.)

Mathieu & Co., J. P. (Kid)
A
Matthews & Co., C. J. (Kid)
A
Mitchell & Peirson (Kid).A
McNeely & Co. (Kid).AAAA
McNeely, Price & Brooks
(Kid) ....A
Schulte Bros. Co. (Sheepskins) ....B
Shoemaker, J. L. & Co.
(Sheepskins) ....A
Swoboda & Son, H. (Horse
Hide) ....A
Wolff Process Leather Co.
(Kid) ....B
PA.—Pine Grove
Gensemer, G. & H. (Oak
Sole; Rough; Harness)..B
PA.—Ridgway
Elk Tanning Co. .....AAA
PA.—St. Mary's
St. Mary's Tanning Co.
AAAA
PA.—Saltillo
Greene & Son Calvin......A
PA.—Sheffield
Penn. Tanning Co. (Hemlock Sole) ....B
PA.—Troy
Van Dyne & Sons, E. (Union
Backs) ....B
PA.—Westover
Mosser, W. F. (Union; Hemlock in Backs and Sides)B
PA.—Williamsport
Crawford & Son, J. K. (Oak;
Harness, Calf; Kip; Upper Fly Net) ....B
Union Tanning Co. .....AAA
R. I.—Providence
Burgess & Son, A. (Picker)
X
Holbrook, A. & C. W. (Picker) ....B
TENN.—Harriman
Harriman Leather Co.....B
TENN.—Niota
Niota Leather Co........B
VT.—Morrisville
Warren Leather Co. (Harness) ....B
VA.—Alexandria
Smoot & Sons Co., C. C.
(Belting; Butts; Oak
Backs; Bellies; Heads).A
VA.—Elkton
Cover, J. R. (Oak Sole)..A
VA.—Fredericksburg
Hurkamp & Co., Jno. G.
(Rough Skirting; Harness; Fair Skirting; Insole; Upper) ....B
VA.—Manchester
Shotwell & Co., A. D.
(Rough; Belting; Butts;
Harness; Collar) ....B
VA.—Winchester
Graischen, F. A. (Glove).B
Shearer, A. L...........C
W. VA.—Charlestown
Goetz, A. D............B
W. VA.—Franklin
Franklin Tanning Co.....B
W. VA.—Wheeling
Hoffman Sons Co., Jno. G.
(Oak Harness) ......AAA
WIS.—Eau Claire
Rueping Leather Co., Fred
(Wax; Calf; Veals; Kips;
Kangaroo; Chrome)...AA
WIS.—Kenosha
Allens' Sons, N. R. (Harness; Deerskin; Slaughter Sole; Collar; Calf)...
AAAA
WIS.—Milwaukee
Anstedt Leather Co., C.
(Collar; Fly Net)......A
Conrad Bros. (Harness;
Collar) ....AA
Gallun & Sons, A. F. (Grain;
Wax Upper; Calf; Harness) ....AAA
Martin Leather Co., Geo.
(Calf; Kip) ......AAA
Pfister & Vogel Leather Co.
(Grain; Upper; Russia;
Kangaroo; Calf; Colored;
Sole; Harness; Splits)...
AAAA
Trostel & Sons, Albert (Rus-

LEATHER (Con.)

sia; Kangaroo; Wax Calf; Boot; Oil; Bright Grain; Slaughter Sole; Splits; Collar; Fly Net; Lace).. AAAA

Zohrlant Leather Co., Herman (Oil; Russia; Boot; Grain; Wax Upper; Satinette; Splits; Kangaroo; Calf; Kip; Harness; Skirting; Collar; Glove).. AA

WIS.—Racine

Eisendrath Tanning Co., B. D. (Kangaroo; Dongola; Calf; Horse Hide)......B

Huffner, E. J. ....A

WIS.—Sheyboygan Falls

Weisse & Co., Chas. S. (Harness; Collar) .....A

LEATHER GOODS

CAL.—Los Angeles

Blust Co., A. (Belts; Leggins) ....D

ILL.—Chicago

Chicago Case Mfg. Co., 142 W. Washn. (Jewelers' Cases) ....E

Chicago Leather Goods Co., 180 Washn. ....D

Eiseman, Kaiser & Co., 146 Franklin ....B

Fitzgerald Trunk Co., (Traveling Bags) .....A

Hartman Trunk Co., 176 Market (Traveling Bags) A

Lanz, Owen & Co., 188 Lake (Bags; Cases; Hat Boxes, &c.) ....A

Riordan Mfg. Co., T. G., 731 King (Traveling Bags) C

Webster, G. A., 14 Wabash Av. (Pocket Books)....C

Weick Mfg. Co., Martin, 1651 N. 41st (Musical Instrument Case) ....E

Weiffenbach Mfg. Co., 622 Humboldt (Razor Strops) D

Western Leather Mfg. Co., 622 Humboldt (Collar; Cuff Boxes) ....D

MASS.—Amherst

Arms Pocketbook & Leather Novelty Co. (Pocket Books) X

MASS.—Athol

Bates Bros. (Pocket; Bill Books) ....B

MASS.—Boston

White & Son. W. B., 105 Summer (Spectacle Cases) ....D

MASS.—Greenfield

Weisbrod & Sons, Emil (Pocket Books) ....A

MASS.—South Deerfield

Ars Mfg. Co. (Bill; Pocket Books) ....B

MASS.—Westboro

Hunt Leather Goods Co. (Cases; Bags, &c)......B

MASS.—Worcester

Warren Leather Goods Co. (Bait; Lunch; Collar; Cuff; Hat Boxes; Dress Suit Cases; Bags; Music Goods, etc.) ....A

Manufacturers of Leather and Canvas Goods, Bag Tags, Traveling Bags, Collar and Cuff Boxes, Rollups, Card Cases, Leather Corners, Cornet Cases, Caddy Bags, Dress Suit Cases, Toilet Cases and Rolls, Mail Bags, Extension Cases, Fish Rod Cases, Fish Basket Straps, Sample Cases, Trunk and Bag Handles, Hat Boxes, Shirt Waist Cases, Hand

LEATHER GOODS Con.

Trunks, Lunch Boxes, Military Brush Cases, Music Rolls, Money Belts, Manicure Cases, Bottle Cases, Shawl Straps, Single Straps, Trunk Straps, Shoulder Straps, School Bags, Steamer Trunks, Goods to order.

N. J.—Hoboken

Lehman & Co. ....A

N. J.—Jersey City

Mehl & Co., John (Pocket Books) ....AA

N. J.—Newark

Beck, A., 231 N. J. R. R. Av. (Suit Cases, &c.)..X

Caille Co., P. (Satchels)..D

Eckelhofer Bros. (Pocket Books) ....E

Peddie & Co., S. B. (Collar; Cuff; Hat Boxes; Pocket Books) ....AA

N. J.—Trenton

Novelty Mfg. Co. (Dress Suit Cases) ....D

N. Y.—Binghamton

Sportsmen's Supply Co...C

N. Y.—Buffalo

Buffalo Jewelry Case Co. (Jewelry Cases) ......B

Pierce Mfg. Co., W. W. (Pocket Books) ....B

N. Y.—Gloversville

Mills, F. S. (Pocket Books) D

Wilkins & Co., E. J. (Pocket Books) ....B

New York City

Acme Leather Co., 558 B'way (Fancy Novelties) B

Altenberg, Jos., 78 Reade (Cases; Bags) ....E

Averbeck, M. J., 19 Maiden Lane (Fancy Novelties).A

A. & E. Leather Goods Co., 419 Broome (Frames; Bags, &c.) ....D

Berner & Freedman. 34 Howard (Cases; Bags; Valises, &c.) ....D

Bienenzucht Bros., 109 Spring C

Boyle & Co., Jno., 112 Duane (Bags; Suit Cases; Trunks; Hat Boxes)..AA

Bronner, Louis H., 39 E. 21st (Card Cases; Bags; Pocket Books, &c.) C

Carow & Co., J., 51 Mercer (Cases) ....E

Cohn, J. J., 19 Maiden Lane (Fancy Novelties) ....A

Columbia Leather Goods Co. 454 B'way C

Comstock-Hoff Mfg. Co., 45 B'way (Collar; Cuff; Boxes) ....D

Conland & Mittenthal, 456 Broome C

Dietsch Bros., 14 E. 17th (Fancy Novelties) ...AA

Eckhardt & Co.. Ph., 53 Crosby (Bags; Cases, &c.) E

Epstein & Kowarsky, 351 B'way (Ad. Novelties).D

Freund Bros. Co., 524 B'way (Fancy Novelties) .....D

Galewski, A., 90 Chambers (Hat Boxes; Bags; &c.) D

Galewski, S., 321 B'way (Dress Suit Cases).....E

Graham Mfg. Co., 19th & B'way (Fancy Novelties) AAAA

Hacker, J. C. (Pocket Books) ....A

Hahn & Co., A., 21 Bond.B

Harrel Leather Goods Co., 522 B'way (Collar; Cuff Boxes) C

Headley & Farmer Co., 14 Astor Pl. (Traveling Goods) ....A

Hemrich, Herman & Weiss, 27 Howard (Fancy) ....D

Hraba, Louis W., 29 E.

LEATHER GOODS Con.

19th (Fancy Novelties).C

Kapp Bros. (Pocket Books) D

Katz Bros. Leather Goods Co., 38 Vesey (Bags; Cases, &c.) C

Kleinstuber, Jno., 536 B'way (Pocket Books)..C

Kraus & Deitsch, 170 5th Av. ....D

Lambert & Co., P. W., 64 Lispenard (Fancy Novelties; Pocket Books)..B

Lange & West, 126 Greene (Bag Cases) ....G

Lefkowitz & Bro., S. (Pocket Books) C

Littauer & Co., Wm. (Pocket Books) ....B

Livingston & Bro., L., 537 B'way (Pocket Books)..B

Loeb, H., 42 E. 12th (Fancy) ....D

Maas, Blum & Co., 424 B'way (Pocket Books).A

Margolin & Hoppenfeld, 126 Wooster C

Menster, George (Pocket Books) ....A

Naidis & Co., M., 122 Chambers (Alligator Bags)..D

Randnitz & Pollitz, 521 B'way (Bags; Belts)...A

Ripple & Fine, 68 Thomas (Dress Suit Cases)....G

Ritter Bros., 50 Howard (Bags; Belts) C

Rosenkaupt, S., 97 Chambers (Bags; Dress Cases, &c.) C

Scheuer, Herman, 435 Broome (Fancy) .....AA

Scheuer & Sons, S., 358 B'way ....AA

Schmickl & Co., F., 558 B'way (Satchels) .....B

Sherman Bros., 93 Chambers (Suit Cases) ....H

Spector & Shpetner, 316 Church (Fancy) ....E

Spier & Co., C. (Pocket Books) ....H

Stember, John, 83 Walker (Pocket Books) C

Tager & Epstein, 420 B'way, (Adv. Novelties)........D

Waxman Bros., 398 Madison (Dress Suit Cases).....E

Whiting Mfg. Co., 18th & B'way (Fancy Novelties) AAA

Wolff, Louis (Pocket Books) ....D

Wolff & Co., R. (Pocket Books) ....B

Zweig, Julius, 81 Chambers (Shawl; Trunk Straps).E

N. Y.—Rochester

Likly & Co., Hy. (Traveling Bags) ....A

OHIO—Cincinnati

American Trunk Co. (Trunks) X

Drucker & Co., N. (Traveling Bags) ....A

OHIO—Cleveland

Likly & Rockett Trunk Co. (Trunks) ....B

OHIO—Columbus

Stallman, F. A. (Traveling Bags) C

Lilly Co., The M. C. (Suit Cases) ....A

OHIO—Coshocton

Meek & Beech Co. (Adv. Specialties) ....AA

PA.—Philadelphia

Bains & Sons, Geo. B. (Trunks; Bags; Cases).A

Belber Trunk & Bag Co. (Bags, &c.) ....B

Haines, Wm. A. (Pocket Books) ....A

Klinger, F. W. Pocket Books) C

Kuester & Gerding, 405 Com. (Suit Cases) .....F

Langfeld Bros. & Co., 10th & Filbert (Bags; Pocket Books) ....AA

Mayer, Max, 44 N. 9th

LEATHER GOODS Con.

(Bags; Suit Cases, &c.) X

Reis & Hoelzel, 10th & Arch (Bags) X

Rosenblatt & Co., H. M., 22d & Oxford (Golf; Traveling Bags; Hat Boxes).A

Rumpp & Sons, C. F. (Collar; Cuff; Match Boxes; Pocket Books) ......AAA

Seitz & Son, J. H., 414 Brown (Bags; Suit Cases) D

Stelz & Bro., Louis E., 155 N. 4th (Society) ......D

Sutterly & Co., Gilbert T. (Match Boxes) C

White Co., F. H., 443 N. 10th (Bags; Cases, &c.).E

VA.—Richmond

Rountree & Bro. Trunk & Bag Co. H. W. (Traveling Bags) ....A

WIS.—Milwaukee

Abel & Bach Co. (Trunks; Bags; Suit Cases) ....A

Burroughs & Sons, Geo. (Traveling Bags, &c.)..B

Romadka Bros. (Traveling Bags, &c.) ....AA

Western Grip & Trunk Co. D

WIS.—Racine

Racine Trunk Co. (Traveling Bags) C

LEAVES

New York City

McKesson & Robbins (Senna) ....AAAA

Schieffelen & Co., (Matico Strontium) ....AA

LEDGERS: LOOSE LEAF

ILL.—Chicago

Baker-Vawter Co., 144 Washn. ....AA

Hoffman & Co., H. H., 176 Monroe ....D

Plew & Motter, Monadnock Blk. ....B

Rubil Mfg. Co. ....D

Tengwall File & Ledger Co. B

Volkers & Co., F. N., 83 5th Av. ....F

MICH.—Detroit

Richmond & Backus Co...A

MICH.—Kalamazoo

Kalamazoo Loose Leaf Ledger Co. X

MO.—Jefferson City

Tribune Printing Co.....B

MO.—St. Louis

Silber & Trussell Mfg. Co. B

New York City

Sheppard Co., C. E., 87 Maiden Lane ....F

MO.—No. Tonawanda

Rand Co. ....D

N. Y.—Rochester

Moore Corp., Jno. C......A

OHIO—Cincinnati

Twinlock Co., 310 Walnut D

PA.—Philadelphia

Mann Co., Wm. ......AA

R. I.—Providence

Park Mfg. Co. X

WIS.—Milwaukee

Heinn Co. ....D

Miller Co., A. C..........B

Razall-Bruel Co., 380 E. Water ....D

Razell Mfg. Co., H. G., 383 Water ....B

West. Williams Co., 389 E. Water C

LEECHES

New York City

Berkitz & Co., B., 429 E. 120th ....F

LEGGINGS

CONN.—Hartford

618

LEGGINGS (Con.)

Wiley & Son Co., Wm. H.
(Gaiters; Hunting; Military; Riding) ....A

ILL.—Chicago
Columbia Overgaiter & Legging Co. C
Cook & Bros., E. C.......A
Weller Mfg. Co., 118 North
Av. (Elevator) ....A

ILL.—Dubuque
Rider-Wallis Co... ....A

MASS.—Boston
Clapp Rubber Co., E. H.
(Rubber) ....A
Stoughton Rubber Co.
(Rubber) ....AA

MICH.—St. Joseph
Cooper, Wells & Co. (Knit)
AA

MINN.—Mankato
Mankato Mills Co........A

MO.—St. Louis
Strauss Saddlery Co., Jacob
A
Zittlosen Mfg. Co.......C

N. H.—Manchester
Rief, Geo. W. (Knit)....D

N. J.—Newark
Peters Harness & Saddlery
Co. (Riding) C

N. Y.—Jamestown
Broadhead & Sons. Wm.
(Knit) ....AAAA

New York City
Borchardt & Co., S.....AA
Goodyear's India Rubber
Glove Mfg. Co. (Rubber)
AAAA
Goodyear Rubber Co. (Hunting; Rubber) .....AAAA
Hodgman Rubber Co. (Hunting; Rubber) ....AA
Mechanical Rubber Co.
(Rubber) ....AAAA
Rauh & Co., S., 310 6th
Av. ....D
Stimpson Son. E. B., 31
Spruce (and Gaiters)....B

N. Y.—Syracuse
Sager, A. ....A

OHIO—Cincinnati
Pettibone Bros. Mfg. Co.
(Gaiters) ....A

TEXAS—Dallas
Padgitt Bros. Co........A

WIS.—La Crosse
La Crosse Rubber Mills Co.
(Hunting; Rubber) ...A

WIS.—Milwaukee
Kalt-Zimmers Mfg. Co....C

WIS.—Racine
Chicago Rubber Clothing Co.
(Hunting; Rubber).....A

LEGS

For Artificial Legs, see Limbs

CONN.—New Britain
New Britain Machine Co.
(Bench) ....A

CONN.—Waterbury
Amer. Pin Co. (Brass Lavatory) ....AA

ILL.—Chicago
Clow & Sons, Jas. B., 222
Lake (Lavatory)...AAA
Illinois Malleable Iron Co.,
30 W. Monroe (Lavatory(
AAAA

ILL.—Edwardsville
Edwardsville Brass Co.
(Lavatory) ....B

IND.—South Bend
Stephenson Mfg. Co.
(Beaded Chair) ....B

KY.—Covington
Ohio Scroll & Lumber Co.
(Chair; Table) ....D

MASS.—Worcester
Warren Leather Goods Co.
(Boots; Tops)........B

MO.—St. Louis
Nelson Mfg. Co., N. O.
(Sink; Stall) ......AAA

N. Y.—Manlius
Cheney & Son, S. (Counter)
A

LEGS (Con.)

New York City
Du Bois & Co., F. N., 243
9th Av. (Lavatory)..AAA
Mott Iron Wks., J. L., 88
Beekman (Lavatory)..AA
Mullaney's Son, Jas., 25th
& Lex. Av. (Brass Basin
Lavatory) ....D
Stimpson & Son, E. B.
(Boot; Tops) ....B
Victor Excelsior Brass Wks.
42 Mott (Lavatory) ...A

N. Y.—Rome
Wilson Mfg. Co., R. M.
(Lavatory) ....B

OHIO—Cleveland
Ohio Brass & Iron Mfg. Co.
(Lavatory) ....B
Sanitary Co., 335 Huron
(Brass Lavatory) ......B

PA.—Philadelphia
Blatchley, Chas. G. (Chair;
Table) ....B
Haines, Jones & Cadbury
Co., 1136 Ridge Av. (Lavatory) ....AA
McCambridge & Co. (Ltd.)
527 Cherry (Lavatory).B
Newell-Booth Co., Broad,
cor. Buttonwood (Lavatory) ....D

PA.—Pittsburg
Pittsburg Brass Mfg. Co.
(Lavatory) ....D

LEMONS
See Oranges & Lemons

LENOS
R. I.—Pawtucket
Slater Cotton Co........AA

LENSES
See also Optical Goods

ILL.—Chicago
Adams & Westlake Co., Ontario, cor. N. Franklin
(Signal Lamps) ....AAAA
Fowler, E. S. & W. S....D

IND.—Hartford City
Sneath Glass Co. (Semaphore; Bulls' Eye)......B

MASS.—Cambridge
Clark & Sons, Alvan (Astronomical Instrument).F

MASS.—Southbridge
Amer. Optical Co. (Optical;
Bicycle Lantern; Spectacle; Eye Glass)...AAA

N. H.—Tilton
Tilton Optical Co. (Optical)
D

New York City
Anthony & Scovill Co., 122
5th Av. (Photographic).D
Gennert, G. (Photographic)
B
Gregg, Wm. T. (Photographic) ....F
McAllister, T. H. ....B
Myers Co., S. F.........D
Spencer Optical Co. (Optical; Spectacle; Eye Glass;
Astronomical Instrument;
Ophthalmoscopic Test)..C

N. Y.—Rochester
Bausch & Lomb Optical Co.
(Spectacle; Eye Glass;
Astronomical Instrument;
Photographic) ......AAA
Gundlach Optical Co.
(Photographic) ....A

OHIO—Toledo
Libbey Glass Co. (R. R.
Signal Lamp) ....AA

PA.—Pittsburg
Macbeth-Evans Glass Co.
(Railroad Signal).AAAA

VT.—North Bennington
White & Co., H. C.
(Stereoscopic) ....B

WIS.—Milwaukee
Milwaukee Optical Mfg. Co.
(Optical) ....D

LEPTANDRIN

MO.—St. Louis
Larkin & Scheffer Chem.
Co. ....A

LETTERS

**See also Figures; Numbers;
Alphabets.**

CONN.—Bridgeport
Schwerdtle Stamp Co.
(Steel) ....F
CONN.—Meriden
Bradley & Hubbard Mfg.
Co. (Brass) ......AAAA
CONN.—New Haven
Hoggson & Pettis Mfg. Co.
(Steel) ....A
CONN.—Winsted
Goodwin & Kintz Co.
(House) ....B
ILL.—Chicago
Besley Co., Chas. H.
(House) ....AA
Chicago Spring Butt Co.
(House) ....B
Meyercord Co. (Decalco-
mania) ....A
ILL.—Elgin
Zeigler Bros. (Removable
Metallic Sign) C
ILL.—Freeport
Arcade Mfg. Co. (House).A
Stover Mfg. Co. (Brass).AA
Ｉ.—Boston
Bay State Fdry. Co., 155 A
(Bronze) ....D
Dennison Mfg. Co. (Paper
Gummed) ....AAAA
Murdock Corporation, 156
Boylston (Bronze)......B
Woodman Mfg. & Supply
Co., R. (Steel) ....F
MO.—St. Louis
St. Louis Electrotype Fdry.,
211 N. 3d (Metallic Pat-
tern) ....D
N. J.—Newark
Benfield & Milne Mfg. Co.
(Sign; Cast Iron) .....D
Spanjer Bros. (Wooden)..E
New York City
Am. Railway Supply Co.
(House) X
Brooks & Co., E. J. (Metal-
lic Pattern; Steel).....B
Butler, A. G., 284 Pearl
(Metal Pattern) ....D
Caesar Bros. (Enamelled).D
Fac-Simile Typewriting Co.,
180 Fulton (Imitation
Type Written) C
Ness, Jr., Geo. M. (Steel)
H
New York Stencil Wks.
(Brass; Steel) X
Palm-Fechteler Co. (Decal-
comania) ....A
Russell & Erwin Mfg. Co.
(House) ....AAAA
Sargent & Co. (House)
AAAA
Stafford Co., N. (Brass).F
Tiebout, W. & J. (House).B
Wiebusch & Hilger
(House) ....A
Yale & Towne Mfg. Co.
(House) ....AAAA
N. Y.—Seneca Falls
Brim, A. W. (Pattern)..F
Knight & Son, H. W. (Pat-
tern) C
OHIO—Akron
Enterprise Mfg. Co. (Block)
A
OHIO—Canton
Berger Mfg. Co. (Cornice;
Sign) ....AA
OHIO—Cincinnati
Obermayer Co., S. (Metal-
lic Pattern) ....AA
Palm Bros. & Co. (Decal-
comania) ....A
Palm Letter Co., 316 Main
(Transfer) ....A
OHIO—Cleveland
Cleveland Galvanizing Wks.
(House) C
Globe Machine & Stamping
Co. (Steel) C

LETTERS (Con.)

Konislow Stamping & Tool
Wks. (Steel) ....D
National Decalcomania Co.
(Decalcomania) ....F
Taylor & Boggis Fdy. Co.
(House) ....AA
OHIO—Dayton
Howard, Wm. H. (Brass).E
PA.—Philadelphia
Natl. Decalcomania Co.
(Paper Gummed) .....F
Paxson Co., J. W. (Metal-
lic Pattern) ....AA
Quint & Sons, S. H. (Metal-
talic Pattern) ....B
PA.—Reading
Reading Hdw. Co. (House)
AAAA
R. I.—Providence
Brown & Sharpe Mfg. Co.
(Sign; Cast Iron)..AAAA

LEVELERS

ILL.—Chicago
Austin Mfg. Co., Manhattan
Bldg. (Road) ....AAA
ILL.—Harvey
Austin Mfg. Co. (Road)
AAA
MICH.—Detroit
Amer. Harrow Co. (Road)
AA
N. Y.—Frankfort
Acme Road Machy. Co.
(Road) ....B
N. Y.—Marathon
Climax Road Machine Co.
(Road) ....B
OHIO—Columbus
Kilbourne & Jacobs Mfg.
Co. (Road) ......AAAA
PA.—Kennett Square
Amer. Road Machine Co.
(Road) ....AA

LEVELS

COLO.—Denver
Ainsworth & Sons, Wm.
(Engineers') ....B
CONN.—New Britain
Stanley Rule & Level Co.
(Bit; Square; Iron Pock-
et) ....AAA
CONN.—Pine Meadow
Chapin-Stephens Co. (Ad-
justable; Non-Adjustable
Machinists' Brass Col-
ored; Track; Masons';
Pocket) ....A
CONN.—Rockfall
Smith, Otis A. (Carpenters')
B
ILL.—Chicago
Dietzgen Co., Eugene, 149
5th Av. ....A
Fairbanks, Morse & Co.,
Franklin & Monroe
(Track) ....AAAA
Webster Mfg. Co. (Hydro-
static) ....AA
ILL.—Harvey
Buda Fdry. & Mfg. Co.
(Track) ....AA
MASS.—Athol
Athol Machine Co. (Iron
Pocket; Plumbers'; Ma-
chinists'; Iron Bench;
Carpenters') ....B
Richardson-Oliver Co. (Ma-
chinists'; Pocket; Iron)
E
Starrett Co., L. S. (Iron;
Machinists') ....A
MASS.—Boston
Berger & Sons, C. L. (En-
gineers') ....A
MASS.—Fitchburg
Putnam Machine Co. (Iron;
Machinists') ....A
Sawyer Tool Mfg. Co. (Iron;
Steel Spirit; Cross)....C
MASS.—Greenfield
Stratton Bros. ....E
MASS.—Millers Falls
Millers Falls Co. (Iron).AA
MICH.—Detroit
Anderson & Sons, W. H.
(Track) C
Strelinger Co., Chas. A., 98

LEVELS (Con.)
Bates (All Kinds).....A
MICH.—Kalamazoo
Kalamazoo Railway Supply
Co. (Track) ....B
MICH.—Three Rivers
Sheffield Car Co. (Track)
AA
MO.—St. Louis
Handlan Buck Mfg. Co., 212
N. 3d (Track) ....AA
N. J.—Newark
Smith, S. O. (Boxwood)...D
N. Y.—Albany
Van Hoesen, Theo. W.
(Glass Spirit for Scientific Instruments) .....F
New York City
Bender & Sons, Ph. J., 87
Frankfort (Machinists') E
Fox Bros. & Co., 24 Vesey
(Track) ....A
Gardam & Sons, Wm., 47
Rose (Architects'; Builders') ....D
Jennings Co., C. E. (Hand
Bench) ....B
Keuffel & Esser Co. 127 Fulton (Architects'; Engineers'; Iron; Machinists';
Pocket; Shafting; "Y")
AA
Peck, Stow & Wilcox Co.
27 Murray (Bit; Square)
AAAA
Soltmann, E. G., 125 E. 42d
(Architects'; Engineers')
B
Tower & Lyon Co., 95
Chambers (Masons; Pocket) ....B
N. Y.—Troy
Gurley, W. & L. E. (Architects'; Engineers') ....A
OHIO—Akron
Akron Spirit Level Wks..B
OHIO—Cincinnati
Pfister, Herman, 428 Plum
(Architects'; Builders').E
PA.—Columbia
Smith, E. G. (Pocket)...E
PA.—Philadelphia
Disston & Sons (Inc.), Hy.
(Iron; Shafting; Pocket;
Machinists') .....AAAA
Queen & Co. (Inc.), 1010
Chestnut (Architects'; Engineers') ....AA
Young & Sons, 47 N. 7th
(Engineers') ....B

LEVERS
CONN.—Stamford
Yale & Towne Mfg. Co.
(Bell; Bronze) ....AAAA
GA.—Toccoa
Reeves Spool & Bobbin Co.
(Pick) ....D
ILL.—Rockford
Emerson Mfg. Co. (Steel
Harrow) ....AAA
MINN.—Duluth
La Dow Implement Co.
(Harrow) ....B
New York City
Peck, Stow & Wilcox Co.,
27 Murray (Door Bell)...
AAAA
Russell & Erwin Mfg. Co.
(Door Bell) ......AAAA
Sargent & Co. (Door Bell;
Machine) ....AAAA
OHIO—Cleveland
Federal Mfg. Co. (Automobile Steering) ..AAAA
OHIO—Dayton
Dayton Malleable Iron Co.
(Brake) ....AAA
PA.—Lebanon
Amer. Iron & Steel Mfg. Co.
(Brake) ....AAAA
PA.—Pittsburg
Oliver Iron & Steel Co.
(Brake) ....AAAA
PA.—Reading
Reading Hdw. Co. (Door
Bell) ....AAAA
R. I.—Bristol
Dixon Lubricating Paddle
Co. (Cotton Machine)...B

LEVERS (Con.)
R. I.—Pawtucket
Haskell Mfg. Co., Wm. H.
(Machine) ....AA

LICORICE
KY.—Louisville
Jungbluth & Rautenberg,
831 W. Main ....B
MD.—Baltimore
Young Co., J. S........AA
N. Y.—Brooklyn
Natl. Licorice Co., 375
Lorimer ....A
New York City
Amer. Licorice Co., 18
Wooster X
Carenou & Tus, 3 Union Sq.
(Powd.; Root) ....B
Dean & Son, W. G., 361
Washn. ....A
MacAndrews & Forbes, 111
5th Av. ....AAAA
Stamford Mfg. Co., 88 Wall
(Root) ....AAAA
Weaver & Sterry, 79 Pine
B
OHIO—Cincinnati
Mueller Licorice Co., Jno.,
2117 Redding Road.....X
OHIO—Toledo
Toledo Licorice Co. (Powd.)
C
PA.—Hanover
Young & Co., J. S........A

LIDS
DEL.—Wilmington
Davis Pressed Steel Co.
(Journal Box) ....B
ILL.—Chicago
McCord & Co., Old Colony
Bldg. (Journal Box)...B
N. Y.—Brooklyn
Continental Iron Wks., Calyer & West (Gas Works
Retort) ....A

LIFTERS
CONN.—Bristol
Sessions & Son, J. H.
(Trunk) ....AA
CONN.—New Britain
Stanley Works (Sash).AAA
CONN.—New Haven
Ives Co., H. B. (Sash)...A
Miner & Peck Mfg. Co.
(Drop Press; Hammer).X
CONN.—Plainville
Hills, Edwin (Stove Lid).A
ILL.—Chicago
Barbee Wire & Iron Wks.
(Pie; Turners) ....B
Nicol & Co., 55 W. Washington (Stove Lid)......D
Wing Mfg. Co., 13 N. Jeff
(Stove Lid) ....B
ILL.—Freeport
Arcade Mfg. Co. (Sash;
Stove Lid; Pot; Plate)..A
Stover Mfg. Co. (Stove Lid;
Sash; Window Screen)..
AA
ILL.—Moline
Williams, White & Co.
(Drop Hammer) ......AA
ILL.—Paxton
Paxton Hdw. Mfg. Co.
(Hot Dish) X
ILL.—Sterling
National Mfg. Co. (Sash).C
IOWA—Dubuque
Adams Co. (Stove Lid)..A
MASS.—Boston
New England Novelty Mfg.
Co. (Pie; also Turners).A
MASS.—Lowell
Woods, Sherwood Co. (Wire
Plate) ....E
MASS.—Worcester
Hamblin & Russell Mfg. Co.
(Wire Stove Cover)....B
Wire Goods Co. (Stove Lid;
Window Screen) ......A
MICH.—Bellaire
Richards & Bechtel (Wooden Clothes) ....B

LIFTERS (Con.)

MICH.—Kalamazoo
Hill & Co., Wm. E. (Steam
Gang Stock) ....B

MINN.—Minneapolis
Diamond Iron Wks. (Steam
Skid) ....B

MO.—St. Louis
Pleuger & Henger Mfg. Co.
(Sash) ....A

N. J. Newark
Ohl & Co., Geo. A. (Drop
Press; Hammer) ......B
Williamson Wire Novelty
Co., C. T. (Window
Screen) ....B

N. Y.—Albany
Troy Nickel Wks. (Stove
Lid) C

N. Y.—Brooklyn
New York Stamping Co.
(Stove Lid) ....A

New York City
Eagle Chain & Novelty Mfg.
Co., 135 Elm (Brass Plate
Skirt) C
Peck, Stow & Wilcox Co.
(Sash; Stove Lid).AAAA
Russell & Erwin Mfg. Co.
(Transom; Sash; Shutter)
..................AAAA
Sargent & Co. (Sash; Shut-
ter; Stove Lid; Transom;
Window Screen) ..AAAA
Stoutenborough, X. (Pie
Plate) ....D
Yale & Towne Mfg. Co.
(Sash; Transom) .AAAA

OHIO—Cincinnati
Obermayer Co., S. (Mould-
ers' Pattern) ....AA

OHIO—Cleveland
Cleveland Foundry Co.
(Stove Lid) ....A
Fanner Mfg. Co. (Stove
Lid) ....A
Taylor & Boggis Fdry. Co.
(Sash) ....AA

OHIO—Ravenna
Williams, A. C. (Stove Lid)
....................A

OHIO—Shelby
Shelby Spring Hinge Co.
(Sash) ....B

PA.—Erie
Griffin Mfg. Co. (Sash) ..A

PA.—Lancaster
Chalfant Hdw. Mfg. Co.
(Stove Lid) X

PA.—Mount Joy
Iron Casting Co. (Stove
Lid) ....AAAA

PA.—Norristown
Reading Screw Co. (Tran-
som) ....

PA.—Philadelphia
Pease Mfg. Co. (Pan)....F

PA.—Reading
Reading Hdw. Co. (Sash;
Shutter; Transom).AAAA

PA.—Wrightsville
Wrightsville Hdw. Co.
(Stove Lid; Sash) ....AA

R. I.—Providence
Standard Machy. Co. (Drop
Press; Hammer) ......B

WIS.—Milwaukee
Allis-Chalmers Co. (Steam
Board; Steam Gang Stock)
..................AAAA

LIFTS

CONN.—Bridgeport
Gaynor & Mitchell Mfg. Co.
(Sash) C

CONN.—Hartford
Rhodes, L. E., 28 High
(Automatic Water).....F

CONN.—Middletown
Wilcox-Crittenden & Co.
(Sash) ....A

CONN.—New Britain
Corbin, P. & F. (Sash;
Flush Sash) ......AAAA
Judd, Oliver S. (Sash)....B
Russell & Erwin Mfg. Co.
(Sash) ....AAAA
Stanley Wks. (Sash) ..AAA

CONN.—New Haven
Ives & Co., B. (Sash)......A
Mallory-Wheeler Co. (Sash)
....................AA

LIFTS (Con.)

CONN.—Southington
Peck, Stow & Wilcox Co.
(Sash) ....AAAA

CONN.—South Norwalk
Norwalk Lock Co. (Sash)..A

CONN.—Stamford
Yale & Towne Mfg. Co.
(Transom; Sash; Safety
Double) ....AAAA

ILL.—Aurora
Amer. Well Wks. (Air;
Water) ....AA

ILL.—Chicago
Clow & Sons, Jas. B., 344
Franklin (Water) .....AA
Hine-Watt Mfg. Co., 60 Wa-
bash Av. (Transom)....D
Payson Mfg. Co., 1319 W.
Jackson Boul. (Transom)
....................D

ILL.—Freeport
Arcade Mfg. Co. (Sash)...A
Stover Mfg. Co. (Sash) AA

MAINE—Portland
Cox & Son, A. F. (Shoe;
Top) ....A

MASS.—Boston
Coffin Valve Co. (Hydraulic)
....................D
Thayer Co., N. F. (Shoe) C

MAINE—Salem
Patten, Paul B. (Motor; Car
Pitt) ....E

N. J.—Newark
Storm Mfg. Co. (Invalid) B

New York City
Amer. Air Compressor Wks.,
26 Cortlandt (Pneumatic)
....................F
Braender, Philip, 47 W.
125th (Automatic Water)
....................B
Creamer & Co., W. G., 96
John (Sash; Railway
Car) ....A
Krieg & Co., J. K. (Shoe
Top) ....A
Sargent Co., Geo. F. (In-
valid Transfer) X
Watson-Stillman Co. (Elec-
tric Motor) ....A

N. Y.—Poughkeepsie
Sedgwick Machine Wks.
(Trunk) ....D

N. Y.—Rochester
Rochester Top Lift Co.
(Boot Top) ....B

OHIO—Cleveland
Bishop & Babcock Co., Ham-
ilton & Kirtland (Automa-
tic Water) ....AAA
Cleveland Faucet Co., 21
Frankfort (Automatic
Water) ....AAA
Columbian Hdw. Co., Coe &
Hamilton (Sash) .....AA
Taylor & Boggis Fdy. Co.,
521 Seneca (Sash) ..AA

OHIO—Columbus
Ohio Pump & Brass Co.,
18th & Oak (Water)....C

OHIO—Mansfield.
Ohio Brass Co. (Motor; Car
Pitt) ....AA

OHIO—Shelby
Shelby Spring Hinge Co.
(Sash) ....B

PA.—Atglen
Chalfant Hdw. Mfg. Co.
(Sash) X

PA.—Norristown
Reading Screw Co. (Self-
Locking Push Button
Transom) ....A

PA.—Philadelphia
Wood & Co., R. D., 400
Chestnut (Hydraulic)
..................AAAA

PA.—Pittsburg
Lewis Fdy. & Machine Co.,
1001 Bingham (Hydrau-
lic) ....A

PA.—Reading
Penn. Hdw. Co. (Sash) .AA
Reading Hdw. Co. (Sash;
Transon) ....AAAA

PA.—South Bethlehem
Bethlehem Fdy. & Mach.
Co. (Acid) C

PA.—Wrightsville
Wrightsville Hdw. Co.
(Sash) ....B

LIFTS (Con.)
WIS.—Milwaukee
Willer Mfg. Co. (Sash)..A

LIGHTERS

CONN.—Meriden
Bradley & Hubbard Mfg. Co.
(Cigar) ....AAAA
ILL.—Chicago
Braun Mfg. Co., D. J.,
Washington & Union (Ci-
gar) ....B
Eldred Mfg. Co., 291 N.
State (Cigar) C
KY:—Newport..
Higgin Mfg. Co. (Vehicle)
A
MASS.—Boston
Edson Mfg. Co. (Side;
Deck) ....B
New England Novelty Mfg.
Co. (Cigar) ....H
MASS.—Brookline
Holtzer-Cabot Electric Co.
(Gas; Electric) ....A
N. Y.—Belmont
Clark Bros. Co. (Gas)....A
New York City
Houchin Co., Thos. W.
(Candle) ....D
Ostrander & Co., W. R.
(Side; Deck) ....A
Roche, Wm. (Electric Gas)
D
PA.—Erie
Erie Specialty Co. (Cigar)
B
WIS.—Milwaukee
Bagley & Sons Co., W.
(Side; Deck) X

LIGHTS

See also Lamps

CAL.—San Francisco
Jackson & Co., P. H., 228
1st (Sidewalk; Vault Floor)
D
ILL.—Chicago
Brown Bros. Mfg. Co., W.
22d & Campbell Av. (Side-
walk; Vault Floor) ....B
Chicago Sidewalk Light Co.,
101 Wash'n (Sidewalk;
Vault Floor) ....F
Dauchy Iron Wrks., 88 Illi-
nois (Prismatic Sidewalk;
Vault Floor) ....B
Richards & Kelly Mfg. Co.,
389 23d (Sidewalk; Vault
Floor) ....D
Smith Wire &Iron Wrks.,
100 Lake (Sidewalk; Vault
Floor) ....AA
IND.—Indianapolis
Brown & Ketcham Iron
Wrks. (Sidewalk; Vault
Floor) ....AAA
Hetherington & Berner, 19
W. South (Sidewalk;
Vault Floor) ....A
IND.—Lafayette
Wallace Fdry. & Machine
Co. (Sidewalk; Vault
Floor) ....D
KY.—Louisville
Snead Arch'l Iron Wks., 710
14th (Sidewalk; Vault
Floor) ....B
KY.—Newport
Higgin Mfg. Co. (Curtain)
A
MAINE—Portland
Fletcher & Crowell Co.,
(Sidewalk; Vault Floor
D
Megquier & Jones Co., 33
Pearl (Sidewalk; Vault
Floor) ....B
MD.—Baltimore
Bartlett, Haywood & Co.,
Continental Trust Bldg.
Sidewalk; Vault Floor) .B
MASS.—Boston
Amer. Mason Safety Tread
Co., 40 Water (Sidewalk;
Vault Floor) X
Carr & Andrews Corpn, 64
Federal (Sidewalk) ....D
Chelmsford Fdry. Co., 177
Devonshire (Sidewalk;
Vault Floor) ....A

LIGHTS (Con.)
Ham & Co., L. M., 152 Port-
land (Sidewalk; Vault
Floor) ....B
Smith & Lovett Co., 125 Al-
bany (Sidewalk; Vault
Floor) ....D
Wheeler Reflector Co.
(Church; Picture) C
MICH.—Detroit
Barnum Wire & Iron Wks.,
E. T., 99-105 Shelby
(Sidewalk; Vault Floor)
B
Russell Wheel & Fdry. Co.
(Sidewalk; Vault Floor).
AA
Vulcan Co. (Concrete; Cast
Iron Sidewalk; Vault
Floor) ....F
MICH.—Three Rivers
Sheffield Car Co. (Car
Signal) ....AA
MINN.—Minneapolis
Crown Iron Wks. 115 2nd
Av. (Sidewalk; Vault
Floor) ....B
Minneapolis Steel & Mchry.
Co. (Sidewalk; Vault
Floor) ....AAA
Northwestern Foundry (S.
T. Ferguson, Prop.), 312
S. 10th (Sidewalk; Vault
Floor) ....A
MINN.—St. Paul
St. Paul Fdry. Co., Como
Av. & Mackabin (Side-
walk; Vault Floor)....AA
MO.—St. Louis
Christopher & Simpson
Arch'l Iron & Fdry. Co.,
811 Park Av. (Sidewalk;
Vault Floor) ....AA
Globe Iron & Fdry. Co., cor.
9th & Victor (Sidewalk;
Vault Floor) ....B
NEBR.—Omaha
Paxton & Vierling Iron
Wks., 17th & U. P. Ry.
(Sidewalk) ....AA
N. J.—Jersey City
Snead & Co. Iron Wks.
(Sidewalk) ....A
N. Y.—Binghamton
Crandal, Stone & Co. (Cur-
tain) ....A
N. Y.—Brooklyn
Brooklyn Vault Light Co.,
481 Driggs Av. (Sidewalk;
Vault Floor) ....A
N. Y.—Buffalo
Ernst, Chas. F., 311 Walnut
(Sidewalk) ....B
New York City
Cornell Co., J. B. & J. M.,
26th & 11th Av. (Side-
walk; Vault Floor) ...AA
Dimond, Thos. (Floor; Side-
walk) ....A
Dietz Co., R. E., 60 Laight
(Search) ....A
Frink, I. P. (Pulpit; Dome
Ceiling; Foot; Picture)..
AA
Jacobs & Sons, 510 Pearl
(Sidewalk; Vault Floor) D
Joosten, C. H., 201 West
(Wax Night) X
Lamb, J. & R. (Church)..D
Mark, Jacob, 7 Worth (Side-
walk; Vault Floor) ....D
Metal Stamping Co. (Cur-
tain) ....A
N. J. Foundry & Machine
Co., 9 Murray (Sidewalk;
Vault Floor) ....D
N. Y. Prism Co., 473 W.
B'way (Sidewalk; Vault
Floor) ....E
Ransome & Smith Co., 11
B'way (Sidewalk; Vault
Floor) ....D
Tiebout, W. & J. (Side;
Deck) ....B
Tucker & Vinton (Inc.),
156 5th Av. (Steel Con-
crete Sidewalk; Vault
Floor) ....D
Wells Light Mfg. Co. (Con-
tractors') ....B
N. Y.—Rochester
Heughes & Co., F. L., 190
South Av. (Sidewalk;

LIGHTS (Con.)
Vault Floor) ....A
Star Headlight Co. (Car
Signal) X
N. Y.—Troy
Mahony Mfg. Co., 5th Av.,
cor. Liberty (Sidewalk;
Vault Floor) ....B
OHIO—Bellaire
Rodefer, T. G. (Floor;
Vault) ....A
OHIO—Cincinnati
Craighead Engineering Co.
(Head) ....D
Macleod & Co., Walter
(Search) ....B
Monarch Carriage Goods Co.
(Curtain) ....B
Schreiber & Sons Co., L.,
8th & Eggleston Av.
(Sidewalk; Vault Floor).
AA
OHIO—Cleveland
Brooks & Co., T. H., 960
Lake (Sidewalk; Vault
Floor) ....A
Madison Av. Fdry. Co., 155
E. Madison Av. (Side-
walk; Vault Floor) ....D
Van Dorn Iron Wks. Co.,
1793 E. Madison Av. (Side-
walk; Vault Floor) ..AA
OHIO—Kenton
Champion Iron Co. (Side-
walk; Vault Floor) ...AA
OHIO—Youngstown
Youngstown Wire & Iron
Co. (Sidewalk) ....G
PA.—Allegheny
Rieseck, P., cor. Allegheny
Av. & Rebecca (Sidewalk;
Vault Floor) C
PA.—Philadelphia
Brill Co., J. G. (Car Sig-
nal) ....AAAA
Creswell Iron Wks., S. J.,
23rd & Cherry (Sidewalk;
Vault Floor) ....B
Horrocks Iron Wks., 234 N.
Broad (Sidewalk; Vault
Floor) ....D
Merritt & Co., 1024 Ridge
Av. (Sidewalk; Vault
Floor) ....B
Steward & Stevens Iron
Wks., 9th, cor. Montg'y
Av. (Sidewalk; Vault
Floor) ....B
PA.—Pittsburg
Phoenix Steel Construction
Co., Penn Av. & 3rd (Il-
luminated Sidewalk; Vault
Floor) ....D
Pittsburg Brass Mfg. Co.
(Church) ....D
TENN.—Memphis
Chickasaw Iron Wks. (Side-
walk) ....A
WIS.—Milwaukee
Bayley & Sons Co., Wm.,
732 Greenbush (Sidewalk;
Vault Floor) X

LIMBS

ILL.—Chicago
Haussmann & Dunn (Arti-
ficial) C
Merrick-Hopkins Co. (Arti-
ficial) ....F
Truax, Green & Co., Chas.
(Artificial) ....A
LA.—New Orleans
McDermott Surgical Instru-
ment Co. (Ltd.) (Artifi-
cial) ....D
MICH.—Detroit
Simpson, Wm. T. (Artifi-
cial) ....F
MINN.—Minneapolis
Winkley Artificial Limb Co.
(Artificial) ....D
MO.—St. Louis
Kane Co., Daniel P.
(Artificial) X
New York City
Condell, A. (Artificial)...D
Frees, C. A. (Artificial)..X
Marks, A. A., 701 B'way
(Artificial; Artificial
Rubber) ....AA
N. Y.—Rochester
Fuller Co., Geo. R. (Arti-

LIMBS (Con.)
ficial; Artificial Rubber)
E
OHIO—Columbus
Triumph Artificial Limb Co.
(Artificial) ....H
PA.—Philadelphia
Kolbe Co., D. W. (Arti-
ficial) X
PA.—Pittsburg
Artificial Limb Mfg. Co.
(Artificial) X
Feick Bros. Co. (Artificial)
D

LIME

**For Chloride of Lime see
next Heading**

ALA.—Gadsden
Legarde Lime & Stone Co.
B
ALA.—Long View
Long View Lime Wks.....C
ARK.—Little Rock
Leiper & Mills...........B
CAL.—Los Angeles
California Portland Cement
Co. (Ground & Crushed).D
Union Lime Co. ....A
CAL.—San Francisco
Cowell & Co., Henry..AAA
Hearfield, Bannister & Co.
C
CONN.—Brookfield
New England Lime Co.
AAAA
FLA.—Lowell
Meffert, J. M...........C
GA.—Lime Kiln
Grove Lumber Co., M. J..A
GA.—Savannah
Hanley Co., Andrew......B
ILL.—Chicago
Artesian Stone & Lime Wks.
B
Chicago Union Lime Wks.
Co. ....A
Marblehead Lime Co.,
Mason Temple ....A
Shultz, Fred. T., 658 So.
Halstead ....A
Wis. Lime & Cement Co.
Chamb. Com. Bldg......B
ILL.—Fulton
Alden Lime Co...........A
ILL.—Kankakee
Kankakee Stone & Lime Co.
B
ILL.—Kinderhook
Marblehead Lime Co......A
ILL.—Quincy
Menke Stone & Lime Co.,
F. W. C
IND.—Evansville
Eichel Stone & Lime Co.
C
IND.—Fort Wayne
Bates & Co., E. M........B
IND.—Mitchell
Mitchell Lime Co........C
IND.—Putnamville
Keeport & Co., A. B.....C
IOWA—Fort Dodge
Superior Mfg. Co........A
IOWA—Maquoketa
Hurst & Co., A..........A
MAINE—Rockport
Eells Lime Co. ....A
MAINE—Thomaston
Creighton & Co., Jno. A..B
MD.—Baltimore
Maryland Lime & Cement
Co. ....B
Platt & Co. ....B
Stand. Lime & Stone Co..B
Wash. Building Lime Co..A
MD.—Buckeyetown
Stand. Lime & Stone Co..B
Washington Building Lime
Co. ....A
MD.—Frederick
Grove Lime Co., M. J. ...A
MD.—Lee
Lee Lime Co. (Magnesian
White) ....B
MD.—Le Grove
Le Grove Comb. Lime Co. B
MASS.—Adams
New England Lime Co.
AAAA
MICH.—Bay Shore
Bay Shore Lime Co. ......A

LIME (Con.)

MICH.—Detroit
Burrell Chemical Co.
(Acetate of) ....AA
Houghton, Hy. ....B
MICH.—Manistique
White Marble Lime Co.
(White) ....B
MICH.—Petoskey
Coughlan, T. R. ....AAAA
MICH.—Traverse City
Desmond Chemical Co.
(Acetate) C
MINN.—Mankato
Fowler & Pay ....B
MINN.—St. Paul
Northwestern Lime Co. .C
MO.—Auxvasse
Marblehead Lime Co. ....A
MO.—Centaur
Centaur Lime Co. ......B
MO.—Hannibal
Hannibal Lime Co. .....B
MO.—Kansas City
Ash Grove White Lime
Ass'n. ....A
MO.—St. Louis
Centaur Lime Co. ......B
N. J.—German Valley
Neighbor, E. J. C
N. J.—Lincoln
Atlas Mineral & Machine Co.
(Flour; Vienna) ......D
N. J.—McAfee
N. J. Lime Co. ....A
N. J.—Newark
Newark Lime & Cement
Mfg. Co. ....AAA
Newark Rosendale Lime &
Cement Co. ....A
N. Y.—Brooklyn
Wiarda & Co., John C.
(Hydrated) ....AA
N. Y.—Chazy
Chazy Marble Lime Co. ..C
N. Y.—Glens Falls
Sherman Lime Co. ....A
N. Y.—Rochester
Whitmore, Rauber & Vicini-
us ....A
N. Y.—Troy
Smith, Milo C
OHIO—Cincinnati
Strunk-Meyer Lime Co. .B
OHIO—Cleveland
James, Ralph T. C
OHIO—Columbus
Rock Plaster Mfg. Co. ....B
OHIO—Duhring
Bemis & Son, J. M. .....A
OHIO—Easton
Easton Lime Co. ....A
OHIO—Frazier
Knickerbocker Lime Co. ..A
OHIO—Ironton
Kelley, Mrs. Lindsey ....B
OHIO—Lime City
Lime City Co. C
OHIO—Marion
Evans Lime & Stone Co.,
Jno. ....
OHIO—Owens
Owens & Son, Jno. D. .....A
OHIO—Rocky Ridge
Kingman, Joseph ....B
OHIO—Springfield
Mills Bros. ....A
OHIO—Sugar Ridge
Buckeye Lime Co. ......B
Urschel Lime Co. C
OHIO—Toledo
Toledo White Lime Co.
(Ground; Crushed) ....A
OREGON—Portland
McCracken Co., J. ....B
PA.—Bradford
Lewis Run Mfg. Co.
(Acetate of) C
Smith Chemical Co., A. B.
(Acetate) ....B
PA.—Brandt
Kesler & Co. (Acetate) ..D
PA.—Bridgeport
David & Co., W. P. .....B
PA.—Kane
Forest Chemical Co.
(Acetate of) ....B
PA.—Norristown
Lukens & Yerkes ....B
Rambo, W. B. ....B
PA.—Philadelphia
Knickerbocker Lime Co. ..B
PA.—Port Allegheny
Wyman Chemical Co.
(Acetate) C

LIME (Con.)

PA.—Scranton
Keller, Luther ....A
PA.—Tyrone
Amer. Lime & Stone Co.
(Caustic; Ground; Cruched
Limestone; Hydrated)
AAA
S. C.—Gaffney
Carrol & Co. ....B
TENN.—Erin
Rauscher, E. W. ....B
TEXAS—Austin
Austin White Lime Co. ..B
VA.—Riverton
Carson Lime Co. ....B
VA.—Stevens City
Grove Lime Co., M. J. ..B
WASH.—Freeman
Wash. Brick & Lime Mfg.
Co. ....B
WASH.—Tacoma
Tacoma & Roche Harbor
Lime Co. ....B
W. VA.—Bakerton
Wash. Building Lime Co. A
WIS.—Eden
Marblehead Lime Co. ...A
WIS.—Mayville
Mayville White Lime Wks.
D
WIS.—Milwaukee
Western Lime & Cement Co
B
Northwestern Chemical Co.
(Bi-Sulphite) ....B
WIS.—Oshkosh
Cook & Brown Co. ....A

LIME: CHLORIDE

CAL.—San Francisco
Griswold & Co., E., 16th &
R. I. Av ....B
ILL.—Chicago
Brookman Bros. (Columbia
Chem. Wks.) 149 Huron E
Brookman Mfg. Co., 79 La
Salle Av. ....D
Champion Chem. Wks., 208
Michigan C
MICH.—Detroit
Acme White Lead & Color
Wks. ....A
N. J.—Hoboken
Vanderbilt & Son, J., ft. 7th
D
N. J.—Jersey City
Brookman Mfg. Co., 193
Front ....D
Champion Chem. Wks., 177
Franklin ....B
Fuerst Bros. & Co., 2 Stone
B
Hirsch & Son, L., 368 Green-
wich C
Platt, H. B., 52 Cliff ....B

LIMES

LA.—New Orleans
Dunbar's Sons, G. W.
(Preserved) ....AA
N. Y.—Buffalo
Erie Preserving Co. (Pre-
served) ....AA
N. Y.—Community
Oneida Community (Ltd.)
(Preserved) ....AAA
New York City
Gordon & Dilworth (Pre-
served) ....A

LIMESTONE

OHIO—Cleveland
Malone Stone Co. ....A
OHIO—Columbus
Columbus Iron & Steel Co.
AAAA
OHIO—Youngstown
Bessemer Limestone Co.
(Concrete) ....A
PA.—Harrisburg
Spong, L. R. (Crushed) E
PA.—New Castle
Croton Limestone & Brick
Co. (Crushed) C
PA.—Pittsburg
Blair Limestone Co.
(Crushed) ....B

LIMESTONE (Con.)

TEXAS—Jacksboro
Risley Bros. Co. (Blue) ..D

LINCRUSTA

New York City
Beck & Co., F. (Walton) A

LINDSEYS

See Woolen Goods

LINEN GOODS

MAINE—Snows Falls
Linen Mfg. Co. ....A
MASS.—Boston
Mackintire, Lawrie Co.
    (Importers) ....A
Nevins Co., 78 Chauncey ..A
N. J.—Wortendyke
Granite Linen Co. ......B
New York City
Anderson & Co., Wm.
    (Import.) ....AAAA
Bacon & Co. (Com.) ..AAA
Ballin & Taylor (Import.)B
Ballinger & Elkin, 377
    Bway. ....E
Beveridge, Erskine & Co.
    (Ltd.) (Import.) ......A
Brice & Johnson (Import.)
    ....B
Broadway Damask Co.
    (Import.) ....A
Brookfield Linen Co.
    (Import.) ....A
Brown & Co., Chas.
    (Import.) ....A
Campbell, Metzger & Jacob-
    son (Import.) ....B
Castle Island Linen Co.
    (Import.) C
Conrad & Co., W. B. (Com.;
    Import.) ....AA
Don & Co., Wm. & Jno.
    (Import.) ....AAAA
Douglas & Berry (Import.)
    ....A
Duff & Benton (Import.) B
Duke, McMahon & Co.
    (Import.) ....A
Duncan & Co., Jas.
    (Import.) ....AA
Elliott & Co., Jas. (Import.)
    ....A
Ewart & Son, (Ltd.) Wm.
    (Import.) ....AAAA
Freund, Foise & Co.
    (Import.) ....B
Gardner & Co., M. (Import.)
    ....A
Girdwood & Co., Jas.
    (Import.) ....A
Glass & Co., H. (Import.) A
Glendenning, McLeish & Co.
    (Import.) ....A
Graham & Co., Jno.
    (Import.) ....B
Grande Maison de Blanc
    (Import.) ....B
Gribbon & Sons, E.
    (Import.) ....AA
Haas & Co., S. (Import.) B
Inglis & Co. (Import.)AAAA
Jaffe & Pinkus, O.
    (Import.) ....AA
Lamb, Finlay & Co.
    (Import.) ....AA
Liddell & Co., Wm.
    (Import.) ....AAAA
McBratney, Robt. (Import.)
    ....B
McCann & Co., Jno.
    (Import.) ....A
McConnell & Co., Edw.
    (Import.) ....A
McCutcheon & Co., Jas.
    (Import.) ....AA
McGibbon & Co. (Import.) A
McLeod & Co., Donald W.
    (Import.) ....A
Macdermott, Wm. H.
    (Import.) ....B
Matier & Co., H. (Import.)
    ....AAA
Murphy & Stevenson & Co.
    (Import.) ....A
Neuss, Hesslein & Co.
    (Import.) ....B
Nevins Co., The (Com.) ..A
Reid & Co., Andrew
    (Import.) ....AAAA
Remy, Schmidt & Pleissner

LINEN GOODS (Con.)
    (Com.; Import.) ......AA
Richardson Sons & Owen, J.
    N. (Import.) ....AAA
Riggs & Co., Geo. (Import.
    Com.) ....A
Scott & Sons, Jas. (Import.
    Com.) ....AAA
Thompson & Co., Jas.
    (Import.) ....A
Ulmann & Co., Bernhard
    (Import.) ....AAAA
Waentig, Chas. R.
    (Import.) ....B
White & Co., Jas. F. (Com.;
    Import.) ....AAAA
Wilmerding & Bisset (Com.)
    ....AA
York Street Flax Spinning
    Co. (Import.) ....AAAA
PA.—Philadelphia
O'Neill, Wm. (Damask) ..C
Wardlow, Jno. & W., 1617
    Frankfort (Damask) ..D

LINERS

IND.—Kokomo
Petroleum Hoop & Lumber
    Co. (Head) ....B
MASS.—Athol
Starrett Co., L. S.
    (Draughts-men's; Section)
    ....A
MO.—St. Louis
Christy Fire Clay Co. (Ce-
    ment Kiln) ....AAA
N. Y.—Brooklyn
Adams & Co., J. J. (Brick)
    ....A
New York City
Bradley & Smith (Brick) AA
Gardam & Sons, W.
    (Draughtsmen's) ......D
Hanlon & Goodman (Brick)
    ....A
Keuffel & Esser Co.
    (Section) ....AA
OHIO—Akron
Robinson Clay Product Co.
    (Flue) ....AAAA
OHIO—Hamilton
Black-Clawson Co. (Sheet;
    Paste) ....AAA
WIS.—Beloit
Beloit Iron Wks. (Paste;
    Sheet) ....A

LINES

See also Cordage

ALA.—Anniston
Anniston Cordage Co.
    (Clothes) ....B
CONN.—Moodus
New York Net & Twine Co.
    (Fishing) ....A
CONN.—New Haven
Ives & Co., Hobart B.
    (Sash) ....A
CONN.—Norwich
Ossawan Mills Co. (Masons';
    Awning; Braided; Chalk;
    Clothes; Solid Braided;
    Trot; Twisted; Window)B
Turner Emerson Mfg. Co., P.
    (Chalk; Masons'; Cotton
    Clothes; Wire Clothes;
    Garden) X
CONN.—Westport
Lees Mfg. Co. (Chalk) ...A
GA.—Macon
Bibb Mfg. Co. (Chalk;
    Tarred) ....AAAA
ILL.—Chicago
American Steel & Wire Co.,
    The Rookery (Deep Sea
    Sounding) ....AAAA
Carpenter Co., Geo. B. (Cot-
    ton Clothes) ....AA
Roberts & Co., E. L.
    (Awning) ....A
KY.—Maysville
January & Wood Co. (Cotton
    Clothes; Fishing) .....A
MASS.—Arlington
Dale, Mrs. M. (Clothes) ..E
MASS.—Boston
Amer. Net & Twine Co.
    (Chalk; Fishing) ....AAA
Dame, Stoddard & Co.
    (Fishing) ....A
Gloucester Net & Twine Co.

LININGS (Con.) ..
Fuller, B., 95 Albany (Shoe)
  B
Munroe Felt & Paper Co.
  (Carpet) ....A
Union Carpet Lining Co.
  (Stitched Carpet) ....AA
MASS.—Canton
Draper Bros. & Co. (Boot;
  Glove; Rubber Shoe) ..A
MASS.—Chicopee
Olmstead & Tuttle Co.
  (Carpet) ....A
MASS.—Dighton
Dighton Stove Lining Co.
  (Stove) ....D
MASS.—Lynn
Houghton Heel & Leather
  Co. (Rubber Shoe) X
MASS.—Methuen
Knitted Fabrics Co. (Fancy)
  B
MASS.—Somerset
Somerset Stove Fdry. Co.
  (Grate) ....D
MASS.—Springfield
Chapman & Co., J. B.
  (Steam Pump) ....E
MASS.—Taunton
Presbrey Stove Lining Co.
  (Stove; Fire Brick; Grate)
  B
Taunton Stove Lining Co.
  (Stove) ....B
Union Stove Lining Co.
  (Stove) C
Williams Stove Lining Co.
  (Stove) ....B
MASS.—Walpole
Lewis Batting Co. (Stitched
  Carpet) ....B
MASS.—Watertown
Union Carpet Lining Co.
  (Carpet) ....A
MINN.—Winona
Union Fibre Co. (Car, Re-
  frigerator) ....B
MO.—Kansas City
Brockett Cement Co. (Flue)
  B
Dickey Clay Mfg. Co., W. S.
  (Flue) ....A
MO.—St. Louis
Evans & Howard Fire Brick
  Co., 920 Market (Flue)
  AAAA
Laclede Fire Brick Mfg. Co.,
  105 N. 7th (Flue) ..AAA
Missouri Fire Brick Co.
  (Cupola) ....B
Mound Coffin Co. (Coffin) A
Parker & Russell Mining &
  Mfg. Co., 417 Pine (Flue;
  Blast Furnace; Cupola)
  AAA
N. H.—Rochester
Kiesel Fire Brick Co.
  (Stove) ....F
N. H.—Troy
Troy Blanket Mills (Coat) B
N. J.—Hoboken
Woodman, Joel H. (Veneer
  Car) ....A
N. J.—Passaic
Alexander Silk Mills
  (Mohair) ....B
N. J.—Woodbridge
Valentine Bros. Co., M. D.
  (Blast Furnace; Cupola)
  AA
N. Y.—Albany
Jackson, Jno. H., 142 S. 3rd
  Av. (Flue) ....B
N. Y.—Brooklyn
Brooklyn Fire Brick Wks.,
  88 Van Dyke (Flue; Stove)
  A
N. Y.—Buffalo
Hall & Sons, 69 Tonawanda
  (Stove) ....A
N. Y.—Cossayuna
Alexander Blanket Co.
  (Blanket Cloth) ....D
N. Y.—Fonda
Fonda Glove Lining Co.
  (Glove) C
N. Y.—Gloversville
Gloversville Textile Co.
  (Glove) C
N. Y.—Lockport
Lockport Paper Co. (Carpet)
  A
New York City
Abegg & Rusch (Worsted
  Dress) ....AAAA

LININGS (Con.)
Brenack Paper Co., 16 Des-
  brosses (Barrel) X
Duffy & Co., J. P., 440 E.
  138th (Flue) ....B
Federal Clay Mfg. Co., 170
  Bway. (Flue) ....B
Jackson Co., Wm. K. (Fire-
  place) ....A
Kennedy Valve Mfg. Co.
  (Valve) ....AAA
Marcus & Bro., M. H.
  (Carpet) ....A
Maurer & Son, Henry, 420 E.
  23rd (Flue) ....AA
Murray & Brooking, 212
  Church (Trunk; Bag;
  Dress Suit Case, etc.) ..B
New York Carpet Lining Co.
  (Paper Carpet) ....F
Pierson & Co., Arthur N., 1
  Park Row (Flue) C
Reconstructed Granite Co.,
  14 Dey (Sulphate Diges-
  ter) ....D
Scott & Sons, Jas. (Cotton)
  AAAA
N. Y.—Rochester
National Casket Co.
  (Casket) ....AAAA
Rochester Sewer Pipe Co.,
  Powers Blk. (Flue) ...B
N. Y.—Troy
Adams Laundry Machine Co.
  (Asbestos Stove) .....B
Connors Paint Mfg. Co.,
  Wm. (Stove) ....A
McLeod & Henry Co. (Stove;
  Blast Furnace; Cupola) B
Ostrander Fire Brick Co.
  (Stove) ....A
N. C.—Pomona
Pomona Terra Cotta Co.
  (Chimney Flue) ....B
OHIO—Akron
Akron Fire Brick Co. (Stove)
  B
Robinson Clay Product Co.
  (Flue) ....AAAA
OHIO—Alliance
Alliance Asbestos Mfg. Co.
  (Asbestos Stove) .....B
OHIO—Cincinnati
Cinn. Sewer Pipe Co.
  (Chimney Flue) ....E
OHIO—Columbus
Wassall Fire Brick Co.
  (Flue) ....D
OHIO—Empire
Stratton Fire Clay Co.
  (Flue) ....A
OHIO—Haydensville
Haydensville Co. (Chimney
  Flue) ....A
OHIO—Lockland
Haldeman Paper Co. (Car-
  pet) ....A
OHIO—Logan
Hocking Clay Mfg. Co.
  (Flue) ....B
OHIO—Toronto
Francy's Sons & Co., Jno.
  (Chimney Flue) ..AAAA
OHIO—Uhrichsville
Buckeye Fire Clay Co.
  (Flue) ....B
PA.—Allegheny
Pittsburg Clay Pot Co.
  (Blast Furnace; Cupola) A
PA.—Beaver Falls
Ingram-Richardson Mfg. Co.
  (Enameled Refrigerator)D
Knott, Harker & Co., (Fire-
  place) ....AA
PA.—Castasauqua
Dery, D. G. (Silk) ......A
PA.—Clearfield
Clearfield Clay Wkg. Co.
  (Flue) ....B
PA.—Erie
Watson Co., H. F. (Paper
  Carpet) ....AAA
PA.—Franklin
Franklin Mfg. Co. (Asbestos
  Stove) ....AA
PA.—New Brighton
Pittsburg Clay Mfg. Co.
  (Chimney Flue) ..AAAA
PA.—Patton
Patton Clay Mfg. Co. (Flue)
  AA
PA.—Philadelphia
Garrett & Son Co., C. S.
  (Carpet) ....AA
Harvey, Moland & Co., 620

LININGS (Con.)
Arch (Flue) X
Sheppard & Co., Isaac A.
(Fireplace) ......AAA
Sweeney & Co., Geo., 1334
Ridge Av. (Stove) ....AA
Wolgamuth's Sons, F. F.
(Silk Dress, etc.) ......D
PA.—Pittsburg
Amer. Sewer Pipe Co., 2nd
Natl. Bk. Bldg. (Flue)
AAAA
Manown Mfg. Co. (Blast
Furnace; Cupola) .....B
Welch Gloninger & Maxwell
(Blast Furnace.. Cupola)
B
PA.—Reading
Fox & Co., E. S. (Stove) ..C
R. I.—Pawtucket
Goff & Sons, D. (Mohair)
AAA
Lebanon Mill Co. (Rubber)B
S. C.—Spartanburg
Morgan Wood & Iron Wks.
(Stove) ....D
TENN.—Chattanooga
Montague & Co. (Chimney
Flue) ....A
VT.—Rutland
Rutland Fire Clay Co.
(Plastic Stove) ....B
WASH.—Little Falls
Little Falls Fire Clay Co.
(Flue) ....B
WASH.—Seattle
Denney Clay Co. (Flue) ..A

LINKS

See also Jewelry

CONN.—Bridgeport
Bridgeport Chain Co.
(Repair; Lap) X
Smith & Egge Mfg. Co.
(Split) ....A
CONN.—New Haven
Kilborn & Bishop Co. (Re-
pair; Lap) C
ILL.—Aurora
Richards Mfg. Co. (Fusible)
B
ILL.—Chicago
Ajax Forge Co. (R. R.
Coupling) ....AA
Gibson Co., Wm. D., 23 N.
Clinton (Bed) ....B
Union Drop Forge Co., 66 N.
Ohio (Punched Chain)...X
ILL.—Evanston
Mark Mfg. Co. (Chain Belt)
AA
IND.—Indianapolis
Over, Ewald (Chain) .....D
MAINE—Portland
Laughlin Co., Thos.
(Chain) ....A
MAINE—So. Portland Sta.
Marine Hdw. Equipment
Co. (Repair; Lap) .....D
MASS.—Boston
Harvey, Henry H. (Adjus-
table Chain) ....B
MASS.—Lowell
Amer. Bolt Co. (Chain) ..X
MASS.—Worcester
Smith & Co., Thos.
(Punched Chain) '.......D
N. Y.—Binghamton
Titchener & Co., E. H.
(Bed) ....B
N. Y.—Buffalo
Buffalo Forge Co. (R. R.
Coupling) ....AA
Pratt & Letchworth (Plow)
AA
N. Y.—Kenwood
Oneida Community (Repair;
Lap) ....AAAA
New York City
New Jersey Fdry. & Ma-
chine Co.. 15 Murray
(Punched Chain) ....D
Sargent & Co. (Repair;
Lap) ....AAAA
Tiebout, W. & J. (Repair;
Lap) ....B
N. Y.—Utica
Foster Bros. Mfg. Co.
(Wire) ....A
OHIO—Akron
Whitman & Barnes Mfg. Co.
(Belting) ....AAAA

LINKS (Con.)
OHIO—Cleveland
Cleveland City Forge & Iron
Co. (R. R. Coupling)..AA
Federal Mfg. Co., Amer.
Trust Bldg. (Punched
Chain) ....AAAA
PA.—Chester
Keystone Drop Forge Wks.
(Open Connecting; Car
Coupling; Repair; Lap).A
PA.—Lebanon
Amer. Iron & Steel Mfg. Co.
(Chain) ....A
PA.—Newcastle
Newcastle Forge & Bolt
Co. (Punched Chain)...B
PA.—Philadelphia
Hoopes & Townsend Co.,
1330 Buttonwood (Chain)
AAA
Phosphor Bronze Smelt Co.
(Ltd.) (Split) ....A
PA.—Pittsburg
Carnegie Steel Co. (Ltd.)
(R. R. Couplings).AAAA
Jones & Laughlin Steel Co.
(Car Coupling).....AAAA
Pittsburg Forge & Iron Co.
(R. R. Coupling) ......A
Pittsburg Malleable Iron
Co. (Chain Belt) ....A
Standard Chain Co. (Car
Coupling; Repair; Lap)..
AAAA
PA.—Scranton
Scranton Forging Co. (Con-
veyors' Chain) ....A
PA.—Wilkesbarre
Vulcan Iron Wks. (R. R.
Coupling) ....AAAA
PA.—York
Schmidt & Co., Jno. C. (Br.
Standard Chain Co.) (Re-
pair; Lap) ....AAAA
R. I.—Pawtucket
Haskell Mfg. Co., Wm. H.
(Punched Chain) ....A
Pawtucket Mfg. Co.
(Punched Chain) ....A
R. I.—Providence
Rhode Island Tool Co.
(Punched Chain) ..AAA
VA.—Richmond
Tredegar Co. (R. R.
Coupling) ....AAAA
W. VA.—Wheeling
Wheeling Hinge Co. (Re-
pair) ....AA
WIS.—South Milwaukee
Stowell Mfg. & Fdry. Co.
(Belting) ....A

LINOLEUM

ILL.—Chicago
Chicago Linoleum Co., 371
Hawthorne Av. ....A
N. J.—Camden
Farr & Bailey Mfg. Co....
AAA
N. J.—Kearney
Nairn Linoleum Co....AAA
N. J.—Trenton
Standard Inlaid Mfg. Co..B
Trenton Oil Cloth & Lino-
leum Co. ....A
New York City
Amer. Linoleum Mfg. Co.,
11 Thomas ....AA
Wild & Co., Joseph, 11
Thomas ....AAA
N. Y.—Troy
Powers & Sons, Deborah
(Also Oil Cloth) ......A
PA.—Philadelphia
Blabon Co.. Geo. W., 34 N.
5th ....AAAA
Potter Sons & Co. (Inc.),
Thos., 522 Arch ....AAA

LINTELS

KAN.—Emporia
Emporia Fdry. & Mach.
Wks. (Iron) ....D
MICH.—Detroit
Bolles Iron & Wire Wks.,
J. E. (Iron) ....E
MO.—St. Louis
Christopher & Simpson Arch.
Iron Fdry. Co. (Cast Iron)
AA

LINTELS (Con.)
N. Y.—Brooklyn
Taylor & Co. (Inc.) (Iron)
.................................D
Diamond, Thos. (Iron) ..A
Dunn, Thos. J. (Stone)...C
N. Y.—Oxford
Clark Bluestone Co., F. G.
(Stone) ....A
N. Y.—Warsaw
Warsaw Bluestone Co.
(Stone) ....B
OHIO—Cleveland
Duplex Hanger Co., 176 Co-
lumbus (Concrete Trussed)
.................................D
OHIO—Kenton
Champion Iron Co. (Iron)..
.................................AA
PA.—Pittsburg
Pittsburg Fdry. & Machine
Co. (Brick Building) ..D
TENN.—Memphis
Chickasaw Iron Wks.
(Iron) ....A

LINTERS

ALA.—Jacksonville
Jacksonville Oil Mill Co.
(Cotton Seed) ....B
CONN.—New London
Brown Cotton Gin Co.
(Cotton Seed) ....AA
GA.—Atlanta
Van Winkle Gin & Mach.
Wks., E. (Cotton Seed)·
.................................AAA
GA.—Columbus
Mutual Cotton Oil Co.
(Cotton Seed) ....AAAA
MISS.—Vicksburg
Advance Gin & Mill Co.
(Cotton Seed) ....B
TEXAS—Belton
Belton Oil Co. (Cotton
Seed) ....D
TEXAS—Taylor
Taylor Cotton Oil Wks.
(Cotton Seed) ....B

LIQUIDS

CONN.—New Milford
Bridgeport Wood Finishing
Co. (Bronzing) ....AA
ILL.—Chicago
Matchless Metal Polish Co.
(Polishing) ....D
MICH.—Detroit
Acme White Lead & Color
Wks. (Bronzing) .....AA
New York City
Watts Sons, Jno. M.
(Polishing) ....D
PA.—Philadelphia
French & Co., Saml. H., 4th
& Callowhill (Bronzing)..
.................................AAA
Lucas & Co., Jno., 322 Race
(Bronzing) ....AAAA

LIQUORS

**Wines; Brandy; Whiskey;
Cordiales; Gin; etc.**

CAL.—Esparto
Esparto Winery (Wine
(Growers) X
CAL.—Fresno
Caliva Winery (Wine
Growers) X
Kohler & Frohling (Wine
Growers) X
St. George Vineyard Co.
(Wine Growers) ....D
CAL.—Irvington
Grau & Werner (Wine
Growers) ....D
CAL.—Lamanda
Sierra Madre Vintage Co.
(Wine Growers) C
CAL.—Livermore
Pioneer Winery (Wine
Growers) X
CAL.—Los Angeles
Goldschmidt Bros. (Wine
Growers) ....D
South Cal. Wine Co. (Wine
Growers) C
Stern & Sons, Chas. (Wine
Growers) ....A

LIQUORS (Con.)
CAL.—Mission San Jose
Salazar, A. J. (Wine
Growers) X
CAL.—Napa
Napa Valley Wine Co.
(Wine Growers) X
CAL.—Oakland
Gier Co., Theo. (Wine
Growers) C
CAL.—Oakville
Brun & Chaix (Wine
Growers) ....B
To-Kalon Vineyard Co.
(Wine Growers) ....A
CAL.—Rutherford
Ewer, S. (Wine Growers).C
CAL.—Sacramento
Calif. Winery (Wine
Growers) ....A
Kohler & Van Bergen
(Wine Growers) X
CAL.—St. Helena
Beringer Bros. (Wine
Growers) ....A
Greystone Winery (Wine
Growers) X
CAL.—San Francisco
Berges & Dominiconi
(Wine Growers) ....A
Calif. Wine Assn. (Wine
Growers) ....AAAA
Chevalier Co., F. (Wine
Growers) ....A
Frapolli & Co., B. (Wine
Growers) ....A
French-Am. Wine Co. (Wine
Growers) ....A
Gundlach-Bundschu Wine
Co. (Wine Growers) ...A
Italian Swiss Colony (Wine
Growers) ....AAA
Lachman & Jacobi (Wine
Growers) ....AAA
Mt. Diablo Wine Co.
(Wine Growers) ....A
Napa Sonoma Wine Co.
(Wine Growers) C
Schilling & Co. (Wine
Growers) ....A
Wetmore-Bowen Co. (Wine
Growers) ....B
CAL.—San Gabriel
Golden Gate Fruit Co.
(Orange Wine; Apricot
Brandy) C
CAL.—San Jose
Mason, Paul (Wine
Growers) ....D
Pacific Winery (Wine
Growers) X
CAL.—Sonoma
Drecel & Co. (Wine Grow-
ers) ....B
CAL.—Stockton
West & Son, Geo. A. (Wine
Growers) ....A
CAL.—Vina
Vina Distillery (Wine
Growers) ....AAAA
CAL.—Windsor
Windsor Winery (Wine
Growers) ....D
CONN.—Hartford
Heublin & Bros., G. F.
(Bitters) ....AA
DEL.—Dover
Levy, Louis A. (Whiskey
Dist.) ....E
ILL.—Belleville
Belleville Distillery Co.
(Whiskey Dist.) ....G
ILL.—Chicago
Am. Bitters & Cordial Co.
(Bitters; Cordials) ...X
Delaney & Murphy (Whis-
key Dist.) ....A
Devinehy & Co., Chas.
(Whiskey Dist.) X
Hessler & Co., Julius
(Whiskey Dist.) ..AAAA
Rosenfeld Bros. & Co.
(Whiskey Dist.) ...AAA
Shufeldt & Co., H. H.
(Gin) ....B
Triner, Joseph (Bitters)...E
ILL.—Jacksonville
Seligman Bros. Whiskey
Dist.) C
ILL.—Pekin
Am. Distilling Co. (Whiskey
Dist.) ....A
Globe Distillery (Whiskey

LIQUORS (Con.)

Dist.) X
ILL.—Peoria
Am. Spirits Mfg. Co.
(Whiskey Dist.)...AAAA
Clarke Bros. & Co. (Whiskey
Dist.) ....AA
Corning & Co. (Whiskey
Dist.) ....AAA
Stand. Distilling & Distrib.
Co. (Whiskey Dist.)..AA
ILL.—Rockford
Graham Bros. (Whiskey
Dist.) ....E
IND.—Hammond
Hammond Distilling Co.
(Whiskey Dist.) ......AA
IND.—Lawrenceburg
Greendale Distillery Co.
(Whiskey Dist.) ....B
Squibb & Co., W. P.
(Whiskey Dist.) ....A
IND.—Terre Haute
Commercial Distilling Co.
(Whiskey Dist.) ......H
Indiana Distilling Co.
(Whiskey Dist.) ......B
Merchants Distilling Co.
(Whiskey Dist.) ....A
Terre Haute Dist. Co.
(Whiskey Dist.) ..AAAA
IND.—Vincennes
Inter-State Distilling Co.
(Whiskey Dist.) X
KANS.—Atchison
Doniphan Vineyards & Wine
Co. (Wine Growers) ...F
KY.—Bardstown
Early Times Distilling Co.
(Whiskey Dist.) X
Mattingly & Moore Distill-
ing Co. (Whiskey Dist.).
D
Moore, Tom (Whiskey
Dist.) ....D
Sutherland, Hy. (Whiskey
Dist.) ....G
Walker Co., F. G.
(Whiskey Dist.) ....D
KY.—Berry Station
Craig, F. G. (Whiskey
Dist.) X
KY.—Bloomfield
McClackey Son, B.
(Whiskey Dist.) ....G
KY.—Burgin
Dowling Bros. (Whiskey
Dist.) C
KY.—Carrollton
Jett Bros. Dist. Co.
(Whiskey Dist.) ......H
KY.—Chicago
Smith & Smith (Whiskey
Dist.) ....E
KY.—Coonhollow
Willow Springs Dist. Co.
(Whiskey Dist.) ....D
KY.—Covington
Crigler & Crigler
(Whiskey Dist.) ....D
Woodland & Buffalo Springs
Distillery (Whiskey Dist.)
X
N. E. Distilling Co. (Rum
Distillers) C
KY.—Cynthiana
Ashbrook Distilling Co., F.
S. (Whiskey Dist.) ....B
KY.—Dant
Dant Distilling Co.
(Whiskey Dist.) ....D
KY.—Deatsville
Samuels, T. W. (Whiskey
Dist.) ....D
KY.—Eminence
Eminence Distillery Co.
(Whiskey Dist.) ....B
KY.—Fairfield
McKenna & Co., H.
(Whiskey Dist.) C
KY.—Frankfort
Frankfort Distillery Co.
(Whiskey Dist.) ....B
Gaines & Co., W. A.
(Whiskey Dist.) ....A
Kty. Distilleries & Ware-
house Co. (Whiskey Dist.)
AAAA
Labrot & Graham (Whiskey
Dist.) ....A
Stagg Co., Geo. T. (Whis-
key Dist.) ....A

LIQUORS (Con.)

KY.—Gethsemane
Beam & Co., M. C.
(Whiskey Dist.) ......D
Head & Co., F. M.
(Whiskey Dist.) ......E
KY.—Greenbrier
Greenbrier Distillery Co.
(Whiskey Dist.) ....A
KY.—Harrodsburg
Thompson, J. B. (Whiskey
Dist.) X
KY.—Henderson
Kraver, Hy. (Whiskey
Dist.) ....D
Winsted & Son, A. S.
(Whiskey Dist.) ......E
KY.—Lawrenceburg
Dowling & Co., Jno.
(Whiskey Dist.) C
Hoffman Distilling Co.
(Whiskey Dist.) ....D
Moore, D. L. J. (Whiskey
Dist.) X
Saffel, W. B. (Whiskey
Dist.) ....B
KY.—Lexington
Mueller, Wathen & Kobert
(Whiskey Dist.) ....A
KY.—Lexington
Curley & Co., E. J.
(Whiskey Dist.) ......B
Pepper & Co., Jas. E.
(Whiskey Dist.) ....A
Stoll & Co. (Whiskey Dist.)
A
KY.—Lovetto
Burks Spring Distillery Co.
(Whiskey Dist.) ....D
Cummins & Co., K.
(Whiskey Dist.) ......E
KY.—Louisville
Barbee & Co., Jno. T.
(Whiskey Dist.) ....A
Bernheim Distilling Co.
(Whiskey) ....AAAA
Bonnie Bros. (Whiskey
Dist.) ....AA
Brown Founder Co.
(Whiskey Dist.) ....B
Brown & Sons, J. T. S.
(Whiskey Dist.)...AAAA
Ehrmann, Hilmar & Co.
(Whiskey Dist.) C
Ferncliff Distillery Co.
(Whiskey Dist.) ....B
Glencoe Distilling Co.
(Whiskey Dist.) ....B
Grabfelder & Co., S.
(Whiskey Dist.) ....AAA
Greenbaum, S. J.
(Whiskey Dist.) ......AA
Mellwood Distillery Co.
(Whiskey Dist.) ....A
Moore, Jesse, Hunt Co.
(Whiskey Dist.) ....A
Old Kty. Distillery
(Whiskey Dist.) ....A
Rugby Distilling Co.
(Whiskey Dist.) ....A
Sachs & Sons, D.
(Whiskey Dist.) ......AA
Selliger & Co., Max
(Whiskey Dist.) ....AAA
Stitzel Distilling Co.
(Whiskey Dist.) C
Thixton, Millett & Co.
(Whiskey Dist.) ....A
Uri & Co., Nathan M.
(Whiskey Dist.) ....A
Wathen & Co., R. E.
(Whiskey Dist.) ....A
Wright & Taylor
(Whiskey Dist.) ......AA
Rogers & Co., J. H .
(Whiskey Dist.) ....B
KY.—McBrayor
Searcy, Wiley (Whiskey
Dist.) ....E
KY.—Maysville
Pogne Distillery Co., H. E.
(Whiskey Dist.) ....B
Poyntz Bros. (Whiskey
Dist.) ....G
KY.—Memphis Junction
Spring Water Distilling Co.
(Whiskey Dist.) X
KY.—Murphy
Murphy & Co., Ed.
(Whiskey Dist.) ....D
KY.—Orr
Day, Jno. E. (Whiskey
Dist.) ....D

LIQUORS (Con.)

KY.—Owensboro
Daviess Co. Distilling Co.
(Whiskey Dist.) ....H
Field & Son, J. W. M.
(Whiskey Dist.) ....E
Glenmore Distilling Co.
(Whiskey Dist.) ......A
Greene River Dist. Co.
(Whiskey Dist.) ....A
Mattingly, M. P. (Whiskey
Dist.) C
Rock Spring Distilling Co.
(Whiskey Dist.) ....A

KY.—Paducah
Friedman, Keiler & Co.
(Whiskey Dist.) .....AA

KY.—Pleasure Ridge Park
Pleasure Ridge Park Dist.
Co. (Whiskey Distillers)
................A

KY.—Poindexter
Wiglesworth Bros. Co.
(Whiskey Dist.) ....D

KY.—Raywick
Head Distilling Co., W. H.
(Whiskey Dist.) ....D

KY.—Salvisa
Dedman, C. M. (Whiskey
Dist.) ....D

KY.—Samuels
Samuels & Co., W. B.
(Whiskey Dist.) ......E

KY.—Silver Creek
Burnam, Bennett & Co.
(Whiskey Dist.) ....A

KY.—Versailles
Frazier, W. T. (Whiskey
Dist.) ....F

LA.—New Orleans
Dunbars' Sons, G. W., 3400
Charters (Cordials) ....A
La. Distilling Co. (Whiskey
Dist.) ....B

MD.—Accident
Miller Sons, M. J. (Whiskey
Dist.) ....F

MD.—Baltimore
Abbott & Co., C. W. 17 S.
Charles Angostura Bit-
ters) ....A
Balto. Distilleries Co.
key Dist.; Bitters) ...A
Canton Distilleries Co.
(Whiskey Dist.) ....B
Carroll Springs Distilling
Co. (Whiskey Dist.)....B
Highspire Distillery Co.
(Ltd.) (Whiskey Dist.).D
Md. Distilling Co. (Whiskey
Dist.) ....A
Milvale Distillery Co.
(Whiskey Dist.) .....AA
Monticello Distilling Co.
(Inc.) (Whiskey Dist.)AA
Roxbury Distilling Co.
(Whiskey Dist.) ....A
Sharpe & Dohme (Cordials)
................AAA
Sherwood Distilling Co.
(Whiskey Dist.) ....A
Wineke-Bauernschmidt Co.
(Whiskey Dist.) ....B

MD.—Burkittsville
Pure Rye Distilling Co.
(Whiskey Dist.) ....B
Horsey, Outerbridge Co.
(Whiskey Dist.) C

MD.—Carrollton
McGinnis Co., A. (Whiskey
Dist.) ....D

MD.—Cumberland
Clark Dist. Co., Jas.
(Whiskey Dist.) ....B

MD.—Hyattstown
Price, Levi (Whiskey Dist.)
................E

MD.—Kings Valley
King, Luther G. (Whiskey
Dist.) C

MD.—Leitersburg
Rock Forge Dist. Co.
(Whiskey Dist.) X

MD.—Mt. St. Marys
Cretin, Jno. T.
(Whiskey Dist.) ....E

MD.—Pikesville
Winand Distilling Co.
(Whiskey Dist.) C

MASS.—Boston
Chapin, Truell & Co.
(Whiskey Dist.) ....A
Chase & Co., Danl. E.

LIQUORS (Con.)
(Rum Dist.) ....A
Everett Distilling Co.
(Rum Dist.) X
Farris & Co., Wm. A.
(Bitters) ....H
Felton & Son (Rum Dist.)B
Lawrence & Son, Danl.
(Rum Dist.) ......AAAA

MASS.—Newburyport
Caldwell, A. & G. T.
(Rum Dist.) ....AA

MINN.—St. Paul
Benz & Sons, Geo. (Whiskey
Dist.) ....AAA

MO.—Herman
Stone Hill Wine Co. (Wine
Growers) ....A

MO.—St. Louis
American Wine Co. (Cham-
pagne) ....A
Mound City Distilling Co.
(Whiskey Dist.) .....AA
Tilden Co., 1718 Olive
(Cordials) ....A

NEBR.—Omaha
Iler & Co. (Whiskey Dist.)
................G

N. Y.—Albany
Columbia Distilling Co.
(Whiskey Dist.) ......A

N. Y.—Brockton
Am. Chianti Wine Co.
(Wine Growers) ......E
Ryckman & Son, G. E.
(Wine) ....B

N. Y.—Brooklyn
Hasbrouck & Co., John L.
(Gin) ....B

N. Y.—Buffalo
Buffalo Distilling Co. (Gin;
Whiskey Dist.) ...AAAA
Meadville Distilling Co.
(Whiskey Dist.) ......A

N. Y.—Hammondsport
Columbia Wine Co. (Wine)
................A
Freidell Winery Co. (Wines)
................X
Germania Wine Cellars
(Wines) ....A
Hammondsport Valley Wine
Cellars (Wines) X
Monarch Grape & Wine Co.
(Wine) ....B
New Hammondsport Wine
(Co. (Wine) ....A
Ronalet Wine Co. (Wine).D
White Top Champagne Co.
(Champagne) ....B

N. Y.—Himrod
Severne Wine Co.
(Champagne) ....A

New York City
Adams & Co., 220 Front
(Cordials) ....A
Alexander & Co., J., 97
Water (Cordials).....D
Ardin, L. (Import.) ......E
Arnold & Co., C. H. (Imp.
Champagne) ....D
Baird-Daniels Co., 75 Dey
(Gin) C
Baldwin Bros. & Co.
(Imp.) ....E
Bass, Batcliff & Gretton
(Imp.) X
Batjer & Co. (Imp. Brandy;
Rum; Wines; Bitters;
Cordials) ....AAA
Bell Co., J. M. (Imp.)....A
Benedict Co., Jos. (Imp.
Wines; Brandies; Gin,
etc.) ....D
Blache & Co., Oct. C. (Imp.
Rum; Brandy; Gin; Bit-
ters) ....B
Blackburn & Co., Edw.
(Imp.) ....B
Blum Jr.'s Sons, A. (Imp.)
................X
Bouche Fils & Co. (Imp.
Cordials) X
Buchanan & Co., Jas. (Imp.)
................X
Burke, Edw. & John (Ltd.)
(Imp.) ....AAAA
Burke Imp. Co., John (Imp.)
................A
Burnham Co., E. S. (Bit-
ters) ....A
Calif. Wine Assn. (Wine
Assn.) ....AAAA

LIQUORS (Con.)

Carter Medicine Co., 57 Murphy (Bitters) ....B
Cazanove Champagne Co. (Imp. Champagne) X
Chapin & Co., N. (Imp.)...X
Conti, Cesaere (Imp.)...A
Cook & Bernheimer Co. (Inc.), 150 Franklin (Whiskey; Cordials; Impts.) ....AAA
Cusinier Co., 110 Broad (Imp. Wine; Brandy; Champagne; Gin) X
De Bary & Co., Fredk. (Imp. Champagne) .....A
De Luze & Co., Francis O., 18 S. William (Imp. Wines; Brandies; Champagnes; Irish Whiskey).D
De Montebello, Alfred & Co. (Imp. Champagne) ....A
Du Vivier & Co. (Imp. Champagne) X
Engs & Sons (Inc.), P. W., 208 B'way (Import Wines; Brandies; Cordials) ....A
Federal Distilling Co. (Whiskey Dist.) X
Feldmann, Ernst (Imp.)..X
Finlay & Co., H. P. (Imp.) X
Fleischmann & Co. (Whiskey; Gin Dist.)...AAAA
Fleischmann & Co., 600 W. 34th (Whiskey; Gin Dist.) ....AAAA
Francklyn & Co., R. (Imp.) ....D
Funke, Jr., L., 72 Beekman (Cordials) ....A
Gandolfi & Co., L. (Imp.).A
Glassup, Fredk. (Imp.)...X
Gourd, Hy. E. (Imp.) ...B
Graef & Co., Chas. (Imp. Champagne) ....B
Gretsche & Birth (Imp.)..X
Gundlach-Bundschu Wine Co. (Wines) ....AA
Habernicht & Co., A. (Imp. Champagne) ....E
Habbenden & Van Biel (Imp. Champagne) C
Hall & Co., F. de Peyster (Imp.) X
Halliday & Co., A. (Imp. Irish Whiskey) ....A
Handrich & Son, Fritz (Imp.) ....A
Hartman, Goldsmith & Co. (Imp.) ....A
Hauselt & Luneschloss (Imp. Champagne) ....D
Henry & Co., R. B., 30 Beaver (Imp.) ....B
Hochstadler Co., 227 Front (Cordials) ......B
Hossfeld & Wierl (Imp.)..B
Jacquin et Cie., 227 Front (Cordials) ....A
Johnstone & Ross Bros. (Imp.) X
Jameson & Son, Jno., 29 B'way (Irish Whiskey; Italian Vermuth) X
Joseph, James (Imp.) X
Karatsonyi & Kmetz (Imp.) X
Kty. Distilleries & Warehouse Co. (Whiskey Dist.) ....AAAA
Kessler & Co., Geo. A. (Imp.) ....B
Kirk & Co., H. B. (Imp.).A
Kitz, Augustus J., 70 Broad (Imp. Champagne) X
Krans & Bro., S. (Imp.). ....AA
Krauss & Kinef (Imp.)...X
Kroger & Co., Hy. (Imp.) ....AA
La Montagne & Sons, E., 45 Beaver (Imp. Clarets; Sauternes; Gin) ....AA
Luders, Oscar B. (Imp.)..X
Luyties Bros. (Imp.)....B
McCunn, Jas. M. (Imp.)..D
McMullen & Co., Thos. (Imp.) ....AA
May, J. S. (Imp.) X
Moehring & Co., Wm. G. (Imp.) ....A

LIQUORS (Con.)

N. Y. & Kty. Co. (Imp.).... ....AAA
Nicholas, Geo. S. (Imp.)..A
Nohn & Sons (Imp.) X
Oberfelder, Max (Imp.)..B
Oechs, Anthony (Imp. Champagne) ....AA
Osborn, Chas. R. (Imp.)..X
Paris, Allen & Co. (Imp.) ....AAAA
Phelan & Duval (Imp.)...A
Pick Import. Co. (Imp.)..F
Psiaki Bros., 104 Wall Imp. Greek Brandy) ...X
Regent Cordial Co., 330 Spring (Cordials) .....F
Reid & Co., Jas. (Imp.)..X
Rath & Co., Nicholas, 30 S. William (Imp. Scotch Whiskey; Gin; Rum; Wines, etc.) ....AA
Renauld & Niederstadt (Imp.) ....AA
Ripin & Co. (Imp. Champagne) C
Roche, Jas. B. (Imp.)...F
Roederer, Louis (Imp. Champagne) X
Roosevelt & Schuyler, 62 Stone (Imp. Champagne Scotch Whiskey) ....A
Rose, J. G. (Imp.).......X
Rose & Bro., W. A. (Imp. Gin) ....B
Ross & Bro., W. A. (Imp. Gin) ....B
Rinnart & Co., Paul (Imp. Champagne) X
Schmidt & Peters, C. F. (Imp.) ....A
Shaw & Co., Alex. D. (Imp.) ....B
Smith, Julius Paul (Cal. Wine Growers) ......B
Solomon, Jr., & Co., A. A., 37 Beaver (Imp. Brandies; Wines; Cordials) ......E
Spiegel & Steiner, Chas. (Imp.) ....AA
Stand. Distilling & Distributing Co. (Whiskey Dist.) ....AAAA
Starace, Achille (Imp.)..,B
Streit & Co., Saml. (Imp.) ....A
Taylor & Co., W. A. (Imp.) ....D
Thomson, Duntze & Co. (Imp.) X
Van Rensselair, S. & C. A. (Imp.) ....B
Walden, Franklin (Imp.).X
Werner & Co., A., 42 Broad (Champagne) X
Wildersinn, E. (Imp.)...X
Wile, Sons & Co., Julius, 148 Duane (Imp. Wines; Cordials; Bitters; Gin).A
Wilson, J. & R. (Imp.)...D
Wolfe Co., Udalpho (Imp.) ....B
Wuppermann, I. W., 29 B'way (Bitters; Cordials) ....D

N. Y.—Penn Yan

Empire State Wine Co. (Wine Growers) ....A

N. Y.—Rheims

Pleasant Valley Wine Co. (Champagne) ....AAA

N. Y.—Urbana

Urbana Wine Co. (Champagne) ....A

N. C.—Weldon

Garrett & Co. (Wine Growers) X

OHIO—Cincinnati

Berkeley Dist. Co., Wm. (Whiskey Dist.) ......D
Block & Sons, Chas. (Whiskey Dist.) ..AAAA
Clifton Springs Dist. Co. (Whiskey Dist.) ......AA
Edgewood Distilling Co. (Whiskey Dist.) ......AA
Fleischmann & Co. (Dist.) ....AAAA
Freiburg & Workum (Whiskey; Gin Dist.)... ....AAAA
Hofheimer Bros. Co. (Whiskey Dist.) X

LIQUORS (Con.)

Johnson & Co., W. W.
  (Whiskey Dist.) X
Levy & Bro., Jas. (Dist.)..
  AAAA
Mihalovitcr, Fletcher & Co.,
  516 E. Pearl (Cordials)
  AA
Mill Creek Dist. Co.
  (Whiskey Dist.) X
Old '76 Distilling Co.
  (Whiskey Dist.) ....A
Peacock Distillery Co.
  (Whiskey Dist.) ....A
Rheinstrom, Bettman, John-
  son & Co. (Brandy)..AA
Rheinstrom Bros. (Cham-
  pagne; Liqueurs; Cor-
  dials Vermouth) ......AA
Sunny Side Distilling Co.
  (Whiskey Dist.)...AAAA
Union Distilling Co.
  (Whiskey Dist.) ....AAA
Walsh & Co., Jas. (Whis-
  key Dist.) ....AAAA
Westheimer & Sons, F.
  (Whiskey Dist.) ...AAAA

OHIO—Dayton

Haynes Distilling Co.
  (Whiskey Dist.) .....AA

OHIO—Germantown

Rohrer, D. (Whiskey Dist.)
  A

OHIO—Kelleys Island

Kelley's Island Wine Co.
  (Wine Growers) ....A
Union Wine Co. (Wine
  Growers) ....B

OHIO—Newark

Styron, Beggs & Co.
  (Cordials) ....A

OHIO—Sandusky

Dorn, Jno. (Wine Growers)
  A
Duroy & Haines Co.
  (Wine Growers) ....A
Engels & Krudwig Wine Co.
  (Wine Growers) ....A
Hommel Wine Co., M.
  (Champagne) ....A
Moos, Edw. R. (Wine
  Growers) ....D
Sandusky Wine & Brandy
  Co. (Wines; Brandy)..B
Schmidt & Bro., A., Jr.
  (Wine Growers) ....A
Stenck, Edw. L. (Wine
  Growers) ....D
Strobel, Jno. E. (Wine
  Growers) ....D
Sweet Valley Wine Co.
  (Wine Growers) ....A

OHIO—Toledo

Brand Wine Co., Hy.
  (Wine) ....A
Lenk Wine Co. (Wine
  Growers) ....AA

OHIO—Trebein

Colonial Distillery Co.
  (Gin; Whiskey Dist.)..X

PA.—Benton

McHenry-Rohr Dist. Co.
  (Whiskey Dist.) ....A

PA.—Exeter Station

Neversink Distilling Co.
  (Whiskey Dist.) X

PA.—Glen Rock

Foust, Wm. (Whiskey
  Dist.) ....AA

PA.—Grays Landing

Gray, J. R. (Whiskey Dist.)
  D

PA.—Lucesco

Schenley Distilling Co.
  (Whiskey Dist.) ......AA

PA.—McKeesport

Moore Dist. Co., Thos.
  (Whiskey Dist.) ....A

PA.—Philadelphia

Carstairs Bros. (Whiskey
  Dist.) ....AAA
Catherwood, H. & H. W.
  (Whiskey) ....A
Dougherty's Sons, J. A.
  (Whiskey Dist.) ......AA
Hannis Distilling Co.
  (Whiskey Dist.) .....AAA
Miller Pure Rye Distilling
  Co. (Whiskey Dist.)....B
Moore & Sinnott (Whiskey
  Dist.) ....AAA
Phila. Pure Rye Whiskey

LIQUORS (Con.)

Dist. Co. (Whiskey Dist.)
  A
Young Co., Alex. (Whiskey
  Dist.) ....A

PA.—Pittsburg

Economy Distilling Co.
  (Whiskey Dist.) ....B
Hamburger Co., Ph.
  (Whiskey Dist.) .....AA
Hostetter Co. (Bitters;
  Cordials) ....A
Large Distilling Co.
  (Whiskey Dist.) ....B
Moore Distillery Co.
  (Whiskey Dist.) C
Overholt & Co. (Whiskey
  Dist.) ....AAAA
Thompson Dist. Co.
  (Whiskey Dist.) .....AA
Vandergrift Dist. Co.
  (Distillers) ....F

PA.—Ruffs Dale

Dillings & Sons, S.
  (Whiskey Dist.) ...AAAA

PA.—Waynesboro

Pen-Mar Dist. Co.
  (Whiskey Dist.) C

TENN.—Nashville

Nelson, Chas. (Whiskey;
  Apple; Peach Brandy)...
  AAA

TEXAS—Dallas

Star Mfg. Co. (Cordials)..G

WIS.—Milwaukee

Herbst Importing Co.
  (Whiskey) ....A
Lake Side Dist. Co.
  (Whiskey Dist.) ....A
Nat. Distilling Co. (Whis-
  key; Gin Dist.) ......AA

WIS.—Oshkosh

Roewekamp Bros. (Bitters)
  D

LISTERS

See Agr. Implements

LITHARGE

See also Lead; Paints.

CAL.—Los Angeles

Braum Co., F. W. ....AAA

CAL.—San Francisco

Fuller & Co., W. P. ..AAAA

ILL.—Chicago

Carter White Lead Co..AAA
Rubber Paint Co. ....A

MASS.—Boston

Chadwick-Boston Lead Co.
  AAA

N. Y.—Brooklyn

Wiarda & Co., Jno. C. .AA

New York City

F. W. Devoe & C. T.
  Reynolds Co. ......AAAA
Longman & Martinez..AAA
Valentine & Co. ....AAA

OHIO—Cincinnati

Eagle White Lead Co...
  AAAA

OHIO—Cleveland

Morley Lead Wks., J. H...
  AAAA

PA.—Philadelphia

Harrison Bros. & Co..AAAA
Lewis & Bros., Jno. T.....
  AAAA
Wetherill & Bro., White
  Lead Wks. ....AAA

PA.—Pittsburg

National Lead & Oil Co. of
  Pa. ....AAAA
Pennsylvania Smelting Co.
  C
Sterling Varnish Co. ....A

PA.—Reading

Wilhelm & Co., A. ......AA

LITHOPONE

New York City

Bartels & Co., Ernest ....B
Gabriel & Schall ....B
Heller & Merz Co. ......AA

LITMUS

PA.—Easton

Baker & Adamson Chem. Co.
  A

634

LITTERS

ILL.—Bradley
Bradley Mfg. Co., David
(Vehicle) ....AAA
IND.—Indianapolis
Armstrong & Co., Wm. H.
(Vehicle) ....B
WIS.—Racine
Gold Medal Camp Furniture
Co. (Army) ....B

LIZARD

See Leather

LOADERS

See also Agr. Implements

ARK.—Newport
Pond-Decker Mfg. Co.
(Log) ....A
ILL.—Allenville
Ideal Car Loader Co.
(Grain Car) X
Western Wheeled Scraper
Co. (Wagon) ....AA
ILL.—Canton
Parlin & Orendorff Co.
(Hay) ....AAAA
ILL.—Chicago
Eaton Mfg. Co., W. T., 4
Sherman (Grain) ......A
National Drill & Mfg. Co.,
Pullman Bldg. (Wagon).B
Park-Gate Mfg. Co., Ash-
land Blk. (Ore; Coal)..D
Webster Mfg. Co., 1075 W.
15th (Grain Car) ....AA
ILL.—Decatur
Williams Mfg. Co. (Also
Weighers; Baggers;
Grain) ....H
ILL.—Harvey
Austin Mfg. Co. (Wagon)..
AA
ILL.—Litchfield
Litchfield Fdry. & Machine
Co. (Box Car) ....A
ILL.—Maroa
Maroa Mfg. Co. (Car) ....B
ILL.—Marseilles
Marseilles Mfg. Co. (Hay).A
ILL.—Meadows
Meadows Mfg. Co. (Car)..E
ILL.—Moline
Deere & Mansur Co. (Hay)
AA
ILL.—Ottawa
Porter Co., J. E. (Hay) ..A
ILL.—Peoria
Hart Grain Weigher Co.
(Also Weighers; Baggers;
Grain) ....A
ILL.—Rock Island
Rock Island Plow Co.
(Hay) ....AAA
ILL.—Sandwich
Sandwich Mfg. Co. (Clean
Sweep Hay) ....AA
ILL.—Springfield
Aetna Fdry. Machine Co.
(Box Car) ....B
ILL.—Sterling
Keystone Mfg. Co. (Hay).
AA
Sterling Mfg. Co. (Hay)..A
IND.—Connorsville
Roots Co., P. H. & F. M.
(Steam Log) ....AA
IND.—Indianapolis
Pneumatic Elevator &
Co. (Also Weighers; Bag-
gers; Grain) ....A
IOWA—Ottumwa
Ottumwa Box Car Loader
Co. (Box Car; Coal) ...B
KANS.—Leavenworth
Great Western Mfg. Co.
(Grain Car) ....AA
MICH.—Battle Creek
Advance Thresher Co. (Also
Weighers; Baggers; Grain)
AAA
Nichols & Shepard Co.
(Also Weighers; Baggers;
Grain) ....AAA
MICH.—Port Huron
Port Huron Engine &
Thresher Co. (Also Weigh-
ers; Baggers; Grain)....
AAAA

LOADERS (Con.)
MICH.—Saginaw
Wickes Bros. (Steam Log)
AAA
MINN.—Minneapolis
Kilgore Machine Co. (Direct
Acting Steam Log) ..X
MINN.—Stillwater
Northwest Thresher Co.
(also Weighers; Baggers;
Grain) ....AA
MISS.—Meridan
Soule Steam Feed Wks.
(Log) C
MO.—St. Louis
Ellison & Sons Mfg. Co.
Wm., 1018 N. 6th (Box
Car) ....B
Leschen & Sons Rope Co.,
920 N. 1st (Log) ..AAA
New York City
Lidgerwood Mfg. Co., 96
Liberty (Steam Log) AAA
OHIO—Cleveland
Garry Iron & Steel Co. (Log)
A
OHIO—Columbus
Kilbourne & Jacobs Mfg. Co.
(Horse) ....AA
OHIO—Dayton
Ohio Rake Co. (Hay) ..AA
OHIO—Lancaster
Hocking Valley Mfg. Co.
(Hay) C
OHIO—Marion
Huber Mfg. Co. (also
Weighers; Baggers Grain)
AAA
Marion Mfg. Co. (also
Weighers; Baggers Grain)
AA
OHIO—Mt. Gilead
Hydraulic Press Mfg. Co.
(also Weighers; Baggers;
Grain) ....A
OHIO—Springfield
Thomas Mfg. Co. (Hay)AAA
WIS.—Marinette
Stevens Co., A. W. (also
Weighers; Baggers; Grain)
AA
WIS.—Racine
Case Threshing Machine Co.,
J. I. (also Weighers; Bag-
gers, Grain) ......AAAA

LOBSTER: CANNED

See Canned Goods

LOCKERS

MASS.—Worcester
National Mfg. Co. (Office)
A
Wright Wire Co. (Office;
Shop) ....AA
N. Y.—Jamestown
Art Metal Const. Co. (Metal
for Clothing, etc.) ..AAA
OHIO—Canton
Berger Mfg. Co. (Metal) AA
OHIO—Hamilton
Meyers Mfg. Co., Fred J.
(Office; Shop) ....B
OHIO—Salem
Clark Co., W. J. (Office;
Shop) ....B
PA.—Ellwood City
Glen Mfg. Co. (Office;
Shop) ....D
PA.—Philadelphia
Darby & Sons, Edward
(Office; Shop) ....A
Merritt & Co., 1000 Ridge
Av. (Metal; Wire) ....B
R. I.—Providence
Narragansett Machine Co.
(Office) ....A

LOCKETS

See also Jewelry
CONN.—Mt. Carmel
Woodruff & Sons, Walter
W. (Hame) ....A
MASS.—Attleboro
Fisher & Co., J. M. ....A
MASS.—Chartley
Freeman, Daughaday & Co.
C

LOCKETS *(Con.)*

N. J.—Newark
Durand & Co. (Inc.) ...AA
Hedges & Co., A. J. .....A
New York City
Alling & Co. ....AA
Myers Co., S. F. ....D
Richards & Co., E. Ira AAA
Rothschild Bros. C
Trenkmann, August (Shell)
...........AAA
PA.—Philadelphia
Bingham, James ....H
R. I.—Providence
Albro & Kettlety X
Cory & Reynolds Co. C
Devereux & Co., O. C. ...D
Foster & Bro. Co., Thos. W.
...........AA
Hamilton & Hamilton, Jr. A
Lederer Co., S. & B. C
Luther & Son, Wm. H. ...B
Potter. W. K. (Shell) ....F
Snow & Westcott ....A
Waite, Mathewson & Co. B

LOCKS

See also Hardware; Carriage; Rowlocks.
CAL.—Stockton
Universal Nut Lock Co.
(Nut) ....A
CONN.—Branford
New York Lock Co. (Ship;
Sliding Door) ....B
CONN.—Bridgeport
Smith & Egge Mfg. Co. (Toe
Clips; Casters Padlock;
Piano; Organ; Sewing Machine; Bicycle; Pad) ..A
CONN.—Bristol
Root, C. J. (Sash) ....D
CONN.—Meriden
Chapman Mfg. Co. (Dog
Collar) ....A
CONN.—Middletown
Chapman Co., W. H. (Padlocks) ....B
Wilcox, Crittenden & Co.
(Padlock; Dead) .....A
Wilcox Mfg. Co., Wm.
(Pad) ....A
CONN.—Mt. Carmel
Woodruff & Sons Co., W. W.
(Carriage Door; Automobile) ....A
CONN.—New Britain
Corbin Cabinet Lock Co.
(Cabinet) ....AA
Corbin, P. & F. (Amer.
Hdw. Corp'n) (Padlock;
Sash; Door; Drawer; Mortise; Piano; Organ; Rim;
Sliding Door; Trunk;
Sash & Lifts Combined)
...........AAAA
Russell & Erwin Mfg. Co.
(Amer. Hdw. Corp'n)
(Car; Switch; Padlock;
Sash; Sliding Door; Basement Door; Cabinet; Door;
Knob; Mortise; Store
Door) ....AAAA
CONN.—New Haven
Cowles & Co., (Inc.) C. (Carriage; Lever) ....A
English & Merrick Co.
(Carriage) C
Fitch Co., W. & E. T.
(Sash) ....AA
Ives & Co., Hobert B. (Sash;
Burglar Proof Sash) ..C
Mallory, Wheeler & Co.
(Padlock; Barn Door;
Basement Door; Burglar
Proof; Cupboard; Door;
Front Door; Knob; Mortise; Rim; Sash; Sliding
Door; Spring; Tumbler)
...........AA
Marlin Fire Arms Co. (Pad)
.......A
Reeves Mfg. Co. (Bicycle) C
Sargent & Co. (Car; Switch;
Padlock; Sash; Basement
Door; Cabinet; Door;
Knob; Mortise; Sliding
Door; Store Door; Refrigerator; Ship; Elevator
Door) ....AAAA
CONN.—Southington
Peck, Stow & Wilcox Co.
(Sash) ....AAAA
CONN.—Stamford

LOCKS *(Con.)*

Yale & Towne Mfg. Co.
(Keyless Combination;
Padlock; Time; Barn &
Basement Door; Burglar
Proof; Cabinet; Chest;
Cupboard; Dead; Desk;
Door; Drawer; Front Door;
Hasp; Knob; Latch; Lever; Mortise; Post Office;
Refrigerator; Rim; Burglar Proof Sash; Spring;
Store Door; Tumbler; Jail;
Safe; Bank; Bicycle; Pad;
Prison; Trunk; Bag)
...........AAAA
CONN.—Terryville
Eagle Lock Co. (Padlock;
Book; Cabinet; Chest;
Cupboard; Desk; Door;
Drawer; Hasp; Mortise;
Piano; Organ; Post Office; Sewing Machine; Sliding Door; Trunk; Wardrobe; Cigar Box) ...AAA
CONN.—Torrington
Union Hdw. Co. (Jail) ..A
CONN.—Waterbury
Amer. Pin Co. (Brass Nut)
.......A
DEL.—Wilmington
Diamond State Steel Co.
(Diamond Spring Nut)
...........AAA
ILL.—Alton
Illinois Box Co. (Wooden
Box) C
ILL.—Chicago
Adams & Westlake Co., Ontario & N. Franklin (Car;
Switch) ....AAA
Burton & Son, A. G. (Burglar Proof) ....D
Chicago Hdw. Co., 132 Lake
(Sash) ....D
Cutter Mfg. Co., Geo., Union
& Fulton (Pole) C
Gardner Sash Balance Co.,
1st Nat. Bank Bldg. (Steel
Sash) ....D
Harley Burglar Proof Ventilating Sash Lock Mfg.
Co., 92 La Salle (Ventilating Sash) ....D
Haussmann & Dunn (Bicycle) C
Jones Positive Nut Lock Co.,
112 Clark (Nut) ......E
Keyless Lock Co. (Door;
Keyless) ....D
Payson Mfg. Co., 1319 W.
Jackson Boul. (Sash) ..B
Solid Steel Tool Co., 11 S.
Jefferson (Nut) ....F
ILL.—Freeport
Stover Mfg. Co., 165 River
(Burglar Proof; Sash) ..A
ILL.—Kewanee
Western Tube Co. (Steamfitters' Nut) ....AAA
ILL.—Sterling
Lawrence Bros. (Latches,
etc.) ....AA
National Mfg. Co. (Latches,
etc.) ....D
IND.—Elkhart
Buescher Mfg. Co.
(Bicycles) C
IND.—Indianapolis
Jordan, Arthur (Keyless)..
...........AAA
Keyless Lock Co., 1401
Newman (Cabinet, all
kinds; Keyless Combination) ....AAA
IOWA—Cedar Falls
Wagner Mfg. Co. (Latches,
etc.) ....D
IOWA—Clinton
United States Steel Lock
Co. (Latches, etc.; Pad)
.......B
IOWA—Fairfield
Louden Mchry. Co. (Sliding
Door) ....D
KANS.—Iola
Edgar Car Lock & Seal Co.
(Box Car) ....D
KY.—Louisville
Peerless Mfg. Co., 15th &
Ormsby Av. (Nut) .....A
MD.—Baltimore
Kemp Mfg. Co., C. M.

LOCKS (Con.)

(Sash) C

MASS.—Boston

Ham & Co., L. M., 152
Portland (Prison Cell
Door) C

Hamlin & Emery, 26 Island
(Brass Nut) ....D

Harrington, Robinson & Co.
(Automatic Nut) ......D

MASS.—Chicopee

Ames Sword Co. (Barn
Door; Dog Collar; Bicy-
cle; Pad) ....B

MICH.—Bay City

Garland Co., M. (Log) ...C

MICH.—Detroit

Detroit Ship Bldg. Co. (Br.
Am. Ship Bldg. Co., Cleve-
land, O.) (Car; Switch;
Brass Dept.; Padlock)....
                    AAAA

Smith & Co., Jos. N., 35 W.
Larned (Automobile Door)
                        C

MICH.—Grand Rapids

Grand Rapids Brass Co.
(Door) ....A

MICH.—Ypsilanti

Michigan Mfg. Co. (Sash;
Ventilator) ....AA

MO.—St. Louis

Climax Nut Lock Mfg. Co.,
1132 Collins (Nut) ....D

Pauly Jail Building Co.
(Prison Cell) ....A

U. S. Box Lock Co., 154
Blair Av. (Wooden Box)
                        X

N. J.—Newark

Ahrend & Son, H. (Trunk;
Dress Suit Case, &c.)...B

Gould's Son & Co., M.
(Trunk) ....A

Huebel Mfg. Co. (Dog Col-
lar) ....D

Jenkinson & Co., R. C.
(Trunk; Bag) ....A

National Lock Washer Co.,
65 Johnson (Nut; Sash).A

Positive Lock Washer Co.,
291 N. J. R. R. Av.
(Nut) ....D

Romer & Co. (Car Door;
Latch; Pad; Rim; Jail).B

Slaight Lock & Mfg. Co.,
Thomas, 113 N. J. R. R.
Av. (Car; Switch) ....E

N. Y.—Binghamton

Crandal, Stone & Co. (Nut)
                        A

N. Y.—Brooklyn

Bohannon, Wilson, 760 Lex-
ington Av. (Padlock; Car
Door; Chest; Desk; Door;
Drawer; Drawn Combina-
tion; Latch; Mortise;
Rim; Spring; Store Door;
Tumbler; Wardrobe;
Switch) ....A

Schade & Co., 56 Ainslie
(Padlock) ....F

N. Y.—Elmira

Cronk & Carrier Mfg. Co.
(Sliding Door) ....E

Medford Fancy Goods Co.
(Dog Collar) ....E

New York Guardant Lock
Co., 74 Cortlandt (Time)
                        F

Russell & Erwin Mfg. Co.
(Am. Hdw. Co.) (Pad;
Brass Pad) ....AAAA

Surpless, Dunn & Co., 55
Warren (Pad) C

Tiebout, W. & J. (Ship;
Pad) ....B

Tower & Lyon (Pad; Bi-
cycle Pad; Brass Pad;
Scandinavian Pad) ....B

Universal Lock Co. (Door).F

New York City

Bickelhoupt Skylight Wks.,
Geo. 243 W. 47th (Sash
Ventilating) ....F

Creamer & Co., W. G., 96
John (Car and Switch;
Railway Car Sash)......B

Eagle Lock Co. (Pad; Bi-
cycle Pad; Brass Pad;
Mail Pad; Spring Pad)
                      AAA

Edwards & Co., 144th &
4th Av. (Electric) C

LOCKS (Con.)

Graham & Co., Jno. H.
(Bicycle) ....AA

Weber Railway Joint Mfg.
Co., 71 B'way (Nut Auto-
mobile) ....B

Wendell & MacDuffie (Au-
tomobile Nut) ....B

N. Y.—Poughkeepsie

Lane Bros. Co. (Sliding
Door) ....A

N. Y.—Rochester

Caldwell Mfg. Co., 8 Jones
(Sash) ....E

Pullman Mfg. Co. (Sash)..C

Rochester Automatic Ele-
vator Door Co. (Elevator)
                        E

Rochester Sash Lock Co.
(Automatic Steel Sash,
for railroad coaches) ..D

Sargent & Greenleaf Co.
(Keyless Combination;
Time; Cabinet; Cupboard;
Desk; Door; Mortise; Rim;
Spring; Trunk; Wardrobe;
Safe) ....AA

N. Y.—Syracuse

Stearns & Co., E. C. (Barn
Door; Door; Sliding Door)
                        AA

N. Y.—Warsaw

Warsaw Elevator Co. (Ele-
vator Safety) .....'....B

N. Y.—Watervliet

West Side Fdy. Co., Troy
P. O. (Br. Troy) (Nut).A

OHIO—Canton

Diebold Safe & Lock Co.
(Time; Jail; Safe) ..AAA

OHIO—Cincinnati

Consolidated Time Lock Co.,
315 W. 4th (Time)....AA

Hall's Safe & Lock Works
(Safe) ....A

Victor Safe & Lock Co.
(Jail; Safe) ....A

OHIO—Cleveland

Bourne & Knowles Mfg. Co.,
68 S. Main (Nut) .....A

Chisholm & Moore Mfg. Co.
(Elevator Door) ......AA

National Safe & Lock Co.
(Safe; Combination) ...D

Pennington & Son, A. W.,
34 S. Water (Ventilating;
Burglar Proof Sash)...D

Taylor & Boggis Fdy. Co.
(Sash) ....AA

Universal Fastener Co. (Refrigerator) ....F

Van Dorn Iron Works Co.
(Prison Cell) ....AA

OHIO—Columbus

Simpson Iron Co., West End
Buttles Av. (Sash)......D

OHIO—Dayton

Dayton Mfg. Co. (Car;
Switch; Padlock; Store
Door) ....A

Dayton Supply Co. (Sash
Ventilating) ....B

OHIO—Hamilton

Macneale & Urban Co.
(Time; Safe; Combina-
tion) ....B

Mosler Safe Co. (Time;
Safe; Keyless; Combina-
tion) ....AAA

OHIO—Kenton

Champion Iron Co. (Prison
Cell) ....AA

PA.—Lancaster

Fraim, E. T. (Pad; Brass
Pad; Mail Pad; Spring
Pad) ....AA

Hubley Mfg. Co. (Door)..A

Keystone Lock Works (Pad-
locks; Jail) ....AA

Slaymaker, S. R. (Padlock;
Car; Switch) ....A

PA.—Lebanon

American Iron & Steel Mfg.
Co. (Nut) ....AAAA

PA.—Milton

Milton Mfg. Co. (Nut)...AA

PA.—Philadelphia

Brohard Co., 1684 N. 9th
(Sash) ....B

Mayer & Englund (Automat-
ic Nut) ....A

Miller Lock Co., 4519 Ta-
cony (Car; Switch; Pad-
lock; Automatic Ventilat-

LOCKS *(Con.)*

ing Sash; Cabinet; Door;
Latch; Wardrobe; Sliding
Door; Drawer; Keyless;
Combination; Bicycle)..B
Ruffner & Son (Automatic
Single & Double Nut)...B
Wharton & Co., Jr., Wm.
(Automatic Nut) ...AAA

PA.—Pittsburg
Barnes Safe & Lock Co.
(Time; Safe; Combina-
tion) ....F
Eureka Nut Lock Co., 32d
& Smallman (Nut) ....A
Verona Tool Works, Murt-
land Bldg. (Br. Verona,
Pa.) (Nut) ....A

PA.—Reading
Penna. Hdw. Co. (Door).AA
Reading Hdw. Co. (Sash;
Sliding Door; Door; Car
Window; Elevator Door)
AAA

PA.—Wrightsville
Wrightsville Hdw. Co.
(Shutter; Bowers) C

PA.—York
York Safe & Lock Co. (Safe)
B

R. I.—Pawtucket
Haskell Mfg. Co., Wm. H.
(Nut) ....A

R. I.—Providence
New England Butt Co. (Cab-
inet, all kinds; Mortise;
Door; Knob) ....A

VT.—Montpelier
Lane Mfg. Co. (Log) ....A

WIS.—Milwaukee
Filer & Stowell Co. (Ltd.)
(Log) ....AAA
National Elastic Nut Co.
(Self-Locking Nut) ....A
Stowell Mfg. & Fdy. Co.
(Elevator Door; Sliding
Door) ....A

LOCOMOTIVES

ALA.—Anniston
Kilby Locomotive & Machine
Works (Logging) ......B

ARK.—Pine Bluff
Dilley Foundry Co. (Log-
ging) ....A

CAL.—San Francisco
Risdon Iron & Locomotive
Works (Steam) ....AAA

ILL.—Chicago
Chicago Car & Locomotive
Works (Industrial; Mine)
X
Contractors Supply & Equip-
ment Co., 232 5th Av. (In-
dustrial; Mine) C
Goodman Mfg. Co., S. Hal-
sted & 48 Place (Electric;
Electric Mining) ......A
Hicks Locomotive & Car
Works, 277 Dearborn
(Logging) ....AA
Link Belt Machinery Co.,
39th & Stewart Av. (Elec-
tric Mining) ....A
McGuire Mfg. Co., 122 N.
Sangamon (Electric) ...A
Morgan Electric Machine
Co., Monadnock Block
(Electric Mining) X
Shaw, Willis, 171 La Salle
(New & Second Hand In-
dustrial & Mine) ......D

IND.—Terre Haute
Prox & Brinkmann Mfg. Co.
(Gasoline) ....A

IOWA—Davenport
Davenport Machine Works
(Contractors'; Mine) ...A

KANS.—Abilene
Parker, C. W. (& Railways;
Miniature) X

MAINE—Portland
Portland Co. (Steam; Light
Steam) ....AA

MD.—Baltimore
Ryan-McDonald Mfg. Co.,
44 South (Industrial;
Mine; Narrow Gauge;
Steam; Light) ....A

MASS.—Taunton
Mason Mach. Wks. (Steam)
AAA

LOCOMOTIVES *(Con.)*

Taunton Locomotive Mfg.
Co. (Electric) ....AA

MICH.—Lansing
Prouty Locomotive Co.
(Gas) X

MICH.—Port Huron
Port Huron Engine &
Thresher Co. (Traction
Dirt Road) ....AAAA

N. H.—Manchester
Manchester Locomot. Wks.
(Br. Amer. Locom. Co.,
N. Y. C.) (Steam).AAAA

N. J.—Paterson
Cooke Locomotive & Ma-
chine Co. (Br. Amer. Lo-
comotive Co., N. Y. C.)
(Steam) ....AAAA
Rogers Locomotive Works
(Steam) ....AAAA

N. Y.—Buffalo
Buffalo Pitts Co. (Dirt
Road) ....AAA

N. Y.—Dunkirk
Brooks Locomotive Works
(Br. Amer. Locomotive
Co., N. Y. C.) (Steam)
AAAA

New York City
American Locomotive Co.,
25 Broad (Compressed
Air; Electric; Oil Burn-
ing; Industrial; Mine;
Logging) ....AAAA
Compressed Air Co., 24
State (for Street Rail-
ways) ....AA
Davies, Frank, 68 Broad
(Electric; Electric Min-
ing; Industrial) ......AA
Hunt Co. C. W. 45 B'way
(Electric for Industrial
Railway; Mine) ......A
Koppel Arthur, 68 Broad
(Electric; Electric Mining
& Industrial) ....AA
Leavitt & Co., C. W., 15
Cortlandt (Electric; Elec-
tric Mining; Industrial).D

N. Y.—Schenectady
General Electric Co. (Elec-
tric; Electric Mining)
AAAA
Schenectady . Locomotive
Works (Br. Amer. Locom.
Co., N. Y. C.) (Steam)
AAA

N. Y.—Troy
Knowlson & Kelly (Light).B

OHIO—Akron
Akron Electrical Mfg. Co.
(Electric; Electric Min-
ing) C
Webster Camp & Lane Ma-
chinery Co. (Electric)..A

OHIO—Cincinnati
Bullock Electric Mfg. Co.
(Electric) ....AAAA

OHIO—Cleveland
Atlas Car & Mfg. Co., J. A.
(Br. Atlas Bolt & Screw)
(Steam; Electric) .....A

OHIO—Columbus
Jeffrey Mfg. Co. (Electric;
Narrow Gauge; Electric
Mining) ....AA

OHIO—Lima
Lima Locomotive & Machine
Co. (Industrial; Mine;
Logging; Geared & Direct
Connected; Steam; Light)
AA

OHIO—Ravenna
Byers Machine Co., Jno. F.
(Industrial; Mine; Con-
tractors') ....B

PA.—Corry
Climax Mfg. Co. (R. S.
Battles) (Tramway; In-
dustrial; Mine; Logging)
AA

PA.—Erie
Erie City Iron Works (Electric Mining) ......AAAA
Heisler Pumping Engine Co.
(for mountain use) X
Stearns Mfg. Co. (Indus-
trial; Mine; weight, 14-60
tons; Geared) ....AA

PA.—Philadelphia
Baldwin Locomotive Works
(Burnham, Williams &

LOCOMOTIVES (Con.)

Co.), 500 N. Broad (Compressed Air; Electric; Steam: Electric Mining; Industrial Oil Burning; Light) ....AAAA

Brill Co., J. G., 62d & Woodland Av. (Electric; Electric Industrial; Mine) ....AAA

Conard, Thos. P. (Steam; Electric) ....D

Girard Machine Works, 2616 Girard Av. (Miniature Railways, 15-inch gauge) ....D

Wharton & Co., Jr., Wm. (Steam) ....AAA

PA.—Pittsburg
Carlin Co., W. J. (Industrial: Mine) ....A

Porter Co., H. K., Industrial, 6th & Wood (Compressed Air; Electric; Industrial; Mine; Steam; Pneumatic; L o g g i n g; Light) ....AA

Rees & Sons' Co., James (Light) ....AA

Westinghouse Electric & Mfg. Co. (Br. N. Y. C.) (Electric; Electric Mining; Industrial) ..AAAA

PA.—Wilkesbarre
Vulcan Iron Works (Industrial; M i n e; S t e a m; Light) ....AAAA

VA.—Norfolk
Godwin & Co., Thos. W...B

VA.—Petersburg
Petersburg Iron Works Co. (Industrial; Mine; Logging) ....D

W. VA.—Fairmont
Wagner-Palmros Mfg. Co. (Electric; Electric Mining) ....A

LOGS

MICH.—Bay City
Michigan Pipe Co. (Liquor) ....AA

MICH.—Saginaw
Wickes Bros. (Marine).AAA

New York City
Bliss & Co., John (Taffrail) ....D

Crane Co., Wm. N. (Gas).A

OHIO—Cincinnati
Eureka Foundry Co. (Gas) ....A

OHIO—Cleveland
Nicholson Ship Log Co. (Ship) ....AA

OHIO—Zanesville
Owens Pottery Co., J. B. (Gas) ....A

PA.—Allegheny
Superior Mfg. Co. (Gas)...C

PA.—New Brighton
Pittsburg Clay Mfg. Co. (Gas) ....AAAA

PA.—Philadelphia
Cassell. Jacob C. (Gas)...D
Riggs & Bro. (Marine)...B

WIS.—Racine
Winship Mfg. Co. (Liquor) ....E

LOGWOOD

CONN.—Hartford
Beach & Co. (Cut; Ground) ....AAA

New York City
New York & Boston Dyewood Co. (Cut; Ground) ....AAAA

Stamford Mfg. Co., 82 Wall (Cut; Ground) ....AAAA

LOOMS

See also Machinery
CONN.—Staffordsville
Amidon, S. E. ....G

CONN.—Stonington
Atwood-Morrison Co. (Silk) ....AA

MD.—Baltimore
Poole & Son Co., Robert (Duck; Cotton Duck)...A
Pool Engineering & Machine Co. (Cotton Duck) ...AA

LOOMS (Con.)

MASS.—Boston
Leigh, Evan Arthur. 35 & 36 Mason Bldg. (Carpet; Cotton; Woolen; Worsted) X

Stoddard, Haserick, Richards & Co., 152 Congress (Carpet; Fancy) ....AAA

MASS.—Fall River
Fall River Foundry & Machine Co. (Cotton) ....F
Kilburn, Lincoln & Co. (Cotton; Fancy; Silk) .....A

MASS.—Hopedale
Draper Co. (Cotton; Gingham) ....AAAA

MASS.—Lowell
Lowell Machine Shop (Cotton; Cotton Duck).AAAA

MASS.—Readville
American Loom Co. X

Stafford Co., Geo. W. (Cotton; Silk) ....A

MASS.—Taunton
Mason Machine Works (Cotton; Fancy; Silk; Ribbon) ....AAA

MASS.—Whitinsville
Whitin Machine Works (Axminster; Cotton) ..AAAA

MASS.—Worcester
Crompton & Knowles Loom Works (Axminster; Bag; Carpet; Cassimere; Cotton; Dress Goods; Fancy; Gingham; Jacquard; Jean; Jute Carpet; Plush; Ribbon; Rug; Silk; Suspender; Upholstery; Velvet; Webbing; Woolen; Weft; Goring; Felting; Curtain; Worsted) ....AAAA

Crompton & Thayer Loom Co. (Silk) ....AAA

Gilbert Loom Co. (Carpet; Cassimere; Cotton; Fancy; Jean; Plush; Ribbon; Velvet; Woolen; Worsted; Gingham) X

Steele & Bro., A. H., 54 Hermon ....D

N. J.—Passaic
Lyall, J. & W. (Carpet).AA

N. J.—Paterson
Atherton Machine Co. (Suspender Webbing) .....B

Eastwood Co., Benj. (Broad; Jacquard; Silk) ....A

Jackson & Son, Jas. (Inc.) (Jacquard) ....B

Paterson Machine Works, 46 Warren (Broad Silk).F

Royle & Sons, John (Inc.) (Jacquard) ....A

Widmer Bros., 108 N. 7th (Ribbon; Suspender) ..F

N. J.—Smithville
Smith Machine Co., H. B. (Carpet; Cotton) .....A

New York City
Ehrenberg, Theo. (Fringe; Ribbon; Suspender) ....G

Voelmy Bros., 507 W. 30th ....F

PA.—Bridgeport
Lees & Sons' Co., James (Broad) ....AAAA

PA.—Philadelphia
Fairmount Machine Co., 2106 Wood (Cassimere; Cotton; Cotton Duck; Dress Goods; Fancy; Gingham; Jacquard; Jean; Woolen; Worsted) ....A

Furbush & Son Machine Co., M. A. (Carpet; Cassimere; Cotton; Fancy; Jacquard; Jean; Rug; Woolen; Worsted) ....A

Halton's Sons, Thomas (Jacquard) ....B

Hughes & Russum (All Kinds Cotton; Fancy; Silk; Woolen; Worsted) ....E

Jefferson & Bro., Edward, 127 S. 2d ....D

Klein, Chas. C., 2850 N. Marshall ....D

Mutual Machine Works (Cot-

LOOMS (Con.)

ton; Broad; Cotton Duck;
Jacquard; Plush; Woolen)
.................................X
Schaum & Uhlinger (Cotton; Ribbon; Suspender
Swivel) ....AA
Smith Woolen Machinery
Co., Jas., 411 Race (Woolen) ....AA
R. I.—Woonsocket
Woonsocket Machine & Press
Co. (Cassimere; Cotton;
Worsted) ....AA

LOOPERS

N. Y.—Cohoes
Beattie & Son, Wm. ....D
N. Y.—Lockport
Ward & McLean.........C
PA.—Philadelphia
Hepworth & Co., John W.
.................................B

LOOPS

See also Trimmings; Upholstery; etc.
CONN.—Bristol
Sessions & Son, J. H.
(Trunk) ....AA
CONN.—Danielson
Jacobs Mfg. Co., E. H.
(Picker) ....B
CONN. -Meriden
Meride Curtain Fixture Co.
(Shade) ....B
CONN.—Mount Carmel
Woodruff & Sons, W. W.
(Breeching) ....A
CONN.—New Britain
North & Judd Mfg. Co.
(Halter; Ring; Horse
Belt; Horse Blanket;
Trace) ....A
CONN.—New Haven
North & Co., O. B. (Breeching; Buckle) ....AA
CONN.—Plantsrille
Atwater Mfg. Co. (Carriage) ....A
Blakeslee Forging Co. (Carriage) ....B
Smith & Co., H. D. (Carriage) ....A
CONN.—Torrington
Turner & Seymour Mfg. Co.
(Curtain) ....A
CONN.—Waterbury
Waterbury Mfg. Co. (Trace)
.............................AAAA
CONN.—West Haven
American Buckle Co. (Sap
Pail; Wire; Button)....D
ILL.—Chicago
Boyer, F. (Shade) ......B
Great Western Shade Co.
(Shade) ....F
Hutchinson & Son, W. H.
(Inc.) (Wire) ....A
Opaque Shade Cloth Co.
(Shade) ....AA
Western Shade Cloth Co.
(Shade) ....A
IND.—Indianapolis
Automatic Grip Neck Yoke
Co. (Neck Yoke) ......B
KY.—Newport
Higgin Mfg. Co. (Buckle).A
MAINE—South Paris
Paris Mfg. Co. (Shade)...A
MASS.—Lowell
Lahne & Co., M. M. (Picker)
.................................E
MASS.—Worcester
Spencer Wire Co. (Bottle).A
Wright Wire Co. (Wire).AA
N. J.—Newark
Peters Harness & Saddlery
Co. (Breeching; Buckle;
Trace) C
Sargeant Mfg. Co. (Trace)
.................................A
Wiener & Co. (Trace) ....B
N. Y.—Auburn
Clapp Mfg. Co., E. D. (Carriage) ....B
N. Y.—Binghamton
Crandal, Stone & Co. (Curtain; Buckle) ....A
New York City
Columbia Shade Cloth Co.
(Shade) ....A
Metal Stamping Co. (Car-

LOOPS (Con.)

riage) ....A
Union Upholstery Trimming
Co. (Curtain) ....D
Wemple Co., J. C. (Shade)
.................................AA
OHIO—Canton
Elbel & Co. (Breeching;
Hame) ....A
OHIO—Cincinnati
Monarch Carriage Goods Co.
(Buckle) ....B
OHIO—Cleveland
Cleveland Hardware Co.
(Carriage) ....AA
PA.—Mechanicsburg
Wilcox Mfg. Co., D. (Carriage) ....A
PA.—Philadelphia
Horstmann Co., Wm. H.
(Curtain) ....AAAA
Schrack & Sherwood (Curtain) ....A
R. I.—Providence
American Supply Co. (Picker) ....AA
Burgess & Son, A. (Picker)
.................................X
VT.—Burlington
Vermont Shade Roller Co.
(Shade) ....A
WIS.—Racine
Racine General Mfg. Co.
(Trace) ....E

LORGNETTES

MASS.—Attleboro
Briggs Co., D. F. ......AA
MASS.—North Attleboro
Barrows & Co., H. F......A
Blackinton & Co., R.....A
N. J.—Newark
Bippart, Griscom & Osborn
.................................A
Krementz & Co. ....AAA
Stevens & Leithoff ......F
New York City
Briggs Co., D. F., 180
B'way ....AA
Carter, Howe & Co., 9
Maiden Lane ....A
Spencer Optical Co. C
R. I.—Providence
Kirby, Hy. A. ....AAA
Lederer Co., S. & B......C
Waite, Thresher Co. .....A

LOTIONS

IOWA—Des Moines
Dawn Mfg. Co. ....H
Humane Remedy Co. ....F
MASS.—Boston
Brown & Sons, Jno. I.
(Skin) ....A
Kutcko Co., 373 Washington
(Skin) X
OHIO—Cincinnati
Remmers Soap Co. ......D
OHIO—Toledo
Ohio Toilet Mfg. Co......X
TEXAS—Waco
Artesia Cream Company
(Wrinkle) ....F

LOUNGES

See Furniture

LOZENGES

MASS.—Boston
New England Confectionery
Co. ....AAA
MICH.—Detroit
Parke, Davis & Co. (Medicated) ....AAAA
N. Y.—Newburgh
Cough Checker Mfg. Co.
(Cough) ....G
OHIO—Cincinnati
Merrell Chemical Co., Wm.
S. (Medicated) ....AAA
PA.—Philadelphia
Mason Chemical Co., 515
Arch ....B

LUBRICANTS

See also Grease; Oils.

LUBRICANTS (Con.)

ILL.—Chicago
Arnstein, Eugene, 35th & Shields Av. (Bicycle Chain) ....A
Excelsior Supply Co., Wabash Av. (Bicycle Chain) A

IOWA—Council Bluffs
Monarch Mfg. Co. (Graphite Oil) ....B

MASS.—New Bedford
Nye, Wm. F. (Bicycle Chain) ....A

MICH.—Detroit
Detroit Graphite Mfg. Co., 540 River (Graphite) ..A

MICH.—Saginaw
U. S. Graphite Co. (Graphite) ....A

MO.—St. Louis
Leschen & Sons' Rope Co., A. (Rope; Wire Rope) AAA

N. J.—Jersey City
Dixon Crucible Co., Joseph (Graphite; Wire Rope; Bicycle Chain) ......AAA

N. J.—Lincoln
Atlas Mineral Machine Co. (Soapstone) ....D

New York City
Cole & Co., G. W., 141 B'way (Bicycle Chain).D
Robins Conveying Belt Co. A
Standard Graphite Co., 11 B'way (Graphite) ......B

OHIO—Columbus
Ironsides Co. (Wire Rope; Gear) C

PA.—Allegheny
Wisconsin Graphite Co. (Graphite; Graphite Wire Rope) X

PA.—Philadelphia
McIlvaine Bros., 1500 Hamilton (Soapstone) ......B

PA.—Pittsburg
American Supply Co., 960 2d Av. (Wire Rope)....X
Atlas Paint Co. (Ltd.), 2638 Liberty Av. (Wire Rope) X

WIS.—Milwaukee
Force Feed Lubricating Co. (Graphite) ....F

LUBRICATORS

See also Cups; Oil.

CONN.—Bridgeport
Belknap Mfg. Co. C

ILL.—Chicago
Besly & Co., Chas. H....AA
Chicago Engineer Supply Co., 114 Lake ....AAAA
Crane Co. (Sight Feed) AAAA
Hills-McCanna Co., 50 N. Wells (Pump) X
Illinois Malleable Iron Co., 30 W. Monroe .....AAAA
Lang & Co., J., 44 Michigan F
McCanna Co., Jno. F., 244 Wells ....D
Norris & Co., T. A., 43 S. Jefferson (Candle, for Shafting & Loose Pulleys) X
Phenix Metallic Packing Co., 7 S. Jefferson (Automatic Pump) ....H
Scott Valve Co., 32 W. Randolph ....D

ILL.—Waukegan
Thomas Brass & Iron Co. (Sight Feed) ....A

MASS.—Boston
Crosby Steam Gauge & Valve Co., 95 Oliver (Locomotive; Sight Feed; Cylinder) ....AA
Seibert Cylinder Oil Cap Co., 53 Oliver (Pump; Sight Feed) ....E
Walworth Mfg. Co., 132 Federal (Sight Feed; Cylinder) ....AAAA

MICH.—Detroit
American Injector Co.....D

LUBRICATORS (Con.)
Detroit Lubricator Co., Hodges Bldg. (Candle, for Shafting & Loose Pulleys; Locomotive; Pump; also Hand Feed; Sight Feed; Dynamo; Cylinder)....AA
Detroit Shipbuilding Co. (Br. Amer. Shipbuilding Co., Cleveland, O.) (Brass Dept. - Air Compressor; Pump) ....AAAA
Essex Brass Co., G. B. (Pump) C
McRae & Roberts Co. (Sight Feed) ....A
Michigan Lubricator Co. (Locomotive; Sight Feed) B
Penberthy Injector Co., 346 Holden Av. ....A

MICH.—South Park
Lee Injector Mfg. Co.....D

MO.—St. Louis
Hanlan-Buck Mfg. Co., 212 N. 3d (Sight Feed)....AA
Siegrist Lubricator Co., 200 N. 2d C

N. Y.—Albany
Stephenson Mfg. Co. (Auto. Forced Feed Cylinder)..D

N. Y.—Buffalo
Manzel Bros., 46 B'way (Gas Engine; Locomotive; Sight Feed Automatic Pump) ....F
Sherwood Mfg. Co., 34 Washington (Hand, Cylinder & Automatic Sight Feed Pump; Dynamo) ..B

N. Y.—Elmira
Swift Lubricator Co. (Sight Feed) ....D

N. Y.—Jamestown
Engineering & Power Co...A

New York City
Eaton, Cole & Burnham Co., 253 B'way. .....AAAA
Fairbanks Co., 186 Elm AAAA
Greene, Tweedy & Co., 17 Murray (Pump) ....B
McNab & Harlin Mfg. Co., 56 John ....AA
Nathan Mfg. Co., 92 Liberty (Locomotive; Sight Feed) A
Worthington Pumping Engine Co. (Cylinder) AAAA

N. Y.—Rochester
Sterling Lubricator Co., Powers Blk. (Automatic Force Feed; Force Feed Locomotive; Force Feed Pump; Sight Feed) ....B

N. Y.—Troy
Hammett, H. C., 476 8th D

OHIO—Cincinnati
Lunkenheimer Co., Beekman & Waverly (Air Compressor; Candle, for Shafting & Loose Pulleys; Gas Engine; Sight Feed; Locomotive; Pump; Cylinder) ....AAA
Powell Co., Wm., 2529 Spg. Grove Av. (Air Compressor; Gas Engine; Locomotive; Pump; Dynamo; Sight Feed) ....AAA
Queen City Brass Works (R. Hesterburg) C

OHIO—Cleveland
Crescent Mfg. Co., 24 Centre X
Farnan Brass Works, 25 Centre (Pump) ....A
Talmage Mfg. Co., 270 St. Clair ....B

OHIO—Dayton
Buckeye Iron & Brass Wks. A

OHIO—Mansfield
Ohio Brass Co. (Sight Feed) B

OHIO—Salem
Deming Co. (Oil Pump) ..A

OHIO—Springfield
Nolte Brass Co. ....D
Springfield Brass Co. ....D

OHIO—Toledo
Harrison-Williams Co. (Car

LUBRICATORS (Con.)

Journal) ....D

PA.—Connellsville
Lackawanna Lubricator & Mfg. Co. (Locomotive; Sight Feed, for Stationary, Locomotive & Marine Engines) X

PA.—Erie
Jarecki Mfg. Co. (Pump; Sight Feed) ......AAAA

PA.—Philadelphia
Belfield & Co., H., 435 N. Broad ....AA
Eynon-Evans Mfg. Co., 1519 Clearfield (Pump) ....B
Lonergan & Co., J. E., 214 Race (Steam Engine; Sight Feed; Cylinder)..A

PA.—Pittsburg
Bonar & Co., James, Carnegie Bldg. (Pump) ......B
Carron & Co., A. M., 108 Market (Pneumatic Tool) D
Gem Mfg. Co., Spruce, nr. 23d (Loose Pulley) ...D
Kelly & Jones Co., 135 Water (Plain) ....AA
Mansfield Mfg. Co., 57 1st Av. (Sight Feed) ....B
Pittsburg Brass Mfg. Co., 107 Wood (Sight Feed).D

WIS.—Madison
Mason & Kipp Mfg. Co. (Force Feed) C

WIS.—Milwaukee
Force Feed Lubricating Co. (Force Feed) ....F
Sight Feed Oil Pump Co. (Cylinder Oil Pump)....E

LUGS

CAL.—San Francisco
Pacific Tank Co. (Tank)..A

ILL.—Chicago
Fairbanks, Morse & Co. (Rivetless; Eclipse Steel Tank) ....AAAA

PA.—Coatesville
Lukens Iron & Steel Co. (Boiler) ....AAAA
Worth Bros. Co. (Boiler).AA

PA.—Pittsburg
Lanz & Sons. M. (Tank).AA

PA.—Pottstown
Glasgow Iron Co. (Boiler) AAA

WIS.—Racine
Racine Tank Lug Co. (Tank) ....F
Tecktonius, E. C. (Tank).E

LUMBER

ALA.—Atmore
Carney & Co., A. M. (Long Leaf Yellow Pine) .....A

ALA.—Birmingham
Kaul Lumber Co. ....A

ALA.—Brewton
Cedar Creek Mill Co. (Yellow Pine) ....A

ALA.—Chapman
Smith Lumber Co., W. T. (Yellow Pine) ....A

ALA.—Marbury
Marbury Lumber Co. ....A

ALA.—Mobile
Baird Lumber Co. (Yellow Pine) ....A
Blackshar Co. (Yellow Pine) A
Hubbard Bros. (Pitch Pine Exporters) ....A
Sullivan Timber Co. (Yellow Pine) ....AA

ALA.—Oak Grove
Davis, M. L. (Yellow Pine) A

ALA.—Riverside
Lathrop-Hatton Lumber Co. (Yellow Pine) ....A

ALA.—Daleville
Arkadelphia Lumber Co. (Yellow Pine) ......AAA

ARIZ.—Flagstaff
Arizona Lumber & Timber Co. X

ARK.—Eagle Mills
Eagle Lumber Co. (Yellow Pine) ....A

LUMBER (Con.)

ARK.—Frostville
Red River Lumber Co. (Yellow Pine) ....A

ARK.—Greenfield
Greenfield Lumber Co. (Cypress; Hardwood; Oak; Ash, &c.) ....A

ARK.—Gurdon
Gurdon Lumber Co. (Yellow Pine) ....AAA

ARK.—Kearney
Kearney Lumber Co. ...AA

ARK.—Lester
Lester Mills Co. (Yellow Pine Finish, Moulded Casings; Bass) ....A

ARK.—Onalaska
Carlisle & Co., Wm. (Yellow Pine) ....AAAA

ARK.—Pine Bluff
Bluff City Lumber Co. (Yellow Pine; Cypress).....AA
Sawyer & Austin Lumber Co. ....AAA

ARK.—Sayre
Sayre Lumber Co. (Yellow Pine) ....AA

ARK.—Stamps
Bodcaw Lumber Co. (Yellow Pine) ....AAA

ARK.—Texarkana
Southern Pine Lumber Co. (Yellow Pine) ....A

ARK.—Wilmar
Gates Lumber Co. (Yellow Pine; Cypress Shingles) A

CAL.—Albion
Albion Lumber Co. (Redwood Shingles; Ties)..A

CAL.—Bella Vista
Terry Lumber Co. ....AAA

CAL.—Eureka
McKay & Co. ....AA
Vance Redwood Lumber Co. (Pine; Redwood; Shingles) ....AAA

CAL.—Fort Bragg
Union Lumber Co. (Redwood Shingles; Ties) .....AA

CAL.—Fresno
Fresno & Pine Ridge Flume & Irrigation Co. ......AA

CAL.—Gualala
Gualala Lumber & Mill Co. AAA

CAL.—Kernville
Brown, A. ....A

CAL.—Korbel
Humboldt Mill Co. ......A

CAL.—Occidental
Meeker M. C. ....AAA

CAL.—Pescadero
Levy Bros. ....A

CAL.—San Francisco
Bellingham Bay Improvement Co. ....AA
Casper Lumber Co. (Redwood Ties; Shingles, &c.) A
Dolber & Carson (Redwood; Shingles) ....AAAA
Duncan Mills Land & Lumber Co. ....A
Gardiner Mill Co. ......A
Gray's Harbor Commercial Co. (Fir; Spruce; Red Cedar; Shingles) ......AAA
Gualala Mill Co. ......AAA
Hooper, J. A. & F. P...AAA
Humboldt Lumber Mill Co. A
Loma Prieta Lumber Co..A
Mendocino Lumber Co. ...A
Pacific Lumber Co. (Redwood; Pine; Shingles) AAAA
Pacific Pine Co. (Rough Douglas; Fir Railroad Ties; Rustic Sidings; Bridge; Timber; Carsills, &c.) ....A
Puget Sound Lumber Co...A
Renton, Holmes & Co.....A
San Diego Lumber Co......A
Santa Clara Valley Mill & Lumber Co. ....A
Scott & Van Arsdale Lumber Co. (Pine; Redwood; White Cedar) ....AAAA
Sierra Lumber Co. (Pine;

LUMBER (Con.)
Spruce; Fir) ......AAAA
Sonoma Lumber Co. .....A
Stimson Mill Co. ....A
Tacoma Mill Co. ....B
Vance Redwood Lumber Co.
AAA
Washington Mills Co. ...AA
White Bros., Spear & Howard (Maple) ....A
CAL.—Sanger
Sanger Lumber Co. (Redwood of finest finish work; also Sugar Pine & Cal .White for pattern lumber; Posts; Shingles; Mouldings; Boxes; Trays; General Mill Work)....A
CAL.—Santa Clara
Pacific Mfg. Co. ......AAA
CAL.—Santa Cruz
Hihn Co., F. A......AAA
CAL.—Towle
Towle Bros. Co. ......AA
COLO.—Durango
Stubbs & Jakway ....A
CAL.—Victor
Cunningham, J. B. ......A
FLA.—Escambia
Skinner Mfg. Co. (Yellow Pine) ....AA
FLA.—Jacksonville
Cummers Lumber Co. (L. L. Yellow Pine) .....AA
Dexter, Hunter (Yellow Pine) ....A
FLA.—Milton
Chaffin & Co., James A. (Inc.) ....A
FLA.—Montbrook
Wade & Arthur Lumber Co.
A
FLA.—Muscogee
Southern States Lumber Co. (Yellow Pine) ......AAA
FLA.—Palatka
Selden Cypress Door Co...A
Wilson Cypress Co. (Cypress Lumber; Siding Shingles)
A
FLA.—Pensacola
Keyser & Co., Wm. S. (Export) ....A
Pensacola Lumber Co. (Export Pitch Pine) ......B
Southern States Lumber Co.
B
GA.—Ashburn
Betts & Co., J. S. (Yellow Pine; Lath; Shingles)...B
GA.—Atlanta
Enterprise Lumber Co. ..A
GA.—Augusta
Perkins Mfg. Co. (Yellow Pine) ....A
GA—Dalton
Cherokee Mfg. Co. C
Farrar Lumber Co. (Yellow Pine Brackets; Blocks; Mill Finish) C
GA.—Dawson
Variety Works Co. (Sash; Door; Blind) ....D
GA.—Macon
Masse & Felton Lumber Co.
A
Red Cypress Lumber Co. (Lumber; Shingles) ....A
GA.—Savannah
Georgia Lumber Co. (Yellow Pine) C
Southern Pine Co. (Yellow Pine; Rough & Dressed Shingles; Lath; Mouldings; Newell Posts; Balluster; Flooring; Heavy Timber) ....AAAA
IDAHO—Boise
Ridenbaugh, W. & H.....B
ILL.—Cairo
Carey, Holliday Lumber Co. (Hardwood) ....B
Creelman Lumber Co., F. E. (Hardwood) ....B
Himmelberger & Friant Co. (Hardwood) ....AA
Three States Lumber Co. (Hardwood) ....B
ILL.—Chicago
Baker Lumber Co. ......B
Bay De Noquet Co. ....AA
Bigelow Bros. & Walker Co.

LUMBER (Con.)
(Yellow Pine; Cypress; Hardwood) ....AAA
Detour Lumber & Cedar Co.
Dodge & Co., P. G. (Hardwood) ....B
Dunfee & Co., 106 Franklin (Hardwood) ....B
Heath, Witbeck & Co. (Maple; Cypress; Basswood)
A
Holt Lumber Co. ....A
Houston & Co., Geo. T. (Yellow Pine; Hardwood; Cypress) ....AAA
Marsh & Bingham Co. (L. L. Yellow Pine; Fir; Oak; Hemlock) ....A
Martin Lumber Co., S. K.
A
Mississippi Lumber Co. (L. L. Yellow Pine) ......AA
Paepcke-Leicht Lumber Co. (Box Shooks; Nail Work)
AAA
Rittenhouse & Embree Co., 3500 S. Central Av. (Maple) ....AA
Ross Lumber Co. ....A
Schultz Bros. (Pine Flooring; Cedar Poles; Maple)
B
South Side Lumber Co. (Maple; Oak Flooring)..AAA
Upham Lumber Co., Fred W. (Basswood) ....B
Ward Lumber Co. (Hardwood) ....A
White Lake Lumber Co...B
Wiloe Co.. T. (Maple; Hardwood Flooring) .AAA
Wood Lumber Co., Geo. E. White Pine) ....AA
ILL.—East St. Louis
Goedde & Co., B. ....B
ILL.—Pekin
Smith & Co., T. H......A
ILL.—Rockford
Woodruff & McGuire (White; Norway Pine).B
ILL.—Rock Island
Rock Island Lumber & Mfg. Co. (Lumber; Lath; Shingles) ....A
Weyerhaeuser & Denkmann (White Pine) ....AAAA
IND.—Anderson
Wilke Mfg. Co. (Hardwood Flooring) ....B
IND.—Brazil
Excelsior Clay Works (Maple) ....D
IND.—Clay City
Guir, W. H. (Hardwood).B
IND.—Edinbury
Maley, Hy. (Hardwood)..A
IND.—Evansville
Helfrich Lumber & Mfg. Co.
A
Maley Lumber Co.. Hy. (Indiana Hardwoods) .....A
Maley & Wertz (Hardwoods; Quartered Oak, &c.)....A
May. Thompson & Thayer (Hardwoods) ....A
IND.—Fort Wayne
Ferguson, Jno. (Hardwood)
B
Gilmartin, Edw. (Hardwood) ....B
IND.—Goshen
Sanders & Egbert Co. (Hardwood) ....B
IND.—Indianapolis
Bachman Co.. F. M......B
Christian, Jno. E. (Hardwood) ....B
Coburn Lumber Co.. Hy...A
IOWA—Bellevue
Dorchester & Hughey (White Pine) ....A
IOWA—Burlington
Burlington Lumber Co. (White Pine) ....A
Nairne, Giles & Co......B
IOWA—Cedar Falls
Harris & Cole Bros. (Poplar; Oak Lumber Wagon Box Material; Turned Work; House Trimmings)
A

643

LUMBER (Con.)

IOWA—Clinton
Curtis Bros. & Co. (Mill Work) ....AA
Lamb & Sons, C. (Lumber; Lath; Shingles; Pickets; Flooring; Siding; Ceilings) ....A

IOWA—Davenport
Lindsay & Phelps Co. ....B
McClelland Co., T. W.....B
Mueller & Sons, Chris. (White Pine) ....A
Roberts Co., N. N. ....A

IOWA—Des Moines
Getchel & Martin Lumber & Mfg. Co. ....A
Gilchrest Co., J. K. & W. H. ....A
Green Bay Lumber Co. .AAA

IOWA—Dubuque
Carr, Ryder & Adams Co. A
Farley & Loetscher Mfg. Co. A
Rumpf-Frudden Lumber Co. A
Standard Lumber Co. ..AA

IOWA—Ft. Madison
Atlee, S. & J. C. (White Pine) ....AAA

IOWA—Guttenberg
Zimmerman, J. & Ives....A

IOWA—Keokuk
Taber Lumber Co. ....A

IOWA—Marshalltown
Moore, A. A. ....A

IOWA—Muscatine
Hershey Lumber Co. .....A
Musser Lumber Co. (White Pine) ....A
South Muscatine Lumber Co. (Box Shooks) ....A

IOWA—Sioux City
Edwards & Bradford Lumber Co. ....AAA

IOWA—Waterloo
Ricker & Bratnaber Lumber Co. ....A

KY.—Ashland
Ashland Lumber Co. ....A
Van Sant-Kitchen Co. (Yellow Poplar) ....A

KY.—Burnside
Kentucky Lumber Co.....AA

KY.—Ford
Burt & Brabb Lumber Co. (Hardwood) ....A

KY.—Louisville
Hughes Co., E. L. (Sash; Doors. &c.) ....B
Hughes & Sons' Co., W. J. A
Koehler & Co., Hy. (Hardwood; Yellow Pine)...B
Mengel & Bro. Co., Jr.. C. C. (Hardwood; Box Shooks) ....AAAA
Louisville Veneer Mills (Thin) ....A

KY.—Paducah
Ferguson & Palmer Co. ..B
Longstaff-Orm Mfg. Co....A

KY.—Pineville
Asher. A. J. ....A

KY.—Warsaw
McDaniel's Sons, J. H. (Poplar; Oak; Interior Finish) B

LA.—Antrim
Antrim Lumber Co. (Yellow Pine) ....A

LA.—Bolinger
Arkansas Central Lumber Co. ....A

LA.—Bonami
King-Ryder Lumber Co...A

LA.—Bowie
Bowie Lumber Co. (Lumber; Shingles) ....B

LA.—Bunkie
Haas & Co.. W. D.....AAA

LA.—Donaldsonville
Wilber & Sons Lumber & Shingle Co.. A.........A

LA.—Dubach
Dubach Lumber Co., Fred. B. ....A

LA.—Fisher
Louisiana Long Leaf Lumber Co. (Yellow Pine) AAA

LUMBER (Con.)

LA.—Franklin
Hanson Lumber Co., Alb. (Cypress) ....A

LA.—Harvey
Louisiana Cypress Lumber Co. (Red Cypress Lumber; Shingles) ....A

LA.—Jacoby
Dodge & Sundberry (Cypress; Yellow Pine; Hardwood) ....B

LA.—Jonesboro
Huir-Hodge Lumber Co..AA

LA.—Kentwood
Kent Brick & Lumber Co., Amos (Yellow Pine)..AA

LA.—Lake Charles
Bradley - Ramsey Lumber Co. (L. L. Yellow; Pitch Pine) ....AAAA
Hodge Fence & Lumber Co. B
Powell, J. G. ....B

LA.—Monroe
Monroe Lumber Co. .....A
Southern Lumber Co. ..AAA

LA.—Morgan City
Brownell & Son Lumber Co. (Lumber; Shingles).....B

LA.—Montrose
Montrose Lumber Co. (Yellow Pine) ....A

LA.—Myrtistown
Black Bayou Lumber Co. (Yellow Pine) ....B

LA.—Natalbany
Natalbany Lumber Co. (Yellow Pine) ....AAA

LA.—New Orleans
Carre, W. W. (Export Yellow Pine) ....A
Fischer Lumber & Mfg. Co. (Cypress) ....A
Lambon & Noel Lumber & Mfg. Co. ....B
New Orleans Cypress Co. (Red Cypress) ....B
Otis Mfg. Co. ....A
Ruddock Cypress Co. ....A
Salman Brick & Lumber Co. (Yellow Pine; Cypress).A

LA.—Patterson
Cypress, Tank & Mfg. Co. (R. R. Lumber; Piling).B
Trellue Cypress Lumber Co. (Cypress Shingles; R. R. Lumber) ....A
Williams, F. B. (Cypress) AAAA

LA.—Plaquemine
Wilbert Sons Lumber & Shingle Co.. A. (Red Cypress Lumber; Shingles) A

LA.—Ramos
Ramos Lumber & Mfg. Co. (Red Cypress Lumber; Lath; Shingles) ....AAA

LA.—Ruddock
Ruddock Cypress Co. (Cypress) ....AA

LA.—St. Martinsville
Burdin & Bro.. J. J.......B

LA.—Shreveport
Allen & Curry Mfg. Co. (Yellow; Pine; Lumber; Cypress Pickets; Mouldings) ....A
Henderson Lumber Co.. W. K. ....B

LA.—Tremont
Tremont Lumber Co. (Yellow Pine) ....AA

LA.—Victoria
Louisiana Long Leaf Lumber Co. (Yellow Pine)..B

LA.—West Lake
Perkins & Miller Lumber Co. (Yellow Pine) ...AAA

LA.—Yellow Pine
Globe Lumber Co. (Yellow Pine) ....AA

LA.—Zimmerman
Bentley Lumber Co., J. A. (Yellow Pine) ....AA

MAINE—Augusta
Augusta Lumber Co. (Pine; Spruce Laths; Shingles) A

MAINE—Bangor
Ashland Mfg. Co ....B

LUMBER (Con.)

Ayer & Co., F. W.........A
Cassidy & Son, John....AA
Engel, Wm. ....AA
Lowell & Engel ....AA
Morse & Co. ....AA
Rice & Co., James......B
MAINE—Calais
Murchie & Sons, Jas.....AA
MAINE—Ellsworth Falls
Whitcomb, Haynes & Co.
  (Spruce; Hemlock; Lath;
  Shingles) ....A
MAINE—Gardiner
Gray & Sons, Joshua (Lath;
  Shingles) ....A
MAINE—Guilford
Hussey, Goldwaite & Hudson ....B
MAINE—New Glouster
Chandler Bros. ....A
MAINE—Portland
Berlin Mills Co., 404 Commercial (Spruce; Clapboards; Shingles; Lath;
  Pickets; Dimension
  Boards, &c.) ..AAAA
MAINE—Shawmut
Lawrence, Newhall & Co...A
MAINE—South Beaver
Sargent Lumber Co. ....B
MD.—Baltimore
James & Co., N. W...AAAA
Shryock & Co., Thos. J.
  (Pine; Hardwood, &c.)
                      AA
Sloan & Bro., Geo. F. (N.
  C. Pine; Flooring; Mouldings, &c.) ....A
Surry Lumber Co. ....AAA
Womble, Jr., Pembroke M.
                       B
Jackson Bros. Co. .....AA
Miller & Co., W. B.......A
MASS.—Boston
Atlantic Lumber Co. (Hardwood) ....B
Bartlett Lumber Co. (Cal.
  Redwood; Shingles, &c.)
                        A
Conn. Valley Lumber Co.
                      AAA
Cypress Lumber Co., 153
  Milk (Cypress; Shingles;
  Doors; Sashes; Blinds).AA
Palmer, Parker & Co. (Mahogany; Hardwood; Veneers) ....A
Stearns Lumber Co., A. T.
  (Cypress; Yellow; Pine;
  Ash, &c.; Doors; Blinds;
  Trim.; Cabinet Work;
  Flooring; Shingles; Tanks,
  &c.) ....AA
MASS.—Chelsea
Emery, Geo. D. (Imported&
  Domestic Cabinet Wood &
  Veneers; Spanish Cedar)
                        AA
MASS.—Lowell
Allen & Son, Otis (Kyanized) ....B
Pratt & Co., Amasa (Veneered Doors, &c.).....A
MASS.—Worcester
Baker Lumber Co. (Kiln
  Dried) C
MICH.—Alpena
Comstock Bros. ....AAAA
Gilchrist, F. W. (Maple)
                      AAAA
MICH.—Ausable
Londs Co., H. M. (Pine;
  Cedar Poles) ....A
MICH.—Bay City
Chesborough Bros. ....A
Foss & Co., E. B. (White
  Pine Lath; Shingles)...A
Michigan Pipe Co. (Creosoted) ....AA
Spanish River Lumber Co.
                        A
MICH.—Bay Mills
Hall & Monson Co. (Moulding; Box Shooks) ......A
MICH.—Boyne City
White & Co., W. H. (Hemlock; Maple; Soft & Rock
  Elm; Basswood; Beech;
  Cedar; Tan Bark, &c.)..A
MICH.—Cadillac
Cobb & Mitchell (Maple

LUMBER (Con.)

Flooring, &c.) ....A
Mitchell Bros. (Maple Flooring, &c.) ....AAA
MICH.—Cheboygan
McArthur Co., W. & A....A
Nelson & Clark ....A
Pelton & Reid ....A
MICH.—Detroit
Alger, Smith & Co. (Long
  Pine Timber) .....AAAA
Brownlee & Co. (Telegraph
  Poles) ....A
Detroit Lumber Co. .....A
Dwight Lumber Co. (Maple;
  Oak Flooring; Cigar Box)
                        A
Hunton, A. K............A
MICH.—Detroit
Miller Lumber Co., W. A.
  C. ....A
Nester, Thos. (Est.) AAAA
Stephens & Co., Henry
  (Norway Pine)......AAA
MICH.—Eastlake
Peters, R. G............AA
MICH.—Emerson
Chesbrough Bros. ....A
MICH.—Escanaba
Pittsburg & Lake Superior
  Iron Co. (White Cedar,
  &c.) ....A
MICH.—Filer City
Filer & Sons ....AAAA
MICH.—Grand Rapids
Dennis Bros. (Hardwood).A
Foster-Winchester Lumber
  Co. (Hemlock; Hardwood)
                        A
Fuller & Rice Lumber &
  Mfg. Co. (Hemlock; Hardwood) ....A
Grand Rapids Bark & Lumber Co. (Bark; Hemlock;
  Hardwood) ....A
MICH.—Grayling
Sailing, Hanson & Co.
  (White; Cork; Norway
  Pine) ....AAAA
MICH.—Hermanville
Wisc. Land & Lumber Co.
  (Hemlock; White; Pine;
  White Cedar; Shingles;
  Basswood; Ceiling Siding;
  Mouldings; Hardwood;
  Flooring) ....AAAA
MICH.—Honor
Guelph Patent Cast Co.
  (Saw; Shingle; Tie Mill)
                        A
MICH.—Ironwood
Scott & Howe .... .A
MICH.—Kenton
Sparrow-Kroll Lumber Co.
                      AA
MICH.—Lewiston
Michelson & Hanson......A
MICH.—Manistee
Buckley & Douglass Lumber Co. (Timber; Lath;
  Shingles) ....AAA
Canfield Salt & Lumber Co.
                      AA
Manistee Lumber Co. (Lath;
  Timber) ....AAAA
Sands, Louis (Pine; also
  Lath; Shingles)....AAAA
State Lumber Co. (Shingles)
                      AA
MICH.—Manistique
Chicago Lumbering Co.
                      AAAA
Weston Lumber Co.....AAA
MICH.—Marquette
Read & Co., F. W. (Lath;
  Shingles; Pickets; Mouldings) ....AA
MICH.—Marysville
Mills, N. & B. (Pine;
  Bridge Timber) .....AAA
MICH.—Menominee
Girard Lumber Co. (Pine;
  Hemlock; Hardwood; Cedar Lath; Pickets; Piling)
                      AA
Menominee Bay Shore Lumber Co. (Pine; Hemlock;
  Hardwood; Cedar Lath;
  Shingles) ....A
MICH.—Monroe
Sterling & Son, W. C.
  (Hardwood; Hemlock).A

LUMBER (Con.)

MICH.—Muskegon
Thayer Lumber Co. (Lath; Shingles) ....A

MICH.—Pentwater
Sands & Maxwell Lumber Co. ....A

MICH.—Pequaming
Hebard & Son, Chas...AAA

MICH.—Saginaw
Avery & Co. (Lath; Shingles, &c.)........AAA
Bliss & Van Auken (Maple Flooring; Lath; Shingles) AA
Booth & Boyd Lumber Co. (Lath; Shingles).......A
Germain, Edw. ....AA
Jackson & Co., Thos......A
Saginaw Lumber & Salt Co. ....AA
Saginaw Mfg. Co. ....AA

MICH.—Sebewaing
Liken & Bach (Staves; Headings) ....A

MICH.—Spring Lake
Cutler & Savidge Lumber Co. ....A

MICH.—Traverse City
Fulghum Mfg. Co. (Maple) B

MICH.—West Bay City
Young & Co., W. D. (Hardwood; Maple Flooring)..A

MINN.—Carlton
Sauntry-Cain Co..........A

MICH.—Cloquet
Cloquet Lumber Co. (White Pine) ....AAA
Johnson Wentworth Co. (White Pine Lath; Shingles) ....A
Northern Lumber Co. (White Pine) ......AAA

MICH.—Duluth
Clark-Jackson Lumber Co. A
Gilbert, F. L.............A
Hill Lumber Co., C. M.....A
Richardson & Avery..AAAA
Scott-Graff Lumber Co...A
Split Rock Lumber Co....A
Swallow & Hopkins......A

MICH.—Frazee
Commonwealth Lumber Co. (White Pine) ....A

MINN.—Milaca
Foley-Bean Lumber Co. (White Pine) ......AAA

MINN.—Minneapolis
Backus-Brooks Co. (White Pine) ....AAA
Bovey-de Laittre Lumber Co. ....AA
Bradley-Watkins Co. (White Cedar; White; Norway Pine) ....A
Brainerd Lumber Co. (Lath; Shingles) ....AAA
Coolidge-Schwessler Co. (Car Builders).........B
Nelson-Tuthill Lumber Co. (White Pine) ....A
Scanlon-Gipson Lumber Co. (White Pine) ....AAAA
Shevlin-Carpenter Co. (White Pine Shingles; Lath) ....AAAA
Waite Lumber Co., H. R. (Pine; Red Cedar Shingles) ....A

MINN.—Red Wing
Betcher Lumber Co., Chas. A

MINN.—St. Paul
Coast Lumber Co. (Shingles) AAAA
Jefferson & Kasson (White Pine; Shingles) ....A
Nolan Bros. & Laird (White Pine; Hardwood) ....A
Osgood & Blodgett Mfg. Co. (Hardwood Flooring; Box Shooks; Mouldings) ....A
Villaume Box & Lumber Co. (Hardwood) ....A
Weyerhaeuser & Co. (White Pine) ....AAAA

MINN.—Stillwater
Tozer, David (White Pine) AAAA

LUMBER (Con.)

MINN.—Thief River Falls
Thief River Falls Lumber Co. ....A

MINN.—Virginia
Bailey Lumber Co., W. T. A

MINN.—Willow River
Atwood Lumber Co. (White Pine)................A

MINN.—Winona
Bolcomb & Co., H. C. (White Pine) ....A
Empire Lumber Co. (White Pine Lath; Shingles)....A
Laird; Norton Co. (White Pine) ....AAAA
Schroth & Aheens (Doors, &c.) ....A
Winona Lumber Co. (White Pine) ....AA
Youmans Bros. & Hodgins (White Pine) ....A

MISS.—Collins
Williamsburg Lumber Co. (L. L. Yellow Pine Bridge Timber. &c.) ....A

MISS.—Ellisville
Ellisville Lumber Co. (L. L. Yellow Pine) ....A

MISS.—Glover
Knight Lumber Co. (Cypress, &c.) ....A

MISS.—Hattiesburg
Newman Lumber Co., J. J. (Yellow Pine) ....A

MISS.—Jackson
Enochs Lumber & Mfg. Co. (Yellow Pine) ....A

MISS.—Laurel
Eastman, Gardiner & Co. (L. L. Yellow Pine)..AA

MISS.—Logtown
Weston Lumber Co., H. (L. L. Yellow Pine).AAA

MISS.—Moss Point
Dantzler Lumber Co., L. N. (Yellow Pine; Rift Flooring) ....AA
Denny & Co., W. (L. L. Yellow Pine) ....A
Moss Point Lumber Co. (Yellow Pine) ....A

MISS.—Mt. Olive
Mt. Olive Planing Co. (Flooring; Ceiling, &c.).A

MISS.—Natchez
Learned, R. F. (Cypress) AA

MISS.—Norfield
Norwood & Butterfield Co. (Yellow Pine) ....A

MISS.—Orvisburg
Champion Lumber Co. (Yellow Pine; Timbers).A

MISS.—Wellman
Keystone Lumber & Improvement Co. (Yellow Pine) ....A

MO.—Bethany
Miner & Frees ....A

MO.—Doniphan
Doniphan Lumber Co. (Yellow Pine) ....AA

MO.—Grandin
Mo. Lumber & Mining Co. (Mo. Soft Pine)....AAA

MO.—Kansas City
Bowman-Hicks Lumber Co. A
Buchanan, Wm. (Yellow Pine) ....AAA
Clark & Bates (Yellow Pine; Cypress) ......A
Gloyd Lumber Co.(Yellow Pine. &c.) ....A
Pickering Lumber Co., W. R. ....AA
Swartz Co.. E. G..........A

MO.—Morehouse
Himmelberger-Luce Land & Lumber Co. (Hardwood).. AA

MO.—St. Louis
Chicago Lumber & Coal Co. (Yellow Pine; Oak; Cypress; Hemlock; Gum Lumber; Cedar; White Oak; Black Locust Poles; Posts; Pilings; Red Cedar; Cypress Shingles; White Pine Cypress;

LUMBER (Con.)
  Yellow Pine Laths......
                    AAAA
Degenhart Lumber Co., J.
  H. ....A
Detroit Timber & Lumber
  Co. (Long; Short Leaf
  Yellow Pine) ....A
Eau Claire-St. Louis Lumber
  Co. ....A
Ferguson Lumber Co., W. T.
  (Yellow Pine) .....AAAA
Frost Trigg Lumber Co.
  (Yellow Pine) ....A
Garetson-Greason Lumber
  Co. ....A
Liebke Hardwood Mill &
  Lumber Co., C. F.......A
Little Lumber Co. (Hard-
  wood) ....A
Luehrmann Hardwood Lum-
  ber Co., C. F. (All Kinds)
                      AA
Malvern Lumber Co.
  (Yellow Pine) ....A
Moss Tie Co., T. J.......AA
Saginaw Lumber Co.......A
St. Louis Refrigerator &
  Wood Gutter Co. (Yellow
  Pine; Oak; Cypress)..AA
So. Ark. Lumber Co. (Yel-
  low Pine; Rift Flooring;
  Finish) ....AA
Swartz Lumber Co........A
Werner Saw Mill Co., Louis
  (Oak; Ash; Poplar; Gum;
  Short; L. L. Yellow Pine)
                      AA
Western Tie & Lumber Co.
  (Mo. Soft Pine)......AA
MONT.—Bonner
Big Blackfoot Milling Co.
                    AAAA
MONT.—Butte
Anaconda Copper Mining Co.
  (Oak; Maple, &c.).AAAA
NEBR.—Lincoln
Foster & Smith Lumber Co.
                       A
N. H.—Gorham
Libby & Sons, E..........A
N. H.—Hookset
Thompson, Jas. ....A
N. H.—Laconia
Cooks Lumber Co. ......A
N. H.—Lincoln
Henry & Sons, Jas. E......
                    AAAA
N. H.—Pierce Bridge
Pierce, Jno., Jr. ....A
N. J.—Newark
Backus Lumber Co., E. P.
                       A
N. Y.—Addison
Park, Winton & True....A
N. Y.—Binghamton
Bartlett & Co. ....A
Middlebrook & Son, C. D..A
Weed & Co., J. B......AAA
N. Y.—Brooklyn
Grupe & Gloeckner (Spanish
  Cedar) ....A
N. Y.—Buffalo
Buffalo Hardwood Lumber
  Co. (Hardwood) ....A
Buffalo Maple Flooring Co.
  (Maple) C
Empire Lumber Co. (Hard-
  wood) ....A
Emporium Lumber Co.
  (Hardwood) ....A
Goodyear Lumber Co.
  (Penna. White Hemlock)
                    AAAA
Holland, Graves, Manbert
  & George ....A
McNeil Lumber Co........A
Montgomery Bros. & Co.
  (Yellow Pine; Hardwood)
                      AA
N. Y.—Canton
Bucks Bridge Lumber Co.
  (Spruce; Hemlock; Pine)
                       A
N. Y.—Elmira
Doane & Jones Lumber Co.
  (Car Trade a Specialty).A
N. Y.—Glens Falls
Finch, Pruyn & Co...AAAA
Kendrick & Brown Co.....A
N. Y.—Gloversville
Holden, Chas. J...........A

LUMBER (Con.)
N. Y.—New Hamburg
Millard Lumber Co. (White
  Pine; Spruce; Hemlock;
  Box Shooks) ....A
N. Y.—Brooklyn
Brooklyn Lumber Co.
  (Timber) ....A
New York City
Cooney, Eckstein & Co.
  (Yellow Pine; R. R. Ties)
                      AA
Price & Hart (Furniture;
  Cabinets) ....A
Sizer & Co., Robt. R.
  (Yellow Pine) ....A
Skillings, Whitneys &
  Barnes Lumber Co. (Tim-
  ber; Piling) ....AAA
Wiley, Harker & Camp Co.
  (N. C. Pine)..........A
Yellow Pine Co. (White;
  Yellow Pine; Spruce;
  Hemlock) ....AA
N. Y.—North Tonawanda
Charlton & Thomas, Jno.
  (Timber; Planing)...AA
Sawyer Lumber Co., W. H.
  (White Pine) ....A
Shepard & Morse Lumber
  Co. (White Pine) .....A
Thompson, Hubman &
  Fisher ....A
White, Gratwick & Co...A
White, Rider & Frost
  (White Pine; Spruce; N.
  C. Pine; Shingles).....A
N. Y.—Potsdam
Sherman Lumber Co., A.
  (Spruce; White Pine)..A
N. Y.—Salamanca
Ostrander, H. A. ....A
N. Y.—Sandy Hill
Griffin Lumber Co.......A
Kenyon Lumber Co. (Lath)
                       A
N. Y.—Tonawanda
Eastern Lumber Co. (Mill
  Work) ....AA
N. Y.—Waterford
Burton's Sons, Wm. (Ma-
  hogany; Quartered Oak;
  Red Cedar Veneer, &c.)A
N. Y.—Weston's Mills
Weston Lumber Co. ......A
N. C.—Boardman
Butler's Lumber Co. (N. C.
  Pine) ....A
N. C.—Dover
Goldsboro Lumber Co. (Yel-
  low Pine Flooring; Finish)
                       A
N. C.—Edenton
Branning Mfg. Co. (N. C.
  Pine; Box Shooks).....A
N. C.—Elizabeth City
Blades Lumber Co. (N. C.
  Pine) ....A
East Coast Cedar Co......A
N. C.—Highpoint
Snow Lumber Co..........A
N. C.—Lenoir
Wilson Lumber & Milling
  Co. ....A
N. C.—Williamston
Simmons Lumber Co.,
  Dennis (N. C. Pine)...A
N. C.—Wilmington
Bridges & McKeithan
  (Yellow Pine) ....A
Hilton Lumber Co........A
OHIO—Bluffton
Althans & Balmer (White
  Ash) ....A
OHIO—Cincinnati
Cincinnati Cigar Box Lum-
  ber Co. (Spanish Cedar).A
Cypress Lumber Co.......A
Maley, Thompson & Moffat
  (Hardwood; Mahogany;
  Veneer) ....A
Pease Co. (Lath; Shingles)
                       A
OHIO—Cleveland
Cleveland Saw Mill & Lum-
  ber Co. (Hardwood; Pine;
  Red Cedar; Shingles)..AA
Garry Iron & Steel Co.
  (Fire Proof) ....A
Jenks Lumber Co., Robt. H.
  (Pine; Red Oak; Hem-
  lock; Shingles) ....A

LUMBER (*Con.*)

Martin-Barriss Co. (Mahogany; Cabinet Wood Mfg.) ....A

OHIO—Coal Grove

Yellow Poplar Lumber Co. (Yellow Poplar; White Woods) ....AA

OHIO—Columbus

Ritter & Co., W. M. (Oak; Poplar) ....AAA

OHIO—Dayton

Dayton Lumber & Mfg. Co. ....A

OHIO—Portsmouth

Portsmouth Veneer & Panel Co. (Compound) ......B

OHIO—Sandusky

Bennett Bros. Lumber Co.A

Gelaher & Schuck.......AA

OHIO—Toledo

Barbour & Starr (Cork; Pine; Sash Stock).....A

Empire Lumber Co. (White; Yellow Pine) ....A

Jacoby Co., Edwin ......A

McLaren & Sprague Lumber Co. (White Pine)......A

Mitchell & Rowland Lumber Co. (White; Norway Pine) ....AA

Peters, Wm. ....A

Rib River Lumber Co. (White Pine) ....A

Smith Co., W. H. H. (White; Norway Pine).A

OHIO—Winton Place

Farrin, M. B. (Oak Flooring) ....AA

OREGON—Bridal Veil

Bridal Veil Lumbering Co. (Ore. Fir; Larch Siding; Ceiling; Finish)........A

OREGON—Empire

Southern Oregon Co.......AA

OREGON—Eugene

Booth-Kelly Lumber Co. ....AAA

OREGON—Fossil

Butte Creek Land Live Stock & Lumber Co....A

OREGON—Mill City

Curtis Lumber Co.......A

OREGON—Perry

Grande Pond Lumber Co..AA

OREGON—Portland

Eastern Lumber Co.......AA

Inman, Poulsen Co. (Oregon Pine) ....AA

Nortn Pacific Lumber Co. ....AA

Haseltine & Co., J. E. (Hardwood) ....A

PA.—Ambler

Keasbey & Matteson Co. ....AAAA

PA.—Bellefonte

Crider & Son, P. B.....AA

PA.—Bradford

Bemis & Son, J. M.....AA

Bradford Hardwood Lumber Co. ....A

Weed & Co., W. S.......A

PA.—Brookville

Dickey, Wm. ....A

PA.—Clearfield

Clearfield Lumber Co., Ltd. (Hemlock; Pine; Oak; Hardwood) ....A

PA.—Cooksburg

Cook's Sons, A. ....A

PA.—Dubois

Du Bois, Jno. E. ....AAAA

PA.—Ebensburg

Griffith, Webster (Maple; Flooring; Hemlock; Hardwood) ....A

PA.—Elk Grove

Hummer & Yorks ......A

PA.—Empire

Raine & Raine (Hemlock, &c.) ....A

PA.—Emporium

Howard Co., C. B. (Hemlock Lath; Pickets)...A

PA.—Evans City

Dambaugh, Edw. ....A

PA.—Hallton

Hall, Gardner & Co....AAA

PA.—Johnstown

Murdock & Bro., J. M. (White Oak; Hemlock;

LUMBER (*Con.*)

White Pine; Hardwood).A

PA.—Keating Summit

Emporium Lumber Co. (Hardwood) ....A

PA.—Kutztown

Gonser, John R. ....A

PA.—Lock Haven

Hopkins, A. C. (Hemlock, &c.) ....AAA

Hopkins & Weymouth (Hardwood; Pine; Oak) ....AAA

Kreamer, Chas. (Hemlock; Oak) ....A

Kreamer, Stevenson & Co. (Pine; Hemlock; Hardwood) ....A

PA.—Lopez

Jennings Bros. (Hemlock; Spruce; Maple, &c.).... ....AAAA

PA.—Milton

Clinger, D. (Planing Mill) ....A

PA.—Marionville

Wagner & Wilson ....A

PA.—Parnassus

Logan & Sons, J. W. (Planing Mills) ....A

PA.—Philadelphia

Bayard & Co., Henry ....A

Fox, W. M. & A. M. ....A

Lippincott, Robt. C. (Mich.; N. C. Pine) ....A

Lukens Lumber Co.......A

Rice, Thos. B...........A

Sheip Mfg. Co., Henry H. (Cigar Box) ....A

Strong & Co., Jas. (Hemlock; Poplar; Oak; White Pine; Chestnut) ....A

PA.—Pine Grove

Boyer, Mahlon H........A

PA.—Pittsburg

American Lumber & Mfg. Co. (Timbers; Glazed Factory Sash; Factory Mill Work) ....A

Empire Lumber Mfg. Co. (White; Yellow Pine; Maple Flooring) ......A

Flint, Erving & Stormer (White; Yellow Pine; Oak; Poplar; Hemlock Lath; Shingles) ....A

Huster Lumber Co.......A

Lindsay & Hamilton (White; Yellow Pine; Oregon Fir; Hardwood, &c.) .....A

PA.—Ridgway

Hyde & Co., W. H......AAA

Hyde & Thayer ....A

Thayer, H. S...........A

PA.—St. Marys

Kaul & Hall Lumber Co... ....AAA

Portland Lumber Co....AA

PA.—Rickets

Trexler-Terrell Lumber Co. (Hemlock; Spruce, &c.).. ....AAA

PA.—Sunbury

Whitmer & Sons, Wm. (All Kinds) ....A

PA.—Tidioute

Robinson, G. W..........A

PA.—Vowinkle

Rowman Lumber Co. ....A

PA.—Warren

Wetmore Lumber Co.......A

PA.—Williamsport

Bowman, Forseman & Co. (Hemlock, &c.) ....A

Brown, Clarke & Howe (Lumber; Lath, &c.).AAA

Emery Lumber Co. (Hemlock; Long Large Bills).A

Hall, John L. ....A

Payne, Cochran & Co.AAAA

Righter's Sons & Co., W. (White Pine, &c.).....A

Sones, C. W. ....A

Weis, Chas. W. ....A

West Branch Lumber Co..A

Williamsport Planing Co. ....A

PA.—Wyalusing

Welles, M. H. & G. H...A

Welles, N. A. ....A

S. C.—Alcoln

Alderman & Sons Co......A

648

LUMBER (*Con.*)

S. C.—Prosperity
Wheeler, D. H...........A
TENN.—Bristol
Strong Lumber Co., Jas. (Poplar; Oak; Chestnut) ....A
TENN.—Chattanooga
Loomis & Hart Mfg. Co...A
Snodgrass & Field........A
TENN.—Crossville
Powell Lumber & Mining Co. ....A
TENN.—Duck Town
Tennessee Cooperage Co. ....AAAA
TENN.—Dyersburg
Stevens Lumber Co., A. M. ....A
TENN.—Memphis
Anderson-Tully Co. (Box Shooks, &c.)............A
Cole Mfg. Co. ....A
Darnel & Son Co., I. M. (Hardwood) ....A
Darnell, R. J. (Hardwood) ....A
Thompson Lumber Co., J. W. (Hardwood) ....A
Williams & Co. (Poplar; Oak) ....A
PA.—Murfresboro
Earthman & Co., W. B. (Red Cedar; Hardwood; Fence Posts; Bevel; Poplar Siding; Yellow Pine Ceiling) ....A
TENN.—Nashville
Lieberman, Loveman & O'Brien ....A
Ransom & Co., John B...A
TEXAS—Boren
Smith, Cicero (Yellow Pine) ....A
TEXAS—Dallas
Conway-Leeper Co........A
TEXAS—Galveston
Moore & Goodman (Lath; Shingles) ....A
TEXAS—Houston
Campbell, Jas. I........AA
Emporia Lumber Co. (L. L. Yellow Pine) ....AA
Jones Lumber Co., M. T. (L. L. Yellow Pine; Shingles) AA
TEXAS—Keltys
Angelina Lumber Co......A
TEXAS—Olive
Olive & Sternenberg (Yellow Pine) ....A
TEXAS—Orange
Gilmer, A. (Yellow Pine)...AAA
Jones Lumber Co., M. T. (L. L. Yellow Pine; Shingles) ....A
Wingate Lumber Co., D. R. (Yellow Pine) ....A
TEXAS—Rockland
Cameron & Co., Wm. (Yellow Pine) ....AAAA
TEXAS—Texarkana
Buchanan, Wm. (Yellow Pine) ....A
Sabine Valley Lumber Co. (Yellow Pine) ....AAAA
Southern Pine Lumber Co. (Yellow Pine) ....A
TEXAS—Timpson
Ragley, W. G.............A
TEXAS—Waco
Brazelton & Johnson (Cypress; Yellow Pine; Shingles) ....A
Cameron, Wm. (Yellow Pine; Red Cypress Shingles; Lath; Mouldings; Tirs; Poles; Posts, &c.) ....AAAA
TEXAS—Willard
Thompson & Tucker Lumber Co. (Yellow Pine)...AAA
VT.—Danby
Griffith, S. L...........AA
VT.—Island Pond
Fitzgerald Land & Lumber Co. ....A
VT.—Moretown
Ward. H. O. ....A
VT.—Peru
Peru Lumber Co..........A

LUMBER (*Con.*)

VA.—Franklin
Camp Mfg. Co. (N. C. Pine; Rough; Dressed) ....A
VA.—Norfolk
Roanoke Railroad Lumber Co. (N. C. Pine; Kiln Dried) ....AA
Roper Lumber Co., Jno. L. (N. C. Pine; Flooring; Ceiling, &c.) ....AAA
WASH.—Aberdeen
West & Slade Mill Co. (Pine; Shingles) ......A
Wilson Bros. & Co.......A
WASH.—Blaine
Monarch Mill Co........A
WASH.—Deming
United Shingle Co. (Shingles) ....A
WASH.—Enumclaw
White River Lumber Co. (Fir; Cedar; Spruce; Red Cedar Shingles).......A
WASH.—McMurray
Atlas Lumber & Shingle Co. ....A
WASH.—Seattle
Moran Bros. (Spruce; Cedar, &c.) ....A
Seattle Cedar Lumber Mfg. Co. (Red Cedar; Shingles) ....A
Seattle Lumber Co.....AAA
Statson & Post Mill Co...A
Stimson Mill Co. (Shingles) ....AA
WASH.—Tacoma
St. Paul & Tacoma Lumber Co. (Fir; Cedar; Shingles) ....AAAA
Wheeler, Osgood & Co. (Cal. Redwood; Red Cedar; Doors; Finish)....A
WASH.—Walla Walla
Whitehouse, Crimmins & Co. ....A
W. VA.—Charleston
Branch Veneer & Lumber Co. (Lumber for Built Up Work) ....A
Charleston Lumber Co....A
Devereux Lumber Co. (Hardwood) ....A
W. VA.—Davis
Blackwater Lumber Co. (Hemlock; Spruce)..AAA
W. VA.—Lock Seven
Mohler Lumber Co. (Poplar; Oak; Walnut; Ash)..AA
W. VA.—St. Albans
Bowman Lumber Co......A
W. VA.—Wilson
Wilson Lumber Co......A
WIS.—Arber Vitas
Ross Lumber Co. (Long Joist; Heavy Timber)..A
WIS.—Ashland
Ashland Lumber Co. (White Yellow Pine) ....A
Gilbert, W. H. (Norway Pine) ....A
Keystone Lumber Co. (White; Norway Pine)..AAA
WIS.—Boscobel
Ruka Bros. Mfg. Co. (Hardwood) ....A
WIS.—Chippewa Falls
Chippewa Lumber & Boom Co. (White Pine)....AAA
WIS.—Cumberland
Beaver Dam Lumber Co..A
WIS.—Drummond
Rust-Owen Lumber Co. (Cork; White Pine).AAA
WIS.—Eau Claire
Northwestern Lumber Co...AAA
Owens Lumber Co., John S.
WIS.—Fairchild
Foster Lumber Co., N. C. AAA
WIS.—Fond du Lac
Moore & Galloway Lumber Co. ....A
WIS.—Gile
Montreal River Lumber Co. AA
WIS.—Grand Rapids
Arpin Hardwood Co.......A

LUMBER (Con.)

WIS.—Green Bay
Murphy Lumber Co. (Box Shooks) ....AAAA
WIS.—Hayward
North Wisconsin Lumber Co. (White Pine) ....AAAA
WIS.—Independence
Sprecher & Shafer ....A
WIS.—Iron River
Alexander & Edgar Lumber Co. ....A
WIS.—Jeffris
Jeffris, D. K. ....A
WIS.—Kiel
Laum, J. B..............A
WIS.—Knapp
Hall, A. R. ....A
WIS.—La Crosse
Coleman Lumber Co., C. L. (Shingles) ....AAA
Goddard, Hiram ....A
Holway, N. B. (Est. of)..A
Trow & Co., A. S.........A
WIS.—Lake Nebagemain
Nebagemain Lumber Co... AAAA
WIS.—Madison
Brittingham & Hixon Lumber Co. ....AA
WIS.—Marinette
Hamilton & Merryman Co. (White Pine; White Cedar Shingles; Lath, &c.) AA
Marinette Lumber Co. (Pine; Hemlock; Hardwood; Lath; Shingles; Barrel Staves) .....AAA
Merryman & Co., R. W. (Lath; Shingles)......A
Sawyer-Goodman Co. (Pine; Hemlock; Hardwood Shingles; Lath) .....AAA
WIS.—Marshfield
Conner Lumber & Land Co. A
Connor Co., R. (Pine; Hemlock; Hardwood; Cedar; Pine; Shingles; Cedar Posts; Poles; Basswood Sidings; Ceiling, &c.; End Matched Hardwood; Flooring, &c.) .....AAA
WIS.—Mason
White River Lumber Co... AAA
WIS.—Mellen
Foster-Latimer Lumber Co. A
WIS.—Merrill
Gilkey & Anson Co. (Box Shooks) ....A
Heineman Lumber Co.....A
WIS.—Milwaukee
Cream City Sash & Door Co. (Maple) ....AAAA
Land Log & Lumber Co... AAAA
Rietbrook Land & Lumber Co. ....A
Schroeder Lumber Co., John (Maple) ....A
Wilbur Lumber Co. ......A
WIS.—Odanah
Stearns Lumber Co., J. S. (White Pine) ....AA
WIS.—Oshkosh
Paine Lumber Co. (Mill Work) ....AAAA
WIS.—Owen
Owen Lumber Co., John S. (Pine; Hardwood) ....AA
—Phillips
Davis Lumber Co., John R. (Pine; Hemlock; Hardwood, &c.) ....A
WIS.—Platteville
Eastman Lumber Co., M...A
WIS.—Rice Lake
Rice Lake Lumber Co. (White Pine) ....AA
WIS.—Richland Centre
Kronskop, A. H. (Maple)..A
WIS.—Sawyer
Shaw & Co., A. (Shingle Mill) ....A
WIS.—Schofield
Brooks & Ross Lumber Co. (Pine; Hemlock; Lath Shingles; Pickets, &c.).A
WIS.—Star Lake
Salsich & Wilson.........A

LUMBER (Con.)

WIS.—Stevens Point
Weeks Lumber Co., John.A
WIS.—Stiles
Eldred Co., Anson ....A
WIS.—Sturgeon Bay
Washburn & Co., N. S.....A
WIS.—Three Lakes
Woodruff & McGuire Lumber Co. ....A
WIS.—Tomahawk
Bradley Co. (Lath; Shingles) ....A
WIS.—Two Rivers
Two Rivers Mfg. Co........A
WIS.—Wausau
Curtis & Yale Co. (Hardwood; Basswood; Pine, &c.) ....A
Goodwillie Bros. (Box Shooks) ....A
Stewart, Alex (Lath Shingles) ....AAAA

LUMPERS

MASS.—Athol
Gerry & Son, Geo.........X
PA.—Philadelphia
Smith Woolen Machy. Co., James, 411 Race......AA

LYE

ILL.—Chicago
Brookman Bros. (Col. Chem. Wks.), 149 Huron.....E
Champion Chem. Wks., 208 Mich. C
MICH.—Detroit
Acme White Lead & Color Wks. ....A
MO.—St. Louis
Myers Lye Co., E., 3d & Clark Av. (Concentrated) B
Priesmeyer, W. H., 1001 Carr ....A
N. Y.—Albany
Mendelsohn & Sons (Concentrated) ....A
New York City
Champion Chem. Wks., 177 Franklin ....B
Hall, E. N., 396 B'way....A
OHIO—Cincinnati
Amer. Chem. Co. (Concentrated) ....D
PA.—Philadelphia
Penn. Chem. Wks. (Concentrated) ....AAAA
Penn. Salt Mfg. Co. (Concentrated) ....AAAA
Phila. Lye & Chem. Wks. 10th & Jackson (Con.).C
Tomson & Co., P. C., 25 Wash. Av. (Con.) ..AAA
WIS.—Milwaukee
Eagle Lye Works, 28 Erie.A

LYGOSINE

New York City
Bischoff & Co., C., 88 Park Pl.. ....B

LYSOL

New York City
Lehn & Fink ....AAA

MACARONI & VERMICELLI

CAL.—Los Angeles
Kahn-Beck Co. C
So. Calif. Macaroni Co. ..D
CAL.—San Francisco
Chichizola & Sons, A. (Italian Delicacies) 316 Pacific A
Granucci Bros (Ital. Gds.) 521 Front C
Lavaggi, G. B., 543 Wash'n C
Mattencci & Co., F., 411 Francisco ....D
Splivalo & Co., C. R., 347 Sacramento ....B
Valente, L., 214 B'way ..D

650

MACARONI, ETC. (Con)
COLO.—Coal Creek
Fremont Co. Macaroni Fcty.
D
DEL.—Wilmington
Natl. Macaroni Co......D
ILL.—Braidwood
Rossi & Son, Peter ......D
ILL.—Chicago
Amer. Macaroni Co. (&
Noodles) 135 Adams ..B
Busam, J., 278 Mohawk..B
Canepa Bros. (also German
Home Made Egg Noodles)
101 Indiana ....B
Foulds Milling Co., 185 Kin-
zie ....B
Meyer Mrs. C., 1029 Milwau-
kee Av. C
Nardi, L., 499 W. North..E
IND.—Indianapolis
Van Camp Pack. Co., 600
Ky. Av. ....AA
IOWA—Davenport
Crescent Macaroni Co.
(Spaghetti) ....B
Crescent Macroni Co.
(Noodles) ....B
LA.—New Orleans
Cusinano, J., 1238 Chartres
D
Impastato, G., 612 Du-
maine ....D
Southern Italian Paste
Fcty., 602 S. Peters ...D
MASS.—Springfield
Castle, W. A. ....B
MINN.—St. Paul
Minnesota Macaroni Co., 44
E. Isabel ....D
MO.—Kansas City
Continental Cereal Co., 528
Walnut C
MO.—St. Louis
Amer. Macaroni Co. (also
Noodles) 7 N. 2d .....B
Maull Bros., St. Louis Av. &
13th ....B
Stobie Cereal Mills ......B
MONT.—Butte
Imperial Paste Co. ......D
MFONT.—Great Lake
Imperial Paste Co. ......D
N. J.—Jersey City
Mueller & Co., C. F. (also
Egg Noodles) 93 Boyd Av.
D
N. Y.—Brooklyn
Castruccia & Son, A., 66
Sackett ....B
Savarese & Bros. V., 56
Irving ....A
Zeregas Sons, A., (Ital.
Spec.) 61 Front ....B
N. Y.—Buffalo
Antoniazzi, C., 161 Senaca
D
New York City
Archibald & Lewis, 193
Front C
Atlantic Macroni Co., 508
W. 22d ....B
Columbia Mfg. & Impt'g Co.,
69 Cliff ....B
Falcon Packing Co., 158
Franklin C
Goodman & Son, A.,
(Noodles) C
Maspero, C., 338 Gwich. .B
Moos & Co., 171 Duane..D
Regensburger, Albt., 418 W.
27th ....D
Sholl & Co., E. P., (Imptr's)
118 Duane ....A
Starace, Achille, 76 Pearl
B
N. Y.—Rochester
Eddy Co., L. B. (& Noodles)
C
N. Y.—Syracuse
Hotaling-Warner Co. ....D
N. Y.—Utica
Italian Macaroni Co.
(Noodles Spaghetti) ...C
OHIO—Cincinnati
Foulds Milling Co., 1225
Budd C
Goddum Co., A. L., 112 W.
Court ....D
Wuerdeman Co., 427 E.
Pearl ....D
OHIO—Cleveland
Cleveland Macaroni Co.,
Shaw & Big 4 R. R. ...C
Pfaffman Egg Noodle Co.

MACARONI, ETC. (Con)
(& Noodles) 278 Seneca
D
OHIO—Sandusky
Peninsular Macaroni Co.
C
ORE.—Portland
Allers Bros. Milling Co...C
PA.—Allegheny
Pittsburg Macaroni Fcty.
C
PA.—Carnegie
Bisi, E. ....A
PA.—Harrisburg
Smith & Co., S. R. (Noodles)
D
PA.—Philadelphia
Cuneo, Frank, 832 So. 8th
C
Cuneo & Co., J., 901 So.
8th C
Guano & Raggio, 924 So. 7th
B
PA.—Pittsburg
Piccardo, B. (also Noodles)
185 1st ....B
PA.—Scranton
Cassesse Bros. ....D
PA.—Wakers Mills
Bisi, E. ....A
TEXAS—Galveston
Martinelli & Co., G. ....D

MACERATORS

KANS.—Fort Scott
Ft. Scott Fdry. & Mach. Co.
H

MACHETS

CONN.—Collinsville
Collins Co. ....AAAA
MAINE—East Wilton
Clarke & Parsons Co. X
N. Y.—New York City
Abercrombie & Fitch, 314
B'way C
Collins & Co., 212 Water
A
PA.—Beaver Falls
Emerson, Smith & Co. ...A
PA.—Philadelphia
Disston & Sons (Inc.), Hen-
ry ....AAAA

MACHINERY

Of all kinds, fully indexed,
see Appendix; see also
Mills; Tools; also look for
Machinery or Machine
Wanted)
Also Agricultural Imple-
ments

MACKEREL

See Fish

MACKINAWS

See Clothing; Mens.

MACK-
INTOSHES

MD.—Baltimore
Adler, L. & D. C
MASS.—Boston
Amer. Rubber Co. ..AAAA
Boston Rubber Shoe Co.
AAAA
Columbia Rubber Shoe Co.
Co-operative Rubber Co., 175
Hanover (Rubber) ....B
McIntyre & Co., J. C., 20
Chauncy ....D
Stoughton Rubber Co. ...AA
Union Rubber Co., 65 Es-
sex ....A
N. Y.—New York City
Goodyear India Rubber Glove
Mfg. Co., 503 B'way
AAAA
Goodyear Rubber Co., B'way
AAAA
Hodgman Rubber Co., 806
B'way ....AA
Mandelberg & Co., J., 20 W.
20th ....A

MACKINTOSHES (Con)

Mechanical Rubber Co.
.... AAAA

Pantastote Leather Co.
(Army; Automobile;
Sportmen's) .... AA

OHIO—Akron
Goodrich Co., B. F.
.... AAAA

PA.—Philadelphia
Delaware Rubber Co., 631
Market X

WIS.—La Crosse
La Crosse Rubber Mills Co.
A

WIS.—Racine
Chicago Rubber Clothing Co.
A

MADRAS

See Cotton Goods

MAGAZINES

OHIO—Cleveland
Garry Iron & Steel Roofing Co. (Iron) .... A

MAGNESITE

N. Y.—Brooklyn
Wiarda & Co., Jno. C.
(Powdered) .... AA

New York City
Whittaker, W. H., 245
Front (Calcined; Lump;
Powdered) .... E

PA.—Ambler
Keasby & Mattison Co.
(Powdered) ...... AAAA

N. Y.—Easton
Baker & Adamson Chemical
Co. (Powdered) .... A
Williams & Co., C. K, (Powdered) .... A

MAGNESIUM

PA.—Ambler
Keasby & Mattison Co.
.... AAAA

ILL.—Chicago
Western Telephone Mfg. Co.
(Telephone) .... B

MAGNETOS

ILL.—Chicago
Swedish-American Telephone
Co., 88 W. Jack Boul. .. A

IND.—South Bend
Knoblock-Heidman Mfg. Co.
(Sparkling) .... D

MASS.—Brookline
Holtzer-Cabot Elec. Co.
(Testing) .... A

S. C.—Sumter
Sumter Telephone Mfg. Co.
A

MAGNETS

CONN.—Ansonia
Ansonia Electrical Co. (Electro) .... A

CONN.—Manchester
Norton Electrical Instrument
Co. (Horse Shoe) ...... D

ILL.—Chicago
McDermid Mfg. Co., Board
of Trade Bldg., (Electro)
C
Scheutel & Co., W., 171 E.
Randolph (Eye) .... D
Western Electric Co. (Electro; Horse Shoe) .AAAA

IND.—Indianapolis
Nordyke & Marmon Co.
(Electro) .... AAA

IND.—South Bend
Knoblock-Heidman Mfg. Co.
(Electro) .... D

MASS.—Boston
Hall Scientific Co., Arthur
W., 141 Franklin (Electro)
E

N. Y.—New York City
Bunnell & Co., J. H., 20
Park Pl. (Horse Shoe)
C
Glaenzer, Freres & Reinholt,
26 Wash'n Place (Imp't'd
Electro) ....A
McCoy Co., Jos. F., 157
Chambers (Lifting) .... B

MAGNETS (Con.)

Manhattan Electrical Supply Co., 32 Cortlandt
(Electro) .... AA
Splitdorf, Chas. F., 23 Vandewater (Electro) ...... E

N. Y.—Schenectady
General Electrical Co.
(Horse Shoe) ...... AAAA

OHIO—Cincinnati
Electrical Appliance Co., 136
Longworth (Electro) .. C

OHIO—Cleveland
Electric Controller & Supply
Co. (Lifting Electro) .. A
North Electric Co. ...... A

R. I.—Phillipsdale
Varley Duplex Magnet Co.
(Electro) .... A

N. J.—Paterson
Ferrary & Schauble Co. .. D
Ulrich & Co. (Brass & Steel)
C
Walder, Jacob (Brass &
Steel) .... AA

MAHOGANY

See Lumber

MALLETS

CONN.—Collinsville
Hartigan, W. R. (Wooden)
H

CONN.—Deep River
Williams & Marvin Mfg. Co.
(Wooden; Lignumvitae;
Calking; Ice Pick; Printers'; Tinners') .... D

CONN.—Middletown
Wilcox, Crittenden & Co.
(Calking; Wooden) ..... A

CONN.—New Britain
Stanley Rule & Level Co.
(Wooden) .... AAA

CONN.—Saugatuck
Dosher Plane & Tool Co.
(Wooden) .... E

CONN.—Southington
Peck, Stow & Wilcox Co.
(Tinners'; Wooden) AAAA

CONN.—Torrington
Union Hdw. Co. (Calking;
Wooden) .... AA

ILL.—Chicago
Chicago Rawhide Mfg. Co.,
75 E. Ohio (Rawhide) .. A
Dental Protective Supply
Co., Champlain Bldg. (Automatic) .... A
Morgan & Wright (Inc.), 333
W. Lake (Rubber) ....AA
Redlich Mfg. Co. (Rubber
Ended) .... B

IND.—Indianapolis
Tucker & Dorsey Mfg. Co.
(Tinners') .... A

MASS.—Boston
Boston Belting Co., 256 Devonshire (Rubber), AAAA
Boston & Lockport Block
Co., 160 Commercial
(Wooden; Lignumvitae)
Harvey, H. H. (Stone Cutters') .... D
Waite, Ranlet & Co.
(Wooden) .... B

MASS.—Brockton
Brockton Mallett Co. (Rawhide) .... E

MASS.—Kingston
Drew & Co., C. (Calking) C

N. J.—Newark
Bernz, Otto, S. 13th & S.
Orange Av. (Wooden) .. B
Sommer's Son, Jno., 355 Central Av. (Wooden) ...... A

MICH.—Ludington
Tubbs Mfg. Co. (Printers)
B

N. Y.—Buffalo
White Co., L. & J., Perry
& Columbia (Calking) .. A

New York City
Estes & Sons, E. B., 45 John
(Wooden) .... AA
Hoe & Co., R. (Printers')
AAAA
New York Belting & Packing Co., 25 Park Pl. (Rubber) .... AAA
Peerless Rubber Mfg. Co.
(Rubber) .... AA
Stimpson & Son, Edwin B.

MALLETS (Con.)
(Rawhide) ....B
Stoutenborough, X. (Ice
Pick) ....D
Tiebout, W. & J., 118 Chambers (Calking) ....B
N. Y.—Stony Brook
Stossel, Carl (Boiler Makers'; Carpenters'; Coppersmiths'; Gavel; Metal
Workers') ....F
N. Y.—Syracuse
New Process Rawhide Co.
(Rawhide) ....B
Stearns & Co., E. C. (Carpenters'; Fibre Head; Lignumvitae; Tinners') ..AA
OHIO—Akron
Baker, McMillen Co. (Wooden) ....B
Goodrich Co., B. F. (Rubber)
AAAA
OHIO—Cincinnati
Obermayer Co., S. (Boxwood; Rawhide) ......AA
OHIO—Cleveland
Osborn Mfg. Co. (Rubber;
Wooden) ....B
OHIO—Columbus
Ohio Tool Co. (Boxwood;
Lignumvitae) ....AA
OHIO—Piqua
Piqua Handle & Mfg. Co.
(Wooden) ....A
OHIO—Sandusky
Sandusky Tool Co. (Wooden;
Carpenters'; Tinners')..A
OHIO—Youngstown
Republic Rubber Co. (Rubber) ....AA
PA.—Erie
Continental Rubber Wks.
(Rubber) ....A
PA.—Philadelphia
Paxson Co., J. W. (Wooden)
AA
R. I.—Pawtucket
Bliss Mfg. Co., R. (Wooden;
Boxwood; Lignumvitae)
AAAA
R. I.—Providence
Holbrook, A. & C. W. (Rawhide) ....B
WIS.—Two Rivers
Hamilton Mfg. Co. (Printers') ....AA

MALT

MD.—Baltimore
McCormick & Co. ....D
MASS.—Boston
Dole Bros., Hops & Malt Co.
B
MINN.—Hastings
Hastings Malting Co. .....A
MINN.—New Ulm
Hauenstein Brewing Co.,
Jno. ....B
MINN.—St. Paul
Hauser & Sons Malting Co.
A
MINN.—St. Peter
Engesser Brewing Co. ....A
MO.—St. Louis
Anheuser-Busch Brewing
Assn. ....AAAA
MONT.—Butte City
Centennial Brewing Co. ...A
N. J.—Newark
Feigenspan, Christain X
N. Y.—Brooklyn
Leavy & Britton Brewing Co
B
N. Y.—Buffalo
Schaefer & Sons Malting Co.
B
N. Y.—East Syracuse
Benedict Mfg. Co., M. S.
AA
N. Y.—Geneva
Nester, S. T. ....AAA
New York City
Beadleston & Woerz ......A
WIS.—Kenosha
Pettit Malting Co., M. H., A
WIS.—La Crosse
Gund Brewing Co., Jno.
AAAA
WIS.—Milwaukee
Gerlach & Co., Wm. ......A
Pabst Brewing Co....AAAA

MANDOLINS

See Musical Instruments

MANDRELS

CAL.—San Francisco
Pacific Saw Mfg. Co. (Circular Saw) X
CONN.—Hartford
Pratt & Whitney Co.
(Taper) ....AAAA
CONN.—Norwich
Rogers & Co., C. B. (Circular Saw) ....AAAA
CONN.—Southington
Peck, Stow & Wilcox Co.
AAAA
CONN.—South Norwalk
Le Count, Wm. G. (Expanding) ....B
GA.—Atlanta
Southern Saw Wks. (Circular Saw) ....B
ILL.—Cairo
Reed, Jos. B. (Saw) .....B
ILL.—Carpentersville
Illinois Iron & Bolt Co. (or
Cones; Blacksmiths') .X
ILL.—Chicago
Rich Mfg. Co., Geo. R. (Expanding) ....D
IND.—Indianapolis
Atkins & Co., E. C., 402 S.
Illinois (Circular Saw)
AAAA
Barry Saw & Supply Co.,
W. B. (Circular Saw) ..C
IOWA—Dubuque
Adams Co. (Stove Pipe) ..A
MAINE—Bangor
Union Iron Wks. (Saw) ..A
MASS.—Boston
Woods Machine Co., S. A.,
445 Dorchester (Saw), AA
MASS.—Canton
Kinsley Iron & Machine Co.
(Circular Saw) ....AA
MASS.—Fitchburg
Putnam Machine Co. (Auto
Cone) ....A
MASS.—Greenfield
Wells Bros. Co. ....A
Wiley & Russell Mfg. Co.
(Taper) ....AA
MASS.—New Bedford
Morse Twist Drill & Machine
Co. (Expanding; Taper)
AAA
MO.—St. Louis
Plunger & Henger Mfg. Co.,
11th & Herbert ....A
N. J.—Elizabeth
Braunsdorf-Mueller Co. ..D
N. J.—Gloucester City
Rogers Gauge & Drill Wks.,
Jno. M. ....A
N. J.—Smithville
Smith Machine Co., H. B.
(Saw, Circular) ....A
N. Y.—Brooklyn
Oldham & Sons, Joshua
(Circular Saw) ....D
N. Y.—Buffalo
Frank Machinery Co. (Circular Saw) C
Niagara Machine & Tool
Kks. ....A
N. Y.—Middletown
National Saw Co. (Saw)...A
New York City
Amer. Woodworking Machine Co., 136 Liberty
(Circular Saw) ....AAAA
Etna Mfg. Co., 253 Bway. X
Fairbanks Co. (Expanding;
Circular Saw) ...AAAA
Hoe & Co., R., 506 Grand
(Saw) ....AAAA
OHIO—Akron
Whitman & Barnes Mfg. Co.
AAAA
OHIO—Carthage
Block-Pollak Iron Co. ..AAA
OHIO—Cincinati
Cincinnati Screw & Tap Co.
A
Cordesman Machine Co., 25
Butler (Saw) X
Fay & Eagan Co., J. A.,
Front & John (Saw)
AAAA
Lane & Bodley Co. (Circular
Saw) ....B

MANDRELS (Con.)

OHIO—Cleveland
Cleveland Twist Drill Co.
(Blacksmiths') ....A
Standard Tool Co. ....AA
OHIO—Columbus
Buckeye Saw Mfg. Co. (Circular Saw) ....D
OHIO—Springfield
Western Mfg. Co. (Expanding) ....D
PA.—Beaver Falls
Champion Saw & Gas Engine
Co. (Saw) X
Emerson, Smith & Co. (Saw)
............A
PA.—East Stroudsburg
Stauffer, Geo. E. C
PA.—Philadelphia
Disston & Sons (Inc.),
Henry (Saw) .....AAAA
Earle Gear & Machine Co., D
Power & Co., L., 20 S. 23d
(Saw) ....A
PA.—Pittsburg
Lippert, E. T. (Saw) X
PA.—Wilkesbarre
Nicholson & Co., W. H. (Expanding; Lathe) C
PA.—York
Farquhar & Co. (Ltd.), A.
B. (Saw) ....AAA
R. I.—Providence
Browne & Sharpe Mfg. Co.
(Taper) ....AAAA
TENN.—Chattanooga
Wheland Machine Wks.
(Saw) ....A
TENN.—Jackson
Southern Engine & Boiler
Wks. (Inc.) (Saw ..AA
VT.—Montpelier
Lane Mfg. Co. (Circular
Saw) ....A

MANGANESE

CAL.—San Francisco
Union Iron Wks. (Bronze) X
D. C.—Washington
Kendall & Flick ....A
MD.—Baltimore
Thomsen Chemical Co. (Carbonate) ....B
MASS.—Boston
Billings, Clapp & Co. (Salts)
AA
MO.—St. Louis
Mallinckrodt Chemical Wks.
(Salts) ....AAAA
N. J.—High Bridge
Taylor Iron & Steel Co.
(Steel; Steel Castings;
Steel Forgings) ....AAAA
N. J.—Jersey City
Williams & Son, E. A.
(Bronze) ....AA
N. Y.—Brooklyn
Wiarda & Co., Jno. C. (Oxide; Salts) ....AA
New York City
Chrystal, Charles B. ...D
Cooper & Co., Chas., 194
Worth ....AA
Feuchtwanger & Co., L.
(Salts) ....B
Klipstein & Co., A .....AA
Lamson & Bro., Jno. S. ..A
Lee & Co., James ......A
Roessler & Hasslacher, 100
William (Chloride, Oxide;
Sulphate) ....AA
Wegelin & Wilckes C
PA.— Chester
Crown Smelting Co.
(Bronze) ....A
PA.—Easton
Baker & Adamson Chemical
Co. (Salts) ....A
PA.—Philadelphia
Pennsylvania Salt Mfg. Co.
(Salt) ....AAAA
Samuel, Frank (Firm of)
1502 Market ....A
Powers - Weightman - Rosengarten Co. (Salts)
AAAA
PA.—Pittsburg
Finkell-Hachmeister Chemical Co. (Oxide; Borate;
Chloride) ....D

MANGERS
ILL.—Chicago

MANGERS (Con.)

Barbee Wire & Iron Wks.
B
Illinois Malleable Iron Co.
(Feed) ....AAAA
N. J.—Burlington
Stewart & Peterson Co.
(Horse Feed) ....A
N. Y.—Greene
Lyon Iron Works (Casein)
B
N. Y.—Manlius
Cheney & Son, S. (Feed)..A
N. Y.—Munnsville
Munnsville Plow Co. (Field)
B
New York City
Fiske Iron Wrks., J. W. .B
N. Y.—Warsaw
Warsaw Elevator Co. (Feed)
B
OHIO—Toledo
Donovan Wire & Iron Co.
(Feed) C
PA.—Elizabethtown
Buch's Sons, A. ....A
PA.—Hamburg
Loose & Son, S. A. (Feed)
B
VA.—Norfolk
Whitehurst Co., R. W.
(Feed) ....B

MANGLES

See also Machinery; Laundry

ILL.—Chicago
Steel Roll Mangle Co., 214
Washn. (Laundry) .....F
MASHS.—Boston
Walworth Mfg. Co. ..AAAA
MICH.—Muskegon
Automatic Wringer Co.
(Laundry) X
N. Y.—New York City
Amer. Wringer Co. ..AAAA
Export Laundry Machry.
Co., 74 W. Houston
(Laundry) X
Oakley & Keating, 40 Cortlandt (Laundry) X
N. Y.—Rochester
Hagen & Co., A. L. (Laundry) ....AA
N. Y. Troy
Adams Laundry Mach. Co.
B
Troy Laundry M'ch'ry Co.
(Ltd.) (Laundry) ....AA
OHIO—Cincinnati
Amer. Laundry Mach. Co.
B
Watkins Laundry Mchy. Co.,
F. M. (Laundry) ....A
OHIO—Hamilton
Betz Mfg.. Co. (Steam
Laundry) ....D
OHIO—Sandusky
Warren Electric Mfg. Co.
A
PA.—Columbia
Nilson Laundry Mach'y Co.
A
PA.—Philadelphia
Butterworth & Sons Co., H.
W. ....A
WIS.—Racine
Collier, T. & P. X
Foster & Williams Mfg. Co.
B
Racine Hwd. Co., (Laundry) X
PA.—Coatesville

MANHEADS

Lukens Iron & Steel Co.
(Yokes; &c.; Pressed
Steel) ....AAAA
Worth Bros Co. (Yokes; &c.;
Pressed Steel) ....AA
PA.—Harrisburg
Central Iron & Steel Co.
(Yokes; &c.; Pressed
Steel) ....AAAA
PA.—Pottstown
Glasgow Iron Co. (Yokes;
&c.; Pressed Steel) .AAAA
PA.—Williamsport
Keeler Co., E. ....A

MANICURE GOODS

See Silverware Novelties

MANHOLES

OHIO—Youngstown
Sennett Co., Geo. B. (Street)
......................................B

MANILLA

See Paper

MANTELS

See also Clothing; Ladies

ALA.—Birmingham
Wood, Dickerson & Putnam
(Wood) ....B
CAL.—San Francisco
Bennett & Schutte, 184 Valencia (Marble; Wood).D
Mangrum & Otter, 581 Market (Wood) ....A
Sterling Furniture Co., 1039
Market (Wood) ....B
COLO.—Denver
Paulson, Jno. P., 1831 Wazee (Wood) ....A
Sayre-Newton Lumber Co.,
22d cor. Blake (Wood)
............................AAA
CONN.—Hartford
Hartford Faience Co.
(Faience) ....B
White & Whitmore (Wood)
............................C
GA.—Augusta
Perkins Mfg. Co. (Wood)
............................A
GA.—Tate
Sickels Co., Geo. B. (Marble ....B
ILL.—Chicago
Andrews Co., A. H. (Wood)
............................AA
Ayers Mantel Co.., John W.
(Wood) ....E
Foster-Munger Co., W. 20th
& S. Sagamon (Wood)
............................AA
Gauger & Co., John A., W.
22d & Laflin (Wood).AA
Hawes & Dodd, 24 Adams
(Mosaic) C
Palmer-Fuller & Co., 2244
Lumber (Wood) ......A
Petersen Co., Geo. L.
(Wood) ....B
Roberts & Co., E. L., W.
22d & Union (Wood) ..A
Sherman & Flavin, 2511
State (Marble; Mosaic;
Onyx) ....B
ILL.—Dixon
Fletcher Mfg. Co. (Wood)
............................B
ILL.—Edwardsville
Leclair Mfg. Co. (Wood).B
ILL.—Moline
Moline Furniture Wrks.
(Wood) ....B
ILL.—Peoria
Peoria Stone & Marble Wrks.
(Marble) ....A
ILL.—Quincy
Quincy Show Case Wrks.
(Wood) ....A
ILL.—Rockford
Rockford Mantel Co. (Wood)
............................A
ILL.—Rock Island
Rock Island Sash & Door
Wrks. (Wood) ......AA
IND.—Indianapolis
Huey Co., M. S. (Wood)
............................B
IND.—Tell City
Tell City Desk Co. (Wood)
............................B
IOWA—Clinton
Curtis Bros. & Co. (Wood)
............................AAA
IOWA—Des Moines
Des Moines Marble & Mantel Co. (Marble) C
IOWA—Dubuque
Carr, Ryder & Adams Co.
(Wood) ....A
IOWA—Lyons
Disbrow & Co., M. A.
(Wood) ....A

MANTELS (Con.)
IOWA—Muscatine
Roach & Musser Sash &
Door Co. (Wood) ..AAA
IOWA—Sioux City
Curtis Sash & Door Co.
(Wood) ....AA
KY.—Louisville
Fischer-Leaf Co., 438 High
(Marbleized Iron) ......A
Gernert Bros. Lbr. Co., 6th,
Hill & A. (Wood) ....B
Hegan Mantel Co., 631 4th
(Wood) ....B
Hughes & Sons Co., W. J.,
14th, Cor. Maple (Wood)
............................A
Kentucky Stove Co., 1401
Deleware (Marbleized
Iron) ....B
Voss-Cochrane Mantel Co.,
A. F., 16th & Arbegust
(Wood) C
KY.—Mount Sterling
McCormick, Lyons & Co.
(Wood) ....B
Star Planing Mill Co.
(Wood) C
LA.—Patterson
Cypress Tank & Mfg. Co.
(Wood) ....B
LA.—Shreveport
Allen Mfg. Co. (Wood)..B
MAINE—Bangor
Morse & Co. (Wood)..AA
MAINE—Portland
Allen, W. A., 125 Somerset
(Wood) ....F
Delano Planing Mill Co.
(Wood) ....D
Smith & Rumery, 510 Fore
(Wood) ....D
MD.—Baltimore
Broadbent & Davis Mantel
Co. (Wood) ....D
Evans Marble Co., 204 E.
York (Marble) ....A
Hilgartner & Sons, Inc., 714
W. Baltimore (Marble)
............................C
MASS.—Boston
Boston Fire Brick Co. (Geo.
M. Fiske, Mgr.) 164 Devonshire (Brick) ......A
Boston Mosaic Co., 131
Wash'n N. (Mosaic) ..X
Grueby Faience Co., E. 1st
& K. (Faience) ....D
Irving & Casson, 150 Boylston (Wood) ....A
Paine Furniture Co., 48 Canal (Wood) ....B
Stearns Lumber Co., A. T.,
(Wood) ....AA
MASS.—Cambridge
Hall & Co., C. E., 62 1st
(Marble) ....A
MICH.—Detroit
Christa & Sons, Philip, 504
Lafayette Av. (Marble;
Onyx) ....B
MICH.—Grand Rapids
Aldine Grate & Mantel Co.,
Court, cor. Shawmut Av.
(Wood) C
Ocker & Ford Mfg. Co.
(Wood) ....A
MICH.—Saginaw
Mershon & Co. (Inc.) Wm.
B. (Wood) ....A
MINN.—Minneapolis
Northwestern Mantel Co.,
419 S. 6th (Wood) C
MINN.—St. Paul
St. Croix Lumber Co., Germania Life Bldg. (Wood)
............................AAA
MISS.—Jackson
Enochs Lumber & Mfg. Co.
(Wood) ....A
MO.—Kansas City
Whitcomb Cabinet Co., 1209
Walnut (Wood) ....D
MO.—St. Louis
Beattie Mfg. Co., 2202 Pine
(Wood) ....A
Pickel Marble & Granite Co.,
N. 1907 B'way (Marble)
............................A
NEBR.—Lincoln
Curtis & Bartlett Co.
(Wood) ....A
NEBR.—Omaha
Adams & Kelly Co. (Wood)
............................B

MANTELS (Con.)

Bloom Co., Alfred, 1502 California (Wood) C

N. H.—Milford
Pierce & Co., W. E. (Wood)
......D

N. J.—Perth Amboy
Perth Amboy Terra Cotta Co (Terra Cotta) ....AA

N. Y.—Binghamton
Robertson & Son, A. (Wood)
......AA

N. Y.—Brooklyn
Bossert & Son. Louis, Grand & Newton Creek (Wood)
......AAAA
Hecla Iron Wrks., N. 11th & Berry (Iron, Electro Bronze Plated) ......AA
McGratty & Sons, 313 Butler (Onyx) X
White, Potter & Paige Mfg. Co., 415 Willoughby (Wood) ....A

N. Y. Buffalo
Cooper Marble & Monumental Wrks., W. F., 885 W. Delavan (Marble) ......D
Loutz Co., 861 Main (Marble: Onyx) ....A
Steul & Thuman Co., 278 Johnson (Wood) ....A
Stuhlmiller, Wm. L. (Wood)
......C

N. Y.—Elmira
Kertscher & Co. (Wood) ..A

N. Y.—Jamestown
Munson & Johnson (Wood)
......B

New York City
Batterson & Eisle, 431 11th Av. (Marble; Onyx) ...A
Buess, Wm., 316 E. 95th (Marble; Slate) ....E
Currier Co., E. Bradley 119 W. 23d (Wood) ....B
Graf, Frank H., 322 7th Av. (Marble Wood) ......D
Fisher & Co., Robert C., 97 E. Houston (Marble; Onyx) ....AA
Harris Brick Co., 1123 B'way (Brick) ....A
Jackson Co., Wm. H., 29 E. 17th., (Marble; Slate; Wood) ....A
Kimbel & Sons, A., 398 5th Av. (Wood) ....A
Klaber & Co., S., 47 W. 42d (Marble; Onyx) ....B
Pellarin & Co., 23 W. 8th (Mosaic) ....E
Penrhyn Slate Co., 493 E. 138 (Slate) X
Shipway & Bro., Jno. H. ft. E. 136th (Marble)..A
Stoltzenberg Co., 51 & 53 Barclay (Mosaic) ......B
Traitel Bros. & Co., 133 W. 42d (Mosaic) ....B

N. Y.—Poughkeepsie
Van Wyck & Collins, 170 Main (Marble) ....D

N. C.—Charlotte
Carolina Mfg. Co. (Wood)
......C

N. C.—Greensboro
McClamroch Mantel Co. (Wood) ....E

N. C.—High Point
Grand Rapids Furniture Co. (Wood) ....B

N. C.—Mt. Airy
Mt. Airy Mantel & Table Co. (Wood) ....D

OHIO—Cincinnati
Great Western Marble Wrks. (Philip McDonough. Prop.) cor. Park & 2d (Marble) ....AAAA
Mitchell Furniture Co., Robert, 624e Rac (Wood)
......AAAA
Pease Co. (Wood) ....A
Standard Marble Wrks. (Jno., M. Mueller, Jr. Prop.) 706 W. Front (Marble) ....B
Thauwald & o.., C. F., 1214 Harrison Av. (Wood) ..A
Varwig Mfg. Co. (Wood) .C
Wiggers Furniture Co., The 1423 Plumb (Wood) ..B

OHIO—Columbus
Ohio Furniture & Mantel Co.

MANTELS (Con.)

(Wood) ....B
Taylor Mantel & Grate Co., Wm. M., 26 S. 3d (Marbleized Slate; Slate; Wood) ....B

OHIO—Dayton
Requarth Co., F. A. (Wood)
......B

OHIO—Hillsboro
Enterprise Planing Mill Co. (Wood) ....B

OHIO—Ironton
Ironton Wood Mantel Co. (Wood) ....D

PA.—Bangor
Amer. Slate Co. (Slate)..D
Bangor Crescent Slate Co. (Marbleized Slate; Slate)
......B
Columbus Bangor Slate Co. (Slate) ....A

PA.—East Bangor
East Bangor Consolidated Slate Co. (Marbleized Slate; Wainscoating; Slate) ....AA

PA.—Easton
Penna. Structural Slate Co. (Marbleized Slate; Slate)
......B

PA.—Fallston
Fallston Fire Clay Co. (Brick) ....B

PA.—Lewisburg
Nesbit Co., D. M. (Wood)
......A

PA.—Pen Argyle
Crown Slate Co. (Slate) ..C

PA.—Philadelphia
French & Co., Sam'l H. 4th & Callowhill (Marbleized Slate; Slate; Wood; Marble) ....A
Hale & Kilburn Mfg. Co., 48 N. 6th (Wood)..AAAA
Italian Marble Mosaic Co., 431 Spruce (Mosaic) ..F
Sharpless & Watts, 1522 Chestnut (Mosaic) ....A
Thompson & Co., Lewis. 127 Walnut (Wood) ....D

PA.—Pittsburg
Aiken & Co., 47 7th (Slate)
......B

PA.—Warren
Spinner Heater Co., Wm. (Steel; for Gas) ....F

TENN.—Knoxville
King Mantel Co., 624 Gay (Wood) C

TENN.—Memphis
Wetter Mfg. Co., H. (Iron)
......A

TENN.—Nashville ..
Phillips & Buttorf Mfg. Co. (Wood; Iron) ......AAAA

TEXAS—Austin
Nalle & Co. (Hard & Soft Wood) ....AA

TEXAS—Houston
Bering Mfg. Co. (Wood)
......AA

VT.—Burlington
Mason & Co. (Wood) ....B

VT.—Fair Haven
Allen's Sons. S. (Marbleized Slate; Slate) ....D
Coulman & Wescott (Marbleized Slate) ....D
Fair Haven Marble & Marbleized Slate Co. (Marbleized Slate; Slate) ....B

VT.—Hydeville
McDonough & O'Day (Marbleized Slate) ....D

VT.—Poultney
Fleming Slate Co. (Marbleized Slate) C

VT.—Swanton
Barney Marble Co. (Marble)
......B

WASH.—Spokane
Washington Brick & Lime Mfg. Co. (Brick) ......A

WIS.—Milwaukee
Matthews Bros. Mfg. Co., 61 4th (Wood) ....A
Wallaeger Mfg. Co., 686 N. Water (Wood) ....A

WIS.—Oshkosh
Gould Mfg. Co. (Wood) ..A
McMillen Co., R. (Wood)
......A
Morgan Co. (Wood) ....AA

MANTELS (Con.)
Paine Lumber Co. (Wood)
............AAAA
WIS.—Wausau
Curtis & Yale Co. (Wood)
............AA

MANTLES

CONN.—Stamford
Stamford Gas Stove Co.
(Incandescent Gas) .....B
ILL.—Chicago
Cosmopolitan Co., 41 State
(Incandescent Gas) ....D
Engel & Co., 213 E. Ran-
dolph (Gas) X
Liberty Mantle Mfg. Co.,
108 Franklin (Incandes-
cent Gas) C
Peerless Light Co., 146 5th
(Incandescent Gas) C
Solar Incandescent Co., 73
W. Kinzie (Incandescent
Gas) ....D
Standard Gas Lamp Co.
(Gas) C
IOWA—Sioux City
Whalebone Gas Mantle Co.
(Incandescent Gas) ....G
MICH.—Detroit
Michigan Gas Mantle Co..
1383 Jefferson (Incandescent
Gas) ....D
MINN.—St. Paul
Herz Mfg. Co., 29 E. 7th
(Incandescent Gas)...D
N. J.—Gloucester
Welsbach Co. (Incadescent
Gas) ....A
N. J.—Jersey City
Wiederhold Light Co., (In-
candescent Gas) ......B
N. Y.—Buffalo
Buffalo Lighting Co., 15
Niagara (Incandescent
Gas ....E
New York City
Adams Incandescent Light
Co., (Incandescent Gas)
F
Amer. Incandescent Lamp
Co., 55 Park Place (In-
candescent Gas) ....B
Cremo Incandescent Light
Co., 110 E. 129th (Incan-
descent Gas) ....D
Deutsch, Chas., 538 E. 87th
(Incandescent Gas; Plain
Fancy Webbings) ......D
Mica Mfg. Co., 307 W.
B'way (Incandescent Gas)
C
Raritan Mantle Co., 7 Chat-
ham Sq. (Incandescent
Gas) ....E
Van Houten, E. J. S., 74
Park Place (Incandes-
cent Gas) ....B
OHIO—Cleveland
Fawcett Incandescent Man-
tle Co., 399 Prospect (In-
candescent Gas) X
Forest City Incandescent
Light Co., 437 Woodland
Av. (Incandescent Gas)
E
PA.—Erie
Erie Gas Mantle Mfg. Co.
(Incandescet Gas) ...B
PA.—Pittsburg
Duquesne Incan. Light Co.,
107 Wood (Incandescent
Gas) C
PA.—Vandergrift
Breig, Geo. F. (Incandes-
cent Gas) ....F
TENN.—Memphis
Irby & Gilliland (Incandes-
cent Gas) ....B

MAPLE

See Lumber

MAPS

ILL.—Chicago
Andrews Co., A. H., 300
Wabash Av. ....AA
Rand McNally & Co. (Inc.)
............AAAA
Union School Furnishing
Co., 211 E. Madison (Ge-

MAPS (Con.)
ographical) C
MASS.—Boston
Rand-Avery Supply Co. AA
MASS.—Springfield
Bradley Co., Milton (Dis-
sected) ....A
New York City
Bien & Co., Julius ......D
Bridgman, E. C..........F
Sanborn Map Co. (Ltd.)..B
Schedler, Herman (Relief)
E
OHIO—Cincinnati
Stobridge Lithographing Co.
AA
PA.—Philadelphia
Noll & Co., E. P........D
Smith, John L...........B

MARASCHINO
See Cordials

MARBLE

ILL.—Chicago
Art Marble Co., Flournoy &
Rockwell (Artificial)..B
Bagley & Co., Frederick P.,
18th N. S. Canal.......X
Henry Marble Co., 1626 Wa-
bash Av. (Artificial)...X
Verd Antique Marble Co.,
1118 Marquette Bldg.
(Green) ....B
ILL.—Edwardsville
Illinois Marble Co. (Elec-
tric Work) C
IOWA—Marshalltown
Le Grand Quarry Co.......A
MD.—Baltimore
Evans Marble Co., York &
William ....A
MASS.—Westfield.
Westfield Marble & Sand-
stone Co. (Green; Serpen-
tine) ....D
MASS.—Worcester
Norcross-West Marble Co.,
10 E. Worcester (Electric
Work) ....B
MICH.—Detroit
Mehling, Geo. F. (Artificial)
C
MO.—St. Louis
Bradbury Marble Co., 1129
S. 2nd (Georgia).....D
Carthage Marble & White
Lime Co., Emilie Bldg.
(Georgia; Tennessee)...A
Nelson Mfg. Co., N. O.
Plumbers') ....AAA
Seifert Plastic Relief Co.,
Frank A., 2646 Lawton
Av. (Artificial) ....D
New York City
Artificial Marble Co., 413
E. 91st (Artificial) ....F
Fisher & Co., R. C., 97 E.
Houston (Royal Irish;
Green; Serpentine) ..AA
Graf, Frank H., 322 7th Av.
(for Construction Work)
D
Jackson & Co., C. D., 105th
& E. R. (Carrara; Foreign
Colored; Green; Serpen-
tine) ....A
Klaber, Adolph ....B
Manhattan Marble Co., 282
Locust Av. (Foreign
Colored) ....B
Marine, Arlando, 24 E. 42nd
D
Mycenian Marble Co., 524-
526 W. 34th (Artificial;
Mycenian) ....D
Taber & Co., 24 Corlears.B
Waverly Marble Co., 160
5th Av. (Electric Work)
B
OHIO—Cincinnati
Buckeye Marble & Freestone
Co. (Plumbers) ......D
Great Western Marble Wks.
Co. (Plumbers') C
Standard Marble Wks.
706 W. Front (Plumbers')
B
OHIO—Dayton
Marbleithic Co. (Artificial)

MARBLE (Con.)

OHIO—Zanesville
Townsend & Co., Wm. C. .... AA

PA.—Philadelphia
Amer. Art Marble Co., 609 N. American (Artificial) .... B
Sharpless & Watts .... A
Stephens, Cooper & Co., Real Estate Trust Bldg. (Artificial) .... D
Wiliamson & Co., Frank, 2202 Chestnut .... D

VT.—Proctor
Vermont Marble Co. (Sawed; Finished) .... AAAA

VT.—Rutland
Columbian Marble Quarrying Co. .... B
Temple Bros. .... B

WASH.—Spokane
United States Marble Co. (Black; Green; Serpentine) X

MARBLES

New York City
Bawo & Dotter, 26 Barclay (Art) .... AA
Bing & Co., Ferd., 10 Wash. Pl. (Art) ....
Borgfeldt & Co., Geo., 48 W. 4th (Art) ...... AAAA
Lazarus, Rosenfeld & Lehmann, 62 Murray (Art) B
Levy & Co., L. W., 194 B'way (Art) .... B
Straus & Sons, L., 42 Warren (Art) .... AAAA

OHIO—Akron
American Marble & Toy Mfg. Co. (Clay) .... B
Standard Toy Mfg. Co. (Playing) .... D

OHIO—Limaville
Albright & Lightcap (Toy) .... F

MARKERS

See also Machinery

CONN.—New Britain
Stanley Rule & Level Co. (Clapboard) .... AAA

CONN.—Rockfall
Smith, Otis A. (Clapboard) .... A

GA.—Atlanta
Pearl Laundry Marking Co. (Laundry) X

ILL.—Chicago
Barbee Wire & Iron Wks. (Grave) .... B

MASS.—Boston
McCarter Co., J. G. (Vamp) .... B

MASS.—Greenfield
Wiley & Russell Mfg. Co. (Tire) .... AA

MASS.—Hopedale
Draper Co. (Cut) .... AAAA

MASS.—Springfield
Smith Mfg. Co., R. H. (Price; Sign) C

N. J.—Newark
Celluloid Co. (Whist) .... B

N. Y.—Greenwich
Eddy Plow Co., W. (Furlowers) .... B
Grote & Co., F. (Whist) D

New York City
Krieg & Co., J. K. (Lining) .... B

N. Y.—Seneca Falls
Littlejohn Granite Co. (Granite) .... D

PA.—Elizabethtown
Buchs' Sons Co., A. (Corn) .... A

PA.—Philadelphia
Allen & Co., S. L. (Furrowers) .... AA
Butterworth & Sons Co., H. W. (Cut) .... A

R. I.—Providence
Textile Finishing Mchy. Co., 17 Exch. Pl. (Cut) . AAAA

MARKS

CONN.—Wallingford

MARKS (Con.)
Wallace & Sons Mfg. Co., R. (Metal; Book) .. AAAA

ILL.—Chicago
Burch & Co., F. S. (Animal) .... D
Pralt Mfg. Co., Wm. E., 91 Lake (Stock) .... B

MASS.—Boston
Robbins Mfg. Co., Jno. (Metal; Book) .... E

N.H.—Mount Lebanon
Dana. Chas. H. (Metallic Ear) .... D

New York City
Keller Printing Co., 722 B'way (Glove; Hatters' Size) C
Wintjen, Jno. G. (Hat) E

N. Y.—Rochester
Pulver Co., F. F. (Celluloid Book) .... B

MARLINE

See also Cordage

MASS.—Ludlow
Ludlow Mfg. Co. (Hemp: Jute) .... AAAA

MASS.—New Bedford
New Bedford Cordage Co. X

New York City
Travers Bros. Co. ...... AA

MARMALADES

See Jams; Jellies; Marmalades.

MARQUEES

See Iron & Steel; Architectural.

ILL.—Chicago
Winslow Bros. Co., 368 Carroll Av. .... AA

MICH.—Detroit
Vulcan Co. .... F

N. Y.—Brooklyn
Hecla Iron Wks., N. 11th & Berry .... AA

New York City
Jackson Co., Wm. H., 29 E. 17th (Iron: Bronze) .... A
Pitt Composite Iron Wks., Wm. R., 111 5th Av. (Iron; Glass) .... D

OHIO—Cleveland
Tyler Co., W. S. .... AAAA

PA.—Pittsburg
Phoenix Steel Construction Co., Penn. Av. & 3d .... D

MAR-QUETERIES

MASS.—Boston
Davenport Co., Albert H. .... AA

MARTINGALES

See Harness

MASHERS

CONN.—Collinsville
Hartigan, Wm. R. (Vegetable) .... H

CONN.—Danielson
Parkhurst, L. D. (Vegetable) .... G

CONN.—Deep River
Williams & Marvin Mfg. Co. (Potato; Wooden) ..... D

CONN.—Unionville
Humphrey, H. W. (Potato) .... D

ILL.—Chicago
American Fdy. & Mchy. Co., Monadnock Blk. (Beet) .... AA
Barbee Wire & Iron Wks. (Potato) .... B

ILL.—Paxton
Paxton Hdw. Mfg. Co. (Potato: Wire) X

IND.—Indianapolis
Tucker & Dorsey Mfg. Co. (Potato; Wooden) .... A

MASHERS (Con.)

MASS.—Lowell
Woods, Sherwood Co. (Potato Wire) ....E
MASS.—Worcester
National Mfg. Co. (Potato; Wire) ....A
MICH.—Ludington
Handy Things Co. C
N. H.—Antrim
Goodell Co. (Vegetable)..A
N. J.—Garwood
Beckley Co., A. J. (Ore) D
N. J.—Newark
Sommers' Son, Jno. (Vegetable) ....A
N. Y.—Rochester
Streeter & Co., N. K. (Potato) ....A
OHIO—Canton
Gibbs Mfg. Co. (Vegetable) ....A
Kohler & Co., F. E. (Vegetable) ....B
OHIO—Columbus
Ohio Tool Co. (Potato) AA
OHIO—Hamilton..
Meyers Mchy. Co., Fred. J. (Potato; Wire) ....B
OHIO—Piqua
Piqua Handle & Mfg. Co. (Potato; Wooden) ....A
OHIO—Ravenna
Williams, A. C. (Vegetable) A

MASKS

ILL.—Chicago
Barbee Wire & Iron Wks. (Base Ball) ....B
Chicago Sporting Goods Mfg. (Base Ball) ....B
MASS.—Worcester
Hamblen & Russell Mfg. Co. (Base Ball) ....B
New York City
Dessart Bros., 110 Chambers D
OHIO—Akron
Faultless Rubber Mfg. Co. (Rubber) ....B
OHIO—Barberton
Pure Gum Specialty Co. (Rubber) C
OHIO—Cincinnati
Goldsmiths Sons, P. (Base Ball) ....D
OHIO—Findlay
Amer. Mask Mfg. Co.....C
R. I.—Providence
Davol Rubber Co. (Rubber) AAA

MASS

MASS.—Boston
Billings, Clapp & Co. (Blue) AA
MO.—St. Louis
Herf & Frerichs Chemical Co. (Blue) ....A
Larkin & Scheffer Chem. Co. (Blue) ....AAAA
Mallinckrodt Chem. Wks. (Blue) ....AAAA
New York City
McKesson & Robbins (Blue) AAAA
N. Y. Quinine & Chem. Wks. (Ltd.) (Blue)....A
Pfizer & Co., Chas. (Blue) AAAA
Schieffelin & Co., W. H. (Blue ....AA
PA.—Philadelphia..
Hance Bros. & White (Blue) AA
Powers - Weightman - Rosengarton Co. (Blue) AAAA

MASTS

FLA.—Pensacola
Thornton, H. H. ....F
GA.—Savannah
Southern Pine Co. of Georgia ....AAA
ILL.—Chicago
Cutter Co., Geo. Fulton & Union (Arm) C
MASS.—Gloucester
Andrews, H. N. ....F

MASTS (Con.)

N. Y.—Ogdensburg
Spaulding St. Laurence Boat Co. C
N. Y.—Roslyn
Clapham, Thos. ....F

MATCHERS

See also Machinery

CONN.—Norwich
Rogers & Co., C. B. AAAA
GA.—Atlanta
De Loach Mill Mfg. Co. B
MASS.—Boston
Woods Machine Co., S. A. A
MASS.—Oranges
Chase Turbine Mfg. Co, (Automatic) ....A
N. J.—Smithville
Smith Machine Co., H. B. A
N. Y.—Buffalo
Frank Machinery Co.......C
Holmes Mchy. Co., E. & B. (Box Board) ....B
New York City
Amer. Wood Wkg Mach. Co. (Box Board) ......AAAA
N. Y.—Rochester
Morgan Machine Co.....AA
N. C.—Winston-Salem
Salem Iron Wks. ....A
OHIO—Cincinnati
Cordesman, Meyer & Co. B
Cordesman Machine Co. X
Fay-Egan Co., J. A. (Box Board) ....AAAA
OHIO—Defiance
Defiance Machine Wks...A
OHIO—Hamilton
Bentel & Margedant Co...A
PA.—Philadelphia
Power & Co., L...........A
VT.—Montpelier
Lane Mfg. Co............A
WIS.—Beloit
Berlin Machine Wks. AAAA

MATCHES

CAL.—Madera
Pacific Match Co.........D
CAL.—San Francisco
Leege & Haskins, 3 Front A
Metropolitan Fuse & Match Co., 3 Front............B
CAL.—Stege
Metroplittan Match Co. B
ILL.—Chicago
Diamond Match Co.. 504 Pulman Bldg......AAAA
Ill. Match Mfg. Co., 225 Kinzie ....D
ILL.—Evergreen Park
Merkle-Wiley Broom Co...C
ILL.—Rockford
Graham Match Co.........D
IND.—Crawfordville
Indiana Match Co. ......A
MAINE—Portland
Portland Star Match Co...B
MD.—Baltimore
Diamond Match Co. (Br.) 19 S. Charles......AAAA
MICH.—Detroit
Diamond Match Co.. 8th & River (Br.) ......AAAA
Modern Match Co. (Ltd.)..C
MICH.—Grand Haven
Ruby Match Co............D
MINN.—Duluth
Duluth Match Co.........B
N. J.—Arondale
Amer. Match. Mfg. Co.....D
N. J.—Camden
Ruby Match Co............D
N. J.—Clinton
Mutual Match Co. ....B
N. J.—Passaic
Continental Match Co.....B
N. J.—Paterson
Federal Match Co.........A
New York City
Delapenha & Co., R. U.. 17 Jay C
Diamond Match Co.. 86 Hudson ....AAAA
Huner, J. P.. 40 Hudson..C
Kalmowitz, I., 47 Ludlow A
Rosenstein Co., C., 373 Washington ....D

MATCHES (Con.)

Strohmeyer Arpe Co., 33 Water ....A

N. Y.—Ogdensburg
Adirondack Match Co....B

N. Y.—Oswego
Diamond Match Co. AAAA

OHIO—Ashland
Reliable Match Co.......A

OHIO—Barberton
Diamond Match Co(Fct'y.) AAAA

OHIO—Springfield
Buckeye Match Co......D

OHIO—Wadsworth
Ohio Match Co........AAA

OREGON—Portland
Zan Bros..............B

PA.—Bellefonte
Pennsylvania Match Co. AAA

PA.—Hanover
Hanover Match Co.......B

PA.—Harrisburg
Harrisburg Match Co.,..B

PA.—Philadelphia
Champion Match Co., 217 Race ....D
Diamond Match Co. (Br.) AAAA
International Match Co., 25th & Wharton........A
Weickel & Smith Spice Co., 129 N. Front.........A

PA.—Phoenixville
Ahwaga Mfg. Co.........D

WASH.—Seattle
Washington Match Co.....B

WASH.—Tacoma
Washington Match Co.....B

WIS.—Green Bay
Diamond Match Co. AAAA

WIS.—Milwaukee
Wisconsin Match Co., 543 3d ....D

WIS.—Oshkosh
Diamond Match Co. AAAA

MATS

See also Rugs; Matting; Rubber Goods

CONN.—Hartford
Hartford Woven Wire Mattress Co. (Wire)....X

CONN.—Meriden
Manning, Bowman & Co. (Wire; Table)........AA

CONN.—Watertown
Barlow Mfg. Co., H. P. (Sheepskin) ....G

ILL.—Chicago
Abbott, W. W. (Picture) D
Barbee Wire & Iron Wks. (Wire) ....B
Mueller Bros. Art Mfg. Co. (Picture) ....B
Pratt Mfg. Co., Wm. E. (Wire) C
Smith Wire & Iron Wks., F. P., 100 Lake (Wire) AA

ILL.—Decatur
United States Wire Mat Co. (Wire) ....D

MD.—Baltimore
East India Mfg. Co., P. O. Box 565 (Cocoa).......D

MASS.—Andover
Tyer Rubber Co. (Rubber) AA

MASS.—Boston
Boston Belting Cob. (Rubber) ....AAAA
Clapp Rubber Co., E. H. (Rubber) ....A
Revere Rubber Co. (Rubber) AAAA

MASS.—Cambridgeport
Boston Woven Hose & Rubber Co. (Rubber) ..AAAA

MASS.—Clinton
Clinton Wire Cloth Co. (Wire; Steel) .....AAA

MASS.—Gardner
Heywood Bros. & Wakefield Co. (Cocoa) ......AAAA

MASS.—Lowell
Woods, Sherwood Co. (Wire; Table) ....E

MASS.—Worcester
National Mfg. Co. (Wire;

MATS (Con.)

Table) ....A
Parker Wire Goods Co. (Wire; Steel) ....D
Wire Goods Co. (Wire) A

MICH.—Adrian.
Page Woven Wire Fence Co. (Wire) ....A

MICH.—Detroit
Barnum Wire & Iron Wks., E. T. (Wire).........B

MICH.—Milan
Schmitt, Chas. (Wood Rolling) ....H

MICH.—Wyandotte
Bishop & Co., J. H. (Wool) A

MINN.—St. Paul
American Grass Twine Co. (Grass Door) ....AA

MO.—St. Louis
Ludlow-Saylor Wire Co. (Wire; Steel) ....AA

N. H.—Exeter
Rubber Step Mfg. Co. (Rubber) ....D

N. J.—Jersey City
New Jersey Car Spring & Rubber Co. (Rubber; Rubber Coin; Rubber Table) ....AA
Voorhees Rubber Mfg. Co. (Rubber) ....A

N. J.—Sussex..
Sussex Mills (Bath)......C

N. J.—Trenton
Crescent Belting & Packing Co. (Rubber) ....A
Empire Rubber Mfg. Co. (Rubber) ....AA
Home Rubber Co. (Rubber) AA
Trenton Rubber Mfg. Co. (Rubber) ....A

N. Y.—Brooklyn
Bainbridges Sons, Chas. T., 2 Cumberland (Picture Frame) ....A
Eichman, Martin & Co., 16 Larimer (Street Car)....F
Planet Mills Mfg. Co., 335 Carroll (Cocoanut) ..AAA

N. Y.—Buffalo..
Buffalo Wire Wks. Co. (Wire; Steel) ....A
Shepard & Co., Sidney (Asbestos) ....AAAA

N. Y.—Jamestown
Chautauqua Towel Mills (Bath) ....D

New York City
Colgan, J. B., 675 Hudson (Cork) C
Cordley & Hayes (Spittoon) A
Darragh & Smail, 177 Water (Cocoanut) ....B
Empire Rubber Co. (Rubber) D
Estey Wire Wks. Co., 59 Fulton (Wire; Steel)...D
Goldberg, C. H. & E. S., 114 Reade (Flexible Wood) B
Goodyears' India Rubber Glove Mfg. Co., 503 B'way (Rubber) ....AAAA
Goodyear Rubber Co. (Rubber) ....AAAA
Gutta Percha & Rubber Mfg. Co., 126 Duane (Rubber) AAAA
Hartman Mfg. Co. (Wire) X
Heywood Bros. & Wakefield Co. (Rattan) ......AAAA
International Automobile & Vehicle Tire Co., 346 B'way (Rubber) ....B
Johns-Manville Co., H. W. (Asbestos) ....AAAA
New York Belting & Packing Co., 25 Park Pl. (Rubber) ....AAAA
Rubber Goods Mfg. Co., 253 B'way (Rubber) ..AAAA
Sjoberg & Co., J. P. (Wooden Street Car)....D
Toffler, A., 725 1st Av. (Street Car; Iron; Steel; Wooden; Flexible) X
Wild & Co., Joseph, 11 Thomas (Cocoanut) ...AAA

OHIO—Akron
Goodrich Co., B. T. (Rub-

MATS (Con.)
ber) ....AAAA
Whitman & Barnes Mfg. Co.
(Rubber) ....AAAA
OHIO—Alliance
Alliance Asbestos Mfg. Co.
(Asbestos Stove) ......B
OHIO—Barbeton
Alden Rubber Co. (Rubber
Coin) X
OHIO—Cleveland
Van Dorn Iron Wks. Co.
(Iron; Steel) ....AA
OHIO—Dayton
Barney & Smith Car Co.
(Street Car) .....AAAA
PA.—Ellwood City
Glen Mfg. Co. (Wire; Steel)
C
PA.—Philadelphia
Darby & Sons, Edward
(Wire) ....A
Delaware Rubber Co., 631
Market (Rubber).......X
Hall & Carpenter, 518 Race
(Asbestos) ....AA
Margerison, W. H. & E. A.
Emerald & Sargeant
(Bath) ....B
National Leather Mat &
Belting Co., Real Estate
Bldg. (Leather, for Cars;
Schools; Homes; Eleva-
tors) ....B
Star & Crescent Mills' Co.
(Bath) ....A
PA.—Pittsburg
Armstrong Cork Co. (Bath)
AAAA
Central Expanded Metal Co.
(Expanded Metal) X
Keystone Steel Matting Co.
(Flexible Steel).......X

MATTING

MASS.—Boston
Boston Belting Co. (Rubber)
AAA
MASS.—Cambridge
Boston Woven Hose & Rub-
ber Co. (Rubber)..AAAA
MASS.—Gardner
Heywood Bros. & Wakefield
Co. (Straw) ......AAAA
N. H.—Exeter ..
Rubber Step Mfg. Co. (Rub-
ber) ....D
N. J.—Jersey City
New Jersey Car Spring &
Rubber Co. (Rubber) AA
N. J.—Paterson
Lamond & Robertson Co.
(Napier) C
N. J.—Trenton
Crescent Belting & Packing
Co. (Rubber) ....A
Empire Rubber Mfg. Co.
(Rubber) ....AA
Home Rubber Co. (Rubber)
AA
Trenton Rubber Mfg. Co.
(Rubber ....A
New York City
Amer. Grass Twine Co., 377
B'way (Grass) ....B
Bunnell & Co., J. H., 20
Park Pl. (Electric) ...B
Darragh & Small, 177 Wa-
ter (Cocoa) ....B
Goodyear's India Rubber
Glove Mfg. Co., 503 B'way
(Rubber) ....AAAA
Gutta Percha & Rubber Mfg.
Co. (Rubber) .....AAAA
International Automobile &
Vehicle Tire Co. (Rubber) B
Mitsin & Co., 445 Broome
(Straw) ....AAAA
New York Belting & Packing
Co. (Rubber) .....AAA
New York Rubber Co., 84
Reade (Rubber) ....AA
Smith, Baker & Co., 85 Wall
(Straw; Cocoa) ....B
Wild & Co., Jos. (Cocoa)
AAA
OHIO—Akron
Goodrich Co., B. F. (Rubber)
AAAA
PA.—Philadelphia
Delaware Rubber Co., 631
Market (Rubber) X

MATTOCKS

CONN.—Collinsvill·
Collins Co. ....AAAA
MICH.—Detroit
Anderson & Sons, W. H.
(Asphalt) C
N. Y.—Elmira
Cronk & Carrier Mfg. Co.
(Garden) ....B
New York City
Amer. Axe & Tool Co., 258
B'way ....AAAA
OHIO—Cleveland
Amer. Fork & Hoe Co.
(Garden) ....AAAA
OHIO—Findlay
Findlay Axe & Tool Co...A
PA.—Eldorado..
Colclesser Bros..........D
PA.—Philadelphia
Contrators Supply Co., 118
S. 6th (Asphalt) ......D
Griffiths Co., Geo. ..AAAA
Plumb, Fayette R (Inc.)
AA
PA.—Pittsburg
Iron City Tool Wks., 32d &
Smallman ....&.....A
Jones & Laughlins Steel Co.
AAAA
Klein-Logan Co., S. 13th &
Breed ....A
Oliver Iron & Steel Co.
AAAA
W. VA.—Wheeling
Warwood Tool Co........B

MATTRESSES

**See Bedding; Beds; Furni-
ture.**

MAULS

CONN.—Collinsville
Collins Co. (Railroad or
Spike; Ship or Top)
AAAA
CONN.—Hartford
Billings & Spencer Co.
(Railroad or Spike; Ship
or Top; Woodhchoppers')
AA
CONN.—Middletown
Wilcox, Crittenden & Co.
(Ship or Top)........A
ILL.—Chicago
Chicago Rawhide Co.,
75 E. Ohio (Rawhide) A
Nicol & Co. (Steak)......D
Vaughan & Bushnell Mfg.
Co., 875 Carroll Av. (Ship
or Top; Railroad) .....A
ILL.—Rockford
Sovereign Co., C. E. (Han-
dle Post) C
ILL.—Sycamore
Palten Co., F. C. (Post) ..A
IND.—Evansville
Evansville Tool Wks (Rail-
road or Spike; Ship or
Top; Woodchoppers'; ..A
IND.—Frankfort
Frankfort Handle Mfg. Co.
(Post; Spike) ....E
IND.—Indianapolis
Atkins & Co., E. C. (Ship)
AAAA
Tucker & Dorsey Mfg. Co.
(Steak; Wooden) .....A
IND.—South Bend
Sandage Steel Skein Co.
(Post) X
MASS.—Boston
Harvey, H. H., 608 Atlantic
Av. (Ship or Top; Cast
Steel; Floor; Railroad) D
MICH.—Detroit
Anderson & Sons, W. H.
(Railroad or Spike)....C
Detrot Steel Products Co.
(Ship Woodchoppers')...B
MO.—St; Louis
Kupferle, Jno. C. .....AA
Pleuger & Henger Mfg. Co.
A
Western Fdy & Sash Weight
Co., 2nd & Miller (Post)
D
N. J.—Newark
Atha Tool Co. (Railroad or
Spike; Ship or Top; Wood-

MAULS (Con.)
choppers') ....A
N. Y.—Buffalo
White Co., L. & I. J., Perry
  cor. Columbia (Ship or
  Top) ....A
N. Y.—Cato
Dutton & Co., E. L. (Post)
E
N. Y.—Gowanda
Gowanda Agriultural Wks.
  (Post) X
N. Y.—Horseheads
Weller Hdw. & Fdy. Co.
  (Post) ....D
N. Y.—Little Falls
Cheney Hammer Co., Henry
  (Railroad) ....D
N. Y.—Manlius
Cheney & Son, S. ....A
N. Y.—Medina
Swett Iron Wks., A. L.
  (Woodchoppers') ......A
OHIO.—Ashtabula
Barber Mfg. Co. (Post)....C
OHIO.—Cincinnati
Obermayer Co., S. (Hide
  Faced) ....AA
OHIO.—Fremont
Lehr Agricultural Co.
  (Woodchoppers') ......B
OHIO.—Lancaster
Eagle Machine Co. (Cast
  Iron Post) ....A
OHIO.—Ravenna
Wiliams, A. C. C
PA.—Corry
McInnes Steel Co. (Wood-
  choppers') C
PA.—Ogontz
Hammond & Son, C. (Rail-
  road or Spike; Ship or
  Top; Woodchoppers')...A
PA.—Philadelphia
Pedrick & Ayer Co. (Rail-
  road) ....A
Plumb (Inc.), Fayette R.
  (Ship or Top; Railroad;
  Woodchoppers') ....AA
PA.—Pittsburg
Hubbard & Co., Murtland
  Bldg. (Railroad or Spike)
AA
Iron City Tool Wks., 32nd
  & Stallman (Railroad or
  Spike; Ship or Top; Cast
  Steel; Steel Faced; Wood-
  choppers') ....A
Jones & Laughlins Steel Co.
  (Ship or Top; Woodchop-
  pers') ....AAAA
Klein-Logan Co., S. 13th
  (Solid Cast Steel Ship or
  Top; Woodchoppers') ..A
Verona Tool Wks., Murtland
  Bldg. (Ship or Top) ...A
S. C.—Charleston
Woodstock Hardwood &
  Spool Mfg. Co. (Boiler-
  makers') ....E

MEAL

**See also Corn-meal in
  Appendix**
ALA.—Florence
Florence Milling Co. (Corn)
D
ALA.—Jacksonville
Jacksonville Oil Mill Co.
  (Cotton Seed) ....A
CONN.—Thompsonville
Bushnell Press Co., G. H.
  (Heaters; Oil Seed)...A
DEL.—Wilmington
Lea Milling Co. (Brewers';
  Corn) ....AAA
FLA.—Madison
Florida Mfg. Co. (Cotton
  Seed) ....AA
GA.—Atlanta
Fulton Bag & Cotton Mills
  (Bags) ....AAAA
GA.—Blackshear
Bradley & Co., A. .
  (Cotton Seed) ....AA
GA.—Brunswick
Downing Co. (Corn)......AA
GA.—Columbus
Mutual Cotton Oil Co.
  (Cotton Seed) ....AAAA
GA.—Elberton
Elberton Oil Mill (Cotton

MEAL (Con.)
Seed) ....A
ILL.—Brighton
Hilliard, Geo. W. (Corn).B
ILL.—Chicago
Burch Co., F. S. (Blood)..D
Norton & Co. (Corn)....AA
ILL.—Paris
Kidder & Co., F. L.
  (Brewers') ....B
IND.—Grand View
Cadick Milling Co. (Corn).B
IND.—Lafayette
Lafayette Hominy Mill Co.
  (Corn) ....B
IOWA—Le Mars
Plymouth Milling Co. (Corn)
B
KANS.—Atchison
Blair Milling Co. (Brewers')
A
KANS.—Forsha
Forsha Milling Co. (Corn).B
KANS.—Fort Scott
Goodlander Milling Co.
  (Corn) ....B
KANS.—Lawrence
Bowersock, J. D. (Corn).AA
KANS.—McPherson
Pearl Milling Co. (Corn)..D
KANS.—Wellington
Hunter Milling Co. (Corn)
A
KANS.—White Cloud
White Cloud Mill & Eleva-
  tor Co. (Corn) ....F
KY.—Lexington
Lexington Roller Mill Co.
  (Corn) ....A
MD.—Baltimore
Gambrill Mfg. Co., C. A.
  (Corn) ....AAA
MD.—Pocomoke City
Costen Co., W. A. (Al-
  mond) ....F
MD.—Port Deposit
McClenahan Granite Co.
  (Granite) ....A
MASS.—Salem
Salem Chemical & Supply
  Co. (Almond) ....E
MICH.—Battle Crek
Sanitas Nut Food Co. (Ltd.)
  (Almond) ....B
MICH.—Detroit
Michigan Carbon Wks.
  (Bone) ....AAA
MISS.—Port Gibson
Port Gibson Oil Wks.
  (Cotton Seed) ....A
MO.—Marionville
Marionville Roller Mill Co.
  (Corn) ....B
MO.—Oakgrove
Oak Grove Mill Co.
  (Corn) ....E
NEBR.—Crete
Crete Mills (Corn)......B
NEBR.—North Platte
Iddings, C. F. (Corn).....B
NEBR.—Schuyler
Weels-Abbott-Meinan Co.
  (Brewers') ....AA
N. J.—Milhurst
Snyder & Son, C. H.
  (Corn) C
N. J.—Newark
Peckham Mfg. Co., 244
  South (for Dry Barrel Pol-
  ishing) ....E
N. Y.—Buffalo
Mann Bros. Co. (Linseed
  Cake) ....A
N. Y.—Cuba
Phelps & Sibley Co. (Corn)
B
New York City
Amer. Cotton Oil Co. (Cot-
  ton Seed) ....AAAA
Baker & Bro., H. J. (Bone)
AA
Donovan, Jno. J., 203
  B'way (Granite).......D
Napier Chemical Co., 644 E.
  14th (Almond) C
N. Y.—Troy
Boutwell Milling & Grain
  Co. of Troy (Corn)....A
N. C.—Asheville
Asheville Milling Co. (Corn)
B

MEAL (Con.)

OHIO—Dayton
Durst Milling Co. (Corn).A
OHIO—Mansfield
Mansfield Linseed Oil Co.
(Linseed Cake) ....D
OHIO—Prospect
National Mill Co. (Corn)..D
PA.—Butler
Klingler & Co., H. J.
(Corn) ....A
PA.—Emporium
Emporium Milling Co.
(Corn) C
PA.—Fertility
Groff, I. B. (Corn).......F
PA.—Irwin
Irwin Flour Mills Co.
(Corn) ....B
PA.—Philadelphia
Vail Bros., 2000 N. 10th
(Almond) C
PA.—Roaring Spring
Bare Milling Co. (Corn)..C
PA.—York
York Chemical Wks. (Bone)
A
R. I.—Providence
Union Oil Co. (Cotton
Seed) ....AAA
TENN.—Memphis
Valley Oil Mill (Cotton
Seed) ....A
TEXAS—Belton
Belton Oil Co. (Cotton
Seed) ....D
TEXAS—Denton
Alliance Milling Co. (Inc.)
(Corn) ....A
TEXAS—Taylor
Taylor Cotton Oil Wks.
(Cotton Seed) ....B
UTAH—Salt Lake City
Inter-Mountain Milling Co.
(Corn) ....D
VA.—Alexandria
Roberts, Walter (Corn)..B
VA.—Aylett
Sizer, Augustus (Corn)...E

MEASURES

**See also Enamelled Iron-
ware; Tinware; Wooden-
ware.**

CONN.—Meriden
Bradley & Hubbard Mfg. Co.
(Tape) ....AAAA
CONN.—New Britain
Stanley Rule & Level Co.
(Linear; Rule; Yard)
AAAA
CONN.—Pine Meadow
Chapin-Stephens Co. (Rule;
Yard; Board) ....A
CONN.—Unionville
Union Nut & Bolt Co.
(Rule; Yard) ....A
Upson Nut Co. (Rule; Yard)
AAAA
CONN.—Waterbury
Waterbury Brass Co. (Tape)
AAAA
ILL.—Chicago
Barbee Wire & Iron Co.
(Iron) ....B
Dietzgen Co., Eugene, 181
Monroe (Tape) ....A
Photo-Jewelry Mfg. Co., 464
Carroll Av. (Tape) ..B
Redlich Mfg. Co. (Wooden)
B
Wilson & Co., F. C., 239
Lake (Accurate) ......B
ILL.—Quincy
Quincy Stamping Co. (Gal-
vanized Steel Dry) C
MD.—Hagerstown
Reisner Lens Measure Co.,
W. H. (Lens) ....F
MASS.—Athol
Athol Machine Co. (Rule;
Yard) ....B
Starrett Co., L. S. (Rule;
Yard; Tape) ....A
MASS.—Boston
Strater & Sons, Herman
(Ale; Beer) ....A
MASS.—Fitchburg
Sawyer Tool Mfg. Co.
(Rule; Yard) C

MEASURES (Con.)

Simonds Mfg. Co. (Tape)..
AAA
MICH.—Battle Creek
Nichols & Shepard Co.
(Grain; Automatic) ....
AAAA
MICH.—Bellaire
Richardi & Bechtold
(Wooden Vinegar, etc.).B
MICH.—Grand Rapids
Michigan Barrel Co.
(Wooden) ....A
MICH.—Saginaw
Lufkin Rule Co. (Rule;
Yard; Tape) ....AA
MO.—St. Louis
St. Louis Stamping Co.
(Iron) ....AAAA
N. H.—Wilton
Cragin, D. (Dry) ....E
N. J.—Newark
Celluloid Co. (Tape) .....B
Smith, S. O., 24 Prospect
(Rule; Yard; Horse) ...A
Sommer's Son, John
(Vinegar) ....A
N. Y.—Brooklyn
Eddy & Co., Geo. M. (Ad-
vertising; Tape; Tailors')
A
Sweeney Mfg. Co., W. A.
(Ale; Beer; Copper; Tin)
A
Wesel Mfg. Co., F. (Type)
X
N. Y.—Buffalo
Aldrich Mfg. Co. (Copper)
A
Shepard & Co., Sidney
(Liquid) ....AAAA
N. Y.—Jamestown
American Mfg. Concern
(Rule; Yard) ....A
New York City
Central Stamping Co. (Ale;
Beer; Cooper) ....AA
Chatillon & Sons, John
(Liquid) ....A
Cordley & Hayes (Fibre;
Vinegar) ....A
Estes & Sons, E. B., 45 John
(Rule; Yard) ....AA
Faber, Eberhard, 545 Pearl
(Rule; Yard) ....AAA
Goldbacher, Earnest
(Tailors') C
Keuffel & Esser Co.
(Tape; Linear) .....AA
Kohlbusch, Herman ......B
Lalance & Grosjean Mfg. Co.
(Ale; Beer; Iron) ..AAAA
Reilley Bros. (Iron) ......D
Smith & Hemenway Co.
(Tape) ....D
Stoutenborough, X. (Ale;
Beer; Copper; Oil; Gaso-
line) ....D
Surpless, Dunn & Co., 55
Warren (Rule; Yard)...C
Walbridge & Co., J. H., 337
B'way (Tape) ....B
N. Y.—Patchogue
Roe & Sons, Justus (Steel
Tape) ....D
N. Y.—Rochester
Rochester Stamping Co.
(Galvanized) ....AAA
N. Y.—Seneca Falls
Westcott-Jewell Co. (Adver-
tising; Cork; Type; Rule;
Yard) ....D
N. Y.—Troy
Gurley, W. & L. E.
(Tape) ....A
Troy Stamping Wks.
(Tin) ....AAAA
OHIO—Cleveland
Upson Nut Co. (Linear).:.
AAAA
OHIO—Salem
Clark Co., W. J. (Iron;
Steel) ....A
PA.—Philadelphia
Clad & Sons, Valentine
(Ice Cream) ....A
Mills & Bro., Thos.
(Cream; Gauges) ......A
R. I.—Providence
Brown & Sharpe Mfg. Co.
(Rule; Yard) .....AAAA

MEASURES (Con.)
VA.—Richmond
Richmond Cedar Wks. (Dry Wooden) ....AAAA

MEAT: MINCE

ARK.—Ft. Smith
Oklahoma Vinegar Co. ...C
CAL.—Los Angeles
Shaw Pres. Co. ....B
CAL.—San Francisco
Pacific Coast Syrup Co., 713 Sansome ....B
CONN.—Southington
Pratt & Owen Co. ....D
DEL.—Delaware City
Pancoast, C. W. ....D
ILL.—Chicago
Armour Co., 205 La Salle .. AAAA
Maine Packing Co., 1707 S. Clark ....D
Morris & Co., Nelson .... AAAA
Reid, Murdoch & Co., Lake & Market ....AAAA
Rice Co., Erwin A., 1707 S. Clark ....B
IND.—Brookville
Brookville Mfg. Co. ....B
IND.—Indianapolis
Bessire & Co., 118 S. Del. (Mince; Packers of Bulk; Canned) ....D
Columbia Conserve Co., So. Meridian & Belt Ry....A
IOWA—Glenwood
New Glenwood Can. Co...C
KY.—Louisville
Goodwin Pres. Co., 407 9th A
MAINE—Rockland
Thorndike & Hix C
MD.—Baltimore
Van Lill Pres. Co., 108 Concord ....B
MICH.—Detroit
Williams Bros. Co., Gr. River Av. ....A
MICH.—Grand Rapids
Fallas, Edwin C
United States Packing Co..A
MICH.—Saginaw
United States Horse Radish Co..................D
MICH.—West Bay City
Bentel Co., R. ....A
MINN.—St. Paul
Gedney Pickling Co., M. A., 59 S. Wabash Av......A
MO.—St. Louis
Bayle, Geo. A., 113 S. 2nd B
N. J.—Bordentown
Brakeley, Asher ....B
N. J.—Camden
Cmapbell Pres. Co., Jos..AA
N. J.—Crosswicks
Brick E. ....B
N. Y.—Buffalo
La Clair, Jos., 128 Grey ..D
Heinz Co., H. J., 106 Main AAAA
N. Y.—Glens Falls
Harrison, Everett ....D
N. Y.—Kenwood
Oneida Community (Ltd.) AAA
N. Y.—Liverpool
Woerner Pres. & Pack. Co. AA
New York City
Ams, Max., 372 Greenwich AA
Oneida Community ...AAA
N. Y.—Pt. Byron
Gutchess, H. C. C
N. Y.—Rochester
Curtice Bros. Co. ......AA
N. Y.—Syracuse
Merrell-Soule Co. ......AA
OHIO—Cincinnati
Spencer & Son, W. M., 324 E. 2nd ....D
OHIO—Cleveland
Haserot Canneries Co., 39 Woodland ....B
OHIO—Creston
Lutz & Schramm Co.....AA
OHIO—Urbana
Marvin Co., W. H. ....A

MEAT: MINCE (Con.)
OHIO—Wooster
Wooster Pres. Co. ....B
PA.—Allegheny
Lutz & Schramm ....AA
PA.—Lebanon
Henry, L. W. ....D
PA.—Philadelphia
Amer. Pres. Co., 946 Beach ....A
Atmore & Son, 110 Tasker.A
Brenneman, W. H., 813 N. 11th ....D
Ritter Conserve Co., Philip J., 2156 E. Dauphin.....A
W. VA.—Wheeling
Exley, Watkins & Co. ....B
Flaccus Bros ....A
McMechen & Son Co., G. K. A

MEAT PACKERS

CAL.—Los Angeles
Maier Packing Co., 149 N. Spring ....AA
CAL.—Sacramento
Mohr & Yoerk Packing Co. (Pork) ....A
Swanston & Son, C.......C
CAL.—San Francisco
Dairymens Union of Calif., 124 Davis ....A
Roth, Blum & Co. ....A
Schweitzer & Co., J., 416 Clay ....AAA
Silverberg, Simon, 320 Sansome ....A
South San Fran. Packing & Provision Co. ....A
Western Meat Co. ..AAAA
COLO.—Colorado Springs
Colorado Packing & Provision Co. (Br. Denver)..AA
COLO.—Denver
Colo. Packing & Provision Co. ....AA
Standard Meat & Live Stock Co. ....B
COLO.—Pueblo
Nuckolls Packing Co. ....A
CONN.—Allington
Merwin Provision Co. (Pork) ....A
CONN.—Bridgeport
McElroy Bros. Co. ....B
Plumb & Winton Co. ....A
CONN.—New Britain
Andrews, Swift & Co.... AAAA
Merwin Provision Co. ...A
Sperry & Barnes ......AAA
DEL.—Wilmington
Hart & Bro. ....AA
ILL.—Alton
Alton Packing Co. ....A
Kirsch Co. ....B
Luer Bros. Packing & Ice Co. ....B
ILL.—Aurora
Sinclair & Co., T. M. (Ltd.) (Beef; Pork) ......AAAA
ILL.—Bloomington
Cont. Packing Co.......AA
ILL.—Chicago
Armour Packing Co..AAAA
Anglo-Amer. Prov. Co., 60 B. of T. Bldg. ....A
Arnold Bros., 145 W. Randolph ....AA
Boyd, Lanham & Co., 169 Jackson Boul. ....AA
Cont. Packing Co. ......AA
Cudahy- Packing Co..AAAA
Fairbanks Canning Co. (Canned Meats) ...AAAA
German-Amer. Provision Co. A
Guth, Henry, 3911 S. Halsted ....B
Libby, McNeill & Libby (Canned Meats) ...AAAA
Lipton Co., T. J., Union Stock Yards (Canned Meats) ....AAAA
Mayer & Bro., O. F., 285 Sedgwick ....A
Miller & Hart ....A
Morrell & Co., John ...AA
Nelson & Co., Morris.AAAA
Morton, Gregson Co., 77 Jackson Boul. ....A
Nebraska City Packing Co.,

664

84 Van Buren ....B
Omaha Packing Co....AAA
Pfaelzer & Co., L., 4177
  Emerald Av. ....A
Schwarzschild & Sulzberger
  Co., Exch. Bldg. ..AAAA
Swift & Co., Union Stock
  Yards ....AAAA
ILL.—Decatur
Danzeisen & Sons, G. J....B
ILL.—Galena
Vogel, John (Pork) ......B
ILL.—Peoria
Godel & Sons, E. ....B
Peoria Packing Co. (Beef;
  Pork) ....AA
Sinclair & Co., T. M..AAA
ILL.—Quincy
Bloomer & Michael Co. ...A
Hammond Packing Co....
  ....AAAA
ILL.—Rochelle
Cooper, Peter............B
ILL.—Rock Island
Gilmore, James S. ....A
Hammond Packing Co....
  ....AAAA
ILL.—Springfield
Franz Bros. Packing Co...A
ILL.—Teutopolis
Uptmor & Son, C. ....B
IND.—Evansville
Akin & Son, W. M. .....A
Evansville Packing Co...B
IND.—Ferdinand
Beekman, J. G...........B
IND.—Fort Wayne
Bash. Packing Co. ......B
Eckert Packing Co. .....B
IND.—Hammond
Hammond Co., G. H. ...
  ....AAAA
Hammond Packing Co....
  ....AAAA
IND.—Indianapolis
Coffin-Fletcher Packing Co.
  ....AA
Gardner, C. J. (Beef)....A
Kingan & Co. ....AAAA
Moore & Co. ....AA
IND.—Lafayette
Dreyfus Packing & Provision
  Co. ....B
IND.—Logansport
Routh, W. C. ....B
IND.—Vincennes
Bierhaus & Sons, E. ....AA
IOWA—Burlington
Boeck, George ....B
IOWA—Cedar Springs
Sinclair & Co., T. M..AAAA
IOWA—Clinton
Iowa Packing Co. ......B
IOWA—Davenport
Kohrs, Henry ....A
Tri-City Packing Co. ....A
IOWA—Des Moines
Hammond Packing Co....
  ....AAAA
Morrell & Co., John ..AAA
Zoecklers' Sons, J. L. ...B
IOWA—Dubuque
Hammond Packing Co. ...
  ....AAAA
IOWA—Marshalltown
Brittain & Co. ....A
IOWA—Mason City
Decker & Son ....B
IOWA—Muscatine
Blanchard Packing Co.....B
IOWA—Ottumwa
Morrell & Co., John (Ltd.)
  ....AAA
KANS.—Kansas City
Fowler Packing Co. .....A
KANS.—Leavenworth
Leavenworth Packing Co..B
Thudium Packing Co. ..B
KANS.—Topeka
Wolff Packing Co. ......A
KANS.—Wichita
Dold Packing Co., J. ....
  ....AAAA
KY.—Louisville
Bornwasser, L. P., 937
  Geiger ....B
Louisville Packing Co. 1318
  Storey Av. ....AAA
Pfaffinger & Co., 922 E.
  Market ....B
Vissman & Co., C. F., 417
  Bickel Av. ....B

MAINE—Portland
Cummings Bros. ....B
MD.—Baltimore
Harney Co., 500 North....A
Hohman & Sons, C., 2026
  E. Monument ....B
Jones & Co., R. M., 2802
  Pa. Av. ....A
Miller & Miller, 12 N. Paca
  ....B
Schludderburg & Son, W...B
Shafer & Co., J. C., 520 W.
  Lexington ....A
MASS.—Boston
Boston Packing & Provision
  Co., 77 N. Market ...AA
Clinton Market Beef Co., 116
  S. Market ....AAAA
Dyer & Co., L. M., 45 N.
  Market ....B
Hollis, N. E., 51 N. Mar-
  ket ....A
Learned. S. S., 50 F. H.
  Market ....AA
Mentzer & Co., W. C., 3 N.
  Market ....B
N. E. Beef Co., 103 Clinton
  ....B
North Packing & Provision
  Co., 33 N. Market..AAAA
Potter & Wrightington, 66
  Commerce ....AA
Squire & Co., J. P., 39 N.
  Market (Hams; Bacon)..
  ....AAAA
Wheeler Co., T. H., 101
  Clinton ....B
Woodbridge Meat Co., 6
  Quincy Row ....A
MASS.—Holyoke
Springfield Provision Co...
  ....AAAA
MASS.—Peabody
Thomas Co.. J. B. ....A
MASS.—Springfield
Handy, H. L. ....B
Hunt & Co., A. C. ......B
MASS.—Worcester
White, Pevey & Dexter Co.
  ....AA
MICH.—Detroit
Hammond, Standish & Co...
  ....AA
Parker-Webb Co., 87 Rose..
  ....AA
MICH.—Flint
Putnam & Co., R. ....A
MICH.—Ishpeming
Ishpeming Beef Co. .....B
MICH.—Saginaw
Saginaw Beef Co. ....A
MINN.—Austin
Hormel & Co., G. A. .....A
MINN.—Duluth
Omaha Packing Co. ...AAA
MINN.—St. Paul
McMillan, J. T. ....A
MO.—Kansas City
Armour Packing Co.
  (Canned) ....AAAA
Cudahy Packing Co. .AAAA
Dold Packing Co., Jacob...
  ....AAAA
Schwarzschild & Sulzberger
  ....AAAA
Swift & Co. ....AAAA
MO.—La Belle
La Belle Packing & Provis-
  ion Co. ....B
MO.—St. Joseph
Krug Packing Co., H. ..AA
MO.—St. Louis
Cox & Gordon, 1019 S. 3rd
  ....AA
Getty's & Son Prov. Co.,
  113 N. Main ....B
Grant, W. D., 3830 Garfield
  ....AA
Heil, C. P., 3857 Chouteau
  ....B
Krey Packing Co., 21st &
  Bremen Av. ....B
Murphy, J., 2315 Morgan.A
St. Louis Dressed Beef &
  Prov. Co., 701 N. 3rd..AA
Wissmath & Son, C., 1113 N.
  12th ....B
MO.—St. Joseph
Hammond Co., G. H..AAAA
NEBR.—Lincoln
Lincoln Packing Co. .....A

NEBR.—Nebraska City
Morton-Gregson Co. (Pork) .....A

NEBR.—South Omaha
Armour & Co.......AAAA
Cudahy Packing Co..AAAA
Hammond Packing Co..... AAAA
Omaha Packing Co. ..AAA
Swift & Co. ....AAAA

N. J.—Jersey City
Bender Co., Wm. ....A

N. J.—Newark
Bailey & Co., C. M., 101 S. Orange Av. (Cured Meats) ....B

N. J.—Passaic
Muhs Co., H. ....AA

N. J.—Paterson
Muhs Co., H. ....AA

N. J.—Phillipsburg
Shiner, J. R. (Smoked Meats) ....B

N. Y.—Albany
Holland Bros. ....B

N. Y.—Amsterdam
Carpenter, W. N. (Pork)..B

N. Y.—Buffalo
Danahy Packing Co., Metcalf & Clinton ....A
Dold Packing Co., 745 William ....AAAA
Kamman Bros., 759 Seneca ....B
Klinch, C., 101 E. Market ....AA
Sahlem, Joseph, Howard & Detroit ....A
Weppners' Sons, A., Louisiana & Elk ....B
Weppner's Provision Co., 597 Perry ....B
Western Beef Co., 72 River ....A

N. Y.—Elmira
Elmira Beef Co. .....AAAA

N. Y.—Hamburg
Hamburg Canning Co. ....A

N. Y.—Newburgh
Heyer Co., A. L. ....B

New York City
Ams, Max., 372 Greenwich (Lamb's Tongues; Pres. Meats) ....AA
Beardsley's Sons, J. W., 476 Greenwich ....A
Ferris & Co., F. A., 264 Mott (Hams; Bacon)..AA
Fairbanks Canning Co. 46 10th Av. (Canned Meats) AAAA
German-Amer. Prov. Co., 342 Washington ....A
Halsted & Co., Produce Exchange ....AA
Hammond Co., G. H. 52 10th Av. ....AAAA
Heyer Packing Co., A. L. 318 E. 39th ....B
Kingan Provision Co., 20 Manhattan Mkt....AAAA
North Packing & Provision Co. Produce Exchange (Pork) ....AAAA
Oneida Community, 413 B'way (Canned) ......AA
Rohe & Bro., Produce Exch. AAA
Schwarzchild & Sulzberger Co. ....AAAA

N. Y.—Rochester
Curtice Bros. Co. (Potted Meats) ....AA

N. Y.—Syracuse
Hammond Co., G. H..AAAA
Kingan Provision Co.AAAA

N. Y.—Utica
Lee, A. ....B

OHIO—Cincinnati
Cincinnati Abattoir Co. (Canned) ....AA
Hoffman, John, Baymiller & Central ....A
Hoffman & Sons, John, 2162 Colerain Av. ....A
Maescher & Co., 1754 Central Av. ....A
Morrison & Co., Thos., Bank & Winchell Av. .....AA
Rawsons' Sons, Jos..AAAA
Roth Packing Co., J. C. 1010 Gest ....AA

Sander Packing Co., A., 1022 Gest (Hams) ....A
Schroth Packing Co., J. & F., Cormany Av. & Township ....AA
Vogel & Son, Jacob, 2604 Colerain Av. ....A
Zehler Provision Co., Geo., 1705 Logan ....A

OHIO—Cleveland
Cleveland Provision Co., 8 Boliver ....AAA
Ohio Provision Co.. Clark Av.. at C. C. C. & St. L. R. R. ....A
People's Provision Co., Gordon Av., opp. Stock Yards ....B

OHIO—Dayton
Burkhardt Packing Co....B
Focke's Sons Co.. W......A
Jacobs & Co., N. ....B

OHIO—Newark
Metz & Bro., Chas. .....B

OHIO—Sandusky
Bear & Ruth Bros. ......B

OHIO—Wooster
Wooster Preserving Co...B

OREGON—Baker City
Geddes & Pollman ......B

OREGON—Portland
Omaha Packing Co. ..AAA
Sinclair & Co., T. M..AAA
Union Meat Co. ....AA

PA.—Allegheny City
Zoller & Co., W. ....A

PA.—Allentown
Arbogast & Bastian .....B

PA.—Blairsville
Brown & Bro., M. E. ....B

PA.—Bridgeport
March Packing Co., A. H. (Pork) ....A

PA.—Chester
Buckley, J. J. ....B

PA.—Harrisburg
Brelsford Packing Co....A
Dold Packing Co., Jacob... AAAA

PA.—Lehighton
Obert, J. (Est.) ....B

PA.—Mt. Carmel
Weissinger, Jr., & Bro., L. W. ....AA

PA.—Philadelphia
Alburger & Co., J. T., S. 2nd & Snyder Av. ....A
Felin & Bro., J. J., 4142 Germantown Av. (Pork).B
Michener & Co., J. H., 956 N. Front ....AA
Penn. Packing & Prov. Co., N. 30th & Race ....A
Warthman & Co., 705 Callowhill ....A

PA.—Pittsburg
Dunlevy & Bros., 615 Liberty Av. ....A
Fried & Reinman, 16 Diamond Mkt. ....B
Myers & Co., E. H., 248 Va. Av. ....AAA
Rea & Co., 612 2nd Av...AA
Stevenson & Co., J., 637 Liberty Av. ....A

PA.—Pottsville
Seltzer Packing Co. (Beef; Pork) ....A
Ulmer Packing Co., J.....A

PA.—Sandy Run
Millhopper Packing Co..AA

PA.—Scranton
Scranton Packing Co......A
Stowers Park Packing & Provision Co. (Pork) ...A

R. I—Providence
Kimball & Colwell Co....B
Mason & Sons, I. B. ....AA

R. I.—Woonsocket
Woonsocket Beef & Provision Co. ....AAAA

TENN.—Knoxville
East Tenn. Packing Co...A

TENN.—Morristown
Nance & Co., F. T. (Pork) B

TENN.—Nashville
Nashville Packing Co. ..AA

TENN.—Paris
Paris Packing Co. ......A

TEXAS—Dallas
Doran, F. H. ....B

MEAT PACKERS (Con.)
Hahn Packing Co., Max...B
TEXAS—Ft. Worth
Ft. Worth Packing & Provision Co. (Pork) ....AA
TEXAS—Houston
Houston Packing Co. ....B
TEXAS—McKinney
Shain Packing Co. (Beef; Pork) ....B
TEXAS—Sherman
Sherman Packing Co. ..B
TEXAS—Waco
Brazos Packing Co. .....B
VA.—Richmond
Kingan & Co. ......AAAA
VA.—Rosslyn
Rosslyn Packing Co. (Pork) ....B
WASH.—Tacoma
Pacific Meat Co. ....A
W. VA.—Wheeling
McMechen & Son Co., G. K. ....A
Schenck & Sons Co., F...AA
WIS.—Eau Claire
Drummond Bros. ....B
WIS.—Jefferson
Stoppenbach's Sons, Chas..A
WIS.—Milwaukee
Bodden Packing Co., Muskego Av. & N. Canal....A
Frank & Son Packing Co., L. A
Gross Bros. Co., F. C., Muskego Av. & Canal .....B
Layton Co. ....AA
Plankinton Packing Co..AA

MEATS

For Canned Meats see Canned Goods

COLO.—Denver
Kreiner, F. (Pickled) ....D
D. C.—Washington
Briggs, P., 16 Center Mkt. E
Columbia Packing Co., 2713 Brightwood Av. (Sund.).E
Nash, W. F., 500 Center Mkt. (Smoked) ....E
Ruppert, J. H., 23 Riggs Mkt. (Smoked) ....B
Schaper, A. (Smoked) ....F
Schroth, A. T. (Smoked)..D
ILL.—Chicago
Armour & Co. (Deviled; Potted) ....AAAA
Cudahy Packing Co. (Deviled; Potted) .....AAAA
German-Amer. Provision Co. (Deviled; Potted) .....A
Libby, McNeill & Libby (Deviled; Potted; Canned; Lamb's Tongues)..AAAA
Nelson & Co., Morris (Deviled; Potted; Canned; Lamb's Tongues)...AAAA
MASS.—Boston
North Packing & Provision Co. (Dressed) ....AAAA
Potter & Wrightington (Deviled) ....AA
Underwood Co., Wm. (Deviled) ....A
N. J.—Newark
Schriehoffer, Jacob (Pickeled) ....E

MEDALLIONS

See Jewelry

MASS.—Springfield .. ....
Taber-Prang Art Co. (Photograph) ....AA
N. J.—Newark
Reynolds & Zahn (Robe)..B
N. Y.—Brooklyn
Parkes Machine Co., 290 Graham Av. (Embroidered) ....D
OHIO—Cincinnati
Reuhl Moulding Mfg. Co. A
R. I.—Providence
Pollard & Co., A. ....E
Wightman & Hough Co...A
WIS.—Milwaukee
Schwab Stamp & Seal Co. X

MEDALS

See Jewelry

MEDIUMS

MD.—Baltimore
Bennett Pottery Co., Edwin (Filtering) ....A
N. J.—Newark
Murphy Varnish Co. (Artists) ....AAAA
N. Y.—New York City
Devoe, F. W. & C, T. Raynolds Co. (Artists, China Decorators) ....AAAA

MEGAPHONES

MASS.—Boston
Merriman Bros. ....F
MASS.—Westfield
Crane Bros. (Linonoid) AAA
N. Y.—New York City
Bunnell & Co., J. H., 20 Park Pl...............B

MELTERS

N. Y.—New York City
American Gas Fixtures Co., 23 John (Babbitt Metal) A
N. Y.—Rochester
Werner, John (Cream) ..D
PA.—Allegheny
Pittsburg Clay Pot Co. (Glass) ....AA

MELTONS

See Woolen Goods

MENDERS

MASS.—Boston
Eyelet Tool Co. (Steel Tape) X
MASS.—Cambridge
Boston Woven Hose & Rubber Co. (Rubber Hose) AAAA
MASS.—Worcester
Hamblin & Russell Mfg. Co. (Wire Hose) ....B
N. J.—Newark
Sommer's Son John (Hose) A
OHIO—Canton
Kohler & Co., F. E. (Hose) B
PA.—Bradford
Hudson & Co., Chas. (Hose) D
PA.—Philadelphia
Stortz & Son, Jno., 210 Vine (Hose) ....E

MENTHOL

MICH.—Detroit
Parke, Davis & Co...AAAA
MO.—St. Louis
Mallinckrodt Chemical Wrks. ....AAAA
N. Y.—New York City
Schieffelin & Co., W. H. AA
Wetmore Co., S. H. ....D
Wyeth & Bro., J. ....AAAA

MERCURY

N. J.—Secaucus
Eagle Chemical Co. (Redistilled) ....D
PA.—Easton
Baker & Adamson Chemical Co. ....A
PA.—Philadelphia
Hagstoz Co., L. B., 709 Sansome ....F

MERRY-GO-ROUNDS

See Carousels; Galleries.

METAL

See also Metals; for Expanded Metal see also Fire-proofing.

METAL (*Con.*)

CAL.—San Francisco
Finn Metal Wks., John
(Babbitt) C
Garrett & Co., W. T., 140
Fremont (Babbitt) ....AA
Great Western Smelting &
Refining Co., 217 1st
(Babbitt) ....E
O'Brien, Michael, 142 First
(Babbitt) ....E
Pacific Metal Wks., 139
First (Babbitt) ....B
Pickthall & Co., M., 105
Fremont (Babbitt) ...H
Selby Smelting & Lead Co.,
416 Montgomery (Babbitt)
AAA

COLO.—Denver
Bogue Lead Co., 1810 Blake
(Babbitt) ....D

CONN.—Ansonia
Ansonia Brass & Copper Co.
(Tobin Bronze) ....AAAA

CONN.—Bridgeport
Bridgeport D e o x i d i z e d
Bronze Metal Co. (Babbitt,
Ingot; Type) C
Rowell & Co., W. G.
(Babbitt) ....F

CONN.—Hartford
Blake & Son, T. J. (Babbitt)
E

CONN.—New Haven
Graham & Co., Jas., 293
Wooster (Babbitt) ....E
Magnus Metal Co., 248 Cedar
(Anti Friction) ....A

CONN.—Waterbury
Plume & Atwood Mfg. Co.
(Jewelers) ....AAA
Waterbury Brass Co. (Cart-
ridge) ....AAAA

ILL.—Aurora
Aurora Metal Co. (Babbitt)
F

ILL.—Cairo
Reed, Jos. B. (Babbitt) ..B

ILL.—Chicago
Besly & Co., Chas. H. (Bab-
bitt) ....AAA
Blatchford & Co., E. W., 70
N. Clinton (Babbitt) .AA
Channon Co., H. (Babbitt) A
Edna Smelting & Refining
Co., Monadnock Blk. (Bab-
bitt; Porteous Graphite) B
Gould & Gould, 84 Market
(Babbitt) ....F
Great Westrn Smelting &
Refining Co., 173 W. Kin-
zie (Babbitt) ....A
Illinois Smelting & Refining
Wks. (Babbitt).......A
Kramer & Son. H., 401 So.
Canal (Babbitt) ......A
Lammert & Mann, 157 So.
Jeff. (Anti Friction; Bab-
bitt) ....E
Magnolia Metal Co., Fisher
Bldg. (Babbitt) ....A
National Lead Co., 1510
State (Babbitt) ..AAAA
Railroad Supply Co., Old
Colony Bldg. (Babbitt) .A
Raymond Lead Co., 54 W.
Lake (Babbitt) ....AAAA
Ryan & Co., J. J., 68 W.
Monroe (Babbitt) C

ILL.—Granite
Illinois Metal Co. (Babbitt)
D

LA.—New Orleans
New Orleans Roofing &
Metal Wks., 926 Lafayette
(Babbitt) ....B

MAINE—Portland
Babbitt, Chas. E. (Babbitt)
F

MD.—Baltimore
Aumen & Garrett, 102 South
(Babbitt) ....D
Codd Co., E. J., 708 S. Caro-
line (Babbitt) ....A
Schultz & Co., A., 1016 E.
Balt. (Babbitt; Type) ..G

MASS.—Boston
Blaney & Co., W. D., 6
Northampton (Babbitt) G
Butler & Co., Saml., 549
Atlantic Av. (Babbitt) C
Mowry & Phillips, 197 High
(Babbitt; Journal Lining)
D
Priest, Page & Co., 143

METAL (*Con.*)

Franklin (Babbitt) ..A
Rogers, C. E., 34 Beach
(Babbitt) ....G
Star Refining Co., 170 Sum-
mer (Babbitt) ....B
Walworth Mfg. Co., 136
Federal (Babbitt) AAAA

MASS.—Clinton
Clinton Wire Cloth Co.
(Perforated) ....AAA

MASS.—Fitchburg
Hardy & Son Co., Wm. A.,
(Babbitt) ....B

MASS.—Taunton
Reed & Barton Corporation
(White) ....AAA

MASS.—Worcester
Kindred & Taylor (Babbitt)
F

MICH.—Detroit
Bostwick, James, 372 Abbott
(Babbitt) ....F
Duro Metal Co., ft. Ran-
dolph (Babbitt) ....D
Muzzy-Lyon Co., 56 Wood-
ward Av. (Babbitt) ....F
National Fulton Brass Mfg.
Co. (Babbitt) ....AA
Wing & Co., J. T., 19 Wood-
ward (Babbitt) ....D

MICH.—Grand Rapids
Hayden & Co., J. M., 58
Pearl (Babbitt) ......D

MICH.—Kalamazoo
New Era Mfg. Co. (Babbitt)
D

MO.—St. Louis
Hiertz Metal Co., Theo.,
10th & Poepping (Electro-
type; Linotype; Babbitt)
D
Hoyt Metal Co. 4153 Clay-
ton Av. (Babbitt; Type) A
Leschen & Sons Rope Co., A.
(Babbitt) ....AAA
Markle Lead Wks., Realto
Bldg. (Babbitt) ....B
More-Jones Brass & Metal
Co., 3144 N. Bway. (Bab-
bitt) ....A
National Lead Co. (Babbitt)
AAAA
Spring Supply Co., H. C., 715
N. 2nd (Babbitt; Graph-
ite) ....A
Zelnicker Supply Co., Walter
A., 408 N. 4th (Babbitt) C

N. J.—Arlington
Hoyt Metal Co. (Babbitt)
AA

N. J.—Belleville
Eastwood Wire Mfg. Co.
(Anti-Friction; Babbitt) A

N. J.—Camden
Fullmer & Co., A. J. (Babbitt) ....E

N. J.— Jersey City
Brady Brass Co., 204 10th
(Babbitt) ....B
Magnus Metal Co., 364 9th
(Babbitt) ....AA
Williams & Son, E. A., 105
Plymouth (Babbitt; Bottle
Leaf; Gun; Ingot; Needle;
Umbrella Tip; Type; Bol-
ster; Rubber Mould) AAA

N. Y.—Brooklyn
Lissberger, Marks & Son, 375
Driggs Av. (Babbitt) ..B

N. Y.—Buffalo
Buffalo Metal Goods Co.
(Ornamental; Embossed) C
Hayman & Co., M., 38 Perry
(Babbitt) ....A
Squier Mfg. Co., Geo. L.
(Anti-Friction; Babbitt;
Electrotype, etc.) ...AAA
New York City
Amer. Gas Furnace Co., 23
John (Babbitt) ....A
Amer. Metal Co., 52 Bway.
(Babbitt) ....AAA
Baker, John W. (Babbitt) D
Columbia Smelting & Refin-
ing Wks., 307 Water
(Babbitt) ....AA
Fairbanks Co., 186 Elm
(Babbitt) ....AAAA
Hungerford Brass & Copper
Co., U. T., 497 Pearl (To-
bin Bronze) ....A
Kahn Bros., 525 E. 19th
(Babbitt) ....AA
Magnolia Metal Co., 511 W.

METAL (Con.)

13th (Balbitt; Journal) A

Nassau Smelting & Refining Wks., 29th & 11th Av. (Babbitt) ....AA

National Metal Co., 129 Liberty (Babbitt) ....A

Pittsburg White Metal Co., 160 Leroy (Babbitt) ..D

Wildes, M. L., 246 Water (Babbitt) ....D

N. Y.—Rochester

Clum & Co., P. A., 18 Jay (Babbitt) C

Nunn Brass Wks., 17 Wentworth (Babbitt) ....F

Rochester Lead Wks., 380 Exchange (Babbitt) ...B

N. Y.—Syracuse

Empire Metal Co. (Babbitt) A

N. Y.—Tonawanda

Gillie Engine & Machine Co. (Babbitt) C

OHIO—Cincinnati

Amer. Valve & Meter Co. (Babbitt; Graphite) ...C

McDonald & Sons Co., Jas., 654 Main (Babbitt) .....B

Morris & Co., E. K., 315 W. 2nd (Babbitt) ....B

Powell Co., Wm., Spring Grove Av. (Anti-Friction; Babbitt) ....AAA

Van Duzen Co., E. W., 428 E. 2nd (Anti-Friction; Babbitt) C

OHIO—Cleveland

Metal Sales Co., 15 S. Water (Babbitt) ....G

OHIO—Lorain

Lorain Foundry Co. (Babbitt) ....A

OHIO—Mansfield

Ohio Brass Co. (Babbitt) B

OHIO—Springfield

Springfield Brass Co. (Babbitt) ....E

OHIO—Youngstown

Falcon Bronze Co. (Babbitt) D

OREGON—Portland

Arthur & Co., J. M. (Babbitt) ....B

Pacific Metal Wks. (Babbitt) ....B

Simonds Mfg. Co. (Babbitt) AA

PA.—Allegheny

Damascus Bronze Co. (Babbitt) ....A

PA.—Chester

Crown Smelting Co. (Ingot; Journal Lining) ....A

PA.—Easton

Baker & Adamson Chem. Co. (Babbitt) ....A

PA.—Philadelphia

Ajax Metal Co., 48 Richmond (Babbitt) ....AA

Atlas Smelting & Refining Co., 1008 Germantown Av. (Babbitt) ....E

Delaware Metal Refinery, 18th & Wash. Av. (Babbitt) ....A

Fullerton, Frank S., 438 E. Girard Av. (Babbitt) ...A

Hagstoz Co., T. B., 709 Sansom (Babbitt) ....F

Hand & Co., E. L., 616 Market (Babbitt) C

Hooks Smelting Co., Broad & Hamilton (Babbitt) ...A

King Smelting Wks., Jno., 1330 S. 10th (Babbitt) D

Lewis & Bros., Jno. T., 231 So. Front (Babbitt)AAAA

McHatton Smelting Co., 1500 Washn. Av. (Babbitt) ..A

Merchant & Co. (Linotype) AA

North American Smelting Co., 9th & Thompson (Babbitt) ....AA

Paxson Co., J. W. (Pattern) ....AA

Pennsylvania Smelting & Refining Co., 901 Filbert (Babbitt) ....F

Phillips & Sons Co., F. R., Penn Bldg. (Babbitt) ..D

Phosphor Bronze Smelting Co., 2202 Wash. Av. (Bab-

METAL (Con.)

bitt) ....B

Reeves & Son, Paul S., 1415 Catherine (Babbitt) ..B

Shimer & Co., H. M., 19th & Wash. Av. (Babbitt) F

Taylor & Co., N. & G., Third & Chestnut (Babbitt; Type) ....AAAA

U. S. Smelting Wks., Spring Garden St. (Babbitt)..B

White & Bro., 1506 E. Montg. Av. (Babbitt) ..B

Woodfall Bros., 1005 Fairmount Av. (Babbitt) ..B

PA.—Pittsburg

Bailey-Farrell Mfg. Co., 619 Smithfield (Babbitt) AA

Best Mfg. Co., 25th & A. V. Railway (Babbitt) ...A

Cadman Mfg. Co., A. W., 2814 Smallman (Babbitt) D

Epping Carpenter Co., 41st & A. V. Ry. (Babbitt) .A

Fox Copper & Bronze Mfg. Co., 2624 Smallman (Babbitt) ....F

Hyde Bros. & Co., Lewis Block (Babbitt) ....B

Lawrenceville Bronze Co., 3046 Penn Av. (Babbitt) D

Mansfield Mfg. Co., 61 1st Av. (Babbitt) ....B

Phoenix Fdry. Co., 28th & A. V. Ry. (Babbitt) ...D

Pittsburg Brass Mfg. Co., 107 Wood (Babbitt) ....D

Pittsburg White Metal Co., 1739 Liberty Av. (Babbitt) B

S. C.—Charleston

Bailey-Libby Co. (Babbitt)B

TENN.—Chattanooga

Frictionless Metal Co. (Anti Friction) C

TENN.—Memphis

Lee Bros. (Babbitt) ......A

VA.—Richmond

Smith-Courtney Co. (Babbitt) ....D

WASH.—Seattle

Finn Metal Wks., John (Babbitt) ....D

Puget Sound Metal Wks. (Babbitt) ....G

METALLOPHONES

PA.—Philadelphia

Schoenhut & Co., A., 2215 Adams ....A

METALS

See also Metal

CAL.—San Francisco

California Perforating Screen Co., Howard & Fremont (Perforated) ..D

Quick, John W., 221 1st (Perforated) ....B

CONN.—Torrington

Union Hardw. Co. ....A

CONN.—Waterbury

Benedict & Burnham Mfg. Co. (Platers') ....AAAA

Novelty Mfg. Co. (Perforated; Embossed) ....A

ILL.—Chicago

Aitchison Perforated Metal Co., Robt., 303 Dearborn (Perforated) ....B

Allis-Chalmers Co., Home Ins. Bldg. (Perforated) AAAA

Harrington & King Perforating Co., 224 N. Union (Perforated) ....A

Johnston & Chapman Co., 42 Michigan (Perforated) .D

Northwest Expanded Metal Co. (Expanded) ....B

MO.—St. Louis

St. Louis Expanded Metal Fire Proofing Co. (Expanded) ....B

Seibel-Snessdorf Copper & Iron Mfg. Co. (Perforated) A

N. J.—Garwood

Beckley Co., A. J. (Per-

METALS (Con.)
forated) ....D
N. J.—Riverside
Riverside Metal Co.
(Platers') ....A
New York City
Clinton Wire Cloth Co., 76
Beekman (Perforated)
............AAA
Manhattan Perforated Metal
Co., 237 Centre (Per-
forated) ....F
Mundt & Sons, Charles, 88
Walker (Perforated) ..B
Stimpson & Son, Edwin B.,
31 Spruce (Perforated) A
N. Y.—Rochester
Erdle & Schenck cor. Mill &
Factory (Perforated) ..B
OHIO—Cincinnati
Littleford Bros., 453 E.
Pearl (Perforated) ....D
PA.—Carbondale
Carbondale Machine Co.
(Perforated) ....AA
Hendrick Mfg. Co. (Ltd.)
(Perforated) ....AA
PA.—Philadelphia
Merritt & Co., 1024 Ridge
Av. (Perforated) ......E
PA.—Pittsburg
Central Expanded Metal Co.
(Expanded) ....A
Duquesne Co., (Chas. C.
Morrow Prop.) (Decorated
sheet) C
Pittsburg White Metal Co.,
1739 Liberty Av. (Electro-
type; Linotype; Monotype;
Stereotype) ....B
R. I.—Pawtucket
Fuller & Son, Geo. M.
(Platers') ....A
R. I.—Providence
Linton & Co., W. H.
(Platers') ....F

METERS

See also Wattmeters; etc..

CAL.—San Francisco
San Francisco Tool Wks.
(Water) ....F
CONN.—Bridgeport
Sprague Co., H. H. (Gas) D
CONN.—Manchester
Norton Elec. Instrument Co.,
Chas. (Ampere; Volt) ..E
CONN.—New Haven
New Haven Novelty Machine
Co. (Gas, Prepayment
Mechanism) ....A
CONN.—Waterbury
Bristol Co. (Ampere; Volt;
Recording Watt) ......D
Standard Electric Time Co.
(Ampere; Volt) ......E
ILL.—Chicago
Jewell Elec. Instrument Co.,
358 Dearborn (Ampere;
Volt) ....E
Western Elec. Co., 259 So.
Clinton (Ampere; Volt)
............AAAA
ILL.—Springfield
Sangamon Elec. Co. (Water)
............B
IND.—Fort Wayne
Ft. Wayne Elec. Wks. (Am-
pere; Volt; Primary; Re-
cording; Ampere-Hour;
Lamp-Hour) ....AA
IND.—Lafayette
Duncan Electric Mfg. Co.
(Electric) ....B
IND.—Richmond
Henly Bicycle Wks. (Nat-
ural Gas) ....A
MD.—Baltimore
Maryland Meter Co., 229
North (Gas) X
MASS.—Boston
Berger & Sons, C. L., 37
Williams (Current) ....A
Hersey Mfg. Co., 314 W.
2d S. B. (Water; Gas
Naphtha; Oil) ....AA
Knott Apparatus Co., L. E.
(Ampere; Volt) ......E
Tufts Meter Co., Nathaniel,
8 Medford (Experimental;
Proves'; Test; Repay-
ment; Station Gas) ..AA

METERS (Con.)
MASS.—Great Barrington
Stanley Instrument Co.
(Electric) ....AA
MASS.—Peabody
American Iron Electricity
Meter Co. (Electric) ..D
MASS.—Pittsfield
Stanley Elec. Mfg. Co., (Am-
pere; Volt) ....AA
MASS.—Springfield
Eldridge Elect. Mfg. Co.
(Ampere; Volt) ......F
MASS.—Worcester
Union Water Meter Co.
(Water) ....B
MICH.—Detroit
Buhl Stamping Co. (Gas) A
Byram & Co., 435 Guoin
(Blast) ....D
Detroit Meter Co., 206 W.
Larned (Gas; Electric) B
MO.—St. Louis
Wagner Elec. Mfg. Co., 2015
Locust (Ampere; Volt) A
N. H.—Lebanon
Kendrick & Davis (Ampere;
Volt) ....A
N. H.—Penacook
Whitney Electrical Instru-
ment Co. (Dynamo; Am-
pere; Volt) ....D
N. J.—Newark
Hanson & Van Winkle Co.
(Ampere; Volt) ......AA
Weston Electrical Instru-
ment Co. (Dynamo; Am-
pere; Volt) ....A
N. Y.—Albany
McDonald & Co., D. (Pre-
payment Gas) ....A
N. Y.—Brooklyn
Schaeffer & Budenberg, 10
Division (Dynamo; Water)
............A
Thomson Meter Co., 79
Washington (Water) ..A
Universal Gas Meter Co., 192
24th (Gas) ....E
N. Y.—Buffalo
Buffalo Meter Co., 290 Ter-
race (Oil; Water) ......D
N. Y.—Lockport
Amer. District Steam Co.
(Steam) ....AAA
New York City
Amer. Meter Co., 561 W.
47th (Gas) ....A
Automatic Meter Co., 115
Bway. (Gas) X
Empire Elec. Instrument
Co. 656 Hudson (Ampere;
Volt) ....D
General Incandescent Arc
Light Co., 572 1st Av.
(Ampere; Volt) ......A
Gilbert & Barker Mfg. Co.
(Water) ....A
Griffin & Co., J. J., 52 Dey
(Gas) ....AA
International Steam Pump
Co., 120 Liberty (Gas; Oil)
............AAAA
Jones & Son, J., 64 Cort-
landt (Ampere; Volt) ..D
Keuffel & Esser Co., 127
Fulton (Water Current) A
National Meter Co., 86
Chambers (Oil; Water;
Gas; Experimental; Water
& Gas Station; Test) ..A
Neptune Meter Co., 253
Bway (Water) ....A
Pignolet, Louis M. (Ampere;
Volt) ....D
Standard Meter & Mfg. Co.
(Gas) ....H
Worthington, Henry R., See
Interl. Steam Pump Co.,
114 Liberty (Water;
Naphta; Oil)
Zucker & Levett & Loeb Co.
(Ampere; Recording Volt)
............A
N. Y.—Schenectady
General Electrical Co. (Elec-
tric Ampere; Volt; Re-
cording Watt) ....AAAA
N. Y.—Syracuse
Syracuse Electric Instrument
Co. (Ampere; Volt) X
N. Y.—Troy
Gurley, W. & L. E. (Alter-
nating Current) ......AA

670

METERS (Con.)

OHIO—Cincinnati
Amer. Valve & Meter Co.
(Water) C

OHIO—Cleveland
Cleveland Gas Meter Co., 42
Glendale Av. (Gas) ....E
Elwell-Parker Electric Co.,
1066 Hamilton (Dynamo)
..............................A

PA.—Erie
Metric Metal Wks. (Br.
Am. Meter Co., N. Y.
City) (Fuel Gas; Gas)..A

PA.—Philadelphia
Harris Bros. & Co., 12th &
Brown (Gas) ....F
Helme & McIlhenny, 1339
Cherry (Experimental;
Provers' Gas) ....AA
Keystone Elect. Instrument
Co., 9th & Montgomery
(Ampere; Volt) ....B
Paxson Co., J. W. (Blast)
..............................AA
Queen & Co.. (Inc.) 1010
Chestnut (Dynamo; Am-
pere; Volt) ....AA
Wirt Elect. Co. (Volt) ...D

PA.—Pittsburg
Chaplin-Fulton Mfg. Co., 28
Penn Av. (Fuel Gas) ..A
Equitable Meter Co. (Dry) B
Pittsburg Meter Co. (Tin;
Westinghouse Gas; Pro-
portional Gas; Water)AA
Pittsburg Supply Co., 226 1st
Av. (Fuel Gas; Gas) ...A
Westinghouse Elect. & Mfg.
Co. (Ampere; Volt; Alter-
nating Current; Electric;
Recording Watt) ..AAAA

PA.—Reading
Reading Electric Mfg. Co.
(Volt) ....E

PA.—Royersford
Keystone Meter Co. (Gas;
Prepaid Gas) ....A

R. I.—Providence
Builders' Iron Fdry. (Water)
..............................AA

WIS.—La Crosse
Benton & Son. Thos. P.
(Ampere; Volt) ....F

METHYL

New York City
Salomon & Bro., L. A. ..AA

MICA

ILL.—Chicago
Sills Eddy Mica Co., 34
Clark (Micabeston) X

MASS.—Boston
North Carolina Mica Co., 84
North ....D

MO.—St. Louis
Braner, A. G. C

N. J.—Lincoln
Atlas Mineral & Machine Co.
(Ground) ....D

New York City
Francklyn & Ferguson. Cot-
ton Exch. Bldg. (Electri-
cal; Ground; Pulp) ...F
Johns-Manville Co.. H. W.,
100 William (Moulded)
..............................AAAA
Mica Insulator Co., 218 Wa-
ter (Micanite) ....B
Mica Mfg. Co. C
Munsell & Co.. Eugene ..B
National Gum & Mica Co.,
502 W. 45th (Ground;
Pulp) ....A
Schoonmaker, A. O., 221
Fulton (Importer) ....D
Whittaker. W. H., 245
Front (Ground) ....E

N. C.—Asheville
Asheville Mica Co. ......B

PA.—Philadelphia
Merchant & Co., 517 Arch
..............................AA
Paxson Co.. J. W. (Shist)
..............................AA

VA.—Richmond
Richmond Mica Co. (Ground)
..............................B

MICROMETERS

CONN.—Hartford
Pratt & Whitney Co. AAAA

MICROMETERS (Con.)

MASS.—Athol
Athol Machine Co. ....B
Starrett Co., L. S. (Outside;
Inside) ....A

MASS.—Fitchburg
Sawyer Tool Mfg. Co. (In-
side) C

MASS.—Greenfield
Massachusetts Tool Co. ...C

New York City
Hammacher - Schlemmer &
Co.. 209 Bway. ......AAA

N. Y.—Syracuse
Syracuse Twist Drill Co. ..B

PA.—Columbia
Smith, E. G. ....F

R. I.—Providence
Brown & Sharpe Mfg. Co.
(Paper) ....AAAA
Slocomb & Co., J. T. .....E

MICROSCOPES

CONN.—Bridgeport
Gaynor & Mitchell Mfg. Co.
(Toy) ....D

ILL.—Chicago
Martin Co., Edw. P. C

MASS.—Boston
Thompson & Co.. A. T., 15
Tremont Pl. (Projecting)
..............................X

New York City
King Optical Co., Julius
(Dlrs.) C
Meyrowitz Co. (Dlrs.) ....E

N. Y.—Rochester
Bausch & Lomb Optical Co.
(Mfrs.) ....AAA
Gundlach Manhattan Optical
Co. ....A

PA.—Philadelphia
Thomas Co., A. H., 12th &
Walnut (Importers) ...B

MIDDLES: CARD

See Paper

MILK

CAL.—Hanford
Valley Cond. Milk & Cream
Co. (Condensed) .....E

CAL.—Loleta
Cold Brook Creameries (Condensed) ....B

CAL.—Los Angeles
Pacific Creamery Co. (Con-
densed; Sterilized Cream)
..............................B

CAL.—San Francisco
Hilmer & Bredhoff (Con-
densed) C

CAL.—Visalia
Valley Cond. Milk & Cream
Co. (Condensed) .....E

COLO.—Fort Lupton
Colorado Condensed Milk Co.
(Condensed) ....A

ILL.—Effingham
Van Camp Cond. Milk Co.
(Condensed) ....A

ILL.—Elgin
Elgin Condensing Co. (Con-
densed) ....A
Huntley Cond. Milk Co.
(Condensed) ....B

ILL.—Geneva
Kleinbeck, C. H. (Con-
densed) ....D

ILL.—Highland
Helvetia Milk Condensing
Co. (Condensed; Evapor-
ated Cream) ....AA

ILL.—Pearl City
Great Western Cond. Milk
Co. (Condensed) ......B

ILL.—St. Charles
St. Charles Condensing Co.
(Condensed; Evaporated
Cream) ....AAA

ILL.—Trenton
St. Louis Cond. Milk Co.
(Condensed) ....D
Trenton Evaporated Cream
Co. (Condensed) ......B

IND.—Anderson
Indiana Cond. Milk Co.
(Condensed) ....D

IND.—Centerville
Centerville Cond. Milk &

MILK (*Con.*)
Creamery Co. (Condensed)
    A
IND.—Indianapolis
Centerville Cond. Milk &
  Creamery Co. (Condensed)
Van Camp Cond. Milk Co.,
  (Condensed) ....A
IOWA—Waverly
Wisconsin Cond. Milk Co.
  (Condensed) ....B
IOWA—West Liberty
Iowa Cond. Milk Co. (Con-
  densed) ....:.....A
MASS.—Cambridge
Brigham Co., C. (Condensed)
    A
MASS.—Newburyport
Newburyport Cond. Milk Co.
  (Condensed) C
MICH.—Detroit
Jersey Cond. Milk Co.,
  (Phelps, Brace & Co.)
  (Condensed) ....AA
MICH.—Durand
Durand Cond. Milk Co. (Con-
  densed) C
MICH.—Howell
Michigan Cond. Milk Co.
  (Condensed) ....A
ICH.—Jackson
Amer. Cond. Milk Co. (Ltd.)
  (Condensed) ....A
MICH.—Lansing
Michigan Cond. Milk Co.
  (Condensed) ....A
MICH.—Morenci
Ohio Dairy Co. (Condensed)
    B
MICH.—Northville
Northville Condensing Co.
  (Condensed) C
MICH.—Ubly
Hands Cond. Milk Co., Dr.
  (Condensed) ....B
MINN.—Rochester
Minnesota Milk Condensing
  Co. (Condensed) ....G
MO.—St. Louis
St. Louis Cond. Milk Co.
  (Condensed) ....D
N. J.—Bridgeton
Bridgeton Cond. Milk Co.
  (Condensed) ....A
N. J.—Glenwood
Brown & Bailey (Condensed)
    C
N. Y.—Dansboro
U. S. Condensed Milk Co.
  (Condensed) C
N. Y.—Delphi
Delphi Milk Condensing Co.
  (Condensed) C
N. Y.—Frankfort
Michigan Cond. Milk Co.
  (Condensed) ....AA
N. Y.—Fulton
Nestle, Henri (Condensed) B
N. Y.—Goshen
Howell Cond. Milk & Cream
  Co. (Condensed; Evapo-
  rated Cream) ....A
New York City
Borden's Cond. Milk Co.
  (Condensed; Malted)
    AAAA
Canfield, H. Y. (Condensed)
    A
Leeming & Co., T. (Con-
  densed Nestles' Swiss) B
Michigan Cond. Milk Co.
  (Condensed) ....A
Mohawk Cond. Milk Co.
  (Condensed) ....A
Wisconsin Cond. Milk Co.
  (Condensed) ....B
N. Y.—Rochester
Mohawk Cond. Milk Co.
  (Condensed) ....A
N. Y.—St. Johnsville
Mohawk Cond. Milk Co.
  (Condensed) ....A
N. Y.—Walton
Consumers' Cond. Milk Co.
  (Condensed) C
OHIO—Cleveland
National Cond. Milk Co.
  (Condensed) ....B
OHIO—Kent
National Cond. Milk Co.
  (Condensed) ....B
PA.—Corry
Corry Cond. Milk Co.
  (Condensed) C

MILK (*Con.*)
PA.—Condersport
Northern Cond. Milk Co.
  (Condensed) ....B
PA.—Kennett Square
Eastern Cond. Milk Co.
  (Ltd.) (Condensed) ...B
PA.—Malvern
Hires' Cond. Milk Co. (Con-
  densed) ....AA
PA.—Philadelphia
Hires' Cond. Milk Co.
  (Condensed) ....AA
Northern Cond. Milk Co.
  (Condensed) ....B
PA.—Scranton
Hand Cond. Milk Co., Dr.
  (Condensed) ....A
Lackawanna Dairy Co., The
  (Condensed) ....F
Laplume Cond. Milk Co.
  (Condensed) ....A
UTAH—Richmond
Utah Cond. Milk Co.
  (Condensed) ....A
VT.—Burlington
Vermont Cond. Milk Co.
  (Condensed) ....B
WASH.—Kent
Pacific Coast Cond. Milk Co.
  (Condensed) ....A
WASH.—Seattle
Pacific Coast Cond. Milk Co.
  (Condensed) ....A
WIS.—Burlington
Wisconsin Cond. Milk Co.
  (McCanna & Fraser)
  (Condensed) ....B
WIS.—Elkhorn
Badger State Cond. Milk Co.
  (Condensed) C
WIS.—Racine
Horlick's Food Co. (Malted)
    A

MILLINERY

See Hats; Flowers; also List
in Appendix; Feathers,
    etc.

MILLS

See also Windmills; Agr.
  Imps.; Tools; Machy.;
  Grinders; Pulverizers;
  Crushers, etc.

ALA.—Huntsville
Huntsville Fdry. & Machine
  Wks. (Sugar Cane) ....B
ALA.—New Decatur
North Alabama Engineering
  Co. (Sugar Cane) ....F
ARIZ.—Nogales
Arizona & Sonora Mfg. Co.
  (Cyanide; Stamp) C
CAL.—Benecia
Benecia Agricultural Wks.,
  (Baker & Hamilton)
  (Feed Grinding) ....AAA
CAL.—Los Angeles
Stearns Mfg. Co. (Wind)..D
CAL.—San Francisco
Dyer Mill Co. 240 Mont-
  gomery (Improved Canon
  Ball Quarz) ....A
Harron, Rickard & McCone
  (Inc.), 21 Fremont
  (Quartz) ....B
Hendy Machine Wks.,
  Joshua (Quartz; Stamp)..
    AA
Jackson Machine Wks., By-
  ron (Wind) ....A
Krogh Mfg. Co., 9 Steven-
  son (Quartz) C
Marshutz & Cantrell, Main,
  cor. Howard (Quartz)..A
Risdon Iron & Locomotive
  Wks., Stewart & Folsom
  (Quartz; Sugar Cane)...
    AAA
Union Iron Wks., 222 Mar-
  ket (Prospecting; Stamp)
    AAAA
Woodin & Little (Wind)..A
CAL.—Stockton
Globe Iron Wks. (Inc.)
  (Stamp) ....B
COLO.—Denver
Davis Iron Wks., F. M., 8th
  & Larimer (Stamp) ...A
McFarlane & Co., 1734 15th

MILLS (Con.)

(Stamp) ....A
Mine & Smelter Supply Co.,
  Blake & 17th (Stamp) ...
                              AAA
Montgomery Mchry. Co., J.
  H. (Concentrating; Stamp)
                                C
Stearns-Roger Mfg. Co.,
  1718 California (Chlorina-
  tion; Stamp) ....A
CONN.—Ansonia
Farrel Fdry. & Machine Co.
  (Cane; Rolling) ..AAAA
CONN.—Bridgeport
Bullard Mach. Tool Co.
  (Boring; Turning) ....A
CONN.—Derby
Birmingham Iron Fdry.
  (Wire Flattening; Rail)
                               A
CONN.—Hartford
Pratt & Whitney Co. (Bor-
  ing; Horizontal; End;
  with Inserted Teeth)....
                            AAAA
CONN.—Higganum
Cutaway Harrow Co. (Cider)
                               A
CONN.—Meriden
Parker Co. (The), Chas.
  (Coffee; Drug; Spice)..
                            AAAA
CONN.—New Britain
Landers, Frary & Clark
  (Coffee: Drug) .....AAA
CONN.—New Haven
Geometric Drill Co. (Hol-
  low; Adjustable) C
Harrison, Leonard D.
  (Paint; Color; Corn) ..H
New Haven Mfg. Co. (Bor-
  ing; Turning) ....AA
Shuster Co., F. B. (Wire)
                               X
CONN.—Southington
Peck, Stow & Wilcox Co.
  (Drug; Spice; Coffee)..
                            AAAA
CONN.—Thompsonville
Bushnell Press Co., Geo. H.
  (Cider; Oil) ....A
CONN.—Waterbury
Blake & Johnson (Rolling;
  Wire Flattening) ......A
Waterbury Farrel Fdry. &
  Machine Co. (Rolling
  Brass; Rolling Copper;
  Rolling Sheet Metal;
  Wire) ....AA
Waterbury Machine Co.
  (Rumbling) ....B
DEL.—Wilmington
Betts Machine Co. (Boring;
  Turning; Vertical, 5 to 20
  ft. Swing) ....
                              AA
Poole Co., Morton J. (Ink)
                              AA
Pusey & Jones Co. (Sugar
  Cane) ....AAA
Walker & Elliott (Cement;
  Phosphate Fertilizer
  Grinding) ....B
GA.—Atlanta
De Loach Mill Mfg. Co.
  (Buhr Stone; Corn Meal;
  Corn; Shingle) X
Van Winkle Gin & Machine
  Wks.. E. (Oil Cake)....A
GA.—Augusta
Lombard Iron Wks. & Sup-
  ply Co. (Band Saw; Grist;
  Cane; Stamp) ....A
GA.—Columbus
Southern Plow Co. (Sugar
  Cane) ....AA
GA.—Macon
Schofield Sons & Co., J. S.
  (Sugar Cane) ....A
GA.—Newnan
Cole Mfg. Co., R. D.
  (Grist) ....A
GA.—Savannah
Kehoe & Sons, Wm. (Sugar
  Cane) ....A
Rourke & Sons, Jno. (Sugar
  Cane) ....B
GA.—West Point
West Point Iron Wks.
  (Grist) C
ILL.—Aurora
Amer. Well Wks. (Wind)..
                              AA

MILLS (Con.)

ILL.—Batavia
Appleton Mfg. Co. (Grist;
  Feed; Wind) ....A
Batavia Wind Mill Co.
  (Corn; Cob; Feed Grind-
  ing) ....D
Challenge Wind Mill & Feed
  Mill Co. (Grist; Grist
  Wind Fanning; Feed;
  Wind) ....A
U. S. Wind Engine & Pump
  Co. (Grist; Corn; Feed;
  Wind) ....A
ILL.—Chicago
Allis-Chalmers Co., Home
  Ins. Bldg. (Ball; Pebble;
  Car Wheel Boring; Cya-
  nide; Prospecting; Quartz;
  Steam Pump) .....AAAA
Chicago Scale Co. (Corn;
  Feed) ....A
Elmes Engineering Wks..
  Chas. F. (Corn; Linseed
  Oil) ....A
Fairbanks, Morse & Co.
  (Grist; Wind) ....AAAA
Kaestner & Co., Chas.
  (Malt; Grinding Paint;
  Drug; Spice) ....A
Olsen & Tilgner (Malt)...D
Raymond Bros. Impact Pul-
  verizer Co., 143 Laflin
  (Grinding; Quartz; Paint;
  Drug; Spice) C
Stroud & Co., E. A., 36 La
  Salle (Drug; Grinding).D
ILL.—Elgin
Elgin Wind Power & Pump
  Co. (Grist; Wind) C
Woodruff & Edwards Co.
  (Coffee; Spice) ....B
ILL.—Freeport
Arcade Mfg. Co. (Coffee;
  Spice) ....A
Hoefer Mfg. Co. (Boring;
  Turning) ....D
Stover Mfg. Co. (Grinding;
  Family Grist; Grist; Corn
  Meal; Cob; Corn; Feed;
  Feed Portable; Feed
  Horse Powers; Combined;
  Rumbling; Wind) .....A
Woodmanse & Hewitt Mfg.
  Co. (Wind) ....B
ILL.—Galesburg
Colton & Co., G. D. (Corn
  Cob; Feed Grinding;
  Grist; Wind) ....D
Frost Mfg. Co. (Grist)....A
May Bros. (Wind) ......B
ILL.—Geneva
Snow Mfg. Co. (Feed
  Grinding) ....B
ILL.—Harvey
Austin Mfg. Co., F. C.
  (Wind) ....AA
ILL.—Henry
Aera Mfg. Co. (Wind)...D
ILL.—Joliet
Adam, W. J. (Bone; Corn;
  Feed) ....B
ILL.—Marseilles
Marseilles Mfg. Co. (Fan-
  ning; Feed Grinding;
  Grist; Wind) ....A
ILL.—Mascoutah
Trappe, Chas. H. (Fanning)
                               H
ILL.—Moline
Barnard & Leas Mfg. Co.
  (Grist; Roller) ....AA
Moline Pump Co. (Wind).
                               A
ILL.—Peoria
Avery Mfg. Co. (Fanning)'
Avery Planter Co. (Wind).A
Kingman & Co. (Fanning)
                              AAA
ILL.—Rockford
Rockford Well Drill Co.
  (Sugar Cane) ....F
ILL.—St. Charles
Goodhue Rotary Grinder Co.
  (Corn; Cob) ....D
ILL.—Sandwich
Sandwich Mfg. Co. (Feed;
  Grist; Wind) ....AA
ILL.—Sterling
Sterling Mfg. Co. (Grist;
  Feed) ....A

MILLS (*Con.*)

IND.—Alexandria
Miller Bros. Mfg. Co.
(Fanning) X
IND.—Auburn
Zimmerman Mfg. Co.
(Wind) ....B
IND.—Aurora
Stedman's Fdry. & Machine
Wks. (Grinding; Bone;
Clay Grinding) C
IND.—Butler
Butler Co. (Feed Grinding)
B
IND.—Frankfort
Wallace Mfg. Co. (Pug)..C
IND.—Indianapolis
Chandler & Taylor Co.
(Band Saw) ....AA
Nordyke & Marmon Co., 1101
W. Morris (Cement; Drug;
Spice; Paint; Color; Fam-
ily Grist; Plantation;
Portable; Rye; Under
Runner; Upper Runner;
Starch; Buhr Stone; Buck-
wheat; Buckwheat Roller;
Corn Meal; Corn Roller;
Hominy; Pearl Barley;
Roller; Cob; Corn; Feed;
Feed Portable) .....AAA
Potts & Co. (Inc.), C. & A.
(Pug) ....B
Sinker-Davis Co. (Grist)..B
IND.—Kendallville
Flint & Walling Mfg. Co.
(Wind) ....AA
IND.—La Porte
Michael, Chas. H. (Fanning)
D
IND.—Mishawaka
Perkins Wind Mill & Axe
Co. (Grist; Wind)......A
IND.—Richmond
Eureka Fence Mfg. Co.
(Feed Grinding) ....E
Richmond City Mill Wks.
(Buhr Stone; Grist;
Corn Meal; Roller; Corn;
Cob; Brown Stone; Porta-
ble) ....A
Robinson & Co. (Grist) ...A
IND.—South Bend
Bowsher Co., N. (Corn; Cob;
Feed Grinding) ....B
South Bend Fdry. Co. (Feed
Grinding. ....B
Sundries Mfg. Co. (Feed
Grinding) ....B
IOWA—Centerville
Hercules Mfg. Co. (Feed
Grinding) ....G
IOWA—Dubuque
Cooper Wagon & Buggy Co.
(Feed Grinding) ......A
Dubuque Turbine & Roller
Mill Co. (Roller) .....B
IOWA—Lone Tree
Monarch Grubber Mfg. Co.
(Feed) ....B
IOWA—Ottumwa
Dain Mfg. Co. (Feed Grind-
ing) ....AA
IOWA—Waterloo
Kelly & Taneyhill Co.
(Feed Grinding) ....G
IOWA—Webster City
Litchfield Mfg. Co. (Feed
Grinding) ....A
KANS.—Enterprise
Ehrsam Machine Co., J.
B. (Grist; Roller) C
KANS.—Leavenworth
Great Western Mfg. Co. (Ce-
ment; Buhr Stone; Grist;
Plantation; Portable;
Rye; Upper Runner; Buck-
wheat; Buckwheat Roller;
Corn Meal; Flour; Cylin-
drical; Roller; Corn; Cob;
Feed; Feed Portable) ..AA
KANS.—Manhattan
Blue Valley Mfg. Co. (Feed;
Feed Sweep) ....F
KY.—Louisville
Avery & Sons, B. F.
(Sugar Cane) ......AAA
Brennan & Co., 801 W.
Green (Cider; Fanning;
Sugar Cane) ....A
LA.—New Orleans
Coleman, H. Dudley (Cane;
Corn) X

MILLS (*Con.*)

Payne & Joubert, 423 Caron-
delet (Sugar Cane) C
Swoop, Julian M., 913
Girod (Sugar Cane) ...A
Whitney Iron Wks. Co.
(Cane) ....A
MD.—Baltimore
Adt, Jno. B. (Snuff) .....B
Detrick & Harvey Machine
Co. (Horizontal Drilling;
Boring; Milling) .....AA
Murray & Son. Jas., 102 E.
York (Grinding) ....B
Poole & Son Co., Robt. (Oil;
Paint; Color; Rolling
Brass; Rolling, Copper;
Fertilizer; Snuff) ......A
Ryan-McDonald Mfg. Co.
(Portable) ....A
Starr & Co., B. F. 455
North (Buhr Stone;
Grinding; Portable) ...D
MASS.—Athol
Gay & Wood (End) ......A
MASS.—Boston
Ames Plow Co. (Drug;
Spice; Grist; Corn Meal;
Coffee; Fanning) .....AA
Blanchard Machine Co.
(Bone; Soap Powder)...D
Bradley Fertilizer Co.
(Bone; Fire Brick; Min-
eral; Paint; Color; Uni-
versal; Quartz) X
McLauthlin, Geo. T. (Oil
Cake) ....H
Sturtevant Mill Co. (Bone;
Cement; Fire Brick;
Paint; Color; Fertilizer).D
MASS.—Chicopee Falls
Belcher & Taylor Agrl. Tool
Co. (Fanning) ....A
MASS.—Fitchburg
Putnam Machine Co. (Bor-
ing; Turning) ....AA
MASS.—Lowell
Lowell Machine Shop (In-
digo) ....AAAA
MASS.—New Bedford
Morse Twist Drill & Mach.
Co. (Hollow Adjustable;
End; with Inserted Teeth)
AAA
MASS.—North Adams
Hunter Machine Co., Jas.
(Fulling) ....A
MASS.—North Wilbraham
Cutler Co. (Buhr Stone;
Grist) ....A
MASS.—Orange
Chase Turbine Mfg. Co.
(Lath) ....A
Hunt, Rodney Machine Co.
(Fulling) ....A
MASS.—Plymouth
Bennett. L. H. (Fanning).X
MASS.—Springfield
Baush Machine Tool Co.
(Boring; Turning) .....B
MASS.—Woburn
Freeman & Co.. J. T.
(Leather Stuffing) ....D
MASS.—Worcester
Amer. Card Clothing Co.
(Fulling) ....AAA
Blaisdell Co., P. (Boring;
Horizontal) ....A
Draper Mach. Tool Co.
(Boring; Horizontal) ..A
Morgan Construction Co.
(Blooming; Continuous
Billet; Rod; Hoop; Cot-
ton; Tie; Merchant Bar)
A
MICH.—Albion
Cook Mfg. Co. (Feed
Grinding) ....E
MICH.—Bay City
Garland Co.. M. (Lath; Log)
C
MICH.—Detroit
Byram & Co. (Rumbling;
Cinder) ....D
Campbell Fanning Mill Co..
M. (Fanning) ....A
Durling, A. N. (Fanning).F
Huetteman & Cramer Co.
(Malt) ....A
MICH.—Grand Rapids
Butterworth & Lowe (Lath)
A
Fox Machine Co. (Boring;

MILLS (*Con.*)
Turning) X
MICH.—Hancock
Portage Lake Fdry. & Machinery Co. (Stamp) ...B
MICH.—Kalamazoo
Phelps & Bigelow Wind
Mill Co. (Wind) ......B
Smith & Pomeroy Wind
Mill Co. (Feed; Wind)..B
Williams Mfg. Co. (Wind)
B

MICH.—Lansing
Lansing Boiler & Engine
Wks. (Lath) ....B
Lansing Wheelbarrow Co.
(Cider;) ....AAA
MICH.—Manistee
Manistee Iron Wks. & Supply Co. (Band Saw)....B
MICH.—Morenci
Michigan Brick & Tile
Mch. Co. (Pug) C
MICH.—Otsego
Bardeen Paper Co. (Felt)..
AA
MICH.—Port Huron
Port Huron Engine &
Thresher Co. (Corn; Cob;
Feed Grinding) ...AAAA
MICH.—Saginaw
Ferrell & Co., A. T.
(Fanning) ....B
Mitts & Merrill (Bark;
Lath) ....B
Wickes Bros. (Band Saw;
Lath; Stave) ....AA
MICH.—Tecumseh
Brewer & Co., H. (Pug)..A
MICH.—Ypsilanti
Ypsilanti Machine Wks.
(Roller) ....D
MINN.—Faribault
Winter & Co., F. W.
(Wind) ....E
MINN.—Fergus Falls
Grollimund, M. (Fanning).G
MINN.—Minneapolis
Beeman & Co. (Fanning)..F
Cleland, A. V. (Fanning)..B
Howell & Co., R. A. (Grist;
Cob; Feed; Lath) ....B
Owens Co., J. L. (Fanning)
B
Schutz-O'Neill Co. (Grinding) C
Twin City Iron Wks.
(Minn. Steel & Mchry.
Co.) (Feed Grinding)...A
Twin City Separator Co.
(Fanning) ....B
Wellford Mfg. Co. (Roller)
C
MINN.—Owatonna
Owatonna Fanning Mill Co.
(Fanning) ....F
Sperry Mfg. Co. (Fanning)
D
MINN.—Sauk Center
Keller Mfg. Co. (Fanning)
B
MINN.—Winnebago City
Dewey Mfg. Co. (Fanning)
X
MINN.—Winona
New Winona Mfg. Co.
(Corn; Cob; Feed Grinding) ....AAA
MO.—Browning
Jenkins Hay Rake & Stacker Co. (Feed Grinding).A
MO.—Carrollton
Farm Tool Mfg. Co.
(Feed Grinding) C
MO.—Kansas City
Kansas City Hay Press Co.
(Feed Grinding) ......AA
Midland Asbestos Mfg. Co.
(Felt) ....D
MO.—St. Louis
Curtis & Co. Mfg. Co.
(Lath) ....A
Fritz, Geo. J. (Roller) ...C
Kingsland Mfg. Co. (Grist)
B
Rumsey Mfg. Co., L. M.
(Feed) ....AAA
Whitman Agrl. Co. (Grist;
Feed) ....A
MONT.—Helena
Caird & Harksworth
(Stamp) ....B

MILLS (*Con.*)
NEBR.—Beatrice
Dempster Mill Mfg. Co.
(Wind) ....A
N. H.—Keene
Humphrey Machine Co.
(Indigo) C
N. H.—Lakeport
Bickford, H. (Boring or
Turning) ....D
N. J.—Bartley
Bartley & Sons, Wm. (Sectional Bark) C
N. J.—Gloucester City
Rogers' Boat, Gauge & Drill
Wks., J. M. (Adjustable
Hollow) ....B
N. J.—Jersey City
Smith & Sons Co., Theo., ft.
of Essex (Grinding) ..A
N. J.—Newark
Binsse Machine Co. (Boring;
Facing) C
N. J.—Paterson
Paterson Machine Wks.
(Warping) ....F
N. J.—Plainfield
Pond Mach. Tool Co.
(Boring) ....AAAA
N. J.—Phillipsburg
Phillipsburg Mfg. Co.
(Grinding) ....F
N. J.—Raritan
Kenyon & Son, D. R.
(Filling) ....A
N. J.—Smithville
Smith Machine Co., H. B.
(Lath) ....A
N. Y.—Albany
Townsend Fdry. & Machine
Shop (Ball; Indigo) ....B
N. Y.—Auburn
New Birdsall Co. (Portable) ....AA
N. Y.—Belmont
Clark Bros. (Band Saw)..A
N. Y.—Brooklyn
Acton, Jno., 118 John
(Grinding) ....F
Alsing Co., J. R., 75 Guernsey (Ball; Pebble; Drug;
Grinding; Quartz) .....E
Bliss Co., E. W. (Boring
Horizontal) ......AAAA
Houchin & Huber (Ink;
Paint; Color; Chocolate)
E
Kent Machine Wks., 246
Plymouth (Grinding; Ink)
E
Nebel, M. A., 72 Grand Av.
(Grinding) ....D
Pioneer Iron Wks., 151 William (Sugar Cane) ....A
Ross & Son, Chas. (Drug;
Spice; Fire Brick;
Grease; Mineral; Paint;
Color; Salt; Starch; Universal; Upper Runner;
Buhr Stone; Chocolate;
Clay) ....D
Simpson, J. S. & G. F.
(Bone; Drug; Spice; Ink;
Mustard; Oil; Paint; Color; Starch; Universal;
Eccentric) ....A
Simpson Fdry. Co., 26 Rodney (Drug; Bone; Cork;
Spice; Oil Cake; Paint
Grinding) C
Taylor & Co. (Inc.) (Oil;
Paint; Color) ....D
N. Y.—Buffalo
Frank Mchry. Co. (Lath)..D
Holmes Mchry. Co., E. &
B. (Shingle) ....B
Nove Mfg. Co., Jno. T.
(Bone; Drug; Salt; Spice;
Mineral; Paint; Color;
Starch; Grist; Plantation;
Portable; Universal; Upper Runner; Buhr Stone;
Buckwheat; Buckwheat
Roller; Corn Meal; Corn
Roller; Pearl Barley;
Roller; Corn; Coffee;
Feed; Malt) ....D
Oliver Mfg. Co., W. W.,
1483 Niagara (Rolling).C
Smith's Sons, Jno. E.
(Drug; Spice) ....B
Squier Mfg. Co., Geo. L.
(Tortilla; Corn Meal;

MILLS (Con.)
Cane; Coffee) ....A
N. Y.—Cato
Dutton & Co., E. Q. (Feed
Grinding) ....E
N. Y.—Cattaraugus
Oakes & Burger (Curd) ..B
N. Y.—Cobleskill
Harder Mfg. Co. (Fanning)
.....................B
N. Y.—Croton-on-Hudson
Talcott & Co., W. E. (Pug)
.....................D
N. Y.—Groton
Groton Bridge & Mfg. Co.
(Grist) ....B
N. Y.—Little Falls
Burrell & Co., D. H. (Curd)
.................AAAA
Kingston's Sons, Wm.
(Felt) ....D
N. Y.—Lockport
Trevor Mfg. Co. (Shingle).B
N. Y.—Lyons
Aul & Sons, Henry (Fanning) ....F
N. Y.—Mt. Morris
Genesee Valley Mfg. Co.
(Fanning) ....B
N. Y.—Newburgh
Coldwell-Wilcox Co. (Sugar
Cane) ....B
Stroock Felt Co. (Felt) ..AA
New York City
Abbe Engineering Co., 220
B'way (Ball; Pebble;
(Paint; Drug; Spice)....E
Abele, Christian, 537 W.
50th (Grinding) .....A
Amer. Felt Co., 110 E. 13th
(Felt) ....AAAA
Amer. Wood Working Mach.
Co. (Lath) ......AAAA
Brown Co., A. & F., 26
Cortlandt (Grinding; Oil
Cake) ....A
Burns & Sons, Jabez (Coffee) C
Carey, Samuel (Cement;
Drug; Spice; Chaser; Ink;
Paint; Color; Salt; Grist;
Portable; Buhr Stone;
Corn Meal; Corn Roller;
Chocolate; Feed; Fertilizer) C
Chatillon & Sons, Jno. (Coffee; Spice; Drug) ...A
Colwell, A. W. (Bagasse;
Salurators) ....A
Corcoran, Andrew J.
(Wind) ....
Cornell Co., J. B. & J. M.,
26th & 11th Av. (Sugar
Cane) ....AA
Deeley & Co., Robert, 507
W. 32nd (Sugar Cane)...
.....................AA
Fairbanks Co. (Coffee)....
.................AAAA
Field & White, 116 Nassau
(Felt) ....D
Huntington Dry Pulverizer
Co., 120 B'way (Grinding)
.....................G
Kent Mill Co., 170 B'way
(Grinding; Quartz) ....E
Krajewski-Peasant Co., 32
B'way (Sugar Cane)..AA
Manning, Maxwell & Moore,
85 Liberty (Boring;
Turning) ....AAA
Morgan Iron Wks., 814 E.
9th (Sugar Cane) .....B
Newell Mfg. Co., 149 B'way
(Grinding) ....D
New York Agrl. Co., 53
Cliff (Feed Grinding; &
Cider Presses) ....D
Niles-Bement-Pond Co., 136
Liberty (Boring; Turning;
Car Wheel Boring).AAAA
Pedrick & Ayer Co. (Boring;
Turning) ....A
Pierce Well Engineering &
Supply Co. (Wind) C
Prosser & Son, Thos., 15
Gold (Ball; Pebble) ....A
Schock, G. (Malt) ....D
Slotkin & Praglin, 210 Canal (Foot Power) ......B
Smidth & Co., F. L., 66
Maiden Lane (Ball; Pebble) ....P

MILLS (Con.)
N. Y.—Poughkeepsie
Lane Bros. Co. (Coffee;
Drug; Grist; Spice) ...A
N. Y.—Rome
Adams & Son, S. (Lath)..C
N. Y.—Silver Creek
Ehmke, C. (Grist) ......H
Howes Co., S. (Grist; Coffee) ....A
Huntley Mfg. Co. (Grist).A
N. Y.—Syracuse
Boomer & Boschert Press
Co. (Cider) ....A
N. Y.—Troy
Grant-Ferris Co. (Drug;
Spice; Cleaning) ......F
N. Y.—Utica
Millar & Son, Chas. (Card)
.....................AA
Munson Bros. (Grist; Under
Runner; Corn; Feed) ..A
N. Y.—Waterville
Berrills' Sons, J. A. (Paint;
Color) ....B
Waterville Fdry. & Mfg. Co.
(Bark; Paint) ....F
N. C.—Charlotte
Mecklemburg Iron Wks.
(Stamp) X
N. C.—Statesville
Steele & Sons, J. C. (Pug)
.....................C
N. C.—Winston-Salem
Salem Iron Wks. (Corn;
Cob; Feed Grinding;
French Buhr Grinding;
Steam; Water; Animal
Power Sugar Cane) ....B
OHIO—Akron
Taplin, Rice & Co. (Clay).A
OHIO—Bucyrus
Amer. Clay Working Mach.
Co. (Clay Grinding; Pug;
Tile; Reduction) ......B
OHIO—Canton
Bonnot Co. (Ball; Pebble;
Pug) ....B
OHIO—Cincinnati
Amer. Tool Wks. Co., 6th &
Eggleston Av. (Boring;
Turning) ....AAA
Bickford Drill & Tool Co.,
3 Pike (Boring; Turning;
Car Wheel Boring) ....A
Blymer Iron Wks. (Portable; Tortilla; Cane; Corn;
Cob; Sorghum) ....D
Day & Co., J. H. 1144 Harrison Av. (Ball; Pebble;
Buhr Stone; Drug; Grinding; Paint; Spice) C
Fosdick Machine Tool Co.
(Boring; Turning) C
Fritsch-Francis Mfg. Co.
(Malt) X
Haven Co., Jas. L., (Cane;
Feed; Sorghum) X
King Machine Tool Co.
(Boring; Turning) C
Lane & Bodley Co. (**Band
Saw**; Grist; Stamp) ....A
McGowan Co., Jno. H. (Oil)
.....................A
Miller, L. J. (Grinding;
Bone; Chicory; Crushing;
Drug; Spice; Salt; Cob;
Corn; Coffee; Feed; **Feed
Crushing**) X
Straub Mchry. Co., 1956 W.
6th (Buhr Stone; Cocoa;
Feed Grinding; Grinding;
Roller Grinding) C
OHIO—Cleveland
Bartlett & Snow Co., C. O.
(Feed Grinding; Cement;
Drug; Paint; Spice Grinding) ....B
Bronson-Walton Co. (Coffee;
Spice, etc.) ....B
Cleveland Twist Drill Co.,
cor. Lake & Kirtland
(End) ....A
Fanner Mfg. Co. (Coffee;
Spice, etc.) ....A
Kilby Mfg. Co. (Sugar Cane)
.....................AA
Sly Mfg. Co., W. W. (Cylinder, with Pump Attached;
Exhaust Steel Tumbling;
Water Polishing) ......B
Standard Sand & Fdry. Supply Co., 1434 **Superior**
(Ball Bearing Centrifugal

MILLS (Con.)

Sand) ....D
Standard Tool Co., 1260 Central Av. (Straight; Fluted; End) ....AAA
Warner & Swasey Co. (Boring; Turning) ....A

OHIO—Columbiana
Enterprise Mfg. Co. (Grist; Feed) ....B

OHIO—Columbus
Case Mfg. Co. (Rye; Buckwheat; Buckwheat Roller; Roller; Corn; Feed) ..AA
Sun Mfg. Co. (Hand Coffee) A

OHIO—Dayton
Buckeye Iron & Brass Wks. (Oil Cake) ....A

OHIO—Galion
Freese & Co., E. M. (Pug) C

OHIO—Greenfield
Waddell Wooden Ware Wks. (Coffee; Spice) ....B

OHIO—Hamilton
Black & Clawson Co. (Ink) AA
Niles Tool Wks. Co. (Boring, Horizontal) ..AAAA

OHIO—Hillsboro
Bell Co., C. S. (Corn; Cob; Feed Grinding; Sugar Cane) ....A

OHIO—Lancaster
Eagle Machine Co. (Feed Grinding) ....A
Hocking Valley Mfg. Co. (Cider; Grist).........A

OHIO—Lockland
Carey Mfg. Co., Philip (Felt) ....AAA
Holdeman Paper Co. (Felt) A

OHIO—Mansfield
Aultman & Taylor Machry. Co. (Grist) ....AA

OHIO—Massillon
Hess, Snyder & Co. (Cinder; Wind) ....AA

OHIO—Middleport
Ohio Machine Co. (Pug) ..C

OHIO—Monroeville
Hosford, Jno. (Fanning), X

OHIO—Newark
Newark Machine Co. (Fanning) ....A

OHIO—New Lexington
Star Mfg. Co. (Feed Grinding; Sweep Feed) C

OHIO—Salem
Silver Mfg. Co. (Feed; Feed Sweep) ....AA

OHIO—Sandusky
Klotz Machine Co. (Cider) B

OHIO—Springfield
Amer. Drill Co. (Feed Grinding) ....F
Amer, Engineering Co. (Attrition Grinding) C
Foos Mfg. Co. (Attrition; Grinding; Bone; Crushing; Grist; Corn Meal; Feed) A
Kelly Co., O. S. (Feed Grinding) ....AA
Mast & Co., P. P. (Cider) AAAA
Mast, Foos & Co. (Wind) AA
Rogers Iron Co. (Feed Grinding) ....)C
Ross Co., E. W. (Feed Grinding) ....A
Springfield Machine Tool Co. (Wind) ....B

OHIO—Steubenville
Means Fdry. & Machine Co. (Pug) ....B

OHIO—Tiffin
Nat'l Mchry. Co. (Rumbling) ....AA

OHIO—Toledo
Baker Bros. (Boring; Turning) ....A
Toledo Machine & Tool Co. (Rolling) ....A

OHIO—Upper Sandusky
Beery Mfg. Co. (Feed Grinding) ....D

OHIO—Wellington
Wellington Machine Co. (Pug) ....B

OHIO—Wellsville
Stevenson Co. (Pug) .....B

OHIO—Winton Place
King Machine Tool Co. (Ver-

MILLS (Con.)

tical Boring; Turning, 42, 50, 60, 72 inch size) C

OHIO—Youngstown
Andrews Bros. Co. (Rolling) X

OHIO—Zanesville
Griffith & Wedge Co. (Stamp) ....A

OREGON—Ashland
Ashland Iron Wks. (Stamp) F

OREGON—Portland
Hammond Mfg. Co. (Stamp) X

PA.—Allegheny
Ajax Mfg. Co. (Feed Grinding) ....D
Carlin's Sons, Thos. (Pug) A

PA.—Allentown
Allentown Fdry. & Machine Wks. (Bark; Cement; Paint Color) ....A
Mosser & Son, Wm. F. (Ball; Pebble) ....A

PA.—Easton
Wilson Bros. (Bone; Drug; Spice; Family Grist; Grist; Corn; Cob) .....A

PA.—Elizabethtown
Buch's Sons, A. (Fanning) B

PA.—Erie
Stearns Mfg. Co. (Band Saw) ....AA

PA.—Franklin
Colburn Mach. Tool Co. (Boring; Turning) .....A

PA.—Harrisburg
Reist & Son, J. R. (Fanning) X

PA.—Lancaster
Eureka Bark Mill Co. (Jno. Best) (Bark; Corn Meal; Cob) ....B
Martin Brick Machine Mfg. Co. (Mortar)...........B

PA.—Landsdale
Heebner & Sons (Feed Grinding) ....A

PA.—Lebanon
Weimer Machine Wks. (Rolling) ....AA

PA.—Mechanicsburg
Comstock, Geo. S. (Cider) D

PA.—Muncy
Sprout, Waldron & Co. (Drug; Spice; Emery; Paint; Color; Buhr Stone; Corn Meal; Roller; Carbon; Corn; Cob; Feed)..A

PA.—New Holland
Zimmerman, A. A. (Feed Grinding) ....F

PA.—Philadelphia
Bement, Niles & Co. (Boring; Horizontal) ...AAAA
Campbell, P. F., 55 Laurel (Buhr Stone; Drug; Paint Fertilizer Grinding; Whiting; Oil Cake Spice)...D
Coles Mfg. Co., 1615 N. 23d (Coffee; Spice) ....D
Dell & Son, J. C. (Elect. Geared Coffee) ....G
Devlin & Co., Thos. (Coffee) AAA
Enterprise Mfg. Co., of Pa. (Coffee; Spice; Bone; Drug; Corn Meal; Coffee) AAAA
Espen-Lucas Machine Wks., Broad & Noble (Boring; Turning) ....D
Fairmount Machine Co., 2106 Wood (Fulling; Indigo), A
Furbush & Son Mach. Co., M. A. (Warping) ......A
Garrett & Co., C. S., 21 Decatur (Felt) ....A
Griscom & McFeeley (Roller) X
Hance Bros. & White (Drug; Spice) ....AA
Harrington Son & Co. (Inc.), E. (Boring) ....AA
Horn & Bros., Wm. H. (Bark) ....B
Howard Fdry. & Machine Wks. (Drug; Spice; Paint; Color) C
Keystone Machine Tool Wks., 1037 Ridge Av. (Boring; Turning) ...AA

MILLS (Con.)

Moore & White Co. (Rolling) AA

Morris, Henry G., Phila. Bourse (Sugar Cane)....F

Natl. Specialty Mfg. Co., 3d Cor. Lehigh Av. (Drug) AA

Newton Machine Tool Wks., 2347 Vine (Boring; Turning) A

Phila. Roll & Mach. Co. (Rolling) A

Power & Co., L. (Lath), AA

Sellers & Co. (Inc.), Wm., 1600 Hamilton (Boring; Turning; Car Wheel Boring) AAAA

Straub Co., A. W., 3737 Filbert (Hand Drug) D

Thompson & Campbell (Bone; Drug; Spice; Paint; Color; Portable; Roller; Fertilizer; Malt) X

Troemner, Henry (Coffee) AAA

PA.—Pittsburg

Huber & Co., S. V., Ferguson Bldg. (Continuous)..D

Machintosh, Hemphill & Co. (Ltd.) AAA

Mesta Machine Co. (Rolling; Tin Plate) AAA

Phillips & McLaren (Pug) B

PA.—Reading

Reading Hdw. Co. (Coffee) AAAA

Reading Iron Co. (Cane; Rolling) AAAA

PA.—Ridgeway

Ridgeway Machine Tool Co. (Boring; Turning) .....B

PA.—Royersford

Royersford Fdry. & Machine Co. (Cinder) C

PA.—South Bethlehem

Bethlehem Fdry. & Machine Co. (Ball; Pebble) C

PA.—Tatamy

Messinger Mfg. Co. (Bone; Shell; Fanning; Feed Grinding) B

PA.—Wilkesbarre

Vulcan Iron Wks. (Chaser) AAAA

PA.—York

Farquhar Co., A. B. (Cider; Corn; Cobb; Food Grinding) AAA

Hench & Dromgold Co. (Cider) A

Keystone Farm Machine Co. (Cider; Corn; Cob; Feed Grinding) F

Variety Iron Wks. (E. G. Smyser's Sons) (Roller) A

York Felt & Paper Co. (Felt) C

R. I.—Bridgeton

Hopkins Machine Wks. (Fulling) C

R. I.—Providence

Brown & Sharpe Mfg. Co. (Rumbling; End) AAAA

Standard Mchry. Co. (Rod Tapering; Wire Flattening) A

Textile Finishing Mchry. Co. 17 Exchange Place (Indigo) AAAA

S. C.—Charleston

Valk & Murdoch Iron Wks. (Grist) B

TENN.—Chattanooga

Chattanooga Plow Co. (Sugar Cane) A

TENN.—Clarksville

Patch, A. H. (Feed Grinding) B

TENN.—Jackson

Southern Engine & Boiler Wsk. (Inc.) (Corn; Cob) A

TENN.—Memphis

Livermore Fdry. & Machine Co. (Grist) A

TEXAS—Bryan

Chatham Mchry. Co. (Grist) B

VT.—Bennington

Scott, Olin (Fulling) A

VT.—Montpelier

Lane Mfg. Co. (Lath; Shingle) A

MILLS (Con.)

VT.—Rutland

Howe Scale Co. (Coffee; Spice) AAAA

VT.—St. Albans

St. Albans Fdry. Co. (Feed) B

VA.—Norfolk

Billups Son & Co., C. (Fanning) A

White & Bros., S. R. (Cider; Sugar Cane) A

Whitehurst Co., R. W. (Cider; Corn) B

VA.—Richmond

Cardwell Machine Co. (Cider; Oil Cake) A

WASH.—Spokane

National Iron Wks. (Inc.) (Stamp) C

WIS.—Appleton

Appleton Machine Co. (Grist) B

WIS.—Beaver Dam

Rowell Mfg. Co., J. S. (Fanning) A

WIS.—Cudahy

Power & Mining Mchry. Co. (Chlorination; Quartz; Cyanide; Stamp) AAAA

WIS.—Eau Claire

Phoenix Mfg. Co. (Band Saw; Lathe) A

WIS.—Evansville

Baker Mfg. Co. (Feed Grinding) A

WIS.—Fort Atkinson

Cornish, Curtis & Greene Mfg. Co. (Curd; Wind). A

WIS.—Kaukauna

Solar Mfg. Co. (Fanning) E

WIS.—La Crosse

James Co., Jno. (Roller) ..B

Ott & Sons, Benj. (Bark). D

WIS.—Madison

Gisholt Machine Co. (Boring; Turning) AA

WIS.—Manitowoc

Smalley & Co. (Grist; Feed) B

WIS.—Marinette

Stevens Co., A. W. (Feed Grinding, also French Buhr) AA

WIS.—Milwaukee

Allis-Chalmers Co. (Band Saw; Cyanide; Roller; Chilian; Lath; Stamp) AAAA

Filer & Stowell Co. (Ltd.) (Band Saw; Lath; Log; Shingle) AAA

Hirsch Bros. (Fanning) ...D

Kiewert Co., Chas. L. (Malt) A

Pawling & Harnishfeger (Boring; Turning) ...AA

Vilter Mfg. Co. (Malt) ..AA

WIS.—Racine

Dickey Mfg. Co., A. P. (Fanning) F

Foster & Williams Mfg. Co. (Fanning) B

Freeman & Sons Mfg. Co., S. (Feed; Grist; Corn; Cob; Fanning; Wind) A

Johnson & Field Co. (Fanning) F

Racine Implement Co. (Fanning) E

WIS.—Sheboygan

Kohler, Hayssen & Stehn Mfg. Co. (Grist) A

WIS.—Superior

Duplex Mfg. Co. (Grist; Feed; Wind) A

WIS.—Waupun

Althouse-Wheeler Co. (Feed Grinding) A

MILLSTONES

CONN.—New Haven

Harrison, Leonard D. .....H

IND.—Indianapolis

Nordyke & Marmon Co. AAA

MD.—Baltimore

Starr & Co., B. F. C

N. Y.—Buffalo

Noye Mfg. Co., Jno. T. ...X

New York City

Carey, Samuel (Buhr)....C

N. Y.—Utica

Munson Bros. Co. (Buhr)..A

MILLSTONES (Con.)
OHIO—Cleveland
Cleveland Stone Co. ..AAAA
PA.—Philadelphia
Campbell, P. T., 55 Laurel D

MIMEOGRAPHS

ILL.—Chicago
Dick Co., A. B., 161 W.
  Jackson Boul. ....AA
Rider & Co., M. D........E
N. Y.—Carthage
Mason, M. P. ....A

MINCE MEAT

See Meat; Mince.

MINERALS

See Clays

MIRRORS

See also Furniture; Glasses.

CONN.—Derby
Derby Silver Co. (Hand)
  ....AAAA
CONN.—Meriden
Bradley & Hubbard Mfg. Co.
  (Framed; Hand) .AAAA
Meriden Britannia Co.
  (Hand) ....AAAA
CONN.—Wallingford
Wallace & Sons Mfg. Co., R.
  (Hand; Toilet) ....AAAA
ILL.—Chicago
American Specialty Mfg. Co.
  70 W. Wash. (Adjustable)
  ....E
Galloway Glass Co. C
Mills Novelty Co., 11 S. Jeff
  (Carousel) ....A
Parisian Novelty Co., 163 S.
  Canal (Advertising) ...C
Rubin Bros. Mfg. Co., 345 S.
  Canal (Bath Room) ....E
IND.—Shelbyville
Conrey-Davis Mfg. Co. (Bath
  Room) ....B
MD.—Baltimore
Bereger & Co. (Hand) ...X
MASS.—Boston
Boston Mirror Co., Inc. ...D
MASS.—Florence
Florence Mfg. Co. (Framed;
  Hand; Toilet) ....A
MICH.—Detroit
Hargreaves Mfg. Co.
  (Framed; Toilet) ......A
Moore & Son, E. C., 103
  Miami Av. (Dental,
  Mouth) ....F
Widman & Co., C. D.
  (Framed) ....A
MICH.—Grand Rapids
Royal Furniture Co.
  (Framed) ....A
MICH.—Lansing
Lyons & Co., Hugh
  (Counter) ....A
MO.—St. Louis
Pauk & Sons Mfg. Co., H.
  (Framed) ....A
Western Glass Bending
  Wks. 1520 Gratiot (Bent)
N. J.—Hoboken
Schniper & Co., Wm.
  (Hand) ....AA
N. J.—Newark
Celluloid Co. (Hand; Shav-
  ing; Toilet) ....B
N. Y.—Brooklyn
Donnelly Co., J. R. (Convex;
  Folding; Foot; Hall; Man-
  tle; Pier) ....D
N. Y.—East Syracuse
Benedict Mfg. Co., M. S.
  (Toilet) ....A
New York City
Arlington Co., 475 Bway.
  (Hand) ....AAAA
Blum, Toch & Co. (French
  Mirror Plate; Amer.
  Beauty Plate).........B
Consolidated Dental Mfg. Co.
  (Dental) ....B
Denzi & Phillips (Foot) ...C
Gorham Mfg. Co., Bway &
  19th (Hand) ......AAAA
Grote & Co., F. (Hand; Toi-
  let) ....D

MIRRORS (Con.)
Herter Bros. (Inc.) (Hall;
  Mantle; Pier) ....D
Judd & Co., H. L. (Ornamen-
  tal; Toilet) ....AA
Meyer-Sniffen Co. (Ltd.)
  (Framed) ....A
Pottier & Stymus Co. (Hall;
  Mantel; Pier) ....D
Souto & Co., B. (Hall) ..B
Swain & Son (Inc.), H. C.
  (Hall) ....B
Vogel & Co., F. (Hall)....X
N. Y.—Rochester
Bausch & Lomb Optical Co.
  (Search Light) .....AAA
OHIO—Toledo
Meilink Mfg. Co. (Hand), C
PA.—Philadelphia
Behrend, Jacob, 118 Wallon
  (Bath Room) C
Johnson & Lund (Dental)
  ....AA
White Dental Mfg. Co., S. S.
  (Dental) ....AAAA
PA.—Pittsburg
Gillespie & Co., J. J.
  (Framed) ....B
PA.—Reading
Natn. Brass & Iron Wks.
  (Framed) ....A
R. I.—Providence
Foster & Bros. Co., Theo. W.
  (Hand) ....AA
Pollard & Co., A. (Pocket;
  Hand) ....E

MITRES

CONN.—New Haven
Reeves Mfg. Co. (Gauge)..C
CONN.—Waterbury
Waterbury Clock Co.
  (Gauge) ....AAAA
MASS.—Lynn
Frego, Alex J. K. (Gauge)
  ....H
N. J.—Newark
Plumb, David S. (Gauge)..D
OHIO—Canton
Berger Mfg. Co. (Eaves
  Trough) ....AA
Canton Steel Roofing Co.
  (Eaves Trough) ....A
OHIO—Cleveland
Garry Iron & Steel Co.
  (Eaves Trough) ....A
PA.—Philadelphia
Berger Bros. Co., 231 Arch
  (Eaves Trough) ....A

MITTENS

See Gloves & Mittens

MIXERS

See also Mills; Machinery.

CONN.—Ansonia
Farrell Fdy. & Machine Co.
  (German Linoleum).AAAA
CONN.—Danbury
Peck Fur Co. (Fur) .....D
CONN.—Derby
Birmingham Iron Foundry
  (Rubber) ....AA
CONN.—New Britain
Landers, Frary & Clark
  (Bread) ....AAA
DEL.—Wilmington
Pusey & Jones Co. (Sugar)
  ....AAA
Walker & Elliott (Mortar;
  Clay) ....B
D. C.—Washington
Fisher & Saxton Co. (Ce-
  ment) ....D
ILL.—Chicago
Caldwell & Son Co., H. W.
  (Concrete) ....AA
Drake Standard Machine
  Works, 300 W. Jackson
  Boul. (Concrete; Motar;
  Asphalt) ....B
Kaestner & Co. (Paint)...A
Municipal Engineering &
  Contracting Co. (Mortar)
  ....A
Wolf Co., F. W., 139 Rees
  (Sugar) ....AAA
ILL.—Decatur
Decatur Iron Works (Clay)
  ....D

MIXERS (Con.)

ILL.—Edwardsville
Edwardsville Brass Company (Gas) ....B

IND.—Indianapolis
Hetherington & Berner, 19 W. South (Asphalt) ....A
Nordyke & Marmon Co. (Flour; Feed) ......AAA

IOWA—Burlington
Murray Iron Works Co. (Meat) ....A

IOWA—Keokuk
Scott Mfg. Co. (Clay)....D

KANS.—Enterprise
Ehrsam & Sons Mfg. Co. J. B. (Plaster) ....B

KANS.—Leavenworth
Great Western Mfg. Co. (Flour; Feed) ......AA

LA.—New Orleans
Payne & Joubert, 423 Carondelet (Sugar) ......A

MD.—Baltimore
Poole Engineering & Machine Co. (Fertilizer; Paint) ....AA

MASS.—Boston
American Soda Fountain Co. (Beverage) ......AAAA
American Tool & Machine Co. (Sugar) ......AA
Johnson & Co., H. A. (Dough) ....A

MICH.—Detroit
Anderson & Sons, W. H. (Concrete; Mortar) C

MICH.—Morenci
Michigan Brick & Tile Machine Co. (Gas) ......D

MO.—St. Louis
Brecht Butchers' Supply Co., G. V., 1201 Cass Av. (Lard) ....AAA

N. J.—Jersey City
Cockburn Barrow & Machine Co. (Concrete) ....B

N. J.—Trenton
Crossley Mfg. Co. (Clay)..B
Thropp, Wm. R. (Sand)..A

N. Y.—Brooklyn
Nebel M. A., 72 Grand Av. (Paint) ....D
Pioneer Iron Works, 151 William (Asphalt) ....A
Ross & Son, Charles, 16 Steuben (Baking Powder) D

N. Y.—Buffalo
Contractors Plant Mfg. Co. (Concrete) ....B
Dopp Co., H. W. (Lard; (Paint) ....D
Iroquois Iron Works, 178 Walden Av. (Asphalt)..A
Noye Mfg. Co., Jno. T. (Flour; Feed) X
Shepard & Co., Sidney (Cake) ....AAAA
Smith's Sons, Jno. E. (Lard; Stuffing) ....B
Squier Mfg. Co., Geo. L. (Sugar) ....AAA

N. Y.—Newburgh
Coldwell-Wilcox Co. (Asphalt) ....B

New York City
Bartlett, Haywood & Co., 100 B'way (Sugar) ....B
Cornell Co., J. B. & J. M., 26th & 11th Av. (Sugar) AA
Deeley & Co., Robert, 507 W. 32d (Sugar) ......AA
Faust Machine Wks. (Paint) D
Fowler & Rockwell, 9 Elizabeth (Asphalt; Cement)X
Henworth Co., S. S., 92 Willis Av. (Sugar) ....D
Houchin & Huber (Paint).D
Jamieson Co., R. W., 5C Warren (Bread; Dough).X
Krajewski-Pesant Co., 32 B'way (Sugar) ....AA
One Minute Churn Co., 9 Old Slip (Paint) X
Ransome Concrete Machry. Co., 11 B'way (Concrete; Mortar) C
Reilley Bros. (Paint) ....D
Staubach, B. (Lard) ......A
Wing Mfg. Co.. L. J., 256

MIXERS (Con.)

W. B'way (Beverage)..D

N. Y.—Rochester
Werner, John (Chocolate).D

N. Y.—Silver Creek
Huntley Mfg. Co. (Feed).A

N. Y.—Syracuse
Dunning, W. D., 300 Water (Plaster) ....AA

N. Y.—Waterville
Waterville Fdy. & Mfg. Co. (Paint) ....F

N. C.—Charlotte
Tompkins Co., D. A. (Fertilizer) ....AA

OHIO—Bucyrus
American Clay Working Machine Co. (Clay) X

OHIO—Canton
Canton Fdy. & Machine Co. (Paint) ....B

OHIO—Cincinnati
Day & Co., J. H., 1144 Harrison Av. (Fertilizer; Cake; Plaster; Flour; Feed; Paint) ....A

OHIO—Cleveland
Bartlett & Snow Co., C. O. (Paint) ....A

OHIO—Columbus
Jeffrey Mfg. Co. (Concrete) AAAA

OHIO—Hamilton
Black-Clawson Co. (Lard) AAA

PA.—Allegheny
Carlins' Sons, Thos. (Concrete) ....A

PA.—Erie
Campbell Brass Works, J. B. (Gas) ....A
Erie Machine Shops (Asphalt) ....B
Erie Specialty Co. (Beverage) ....B
Hays Mfg. Co. (Gas)....A
Hollands Mfg. Co. (Natural Gas) ....B

PA.—Philadelphia
Campbell, P. F. (Paint)..D
Nittinger, August (Lard) A

PA.—Pittsburg
Riter-Conley Mfg. Co. (Metal) ....AAA

PA.—Williamsport
Darling Pump & Mfg. Co. (Gas) ....B

PA.—York
Dempwolf & Co., O. H. (Fertilizer) ....A

MOCCASINS

MAINE—Bangor
Buck & Co., E. A.........D

MINN.—St. Paul
St. Paul Mocassin Co.....G

New York City
Abercrombie & Fitch, 314 B'way C

PA.—Harrisburg
Waters Co., E. H.........C

WIS.—Berlin
Wright Co. ....B

WIS.—Eau Claire
Cutter, A. A. ....A

WIS.—Milwaukee
Kalt, Zimmers Mfg. Co...B

MODELS

COLO.—Denver
Flint Lomax Electric & Mfg. Co., 1937 Curtis (& Patterns) ....B

CONN.—Bridgeport
Grant Mfg. & Machine Co. (& Patterns; Experimental Metal) ....E

CONN.—Hartford
Fenn-Sadler Mach. Co. ...E

CONN.—New Haven
Griswold, Geo. M. (& Experimental Work) .....D
Reeves Mfg. Co. (& Patterns) C

CONN.—Plantsville
Shepard, Amos (Metal) .E

CONN.—Waterbury
Electrical Appliance Mfg. Co. (& Experimental Work) ....G

CONN.—Winsted
Goodwin & Kintz Co. (Inventors' Sheet Metal)..B
ILL.—Chicago
Andrews Co., A. H. (Drawing; Geometrical) ...AA
Lang Electric Co., J., 44 Michigan (& Experimental Work) ....D
Turner Brass Works, Franklin & Michigan (& Patterns; Brass) ....A
ILL.—Quincy
Reliable Foundry Co. (& Patterns) ....E
KANS.—Wichita
Wichita Mfg. Co. (& Patterns; Wood; Metal)....C
LA.—New Orleans
Buchel Machine Works, 827 Conti (& Patterns; Experimental Work) X
MASS.—Boston
Ziegler Apparatus Co., 200 Summer (& Experimental Work) X
MASS.—Fitchburg
Tenny & Merriam (& Patterns) X
MASS.—New Bedford
Acushnet Iron Co. (& Patterns) ....F
Blossom Bro. (& Patterns) X
Washburn & Co., Lettie R. (& Patterns) C
MASS.—Springfield
Bradley Co., Milton (Sunday School) ....A
MASS.—Waltham
Ames & Co., B. C. (& Experimental Work) X
MASS.—Westfield
Crane Bros. (Yacht Hull; Linenoid) ....AAA
MASS.—Worcester
Kidder, R. E., 2 Hermon (& Patterns; all kinds).E
MICH.—Detroit
Hardoin Brass Works, 180 Brush (& Patterns) ....H
MICH.—Grand Rapids
Harring, Atwood Brass Mfg. Co. (& Patterns; Metal).F
MO.—Kansas City
Hervey Machine Works (& Experimental Work) ...F
MO.—St. Louis
Banner Iron Works (& Patterns) X
Gaisler, Pattern Co., O. Jr. (& Patterns) ....G
Gorning & Luley (& Patterns) ....G
Kiburz Pattern Co., Jno. (& Patterns) ....F
Knight & Co., W. B., 1518 Olive (& Patterns; Metal) E
Medart, Fred, 3540 De Kalb (& Patterns) ....E
Neslage, Herman F., 1023 S. 11th (& Patterns) ...H
Reliance Machine & Tool Works (& Experimental Work) ....AAA
N. H.—Lakeport
Cole Mfg. Co. (& Patterns) A
N. J.—Jersey City
Spindler & Derringer, 18 Morris (& Experimental Work) ....D
N. J.—Newark
McClure, Jno. C., 28 Orange (& Patterns) X
N. Y.—Albany
Townsend Furnace & Machine Shop Co. (& Patterns) ....B
N. Y.—Brooklyn
Columbia Machine Works & Malleable Iron Co., 167 Chestnut (& Patterns; Metal) ....A
Wiarda & Co., Jno. C. (Drawing) ....AA
N. Y.—Newburgh
Chadborn Mfg. Co. (& Patterns) X
New York City
Arthur Co., 188 Front (Ex-

perimental Work) .....A
Baillard, E. V., Fox Bldg. Franklin Sq. (& Experimental Work) ....D
Devoe, F. W. & C. T. Raynolds Co. (Drawing; Geometrical) ....AAAA
Dressler & Bro., C. E., 17 Lexington Av. (& Experimental Work) ....D
Hinchcliff, H. C., 170 Centre (Metal; Experimental Work) ....E
Hurd & Co., 570-576 W. B'way (& Experimental Work) ....D
Kny-Scheerer Co., 255 4th Av. (Anatomical; Biological) C
Parsell & Weed, 129 W. 31st (& Experimental Work).D
Spencer Optical Co. (Eye).C
N. Y.—Rome
Doyle, W. J. ....D
N. Y.—Syracuse
Lewis, Chas. H., 120 S. State (& Patterns) ....F
Lipe, C. E. (Est.), 208 S. Geddes (& Patterns)...D
N. Y.—Troy
Tolhurst & Son, Wm. H., Fulton & 6th Av. (& Experimental Work) .....B
OHIO—Akron
Adamson, Alex. (& Patterns) ....D
OHIO—Canton
Canton Malleable Iron Co. (& Patterns; Brass)...B
Frankham, Wm. (& Patterns) ....F
OHIO—Cleveland
Gobeille Pattern Co. (& Patterns; Wood) ....D
OHIO—Columbus
Ohio Pump & Brass Co., 18th & Oak (& Patterns) C
Simpson Iron Co. (& Patterns; Metal) ....F
OHIO—Norwood
Dittgen & Rapp (Clay) ...D
OHIO—Springfield
Parker Mfg. Co., W. T. (& Patterns) ....G
Pauly Bros. (& Patterns) H
Tittle, R. D. (& Patterns) F
OREGON—Portland
Phoenix Iron Works (& Patterns) ....D
Portland Iron Works (& Patterns) ....A
Willamette Iron & Steel Works (& Patterns) ....A
PA.—Allegheny
White, Jno. ....H
PA.—New Castle
New Castle Asphalt Block Co. (& Patterns) ......A
PA.—Philadelphia
Allen, Geo. R., 500 N. 13th (& Patterns) C
Jenkins & Beach, 1535 Ridge Av. (& Patterns) ....H
Luzler & Son, T. B., 429 N. 5th (& Patterns) ....D
McLaughlin, Jno. K., 215 N. 2d (& Patterns) .....H
Nacke & Son, A., 723 Sansom (& Patterns; Metal) E
Rudolph, Wm. F., 234 N. Broad (& Experimental Work) ....E
PA.—Pittsburg
Reliance Pattern Works, 3204 Smallman (& Patterns) X
Sommerfeld Machine & Mfg. Co. 224 3d Av. (& Experimental Work) .....B

MOHAIR
See Woolen Goods

MOISTENERS

ILL.—Chicago
Baird Mfg. Co. (Envelope;

MOISTENERS (Con.)

Stamp) C
Eureka Blotter Bath Co.
(Dried Fruit; Cigar; Envelope; Postage Stamp).E
Knapp Co., Fred H., 80
Wabash Av. (Label)....D

MASS.—Boston
American Moistening Co.
(Air) ....B
Eureka Novelty Co. (Envelope) X
Sturtevant Co., B. F. (Air)
AAA

N. Y.—Binghamton
Binghamton Novelty Co.
(Envelope) ....E
New York City
Faber, Eberhard (Pen).AAA
PA.—Philadelphia
Phila. Textile Machine Co.
(Air) ....AA

MOLASSES & SYRUPS

CAL.—Oakland
California Mercantile Co.
(Refined) ....B
Columbia Mercantile Co.
(Refiners) C
CAL.—San Francisco
Long Syrup Refining Co.,
8th & Brannan ....B
Pacific Coast Syrup Co., 713
Sansome ....B
CONN.—New Haven
Stoddard & Co., G. (Importers) ....AA
GA.—Atlanta
Eagle Mfg. Co. (Refiners).C
Planters Syrup Refining Co.
A
GA.—Cairo
Quitman Syrup & Produce
Co. C
GA.—Thomasville
Cooper Co., C. W. C
ILL.—Chicago
Berry, Maybrun Co., 59 Larrabee C
Bradshaw, J. H., 188 C. H.
Place ....A
Corn Products Co. ...AAAA
Durand & Kasper Co., 153
W. Lake (Ref.) ....AAA
Glucose Sugar Refining Co.,
The Rookery ......AAAA
Manierre-Yoe Syrup Co., 30
River ....A
Oelerich & Laux, 6 Austin
Av. ....B
Reid, Murdock & Co., Lake
& Market ....AAAA
Scudder Syrup Co., 43 River
C
Scully Syrup Co., D. B., 416
Illinois (Rock Candy Syrup) ....A
Wogan Bros., 287 Kinzie..A
ILL.—Peoria
Oakford & Fahnestock (Refiners) ....AA
IND.—Evansville
Indiana Canning Co. (Packers) C
IND.—Indianapolis
Champion Syrup Refining
Co., W. 10th & Belt R. R.
AA
Schnull & Co. (Refiners)
AAAA
IOWA—Benson
Morgan Bros. C
IOWA—Davenport
Glucose Sugar Refining Co.
AAAA
KANS.—Fort Scott
Fort Scott Sugar & Sorghum
Syrup Co. ....B
KANS.—Independence
Adamson Mfg. Co. (Sorghum
Syrup) ....B
KY.—Louisville
Torbitt & Castleman, 127
2d ....A
LA.—Baldwin
Borg, Joe (Planter) .....A
LA.—Bancker
Code, Wm. (Planter).....C
LA.—Baton Rouge
Goyer & Co., R. L. .....AA

MOLASSES & SYRUPS
LA.—Bayou Goula
Murrell Mfg Co., G. M....A
LA.—Belle Rose
Dehom & Pryeau (Planters)
B
Kessler Bros. (Planters).B
LA.—Caspiano
Hughes, J. V. (Planter)..A
Hutchinson, W. J. (Planter)
B
LA.—Chenal
Rongon Bros. (Planters)..B
LA.—Houma
Minor, H. C. (Planter)....A
Minor, J. D. (Planter)....B
LA.—Illawara
Graham, H. H. (Planter).B
LA.—Klotzville
Klotz, A. (Planter).....A
LA.—Lindsay
McKowen, T. C. (Planter)
C
LA.—Lordells
Kahoa, M. I. (Planter)...B
LA.—Longbridge
Bordelow & Cappel (Planters) C
LA.—Loreauville
Gonsaulin, A. (Planter)..C
LA.—Louisa
Burguieres, M. E. D. (Planter) ....AA
Burguieres, Jules M. (Planter) ....AA
LA.—Lucy
Burch & Champagne (Planters) C
LA.—McCall
McCall Bros. Planting Co.
A
LA.—Mabel
Smart, Alex. (Planter)...A
LA.—Manchac
Lefebun, V. M. (Planter).B
LA.—Mansura
Regard, Fereal. (Planter).B
LA.—Monroe
Monroe Sugar & Molasses
Co. ....A
LA.—Natchez
Williams, R. B. & J. W.
(Planters) ....A
Williams & Son, R. B.
(Planters) ....A
LA.—Newellton
Marks, S. (Planter) C
LA.—New Orleans
Alexander Co., M. H., 319
Decatur (R. C. Syr.)...A
Aaron & Co., J., 416 Poydras (Molasses) ....A
Bloomfield, W. B., 207 N.
Peters ....B
Bodenhemier & Bro., 209 N.
Peters ....A
D'Aquin, J. J., 223 N. Peters ....B
Dunbar Sons', G. W., 3400
Chartres ....A
Ellington Planting Co., Ltd.,
219 N. Peters ....A
Ermann & Cahn, 233 N. Peters ....A
Feibelman, Sons & Co., E.,
418 S. Peters.........A
Godchaux Co., Leon (Planters) ....AAAA
Harral, J. A., 319 Carondelet C
Hearn & Jones, 204 Fulton
A
Henderson, T. J., 235 N.
Peters C
Henderson, W., 237 N. Peters ....AA
Hobart & Co., H. L., 307
N. Front ....A
Israel, Leon. 417 Poydras..B
Louisiana Molasses Co., 414
St. Joseph ....A
McDermott, Thos., 225 N.
Peters ....A
Miles Planting & Mfg. Co.,
217 N. Peters ....AA
Scudder, R. B., N. Front &
Bienville C
Taussig Co., N. W......AA
Westerfield, J. R., 235 N.
Peters C
Wogan Bros., N. Peters &
Port ....A

682

MONOGRAMS

MONUMENTS

See also Stone

MO**NUMENTS** (Con.)   MORTAR (Con.)

MONUMENTS (Con.)
(Bronze) ....F
Gorham Mfg. Co., 19th &
B'way (Bronze) ..AAAA
Henry-Bonnard Bronze Co.,
430 W. 16th (Bronze)..C
Lamb, J. & R. (Cemetery)
D
PA.—Philadelphia
Bureau Bros., cor. 21st &
Allegheny Av. (Bronze).D
Phila. White Bronze Monu-
ment Co. (Cemetery)...X
Tacony Iron & Metal Co.,
(Bronze) ....A
WIS.—Sheboygan
Kohler, Hayssen & Stehn
Mfg. Co. (Cemetry) ...X

MOPS

CONN.—Bristol
Conzelman, C. (Cotton)...F
ILL.—Freeport
Arcade Mfg. Co..........A
Stover Mfg. Co..........AA
MASS.—Fall River
Estes & Son, Jno. ....A
MASS.—Winchendon
Clark, Wilder P. ....A
MICH.—Fenton
Phillips Co., A. J........A
New York City
Massasoit Mfg. Co., 56 Leon-
ard (Cotton) ....AA
Naurath & Co., J. P., 109
Wooster ....B
N. Y.—Rochester
Castel & Co., Wilmot....X
N. Y.—Troy
Parks & Parks ....D
N. Y.—Warsaw
Martin, W. D. ....G
OHIO—Canton
Kohler & Co., F. E......B
OHIO—Cincinnati
Ault Woodenware Co., 6th
& Carr ....A
De Roo, P., 105 E. Canal..D
Meyer, Sr., B., 19 E. Ca-
nal ....D
OHIO—Oxford
Ohio Mop, Pail & Wringer
Co. ....E
OHIO—Sidney
Donaldson & Boal Broom Co.
B
PA.—Erie
Erie Mop & Wringer Co...D
PA.—Reading
Reading Hdw. Co. ...AAAA
VT.—Wallingford
Hoadley, F. H. ....D

MORPHINE ..

MO.—St. Louis
Mallinckrodt Chemical Wks.
AAAA
New York City
McKesson & Robbins.AAAA
Merck & Co. ....AAAA
N. Y. Quinine & Chemical
Works (Ltd.), 114 Wil-
liam ....A
PA.—Philadelphia
Powers-Weightman-Ro-
sengarten Co. ....AAAA

MORTAR

DEL.—Wilmington
Warner Co., Charles (Ma-
chine Mixed) ....AA
D. C.—Washington
National Mortar Co., 625 F.,
N. W. (Machine Mixed).B
N. Y.—Buffalo
Buffalo Paragon Wall Plas-
ter Co., 11 Brecken-
bridge (Machine Mixed).C
New York City
U. S. Mortar Supply Co.,
1123 B'way (Machine
Mixed) ....B
PA.—Philadelphia
Knickerbocker Lime Co.,
366 N. 24th (Machine
Mixed) ....A
VT.—Chester Depot
American Soapstone Finish
Co. (Patent Soapstone).F

MORTAR (Con.)
VA.—Norfolk
Builders' Supply Co. (Ma-
chine Mixed) ....B

MORTARS

N. J.—Burlington
Stuart & Peterson Co.
(Druggists' Iron) ......A
N. J.—Trenton
Trenton Potteries Co...AAA
New York City
Hughes, Thomas (Druggists'
Display) ....D
Maris & Co., John M., 219
Fulton ....B

MORTISERS

See also Machinery

CONN.—New Britain
New Britain Machine Co.
(Chain Saw) ....A
CONN.—Norwich
Rogers & Co., C. B. (Foot
Power) ....AAAA
ILL.—Rockford
Barnes Co., W. F. & Jno.
(Foot Power) ....AA
MD.—Baltimore
Sloan & Co., Frank B., 10
S. Charles (Sash Pulley)
C
MASS.—Boston
Austin & Eddy, 117 Broad
(Sash Pulley) C
Woods Machine Co., S. A.
(Hollow Chisel; Horizon-
tal; Vertical) ......AA
MASS.—Worcester
Hobbs Mfg. Co. (Power)..A
N. J.—Newark
Gould & Eberhardt (Foot
Power) ....A
Seymour & Whitlock (Foot
Power) ....B
N. J.—Smithville
Smith Machine Co., H. B.
(Foot Power) ....A
New York City
American Wood Working
Mach. Co. (Foot Power)
AAAA
N. Y.—Seneca Falls
Seneca Falls Mfg. Co. (Foot
Power) ....B
N. Y.—Troy
Kellogg, Wm. P. (Foot
Power) X
OHIO—Cincinnati
Fay, J. A. & Egan Co.
AAAA

MOSAICS

CAL.—San Francisco
California Marble Co. (Cera-
mic; Marble) ....D
Giletti System Co., Builders'
Exchange (Marble) ...X
CONN.—Hartford
Hartford Mantel & Tile Co.,
164 State (Marble) X
White & Whitmore, 38 Ann
(Marble) C
D. C.—Washington
Corning, Jno. Herbert, 520
13th. N. W. (Marble)..E
Hutchinson, Wm. Seeley,
1331 G., N. W. (Marble)
X
National Mosaic Co., 207
John Marshall Place
(Marble) ....D
ILL.—Chicago
Caretti & Co., Jno., 232
Michigan (Ceramic; Mar-
ble) ....G
Davidson Bros. Marble Co..
ft. of Orleans (Marble).B
Davis Mosaic Co., 302 Mich-
igan Av. (Ceramic; Ro-
man; Marble: Venetian)
E
Hawes & Dodd, 24 Adams
(Ceramic; Marble) C
Henry Marble Co., 1628 Wa-
bash Av. (Marble) X
Keating & Sons' Co., M.,
224 Washn. (Marble)...D
Lorenzen & Co., Chas. F.,

MOSS (Con.)

New York City
Schwenker, W. M. (Irish) .B

PA.—Philadelphia
Baeder, Adamson & Co. (Artificial; Upholsterers') ....AAAA
Keller, Robert (Irish) ....D

WIS.—Milwaukee
Kiewert Co., Chas. L. (Irish) ....A

MOTIONS

MASS.—Boston
Riley & Co., C. E., 65 Franklin (Drawing Frame Stop) ....A

MASS.—Fall River
Fall River F'dy. & Machine Co. (Spooler Stop) ....F

MASS.—Hopedale
Draper Co. (Loom Stop; Warp Stop; Spooler Stop; Spooler Traverse) .AAAA

MASS.—Lowell
Lahue & Co., H. M. (Steel Lug Pick) ....E
Lowell Machine Shop (Evener; Spooler Stop)..AAAA

MASS.—Newton Upper Falls
Saco & Pettee Machine Wks. (Evener) ....AAA

MASS.—Readville
Stafford Co., Geo. W. (Warp Stop) ....A

MASS.—Taunton
Mason Machine Wks. (Evener) ....AA

MASS.—Worcester
Cleveland Machine Works (Doffer Comb) ....A
Crompton & Knowles Loom Wks. (Selvage) .AAAA

N. J.—New Brunswick
Crawford Mfg. Co. (Mechanical Stop) ....F

PA.—Philadelphia
Barker, James, Cayuga & N. 6th (Doffer Comb)..A
Nye & Fredick Co., 666 Arch (Knitting Machine Stop) D

R. I.—Pawtucket
Howard & Bullough American Machine Co. (Ltd.) (Drawing Frame Stop) AAA

R. I.—Providence
Curry & Co., Albert, 102 Friendship (Spooler Stop) H

MOTORS

See also Engines; Dynamos

CAL.—San Francisco
Jackson Machine Works, Byron (Oil Fuel) ......A

CONN.—Bristol
Smith, Ira B. (Water)....E

CONN.—Cos Cob
Palmer Bros. (Gasoline Automobile) C

CONN.—Hartford
Organ Power Co. (Organ; Water) ....E

CONN.—Windsor
Eddy Electric Mfg. Co. (Electric) ....D

ILL.—Chicago
American Gasoline Motor Co., 88 W. Jackson Boul. (Gasoline: 1 1-2 to 8 h. p.) X
Chicago Pneumatic Tool Co., Fisher Bldg. (Pneumatic) AAAA
Chicago Water Motor & Fan Co., 22 S. Canal (Water) E
Fairbanks, Morse & Co., Franklin & Monroe (Gasoline Turntable) .AAAA
Hoffman Motor Co., H. L., 30 W. Randolph (4-Cycle Gasoline Automobile) ..X
Illinois Malleable Iron Co., 30 W. Monroe (Water) AAAA
Roth Bros. & Co. (Electric

MOTORS (Con.)

Electric Fan) ....F

ILL.—Decatur
Faries Mfg. Co. (Revolving Spring) ....A

ILL.—Downer's Grove
Dicke Tool Co. (Water, for Washing Bottles) C

IND.—Connersville
Connersville Blower Co. (Water) ....B

IND.—Ft. Wayne
Fort Wayne Electric Corporation (Electric, Alt. Current; Electric Direct Connected; Electric Multi-Polar) ....AA

IND.—Hagerstown
Light Inspection Car Co. (Gasoline) ....D

IND.—Indianapolis
Commercial Electric Co., 220 W. Merrill (Electric Crane; Electric Elevator) A
Jenney Electric Mfg. Co. (Electric; Electric Direct Connected; Electric Elevator; Electric Multi-Polar; Electric Printing Press) ....A
Specialty Mfg. Co., 400 S. Meridian (Water) ....E

KANS.—Topeka
Baird Portable Machine Co. (Pneumatic Wood Boring) ....B

MAINE—Brunswick
Brunswick Mfg. Co. (Water) ....D

MD.—Baltimore
Rosenberg Co., A. (Water; Electric Manicuring; Dental) ....H

MASS.—Boston
Clark & Mills, 543 Boylston (Electric Fan) ....D
Gilmore Electric Co. (Electric; Water) ....A
Sturtevant Co., B. F. (Electric; Electric Street; Railway) ....AA
Whitney, F. E., 65 Sudbury (Organ; Water) ....E
Wood-Gleeson Motor Co., 106 Sudbury (Gasoline).X

MASS.—Cambridge
Crest Mfg. Co. (Gasoline Automobile) ....D

MASS.—Lowell
Barker Mfg. Co., H. R. (Organ) ....B

MASS.—Springfield
Elektron Mfg. Co. (Electric; Organ; Electric Organ Blowing) ....B
Russell, Jno. W. (Water).D

MASS.—Waltham
Waltham Mfg. Co. (Automobile) ....AA

MICH.—Battle Creek
American Steam Pump Co. (Hydraulic Organ) .AAA

MICH.—Detroit
Leland & Faulconer Mfg. Co., 480 Twombly Av. (Gasoline) ....B
Michigan Steel Boat Co. (Marine Gasoline) .....D
Northern Engineering Wks. (Compressed Air) .....A

MICH.—Grand Haven
Dake Engine Co. (Reversible Air) ....A

MICH.—Grand Rapids
Wolverine Motor Works (Gasoline; Benzine; Marine) C

MICH.—Menominee
Menominee Electric Mfg. Co. (Electric Fan) C

MICH.—Port Huron
Lansing Motor Wks. (Gasoline; Mine Gas) X

MICH.—St. Joseph
St. Joseph Iron Wks. (Gasoline) ....B
Truscott Boat Mfg. Co. (Marine) ....A

MICH.—Three Rivers
Sheffield Car Co. (Electric) AA

MOTORS (Con.)

MINN.—Minneapolis
D. & D. Electric Mfg. Co.,
4th & 11th Av. (Electric) X
MINN.—St. Paul
Eureka Mfg. & Supply Co.
(Cycle) ....H
Graves Motor Mfg. Co.
(Cycle) X
Helwig Mfg. Co. (Reversible Pneumatic; Compressed Air) ....F
MO.—St. Louis
Emerson Electric Mfg. Co.,
718 St. Charles (Electric;
Alt. Desk, Bracket & Ceiling Electric Fan) .....B
Nelson Mfg. Co., N. O.
(Water) ....AAA
Neustadt-Perry Co., 826 S.
18th (Automobile) C
St. Louis Gasoline Motor Co.
(Automobile; Gasoline).F
St. Louis Gas & Gasoline
Engine Works, 2519 S. 2d
(Automobile) ....F
Standard Railway Equipment Co., Union Trust
Bldg. (Pneumatic) .....D
N. H.—Lebanon
Kendrick & Davis (Battery;
Electric Toy; Water)...A
N. J.—Ampere
Crocker-Wheeler Co. (Electric Crane; Electric Elevator; Electric Direct
Connected; Electric Fan)
AAA
N. J.—Belleville
Eck Dynamo & Motor Wks.
(Types: 1-32 to 5 h. p.
Electric) C
N. J.—Boundbrook
American Engine Co. (Electric; Electric Street; Railway) ....A
N. J.—Elizabethport
Diel Mfg. Co. (Electric)..A
N. J.—Harrison
Storey General Electric Co.
(Electric, for Flexible
Shaft) ....AA
N. J.—Jersey City
Holland Auto. Co. (Automobile) X
N. J.—Newark
Backus Water Motor Co.,
174 Penna. Av. (Water).B
Blevney, J. C. (Hydrocarbon) X
Seymour & Whitlock, 43
Lawrence (Water) .....B
N. Y.—Auburn
Fay & Bowen (Gasoline)..D
N. Y.—Binghamton
G. & E. Electric & Construction Co. (Water).......E
Stow Mfg. Co. (Portable;
Electric) ....B
N. Y.—Brooklyn
Houchin & Huber (Gasoline)
E
Industrial Machine Co., 302
Pearl (Gasoline) .....E
Regent Auto. & Mach. Co.,
12 Clinton (Gas; Gasoline
Automobile) X
N. Y.—Buffalo
Buffalo Gasoline Motor Co.
(Automobile) ....D
Thomas Motor Co., E. R.
(Gasoline Automobile;
Cycle; Gasoline) .....A
N. Y.—Elbridge
Elbridge Electrical Mfg. Co.
(Electric) C
N. Y.—Fulton
Hunter Fan & Motor Co.
(Water) ....B
N. Y.—Long Island City
Daimler Mfg. Co. (Marine;
Vehicle Gasoline; Marine
& Vehicle Gas; Marine &
Vehicle Oil Fuel) ...AA
New York City
American Hydraulic Motor
Co., 116 Nassau (for Gas
Compressing) X
American Impulse Wheel
Co. (Water) ....E
American Motor Co. (Gaso-

MOTORS (Con.)

line) X
C. & C. Electric Co. (Electric; Electric Battery)AA
Compress Air Co., 621 B'way
(Air) ....AA
Falcon Electric Mfg. Co.,
432 E. 71st (Electric Fan)
X
General Incandescent Arc
Light Co., 572 1st Av.
(Electric) ....A
Goldmark & Wallace, 67
Cortlandt (Hurricane Direct Current Electric Fan)
D
International Brass & Electric Co., 76 Beekman
(Small Electric) .....D
Jordan Bros., 74 Beekman
(Organ) ....F
Manhattan Machinery Co.
(Electric; Automobile Carriage) X
Ostrander & Co., W. R.
(Electric Fan) ....B
Rider Boiler Co., 131 Liberty (Steam Automobile)
X
Sprague Electric Co., 527
W. 34th (Electric; Fan
Electric) ....AAAA
Swan Electric Mfg. Co., 59
William (Gasoline) ...B
Worthington Pumping Engine Co. (Int. Steam
Pump Co.) (Water).AAAA
N. Y.—North Tonawanda
Armitage & Herschell Co.
(Electric) ....A
N. Y.—Oneida
Oneida Automobile Co.
(Steam Automobile) ...F
N. Y.—Orangeburg
Empire Engine & Motor Co.
(Pneumatic Crane; Electric) ....B
N. Y.—Ossining
Kipp, Jr., A. (Organ)....D
N. Y.—Rochester
Burns, M. F., 20 Spring
(Electric) ....H
Rochester Electric Motor
Co. (Electric; Direct Connected) ....F
N. Y.—Schenectady
General Electric Co. (Electric; Electric Crane; Induction; Street & Railway
Electric; Electric Fan)
AAAA
N. Y.—Syracuse
Brennan Motor Co. (Gasoline Automobile) .....F
N. Y.—Troy
Bernard Co., E. G. (Electric; Electric Direct Connected; Electric Inclosed)
D
Ross Valve Co. (Organ;
Water) C
OHIO—Akron
Akron Electrical Mfg. Co.
(Electric) C
Webster, Camp & Lane
Mach. Co. (Electric) ..A
OHIO—Cincinnati
Bullock Electric Mfg. Co.
(Electric; Electric Direct
Connected; Electric Printing Press) ....AAAA
Carlisle & Finch Co., 229
E. Clifton Av. (Water).C
Cincinnati Electric Motor
Co. (Electric, 1-2 to 10
h. p.) X
Jantz & Leist Electric Co.,
808 Elm (Electric, Enclosed Type 1 1-2 to 15
h. p.) ....E
Scott, Kornhoff & Co., 682
Webb (Gasoline, for Vehicles) ....H
Triumph Electric & Ice Machine Co., 610 Baymiller
(Electric Elevator; Electric Direct Connected;
Electric Printing Press;
Electric Street & Railway) ....A
OHIO—Cleveland
Bishop & Babcock Co., Han-

MOTORS (Con.)

ilton cor. Kirtland (Organ Water) ....AA
Chisholm & Moore Mfg. Co. (Compressed Air) ...AA
Cleveland Faucet Co. (Water) ....AA
Elwell-Parker Electric Co. (Slow Speed Electric Automobile) ....A
Excelsior Elec. Mfg. Co. (Water) ....G
Lincoln Electric Co. (Automobile; Small Electric; Electric Elevator) .....F
Ohio Electric Works, 76 Ellen (Battery; Electric Fan; Electric) ....F

OHIO—Columbus

Columbus Brass Co. (Water) ....B
Jeffrey Mfg. Co. (Electric) ....AA

OHIO—Dayton

Bates & Bro., D. L. (Water) ....B
Dayton Fan & Motor Co. (Water) C
Roberts & Co., Geo. L. (Water) ....A
Thresher Electric Co. (Automobile; Electric, Direct Connected; Electric Elevator; Electric Enclosed; Electric Multi-Polar)....C

OHIO—Loraine

Loraine Steel Co. (Br. Federal Steel Co., N. Y. City) (Street; Railway Electric) ....AAAA

OHIO—Mansfield

Humphryes Mfg. Co. (Water) ....A
Phoenix Electric Mfg. Co. (Electric) ....B

OHIO—Ravenna

Colonial Electric Co. (Direct Current Desk; Ceiling Electric Fan) ....B

OHIO—Springfield

Leffel & Co., Jas. (Water) ....AA
Robbins & Myers Co. (Electric; Electric Fan).....B

OHIO—Warren

Warren Electric & Specialty Co. (Electric Fan)...,..A

PA.—Erie

Erie City Iron Wks. (Electric; Electric Multi-Polar) ....AAAA
Federal Electric Co. (Electric) ....D
Keystone Electric Co. (Electric Elevator; Electric Reversible) ....A

PA.—Lancaster

Towle Mfg. Co., Geo. C. Electric Fan) ....F

PA.—Philadelphia

Baldwin Locomotive Wks. (Burnham, Williams & Co.,) Street Railway Electric) ....AAAA
Dallett & Co., Thos. H. (Electric) ....A
Howard Fdry. & Machine Wks. (Electric)........C
Motor Vehicle Power Co., 1221 Spg. Garden (Gasoline Automobile)........D
Quaker City Electric Co. (Electric) ....D
Stow Flexible Shaft Co., N. 26th & Buttonwood (Air; Flectric for Flexible Shaft; Steam; Compressed Air) ....B
Underwood & Co., H. B., 1025 Hamilton (Air)...B

PA.—Pittsburg

Marshall Bros. (Electric)..................AA
Porter Co., H. K. (Street; Railway; Steam).....AA
Westinghouse Elec. & Mfg. Co., Westinghouse Bldg. (Electric Railway; Electric Street) ......AAAA

PA.—Reading

Reading Electric Co. (Electric) ....B

MOTORS (Con.)

VT.—Montpelier

Lane Mfg. Co. (Water)...A

VA.—Richmond

Coffee & Sons (Inc.), R. W. (Gasoline).........F

W. VA.—Wheeling

Little, Thos. A. (Water)..C

WIS.—Madison

Northern Electrical Mfg. Co. (Electric, ⅛ to 2 H. P.) ....A

WIS.—Menominee

Submerged Electric Motor Co. (Electric) C

WIS.—Milwaukee

Erwin Hydraulic Machy. Co. 204 Grand Av. (Water).D
Mechanical Appliance Co. (Electric) C
Milwaukee Electric Co. (Electric) X
Pawling & Harnischfeger (Electric) ....AA

WIS.—Racine

Racine Malleable & Wrought Iron Co. (Water).......B

MOULDERS

CONN.—Thompsonville

Bushnell Press Co., G. H. (Seed Meal) ....A

MICH.—Saginaw

Werner & Pfleiderer (Dough) ....A

MO.—St. Louis

Fritz, Geo. J. (Seed Meal).B

N. Y.—Buffalo

Holmes Machinery Co., E. & B. (Variable Feed)...B

MOULDINGS

See also Woodwork; Pictures

CONN.—Ansonia

Ansonia Brass & Copper Co. (Copper; Brass; Bronze) ....AAAA

CON.—Bridgeport

Bridgeport Brass Co. (Copper; Brass; Bronze).AAA

CONN.—Essex

Essex Wood Turning Co. (Carved; Rope; Twisted; Furniture) X

CONN.—New Haven

Cowles & Co., (Inc.) C. (Metal; Ratan) ....A
English & Mersick Co. (Carriage) ....B

CONN.—Torrington

Coe Brass Mfg. Co. (Copper; Brass; Bronze) ....AAAA

CONN.—Waterbury

Benedict & Burnham Mfg. Co. (Copper; Brass; Bronze) ....AAAA
Holmes, Booth & Haydens Co. (Copper; Brass; Bronz) ....AAAA
Plume & Atwood Mfg. Co. (Brass) ....AAA
Randolph-Clowes Co. (Brass; Piano; Carriage) ..AAA

FLA.—Apalachicola

Cypress Lumber Co. (Cypress) ....AA

GA.—Dawson

Variety Wks. Co. (Sash; Door; Blind) ....D

ILL.—Chicago

Anderson & Lind, 131 N. May (Embossed) ......D
Bilek Co., Stephen. 306 S. Clinton (Embossed) ....D
Boynton & Co., 67 W. Washington (Embossed; Rope; Twisted) ....B
Braun, J. G., 322 S. Paulina (Steel, for Store Fronts; Stairways; Elev. Enclosures) ....A
Ehnborn & Co., C. 214 S. Clinton (Rope; Twisted) ....G
Foster Munger Co., W. 20th S. Sangamon (Carved; Rope; Twisted) ......AA
Friedley & Voshart, 196 Mather (Sheet Metal)..A
Gouger & Co., Jno. A., W.

22nd & Laflin (Carved)
........AA
Hartman, Jno., 13 N. Jefferson (Carved) ....E
Klicka Co., Joseph (Gilt).B
Lever Mfg. Co., C. H., 19 N. Jefferson (Electrical Wood) ....D
Mc Kay & Co., A. 792 W. Madison (Carved) ......D
Mueller Bros. Art & Mfg. Co. (Picture Frame)....B
Noblett Co., E. J., 898 35th (Electrical; Wood) C
Palmer, Fuller & Co., 2244 Lumber (Carved) ....A
Prendergast, J. 143 N. Hermitage (Rope; Twisted).F
Roberts & Co., E. L., W. 22nd & Union Place (Carved; Rope; Twisted)....A
Standard Carriage Lamp Co. (Carriage) ....D
Wright & Craycroft, 542 W. 21st (Electrical; Wood).C

ILL.—Rock Island
Rock Island Sash & Door Wks. (Embossed) ....AA

IOWA—Clinton
Curtis Bros. & Co. (House Finishing) ..AAA

KY.—Covington
Ohio Scroll & Lumber Co. (Carved; Embossed; Rope & Twisted; Carriage; Furniture) ....D

KY.—Louisville
Central Planing Mill & Lumber Co., 3d & Q. (Carved)
D

LA.—New Orleans
L'Hote Lumber Mfg. Co., N. Liberty & Toulouse (Embossed; Rope; Twisted) ....AA

LA.—Ramos
Ramos Lumber Mfg. Co., (Ltd.) (Cypress) ....AA

MAINE—Ellsworth
Ellsworth Hdw. Co. (Rope; Twisted, also Ball).....E

MASS.—Boston
Ceppi & Co., Alexander (Frame) ....A
Cypress Lumber Co., 153 Milk (Cypress) ......AA
Matthews Consolidated Slate Co., 199 Wash'n (Slate).X
Stearns Lumber Co., A. T. (Carved) ....AA

MASS.—Springfield
Taber-Prang Art Co. (Frame) ....AA

MICH.—Detroit
Dwight Lumber Co., Cor. Congress & 1st (Carved)
A
Hargreaves Mfg. Co. (Frame) ....A

MICH.—Grand Rapids
Amer. Carving & Mfg. Co., 900 Granville Av. (Carved; Rope; Twisted; Beaded).D
Grand Rapids Carved Moulding Co. (Carved; Rope; Twisted; Frame) X
Waddell Mfg. Co. (Carved; Rope; Twisted) ....B

MICH.—Holland
Michigan Toy & Novelty Co. (Carved; Embossed; Rope; Twisted) ....E

MO.—St. Louis
Baxter Moulding Co. (Frame) ....B
Webber Moulding Co., J. R. (Frame) ....B

N. H.—Milford ●
Pierce & Co., W. E. (Carved; Embossed; Rope; Twisted) ....D

N. J.—Edgewater
Hinner's Sons, E. H. (Carved) ....B

N. J.—Newark
Lockwood Mfg. Co. (Carriage) ....B
Schrafft Moulding Co., (Inc.) A.. 69 Polk (Picture; Room; Carved; Turned; Casket) C

N. Y.—Binghamton
Robertson & Son, A. (Frame) ....AA

N. Y.—Brooklyn
Gebhardt, J. F., Calyer & Newell (Embossed) ....E
Johnson Bros., 45 Classon Av. (Electrical; Wood).B
Miller & Doing, 83 Wash'n (Sheet Metal) ....F
White Co., James 446 Adelphia (Sheet Metal)....D

New York City
Broschart & Braun, 607 W. 130th (Sheet Metal)....X
Hungerford Brass & Copper Co., U. T., 497 Pearl (Copper; Brass; Bronze)...AA
Jones & Co., Trevor F., 374 W. B'way (Copper; Brass; Bronze) X
Leslie, Jno., 138 W. 15th (Carved) ....B
Lincoln & Co., F. W. (Frame) ....F
Lippe Gold Frame Mfg. Co. (Frame; Gilt) ....B
Manhattan Brass Co.. 334 E. 28th (Copper; Brass; Bronze) ....A
Metal Stamping Co. (Metal; Carriage) ....A
New York Carved Moulding Co. 771 1st Av. (Carved; Embossed; Rope; Twisted)
D
Parker, Edwin C., 519 W. 30th (Carved) ....F
Saulpaugh's Sons, J. M., 706 E. 12th (Electrical; Wood) ....D
U. S. Frame & Picture Co. (Frame) ....D

N. Y.—Portchester
Mertz's Sons, Geo. (Embossed; Rope; Twisted)....B

N. Y.—Rochester
Gillis & Co., J. W. (Frame) ....A
Nat'l Casket Co. (Casket)
AAAA

N. Y.—Rome
Rome Brass & Copper Co (Copper; Brass; Bronze)
AAAA

OHIO—Cincinnati
Lee, Thos., 209 Race (Circular Sheet Metal).C
Reuhl Moulding Mfg. Co. (Frame) ....A
Stoehr Co., A., 1911 Elm (Embossed) ....G

OHIO—Cleveland
Schaber, Reinthal & Co. (Hardwod; Bronze; Gilt)
AA

OHIO—Columbus
Nelson Co., C. T. (Carved)
D

OHIO—Salem
Mullins, W. H. (Sheet Metal) ....A

OHIO—Toledo
Toledo Moulding Co. (Bronze; Frame; Gilt)..A

PA.—Pen Argyl
Fitzgerald, Speer & Co. (Embossed) ....A

PA.—Philadelphia
Hall & Garrison Mfg. Co. 1124 Washn. (Carved).X
Sheip Mfg. Co., H. H., 529 Columbia Av. (Electrical; Wood) ....AA

PA.—Pittsburg
Diebold Lumber & Mfg. Co.. 99 Wabash (Embossed).A

WIS.—Milwaukee
Ponpert Mfg. Co., Geo., 419 Poplar (Carved) ......A

WIS.—Oshkosh
Gould Mfg. Co., (Carved).A
Mc Millen Co., R. (Carved) ....A
Morgan Co. (Carved; Rope; Twisted) ....AA
Paine Lumber Co. (Embossed) ....AAAA

MOULDS

COLO.—Denver

MOULDS (*Con.*)

Creswell Mfg. Co., Jas.
(Tack) ....A
CONN.—Danielson
Warren & Danielson
(Butter) ....D
CONN.—Lebanon
Turner, Robert E. (Butter)
D
CONN.—New Haven
Hoggson & Pettis Mfg. Co.
(Rubber) ....A
Ideal Mfg. Co. (Bullet)..C
Peck Bros. & Co. (Tack)..A
CONN.—South Windham
Smith & Winchester Co.
(Cylinder) ....A
ILL.—Chicago
Allis-Chalmers Co., Home
Ins. Bldg. (Ingot; Bullion)
AAAA
Creamery Package Mfg. Co.
(Butter) ....AAAA
Crosby & Co., G. A.
(Solder) X
Elmes Engineering Wks.,
Chas. F., Fulton Cor. N.
Morgan (Rubber; Tire).A
Street & Kent Mfg. Co., 41
Fulton (Tack) ......D
Wolff Mfg. Co., L., 117 W.
Lake (Tack) .....AAAA
ILL.—Decatur
Mueller Mfg. Co., H. (Tack;
Lead; Flange; Lead Tack)
A
ILL.—Quincy
Modern Iron Wks. (Half
Round Bar Solder) .....B
IND.—Indianapolis
Potts & Co., (Inc.), C. A.
(Brick) ....B
IND.—Richmond
Richmond Machine Wks.
(Brick) ....B
IOWA—Davenport
Sternberg Mfg. Co.
(Cigar) ....D
IOWA—Keokuck
Scott Mfg. Co. (Brick)..E
KANS.—Fort Scott
Fort Scott Fdy. & Machine
Co., (C. Eller) (Ingot)..H
MASS.—Boston
National Machine Co.
(Rubber) ....A
Steers, Wm. (Rubber)...F
MASS.—Cambridge
Barbour-Stockwell Co.
(Rubber) ....A
MASS.—Haydenville
Haydenville Co. (Solder;
Tack) ....B
MASS.—Springfield
Cheney-Bigelow Wire Wks.
(Cylinder) ....A
Springfield Brass Co. (Tack)
X
MASS.—Taunton
Wheeler, Geo. H. (Brick).F
MASS.—Williamsburg
Hill Bros. & Co. (Button).C
MICH.—Kalkaska
Freeman Mfg. Co. (Butter)
B
MASS.—Ludington
Ludington Woodenware Co.
(Butter) ....B
MO.—St. Louis
Fernholtz Brick Machinery
Co., Boyle & Old Manches-
ter Avs. (Brick)......E
Kupferle, Jno. C., 2nd &
Mound (Solder) ......A
N. J.—Belleville
Eastwood Wire Mfg. Co.
(Cylinder) ....A
N. J.—Bridgeton
More-Jonas Glass Co.
(Bottle) X
N. J.—Newark
Bernz, Otto, S. 13th & S.
Orange Av. (Lead Casting;
Solder; Tack) ....A
Brass Founders' Supply Co.
(Brass) ....
B
Osborne & Co., C. S. (Solder)
Sayre & Co., L. A.
(Solder) ....B
N. J.—New Brunswick
Empire Machine & Fdy. Co.
(Rubber) X

MOULDS (*Con.*)

N. J.—Paterson
Royle & Sons, Jno. (Rubber)
A
N. J.—Salem
Ayres Machine Co. (Glass
House) ....B
N. J.—Trenton
Empire Rubber Co. (Rubber)
A
Home Rubber Co. (Rubber)
AA
N. Y.—Albany
Dederick's Sons, P. K.
(Brick) ....AA
N. Y.—Brooklyn
Fanning, J. P., 678 Jeff'n
(Lead Casting, for Bab-
bitt Metal; Solder; Bar
Lead; Bullets) ....E
Sweeney Mfg. Co., W. H.
(Cake; Ice Cream; Jelly;
Pudding) ....B
Vogel & Bros., Wm.
(Confectioners) ......AA
N. Y.—Buffalo
Shepard & Co., Sidney
(Candle) ....AAAA
N. Y.—Geneva
Chapman, C. A. (Cake)..E
N. Y.—Grassy Point
Wiles Co., Alfred M. & W.
H. (Brick) ....B
New York City
Behr & Co., Herman
(Glassware) ....AA
Brooks & Co. (Glassware;
Rubber Solder) ......E
Consolidated Fruit Jar Co.,
290 B'way (Glass Mfrs.)
AA
Crandall & Godley (Ice-
Cream) ....AA
Eppelsheimer & Co. (Con-
fectioners; Chocolate)..E
Hart, William (Ice Cream)
A
Houchin Co., Thos. W.
(Candle) ....D
Knapp Mfg. Co., 22 Frank-
fort (Tack) ....D
Kulenkampff Mfg. Co., 62
Centre (Confectioners').F
Lalance & Grosjean Mfg. Co.
(Cake; Jelley; Ice Cream;
Pudding; Confctionrs')
AAAA
Mott Iron Wks., J. L. 88
Beekman (Solder) ....AA
Stoutenborough, X. (Cake;
Ice Cream; Pudding)...D
Wicke Co., Wm. (Cigar).A
N. Y.—Walkill
Crowell & Son, J. B. (Brick)
E
OHIO—Bellaire
Rodefer Bros. (Glass;
Special) ....A
OHIO—Cambridge
Cambridge Fdy. Co. (Glass
House) ....F
OHIO—Cincinnati
American Cigar Mould Co.
(Cigar) ....D
Laidlaw-Dunn-Gordon Co.
(Br. Int. Steam Pump Co.,
N. Y. City) (Plug Tobac-
co) ....AAAA
Mc Gowan Co., Jno. H.
(Plug Tobacco) ....A
Miller, Duburl & Peters
Mfg. Co. (Cigar) .....B
Obermayer Co., S., 647
Evans (Ingot).........A
Randall & Co. (Harness).D
OHIO—Cleveland
Smith Fdy. Supply Co., J.
D., 40 S. Water (Ingot)
D
Ulmer & Co., J. C., 225
Champlain (Cement)...H
OHIO—Dayton
New Century Mfg. Co. (Con-
fectioners' Rubber) ....E
Raymond & Co., Chas. W.
(Brick) ....A
OHIO—Hamilton
Black & Clawson Co.,
(Cylinder) ....AA
OHIO—Lorain
Lorain F'dry Co. (Ingot).A
OHIO—New London
Arnold. Creager Co.

MOULDS (Con.)
  (Brick) C
OHIO—Portsmouth
Simpson Bros. (Fire Brick)
                    E
OHIO—Zanesville
Griffith & Wedge Co.
  (Ingot) ....
                    B
Union Machine Co. (Glass)
                    B
PA.—Allegheny
Rosedale Foundry Co.
  (Steel) ....B
PA.—Erie
Griswold Mfg. Co. (Solder)
                    A
PA.—Harrisburg
Harrisburg Pipe Bending
  Co. (Ltd.) (Ice) .....AA
PA.—Lancaster
Martin Brick Machine Mfg.
  Co., Henry (Brick).....B
PA.—New Castle
Penn. Engineering Wks.
  (Ingot) ....A
Vulcan F'dy & Machine Co.
  (Ingot) ....B
PA.—Philadelphia
Clad & Sons, Velentine
  (Ice Cream) ....A
PA.—Phoenixville
Logan Mfg. Co. (Ingot)...B
PA.—Pittsburg
Bailey-Farrell Mfg. Co.
  (Tack) ....AA
Blair & Co., Reed F.
  (Ingot) C
Mc Kee, W. S., 231 1st Av.
  (Glass House) ....D
Marshall Foundry, 28th &
  R. R. (Steel Ingot) AAA
Mesta Machine Co. (Steel
  Ingot) ....AAA
Phillips & Mc Laren
  (Brick) ....B
Pittsburg Mfg. Co., 28th R.
  R. (Ingot) ....A
United Engineering & F'dy
  Co., 54th & A. V. Ry.
  (Steel Ingot) .....AAAA
Mather Mfg. Co. (Lead;
  Plug) ....AA
Mills & Bros., Thos. (Ice
  Cream) ....A
Paxson Co., J. W., 1021 N.
  Del. Av. (Ingot)......AA
Phila. Tool & Machine Co.
  (Ingot) ....A
Reid, A. H. (Butter).....A
Wirz, A. H. (Suppository)
                    A
Yagle & Co., (Ltd.), Wm.,
  500 32nd (Ingot).......C
Yockel & Sons, Chas., 1220
  N. Lawrence (Glass)...D
PA.—Rankin Station
Duquesne Forge Co. (Print-
  ers' Rollers) ....A
PA.—Sharpsville
West F'dy Co., Thos. D.
  (Steel Ingot) ....B
PA.—South Bethlehem
Bethlehem Steel Co. (Ingot)
                  AAAA
PA.—Uniontown
Evans Mold & Machine Co.
  (Glass House) X
PA.—Wheatland
Sharon F'dy Co. (Steel
  Ingot) ....AA
R. I.—Pawtucket
Atwood, Crawford Co.
  (Button; Tassel) ......B
R. I.—Providence
Miller Iron Co. (Solder)..B
VT.—Bellows Falls
Vermont Farm Machine Co.
  (Butter) C
VT.—Rutland
Moseley & Stoddard Mfg.
  Co. (Butter) ....B
VA.—Richmond
Cardwell Machine Co.
  (Plug Tobacco) ....A
W. VA.—New Cumberland
Davis-Price Fdy. & Mchy.
  Co. (Brick) C
W. VA.—Wheeling
Central Fdy. & Machine Co.
  (Glass House) C
Wheeling Mold & F'dy Co.
  (Ingot; Glass House)..A

MOULDS (Con.)
WIS.—Beloit
Beloit Iron Wks. (Cylinder)
                    A
WIS.—Fort Atkinson
Cornish, Curtis & Green
  Mfg. Co. (Butter)......A
WIS.—Milwaukee
Allis-Chalmers Co. (Bul-
  lion) ....AAAA
Rundle-Spence Mfg. Co.
  (Tack) ....AAAA
Schwab & Sons, R. J.
  (Cement) ....AA
WIS.—Sheboygan
Sheboygan Cigar Mould Co.
  (Cigar) C

MOUNTINGS

See also Jewelry; Trim-
mings; Hardware; Car-
riage

CONN.—Bridgeport
White Mfg. Co. (Carriage &
  Hearse) ....B
CONN.—Mt. Carmel
Woodruff & Sons, Walter
  W. (Coach! Carriage)...A
CONN.—New Haven
Fitch Co., W. & E. T.
  (Harness) ....A
CONN.—Waterbury
Novelty Mfg. Co. (Cane;
  Umbrella; Smoking) ...A
ILL.—Chicago
Hanish Bros. Mfg. Co., 2489
  W. Lake (Harness)....E
ILL.—Sterling
Rock Falls Mfg. Co.
  (Hearse) ....A
MD.—Baltimore
Day, Son & Co., O. F.
  (Harness) C
MASS.—Amesbury
Atwood Mfg. Co. (Coach;
  Carriage; Carriage Lamp)
                    C
Gray & Davis (Coach
  Carriage) ....B
MASS.—Chicope
Ames Sword Co. (Regalia;
  Belt; Sword) ....B
N. J.—Newark
Conlon & Co., B. (Bag)..B
Gould's Son Co., (Bag)...A
Greacen & Co., Walter
  (Coach; Carriage; Har-
  ness) ....E
Harper, W. J., 229 Mulberry
  (Hearse) ....E
Jenkinson & Co., R. C.
  (Bag) ....AA
Lochwood Mfg. Co. (Coach;
  Carriage; Carriage Lamp)
                    B
Sargeant Mfg. Co. (Har-
  nes) ....A
Searle Mfg. Co. (Coach;
  Carriage) ....B
New York City
Deeley & Co., Robert
  (Sugar Machinery).....A
Johnson, Hayward & Piper,
  590 B'way (Comb) ....B
Winckler & Son, L. (Cane;
  Umbrella; Whip; Smok-
  ing) C
N. Y.—Utica
Clark, Horrocks Co. (Fish-
  in Rod) ....A
OHIO—Canton
Elbel Co. (Harness)......A
OHIO—Cincinnati
Corcoran's Sons, Thos. H.
  (Coach; Carriage; Hearse)
                    B
Monarch Carriage Goods Co.
  (Coach; Carriage) .....B
PA.—Lancaster
Lancaster Silver Plate Co.
  (Umbrella) C
PA.—Philadelphia
Chesterman & Co., F. E.,
  243 Arch (Harness)....D
Evans & Son, S. W.
  (Umbrella; Whips) ....B
Simons Bros. & Co. (Cane;
  Umbreila) ....A
R. D.—Prividence
Briggs & Sons Co., J.
  (Umbrella) ....A

MOUN..... S (Con.)
Dover Co., Geo. W.
(Umbrella) ....B

MOUNTS

MASS.—Holyoke
Whitmore Mfg. Co.
(Photograph) ....A
New York City
Gennert, G. (Photograph).B
Trier & Bergfield
(Photograph) ....B
PA—Philadelphia
Collins Mfg. Co., A. M.
(Photograph) ....AA
R. I.—Providence
American & British Mfg.
Co. (Gun) ....AAA

MOUTHPIECES

MASS.—Springfield
Dickinson Hard Rubber Co.
(Telephone) X
MINN.—St. Paul
Rauscher, John, 98 W. 3d
(Telephone) ....H
N. Y.—Brooklyn
Electrose Mfg. Co., 127 N.
10th (Transmitters Tele-
phone) ....B
New York City
Amer. Hard Rubber Co., 9
Mercer (Telephone).AAAA
Vulcanized Rubber Co., 568
B'way (Telephone) ....A
OHIO—East Liverpool
Thomas & Sons Co., R.
(Telephone) ....A
PA.—Scranton
Everhart Brass Wks.
(Speaking Tube) ......A

MOVEMENTS

See also Watches; Clocks

CONN.—Ansonia
Phelps & Bartholomew Co.
(Clock) ....D
CONN.—Bridgeport
Bridgeport Brass Co.
(Clock) ....AAA
CONN.—Bristol
Bristol Brass Co. (Clock)
AAA
CONN.—New Haven
New Haven Clock Co.
(Clock) ....AAA
Reeves Mfg. Co. (Clock for
Meters; Gauges, etc.)...C
CONN.—Thomaston
Thomas Clock Co., Seth
(Clock) ....AAA
CONN.—Waterbury
Waterbury Clock Co. (Clock
for Meters; Gauges, etc)
AAAA
Waterbury Electric Co.
(Electric) ....F
Waterbury Mfg. Co.
(Steam Gauge) ...AAAA
CONN.—Winsted
Gilbert Clock Co., Wm. L.
(Clock) ....AA
ILL.—Chicago
Elgin Nat'l Watch Co.
(Watch) ....AAAA
MASS.—Boston
Crosby Steam Gauge &
& Valve Co. (Steam
Gauge) ....AA
Star Brass Mfg. Co.,
(Steam Gauge) ....A
MASS.—Lynn
Fiego, Alex. J. R. (Clock
for Meters; Gauges, etc.)
H
N. J.—Newark
Plumb, David S., 24 Boud-
inot (Clock for Meters;
Gauges, etc. Electrical
Clock; Steam Gauge)....D
New York City
Ansonia Clock Co. (Clock)
AAAA
Doll Mfg. Co., W. F.
(Watch) ....D

MOVERS

ILL.—Chicago

MOVERS (Con.)
Borden & Selleck Co., 48
Lake (Double Clutch)...B
Fairbanks, Morse & Co.,
Franklin & Monroe (Car)
AAAA
Hoisting & Conveying Ma-
chinery Co., 44 N. Eliz-
abeth (Car) ....E
Railway Appliances Co., Old
Colony Bldg. (Car).......A
Skilling & Richards Mfg.
Co., 147 Fulton (Car)...C
Stafford & Bros., E. H. 262
Wabash (Car) C
Webster Mfg. Co., 1075 W.
15th (Car) ....E
ILL.—Marseilles
Marseilles Mfg. Co. (Car)
A
ILL.—Moline
Barnard & Leas Mfg. Co.
(Car) ....AA
IND.—Indianapolis
Nordyke & Marmon Co.
(Car) ....AAA
IND.—Mishawaka
Dodge Mfg. Co. (Car).AAA
MASS.—Boston
Boston & Lockport Block
Co. (Car) ....A
Pearson Co., Jack, 64 Fed-
eral (Car).............G
Woodman Mfg. & Supply
Co., 63 Oliver (Car)....F
MICH.—Detroit
Buhl Malleable Co., Wight
& Adair (Car).........A
MICH.—Kalamazoo
Kalamazoo Railway Supply
Co. (Car) ....B
MINN.—Minneapolis
Howell & Co., R. R. (Car)
B
MO.—St. Louis
Cahill, Swift Mfg. Co., 20
S. 12th (Car)...........B
Zelnicker Supply Co., Wal-
ter A., 408 N. 4th (Car;
Double Clutch) ....A
OHIO—Alliance
Morgan Engineering Co.
(Car) ....AAAA
OHIO—Cleveland
Osborn Mfg. Co. (Car)...B
OHIO—Dayton
Boyer-Bradford Mfg. Co
(Car) C
PA.—Pittsburg
Eichley Co., John, Jr.
(House) ....A
WIS.—Appleton
Appleton Car Mover Co.
(Car) ....H

MOWERS

**See also Agricultural
Implements**

ILL.—Chicago
Lawson Mfg. Co., (Lawn).E
ILL.—Dixon
Clipper Lawn Mower Co.
(Lawn) ....D
IND.—Richmond
Dille & Mc Guire Mfg. Co.
(Lawn) C
F. & N. Lawn Mower Co.
A
MASS.—North Attleboro
Blackington Co., W. S.
(Lawn) ....A
MASS.—Springfield
Blair Mfg. Co. (Lawn)...B
Rogers Iron Wks. (Lawn)
C
Thomas Mfg.. Co. (Lawn)
AAA
N. Y.—Newburg
Coldwell Lawn Mower Co.
(Lawn) ....A
OHIO—Akron
Whitman & Barnes Mfg.
Co. (Lawn) ......AAAA
OHIO—Canton
New Mfg. C. (Lawn)....B
OHIO—Springfield
Mast, Foos & Co. (Lawn)
AA
PA.—Philadelphia
Enterprise Mfg. Co. (Lawn)
AAAA

MOWERS (Con.)

Philadelphia Lawn Mower Co., 3100 Chestnut (Lawn) ....B

Supplee Hdw. Co. (Lawn) ....AA

MUCILAGE

COLO.—Denver
Cannon, W. F............D
CONN.—Hartford
Barber Ink Co............D
ILL.—Chicago
Sanford Mfg. Co..........B
Thomas Co., L. H.........D
MD.—Baltimore
Mc Cormick & Co........D
MASS.—Boston
Carters' Ink Co...........A
MASS.—Cambridge
Whittemore Bros. Co....AA
MASS.—Gloucester
Gloucester Isinglass & Glue Co. ....A
Russia Cement Co.........A
MICH.—Detroit
Keller Ink Co., Robt.....F
Michigan Paste & Mfg. Co. ....F
MO.—St. Louis
Levison & Blyth Mfg. Co., 209 Locust ....E
N. J.—Newark
Dovell Son Mfg. Co., R. B. ....D
Pomeroy Co., I...........F
N. J.—Rahway
Harrison Mfg. Co.........F
N. Y.—Brooklyn
Higgins & Co., Chas. M., 271 9th.................A
New York City
Arabol Mfg. Co., 100 William ....A
Davids Co., Thaddeus, 127 William C
Moss, George A.,, 165 Reade X
Soltmann, E. G., 125 E. 42 (Drawing Board; Library) ....B
Stafford, S. S., 603 Washington ....B
N. Y.—Rochester
Dutcher, M. H...........E
PA.—Philadelphia
Continental Mfg. Co......D
Diamond & Onyx, 317 De Lancey ....B
Mann Co.. Wm...........AA
WIS.—Milwaukee
Diamond Ink Co., Irving Pl. & Bartlett.........D

MUDDLERS

N. J.—Newark
Sommer's Son John (Wooden) ....A

MUFFLERS

See also Neckwear

CONN.—South Manchester
Cheney Bros. ....AAAA
KY.—Louisville
Moran Flexible Steam Joint Co. (Exhaust).....E
MICH.—Detroit
Briscoe Mfg. Co., 1427 Woodward Av. (Automobile) ....A
N. J.—Paterson
Dexter Lambert & Co. ....AAAA
New York City
Roberts & Bros., Geo. I (Exhaust) ....A
Standard Steam Specialty Co., 542 W. B'way (Exhaust) ....A
OHIO—Cuyahoga Falls
Turner, Vaughan & Taylor Co., (Annealing) .....B
VT.—Rutland
Rutland Fire Clay Co (Enamelers') ....B

MUFFLES

COLO.—Denver

MUFFLES (Con.)

Denver Fire Clay Co. (Clay) ....AA
N. Y.—Brooklyn
Broolykn Fire Brick Wks. (Enamelling) ....A
New York City
Maurer & Son, Henry, 420 E. 23d (Assay).......AA

MUFFS

IND.—La Grange
La Grange Robe & Fur Co. (Fur) ....H
MO.—St. Louis
Singer Bros. (Fur).....AA
N. Y.—College Point
Kleinert Rubber Co., Isaac B. (Ear) X
New York City
Frankenthal Bros. Co. (Plush) ....D
Gunther's Sons, C. G. (Fur) ....AAA
Kessler Bros. & Schachter ....E
Kleinert Rubber Co., I. B., 725 B'way (Ear) ....A
Kohn & Bear, 597 B'way (Fur) ....A
Mischo & Muller (Fur)...B
Reineman, Albert (Fur; Plush) ....D

MUGS

See also Silverware; Enamelled Ware; Chinaware

CONN.—Meriden..
Manning, Bowman & Co. (Enameled) ....AA
MO.—St. Louis
St. Louis Stamping Co. (Enameled) ....AAAA
New York City
Lalance & Grosjean Mfg. Co. (Enameled) ..AAAA
OHIO—Newark
Heisey & Co., A. H. (Inc.) (Beer) ....A
OHIO—Toledo
Libbey Glass Co. (Beer) ....AA
PA.—Beaver Falls
Co-Operative Flint Glass Co. (Beer) ....A
PA.—Philadelphia
Gillinder & Sons (Inc.) (Beer) ....A
PA.—Pittsburg
Mc Kee Glass Co., S. (Beer) ....D
W. VA.—Moundsville
Fostoria Glass Co. (Beer) ....AAA
W. VA.—Wellsburg
Riverside Glass Wks (Beer) C
W. VA.—Wheeling
Central Glass Wks. (Beer) ....A
North Wheeling Glass Co. (Inc.) (Beer) ....A

MULES

MASS.—Boston
Firth Co., Wm., 150 Devonshire (Cotton; Self-Acting Worsted) ....D
Lowe, Stephan C., 186 Devonshire (Cotton; Self-Acting; Woolen) ......B
McKerrow & Co., H. G., 31 State (Cotton; Self-Acting) X
Riley & Co., C. E., 65 Franklin (Self-Acting Cotton; Woolen; Worsted) ....A
Stoddard, Haserick, Richards Co., 152 Congress (Self Acting; Woolen; Worsted) ....B
MASS.—Lowell
Lowell Machine Shop (Cotton; Woolen) ....AAAA
MASS.—Newton Upper Falls
Saco & Pettee Machine Shops (Cotton) ....AAA
MASS.—Taunton

MULES (Con.)

Mason Machine Wks. (Cotton; Self-Acting) ....AA
MASS.—Worcester
Amer. Card Clothing Co. (Woolen) ....AAA
Johnson & Bassett (Woolen) A

PA.—Philadelphia
Diamond Textile Machine Wks. (Cotton; Worsted) E
Smith Woolen Mchy. Co., Jas., 41 Race (Self-Acting; English; Moulton Styes; Woolen) ......AA
R. I.—Pawtucket
Brown Machine Co., Jas. (Cotton; Self-Acting) A

MUSIC GOODS LEATHER

MASS.—Worcester
Warren Leather Goods Co.A

Manufacturers of Music Rolls and Satchels, Violin Cases, Guitar Cases, Banjo Cases, Mandolin Cases, Music Folios, Cornet Cases, Music Stand Cases.

MUSICAL INSTRUMENTS

See Appendix

MUSKETS

CONN.—New Haven
Marlin Fire Arms Co. (Repeating) ....AA

MUSLIN

See Cotton Goods

MUSTARD

See Condiments; Relishes

MUTTON

See Meat Packers

MUZZLES

CONN.—Georgetown
Gilbert & Bennett Mfg. Co. (Horse; Ox) ....AAA
CONN.—Southport
Jeliff Mfg. Corporation, C. O. (Ox) C
CONN.—Torrington
Union Hdw. Co. (Dog) AA
ILL.—Chicago
Barbee Wire & Iron Wks. (Dog; Horse; Ox)......B
Cook & Bros., E. C. (Dog; Horse) ....A
IOWA—Carroll
Carroll Muzzle Co. (Calves; Colt; Cow) C
MASS.—Worcester
Hamblin & Russell Mfg. Co. (Horse; Ox).........B
National Mfg. Co. (Dog) A
Wire Goods Co. (Horse; Ox) A
Wright Wire Co. ......AA
MO.—St. Louis
Ludlow-Saylor Wire Co. AA
N. J.—Newark
Peters Harness & Saddlery Co. (Horse) C
New York City
Medford Fancy Goods Co., 75 Duane (Dog) ......E
OHIO—Cincinnati
Bromwell Brush & Wire Goods Co. (Horse; Ox) AA
OHIO—Hamilton
Meyers Mfg. Co., Fred. J. (Horse; Ox) ....B
PA.—Philadelphia
Darby & Sons, Edward (Horse; Ox) ....A

MYRBANE

N. Y.—Buffalo
Schoellkopf, Hartford & Hanna Co. ....AAA
New York City
Berlin Aniline Wks. ....B
Selling Co., The C
PA.—Philadelphia
Barrett Mfg. Co.....AAAA

NAILS

See also Hardware; Carriage, etc.

CAL.—San Francisco
Judson Mfg. Co., Howard & Beale (Cut; Shoe; Wire; Horse) ....AA
COLO.—Denver
Colorado Fuel & Iron Co. (Wire) ....AAAA
CONN.—Bridgeport
Bridgeport Brass Co. (Brass; Copper) ....AA
Canfield, H. O. (Fender) ..D
Knapp & Cowles Mfg. Co. (Rubber) C
CONN.—Derby
Shelton Co. (Small; Brush; Copper; Clout; Cut; Shoe; Wagon Hinge, etc.) ....A
CONN.—Hartford
Capewell Horse Nail Co. (Horse) ....AA
CONN.—Mt. Carmel
Woodruff & Sons, Walter W. (Band; Name Plate) A
CONN.—New Britain
American Hdw. Co. (Picture) ....AAAA
Stanley Wks. (Basket; Box; Cigar Box; Finishing; Hob; Hungarian; Iron) AAA
CONN.—New Haven
Cowles & Co., C. (Inc.) (Cloth Covered; Lining) A
Grilley Co. (Picture) .....B
Natl. Steel & Wire Co. (Small; Wire) ......AAAA
New Haven Wire Mfg. Co. (Wire Finishing) C
CONN.—Norwich
Ossawan Mills Co. (Gilt; Picture; Cupped Brass; Upholstery) ....B
CONN.—Seymour
Fowler Nail Co. (Horse) ..A
CONN.—Torrington
Eagle Bicycle Mfg. Co. (Horse) ....A
Torrington Mfg. Co. (Small Furniture; Upholstery), C
Turner & Seymour Mfg. Co. (Picture; Gilt; Screw Head) ....A
CONN.—Waterbury
Amer. Ring Co. (Brass Headed; Copper; Cut; Upholstery) ....A
Blake & Johnson (Copper) A
White Co., L. C. (Cloth Covered; Saddle) ......D
CONN.—Waterville
Berbecker & Rowland Mfg. Co. (Brass; Copper) C
ILL.—Belleville
Hartman, Hays & Reis (Small) ....AA
Stanley Co., Geo. W. (Barrel; Clout; Hoop; Small Wire; Cut) ....F
ILL.—Chicago
Amer. Steel & Wire Co. Rookery (Barrel; Box; Brass; Copper; Casing; Clinch; Finishing; Roofing; Slating; Small; Wire, all sizes) ....AAAA
Chicago Tack Co. (Basket; Chair; Finishing; Hungarian; Lining Saddle; Shoe; Small; Trunk; Wire) ...B
Grand Crossing Tack Co. (Brass; Copper; Roofing; Slating; Shoe; Wire, all sizes; Box; Cigar Box; Heel; Hob; Iron; Lining; Saddle; Steel; Trunk; Clout; Cut; Last) .....A
Illinois Nail Co., 3 Dix (Wire; Cement Coated), A

NAILS (Con.)

Republic Iron & Steel Co.,
Stock Exchange Bldg.
(Cut) ....AAAA
Union Horse Nail Co., 583
W. 22d (Horse) ....B
Wilson & Co., C. S., Rialto
Bldg. (Cement Coated), D
ILL.—East St. Louis
New Process Steel & Wire
Co. (Wire) ....A
ILL.—Kankakee
Kankakee Nail Co. (Horse)
X
ILL.—Sterling
Dillon-Griswold Wire Co.
(Wire, all sizes) ....A
Lawrence Bros. (Wire)..AA
Northwestern Barb Wire Co.
(Wire) ....A
IND.—Crawfordsville
Crawfordsville Wire & Nail
Co. (Wire) ....B
IND.—Hammond
Chicago Steel Mfg. Co. (Cut;
Steel; Iron) X
IND.—Kokomo
Kokomo Steel & Wire Co.
(Barrel; Box; Casing;
Clinch; Finishing; Roof-
ing; Slating; Wire), AAA
IND.—Madison
Tower Mfg. Co. (Clout; Fin-
ishing; Small Hoop; Bas-
ket; Cigar Box; Roofing;
Slating; Shoe; Trunk;
Wire; Steel; Heel) C
IND.—Muncie
Indiana Steel & Wire Co.
(Wire) ....A
KY.—Ashland
Norton Iron Wks. (Inc.)
(Cut; Wire; Steel) ...AA
MASS.—Boston
Baker & Co., Chas. F.
(Wire) ....A
Pearson & Co., J. C., 130
State (Cement Coated)
AAAA
Putnam Nail Co. (Horse)
AA
MASS.—Bridgewater
Miller's Sons. H. J. (Genu-
ine Iron Shingle; Shoe;
Machine Shoe; Cut; Horse-
shoe; Wire) ....D
MASS.—Brockton
Cross & Co., W. W. (Shoe)
B
MASS.—Lynn
Houghton & Sons, Jas.
(Shoe) X
AA
MASS.—New Bedford
Taunton & New Bedford
Copper Co. (Yellow Metal
Copper; Roofing; Slating)
AAA
MASS.—Plymouth
Cobb & Drew (Small; Cigar
Box; Clout; Brush; Cop-
per; Trunk) ....AA
Plymouth Mills (Cut; Small
Wire; Clout; Trunk) ...B
Ripley & Bartlett (Car;
Steel; Clout; Shoe ; Boot)
B
MASS.—Somerset
Mount Hope Iron Co. (Cut)
A
MASS.—South Hanover
Phillips & Sons, E. (Brass;
Iron; Corrugated; Cement
Coated Wire; Clout;
Roofing; Slating; Brass;
Copper Shoe; Small Iron;
Steel; Zinc; Coppered;
Galvanized; Hob; Tinned;
Trunk) ....A
MASS.—Taunton
Atlas Tack Corporation (all
kinds) ....AAAA
Globe Mfg. Co. (Shoe;
Brush; Copper; Corruga-
ted; Countersink; Head;
Last; Wire) ....F
Rhodes & Son Co., M. M.
(Small Upholstery) X
Taunton Tack Co. (Wire up
to 4 in.) X
Taunton Wire Nail Co.
(Blind; Rugby Box;
Small; Wire 1-8 to 8 in.)
D

NAILS (Con.)

MASS.—Whitman
Gurney, D. B. (Wire up to
20 penny) ....A
MASS.—West Wareham
Tremont Nail Co. (Cut) ..A
MASS.—Worcester
Morgan Spring Co. (Wire) B
Parker Wire Goods Co.
(Picture; Wire) ....E
Wire Goods Co. (Roofing;
Slating; Wire Finishing;
Galvanized; Small; Wire)
B
Wright Wire Co. (Wire)
AA
MICH.—Detroit
Crescent Machine Co., 101
W. Adams Av. (Cigar
Box) ....D
MO.—St. Louis
Ludlow-Saylor Wire Co.
(Wire) ....A
St. Louis Wire & Iron Co.
(Wire) ....D
N. H.—East Jaffrey
Granite State Tack Co.
(Shoe) ....D
N. H.—Keene
Fuller, G. E. & A. I. (Small)
E
N. J.—Newark
Howell & Co. (Leather
(Headed) ....A
Peters Harness & Saddlery
Co. (Saddle) C
Sacks, Louis, Iron Foundry
(Hob) ....A
N. J.—Trenton
Roebling Sons Co., Jno. A.
(Screw Head; Wire, all
sizes) ....AAAA
N. Y.—Au Sable Chasm
Mooney & Co., W. M.
(Horse) ....B
N. Y.—Au Sable Forks
Rogers, J. & J., (Inc.)
(Horse) ....AA
N. Y.—Binghamton
Beman & Co. (Clinch; Shoe)
B
Crandal, Stone & Co. (Band;
Lining; Saddle) ....A
Titchener & Co., E. H.
(Wire, up to 3 in.) ....B
N. Y.—Brooklyn
Hassell, John (Wire) .....B
Hay-Budden Mfg. Co. (Wag-
on; Hinge, etc.) ....B
Igoe Bros.. 226 N. 9th
(Wire, 3-8 to 6 in.) ...C
N. Y.—Buffalo
Western Wire Goods Co.
(Upholsterers') ....E
N. Y.—Cortland
Wickwire Bros. (Wire)
AAAA
N. Y.—Essex
Essex Horse Nail Co., Ltd.
(Horse) C
N. Y.—Keeseville
Ausable Horse Nail Co.
(Horse) ....A
New York City
Ansonia Brass & Copper Co.
(Copper) ....AAAA
Bruce & Cook (Cut) ....AA
Erfert, Hy. F., 238 4th Av.
(Leather) ....F
Fuller Bros. (Cut) ....D
Gould-Mersereau Co. (Stair)
C
Hassell Jno. 169 Elm
(Screw Head; Small;
Wire, 1-8 to 4 in.)......D
Hungerford Brass & Copper
Co. U. T. (Brass; Copper;
Roofing; Slating; Uphols-
terers') ....A
International Brass & Elec.
Co., 76 Beekman (Hexagon
Machine made Brass; Cop-
per) ....D
Johnson Leather Co., 41 E.
21st (Leather) ....B
Judd & Co., H. L. (Picture;
Upholstery) ....AA
Lefferts Galvanizing Wks.
(Galvanized) ....D
Livingston Nail Co., 104
Reade (Horse) ....B
Metal Stamping Co. (Lining)
B
National Horse Shoe Co.

695

NAILS (Con.),
(Horse) X
Russell & Erwin Mfg. Co.
  (Wire) ....AAAA
Salem Nail Co., 279 Pearl
  (Copper; Galvanized; Tin-
  ned; Steel; Cut; Yellow
  Metal; Zinc; Lead; Small;
  Roofing; Slating; Wire,
  all sizes and kinds) .....B
Sargent & Co. (Picture;
  Wagon; Hinge, etc.)
                      AAAA
Stebbins, Chas. J. (Cut) ..D
Wiebusch & Hilger (Horse-
  shoe) ....A
Yale & Towne Mfg. Co.
  (Ornamental) .....AAAA
N. Y.—Penn Yan
Superior Tack & Nail Co.
  (Clout; Small Cut; Trunk;
  Wire) ....B
N. Y.—Rome
Rome Brass & Copper Co.
  (Brass; Copper), ..AAAA
N. Y.—Troy
Burden Iron Co. (Iron)
                      AAAA
OHIO—Canton
Kohler & Co., F. E. (Cut;
  Wire) C
OHIO—Cincinnati
Evans Steel & Iron Co., C.
  W., 22 W. 2d (Cement
  Coated Wire) ....B
Robertson Steel & Iron Co.,
  W. F. (Cement Coated
  Wire) ....A
Tower Mfg. Co. (Shoe) ...C
OHIO—Cleveland
Cleveland Rolling Mill Co.
  (Wire) ....AAAA
Garry Iron & Steel Co.
  (Sheathing; Roofing) ..A
H. P. Nail Co. (Barbed;
  Wire Finishing; Galvan-
  ized; Wire)............X
Kirk-Latty Mfg. Co. (Small
  Clout; Truck) ....B
Lake Erie Iron Co. (Boat)
                      AAAA
Natl. Screw Tack Co.
  (Small) ....AA
OHIO—Cuyahoga Falls
Cuyahoga Steel & Wire Co.
  (Wire) X
OHIO—Ironton
Belfont Iron Wks. Co. (Cut)
                      AAA
Kelly Nail & Iron Co. (Cut)
                      AA
OHIO—Salem
Salem Wire Nail Co. (Wire)
                      X
OHIO—Springfield
Corrugated Steel Nail Co.
  (Steel Corrugated) .....E
OHIO—Steubenville
La Belle Iron Wks. (Barrel;
  Box; Casing; Clinch;
  Clout; Finishing; Hoop;
  Roofing; Slating; Special;
  Basket; Boat; Car; Cut;
  Iron; Lining; Small;
  Steel) ....AAAA
OHIO—Youngstown
Mahoning Valley Iron Co.
  (Cut; Steel) C
PA.—Birdsboro
Brooks Iron Co., E. & G.
  (Cut; Iron) ....AAA
PA.—Griswold Wire Co.
  (Wire) ....B
PA.—Duncannon
Duncannon Iron Co. (Cut;
  Box; Car; Clinch; Clout)
                      AA
PA.—Harrisburg
Bailey & Co., Chas. L. (Inc.)
  (Cut; Box; Clinch; Clout;
  Finishing; Iron; Slating;
  Steel; Roofing) ......AA
PA.—Hollidaysburg
Hollidaysburg Iron & Nail
  Co. (Cut) ....A
PA.—Milton
Godcharles & Co., F. A.
  (Cut) ....A
PA.—New Brighton
Standard Horse Nail Co.
  (Horse) ....AA
Townsend, C. C. & E. P.
  (Wire, Cut; Barbed Wire)
                      AA

NAILS (Con.)
PA.—Morristown
Reading Screw Co. (Wire) B
PA.—Northumberland
Van Alen & Co. (Cut; Bar-
  rel; Box; Clinch; Clout;
  Iron; Steel; Finishing;
  Roofing; Slating) ......A
PA.—Philadelphia
Morris, Wheeler & Co. (Cut)
                      AAAA
Phillips, Townsend & Co.
  (Wire, all sizes) ......E
Phosphor Bronze Smelt Co.,
  Ltd. (Phosphor Bronze), A
PA.—Pittsburg
Anchor Nail & Tack Wks.
  (Shoe; Small Cut) .....B
Chess Bros. (Shoe; Steel)
                      A
Hussey & Co., C. G., 2850 2d
  Av. (Brass; Copper), AAA
Marland, Neeley & Co.
  (Wire) ....A
Oliver Wire Co. (Wire)
                      AAAA
Pittsburg Steel Co., Fergu-
  son Bldg. (Wire) ..AAAA
Pittsburg Wire Co. (Wire)
                      X
Union Steel Co., Carnegie
  Bldg (Box) ....D
U. S. Wire & Nail Co.,Lewis
  Block (Wire) ....A
PA.—Pottstown
Ellis & Lessig Steel & Iron
  Co. (Cut) ....AA
Pottstown Iron Co. (Boat;
  Box; Clinch; Cut; Finish-
  ing; Iron; Roofing; Slat-
  ing; Steel; Tufting)....X
PA.—Sharon Hill
Pickering, R. S. (Cut) ..F
PA.—Steelton
Penna. Steel Co. (Steel)
                      AAAA
PA.—Williamsport
Williamsport Iron & Nail
  Co. (Cut) ....A
PA.—York
York Tack & Nail Wrks.
  (Basket; Boat; Box; Car;
  Chair; Cigar Box; Clinch;
  Cut; Finishing; Small;
  Stair; Steel; Trunk) ..A
R. I.—Pawtucket
Coleman Nail Co. (Horse)
                      B
R. I.—Providence
Am. Screw Co. (Wire all
  sizes) ....AAAA
Tockwotton Co. (Upholster-
  ers' Bag Bottom; Leather
  Carriage; Decorative; Fur-
  niture; Headed; Saddle)
                      E
TENN.—Harriman
Harriman Tack Co. (Iron)
                      X
VT.—Vergennes
Natl. Horse Nail Co.
  (Horse) ....A
VA.—Richmond
Old Dominion Iron & Nail
  Wrks. Co. (Cut Iron;
  Roofing; Slating Box;
  Car; Clinch; Finishing;
  Heel; Small; Steel) ...A
W. VA.—Wheeling
Laughlin Nail Co. (Steel)
                      AA
Wheeling Corrugating Co.
  (Galvanized) ....A
Wheeling Hinge Co. (Iron)
                      AAA
Wheeling Iron & Steel Co.
  (Cut; Finishing; Hoop;
  Roofing; Slating; Small;
  Special) X
WIS.—Cedarburg
Cedarburg Wire, Wire Nail
  & Screw Co. (Wire 1-4 to
  4 inch) ....D
WIS.—Janesville
Janesville Barb Wire Co.
  (Wire 2 to 60 Penny)..B
WIS.Milwaukee
Milwaukee Tack Co. (Brass;
  Copper; Roofing; Slating;
  Small Wire; Basket;
  Boat; Cigar Box; Cut;
  Finishing; Heel; Hob;
  Hungarian; Iron; Steel.C

NAINSOOKS

See Cotton Goods

NAPKINS

MASS.—Holyoke
Japanese Tissue Mills (Paper) ....A
MASS.—Lowell
Lowell Textile Co. (Damask;
D
N. Y.—Brooklyn
Gair Co., Robt. (Paper) ..A
N. Y.—Carthage
Carthage Tissue Paper Mills
(Paper) ....A
New York City
Dennison Mfg. Co., John
(Paper) ....AAAA
PA.—Philadelphia
Providence Mills Mfg. Co.,
Girard Av. & 45th C
WIS.—Green Bay
Hoberg Co., John (Paper)
D

NAPHTHA

MASS.—Boston
Billings, Clapp & Co.
(Wood) ....B
MO.—St. Louis
Mallinckrodt Chemical
Wrks. (Wood) ....AAAA
N. Y.—Buffalo
Schoelkopf, Hartford &
Hanna Co. (Coal Tar)
AAA
New York City
Borrett Mfg. Co.....AAAA
Standard Oil Co. of N. Y.
AAAA
Tide Water Oil Co. ..AAAA
White Tar Co. (Coal Tar)
E
N. C.—Wilmington
Spirittine Chemical Co.
(Wood) C
OHIO—Cleveland
National Refining Co.
(Deodorized) ....AAA
OHIO—Toledo
Paragon Refining Co. ..AA
PA.—Bradford
Emery Mfg. Co. ....AAAA
PA.—Freedom
Freedom Oil Works Co. (Deodorized) ....A
PA.—North Clarendon
Smith, Levi ....A
PA.—Philadelphia
Barrett Mfg. Co. ....AAAA
Crew, Levick Co. ....AAAA
PA.—Warren
Conewango Refining Co...B
Superior Oil Works C
PA.—Titusville
American Oil Wrks. ......A

NAPHTHALINE

N. Y.—Buffalo
Schoelkopf, Hartford &
Hanna Co. ....AAA
New York City
Wegelin & Wilckes Mfg. Co.
C
White Tar Co. 101 N. Moore
(Balls; Flake; Powder;
Crystals) ....E
PA.—Philadelphia
Barrett Mfg. Co. ....AAAA
Jordan, W. H., Jr. & F.
(Powdered) ....AA

NECKLACES

See Jewelry

NECKWEAR

CAL.—San Francisco
Heineman, H. M. ....B
Kraker, M. (Ruching) ...C
Samter, L. & Son........D
CONN.—Williamantic
Thread City Collar Co. (Rubber) ....B
CONN.—Windsor
Windsor Collar & Cuff Co.
C

NECKWEAR (Con.)
GA.—Atlanta
Robinson Neckwear Co. ..D
ILL.—Chicago
Carter & Holmes (Men's)
B
Cronin & Friedman (Men's)
C
Cutter & Crossette (Men's)
B
Michael, John C. (Women's)
D
Rawitsch Bros. (Men's)..D
Salk, M. (Men's) ....D
Shields, J. E. & Co.
(Men's) C
Shoninger Bros. Mfg. Co.
(Women's Lace) C
Squiers, Vandervoort & Co.
(Men's Mufflers) .....B
Thomas & Hayden (Men's)
B
Wilson Bros. ....AAAA
IND.—New Albany
Robinson, Norton & Co.
(Ladies) ....AAA
KY.—Louisville
Platt Co., N. Sid. (Silk &
(Cotton) ....D
MASS.—Boston
Bergheim Bros. (Men's)..C
Bradstreet, Tilton & Co.
(Men's) C
Brown & Co. (Men's) ...C
Cleveland Co. (Men's & Women's) C
Hawley, Folsom & Ronimus
A
Ideal Neckware Co. (Men's)
D
Sharaf, M. & Co. (Men's &
Women's) ....D
Simons, Hatch & Whitten
Co. ....AA
Trafton, H. O. ....E
MASS.—Fitchburg
Cornforth & Marx (Silk
Mufflers) ....B
MASS.—Reading
Temple, J. S. (Men's) ..D
MASS.—Springfield
M. & M. Mfg. Co. (Rubber)
E
MINN.—St. Paul
Conhaim Neckwear Co.
(Men's) C
MO.—St. Louis
Ferguson, McKinney Dry
Gds. Co. (Men's) ..AAAA
Fischlowitz & Franks
(Men's) C
Hurst, Zucker Neckwear
Co. (Men's) ....D
Korngold, J. B. & Co.
(Men's) ....D
Ornstein & Rice Neckwear
Co. (Men's) ....B
N. J.—Paterson
Ball, Wm. (Silk Mufflers)
C
Holmes Silk Co. (Silk Mufflers) ....A
Kattermann & Mitchell Co.
(Silk Mufflers) ....A
Taylor Silk Mfg. Co.
(Silk Mufflers) C
N. Y.—Brooklyn
Roach & Co., John C. ....E
New York City
Altman Neckwear Co.
(Men's) C
Auerbach, Louis (Men's) .B
Bendix & Eisenstaedt
(Men's) C
Benioff Bros. (Men's)...D
Berliner, Strauss & Meyer
(Men's) ....A
Blanchard & Price (Men's)
D
Burger, L. & Co. (Men's)
C
Cohn & Co. (Men's) ....B
Cowen, A. W. & Bros.
(Men's) ....B
Engel, Mayer & Co. (Women's) ....D
Fisk, Clark & Flagg ....A
Frankenstein, Son & Bettelheim (Women's) ......B
French & Co., (Inc.) (Men's)
B
Goodman, M. & Co. (Women's) C
Goodman, Leo & Bro.

NECKWEAR (*Con.*)
(Men's) C
Guiterman Bros. Men's
Silk Mlfflers) ....A
Gumport, I. J. (Men's) ..D
Haslam, Wm. Co. (Men's
& Women's) ....D
Heller, Maurice (Men's).D
Horikoshi & Co., Z. (Silk
Mufflers) ....B
Horn, W. O. & Bro. (Men's
Lawn) ....B
Igelheimer, Middle & Alt-
man (Men's) ....D
Isaac, I. & Co. (Men's) ..C
Kaskel & Kaskel ....B
Keep Mfg. Co. (Men's) ..A
Keiser, James R. (Men's.D
Levy & Marcus (Men's) ..C
Lewine Bros. (Men's)...D
Lowenstein, Morris W.
(Men's) ....D
Lyford, Chas. W. & Son
(Men's) ....D
McCurrach, Jas. & Bro.
(Mens' Mufflers) .....A
Majestic Neckwear Co.
(Men's) ....D
Mannheimer, H. (Men's).D
Mayer, D. & E. L. (Men's)
Meinhard, Dalsimer Co.
(Women's) ....B
Modry, I. & Co. (Women's)
A
Monheimer & Weil (Men's)
C
Nashley, Louis (Men's).D
New York Neckwear Co.
(Men's Silk) ....D
Opper & Levinson (Men's &
Women's) C
Parker & Finn (Men's) ..D
Plonsky & Solomon (Men's)
B
Prenowitz, J. (Men's) ....B
Rabinowitz, J. & Co.
(Men's) ....D
Reiner, Samuel (Men's) ..B
Richters, H., Sons (Men's)
AA
Roche, Croll & Co. ....D
Rosenthal & Grotta (Wo-
men's Lace Novelties;
Rufflings) ....A
Ryerson, A. N. & Co.
(Men's; Women's) ....D
Silberberg Bros. (Ladies')
C
Simon, Morris & Son
(Men's Silk) ....B
Simon, L. & Co. (Men's) ..A
Standard Summer Neckwear
Co. (Men's Lawn; Cotton)
B
Stanton Bros. (Men's; Wo-
men's) C
Stark, James H. & Co.
(Men's) ....B
Stern, C. & Mayer (Men's)
Trevor, Wm. (Men's) ...C
Walton, F. M. & Co.
(Men's) ....B
Waterhouse, Rufus, Co.
(Men's) ....B
Wechsler Bros., (Am. Sus-
pender Co.) ....E
Weld, Colburn & Wilckens
(Men's) ....A
Williamson Bros. (Men's)
B
Wolgamot & Co. (Men's)..C
N. Y.—Port Jervis
Cohn, H. C. & Co. (Men's)
B
N. Y.—Rochester
Cohn & Co., H. C.........A
Randall, F. A. Co. (Men's)
D
Rochester Neckwear Co.
(Men's) ....D
N. Y.—Troy
Dingman, J. B. (Women's)
F
OHIO—Baltimore
Griffith Mfg. Co. (Men's &
Ladies') ....D
OHIO—Cincinnati
Baer, Kronacher & Co.
(Men's) ....D
Ornstein & Rice (Men's)..B
OHIO—Cleveland
Cleveland Neckwear Co.
(Women's) ....D

NECKWEAR (*Con.*)
OREGON—Portland
Olds, Wortman & King ..A
PA.—Philadelphia
Apple, Lou W. & Co.
(Men's) ....D
Davis, Joel Baily Co. (Un-
ion Mfg. Co.) (Men's)..A
Howell, Stein & Co. (Men's)
D
Hughes & Bradley (Men's)
C
Klemm, W. G. (Men's)..B
Levy & Co. (Men's) C
McCutcheon, T. P. & Bro.
(Men's) ....B
Rothschild, I. & Co. (Men's)
D
Ticktin, M. (Men's) ....B

NEEDLES

CONN.—Bridgeport
Beers & Son, P. M. (Sewing
Machine) ....D
Klein & Bro. (Crochet)...B
Wheeler & Wilson Mfg. Co.
(Sewing Machine) .AAAA
CONN.—Chester
Bates, C. J. (Crochet; Knit-
ting) ....D
CONN.—Deep River
Potter & Snell (Crochet)
C
CONN.—Essex
Tiley-Pratt Co. (Crochet).D
CONN.—Hartford
Merrow Machine Co. (Cro-
chet Machine) ....B
CONN.—Manchester
Lydall & Foulds, H. (Knit-
ting Machine) ....B
CONN.—New Haven
Smith Co., A. H. (Sewing
Machine) ....D
CONN.—Torrington
Excelsior Needle Co. (Knit-
ting; Sewing Machine;
Wax Thread) .... AAAA
CONN.—West Cheshire
Jerald & Lawton (Sewing
Machine) ....A
ILL.—Chicago
Excelsior Supply Co. (Sew-
ing Machine) ....A
IOWA—Ottumwa
Hardsocg Mfg. Co. (Coal
Miners') ....B
MASS.—Boston
New England Novelty Mfg.
Co. (Crochet; Self Thread-
ing) ....H
Sewing Machine Supplies Co.
(Sewing Machine) ....B
MASS.—Chicopee Falls
Lamb Knitting Machine Co.
(Latch) ....B
Page Needle Co. (Knitting
Machine; Latch) ......D
MASS.—Lowell
Bagshaw. W. H. ....B
MASS.—Lynn
Eastham, Henry W. (Sewing
Machine; Wax Thread
Sewing Machine) ......D
MASS.—North Hadley
Dickinson & Son, C. D.
(Broom Makers') .....D
MASS.—Springfield
Natl. Needle Co. (Sewing
Machine) ....A
MASS.—Westfield
Crane Bros. (Spring Knit-
ting) ....AAA
MICH.—Detroit
Schimmel, Gustave R. (Hy-
podemic) ....D
N. H.—Franklin
Franklin Needle Co. (Latch;
Sewing Machine) ......B
N. H.—Hill
Adams & Co., G. H. (Knit-
ting Machine) C
N. H.—Lakeport
Crane Mfg. Co. (Spring
Knitting) ....B
Wardwell Needle Co. (Knit-
ting Machine) ....B
N. H.—Manchester
Corey Co., Wm. (Knitted
Machine; Latch) ......B
Dodge Needle Co. (Knitting
Machine; Latch) ......D
N. J.—Newark
Crabb & Co., Wm. (Comber;

698

NEEDLES (Con.)
  Wool Comb) ....A
N. J.—New Brunswick
Ives Co., Loyal S. (Knit-
  ting Machine; Spring
  Knitting) ....B
N. Y.—Amsterdam
Breedon's Son, W. (Knitting
  Machine; Spring Kniting)
                            B
New York City
Barker & Co., C. B. (Sew-
  ing Machine) ....B
Brabant Needle Co. (Cro-
  chet) ....D
Estes & Sons, E. B., 45
  John (Seine Wood) ..AA
Green, Frank P. (Sewing
  Machine) ....D
Hoehn Co., R., 80 Chambers,
  (Dentists') ....B
Shrimpton Mfg. Co., 273
  Church (Glove; Harness;
  Hand sewing; Knitting;
  Sail Makers'; Packing;
  Sewing Machine; Spey-
  ing) ....G
Singer Mfg. Co. (Sewing
  Machine) ....AAAA
Tiebout, W. & J. (Sailmak-
  ers': Packers, etc.).....B
N. Y.—Philmont
Ames, David J. (Knitting
  Machine; Spring Knit-
  ting) X
N. Y.—Troy
Tompkins Bros. Co. (Com-
  ber) ....B
OHIO—Cleveland
United States Dental Mfg.
  Co. (Dental Hypodermic)
                            D
PA.—Mount Clare
Mount Clare Needle Co.
  (Hosiery) ....D
PA.—Philadelphia
Branson Machine Co., 506
  No. American (Knitting
  Machine) ....A
Keystone Kniting Machine
  Mfg. Co. (Knitting Ma-
  chine) ....D
Manufacturers' Supplies Co.,
  66 N. 4th (Knitting Ma-
  chine) ....D
Nat'l Automatic Knitter Co.
  (Knitting Machine) ....B
PA.—Pittsburg
Hubbard & Co., Murtland
  Bldg. (Miners') ......AA
Klein-Logan Co. (Miners')
                            A
Pittsburg Tool & Drop Forge
  Co., Arrott Bldg. (Mi-
  ners') ....D
R. I.—Providence
Townsend, Thos., 157
  Orange (Comber) ......E
VT.—Bennington
Cooper, Chas. (Knitting Ma-
  chine) ....B

NESTS

ILL.—Chicago
Barbee Wire & Iron Wrks.
  (Hens' Wire) ....B
MO.—St. Louis
Ludlow- Sayloe Wire Co.
  (Hens' Wire) ....AA
N. Y.—Cortland
Wickwire Bros. (Hens', &c.)
                         AAAA
New York City
Gilbert & Bennett Mfg. Co.
  (Hens' &c.) 42 Cliff
                       AAA

NETS

CAL.—San Francisco
Neville & Co. (Fishing) ..A
CAL.—Stockton
Shaw Co., H. (Hay) ....A
CONN.—East Hampton
Star Net & Twine Co., The
  (Linen; Cotton Fish)...B
CONN.—Moodus
New York Net & Twine Co.
  (Fishing) ....B
CONN.—Naugatuck
Dunham Hosiery Co. (Net
  for Rubber Shoe Linings)
                           A

NETS (Con.)
CONN.—Norwich
Turner Mfg. Co. (Bicycle;
  Dress Guard) X
CONN.—Rockville
Regan Mfg. Co., Jas. J.
  (Cotton; Wool) ......AA
CONN.—Tariffville
Tariffville Lace Mfg. Co.
  (Fish) ....B
ILL.—Chicago
Carpenter & Co., Geo. B.
  (Fishing) ....AA
Chicago Net & Twine Co.
  (Fish; &c.) ....D
Chicago Rawhide Mfg. Co.
  (Leather; Fly) ....A
Cook & Bro., E. C. (Fishing)
                            A
ILL.—Ottawa
Bach & Co., M. W. (Fly)
                            C
MASS.—Boston
Amer. Net & Twine Co.
  (Fishing; Gymnasum)
                         AAA
Chase & Co. (Fly) ....AAA
Lord Co., G. W. (Fishing)
                            A
MASS.—Gloucester
Gloucester Net & Twine Co.
  (Fish Nets; Sienes) ....A
MICH.—Kalamazoo
Lull Carriage Co. (Fly) ..B
MINN.—St. Paul
Hardenburg, P. R. L. (Fly)
                            A
MO.—St. Louis
Missouri Tent & Awning Co.
  (Fishing) ....B
N. J.—Jersey City
Hall, H. S. (Silk Hair) ..D
N. J.—Newalk
Peters Harness & Saddlery
  Co. (Horse; Fly) C
N. Y.—Brooklyn
Jennings Lace Wrks. (Silk
  Hair; Lace) ......AAAA
Kelsey, Albert (Fly) ....B
Hepner & Horwitz (Knit
  Millinery) C
New York City
Spaulding & Bro., A. G.
  (Tennis) ....AAAA
Taylor & Co., H. E., 510 E.
  72nd (Fly) ....A
Tiebout, W. & J. (Scoop)
                            B
N. Y.—Utica
Clark, Horrocks Co. (Fish
  Landing) ....A
PA.—Dillsburg
Altland, A. D. (Cotton Knit)
                            D
PA.—Milton
Wilson & Co., R. F. (Fly)
                            A
PA.—Philadelphia
Ayres & Son, Wm. (Gym-
  nasium; Fly) ....AA
Loeb, Lepper & Co. (Lace)
                            A
PA.—Quakertown
Harley, J. S. (Leather; Fly)
                          AA
PA.—Wellsville
Pennsylvania Net Co. (Horse
  Fly) C
W. VA.—Moundsville
Bardall & Co., J. C. (Fly)
                            B
WIS.—Milwaukee
Gem Hammock & Fly Net
  Co. (Fly; Leather) ....A

NETTING

CAL.—San Francisco
California Wire Cloth Co.
  (Wire: Poultry) ....D
Hallidie-Painter Tramway
  Co., 46 Fremont (Wire:
  Poultry) ....D
West Coast Wire & Iron
  Wrks. (Wire; Poultry).F
CONN.—Georgetown
Gilbert & Bennett Mfg. Co.
  (Wire; Poultry; Galvaniz-
  ed; Glue; Steel Wire)
                         AAA
CONN.—Middletown
Palmer, I. E. (Imitation
  Wire) ....AAA
CONN.—New Haven
Nat'l Steel & Wire Wrks.

NETTING (Con.)

Wire; Poultry) ....AAAA
ILL.—Chicago
Am. Steel & Wire Wks. Co.
(Wire; Poultry) ..AAAA
Barbee Wire & Iron Wrks.
(Wire; Poultry) ......B
Booth, Jno., 114 Lake
(Wire; Poultry) .....B
Smith Wire & Iron Wrks., F.
P., 100 Lake (Wire; Poultry) ....AA
ILL.—DeKalb
DeKalb Fence Co. (Wire;
Poultry) ....AA
IND.—Crawfordsville
Crawfordsville Wire & Nail
Co. (Wire) ....A
IND.—Richmond
Eureka Fence Mfg. Co.
Wire; Poultry) ......F
KY.—Louisville
Dow Wire Wrks. Co., 730
W. Market (Wire; Poultry) ....D
MD.—Baltimore
Dufur & Co., 311 N. Howard (Wire; Poultry) ....B
MASS.—Clinton
Clinton Wire Cloth Co.
(Wire; Poultry; Galvanized Wire) ....AAA
MASS.—Springfield
Bigelow-Cheney Wire Wrks.
(Wire; Galvanized Wire;
Poultry; Steel Wire) ..A
MASS.—Worcester
Wright Wire Co. (Wire;
Poultry) ....AA
MO.—St. Louis
Ludlow-Saylor Wire Co.
(Wire) ....AA
N. J.—Belleville
Eastwood Wire Mfg. Co.
(Wire; Poultry) ......A
N. J.—Trenton
New Jersey Wire Cloth Co.
(Wire; Poultry) ......A
N. Y.—Buffalo
Buffalo Wire Works Co.
(Wire) ....A
N. Y.—Cortland
Wickwire Bros. (Wire; Galvanized Wire; Poultry)
................AAAA
New York City
Estey Wire Wrks. Co., 59
Fulton (Wire; Poultry)
................AA
Fiske Iron Wrks, J. W., 39
Park Pl. (Wire; Poultry)
................B
Howard & Morse, 45 Fulton
(Wire; Poultry) ......D
Roebling's Sons, Jno. A.
(Wire; Poultry; Galvanized Wire) ....D
OHIO—Cincinnati
Bromwell Brush & Wire
Goods Co. (Wire) ....AA
Cincinnati Mfg. Co., 512
Main (Wire; Poultry) ..B
Nimmo Fence Co., 324 E. 4th
(Wire; Poultry) ......E
OHIO—Cleveland
Tyler Co.. W. S., 1150 St.
Clair (Poultry; Locomotive Stack) ......AAAA
OHIO—Hamilton
Meyers Mfg. Co., Fred J.
(Wire) ....B
PA.—Philadelphia
Darby & Sons, Edw., 233
Arch (Wire; Poultry) ..A
De Witt Wire Cloth Co.. 703
Market (Wire; Galvanized
Wire; Poultry) ....A
PA.—Pittsburg
Pittsburg Steel Co.. Peoples
Sav. Bank Bldg. (Wire;
Poultry) ....AAAA

NETTING: MOSQUITO

CONN.—Middleton
Arawana Mills (I. E. Palmer) (Cotton; Sand Fly)
................AAA
CONN.—Shelton
Derby Cotton Mills (Robt.
Franklyn Adams) (Cotton)
................A

NETTING: MOSQUITO

N. J.—Passaic
McLean Co., Andrew ..AA
N. Y.—Valley Falls
Thompson & Co., Jas. ..AA
R. I.—Scituate
North Scituate Cotton Mills
................C
WIS.—Racine
Gold Medal Camp Furniture
Mfg. Co. C

NEWELS

ALA.—Florence
Florence Wagon Wrks.
(Porch) ....A
ALA.—Stanton
Dyer, W. C. ....E
MASS. Worcester
Hatch & Barnes C
N. Y.—New York City
Bird, Wm. S., 42 W. 67th
(Stair) ....E
TENN.—Cookville
Dow, D. L. (Stair) ......E
WIS.—Oshkosh
McMillen & Co., R. (Hardwood Stair) ....A

NICKEL

ILL.—Peru
Illinois Zinc Co. ......AAA
MASS.—Boston
Waite, Ranlet & Co. ....B
N. J.—Newark
Hanson & Van Winkle Co.
................AA
N. Y.—New York City
American Metal Co. ..AAAA
Boker & Co., Hermann
................AAAA
Orford Copper Co. ....AAA
N. Y.—Rome
Rome Mfg. Co...........B

NICKELINE

N. Y.—New York City
Boker, Hermann & Co., 101
Duane ....AAA
Hirsch. Isaac E., 468 W.
B'way ....D

NICKELOID

ILL.—Peru
Am. Nickeloid Mfg. Co.
(Nickeloid: Copperoid;
Steeloid; Brassoid; Nickelized Sheet Steel; Zinc;
Copper; Brass; &c.) ..F

NIPPERS

CONN.—Bridgeport
Bridgeport Hwd. Mfg. Co.
(End Cutting) ....B
CONN.—New Haven
Schollhorn Co.. Wm. (Cutting) ....A
CONN.—Rockfall
Smith, Otis A. (Cutting) .B
CONN.—Southington
Peck, Stow Wilcox Co.
(Cutting; Hoof) ..AAAA
CONN.—Waterbury
Mattatuck Mfg. Co. (Automatic) C
Scovill Mfg. Co. (Bicycle)
................AAAA
ILL.—Chicago
Chicago Pneumatic Tool Co.,
Fisher Bldg. (Pneumatic
Bolt) ....AAAA
Vaughn & Bushnell Mfg.
Co., 875 Carroll Av. (Cutting) ....A
MASS.—Athol
Starrett & Co., L. S. (Cutting) ....A
MASS.—Boston
Whitcher & Co., Frank W.
(Cutting) ....A
MASS.—Chicopee Falls
Stevens Arms & Tool Co., J.
(Bicycle) ....A
MICH.—Grand Rapids
Wolverine Brass Wrks. (Soldering) ....A
N. J.—Newark
Heller & Bros (Cutting)

NIPPERS (Con.)

Krauter & Co., (Cutting)
....X

Osborn & Co., C. S. (Cutting) ....B

Sacks Iron Fdy, Louis (End Cutting) ....A

N. Y.—Elmira
Cronk & Carrier Mfg. Co. (End Cutting) ....B

New York City
Morrill, Charles (End Cutting) ....D

Smith & Hemenway Co., 296 B'way (Bicycle) ......D

Tower & Lyon, 95 Chambers (Police) ....B

Weed, Riley & Co., 11 Gold (Cutting) ....D

Wiebusch & Hilger (Cutting) ....A

N. Y.—Utica
Utica Drop Forge & Tool Co. (Bicycle; Cutting) ....B

OHIO—Cincinnati
Cincinnati Tool Co. (Cutting) ....B

OHIO—Cleveland
Peck, Stow & Wilcox Co. (Cutting) ....AAAA

OHIO—Ravenna
Williams, A. C. (Cutting)
....A

R. I.—Providence
Amer. Supply Co. (Point)
....AA

VT.—Windsor
Hubbard & McClary (Cutting) ....B

NIPPLES

CONN.—Bridgeport
Belknap Mfg. Co. (Hose & Nursery Rubber) C

CONN.—Essex
Tiley-Pratt Co. (Bicycles)
....D

CONN.—Hartford
Hartford Machine Screw Co. (Bicycle) ....AAAA

CONN.—New Haven
Seamless Rubber Co. (Nursery Rubber) ....AA

CONN.—Torrington
Excelsior Needle Co. (Bicycle) ....AAAA

CONN.—Waterbury
Mamille Machine Co., E. J. (Bicycle; Automobile) .C

ILL.—Chicago
American Steel & Wire Co. (Bicycle) ....AAAA

Blatchford & Co., E. W., 70 N. Clinton (Soldering)
....AAAA

Chicago Screw Co. (Bicycle)
....AAA

Illinois Malleable Iron Co. (Soldering) ......AAAA

ILL.—Decatur
Mueller Mfg. Co., H. (Soldering) ....AAA

ILL.—Edwardsville
Edwardsville Brass Co. (Soldering) ....B

ILL.—Kewanee
Western Tube Co. (Pipe; Soldering) ....AAA

IND.—Erkhart
Erkhart Brass Mfg. Co. (Hose) ....E

MD.—Baltimore
Robertson Mfg. Co., James (Soldering; Brass) ....A

MASS.—Andover
Tyer Rubber Co. (Nursery Rubber) ....AA

MASS.—Boston
Boston Brass Co., 36 Oliver (Hose) C

Davidson Rubber Co. (Nursery Rubber) ....AA

Walworth Mfg. Co. (Brass)
....AAAA

MASS.—Holliston
Wilder & Co., Sidney (Brass Hose) ....E

MASS.—Lexington
Jefferson Mfg. Co. (Soldering) X

MASS.—Worcester
Wire Goods Co. (Bicycles; Au   ile) ....A

NIPPLES (Con.)

MICH.—Detroit
Park & MacKay Co. (Brass)
....C

MICH.—Jackson
McKeel & Co., Geo. A. (Boiler; Radiator) ....B

MO.—Kansas City
Platt Mfg. Co. (Brass Soldering) ....F

N. Y.—Jamesville
Jamesville Mfg. Co. (Automobile) ....D

New York City
Goodyear Rubber Co. (Nursery Rubber) ....AAAA

Goodyear's India Rubber Glove Mfg. Co. (Nursery Rubber) ....AAAA

Gotham Co. (Nursery Rubber) ....D

Mattson Rubber Co. (Nursery Rubber) ....B

Parker, Stearns & Sutton (Nursery Rubber) ......B

Schrader's Son, A., 30 Rose (Hose) ....B

OHIO—Akron
Goodrich Co., B. F. (Nursery Rubber) ....AAAA

Miller Rubber Co. (Nursery Rubber) ....B

OHIO—Cincinnati
Powell & Co., Wm., 2529 spg. Grove Av. (Hose)
....A

Queen City Brass & Iron Wrks. (Hose; Soldering)
....B

OHIO—Cleveland
Cleveland Bronze & Brass Wrks. (Soldering) C

Glauber Brass Mfg. Co., 88 & River (Soldering) ....AA

Sanitary Co., 335 Huron (Soldering) ....B

OHIO—Springfield
Nolte Brass Co. (Soldering)
....D

PA.—Erie
Cambell Brass Wrks., J. B. (Soldering) ....A

PA.—Philadelphia
Haines, Jones & Cadbury, 1136 Ridge Av. (Soldering) ....AA

Saville, Thos., 11th & Wood (Soldering) C

Ware Co., Walter F. (Nursery Rubber) ....B

R. I.—Providence
Davol Rubber Co. (Nursery Rubber) ....AA

NITRE

MO.—St. Louis
Herf & Frerichs Chemical Co. (Spirits of) ....A

Mallinckredt Chemical Wks. (Spirits of) ......AAAA

Powers-Weightman-Rosengarten Co. (Spirits of)...
....AAAA

NOILS

MASS.—Westford
Abbott Worsted Co. (Camels Hair; Carpet Wool)...AA

N. J.—Newark
Basch & Greenfield Co. (Silk) ....A

N. Y.—Whitehall
Champlain Silk Mills (Silk)
....A

PA.—Philadelphia
Tilden, W. T. ....A

NOODLES

See Macaroni & Vermicelli

NOSES

New York City
Condell, A. (Artificial)..D

PA.—Philadelphia
Kolbe Co., D. W. (Artificial) X

NOTES

ILL.—Chicago

NOTES (Con.)

Western Bank Note & Engraving Co. (Bank)...AA

New York City

Am. Bank Note Co. (Bank)
................AAAA

International Bank Note Co. (Bank) ....B

New York Bank Note Co. (Bank) ....A

NOTIFIERS

OHIO—Dayton

Dayton Supply Co. (Burglar) ....A

NOVELTIES

See also Silverware; Jewelry; Millinery

ARK.—Texarkana

Standard Novelty Wks. (Wood Turned) ....A

CONN.—Bridgeport

Gaynor & Mitchell Mfg. Co. (Special Sheet Metal)..C

Ives Mfg. Co. (Toy)......C

CONN.—Bristol

Root, C. J. (Hardware)...B

CONN.—Deep River

Williams & Marvin Mfg. Co. (Wood Turned) ....D

CONN.—Derby

Derby Silver Co. (Silver Plate) ....AAAA

CONN.—Essex

Essex Wood Turning Co. (Furniture) X

CONN.—Meriden

Hall, Wilbur B. (White Metal) X

Meriden Britannia Co. (Thermometr) ....AAAA

Meriden Silver Plate Co. (Silver Plate)......AAAA

CONN.—New Britain

Landers, Frary & Clark (Hardware) ....AAA

CONN.—New Haven

Ives Co., Hobart B. (Hardware) ....A

CONN.—Torrington

Torrington Mfg. Co. (Metal)
................C

Turner & Seymour Mfg. Co. (Hardware) ....A

CONN.—Wallingford

Wallace & Sons Mfg. Co., R. (Silver) ....AAAA

CONN.—Waterbury

Amer. Pin Co. (Metal Stamped; Spun Turned from Rod) ....AA

Novelty Mfg. Co. (Metal; Plush) ....A

Steele & Johnson Mfg. Co. (Brass; Plush) ....A

White Co., L. C. (Brass).C

CONN.—Winsted

Goodwin & Kintz Co. (Brass; Aluminum; Nickel) ....B

ILL.—Chicago

Caldwell & Co., W. D. (Wood) C

Turner Brass Wks. (Metal)
................A

Shafer Co., F. L., 263 Dearborn (Advertising).X

ILL.—Freeport

Stover Mfg. Co. (Hardware)
................AA

IND.—Fort Wayne

Anthony Wayne Mfg. Co. (Show Window) X

IND.—Indianapolis

Union Novelty Mfg. Co., 1338 Charles (Wood; Iron; Metal) X

MASS.—Attleboro

Mossberg Co., Frank (Sheet Metal; Stamped; Punched) ....A

MASS.—Chelsea

Chelsea Mfg. Co. (Metal).X

Low Tile Co. (Stationers')
................F

MASS.—Fitchburg

Mossmon, Jerome (Wood Turned) ....F

NOVELTIES (Con.)

MASS.—Leominster

Whitney Reed Chair Co. (Toy) ....AAAA

MASS.—Lowell

Woods, Sherwood Co. (Wire)
................E

MASS.—North Attleboro

Barrows & Co., H. F. (Jewelry; Silver)......A

Codding & Hailborn Co. (Silver) ....A

Whiting Co., F. M. (Jewelry; Silver) ....B

MASS.—Springfield

Bradley Co., Milton (Toy)
................A

Smith Mfg. Co., R. H. (Stationers') C

MASS.—Westfield

Hampden Toy Co. (Advertising) ....D

ASS.—Woburn

Curtis, Wm. H. (Cotton).G

MASS.—Worcester

Warren Leather Goods Co. (Leather Advertising)..B

MICH.—Bellaire

Richardi & Bachtold (Wood Turned) ....B

MICH.—Cadillac

Cummer Mfg. Co. (Wooden)
................B

MICH.—Detroit

Widman & Co., C. D. (Furniture) ....A

MICH.—Grand Rapids

Grand Rapids Brass Co. (Brass) ....A

MICH.—Holland

Michigan Toy & Novelty Co. (Wood) ....E

MICH.—Jackson

McKeel & Co., Geo. A. (Sheet Metal) ....B

MICH.—Saginaw

Berst Mfg. Co. (Wood Turned) ....B

N. H.—Milford

Price & Co., W. E. (Wood Turned) ....D

N. H.—State Line

Cudworth & Petts ....F

N. J.—Jersey City

Koenig Bros. (Plush).....D

Mehl & Co., John, Inc. (Leather) ....AA

N. J.—Newark

Benfield & Milne Mfg. Co. (White Metal) ....B

Block & Bergfield (Jewelry Roman) ....B

Crabb & Co., Wm. (Wire)
................A

Domestic Novelty Co. (Metal) X

Durand & Co., Inc. (Jewelry; Silver) ....AA

Havel Mfg. Co., 284 Wash. (Metal) ....A

Hedges & Co., A. J. (Jewelry) ....A

Newark Street Metal Ware Co., 50 Elm (Metal)...D

Sommer's Sons, Jno. (Wood Turned) ....A

Whitehead & Hoag Co. (Celluloid Advertising)..
................AAA

Williamson Wire Novelty Co., C. T. (Wire)......B

N. J.—New Brunswick

Consolidated Fruit Jar Co. (Metal) ....AA

N. Y.—Bliss

Bliss Mfg. Co. (Wooden).E

N. Y.—Brooklyn

Bommer Bros. (Hardware)
................A

N. Y.—Buffalo

Buffalo Scale Co. (Stationers') ....AA

New York City

Bronze & Papier Mache Co., 388 Hudson (Advertising)
................A

Cohn, J. J. (Leather)....A

Cottle, C. S. (Jewelry; Silver) ....E

Eagle Novelty Wks. (Millinery) ....D

Eagle Pencil Co. (Station-

NOVELTIES (Con.)

ers') ....AAA
Faber, Eberhard (Station-
ers') ....AAA
Grote & Co., F. (Ther-
mometer) ....D
Illustrated Postal Card &
Novelty Co. (Advertising)
............................X
Jansen, Edward (Straw
Braid) ....A
Judd & Co., H. L. (Metal;
Thermometer) ....AA
Kaufman & Strauss Co.
(Advertising) ....A
Larter & Sons (Jewelry)..A
Maas-Blum Co. (Leather)..
............................AA
Manhattan Silver Plate Co.
(Jewelry; Silver) ..AAAA
Meyers Co., S. F. (Jewelry;
Silver) ....D
N. Y. Aluminum Co. (Ad-
vertising) C
Pairpont Corpn. (German
Silver) ....AA
Rice's Sons, Bernard (Glass
with Plated Mountings;
Jewelry) ....A
Richards & Co., C. Ira
(Roman; Silver Jewelry)
............................AAA
Shiebler & Co., Geo. W.
(Silver) ....A
Sloan & Co. (Jewelry;
Silver) ....B
Waring, Vechten (Adver-
tising) ....F
Whitehead & Hoag Co.
(Advertising) ......AAA
N. Y.—Rochester
Streeter & Co., N. R.
(Hardware) ....A
N. Y.—Rome
Doyle, W. J. (Metal)....D
N. Y.—Seneca Falls
Westcott Jewell Co. (Ad-
vertising) ....D
OHIO—Belaire
Rodefer, T. C. (Glassware)
............................A
OHIO—Cincinnati
Globe-Wernicke Co. (Sta-
tioners') ....AAAA
Tatum Co., Saml. C.
(Hardware) ....B
OHIO—Cleveland
Ohio Electric Wks. (Elec-
tric) ....D
OHIO—Coshocton
Beach Co., H. D. (Ad-
vertising) X
Coshocton Novelty Co.
(Advertising) X
Meek-Beach Co. (Adver-
tising) ....s....AA
Novelty Advertising Co.
(Advertising) ....B
OHIO—Piqua
Piqua Handle & Mfg. Co.
(Wood Turned) ....A
PA.—Allentown
Grammes & Sons, L. F.
(Wrought Brass) .....A
PA.—Beaver Falls
Co-operative Flint Glass Co.
(Glassware) ....A
PA.—Corapolis
Consolidated Lamp Glass
Co. (Glassware)........A
PA.—Grapeville
Westmoreland Specialty Co.
(Glassware) ....A
PA.—Jeannette
McKee-Jeanette Glass Co.
(Glassware) ....B
PA.—Philadelphia
Gillinder & Sons (Glass-
ware) ....A
Natl. Metal Edge Box Co.
(Advertising) ....AA
Phila Novelty Mfg. Co.
(Cutlery; Hardware; Sta-
tioners) ....D
Rumpf & Sons, C. F.
(Leather) ....AAA
Schoenhut & Co., A. (Toy)
............................A
Wiland & Co., 205 Willow
(Metal) X
Wirz, A. H. (Metal) ....A
PA.—Pittsburg
McKennan Bros. (Metal)..A

NOVELTIES (Con.)

Phoenix Glass Co. (Glass-
ware) ....A
PA.—Scranton
Scranton Button Co. (Ad-
vertising) ....A
PA.—Tarentum
Tarentum Glass Co. (Glass-
ware) ....A
PA—Washington
Duncan & Miller Glass Co.
(Glassware) ....A
R. I.—Providence
Adams, D. F. (Jewelry).C
Amer. Enamel Co. (Wood
Turned; Metal) ....B
Bassett Jewelry Co. (Sil-
ver) ....B
Cory & Reynolds Co.
(Silver) C
Crossin & Co. (Jewelry)..F
Foster & Bros. Co., T. W.
(Silver) ....AA
Hamilton & Hamilton, Jr.
(Jewelry; Silver) ......A
Lederer Co., S. & B. (Jew-
elry; Roman; Silver)....C
Luther & Son, Wm. H.
(Jewelry) ....B
New England Butt Co.
(Hardware) ....AA
New England Pearl Co.
(Jewelry) ....F
Nickerson, N. B. (Jewelry;
Roman) X
Read & Lincoln (Silver)..D
Waite, Mathewson & Co.
(Jewelry) ....B
W. VA.—Wellsburg
Eagle Glass & Mfg. Co.
(Glassware) ....A
Riverside Glass Wks.
(Glassware) C
W. VA.—Wheeling
Central Glass Works
(Glassware) ....A
WIS.—Dundas
Dundas Woodenware Co.
(Wooden) ....D
WIS.—Milwaukee
Meinecke & Son, A. (Fur-
niture) ....AA
WIS.—Two Rivers
Aluminum Mfg. Co. (Alu-
minum; Advertising)...A
WIS.—Wausau
Wausau Novelty Co.
(Wood Turned) ....B

NOZZLES

CAL.—San Jose
Bean Spray Pump Co.
(Spray) ....D
CONN.—Bridgeport
Amer. Tube & Stamping
Co. (Oiler) ......AAAA
CONN.—New Haven
Peck Bros. & Co. (Spray;
Hose) ....AA
ILL.—Chicago
Allen Mfg. Co., 151 Lake
(Hose) ....A
Crane Co. (Hose) ...AAAA
IND.—Indianapolis
Armstrong & Co., W. H.
(Spray) ....B
MASS.—Boston
Boston Coupling Co., 156
Pearl (Hose) ....E
Hersey Mfg. Co. (Spray;
Hose) ....AA
Morse & Son. A. J., 140
Congress (Hose; Hy-
draulic) ....B
MASS.—Cambridge
Boston Woven Hose & Rub-
ber Co. (Hose) ....AAAA
MO.—St. Louis
Pleuger & Henger Mfg. Co.
(Hose) ....A
N. J.—Trenton
Empire Rubber Mfg. Co.
(Spray; Hose) ....AA
New York City
Eaton, Cole & Burnham Co.,
253 B'way (Hose; Spray;
Hydraulic) ....A
Empire Rubber Mfg. Co., 88
Reade (Hose) ....AA
Pedrick & Ayer Co. (Hose)
............................A
Schrader's Son, A., 30 Rose

NOZZLES (Con.)
(Hose) ....B
N. Y.—Rochester
Pullman Mfg. Co. (Hose;
Spray) ....B
OHIO—Ashland
Myers & Bro., F. E.
(Hose) ....AAAA
OHIO—Canton
Kohler & Co., F. E. (Hose)
B
OHIO—Mansfield
Barnes Mfg. Co. (Hose)..A
OHIO—Massillion
Hess, Snyder Co. (Spray)..
AA
OHIO—Salem
Deming Co. (Hose)......AA
PA.—Philadelphia
Clay, Jno. H., 1320 Ridge
Av. (Hose) ....B
Eynon-Evans, 1519 Charfield
(Blast) ....B
Seidel, R. B., 1334 Callow-
hill (Ladle) ....A
PA.—Pittsburg
Gem Mfg. Co. (Oiler)...D
McCullough-Dalzell Crucible
Co. (Plumbago for Besse-
mer; Open Hearth Fur-
naces) ....A
PA.—Williamsport
Darling Pump & Mfg. Co.
(Hose) ....B
WIS.—Milwaukee
Loeffelholz & Co., 170 Clin-
ton (Combination; Judge
Distributing Hose)......A

NUMBERS

**See also Figures; Letters;
Alphabets**
CONN.—Middletown
Wilcox, Crittenden Co.
(Metal) ....A
CONN.—New Haven
Hoggson & Pettis Mfg. Co.
(Door; Metal) ....A
CONN.—South Norwalk
Norwalk Lock Co. (Metal)
A
ILL.—Chicago
Chicago Spring Butt Co., 491
Carroll Av. (Metal) ....B
Kienzle, W. F., 92 Ohio
(Metal) ....D
Meyercord Co. (Decalco-
mania) ....A
Nicol & Co., 57 W. Washn.
(Metal) ....D
Turner Brass Wks. (Metal)
A
ILL.—Elgin
Zeigler Bros. (Metal)....C
ILL.—Freeport
Arcade Mfg. Co. (Brass;
Aluminum House; Pat-
tern) ....A
Stover Mfg. Co. (Door;
Metal) ....AA
MASS.—Boston
Robbins Mfg. Co., 58 Knee-
land (Metal; Door)....E
MASS.—Springfield
Kendall, W. E. (Door)....F
MICH.—Detroit
Buhl Stamping Co. (Metal)
AA
Thorpe Mfg. Co. (Metal).X
N. J.—Newark
Benfield & Milne Mfg. Co.,
67 Halleck (Metal) ....B
Reynolds & Zahn, 46 Me-
chanic (Metal) ....A
Schneider, Louis (Chair).H
N. Y.—Brooklyn
Brass Goods Mfg. Co.
(Metal) ....B
New York City
Caesar Bros., 112 Fulton
(Enameled) ....B
New York Stencil Wks.
(Door) X
Palm-Fetcheler Co. (Decal-
comania) ....A
Tablet & Ticket Co., 381
B'way (for Signs)......B
N. Y.—Seneca Falls
Brim, A. W. (Metal)....F
Knight & Son, H. W.
(Metal) C

NUMBERS (Con.)
N. Y.—Utica
Blasier & Co., M. E.
(Metal) C
OHIO—Cleveland
Taylor & Boggs Fdry. Co.,
521 Seneca (Metal) ...AA
OHIO—Columbus
Simpson Iron Co. (Metal).F
PA.—Philadelphia
National Decalcomania Co.
(Decalcomania) ....A
Quint's Sons, S. H. (Pew;
Pattern; Door) ....B
PA.—Reading
Reading Hdw. Co. (Metal)
AAAA
R. I.—Providence
Providence Aluminum Co.
(Metal) ....F
W. VA.—Wheeling
Wheeling Glass Letter &
Novelty Co. (Glass)....C
WIS.—Clinton
Smith & Holtam Mfg. Co.
(House) ....F

NUTMEGS

See Teas; Coffees & Spices

NUTS: EDIBLE

For Nuts Pea; See Peanuts

CAL.—Chico
Warren, E. A.............C
CAL.—Fullerton
Amerige, E. R. & G. H.
(Walnuts) ....B
CAL.—Los Angeles
Armsby Co., J. K., 121 W.
3d ....A
Germain Fruit Co. (Inc.).A
Inderrieden & Co., J. B.
(Br. Chic.) 109 Henne
Blk. ....AA
Simpson & Hack Fruit Co.
C
CAL.—Modesta
McHenry Seeded Raison Co.
AA
CAL.—Sacramento
Castle Bros. ....AA
CAL.—San Francisco
Guggenhime & Co., 118
Davis ....A
Hromada, A., 222 Battery
B
Ivancovich & Co., J., 211
Washn. ....A
Rosenberg Bros. & Co., 211
Cal. (Nut Meats) .....A
Scatena & Co., L., 104
Washn. ....B
Ulrichs & Co., J. F., 20
Clay C
CAL.—Santa Ana
Santa Ana Prod. Co.......C
CAL.—Suisun
Alden-Anderson Fruit Co.
(Almonds) C
CAL.—Yuba City
Rosenberg Bros. & Co.
(Br. San Francisco)....A
GA.—De Witt
Bacon Pecan Co., G. M.
(Pecans) ....B
ILL.—Chicago
Barsotti & Co., J., 119 So.
Water C
MO.—St. Louis
Barnhart Merc. Co., 518
No. 2d (Pecans)........B
Bayle, Geo. A., 113 So.
2d (Salted Almonds)..B
Funsten & Co., R. E., 300
N. Com'l (Pecans) ....B
St. Louis Edible Nut Co.,
216 N. Com'l (Pecans)..C
New York City
Arquimbau & Ramee, 84
Thomas ....B
Bennett, Day & Co., 96
Hudson ....A
Crooks & Co., Robt., 136
Front ....AA
Hills Bros. Co., 377 Washn.
AA
Spencer & Co., 163 Gwich.
C

704

NUTS: EDIBLE (Con.)

PA.—Philadelphia
Birdsong & Co., 38 No. Del.
Av. ....B
Lummis & Co., 148 N, Del.
Av. ....B
TENN.—Memphis
Barlow & Co., A. S.......B
TEXAS.—Austin
Orr, John (Pecans)......A
TEXAS—Dallas
Jackson & Co., A. A.......B
Nigro & Co., N...........B
TEXAS—Llano
Orr. John (Pecans) ......A
TEXAS—San Antonio
Duerler Mfg. Co., G. A.
(Shelled Pecans).......A
TEXAS—Tyler
Woldert Gro. Co. (Pecans)
C

NUTS: IRON; STEEL; BRASS, ETC.

See also Bolts

ALA.—Birmingham
Southern Bolt & Nut Wks.
(Bicycle, &c.).........B
COLO.—Denver
Colorado Fuel & Iron Co.,
Boston Bldg. (Tapped)..
AAAA
CONN.—Hartford
Billings & Spencer Co.
(Thumb; Wing).......A
CONN.—Milldale
Clark Bros. & Co. (Special;
all Kinds) ....A
CONN.—Mt. Carmel
Mt. Carmel Bolt Co. (Stove;
Bolt; Rod) ....B
CONN.—Southington
Aetna Nut Co. ....A
Southington Cutlery Co.
(Cold; Punched; Tapped;
Tire Bolt) ....AA
CONN.—Unionville
Union Uut & Bolt Co. (Hot
Pressed; Iron) ....A
Upson Nut Co. (Bicycle;
Case Hardened; Check;
Jam; Cold Punched; Hot
Pressed; Joint; Machine
Screw; Semi-Finished;
Tapped; Thumb; Wing;
Tire Bolt) ....AAA
CONN.—Winsted
Moore-Franklin Co. (Bi-
cycle; Joint) ....A
Richards Hdw. Co. T. C.
(Bicycle; Tire Bolt)...C
ILL.—Chicago
Ill. Screw Co. 19 Lake
(Boiler Patch; Planer
Herd) C
Republic Iron & Steel Co.,
Stock Exch. Bldg. (Hot
Pressed; Joint Sleeve;
Stove Bolt; Rod; Tapped;
Thumb; Wing; Tire
Bolt) ....AAAA
Standard Screw Co., 2 N.
Canal.. (Bicycle; Iron;
Brass Cap; Check; Jam;
Double Cupped; Machine
Screw; Collars; Semi-
Finished; Tapped; Thumb;
Wing) ....AAAA
MD.—Baltimore
Natl. Supply Co.. 7 W.
Lombard (Cold Punched;
Hot Pressed) ....B
MASS.—Boston
Boston Bolt Co., 33 Pur-
chase (Sleeve; Thumb)
B
MASS.—Worcester
Worcester Ferrule & Mfg.
Co. C
MICH.—Detroit
Mich. Bolt & Nut Works,
Meldrum Av. (Iron; Hot
Pressed; Tapped; Thumb;
Wing) ....B
MO.—Kansas City
Kansas City Bolt & Nut
Co.. Inde. Av., cor. Bris-
tol (Check; Jam; Hot

NUTS: IRON; STEEL
Pressed; Sleeve; Tapped)
A
MO.—St. Louis
Moran Bolt & Nut Mfg. Co.
Florida & Main (Cold
Punched; Hot Pressed;
Joint; Sleve; Stove; Bolt;
Rod; Tapped) ....A
St. Louis Screw Co., 3017 N.
13th (Bicycle; Brass Cap;
Brass; Copper; Case Hard-
ened; Check; Jam; Cold
Punched; Double Cupped;
Hot Pressed; Joint;
Knoiled; Mach. Screw;
Nuts; Collars; Semi-Fin-
ished; Stove Bolt; Rod;
Wing) ....B
New York City
Greenlie, Wyatt & Co., 499
Water (Tapped) ....B
Union Nut & Bolt Co., 107
Chambers (Hot Pressed)
B
N. Y.—Port Chester
Russell. Burdsall & Ward
Bolt & Nut Co. (Bicycle;
Case Hardened; Check;
Jam; Cold Punched; Joint;
Semi-Finished) ....AA
N. Y.—Rochester
Rochester Mach. Screw Co.
B
OHIO—Cleveland
Bourne & Knowles Mfg. Co.
8 Main (Cold Punched) A
Eberhard Mfg. Co., Tenny-
son & C. & P. R. R.
(Wing) ....AA
Kirk-Latty Mfg. Co., Mal-
colm, at Nickelplate R.
R. (Cold Pressed) .....B
Lamsen & Sessions Co., 412
Scranton Av. (Stove; Hot
Pressed; Bolt; Rod;
Tapped; Wing) ......AA
National Screw & Tack Co.,
Stanton & C. & P. R. R.
(Tapped) ....AA
OHIO—Columbus
Berry Bros. (Tire Bolt)...B
Lanman Co., E. B. (Cold
Punched) C
PA.—Allegheny
Graham Nut Co., 755 Re-
becca (Check; Jam; Cold
Punched; Tapped) C
PA.—Lancaster
Penn. Iron Co. (Cold
Punched; Hot Pressed;
Tapped) ....A
PA.—Lebanon
Am. Iron & Steel Mfg. Co.
(Case Hardened; Cold
Punched; Joint; Semi-Fin-
ished; Tapped; Wing)
AAAA
PA.—Milton
Milton Mfg. Co. (Case Hard-
ened; Cold Punched; Hot
Pressed; Semi-Finished) A
PA.—Philadelphia
Hooper & Townsend Co..
1330 Buttonwood (Case
Hardened; Cold Punched;
Double Cupped; Hot
Pressed; Joint; Collars;
Semi-Finished; Tapped;
Wing) ....AAA
Phosphor Bronze Smelting
Co., 220 Wash. Av. (Phos-
phor Bronze) ....B
PA.—Pittsburg
Lanz & Sons, M.. 101 S.
29th (Hot Pressed;
Tapped) ....B
Oliver Iron & Stel Co.. S.
10th & Muriel (Hot
Pressed; Joint; Tapped)
AAAA
Pittsburg Malleable Iron
Co. ....A
Pittsburg Screw & Bolt Co..
25th & Liberty (Case
Hardened; Cold Punched;
Semi-Finished) ....B
Pittsburg Mfg. Co.. 28th &
A. V. Ry. (Hot Pressed)
B
PA.—Scranton
Scranton Bolt & Nut Co.

NUTS: IRON; STEEL
(Hot Pressed) ....A
R. I.—Pawtucket
Haskell Mfg. Co., Wm. H.
(Case Hardened; Check;
Jam; Cold Punched;
Double Cupped; Joint;
Collars; Semi-Finished;
Wing) ....A
Pawtucket Mfg. Co. (Cold
Punched; Semi-Finished;
Iron) ....A
R. I.—Providence
Am. Screw Co., 21 Stevens
(Stove Bolt; Rod; Tire
Bolt) ....AAAA
R. I. Tool Co. (Brass; Cop-
per; Case Hardened; Col-
lar; Joint; Mach. Screw;
Semi-Finished; Tapped;
Wing) ....AAA
VA.—Richmond
Old Dom. Iron & Nail Wks.
Co. (Hot Pressed; Ma-
chine Screw; Semi-Fin-
ished; Tapped) ....A

OAK

See Lumber

OAKUM

CONN.—Cobalt
Tibbals Oakum Co.
(Carded) ....B
MAINE—Camden
Alden, H. L. ....A
MD.—Baltimore
Balto. Oakum Wks., 916
S. B'way ....A
MO.—St. Louis
Broderick & Bascom Rope
Co., 809 N. Main ......AA
Leschen & Sons Rope Co.,
A., 920 N. 1st ......AAA
N. J.—Jersey City
Baker, Wm. T...........D
Stratford Oakum Co., Geo.
(Navy) ....A
N. Y.—Brooklyn
Chelsea Jute Mills....AAAA
Planet Mills Mfg. Co., 335
Carroll ....AAA
New York City
Amer. Mfg. Co., 63 Wall..
AAAA
Davey's Sons, W. O., 47
South ....A
De Grauw, Aymar & Co...
AA
Disbrow & Co., 56 Warren
F
Hoffman-Corr Mfg. Co., 107
Duane ....AA
Lawrence Cordage Wks., 46
South ....A
Marine Mfg. & Supply Co.
156 South ....B
Mayer, Lane & Co., 128
White X
Sealy, Thomas. 142 Front.C
Travers Bros. Co., 41 Worth
AA

OARS

ARK.—Devall Bluff
Wells Boat Oar Co., C. F.
D
ARK.—Silica
Lena Lumber Co. (Car)..X
LA.—Baton Rouge
Moorman Eli S...........D
MASS.—Boston
Hinckley Bros. & Co.....B
Shaw & Co., T. J........E
Sheldon & Co., O. (also
Paddles) ....D
MICH.—Detroit
Dodge, Jasper N.........E
N. Y.—Canton
Rushton, J. H...........F
New York City
De Grauw. Avmar & Co.
(Also Paddles) ......AA
Estes & Sons, E. B., 45
John (Also Paddles)..AA
New York Boat Oar Co., 69
West(Rough; Spoon)..A
Smith, John T...........E
OHIO—West Unity
West Unity Mfg. Co. ....D

OATMEAL

See Cereals

OBOES

See Musical Instruments

OCHRE

See also Colors

GA.—Cartersville
Amer. Ochre Co..........E
MICH.—Detroit
Acme White Lead & Color
Wks. ....AAA
Detroit White Lead Wks.
AAA
New York City
Bartels Co., Ernest C.....B
Longman & Martinez...AAA
Smith & Co., J. Lee, 59
Frankfort (French; Gold-
en) ....AA
Tiemann & Co., D. F.....A
OHIO—Cleveland
McNairy & Co., Amos B...B
PA.—Easton
Williams & Co., C. K.....A
PA.—Philadelphia
Lucas & Co., John...AAA
Wetherill Co., S. P., 925
Chestnut ....B
PA.—Reading
Wilhelm Co., A.........AA
VT.—Bennington
Adams Co., Enos..........D

ODOMETERS

CONN.—Hartford
Veeder Mfg. Co. (Auto-
mobile) ....A
ILL.—Chicago
McDonnell Odometer Co...X
New York City
Keuffel & Essex Co.....AA
N. Y.—Troy
Gurley, W. & L. E........A

OFFSETS

CONN.—Plantsville
Smith & Co., H. D. (Ve-
hicle) ....A
MINN.—Minneapolis
Union Iron Wks. (Car-
riage) ....A
N. Y.—Auburn
Clapp Mfg. Co., E. D.
(Vehicle) ....B
WIS.—Milwaukee
Filer & Stowell Co. (Band
Saw Carriage) ......AAA

OHMMETERS

CONN.—Hartford
Veeder Mfg. Co. ....A
ILL.—Chicago
Illinois Elect. Specialty Co.,
Tacoma Bldg. (Direct
Reading) X
Jewell Elect. Instrument
Co., 358 Dearborn ......E
IND.—Fort Wayne
Fort Wayne Electric Corpn.
AAAA
N. H.—Penacook
Whitney Elec. Instrument
Co...................D
New York City
Bunnell & Co., J. H., 20
Park Pl................B
PA.—Philadelphia
Keystone Electrical Instru-
ment Co. ....B
Wirt Electric Co.........D

OIL

See also Petroleum; Grease,
etc.
For Cottonseed Oil see Following Heading
For Olive Oil—See Olives

CAL.—Berkeley
El Dorado Linseed Oil Wks
(Linseed) ....B
CAL.—Los Angeles
Hercules Oil Refining Co.

OIL (Con.)

(Lubricating) C

Warren & Bally Mfg. Co.
(Lubricating) C

CAL.—Pasadena

San Gabriel Valley Essential Oil Co. (Essential) ..C

CAL.—San Francisco

Clinch & Co., C. G., 9 Front (Lubricating) ...A

Dixon Crucible Co., Jos., 304 Mkt (Lubricating) ....AAA

Fuller & Co., W. P. (Lubricating) .....AAAA

Herrmann Co., Geo. (Essential) ....B

Mason & Co., R. N., 115 Front (Lubricating) ...A

New York Lubricating Oil Co., 530 California (Lubricating) ....A

Pacific Coast Oil Co. (Machinery; Illuminating) ....AAAA

Pacific Steam Whaling Co. (Fish) ....A

Redington & Co. (Essential) ....AAA

Whittier, Coburn Co., 18 Fremont (Lubricating) ....AAA

CAL.—Santa Barbara

Cooper - Ellwood (Salad Olive) ....B

CONN.—Essex

Dickinson & Co., E. E. (Essential) ....A

CONN. Hartford

Tracy Oil & Varnish Co. (Castor, Machinery; Harness) X

GA.—Savannah

Shotter Co., S. P. (Rosin; Linseed) ....AAAA

ILL.—Aurora

Akron Mining, Milling & Mfg. Co. (Lubricating) B

ILL.—Chicago

Armour & Co. (Lubricating; Neatsfoot) .....AAAA

Besly & Co., Chas. H. (Lubricating; Helmet) ....AA

Champion Oil Co. (Lubricating, also for Hot Box) ....B

Chicago White Lead & Oil Co. (Linseed) ....AA

Clark, F. C. (Lubricating) ....D

Crew, Leveck Co. (Lubricating; Cylinder; Machinery; Mineral; Rope Wool; Illuminating; Jute) AAA

Dearborn Drug & Chemical Wks., Rialto Bldg. (Lubricating) ....A

Fairbank Co., N. K. (Tallow) ....AAAA

Frazer Lubricator Co., 35 Superior (Lubricating) ....AAAA

Glucose Sugar Refining Co. (Cooking) ....AAAA

Magie Bros., 9 N. Canal (Lubricating) ....B

Morris & Co., Nelson (Tallow) ....AAAA

Reid, Murdock & Co. (Cocoanut) ....AAAA

Roemheld & Co., J. (Cognac) ....F

Speare's Sons Co., 54 N. Canal (Lubricating) ..AA

Stuart & Co., D. A. (Inc.) (Cylinder; Machinery; Wool) C

Sullivan Oil Co., 48 N. Wells (Lubricating) ...B

ILL.—Quincy

Richardson Lubricator Co. (Lubricating) C

ILL.—Rockford

West Mfg. Co., L. M. (Harness) X

ILL.—Rock Island

Lewis Roofing Co. (Creosote) ....B

IND.—Hammond

Hammond Co., G. H. (Tallow) ....AAAA

IND.—Indianapolis

Miller Oil & Supply Co. (Lubricating) C

IND.—Jeffersonville

Pfau & Sons, Geo. (Lubricating) ....A

IND.—South Bend

O'Brien Varnish Co. (Linseed) ....A

IOWA—Cedar Rapids

Sinclair & Co., T. M. (Inc.) (Lard) ....AAA

IOWA—Council Bluffs

Monarch Mfg. Co. (Lubricating) ....B

IOWA—Sioux City

Sioux City Linseed Oil Wks (Linseed) ....B

KANS.—Fredonia

Lyster, F. E. (Linseed) A

KANS.—Topeka

Topeka Linseed Oil Wks. (Linseed) ....B

LA.—Crowley

Lawrence Feed Co. (Rice) ....A

LA.—New Orleans

McWilliams, R. (Ltd.) (Bicycle; Sewing Machine; Cylinder; Engine; Machinery; Harness) X

MD.—Baltimore

Bullock & Son, John (Neatsfoot) X

Chesapeake Oil Co. (Lubricating) ....D

McCormick & Co. (Castor, Wintergreen; Synthetic) ....D

Red C. Oil Mfg. Co., 38 S. Calvert (Lubricating) D

Robinson & Son, Wm. C., 217 South (Lubricating) ....B

MASS.—Boston

Billings, Clapp & Co. (Fusel) ....B

Bird & Co., J. A. & W., 34 India (Dust Absorbing Floor) ....AA

Boston Belting Co. (Hose) ....AAAA

Hoskins, Leander M. (Curriers') ....A

Jenney Mfg. Co., 291 W. 1st (Lubricating) ......A

Leonard & Co., Geo. H. (Lubricating; Menhaden; Cod Liver) ....A

Macomber & Co., H. S. (Lubricating) ....D

Masury, Young & Co., 198 Milk (Lubricating) ...B

Union Grease Co. (Signal) X

Vacuum Oil Co., 101 Milk (Lubricating) .....AAAA

Wood & Co., W., 373 Atlantic Av. (Lubricating) ....B

Young, Frank L. & Kimball (Sperm; Menhaden) ....A

MASS.—Cambridge

Whittemore Bros. & Co. (Sewing Machine) ..AA

MASS.—Gloucester

Dodd & Co., A. W. (Cod Liver; Sperm; Whale; Fish) ....B

MASS.—New Bedford

Kelley Oil Wks. (Clock; Watch; Sewing Machine; Typewriter; Machinery) ....B

Nye, W. F. (Anti Rust; Bicycle; Clock; Watch; Gun; Jewelers Lathe Sewing Machine; Typewriter; Fish; Cylinder; Dynamo; Engine; Machinery; Spindle; Sperm; Whale; Harness; Signal) ....A

Robinson & Co., W. A. (Fish; Whale; Menhaden; Sea Elephants) ....B

MASS.—Worcester

White & Bagley Co., 100 Foster (Lubricating) ..C

MICH.—Bronson

Rudd, F. M. (Spearmint; Tansy; Wormwood; Brigeron) ....A

OIL (Con.)

MICH.—Detroit
Acme White Lead & Color Wks (Gold Size)....AAA
Detroit Graphite Mfg. Co., 540 River (Lubricating) A
Michigan Carbon Wks. (Neatsfoot) ....AAA
Parke, Davis & Co. (Cod Liver) ....AAAA
Republic Oil Co., 701 Bellevue Av. (Lubricating) AA
Wing & Co., J. T., 19 Woodward Av. (Lubricating) ....A

MICH.—Kalamazoo
Todd Co., A. M. (Peppermint; Spearmint; Wintergreen) C

MICH.—Mendon
Beebe, Albert E. (Essential) C

MICH.—Pearl
Todd, A. M. (Essential) A

MICH.—Three Rivers
Hall, H. (Essential)......D

MINN.—St. Paul
Craig Oil Co. (Lubricating) AA
St. Paul Linseed. Oil Co (Linseed) ....B
St. Paul White Lead & Oil Co. (Linseed) ....B

MO.—East Lynne
Zook Bros. (Linseed) ....E

MO.—Kansas City
Amer. Linseed Co. (Linseed) AAAA
Interstate Oil Co. (Lubricating) C
Keystone Oil Co. (Armour Bldg.) (Lubricating)....C
Marsh Oil Co. (Lubricating; Castor) ....A

MO.—St. Louis
Crown Linseed Oil Wks. (Linseed; Boiled Linseed) B
Goodwin Mfg. Co. (Red) AA
Herf & Frericks Chem. Co. (Fusel; Wintergreen; Synthetic) ....A
Jones & Co., Geo. P., 704 N. Main (Lubricating) A
Mallinckrodt Chem. Wks. (Fusel) ....AAAA
Mound City Paint & Color Co. (Linseed) ....AA
National Lead Co. (Linseed) AAAA
Waters-Pierce Oil Co. (Machinery; Illuminating)... AA

N. J.—Bloomfield
McKenzie Bros. & Hill (Essential) ....B

N. J.—Camden
Hollingshead & Co., R. M. (Harness) ....B

N. J.—Elizabeth
Borne, Scrymser & Co. (Lubricating) ....A

N. J.—Garfield
Fritzsche Bros. (Essential) AA

N. J.—Jersey City
Dixon Crucible Co., Jos. (Graphited) ....AAA
N. J. Car Spring & Rubber Co. (Hose) ....AA

N. J.—Kearney
Cromwell-Walker Co. (Creosote) C

N. J.—Newark
Atlas Refinery (Neatsfoot) D
Gladding Oil Co. (Hose)..F

N. Y.—Albany
Albany Chemical Co. (Fusel) A
Murphy, E. W., 109 Montgomery (Lubricating) AA
Wing & Son, Robt., 82 Quay (Lubricating) ....B

N. Y.—Amsterdam
Kellogg & Miller (Linseed) AAA

N. Y.—Binghamton
Binghamton Oil Refining Co. (Anti-Rust; Carriers; Bicycle Sewing Machine;

OIL (Con.)

Cylinder; Drill; Dynamo Engine; Machinery; Railway; Spindle; Valve; Rope; Whale; Miners') A

N. Y.—Brooklyn
Crombie & Co., J. A. (Essential) ....B
Davis Oil Co. (Neatsfoot; Lard) ....B
Livingston Laboratory, 190 Wyona (Bead; Agene; Elixir) ....D
Miller Co., W. P. (Car Axle; Cylinder; Dynamo Engine; Machinery; Spindle; Valve) ....D

N. Y.—Buffalo
Buffalo Specialty Mfg. Co. (Harness) ....B
Mann Bros. & Co. (Linseed) A
Merchants Refining Co. (Cylinder Stocks, &c.)..C
Schoelkopf, Hartford & Hanna Co. (Cod Liver; Fusel) ....AAA

N. Y.—Le Roy
Rogers, F. C. (Linseed) D

N. Y.—Newark
Pierson & Co., E. V. (Essential) ....B
Stuart & Co., C. H. (Essential) ....A

New York City
Alexander Co., H. T., 34 Water (Lubricating)....C
Amer. Dust Absorbing Floor Oil Co., 441 B'way....F
Amer. Linseed Co. (Linseed) AAAA
Baker & Bro., H. J., 100 William (Castor) ...AA
Benners Co., E. H., 61 Pearl (Lubricating) C
Bliven & Carrington (Lubricating) ....B
Borne Scrymser & Co. (Lubricating; Belting; Car Axle; Cylinder; Drill; Engine; Machinery; Railway; Valve; Mineral; Sperm; Whale; Lard)...A
Buxton, Heins & Co., 12 Jacob (Lubricating) C
Calif. Essence Distilling Wks. (Essential) ......B
Cambell & Thayer (Linseed; Illuminating; Boiled Linseed) ....B
Carter, C. W. H. (Engineers Plate) ....A
Casey & Co., J. A. (Lubricating) ....B
Caswell Massey Co. (Hair) X
Centaner Co. (Castor ....B
Chaskel Chemical Wks. (Cognac; Essential; Fruit; Ageing) X
Chiris, Antoine, 18 Platt (Bay; Bergamot; Lavender; Orris; Rose; Rosemary; Peppermint) ....A
Clarkson & Ford, 224 Front (Lubricating) C
Colgate & Co. (Sperm) AAAA
Columbia Oil Co. (Lubricating) ....B
Columbia Refining Co. (Machinery; Whale; Illuminating) ....B
Cook's Sons, Adam (Lubricating; Cylinder; Dynamo Engine; Machinery)....B
Cooper & Co., Chas. (Fusel) AA
Corn Products Co., 25 Broad (Corn) ....AAAA
Coward, M., 279 Greenwich (Haarlem) X
Devce, F. W. & C. F. Raynolds Co. (Artistic; China; Decorative) ......AAAA
Dodge & Olcott (Essential) AAA
Dreyer & Co., P. R., 16 Cedar (Cod Liver) X
Elbert & Co., Job (Menhaden; Cod Liver)........X
Ellis & Co., John (Lubricating) ....AAA

Euler & Robeson (Essential) C

Fischer Chemical Importing Co. (Essential C

Fiske Bros. Refining Co., 59 Water (Belting; Carriers; Sewing Machine; Lubricating; Car Axle; Cylinder; Drill; Dynamo; Engine; Machinery; Wagon Axle; Railway; Red; Spindle; Valve; Rope; Wool; Illuminating; Jute; Lard) ....A

Flanagan-Blanchet (Essential) ....D

Fuerst Bros. & Co. (Cocoanut; Castor; Essential) B

Giese & Son, A. (Essential) D

Goldsticker, L. & M. (Essential) ....B

Grossmith, T. T. (Essential) ....A

Gutta Percha & Rubber Mfg. Co. (Hose)...AAAA

Haggerty Refining Co., 50 South (Lubricating) ....B

Harrison Bros. & Co. (Artists) ....AAAA

Haws, Geo. A., 25 Bridge (Lubricating; Neatsfoot, for Silk Mfrs.) C

Hill's Sons Co., Edw. (Cocoanut) ....AA

Horner, J. B. (Essential) AA

Hutchinson, D. W. (Essential) ....D

Ilsley, Doubleday & Co. (Linseed) Harness; Curriers; Sewing Machine; Car Axle; Wagon Axle; Cylinder; Drill; Dynamo; Engine: Machinery; Railroad; Valve: Signal)....C

Job, Elbert & Co., 68 Broad (Corn; Fish; Seal; Cod) B

Kanter & Co., 647 Water (Lubricating) ....B

Keith & Co., B. (Essential) F

Kellogg & Co. (Anti-Rust; Gum; Car Axle; Cylinder; Dynamo; Engine; Machinery; Signal).......B

Lanman & Kemp (Cod Liver) ....AAA

Lerberger Bros. (Essential) A

Lehn & Fink (Cod Liver) AAA

Leonard & Ellis (Lubricating; Machinery) ....AAA

Loeb & Co., Herman (Menhaden) ....B

Longman & Martinez (Cylinder; Machinery; Illuminating: Linseed) ..... AAA

Lueders & Co., G. (Essential) ....A

Maas & Walstein (Essential; Fusel) ....A

Micesson & Robbins (Essential; Sewing Machine; Cod Liver) ....AAAA

Magnus & Lauer (Essential; Cocoanut) ....B

Manhattan Oil Co., 51 Front (Refined Cotton Seed, Elaine Sewing Machine; Fish; Cylinder; Engine; Machinery; Railway; Red; Spindle; Valve; Mineral; Neatsfoot; Sperm; Whale: Lard; Salad: Animal)..D

Manheimer & Eben (Essential) C

Marchie, E. (Essential)...C

Matheson & Co., Wm. J. (Essential) ....A

Mergentine & Lamm (Essential) ....B

Michaels, L. J. (Essential) A

Miller Co., Frank (Sewing Machine; Car Axle; Wagon Axle; Harness) .....B

National Lead Co. (Castor) AAAA

N. Y. Lubricating Oil Co. (Lubricating) ....B

Orvine Co. (Essential)....D

Paterson, Boardman & Co. (Cocoanut) ....AAA

Post & Co. (Belting).....X

Pulver & Sons, Peter (Car Axle) ....D

Reed & Hewlett (Castor; Refined Cotton Seed Cylinder; Engine; Machinery; Valve; Mustard Seed; Rope Seed; Signal)....B

Rockhill, C. (Essential) B

Rudkin Co., Wm. H. (Cognac; Essential; Fruit) D

Schieffelin & Co., W. H. (Cod Liver) ....AA

Scott & Bowne (Castor; Cod Liver) ......AAAA

Shafer & Co., I. (Essential) A

Shipkoff & Co. (Essential) A

Smith & Nichols (Machinery) ....A

Solary & Co., J. (Essential) D

Stallman & Fulton (Cod Liver) ....A

Standard Oil Co. of N. Y. (Lubricating; Belting; Bicycle; Gun; Wagon Axle; Cylinder; Drill; Dynamo; Engine; Machinery; Railway; Valve; Mineral Rope; Wool; Illuminating; Signal; Jute) ....AAAA

Stiwell, A. A. (Essential; Fruit) ....A

Swan & Finch Co. (Lubricating; Crude; Refined; Bicycle; Cylinder; Dynamo; Engine; Machinery; Railway; Spindle; Mineral; Neatsfoot Illuminating; Jute; Lard; Salad; Fish; Whale; Seal)....A

Tide Water Oil Co. (Black; Curriers; Fish; Cylinder; Dynamo; Engine; Machinery; Red; Spindle; Paraffine; Wool; Illuminating; Signal) .AAAA

Ungerer & Co. (Essential) D

Warrick Freres & Co. (Essential) ....B

Wilcox Lard & Refining Co., W. J. (Tallow) ......AA

Winn, Wm. R., 143 Maiden Lane (Lubricating) ...C

Winterbourne & Co., S., 94 Pine (China Wood) ....B

Wergreen Chemical Co., 130 Fulton (Flower) X

Wood & Selick (Essential) A

Zinkeisen & Co. (Essential) C

N. Y.—Orangeburg

Empire Engine & Motor Co. (Pneumatic Tool) ......B

N. Y.—Rochester

Southwick, T. T. (Lubricating) C

Vacuum Oil Co. (Lubricating; Sewing Machine; Hoof; Cylinder; Engine; Machinery ; Railway ; Spindle; Valve; Harness; Signal) ....AAAA

N. Y.—Syracuse

Syracuse Reduction & Mfg. Co. (Lubricating)......C

Will & Baumer Co. (Red).. AA

N. Y.—Troy

Troy Belting & Supply Co. (Cylinder ; Machinery ; Wool) C

Troy Oil Wks (Engine; Cylinder; Wool) ......B

N. C.—Beaufort

Dey, C. P. (Fish) ....D

N. C.—Wilmington

Spiritine Chem. Co. (Tar)C

N. DAK.—Fargo

Fargo Linseed Mills (Linseed) ....U

OIL (*Con.*)

OHIO—Cincinnati
Amer. Cotton Oil Co. of Ohio (Miners; Salad; Cooking) ....AA
Burckardt & Co., 323 Syracuse (Lubricating) ..AA
Cinn. Linseed Oil Co. (Linseed) ....A
Emery Candle Co. (Black; Red; Elaine) ....AA
Fries & Bros., Alex (Essential; Ageing) ......AA
Harkness & Cowing Co. (Red) ....A
Moore Oil Co., Chas. H. (Linseed) ....A
New Process Oil Co., 50 Elm (Lubricating) ...B
Ogiloy, David J. (Rope) ..B
Paragon Refining Co. (Cylinder; Valve; Engine).AA
Star Oil Co., Brighton St. (Lubricating) ......AAA
Valvoline Oil Co., 1755 Elmore (Lubricating) AAA
Winkler & Co., Isaac (Cocoanut) ....AA

OHIO—Cleveland
Atlantic Refining Co. (Garfield Bld'g (Lubricating; Floor) ....A
Brooks Oil Co. (Sewing Machine; Car Axle; Machinery; Neatsfoot; Harness) ....A
Climax Refining Co. (Castor) ....D
Commercial Oil Co. (Linseed;; Castor; Harness) E
Crystal Oil Refining Co., 135 St. Clair (Headlight) D
Ensign Refining Co. (Illuminating) ....F
Globe Oil Co. (Black Curriers; Cylender; Engine; Machinery) ....A
Harbaugh Co., A. G. (Tallow; Miners'; Lard) ..A
Monitor Oil Co. (Cylinder; Red; Spindle; Neutral).. C
National Refining Co., Rose Bldg. (Cylender; &c.) AAA
Reliance Oil & Grease Co., (Car Axle; Drill; Engine; Dynamo; Machinery; Cylender; Mustard Seed)..X
Republic Oil Co. (Lubricating) ....AAA

OHIO—Columbus
Ironsides Co. (for Gearing; &c.) C
Janton & Sons, G. (Lard) B

OHIO—Dayton
Buckeye Iron & Brass Wrks. (Linseed) ....AA
Pope & Co., H. L. (Linseed) B
Thresher & Co. (Linseed; Boiled Linseed) ......AA

OHIO—Mansfield
Mansfield Linseed Oil Co. (Linseed) ....A

OHIO—Newark
Styron, Beggs & Co. (Lubricating; Castor) ....A

OHIO—St. Marys
American Linseed Oil Co. (Linseed) ....AAAA

OHIO—Sandusky
Jarecki Chemical Co. (Fish) AAA

OHIO—Toledo
National Cement & Rubber Mfg. Co. (Almond; Bicycle; Lubricating; Miners') C
Sun Oil Co., The (Petroleum; Parafine) ..AAAA

OHIO—Warren
Griswold Linseed Oil Co. (Linseed; Boiled Linseed) AA

PA.—Allegheny
Miller's & Sons Co., A (Cylinder; Engine; Dynamo) B
Sipe & Co., Jas. B. (Japan) B

OIL (*Con.*)

Thompson & Co. (Linseed) A

PA.—Bradford
Emery Mfg. Co. (Steam Refined Cylinder Stock) AAAA
Hoffman, R. J. (Lubricating) ....A
Penn. Lubricating Co., of Pa. (Lubricating) ......B

PA.—Chester
Manufacturers' Paraffine Co. (Paraffine) ....B

PA.—Easton
Heft Lubricating Oil Co. (Lubricating) ....A
World Refining Co. (Lubricating; Castor; Belting; Bicycle; Clock & Watch; Sewing Machine; Car Axle; Cylinder Drill; Dynamo; Engine; Machinery; Red; Spindles; Neatsfoot; Rubbing; Tallow; Wool; Harness; Linseed) ....D

PA.—Emlenton
Emlenton Refining Co. (Cylinder; Engine; Spindle; Dynamo) ....AA

PA.—Erie
Erie Oil Co. (Lubricating) A

PA.—Franklin
Eclipse Lubricating Oil Wrks. (Valve; Wool; Illuminating) X
Franklin Oil Wrks. (Sewing Machine; Lubricating; Machinery Valve) X
Galena Oil Wrks. (Lubricating) ....AAA
Galena Signol Oil Co. (Coach; Engine; Car Oils; Valve; Signal) ....AAAA

PA.—Freedom
Freedom Oil Wrks. (Castor; Lubricating; Cylinder; Dynamo; Engine; Machinery; Spindle; Mineral; Rubbing; Neutral; Wool; Harness; Illuminating; Signal; Linseed) ......A

PA.—Oil City
Crystal Oil Wrks. (Railroad) ....B
German Refining Co. (Cylinder; Spindle; Engine; Valve; &c.) ....A

PA.—Pennsburg
Hillegas & Krauss (Linseed) E

PA.—Philadelphia
Atlantic Refining Co. (Cylinder; Engine; Machinery; Railway; Illuminating) AAAA
Barrett Mfg. Co. (Creosote) AAAA
Blabon, Geo. W. Co. (Linseed) ....AAAA
Continental Mfg. Co. (Sewing Machine) ....D
Crew, Levick Co.. 113 Arch (Cylinder; Spindle; Paraffine &c.) ....AAA
Dodge & Olcott (Essential) AAAA
Eclipse Cement & Blacking Co. (Harness) C
France Packing Co., 6512 State Road (Lubricating) B
Fricke, Arthur (Hair) C
Hires, Chas. E. (Essential) AA
Houghton & Co., E. F., 240 W. Somerset (Cutting; Polishing; Drilling; Tempering; Lubricating ..AA
Lewis & Bros. Co., J. T. (Linseed) ....AAAA
Powers-Weightman-Rosengarten Co. (Essential) AAAA
Stevenson Bros. & Co. (Anti-Rust; Lubricating ....B
Sunlight Oil & Gasoline Co., ..217 Arch (Lubricating & Cylinder) ....B
Union Petroleum Co. (Lubricating; Illuminating) AA
Vail Bros. (Sewing Ma-

OIL (Con.)
chine; Hair) C
Zurn Co., O. F., 408 Vine
(Lubricating) ....B
PA.—Pittsburg
Atlas Paint Co., (Ltd.) 2638
Liberty Av. (Japan) ...X
Dalzell & Son Co., Jas., 109
Water (Lubricating) ..C
Guffey Petroleum Co., J. M.,
Frick Bldg. (Petroleum;
Refiners) ....AAAA
Japan Linseed Oil Co. (Lin-
seed; Japan) X
McClintock & Irvine Co.
Neville & P. R. R.; (Lu-
bricating) ....B
Miller's Sons Co., A. D. (Cyl-
inder; Engine; Harness;
Illuminating; Miners';
Signal) ....B
National Lead & Oil Co.,
of Penn. (Linseed; Re-
fined Linseed) ....AAAA
Pittsburg Oil Refining Co.,
425 1st Av. (Cylinder;
Spindle; &c.) ....A
Willock, S. M., 54th & A
V. Ry. (Lubricating) AA
Walker, W. & H. (Tallow)
AAAA

PA.—Titusville
Pennsylvania Paraffine
Wrks. (Paraffine) ....A
PA.—Warren
Cornplanter Refining Co.
(Cylinder; Spindle; En-
gine; &c.) ....AA
Glade Oil Works (Mineral)
AAA
Senaca Oil Works (Cylinder;
Machinery) ....AA
United Refining Co. (Lubri-
cating) ....B
Warren Refining Co. (Cyl-
inder; Engine, etc.)..AA
R. I.—Providence
Amer. Oil Co. (Bicycle;
Sewing Machine; Cylin-
der; Dynamo; Engine; Ma-
chinery; Railway; Spin-
dle; Valve; Mineral;
Sperm; Paraffine; Whale
Signal; Lard) ....B
Amer. Supply Co., 13 Eddy
(Lubricating) ....AA
Place Mfg. Co., Wm. H.
(Lubricating; Machinery;
Neatsfoot; Lard) C
Union Oil Co..........AAA
U. S. Gutta Percha Paint
Co. (Restorated) ......A
TENN.—Memphis
Coffin & Co., J. H. (Lubri-
cating) ....A
Royal Refining Co. (Castor)
C
TEXAS—Houston
Southwestern Oil Co. (Lubri-
cating) ....AA
VA.—Norfolk
Cotton Oil and Fibre Co.
(Linseed) ....AAAA
W. VA.—Parkersburg
Upson Oil and Soap Co.
(Lubricating) ....D
West Virginia Oil Co. (Inc.)
(Machinery) ....A
WIS.—Lodi
Drew, L. S. (Essential; Ab-
sinthe) C
Wis.—Milwaukee
Delaney Oil and Lubricant
Co. (Hoof; Belting; Sew-
ing Machine; Floor; Car
Axle; Cylinder; Dynamo;
Engine; Machinery; Spin-
dle; Valve; Neatsfoot;
Sperm; Harness; Miners;
Signal; Lard; Linseed).X
Halstead Oil Co., W. D. 318
E. Water (Lubricating) A
O'Neil Oil & Paint Co., 297
Water (Lubricating) ..A
Wadhams Oil & Grease Co.
215 National Av. (Lubri-
cating) ....A

OIL CLOTH
MAINE—Winthrop
Bailey's Sons & Co., C. M.
(Floor) ....B

OIL CLOTH (Con.)
MASS.—Taunton
Chandler Oil Cloth & Buck-
ram Co., (Carriage) ...X
Tauton Oil Cloth Co. (En-
ameled Stair) ....B
MO.—St. Louis
Zettlosen Mfg. Co. ....B
N. J.—Camden
Dunn & Co., J. C. (Floor) A
Farr & Bailey Mfg. Co.,
(Floor) ....AAA
Murphy & Co., P. J. (Floor)
A
N. J.—Kearney
Nairn Linoleum Co. (Floor)
AAA
N. J.—Trenton
Trenton Oil Cloth & Linol-
eum Co. (Carriage; Enam-
eled: Floor; Table; Up-
holstery) ....A
New York City
American Oil Cloth Co., 262
Canal (Table) ....B
Sampson & Sons, Alden
(Floor) ....AAA
Standard Table Oil Cloth Co.
320 B'way (Floor; Table)
AAAA
Wild & Co., Joseph, 11
Thomas ....AAA
N. Y.—Troy
Haskell & Co., Robt. C.
(Floor) ....B
Powers & Sons, Deborah
(Floor; Table) ....A
OHIO—Columbus
Columbus Oil Cloth Co.
(Carriage; Enamelled Ta-
ble) ....B
PA.—Philadelphia
Blabon, Geo. W. (Carriage;
Enameled; Floor) .AAAA
Monarch Rubber & Oil Cloth
Co. (Carriage) ....E
Potter Sons & Co., Thos.
(Carriage; Enameled;
Floor; Table) ....AAA

OIL: COTTONSEED
ALA.—Birmingham
Kinney & Co., F. C. ...AAA
ALA.—Florence
Ashcroft Cotton Mills ....A
ALA.—Jacksonville
Jacksonville Oil Mill Co.
(Crude) ....B
ALA.—New Decatur
Decatur Cotton Oil Co. ...C
ALA.—Oxford
Oxford Oil Mill Co. C
ALA.—Piedmont
Calhoun Cotton Seed Oil Co.
C
ALA.—Selma
Alabama Cotton Oil Co. (Br.
Amer. Cotton Oil Co.)
AAAA
International Cotton Seed
Oil Co. ....A
ALA.—Troy
Troy Fertilizer Co. ......A
ALA.—Tuscaloosa
Tuscaloosa Cotton Seed Oil
Co. ....B
ALA.—Uniontown
Uniontown Cotton Oil Co. B
ARK.—Argenta
Ark. Cotton Oil Co. (Br.
Am. Cotton Oil Co.) AAAA
ARK.—Little Rock
Southern Cotton Oil Co.
AAAA
ARK.—Pine Bluff
Pine Bluff Cotton Oil Co...
C
FLA.—Jacksonville
Florida Cotton Oil Co.....B
FLA.—Madison
Florida Mfg. Co. (Crude)
AA
GA.—Atlanta
Gate City Oil Co. ....AA
Georgia Cotton Oil Co.
AAAA
GA.—Augusta
Georgia Cotton Oil Co. ..A
Interstate Cotton Oil Co. B

OIL: COTTONSEED

GA.—Blackshear
Blackshear Mfg. Co. C
Brantley Co., A. P. (Crude)
AA
GA.—Carrollton
Carrollton Oil Mills C
GA.—Columbus
Mutual Cotton Oil Co.
(Crude) ....AAAA
GA.—Elberton
Elberton Oil Mills (Crude) A
GA.—Forsythe
Maynard & Co., P. B. C
GA.—Griffen
Walker Bros. ....B
GA.—La Grange
La Grange Mill Co. ......A
GA.—Macon
McCaw Mfg. Co. .....AAA
GA.—Savannah
Southern Cotton Oil Co.
AAAA
GA.—Smithsonia
Smithsonia Cotton Oil Mills
AA
GA.—Social Circle
Walton Oil Co. ....B
ILL.—Chicago
Atwood & Steele, 18 River C
Consumers Cotton Oil Co.
AAA
I. T.—Ada
Ada Cotton Oil Co. C
I. T.—Ardmore
Ardmore Oil & Milling Co.
B
I. T.—Durant
Durant Cotton Oil Co. ....B
I. T.—Eufaula
Eufaula Cotton Oil Co....C
I. T.—Muskogee
Muskogee Cotton Oil Co...C
I. T.—Wynnewood
Wynnewood Oil Mill Co. ..B
KANS.—Independence
Kansas Cotton Mill Co. ...C
KY.—Louisville
Globe Refining Co. ......A
Kentucky Refining Co.
AAAA
Louisville Cotton Oil Co. B
LA.—Lafayette
People's Cotton Oil Co. ..C
LA.—Monroe
Planters Oil Mill Co. ....B
LA.—New Orleans
Armbruster, Hy., 341 Girod
(Independence Oil & Re-
fining Co.) ....B
N. O. Cotton Seed Oil &
Mfg. Co., 319 Carondelet
X
Southern Cotton Oil Co.,
Hennen Bldg. .....AAAA
Standard Cotton Seed Oil Co.
B
Standard Guano & Chemical
Co. ....AA
Steinhardt & Co. ......AA
Union Oil Co. (Crude) AAAA
LA.—Opelousas
St. Landry Cotton Seed Oil
Co. C
LA.—Shreveport
Shreveport Cotton Oil Co. B
MD.—Baltimore
McCormick & Co. ....D
MISS.—Clarksdale
Mississippi Cotton Oil Co.
AAAA
MISS.—Grenada
Mississippi Cotton Oil Co.
AAAA
MISS.—Indianola
Indianola Cotton Oil Co. ..B
MISS.—Jackson ..
Capitol City Oil Works
AAAA
Central Cotton Oil Co. ..C
Jackson Cotton Oil Co. ..B
MISS.—Meridan
Eagle Cotton Oil Co. ....B
Miss. Cotton Oil Co. AAAA
MISS.—Natchez
Natchez Oil Co. ....B
MISS.—Port Gibson
Miss. Cotton Oil Co. AAAA
Port Gibson Oil Works
(Crude) ....A
MISS.—Starkville
Starkville Cotton Oil Co. C

OIL: COTTONSEED

MISS.—Vicksburg
Lever Bros. ....A
Refuge Oil Mills ....B
MISS.—West Point
Mississippi Cotton Oil Co.
AAAA
MISS—Yazoo City
Mississippi Cotton Oil Co.
AAAA
Producers Cotton Oil Co. A
MO.—Holcomb
Roberts Cotton Co. ......A
MO.—Kennett
Roberts Cotton Co. ......A
New York City
American Cotton Oil Co., 27
Beaver ....AAAA
Falcon Packing Co., 158
Franklin C
Hopkins Dwight & Co., Cot-
ton Exchange Bldg. ..AA
Manhattan Oil Co., 51 Front
D
Swan & Finch Co. ....A
Southern Cotton Oil Co.,
Bowling Green Bldg.
AAAA
Welch, Holme & Clark Co.,
381 West ....A
N. C.—Charlotte
N. Carolina Cotton Oil Co. A
N. C.—Davidson
Davidson Cotton Oil Co...C
N. C.—Goldsboro
Goldsboro Oil Co ....B
N. C.— Laurinburg
Laurinburg Cotton Seed Oil
Mill & Mfg. Co. C
N. C.—Raleigh
No. Carolina Cotton Oil Co.
AAAA
N. C.—Tarboro
Edgecomb County Oil Co.
(Crude) ....AAAA
N. C.—Washington
Havens Oil Co. C
OHIO—Cincinnati
Amer. Cotton Oil Co. of
Ohio, 443 E. 6........AA
Moore Oil Co., C. H., 641 W.
Front ....A
Procter & Gamble Co. AAAA
OHIO—Newark
Styron, Beggs & Co. .....A
OKLA.—Chandler
Chandler Cotton Oil Co. ..A
OKLA.—Narman
Narman Cotton Oil Mill Co.
C
OKLA.—Oklahoma City
Southwestern Cotton Seed
Oil Co. ....A
OKLA.—Shawnee
Shawnee Cotton Oil Co. .B
R. I.—Providence
Union Oil Co. ....AAA
S. C.— Aiken
Aiken Industrial Co. C
S. C.—Bamberg
Cotton Oil Co. C
S. C.—Barnwell
Southern Cotton Oil Co.
AAAA
S. C.—Belton
Belton Oil & Fert. Co. ..C
S. C.—Bennettsville
Marlboro Mill Co. ....B
S. C. Columbia
S. C. Cotton Oil Co. ..AAAA
Southern Cotton Oil Co.
AAAA
S. C.—Greenwood
Greenwood Oil Mill C
S. C.—Newberry
Newberry Cotton Seed Oil &
Fert. Co. C
S. C.—Ridge Springs
Ridge Springs Oil Mills ..C
S. C.—St. Mathews
St. Mathews Mfg. & W. H.
Co. C
S. C.—St. Stephens
Seneca Oil Mills ....A
S. C.—Sumter
Sumter Cotton Oil & Fert.
Co. C
TENN.—Covington
Covington Cotton Oil Co. C
TENN.—Dyersburg
Dyersburg Oil & Fert. Co. C

TENN.—Jackson
Tenn. Cotton Oil Co. ..AAA
TENN.—Memphis
Southern Cotton Oil Co.
(Crude & Refined) AAAA
Valley Oil Mills (Crude &
Refined) ....A
TENN.—Nashville
Tenn. Cotton Oil Co. ....B
TENN.—Trenton
Tenn. Cotton Oil Co. ..AAA
TEXAS—Abilene
Abilene Cotton Oil Co. ..B
TEXAS—Alvarado
Planters Oil Mill Co. ....B
TEXAS—Arlington
Arlington Cotton Oil Co. ..C
TEXAS—Austin
Austin Oil Mfg. Co. ....B
TEXAS—Bastrop
Powell Oil Mill Co. .....A
TEXAS—Belcherville
Belcher Cotton Oil Co. ..C
TEXAS—Belton
Belton Oil Co. C
TEXAS—Bonham
Bonham Cotton Oil Co. ..B
TEXAS—Bowie
Bowie Cotton Seed Oil Co. B
TEXAS—Brenham
Brenham Compress & Oil
Mfg. Co. ....A
TEXAS—Brownwood
Brownwood Oil Mill Co. ..B
TEXAS—Caldwell
Caldwell Oil Mill Co. C
TEXAS—Cameron
Milan Co. Oil Mill Co. C
TEXAS—Cisco
Cisco Oil Mill ....B
TEXAS—Clarksville
Clarksville Cotton Seed Oil
Mill Co. ....B
TEXAS—Cleburne
Cleburne Oil Co. ....B
TEXAS—Corsicana
Corsicana Cotton Oil Co. A
TEXAS—Cuero
Cuero Cotton Oil & Mfg. Co.
B
TEXAS—Dallas
Trinity Cotton Oil Co. ....A
TEXAS—Decatur
Decatur Cotton Seed Oil Co.
B
TEXAS—Dennison
National Cotton Oil Co.
AAAA
TEXAS—Denton
Denton Cotton & Oil Mill Co.
B
TEXAS—Dublin
Dublin Cotton Seed Oil Mill
Co. ....B
TEXAS—Gainesville
Gainesville Cotton Seed Mill
Co. ....A
TEXAS—Galveston
National Cotton Oil Co.
AAAA
TEXAS—Greenville
Greenville Oil & Cotton Co.
A
TEXAS—Hearne
National Cotton Oil Co.
AAAA
TEXAS—Hico
Hico Oil Mills ....B
TEXAS—Hillsboro
Hillsboro Oil Co. ....B
TEXAS—Honey Grove
Honey Grove Cotton Oil Co.
A
TEXAS—Houston
Consumers' Cotton Oil Co.
AA
Nat'l Cotton Oil Co. AAAA
Southern Cotton Oil Co.
AAAA
TEXAS—Italy
Italy Cotton Oil Co. ....B
TEXAS—Itaska
Itaska Cotton Seed Oil Mill
Co. ....B
TEXAS—Jacksboro
Jacksboro Cotton Oil Co. B
TEXAS—Jefferson
Jefferson Cotton Oil & Re-
fining Co. ....B
TEXAS—Kaufman
Kaufman Cotton Oil Co. ..C

TEXAS—Ladonia
Ladonia Cotton Oil Co. ..B
TEXAS—La Grange
La Grange Oil Mill Co. ..B
TEXAS—Leonard
Leonard Cotton Oil Co. ..C
TEXTS—Lockhart
Lockhart Cotton Oil Co..B
TEXAS—McGregor
McGregor Cotton Oil Co. ..C
TEXAS—McKinney
McKinney Cotton Oil Mill
Co. ....B
TEXAS—Marlin
Marlin Oil Co. ....A
TEXAS—Midlothian
Midlothian Cotton Oil Co. C
TEXAS—Nacogdoches
Merchants & Farmers Cotton
Oil Co. C
TEXAS—New Braunfels
Landa Cotton Oil Co. ....B
TEXAS—Palestine
Palestine Cotton Seed Oil Co.
B
TEXAS—Paris
Lamar Cotton Oil Co. C
Paris Oil & Cotton Co....A
TEXAS—Pilot Point
Pilot Point Cotton Oil Mill
Co. C
TEXAS—Rockdale
Rockdale Oil Co. C
TEXAS—San Marcos
San Marcos Oil & Gin Co. C
TEXAS—Sherman
Sherman Oil & Cotton Co.
AA
TEXAS—Sulphur Springs
Greenville Oil & Cotton Co.
A
Sulphur Springs Cotton Oil
Co. ....B
TEXAS—Taylor
Taylor Cotton Oil Works C
TEXAS—Temple
Central Texas Cotton Oil Co.
C
Empire Mill Co. ....B
TEXAS— Terrell
Terrell Cotton Oil Co. ..B
TEXAS—Waco
Consumers Cotton Oil Co. A
TEXAS—Waxahachie
Waxahachie Cotton Oil Co.
A
TEXAS—Weatherford
Planters Oil Co. ....B
TEXAS—Weinar
Weinar Oil Works ......B
TEXAS—Whitewright
Whitewright Cotton Oil
Mfg. Co. C
TEXAS—Wortham
Wortham Cotton Oil Co. C
VA.—Norfolk
Cotton Oil & Fibre Co.
AAAA

OILED COATS

See Clothing; Men's

OILERS

See also Cups; Oil; Lubri-
cators, etc.
CONN.—Bridgeport
American Tube & Stamping
Co. (Steel; Machine;
Shafting; Spring) .AAAA
Bridgeport Brass Co. (Ma-
chine; Spring) ......AAA
CONN.—Meriden
Miller & Co., Edward
(Machine) ....AAAA
CONN.—Waterbury
Noera Mfg. Co. (Brass) ..B
Scovill Mfg. Co. (Bicycle;
Shafting; Spring) .AAAA
ILL.—Chicago
Besly, Co., Chas. H. (Shaft-
ing) ....AA
Nugert & Co., Wm. W., 18
W. Randolph (Crank;
Crosshead Pin, Machine)
E
Swain Lubricator Co., 250
Lake (Loose Pulley) ..B
ILL.—Decatur
Tait Mfg. Co., F. B. (Fel-

OILERS (Con.)
loe) ....A
ILL.—Evanston
Mark Mfg. Co. ....AA
ILL.—Keithsburg
Smith, S. W. (Machine) .D
ILL.—Sycamore
Palten Co., F. C. (Felloe) A
IND.—Bluffton
Red Cross Mfg. Co. (Auto-
matic Windmill) .....B
IND.—Evansville
Vandegrift Coupling Co.
(Loose Pulley) ....E
LA.—New Orleans
Haller Mfg. Co., H. X
MASS.—Boston
Crosby Steam Gauge &
Valve Co., 95 Oliver (S.
L. V. Imported) .....AA
Starr Brass Mfg. Co.
(Crank Pins) ....A
MASS.—Worcester
Bay State Stamping Co.
(Bicycle) ....E
MICH.—Detroit
Detroit Lubricator Co. (Ma-
chine; Brass; Mill; Rail-
road; Crank Pin).....AA
Essex Brass Co., G. B.
(Machine) C
Michigan Lubricator Co. A
Northern Engineering Wrks.
A
MICH.—Port Huron
Lee Mfg. Co. (Ball Crank
Pin) ....B
MO.—St. Louis
Handlan-Buck Mfg. Co., 212
N. 3rd (Valve; Machine)
AA
N. J.—New Brunswick
Consolidated Fruit Jar Co.
(Machine) ....AA
N. Y.—Brooklyn
Deverell Perfection Mfg.
Co., 36 Bridge (Machine;
Mill; Railroad) ....D
Hauck & Son. Chas. J., 36
Stagg (Pocket) ....B
Miller Co., Wm. P. (Crank
Pin) ....D
Vogel & Bros., Wm., 37 S.
9th (Brass) ....AA
N. Y.—Buffalo
Shepard Sidney Co. (Spring)
AAAA
Sherwood Mfg. Co. .....B
New York City
Consolidated Fruit Jar Co.,
290 B'way ....AA
Cushman & Denison Mfg.
Co., 240 W. 23rd (Pocket;
Bicycle) ....B
Goodyear's India Rubber
Glove Mfg. Co. (Machine)
AAAA
Gould-Mersereau Co. (Ma-
chine) ....G
Hill Mfg. Co., 40 Cortlandt
(Machine) ....G
Knapp Mfg. Co., 24 Frank-
fort (Locomotive) ....D
Manhattan Brass Co., 334
E. 28th (Brass; Zinc;
Machine) ....A
Nason Mfg. Co. (Machine) B
Tower & Lyon Co., 95 Cham-
bers (Melleable Iron; Ma-
chine; Spring) ....B
N. Y.—Rochester
Rochester Automatic Oiler
& Supply Co. (Automatic)
D
OHIO—Akron
Akron Mfg. Co. (Machine) D
OHIO—Cincinnati
Lunkenheimer Co. (Loose
Pulley; Shafting) ....AA
Powell Co., Wm., 2529
Spring Grove Av. (Glass;
Plain; Light; Seed Ma-
chine) ....A
Van Duzen Co., E. W., 428
E. 2d (Loose Pulley) ..B
OHIO—Columbus
Ironsides Co. (For Mine Car
Wheels; etc.) C
OHIO—Cuyahoga Falls
Falls Rivet & Mchry. Co.
(Ring; Chain) ....A
PA.—Allegheny

OILERS (Con.)
Sands Mfg. Co. (Steel Braz-
ed Machine) ....H
Wall Mfg. Supply Co., P.
(Brazed Steel Machine) B
PA.—Bausman
Bausman, D. H. (Wagon
Wheel) C
PA.—Philadelphia
Hero Fruit Jar Co. (Ma-
chine) ....AA
Lonergan & Co., J. E. (Ma-
chine; Mill; Railroad) AA
PA.—Pittsburg
Gem Manufacturing Co.,
Spruce near 33rd (Brass &
Steel Machine; Engineer-
ing; Loose Pulley; Spring)
D
McClintock & Irvine .....B
R. I.—Providence
American Supply Co. (Mills)
AA

OINTMENTS

ILL.—Chicago
Baker Co., Chas. S.......C
Hamlin's Wizard Oil Co..B
MD.—Baltimore
Burrough Bros. Mfg. Co..A
Resinol Chemical Co.....B
Thomsen Chemical Co.
(Mercurial) ....B
MASS.—Boston
Kennedy, Donald ....AA
Potter Drug & Chemical Co.
A
MASS.—New Bedford
Ashley, A. Davis C
N. Y.—Brooklyn
Morgan Drug Co.........D
N. Y.—Buffalo
Smith & Cutler Co., W. S.
X
New York City
Carbolic Soap Co., 230 Pearl
B
Gotham Co. ....D
Lanman & Kemp ......AAA
New York Quinine & Chemi-
cal Wks., Ltd. ....A
Schieffelin & Co., W. H.
AA
OHIO—Cleveland
Atlantic Refining Co.
(Hoof) ....A
OHIO—Dayton
Applegate & Co., J. L.
(Hoof) ....F
OHIO—Tiffin
Capitol Food Co. (Blister).D
PA.—Philadelphia
Hance Bros. & White, 621
Callowhill ....AA
Mason Chemical Co., 515
Arch ....B

OLEATES

ILL.—Chicago
Baker Co., Chas. S C
MD.—Baltimore
Sharpe & Dohme ......AAA
MICH.—Detroit
Parke, Davis & Co. ..AAAA
New York City
McKesson & Robbins, AAAA
Schieffelin & Co., W. H. AA

OLEO-MARGARINE

See also Butterine

ILL.—Chicago
Braun & Fitts, 187 No.
Union ....AA
Cudahy Packing Co...AAAA
Friedman Mfg. Co.........A
Moxley, Wm. J...........A
Railton, B. A...........B
Swift & Co. ....AAAA
ILL.—East St. Louis
Dold Butterine Co., Jacob
AAAA
IND.—Indianapolis
Columbia Butter Co.......D
Jordan Co., Arthur ......A
MASS.—Cambridge

OPENERS

CONN.—Bridgeport
Bridgeport Hdw. Mfg. Co.,
481 Iranstan Av. (Can) B
Drouve Co., G. (Sash; Window) ....B
Knapp & Cowles Mfg. Co.
(Can) C
CONN.—Bristol
Barrett, W. L. (Can) ...D
CONN.—Collinsville
Hartigan, Wm. R. (Egg) H
CONN.—Danielson
Parkhurst, L. D. (Can) ..G
CONN.—Essex
Tiley, Pratt & Co. (Letter)
D
CONN.—Meriden
Brown & Dowd Mfg. Co.
(Can) ....E
Meriden Brittania Co. (Letter) ....AAAA
CONN.—New Britain
Landers, Frary & Clark
(Can) ....AAA
Taplin Mfg. Co. (Bottle) D
CONN.—New Haven
Henn & Co., A. S. (Can) F
Kilborn & Bishop Co. (Box;
Cigar Box) C
CONN.—Unionsville
Humphrey, H. W. (Egg) D
CONN.—Wallingford
Wallace & Sons Mfg. Co., R.
(Letter) ....AAAA
ILL.—Chicago
American Cutlery Co. (Can;
Cigar Box; Letter) ..AA
Nicol & Co. (Cigar Box;
Can) ....D
Radecke Mfg. Co., 34 So.
Clark (Can) ....E
Vaughan & Bushnell Mfg.
Co. (Crate) ....A
Western Electric Co., 259
S. Clinton (Electric Door)
AAAA
ILL.—Decatur
Illinois Cutlery Co. (Can) B
ILL.—Freeport
Arcade Mfg. Co. (Box) ..A
ILL.—Paxton
Paxton Hardware Mfg. Co.
(Can) X
MD.—Baltimore
Perfection Couch Opener Co.
F
Sinclair Scott Co. (Can) ..E
MASS.—Attleboro
Mossberg Co., Frank (Letter) ....A
MASS.—Boston
Boston Electric Co. (Electric Door) ....B
Dame, Stoddard & Co. (Cigar Box) ....A
Harwood & Son, Geo. S., 53
State (Feeders; Wool-Washer) ....A
Leigh, Evan Arthur, Mason
Bldg. (Lapper; Cotton) .B
MASS.—Lowell
Kitson Machine Co. (Lappers; Cotton) ......AAA
MASS.—Melrose
Ormsby, E. A. (Sash; Window; Skylight Window) H
MASS.—North Easton
New England Specialty Co.
(Can) C
MASS.—Springfield
Bemis & Call Hardware &
Tool Co. (Box) ....A
Springfield Machine Screw
Co. (Can) ....D
MASS.—Taunton
Mason Machine Works (Lappers; Cotton) ......AA
M ss.—Whitinsville
Whitin Machine Works
(Lappers; Cotton) AAAA
MASS.—Worcester
Bigelow Mfg. Co., J. F.
(Can) ....E
N. H.—Antrim
Goodell Co. (Can) ......A
N. J.—Newark
Celluloid Co. (Letters) ..B
Kraeuter & Co. (Can).....X
Osborn & Co., E. S. (Cigar
Box; Can) ....R
Sharp, Fdk. (Can) .....F

N. Y.—Brooklyn
Ranken, Herman, 71 S. 1st
X
N. Y.—Buffalo
Union Mfg. & Specialty Co.
(Can) C
N. Y.—East Syracuse
Benedict Mfg. Co., M. S.
(Letter) ....AA
N. Y.—Irvington
Lord & Burnham Co. (Sash
& Window) ....A
New York City
Bickelhoupt Skylight Wks.,
245 W. 47th (Automatic
Scuttle) ....F
Bunnell & Co. J. H., 20
Park Pl. (Electric Door)
B
Graham, John H., & Co.
(Cigar Box) ....AA
Keil & Son, Francis, (Electric Door) ....AA
Peck Stow & Wilcox Co.,
(Can) ....AAAA
Sargent & Co. (Can) AAAA
Smith & Hemenway (Can)
D
Thurnauer & Bros., G. M.,
35 Park Pl. X
N. Y.—Rochester
Kron, P. (Can) ....G
Streeter & Co., N. R. (Can)
B
OHIO—Canton
Gibbs Mfg. Co. (Can) ....A
OHIO—Cleveland
Fanner Mfg. Co. (Box) ..A
OHIO—Hamilton
Meyers Mfg. Co., Fred J.,
(Can) ....B
PA.—Erie
Erie Specialty Co. (Cigar
Box) ....B
Reed Mfg. Co. (Bottle) ..A
PA.—Philadelphia
Able & Willing Co., 144 Lehigh Av. (Envelope) ..B
Partrick, Carter & Wilkens
(Electric Door) ....B
Philadelphia Novelty Mfg.
Co. (Can) ....D
Philadelphia Textile Machinery Co., Hancock &
Somerset (Lappers; Cotton) ....AA
PA.—Wrightsville
Wrightsville Hardware Co.
(Can) ....B
R. I.—Pawtucket
Atherton Machine Co. (Lappers; Cotton) ....B
Howard & Bullough Amer.
Machine Co., Ltd. (Lappers; Cotton) ......AAA
WIS.—South Milwaukee
Stowell Mfg. & Foundry Co.
(Can) ....A

OPTHALMO-SCOPES

ILL.—Chicago
Fowler, E. S. & W. S. ....D
IND.—Indianapolis
Armstrong & Co., Wm. H. B
New York City
Meyrowitz, E. B. ....A
Spencer Optical Co., 12
Maiden Lane C
N. Y.—Rochester
Bausch & Lomb Optical Co.
AAA

OPIUM

New York City
Hill's Sons Co., Edw. ..AA
McKesson & Robbins AAAA
Merck & Co. ....AAAA
New York Quinine & Chemical Works ....A
Schieffelin & Co. ....AA

OPTICAL GOODS

ILL.—Chicago
Chicago Mfg. & Optical Co.,
133 Wabash Av. X
King Optical Co., Julius ..E

OPTICAL GOODS (Con.)

Manasse Co., L., 88 E. Madison C
Martin Co., Edw. P. C
Peerless Optical Co., 84 Wabash Av. X
MASS.—Attleboro
Bay State Optical Co. (Eye Glasses; Frames) ......B
MASS.—Boston
Boston Optical Works, 48 Hanover ....F
Lloyd & Co., Geo. H., 23 Winter ....F
MASS.—Southbridge
American Optical Co. ..AAA
Central Optical Co. ....D
Dupaul, Young Optical Co. B
Quimette, J., Jr. ....D
MICH.—Detroit
Johnston Optical Co. .....A
Michigan Optical Co. ....B
MO.—Kansas City
Merry Optical Co. ....A
MO.—St. Louis
Western Optical Co. ....D
N. H.—Tilton
Tilton Optical Co. ....D
N. Y.—Buffalo
King & Eisel ....AA
N. Y.—Geneva
Geneva Optical Co. ......D
Spengler Optical Co. ....F
Standard Optical Co. ....A
N. Y.—Horseheads
Winchester Optical Co. ..D
New York City
American Spectacle Co., 177 Broadway (Spectacles) B
Apfel Philip, 95 Nassau (Lenses) ....D
Berger & Co., Albert, 45 Maiden Lane ....AA
Cross Optical Co., A. J., 20 E. 23rd (Instruments) E
Fay, W. G., 178 Broadway (Instruments) ....F
Goerz, C. P., 52 Union Sq. E. X
Green & Co., W., 6 Maiden Lane C
King Optical Co., Julius, 4 Maiden Lane ....A
Hammel, Riglander & Co., 35 Maiden Lane ......AA
Koenen & Bro., A., 57 Fulton (Spectacles) .....B
Meyrowitz Mfg. Co., 104 E. 23rd C
New York Mutual Optical Co., 9 Maiden Lane .....F
Miller, Mark, 86 Nassau 23rd ....A
Oelschlaeger Bros., 42 E. 23rd ....A
Singer & Rothenberg, 116 Fulton ....D
Spencer Optical Co., 12 Maiden Lane C
N. Y.—Rochester
Bausch & Lomb Optical Co. ....AAA
Briggs Optical Co. ......D
Gundlach-Manhattan Optical Co. ....A
N. Y.—Syracuse
Empire Optical Co. X
Morse Optical Co., Jas. H. D
Syracuse Optical Co. X
OHIO—Cincinnati
Standard Optical Co., 13 Emery Arcade ....F
OHIO—COLUMBUS ..
Columbus Aseptic Furniture Co. X
White-Haines Optical Co. D
OHIO—Springfield
Fay, C. S. (Instruments) H
OHIO—Toledo
Swegart Optical Co. .....D
PA.—Philadelphia
Borsch & Co., Jno. L., 1324 Walnut ....A
Brown, Daniel V., 740 Sansom ....A
Limeburner & Co., J. E., 315 Vine ....B
McIntire, Magee & Brown, 723 Sansom ....A
Mayer & Co., Geo., 134 So 8th ....B
National Optical Co., 11th & Mifflin ....B
Neill, J. F., 727 Sansom D

OPTICAL GOODS (Con.)

Queen & Co., 1010 Chestnut ....AA
Standard Optical Institute, 315 Vine ....E
Wedge Mounting Co., 833 Arch ....D
Williams, Brown & Earle, 918 Chestnut ....A
Zineman & Bro., M., 21 N. 11th ....B
PA.—Reading
Pennsylvania Optical Co. ..A
Willson & Co., T. A. ...AA
PA.—Richmond
Galeski Optical Co. X
R. I.—Providence
Wilkerson & Co., C. A. (Gold Filled Frames) AA
WIS.—Milwaukee
Milwaukee Optical Mfg. Co. ....D
Reinhard Mfg. Co. .,....D

ORANGES & LEMONS

CAL.—Bonita
Sweetwater Farm Co. ..B
CAL.—Colton
Colton Fruit Exch. C
CAL.—Fresno
Earl Fruit Co. (Br. Sacramento) ....A
CAL.—Fullerton
Placentia Orange Growers' Assn. C
CAL.—Highland
Earl Fruit Co. (Br. Sacramento) ....A
CAL.—Los Angeles
Earl Fruit Co. (Br. Sac.) A
Fay Fruit Co., 216 S. Bway. ....A
Rudock, French & Co., 314 W. 4th ....AA
Simpson & Hack Fruit Co. C
Southern Calif. Fruit Exch. ....AA
CAL.—North Ontario
Lemon Growers' Exch. ...C
CAL.—Pacific Beach
Baker & Son, R. M. (Lemons) C
CAL.—Redlands
Earl Fruit Co. (Br. Sac.) A
Gregory Fruit Co. C
Redlands Orange Growers' Assn. ....B
CAL.—Riverside
Arlington Heights Fruit Co. ....B
Earl Fruit Co. (Br. Sac) A
Everest Rancho (Oranges only) ....A
Johnson, A. P. (Pack. Oranges) ....A
Riverside Fruit Co. .....AA
Riverside Orange Co. (S.) A
CAL.—Sacramento
Earl Fruit Co. ....A
CAL.—Visalia
Earl Fruit Co. (Br. Sac.) A
Kaweah Lemon Co. ....B
FLA.—Sanford
Chase & Co. ....B
FLA.—Tampa
Fuller & Co., W. A. (Oranges) ....A
ILL.—Chicago
Evans & Co., D. E., 71 S. Water ....B
Zucca & Co., J., 63 S. Water C
ILL.—Joliet
Seaver Co., C. S. ....B
IOWA—Burlington
Lagomareino & Co., A. ..B
IOWA—Cedar Rapids
Lagomarcino & Co., A. ..B
IOWA—Sioux City
Haley & Lang Co. ....A
KY.—Louisville
Allen & Co., J. T. C
MD.—Baltimore
West India Trading Co. ..X
MICH.—Detroit
Lichtenberg & Sons, Woodbridge & Griswold .....B
N. Y.—Buffalo
Brennison & Son, F., 156 Mich. ....B

717

ORANGES & LEMONS

New York City
Contencin & Son, Louis, 4
  Stone ....A
Hutcheson & Co., A. G., 106
  Front ....A
Lyon Bros. Co., 330 Washn.
 C
Pierce, L., 208 Duane C
Ruhlman & Co., P., 261
  Washn. ....B
Schott & Franke, 120
  Warren ....B
Thompson, Geo. H., (Imp.)
  107 Hudson ....B
Zucca & Co., 235 West ...C

ORDERS

CONN.—Clintonsville
Vibbert & Co., Geo. S.
  (Dance) ....F
New York City
Hake Mfg. Co., Philip
  (Dance) ....A
Koehler, Joseph, 148 Park
  Row (Fancy Dance) ...C
Tobin, Michael F. (Dance) B

ORE

ALA.—Birmingham
Birmingham Rolling Mill Co.
  (Iron) ....AAA
Cahala Southern Mining Co.
  (Iron) ....A
Pioneer Mining & Mfg. Co.
  (Iron) ....AAAA
Sloss Sheffield Steel & Iron
  Co. (Iron) ....AAAA
Tennessee Coal Iron & Rail-
  road Co. (Iron) ....AAAA
ALA.—Woodward
Woodward Iron Co. (Iron)
  ....AAAA
ARIZ.—Morenci
Detroit Copper Mining Co.
  of Arizona (Copper)
  ....AAAA
CAL.—San Francisco
Selby Smelting & Lead Co.
  (Tin) ....AAA
COLO.—Denver
Boston & Colorado Smelting
  Co. (Copper) ....AAA
COLO.—Leadville
Hunter Co., V. (Gold; Lead)
  ....AAAA
ILL.—Chicago
Pickands, Brown & Co.
  (Iron) ....AAAA
MICH.—Hancock
Quincy Mining Co. (Copper)
  ....AAAA
MICH.—Ishpeming
Cleveland Cliffs Iron Co.
  (Iron) ....AAAA
MONT.—Butte
Anaconda Copper Mining Co.
  (Copper; Lead; Silver)
  ....AAAA
Boston Montana Can Copper
  & Silver Mining Co. (Cop-
  per; Silver) .....AAAA
New York City
Cooper Hewitt & Co. (Iron)
  ....AAAA
Dana & Co., 32 Bway. (Man-
  ganese) ....A
Oxford Copper Co. (Copper;
  Nickel) ....AAA
N. Y.—Poughkeepsie
Poughkeepsie Iron Co.
  (Iron) ....A
N. Y.—Rochester
Rochester & Pittsburg Coal
  & Iron Co. (Iron) AAAA
OHIO—Cleveland
Cleveland Iron Mining Co.
  (Iron) ....AAAA
OHIO—Steubensville
La Belle Iron Works (Iron)
  ....AAAA
PA.—Philadelphia
Phila. & Read. Coal & Iron
  Co. (Iron) ....B
Billing & Crane (Iron) ..AA
Pullman, J. Wesley (Iron) B
TENN.—Dayton
Dayton Coal & Iron Co.
  (Iron) ....AAAA
UTAH—Salt Lake City
Centennial Eureka Mining
  Co. (Silver) ....B

ORE (Con.)
Daly-West Mining Co.
  (Silver) ....A
Eureka Hill Mining Co.
  (Silver) ....B
Ontario Silver Mining Co.
  (Lead; Silver) ......B

ORGANETTES

New York City
Aeolian Co., 362 5th Av.
  ....AAAA

ORGANS

CAL.—San Francisco
Sherman Clay & Co. (Inc.)
  (Church) ....AAAA
CONN.—Bridgeport
Bridgeport Organ Co.
  (Cabinet Reed) ......B
CONN.—Derby
Sterling Co. (Cabinet Reed)
  ....AA
CONN.—Meriden
Wilcox & White Co. (Cabi-
  net Reed, Church) ...A
CONN.—New Haven
Hall & Co., H. (Church) ..F
Shoninger Co., B. (Cabinet
  Reed) ....AAA
ILL.—Chicago
Bent, Geo. P. (Cabinet
  Reed) ....AAA
Bilhorn Bros., 56 5th Av.
  (Folding, Reed) C
Kimball Co., W. W., Wa-
  bash Av. & Jackson Boul.
  (Church, Cabinet Reed,
  Pipe) ....AAAA
Lyon & Healy (Cabinet
  Reed, Pipe) ....AAAA
Newman Bros. Co. (Cabinet
  Reed) ....AA
Storey, J. B. & E. A. Clark
  Co. (Cabinet Reed) ..C
KANS.—Abilene
Parker, C. W. (Military
  Band) ....A
MAINE—Foxcroft
Hughes & Son Piano Mfg.
  Co. (Cabinet Reed) ..B
MD.—Baltimore
Niemann, Henry, 655 W.
  Lombard (Church) ....H
Stein, Adam, 665 W. Ger-
  man (Church) X
MASS.—Boston
Cole Church Organ Co., 99
  Bristol (Church) X
Hutchings Votey Organ Co.
  (Pipe) ....B
Woodberry & Co., Jesse, 520
  Harrison Av. (Church,
  Pipe) ....D
MASS.—Kendal Green
Hook & Hastings Co.
  (Church, Pipe) ......A
MASS.—Westfield
Howard & Emmons (Church)
  ....D
MICH.—Detroit
Clough & Warren Co.
  (Cabinet Reed) ......A
Farrand Organ Co. (Cabinet
  Reed, Pipe) ....AA
N. H.—Concord
Prescott Piano Co. (Cabinet
  Reed) ....B
N. J.—Camden
Furbush & Son Machine Co.,
  M. A. X
N. Y.—Brooklyn
Looff, Chas., Normann Av.
  & Russell ....A
Midmer & Son, Reuben (Cab-
  inet Reed, Church) ..B
N. Y.—Buffalo
Niner & Sons, 428 Pearl
  (Church) ....E
N. Y.—Ithaca
Autophone Co. (Automatic,
  Mechanical, Roller) .B
New York City
Aeolian Co. (Cabinet Reed,
  Mechanical) ......AAAA
Mason & Hamlin Co. (Cab-
  inet Reed, Church) ..A
Molinari & Son, 153 Eliza-
  beth (Hand) X
Needham Piano & Organ Co.
  (Cabinet Reed) ......A
Odell & Co., J. H. & C. S.
  409 W. 42d (Church) ...B

ORGANS (Con.)

N. Y.—North Tonawanda
Armitage Herschell Co.
(Steam; Electric) .....B
Herschell, Spillman & Co. A
N. Y.—Tonawanda
Gillie Engine & Machine Co.
C
OHIO—Alliance
Hillgreen Lane & Co.
(Church) ....A
OHIO—Cincinnati
Foley & Williams Mfg. Co.,
123 W. 5th (Church) ..A
OHIO—Cleveland
Raymond, Frank L. T. Co.
(Cabinet Reed) ....B
OHIO—Norwalk
Chase Co., A. B. (Cabinet
Reed) ....AA
PA.—Erie
Felgemaker, A. B. (Pipe) A
PA.—Lebanon
Miller Organ & Piano Co.
(Cabinet Reed) ....A
PA.—Philadelphia
Bates & Culley, 706 Mercer
(Church) ....F
Dentzell, G. A., 3635 Ger-
mantown Av. ....B
PA.—Pittsburg
Ingersoll Construction Co.,
307 4th Av............B
VT.—Brattleboro
Carpenter Co. (Cabinet
Reed) ....B
Estey Organ Co. (Cabinet
Reed, Church, Pipe)AAAA
WIS.—Milwaukee
Schuelke, Wm., 2219 Wal-
nut (Church) X
Foerster, Carl (Carousel) A

ORGANZINE

See Silk Goods

ORNAMENTS

See also Millinery

CAL.—Los Angeles
Betkonskie, Martin F., 451
E. 3d (Plastic) ....D
CONN.—Bristol
Ingraham Co., E. (Bronze)
AAA
CONN.—Hartford
Root, C. R., 286 Sheldon
(Composition) ....G
CONN.—Meriden
Bradley & Hubbard Mfg. Co.
(Bronze; Stone) ..AAAA
North & Co., O. B. (Saddle)
AA
CONN.—Waterbury
Amer. Ring Co. (Harness;
Saddle) ....A
Matthews & Willard Co.
(Bronze) ....AAAA
Novelty Mfg. Co. (Brass) A
Plume & Atwood Mfg. Co.
(Harness) ....AAAA
Steele & Johnson Mfg. Co.
(Brass) ....A
Waterbury Button Co. (Mili-
tary) ....A
ILL.—Chicago
Architectural Decorating
Co., 204 Illinois (Composi-
tion; Plastic) ....D
Barnhardt Bros. & Spindler
(Printers) ....AA
Braun, J. G., 322 S. Paulina
(Steel for Ornamental Iron
Work) ....
Decorators' Supply Co., 209-
219 So. Clinton (Composi-
tion; Plastic) ....B
Fiedler & Sons, A. B. (Inc.)
(Silk) ....A
Foster-Munger Co., W. 20th
& So. Sagamon (Wood)AA
Friedley & Noshardt, 196
Mather (Sheet Metal) ..A
Ganger & Co., Jno. A., W.
22d & Laflin (Wood)..AA
Harsha Mfg. Co., L. R., 793
Carroll (Composition) ..B
Hartmann, Jno., 13 N. Jeff-
erson (Composition) ....E
Meyercord Co. (Transfer) A
Palmer, Fuller & Co., 2244
Lumber (Wood) ....A
Plastic Relief Mfg. Co., 298

ORNAMENTS (Con.)

N. Halsted (Composition;
Plastic) ....E
Raubold & Lambkin, 19 N.
Ann (Composition) C
Roberts & Co., E. L., 22d
& Union Pl. (Wood) ...A
Stubb, A., 2 Nebraska Av.
(Composition) X
Thoresen, Wm., 816 N.
Western Av. (Sheet
Metal) ....E
Warren & Co., James P.
(Copper) X
Weary, Edwin D., Mar-
quette Bldg. (Composi-
tion) ....B
IND.—South Bend
Studebaker Bros. Mfg. Co.
(Harness) ....AAAA
IOWA—Clinton
Curtis Bros. & Co. (Wood)
AAA
KY.—Covington
Ohio Scroll & Lbr. Co.
(Wood Furniture) ......D
MD.—Baltimore
Meislahn & Co., C. F., 19
Clay (Composition) ..D
MASS.—Boston
Emmel, Chas., 383 Albany
(Composition; Plastic) .B
Lombard & Co., A. P., 99
Bristol (Composition) ..D
Mathews Consolidated Slate
Co., 199 Washn. (Slate) X
Stearns Lumber Co., A. T.
(Wood Gable) ....AA
MASS.—Haverhill
Dalrymple & Co., J. A.
(Millinery) ....B
MASS.—Leominster
Earl & Co., W. D. (Hair) C
Tilton & Cook (Hair) ...A
MASS.—Attleboro
Barrows & Co., H. F. (Hair)
A
Whiting & Co., F. M. (Hair)
B
MICH.—Detroit
Bailey Co., 224 21st (Plas-
tic) ....E
Detroit Shipbuilding Co.
(Brass Dept.; Flag Pole;
Banner) ....AAAA
Wilton-Reuter Co., 472 Fort
W. (Composition) X
MICH.—Grand Rapids
Grand Rapids Brass Co.
(Metal) ....A
Grand Rapids Carved Mould-
ing Co. (Wood) X
Novelty Wood Works (Wood
Furniture) ....F
Waddell Manufacturing Co.
Wood; Rosettes; Carved;
Grilles, etc.) ....B
MICH.—Holland
Michigan Toy & Novelty Co.
(Wood; Rosettes; Turned
Specialties) ....E
MINN.—St. Paul
St. Paul Roofing Cornice &
Ornament Co. (Sheet Met-
al; Zinc) ....B
MO.—Kansas City
Jennens Mfg. Co., W., 1700
Wyandotte (Composition)
F
MO.—St. Louis
Beattie Manufacturing Co.,
2202 Pine (Composition) A
Eastman & Johnstone, 1711
St. Charles (Composition;
Plastic) ....F
Gerock Bros. Mfg. Co., 1252
Manchester Av. (Sheet
Metal) C
Prall, Alfred A., 25 So. 8th
(Plastic) ....H
Seifert Plastic Relief Co.,
Frank A., 2646 Lawton
Av. (Composition; Plastic)
..D
NEBR.—Lincoln
Curtis & Bartlett Co.
(Wood) ....A
N. H.—Milford
Pierce & Co., W. E.
(Wood) ....D
N. J.—Camden
Frand & Co., Martin J., 110
Arch (Sheet Metal) C

ORNAMENTS (Con.)

N. J.—Newark
Dorn, Wm. J., 268 Market (Composition) X
Peters Harness & Saddlery Co. (Saddle) C
Prior, James N., 288 Washington (Plastic) ......F
Reynold & Zahn (Harness) C
Spanjer Bros. (Wood) ....E

N. J.—New Brunswick
New Jersey Lamp & Bronze Works (Brass; Bronze; Clock) ....AA

N. Y.—Brooklyn
Forman Bros., 645 Gates Av. (Composition; Plastic) D
Heilman Co., R., 207 State (Composition; Plastic) .E
Miller & Doing, 83 Washington Av. (Sheet Metal) F
Nogt, Walter J. (Cap; Tinzel) ....D
White Co., James, 446 Adelphi (Sheet Metal) ....D
White, Potter & Paige Mfg. Co., 415 Willoughby Av. (Composition) ....A

New York City
Benziger Bros. (Church) ..A
Berger Sons, H., 101 4th Av. (Plastic) ....E
Broschart & Braun, 601 W. 130th (Sheet Metal) ..X
Day Clark & Co. (Hair) B
French, S. A. (Military; Society) ....
Hergert, Theo. E., 384 2d Av. (Sheet Metal for Cornices) C
Judd & Co., H. L. (Brass) ....AA
Klee Thomson Co., 327 E. 40th (Plastic) ....D
Maas & Co., Wm. (Hair)AA
Masset, A., 78 E. 10th (Church) ....D
Meyer, Bernard (Christmas Tree) ....D
Moore Bronze & Plate Co., M. E. (Bronze; Clock) B
Newcombe Mfg. Co., F. J., 44 W. 13th (Composition) ....B
New York Carved Moulding Co., 771 1st Av. (Wood) D
New York Composition & Decorative Co., 228 W. Houston (Composition; Plastic) X
Palm Fechtler Co. (Transfer) ....A
Parker, Edwin C., 519 W. 30th (Wood) ....F
Richards & Co., E. Ira (Hair) ....AAA
Rudolph, Oscar, 32 E. 22d (Composition) ....D
Sloan & Co. (Inc.) (Hair) B
Stoltzenberg Co. (Charcoal) ....B
Veit, Son & Co., (Millinery) ....A
Waldron & Carroll (Harness) ....D
Walter, G. E., 157 E. 44th (Composition; Plastic) ..C

N. Y.—Syracuse
Schneider, F. H., 439 E. Water (Composition; Plastic) F

N. Y.—Watervleit
Covert Manufacturing Co. (Harness) ....A

OHIO—Akron
Enterprise Mfg. Co. (Harness) ....A

OHIO—Canton
Berger Mfg. Co. (Gable) AA

OHIO—Cincinnati
Edwards Mfg. Co. (Copper)
Marks, W. A. Plaster Ornamentl Mfg. Co., 726 W. 5th (Plastic) ....E
Messmer Co., Andrew (Church) ....B
Palm Bros. & Co., (Inc.) 316 Main (Transfer; Carriage) ....E

OHIO—Salem
Mullins, W. H. (Sheet Metal; Brass; Copper; Zinc)A

PA.—Allentown
Grammes & Sons, L. F.

ORNAMENTS (Con.)

(Brass) ....A
PA.—Philadelphia
Cassell, Jacob C. (Aquarium) ....D
De Plange, F. R., 1349 Ridge Av. (Plastic) ...D
Farley & Bros., Wm. E., 3635 Market (Plastic) ..X
French & Co., Saml. H., 4th & Callowhill (Plastic) A
Gara & McGinley Co., 33 So. 17th (Sheet Metal) ...A
Geilfuss, H. H., 1202 Vine (Confectioners') ......D
Gossert, Henry, 320 Harmony (Composition) ..H
Heath, John A. S., 42 N. 11th (Plastic) ......H
Horstman Co., Wm. H. (Cap) ....AAAA
Loeb, Lipper & Co. (Silk; Millinery) ....A
McCune, Alex., 1303 Race (Composition) ....F
National Decalcomania Co. (Transfer) ....F
Stephens, Cooper & Co., 15 So. 18th (Composition; Plastic) ....D
Thorn Co., J. S., 1227 Callowhill (Sheet Metal) ...A
Whitman & Co., J. Franklin, 212 So. 5th (Composition)C

PA.—Union City
Novelty Wood Work Co. (Wood Furniture) ......B

R. I.—Providence
Feeley Co., W. J. (Church) ....B
Hancock, Co., Chas. E. (Hair) ....B
Pollard & Co., A. (Millinery) ....E

WIS.—Milwaukee
Milwaukee Ornamental Carving Co., 423 Poplar (Plastic; Wood) ....F

WIS.—Oshkosh
Gould Mfg. Co. (Wood) ..A
McMillen Co., R. (Wood) A
Morgan Co. (Wood) .....AA
Paine Lumber Co. (Wood) ....AAAA

OSNABURGS
See Cotton Goods

OTTOMANS
See also Furniture

MINN.—Minneapolis
McLeod & Smith ....B
New York City
Judd & Co., H. L. (Brass) ....AA
N. Y.—Rochester
Archer Mfg. Co. (Piano) A

OUTFITS
CONN.—Deep River
Williams & Marvin Mfg. Co. (Button Makers) ......D
CONN.—Waterbury
Scovill Mfg. Co. (Photographic; Amateur) ....AAAA
ILL.—Chicago
Liquid Carbonic Acid Mfg. Co. (Liquid Gas Charging) ....AAAA
LA.—Amite City
Gullett Gin Co. (Cotton Gin) ....A
LA.—New Orleans
Coleman & Co., H. Dudley (Cotton Gin) ....D
N. J.—Newark
Gould & Eberhardt (Button Makers) ....A
Sacks Iron Foundry, Louis (Cobblers') ....A
New York City
Abercrombie & Fitch (Camping) C
Gennert, G. (Photographic; Amateur) ....B
Gordon Battery Co. (Table; Shelf) ....D
Horsman Co., E. I. (Photographic; Amateur) C
Kohlbusch, Herman (Sugar

OUTFITS (Con.)

Chemists) ....B
Lovejoy Co. (Stereotypers) B
Pierce Well Engineering &
  Supply Co. ....D
Wesel Mfg. Co., F. (Stereo-
  typers) X
N. Y.—Rochester
Eastman Kodak Co. (Photo-
  graphic; Amateur) AAAA
OHIO—Cincinnati
Western Tray Factory
  (Trunk) ....F
OHIO—Cleveland
Cleveland Dental Mfg. Co.
  (Dental) ....B
OHIO—Plymouth
Root Bros. Co. (Cobblers;
  Tinware Repairing) ..B
PA.—Philadelphia
Enterprise Mfg. Co., N. 3d
  & Dauphin (Cobblers')
              AAAA
TEXAS—Fort Worth
Fort Worth Iron & Steel
  Mfg. Co. (Drive Well) A

OUTING SUITS
See Clothing: Men's

OVENS

CONN.—Stamford
Oven Equipment & Mfg. Co.
  (Enameling; Gas) ......B
ILL.—Chicago
Arnstein, Eugene, 35th &
  Shields Av. (Enameling)
              A
Hubbard Portable Oven Co.,
  112 Mich. (Portable) ..C
White Mfg. Co., 158 Indiana
  (Enameling) X
ILL.—Harvey
Whiting Foundry & Equip-
  ment Co. (Core) ......AA
ILL.—Paxton
Paxton Hdw. Mfg. Co.
  (Portable) X
IND.—Mishawaka
Dodge Mfg. Co. (Square;
  Rotary Core) ......AAA
KANS.—Fort Scott
Fort Scott Foundry & Ma-
  chine Co. (Ore Roasting) E
MASS.—Boston
Howes Co., S. M. (Gas;
  Gasoline; Oil) ....B
MASS.—Cambridge
Barbour-Stockwell Co.
  (Bakers') ....B
MICH.—Detroit
American Electric Heater
  Co. (Bakers') ....B
Byram & Co. (Core) .....D
Detroit Vapor Stove Co.
  (Gas; Oil Stove) ......B
Northern Engineering Works
  (Core) ....A
MICH.—Jackson
Novelty Mfg. Co. (Gas; Gas-
  oline; Oil; Portable) ..A
MICH.—Saginaw
Werner & Pfleiderer
  (Bakers') ....A
MO.—St. Louis
American Stove Co. (Porta-
  ble) ....AAAA
N. Y.—Buffalo
Reid Portable Oven Co., H.
  (Combination Portable;
  Roaster) ....G
Ruger Mfg. Co., J. W.
  (Mechanical) ....B
New York City
American Gas Furnace Co.
  (Enameling; Gas Enamel-
  ing) ....A
Crandall & Godley Co., 157
  Franklin (Portable) ..AA
OHIO—Cincinnati
Hill & Griffith Co. (Core) D
Obermayer Co., S. (Core) AA
Van Range Co., John (Port-
  able) ....A
OHIO—Cleveland
Cleveland Foundry Co.
  (Portable) ....A
Dangler Stove & Mfg. Co.
  (Gas; Gasoline; Oil)
              AAAA
Schneider & Traucamp (Gas;
  Gasoline; Oil) ....AAAA

OVENS (Con.)

Smith Fdry. Supply Co., 40
  S. Water (Core) ......D
Van Dorn Iron Works Co.
  Enameling; Japan) ..AA
Wellman-Seaver Organ Co.
  (Coke) ....AAAA
OHIO—Toledo
National Cement & Rubber
  Mfg. Co. (Enamelled;
  Gas; Gasoline) C
PA.—Philadelphia
Paxson Co., J. W., 1021 W.
  Del. Av. (Core) ......AA
PA.—Pittsburg
McCormick Co., J. S., 25th
  & A. V. Ry. (Core) ...E
R. I.—Providence
American Enamel Co.
  (Enameling) ....B
VT.—Burlington
Blodgett Co., G. S. (Baking;
  Japaning Core; Cabinet;
  Portable; Enameling) ..C

OVERALLS
See Clothing: Men's

OVERCOATS
See Clothing: Men's

OVER-COATINGS
See Woolen Goods

OXIDE

MO.—St. Louis
Mallenckrodt Chemical
  Works (Chrome) ..AAAA
Ozark Zinc Oxide Co.
  (Zinc) ....B
N. J.—Lincoln
Atlas Mineral & Machine Co.
  (Iron) ....D
N. Y.—Brooklyn
Wiarda & Co., John C.
  (Chrome; Cobalt; Manga-
  nese; Nickel; Iron; Cop-
  per; Silver; Tin; Uranium;
  Zinc) ....AA
N. Y.—Clinton
Clinton Metallic Paint Co.
  (Red) C
New York City
Cooper & Co., Chas.
  (Chrome; Gold) .....AA
Feuchtwanger & Co., L.
  (Chrome) ....B
Gabriel & Schall, 205 Pearl
  (Zinc) ....B
Johns-Manville Co., H. W.
  (Red) ....AAAA
New Jersey Zinc Co. (Zinc)
              A
Prince Mfg. Co. (Red) ...B
Tiemann & Co., D. F. (Red)
              A
N. Y.—Randolph
Elko Paint Co. (Dry;
  Enamel) C
PA.—Easton
Williams & Co., C. K. (Red;
  Yellow) ....A
PA.—Philadelphia
Drueding Bros. Co. (Magne-
  sium) ....AA
Powers-Weightman-Rosen-
  garten Co. (Gold) AAAA
White Dental Mfg. Co., S.
  S. (Nitrous; Liquefied)
              AAAA
PA.—Pittsburg
Davis Lead Co. (Lead) ..A
PA.—Williamsport
National Paint Works (Red;
  Zinc) ....B
TENN.—Chattanooga
Chat. Paint Co. (Red) C
WIS.—Mineral Point
Mineral Point Zinc Co.
  (Zinc) ....AA

OXYGEN
See Gas

OYSTERS: CANNED

See Canned Goods

OZOKERITE

New York City
Brunn, A. W. X

PACKAGES

See also Baskets; Cooperage; Boxes

ILL.—Chicago
Creamery Package Mfg. Co. (Beer; Butter; Lard)
AAAA
ILL.—Mound City
Metal Bound Package Co. (Metal Bound) ....A
MASS.—Townsend
Fessenden, B. & A. D. (Fish; Lard; Paint; Varnish; Pickle) ....A
N. H.—Keene
Beaver Mills (Fish; Jelly).A
Impervious Package Co. (Lard; Oil; Pickle; Syrup)
B
N. Y.—Buffalo
Wright & Co., R. G. (Oil; Paint; Varnish) ....AA
OHIO—Cincinnati
Cincinnati Cooperage Co. (Beer; Ale) ....AAA
OHIO—Defiance
American Steel Package Co. (Steel Bottle) ....B
OHIO—East Liverpool
Williams & Co., S. C. (Pottery) ....A
WIS.—Menasha
Menasha Woodenware Co. (Butter; Fish; Jelly; Lard; Syrup) ....AA

PACKERS

See Canned Goods; Machinery

GA.—Atlanta
De Loach Mill Mfg. Co. (Shingle) ....B
ILL.—Moline
Barnard & Leas Mfg. Co. (Bean; Flour) ....AA
IND.—Indianapolis
Nordyke & Marmon Co. (Flour) ....AAA
IND.—Richmond
Richmond City Mill Works (Flour) ....B
KANS.—Leavensworth
Great Western Mfg. Co. (Flour) ....AA
MASS.—Boston
Hersey Mfg. Co. (Barrel)
AA
MICH.—Saginaw
Mitts & Merrill (Shingle).B
N. Y.—Brooklyn
Ross & Son, Chas. (Barrel)
D
N. Y.—Buffalo
Noye Mfg. Co., Jno. T. (Flour) X
N. Y.—Lockport
Trevor Mfg. Co. (Shingle)
B
N. Y.—Silver Creek
Howes Co., S. (Bean; Flour; Cement) ....A
OHIO—Cincinnati
Day & Co., J. H. (Flour; Spruce) ....A
OHIO—Columbus
Case Mfg. Co. (Flour) ....A
PA.—Bradford
Dresser, S. R. (Oil Well)
AA
McElwaine Co. (Oil Well)
D
PA.—Muncy
Sprout, Waldron & Co. (Flour) ....A
VT.—Montpelier
Lane Mfg. Co. (Shingle)..A
WIS.—Milwaukee
Ellis-Chalmers Co. (Flour)
AAA

PACKERS (Con.)
Filer & Stowell Co. (Shingle
AAA

PACKING

CAL.—San Francisco
American Balance Valve Co. (Ring) ....D
CONN.—Hartford
Hartford Rubber Wks. Co. (Rubber; Steam) ..AAAA
Johns-Pratt Co., 555 Capitol (Vulcanized Asbestos; Steam) ....A
DEL.—Wilmington
American Vulcanized Fibre Co. (Vulcanized Fibre)
AAAA
Delaware Hard Fibre Co. (Hard Fibre; Steam) ...B
Planet Mills Mfg. Co. (Jute)
AAAA
ILL.—Aurora
Udstad, S. (Plaster)......E
ILL.—Chicago
Advance Packing & Supply Co., 155 S. Canal (Asbestos; Metallic Sheet; Steam) C
Allen Mfg. Co., W. D., 151 Lake (Steam) ....B
Carpenter, Geo. B. & Co. (Valve; Rod; Piston) .AA
Chicago Fireproof Covering Co., 18 N. Canal (Steam)
A
Chicago Rawhide Mfg. Co., 75 E. Ohio (Rawhide; Rawhide Hydraulic Steam) ....A
Goodsell Packing Co., 33 So. Canal (Improved Metallic; Flax; Metallic Steam).B
Hennebohle, Frank (South) (Metallic) ....D
Jenkins Bros. of New York, 31 N. Canal (Steam; Valve; Rod; Piston) ..AA
Jerome & Elliott, 35 So. Canal (Metallic; Ring; Metallic Steam) ....A
Johns-Manville Co., H. W., of New York (Steam; Asbestos; Metallic) AAAA
New York Belting & Packing Co. (Ltd.), 150 Lake (Rubber; Steam) ..AAA
Phenix Metallic Packing Co. 70 So. Jefferson (Metallic) ....F
Railway Appliances Co. Old Colony Bldg. (Metallic; Ring) ....A
Revere Rubber Co., of Boston, Mass., 168 Lake (Steam) ....AAAA
Swain Lubricator Co., 252 Lake (Metallic; Metallic Steam) ....B
ILL.—Evanston
Mark Mfg. Co. (Leather)
AA
IND.—Indianapolis
Pioneer Brass Wks. (Piston; Rod) C
IND.—Terre Haute
American Asbestos Co. (Valve; Rod; Piston; Vault) ....D
KY.—Covington
Overman & Schrader Cordage Co. (Jute) ......AA
KY.—Louisville
Cook, C. Lee (Metallic)..D
LA.—New Orleans
Fairbanks Co. (Semi-Bronze; Asbestos, for high and low and Hydraulic Pressure; Steam) ....AAAA
MAINE—Portland
Lang Co., E. M. (Metallic)
C
MASS.—Boston
American Steam Packing Co., 60 Federal (Asbestos; Metallic; Steam) ....B
Anderson, G. P., 73 Oliver (Ring) ....D
Bay State Belting Co., 119 Franklin (Steam) .....A
Boston Belting Co. 256 Metallic: Wire Rope Pul-Devonshire (Combination

722

PACKING (*Con.*)

ley; Rubber; Ammonia; Plumbago; Piston; Spiral Piston; Ring &c.; Steam; Engine) ....AAAA

Chesterton & Co., A. W., 64 India (Metalbestos; Rubberbestos; Steam; Engine) A

Knowlton Rubber Co., Geo. W., 72 Broad (Ring) .F

Lubron Mfg. Co., 51 India (Ring) ....F

Silver Lake Co. (Locomotive) ....A

Standard Packing Mfg. Co., 404 Atlantic Av. (Metallic Fibred Compound) X

Watson Co., H. F. (of Erie, Pa.) 233 Congress (Steam; Asbestos) ....AAA

MASS.—Cambridge

Gould Packing Co. (Ring) .H

MASS.—Newton

Silver Lake Co. (Steam) ..A

MICH.—Detroit

Detroit Leather Specialty Co. (Hydraulic Leather) .C

Detroit Lubricator Co. (Metallic; Steam) ....AA

Harvey's Sons Mfg. Co., A., 1st, cor. Woodbridge (Steam) ....A

MICH.—Menominee

Prescott Co., D. Clint. (Metallic; Metallic Steam) .B

MO.—St. Louis

Broderick & Bascom Rope Co. (Hemp; Flax; Valve Rod; Piston) ....AA

Hoyt Metal Co. (Metallic) A

Leschen & Sons Rope Co., A. 920 N. Main (Steam; Valve Rod; Piston) ..AAA

Pilley Packing & Fluebrush Co., 606 So. 3d (Ring) .D

Zelrucker Supply Co., Walter A., 408 No. 4th (Brassbestos; Sheet; Steam) ..C

N. J.—Bloomfield

Combination Rubber & Belting Co. (Steam) ....A

N. J. Jersey City

Johnson Co., Henry (Ring) D

Lane & Co., Rodney D., 484 Johnson Av. (Ring)....H

New Jersey Car Spring & Rubber Co. (Antimony; Rod; Sheet; Steam) ..AA

N. J.—Paterson

Barbour Flax Spinning Co. (Flax) ....AAAA

N. J.—Trenton

Empire Rubber Mfg. Co. (Cloth Insertion; Engine) AA

Hamilton Rubber Mfg. Co. (Rubber; Steam) ......A

Hunt Mfg. Co., Jas. B. (Gum; Core; Flax; Steam) C

Trenton Rubber Mfg. Co. (Gum) ....A

N. Y.—Auburn

Columbian Cordage Co. (Jute) ....AA

Leather & Brass Mfg. Co. (Leather) ....F

N. Y.—Brooklyn

Clinton Mfg. Co., 83 Grand Av. (Flax) C

Excelsior Ring Packing Co., 430 Kent Av. (Ring)...D

Ward & Upright Engineering Co., 41 York (Metallic) ....D

N. Y.—Jamestown

Engineering & Power Co. (Steam) X

New York City

American Mfg. Co., 63 Wall (Jute) ....AAAA

Asbestos Felting Works (Asbestos) ....D

Brandt, Randolph (Cotton; Engine; Flag; Gum; Hemp; Ice Machine) ...E

Common Sense Metallic Packing Mfg. Co., 393 Pearl (Metallic) ......D

Green, Tweed & Co., 17

PACKING (*Con.*)

Murray (Steam) ......B

Gutta Percha & Rubber Mfg. Co., 126 Duane (Steam) AAAA

Hall Mfg. Co., 40 Cortlandt (Ring) C

Katzenstein & Co., L., 358 West (Metallic; Metallic & Flexible Tubular Metallic Steam) ....A

Keasbey & Mattison Co., 84 John (Steam) ....AAAA

Lawrence Cordage Works (Hemp; Jute) ....A

Magnolia Metal Co., 260 W. Bway (Ring) ......B

Massasoit Mfg. Co. (Cotton) ....AA

Mayer, Lane & Co., 128 White (Asbestos) X

Mineralized Rubber Co., 18 Cliff (Steam) ....A

New Jersey Asbestos Co., 47 Dey (Asbestos) ......AA

New York Rubber Co., 84 Reade (Steam) ......AA

Peerless Rubber Co.. 16 Warren (Spiral; Piston Rod; Valve Rod; Steam) AAAA

Roberts & Bros., Geo. J. (Inc.), 471 4th Av. (Square; Flax; Steam) .B

Robertson & Sons, Jas. L. 204 Fulton (Steam; Asbestos; Cotton; Engine; Jute; Hemp) C

Travers Bros. Co., 41 Worth (Jute; Hemp) ......AA

Union Selling Co. (Hemp) AAA

Watson-Stillman Co. (Cup) A

Whitman & Barnes Mfg. Co., 111 Chambers (Rubber; Steam Valve; Rod; Piston) ....AAAA

N. Y.—Palmyra

Garlock Packing Co. (Metallic; Ring; All Kinds, for all purposes; Steam) ...A

OHIO—Akron

Akron Belting Co. (Leather) A

OHIO—Cincinnati

Bradford Belting Co., cor. 2d & Walnut (Steam) ..A

Jacobs Cordage Co., Harriot & Budd (Hemp) ....A

OHIO—Cleveland

American Metallic Packing & Supply Co.. Williamson Bldg. (Self-Lubricating Metallic) ....F

Cleveland Tool & Supply Co. 8 So. Water (Steam) ..C

OHIO—Columbus

Hayden Mfg. Co., N. L. (Metallic; Steam) C

OHIO—Lockland

Carey Mfg. Co., Philip (Asbestos) ....AAA

PA.—Bridgeport

Wilkinson Mfg. Co. (Piston Rod; Steam) C

PA.—Chester

Harper Mfg. Co. (Metallic) D

PA.—Erie

Watson Co., H. F. (Asbestos) ....AAA

PA.—Franklin

Franklin Mfg. Co. (Piston Rod; Steam) C

PA.—Hoboken

Flocker & Co.. John (Cotton; Hemp; Sisal) C

PA.—Jersey Shore

American Balance Valve Co. (Metallic) C

PA.—Philadelphia

Asbestos Mfg. Co., 426 Market (Steam) ....B

Bailey & Co., Jno. T.. cor. Water & Tasker (Jute) AAAA

Billington Co.. Jas. H., 113 Chestnut (Steam) .....A

Cancos Mfg. Co., 146 N. 2d (Metallic) ....D

Canfield Mfg. Co. (Ltd.), 1112 Noble (Braided Gum

PACKING (Con.)

Core; Square Flax Spiral;
Ring; Steam) C
Eureka Packing Co., 14 No.
4th (Steam) C
France Packing Co. (Inc.),
6506 State Road Tacony
(Piston Rod; Valve Rod,
&c.; Metallic Steam) ..C
Glanding Co., James (Gum)
X
Houghton & Co., E. F., 240
W. Somerset (Leather;
Hydraulic L e a t h e r;
Steam) ....B
Mulconroy Co. (Inc.) 1213
Market (Rubber Steam).A
Sayen & Schultz, 13th &
Commerce (Metal Wedge;
Oxidized White Sheet;
Gum; Steam) C
Smith & Co., Jas. (Inc.), 421
Race (Steam; Locomotive;
Hydraulic) ....AA
Underwood & Co., H. B.,
1025 Hamilton (Cylinder;
Steam) ....B
United States Metallic Pack-
ing Co., 427 N. 13th (Me-
tallic Steam) ....B
Walker & Sons, Thos., 4619
Tacony (Metallic; Steam)
C
Williamson & Cassedy, 526
Market (Steam) ....A
PA.—Pittsburg
Chaplin-Fulton Mfg. Co., 30
Penn Av. (Steam) ....A
Flocker & Co. (Ltd.), Jno.,
618 Liberty (Steam) ..B
Frick & Lindsay Co., 109
Wood (Steam) C
Hartley-Rose Belting Co.,
634 Smithfield (Steam) .A
Larkin Metallic Packing Co.,
Imperial Power Bldg.
(Metallic) ....F
McClintock & Irvine, Neville
& P. R. R. (Steam Hemp;
Jute) ....B
Pennsylvania Electric &
Railway Supply Co., 3d
& Penn Av. (Self-Lubri-
cating Metallic) ......D
Pittsburg Mfg. Co., Imperial
Power Bldg. (Metallic
Steam) ....A
Pittsburg Rubber & Leather
Co., 10 Wood (Steam).AA
Pittsburg Supply Co., 226
1st Av. (Steam) ....A
Turner, C. A., 16 Market
(Steam) ....B
PA.—Wilkesbarre
Holmes Metallic Packing
Co. (Piston Rod) .....F
S. C.—Charleston
Charleston Metallic Packing
Co. (Semi-Bronze; Steam)
C
TENN.—Memphis
Livermore Fdy. & Machine
Co. (Hemp) ....A
WIS.—Milwaukee
Delaney Oil & Lubricant Co.,
45 3d (Metallic) X
Western Raw Hide & Belt-
ing Co. (Rawhide) ....D

PADDING

MASS.—Boston
Boston Regalia Co., 7 Tem-
ple Pl. (Military) ....F
MASS.—Canton
Knitted Mattress Co. (Up-
holstery; Table) C
New York City
Sperry & Beale Co., 39 Un-
ion Sq. (Floor) ....B

PADDLES

MAINE—Orono
Taylor & Co., W. C. (Canoe)
E
MASS.—Boston
Hinckley Bros. & Co. (Boat)
B
Shaw & Co., T. J. (Boat)
E
Sheldon & Co., O. (Boat).D

PADDLES (Con.)

N. Y.—Canton
Rushton, J. H. (Boat) ..F
New York City
De Grauw, Aymar & Co.
(Boat) ....AA
Estes & Sons, E. B., 45
John (Boat) ....AA
New York Boat Oar Co.
(Boat) ....A
Smith, John T. (Boat)...E
OHIO—West Lafayette
West Lafayette Mfg. Co.
(Paint) ....E
WIS.—Menasha
Menasha Wood Split Pulley
Co. (Beater) ....D

PADLOCKS

See Locks

PADS

CONN.—Bethel
Shepard & Son, Geo. A.
(Hat) ....F
CONN.—Hartford
Jewell Pad Co. (Collar;
Medicated; R a w h i d e)
AAA
CONN.—New Haven
Cowles & Co., C. (Inc.)
(Step) ....A
National Waste Product Co.
(Leather; Rubber Horse-
shoe) ....G
CONN.—Plantsville
Atwater Mfg. Co. (Step).A
Blakeslee Forging Co. (Step)
B
Smith & Co., H. D......A
ILL.—Chicago
Eureka Blotter Bath Co.
(Copying Cloth) ......E
Kiper & Son, S. (Coach Hard
Rubber) ....AA
Ortmayer & Son, A. (Har-
ness) ....AA
Thacker Magnetic Shield Co.
(Magnetic) ....B
ILL.—Quincy
Schott Saddlery Co., J. B.
(Coach) ....AAA
IND.—Kokomo
Ulrich Mfg. Co. (Coach)..E
IND.—South Bend
Studebaker Bros. Mfg. Co.
(Coach) ....AAAA
IOWA—Dubuque
Dubuque Harness & Saddlery
Co. (Coach; Harness;
Sweat; Team) X
IOWA—Waterloo
Powers Mfg. Co. (Sweat).E
KY.—Louisville
Harbison & Gathright (Har-
ness) ....AA
MD.—Baltimore
American Coat Pad Co.
(Coat) ....E
Marcus & Bro., M. H.
(Stair) X
MASS.—Boston
Cutter-Tower Co. (Writing;
Desk; Blotting) ......B
Neverslip Horseshoe Co.
(Horseshoe) ....D
Union Carpet Lining Co..AA
Webster Co., F. S. (Stamp)
AA
MASS.—Holyoke
American Pad & Paper Co.
(Writing; Desk; Blotting)
A
MASS.—Springfield
Smith Mfg. Co., R. H.
(Stamp) C
MICH.—Buchanan
Zinc Collar Pad Co. (Collar;
Medicated; Sole Leather;
Collar, Zinc) ....D
MICH.—Three Rivers
Initial Toe Pad Co. (Coach
Hard Rubber) ....D
MINN.—St. Paul
Hardenbergh & Co., P. R. L.
(Harness) ....A
MINN.—Winona
Minnesota Harness Factory
(Collar) C

PADS (*Con.*)

MO.—St. Louis
Homann Saddlery Co., Wm. (Harness) ....B
N. H.—Concord
Hill & Co., Jas. R. (Inc.) (Harness; Sweat) .....D
N. J.—Newark
Peters Harness & Saddlery Co. (Bridge Collar; Coach; Collar; Felt; Gig; Harness; Horseshoe; Perforated; Rawhide; Sole Leather; Sweat; Sweat Hair; Team) C
Pomeroy Co., J. (Stamp)..F
Rubber & Celluloid Harness Trimming Co. (Coach).AA
Sargeant Mfg. Co. (Coach) A
N. Y.—Auburn
Clapp Mfg. Co., E. D. (Step) B
N. Y.—Buffalo
Pratt & Letchworth Co. (Step) ....AAA
N. Y.—Castleton
Fort Orange Paper Co. (Writing) X
N. Y.—East Syracuse
Benedict Mfg. Co., M. S. (Silver Ink) ....AA
New York City
Boorum & Pease Co. (Writing; Desk; Blotting).AAA
Excelsior Quilting Co., Laight & Varick (Table) A
Faber, Eberhard (Hand Ink) AAA
Ferris Bros. Co., 341 B'way (Dress) ....B
Force & Co., Wm. A. (Stamp) ....B
Goodyear's India Rubber Glove Mfg. Co. (Teething) AA AA
Hodgman Ruber Company (Teething) ....AAAA
Marcus & Bro., M. H. (Stair) ....A
Massasoit Mfg. Co. (Stair) AA
New York Blank Book Co. (Writing) ....AAAA
New York Stencil Works (Stamp) X
Sperry & Beale Co. (Stair) B
Stafford Co. (Stamp) ...F
Tingue Brown & Co. (Felt) D
Weatjen, Jno. G. (Hat)..E
N. Y.—Syracuse
Frazer & Jones Co. (Coach) AA
OHIO—Akron
Enterprise Mfg. Co. (Sweat; Sweat Cork) ....A
Goodrich Co., B. F. (Truss) AAAA
OHIO—Canton
Gilliam Mfg. Co. (Coach; Harness; Team) ....A
OHIO—Cincinnati
Columbia Mfg. & Supply Co. (Coach) X
Globe-Wernicke Co. (Desk Blotting) ....AAAA
Monarch Carriage Goods Co. (Step) ....B
Perkins-Campbell Co. (Collar) ....AA
OHIO—Cleveland
Cleveland Hardware Co. (Step) ....AA
OHIO—Greenfield
McClain Mfg. Co., E. L. (Collar; Sweat) .AAAA
OHIO—New Berlin
Hoover, W. H. (Coach; Harness; Team) ....A
OHIO—Wooster
Standard Coach Pad Co. (Coach) C
PA.—Huntington
Blair Co., J. C. (Writing) AA
PA.—Philadelphia
Delaware Rubber Co., 631 Market (Rubber; Horse) X

PADS (*Con.*)

Mann Co., Wm. (Writing; Desk Blotting) ....AA
R. I.—Providence
Davol Rubber Co. (Teething) ....AA
R. I.—Woonsocket
Perforated Pad Co. (Perforated; Step Saddle) ....B
TENN.—Chattanooga
Southern Saddlery Company (Coach) ....A
VA.—Glen Allen
Cussons, May & Co. (Calendar; Desk; Blotting)..B
VA.—Richmond
Randolph Paper Box Co. (Wrapping Paper) .....A
VA.—Madison
Curtis, Dexter Co. (Collar) B

PADS & TABLETS

COLO.—Denver
Kistler Stationery Co., W. H. ....B
CONN.—Burnside
Taylor-Atkins Paper Co...C
CONN.—Waterbury
Waterbury Blank Book Co. C
GA—Atlanta
Montag Bros. C
ILL.—Aurora
Hodder & Co., J. H.....C
ILL.—Bloomington
Pantagraph Printing & Stationery Co. C
ILL.—Quincy
Stationers' Mfg. Co. C
IND.—Elkhart
Garden City Stationery Co. C
IND.—Fort Wayne
Fisher Bros. ....A
Burt-Terry-Wilson Co. C
IOWA—Sioux City
Perkins Bros. Co. ....B
MASS.—Boston
Adams, Cushing & Foster, 170 Devonshire ......B
Perry & Co., Chas. E., 183 Congress C
MASS.—Holyoke
Judd Paper Co. C
Powers Paper Co. ....AA
U. S. Env. Co. (Holyoke Env. Co. Div.) ..AAAA
White & Wyckoff Mfg. Co. B
MASS.—Pittsfield
Eaton-Hurlbut Paper Co...A
MASS.—Westfield
Crane Bros. ....AAA
MASS.—Worcester
Whitney Mfg. Co. C
MICH.—Benton Harbor
Hopper Mfg. Co. ....A
MINN.—Minneapolis
McClellan Paper Co. C
Leslie Paper Co., The John B
MO.—St. Louis
Barnard & Co., G. D....AA
N. Y.—Brooklyn
Acme Stationery & Paper Co., N. 9th & Wythe Av. B
Bainbridge's Sons, Chas. T., 12 Cumberland ....A
New York City
Acme Stationery & Paper Co., 302 B'way ......B
American Pad & Paper Co., 320 B'way ....B
Boorum & Pease Co., 101 Duane ....AA
Hake Mfg. Co., Ph., 132-134 Essex ....B
Hurd & Co., Geo. B., 425 Broome ....AA
N. Y. Blank Book Co., 7 Laight ....AAAA
Vernon, S. E. & M., 69 Duane ....A
Whiting Paper Co., 150 Duane ....AAAA
N. Y.—Rochester
Myers, R. M. ....A

PADS & TABLETS

N. Y.—Watertown
Hopper-Morgan Co. ......B
OHIO—Columbus
Nitsche Paper Co. ....B
Ruggles-Gale Co. C
OHIO—Dayton
Reynolds & Reynolds Co...A
OHIO—Toledo
Blade Printing & Paper Co.
    B
OHIO—West Carrollton
Friend Paper & Tablet Co.,
    Geo. H. ....AAA
OREGON—Portland
Blake, McFall Co. ......B
Pacific Paper Co. ....B
PA.—Huntingdon
Blair Co., J. C...........A
PA.—Johnstown
Johnstown Tribune Pub. Co.
    B
PA.—Mt. Holly Springs
Mt. Holly Paper & Station-
    ery Co. ....A
PA.—Philadelphia
Stern & Co., Ed., 112-114
    N. 12th ....B
Sherman Supply Co. .....A
PA.—Pittsburg
Johnston & Co., W. G., 900
    Penn Av. ....AA
PA.—Reading
Earl, M. J. ....B
VA.—Richmond
Baughman Stationery Co...B
Bell Book & Stationery Co.
    A
Waddey Co., E. C
WASH.—Seattle
Lowman & Hanford Station-
    ery & Printing Co......B

PAILS

**See also Woodenware; Tin-
ware; Enamelled Ware, etc.**

CAL.—San Francisco
California Barrel Co. (Sy-
    rup; Candy; Grease;
    Olive; Pickle) ......AA
CONN.—Meriden
Manning, Bowman Company
    (Chamber; Milk; Milk
    Strainer) ....AA
GA.—Savannah
Pierpont Mfg. Co. (Candy)
    A
ILL.—Chicago
Creamery Package Mfg. Co.
    (Candy) ....AAAA
ILL.—Moline
Dimock, Gould & Co.
    (Paper) ....AA
ILL.—Rockford
Palmer Co., H. H. (Milk)
    D
IND.—Indianapolis
Indianapolis Sheet Metal
    Works (Combination Milk
    Strainer) ....D
MICH.—Detroit
Briscoe Mfg. Co. (Fire; Gal-
    vanized Iron) ....A
Buhl Stamping Co. (Fire;
    Galvanized Iron; Cham-
    ber; Enamelled) .....AA
Zenner Disinfectant Co.
    (Garbage) C
MICH.—Flint
Flint Cabinet Creamery Co.
    (Milk) ....E
MINN.—Minneapolis
Bonsfield Woodenware Co.
    (Candy; Jelly; Oyster;
    Water; Wood) ....A
MO.—St. Louis
Brecht Butchers' Supply Co.
    G. V. (Lard) ......AAA
St. Louis Stamping Co.
    (Butter; Chamber; Enam-
    elled; Covered; Milk;
    Slop; Water, Enamelled)
    AAAA
N. H.—Keene
Beaver Mills (Butter;
    Candy; Grease; Spice;
    Pine) ....A
N. H.—Sandown
Lovering, J. W. (Mortar;
    Army) C

PAILS (Con.)

N. J.—Haddonfield
Star Milk Cooler Co. (Milk)
    C
N. Y.—Albany
Hay & Co. (Lard; Dinner;
    Milk Strainer; Water;
    Tin) ....A
N. Y.—Brooklyn
Sweeney Mfg. Co., W. H.
    (Butter; Covered; Dinner)
    A
Vogel & Bros., Wm. (Fish;
    Grease; Oyster) ......AA
N. Y.—Buffalo
Shepard & Co., Sidney (Fire;
    Galvanized Iron; Lard;
    Dinner; Milk; Tin).AAAA
New York City
American Paper Pail & Box
    Co. (Paper) C
Central Stamping Co.
    (Valve; Galvanized; Milk)
    AA
Cordley & Hayes (Chamber;
    Fibre; Commode; Fibre;
    Ice Water; Indurated;
    Fibre; Paper; Slop; Wa-
    ter; Fibre) ....A
Crandell & Godley Co.
    (Wood) ....AA
Goodyear's India Rubber
    Glove Mfg. Co. (Rubber)
    AAAA
Gutter Percha & Rubber Co.
    (Rubber) ....AAAA
Lalance & Grosjean Mfg. Co.
    (Chamber; Enamelled;
    Garbage; Milk; Slop; Wa-
    ter; Enamelled) ..AAAA
Mace & Co., L. H. (Water;
    Wood) ....B
National Enameling &
    Stamping Co., 81 Fulton
    (Fire; Galvanized Iron)
    AAAA
Reilly Bros. (Painters')..D
Stoutenborough, H. (Cov-
    ered; Galvanized; Ice
    Water) ....D
N. Y.—Rochester
Rochester Stamping Co.
    (Chamber) ....AAA
N. Y.—Troy
Troy Stamping Works
    (Lard; Dinner; Water;
    Tin; Seaside; Shovels)
    AAAA
N. Y.—Utica
Miller & Son, Chas. (Slop;
    Milk) ....AA
OHIO—Cincinnati
Obermayer Co., S. (Foun-
    dry; Factory) ......AA
OHIO—Cleveland
Cleveland Wire Spring Co.
    (Steel) ....A
Osborn Mfg. Co. (Foundry;
    Factory; Galvanized)...B
OHIO—Dayton
Dayton Paper Novelty Co.
    (Oyster) ....A
OHIO—Middlefield
Ohio Pail Co. (Candy) ...D
OHIO—Salem
Clark Co., W. J. (Steel;
    Foundry) ....A
PA.—Allegheny
Star Enameling & Stamping
    Co. (Dinner) ....B
PA.—Philadelphia
Pfeiffer & Co., John .....A
R. I.—Providence
Hill Mfg. Co., Jas. (Cham-
    ber, Galvanized; Iron,
    Galvanized) ....B
VA.—Richmond
Richmond Cedar Works
    (Horse; Wood; Water;
    Wood; Cedar; Ice Cream;
    Lard; Spice; Wooden)
    AAAA
WIS.—Menasha
Menasha Woodenware Co.
    (Candy; Oyster; Tobacco)
    AA
WIS.—Racine
Johnson & Field Mfg. Co.
    (Milk) ....F

PAJAMAS
See also Clothing

PAJAMAS (Con.)

CAL.—San Francisco
Ulman, Seeligsohn & Brown
.... B
MAINE—Lewiston
Bates Street Shirt Co.....C
MD.—Baltimore
Heineman, Fred. ....D
Towles Mfg. Co., Wm. H..C
N. J.—Newark
Smith-Linnett Shirt Co.....C
N. Y.—Albany
Munson, S. L. ....A
N. Y.—Binghamton
McHenry Shirt Co. .....D
N. Y.—Lockport
Sillesky & Co., D. R......C
New York City
Keep Mfg. Co. ....A
Keep Shirt Co., H. V.....D
Newell, E. A. ....B
Millen & Co., E. C
Simon, Julius C
Steiner & Son ....A
N. Y.—Peekskill
Janowitz-Maxwell Co. ...D
N. Y.—Troy
United Shirt & Collar Co.
.... AAAA
PA.—Philadelphia
Needles & Co., L. ....D

PAINTS

CAL.—Los Angeles
Silica Aluminum Paint Co.
Wilcox Bldg. (Anti-Rust)
CAL.—San Francisco
Bass, Hueter Paint Co., 46
Ellis ....A
California Paint Co., 236
First ....A
Chemical Paint Co., 26 Mont-
gomery ....A
Fuller & Co., W. P., Pine
& Front ....AAAA
Nason & Co., R. A., 115
Front ....A
Pacific Oil & Lead Works,
155 Townsend ......AAAA
Pacific Rubber Paint Co.
(Rubber) ....AAAA
Paraffine Paint Co., 116
Battery ....B
COLO.—Denver
Hallack Paint, Oil & Glass
Co., 1741 Arapahoe .....A
Humphrey-Jones Mercantile
Co., 1621 Arapahoe C
James Mercantile & Mfg.
Co., B. L. ....B
CONN.—Bridgeport
Crockett Co., D. B., 24 P. O.
Arcade ....B
CONN.—Essex
Essex Paint Works ......A
CONN.—New Milford
Bridgeport Wood Finishing
Co. ....A
DEL.—Wilmington
Bradford Co., Jas. (Roofing)
.... B
Bryan, Jas. M. & W. R...C
D. C.—Washington
Grafton & Son, 714 9th, N.
W. ....D
GA.—Atlanta
Cooledge & Bro., F. J., 12
N. Forsyth ....A
Parian Paint Co. (Mixed).D
Tripod Paint Co., 37 N.
Pryor C
GA.—Augusta
Augusta Sienna & Ochre Co.
(Mineral) ....F
O'Connor & Schweers Paint
Co. ....D
ILL.—Aurora
Akron Mining, Milling &
Mfg. Co. (Fire Resisting;
Graphite; Roofing; Rust
Proof; Waterproof) ....B
ILL.—Bloomington
Globe Chemical Co. (Tree)
.... D
ILL.—Chicago
Adams & Elting Co., 155
Washington Boul. (Cold
Water; Enamel) ......B
Alston Mfg. Co., 177 Ran-
dolph (Asphalt; Brick;

PAINTS (Con.)
Car; Carriage; Copper;
Dipping; Dry; Enamel;
Family; Floor; Gold;
House; Iron; Iron Cast-
ing; Machinery; Metallic;
Mineral; Oxide; Paste;
Preservative; Priming;
Ready Mixed; Roofing;
Zinc) ....B
Bradley & Vrooman Co.,
2633 Dearborn ....B
Cabot, Samuel, 28 Dearborn
Av. (Fire Resisting; Trol-
ley Pole) ....A
Chicago Fire Proof Cov. Co.,
20 N. Canal (Fireproof).D
Chicago White Lead & Oil
Co., N. Green & Fulton
.... AA
Chicago Wood Finishing Co.,
259 Elston Av. ....A
Colt & Co., 33 Washn.....A
Copper Cliff Mining Co., 79
Dearborn (Graphite)..AA
Enterprise Paint Mfg. Co.,
211 S. Clinton C
Eureka Elastic Paint Co.,
154 Van Buren ....D
Fowler Elastic Enamel
Paint Co., 289 W. Lake.C
Freund Bros. Mfg. Co., S.
Canal ....B
Fuller & Fuller Co., 220
Randolph ....AA
Haines, E. H., 503 Ashland
Blk. ....D
Hanna & Andrus Mfg. Co.,
Weed & Hawthorne C
Heath & Milligan Mfg. Co.,
170 Randolph (Iron; Steel)
.... AAA
Henderson Varnish Co.,
Thos. D., 1088 N. Wood
.... D
Inland White Lead Co., 361
S. Clinton ....A
Johnson Magnetic Paint Co.,
232 Clinton C
Milran Paint & Varnish Co.,
N. 51st Av. (Fire Resist-
ing; Iron; Machinery)..D
Pitkin Co., Geo. W., Ful-
ton & Carpenter ....B
Rubber Paint Co., 154 W.
Van Buren (Roofing)..AA
Senour Mfg. Co., 2516
Quarry ....B
Thurston & Co., F. W., 29
River ....A
Vilas Bros., 227 5th Av...B
Wadsworth-Howland Co.,
Indiana Av. & 13th (Coat-
ings & Preserving for Iron
& Steel Graphite & Roof-
ing) ....A
Watson Co., Geo. E., 108
Lake ....B
Williams, T. D., 155 La
Salle ....D
ILL.—East St. Louis
Illinois Mineral Milling Co.
.... C
IND.—Indianapolis
Burdsall & Co., 102 S. Mer-
idian ....AA
Indiana Paint & Color Co.,
240 Mass. Av. ....D
Lily Enamel & Paint Co.,
Rose & Norwood ......E
IOWA—Davenport
Stearns Paint Mfg. Co.....B
IOWA—Ft. Dodge
Iowa Paint Mfg. Co. (Dip-
ping; Dry; Floor; House
Mineral; Paste; Priming;
Ready Mixed Roof; Zinc)
.... C
IOWA—Pella
Nimwegen & Son, H.....D
KY.—Louisville
Bridges-Strassel Co., 1204
8th C
Louisville Lead & Color
Works, 15th & Lytle..AA
LA.—New Orleans
American Paint Works, 2215
S. Water ....B
Barrett Mfg. Co., Hennen
Bldg. (Acid Proof; As-
bestos; Asphalt; Fire Re-
sisting; Casting & Pre-

PAINTS (Con.)

serving for Iron & Steel; Insulating; Roofing; Rust-Proof; Waterproof) AAAA
Kracke & Flanders, 630 Gravier C
McWilliams (Ltd.), R., 342 Camp C

MAINE—Portland
Burgess, Fores & Co. ....A

MD.—Baltimore
Baltimore Copper Paint Co., 508 E. Hughes ....B
Baltimore Dry Paint Works, Ostend & Stockholm...E
Davis Paint Co., H. B., 215 Smiths W. K..........A
Dunpel & Co., Wm. I., Ostend & Stockholm .....D
Enamel Black Works, Carroll ....B
Foy & Co., E. L., 16 W. Camden (Anti-Rust; Asphalt; Asphaltum; Brick; Bridge; Car; Fireproof; House; Iron; Paste; Railroad; Roof) ....E
Hanline Bros., 23 S. Howard ....B
Hirchberg, Hollender & Co., 25 W. Pratt ....A
Kaufman & Co., E. L., Lafayette & Liberty....D
Litharge Paint Co., 306 N. Holliday ....E
Poppelein, G. & N., 220 North (Machinery) .....B

MASS.—Boston
Briggs & Co., John, 14 Washn. (Aluminum; Asphaltum; Bridge; Car; Carriage; Enamel; Family; Floor; Graphite; House; Iron; Machinery; Mineral; Paste; Priming; Railroad; Ready Mixed; Roofing; Zinc) C
Chadwick-Boston Lead Co., 162 Congress ....AAA
Hoffman Co., J. W., 438 Atlantic Av. ....D
Hot Iron Paint Co. (for Hot Surfaces) ....E
Wiley & Co., L. H., 92 Sudbury C
Prince Paint Co., Jas. H., 5 Lancaster C
Seaver & Co., 120 Milk..D
Speares' Sons, Alden, 369 Atlantic Av. (Cold Water) ....A
Stickney & Co., J. W., 79 Milk (Asphalt; Machinery; Smokestack) .....B
Wheeler, A., 52 High (Gold) ....D

MASS.—Dighton
Anchor Color Works ......A

MASS.—Gloucester
Tarr, Jas. H. (Copper)...D
Tarr & Wonson (Copper; Marine) ....A

MASS.—New Bedford
Kirby, Jr., & Co., Geo....B

MASS.—Salem
Philbrick, L. B. C

MASS.—Springfield
Hampden Paint & Chemical Co. ....B

MASS.—Watertown
Waterproof Paint Co. (Waterproof) ....D

MASS.—Wellesley
Woods Sons' Co., Hy......A

MICH.—Detroit
Acme Lead & Color Co., St. Aubin Av. & M. C. R. R. (Coating & Preserving for Iron & Steel; Graphite; Insulating; Iron Oxide; Roofing; Steam Proof & Water Proof) ......AAA
Boydell Bros. White Lead & Color Co., 18 E. Congress (Brick; Bridge; Car; Carriage; Copper; Dipping; Dry; Enamel; Graphite; House Iron; Machinery; Metallic; Ready Mixed; Roof; Rust-proof) ....AA
Buckeye Paint & Varnish Co., 715 Gratiot ....D
Continental Paint & Varnish

PAINTS (Con.)

Co., Clay & St. Aubin Avs. ....D
Detroit Graphite Co., 10 12th (Coating & Preserving for Iron & Steel; Graphite; Rust-proof)...C
Detroit-Ideal Paint Co., 105 Canfield Av., W......D
Detroit White Lead Works, 532 Milwaukee ....AA
Jarratt Paint & Enamel Co., 92 Griswold ....E
Peninsula Paint & Varnish Co., Aubin Av. & M. C. R. R. (Mixed) ....A

MICH.—Flint
Michigan Paint Co. (Coating & Preserving for Iron & Steel; Graphite) ....D

MINN.—Minneapolis
Atlas Paint Mfg. Co., 515 1st Av. C
Eberson & Co., A. A., 901 N. 2d ....D
Minn. Linseed Oil Paint Co., 240 10th Av. ....A
Northern Paint Co. (Floor; Graphite; Ready Mixed) ....B

MINN.—St. Paul
Blood & Co., T. L., 413 Wacouta ....A

MO.—St. Louis
Becke-Moore Paint Co....B
Flatan Mfg. Co., 706 Chestnut ....A
Gilson Asphaltum Co. (Asphalt) ....A
Hammar Paint Co., F., 1222 Spruce ....A
Kent & Purdy Paint Co., 701 N. 2d C
Mepham & Krausse Mfg. Co., Levee & Sidney ...A
Mound City Paint & Color Co., 811 N. 2d..........A
Ozark Zinc Oxide Co., 308 N. 6th ....B
Platt Thornburgh Paint Co., 620 Franklin Av. .....AA
Reardon Glue Co. (Cold Water) ....B
Thomas Mfg. Co., 215 S. Main (Roofing) ....B
Vane-Calvert Paint Co., 823 Locust ....B
Wieder Paint Co., 1601 N. B'way ....B

NEBR.—Lincoln
Lincoln Paint Co. ....A

N. J.—Boonton
Colonial Works ....D

N. J.—Jersey City
Dixon Crucible Co., Jos., 169 Wayne (Bridge; Car; Coating & Preserving for Iron & Steel; Graphite; Iron; Machry.; Paste; Priming; Ready Mixed; Railroad; Roof; Smokestack) ....AAAA
New Jersey Paint Works, Fremont & Wayne ....A
Wookey Paint & Color Co., 500 Grand (Roofing)....A

N. J.—Newark
Bigelow Varnish Co., 356 Mulberry (Bridge; Iron) ....B
Cawley, Clark & Co., 278 Passaic ....A
Johns Paint Mfg. Co., H. W., Chester Av. (Asbestos; Fire Resisting; Casting & Preserving for Iron & Steel; Iron Oxide Machinery; Roofing; Smokestack; Trolley Pole)..AA
Rice. S. E. M. 554 Broad (Flat White Enameled).A
Wheeler & Mitchell, 317 N. J. R. R. Av. (Bridge; Iron; Roofing) ....D

N. J.—Paterson
Norwood & Berdan ......D

N. Y.—Brooklyn
Darby-McQuade Paint Co., 416 Marcy Av. ....D
Holzapfels Composition Co. 175 Beard ....B
Ingersoll, O. W., 243 Plymouth (Anti-Rust; Brick;

PAINTS (Con.)

Car; Carriage; Dipping; Family; Machry.; Metallic; P r i m i n g; Ready Mixed; Roof) ....B

Johnson, H. M., 82 Washn. (Cold Water) ....A

Johnston, ~. M., 69 Washington ....A

King Paint Mfg. Co., 23 Durham Pl. (Bridge; Carriage; Dry; House; Machinery; Priming; Ready Mixed; Railroad) .....B

Masury & Son, Jno. W., 50 Jay ....AAAA

Moore & Co., Benj., 262 Water ....A

Phillips & Ferguson, 76 9th B

Rahtjens American Composition Co., 69 Van Dyke (Marine) ....B

N. Y.—Buffalo

Buffalo Enamel & Stain Co., Ellicott Sq. ....D

Buffalo Oil Paint & Varnish Co., 1317 Elk ....AA

Deuther & Beck, 50 Niagara B

McDougall White Lead Co., 1317 Elk ....AA

McLennan Paint Co., 205 Rand, (Brick; Carriage; Coating & Preserving for Iron & Steel; Dipping; Dry; Enamel; Family; Fireproof; Floor; Graphite; House; Iron; Iron Coating; Iron Oxide; Machinery; Metallic; Miners'; Oxide; Paste; Priming; Railroad; Ready Mixed; Roofing; Rust Proof) ....B

N. Y.—Clinton

Clinton Metallic Paint Co. (Coating; Preserving for Iron; Steel; Metallic; Rust Proof) C

N. Y.—Ellenville

Kimble & Hombeck Co....D

N. Y.—Elmira

Elmira Oxide Paint Co. (Iron) ....D

Elmira Paint Wks. ....D

N. Y.—Fishkill on Hudson

Hammond, Benj. ....D

N. Y.—Long Island City

L. I. Paint & Color Wks. AAAA

Queens Co. Varnish Wks. (Marine) ....E

N. Y.—New Brighton

Muralo Co. (Cold Water).A

N. Y.—Newburgh

Fabrikoid Co. (Marine; Metallic; Artificial Leather) A

New York City

Am. Lucol Co., 44 B'way.A

Anderton, Robt. J., 107 4th Av. ....D

Austen & Co., L. H., 2 South ....D

Billings, King & Co., 438 Pearl (Coating; Preserving for Iron; Steel; Roofing) ....A

Binney & Smith Co., 81 Fulton ....AAA

Carbolineum Co., 426 Gwich. (Bridge; Pres.; Railroads; Roofing) ....B

Childs & Co., Chas. M., 225 Pearl ....A

Chilton Paint Co., 69 Cortlandt (Roofing) ....A

Connors Paint Mfg. Co., Wm. (Bridges; Car; Carriages; Roofing).......A

Coulston & Co., J. W., 81 West ....A

De Ronde Co., F. S., 46 Cliff (Fire Resisting; Coating; Preserving for Iron; Steel; Insulating; Roofing; Waterproof)..C

Devoe, F. W. & C. T. Raynolds Co., 103 Fulton

PAINTS (Con.)

man (Dry) ....A

Dunham, Thos. C., 68 Murray ....D

Feigel & Bro., M., 149 Mercer (Smoke Stack).A

Fox & Co., M. Ewing, E. 136th & Ridge Av. (Cold Water) ....D

Freed, David, 458 Pearl..D

Gerstendorfer Bros., 231 E. 42d (Enamel; Gold)....A

Graves & Co., N. Z., 296 Pearl ....AAA

Grote, Geo. W., 605 W. 39th ....D

Hacenbalg & Co., F., 714 E. 166th ....D

Heller & Merz Co., 22 Cliff A

Hoyt, Arthur, 90 W. B'way (Cold Water) ....B

Illsley, Doubleday & Co., 229 Front C

Kohnstamm & Co., H., 87 Park Pl. ....AA

Leggett & Bro., 301 Pearl.B

Longman & Martinez, 207 Pearl (Copper; Roofing) AAA

Messner Paint & Color Wks., 383 Pearl ....D

National Lead Co., 100 William ....AAAA

Newcomb, Jas. G., 26 B'way (Aluminum; Anti-Rust; Asphalt; Asphaltum; Brick; Bridge; Car; Carriage; Copper; Dipping; Enamel; Fireproof; Floor; Graphite; House; Iron Casting; Mchry; Metallic; Preservative; Priming; Railroad; Ready Mixed; Roof; Rust Proof) AAAA

Pierce Co., F. O., 170 Fulton ....A

Piper, Geo. W., 54 South..D

Prince Mfg. Co., 71 Maiden Lane (Coating; Preserving for Iron; Steel; Roofing) ....B

Schlegel, Oscar, 182 Grand D

Seabord Paint Co., 11 B'way ....D

Smith & Co., Edw., 45 B'way (Coating; Preserving for Iron; Steel; Smoke Stack) ....A

Standard Graphite Co., 11 B'way (Graphite; Roofing) ....E

Standard Paint Co., 100 William (Coating; Preserving for Iron; Steel; Insulating; Roofing)....A

Stewart Mfg. Co., W. H., 81 Fulton ....B

Tieman & Co., D. F., 44 Duane ....AAA

Toch Bros., 85 Pearl (Coating; Preserving for Iron; Steel; Insulating; Rust Proof; Smoke Stack; Trolley Pole) ....F

Water Paint Co. of America, 100 William (Water)..A

Williams, Sam. J., 11 B'way ....A

Zibell Damp Resisting Paint Co., 290 Front C

N. Y.—Ogdensburg

Rossie Iron Ore Paint Co. (Metallic) ....D

N. Y.—Poughkeepsie

N. Y. Marine Paint Co. (Marine) ....A

N. Y.—Randolph

Elko Paint Co. (Enamel; Oxide; Roofing) ......D

N. Y.—Rochester

Clark Paint Oil & Hdw. Co., 131 State ....A

N. Y.—Schenectady

Eigleman & Bellinger, 212 S. Centre C

N. Y.—Troy

Troy Cold Water Kalsomine Co., 22 Paine (Cold Water) ....A

N. C.—High Point
Alexander, H. ....D
N. C.—Wilmington
Sprittine Chemical Co.
 (Roofing) ....D
OHIO—Akron
Akron Varnish Co. (As-
 phaltum) ....A
OHIO—Barberton
Carara Paint Co. ....A
OHIO—Canton
Goheen Mfg. Co. (Car; Fire-
 proof; Graphite; Iron;
 Machy.; Metallic; Miner-
 al; Prreservative; Rail-
 road; Ready Mixed; Roof-
 ing; Smoke Stack; Trol-
 ley Pole; Waterproof)..B
OHIO—Cincinnati
Allen Anti-Rust Mfg. Co.,
 413 Vine (Rust Proof)..D
Barron, Boyle & Co., 428
 Main ....B
Boice & Co., Louis H., 2311
 Gilbert Av. C
Eagle White Lead Co., 1030
 B'way (Paint) ....AAAA
Iridian Paint Co., 2d &
 Main ....D
Kolbe Co., John, 229 W.
 5th ....B
Long & Co., Edwin, 845
 Clinton ....D
Moser & Co., Chas., 213
 Main ....AAA
Ohio Oil & Varnish Co., 230
 E. Pearl ....A
Peale & Bro., W. C., 904
 Central Av. ....A
Richmond Bros., 177 E.
 6th ....D
Washburn Co., Ira D., 1010
 Central Av. C
Western Paint Co., 117 E.
 6th ....D
OHIO—Cleveland
Atlantic Paint Wks., Besse-
 mer Av. & P. R. R.
 (Bridge; Car; Carriage;
 Graphite; Machy.; Metal-
 lic; Oxide; Paste; Ready
 Mixed; Zinc) ....A
Atlantic Refining Co., Gar-
 field Bldg. (Fire Resist-
 ing; Elastic Carbon)...A
Billings-Chapin Co., 37 Case
 Av. (Coating; Preserving
 for Iron; Steel; Roofing)
 ....A
Cleveland Color Co., Mason
 & Belden ....B
Cleveland Iron Ore Paint Co.
 (Iron Ore) ....A
Colonial Paint & Varnish Co.
 Marquette & St. Clair..B
Forest City Paint & Varnish
 Co., Hamilton & Kirkland
 (Asphalt; Barrel; Graph-
 ite; Iron; Oxide; Machy.;
 Roofing; Rust Proof;
 Smoke Stack; Steam
 Proof; Trolley Pole;
 Waterproof) ....B
Garfield Paint Co., Rose
 Bldg. ....D
Garry Iron & Steel Co., Coe
 & Lake (Iron) ....A
Glenmore Color Wks. ....A
Hascall Wise Co., Garfield
 Bldg. (Roofing) ....A
Iron Clad Paint Co., 535
 Seneca (Coating; Preserv-
 ing for Iron; Steel; Gra-
 phite; Roofing Smoke
 Stack; Rust Proof).....C
McNairy & Co., A. B., 160
 Scranton (Brick; Bridge;
 Car; Carriage; Dipping;
 Enamel; Family; Floor;
 Graphite; House; Iron;
 Iron Casting; Machy.; Me-
 tallic; Mineral; Paste;
 Priming; Railroad; Ready
 Mixed; Proof) ....B
Natl. Paint & Varnish Co.,
 37 St. Clair C
Patterson-Sargeant Co., Wa-
 son & Hamilton (Fire Re-
 sisting; Coating; Preserv-
 ing for Iron; Steel; Roof-
 ing) ....
Peerless Paint & Varnish

Co. ....A
Sherwin Williams Co., 100
 Canal ....AAA
Ullmann & Philpott Mfg.
 Co., 95 Merwin ......B
OHIO—Columbus
Columbus Paint Mfg. Co.,
 272 Kimball ....D
Hanna Paint Mfg. Co. 111
 E. Long (Roofing).....D
Orr, Dean & Barry Co.....D
OHIO—Dayton
Irvin Paint Glass Co., 124
 E. 3d ....D
Jewell & Vinson, 436 E. 5th
 ....D
Lowe Bros. Co., 452 E. 3d
 ....AA
OHIO—Findlay
Ohio Paint & Varnish Co.
 (Coating; Preserving for
 Iron; Steel; Roofing;
 Smoke Stack) ....D
OHIO—Lockland
Carey Mfg. Co., Ph. (As-
 bestos) ....A
OHIO—Marietta
Marietta Paint & Color Co.
C
OHIO—Piqua
Piqua Paint & Putty Co.
 (Brick; Bridge; Car; Car-
 riage; Dipping; Enamel;
 Floor; Graphite; House;
 Iron Casting; Machy.;
 Paste; Priming; Railroad;
 Ready Mixed; Roof)...D
OHIO—Toledo
Buckeye Paint & Varnish
 Co., 719 So. 15th (Coating;
 Preserving; Iron; Steel;
 Graphite; Roofing; Steam
 Proof; Rust Proof).....B
Dolphin Color Wks., 30
 Sunnet C
Neel Glass & Paint Co., Hy.
 418 Monroe ....B
OHIO—Warren
Warren Paint Co. ....B
PA.—Alburtis
Bass Paint Co. (Metallic).C
PA.—Allegheny
Diamond Paint & Oil Co.,
 273 Spring Garden Av...D
Eagle Paint & Varnish Wks.
 225 Grand Av. ....B
Gerdes & Bro., F. W.,
 Grand & South Av.....A
Natl. Lead & Oil Co., 2
 Natl. Bank Bldg. (Quick
 Drying) ....AAAA
Nevin Co. T. H., Preble &
 Island Avs. ....A
Wisconsin Graphite Co.
 Grand Av. & Boquet
 (Coating; Preserving; for
 Iron; Steel; Graphite;
 Iron Oxide; Machy.; Roof-
 ing; Rust Proof; Smoke
 Stack; Trolley Pole)....A
PA.—Allentown
Allentown Mfg. Co., Law
 & Maple (Oil) ....B
Princess Metallic Paint Co.
 (Dry Metallic; Mineral).A
PA.—Bethlehem
Erwin & Sons., Hy. (Metal-
 lic) ....B
Semple, Frank G. (Mineral)
 ....D
PA.—Easton
Wagener & Co., J. O.
 (Mineral) ....A
Williams & Co., C. K.
 (Dry; Earth) ....A
PA.—Franklin
Riesenman Mfg. Co. ......B
PA.—Jamestown
Jamestown Paint & Varnish
 Co. (House) ....B
PA.—Johnstown
Cambria Paint & Color Wks.
 (Brick; Dry; Graphite;
 Machy.; Oxide; Ready
 Mixed; Roofing; Rust
 Proof) ....B
PA.—Lancaster
Schroeder. Smith &
 Schroeder ....D
PA.—Philadelphia
Bennett-Lindeman Co., 1400
 Fkd. Av. ....B

PAINTS (Con.)

Binswanger & Co., B., 115 N. 4th (Coating; Preserving for Iron; Steel; Iron Oxide; Machy.; Porcelain Enamel; Smoke Stack; Rust Proof) ....A

Bowens Sons, S., N. 4th & Venango (Coating; Preserving for Iron; Steel; Roofing) ....A

Butterworth & Co., C. H., 125 Mkt. ....B

Evans & Son, Wm., 56 N. Front ....B

Felton, Sibley & Co., 140 N. 4th (Coating; Preserving for Iron; Steel; Roofing) ....AA

French & Co., Sam. H., 4th & Callowhill (Aluminum; Gold; Barrel; Brick; Copper; Coating; Preserving for Iron; Steel; Graphite; Iron Oxide; Machy.; Roofing; Rust Proof; Smoke Stack) ....AAA

Harrison Bros. & Co., 35th & Grays Ferry Rd.AAAA

Howell & Co., C. H., 212 Race (Roofing ....A

Lewis & Bro., Jno. T., 231 So. Front (Zinc) ..AAAA

Lucas & Co., John, 322 Race (Cold Water; Copper; Fire Resisting; Coating; Preserving for Iron; Steel; Graphite; Iron Oxide; Roofing; Rust Proof).... AAA

Maxwell & Co., John, 1420 S. Front ....D

Nice, Eugene, 272 S. 2d ..B

Phila. Graphite Co., Stephen Girard Bldg. (Graphite) ....B

Phoenix Paint & Varnish Co., 124 Mkt. ....D

Phoenix Plumbago Mining Co. (Graphite) ....A

Pittsburg Plate Glass Co., Frick Bldg. ......AAAA

Rambo, Theo. G., 1134 Beach ....D

Rinaldo Bros., 600 Arch (Anti-Rust; Enamel; Bath Tube; Outside Porcelain; Radiator; Graphite; Iron; Mineral; Priming; Roof) E

Sauter & Co., F. W., 909 N. 9th ....E

Schrack & Co., C., 152 N. 4th ....D

Shoemaker & Co., Robt., 201 N. 4th ....A

Thompson Wood Finishing Co., 115 N. 4th........C

Waterall & Co., Wm., 200 N. 4th (Coating; Preserving for Iron; Steel; Machy.; Roofing) .....A

Wetherill & Co., G. D., 114 N. Front (Iron) ......A

Wetherill & Co., S. P., Penn. Mutual Bldg. (Iron; Metallic; Mineral; Oxide) ....A

Wilbur Co., Job, E. Tioga & Carbon (Dry) ....A

Wocker & Son, H. M., 1218 W. College Av. (Black; Carriage; Floor; House; Marine; Mixing; Shellac) C

Woodhouse, S. F., Trinity & Franklin Fkd. (House; Roofing) ....D

Varnall, H. E. & G. D., 1026 Race ....D

PA.—Pittsburg

Davis Lead Co., Park Bldg. A

Iron City Oil & Varnish Co., Inwood & Frankstown Av. A

Lawrence & Co., M. W., Water & Penn. Av. (Coating; Preserving for Iron; Steel; Graphite; Roofing) A

McClintock & Irvine Co.,

PAINTS (Con.)

Neville & P. R. R. (Coating; Preserving for Iron; Steel; Rust Proof)......B

Pittsburg Iron Paint Co. (Iron) ....B

Pittsburg Paint Supply Co., 713 Liberty Av. ......B

Specialty Paint Co., 3d Natl. Bank Bldg ......D

Suydam Co., M. B., 61st & Butler (Acid Proof; Asphalt; Fire Resisting; Coating; Preserving for Iron; Steel; Graphite; Insulating; Iron Oxide; Machy.; Roofing; Rust Proof; Smoke Stack; Trolley Pole; Waterproof)..B

U. S. Graphite Co. (Graphite) C

PA.—Pulaski

Reno Bros. (Mineral).....C

PA.—Reading

Reading Paint Mills (Car; Bridge; House; Roofing; Rust Proof) ....AA

Ruth & Co., B. F., 216 S. 8th ....AA

Wilhelm Co., A., 217 Poplar (Cold Water; Graphite; Iron Oxide; Roofing) A

PA.—Sharpsburg

Bender & Alldred.........B

PA.—Williamsport

National Paint Wks. (Iron; Bridge; Graphite; Machy.; Metallic; Mineral; Oxide; Paste; Railroad; Ready Mixed; Roofing; Rust Proof) ....B

U. S. Paint Co. (Asphalt; Asphaltum; Bridge; Car; Dipping; Dry; Family; Floor; Graphite; House; Iron; Iron Casting; Mach.; Metallic; Mineral; Oxide; Priming; Ready Mixed; Roofing; Zinc.)........F

R. I.—Providence

Johnson, Oliver & Co.. 3 Exch. ....AA

U. S. Gutta Percha Paint Co., 34 Matthewson (Waterproof; Ready Mixed).A

TENN.—Chattanooga

Chattanooga Paint Co. (Coating; Preserving for Iron; Steel; Metallic Roofing) ....D

TENN.—Memphis

Bartholomew Roofing Co., 412 2d C

Memphis Dry Color Co....D

True Tagg Paint Co., 457 Shelby ....B

TEXAS—Houston

Bute, James ....A

Randolph & Sons, N.......C

UTAH—Ogden

Ogden Paint, Oil & Glass Co. D

VT.—Bellows Falls

Casein Co. of America (Cold Water; Dry) ....A

VT.—Bennington

Adams & Co., Enos........D

Godfrey, S. L...........C

Lyons & Bros., S. C......C

VT.—Saxtons River

Edson Starks & Co. (Cold Water) C

VA.—Lynchburg

Natl. Paint & Manganese Co. ....D

VA.—Richmond

Armitage Mfg. Co., 3200 Williamsburgh Av.....B

Worthington Co., 1424 E. Main ....B

W. VA.—Huntington

Parsons Southern Agency Co. (Rubber) ....D

W. VA.—Wheeling

Wilson & Sons, W. A.....B

WIS.—Milwaukee

Carbolineum Wood Preserving Co. 128 Reed......D

O'Niel Oil & Paint Co...B

Patton Paint Co., 213 Lake A

PAINTS (Con.)
Ricketson Mineral Paint
Wks., 111 Mason......D

PALETTES

New York City
Friedrichs, E. H., 140
Sullivan (Artists)......A
Reilly Bros., (Artists)....D
Pa.—Harrisburg
Hickok Mfg. Co., W. O.
(Lettering) ....AA

PALLETS

IOWA—Keokuk
Scott Mfg. Co (Brick)....D
MICH.—Saginaw
Mershon & Co., W. B.
(Wood; Brick) ....A
OHIO—Cleveland
Avery Stamping Co. (Brick)
B
National Box Co. (Brick)..B
OHIO—New London
Arnold-Creager Co. (Brick)
B
OHIO—Niles
Ohio Galvanizing & Mfg. Co.
(Steel; Brick) ....A
Sheet Metal Mfg. Co.
(Steel) C

PALMS

CONN.—Torrington
Union Hardware Co.
(Sailors) ....AA
N. Y.—Brooklyn
Smith & Sons, James, 40
Franklin Av. (Sailors)..D
New York City
Russell, & Erwin Mfg. Co.
(Sailors) ....AAAA
Tiebout, W. & J. 118 Cham-
bers (Sailors) ....B

PANCREATIN

MICH.—Detroit
Parke, Davis & Co....AAAA
New York City
Fairchild Bros & Foster
(Inc.) ....AA
McKesson & Robbins.AAAA
PA.—Philadelphia
Pennsylvania Chemical W'ks
AAA

PANELS

See also Woodwork; Carriage

CONN.—New Haven
Dann Bros. & Co. (Car-
riage) ....B
ILL.— Chicago
Decorators Supply Co.....B
KY.—Covington
Ohio Scroll & Lumber Co.
(Carriage) ....B
MAINE—Foxcroft
Ranger & Ayers Mfg. Co.
(Veneer; Carriage; Sleigh)
D
MAINE—Newport
Cooper Bros. (Carriage)...E
MASS.—Worcester
Phenix Plate Co. (Photo-
raph) C
MICH.—Grand Rapids
Grand Rapids Veneer Wks.
(Veneer; Carriage) ....AA
N. Y.—Binghamton
Roberson & Son, A.......AA
New York City
Frost Veneer Seating Co. 208
Canal (Veneer) X
Sjoberg & Co., J. P. (Car).D
OHIO—Portsmouth
Portsmouth Veneer & Panel
Co ....A
PA.—Philadelphia
Brill Co., J. G. (Car).AAAA
WIS.—Algoma
Almapee Veneer & Seating
Co. (Veneer)...........A

PANS

See also Tinware; Enamel-
led Iron Ware; Holloware

CAL.—San Francisco

PANS (Con.)
Hendy Machine Wks., Josh.
38 Tremont (Amalgamat-
ing) ....AA
Krogh Mfg. Co., 9 Stevenson
(Amalgamating) C
Marshutz & Lantrell, Main
& Howard (Amalgamat-
ing) ....A
Howard (Amalgamating)A
Risdon Iron & Locomotive
Wks., Stewart & Folsom
(Vacuum) ....AAAA
Union Iron Wks., 222 Mar-
ket (Amalgamating; Cyan-
ide, &c) ....AAAA
COLO.—Denver
Mine & Smelter Supply Co.
(Amalgamating; Cyanide,
&c.) ....AAA
CONN.—Meriden
Manning, Bowman & Co.
(Baking; Bread; Sauce;
Copper) ....AA
CONN.—New Britain
New Britain Machine Co.
(Chips) ....A
CONN.—New Haven
Seamless Rubber Co. (Bed)
AA
DEL.—Marshallton
Marshallton Iron & Steel Co.
(Baking; Dripping; Roast-
ing) ....B
DEL.—Wilmington
Pusey & Jones Co. (Vacuum)
AAA
GA.—Savannah
Kehoe & Sons, Wm. (Va-
cuum; Sugar) ....A
Rourke & Sons., Jno. (Va-
cuum) ....A
ILL.—Batavia
Sperry & Co., D. K. (Va-
cuum) ....B
ILL.—Chicago
Allis-Chalmers Co., Home
Ins. Bldg. (Amalgamat-
ing; Dry; Gravel; Grind-
ing; Vacuum; Combina-
tion; Gold; Ore).....AAAA
Amer. Foundry & Machy. Co.
(Vacuum) ....AA
Goetz & Floding Mfg. Co.
(Brewers' Vacuum) ....A
Harris & Bro., Geo. P., 64
W. Lake (Vacuum).....B
Katzinger, Edw., 163 W.
Washn. (Baking) ....D
Laubenheimer Co., Geo. H.
(Brewers' Vacuum) ....A
Lyons Metallic Mfg. Co., 18
So. Ann (Lathe).......F
Stier Mfg. Co., Herman
(Brewers' Vacuum) ....D
Trenkhorst, Frank (Brewers'
Vacuum) ....F
Wolf Co., Fred, 138 Rees
(Vacuum) ....AAA
ILL.—Galesburg
Frost Mfg. Co. (Dry).....A
IND.—Anderson
Anderson Foundry & Mach.
Wks. (Dry) ....B
IND.—Brazil
Crawford & McCrimmon Co.
(Combination) ....A
IND.—Terre Haute
Columbian Enameling &
Stamping Co. (Frying)
AAA
IOWA—Burlington
Murray Iron Wks. Co. (Cool-
ing) ....A
IOWA—Des Moines
Eagle Iron Wks. (Dry)...A
IOWA—Ottumwa
Ottumwa Iron Wks. (Com-
bination) ....B
KANS.—Fort Scott
Fort Scott Foundry & Mach.
Co. (Vacuum) ....A
LA.—New Orleans
Haubtman & Loeb Co.
217 Gravier (Vacuum).AA
Murphy, Jno. H., 643 Maga-
zine (Vacuum).........AA
Payne & Joubert, 423 Caron-
delet (Vacuum) ....A
MASS.—Andover
Tyer Rubber Co. (Bed)..AA
MASS.—Boston
Badger & Sons Co., E. B.,
6 Pitts (Vacuum)......B

PANS (Con.)

Troughs; Charging; Drying; Medicine) ....A

OHIO—Steubenville

Means Foundry & Machine Co. (Dry) C

OHIO—Wellsville

Stevenson Co. (Dry; Dry Grinding) ....B

OHIO—Youngstown

Pollock Co., Wm. B. (Charging; Drying) ..AA

OHIO—Zanesville

Griffith & Wedge Co. (Amalgamating) ....B

PA.—Allegheny

Carlson's Sons, Thos. (Ore; Milling; Clay; Emery Grinding; Grinding)....A

PA.—Allentown

Allentown Foundry & Machine Co. (Vacuum) ....A

PA.—Clearfield

Clearfield Mach. Shops (Ltd) (Dry; also Wet; Grinding) X

PA.—Hazleton

Koenig, M. F. (Baking)..X

PA.—Lancaster

Martin Brick Mach. Mfg. Co., Henry (Dry).....B

PA.—Philadelphia

Borton & Tierney Co., Steph. Girard Bldg. (Grinding; Mgrs, Agts.) ....D

Hibbs, E. A. (Est. of) 213 Quarry (Drip; Gravel)..B

Morris, Henry G., Phila. Bourse (Vacuum) .....B

Morris, P. Hollingsworth, 1501 So. Front (Vac'm)..C AA

North Bros. Mfg. Co. (Cake) (Vacuum) ....AA

Oat & Sons, Jos. 232 Quarry (Vacuum) ....A

Paxson Co., J. W., 1021 N. Del. Av. (Dry Grind).AA

Pfeiffer & Son, Jno. Ltd. (Sheet Iron) ....A

Wood & Co., R. D. 400 Chestnut (Vacuum).AAAA

Whitall, Tatum & Co., Barclay ....AAAA

PA.—Pittsburg

Budke Mfg. Co. (Bread; Dripping; Roasting)....B

Lewis Foundry & Mach. Co., 1001 Bingham (Grinding) A

Phillips & McLaren, 24th & Smallman (Dry; also Wet; Grinding; Clay) ....B

Riter-Conly Co. (Galvanizing) ....AAA

Scaife & Sons Co., Wm. B. (Charging; Clay Mixing; Ore; Cook! Hot Air).AAA

United Engineering & Foundry Co., 54th & A. V. R. R. (Grinding) .....AAAA

PA.—So. Bethlehem

Bethlehem Foundry & Mach. Co. (Dry; Acid)........C

R. I.—Providence

Davol Rubber Co. (Bed).AA

Hill Mfg. Co., Jas. (Refrigerator) ....B

TENN.—Chattanooga

Chattanooga Roofing & Foundry Co. (Drip).....A

WIS.—Cudahy

Power & Mining Machy. Co. (Amalgamating; Chemical; Dry Evaporating; Gravel; Grinding) ..AAA

WIS.—Milwaukee

Allis-Chalmers Co. (Amalgamating) ....AAAA

PANTOGRAPHS

ILL.—Rockford

Air Brush Mfg. Co........X

MASS.—Boston

Amer. Steam Guage & Valve Mfg. Co. ....A

New York City

Keuffel & Esser Co.....AA

N. Y.—Seneca Falls

Westcott-Jewell Co.......D

PANTS

See Clothing: Men's

PAPER

For Wall Paper & Carbon Paper, see following Headings

CAL.—Antioch

Cal. Paper & Board Mills (Straw; Boards; Roofing Felt; Sheathing) ....A

CAL.—Floriston

Floriston Pulp & Paper Co. (Book; Manilla; Tissue) AA

CAL.—Los Angeles

Los Angeles Paper Mfg. Co. (Building; Roofing; Straw; Wrapping; Straw Boards) ....D

CAL.—Soquel

O'Neill Bros. & Callaghan (Manilla; Rag Wrapping) A

COLO.—Denver

Rocky Mountain Paper Co. (Super; News; Manilla; Wrapping) ....E

CONN.—Andover

Case Paper Co., The F. L. (Super; Album; Binders; Jacquard; Leather Board) B

CONN.—Bozrahville

Bingham & Co., W. A. (Tissue; Toilet) ....D

CONN.—Bridgeport

Tait & Sons Paper Co. (Box Boards) ....B

CONN.—Burnside

Case & Marshall (Boards; Rope Manilla) C

East Hartford Mfg. Co. (Bond; Linen) C

Taylor-Atkins Paper Co. (Bonds; Linen; Velum; Tablet) C

Walker, J. H. (Book; Envelope; Linen; Writing).A

CONN.—Chaplin

Wright, Case, Wright Paper Co. (Leather Board) ...D

CONN.—Comstock Bridge

Brown Bros. (Card; Middles; Coating) ....A

CONN.—Danbury

McArthur Bros. (Hardware; Manilla; Wrapping) ....E

CONN.—Glastonbury

Nahbuc Paper Co. (Heavy; Wrapping; Album; Button; Binders; Millboards D

Riverside Paper Co. (Binders; Trunk Boards).....E

CONN.—Hartford

Hartford Board Co. (Trunk; Album; Air Dried Straw Board) ....D

Hartford Paper Co. (Book; Chromo; Colored; Newspaper) ....A

CONN.—Hop River

International Hideite Co. (Leather Board) ....F

CONN.—Manchester

Case, Co., A. Williard (Imitation Press Boards; Decorated; Mat Boards; Cover Papers) ....B

Foulds Co., The Wm. (Button; Straw; B i n d e r s; Leather Board) ....D

Lydall & Foulds Paper Co. (Sheathing) ....B

Oakland Paper Co. (Envelope; Duplex) ....AAAA

CONN.—Montville

Robertson Co., The C. M. Hanging Duplex; Anti-Rust) ....A

CONN.—New Haven

New Haven Pulp & Board Co. (Manilla Boards; Card Middles) C

Parker & Son Co., Joseph (Blotting; Matrix)....AA

CONN.—New London

Robertson, Est. of Jno. (Bogus; Manilla; Bleached; Unbleached; Rope) X

CONN.—No. Westchester

Norton C. H. (Binders; Board) ....F

CONN.—Norwich

PAPER (Con.)

Hubbard Co., A. H. (Colored) ....A

Uncas Paper Co. (Box Board; Card Middles)...B

CONN.—Oneco

Case & Lincoln Paper Co. (Binders; Electric; Bobbin Head Boards)......X

CONN.—Poquonock

Hartford Paper Co. (Book; French Folio) ....A

CONN.—Rainbow

Hartford Paper Co. (Blotting; Manilla; Newspaper; Poster; Colored; Wrapping; Anti-Rust) ......A

Miller Paper Co., O. A. (Press;. Jacquard Card; Electric; Shield; Slate; Fender Boards) X

Vernon, Rich. R. (Tissue; Copy; H. R. R. Impression; Newspaper) .....B

CONN.—Seymour

Beach Paper Co. S. Y. (Colored; Seidlitz) C

CONN.—Shelton

United Box Board & Paper Co. (Manilla Boards) AAAA

CONN.—So. Glastonbury

Wausuc Mills Co. (Album; Binders; Straw Board) C

CONN.—So. Manchester

Brookside Paper Co. (Album; Binders; Straw Board) ....E

Case Bros. (Press; Insulating Board; Jaquared Card) B

Rogers Paper Mfg. Co. (Press Insulating; Jacquard; Insulating Boards) C

CONN.—Talcottville

Swett. B. K. (Leather; Binders; Board) ......A

CONN.—Unionville

Am. Writing Paper Co.(Coupon Bond; Blank Ledger) AAAA

Case Mfg. Co. (Colored; Hardware; Manilla; Pattern; Rope) ....B

CONN.—Versailles

Eastern Straw Board Co. Manilla Lined Folding Box Boards; Mill Wrappers)C

CONN.—Westport

Westport Paper Co. (Binders; Leather; Trunk Board) ....D

CONN.—Westville

Parker & Son Co., Joseph (Blotting) ....A

CONN.—Winsor Locks

Am. Writing Paper Co. (Boards; Manillas).AAAA

Anchor Mills Paper Co. (White; Colored; Manilla Tissue; Toilet; Pattern; White Shoe; French Folio; Stereotype; Yellow; White; Manilla R. R. Copy) ....A

Dexter & Sons. C. H. (Silver Tissue; Colored Tissue; Bristol; Covers Deckle Edge; Manifold; Typewriter) ....A

Whittelsey Frank H. (White & Colored Tissue; Manifold; R. R. Copying; Stereotype; Oiled Board) B

DEL.—Newark

Curtis & Bro. (Book Env.; Writing; Colored; Cover) A

DEL.—Wilmington

Jessup & Moore Paper Co (Book) ....AAAA

DEL.—Wooddale

Marshall & Mitchell (Manilla) ....D

DEL.—Yorklyn

Marshall Bros. (Manilla Wrapping; Roll; Filter; Flour Sack; Hanging; Newspaper) ....A

D. C.—Washington

Dist. of Columbia Paper Mfg. Co. (Blotting; Cover;

PAPER (Con.)

Matrix) ....D

GA.—Atlanta

Atlanta Paper Co. (Wrapping) ....A

GA.—Marietta

Marietta Paper Mills (Book; News; Manilla; Rag Wrapping) ....A

ILL.—Carlyle

Carlyle Paper Co. (Carpet Lining; Straw Wrapping; Wool Felt Sheathing; Express; Straw Board)....D

ILL.—Centralia

Centralia Pulp & Water Power Co. (News) ......A

ILL.—Chicago

Abbott & Co., A. H. (Oil; Sketching) ....B

American Straw Board Co. (Straw Board) ....AAAA

Armour Sand Paper Wks. (Sand) ....AAAA

Chicago Coated Board Co. (Box; Jute; Pulp Boards) AA

Dietzgen Co., Eugene (Oil; Sketching) ....A

Hopkins, H. H. (Building Roofing) ....B

Krembs & Co. (Fly)......C

Peele, C. D. M. (Lace; Shelf) ....H

Smith & Co., Bradner (Inc.) (Manilla; Wrapping) .AA

Union Sand Paper & Factory (Sand) .....AAAA

Utility Mfg. Co. (Fly)....E

Wood & Co., Chas. H. (Carbon; Transferotype).....F

ILL.—Lockport

Am. Straw Board Co. (Straw; Plain; Mill Lined Board) ....AAAA

ILL.—Marseilles

Boyce, W. D. (News)....A

Crescent Paper Co. (Plain; Manilla Lined Straw; Chip Board) C

Marseilles Wrapping Paper Co. (Rag Wrapping; Glazed; Rope Express)......B

ILL.—Morris

Morris Paper Co. (Straw; Wood Pulp; Jute Fibre Boards) C

ILL.—Mt. Carmel

United Box Board & Paper Co. (Straw Board) .AAAA

ILL.—Peoria

United Box Board & Paper Co. (Straw Board) .AAAA

ILL.—Quincy

American Straw Board Co. (Straw; Egg Case; Building Board) ....AAAA

ILL.—Rockford

Ills . Straw Products Co. (Straw; Rags 'Wrapping) X

Rockford Paper Mills (Straw Board; Wrapping) C

ILL.—Rock Island

Lewis Roofing Co. (Building; Roofing; Red Rozin Sized Sheathing) C

ILL.—Rockton

Smith & Co., Bradner Building (Carpet Lining; Wrapping; Straw Board) AA

Coons, Fred M. .(Carpet; Lining; Deadening Felt).C

ILL.—St. Elmo

St. Elmo Paper Co. (Butcher's Manilla; Carpet Lining Rag Wrapping; Roofing) C

ILL.—Taylorville

Prairie State Paper Co. (Bag; Express; Manilla Wrapping) C

ILL.—Wilmington

Am. Straw Board Co. (Straw Board) ....AAAA

ILL.—Vandalia

Ford Mfg. Co. (Roofing; Deadening Felt; Carpet Linings) ....B

ILL.—Waldron

United Box Board & Paper Co. (Straw & Chip Boards) AAAA

736

PAPER (Con.)

MAINE—Orono
International Paper Co.
(News) ....AAAA
Orono Pulp & Paper Co.
(Bag; Sack; Manilla).AA
MAINE—Portland
Berlin Mills Co. (News-
paper) ....AAAA
MAINE—Rumford Falls
International Paper Co.
(News Manilla; Bag)
.................AAAA
Oxford Paper Co. (M. F.
Super; Book; Envelope;
Tablet) ....AAAA
MAINE—South Brewer
Eastern Mfg. Co. (Bond;
Linen; Envelope; R. R.
Writing; Manilla; Wrap-
ping) ....A
MAINE—South Windham
Androscoggin Pulp Co.
(Wood Pulp Board)..AA
MAINE—Winslow
Hollingsworth & Whitney
Co. (Manilla Fibre & Wax-
ed) ....AAAA
MD.—Bentley Spgs.
Young, Sam'l & James R.
(Rag; Manilla Wrapping)
D
MD.—Chesterfield
Am. Straw Board Co.
(Straw Board) ....AAAA
MD.—Childs
Garrett & Son, C. S.
(Hanging) ....AAA
MD.—Cumberland
Southern Paper Co. (Manil-
la; R. R.; Writing; Ex-
press; Water Finish;
Fibre) X
MD.—Hagerstown
Antietam Paper Co. (M. F.;
Super) ....A
MD.—Hoffmanville
Rockdale Powder Co.
(Manilla) ....B
MD.—Lake
W. Va. Pulp & Paper Co
(Super; M. F. Book; En-
velope; Writing; Litho-
graph; Varnish Label)
AAAA
MD.—Providence
Kenmore Pulp & Paper Co.
(Book; Writing; Deckle
Edge) X
MD.—Rowlandsville
West & Co., W. T. (Roof-
ing; Deadening Felt;
Sheathing) ....E
MASS.—Adams
Brown Paper Co., L. L.
(Hand Made Linen Led-
ger; Record; Drawing;
Parchment) ....AA
MASS.—Baldwinsville
Carey Mfg. Co., Phillip
(Asbestos) ....AAA
MASS.—Bancroft
Bulkley, Dunton & Co.
(Card Middles; Book)AAA
MASS.—Boston
Dennison Mfg. Co.
AAAA
Ditson Co., Oliver (Music)
AA
Hollingsworth & Whitney
Co. (Manilla; Newspaper)
AAAA
Hollingsworth & Vose Co.
(Flour Sack; Manilla;
Sand) ....AA
Jones & Co., Melville D.
(Fly) ....A
Tileston & Hollingsworth Co.
(Card; Book; Plate).AAA
Train-Smith Co. (Manilla).B
Valley Paper Co. (Bond;
Linen; Ledger; Photo-
graphic) ....A
Warren & Co., S. D. (Glaz-
ed; Coated; Book).AAAA
Webster Co., F. S.
(Carbon) ....AA
Wheelwright Paper Co., Geo.
W. (Card; Manilla; Book;
Music) ....AA
Whiting Paper Co. (Writ-
ing) ....AAAA
Whitmore Mfg. Co (Coated)
B

PAPER (Con.)

Wilder & Co. (Newspaper)
AA
MASS.—Bridgewater
Jenkins Bros. & Co. (Leath-
er Board; Herling)......A
MASS.—Brightwood
Holyoke Card & Paper Co
(Coated) ....A
MASS.—Dalton
Crane, Z. & W. M. (Extra
Fine Writing) ....AAAA
Crane & Co. (Bank Note;
Bond; Parchment).AAAA
Old Berkshire Mills Co.
(Writing; Bristol Board)
A
Weston Co., Byron
(Linen Ledger; Record)
AA
MASS.—East Pepperell ...
Champion Card & Paper Co.
(Coated) ....AAA
Nashua River Paper Co.
(Book; Envelope; Writ-
ing) ....A
Parker & Co., H. A. (Bogus
Manilla; Rosin Sized
Sheathing) X
MASS.—East Walpole
Bird & Son, F. W. (Hard-
ware; Building; Roofing)
AAA
Hollings & Vose Co. (Rope
Manilla) ....AA
MASS.—Fairfield
Woronoco Paper Co. (Bond;
Linen; Ledger; Writing;
Typewriter) ....A
MASS.—Farley
Farley Paper Co. (Colored
Bristol; Card Middles).B
MASS.—Fitchburg
Croker, Burbank & Co.
(Book; Blotting; Writing;
News; Manilla; Cards;
Bristol Board) ..AAAA
De Jonge & Co., Louis
(Coated) ....AAAA
Falulah Paper Co. (Coated)
B
Fitchburg Paper Co. (Card;
Coating; Book; Hanging)
AAA
Wheelright Paper Co.
(Coating) ....AA
MASS.—Croton Centre
Tileston & Hollingsworth
Co. (Book) ....AAA
MASS.—Haverhill
Haverhill Box Board Co.
(Coated; Folding Box;
Bristol Boards) ......B
MASS.—Holyoke
Amer. Writing Paper Co.
(Wedding Folios; Linen;
Ledger; Cover; Drawing;
Colored Writing; Bristol
Board; Papeterie) .AAAA
Chemical Paper Co. (Enve-
lope; Manilla) ......AA
Crocker-McElwain Co.
(Coated; Colored; Cover;
Embossed; Hardware; Ma-
trix; Ticket, Book)...AA
Excelsior Paper Co. (Book;
Card; Matrix) X
Franklin Paper Co. (Duplex
Envelope; Wrapping) ...A
Griffith, Axtell & Cady
(Fly; Embossed) ......D
Hampden Glazed Paper &
Card Co. (Blotting; Card;
Chromo; Coated; Glazed;
Lithograph; Pattern;
Plate; Silver) ....A
Newton Paper Co. (Build-
ing; Lining; Manilla;
Wrapping) ....A
Parsons Paper Co. (Bond;
Banknote; Colored; Enve-
lope; Parchment) .AAA
Valley Paper Co. (Bond;
Banknote; Typewriter)
AA
Whiting Paper Co. (Bond;
Banknote; Parchment)
AAAA
Whitmore Mfg. Co. (Blot-
ting; Card; Chromo; Coat-
ed; Cover; Glazed; Litho-
graph; Manilla; Plate)..A
MASS.—Housatonic
Rising Paper Co., B. D.

PAPER (Con.)

(Bond; Linen; Ledger;
Wedding Bristol) ....AA
MASS.—Huntington
Am. Writing Paper Co.
(Papeterie) ......AAAA
MASS.—Lawrence
Champion-International Co.,
(Roll for Coating, also
Coated Paper) ......AAA
Merrimac Paper Co. (Super;
M. F. Enamelled; Coated;
Litho.; Writing; Music)
AA
United Box Board & Paper
Co. (Box Board)..AAAA
Munroe Felt & Paper Co.
(Manilla; Hanging; Roof-
ing; Carpet Lining)....A
Nat. Fibre Board Co. (Leath-
er Board) ....A
MASS.—Lee
Am. Writing Paper Co.
(Blotting; Card) .AAAA
Benton Bros. (Writing;
Ledger) C
Eaton-Dikeman Co. (Blot-
ting; Cover; Plate).....A
Smith Paper Co. (Copying;
Silver; Book; Newspaper)
AA
MASS.—Leominster
Leominster Handifold Toilet
Paper Co. ....B
MASS.—Loudville
Loudville Paper Mill (Leath-
er; Binders' Board)....X
MASS.—Middlefield
Bancroft Mill (Hanging;
Manilla; Book; News-
paper) ....D
MASS.—Middleton
Middleton Paper Mills
(Hanging; Book Manilla)
A
MASS.—Millers Falls
Millers Falls Paper Co.
Book; Cover; Folding;
Bristol) ....AA
MASS.—Milton
Tilleston & Hollingsworth
Co. (Book; Litho; Card)
AAA
MASS.—Mittineague
Am. Writing Paper Co.
(Ledger Bond, etc.; Type-
writer; Parchment).AAAA
Mittineague Paper Co.
(Writing; Cover; Draw-
ing) ....AA
Southworth Co. (Bond; Lin-
en Ledger) ....A
Worthy Paper Co, (Bond;
Ledger; Linen) ....A
MASS.—Monroe Bridge
Ramage Paper Co., Jas.
(Manilla; White; Colored
Bristol; Tag; Box Board;
Duplex Paper) X
MASS.—New Bedford
Pairpoint   Corporation
(Straw Board; Heavy
Baling; Case Lining)..A
MASS.—Newton Lower Falls
Crehoe & Son, Chas. F.
(Press Board) ....A
MASS.—Norfolk
Norfolk Paper Co. (Sheath-
ing; Carpet Lining; Wrap-
ping; Box Board; Bristol)
X
MASS.—No. Amherst
Cushman, A. R. (Leather;
Button; Straw Board).D
MASS.—No. Dighton
Lincoln & Co., L. (Manilla;
Sheathing; Pattern) C
MASS.—No. Grafton
Washington Mills Emery
Mfg. Co. (Emery; Flint)B
MASS.—No. Leominster
Nat. Fibre Board Co. (Leath-
er; Fibre Board; Tissue;
Book) ....A
Wheelwright Paper Co.,
Geo. W. (Bristol Board;
White; Tinted Coating;
Book) ....AA
MASS.—No. Wilbraham
Collins Mfg. Co. (Writing)
AA
MASS.—Russell
Chapin & Gould Paper Co.
(Writing) ....A

PAPER (Con.)

MASS.—Somerville
Middlesex Paper Co. (Box
Board; Sheathing; Wrap-
ping) C
MASS.—So. Hadley
Japanese Tissue Mills
(Tissue) C
Stony Book Paper Co.
(Cimmeran Black Paper)
C
MASS.—So. Hadley Falls
Carew Mfg. Co. (Ledger;
Bond; Linen; Typewriter)
AA
Hampshire Paper Co. (Bond;
Banknote; Typewriter;
Card) ....AA
MASS.—So. Lee
Am. Writing Paper Co.
(Bond; Linen; Super.;
Banknote) ....AAAA
MASS.—Springfield
Am. Writing Paper Co.
(Writing) ....AAAA
Holyoke Card & Paper Co.
(Chromo; Coated; Glazed;
Plate; Parchment) ....A
Morgan Envelope Co.
(Toilet) ....AAAA
New England Card & Paper
Co. (Coated; Glazed)...A
Springfield Glazed Paper Co.
(Coated) ....B
MASS.—Townsend Harbor
Spaulding Bros. Co. (Leather
Fibre Board) C
MASS.—Ware
Ware Paper Co. (Book;
Manilla) C
MASS.—Westfield
Columbian Photo Paper Co.
(Photo) ....A
Crane Bros. (Linen Ledger)
AAA
MASS.—West Groton
Groton Leather Board Co.
(Leather Board) C
Hollingsworth & Vose Co.
(Rope Manilla) ....AA
MASS.—Wheelwright
Wheelwright Paper Co.
(Book; Music) ......AA
MASS.—Woronoco
Woronoco Paper Co. (Bond;
Banknote; Hanging; Type-
writer) ....AA
MICH.—Allegan
Dayton Allegan Paper Co.
(Straw; Lining; Rag
Wrapping) X
MICH.—Alpena
Fletcher Paper Co. (Water
Fibre) ....AA
MICH.—Cheboygan
Cheboygan Paper Co.
(News; Fibre) ......AA
MICH.—Childsdale
Childs, Horace H. (Straw
Boards) X
MICH.—Constantine
Constantine Paper Mlls (Ex-
press; Fibre; Rag Wrap-
ping) X
MICH.—Detroit
Decoy Fly Paper Co. (Fly)
C
Detroit Sulphite Fibre Co.
(Sulphite Fibre Wrap-
ping) ....A
Ingram & Co., F. F. (Fly)
B
MICH.—Flint
Lewis Mfg. Co. (Corrugated
Card Board for Cop Tubes)
X
MICH.—Grand Rapids
Grand Rapids Sticky Fly
Paper Co. (Fly)........A
Thum Co., O. & W. (Fly)
AA
MICH.—Jackson
Mich. Paper & Bag Co.
(Waxed; Oiled; Boards)
D
MICH.—Kalamazoo
Bryant Paper Co. (Map;
Lith; Plate; Book; Blot-
ting; Writing) ....A
Gibson Paper Co. (M. F.;
Super Book; Litho; Card;
coating) ....B
Kalamazoo Paper Co. (Book-

PAPER (Con.)

Gandey, Wm. H. (Tissue Manilla; Copying) C

Lambertville Paper Co. (Manifolding; Parchment; Copying; Jute; Manilla Tissue) ....A

N. J.—Millburn

Diamond Mills Paper Co. (Tissue) ....A

Fandango Mills (Binders Board) ....A

Lighttipe & Co., Ernest (Album; Binders; Trunk Boards) ....B

N. J.—Morristown

Muir, Jas. A. (Binders; Leather; Pattern Board) C

N. J.—Newark

Albey Bros. (Binders; Box Button; Trunk Board) ..D

Downs, Geo. W. (Box Board) ....H

N. J.—Passaic

Carlton Paper Mills (Sheathing; Roofing; Felt) C

Paterson Parchment Paper Co. (Lining; Parchment; Wrapping) ....AA

N. J.—Pleasant Mills

Pleasant Mills Paper Co. (Rope; Manilla) ......A

N. J.—Riegelsville

Warren Mfg. Co. (Jute Rope; Cover; Manilla) AA

N. J.—Wanaque

Wanaque River Paper Co. (Chip Straw Board; Heavy Bogus) ....A

N. J.—Waverly Park

Wheeler Mfg. Co. (Chip; Straw Board; Heavy Bogus) ....E

N. J.—Whippany

United Box Board & Paper Co. (News; Combination; Patent Coated Boards) AAAA

McEwan & Bros., A. (Box Boards) X

N. Y.—Albany

Albany Card & Paper Co. (Coated) ....B

Albany Perforated Wrapping Paper Co. (Butter; Roll; Toilet; Tissue; Waxed) ....A

N. Y.—Amsterdam

Smeallie & Co., P. H. (Hanging; News; Lining) AAA

N. Y.—Ancram

Ancram Paper Mill (White; Colored; Manilla; Anti Rust Tissue) C

N. Y.—Ausable Forks

Rogers Co., J. & J. Express; Manilla) ....AAA

N. Y.—Baldwinsville

Colored; Tissue; Wrapping Straw; Manilla Tissue) C

N. Y.—Ballston Spa

Nat. Folding Box & Paper Co. (Box Board) ..AAAA

Union Bag & Paper Co. (Bag; Manilla) ....AAAA

N. Y.—Battenville

Phoenix Paper Co. (White; Manilla Tissue) C

N. Y.—Beaver Falls

Lewis Co., J. P., The (Pulp; Folding Box; Tag; Document; Oyster Pail Jute; Fibre; Mat. Boards) B

Lewis & Slocum (Wood; Pulp; Sulphite Boards in Natural & Tinted Colors) B

N. Y.—Binghamton

Bayless Pump & Paper Co. (Hanging; Newspaper) AA

N. Y.—Black River

Jefferson Paper Co. (Butchers Manilla; Hanging; Wax) ....A

N. Y.—Brooklyn

McLoughlin Bros. (Coated) AAA

Thompson & Morris Co.

PAPER (Con.)

(Cork) ....AA

N. Y.—Brownville

Brownville Board Co. (Tag; Manilla; Folding Box Boards) ....A

Harmon Paper Co. (Book; News; Manilla; Colored Specialties) C

N. Y.—Canajoharie

Arkell & Smith (Coated; Flour Sack) ....

N. Y.—Carthage

Carthage Tissue Paper Mills (Manilla; White; Colored Tissue; Toilet in Rolls) B

Champion Paper Co. (Manilla) ....B

Island Paper Co. (Special Manilla; Screening; Bag; Fibre) ....B

West End Paper Co. (News) B

N. Y.—Castleton

Fort Orange Paper Co. (Pulp Boards; Card Middles. &c.) ....D

Ingalls & Co. (Binders; Friction; Trunk; Wagon; Pattern; Wagon Board) B

N. Y.—Chatham

Hughes, E. T. (Cigarette) D

Stony Brook Box Board Mills (Blue Tint Board) D

N. Y.—Chatham Center

Haner & Son, M. L. (Straw Wrapping; Bogus) ....D

N. Y.—Dansville

McNairn, J. H. (White; Colored Tissue) X

N. Y.—De Feriet

St. Regis Paper Co. (News) AAA

N. Y.—Dexter

Dexter Sulphite Pulp & Paper Co. (Manilla; Fibre) A

N. Y.—Elbridge

Paddock, S. D. (Straw Board for Tubes) ....AA

N. Y.—Evergreens

Lyons, Jas. (Roofing; Deadening Felts; Sheathing) X

N. Y.—Felts Mills

Taggarts Paper Co. (Colored Poster; News; Manilla) ....A

N. Y.—Fort Edward

International Paper Co. (News; Manilla; Hanging; Wrappers) ....AAAA

N. Y.—Fort Miller

Fort Miller Pulp & Paper Co. (Hanging) ....A

N. Y.—Fulton

Eureka Paper Co. (Rope; Tag; Fibre; Oyster Pail; Heavy Wrapping) ....D

United Box Board & Paper Co. (Manilla News; Box Board) ....AAAA

Victoria Paper Mills Co. (Manilla Fibre; Rope) B

Volney Paper Co. (Roofing; Sheathing; Building; Wrapping) ....B

N. Y.—Glens Falls

International Paper Co. (News) ....AAAA

N. Y.—Gt. Bend

Taggarts Paper Co. (Hanging; News; Manilla) AA

N. Y.—Greenwich

Blandy Paper Co. (Spec. for Coating; Card Mills) D

Phoenix Paper Co. (Hanging Newspaper) ....D

N. Y.—Greig

Moyer & Pratt (Drab Express; Manillas) ......D

N. Y.—Hadley

Union Bag & Paper Co. (Bag; Manilla) ..AAAA

N. Y.—Hart Lot

Hart Lot Paper Co. (Manilla) ....B

N. Y.—Herkimer

International Paper Co.

PAPER (*Con.*)

Pettebone-Cataract Paper Co. (News; Manilla; Hanging) ....AAAA
N. Y.—Norfolk
Remington - Martin Co. (News; Hanging; Bag) A
N. Y.—North Hoosick
Stevens & Thompson (Hanging; Newspaper; Colored Specialties) ....AA
N. Y.—Patchogue
Gilmore Mfg. Co. (Board; Sheathing; Wrapping) B
N. Y.—Penn Yan
Andrews & Co., Jno. T. (Butchers'; Manilla; Sheathing) ....A
Fox & Curtis (Straw Wrapping) ....B
United Box Board & Paper Co. (News; Manilla) AAAA
N. Y.—Phoenix
Carrier, Leman J. (Manilla; Tissue) ....E
Oswego River Paper Mills (Toilet) C
Phoenix Toilet & Paper Mfg. Co. (White; Manilla Tissue; Toilet).........C
Sweet Bros. Paper Mfg. Co. (Colored; Manilla Tissue) ....D
N. Y.—Piermont
Piermont Paper Co. (Folding Box Boards)......AA
N. Y.—Pyrites
De Grasse River Paper Co. A
N. Y.—Pt. Leyden
Gould Paper Co. (Heavy Manilla; Drab) ....A
N. Y.—Potsdam
Raquatte River Paper Co. (Manilla; Fibre) ......AA
N. Y.—Raymondville
Raymondville Paper Co. (News) X
N. Y.—Rochester
Amer. Ribbon & Carbon Co. (Carbon) ....D
Eastman Kodak Co. (Bromide; Negative; Transferotype) ....AAAA
Elbs, John G. (Fly) .....D
Genesee Paper Co. (News; Tissue) ....B
Reed Chemical Co. (Fly) E
N. Y.—Rock City Falls
Union Waxed & Parchment Paper Co. (Flexible; Non Flexible Parchment) AA
Brown Paper Co., The E. M. (Heavy Card; Duplex) B
N. Y.—Salisbury Mills
Arlington Paper Co. (Book; Writing) ....A
N. Y.—Sandy Hill
Allen Bros. Co. (Blank Wall; Manilla Fibre; Express) AA
Union Bag & Paper Co. (Bag; Manilla Wall) AAAA
N. Y.—Saugerties
Cantner, E. Martin (Coated) A
Diamond Mills Paper Co. (Typwriter; Carbon; Tissue; Copying; Cigarette) X
N. Y.—Schuylerville
Amer. Wood Board Co. (Coating Board) ......B
Schuylerville Paper Co. (Book; News) ....A
United Box Board & Paper Co. (Jute Fibre Boards) AAAA
N. Y.—Seneca Falls
Ingersoll & Son, E. S. (Tissue) ....D
N. Y.—Shortsville
Jones, James (Bogus Manilla) C
Lawless Paper Co. (Manilla; Manilla Tissue) ....D
N. Y.—Skaneateles
Rose & Moses Pulp & Paper

PAPER (*Con.*)

Co. (Hanging) C
Skaneateles Paper Co. (Boards; Mill Wrappers) B
N. Y.—Stillwater
Pemble, W. (Leather Board) ....A
Stillwater Straw Board Co. (Straw Board) ....D
N. Y.—Stockport
Van de Carr, C. R. (Straw Wrapping; Cigarette) ..C
N. Y.—Syracuse
Syracuse Pulp & Paper Co., (Hanging) C
N. Y.—Ticonderoga
International Pulp & Paper Co., (News) .....AAAA
Ticonderoga Pulp & Paper Co,. (News; Book; Drawing) ....AAA
N. Y.—Tonawanda
Tonawanda Board & Paper Co. (Pulp; Manilla; Jute Coated; Duplex Boards)X
N. Y.—Troy
Albia Box & Paper Co. (Box Boards) ....A
Leversee & Snyder Mfg. Co. (Chip Board) X
Manning Paper Co., Jno. A. (Rope Manilla; Flour Sack; Sand) ....AA
Orr Co., The (News; Tissue; Book) ....AA
Smart, R. T. (Toilet; Straw; Wrapping) ....B
N. Y.—Valatie
Davis & Richmond (Straw Wrapping) ....D
N. Y.—Walesville
Oriskany Paper Co. (Tissue Manilla) X
N. Y.—Walloomsac
Walloomsac Paper Co. (Colored) ....AA
N. Y.—Warrensburgh
Schroon River Pulp & Paper Co. (Hanging; News) ..A
N. Y.—Waterford
Gilbert Paper Co., Frank (Book; Cotton Waste News) ....B
N. Y.—Watertown
International Paper Co. (News; Manilla) ..AAAA
Knowlton Bros. (Cover; Colored Laid Writing; Coated) ....AA
Remington-Martin Co. (Manilla; Roll Newspaper)AA
Taggart Bros. Co. (Rope; Coated) ....A
Watertown Paper Co. (Hanging; News; Manilla) B
N. Y.—West Milton
Jacobs, Jno. (Textile Wrappers; Hardware; Bristols, etc.) C
OHIO—Akron
Cleveland-Akron Bag Co. (Rope; Manilla) .AAAA
Phillips Co., Thomas (Rope; Coated Manilla; Flour Sack) ....AA
OHIO—Baltimore
Twin City Paper Co. (Glazed; M. F. Hardware; Rope) C
OHIO—Barberton
Am. Straw Board Co. (News; Coated; Pulp Lined; Combination)AAAA
OHIO—Cedarville
Hagar Straw Board & Paper Co. (Light Straw Board; Straw Wrapping) C
Ohio—Chagrin Falls
Adams Bag Co. (Manilla) A
OHIO—Chillicothe
Mead Paper Co. (Book; Litho; Writing) ....A
OHIO—Cincinnati
Chatfield & Woods Co. (Newspaper) ....A
Church Co., John (Music) AAAA
OHIO—Circleville
Am. Straw Board Co. (Straw Board) ....AAAA
OHIO—Cleveland
Bruce & West Mfg. Co.

PAPER (Con.)

(Fly) ....D
Cleveland Paper Mfg. Co.
(Colored Book; Manilla;
News; Roll) ....B
Cleveland-Akron Bag Co.
(Rope; Manilla) ......A
OHIO—Coshocton
Coshocton Straw Paper Co.
(Straw Wrapping) .....E
OHIO—Cuyahoga Falls
Walsh Paper Co. (Colored;
News; Starch; Lining; To-
bacco) ....B
OHIO—Dayton
Aetna Paper Co. (Bond;
Ledger; Linen; Flat Envel-
ope; Map; Writing) ..B
Am. Straw Board Co.
(Binders' Board) ..AAAA
Dayton Paper Novelty Co.
(Waxed) ....A
Levis Paper Co. (Bond;
Linen; Bristol; Writing)
AAA
Knerr Paper Co., Lewis
(Binders; Trunk Board) X
Mead Paper Co. (Book;
Litho; Writing) ....A
Nixen & Costello Co.
(Colored) ....E
OHIO—Delphos
Hinde & Dauch Paper Co.
(Straw Board; Wrapping)
B
OHIO—Franklin
Am. Writing Paper Co.
(Writing) ....AAAA
Perfect Safety Paper Co.
(Safety) ....B
Perrine Paper Co. (Rope
Manilla; Wrapping) ...X
Richardson Paper Co. (Roof-
ing; Wrapping; News-
paper) C
Union Waxed & Parchment
Paper Co. (Tissue) ..AA
OHIO—Hamilton
Beckett Paper Co. (Colored
Cover; Poster; Starch; To-
bacco) ....A
Champion Coated Paper Co.
(Book for Coating; Coat-
ed; Lithograph) ...AAAA
Rockdale Tissue & Waxed
Paper Co. (Waxed; Plain
(Tissue) X
Sterling Paper Co. (Parch-
ment) C
OHIO—Kenton
Am. Straw Board Co.
(Straw Board) ....AAAA
OHIO—Lima
Am. Straw Board Co. (Straw
Board; Plain; Lined Egg
Case Fillers) ......AAAA
OHIO—Lockland
Bowen, E. (Carpet Lining;
Cloth; Building; Roofing;
Bottle Wrapper; Candy;
Furniture; Tarred Roof-
ing; Slaters' Felt) ....B
Fox Paper Co. (Roofing;
Wrapping; Express; Build-
ing; Manilla) ....AA
Haldeman Paper Co. (Carpet
Lining; Felt Roofing;
Wrapping) ....A
OHIO—Massillon
Massillon Paper Co. (Straw
Wrapping) C
OHIO—Maumee
Fly Button Co. (Fly) ...D
Maumee Paper Co. (Colored
Cover; Bogus; Bristol;
Mask; Porous; Fly; Tobac-
co; Macaroni; Seidlitz Pat-
tern; Rag Wrapping) X
Mitchell-Westcott Paper Co.
(Express; Straw Wrap-
ping) X
OHIO—Miamisburg
Miamisburg Paper Co.
(Book; News; Butchers'
Manilla; Wax) ....B
Ohio Paper Co. (Super Book;
R. R. Manilla) ....A
OHIO—Middletown
Crystal Paper Co. (White;
Manilla; Tissue; Waxed
Tissue; White Waxed) B
Gardiner Paper Co., Colin
(Coated; Box Boards;
White Blanks) ....A
Oglesby Paper Co., The W.

PAPER (Con.)

B. (High Grade Bag;
Book) ....AAAA
Sorg Paper Co., The Paul A.
(Flour Sack; Wax) ....A
United Box Board & Paper
Co. (Coated Cards; Card
Middles; Comb Cards; Ma-
nilla) ....AAAA
Wardlow-Thomas Paper Co.
(Rope; Jute; Manilla;
Coated) ....AA
Wrenn Paper Co. (Blotting;
Filter; Newspaper)....B
OHIO—Monroe Falls
Monroe Falls Paper Co.
(Carpet Lining; Express;
Straw; Rag Wrapping) D
OHIO—Piqua
Am. Straw Board Co.
(Straw; News; Comb.
Pulp; Chip Board) AAAA
OHIO—Sandusky
Hinde-Dauch Paper Co.
(Straw Board; Wrapping)
B
OHIO—St. Mary's
Western Straw Board Co.
(Jute; Pulp Lined; Fold-
ing Box; Straw Boards) C
OHIO—Steubenville
Hartje Paper Mfg Co. (Ma-
nilla; News; Carpet Lin-
ing; Wrapping Straw;;
Pulp Board) ....AAA
OHIO—Tiffin
Am. Straw Board Co. (Straw
Board) ....AAAA
OHIO—Toledo
Shepler, Jno. B. (Binders';
Trunk; Friction Board) F
Ohio—Urbana
United Box Board & Paper
Co. (Straw Board) AAAA
OHIO—West Carrollton
Friend Paper Co., Geo. H.
(Book; Manilla; Roofing;
Tobacco, Newspaper) AAA
Xenia Board & Paper Co.
(White Folding Box
Board) ....B
OREGON—Lebanon
O'Neill Bros. & Callaghan
(Straw Wrapping) ....A
OREGON—Oregon City
Crown Paper Co. (Manilla;
Fruit Bag; Express) ..A
Willamette Pulp & Paper
Co. (News) ......AAAA
PA.—Atglen
Hults, E. H. Jr., (Binders';
Trunk Board) C
Chalfant, Thos. S. (Binders'
Board) C
PA.—Austin
Bayless Pulp & Paper Co.
(Pure Fibre) ....AA
PA.—Avondale
Keating, Jos. M. (Binders';
Box Board) C
PA.—Bloomsburg
Bloomsburg Paper Co.
(Rope; Manilla; Water
Sheathing; Mill Boards) B
PA.—Bridgeport
Diamond State Fibre Co.
(Fibre) ....B
PA.—Buck Run
Garrett & Son Co., C. S.
(Hanging; Card; Middles;
Fibre) ....AAA
PA.—Catawissa
Penna. Paper Mills (Pure
Fibre; Drab; Express; Im-
itation Press Board) ..B
PA.—Chambersburg
Hollywell Paper Mills
(Building; Dry Roofing;
Deadening Felt; Rosin
Sized Sheathing; Heavy
Wrapping; Manilla) ..X
PA.—Cly
Chase Felt & Paper Co.
(Roofing; Rosin Sized
Sheathing; Deadening
Felt; Corrugated Carpet
Lining) ....D
PA.—Darby
Garrett. E. T. (Book; Card
Middles; Fibre; Hanging)
X
PA.—Dowingtown
Bicking. S. Austin, (Wrap-
ping; Rosin Sized Sheath-

743

PAPER (Con.)
Wrapping) ....D
TEXAS—Sugarland
Cunningham & Co., Ed. H.
(Butchers; Grocers Wrap-
ping) X
R. I.—Pawtucket
Linton Bros. & Co. (Coated)
A
Pawtucket Glazed Paper Co.
(Glazed) C
R. I. Cardboard Co. (Coated)
A
VT.—Bellows Falls
Blake & Higgins (Manilla)
C
Flint & Sons Co., Wyman
(Manilla; Roll Newspa-
per) ....A
International Paper Co.
(News; Manilla; Card
Board) ....AAAA
Moore & Sons, Jno. T. (Ma-
nilla; Envelope; Toilet)A
Moore & Thompson Paper
Co. (Manilla; Envelope;
Coating; R. R. Writing;
Wax Writing) ....A
Robertson & Son, Jno. (Tis-
sue Manilla) ....A
Robertson Paper Co. (Envel-
ope; Manilla, R. R. Writ-
ing; Parchment Writing;
Waxed Manilla; Tissue) A
VT.—Brattleboro
Vinton & Son, Wm. H.
(Blotting; Matrix) ....D
VT.—Fitzdale
Dalton Paper Mills (News)
A
VT.—Morrisville
Nat. Fibre Board Co. (Fibre
Board) ....AAAA
VT.—No. Bennington
Stark Paper Co. (Hanging)
A
VT.—Passumpsig
Passumpsic Fibre Leather
Co. (Leather Board) ···E
VT.—Putney
Cole Paper Co., Wm. A.,
(Manilla Tissue; Toilet)
B
Robertson Wm. (Tissue;
Toilet; Tissue Manilla;
Fruit Wrappers) ......D
VT.—Readsboro
Nat. Metal Edge Box Co.
(Wood Pulp Board) ...A
VT.—St. Johnsbury
Pierce Bros. (Leather
Board) ....D
VT.—So. Lunenburg
Dalton Paper Mills (News)
A
VT.—Wells River
Adams Paper Co. (Manilla
Tissue; Toilet; Anti-
Tarnish) ....D
VT.—Wilder
International Paper Co.
(News) ....AAAA
VA.—Big Island
Bedford Pulp & Paper Co.
Manilla; News; Hanging;
Drawing; Fibre; Pad)..B
VA.—Buena Vista
Columbian Paper Co. (Card;
Writing) ....AAA
VA.—Covington
W. Va. Pulp & Paper Co.
(Super & M. F. Book;
Litho; Varnish; Label;
Writing Tablet; Music)
AAAA
VA.—Manchester
Standard Paper Mfg. Co.
(Blotting; Matrix) ....B
VA.—Richmond
Albermarle Paper Mfg. Co.
(Blotting) ....A
Armitage Mfg. Co. (Roof-
ing) ....B
Manchester Paper Twine Co.
(Gray; Rag Wrapping;
Butchers' Manilla Drab;
Express; Mill Wrappers;
Tissue Manilla) ......B
Richmond Paper Mfg. Co.
(Blotting; Book; News)
AA
Wortendyke Mfg. Co.
(Toilet) ....B

PAPER (Con.)
VA.—Winchester
Old Dominion Paper Co.
(News; Board; Chip
Board) X
WASH.—Camas
Columbia River Paper Co.
(Newspaper; Wrapping;
Straw Wrapping) .....AA
Leadbetter, F. W. (News,
Wrapping, Building) ..D
WASH.—Everett
Everett Pulp & Paper Co.
(Super & M. F. Book; R.
R. Writing; Bonds; Car-
tridge) ....AAA
W. VA.—Halltown
Eyster & Son, S. P. (Box
Boards) ....D
W. VA.—Wellsburg
George Co., S., (Rope
Manilla) ....A
Harvey Paper Co. (Flour;
Cement Sack; Gray Wrap-
ping) ....D
WIS.—Appleton
Atlas Paper Co. (Manilla;
Colored Fibre; News) AA
Fox River Paper Co. (Bond;
Ledger; Linen; Map;
Drawing; Ruled) ....AA
Kimberly & Clark Co.
(Book; Manilla; News-
paper) ....AAAA
Patten Paper Co., The
(Book; News) ....A
Riverside Fibre & Paper Co.
(Manilla; Fibre) ......D
Telulah Paper Co. (Book;
Envelope; Writing; R. R.
Manilla) ....AA
Wisc. Tissue Paper Co.
(Tissue) C
WIS.—Beloit
Barrett Mfg. Co. (Roofing;
Building; Box; Straw
Board) ....AAAA
WIS.—Brokaw
Wausau Paper Mills Co.
(Butchers Manilla) ....A
WIS.—Combined Locks
Combined Locks Paper Co.
(News) ....AAA
WIS.—De Pere
Am. Writing Paper Co.
(Bond; Linen Ledger)
AAAA
WIS.—Eau Claire
Dells Paper & Pulp Co. (Ma-
nilla; Fibre; News) AAA
WIS.—Grand Rapids
Cons. Water Power & Paper
Co. (News) ....AA
Grand Rapids Pulp & Paper
Co. (News) ....A
Pioneer Wood Pulp Co.
(Wood Pulp Board) ...D
WIS.—Green Bay
Hoberg Co., Jno. (White;
Manilla; Tissue; Toilet;
Fruit) ....D
Northern Tissue Paper Mills
(Roll Toilet) ....B
WIS.—Kaukauna
Outagamie Paper Co.
(News) ....A
Thilmany Pulp & Paper Co.
(Tissue; Poster; French
Folio; R. R. Manilla) ..A
Union Bag & Paper Co.
(Manilla; Bag) ....AAAA
WIS.—Kimberly
Kimberly & Clark Co.
(Straw Wrapping; Ex-
press) ....AAAA
WIS.—Marinette
Marinette & Menominee Pa-
per Co. (News; Manilla)
AAA
WIS.—Menasha
Menasha Paper Co. (Manil-
la; Colored Poster; News)
A
Gilbert Paper Co. (Ledger;
Bond; Envelope) ....AA
Howard Co., C. W., The
(Fibre) ....B
Strange Paper Co., Jno.
(Poster; Fibre; Manilla;
Rag; Express) ....A
Whiting, Geo. A. (Book;
Writing) ....AA
Wisconsin River Paper &
Pulp Co. (Newspaper) ..A

PAPER (*Con.*)
WIS.—Milwaukee
Milwaukee Lace Paper Co.
(Lace Shelf) ....B
WIS.—Neenah
Kimberly & Clark Co.
(News) ....AAAA
Neenah Paper Co. (Super.;
M. F. Book) ....A
Winnebago Paper Mills
(Flats; Bonds; Env.; Super.; M. F. Book; Matrix)
AA
WIS.—Nekoosa
Nekoosa Paper Co. (News;
Manilla; Fibre Book) AA
WIS.—Niagara
Kimberly & Clark Co.
(News; Manilla) ..AAAA
WIS.—Oconto Mills
Falls Mfg. Co. (Manilla;
Fibre) ....A
WIS.—Oshkosh
Diamond Sticky Fly Paper
Co. (Fly) ....B
WIS.—Park Falls
Flambeau Paper Co.
(News) ....A
WIS.—Port Edwards
Edwards Mfg. Co. (News) A
WIS.—Rhinelander
Rhinelander Paper Co.
(News; Manilla) ......B
WIS.—Shawano
Wolf River Paper & Fibre
Co. (Bag; Manilla; Envelope) ....A
WIS.—Sparta
Newton's Sons, O. J. (Bogus Manilla; Wrapping) C
WIS.—Stevens Point
Plover Paper Co. (Book;
Writing) ....A
Wis. River Paper & Pulp Co.
(News) ....A
WIS.—Tomahawk
Tomahawk Pulp & Paper Co.
(News) C

PAPER:
CARBON

ILL.—Aurora
Miller-Bryant-Pierce Co..C
MASS.—Boston
Carter's Ink Co...........A
MASS.—Lee
Smith Paper Co...........AA
New York City
Cooke, Douglas H., 18
Beaver ....F
Little, A. P., 201 Broadway
AA
Pen Carbon Manifold Co.,
145 Centre ....D
Whitfield Carbon Paper
Works X
N. Y.—Rochester
Little A. P...........AA
Non-Smut Carbon Mfg. Co.
D
Vacuo-Static Carbon Co..D

PAPER STOCK
See Rags

PAPER: WALL

ILL.—Chicago
Art Wall Paper Co.....AA
Audebert Wall Paper Mills,
16th & State..........B
Freund Bros. Mfg. Co.,
2911 Wentworth ....B
Janeway & Carpenter, 265
S. Canal ....AAA
Potter Wall Paper Mills,
408 Illinois ....D
IOWA—Des Moines
Stoner Wall Paper Co.....B
MASS.—Boston
Boston Wall Paper House
C
Middleton Paper Mills,
147 Milk ....B
Munroe & Co., J. S., 79
Summer C
MASS.—Chelsea
Strahan & Co., Thomas...B
MASS.—Worcester
Allen-Higgins Co.........B

PAPER: WALL (*Con.*)
N. J.—Hackensack
Campbell Wall Paper Co.,
Wm. X
N. J.—Hoboken
Benton, Heath & Co., 18th
& Willow Ave. ....B
Potter Wall Paper Mills..A
N. J.—Newark
Essex Wall Peper Co....C
N. J.—New Brunswick
Janeway & Carpenter...AA
Janeway & Co. ....AA
N. Y.—Brooklyn
Graves, Robt. J.........D
N. Y.—Buffalo
Birge & Sons Co., M. H...A
Potter Wall Paper Mills
AAA
N. Y.—Geneva
Fairfax Bros. ....B
N. Y.—Ithaca
Ithaca Wall Paper Mill...C
N. Y.—Cortland
Wallace Wall Paper Co...B
N. Y.—Brooklyn
Graves Co., Robt., 927 3d
Av. ....AA
Mairs & Co., Wm. H., 68
Sackett ....AAAA
New York City
Beck & Co., Fr., 334 7th
AA
Graves Co., Robt., 483 5th
Av. ....AA
James Co., F. E., 483 10th
Av. ....A
Leatherole Co., The, 142 W.
23d ....A
Potter Wall Paper Mills, 1
E. 13th ....A
Standard Wall Paper Co.,
503 5th Av. ....A
Strahan & Co., Thomas, 156
5th Av. ....B
N. Y.—Sandy Hill
Standard Wall Paper Co...
AAA
N. Y.—Syracuse
Empire Wall Paper Co....C
Syracuse Wall Paper Co..A
N. Y.—Tarrytown
Tarrytown Wall Paper Co.
D
N. Y.—Walloomsac
Walloomsac Paper Co...AA
OHIO—Steubenville
Steubenville Wall Paper Co.
B
PA.—New Brighton
Pittsburg Wall Paper Co..B
PA.—Philadelphia
Becker, Smith & Page,
(Inc.) Snyder Av. &
Water C
Carey Bros Co., 2228 N.
10th ....AA
Cresswell & Washburn,
(Ltd.), 1727 Alter Av...A
Gossler & Wilt Wall Paper
Co., The, 802 So. 11th..C
Graves Co., Robt., 319
Held Bldg. ....AA
Hitchener's Wall Paper Co.,
Ashbourne C
Quaker City Wall Paper
Co. C
PA.—York
York Card & Paper Co...B
York Wall Paper Co.....A

PAPETERIES
See also Pads & Tablets;
also Paper

MASS.—Dalton
Crane, Z. & W. M...AAAA
MASS.—Holyoke
Whiting Paper Co....AAAA
MASS.—South Lee
Amer. Writing Paper Co...
AAAA
MASS.—Springfield
Birnie Paper Co..........A
Morgan Envelope Co.....
AAAA
National Papeterie Co.....A
New York City
Berlin & Jones Envelope Co.
AA
Hake Mfg. Co., Philip....A

PAPETERIES (Con.)

Raynor & Perkins Envelope Co. ....A
PA.—Huntingdon
Blair Co., J. C...........AA

PAPIER MACHE GOODS

ILL.—Chicago
Petersen, O. B...........H
New York City
Berger's Sons, H.........E
PA.—Philadelphia
Schoenhut Co., A..........A

PARAFFINE

See also Wax

ILL.—Chicago
Clark, F. C...............D
New York City
Tidewater Oil Co.....AAAA
OHIO—Cincinnati
Moore Oil Co., Chas. H...A
PA.—Petrolia
Petrolia Mfg. Co..........H
PA.—Titusville
Pennsylvania Paraffine Wks. ....B

PARASOLS

See Umbrellas

PARCHMENT

See Paper

PARERS

MD.—Baltimore
Sinclair, Scott C. (Fruit)..E
MASS.—Leominster
Hudson Parer Co. (Apple).E
MASS.—Worcester
Hamblen & Pearsall Mfg. Co. (Wire) ....B
Parker Wire Goods Co. (Apple; Potato) ....D
N. H.—Antrim
Goodell Co. (Apple)......A
N. J.—Newark
Bannister & Co., A. F. (Fruit) ....A
Heller Bros. Co. (Hoof).AA
New York City
Livingston Nail Co. (Apple; Potato) ....A
N. Y.—Rochester
Boutell Mfg. Co. (Power Apple) C
PA.—Reading
Penn. Hardware Co. (Fruit) AA
Reading Hardware Co. (Apple) ....AAA

PARQUETRY

See Floors; Carpet; Wood

PARTITIONS

ILL.—Chicago
Dodge & Co., H. B. (Wood Rolling) ....D
Illinois Terra Cotta Lumber Co., The Rookery Bldg. (Floors; Fireproof)...AA
Imperial Expanded Metal Co., Monadnock Bldg. (Floors; Fireproof)......D
Mackolite Fireproofing Co., 1303 Schiller Bldg. (Mackolite; Floors; Fireproof) B
Voss, Frederick, 621 Austin Av. (Floors; Wire Lath) B
IND.—Kokomo
Kokomo Fence Mach. Co. (Wire) ....AAA
KY.—Bowling Green
Hartman Sliding Blind Co. (Ball Bearing; Wood Rolling) ....D
MASS.—Boston
Eastern Expanded Metal Co. Pemberton Bldg. (Floors; Fireproof) ....A

PARTITIONS (Con.)

MASS.—Clinton
Clinton Wire Cloth Co. (Floors; Fireproof) ..AAA
MICH.—Detroit
Amos & Co., Chas. (Metal) F
MO.—Kansas City
Swearingen Mfg. Co. (Steel Rolling) X
MO.—St. Louis
Lasar Letzig Mfg. Co., 16th & O'Fallon (Floors; Fireproof) C
Schoenthaler Mfg. Co. (Bottle Packing) C
N. Y.—Brooklyn
Forman, Robert J., 127 Court (Stock) ....E
Schratwieser Fire Proof Construction Co., 3d Av. & 7th (Floors; Fireproof).D
N. Y.—Buffalo
Buffalo Expanded Metal Co., D. S. Morgan Bldg. (Floors; Fireproof).....B
New York City
Bailey, Thos., 501 W. 151st (Floors; Fireproof)....B
City Fire Proofing Co., 611 W. 51st (Floors; Fireproof) ....F
Doehring Fireproof Construction Co., 1123 B'way (Floors; Fireproof).....B
Hayes Co., Geo., 71 8th Av. (Floors; Fireproof).....B
Maurer & Son, Henry, 420 E. 23d (Floors; Fireproof) AA
Metropolitan Fire Proofing Co., 13 Burling Slip (Floors; Fireproof) ....D
Monahan, Martin J., 1123 B'way (& Floors; Fireproof) ....F
Roebling Construction Co., 121 Liberty (& Floors; Fireproof) ....B
Sanitary Fireproofing & Contracting Co., 422 E. 106th (& Floors; Fireproof) ..D
White Fireproof Construction Co., 162 W. 27th (Floors; Fireproof) ....D
Wilson Mfg. Co., Jas. G., 3 W. 29th (Steel Rolling; Wood Rolling).........A
OHIO—Cleveland
Garry Iron & Steel Co. (Metal) ....A
National Concrete Fireproofing Co., New England Bldg. (Floors; Fireproof) C
OHIO—Columbus
Columbus Steel Rolling Shutter Co. (Steel Rolling) ....D
International Fence & Fireproofing Co., Buttes Av. (Floors; Fireproof).....A
Kinnear Mfg. Co. (Steel Rolling) ....AA
OHIO—Youngstown
Youngstown Iron & Steel Roofing Co. (Metal)...AA
PA.—Philadelphia
Merritt & Co., 1024 Ridge Av. (Floors; Fireproof).B
PA.—Pittsburg
National Fireproofing Co., Frick Bldg. (Floors; Fireproof) ....AAAA

PASSE-MENTERIES

New York City
Hertlein, Christopher, 15 Mercer ....AA
Ohle & Broeker, 537 B'way C
PA.—Philadelphia
Loeb Lipper & Co.........A

PASSE-PARTOUTS

MASS.—New Bedford
Pierce Mfg. Co........AAA

MASS.—Springfield
Taber-Prang Art Co.....AA

PASTE

ILL.—Chicago
Chapman & Smith Co.
(Almond) ....A
Martell Co. (Shoe Black-
ing) ....E
Sanford Mfg. Co., 223
Fulton (Sticky).......B
ILL.—Geneva
Kleinbeck, C. K. (Caramel)
D
IND.—Indianapolis
Bessire Co., H. (Almond).D
MD.—Baltimore
Meyers & Hicks Co., 104 S.
Howard (Almond) ....E
MASS.—Boston
Baker & Co., Chas. F.
(Shoe Blacking) ....A
Brown & Co., B. F. (Shoe
Blacking) ....B
Carter's Ink Co. (Flour)..A
Wood Co., Geo. H. (Shoe
Blacking) C
MASS.—Cambridge
Whittemore Bros. & Co.
(Shoe Blacking) .....AA
MASS.—Lowell
Hoyt & Co., E. W. (Tooth;
Powders) ....AA
MO.—St. Louis
Lewison & Blythe Mfg. Co.
(Flour) ....D
N. Y.—Albany
Diamond Paste Co. (Flour;
Bookbinders'; Dry; Of-
fice; Paperhangers'
Shoemakers'; Trunkmak-
ers'; Photographers').AA
New York City
Arabol Mfg. Co., 100 Wil-
liam (Bottlers').......A
Bixby & Co., S. M. (Shoe
Blacking) ....B
Caswell, Massey & Co.
(Tooth; Powders)......X
Devoe, F. W., & C. T. Ray-
nolds Co. (Photographers')
AAAA
Heide, H., 88 Vandam
(Almond) ....AA
Hoyt, Arthur S. (Flour;
Bookbinders'; Dry; Paper-
Hangers; Powdered)....B
Johnson & Johnson(Inc.)..
(Tooth; Powders)..AAAA
Lazell, Dalley & Co. (Tooth;
Powders) ....A
Miller Co., Frank (Shoe
Blacking) ....A
Prescott & Co., J. L. (Shoe
Blacking) ....A
Ricksiecker Co., Theo.
(Tooth; Powders)......C
Silberstein, A. L. (Razor)
A
Stafford, S. S. (Photograph-
ers') ....B
Wood & Selick, 36 Hudson
(Almond) ....A
N. Y.—Rochester
Scott's Arabian Hoof Paste
Co. (Hoof) ....E
N. J.—Utica
Tacks Mfg. Co. (Bottlers';
Brewers'; Canners'; Com-
mercial; Condensed;
Liquid) ....F
OHIO—Cleveland
Cuyahoga Chemical Co.
(Chicle) ....D
OHIO—Columbus
Buckeye Paste Co. (Carriage
Trimmers') ....H
PA.—Easton
World Refining Co. (Shoe
Blacking) X
PA.—Philadelphia
Continental Mfg. Co.
(Photographers') ......D
Diamond. McDonnell & Co.
(Shoe Blacking) ....D
Guano & Reggia (Fancy
Italian) ....B
Mason Co., Jas. S.
(Shoe Blacking) ....A
Nice Co., Eugene (Label)..A

PASTE (*Con.*)
Vail Bros. (Tooth; Powders)
X
White Dental Mfg. Co., The
S. S., 120 Chest. (Tooth)
AAAA
PA.—Pittsburg
Atlas Paint Co. (Ltd.), 2638
Liberty Av. (Anti-Rust)
X
R. I.—Providence
Calder Co., A. L. (Tooth;
& Powders) ....B

PASTEURIZERS

See Apparatus; Brewers

PATCHES

N. Y.—Binghamton
Crandal, Stone & Co. (Carriage; Wagon) ....A

PATTERNS

See also Models

CONN.—Bridgeport
Grant Mfg. & Machine Co.
(Metal) ....E
Schwerdtle Stamp Co.
(Metal) ....F
CONN.—Bristol
Smith, Ira B. ....E
CONN.—New Haven
Burgess, E. A., 67 Court
(Wood; Metal) ....F
CONN.—South Norwalk
Colonial Foundry & Machry.
Co. ....B
CONN.—Waterbury
Blake & Johnson (Metal).A
DEL.—Wilmington
Walker & Kyle ....F
ILL.—Chicago
Elmes Engineering Wks.,
Chas. F. ....A
New Idea Pattern Co., 234
5th Av. (Dress) ....A
Ryan & Co., J. J. (Metal).C
Van Pelt, Geo. H. (Boot;
Shoe) C
ILL.—Freeport
Stover Mfg. Co. (Metal)..
AA
ILL.—Harvey
Whiting Foundry Equipment
Co. (Wood; Metal) ....AA
MASS.—Boston
Hartford Bros. (Shoe) ...E
White & Son, W. B. (Boot)
D
Whitemore, W. E. (Shoe)
C
MASS.—Brocton
Brocton Last Co. (Sole) ..B
MASS.—Worcester
Kidder, R. E. (Metal)....E
MICH.—Detroit
Buhl Malleable Co. .....A
Cope Pattern Wks., G. W.
(Stove) ....D
Kahl Pattern Co., Fred
(Wood; Metal) ....D
MO.—St. Louis
Pleuger & Henger Mfg. Co.
(Metal) ....A
N. J.—Jersey City
Williams & Sons, E. A.
(Metal) ....AA
N. Y.—Albany
Clark, Jno. W. (Wood;
Metal) ....D
N. Y.—Buffalo
Acme Steel & Malleable Iron
Wks. (Wood; Metal)...A
Buffalo Gear & Pattern
Wks., 20 Elk (Gear, cut
by Machinery) ....G
Buffalo Pattern Wks. (Edw.
Simon. Prop.) (Wood;
Metal) ....F
N. Y.—Manlius
Cheney & Son. S. ....A
New York City
Butterick Publishing Co.
(Ltd.), 7 W. 13th (Paper)
AAAA
Demorest Pattern Co.
(Paper) X
McCall Co., 113 W. 31st
(Paper) ....A

PATTERNS (Con.)
McDowell Garment Drafting
Mach. Co. (Paper) X
Oldens Son, Geoffry J.
(Shoe) ....E
N. Y.—Rochester
Rochester Last Wks. (Shoe)
D
N. Y.—Syracuse
Smith & Caffrey ....D
N. Y.—Troy
West Side Foundry Co., 3rd
n. 28th (Wood; Metal)..A
OHIO—Canton
Canton Foundry & Machine
Co. ....B
OHIO—Cleveland
Cleveland Punch & Shear
Wks. ....A
Forrest City Brass Wks.
(Metal) ....B
Forrest City Foundry &
Mfg. Co. ....A
Garry Iron & Steel Co....A
Gobeille Pattern Co.
(Stove) ....D
Macbeth Iron Co., 57 W.
Center ....A
Palmers & De Mooy Foun-
dry Co. (Metal) ......A
Taylor & Boggis Foundry
Co. (Metal) ....AA
Wellman-Seaver-Morgan Co.
AAAA
OHIO—Columbus
Case Mfg. Co. ....A
OHIO—Toledo
Baker Bros. ....A
Donovan Wire & Iron Co.
C
OHIO—Warren
Trumbull Mfg. Co. C
OHIO—Youngstown
Forsyth Pattern Co. (for
Castings from ¼ lb. to
75 tons) ....D
Mahoning Pattern Co. (all
Kinds) ....F
Mahoning Foundry & Ma-
chine Co. ....A
PA.—Bloomsburg
Harmon-Cogger Co. C
PA.—Chester
Penn Pattern Wks. ......D
PA.—Columbia
Columbia Gray Iron Co.
(Metal) ....D
PA.—Lancaster
Barry & Zecher (Metal)..F
PA.—Nazareth
Nazareth Foundry & Ma-
chine Co. ....A
PA.—Philadelphia
Eynon-Evans Mfg. Co., 1519
Clearfield ....A
Kempton & Son, C. C.
(Shoe) C
Philadelphia Gear Wks., 135
N. 7th (Wood; Metal).D
PA.—Pittsburg
Brush & Stephens Co., 106
Penn Av. ....D
Carron & Co., A. M., 108
Market (Metal) ....D
Standard Pattern Co., 3rd
Av. & Ferry (All Kinds)
E
PA.—South Bethlehem
Bethlehem Foundry & Mach.
Co. (Metal) C
PA.—Wrightsville
Susquehanna Castings Co.
(Metal) ....AA
PA.—York
York Pattern Wks. (Metal)
E
VA.—Richmond
Richmond Pattern Wks.
(Wood) ....E

PAULINS

ILL.—Chicago
Carpenter & Co., Geo. B...
AA

PAVEMENTS

MD.—Baltimore
Maryland Pavement Co.
(Concrete) ....D
N. Y.—Brooklyn
Wilson & Baillie Mfg. Co.
(Concrete) ....B

PAVEMENTS (Con.)
New York City
Barber Asphalt Paving Co.,
144 Liberty (Asphalt)...
AAAA
Continental Asphalt Paving
Co., 32 B'way (Asphalt)
D
OHIO—Lockland
Carey Mfg. Co., Philip
(Asphalt) ....AAA
PA.—Philadelphia
Krause & Son, Wm. (Arti-
ficial Stone) ....D

PAWLS

MASS.—Boston
Boston Gear Wks.
(Ratchet) ....B

PEACHES:

See Canned Goods
Dried Fruits

PEANUTS

FLA.—Tampa
Crenshaw Bros. C
KY.—Milldale
Weller Co., J. (Br.).....A
MO.—St. Louis
Bayle, Geo. A., 13 S. 2nd B
Barnhart Merc. Co., 518
N. 2nd ....B
St. Louis Edible Nut Co.,
216 N. Coml. C
N. C.—Weldon
Carolina Peanut Co. C
N. C.—Wilmington
American Peanut Co. .....B
Cooper, W. B. ....B
OHIO—Cincinnati
Shinkle, Wilson & Kreis
Co. ....,..AA
PA.—Bedford
Heckerman, H. C. C
PA.—Norristown
Scheetz, Remandus ......A
PA.—Philadelphia
Brown & McMahon, 334 N.
Front ....B
Lummis & Co. (Inc.), 148
N. Del. Av. ....B
TENN.—Britts Landing
Anchor Peanut Co. ....B
TENN.—Nashville
Cooley & Co., J, S. .....A
VA.—Courtland
Bain & Co. ....B
VA.—Franklin
Pretlow Peanut Co. .....A
Virginia Peanut Co. C
VA.—Holland
Holland Edible Nut Co....C
Holland & Lee Co. .....A
VA.—Norfolk
Columbian Peanut Co. ...C
Cotton Oil & Fibre Co.
(Peanut Oil) .....AAAA
Merchants' & Farmers'
Peanut Co. ....B
Norfolk-Va. Peanut Co....C
VA.—Petersburg
Chieves & Co. ....B
Hartley & Bro., E. A. ...B
Levy Peanut Co., M. ...C
Maclin Peanut Co., J. H.
C
Rodgers, McCabe & Co....A
Petersburg Peanut Co.....C
VA.—Smithfield
Gwaltney-Bunkley Peanut
Co. ....A
Smithfield Peanut Co. ...B
VA.—Suffolk
Lummis & Co. (Inc.) ...B
Nausemond Peanut Co....C
VA.—Wakefield
Wakefield Peanut Co. ...B
VA.—Waverly
Waverley Peanut Co......C

PEARL GOODS

See Jewelry for Pearls &
Imitation Pearls

MASS.—Taunton
Taunton Pearl Wks. ....B
N. J.—Newark
Cory & Bro., W. F. .....B

PEARL GOODS (Con.)
Huebner & Sons, C. C
N. Y.—Brooklyn
Union Pearl Works, 235
Berry ....D
Wengenroth, Chas. W., 176
N. 4th ....D
New York City
Freidman, J., 92 Spring..B
Juergens Bros., 83 Chambers ....B
Roberts, A., 239 Centre..X
Wallbot, Hy., 440 Canal..D

PEARS

See Canned Goods; Dried Fruits

PEAS

See also Canned Goods

CAL.—San Francisco
Amer. Milling Co. (Green;
Split, etc.) ....A
Capitol Mills (Green;
Split, etc.) ....AA
Hinz & Plagemann (Green;
Split, etc.) ....B
Volkman & Co., C. S.
(Green; Split, etc.) C
CONN.—Hartford
Fitzgerald, R. N. (Green;
Split, etc.) ....B
DEL.—Seaford
Greenbaum & Bros.
(Canned) ....A
FLA.—Tampa
Crenshaw Bros. (Green;
Split, etc.) C
ILL.—Chicago
Dickinson Co., Albert
(Green; Split, etc.)...AA
M. O. H. Co. (The)
(Roasted; Cooked, etc.).B
KY.—Owensboro
Blue Grass Canning Co.
(Canned) ....B
MD.—Baltimore
Bolgiano & Son, J. (Green;
Split, etc.) C
Gibbs Preserving Co.
(Canned) ....A
MICH.—Adrian
Acme Preserving Co.
(Canned) ....D
MICH.—Carsonville
Tellson Co., E. D. (Green;
Split, etc.) ....A
MICH.—Jackson
Isbell & Co., S. M. (Green;
Split, etc.) ....A
MICH.—Port Huron
McMorran Milling Co.
(Green; Split, etc.) ...A
N. Y.—Buffalo
Erie Preserving Co.
(Canned) ....AAA
N. Y.—Cape Vincent
Cape Vincent Seed Co.
(Ltd.) (Green; Split,
etc.) C
Cleveland Seed Co. (Green;
Split, etc.) ....A
New York City
Jackson, E. N. (Green;
Split, etc.) C
Miles & Holman, 19 Whitehall ....A
Wakeman & Co., Jno.
(Green; Split, etc.) ...A
OHIO—Cleveland
Haserot Canneries Co.
(Canned) ....B
PA.—Philadelphia
Barker & Co. (Green;
Split, etc.) C
VA.—Richmond
Wood & Sons, T. W.
(Green; Split, etc.) ...B
WIS.—Kewaunee
Kewaunee Grain Co.
(Green; Split, etc.) ...A
WIS.—Manitowoc
Schuette Bros. (Green;
Split, etc.) ....A
WIS.—Milwaukee
Courteen, S. G. (Green;
Split, etc.) C
Pierce Co., A. J. W.
(Green; Split, etc.) ...B
Wisconsin Seed Co. (Green;

PEAS (Con.)
Split, etc.) ....D

PEAVIES

MICH.—Evart
Champion Tool & Handle
Wks. (Solid Socket)..AA
MICH.—Saginaw
Morley Bros. ....AA
OHIO—Cleveland
Gerlach Co., Peter ....A
PA.—Eldred
Prouty & Co., C. (also
Peavie Handles) ......B
WIS.—Oshkosh
Sanford Logging Tool Co.,
A. ....D

PECANS

See Nuts: Edible

PEDALS

CONN.—Bridgeport
Bridgeport Gun Implement
Co. (Bicycle) ....AA
ILL.—Chicago
Walker & Ehrman Mfg. Co.
(Bicycle) ....A
IND.—Indianapolis
Leedy Mfg. Co. ....E
MASS.—Worcester
Bay State Stamping Co.
(Bicycle) ....E
N. Y.—Buffalo
Forsyth Mfg. Co. (Bicycle)
.....................C
New York City
N. Y. Belting & Packing
Co. (Bicycle; Rubber)...
.....................AAA
N. Y.—Syracuse
Syracuse Arms Co. (Bicycle)
.....................B
OHIO—Akron
Goodrich Co., B. F. (Bicycle; Rubber) .....AAAA
OHIO—Cleveland
Federal Mfg. Co. (Bicycle)
.....................AAAA
OHIO—Elyria
Topliff & Ely Co. (Bicycle)
.....................B
PA.—Philadelphia
Faxon Co., Geo. H.
(Piano) ....D

PEDESTALS

See also Woodwork; Furniture

CONN.—Meriden
Bradley & Hubbard Mfg.
Co. (Metal) .....AAAA
IND.—Evansville
Bockstege Furniture Co.
(Wooden) C
MD.—Baltimore
Ellicott Machine Co.
(Shaft) C
MICH.—Grand Rapids
Oriel Cabinet Co. ....AAA
N. J.—Trenton
Trenton Potteries Co..AAA
New York City
Homan Co., Andrew ....D
Judd & Co., H. L. (Brass)
.....................AA
OHIO—Cincinnati
Mitchell Furniture Co.
Robert ....AAAA
OHIO—Zanesville
Owens Pottery Co., J. B.
(Jardenier) ....A
Zanesville Art Pottery Co.
(Pottery) ....B
PA.—Allegheny
Pittsburg Lamp Brass
& Glass Co. (Brass)....
.....................AAAA
PA.—Philadelphia
Cresson Co., Geo. V.
(Shaft) ....AA
Smith & Co., Geo. W. ...A
PA.—Wilkesbarre
Vulcan Iron Wks. (Shaft)
.....................AA'A
WIS.—Milwaukee
Filer & Stowell Co. (Ltd.)
(Shaft) ....AAA

PEDESTALS (Con.)
Meinecke & Son, A. ....AA

PEDOMETERS

CONN.—New Haven
American Pedometer Co..F
New York City
Spaulding & Bros., A. G...
AAAA

PEGS

MASS.—Boston
McCarter, J. G. (Shoe)...D
MASS.—Brockton
Brockton Stay Co. (Shoe)
D
N. H.—Bartlett
Kearsarge Peg Co. (Shoe).D
N. H.—Lisbon
Moore Peg Co. (Shoe).....F
N. H.—Plymouth
Foster, Jacob R. (Shoe)..B
N. Y.—Salisbury Center
Kingsley Bros. (Shoe) ....F
OHIO—Dayton
Crawford, McGregor &
Canby (Shoe) ....AA

PENCILS

**For Gold Pencils see Pens:
Gold**

CONN.—East River
Munger & Son (Slate).....C
MASS.—Boston
Cutter-Tower Co. (Lead).B
MASS.—Northampton
Clark's Indelible Pencil Co.
(Indelible) X
N. J.—Jersey City
Dixon Crucible Co., Jos.
(Lead) ....AAA
N. Y.—Albany
Cox Brass Mfg. Co. (Paper)
C
New York City
Aiken, Lambert & Co.
(Gold) ....A
Amer. Lead Pencil Co., 491
B'way (Colored; Automatic; Lead; Nickel).AA
Eagle Pencil Co., 377
B'way (Colored; Automatic; Copying Ink;
Lead; Lumber; Slate)...
AAA
Faber, Eberhard, 545 Pearl
(Colored; Slate; Automatic; Lead; Lumber) ...
AAA
Foley Pen Co., John (Gold)
X
Foley, Jr., John (Gold)..D
Johnson & Co., E. S. (Gold;
Plated; Silver) ......D
Keuffel & Esser Co. (Lead)
AA
Mabbie, Todd & Bard ...A
Soltman, E. G., 125 E.
42nd (Graphite Drawing)
B
Spencerian Pen Co. (Lead)
AA
Wetmore Co., S. H. (Caustic) ....D
OHIO—Cincinnati
Holland Gold Pen Co., John
(Automatic) ....B
PA.—Philadelphia
Blaisdell Paper Pencil Co.
(Paper) ....B
R. I.—Providence
Pearce & Co., F. F. C
TENN.—Chattanooga
American Lava Co. (Slate)
D
Steward Mfg. Co., D. M.
(Slate) ....B

PENDANTS

See also Jewelry

ILL.—Chicago
Baggot Co., E. (Gas) ...D
Edwards Mfg. Co., W. S.
(Gas) ....A
MASS.—Boston
Ripley-Howland Mfg. Co.
(Jewelry) ....A

PENDANTS (Con.)
N. J.—Bound Brook
Standard Gas Fixture Co.
(Harp) ....B
N. J.—Newark
Block & Bergfels (Jewelry)
B
Durand & Co. (Inc.)
(Jewelry) ....AA
Hedges & Co., A. J. (Jewelry) ....A
N. Y.—Brooklyn
Vosburgh Mfg. Co., W. C.
(Ltd.) (Gas) X
New York City
Alling & Co. (Jewelry)...
AA
Ansonia Brass & Copper Co.
(Gas) ....AAAA
Frink, I. P. (Gas) ..AA
Gleason Mfg. Co., E. P.
(Gas) ....B
Mitchell-Vance Co. (Gas)..
AA
Rothschild Bros. (Jewelry)
C
Sloan & Co. (Jewelry) ..B
R. I.—Providence
Corry & Reynolds (Jewelry)
C
Fowler Bros. (Jewelry) ..C
Hancock Co., Chas. E.
(Jewelry) ....B
Moorhead & Co., R. L.
(Jewelry) ....B
Wall & Co., A. T. (Jewelry)
C

PENS

CONN.—Meriden
Miller Bros. Cutlery Co.
(Steel) ....A
CONN.—New Haven
Nickeloid Pen Co. (Steel
Writing) X
D. C.—Washington
Arlington Fountain Pen Co.
(Fountain) X
ILL.—Chicago
Crown Pen Co., 78 State
(Fountain) ....E
Grieshaber, B., 86 State
(Fountain; Gold) .....D
Hyland Pen Co., Francis,
145 La Salle (Steel Writing) X
Mabie, Todd & Bard, 96
State (Fountain; Gold)
A
Madison & Steel Co., Masonic Temple (Fountain)
C
LA.—New Orleans
Hill, A. M.((Gold) ....B
MASS.—Boston
Cutter-Tower Co. (Glass).B
Sterling Fountain Pen Co.,
19 Milk (Fountain) ...A
MICH.—Detroit
Laughlin Mfg. Co. (Fountain) ....D
MICH.—Kalamazoo
Ihling Bros. & Wishard
(Steel Writing) ....B
Richardson & Co., J. M.
X
MO.—St. Louis
Wright Pen Co. (Gold)...H
NEBR.—Omaha
Western Electric Co. (Electric) ....D
N. H.—Wilton
Satisfaction Fountain Pen
Co. (Fountain) X
N. J.—Camden
Estabrook Steel Pen Mfg.
Co. (Silverine; Yellow
Metal; Crow Quill; Quill
Steel) ....AA
Hunt Pen Co., C. Howard
(Writing) ....A
New York City
Aiken, Lambert & Co., 19
Maiden Lane (Fountain;
Gold) ....A
American Lead Pencil Co.,
491 B'way (Steel) ....AA
Armeny & Marion, 90 Nassau (Gold) ....B
Barnes & Co., A. S., 156
5th Av. (Steel) ....AA
Beaumel. D. W., 45 John
(Fountain) ....D

PERCOLATORS

CONN.—Meriden
Manning, Bowman & Co.
  (Coffee) ....AA
ILL.—Chicago
Pelouze Scale & Mfg. Co.,
  118 W. Jackson Boul.
  (Coffee) C
MICH.—Detroit
Cotton, Arthur (Pharmaceu-
  tical) C
N. J.—Burlington
Stewart & Peterson Co....A
New York City
Sternau & Co., S., 204
  Church ....A

PERFORATORS

See also Protectors

ILL.—Chicago
Cummins Co., B. F., 42 W.
  Jackson Boul. (Check)..C
Tengwall File & Ledger Co.
  (Paper) ....B
New York City
Wesley Mfg. Co., 31 Beek-
  man (Check) X
OHIO—Cincinnati
Globe-Wernecke Co. (Paper)
  AAAA
PA.—Harrisburg
Hickok Mfg. Co., W. O.
  (Hand) ....AA
PA.—Philadelphia
Hill Mfg. Co., B. B., 1020
  New Market (Ticket) ..B
Ott, Geo. F., 207 Button-
  wood (Iron) ....A

PERFUMERY

ILL.—Chicago
Kirk Bros. ....F
Wrisley Co., Allen B., 485
  5th Av. X
MD.—Baltimore
McCormick & Co. ....D
MICH.—Detroit
Seeley Mfg. Co. C
Stearns & Co., Fred..AAA
Wright & Co., Chas.....X
MO.—St. Louis
Eddy & Eddy, 500 Main..A
Koken Barbers' Supply Co.
  A
N. Y.—Buffalo
Larkin Co. ....AAAA
New York City
Caswell, Massey & Co....X
Colgate & Co. ......AAAA
Eureka Soap Co., 332 Bway.
  AA
Hall & Ruckel, 215
  Washington ......AAAA
Ladd & Coffin (Colognes)
  AA
Lazell, Dalley & Co.
  (Colognes) ....A
McKesson & Robbins.AAAA
Palmer, Solon ....D
Perfume Tablet Co., 10 E.
  23rd X
Ricksecker Co., Theo., 74
  Reade C
Riker & Son Co., Wm. B.
  AA
Tappan, H. ....AA
Tarrant & Co. (Inc.) ....D
N. Y.—Rochester
Wright, Alfred .. ..A
OHIO—Cincinnati
Freeman Perfume Co.....D
OHIO—Dayton
Sachs-Pruden Ginger Ale
  Co. ....D
OHIO—Findlay
Happer Extract & Perfume
  Co. ....F
OHIO—Toledo
Lorenz Co., Geo. ....D
PA.—Lancaster
Pennsylvania Soap Co..AAA
PA.—Philadelphia
Clauson Co. C
Smith, Kline & French Co.
  AAA
Tetlow, Joseph, 101 Cherry
  A
Vaile Bros. C

PEROXIDE

New York City
American Peroxide & Chem.
  Co., 88 Maiden Lane ..C

PESSARIES

ILL.—Chicago
Huston Bros., 35 Rand...F
MASS.—Andover
Tyer Rubber Co. (Rubber)
  AA
MASS.—Boston
Davidson Rubber Co. (Rub-
  ber) ....A
N. J.—Trenton
Stokes Rubber Co., Jos.
  (Truss) ....A
New York City
Goodyear's India Rubber
  Glove Mfg. Co. (Rubber)
  AAAA
Parker, Stearns & Sutton
  B
OHIO—Akron
Akron Rubber Co. (Rubber)
  AAAA
Miller Rubber Mfg. Co.
  (Rubber) ....B
PA.—Philadelphia
Horn & Bro., Wm. H.
  (Rubber) ....B
Phila. Truss & Bandage Co.
  (Rubber; Spiral Spring).
  X
Seeley, Isaac B. (Rubber)
  F
Ware Co., Walter F. ..B
Whitall, Tatum & Co.
  (Spiral Spring) ..AAAA
R. I.—Providence
Davol Rubber Co. .....AA

PETROLATUM

MD.—Baltimore
McCormick & Co. ....D
N. Y.—Binghamton
Binghamton Oil Refining
  Co. ....A
New York City
Cheesbrough Mfg. Co. ...
  AAAA
Colgate & Co. ....AAAA
Schieffelin & Co., W. H...
  AA
OHIO—Cleveland
Atlantic Refining Co. ..A
Monitor Oil Co. C
PA.—Freedom
Freedom Oil Wks. Co....A
PA.—Philadelphia
Crew, Levick Co., 113 Arch
  AAA

PETROLEUM

N. Y.—Buffalo
Merchants' Refining Co...C
New York City
Born, Schrymser & Co....A
Columbia Oil Co., 13 Wil-
  liam ....A
Standard Oil Co., 26 B'way
  AAAA
Tidewater Oil Co. (Crude)
  AAAA
OHIO—Cleveland
Canfield Oil Co. ....A
Clark Co., Fred. G. .....A
Climax Refining Co., Wil-
  liamson Bldg. ....D
National Refining Co......
  AAA
OHIO—Toledo
Paragon Refining Co. ..AA
Sun Oil Co. ....AAA
PA.—Allegheny
Millers' Sons Co., A. D...B
PA.—Bradford
Barnsdall, Theo. N.
  (Crude) ....AAAA
Bisett Bros. (Crude).....C
Cochrane, Jas. E. (Crude)
  B
Coleman, Penny & Boyne
  (Crude) ....B
Collins, C. P. (Crude).AA
Devonian Oil Co. (Crude)
  AA
Edgett, A. J. (Crude)...C
Emery, Jr., L. (Crude)....
  AAAA

PETROLEUM (*Con.*)
Emery Oil Co. (Crude)....
AAAA
Haskell, J. E. (Crude)...A
Healey, J. H. (Crude)...B
Jones, J. T. (Crude).....
AAAA
Kennedy & Co., W. C.
(Crude) ....AAAA
Lavens, C. H. (Crude)...B
Mallory, L. E. (Crude)..B
Potter, Geo. H. (Crude)..B
Quintuple Oil Co. (Crude)
AAAA
Thompson, T. P. (Crude).A
PA.—Emlenton
Emlenton Refining Co...AA
PA.—Franklin
Atlantic Refining Co. ...
AAAA
PA.—Freedom
Freedom Oil Wks. ....A
PA.—Oil City
Continental Refining Co.
(Ltd.) ....A
Crystal Oil Wks. ....A
Empire Oil Wks. ....A
Germania Refining Co. ..A
Independent Refining Co.
(Ltd.) ....AA
Penn Refining Co. ......A
PA.—Philadelphia
Pure Oil Co., Manhattan
Bldg. ....AAAA
Union Petroleum Co., 138
S. 4th ....AA
PA.—Pittsburg
Guffey Petroleum Co., J.
M., Frick Bldg. (Crude).
AAAA
Gulf Refining Co. ....AAA
Hazlewood Oil Co. .....AA
Pittsburg Oil Refining Co.,
429 1st Av. ....A
Sun Co. ....A
Waverly Oil Works ....AA
PA.—Titusville
Amer. Oil Wks. (Ltd.)..A
McKinney Bros. (Crude)..
AAAA
Rice Soap Co. (Crude)...C
Titusville Oil Works .....A
PA.—Warren
Conewango Refining Co...B
Cornplanter Refining Co...
AA
Crew-Levick Co. .....AAA
Smith, Levi ....A
Superior Oil Works C
Wilburine Oil Wks. (Ltd.)
AAA

PETTICOATS

See Clothing: Ladies'

PEWS

ILL.—Chicago
Evans & Co., R. O., 210
Madison (Church) ....A
IOWA—Charles City
Smith & Co., Geo. P.
(Church) ....D
N. Y.—Brooklyn
Brooklyn Furniture Co.
(Church) ....A
New York City
Lamb, J. & R., 59 Carmine
(Church) ....D

PHAETONS

See Carriages & Wagons

PHONO-
GRAPHS

ILL.—Chicago
Lambert & Co., 12 Sherman
D
Talking Machine Co., 107
W. Madison ....B
N. J.—Orange
Edison Phonograph Wks...
AA
National Phonograph Co.,
83 Chambers ......AAAA
New York City
Amer. Graphphone Co. ...
AAAA
Columbia Phonograph Co..A

PHONOGRAPHS (*Con.*)
Edison Phonograph Agency
D
PA.—Philadelphia
Penn Phonograph Co., 19 S.
9th ....D

PHOSPHATE

See Fertilizers

PHOSPHATE:
ACID, CHERRY,
ETC.

ILL.—Chicago
Thompson Phosphate Co.,
404 Ogden Av. ....B
Victor Chemical Wks.,
Board of Trade .....AA
MD.—Baltimore
Crawford Co., W. H., 112
S. Gay ....E
Thomsen Chem. Co., Equita-
ble Bldg. ....B
MASS.—Natick
Ford Cherry Phosphate Co.
(Wild Cherry) ....F
MICH.—Detroit
Detroit Chem. Works, 238
Junction Av. (Lime) ..B
N. Y.—Kingston
Ceres Chem. Co. (for
Bakg. Powder) ....D
New York City
Burnham Co., E. S., 61
Gansevoort (Wild Cherry)
B
Maas & Waldstein, 107
Murray ....A
Williamson & Co., D. D.,
14 Dey ....B
R. I.—Providence
Rumford Chem. Works ...
AAA
WIS.—Waukesha
Jaynes Bros. (Wild Cherry)
D

PHOSPHOR-
IZERS

PA.—Pittsburg
McCullough-Dalzell Crucible
Co. (Brass Foundry)....A

PHOSPHORUS

New York City
General Chemical Co., 25
Broad ....AAAA
Riker, J. L. & D. S., 46
Cedar ....A
PA.—Easton
Baker & Adamson Chemical
Co. ....A
PA.—Philadelphia
Allen's Sons, J. J., Bourse
Bldg. ....AA
Crescent Phosphorized Metal
Co. ....D
General Chemical Co.....
AAAA

PHOTO-
GRAVURES

MASS.—Springfield
Tabel-Prang Art Co. ...AA
N. Y.—Buffalo
Gies & Co. ....AAA
New York City
Ringler Co., F. A. .....A

PHOTOMETERS

MASS.—Boston
Tufts Meter Co., Nathaniel
A
MASS.—Lynn
Dwyer Machine Co. (Fac-
tory) ....F
N. J.—Newark
Electric Motor & Equip-
ment Co. C
N. Y.—Albany
McDonald & Co., D. .....A
New York City
Am. Gas Light Assn., 58
William X
American Meter Co., 11th

Av. & 47th ....B
Connelly Iron Sponge &
   Governor Co. (Gas) ....B
National Meter Co. ......A
PA.—Philadelphia
Helme & McIlhenny ....AA

PIANOS

COLO.—Denver
Knight-Locke Piano Co...A
CONN.—Derby
Sterling Co. ....AA
CONN.—New Haven
Matushek Piano Mfg. Co.
   ....AA
Shoninger Co., B. ....AAA
Sonnenberg Piano Co., M.
   ....A
GA.—Atlanta
Phillips & Crew Co......A
ILL.—Chicago
Bent, Geo. P., 211 Wabash
   Av. ....AAA
Cable Co., 240 Wabash Av.
   ....AAAA
Detmer, Henry, 337 Wabash
   Av. ....A
Kimball Co., W. W., 26th
   & Rockwell ......AAAA
Moore Organ Co. ....A
Newman Bros. Co., Chicago
   Av. & Dix ....A
Price & Teeple Co., 206
   Wabash Av. ....A
Schaeffer Piano Mfg. Co.,
   215 Wabash ....A
Schulz Co., 373 Milwaukee
   ....AA
Singer Piano Co., 235 Wa-
   bash Av. ....A
Smith & Barnes Piano Co.,
   471 Clyburn Av. ..AAA
Steger & Sons Piano Mfg.
   Co., 225 Wabash Av...
   ....AAA
Story & Clark Co., 255 Wa-
   bash Av. ....AA
ILL.—Oregon
Schiller Piano Co. ......A
ILL.—Ottawa
Western Cottage Piano &
   Organ Co. ....AAA
ILL.—Rockford
Haddorf Piano Co. .....AA
IND.—Fort Wayne
Packard Co. ....AA
IND.—New Castle
Krell-French Piano Co..AA
IND.—Richmond
Starr Piano Co. ....AA
KY.—Dayton
Harvard Piano Co. ..AAAA
MASS.—Boston
Champion & Co., Geo. H.,
   118 Fremont ....A
Chickering & Sons, 791
   Fremont ....AAA
Emerson Piano Co., 120
   Boylston ....AA
Ivers & Pond Piano Co., 114
   Boylston ....AA
McPhail Piano Co., A. M.,
   120 Boylston ....A
Miller & Sons Piano Co.,
   H. F., 88 Boylston ...A
Vose & Sons Piano Co., 158
   Boylston ....AA
MASS.—Cambridge
Mason & Hamlin Co. ...A
MD.—Baltimore
Knabe & Co., Wm. ...AAA
MICH.—Ann Arbor
Ann Arbor Organ Co.....A
MICH.—Detroit
Clough & Warren Co. ...A
MICH.—Muskegon
Chase-Hackley Piano Co..A
MICH.—Saginaw
Germain Piano Co., E.AA
MO.—St. Louis
Bollman Bros. Piano Co.,
   1120 Olive ....AA
French Piano & Organ Co.,
   J. ....AAAA
Kieselhorst Piano Co....A
N. J.—Washington
Cornish Co. ....AA
N. Y.—Auburn
Wegman Piano Co. ......A
N. Y.—Brockport

Brockport Piano Mfg. Co.,
   ....A
N. Y.—Brooklyn
Smith, F. G. ....AAA
Wissner, Otto, 1078 Atlan-
   tic Av. ....AA
N. Y.—Buffalo
Kurtzmann & Co., C.....A
New York City
Cable & Sons, 554 W. 38th
   ....A
Decker & Sons, 971 E.
   135th ....A
Doll & Son, Jacob, 92 5th
   Av. ....AA
Fischer, J. & C., 417 W.
   28th ....AA
Gabler & Bro., Ernest, 109
   E. 107th ....AA
Hardman, Peck & Co., 138
   5th Av. ....AA
Hazleton Bros., 66 Uni-
   versity Pl. ....A
Kohler & Campbell, 601 W.
   50th ....A
Kranich & Bach, 235 E.
   23rd ....AA
Kroeger Piano Co., 81
   Alex Av. ....A
Needham Piano & Organ
   Co., 96 5th Av. .....A
Pease Piano Co., 128 W.
   42nd ....A
Schubert Piano Co., 1 W.
   139th ....A
Sohmer & Co., 170 5th Av.
   ....AA
Steinway & Sons, 109 E.
   14th ....A
Tonk & Bro., Wm., 452
   10th Av. ....A

*Manufacturers of Ern-
est A. Tonk Piano, an
instrument of extraor-
dinary tone quality, ele-
gant in design and finish,
extraordinary durability,
especially constructed for
extreme climates—export
a specialty.*

Waters & Co., Horace, 134
   5th Av. ....A
Weber Piano Co., 105 5th
   Av. ....AA
Weser Bros., 149 W. 33rd
   ....A
N. Y.—Rochester
Armstrong Piano Co. ....A
Foster-Armstrong Co....A
Gibbons & Stone ....A
Marshall & Wendell Piano
   Co. ....A
Martin & Bro., J. W.....A
OHIO—Cincinnati
Baldwin & Co., D. H. ....A
Krell Piano Co. ....A
Smith & Nixon Piano Mfg.
   Co. ....A
OHIO—Norwalk
Chase Co., A. B. ......AA
PA.—Easton
Lehr & Co., H. ....A
PA.—Lebanon
Miller Organ & Piano Co..A
PA.—Philadelphia
Blasius & Sons, 1101 Chest-
   nut ....AA
Cunningham Piano Co., 1105
   Chestnut ....A
Lester Piano Co., 1308
   Chestnut ....AA
PA.—Scranton
Van Dyke Piano Mfg. Co.
   ....A
PA.—York
Weaver Organ & Piano Co.
   ....AA

PICKAROONS

MICH.—Evart
Champion Tool & Handle
   Wks. ....AA
Evart Tool Co. ....D

PICKERS

CONN.—Bridgeport
Acme Shear Co. (Flower;

PICKERS (Con.)
Fruit) ....B
CONN.—Danbury
Heim Machine Co. (Blower)
D
CONN.—Danielsonville
Jacobs Mfg. Co., E. H.
(Loom) ....B
CONN.—Georgetown
Gilbert & Bennett Mfg. Co.
(Fruit) ....AAA
ILL.—Canton
Parlin & Orendorff Co.
(Potato, & Diggers)......
AAAA
MAINE—Saco
Garland Mfg. Co. C
MASS.—Dedham
Abbott Mfg. Co., J. V.
(Loom) ....D
MASS.—Fall River
Union Belt Co. (Loom)...B
MASS.—Franklin
Clark Mach. & Foundry Co.
(Rag; Shoddy; Wool)...X
Milliken & Son, W. (Loom)
D
MASS.—Lawrence
Barlow Co., Jno. W.
(Loom) ....E
MASS.—Lowell
Dodge, C. S. (Rag; Shoddy)
X
Gates & Sons, Josiah
(Loom) ....D
Kimball, L. S. (Loom) ...X
Kitson Mach. Co. (Rag;
Shoddy) ....AAA
Stott, S. E. & T. (Rag;
Shoddy) X
MASS.—New Bedford
Pickles, Joseph (Loom) ..F
MASS.—Newton Upper
Falls
Saco & Pettee Mach. Shop
AAA
MASS.—Westfield
Crane Bros. (Loom) ..AAA
MASS.—Westford
Sargent's Sons, C. G. (Burr)
A
MASS.—Whitinsville
Whitin Mach Co. ....AAAA
MASS.—Worcester
Cleveland Mach. Wks.....A
Crompton & Knowles Loom
Wks. (Loom) ....AAAA
Curtis & Marble Mach.
Wks. (Burr; Wool) ....A
Parker Wire Goods Co.
(Flower; Fruit) ....B
Wire Goods Co. (Flower;
Fruit) ....B
MICH.—Pontiac
Bacon Mfg. Co. (Bean)...X
N. J.—Belleville
Atlas Foundry & Mach. Co.
(Burr; Hair) ....D
N. Y.—Middleport
Knapp, E. (Bean) ......E
New York City
Hungerford Bros. & Co.
(Peanut) ....B
N. Y.—Rochester
Streetor Co., N. R.
(Flower) ....A
N. Y.—Utica
Williams Co., J. H. (Loom)
A
OHIO—Akron
Akron Belting Co. (Loom)
A
OHIO—Cincinnati
Day & Co., J. H. (Hair)..A
OHIO—Clyde
Clyde Cutlery Co. (Grape).C
PA.—Philadelphia
Darby & Sons, Edward, 233
Arch (Fruit) ....A
Phila. Textile Machry. Co.,
Hancock & Somerset...AA
Schofield Co., Wm. (Rag;
Shoddy) ....B
Smith Woolen Machry. Co.,
Jas., 411 Race (Burr;
Loom; Rag; Shoddy;
Wool) ....AA
R. I.—Pawtucket
Atherton Mach. Co., A. T.
B
R. I.—Providence
Brown Bros. Co. (Loom)..B

PICKERS (Con.)
Burgess & Sons, A. (Loom)
X
Holbrook, A. & C. W.
(Loom) ....B
R. I.—Woonsocket
Coburn, Fred. S., 243 Main
(Loom) X
Wilkins Mfg. Co.. 14 S.
Main (Cotton Filled)...X

PICKETS

See also Fences; Lumber

ILL.—Chicago
Barbee Wire & Iron Wks.
(Malleable) ....B
Braun, J. G., 322 S. Pau-
lina (& Rosettes, Steel).A
N. Y.—Albany
Clark, Jno. W. (& Rosettes,
Iron) ....D
New York City
Eckstein, Chas. G., 249 Cen-
tre (& Rosettes, Iron)..D
PA.—Chester
Keystone Drop Forge Wks.
(& Rosettes, Drop Forged
Iron) ....B
PA.—Pittsburg
Oliver Iron & Steel Co.
(Steel Fence) .....AAAA
WIS.—So. Milwaukee
Stowell Mfg. & Foundry Co.
(& Rosettes, Iron) .....A

PICKLES

See Cider; Vinegar, etc.

PICKS

See also Toothpicks

CAL.—San Francisco
Doble Co., Abner (Stone).A
CONN.—Chester
Bates, C. J. (Tooth; Alaska
Ivory) ....D
CONN.—Deep River
Williams & Marvin Mfg. Co.
(Ice) ....D
CONN.—Meriden
Meriden Britannia Co.
(Nut) ....AAAA
Meriden Cutlery Co.
(Nut) ....AA
CONN.—New Britain
Landers. Frary & Clark
(Ice; Nut) ....AAA
CONN.—New Haven
Harrison, Leonard D.
(Mill) ....H
CONN.—Southington
Peck. Stow & Wilcox Co.
(Ice) ....AAAA
CONN.—Unionville
Hmphrey. H. W. (Ice)...D
CONN.—Wallingford
Simpson, Hall, Miller & Co.
(Nut) ....AAAA
Wallace & Sons Mfg. Co.,
R. (Nut) ....AAAA
CONN.—West Port
Bradley's Sons, G. W.
(Mill) ....D
ILL—Chicago
Amer. Cutlery Co. (Nut) AA
Cassaday-Fairbank Mfg. Co.
(Ice; Nut) C
Higgins & Son. Jno. C., 169
W. Kinzie (Mill) ....E
Nicol & Co. (Ice) ....D
Union Drop Forge Co., 66
E. Ohio (Clay; Contrac-
tors'; Drifting; Mining;
Railroad; Tamping) ..A
ILL.—Freeport
Arcade Mfg. Co. (Ice) ....A
Redlinger, M. (Bung) ....F
Stover Mfg. Co. (Ice) ..AA
IND.—Evansville
Evansville Tool Wks. (Mill;
Mining; Poll; Railroad;
Stone) ....A
IND.—Frankfort
Frankfort Handle Mfg. Co.
(Railroad) ....E
IND.—Indianapolis
Nordyke & Marmon Co.
(Mill) ....AAA

PICKS (Con.)

IOWA—Ottumwa
Hardsocg Mfg. Co. (Drifting) ....B

MASS.—Boston
Cutter-Tower Co. (Tooth; Wood) ....B
Harvey, H. H., 606 Atlantic Av. (Mill; Railroad; Stone) ....D
Isele & Son, G. W. (Contractors'; Railroad; Stone)..F

MASS.—Brockton
Tuck Mfg. Co. (Ice) .....E

MASS.—Fiskdale
Snell Mfg. Co. (Ice) ....B

MASS.—Northampton
Northampton Cutlery Co. (Nut) ....A

MASS.—Shelburne Falls
Lamson & Goodnow Mfg. Co. (Nut) ....A
Mayhew Co., H. H. (Ice)..D

MASS.—Turners Falls
Russell Cutlery Co., John (Nut) ....AA

MASS.—West Mansfield
Standard Tool Co. (Ice)..H

MICH.—Detroit
Anderson & Sons, W. H. (Clay; Contractors'; Drifting; Mill; Mining; Railroad; Stone; Surface; Tamping) C

N. J.—Mahwah
Amer. Brake Shoe & Foundry Co. (Coal) ....A

N. J.—Newark
Atha Tool Co. (Contractors'; Mill; Railroad; Stone)..A
Osborne & Co., C. S. (Ice).B

N. Y.—Albany
Troy Nickel Wks. (Jno. E. Gaitley, Prop.) (Nickel Plated Ice; & Breakers) C

N. Y.—Brooklyn
Pollard, Jos. G., 141 Raymond (Contractors'; Mill; Railroad) ....F

N. Y.—Buffalo
Noye Mfg. Co., John T. (Mill) X

N. Y.—Elmira
Cronk & Carrier Mfg. Co. (Ice) ....B

N. Y.—Herkimer
Quackenbush, H. M. (Nut) ....A

New York City
Amer. Axe & Tool Co., 253 B'way (Railroad; Stone) ....AAAA
Carey, Samuel (Mill) C
Grote & Co., F. (Tooth; Ivory) ....D
International Silver Co. (Nut) ...AAAA
Judd & Co., H. L. (Nut)... AA
Koppel, Arthur, 68 Broad (Contractors'; Railroad).A
Leavitt & Co., C. W., 15 Cortlandt (Contractors'; Railroad) ....D
Sargent & Co. (Ice) ..AAAA
Smith & Hemenway (Ice).D
Wabusch & Hilger.......A

N. Y.—Rochester
Tisserand Mfg. Co., Essex Bldg. (Tooth) ....F

N. Y.—Troy
Palmer Hardware Mfg. Co. (Ice) ....D

OHIO—Cleveland
Fanner Mfg. Co. (Ice) ....A
Federal Mfg. Co., Amer. Trust Bldg. (Ice; Nut)... AAAA

OHIO—Dayton
Dayton Malleable Iron Co. (Malleable Iron; Points; Ore; Case Hardened; Locomotive Coal) .....AAA

OHIO—Findlay
Findlay Axe & Tool Co. (Clay; Contractors'; Drifting; Mining; Poll; Railroad; Surface) ....A

OHIO—Ravenna
Williams, A. C. (Ice) ....A

OHIO—Toledo
Hartley, Geo. W. (Mill)..D

PICKS (Con.)

PA.—Allegheny
Hardsocg Mfg. Co., Martin (Drifting; Mining) ....B
Heathcote, Thos. (Stone)..G

PA.—Beaver Falls
Beaver Falls Mfg. Co.(Clay; Mining; Stone) ....B

PA.—Chester
Black & Co., H. B. (Firemen's Truck; Mill; Stone) AA

PA.—Erie
Erie Specialty Co. (Ice).B

PA.—Fleetwood
Kern, Amandus (Mill) ....F

PA.—Honesdale
White Axe Co., G. (Mill).D

PA.—Howard
Howard Iron & Tool Co. (Mining) ....B

PA.—Muncy
Sprout, Waldron & Co. (Mill) ....A

PO.—Ogontz
Hammond & Son, C. (Mill) A

PA.—Philadelphia
Plumb, Fayette R. (Inc.) (Clay; Drifting; Mining; Poll; Railroad; Stone; Surface; Tamping) ...AA
Smith Co., J. Barton, N. 4th & Somerset (Ice)...D
Stortz & Son, Jno. 210 Vine (Boiler; Ice; Mill) ....E

PA.—Philipsburg
Gills Sons, Jno. D. (Mining) ....E

PA.—Pittsburg
Hubbard & Co., Murtland Bldg. (Clay; Locomotive Coal; Coal Mining; Stone; Tamping) ....AA
Iron City Tool Works (Ltd.) 32d & Smallman (Clay Contractors'; Drifting; Mining; Poll; Railroad; Stone Surface; Tamping; Mill) ....A
Jones & Laughlins Steel Co. (Clay; Contractors'; Mining; Stone) .....AAAA
Klein-Logan Co., Breed & S. 13th (Clay; Contractors'; Drifting; Mining; Poll; Railroad; Stone Tamping) ....A
Oliver Iron & Steel Co. (Clay; Contractors'; Drifting; Mining; Poll; Surface; Tamping) ...AAA
Pittsburg Tool & Drop Forge Co., Arrott Bldg (Clay; Mining; Tamping) ....D

PA.—Reading
Franklin Specialty Co. (Nickel Plated; Hickory Handle Ice) ....G

PA.—Wrightsville
Wrightsville Hardware Co. B

W. VA.—Wheeling
Warwood Tool Co. (Mining) B

WIS.—Racine
Foster & Williams Mfg. Co. (Flax Tow) ....B

PICKUPS

OHIO—Cleveland
Electric Controller & Supply Co. (Crane; Electric) A

PICTURES: MOULDINGS & FRAMES

ILL.—Chicago
Cass & Co., B. F. (Pictures; Mouldings; Frames) C
Great Northern Moulding Co. (Mouldings) ....B
Harsha Mfg., L. R. (Mouldings) C
Illinois Moulding Co. (Mouldings) ....B
Kern Co., The A. F. (Mouldings Room; Picture Frames; Easels; Framed

PICTURES: FRAMES

Pictures; Wall Pockets; Art Gds.; Novelties ...C
Klein Co., A. S. (Pictures; Frames) ....A
Larson & Co., C. (Mouldings) C
Mueller Bros. Art Mfg. Co. (Framed Pictures; Picture Frames; Art Gds.) C
Newcomb-Macklin Co. (Mouldings) ....D
Planett Mfg. Co. (Picture Frames; Gilt Furn.) ...D
Raubold & Lambin (Mouldings) C
Schram Bros. (Mouldings) B
Smalley Mfg. Co. (Picture Frames; Easels; Wall Pockets) C
Sparr & Weiss (Picture Mouldings) ....B
Vilas Co., A. H. (Picture Frames; Easels) .....B
KY.—Louisville
Lindsey, T. N. (Picture Frames) ....D
MAINE.—Ellsworth
Ellsworth Hardware Co. (Mouldings) ....E
MD.—Baltimore
Esselmann Co., Geo. (Picture Mouldings) ......D
Furst Bros. & Co. (Picture Frames; Mouldings) C
Hamp Co., Conrad (Picture Mouldings) ....B
MASS.—Boston
Boston Mirror Co. (Inc.) (Frames; Mouldings) ..D
MASS.—Springfield
Bradley Co., Milton (Sectional) ....A
Taber-Prang Art Co. (Framed) ....AA
MICH.—Detroit
Hargreaves Mfg. Co. (Picture Frame Mouldings) A
Lawrence & Co., Leonard (Pictures; Picture Frames; Mouldings) AAA
MINN.—Minneapolis
Bintliff Mfg. Co. (Picture Mouldings) ....D
MO.—St. Louis
Baxter Moulding Co. (Mouldings; Frames; Framed Pictures; Mirrors, etc.) C
Webber Moulding Co., J. R. (Moulding; Frames; Easels; Pictures) C
N. J.—Newark
Schrafft & Co., A. (Picture Mouldings) ....A
N. Y.—Brooklyn
White, Potter & Page Mfg. Co. (Picture Frames) ..A
New York City
Hickok & Pate (Religious Pictures) ....E
Lippe & Co. (Wood) ...C
PA.—Philadelphia
Beck Paper Co. (Relief) B

PIECES: MOUTH

See Mouthpieces

PIERS

PA.—Beaver Falls
Penn Bridge Co. (Iron; Steel) ....AA
PA.—Philadelphia
Phoenix Bridge Co. (Iron; Steel) ....A
PA.—Steelton
Pennsylvania Steel Co. (Iron; Steel) ......AAAA

PIGEONS

New York City
Hartley & Co., M. (Clay) ....AAA
OHIO—Cleveland
Chamberlain Cartridge & Target Co. (Clay) ......A

PIGMENTS

See also Colors

PIGMENTS (Con.)

N. Y.—Niagara Falls
International Acheson Graphite Co. (Graphite) ...B
PA.—Easton
Williams & Co., C. K. ....A

PILING

See also Lumber

FLA.—Pensacola
Thornton, H. H. (Pine) ...F
GA.—Savannah
Southern Pine Co. of Georgia (Pine) ....AAA
MICH.—Bay City
Michigan Pipe Co. (Creosoted) ....AA

PILLOWS

See also Bedding

MASS.—Andover
Tyer Rubber Co. (Air) ..AA
MASS.—Boston
Davidson Rubber Co. (Air) A
New York City
Goodyears' India Rubber Glove Mfg. Co. (Air) AAAA
Goodyear Rubber Co. (Air) AAAA
Hall, Francis A. (Hair) ..B
Hodgeman Rubber Co. (Air) AA
Ostermoor & Co. (Hair) ..A
R. I.—Providence
Davol Rubber Co. (Air) AA
WIS.—Racine
Chicago Rubber Clothing Co. (Air) ....A

PILLS

ILL.—Chicago
Baker Co., Chas. S. (Coated) C
IND.—Indianapolis
Lilly & Co., Eli (Coated; Gelatine) ....AA
MD.—Baltimore
McCormick & Co. (Quinine) D
Sharpe & Dohme (Coated; Gelatine) ....AAA
MASS.—Cambridge
Thayer & Co., Henry (Coated) ....A
MICH.—Detroit
Parke, Davis & Co. (Coated; Gelatine) ....AAAA
Stearns & Co., Fred (Coated) AAA
MICH.—Kalamazoo
Upjohn Co. ....AA
New York City
Keith & Co., B. (Coated) F
McKesson & Robbins (Coated; Gelatine) AAAA
Parke, Davis & Co. ..AAAA
Schieffelin & Co., W. H. AA
Tutt Mfg. Co., Dr. ......B
OHIO—Cincinnati
Merrell Chemical Co., Wm. S. (Sugar Coated) ..AAA
PA.—Ambler
Keasby & Mattison Co. (Coated; Gelatine) AAAA
PA.—Philadelphia
Hance Bros. & White (Coated; Gelatine) ..AA
Nittinger Sr., August ...A
Powers-Weightman-Rosengarten Co. ....AAAA
Wythe & Bro. J. (Coated) AAAA
PA.—Pittsburg
Fleming Bros. Co. X

PILOCARPINE

New York City
Roessler & Hasslacher Chemical Co, ...AA

PINCHERS

CONN.—Bridgeport
Bridgeport Hdw. Mfg. Co. B
CONN.—Southington
Peck, Stow & Wilcox Co. (All Kinds) ......AAAA

PINCHERS (Con.)

ILL.—Chicago
Vaughn & Bushnell Mfg. Co.
877 Carroll Av. (Carpenters) ....A
ILL.—Downer's Grove
Dicke Tool Co. (Farriers') C
ILL.—Freeport
Arcade Mfg. Co. (Cast
Iron) ....A
MASS.—Boston
Whitcher & Co., Frank W.
(Shoemakers') ....A
MO.—Kansas City
Russell Hdw. & Implement
Mfg. Co. X
N. J.—Newark
Atha Tool Co. (Farriers') A
Heller Bros. Co., 879 Mt.
Prospect Av. ....AA
Johnson, Wm. (Shoemakers') ....D
Osborne & Co., C. Louis S.
................B
Sacks Iron Fdry. ....A
New York City
Sargent & Co. ...AAAA
OHIO—Cleveland
Columbian Hardware Co.,
Coe & Hamilton ......AA
OHIO—Ravenna
Williams, A. C. ....A

PINE TREE PRODUCTS

N. C.—Wilmington
Spiritine Chem. Co........C

Manufacturers and Refiners of Pure Pitch Pine Product.
Awarded Medal and Diploma by the World's Columbian Exposition in 1893, and Atlanta, Ga., 1895, Buffalo, 1901 and Charleston, S. C., 1901-2. Spirittine Wood Preserver, Spirittine Mercury Wood Preserver, Oil of Tar, Wood Creosote Oil, Spirittine Wood Filler, Pure Pine Oil, Spirittine Paint Oil, Spirittine Brick Preserver, Soluble Spirittine for Insectiside and Disinfectants, Spirittine Disinfectants No. 1, Spirittine Disinfectants No. 2, Refined Pyrolignous Acid, Sheep Dip, Black Rubber Varnish, Deck Varnish, Wood Naptha, Wood Spirit Turpentine, Pinoleum Cable Coating, Spirittine Pine Rubber Graphite and Metallic Composition Paint, Metallic Brown, Metallic Composition Black, Hanson's Mercury Bottom Coating.

PINE

See Lumber

PINEAPPLES

ALA.—Mobile
Muscat & Lott ....D
CAL.—San Francisco
Brandenstein & Co., M. J.,
118 Mkt. ....AAAA
Macondray & Co., 116
Calif. ....B
D. C.—Washington
Adams & Co., E. J., 907
B. N. W. ....D
MD.—Baltimore
Buckman Fruit Co., 205
Bowleys Whf. ....B
Kirwan-Schall Fruit Co. ..E
Lawder & Sons, Saml., M.,
2215 Boston C
West India Trading Co. ..B
New York City
Brown & Co., W. H., 161
Maiden Lane ....D

PINEAPPLES (Con.)

Courtin, Golden & Co., 87
Front ....D
Hutcheson & Co., A. G., 106
Front ....A
Lester, F. H., 97 Park Pl. D
McCormick, Hobbs & Co.,
279 Washn. ....A
Nix & Co., J., 281 Washn. A
Roberts, J., 158 Front ....E
Ruhlman & Co., P., 261
Washn. ....B
OREGON—Portland
Oriental-American Co.
(Imprts.) C
PA.—Philadelphia
Weinert & Co., Wm., 260
No. Front C

PINIONS

See also Gears

CONN.—Derby
Birmingham Iron Foundry
(Combination Mill) ..AA
ILL.—Chicago
Chicago Raw Hide Mfg. Co.,
75 E. Ohio (Raw Hide) A
KANS.—Leavenworth
Great Western Mfg. Co. AA
MD.—Baltimore
Poole Engineering & Mach.
Co. (Gearing; Elec.
R'way) ....AA
MASS.—Holyoke
Holyoke Machine Co. ..AA
N. J.—High Bridge
Taylor Iron & Steel Co.
...................AAAA
N. Y.—Brooklyn
Bliss Co., E. W., 19 Adams
(Pressed Steel; Electric
Railway) ....AAAA
N. Y.—Buffalo
Pratt & Letchworth Co.
(Steel) ....AAA
N. Y.—Catskill
Catskill Foundry & Mach.
Wks. (Electric Railway)B
New York City
Johns-Manville Co., H. W.,
100 William (Electric
Railway) ....AAAA
OHIO—Cleveland
Cleveland Gear Wks. (Electric Railway) X
Horsburg & Scott Co., 108
Canal (Electric Railway)
...................B
Van Dorn & Dutton Co., 1796
E. Madison Av. (Electric
Railway) ....B
PA.—Chester
Chester Steel Casting Co. AA
PA.—Philadelphia
Phila. Roll & Mchry. Co.,
So. 23d & Washn. Av.
(Roll) ....A
PA.—Pittsburg
Fawcus Machine Co., 2818
Smallman (Electric Railway) ....B
Garrison Foundry Co., A.,
9th & Bingham (Double
Spiral) ....AAA
Hogg Iron & Steel Foundry,
Geo. A., 24th & R. R. ..A
Mesta Machine Co., Lewis
Blk. (Roll) ....AAAA
Nuttall Co., R. D., Lafayette & Garrison Pl. (Electric Railway) ....A
Pittsburg Steel Foundry Co.
...................AA
Seaman-Sleith Co. (Roll) AA
Simonds Mfg. Co. (Electric
Railway) ....B
PA.—Rankin Station
Duquesne Forge Co. (Electric
Railway) ....A
PA.—Wilkesbarre
Vulcan Iron Wks. ...AAAA
R. I.—Providence
Brown & Sharpe Mfg. Co.
(Electric Railway) AAAA
WIS.—Milwaukee
Falk Co., ft. 30th (Electric
Railway) ....AAA
Western Rawhide & Belting
Co. (Rawhide; Elec.
R'way) ....B

PINS

See also Jewelry; also Brackets for Wood Pins

CONN.—Bridgeport
Bridgeport Brass Co. (Escutcheon; Brass; Iron) ....AAA
Nilson Machine Co., A. H. (Safety) ....E

CONN.—Bristol
Sessions & Son, J. H. (Escutcheon) ....AA

CONN.—Collinsville
Hartigan, Wm. R. (Rolling) ....H

CONN.—Deep River
Williams & Marvin Mfg. Co. (Rolling) ....D

CONN.—Derby
Howe Mfg. Co. (Brass; Button; Eye; Hat; Headless; Iron; Mixed; Mourning; Ribbon; Scarf Mfrs.; Shawl; Tape) ....A
Hartford Machine Screw Co. (Taper) ....AAAA
Jewell Belting Co. (Toilet) ....AAA
Jewell Pin Co. (Toilet) ...B
Pratt & Whitney Co. (Tapering) ....AAAA

CONN.—Manchester
Lydall & Foulds, H. (Hackle) ....B

CONN.—Meriden
Foster, Merriman & Co. (Escutcheon; Brass; Hat) AA

CONN.—Middletown
Wilcox Crittenden & Co. (Belaying) ....A

CONN.—New Britain
Humason & Beckley Mfg. Co. (Ox Yoke Bow) ...A
Landers, Frary & Clark (Brass) ....AAA
Russell & Erwin Mfg. Co. (Escutcheon; Shelf) AAAA

CONN.—New Haven
North & Co., O. B. (Picket) ....AA

CONN.—New London
Brown Cotton Gin Co. (Cotton Gin) ....AA

CONN.—Oakville
Oakville Co. (Metal; Safety) ....A

CONN.—Southington
Peck, Stow & Wilcox Co. (Ox Yoke Bow) ..AAAA

CONN.—Torrington
Progressive Mrg. Co. (Brass; Copper; German Silver; Special; Dowell; Taper) A
Turner & Seymour Mfg. Co. (Escutcheon; Rivet; Drapery; Safety) ....A

CONN.—Waterbury
Amer. Pin Co. (Brass Escutcheon; Brass; Hat; Headless; Drapery; Iron; Safety; Hair; Tag) .....AA
Amer. Ring Co. (Hat) .....A
Blake & Johnson (Inc.) (Aluminum; German Silver; Brass; Copper; Steel; Hair; Special) ....A
Holmes, Booth & Hayden Co. (Escutcheon) ....AAAA
Plume & Atwood Mfg. Co. (Escutcheon; Brass; Toilet) ....AAA
Scovil Mfg. Co. (Escutcheon) ....AAAA
Waterbury Brass Co. (Escutcheon) ....AAAA
Waterbury Button Co. (Safety; Toilet) ....A

CONN.—Winsted
New England Pin Co. (Pyramid) ....AA

GA.—Atlanta
Van Winkle Gin & Mach. Wks. E. (Cotton Gin) AAA

ILL.—Chicago
American Steel & Wire Co., The Rookery (Brass; Steel; Escutcheon) AAAA
Escanaba Woodenware Co., Manhattan Bldg. (Clothes) ....A
Gould & Co., L., 48 Wabash Av. (Clothes) ....AAA

PINS (Con.)
Grand Crossing Tack Co. (S. Chicago Av. & 79th (Escutcheon; Dowel; Sash) ....AAA
Illinois Malleable Iron Co. (Pump) ....AAAA
Pratt Mfg. Co., Wm. E., 91 Lake (Husking) ....B
Redlich Mfg. Co. (Ten)...B
Republic Iron & Steel Co., 108 La Salle (&; Links Coupling) ....AAAA
Standard Screw Co., 2 N. Canal (Tapar) ......AAA
Union Drop Forge Co., 66 E. Ohio (& Shafts; Crank), A

ILL.—Freeport
Arcade Mfg. Co. (Husking) ....A
Walker & Ehrman Mfg. Co. (Taper) ....A

ILL.—Lemont
Illinois Pure Aluminum Co. (Hair) X

IND.—Indianapolis
Tucker & Dorsey Mfg. Co. (Rolling) ....A

IND.—Kokomo
Kokomo Steel & Wire Co. (Barbed; Dowel) ....AAA

MAINE—Portland
Laughlin Co., Thos. (Belaying) ....A

MAINE—So. Portland
Marine Hardware & Equipment Co. (Belaying) C

MAINE—West Paris
Mann, Lewis M. (Clothes) C

MAINE—West Peru
Austin & Son, E. G. (Clothes) ....D

MASS.—Attleboro
Bliss Bros. Co. (Bar) .....A
Daggett & Clapp Co. (Bar) ....A
Horton, Angell & Co. (Ladies Cuff) ....A
Regnell, Bigney & Co. (Bar; Bonnet) ....B
Robbins Co., Chas. M. (National Flag) C

MASS.—Boston
Boston Forge Co., 340 Maverick (& Shafts; Crank)..A
Boston & Lockport Block Co., 160 Commercial (Belaying) ....A
Eastern Forge Co., 70 Kilby (& Shafts; Crank) ......B
New England Novelty Mfg. Co. (Button) ....H
Ripley-Howland Mfg. Co. (Brooch; Gold) ....A
Stoddard, Haserick, Richards & Co., 1152 Congress (Gill; Combing) ....B

MASS.—Bridgewater
Perkins Co., Henry (Escutcheon) ....B

MASS.—Chartley
Freeman, Daughaday & Co. (Bar; Scarf; Shawl) C

MASS.—Greenfield
Automatic Machine Co. (Taper) C

MASS.—Leominster
Blodgett & Co., B. F. (Hair; Horn) ....B

MASS.—Lowell
Bagshaw, W. H. (Estate of) (Picker) ....B
Dodge, C. S. (Hot Forged Picker) ....D
Stott, Samuel E. & T. (Picker) X

MASS.—New Bedford
Morse Twist Drill & Mach. Co. (Taper) ....AAA

MASS.—North Attleboro
Barrows & Co., H. F. (Bar; Bonnet) ....A
Blackington & Co., R. (Bar; Scarf; Plated) ....A
Bugbee & Niles Co. (Bar; Brooch) ....A
Cheever, Tweedy & Co. (Hair) ....AAA
Coddington & Heilborn Co. (Bar; Scarf; Hat) .....A
Franklin & Co., E. I. (Bar; Bonnet; Hair; Ladies Cuff; Scarf) C

PINS (Con.)

Whiting Co., F. M. (Brooch) D

MASS.—Plainville

Plainville Stock Co. (Bar; Bonnet; Brooch; Hair; Scarf; Plated Scarf) ..A

MASS.—Plymouth

Plymouth Mills (Brass; Iron Escutcheon) ....B

MASS.—Taunton

Globe Mfg. Co. (Escutcheon; Brass; Iron) ....E
Taunton Wire Nail Co. (Escutcheon) ....D

MASS.—Worcester

Parker & Co., Jno. L. (Escutcheon; Hinge) ..B
Parker Wire Goods Co. (Dowel) ....D
Wire Goods Co. (Escutcheon; Dowel; Shelf; Regalia) .A
Worcester Machine Screw Co. (Taper) ....AAA
Wyman & Gordon (& Shafts; Crank) ....A

MICH.—Bay City

Vance Box Co., E. J. (Ltd.) (Tent) ....B

MICH.—Bellaire

Richardi & Bechtold (Clothes) ....B

MICH.—Crystal Falls

Crystal Falls Woodenware Co. (Clothes) C

MICH.—Custer

Custer Mfg. Co. (Clothes), E

MICH.—Detroit

Anderson & Sons, W. H. (Surveyors' Lining) ...C
Brownlee & Co. (Insulator) AA
Schulenburg Mfg. Co. (Ten) C

MICH.—Escanaba

Escanaba Woodenware Co. (Clothes) ....A

MICH.—Grand Rapids

Grand Rapids Brass Co. (Hat) ....A
Hardware Supply Co. (Shelf) X

MICH.—Ludington

Ludington Woodenware Co. (Clothes) C

MICH.—Northville

Dubuar Mfg. Co., J. A. (Belaying; Tent) X

MINN.—Minneapolis

Clark Co., J. R., 4th Av. & 2d Av. No. (Clothes) .C

MO.—Poplar Bluffs

Armstrong-Dowell Pin Co. (Dowell) ....D

MO.—St. Louis

Helmbacher Forge & Rolling Mills Co.. Cor. Barton & D'eKalb (Coupling; Crank; Links) ....AA
St. Louis Screw Co., 3017 N. 13th (Taper) ....A

N. H.—Manchester

Baldwin Co., Jas. (Insulator) ....AAAA

N. H.—Sutton

Wadleigh, M. B. ....D

N. J.—Jersey City

Mack Mfg. Co., Thos. A. (Dowell; Taper) X

N. J.—Newark

Adams & Co., Thos. W. (Bar; Scarf) ....B
Block & Bergfels (Bonnet; Brooch; Scarf) ....B
Crabb & Co., Wm. (Hackle; Cotton Gin) ....A
Durand & Co. (Inc.) (Bar; Bonnet; Brooch; Gold; Hair; Ladies Cuff; Scarf; Shawl; Society) ....AA
Hedges & Co., A. J. (Bar; Bonnet; Brooch; Gold; Hair; Ribbon; Scarf) ..A
Jenkinson & Co., R. C. (Escutcheon; Brass; Iron), A
Krementz & Co. (Hair; Scarf) ....AAA
Reeves & Brown (Bar; Bonnet; Ladies Cuff; Scarf) B
Sommer's Son, John (Insulator, Rolling) ....A

N. Y.—Binghamton

Titchener & Co., E. H. (Dowel) ....B

PINS (Con.)

N. Y.—Brooklyn

Brass Goods Mfg. Co. (Safety) ....B

N. Y.—Buffalo

Buffalo Forge Co. (Coupling) AAA

N. Y.—East Koy

Campbell, G. A. (Clothes), F

N. Y.—Edinburg

Tennant, S. (Clothes) ....D

N. Y.—Lockport

Western Block Co. (Belaying) C

New York City

Alling & Co. (Scarf) ....AA
Averbeck, M. J. (Bar; Brooch; Gold; Hair; Ladies Cuff) ....A
Braxmar Co., C. G. (Society) B
Brunswick - Balke-Collender Co. (Ten) ....AAAA
Cottle Co., S. (Gold).....E
Estes & Sons, E. B. (Rolling; Thole) ....AA
Etna Mfg. Co. (Taper) ...X
Gould-Mersereau Co. (Escutcheon; Brass Curtain) ..B
Tortoise Shell; Tent ....D
Grote & Co., F. (Hair, Ivory; Brass; Iron; Steel; German Silver; Tinned Escutcheon) ....B
Hassall, Jno., 169 Elm
Henrich, Henry (Scarf) ..E
Hicks, Chas. N., 226 South (Belaying) ....H
Hungerford Brass & Copper Co., 497 Pearl (Brass; Copper Escutcheon) ......AA
Judd & Co., H. L. (Escutcheon; Brass; Carpet; Sockets; Curtain; Hat) AA
Keuffel & Esser Co. (Drawing) ....AA
Maas & Co., Wm. (Bar; Hair) ....AA
Megill, Edward L. (Printing Press Gauge) ....B
Myers Co., S. F. (Bar; Brooch; Ladies Cuff; Plated Scarf) ....D
New York Nickel Plating & Mfg. Co. (Hinge) .....D
Richards & Co., E. Ira (Bar; Black Onyx; Bonnet Brooch, Hair, Ladies' Cuff, Ribbon Rolled Plate, Shawl) ....AAA
Sargent & Co. (Curtain; Ox Box; Shelf) ....AAA
Sexton & Co., Wm. L. (Bonnet; Hair) C
Shardlow, Joseph (Ten) ..D
Shrimpton Mfg. Co. (Household, etc.) ....G
Sloan & Co. (Inc.) (Bar; Bonnet; Brooch; Gold; Hair; Ribbon; Rolled Plate; Scarf; Shawl; Hat) B
Stern Bros. Co. (Bar) AAAA
Tiebout, W. & J. (Belaying; Sash) ....B
Trenkmann, August (Hair; Tortoise Shell) ......AAA

N. Y.—Northbush

Holmes, R. E. (Clothes), D

N. Y.—Rochester

Judson Pin Co. (Safety)...C

N. Y.—Victor

Locke Insulator Mfg. Co. (Insulator) ....A

N. Y.—Watervliet

Covert Mfg. Co. (Picket; Lariat) ....A

OHIO—Bucyrus

Blair Husking Glove Co. (Corn Husking) ....D

OHIO—Carthage

Block-Pollak Iron Co. (& Shafts; Crank) ......AAA

OHIO—Cincinnati

Cincinnati Screw & Tap Co. (Taper) ....A
Creaghead Engineering Co., 313 Walnut (Malleable Iron; High Tension)....D
Tower Mfg. Co. (Escutcheon) C

OHIO—Cleveland

Atlas Car & Mfg. Co.

PINS (Con.)

(Dowel) ....AA
Cleveland City Forge & Iron
   Co., 67 Case Av. (Coupl-
   ling; also Crank) .....AA
Francis. A. E., 780 Cedar
   (Clothes; Wire) ....F
Ohio Electric Co. (Scarf;
   Electric). ....D
Vulcanus Forging Co. (Air
   Brake) ....B
OHIO—Columbus
Ohio Tool Co. (Rolling), AA
OHIO—Elyria
Western Automatic Mach.
   Screw Co. (Carpet; Sock-
   ets; Shoulder; Taper), AA
OHIO—Hicksville
Kerr Bros. Mfg. Co. (Tent)
   C
OHIO—Piqua
Piqua Hndle & Mfg. Co.
   (Coal Mine Cartridge;
   Thole) ....B
OHIO—Toledo
Stevens Co.. B. A. (Bowl-
   ing Alley) ....A
OHIO—Youngstown
Finished Steel Co. (Bridge
   Polished Steel) ....A
PA.—Braeburn
Braeburn Steel Co. (&
   Shafts; Steel Crank)...A
PA.—Burnham
Logan Iron & Steel Co. (&
   Links; Coupling)......AA
PA.—Chester
Chester Steel Castings Co.
   (& Shafts; Crank) ....AA
Keystone Drop Forge Co. (&
   Links; Coupling) ......B
PA.—Candenport
Dodge Clothes Pin Mfg. Co..
   A. W. (Clothes) ....B
PA.—Eddystone
Tindell-Morris Co. (Crank)
   AA
PA.—Erie
Erie Forge Co. (& Shafts;
   Crank) ....A
PA.—Johnstown
Cambria Steel Co. (& Stafts;
   Crank) ....AAAA
PA.—Kushequa
Howells, Davis & Co.
   (Clothes) ....AA
PA.—Lebanon
Amer. Iron & Steel Mfg. Co.
   (Brake; Knuckle), AAAA
PA.—Lopez
Lopez Mfg. Co. (Clothes), A
PA.—McKee's Rocks
Lockhart Iron & Steel Co.
   (& Shafts; Crank) ....AA
PA.—Mechanicsburg
Wilcox Mfg. Co., D. (&
   Links; Coupling) ....A
PA.—Monroeton
Rockwell, John L. (Ten) ..F
PA.—New Castle
New Castle Forge & Bolt Co.
   (Brake; Knuckle; Coup-
   ling; also Links) ......AA
PA.—Philadelphia
Bingham, Jas. (Scarf) ....H
Midvale Steel Co. (& Shafts;
   Nickel Steel Crank) AAAA
Paxson Co., J. W. (Dowel)
   AA
Penna. Steel Co., Girard
   Bldg. (& Shafts; Crank)
   AAAA
PA.—Pittsburg
Carbon Steel Co. (& Shafts
   Nickel Steel Crank) ..AA
Carnegie Steel Co. (& Links;
   Couplin; also Crank)
   AAAA
Crucible Steel Co.. of Amer-
   ica (& Shafts; Crank)
   AAAA
Jones & Laughlins Steel Co.
   (& Links; Coupling: also
   Crank) ....AAAA
Morris & Bailey Steel Co. (&
   Shafts; Crank) ....A
Oliver Iron & Steel Co. (&
   Links; Coupling) ..AAAA
Pittsburg Forge & Iron Co.
   (& Links; Coupling) ....A
Pittsburg Screw & Bolt Co.
   (Taper) ....A
Pittsburg Steel Co. (Dowel)
   AAAA

PINS (Con.)

Steel Car Forge Co. (Con-
   nection) ....B
PA.—Rankin Station
Duquesne Forge Co. (&
   Shafts; Crank) ....A
PA.—Reading
Reading Hardware Co.
   (Shelf) ....AAAA
Reading Iron Co. (& Shafts;
   Crank) .... AAAA
PA.—Scranton
Scranton Bolt & Nut Co.
   (Brake; Knuckle) ....AA
PA.—So. Bethlehem
Bethlehem Steel Co. (&
   Shafts; Nickel Steel
   Crank; also Cross Head
   AAAA
PA.—Titusville
Titusville Forge Co. (&
   Shafts; Centre Throw
   Crank) ....A
PA.—Wilkesbarre
Vulcan Iron Wks. (& Shafts;
   Crank) ....AAAA
R. I.—Pawtucket
Jenckes Mfg. Co. (Wire
   Spring) ....A
R. I.—Providence
Adams & Co., D. F. (Black
   Onyx) C
Amer. Screw Co. (Escut-
   cheon; Brass) .....AAAA
Ballow & Co., B. A. (Bar;
   Ladies Cuff; Safety), AA
Cook Co., C. H. (Bar;
   Brooch; Gold; Hair;
   Ladies Cuff) ....D
Cory & Reynolds Co. (Bar;
   Scarf; Stick) C
Crossin & Co. (Bar; Brooch;
   Scarf; Hair) ....F
Cutler Jewelry Co. (Bar;
   Brooch; Ladies Cuff) ..D
Devereux & Co., O. C. (Bar;
   Scarf; Plated) ....D
Foster & Bros. Co.. Theo. W.
   (Bar; Scarf; Plated) ..AA
Fowler Bros. (Bar) C
Greene & Co., Wm. C.
   (Ladies' Cuff: Scarf)..D
Hancock Co.. Chas. E. (Bar;
   Ladies Cuff; Scarf; Hat)
   B
Irons & Russell (Gold; Soci-
   ety) ....A
Lederer & Co., S. B. (Bar;
   Brooch: Rolled Plate;
   Scarf Plated; Shawl; So-
   ciety) C
Linton Co., P. & A. (Rolled
   Plate; Scarf) ....B
Loeb & Co., Wm. (Stick;
   Hat) ....A
Luther & Son. Wm. H. (Bar;
   Brooch; Scarf; Scarf
   Plated) ....B
Moorehead & Co., R. L.
   (Bar; Brooch; Rolled
   Plate; Scarf; Scarf
   Plated) ....B
Narragansett Machine Co.
   (Ten) ....A
Ostby & Barton Co. (Brooch)
   AAA
Potter & Buffington Co.
   (Bar; Ladies Cuff) .....A
Richardson & Co., Josiah W.
   (Society) ....D
Schofield-Battery & Co.
   (Ladies Cuff) C
Snow & Westcott (Bar;
   Brooch; Ribbon; Scarf), A
Tockwolton Co. (Split) ....F
Waite, Mathewson & Co.
   (Bar; Ladies Cuff; Soci-
   ety) ....B
Waite-Thresher Co. (Scarf)
   A
Wilcox & Co., D. (Scarf)
   AA
VT.—Montpelier
U. S. Clothes Pin Co.
   (Clothes; Spring) ......D
VT.—Springfield
Mason Mfg. Co. (Clothes) H
VT.—Waterbury
Demeritt & Palmer Packing
   Co. (Clothes) ....E
VA.—Richmond
Richmond Cedar Wks.
   (Clothes) ....AAAA
Richmond Standard Steel

PINS (Con.)
Spike & Iron Co. (& Links; Coupling) X
Tredegar Co. (Coupling) AAA
VA.—Standardville
Standard Clothes Pin Co. (Clothes) ....D
VA.—Richwood
Dodge Clothes Pin Mfg. Co., A. W. (Clothes) ....;...A
WIS.—Kenosha
Stewart Mfg. Co. (Clothes) X
WIS.—Milwaukee
Meinecke & Sons, A. (Ten) AA
Milwaukee Tack Co. (Escutcheon) X
WIS.—Two Rivers
Aluminum Mfg. Co. (Hair; Aluminum) ....A

PIPE

See also Lead; also Pipes

ALA.—Bessemer
Bessemer Soil Pipe Co. (Cast Iron Soil; Fittings) .....B
ALA.—Birmingham
Birmingham Pipe & Casting Co. (Cast Iron Soil; Fittings) ....A
Dimmick Pipe Co. (Cast Iron Gas; Water) ....AA
ALA.—Gadsden
Gadsden Pipe & Fdry Co. (Cast Iron Soil & Fittings) C
CAL.—Lincoln
Gladding, McBean & Co. (Sewer) ....AA
CAL.—Los Angeles
Consolidated Pipe Co. (Riveted Steel) ....B
Lacy Mfg. Co. (Riveted Steel) ....AA
Pacific Clay Mfg. Co. (Vitrified; Sewer) ....A
Thompson & Boyle Co. (Riveted Steel) ....B
CAL.—Sacramento
Schaw, Batcher Co., 219 "J" (Riveted Steel) ....J
CAL.—San Francisco
Garrett & Co. (Inc.), W. T. (Brass) ....AA
Hendy Machine Wks., Joshua (Cast Iron; Gas; Steam; Water) ....AA
Montague & Co., W. W., 309 Market (Riveted Steel; Culvert; Sewer; Fire Clay; Stove) ....AAA
Risdon Iron & Locomotive Wks. (Cast Iron; Gas; Steam; Water) ....AAAA
San Fran. Bridge Co. (Riveted Steel) X
Selby Smelting & Lead Co. (Block Tin) ....AAA
Smith & Co., Francis, 83 Fremont (Riveted Steel; Riveted Iron) ....AA
Union Iron Wks., 222 Market (Riveted Steel) X
Woodin & Little (Cast Iron; Gas; Steam; Water) ....A
COLO.—Denver
Colorado Fuel & Iron Co. (Cast Iron 3 to 24 in.; Gas; Water) ....B
CONN.—Bridgeport
Belknap Mfg. Co. (Crown) C
Bridgeport Boiler Wks. Co. (Cast Iron; Gas; Steam; Water) ....D
Bridgeport Brass Co. (Brass) AAA
Pierce Mfg. Co. (Well) ...E
CONN.—Hartford
Stirling Blower & Pipe Mfg. Co., (Galvanized; Riveted) A
Whitlock Coil Pipe Co.....A
CONN.—New Haven
National Pipe Bending Co. (Copper) ....B
CONN.—New London
Burch & Co., H. O. (Culvert; Sewer) X
CONN.—Waterbury
Holmes, Booth & Haydens

PIPE (Con.)
Co. (Inc.) (Brass) .AAAA
Randolph-Clowes Co. (Flush; Supply) ....AAA
CONN.—Willimantic
Vanderman Plumbing & Heating Co. (Cast Iron; Soil; Fittings) C
GA.—Macon
Steven's Sons Co., H. (Culvert; Sewer) ....A
IDAHO—Wallace
Coeur D'Alene Hdw. Co. (Riveted Steel) ....AA
ILL.—Chicago
Aermotor Co., W. 12th & Rockwell Av. (Wrought Iron Pipe; Tube Mills) AAA
Allis-Chalmers Co., Home In.s Bldg. (Riveted Steel) AAAA
Amer. Spiral Pipe Wks. 1173 So. Paulina (Hydraulic; Steel Riveted; Sheet Iron; Spiral Steel Riveted) ...B
Blatchford & Co., E. W., 70 N. Clinton (Block Tin; Lead; Lead Tin Lined) AAAA
Carroll Iron Wks. (C. L. Bowes, Prop.), 719 Carrol Av. (Riveted Steel; Spiral Riveted) C
Clow & Sons, James B. (Cast Iron 2 to 48 in.; Gas; Water) ....AAA
Crane Co. (Wrought Iron; Steam; Gas; Water; Steel; Tube Mills), AAAA
Franklin Fdry. Co., 1155 S. Paulina (Cast Iron; Soil; Fittings) ....D
Illinois Malleable Iron Co. (Cast Iron; Gas; Steam; Water; Iron Soil).AAAA
Raymond Lead Co. (Lead; Tin Lined; Steel) .....AA
Rempe Co. (Welding, by Electricity) ....B
Wolf Co., Fred. W. (Ammonia) ....AAA
Wolff Mfg. Co., L. (Cast Iron Soil; Fittings) AAAA
ILL.—Edwardsville
Edwardsville Brass Co. (Flush; Supply) ....B
ILL.—Paxton
Paxton Hdw. Mfg. Co. (Stove) X
ILL.—Peoria
McAleenan Boiler Co. (Riveted Steel) ....A
ILL.—St. Charles
Glenn Mfg. Co. (Cast Iron Soil; Fittings) ....D
ILL.—Springfield
Springfield Boiler & Mfg. Co. (Riveted Steel) .....A
IND.—Fort Wayne
Kerr Mfg. Co., Murray (Cast Iron; Gas; Steam; Water) ....A
IND.—Terre Haute
Terre Haute Brick & Pipe Co. (Vitrified; Drain) ..X
IOWA—Burlington
Murray Iron Wks. Co. (Cast Iron; Gas; Steam; Water) A
IOWA—Cedar Rapids
Cedar Rapids Pump Co. (Cast Iron Soil; Fittings) AA
IOWA—Des Moines
Iowa Pipe & Tile Co. (Sewer) ....A
IOWA—Oskaloosa
Iowa Mfg. Co. (Cast Iron Soil; Fittings) ....D
MD.—Baltimore
Regester Sons Co. (Soil; Iron) ....A
Robertson Mfg. Co., Jas., 30 Hanover (Block Tin; Lead) ....A
MASS.—Boston
Chadwick-Boston Lead Co., 162 Congress (Block Tin; Lead; Tin Lined; Tin) AAA
Coffin Valve Co. (Water Wks.; Intake) ....D
Cunningham Iron Co. (Enam-

PIPE (Con.)
elled; Galvanized Iron)..B
Hercules Iron & Supply Co.,
Com'l & Hanover (Cast
Iron Soil; Fittings) ....A
Hodge Boiler Wks. (Riveted
Steel) ....A
National Tube Co. (Cast
Iron; Gas; Steam; Water;
Drive Well; Oil Line)
AAAA
Stearns Lumber Co., A. T.
(Wood) ....AA
Sturtevant Co., B. F. (Gal-
vanized Riveted) ....AAA
Van Noorden Co., E. (Lead;
Tin Lined) C
Walworth Mfg. Co. (Cast
Iron; Gas; Steam; Water)
AAAA
MASS.—Cambridge
Lamb & Ritchie (Lead; Tin-
ned Lined; Spiral Lock
Seam; Composition: Wa-
ter) ....AA
MASS.—Hyde Park
Boston Blower Co. (Galvan-
ized Iron) ....B
MASS.—Wakefield
Lead Lined Iron Pipe Co.
(Iron; Lead; Tinned
Lined) ....B
rt. ol.)e...-.... csm
MASS.—Waltham
Davis & Farnum Mfg. Co.
(Inc.) (Cast Iron; Gas;
Steam; Water; Flange), A
MICH.—Bay City
Michigan Pipe Co. (Improved
Wood; Cast Iron; Gas;
Steam; Water; Distillers';
Tan; Liquor; Wooden Wa-
ter) ....AA
MICH.—Big Rapids
Michigan Heater Co. (Cast
Iron Soil; Fittings) C
MICH.—Detroit
Detroit Lead Pipe & Sheet
Lead Wks. (Lead) .....A
Northwestern Fdry. & Sup-
ply Co. (Cast Iron Soil;
Fittings) ....B
MINN.—Minneapolis
Minneapolis Steel & Mchry.
Co. (Riveted Steel), AAA
MO.—Oregon
Schulte Bros. (Grapple for
Lowering Pipe in Wells) E
MO.—St. Louis
Amer. Car & Fdry. Co., 706
Chestnut (Cast Iron, 3 to
16 in.; Gas; Water) AAAA
Blackmer & Post Pipe Co.
(Culvert; Sewer) .....AA
Nelson Mfg. Co., N. O. (Cast
Iron Soil; Fittings; Lead)
AAA
Pleuger & Henger Mfg. Co.
(Cast Iron; Flush; Supply)
A
NEBR.—Omaha
Crane Co. (Wrought Iron;
Steam; Gas; Water) ....A
N. J.—Elizabeth
Braunsdorf-Mueller Co.
(Blow) ....D
N. J.—Newark
Simmons Pipe Bending Wks.
Ave. "D" Cor. Murray
(Cast Iron Soil; Fittings)
E
N. J.—Paterson
Paterson Heater Co. (Double
Wall; Hot Air Furnace;
Stove) ....H
Smith & Son Co., Saml.
(Steel) ....B
N. J.—Phillipsburg
Warren Fdry. & Machine
Co., (Cast Iron; Gas;
Steam; Water; Cast Iron
Culvert; Flange) .....AA
N. J.—Salem
Salem Brass & Iron Mfg.
Co. (Flush; Supply) ....B
N. J.—Sewaren
Baynton, C. W. (Sewer) ..A
N. Y.—Brooklyn
Nat'l Fdry. Co., 32 Sanford
St. (Cast Iron Soil; Fit-
tings) ....B
Ronalds & Johnson Co., 51
Boerum Place (Cast Iron
Soil; Fittings) ....AA

PIPE (Con.)
Wilson & Baillie Mfg. Co.
(Cement, Sewer) ....B
N. Y.—Buffalo
Lyth & Sons, Jno. (Cast Iron
Culvert; Sewer) ....AA
N. Y.—Elmira
Wyckoff & Son, A. (Acid
Proof Wood; Tan Liquor;
Wooden; Water) ....B
N. Y.—Lockport
Amer. District Steam Co.
(Wood) ....AAA
N. Y.—Newburgh
Coldwell-Wilcox Co. (Cast
Iron; High Pressure for
Steam; Hot Water) ....B
New York City
Abendroth Bros., 109 Beek-
man (Cast Iron Soil; Fit-
tings) ....A
Abendroth & Root Mfg. Co.,
99 John (Hydraulic, Steel
Riveted from 16 B. W. G.
to 1-2 in. thick; Spiral
Riveted Steel; Blast; Gal-
vanized Iron; Punched;
Formed; Sheet Iron; Soil)
A
Bishop Gutta Percha Co.
(Gutta Percha) ....B
Central Fdry. Co., 116 Nas-
sau (Cast Iron Soil; Fit-
tings) ....AAA
Colwell Lead Co., 63 Centre
(Block Tin; Lead, Tin
Lined) ....AA
Drummond & Co., M. J., 192
Bway. (Cast Iron Gas;
Water) ....A
Eaton, Cole & Burnham Co.
(Brass) ....AAAA
Fox & Co., Jno., 253 Bway.
Mfrs. Agts.(Cast Iron
Gas; Water) ....B
Gutta Percha & Rubber Mfg.
Co. (Gutta Percha), AAAA
Koven & Bros., L. O., 50
Cliff (Riveted Steel) ....A
Mayor, Lane & Co. (Lead) A
Mott Iron Wks., J. L., 88
Beekman (Cast Iron Soil;
Fittings) ....AA
Mullaney'n Son, Jas., 25th
Cor. Lex. Av. (Flush; Sup-
ply) ....D
Nat'l Lead Co., 100 William
Block Tin; Lead, Tin
Lined) ....AAAA
N. Y.—Orangeburg
Fibre Conduit Co. (Wood
Fibre) ....B
N. Y.—Rochester
Enterprise Fdry. Co., 48
Olean (Cast Iron Soil; Fit-
tings) ....B
Standard Sewer Pipe Co.
(Conduit; Sewer) ......A
N. Y.—Syracuse
Howard & Jenning (Wood-
en; Water) ....D
N. Y.—Troy
Troy Stamping Co. (Stove)
AAAA
N. Y.—Utica
International Heater Co.
(Hot Air Furnace; Tin;
Stove) ....AAA
Millar & Son Co., Chas.
(Cast Iron; Lead; Sewer)
AA
N. C.—Charlotte
Charlotte Pipe & Fdry. Co.
(Cast Iron Soil; Fittings)
B
N. C.—Pomona
Pomona Terra Cotta Co.
(Sewer; Chimney Flue;
Terra Cotta) ....B
OHIO—Akron
Buckeye Sewer Pipe Co.
(Sewer) ....A
Robinson Clay Product Co.
(Sewer; Stove) ....AAAA
OHIO—Calumet
Amer. Sewer Pipe Co. (Cul-
vert; Sewer) ......AAAA
OHIO—Canton
Berger Mfg. Co. (Steel)
AA
Canton Steel Roofing Co.
(Stove) ....A
OHIO—Cincinnati
Cinn. Sewer Pipe Co. (Flue;

PIPE (Con.)
Culvert; Sewer) ....E
Edwards Mfg. Co. (Stove)
........................C
Tudor Boiler Mfg. Co. (Riveted Steel) ....B

OHIO—Cleveland
Avery Stamping Co. (Steel)
........................B
Garry Iron & Steel Roofing Co. (Galvanized Iron; Stove)
King Bridge Co. (Riveted Steel) ....AAAA
Ohio Brass & Iron Mfg. Co. (Brass) ....B
Sanitary Co., 335 Huron (Flush; Supply)) .....B
Van Wagoner Co. (Stove).X

OHIO—Columbiana
Columbiana Boiler Co. (Riveted Steel) C

OHIO—Girard
Girard Boiler & Mfg. Co. (Riveted Steel) ....D

OHIO—Hadenville
Haydenville Co. (Sewer) .A

OHIO—Jackson
Crown Casting Co. (Cast Iron Soil; Fittings) ....B

OHIO—Lowellville
Masillon Iron & Steel Co. (Cast Iron; Gas; Water; also Flange Pipe; Fittings) ....A

OHIO—Masillon
Meehan Boiler & Construction Co. (Riveted Steel)
........................B

OHIO—Nelsonville
Nelsonville Fdry & Machine Co. (Cast Iron Gas; Steam; Water) ....B

OHIO—New Philadelphia
Ohio Stove Pipe & Mfg. Co. (Stove) ....E

OHIO—Salem
Clark Co., W. J. (Sheet Metal; Grooved Steam)
........................A

OHIO—Springfield
Leffel & Co., Jas. (Riveted Steel; Cast Iron Gas; Steam; Water) ....AA

OHIO—Steubenville
La Belle Iron Wrks. (& Tube Mills) .....AAAA

OHIO—Toronto
Francy's Sons & Co., Jno. (Sewer) ....AAAA
Great Western Fire Clay Co. (Sewer) ....AAAA

OHIO—Warren
Warren City Boiler Wrks. (Riveted Steel) ....A

OHIO—Youngstown
Pollock Co., Wm. B. (Hydraulic Riveted Steel; Iron) ....AA
Youngstown Iron Sheet & Tube Co. (Iron; Steel; Boiler Tubes; from 5-8 to 8 inch; Galvanized)
........................AAAA

OREGON—Portland
Oregon Iron & Steel Co., Sherlock Bldg. (Cast Iron 4 to 32 inch; Gas; Water)
........................B
Phoenix Iron Works (Riveted Steel) ....D

PA.—Allegheny
Carlin's Sons, Thos. (Steel; Culvert Steel) ....A
Pittsburg Lamp, Brass & Glass Co. (Brass) ..AAAA

PA.—Allentown
Albright's Son & Co. (Blast; Wrought Iron) ......AA

PA.—Braddock
McVay & Walter (Cast Iron Soil; Fittings) ....A

PA.—Chester
Penn. Steel Casting & Mach. Co. (Cast Steel; from 6 inch up) ......AA
South Chester Tube Co. (Mills) ....AAA

PA.—Coates
Coatesville Rolling Mill Co. (Boiler Tubes) ....AAA
Worth Bros. Co. (Sap Welded; Charcoal Iron; Boiler Tubes) ....AA

PIPE (Con.)
PA.—Conshohocken
Longmead Iron Co. (Black; Galvanized) ....AA

PA.—Emaus
Donaldson Iron Co. (Cast Iron; Gas; Steam; Water; Cast Iron Culvert) ..AA

PA.—Harrisburg
Harrisburg Mfg. & Boiler Co. (Riveted Steel; Flange) ....A
Harrisburg Pipe & Pipe Bending Co. (Mills) .AAA

PA.—McKeesport
Nat'l Tube Co. (Wrought Iron; Steam; Gas; Water)
........................AAAA

PA.—Middletown
Amer. Tube & Iron Co. (Cast Iron; Drive Well; Flange; Galvanized; Oil Line; Steel; Wrought Iron; Gas; Steam Water)
........................AAAA

PA.—Montclare
Hallman, Oliver (Cast Iron Soil; Fittings) ....E

PA.—Nazareth
Nazareth Fdry. & Mach. Co. (Cast Iron) ....B

PA.—New Brighton
Pittsburg Clay Mfg. Co. (Culvert; Sewer; Fire Clay; Stove) ......AAAA

PA.—New Castle
Penna. Engineering Wrks. (Riveted Steel) ......AA

PA.—Philadelphia
Amer. Pipe Mfg. Co., 114 N. Broad (Block Tin; Patent Cement Hydraulic; Wrought Iron; Cement Lined; Cast Iron Steam; Gas; Water; Sewer)
........................AAAA
Berger Bros. Co. (Galvanized Iron) ....A
Blatchley, C. G. (Wooden; Water) ....B
Haines, Jones & Cadbury, 1136 Ridge Av. (Flush; Supply; Cast Iron Soil; Fittings) ....AA
Hibbs, E. A., 213 Quarry (Riveted Steel) ....B
Lewis & Bros. Co., Jno. T., 231 S. Front (Block Tin; Lead; Tin Lined) .AAAA
Pfeifer & Co. (Ltd.) Jno. (Stove) ....A
Thompson & Co., J. (Cast Iron; Gas; Steam; Water)
........................A
Wood & Co., R. D. (Cast Iron; Gas; Steam; Water Cast Iron Culvert)
........................AAAA

PA.—Pittsburg
Amer. Fdry. & Pipe Co., Frick Bldg. (Cast Iron Soil; Fittings) ....B
Bailey-Farrell Mfg. Co., 619 Smithfield (Lead; Tin Lined; Tin) ....AA
Best Mfg. Co., 25th & A. V. Ry. (Hydraulic) ....AA
Budke Mfg. Co. (Stove) ...B
Byers Co., A. M. (Oil Line; Wrought Iron; Steam; Gas; Water; Tube Mills)
........................AA
Carroll-Porter Boiler & Tank Co.. Empire Bldg. (Riveted Steel; Steel) ..B
Childs & Co.. Harvey L. (Wooden; Water) ....AA
Gillespie Co.. T. A., Westinghouse Bldg. (Riveted Steel) ....AAA
McNeil & Bro. Co., Jas. (Riveted Steel) ....A
Monongahela Tube Co., Ferguson Bl'k. (Iron; Steel Boiler Tubes) ....A
Nat'l Tube Co. (Stove; Tube Mills) ....AAAA
Pittsburg Brass Mfg. Co. (Brass) ....D
Pittsburg Seamless Tube Co., Arrott Bldg. (Seamless Boiler Tubes) X
Pittsburg Tube Co. (Wrought Iron; Steam; Gas; Water) ....B

PIPES (Con.)

Hirschel & Bendheim (Cob; Smoking)
Sweetheart Pipe Co. (Cob; Smoking) X
Tibbe & Son Mfg. Co., H. (Cob; Smoking) .....B

N. J.—Elizabeth
Braunsdorf-Mueller Co. (Blow) ....D

N. J.—Newark
Bernz, Otto, S. 13th, cor. S. Orange Av. (Blow) ..B

N. J.—Paterson
Paterson Heater Pipe Co. (Conductor) ....A

N. J.—Town of Union
Smith, J. W. & J. T. (Clay Smoking) ....H

N. Y.—Durhamville
Amer. Clay Pipe Co. (Clay Smoking) ....D

N. Y.—Kingston
Wieber, Henry E. (Blow) ....D

New York City
Baylis Co., 140 Wash'n (Blow) ....D
Eaton, Cole & Burnham Co., 253 B'way (Hose) .AAAA
Empire Rubber Mfg. Co., 88 Reade (Hose) ....AA
De Muth & Co., W. (Smoking; Meerschaum Smoking) ....AAA
Haydenville Co., 150 Nassau (Hose) ....A
Kaldenberg Imptg. & Trading Co. (Smoking ;Meerschaum Smoking) ......D
Kaufmann Bros. & Bondy, 129 Grand (Smoking; all kinds) ....AA
Metropolitan Tob. Co. (Smoking) ....AA
Samter & Co., M. L. (Smoking) X
Stehr, Gus. (Meerschaum; Smoking) ....F

N. Y.—Oneida
Amer. Clay Pipe Co. (Clay Smoking) ....D

OHIO—Canton
Berger Mfg. Co. (Conductor) ....AA
Best Street Light Co. (Blow) ....B

OHIO—Cincinnati
Kiechler Mfg. Co. (Blow) C

OHIO—Cleveland
Garry Iron & Steel Co. (Conductor) ....A
King Bridge Co. (Stand; Railway) ....AAAA

OHIO—Columbus
Rarig Engineering Co. (Stand) X

OHIO—Mogadore
Akron Smoking Pipe Co. (The) (Clay Smoking) ..B

OHIO—Painesville
Painesville Cob Pipe & Mfg. Co. (The) (Cob Smoking) F

PA.—Erie
Felgemaker, A. B. (Organ) A

PA.—Philadelphia
Boekel & Co., Wm., 518 Vine (Blow) ....A
Harvey, Moland & Co. (Chimney) X
Harvey & Watts Co. (Nicotine Absorbent; Smoking) A
Stortz & Son, Jno., 210 Vine (Blow) ....E
Zorn & Co., Geo. (Smoking) A

PA.—Pittsburg
Carroll-Porter Boiler & Tank Co. (Stand) .....B
Marshall Bros. (Stand)..AA
Munroe & Son Mfg. Corp'n, R. (Stand) ....AA
Riter-Conley Mfg. Co. (Stand) ....AAA

PA.—Sharon
Sharon Boiler Wrks. (Stand) A

PA.—Warren
Struthers, Wells Co. (Stand) AA

PIPES (Con.)

PA.—York
York Mfg. Co. (Stand) AAA

TENN.—Chattanooga
Casey & Hedges Mfg. Co. (Stand) ....A

TENN.—Murfreesboro
Central Pipe Co. (Cob Smoking) ....F

VT.—Burlington
Reed & Co., J. G. (Smoking) B

W. VA.—Wheeling
Wheeling Corrugating Co. (Conductor) ....AAAA

WIS.—Racine
Freeman & Sons Mfg. Co., S. (Stand) ....A

PIPING

ILL.—Chicago
Wolf Co., Fred W. (Brine) AAA

PA.—Pittsburg
Best Mfg. Co., 25th & A. V. Ry. (High Pressure)..AA
Pittsburg Piping & Equipment Co., 35th & Smallman (High Pressure)...D
Pittsburg Valve, Fdy. & Construction Co., 5th & Duquesne Way (High Pressure) ....AAA

WIS.—Milwaukee
Vilter Mfg. Co. (Brine)..AA

PISTOLS

See also Firearms

CONN.—Bridgeport
Ives Mfg. Co. (Paper Cap) C

CONN.—Cromwell
Stevens Co., J. & E. (Paper Cap) ....AAAA

CONN.—New Britain
Landers, Frary & Clark (Paper Cap) ....AAA

N. H.—Keene
Wilkins Toy Co. (Paper Cap) ....AAA

N. J.—Newark
Paulus Mfg. Co. (Cap)....F

PA.—Freemansburg
Shimer, Son & Co., Wm. (Paper Cap) ....B

R. I.—Pawtucket
Bliss Mfg. Co., R. (Paper Cap) ....A

PISTONS

N. Y.—Buffalo
Pratt & Letchworth Co. (Locomotive) ....AAA

PA.—Philadelphia
Midvale Steel Co. (Locomotive) ....AAAA

PA.—Pittsburg
Carnegie Steel Co. (Ltd.) AAAA

PITCH

GA.—Atlanta
Southern Roofing Co. (Paving; Roofing) ....D

GA.—Savannah
Shotter Co., S. P. (Brewers'; Brush Makers') AAAA

ILL.—Chicago
Barrett Mfg. Co. (Paving; Roofing) ....AAAA
Falk. Wormser & Co. (Brewers') ....A
Ford Mfg. Co., 731 S. Ashland Av. (Paving; Roofing) ....B
Goldman & Co., E. (Brewers') ....A
Magnus Sons' Co. (Brewers) B
Shotter Co., S. P. (Brewers') ....AAAA

ILL.—Rock Island
Lewis Roofing Co. (Paving; Roofing) ....B

MASS.—Boston
Chapman & Soden, 410 Atlantic Av. (Paving; Roofing) ....A
Warren Bros. Co., 93 Fed-

PITCH (Con.)
eral (Paving; Roofing)
AA

MO.—St. Louis
Asphalt Roofing Co., 808
Theresa Av. (Paving;
Roofing) X
Burch & Co., E. A. (Brewers') X
Trinidad Asphalt Mfg. Co.
(Paving; Roofing) ....A
N. J.—Elizabeth
Rankin Co., W. H. (Paving;
Roofing) ....AA
N. Y.—Brooklyn
Coal Tar Products Co., 71
Commerce (Paving; Roofing) ....D
N. Y.—Buffalo
Schoellkopf, Hartford &
Hanna Co. (Paving; Roofing) ....AAA
New York City
Casey Co., Jno. A., 141
Maiden Lane ....A
Heyman & Fischer (Brewers') C
Longman & Martinez, 207
Pearl (Brewers') ....AA
Marx & Rawolle (Brewers')
AA
Schwenker, W. M. (Brewers') ....B
Sealy, Thomas, 142 Front..C
Tide Water Oil Co. (Paving)
AAAA
Warren Chemical & Mfg.
Co. (Roofing) ....A
Zinsser & Co., Wm., 197
William (Brewers') ....A
Zoller & Co., Chas. (Brewers') C
N. C.—Wilmington
Martin & Co., W. A. (Pine;
Paving; Roofing) .....D
OHIO—Cincinnati
British-American Co., 1256
W. Front ....E
Chatfield & Woods Co., 347
W. 4th (Paving; Roofing)
A
OHIO—Lockland
Carey Mfg. Co., Philip (Asbestos Roofing; Paving;
Asphalt) ....AAA
PA.—Bradford
Smith Chemical Co., A. B.
B
PA.—Johnstown
Cambria Steel Co. (Paving;
Roofing) ....AAAA
PA.—Philadelphia
Barber Asphalt Paving Co.,
Land Title Bldg. (Paving;
Roofing) ....AAAA
Garrett & Son Co., C. S..AA
PA.—Pittsburg
McClintock & Irvine Co.
(Paving; Roofing) .....B
TENN.—Nashville
Nashville Chemical Co., 919
N. Front (Paving; Roofing) ....D
VA.—Richmond
Armitage Mfg. Co., 3200
Williamsburg Av. (Paving; Roofing) ....B
WIS.—Milwaukee
Kiewert Co., Charles L.
(Brewers') ....A

PITCHERS•

See also Glassware; Chinaware; Silverware; Tinware; Enamelled Ware,
etc.

CONN.—Meriden
Manning, Bowman & Co.
(Beer; Enamelled; Milk;
Molasses) ....AA
Meriden Britannia Co.
(Beer) ....AAAA
CONN.—Wallingford
Wallace & Sons' Mfg. Co.,
R. (Beer) ....AAAA
ILL.—Monmouth
Weir Pottery Co. (Porcelain) ....A
MO.—St. Louis
St. Louis Stamping Co.
(Beer; Enamelled).AAAA

PITCHERS (Con.)
N. Y.—Buffalo
Shepard & Co., Sidney (Tin;
Metal) ....AAAA
New York City
Bishop Gutta Percha Co.,
420 E. 25th (Rubber)...B
Cordley & Hayes (Fibre)..A
International Silver Co.
(Beer; Wine; Syrup, &c.)
AAAA
Lalance & Grosjean Mfg.
Co. (Enamelled; Milk; Molasses) ....AAAA
Stoutenborough, X. (Tin).D
N. Y.—Rochester
Rochester Stamping Co.
(Cream) ....AAA
N. Y.—Rome
Rome Mfg. Co. (Metal)...B
PA.—Philadelphia
Fox & Sons, H. C. (Glass;
Molasses) ....AA
PA.—Pittsburg
McKee Glass Co., S. (Glass;
Molasses) ....D
W. VA.—Moundsville
Fostoria Glass Co. (Glass;
Molasses) ....AAA
W. VA.—Wellsburg
Riverside Glass Works
(Glass, Molasses) C
W. VA.—Wheeling
Central Glass Wks. (Glass,
Molasses) ....A

PITS

PA.—Philadelphia
Woolford Wood Tank Mfg.
Co. (Blow; Wooden)....B
PA.—Pittsburg
McClure, Son & Co., G. W.
(Soaking) ....D
Swindell & Bros., Wm.
(Soaking) ....B

PIVOTS

ILL.—Chicago
Lawson Mfg. Co., 115 Lake
(Door) ....E
N. Y.—Brooklyn
Bommer Bros. (Floor)....A
New York City
Sargent & Co., 151 Leonard
(Stool; Chair) .....AAAA

PLACES: FIRE

See Fireplaces

PLAIDS

See Cotton Goods

PLAITERS

See also Machy

PA.—Philadelphia
North Bros. Mfg. Co. (Laundry) ....AA

PLANERS

See also Machy; Tools

CONN.—Ansonia
Farrell Fdy. & Machine Co.
(Stone) ....AAAA
CONN.—Derby
Birmingham Iron Foundry
(Stone) ....AA
CONN.—Hartford
Pratt & Whitney Co. (Metal
Working) ....AAAA
CONN.—New Haven
New Haven Mfg. Co. (Metal
Working) ....:..AA
CONN.—Norwich
Rogers & Co., C. B. (Buzz;
Timber) ....AAAA
CONN.—Torrington
Hendey Machine Co. (Metal
Working) ....AA
DEL.—Wilmington
Betts Machine Co. (Metal
Working) ....AA
Hilles & Jones Co. (Metal
Working Plate) ....AAA
GA.—Atlanta
De Loach Mill Mfg. Co.

PLANERS (Con.)
(Pony; Wood) ....B
GA.—Augusta
Lombard Iron Works & Supply Co. (Buzz) ....A
ILL.—Cairo
Reed, James B. (Metal Working) ....B
ILL.—Chicago
Marshall & Huschart Machinery Co., 62 S. Canal (Metal Working) ......A
IND.—New Albany
New Albany Mfg. Co. (Stone) C
MAINE—Bangor
Union Iron Works (Buzz; Pony; Wood) ....A
MD.—Baltimore
Detrick & Harvey Machinery Co., 508 E. Preston (Metal Working; Open Side; Plate) ....AA
MASS.—Boston
Woods Machine Co., S. A., 445 Dorchester Av. (Buzz; Wood; Timber) ....AA
MASS.—Fitchburg
Fitchburg Machine Works (Frog; Switch; Metal Working) ....B
Putnam Machine Co. (Metal Working Wood) ....A
MASS.—Hyde Park
Becker - Brainard Milling Machine Co. (Rotary) AA
MASS.—Lowell
Carey, W. W. (Buzz) ....B
MASS.—Springfield
Bullock Mfg. Co. (Electrotypers' Wood) ....A
MASS.—Winchendon
Whitney & Son, Baxter D. (Wood; Metal Working) ....AA
MASS.—Worcester
Blaisdell & Co., P. (Metal Working) ....B
Draper Machine Tool Co. (Metal) ....B
Pond Machine & Foundry Co., L. W. (Metal Working) X
Whitcomb Mfg. Co. (Metal Working; Wood) ....B
Woodward & Powell Planer Co. (Frog; Switch; Sandstone; Metal Working) .B
MICH.—Grand Rapids
American Machinery Co. (J. W. Oliver, Prop.) (Buzz; Wood) ....B
Porter, C. O. & A. D. (Hand Power) C
MICH.—Jackson
Dennis Machine Co. (Buzz) ....D
MICH.—Ludington
Tubbs Mfg. Co. (Printers') ....B
MICH.—Muskegon
Bass Machinery Co. (Cabinet) ....E
Morton Mfg. Co. (Portable Metal Working) ....B
MO.—St. Louis
Hall & Brown Wood Working Machine Co. (Wood) A
Yerkes & Finan Wood Working Machine Co. (Wood) B
N. H.—Dover
White & Co., Jno. A. (Wood) C
N. H.—Keene
Humphrey Machine Co. (Wood) C
N. H.—Nashua
Flather Planer Co., Mark (Metal Working) ......B
N. J.—Newark
Gould & Eberhardt (Metal Working) ....A
Seymour & Whitlock (Wood, or Hand Feed Jointing) .B
N. J.—Paterson
Royle & Sons, Jno. (Wood; Electrotypers' Wood) ..A
N. J.—Plainfield
Pond Mach. Tool Co. (Wood) ....AAAA
N. J.—Smithville
Smith Machine Co., H. B. (Buzz; Wood) ....A

PLANERS (Con.)
N. Y.—Brooklyn
Wesel Mfg. Co., F. (Printers') X
N. Y.—Buffalo
Frank Machinery Co. (Buzz; Pony; Wood) C
Holmes Machinery Co., E. & B. (Buzz; Pony Shingle; Wood; Timber) ....B
N. Y.—Lockport
Trevor Mfg. Co. (Wood; Shingle) ....B
N. Y.—Middletown
Morgan & Wilcox Mfg. Co. (Printers') C
New York City
American Wood Working Mach. Co. 136 Liberty (Buzz; Pony; Wood) ....AAAA
Cottrell & Sons' Co., C. B. (Electrotypers' Wood) ....AAA
Fairbanks & Co. (Metal) ....AAAA
Garvin Machine Co., cor. Spring & Varick (Metal Working; Buzz) ......AA
Hoe & Co., R. (Printers') ....AAAA
Lovejoy Co. (Electrotypers' Wood) ....B
McCabe, J. J. (Metal) ....B
Manning, Maxwell & Moore, 85 Liberty (Metal Working) ....AA
Niles-Bement-Pond Co., 136 Liberty (Frog; Switch; Metal Working; Open Side; Plate; Rotary; Buzz; Valve Seat; Wall) ....AAAA
Pryibil, P., 512 W. 41st (Wood; Buzz) ....AA
Sheridan Co., T. W. & C. B. (Book) ....A
N. Y.—Rochester
Gleason Works (Gear; Metal Working) ....A
Wilson Machine Co., W. A., cor. River & Water (Metal Working) ....B
N. C.—Winston-Salem
Salem Iron Works (Inc.) (Wood) ....A
OHIO—Cincinnati
American Tool Works Co., 6th & Eggleston Av. (Metal Working) .....AA
Belmer Mach. Tool Co. (Metal Working, 30-inch upward) ....A
Cincinnati Planer Co., cor. Harrison Av. & Buck (Metal Working, 24-60 inches square, 30-36 inches square) ....A
Cordesman Mach. Co., 27 Butler (Buzz; Pony; Wood) X
Cordesman, Meyer & Co....B
Fay & Egan Co., J. A., cor. Front & John (Pony; Wood; Timber) ...AAAA
Gray Co., G. A., Gest, cor. Depot (Metal Working) ....AA
Greaves, Klusman & Co., Cook, cor. Alfred (Wood) ....B
Rechtin & Bro., Louis E. (Wood) ....D
Shepard Lathe Co., 129 W. 2d (Hand; Foot Power) ....F
OHIO—Cleveland
Cleveland Punch & Shear Works Co. 156 Case Av. (Metal Working; Plate; Rotary) ....A
Lane Tool Co. 1196 Hamilton (Metal Working) ...D
Oram, Jno. S., 160 Coe (Stave) ....A
Strong, Carlisle & Hammond Co., 61 Frankfort (Wood) ....A
OHIO—Hamilton
Bentel & Margedant Co. (Wood) ....A
OHIO—Kenton
Ohio Mach. Tool Co. (Met-

PLANERS (Con.)

al Working) C
OHIO—Leetonia
Crescent Machine Co. (Buzz)
    D

OHIO—Toledo
Baker Bros. (Buzz) ......A
PA.—Allegheny
Pittsburg Mach. Tool Co.
    (Metal Working) ......A
PA.—Bangor
Flory Mfg. Co., S. (Slate)
    A

PA.—Philadelphia
Atlantic Works (Inc.), 23d
    & Arch (Wood) ......B
Chambers Bros. Co. (Book)
    AA
Colladay, Jos. O., 626 Race
    (Buzz; Wood) ....B
Dallett Co., Thos. H. (Elec-
    tric Wood) ....B
Harrington, Son & Co., Ed-
    win, 1505 Penna. Av.
    (Metal Working) .....AA
Newton Mach. Tool Co.
    (Inc.), 2343 Vine (Rotary)
    AA
Pedrick & Ayer Co., 1001
    Hamilton (Valve Seat Ro-
    tary) ....A
Power & Co., L., 20 S. 23d
    (Pony; Wood) ....A
Sellers & Co. Wm. (Inc.),
    1600 Hamilton (Metal
    Working; Plate; Rail;
    Rotary) ....AAAA
Stow Flexible Shaft Co.
    (Radius Link) ......B
PA.—Ridgeway
Ridgeway Mach. Tool Co.
    (Metal Working) ......A
PA.—Stroudsburg
Tanite Co. (Emery) ......A
PA.—Williamsport
United States Machine Co.
    (Buzz, or Hand; Jointer)
    D

R. I.—Providence
Diamond Mach. Co. (Emery)
    B

VT.—Montpelier
Lane Mfg. Co. (Pony; Buzz;
    Wood; Timber) ....A
VT.—Rutland
Lincoln Iron Works (Stone)
    A
Patch Mfg. Co., F. R.
    (Stone) ....B
WIS.—Beloit
Berlin Mach. Wks. (Buzz;
    Wood) ....AAAA
WIS.—Two Rivers
Hamilton Mfg. Co. (Print-
    ers') ....AA

PLANES

CONN.—New Britain
Stanley Rule & Level Co.
    (Adjustable; Bead; Com-
    bination; Iron; Match;
    Rabbet; Slitting; Wood)
    AAA
Union Mfg. Co. (Iron;
    Wood) ....AA
CONN.—New Haven
Sargent & Co. (Match; Ve-
    netian Blind; Routing;
    Slitting; Iron; Wood)
    AAAA
CONN.—Pine Meadow
Chapin-Stephens Co. (Bench;
    Ship Moulding & Groov-
    ing; Adjustable; Bead;
    Combination; Dado; Hol-
    lows & Rounds; Iron;
    Iron Throat; Joiners';
    Match; Ovolo; Rabbet;
    Routing; Slitting; Vene-
    tian Blind; Fillister) ..A
CONN.—Rockfall
Smith, Otis A. (Bench)...B
CONN.—Saugatuck
Doscher Plane & Tool Co.
    E
ILL.—Carpentersville
Illinois Iron & Bolt Co.
    (Rabbet) ....AA
ILL.—Chicago
Allis-Chalmers Co.. Home
    Ins. Bldg. (Incline).AAAA

PLANES (Con.)

MD.—Baltimore
Detrick & Harvey Machine
    Co. (Iron) ....AA
MASS.—Brockton
Snell & Atherton (Edge)..C
MASS.—Fitchburg
Johnson Arms & Cycle Wks.,
    Iver (Iron) ....AA
MICH.—Grand Rapids
Letellier & Co., F. (Adjust-
    able) ....B
N. J.—Vineland
Gage Tool Co. (Adjustable;
    Bench; Iron Throat; Ve-
    netian Blind) ....A
N. Y.—Buffalo
White Co., L. & I. J. (Iron)
    A
N. Y.—Hudson
Giford Bros. (Incline) ....A
New York City
Jennings & Co., C. E. (Iron)
    B
Tower & Lyon Co., 95 Cham-
    bers (Iron; Combination)
    B
N. Y.—Schenectady
General Electric Co. (Elec-
    tric Incline) ......AAAA
OHIO—Columbus
Ohio Tool Co. (Adjustable;
    Bead; Bench; Circular;
    Dado; Fillister; Hollows;
    Rounds; Match; Mould-
    ing; Ovolo; Rabbet; Rout-
    ing; Ship; Slitting; Toy;
    Venetian Blind; Iron;
    Wood; Plane Irons).AA
OHIO—Sandusky
Sandusky Tool Co. (Adjust-
    able; Bead; Bench; Hol-
    lows; Rounds; Moulding;
    Iron Throat; Match; Rab-
    bet; Routing; Slitting;
    Venetian Blind) ....A
PA.—Bangor
Flory Mfg. Co., S. (Incline)
    A
PA.—Pittsburg
Milholland Co., J. & J. B.,
    718 5th Av. (Incline)..A
Scaife Fdy. & Machine Co.
    (Incline) ....B

PLANIMETERS

MASS.—Boston
American Steam Gauge &
    Valve Mfg. Co. (Polar).A
Crosby Steam Gauge &
    Valve Co., 97 Oliver (Po-
    lar) ....AA
Star Brass Mfg. Co., 103
    E. Dedham ....A
N. Y.—Brooklyn
Schaefer & Budenburg (Po-
    lar) ....D
New York City
Ashcroft Mfg. Co., 85 Lib-
    erty ....A
Bushnell Co., Jno. S., 126
    Liberty ....E
Keuffel & Esser Co. .....AA
Robertson & Sons, Jas. L.,
    204 Fulton ....D
Thompson & Co.. Richard,
    126 Liberty ....F
PA.—Scranton
Union Steam Specialty Co.
    A

PLANTERS

See also Agr. Imps.

GA.—Rome
Towers & Sullivan Mfg. Co.
    (Cotton) ....B
ILL.—Bradley
Bradley Mfg. Co., David
    (Cotton; Corn) ....AAA
OHIO—Canton
Parlin & Orendorff Co.
    (Corn; Cotton) ....AAAA
ILL.—Decatur
Chambers. Bering. Quinlan
    Co. (Corn; Potato) .....A
Haworth & Sons Mfg. Co.
    (Corn) ....A
Tait Mfg. Co., F. B. (Corn)
    A

PLANTERS (Con.)

ILL.—Galesburg
Colton & Co., G. D. (Corn)
.................................C

ILL.—Galva
Hayes Pump & Planter Co.
(Corn) ....,......A

ILL.—Moline
Deere & Mansur Co. (Corn;
Cotton; Potato) ....AAAA
Moline Plow Co. (Corn)
.........................AAAA
Sechler Carriage Co., D. M.
(Corn) ....AA

ILL.—Ottawa
Porter Co., J. E. (Corn)..A

ILL.—Peoria
Avery Mfg. Co. (Corn).AAA
Kingman & Co. (Corn,
Hand) ....AAA

ILL.—Rockford
Emerson Mfg. Co. (Corn,
Hand; Corn, Machine;
Cotton) ....AAA

ILL.—Rock Island
Rock Island Plow Co. (Cotton; Corn) ....AAAA

ILL.—Sandwich
Sandwich Mfg. Co. (Cotton)
.........................AA

ILL.—Sterling
Harrison Mfg. Co. (Corn,
Hand) ....F
Keystone Co. (Corn; Rotary
Drill; Check Row)
Sterling Mfg. Co. (Corn)..A

IND.—Bluffton
Bluffton Mfg. Co. (Corn).C

IND.—Richmond
Eureka Fence Mfg. Co.
(Corn, Hand; Corn, Machine) ....F
Wayne Works (Corn) ....A

IOWA—Fort Madison
Morrison Mfg. Co. (Corn;
Cotton) ....AA

KY.—Louisville
Avery & Sons, B. F. (Corn;
Cotton) ....AAA

MASS.—Boston
Ames Plow Co. (Corn)
.........................AAAA

MASS.—Chicopee Falls
Belcher & Taylor Agricultural Tool Co. (Corn; Potato) ....A

MICH.—Adrian
Babcock Planter Co. (Corn,
Hand) ....F

MICH.—Burr Oak
Sheffield Mfg. Co. (Corn,
Hand) ....B

MICH.—Greenville
Greenville Planter Co.
(Corn, Hand) ....B

MICH.—Jackson
Aspinwall Mfg. Co. (Corn;
Potato) ....B

MICH.—Traverse City
Potato Implement Co. (Corn,
Hand) ....D

N. J.—Grenloch
Bateman Mfg. Co. (Potato)
.............................A

N. J.—Millington
Nash, Duane H. (Corn,
Hand) ....B

N. Y.—Batavia
Wiard Plow Co. (Corn,
Hand) ....AA

N. Y.—Jamestown
Chatauqua Planter Co.
(Corn, Hand) ....E
Vandergrift Mfg. Co. (Corn,
Hand) ....A

N. Y.—Lyons
Nagley Mfg. Co. (Corn;
Pumpkin, Hand) ......D

N. Y.—Warsaw
Warsaw Elevator Co. (Corn)
.............................B

OHIO—Akron
Whitman & Barnes Mfg. Co.
(Corn, Hand) .....AAAA

OHIO—Canton
Kohler & Co., F. E. (Corn,
Hand; Corn, Machine)..B

OHIO—Columbus
Brown, Hinman & Huntington Co. (Corn, Hand)...A

OHIO—Dayton
Ohio Rake Co. (Corn)...AA

PLANTERS (Con.)

Stoddard Mfg. Co. (Corn)
.........................AAA

OHIO—Galena
Hughes & Smythe (Corn,
Hand) C

OHIO—Hamilton
Deuscher Co., H. P. (Corn)
.............................A

OHIO—Lancaster
Eagle Machine Co. (Corn,
Hand) ....A

OHIO—Middletown
McSherry Mfg. Co. (Corn)
.............................A

OHIO—Springfield
Foos Mfg. Co. (Corn) ....A

PA.—York
Farquhar & Co., A. B.
(Corn; Cotton) .....AAA
Keystone Farm Mach. Co.
(Ltd.) (Corn) ....B
Spangler Mfg. Co. (Corn).C

VA.—Norfolk
Whitehurst Co., R. W. (Cotton) ....B

VA.—Richmond
Cardwell Mach. Co. (Corn)
.............................A

WIS.—Beloit
Thompson & Sons' Mfg. Co.,
J. (Corn) ....AA

WIS.—Janesville
Kent Corn Planter Co.
(Corn, Hand) ....E
Rock River Mach. Co. (Corn,
Hand) ....D

WIS.—Madison
Fuller & Johnson Mfg. Co.
(Corn) ....AAA

WIS.—Racine
Winship Mfg. Co. (Corn,
Hand) ....E

PLANTS

See also Millinery

ARIZ.—Nogales
Arizona & Sonora Mfg. Co.
(Cyanide) C

CONN.—Hartford
Billings & Spencer Co.
(Drop Forgings) ......AA

ILL.—Chicago
Allis-Chalmers Co. (Cable
Railway Power) ..AAAA
Botanical Decorating Co. of
Chicago (Artificial; also
Flowers) ....F
Macdonald Engineering Co.,
Monadnock Bldg. (Cold
Storage) ....B

IND.—Fort Wayne
Fort Wayne Electric Works
(Electric Lighting) .AAA

MASS.—Boston
Jones & Co., Melville D.
(Iron) ....G

MICH.—Bay City
Industrial Works (Coaling)
.........................AA

New York City
Gerard, S. (Artificial)....D
Howard & Morse (Drying;
Ventilating) ....D
New York Ice Co. (Cold
Storage) ....B
Western Electric Co., 57
Bethune (Electric Lighting) ....AAAA

N. Y.—Schenectady
General Electric Co. (Electric Marine) ....AAAA

OHIO—Cincinnati
Creaghead Engineering Co.
(Electric Lighting) ....D

OHIO—Cleveland
Merriam-Abbott Co. (Electric Lighting) ....D

OHIO—Mt. Vernon
Cooper Co., C. & G. (Textile Mill) ....AA

PA.—Philadelphia
Dodge Cold Storage Co.,
Nicetown (Cold Storage)
.............................A

PA.—Pittsburg
Heyl & Patterson, 51 Water
(Coal & Coke Crushing &
Screening; Sand Handling) ....AA
Mesta Machine Co. (Besse-

PLANTS (Con.)

mer Steel) ....AAAA
Westinghouse Elec. & Mfg.
Co. (Electric Lighting;
Mining) ....AAAA
WIS.—Cudahy
Power & Mining Machinery
Co. (Coal & Coke Crushing
& Screening) ......AAA

PLAQUES

New York City
Judd & Co., H. L. .....AA

PLASTER

CONN.—New Haven
Connecticut Adamant Plas-
ter Co. (Calcined) .....B
ILL.—Chicago
U. S. Gypsum Co., 184 La
Salle (Calcined) ..AAAA
IOWA—Fort Dodge
Fort Dodge Plaster Co.
(Calcined) ....B
KANS.—Lawrence
American Cement Plaster
Co. (Calcined) ....A
MASS.—Boston
Emmel, Charles. 383 Albany
(Fibrous; Staff) ......B
Fowle. Herbert. 43 Bristol
(Fibrous; Staff) ......F
Windsor Cement Co., 446
Albany (Calcined) .....B
MICH.—Grand Rapids
Alabastine Co. (Calcined;
also Land Plaster) ...AA
Grand Rapids Plaster Co.
(Calcined; also Land).AA
MO.—Kansas City
Brockett Cement Co., C. A.,
121 W. 8th (Calcined)..B
MO.—St. Louis
Acme Cement Plaster Co.,
Century Bldg. (Calcined)
                                    B
Seifert Plastic Relief Co..
Frank A., 2646 Chestnut
(Fibrous; Staff) ......D
N. J.—Harrison
New Jersey Adamant Mfg.
Co. (Wall) ....B
N. J.—Newark
Newark Lime & Cement Co..
ft. of Bridge (Calcined)
                                    AAAA
N. Y.—Buffalo
Buffalo Dental Mfg. Co.
(Dental) ....B
Eclipse Wood Fibre Plaster
Co. (Fibrous; Staff)....X
N. Y.—Indian Falls
Gilmore & Co.. S. (Calcined)
                                    D
N. Y.—Newburgh
Higginson Mfg. Co. (Cal-
cined) ....A
New York City
Hammill & Gillespie. 240
Front (Calcined) ......A
King & Co.. J. B.. 1 B'way
(Calcined; Farmers')
                                    AAAA
Rock Plaster Co. of N. Y.
& N. J.. 11 B'way (Cal-
cined) ....B
Wotherspoon Plaster Mills.
1170 B'way (Dental) ..B
N. Y.—Syracuse
Harnish. Ad.. Spencer n.
Chlorine Spgs. (Fibrous;
Staff) ....E
National Wall Plaster Co.
(Calcined) C
PA.—Chester
Keystone Plaster Co.. Lock
Box 76 (Calcined) .....A
PA.—Philadelphia
French & Co.. Samuel H..
4th & Callowhill (Cal-
cined) ....
                                    AA
Johnson & Lund (Dental)
                                    AA
White Dental Mfg. Co.. S. S.
(Surgical & Dental)AAAA
S. DAK.—Hot Springs
Hot Springs Plaster Co.
(Calcined; Dental) ....D

PLASTERS

ILL.—Chicago
Baker Co.. Chas. S. (Medi-
cal; Surgical) C
Bauer & Black (Medical;
Surgical) ....A
MASS.—Boston
Grosvenor & Co.. J. M. (Sur-
gical; Medical) ....B
MASS.—Waverly
Aldrich. D. H. (Court)....B
MICH.—Detroit
Parke. Davis & Co. (Medi-
cal; Surgical) .....AAAA
MICH.—Saginaw
Saginaw Medicine Company
(Corn) ....D
MO.—St. Louis
Mallinckrodt Chemical Wks.
(Medical; Surgical).AAAA
N. J.—New Brunswick
Johnson & Johnson (Court;
Medical; Surgical).AAAA
N. Y.—Albany
Valentine & Son, W. T.
(Court) ....B
New York City
King. V. C. & C. V.. 509
West (Medical) X
McKesson & Robbins (Medi-
cal; Surgical) .....AAAA
Pall Mall Electric Assn..
870 B'way (Electric)...F
Schieffelin & Co.. W. H.
(Medical; Surgical) ..AA
Seabury & Johnson (Medi-
cal; Surgical; Court)..AA
N. Y.—Yonkers
Deane Plaster Co. (Medical;
Surgical: Court) ......B
PA.—Conshohocken
Lee Co.. J. Elwood (Medi-
cal; Surgical) ....AA
PA.—Philadelphia
French & Co.. 4th (Dental)
                                    A
TENN.—Harriman
Dixie Plaster Co. (Medi-
cated) ....D

PLATES

**See also Iron & Steel: Tin-
ware; Chinaware; Silver-
ware; Enamelled Ware;
also Dishes & Hardware;
Carriages.**

ALA.—Birmingham
Birmingham Rolling Mill
Co. (Bridge; Iron; Iron
Boiler) ....AAA
CAL.—San Francisco
Judson Mfg. Co. (Iron Boil-
er; Tank) ....AA
Passavant Printing Co.
(Photograph. Dry) ....H
Tay Co.. Geo. H. (Floor;
Ceiling) ....AA
COLO.—Denver
Colorado Fuel & Iron Co.
(Iron; Steel Boiler; Tank;
Joint) ....B
CONN.—Ansonia
Ansonia Brass & Copper Co.
(Condenser) ....AAAA
CONN.—Beacon Falls
Bronson Co.. Homer D. (Ma-
chinery Name) C
CONN.—Bridgeport
American Tube & Stamping
Co. (Floor) ....AAAA
Belknap Mfg. Co. (Radiator
Floor) C
Bridgeport Deoxidized
Bronze & Metal Co.
(Name) ....B
Rowell & Co.. W. G. (Ma-
chinery Name) ....D
Schwerdtle Stamp Co.. 35
Fairfield Av. (Machinery
Name; Stencil) ....F
CONN.—Bristol
Snyder & Co.. L. H. (Floor;
Ceiling) C
CONN.—Deep River
Denison Bros. (Small Ivory)
                                    D
CONN.—Easthampton
Gong Bell Mfg. Co. (Name)
                                    AAAA

PLATES (Con.)

CONN.—Guilford
Spencers' Sons, I. S. (Name) ....A
CONN.—Hartford
Billings & Spencer Co. (Drop Forged Screw) ....AA
Pratt & Whitney Co. (Screw) ....AAAA
CONN.—Meriden
Manning, Bowman & Co. (Enameled; Soup) ....AA
CONN.—Mt. Carmel
Woodruff & Sons, Walter W. (Carriage Felloe Whiffletree) ....A
CONN.—New Britain
Corbin, P. & F. (Push; Name) ....AAAA
Russell & Erwin Mfg. Co. (Name; Letter Box; Window; Car Door; Door Number; Hinge, Corner & Center; Push) ...AAAA
Stanley Works (Mending) ....AAA
CONN.—New Haven
Cowles & Co., C. (Carriage Bed) ....A
English & Mersick Co. (Carriage Felloe) ....B
Mallory-Wheeler Co. (Push; Door) ....AA
Sargent & Co. (Key; Name; Window; Door Number; Drop Letter; Hand Rail; Hinge, Corner & Center; Looking Glass; Mending; Push) ....AAAA
CONN.—Plantsville
Atwater Mfg. Co. (Carriage Felloe) ....A
Smith & Co., H. D. (Carriage Bed) ....A
CONN.—Southington
Beaton & Corbin Mfg. Co. (Floor; Ceiling) ....D
CONN.—South Norwalk
Norwalk Lock Co. (Name) ....A
CONN.—Stamford
Yale & Towne Mfg. Co. (Push, Door; Key; Drop Letter; Hinge, Corner & Center) ....AAAA
CONN.—Unionville
Upson Nut Co. (Carriage Felloe) ....AAAA
CONN.—Waterbury
American Ring Co. (Hinge) ....A
Plume & Atwood Mfg. Co. (Heel; Hinge; Floor; Ceiling) ....AAA
Randolph, Clowes Company (Screen) ....AAA
Scovill Mfg. Co. (Name) ....AAAA
Steele & Johnson Mfg. Co. (Floor; Ceiling) ....A
Waterbury Mfg. Co. (Floor; Ceiling) ....AAAA
DEL.—Wilmington
Davis Pressed Steel Co. (Pressed Steel) ....B
Diamond State Steel Co. (Tie) X
Seidel & Hastings Co. (Charcoal Iron Boiler; Iron; Steel) ....A
ILL.—Aurora
Richards Mfg. Co. (Mending) ....B
Wilcox Mfg. Co. (Mending) ....B
ILL.—Carpentersville
Illinois Iron & Bolt Co. (Carriage Bolster) ....AA
ILL.—Chicago
Acorn Brass Mfg. Co. (Name) ....D
Aitchison Perforated Metal Co., Robert, 301 Dearborn (Filter Press; Oatmeal Sifter; Stamp Battery).X
American Radiator Co. (Radiator Floor) ......AAA
American Steel & Wire Co. (Iron; Steel Boiler; Tank; Steel Fire Box)....AAAA
Barbee Wire & Iron Works (Sign) ....B
Besly & Co., Charles H.

PLATES (Con.)

(Screw) ....AA
Chicago Art Metal Works (Bicycle Name) ....E
Chicago Hdw. Co., 132 Lake (Push) ....D
Chicago Spring Butt Co., 491 Carroll Av. (Push) ...B
Crane Co., 10 N. Jefferson (Floor; Ceiling; Die; Screw) ....AAAA
Creamery Package Mfg. Co. (Wooden) ....AAAA
Crowe Metal Mfg. Co., 71 W. Jackson (Name) ...E
Davis Co., Jno., 75 Michigan (Floor; Ceiling) ......AA
Harrington & King Perforating Co. (Perforated Filter Press; Iron & Steel Punched) ....A
Illinois Malleable Iron Co., 30 West Monroe (Floor; Ceiling) ....AAAA
Illinois Steel Co., The Rookery (Iron; Steel Boiler; Tank; Steel Bridge; Fire Box; Tie) ....AAAA
Independent Railroad Supply Co., The Rookery (Tie) ....E
Railroad Supply Co., Bedford Bldg. (Tie) ....B
Republic Iron & Steel Co., 108 La Salle (Boiler; Tank; Steel Bridge; Fire Box; Bolster; Fish; Iron; Steel) ....AAAA
Sellers Mfg. Co., 27 W. Chicago Av. (Tie) .....B
Turner Brass Works (Carriage; Machinery Name) ....A
Winslow Bro. Co., 368 Carroll Av. (Push) ....AA
ILL.—Edwardsville
Edwardsville Brass Co. (Name) ....B
ILL.—Freeport
Stover Mfg. Co. (Push, Door; Carriage Bolster) ....AA
ILL.—Galva
Mulford Heater Co. (Floor; Ceiling) X
ILL.—Kawanee
Western Tube Co. (Expansion; Floor; Ceiling).AAA
ILL.—La Salle
Matthiessen & Hegeler Zinc Co. (Lithographers'; Zinc) ....AAAA
ILL.—St. Charles
Glenn Mfg. Co. (Floor; Ceiling) ....D
ILL.—Sterling
Lawrence Bros. (Wagon End Gate) ....AAA
National Mfg. Co. (Mending) C
Novelty Iron Works (Pump Handle; Handle) ......E
IND.—Kokomo
Kokomo Fence Machine Co. (Nickel & Aluminum Name) ....AAA
IOWA—Dubuque
Adams Co. (Floor & Ceiling, for Stove Pipe Register).A
IOWA—Oskaloosa
Iowa Mfg. Co. (Floor; Ceiling) ....D
MAINE—Bath
Torrey Roller Bushing Wks. (Machinery Name) .....B
MD.—Baltimore
Dorman Co., J. F. W. (Name) ....F
Levering Bros. (Building; Wall) C
MD.—Cumberland
Cumberland Steel Co. (Black Metal) ....A
MASS.—Amesbury
Feltch & Co., E. S. (Carriage Bed) C
MASS.—Attleboro
Robbins Co., Chas. M. (Bicycle Name) C
MASS.—Boston
Becker Engraving Co., August, 247 Atlantic Av. (Machinery Name) ....E

773

PLATES (Con.)

Coffin Valve Co. (Floor)..D
Edson Mfg. Co. (Deck, or Manhole) ....B
G. & P. Engraving Co., 185 Franklin (Mach. Name) X
Grundy Brass Wks., 50 Sudbury (Floor; Ceiling)...F
Howes Co., S. M. (Hot).B
Murdock Corporation, 156 Boylston (Mach. Name; Push) X
Robbins Mfg. Co., Jno., 58 Kneeland (Name) .....E
Smith & Thayer Co., 236 Congress (Floor; Ceiling) A
Union Metal Corner Co., 206 Summer (Plasterers' Steel Corner) ....D
Walworth Mfg. Co., 132 Federal (Floor; Ceiling; Screw) ....AAAA
Woodman Mfg. & Supply Co., R., 63 Oliver (Machinery Name) ....F

MASS.—Cambridge
Hews & Co., A. H. (Storage Battery, Porous)...A

MASS.—Fitchburg
Putnam Machine Co. (Surface) ....A
Welch & Co., E. J. (Screen) D

MASS.—Greenfield
Reese Co., E. F. (Screw)..D
Wells Bros. Co. (Screw) .A
Wiley & Russell Mfg. Co. (Screw) ....AA

MASS.—Haydenville
Haydenville Co. (Floor; Ceiling) ....A

MASS.—Holyoke
Holyoke Bar Co. (Carriage Bed) ....E

MASS.—Mansfield
Card Mfg. Co., S. W. (Screw) ....B

MASS.—New Bedford
Morse Twist Drill & Mach. Co. (Screw) ....AAA
Taunton-New Bedford Copper Co. (Singe) ....AAA

MASS.—Newton
Stanley Dry Plate Co. (Photograph, Dry) ....B

MASS.—Somerville
Birch Bros. (Singe)......C

MASS.—South Hanover
Phillips & Sons, Ezra (Zinc; Zinc, Boiler) ....A

MASS.—Springfield
Smith Mfg. Co., R. H. (Stencil) C

MASS.—Westfield
Lamprey Co. (Boiler Arch) F

MASS.—Worcester
Cleveland Machine Works (Press) ....A
Houghton Mfg. Co. (Floor; Ceiling) ....E
Phoenix Plate Co. (Ferrotype; Dry; Sign).......C
Worcester Ferrule & Mfg. Co. (Floor; Ceiling) ...C

MASS.—Wrentham
Winter Bros. Co. (Screw) E

MICH.—Detroit
Ireland & Matthews Mfg. Co. (Bumper, for Plumbers' Woodwork: Spun Brass Floor & Ceiling)..A
Smith & Co., Joseph N. (Carriage Name) C
U. S. Heater Co., 251 Campbell Av. (Floor; Ceiling) A

MICH.—Grand Rapids
Grand Rapids Brass Co. (Electric) ....A
Wolverine Brass Works (Floor; Ceiling) ....A

MICH.—Jackson
Withington & Cooley Mfg. Co. (Felloe) ....AA

MO.—St. Louis
American Brass & Mfg. Co., 409 S. 2d (Machinery Name) ....

PLATES (Con.)

Barnard Stamp Co. (Name) E
Cramer Dry Plate Co., G. (Photograph, Dry) .....A
Ewald Iron Co. (Iron)..AAA
Hammer Dry Plate Co. (Photograph, Dry) ....A
Kupferle, Jno. C., (Floor; Ceiling; Bolster; Hound) AA
Nelson Mfg. Co., N. O., 8 St. Charles (Floor; Ceiling) ....AAA
Pleuger & Henger Mfg. Co. (Floor; Ceiling; Bolster; Hound) ....A
St. Louis Stamping Co. (Pie; Enamelled; Soup)..AAAA

N. H.—Exeter
Exeter Brass Works (Floor; Ceiling) C
Rubber Step Mfg. Co. (Carriage Step) ....D

N. J.—Belleville
Eastwood Wire Mfg. Co. (Machinery Name; Screen; Rolled Brass Screw; Name) ....A

N. J.—Bloomfield
Combination Rubber & Belting Co. (Typewriter) ...A

N. J.—High Bridge
Taylor Iron & Steel Co. (Iron Chute) .....AAAA

N. J.—Jersey City
Griffing Iron Co., A. A. (Floor; Ceiling; Radiator Floor) ....AA

N. J.—Newark
Currier & Sons, Cyrus (Filter Press) ....AA
Jackson Co., Jno. J. (Engravers') ....D
Richmond Bros. Co. (Heel) D
Sacks Iron Foundry, Louis (Heel) ....A
Searls Mfg. Co. (Name) .B

N. J.—Paterson
Annandale Screen Plate Co. (Screen) ....B
Passaic Steel Co. (Bridge; Iron; Steel) ....A

N. Y.—Albany
Clark, Jno. W. (Machinery Name) ....D
Townsend Furnace & Mach. Shop Co. (Floor) ......B

N. Y.—Auburn
Clapp Mfg. Co., E. D. (Carriage Bed) ....B

N. Y.—Brooklyn
Bommer Bros. (Door Bottom; Kick) ....A
Clarke, Robert, 98 Schermerhorn (Floor; Ceiling)..F
Donnelly Co., J. R. (Glass Name) ....D
Hecla Iron Works, N. 11th & Berry (Push) ......AA
Houchin & Huber (Printing Box) ....D
Sweeney Mfg. Co., Wm. H. (Tin) ....A
Union Porcelain Wks. (Sign; Name) ....B
Vogel & Bros., Wm. (Pie; Tin) ....AA

N. Y.—Buffalo
Ashbery, Henry C., 16 Seneca (Machinery Name) .G
Pratt & Letchworth Co. (Carriage Bed; Carriage Step) ....AAA

N. Y.—Fulton
Foster Bros. & Chatillion Co. (Roll) ....A

N. Y.—Goshen
Newbury, Jay H. (Floor; Ceiling) ....B

N. Y.—Manlius
Cheney & Son, S. (Floor; Ceiling) ....A

N. Y.—Monroe
Newbury Mfg. Co. (Floor; Ceiling) ....D

New York City
Arderton, Ralph L., 210 Grand (Machinery Name) B
Baker, Hermann & Co., 101 Duane (Screw) .....AAA

774

PLATES (Con.)

Caesar Bros. (Name) .....D
Carragan & Tilson (Stencil)
    D
Central Stamping Co. (Lettered) ....AA
Cooper & Co., Chas. (Photograph, Dry) ....AA
Crandall & Godley Co. (Tin)
    AA
Eaton, Cole & Burnham Co.,
   253 B'way (Floor; Ceiling) ....AAAA
Every Mfg. Co., 102 John
   (Floor; Ceiling) ....B
Fuchs & Lang Mfg. Co.
   (Lithographers') .....AA
Gardner & Co., A. S. (Jewelers') ....B
Gennert, G. (Ferrotype) .B
Gorham Mfg. Co. (Church;
   Brass) ....AAAA
Gould-Mersereau Co. (Stair)
   B
Goulds' Sons & Co., M.
   (Stair) ....A
Hunt Co., C. W. (Cast Iron
   Ceiling) ....AA
Jackson Co., Wm. H., 29 E.
   17th (Union Sq.) (Push)
   A
Judd & Co., H. L. (Stair)
   AA
Krieg & Co., J. K. (Heel) .B
Lalance & Grosjean Mfg. Co.
   (Egg; Pie; Enamelled)
   AAAA
Lamb, J. & R. (Church;
   Brass) ....D
McNab & Harlin Mfg. Co.,
   56 John (Floor; Ceiling)
   AAA
Metal Stamping Co. (Door
   Number; Name; Vehicle
   License) ....A
Morse & Rogers (Heel) ...A
Mundt & Sons, Chas. (Machine; Filter Press Perforated) ....B
Nason Mfg. Co.. 71 Beekman (Floor; Ceiling) ..B
Ness, Jr., Geo. M., 61 Fulton (Name; Machine
   Name) ....H
New York Steel Corner
   Plate Co., 1133 B'way
   (Plasterers' Steel Corner)
   X
New York Stencil Works.
   100 Nassau (Name; Stencil) X
Ogden & Wallace, 577
   Greenwich (Armor; Never
   Slip Wrought Steel Floor)
   A
Peck. Stow & Wilcox Co.
   (Window; Drop Letter;
   Floor; Ceiling) ....AAAA
Phillips Mfg. Co., 215 E.
   34th (Floor; Ceiling)...D
Rutzler Co., E., 178 Centre
   (Floor; Ceiling) ....A
Sanford Mfg. Co., Wm. P.
   (Wooden) ....D
Shriver & Co.. T.. 333 E.
   56th (Filter Press) ....A
Spencer & Co., E. E. (Heel)
   B
Stafford Co.. N. (Stencil) .F
Stoutenborough, X. (Egg;
   Lettered) ....D
Tiebout, W. & J. (Brass
   Step; Deck, or Manhole)
   B
United Metal Mfg. Co.. 525
   Broome (Floor; Ceiling) .D
United States Steel Corporation. 71 B'way (Steel
   Bridge) ....AAAA
Victor Excelsior Brass Wks..
   44 Mott (Floor; Ceiling)
   A

N. Y.—North Tonawanda

Miller Specialty Co. (Floor;
   Ceiling) X
Niagara Radiator Company
   (Floor; Ceiling) ....A

N. Y.—Rochester

Eastman Kodak Co. (Photograph. Dry) ....AAAA
Forbes Dry Plate Co. (Photograph, Dry) ....D

PLATES (Con.)

N. Y.—Seneca Falls

Climax Specialty Co. (Floor;
   Ceiling) ....B

N. Y.—Syracuse

Franklin Mfg. Co., H. H.,
   208 S. Geddes (Name) .A
Pierce, Butler & Pierce
   Mfg. Co. (Cast Iron Ceiling) ....AAA

N. Y.—Troy

Troy Stamping Wks. (Tin)
   AAAA

N. Y.—Utica

Giblin & Co. (Carriage
   Bolster) ....B

N. Y.—Waterford

Holroyd & Co. (Screw)....A
Snyder & Metcalf (Surface)
   X

OHIO—Akron

Enterprise Mfg. Co. (Name)
   A

OHIO—Cincinnati

Cincinnati Mfg. Co., 512
   Main (Name) ....B
Globe Rolling Mill Co. (Iron
   Boiler; Steel; Tank; Jail;
   Safe; R. R. Frog) ....A
Walton Iron Co. (Prismatic
   Sidewalk) C
Weir Frog Co., cor. Front &
   Smith (Tie) ....A

OHIO—Cleveland

Avery Stamping Co. (Carriage Felloe; Pipe Hook;
   Felloe; Steel) ....B
Chisholm & Moore Mfg. Co.
   (Tie) ....AA
Cleveland Hdw. Co. (Carriage Bolster; Carriage
   Step; Carriage Felloe) .AA
Cleveland Steel Co. (Steel
   Bridge) ....AA
Fanner Mfg. Co. (Hot) ....A
Forest City Steel & Iron Co.
   (Iron; Steel) ....A
Garry Iron & Steel Co.
   (Iron; Steel; Tin; Terne)
   A
Hart Mfg. Co., 22 Wood
   (Screw) ....B
Oster Mfg. Co. (Screw)...B
Otis Steel Co. (Ltd.) cor.
   Lake & Lawrence (Steel
   Boiler; Tank; Fire Box)
   A
Taylor & Boggis Fdy. Co.
   (Hot; Push; Pull; Kick)
   AA

OHIO—Columbus

Ohio Pump & Brass Co.. 18th
   & Oak (Floor) C

OHIO—Dayton

Howard, Wm. H. (Name) .E

OHIO—Hamilton

Black-Clawson Co. (Screen)
   AAA

OHIO—Niles

Bostwick Steel Lath Co.
   (Plasterers' Steel Corner)
   C

OHIO—Piqua

Piqua Handle & Mfg. Co.
   (Wooden Push) ....A

OHIO—Plymouth

Root Bros. Co. (Heel; Sole)
   B

OHIO—Ravenna

Williams, A. C. (Bolster) .A

OHIO—Salem

Clark Co., W. J. (Carriage
   Felloe) ....A

OHIO—Shelby

Shelby-Spring Hinge Co.
   (Stamped, Raised Back
   Push) ....B

OHIO—Steubenville

La Belle Iron Works (Iron;
   Steel; Tack) .....AAAA

OHIO—Toledo

Donovan Wire & Iron Co.
   (Brass Step) C

PA.—Allegheny

McKinney Mfg. Co. (Carriage Felloe) ....AAA
Pittsburg Lamp. Brass &
   Glass Co. (Floor; Ceiling)
   AAAA

PA.—Carbondale

Hendrick Mfg. Co. (Perforated Sifter & Screen) .AA

PLATES (*Con.*)

PA.—Catasauqua
Bryden Horse Shoe Co. (Racing) ....AA

PA.—Coatesville
Lukens Iron & Steel Co. (Steel, Sheared Iron & Steel) ....AAAA
Worth Bros. Co. (Steel Boiler; Tank; Steel, Sheared) AA

PA.—Connellsville
Sligo Iron & Steel Co. (Iron; Steel Boiler; Tank) ....B

PA.—Conshohocken
Wood & Bros. Co., J. (Iron; Steel) ....AA

PA.—Erie
Jarecke Mfg. Co. (Floor; Ceiling) ....AAAA

PA.—Fullerton
Lehigh Fdy. Co. (Tunnel) .A

PA.—Harrisburg
Central Iron & Steel Co. (Iron; Steel Boiler; Tank; Steel Fire Box) ....AAAA
Lucknow Iron & Steel Co. (Steel Bridge) ....E

PA.—Lancaster
Champion Blower & Forge Co. (Screw) ....AA

PA.—Millersburg
Brubaker & Bros., W. L. (Screw) ....B
Polk & Son, A. J. (Screw) C

PA.—Nazareth
Nazareth Fdy. & Mach. Co. (Tunnel) ....B

PA.—Philadelphia
American Pressed Steel Co., 824 Witherspoon Bldg. (Wrought Steel Floor) .B
Belfield & Co., H., 435 N. Broad (Floor; Ceiling) AA
Boekel & Co., Wm., 518 Vine (Floor; Ceiling) ...A
Butterworth & Sons' Co., H. W., 2415 E. York (Singe)
Cambria Steel Co., Arcade Bldg. (Tie; Iron; Steel Boiler; Tank) .....AAAA
Chester Steel Castings Co. (Mining Crusher) ....AA
Cresson Co., Geo. V. (Angle & Bearings; Wall; Pedestal Base) ....AA
Devlin Mfg. Co.. Thos.. 3d & Lehigh Av. (Floor; Ceiling) ....AA
Flagg & Co., Stanley G.. 19th & Penn Av. (Floor; Ceiling) ....AAA
Gara, McGinley & Co.. 23 S. 17th (Plasterers' Steel Corner) ....A
Haworth Co.. Jno. (Photograph, Dry) ....D
Merchant & Co. (Inc.) (Roofing, Tin) ....AA
Merritt & Co., 1024 Ridge Av. (Plasterers' Steel Corner) ....B
Morris, Wheeler & Co. (Steel; Steel Ship Boiler) AAA
Phila. Roll. & Mach. Co. (Crusher) ....A
Phoenix Bridge Co. (Bridge) A
Phoenix Iron Co., 410 Walnut (Steel Bridge) .AAAA
Roberts Co., A. & P. (Iron) AAAA
Taylor Co.. N. & G.. 3d & Chestnut (Iron; Steel Boiler; Tank; Steel Fire Box; Roofing; Black for Deep Stamping) ....AAA
Wharton & Co.. Wm.. Jr.. 25th & Washn. Av. (Tie) AAA
Wood Co.. Allan. 519 Arch (Iron; Steel; Tank) ..... AAAA

PA.—Pittsburg
American Sheet & Tin Plate Co. (Iron; Steel; Tin; Terne) ....AAAA
Canonsburg Iron & Steel Co. (Stamping; Terne) .....B

PLATES (*Con.*)

Carbon Steel Co. (Steel) Boiler; Tank; Fire Box; Steel Bridge) X
Carnegie Steel Co. (Ltd.), Carnegie Bldg. (Armor; Iron Boiler; Floor; Steel Boiler; Tank; Steel) .... AAAA
Clinton Iron & Steel Co. (Iron; Steel Boiler; Tank) AA
Crucible Steel Co. of America (Steel Boiler; Tank; Bridge; Fire Box; Steel Sheared) ....AAAA
Dilworth, Porter & Co., German Natl. Bank Bldg. Claw Tie) ....AAAA
Jones & Laughlin Steel Co. (Iron; Steel; Boiler; Tank; Steel Bridge).... AAAA
Kelly & Jones Mfg. Co., 315 1st Av. (Floor; Ceiling) AA
Lanz & Sons, Mathew (Sheave) ....AA
McKenna Bros. Brass Co. (Push; Pull; Kick)....A
Oliver Iron & Steel Co. (Iron; Steel Boiler; Tank; Tie) ....AAAA
Pope Tin Plate Co. (Tin).B
Scaife & Sons Co., Wm. B., 221 1st Av. (Iron; Steel Boiler; Tank) ......AAA
Spang-Chalfant & Co. (Steel; Steel Boiler)......AAAA

PA.—Pottstown
Glasgow Iron Co. (Iron; Steel Boiler; Tank; Steel Bridge; Steel Sheared).. AAA
Potts Bros. Iron Co. (Iron; Steel Boiler; Tank).....A

PA.—Reading
Penna. Hdw. Co. (Push).AA
Reading Hdw. Co. (Name; Push; Window; Door Number; Drop Letter; Hinge; Corner; Center).. AAAA
Reading Iron Co. (Iron; Joint; Splice).....AAAA
Seyfert, Simon (Iron; Steel Boiler; Tank) ......AA
Seyfert & Bro.. Saml. R. (Iron; Steel Boiler; Tank) AA

PA.—South Bethlehem
Bethlehem Fdry. & Machine Co. (Floor; Ceiling).....C
Bethlehem Steel Co. (Armor) ....AAAA

PA.—Steelton
Penna. Steel Co. (Splice; Rail Fish) ......AAAA

PA.—Wilkesbarre
Vulcan Iron Wks. (Pedestal Base) ....AAAA

R. I.—Pawtucket
Carpenter Tap & Die Co., J. M. (Screw) C
Fuller & Son. Geo. H. (Jewelers) ....A
Pawtucket Mfg. Co. (Screw) ....A

R. I.—Providence
Briggs & Sons Co., J. (Jewelers') ....A
Brown & Sharpe Mfg. Co. (Surface) ....AAAA
Lind Co.. Thos. W. (Jewelers') ....D
Textile Finishing Machy. Co.. 17 Exchange Pl. (Singe) ....AAA
Waterbury Brass Co. (Engravers') .....AAAA

TENN.—Knoxville
Knoxville Iron Co. (Angle; Bearings; Rail Fish).AA

VT.—Derby Line
Butterfield & Co. (Bicycle Screw; Screw; Die)....A

VA.—Richmond
Tredeger Co. (Rail Fish).. AAA

W. VA.—Charleston
Vulcan Iron Wks. (Floor; Ceiling) ....D

PLATES (*Con.*)

W. VA.—Charlestown
Powhattan Brass & Iron
Wks. (Floor; Ceiling)..B
W. VA.—Parkersburg
Parkersburg Iron & Steel
Co. (Steel Bridge)....AA
W. VA.—Wheeling
Portsmouth Steel Co.....A
Whitaker Iron Co. (Black
Metal) ....AA
WIS.—Milwaukee
Hoffman & Billings Mfg.
Co. (Floor; Ceiling)...AA
Hoffman Mfg. Co., B.
(Floor; Ceiling).......B
Pressed Steel Tank Co.
(Flanged; Deep Stamped;
Forged; Drawn to Shape
Pressed Steel) ....B
Rundle-Spence Mfg. Co.
(Floor; Ceiling)......A
Wrought Washer Mfg. Co.
(Felloe) ....A
WIS.—Racine
Racine Malleable &
Wrought Iron Co. (Car-
riage Bolster) ....A

PLATFORMS

ILL.—Chicago
Chicago Sporting Goods Co.,
126 S. Jefferson (Strik-
ing Bag) ....B
Natl. Car Coupler Co., Mon-
adnock Blk. (Steel Car).A
Tothill, W. S., 128 W. Web-
ster Av. (Striking Bag) F
N. H.—Plymouth
Draper & Maynard Co.
(Striking Bag) ....A
New York City
Fairbanks Co., 416 Broome
(Portable) ....AAAA
Krajewski, Pesant & Co.
(Steel) ....AA
Standard Coupler Co., 160
B'way (Steel Car) ....B
Treinis Bros., 498 B'way
(Striking Bag)........F
N. Y.—Oxford
Clarke Blue Stone Co., F.
G. (Stone) ....A
OHIO—Cleveland
Forest City Steel & Iron
Co. (Telephone Pole)..A
PA.—Danielsville
Hower, J. K. (Slate) ....B

PLATING

CONN.—Bristol
Smith, Ira B. (Electro)..E
CONN.—Guilford
Spencer's Sons, I. S.
(Electro; Nickel)......A
CONN.—Waterbury
Blake & Johnson (Electro;
Nickel) ....A
ILL.—Chicago
Acorn Brass Mfg. Co.
(Electro; Nickel).....D
Winslow Bros. Co., Carroll
Av., Ada & Fulton (Elec-
tro; Bronze) ....AA
ILL.—Freeport
Stover Mfg. Co. (Electro)
...................AA
MASS.—Boston
Murdock Corporation (Elec-
tro) X
MO.—St. Louis
Ludlow-Saylor Wire Co.
(Electro; Nickel).....AA
Pleuger & Henger Mfg. Co.
(Electro) ....A
N. Y.—Albany
Clark, J. W. (Electro;
Nickel) ....D
N. Y.—Brooklyn
Hecla Iron Wks., N. 11th
& Berry (Duplex Bronze;
Electro Bronze) ......AA
N. Y.—Manlius
Cheney & Son, S. (Nickel).A
New York City
Jackson & Co., Wm. R., 29 E.
17th (Electro Bronze)..A
OHIO—Cincinnati
Schreiber & Sons Co., L.,
8th & Eggleston Av.
(Electro Bronze) .....AA

PLATING (*Con.*)

OHIO—Cleveland
Taylor & Boggis Fdry. Co.
(Electro) ....AA
PA.—Pittsburg
McKenna Bros. Brass Co.
(Electro) ....A
PA.—Reading
Reading Machine & Tool
Co. (Electro; Nickel)..B

PLATINUM

ILL.—Chicago
Goldsmith Bros., 65 Washn.
...................A
N. J.—Newark
American Platinum Wks.
(Electric) ....A
Croselmire & Ackor (Sheet;
Wire) ....B
New York City
Eimer & Amend........AA
Platt, C. S., 31 Gold......B
Schawel & Co., Jas., 29
John (Sheet; Wire).....B
PA.—Malvern
Bishop & Co., J. (Wares).D

PLAYERS

CONN.—Derby
Sterling Co. (Piano)....AA
CONN.—Meriden
Wilcox & White (Automatic
Piano) ....A
ILL.—Chicago
Kimball Co., W. W.
(Piano) ....AAAA
N. Y.—Buffalo
Chase & Baker Co. (Auto-
matic Piano) ....A
N. Y.—Elbridge
Maestro Co. (Piano).....X
New York City
Needham Piano & Organ Co.,
96 5th Av. (Piano).....A
Roth & Engelhardt, 2 E.
47th (Piano) ....B
OHIO—Cincinnati
Baldwin Co. (Piano).AAAA

PLIERS

CONN.—Bridgeport
Bridgeport Hdw. Mfg. Co.
(Gas; Champagne; Com-
bination; Cutting; Fenc-
ing; Flat; Round Nose).B
Hurwood Mfg. Co. (Cut-
ting) C
Smith & Egge Mfg. Co.
(Gas) ....A
CONN.—Hartford
Billings & Spencer Co. (Gas;
Combination; Cutting
Electricians'; Flat; Round
Nose) ....AA
CONN.—New Haven
Brown & Co., R. H.
(Jewelers') ....B
Kilborn & Bishop Co. (Gas;
Cutting; Combination;
Electricians'; Farmers';
Fencing; Flat; Round
Nose; Knot Tying; Splic-
ing; Lineman's) C
Sargent & Co., (Gas).AAAA
Schollhorn Co., W. (Line-
man's; Gas; Jewelers').A
CONN.—Plainville
Clark & Son, A. N. (Gas).B
CONN.—Rockfall
Smith, Otis A (Cutting)..B
CONN.—Southington
Peck, Stow & Wilcox Co.
(Gas; Jewelers'; Mica
Handled Linemens'; Chain
Needle; Reamer Nose;
Combination; Cutting;
Electricians'; Flat; Round
Nose; Opticians'; Tire
Plugging; Weaver) AAAA
CONN.—Unionville
Monce, S. G. (Glass
Cutters') ....B
ILL.—Chicago
Klein, Mathias & Son. 87
W. Van Buren (Line-
mens') ....B
Vaughan & Bushnell Mfg.
Co., 875 Carroll Av. (Gas)
...................A

PLIERS (Con.)

ILL.—Downers Grove
Dicke Tool Co. (Linemens')...C

MASS.—Athol
Athol Machine Co. (Gas;
Combination)..........B

—.—Boston
Walworth Mfg. Co., 132
Federal (Gas).....AAAA

MASS.—Springfield
Bullock Mfg. Co. (Jewelers')................A

MINN.—Owatonna
Washington Tool Co. (Gas)...D

N. J.—Newark
Bernz, Otto, S. 13th, cor.
S. Orange Av. (Gas).....B
Johnson, William (Gas)..D
Kraeuter & Co., 577 13th
(Gas; Combination)....X
Lowentraut Mfg. Co., P.
(Gas)................A
Osborne & Co., C. S.
(Gas)................B

N. Y.—Elmira
Cronk & Carrier Mfg. Co.
(Gas; Cutting; Lineman's;
Combination; Electricians'; Flat; Round Nose)...B

New York City
Ashcroft Mfg. Co., 85
Liberty (Gas).........A
Graham & Co., Jno. H.
(Buttons; Cutting; Side;
Diagonal; Electricians';
Lineman's).........AA
Jennings Co., C. E., 79
Reade (Gas)..........B
Johns-Manville Co., H. W.,
100 William (Insulated
Lineman's).........AAAA
McCoy Co., Jos. F. (Chain;
Needle; Reamer Nose;
Combination; Cutting;
Side; Diagonal; Duckbill;
Electricians'; Flat; Round
Nose; Gas Burner; Pipe;
Knot Tying; Splicing;
Weavers')..........B
Smith & Hemenway Co.
(Cutting; Gas Burner;
Pipe; Glass).........D
Tower & Lyon Co., 95
Chambers (Gas; Aligning;
Glass; Combination; Flat;
Round Nose; Pianomakers'; Webbing)......B

N. Y.—Seneca Falls
Climax Specialty Co. (Gas)...B

N. Y.—Utica
Utica Drop Forge & Tool Co.
(Gas; Buttons; Lineman's;
Combination; Chain;
Needle; Reamer Nose;
Champagne; Cutting;
Duckbill; Electricians';
Farmers'; Fencing; Flat;
Round Nose; Gas Burner;
Pipe; Glass; Heat Coil;
Knot Tying; Splicing; Opticians'; Plugging; Weavers')..............B

N. Y.—Waterford
King & Co., J. M. (Gas;
Combination)..........A

N. Y.—Yonkers
Saunders' Sons, D. (Gas
Burner; Pipe)........A

OHIO—Hamilton
Meyers Mfg. Co., Fred'k J.
(Gas)...............B

OHIO—Norwood
Cinn. Tool Co. (Gas; Lineman's)...............B

OHIO—Ravenna
Williams, A. C. (Gas
Burner; Pipe)........A

PA.—Erie
Reed Mfg. Co. (Gas)......A

PA.—Philadelphia
Stortz & Son, Jno., 210
Vine (Gas; Glass Cutter)...E

PLOWS

See also Agr. Imps

CONN.—Branchville
Grumann, G. G. (Ice).....E

PLOWS (Con.)

CONN.—Higganum
Cutaway Harrow Co......X

ILL.—Aurora
Western Wheel Scraper Co.
(Snow)..............AA

ILL.—Chicago
McGuire-Cummings Mfg.
Co., 122 N. Sangamon
(Snow)..............AA

ILL.—Rock Island
Donaldson Bros. (Ice)....D

IND.—Fort Wayne
Indiana Road Machine Co.
(Street R. R.; Snow)...A

MAINE—Portland
Portland Co. (Snow)...AA

MASS.—Arlington
Wood & Co., Wm. T. (Ice)...A

MASS.—Boston
Ames Plow Co. (Ice)...AAAA

MASS.—Taunton
Taunton Locomotive Mfg.
Co. (Street; Railroad;
Snow)..............AA

MASS.—Woburn
Smith & Wallace (Electric
Snow)..............D

MASS.—Worcester
Buckley Car Mfg. Co., T.
H. (Snow)..........AA

N. J.—Elizabeth
Stephenson Co., Jno. (Railroad; Street; Snow)..AAA

N. J.—Grenlock
Bateman Mfg. Co. (Hand;
Wheel)..............A

N. J.—Montclair
Heller & Co., W. C......F

N. Y.—Athens
Dernell & Co., H. F. (Ice)...E

New York City
Amer. Locomotive Co., 25
Broad (Steam; Snow)...AAAA
Woodhouse, J. S., 191
Water (Ice)..........C

N. Y.—Niagara Falls
Dobbie Fdry. & Machine Co....D

N. Y.—Staatsburg
Bodenstein & Co., J. G.
(Ice)................E

N. Y.—Syracuse
Syracuse Chilled Plow Co....AA

OHIO—Cleveland
Gerlach Co., Peter, 28 Col.
Av. (Ice)...........A
Van Dorn & Dutton Co.,
1796 E. Madison Av.
(Street; Railroad; Snow)...D

OHIO—Columbus
Kilbourne & Jacobs Mfg.
Co.................AAAA

OHIO—Hamilton
Long & Allstatter Co...AA

PA.—Waynesboro
Geiser Mfg. Co. (Snow)....AAAA

R. I.—Providence
Franklin Machine Co. (Electric Snow).............A

VA.—Norfolk
Whitehurst Co., R. W....B

PLUGGERS

N. Y.—Buffalo
Buffalo Dental Mfg. Co.
(Automatic Dental)....B

New York City
Consolidated Dental Mfg.
Co., 115 W. 42d (Automatic Dental)........B

PA.—Philadelphia
Johnson & Lund (Automatic
Dental)............AA
White Dental Mfg. Co., S.
S. (Automatic Dental)....AAAA

PLUGS

CONN.—Bridgeport
Belknap Mfg. Co. (Fusible)...C

Bryant Electric Co. (Electrical)..............A
Perkins Elect. Switch Mfg.

PLUGS *(Con.)*
Co. (Attachment)......A
ILL.—Chicago
Illinois Malleable Iron Co.,
30 W. Monroe (Soil Pipe
Testing; Fusible)..AAAA
Redlich Mfg. Co. (Wooden;
Deck)¹..............B
Ryerson & Son, Joseph T.
Boiler Flue) ....AAAA
Western Electric Co. (Electrical) ....AAAA
ILL.—Decatur
Mueller Mfg. Co., H. (Attachment; Brass Elec.)..
AAA
IND.—Peru
Peru Electric Mfg. Co.
(Fusible; Electrical)...A
IND.—South Bend
Knoblock-Heideman Mfg.
Co. (Spark) ....D
MD.—Baltimore
Kemp Mfg. Co., 1501 Guilford Av. (Soil Pipe Testing) ....B
MASS.—Boston
Crosby Steam Gauge &
Valve Co. (Fusible)...AA
Walworth Mfg. Co. (Boiler
Flue; Fusible) ...AAAA
MASS.—Braintree
Dow Portable Electric Co.
(Sparkling) C
MASS.—Somerville
Amer. Coil Co. (Double Insulated Mica Cord Spark)
D
MASS.—Webster
Prescott & Son, J. B. (Metal
Wall) ....B
MICH.—Detroit
Amer. Injector Co. (Fusible)
D
Park & McKay Co. (Basin;
Bath Tub, &c) C
MICH.—Northville
Dubuar Mfg. Co., J. A.
(Deck) X
MO.—St. Louis
Nelson Mfg. Co., N. O.
(Basin; Bath Tub, &c.)
AAA
N. H.—Keene
Ellis, Austin A. (Brush)..D
N. J.—Hoboken
New Jersey Plumbing Specialties Co. (Soil Pipe
Testing) ....G
N. J.—Jersey City
New Jersey Spring & Rubber
Co. (Basin; Bath Tub,
&c.) ....AA
N. J.—Newark
Premo-Hall Mfg. Co. (Bath
Tub) X
Sommers' Son, Jno. (Wooden) ....A
N. Y.—Bleeker
Peters' Sons, Jno. M.
(Wood: Paper Mill)....D
New York City
Ashcroft Mfg. Co. (Fusible)
A
Bunnell & Co., J. H. (Electrical) ....B
Connelly Iron Sponge & Gov.
Co. (Fusible) ....B
Drummond & Co., M. J.,
192 B'way (Soil Pipe
Testing) ....AA
Estes & Sons, E. B. (Deck;
Wooden; Paper) .....AA
Jones & Son, J., 64 Cortlandt (Attachment)....X
Reilly Repair & Supply Co.,
James, 229 West (Fusible) ....AA
N. Y.—Syracuse
Pass Seymour (Attachment; Fusible) ....A
N. Y.—Troy
Bernard Co., E. G. (Electrical) ....D
OHIO—Cincinnati
Lunkenheimer Co. (Fusible)
AA
Powell Co., Wm. (Fusible)
A
Vanduzen Co., E. W.
(Fusible) ....B
PA.—Philadelphia
Partrick, Carter & Wilkins

PLUGS *(Con.)*
(Electrical) ....B
Philadelphia Elec. Mfg. Co.
(Electrical) ....E
Pringle, Wm. F. (Electrical) ....D
PA.—Pittsburg
Goldie & Co., Wm., Jr.
(Tie) ....A
PA.—Williamsport
Darling Pump Mfg. Co.
(Ltd.) (Fusible) ....B
VT.—Putney
Stowell Co. (Toilet Paper)
D

PLUMBAGO
MASS.—Springfield
Springfield Facing Co.....C
N. J.—Jersey City
Dixon Crucible Co., Joseph
AAA
New York City
Ilsley, Doubleday & Co., 29
Front ....B
Kelly & Co., Thos. P., 544
W. 22d ....B
Patterson, Boardman & Co.
AAA
Pettit Chemical Co......B
Salomon & Bro., L. A., 216
Pearl ....AA
Standard Graphite Co., 11
B'way ....B
Wegelin & Wilckes Mfg.
Co. C
N. Y.—Rochester
Amer. Chemical Mfg. &
Mining Co. ....B
OHIO—Cincinnati
Obermayer Co., S., 647
Evans ....AA
OHIO—Cleveland
Smith Fdry. Supply Co., J.
D., 40 S. Water (Silver
Lead) ....D
PA.—Bethlehem
Pettinos Bros. ....A
PA.—Philadelphia
McIlvaine Bros. ....B
Paxson Co., J. W......AA
PA.—Pittsburg
McCormack Co., J. S.,
25th & A. V. Ry......B
McCullough-Dalzell Crucible
Co. ....A

PLUMES
CONN.—East Hampton
Bevin Bros. Mfg. Co.
(Horse; Sleigh).......A
Starr Bros. Bell Co. (Horse;
Sleigh) ....B
ILL.—Chicago
Dearborn Duster Co., 124 S.
Green (Horse) ....A
New York City
Taylor & Co., M. J.
(Harness) ....E
Wagner, Otto ....A
OHIO—Cincinnati
Crane & Breed Mfg. Co.
(Harness) ....AA
Pettibone Bros. Mfg. Co..A
PA.—Philadelphia
Horstmann, Wm. H...AAAA
WIS.—Milwaukee
Gem Hammock & Fly Net
Co. ....A

PLUMS
**See Dried Fruit; Canned
Goods**

PLUNGERS
MASS.—Boston
Young, Jos. H., 224 Franklin (Water Closet).....D
MO.—St. Louis
Reliance Machine & Tool
Co. (Pump) ....AAA
OHIO—Cincinnati
Vanduzen & Co., E. W.
(Pump) ....B
OHIO—Piqua
Piqua Handle & Mfg. Co.
(Pump) ....A
OREGON—Portland
Air-Tight Stove Mfg. Co.
(Roof) ....E

PLUNGERS (Con.)
PA.—Philadelphia
Berger Bros. Co., 237 Arch
(Pump) ....A
Holmes Fibre & Graphite
Mfg. Co. (Arc Lamp)..D
PA.—Rankin Station
Duquesne Forge Co.
(Piston) ....A

PLUSH

See also Silk Goods

CONN.—Bridgeport
Salts Textile Mfg. Co., The
(Silk Plush; Velvet)....A
CONN.—Mystic
Rossie Velvet Co. (Velvets)
B
CONN.—Norwich
Martin Co., J. B. (Silk
Velvet) ....AAAA
CONN.—Stonington
American Velvet Co. (Silk
Velvet) ....AAA
MAINE—Sanford
Sanford Mills (Furniture
Plushes) ....AAAA
N. J.—Paterson
Olympia Velvet Mills (Silk
Velvets) ....B
Peerless Plush Mfg. Co.
(Cotton; Silk; Seal)...B
Simon, R. & H. (Velvet)
AAAA
N. Y.—Clark Mills
Hind & Harrison Plush Co.
(Seal; Cotton, &c.)....A
N. Y.—Long Island City
Astoria Silk Wks. (Silk)..AA
N. Y.—Newburgh
Stroock Plush Co. ....B
New York City
Abegg & Rusch (Com.
Velvets) ....AAAA
Butterfield Co., Fred
(Plush) ....AAAA
Caeser & Co., H. A. (Vel-
vets) ....AAA
Chase & Co., L. C. (Mohair,
Com.) ....AA
Cheney Bros. (Plush; Vel-
vet) ....AAAA
Fleitmann & Co. (Com.
Velvets) ....AAAA
Gomprecht, M. (Velvets)..B
Hill Bros. (Velvets).....B
Hoeninghaus & Curtiss
(Com. Plush; Velvets).AA
Jaeger & Schmiedel (Com.
Plush; Velvets).......A
Krindel Sons & Co., J.
(Velvets) ....AAA
Menke & Co., Jno. (Velvets)
A
Oelbermann, Dommerich &
Co. (Com. Velvets) AAAA
Passavant & Co. (Com.
Velvets) ....AAAA
Poncet & Neeser (Velvet).B
Schoolhouse & Son, Chas.
(Velvets) ....A
Stieglitz & Sons, M. L.
(Velvets) ....A
Stroock & Co., C. (Com.).A
Wimpfheimer & Co., A.
(Velvets) ....AAA
PA.—Catasauqua
Wahnetah Silk Co. (Silk;
Seal) ....A
PA.—Easton
Simon, R. & H. (Silk;
Velvet; Plush)....AAAA
PA.—Philadelphia
Bechmann & Son. Geo. F.
(Velvets; Plushes)....A
Collins & Aikman Co. (Ve-
lours; Mohair; Cotton
Plush) ....A
Dobson, J. & J. (Silk; Mo-
hair; Worsted; Seal;
Coat Plushes; Silk Vel-
vets) ....AAAA
PA.—Swarthmore
Victory Plush Mill (Silk;
Velour) ....B
R. I.—Pawtucket
Goff & Sons. D. (Mohair)..
AAA
R. I.—Woonsocket
Eagle Mills ....A

POACHERS

ILL.—Paxton
Paxton Hdw. Mfg. Co. (Egg)
X
IND.—Terre Haute
Columbian Enameling &
Stamping Co. (Egg)..AAA
N. Y.—Brooklyn
Silver & Co., 304 Hewes
(Egg) C
N. Y.—Buffalo
Shepard & Co., Sidney (Egg)
AAAA
New York City
Lalance & Grosjean Mfg.
Co. (Egg) ....AAAA
Silver & Co. (Inc.) (Egg), C

POCKETS

See also Furniture; Pict-
ures, etc.

CONN.—Meriden
Bradley & Hubbard Mfg. Co.
(Brass Wall) ......AAAA
KY.—Louisville
Belcher Mfg. Co., J. V. (Me-
tal Pencil) ....E
MASS.—Ayer
Sigsbee Co. (Chamois Neck)
D
MASS.—Boston
Messer & Co., Geo. E. (Slip-
per) ....E
MICH.—Detroit
Hargreaves Mfg. Co. (Wall)
A
MINN.—Minneapolis
Dodson, Fisher, Brockman &
Co., 15 N. 3d (Leather
Saddle) ....AA
MO.—St. Louis
Webber Moulding Co., J. R.
(Wall) ....B
Western Railway Equipment
Co., Mo. Trust Bldg. (Car
Line) ....A
New York City
Gould-Mersereau Co. (Brass;
Wall) ....B
Hunt Co., C. W. (Coal) ..AA
Judd & Co., H. L. (Brass;
Wall) ....AA
Mason & Co., J. W. (Wall).
B
Tower & Lyon, 95 Chambers
(Rubber; Pistol) ....B
N. Y.—Syracuse
Gaylord Bros. (Office Card)
C
PA.—Philadelphia
Link Belt Engineering Co.
(Coal) ....AA
PA.—Pittsburg
Pressed Steel Car Co. (Steel
Stake) ....AAAA
VT.—North Bennington
Cushman Mfg.Co., Henry T.
(Wall) C

PODOPHYLLIN

MO.—St. Louis
Larkin & Scheffer Chem. Co.
A
OHIO—Cincinnati
Merrell Chemical Co., Wm.
C. ....AAA

POINTERS

CONN.—Guilford
Spencer's Sons, I. S. (Picket)
A
CONN.—Hartford
Cook Co., Asa S. (Bolt) B
Pratt & Whitney Co. (Bolt)
AAAA
CONN.—Waterbury
Waterbury Farrell Fdy. &
Mach. Co. (Wire) ....AA
MD.—Baltimore
Detrick & Harvey Machine
Co. (Bolt) ....AA
N. H.—Antrim
Goodell Co. (Pencil)......A
N. J.—Elizabeth
Braunsdorf - Mueller Co.
(Dowel) ....D
New York City
Millers' Falls Co., 28 Warren

POINTERS (Con.)
  (Spoke) ....AA
New York Silicate Book
  Slate Co., 68 Church
  (Blackboard) ....D
OHIO—Cleveland
Acme Mchy. Co. (Bolt) AA
Reliance Machine & Tool Co.
  (Bolt) ....D
OHIO—Hamilton
Niles Tool Wks. Co. (Bolt)
  AAAA
OHIO—Norwood
Cincinnati Tool Co. (Spoke)
  B
OHIO—Springfield
Webster & Perks Tool Co.
  (Bolt) C
OHIO—Tiffin
National Mchy. Co. (Bolt)
  AA
R. I.—Pawtucket
Pawtucket Mfg. Co. (Bolt)
  A

POINTS

CONN.—Derby
Shelton Co. (Glaziers')....A
CONN.—New Britain
Stanley Rule & Level Co.
  (Trammel) ....AAA
CONN.—Unionville
Humphrey, H. W. (Glaziers)
  D
ILL.—Chicago
Chicago Wheel & Mfg. Co.
  (Diamond Turning) C
Vulcan Iron Wks., 63 Mil-
  waukee Av. (& Pile Caps;
  Bands, &c.) ....AA
ILL.—Grand Crossing
Grand Crossing Tack Co.
  (Glaziers) ....AAA
ILL.—Havana
Havana Metal Wheel Co.
  (Plow) ....A
MASS.—Athol
Athol Machine Co. (Tram-
  mel) ....B
Starrett Co., L. S. (Divider
  Ball; Trammel) ....B
MASS.—Boston
Austin & Eddy, 117 Broad
  (Glaziers) C
Harvey, Henry H. (Stone-
  cutters') ....D
MASS.—Fairhaven
Atlas Tack Co. (Glaziers';
  Picture Frame) ....AAAA
MASS.—Kingston
Drew & Co., C. (Enameled
  Burning) C
MASS.—South Hanover
Phillips & Sons, E. (Gla-
  ziers'; ....A
MICH.—Detroit
Anderson & Sons, W. H.
  (Stonecutters') C
MICH.—Kalamazoo
Harrow Spring Co. (Cultiva-
  tor) ....B
MICH.—St. Johns
Mason & Co., F. C. (Spring
  Tooth; Single; Double
  Pointed; Wheel Cultiva-
  tor) C
N. J.—Newark
Atha Tool Co. (Stone-
  cutters') ....A
New York City
Dickinson, Jno. (Est. of)
  (Carbon: Diamond; Dia-
  mond Graduating; Dia-
  mond Turning) ....B
Sargent & Co. (Veneer)
  AAAA
Tower & Lyon (Trammel)
  B
PA.—Philadelphia
Chester Steel Castings Co.
  (Frog: Plow) ......AAAA
Penna. Steel Co. (Frog)
  AAAA
PA.—Pittsburg
Anchor Nail & Tack Wks.,
  S. 19th & Merrimac (Gla-
  ziers') ....B
Klein-Logan Co., S. 18th &
  Breed (Stonecutters') ..A
VT.—Windsor
Hubbard & McClary (Gla-
  ziers') ....B

POKERS

CONN.—Georgetown
Gilbert & Bennett Mfg. Co.
  (Stove) ....AAA
CONN.—Plainville
Hills, Edwin (Stove) .....A
ILL.—Chicago
Nicol & Co. (Stove)......D
ILL.—Freeport
Arcade Mfg. Co. (Stove) A
Stover Mfg. Co. (Stove) AA
MASS.—Worcester
Wire Goods Co. (Stove) ..A
MICH.—Detroit
Ireland & Matthews Mfg.
  Co. (Stove) ....A
N. Y.—Albany
Troy Nickel Wks. (Stove) C
New York City
Graf, Frank H., 322 7th
  Av. (Stove) ....D
Peck, Stow & Wilcox Co.,
  27 Murray (Stove) AAAA
Russell & Erwin Mfg. Co.,
  43 Chambers (Stove) ....
  AAAA
Sargent & Co., 151 Leonard
  (Stove) ....AAAA
OHIO—Cleveland
Federal Mfg. Co. (Stove)
  AAAA
PA.—Philadelphia
Pfeifer & Co. (Ltd.), Jno.
  (Stove) ....A

POKES

IOWA—Fort Madison
Iowa Farming Tool Co.
  (Animal) ....A
MICH.—Galien
Montross, Richard W. (Ani-
  mal) ....B
MICH.—Lansing
Lansing Wheelbarrow Co.
  (Animal) ....AAA
OHIO—Lancaster
Eagle Machine Co. (Animal)
  A
PA.—Girard
Ely Mfg. Co., Theo. J.
  (Animal) C

POLARISCOPES

MASS.—Boston
Thompson & Co., A. T., 15
  Tremont Pl. X
New York City
Colt & Co., J. B., Barclay
  B
Eimer & Amend ....E
Kohlbush, Herman, 194
  B'way ....B
PA.—Pittsburg
Scientific Materials Co...D

POLES

See also Woodwork: Car-
  riage; also Furniture

CONN.—Bridgeport
Wheel & Wood Bending Co.
  (Vehicle; Shafts) .....B
CONN.—Clinton
Kelsey, Horatio (& Flag-
  staffs) ....E
CONN.—New Haven
Dann Bros. & Co. (Vehicle;
  Shafts) ....B
CONN.—Torrington
Turner & Seymour Mfg. Co.
  (Extension Curtain) ....A
CONN.—Waterbury
Scoville Mfg. Co. (Brass;
  Curtain) ....AAAA
ILL.—Chicago
Central Electric Co., 268
  5th Av. (Iron; Steel Trol-
  ley) ....A
Illinois Malleable Iron Co.
  (Electric Light) .AAAA
Klein, Mathias & Son, 87
  W. Van Buren (Guarded
  or Plain Pike) ....B
Roos Mfg. Co., Edward
  (Wooden; Curtain) ....B
ILL.—Downer's Grove
Dicke Tool Co. (Pike) C
ILL.—Edwardsville
Springer Bros. Mfg. Co. (Ve-

POLES (Con.)
hicle; Shafts) ....F
ILL.—Freeport
Stover Mfg. Co., 165 River
(Iron Flag; Iron; Steel
Trolley) ....AA
IND.—Anderson
Anderson Pole & Shaft Co.
(Vehicle; Shafts) ....E
Buckeye Mfg. Co. (Vehicle;
Shafts) ....E
IND.—Bremen
Wright, Jno. J. (Vehicle;
Shafts) ....B
IND.—Indianapolis
Parry Mfg. Co. (Vehicle;
Shafts) ....AAAA
Wayne Works (Vehicle;
Shafts) ....A
MD.—Baltimore
Arnold Co., W. E. (Wooden;
Curtain) C
MASS.—Amesbury
Bailey & Co., S. R. (Vehicle;
Shafts) ....A
Currier & Cameron Co. (Ve-
hicle; Shafts) ....F
MASS.—Boston
Anderson Mfg. Co., A. & J.
(Trolley) ....A
Harrington, Robinson & Co.,
272 Franklin (Iron; Steel
Trolley) ....D
National Works Co. (Trol-
ley; Telegraph) ......AA
Stearns Lumber Co., A. T.,
Neponset & 166 Devon-
shire (Clothes; Flag)
.....................AA
Walworth Mfg. Co., 132
Federal (Iron; Steel Trol-
ley) ....AAAA
MICH.—Bay City
Michigan Pipe Co. (Creoso-
ted; Turned; Ornamental)
.....................AA
MICH.—Cedar River
Crawford & Sons (Cedar
Telegraph) ....A
MICH.—Evart
Champion Tool & Handle
Wrks. (Pike) ....AA
MICH.—Fenton
Phillips Co., A. J. (Clothes)
.....................A
MICH.—Flint
Durant-Dort Carriage Co.
(Vehicle; Shafts) ..AAAA
Flint Wagon Wrks. (Vehi-
cle; Shafts) ....AA
MICH.—Hermansville
Wisconsin Land & Lumber
Co. (Cedar) ......AAAA
MICH.—Kalamazoo
Star Brass Wrks. (Trolley)
.....................C
MICH.—Manistique
White Marble Lime Co.
(Cedar) ....B
MICH.—Menominee
Lindsley Bros. & Co. (Cedar)
.....................B
MICH.—Oscoda
Loud & Sons Lumber Co., H.
M. (Telegraph) .....AA
MICH.—Port Huron
Tunnel City Regalia Co.
(Banner) ....D
MICH.—Saginaw
Morley Bros. (Pike) ....AA
MINN.—Minneapolis
Coolidge-Schussler Co. (Tele-
graph) ....B
MO.—St. Louis
Pauk & Sons Mfg. Co., H.
(Barber) ....A
Webber Moulding Co., J. R.
(Wooden; Curtain) ...B
Western Electrical Supply
Co. (Trolley) X
N. H.—Manchester
Campbell, Jno. (Exhibition)
.....................H
N. J.—Lambertville
Lambertville Spoke Mfg. Co.
(Vehicle; Shafts) .....A
N. Y.—Binghamton
Wilkinson Mfg. Co. (Vehi-
cle; Shafts) ....A
N. Y.—Buffalo
Howard Iron Wrks. (Iron
Flag) ....A
N. Y.—Gowanda
Gowanda Agr'l Wrks. Co.

POLES (Con.)
(Cast Iron Hitching) ...X
New York City
Amer. Flag. Co. (& Flag-
staffs) ....A
Carey, Geo. H. (Trolley).D
Chesebro, Whitman & Co.
(& Flagstaff; Clothes)
.....................B
Ferguson Bros. Mfg. Co.
(Wooden; Curtain) ....A
Gould-Mersereau Co. (Brass;
Curtain) ....B
Gould's Son & Co., M.
(Brass; Curtain) .....A
Greenlie, Wyatt & Co., 499
Water (Iron Flag) ....B
Judd & Co. H. L. (Brass;
Curtain; Cornice) ....AA
John Kroder & Henry Reu-
bel Co. (Brass; Curtain)
.....................B
Morris Co., Elmer P. (Trol-
ley) ....D
New York Ladder Co., 580
Hudson (Clothes) .....E
Wendell & MacDuffie (Trol-
ley) ....B
N. Y.—Rome
Rome Brass & Copper Co.
(Brass; Curtain) ..AAAA
N. Y.—Schenectady
General Electrical Co. (Iron;
Steel Trolley) ....AAAA
N. Y.—Syracuse
Bradley & Son, C. C. (Ve-
hicle; Shafts) ....A
OHIO—Cincinnati
Creaghead Engineering Co.
(Trolley) ....D
Electric Railway Equipment
Co. 431 E. Front (Iron;
Steel Trolley) ....B
Gholson Fence Co., W. C.,
1746 Reading Pl. (Metal
Flag; for Lawn or House
Tops) X
Nimmo Fence Co., 324 E.
4th (Iron Flag) ......F
Walton Iron Co., Spring
Grove Av. (Iron; Steel
Trolley) C
OHIO—Cleveland
Federal Mfg. Co., Amer.
Trust Bldg. (Iron; Steel
Trolley) ....AAAA
Gerlach Co., Peter (Pike)
.....................A
OHIO—Dayton
Brown & Co., S. N. (Vehicle;
Shafts) ....F
OHIO—Hicksville
Kerr Bros. & Co. (Pike;
Awning; Brush; Tent)..C
OHIO—Lima
Coss & Stinebaugh (Brush;
Tent) ....E
OHIO—Mansfield
Ohio Brass Co. (Iron; Steel
Trolley) ....AA
OHIO—Toledo
Toledo Carriage Woodwork
Co. (Vehicle; Shafts)..A
Toledo Moulding Co. (Wood-
en; Curtain) ....A
OHIO—Van Wert
Gleason Lumber Co. (Vehi-
cle; Shafts) ....A
PA.—Franklin
Franklin Rolling Mill &
Fdry. Co. (Tripartite
Steel Trolley) X
PA.—Lancaster
Downey Bros. Spoke & Bend-
ing Co. (Vehicle; Shafts)
.....................B
PA.—McKeesport
Nat'l Tube Co. (& Flag-
staffs; Trolley) ....AAAA
PA.—Middletown
Amer. Tube & Iron Co.
(Electric Street Railway)
.................AAAA
PA.—Philadelphia
Mayer & England Co., 10 S.
10th (Iron; Steel Trolley)
.....................A
Merritt & Co., 1024 Ridge
Av. (Iron Flag) ......B
PA.—Pittsburg
Nat'l Tube Co. (Iron; Steel
Trolley; Iron Flag).AAAA
Nuttall Co., R. D., Lafayette
& Garrison Place (Iron;

POLES (Con.)
Steel Trolley) ....A
Phoenix Steel Construction
Co., Penn. Av. & 3d
(Iron Flag) ....D
Pittsburg Trolley Pole Co.,
115 Water (Iron; Steel
Trolley) X
Shelby Steel Tube Co., Frick
Bldg. (Iron; Steel Trolley;
Hose; Steel) ......AAAA
Simonds Mfg. Co., 25th &
Liberty (Iron; Steel Trol-
ley) ....B
Supply Mfg. Co. (Iron; Steel
Trolley) X
PA.—Reading
Leippe's Sons, Jacob A.
(Vehicle; Shafts) ......A
R. I.—Providence
Sash Curtain Rod & Novelty
Co. (Brass; Curtain) ..F
VT.—Burlington
Vermont Shade Roller Co.
(Wooden; Curtain; Torch;
Cornice) ....A
VA.—Petersburg
South Side Mfg. Co. (Wood-
en; Curtain) C
WIS.—Milwaukee
Falk Co. (Iron; Steel Trol-
ley) ....AAA
Wisconsin Bridge & Iron Co.,
Pabst Bldg. (Iron; Steel
Trolley) ....AA
WIS.—Oshkosh
Sanford Logging Tool Co.
(Pike) ....D
WIS.—Racine
Gold Medal Camp Furniture
Co. (Folding Jointed Tent)
...........................B
Racine General Mfg. Co.
(Vehicle; Shafts) ....E

POLISH

See also Finish; Blacking;
Paste

CAL.—San Francisco
Bennett & Co., E. W. (Met-
al) 296 Church ....F
CAL.—Los Angeles
Fuller & Co., W. P. (Mfrs.
Agt. Hard Wax Floor)
...........................AAAA
CONN.—Bridgeport
Bridgeport Crucible Co.
(Stove) C
CONN.—Hartford
Jennings Bros. Mfg. Co.
(Metal) ....AA
Tracy Oil & Varnish Co.
(Furniture) X
CONN.—Meriden
Meriden Britannia Co. (Sil-
ver) ....AAAA
CONN.—New Haven
Rostand Mfg. Co. (Gold;
Silver; Metal) ....D
Smith Chemical Co. (Metal)
...........................H
CONN.—New London
Tarbox Mfg. Co. (Metal;
Stove) C
CONN.—New Milford
Bridgeport Wood Finishing
Co. (Carriage; Floor; Fur-
niture; Piano) ....AA
GA.—Atlanta
Tripoline Mfg. Co. C
ILL.—Chicago
Adams & Elting Co. (Furni-
ture) ....A
American Shoe Polish Co.
(Shoe) ....A
Arnstein, Eugene, 35th &
Shields Av. (Metal) ...A
Atwood & Steele, 18 River
(Shoe) C
Ayling Bros., 14 Haddon Av.
(Stove) ....E
Chicago Varnish Co., 35
Dearborn Av. (Hard Wax
Floor) ....AA
Chicago Wood Finishing Co.
(Furniture) ....A
Dearborn Duster Co., 122 S.
Green (Metal) ....D
Hazlitt & Co., Geo. K.
(Metal) ....D
Lustre Chem. Co. (Furni-
ture) ....F
Martin & Martin 1398 Car-

POLISH (Con.)
roll (Stove; Metal; Furni-
ture) ....D
Matchless Metal Polish Co.
(Metal; Nickel; Silver).D
Nickel Plate Stove Polish
Co., 461 Illinois (Stove)
...........................C
Paul & Co., J. C., 91 Ran-
dolph (Metal) ....D
Prescott & Co., J. L., 18 N.
Clark (Stove) ....A
Zeller, F., 3112 Butler ...F
ILL.—Rockford
West Mfg. Co., L. M. (Pat-
ent Leather) X
IND.—Connersville
Golden Gleam Stove Polish
Co. ....H
IND.—Indianapolis
Hoffman, Geo. W. (Metal)
...........................C
Interior Hardwood Co.
(Floor) ....A
IND.—Lafayette
Harvey Chemical Co. (Met-
al) C
LA.—New Orleans
Bernhardt, David, 322
Camp (Mfrs. Agt. Hard
Wax Floor) ....A
MD.—Baltimore
Burchard Blacking & Oil
Co., 520 W. Franklin
(Stove) ....F
Hirshberg-Hollander & Co.
(Mfrs. Agt. Hard Wax
Floor) ....B
Thalman Mfg. Co. (Stove)
...........................D
MASS.—Boston
American Metal Polish Co.,
272 Devonshire (Metal)
...........................E
Baker & Co., Chas. F. (Shoe)
...........................A
Bird & Co., J. A. & W.., 34
India (Hard Wax Floor)
...........................AA
Brown & Co., B. F. (Shoe)
...........................B
Butcher Polish Co., 356 At-
lantic Av. (Hard Wax
Floor) ....F
Dennison Mfg. Co. (Silver)
...........................AAAA
Hauthaway & Sons, C. L.
(Patent Leather; Russet
Leather; Shoe) ....A
New England Novelty Mfg.
Co. (Stove) ....H
Parlor Pride Mfg. Co., 62
Clifford (Stove) C
Wiley & Co., I. H. (Floor
Wax) C
MASS.—Cambridge
Lord Polish Co., T. P.
(Metal) ....H
Reid Mfg. Co., W. W. ..H
Whittemore Bros. Co. (Shoe)
...........................AA
MASS.—Canton
Morse Bros. (Stove)..AAAA
MASS.—Lowell
Lowell Polish Co. (Floor;
Furniture) ....G
MASS.—Taunton
Reed & Barton Corporation
(Silver) ....AAA
MICH.—Detroit
Acme White Lead & Color
Wrks. (Hard Wax Floor;
Furniture) ....AAA
Boydell Bros. Whitelead &
Color Co. (Mfrs. Agt.
Hard Wax Floor) ....AA
Detroit Whitelead Wrks.
(Carriage; Piano; Furni-
niture) ....AAA
Regal Mfg. Co. (D. J.
Smith) ....D
Stevens F. B. (Metal) ...A
MINN.—Winona
Roesner Mfg. Co. ....H
MO.—Kansas City
Campell Glass & Paint Co.
(Mfrs. Agt. Hard Wax
Floor) ....AA
MO.—St. Louis
Herr Floor Co., Jno. (Hard
Wax Floor) ....D
MO.—Warrensburg
Pearle Polish Mfg. Co. ...G
N. J.—Jersey City
Dixon Crucible Co., Joseph

POLISH (Con.)
(Stove) ....AAAA
N. J.—Newark
Hanson & Van Winkle
(Metal) ....AA
N. J.—Passaic
Prescott & Co., J. L. (Stove)
A
N. Y.—Brooklyn
Burns, E. R., 27 Jackson
(Metal) ....D
N. Y.—Buffalo
Buffalo Specialty Mfg. Co.
(Furniture; Metal) ....F
East Mfg. Co. (Furniture) A
Favorite Mfg. Co., 1061 Ni-
agara (Metal) ....D
Liberty Chemical Co., 144
Terrace (Metal; Shoe)..F
Stinson & Co., B. F., 418
Niagara (Stove) ....D
Ulrich & Co., C. 233 E.
North (Metal) C
N. Y.—Hartwick
Bush, J. N. ....F
New York City
Bixby & Co's, S. M. (Russet
Leather) ....B
Borsum Bros. (Metal) ..B
Boston. Artificial Leather
Co., 12 E. 18th (Shoe)..B
Chilton Paint Co., 69 Cort-
landt (Mfrs. Agt. Hard
Wax Floor) ....B
Electro-Silicon Co., 30 Cliff
(Silver) ....D
Gaston, Weston & Ladd, 320
Pearl (Stove) ....D
Gerstendorfer Bros. 235 E.
42d (Furniture) ......B
Green & Co., W., 6 Maiden
Lane (Gold; Silver) ..C
Hoffman, G. W., 1 Ann
(Metal) C
Matchless Metal Polish Co.
(Metal) 69 Frankfort ..D
Mayer & Loewenstein (Car-
riage) ....‹...AAA
Miller Co., Frank (Patent
Leather) ....A
Moss, G. A., 167 Reade
(Stove) ....B
Pittit Chemical Co. (Metal)
B
Pierce Co., F. O. (Floor)
170 Fulton ....A
Prescott & Co., J. L., 90
W. B'way (Stove) .....A
Restorff & Bettman (Shoe)
B
Royal Lubricating Oil Co.,
116 Broad (Gold; Silver;
Piano; Metal) X
Salomon & Bro., L. A. (Sil-
ver) ....AA
Tonk & Bro., Wm., 452 10th
Av. (Piano) C
N. Y.—Palmyra
Vacuum Packing Co. (Metal)
D
N. Y.—Rochester
Amer. Chem. Mfg. & Mining
Co. (Stove) ....B
Nunn, G. L., & E. E., 116
Orange (Metal) ....F
Rochester Chemical Co.
(Metal; Stove) ......B
Wood Mosaic Flooring Co.
(Floor) ....AA
N. Y.—Syracuse
Baum's Castorine Co. (Met-
al) X
Colebrook Sons & Co., W. H.
(Stove) C
N. Y.—Troy
Connors Paint Mfg. Co.,
Wm. (Stove) ....A
Troy Paint & Color Wrks.
(Stove) ....B
OHIO—Akron
American Metal Polish Co.
(Metal) ....F
Smith Bros. (Stove) ....B
OHIO—Cincinnati
Barron, Boyle Co., 424 Main
(Hard Wax Floor) X
Obermayer Co., S. (Stove)
AA
OHIO—Cleveland
Smith Fdry. Supply Co., J.
D. (Stove) ....D
OHIO—Columbus
Citizens Wholesale Supply
Co., 150 3d (Shoe; Stove;
Metal; Silver) ....D

POLISH (Con.)
OHIO—Newark
Styron, Beggs & Co. .....A
OHIO—Piqua
Tice & Co., W. W. (Stove)
F
OHIO—Reading
Kuebler, D. (Shoe) ....H
OHIO—Toledo
National Cement & Rubber
Mfg. Co. (Nickel) C
PA.—Easton
World Refining Co. (Metal;
Stove; &c.) ....D
PA.—Johnstown
McKee & Co., Jas. N.
(Stove) X
PA.—Philadelphia
Colburn Co., A., 110 N. 2d
(Stove) ....AA
Diamond & Onyx, 317 De-
Lancy (Stove) ....B
Heaton & Wood, 1706 Chest-
nut (Dresden Wax Floor)
D
Lucas & Co., Jno. (Floor)
AAA
Mason Co., James S. (Pat-
ent Leather) ....A
Nice, Eugene E. (Floor;
Furniture) ....A
Wrigley Mfg. Co., 4478
Green (Metal) ....B
PA.—Pittsburg
Atlas Paint Co. (Ltd.)
(Stove) X
PA.—West Chester
Rapp, Barnet R. (Metal)
H
PA.—York
World Polish Mfg. Co.
(Stove) ....D
R. I.—Providence
Amer. Oil Co. (Metal) ...B
VT.—Rutland
Rutland Fire Clay Co.
(Stove) ....B
WIS.—Milwaukee
Delany Oil & Lubricant Co.
(Metal) X
Speich Stove Repair Co., 130
W. Water C
WIS.—Racine
Wood Mfg. Co., Lyman
(Stove) ....D

POLISHERS
See also Machy

N. Y.—Buffalo
Squier Mfg. Co., Geo. L.
(Coffee) ....AAA

POLO
See Sporting Goods

PONGEE
See Silk Goods

POMADES
N. Y.—New York City
Dreyer & Co., P. R., 16
Cedar X
Hutchinson, D. W., 5 Cedar
E
PA.—Philadelphia
Vail Bros., 2000 N. 10th..C

POMPONS
N. Y.—New York City
Hepner & Horwitz, 30 How-
ard ....B
PA.—Philadelphia
Horstmann Co., Wm. H.
(Regalia; Uniform)
AAAA
Oehrle Bros. & Co., 425 N.
3d ....B

POPCORN
ILL.—Chadwick
Beede Bros. C
ILL.—Chicago
Dickinson Co., Albert,
(Shelled) W. Taylor &
The River ....AA
Rueckheim Bros. & Eckstein
261 S. Desplaines ......A

POPCORN (Con.)
Weaver & Co., C. H., 129 S.
Water ....A
IOWA—Le Mars
Plymouth Roller Mills ....B
Odebolt
IOWA—Odebolt
Cook's Brookmont Farm
AAA
MICH.—Owosso
Mich. Sanitary Popcorn Co.
(Ltd.) C
MO.—Kansas City
Peppard, J. G., 1101 W. 8th
B
N. Y.—Albany
McDougal & Co. ....A
Wright, H. R. ....A
New York City
Cohen & Co., A. E., 18
Wooster ....B
OHIO—Columbus
Williams Mill. Co., J. F...B
B
TENN.—Memphis
Heinrich & Co., J. J. C
WASH.—Seattle
Bowen, E. J. ....A

POPLAR

See Lumber

POPPERS

ILL.—Chicago
Cretors & Co., C. (Corn) ..E
MASS.—Worcester
National Mfg. Co. (Corn) .A
Parker Wire Gds. Co.
(Corn) ....D
Wire Goods Co. (Corn) ...A
N. Y.—Buffalo
Shepard & Co., Sidney
(Corn) ....AAAA
Western Wire Gds. Co.
(Corn) ....D
N. Y.—Cortland
Wickwire Bros. (Corn)....
AAAA
New York City
Gilbert & Bennett Mfg. Co.
(Corn) ....AAA
OHIO—Cincinnati
Bromwell Brush & Wire
Gds. Co. (Corn) ......AA
OHIO—Delphos
Delphos Can Co. (Corn) ..B
OHIO—Hamilton
Meyers Mfg. Co., Fred J.
(Corn) ....B
PA.—Philadelphia
Darby & Sons, Edward
(Corn) ....A

PORK

See Meat Packers

PORPOISE

See Leather

PORTABLES

CONN.—Waterbury
Matthews & Willard Mfg.
Co. ....AAAA
Plume & Atwood Mfg. Co.
(Brass Electric) ....AAA
New York City
Frink, I. P...........AA
McLeod, Ward & Co......E
PA.—Reading
National Brass & Iron
Wks. ....A

PORTE-
MONNAIES

See also Jewelry; Leather
Goods

CONN.—Meriden
International Silver Co.
AAAA
GA.—Allapaha
Baker, Jos. H. C
MASS.—Athol
Bates Bros. & Co........B
N. J.—Jersey City
Mehl & Co., John........AA

PORTEMONNAIES Con.
New York City
Culbert & Co. X
Deitsch Bros. ....AA
PA.—Philadelphia
Rumpp & Sons, C. F..AAA

PORTFOLIOS

See also Leather Goods

ILL.—Chicago
Landa & Co., A., 1784 E.
Ravenswood Av. (Leather)
H
MASS.—Holyoke
National Blank Book Co. AA
MASS.—Springfield
Taber-Prang Art Co. ....AA
N. Y.—College Point
Gerlach, J. H............E
New York City
Boorum & Pease Co...AAA
Fischman Leather Goods Co.
95 5th Av. (Leather) ...D
Harrell Leather Goods Co.,
552 Bway. (Writing) ...C
PA.—Philadelphia
Rosenblatt & Co., H. M.,
22d & Oxford (Music) ..A

PORTIERES

See also Draperies; Curtains

ILL.—Chicago
Chicago Fringe & Embroid-
ery Co., 55 Market (Rope)
D
Mansure Co., E. L. Mich.
Av. & Lake (Rope) ..AA
MASS.—Boston
Paine Furniture Co.......A
New York City
Bernhard Co., Morris, 35 W.
19th (Rope) ....D
Gould Mersereau Co., 43 E.
19th (Leather) ....B
Union Upholstery Trimming
Co. (Rope) ....D
Waterman, Felix, 152
Wooster (Rope) ....D
PA.—Philadelphia
Horstman Co., Wm. H.
Cherry & 5th (Rope).....
AAAA
Oehrle Bros. & Co., 425
No. 3d (Rope) ....B
Schrack & Sherwood, 233
Market (Rope) ....A

PORTRAITS

ILL.—Chicago
Amer. Terra Cotta & Cera-
mic Co. (Terra Cotta) ..A
MASS.—Somerville
Sprague & Hathaway Co..A
N. J.—Perth Amboy
Perth Amboy Terra Cotta
Co. (Terra Cotta) ....AA

POSTERS

ILL.—Chicago
Kittridge & Co., R. J.
Superior ....A
LA.—New Orleans
Gulf Bag Co. (Ltd.)
(Printed Cotton) ..AAAA
MASS.—Boston
Bufford's Sons Engraving
Co. (Theatrical) X
Forbes Lithograph Mfg. Co.
(Theatrical) ....AA
New York City
Federal Lithographic Co., 91
Horatio ....B
Ottmann Lithographing Co.,
J. (Theatrical) ....B
N. Y.—Rochester
Karle Lithographic Co....A
OHIO—Massillon
Massillon Sign & Show
Printing Co. (Paper)...C
PA.—Philadelphia
Wolf & Co. (Theatrical)...
AAA

POSTS

See also Woodwork

CONN.—Ansonia

POSTS *(Con.)*

Ansonia Electrical Co.
(Binding) ....A
CONN.—Bridgeport
Bridgeport Brass Co. (Binding) ....AA
Bryant Electric Co. (Binding) ....A
CONN.—Hartford
Hartford Mach. Screw Co.
(Binding) ....AAAA
Pope Mfg. Co. (Bicycle
Seat) ....AAAA
CONN.—New Britain
Corbin, P. & F. (Binding)
AAAA
CONN.—New Haven
National Steel & Wire Co.
(Iron; Steel Fence).AAAA
CONN.—South Norwalk
U. S. Foundry & Sales Co.
(Lamp) ....D
GA.—Savannah
Southern Pine Co. of
Georgia (Newel) ...AAA
ILL.—Carpentersville
Illinois Iron & Bolt Co.
(Hitching) ....AA
ILL.—Chicago
Barbee Wire & Iron Wks.
(Barbed Wire; Cast Iron;
Iron Fence; Hitching;
Railing) ....B
Climax Fence Post Co., 204
Dearborn (Iron; Steel
Fence; Base made of Vitrified Shale Clay; Railway Signal) ....E
Clow & Sons, Jas. B., 344
Franklin (Lamp) ...AAAA
Cutter Co., Geo. G., Union
& Fulton (Arc Lamp)..C
Fairbanks, Morse & Co.,
Franklin & Monroe (Car
Bumping) ....AAAA
Illinois Malleable Iron Co.
(Hitching; Lamp)..AAAA
Inland Steel Co., 204 Dearborn (Steel for Railway
Fences) ....AAAA
McCord & Co., Old Colony
Bldg. (Car Bumping)..B
Mechanical Mfg. Co., Union
Stock Yards (Car Bumping) ....A
Pursell & Co., 232 So. Clinton (Lamp) ....E
Railway Appliances Co., Old
Colony Bldg. (Car Bumping) ....A
Railroad Supply Co., Bedford Bldg. (Car Bumping;
Steel for Railway Fences)
B
Smith Wire & Iron Wks., F.
P., 100 Lake (Lamp)..AA
Turner Brass Wks., Franklin & Michigan (Binding)
A
Western Electric Co., 259
So. Clinton (Binding;
Elec. Light; Lamp) AAAA
ILL.—De Kalb
De Kalb Fence Co. (Iron;
Steel Fence) ....AA
Union Fence Co. (Steel
Fence; Hitching).......B
ILL.—Freeport
Stover Mfg. Co. (Hitching)
AA
ILL.—Galva
Hayes Pump & Planter Co.
(Ornamental Cast Iron;
Hitching) ....A
ILL.—Joliet
Adams Steel & Wire Co.
(Steel Fence) ....D
IND.—Anderson
Dwiggins Wire Fence Co.
(Iron; Steel Fence).....B
IND.—Bloomfield
Bloomfield Mfg. Co. (Hitching; Iron; Steel Fence).C
IND.—Goshen
I. X. L. & Goshen Pump Co.
(Veranda) ....B
IND.—Indianapolis
Enterprise Foundry & Fence
Co. (Hitching; Iron; Steel
Fence) ....B
Over. Ewald (Iron Fence).C
IND.—Kendallville
Flint & Walling Mfg. Co.

POSTS *(Con.)*

(Hitching) ....AA
IND.—Kokomo
Kokomo Steel & Wire Co.
(Iron; Steel Fence).AAA
IND.—Peru
Peru Electric Mfg. Co.
(Binding) ....A
KY.—Burnside
Burnside Mfg. Co. (Cedar)
E
MD.—Baltimore
Smyser's Sons, E. G., 4
Light (Lamp) ....A
MASS.—Boston
Dinn & Co., P. J., 278
Dover (Lamp) ....E
Electric Gas Lighting Co.,
195 Devonshire (Binding)
A
Globe Gas Light Co., 79
Union (Lamp) ....D
Smith Iron Co., G. W. & F.,
166 Devonshire (Lamp).A
Stearns Lumber Co., A. T.
(Wood Fence) ....AA
MASS.—Lowell
Pevey & Bros., 224 Walker
(Lamp) C
MASS.—Waltham
Davis & Farnum Mfg. Co.
(Lamp) ....A
MASS.—Worcester
Wright Wire Co. (Fence)
AA
MICH.—Adrian
Bond Steel Post Co. (Iron;
Steel Fence) ....A
MICH.—Albion
Gale Mfg. Co. (Hitching)..
AA
MICH.—Athens
American Cement Post Co.
(Cement) ....F
MICH.—Bay City
Michigan Pipe Co. (Turned;
Ornamental) ....AA
MICH.—Detroit
Majestic Wire Fence Co.
(Fence) ....F
MICH.—Hermansville
Wisconsin Land & Lumber
Co. (Cedar) ......AAAA
MICH.—Manistique
White Marble Lime Co.
(Cedar) ....B
MICH.—Oscoda
Loud & Sons Lumber Co.,
H. M. (Cedar) ....AA
MO.—St. Joseph
Missouri Anchor Fence Co.
(Iron; Steel Fence)....D
MO.—St. Louis
Harry Steel Works, O. K.
(Iron Fence) ....B
Hutting Sash & Door Co.
(Newel) ....A
International Steel Post Co.,
719 Chestnut (Iron; Steel
Fence; Hitching) ......A
Ludlow-Saylor Wire Co.
(Fence; Hitching).....AA
St. Louis Screw Co., 3017
N. 13th (Binding) ....A
NEBR.—Omaha
Paxton & Vierling Iron Wks.
(Lamp) ....AA
N. H.—Concord
Concord Foundry & Mach.
Co. (Lamp) ....B
N. H.—Manchester
Campbell, John (Hitching)
H
N. J.—Jersey City
Snead & Co. Iron Wks.
(Lamp) ....A
N. Y.—Binghamton
Roberson & Son, A. (Newel)
AA
N. Y.—Brooklyn
Hecla Iron Wks., N. 11th
& Berry (Lamp)......AA
N. Y.—Cato
Dutton Co., E. Q. (Hitching) ....E
N. Y.—Coxsackie
Amer. Valve Co. (Indicator)
D
N. Y.—Horseheads
Weller Hardware & Foundry
Co. (Cast Iron Hitching)
D

POSTS (Con.)

N. Y.—Manlius
Cheney & Sons, S. (Cast Iron Hitching) ....A
New York City
Bunnell Co., J. H., 20 Park Pl. (Binding).....B
Cornell Co., J. B. & J. M., 26th & 11th Av. (Lamp) ....AA
Drummond & Co., M. J., 192 B'way (Lamp) ....A
Fiske Iron Works, J. W., 39 Park Pl. (Arc Lamp; Iron Fence: Hitching).B
Fox & Co., John, 253 B'way (Lamp; Mfrs. Agts.)...B
Hartman Mfg. Co. (Hitching) X
International Brass & Elect. Co., 76 Beekman (Brass Binding) ....D
Jackson Co., Wm. H., 29 E. 17th (Lamp) ....A
Kenedy Valve Mfg. Co., 57 Beekman (Valve Indicator) ....AAA
Miner Thos., T. W., 821 Eagle Av. (Lamp).....F
Mott Iron Wks., J. L., 88 Beekman (Arc Lamp; Lamp; Hitching) ....AA
Westervelt, A. B. & W. T., 102 Chambers (Arc Lamp; Lamp) ....B
N. Y.—Troy
West Side Fdry. Co. (Hitching) ....A
N. Y.—Waterford
Eddy Valve Co. (Indicator) ....AA
N. Y.—Watervliet
Covert Mfg. Co. (Hitching) ....A
OHIO—Ashtabula
Barber Mfg. Co. (Painted; Bronzed Hitching) C
OHIO—Canton
Amer. Steel Post Co. (Iron; Steel Fence) ....E
Sun Vapor Street Light Co. (Lamp) ....A
OHIO—Cincinnati
Bourbon Copper & Brass Wks., 618 Front (Indicator) ....A
Electric Railway Equipment Co., 431 E. Front (Arc Lamp) ....A
Gholson Fence Co., W. C., 1746 Reading Rd. (Steel Hitching; Steel Fence; Steel Stayes) X
Stacey Mfg. Co., 239 Mill (Lamp) ....AA
Stewart Iron Wks. (Hitching) ....A
OHIO—Cleveland
Avery Stamping Co. (Iron; Steel; Fence) ....B
Cleveland Automatic Mach. Co. (Binding) ....AAA
Federal Mfg. Co. (Bicycle Saddle) ....AAAA
National Iron & Wire Co. (Hitching) ....B
Standard Tool Co. (Bicycle Seat) ....AA
Van Dorn Iron Wks. Co. (Iron; Fence; Hitching) ....AA
OHIO—Columbus
International Fence & Fireproofing Co. (Hitching).A
OHIO—Hamilton
Meyers Mfg. Co., Fred J. (Hitching) ....B
OHIO—Kenton
Champion Iron Co. (Hitching; Lamp; Iron Fence) ....AA
OHIO—Springfield
Rogers Iron Co. (Iron; Steel Fence; Hitching) ......B
OHIO—Toledo
Donovan Wire & Iron Co. (Hitching) C
PA.—Catasauqua
Davis & Thomas Co. (Lamp) ....AA
PA.—Elwood City
Glen Mfg. Co. (Steel Hitching) C

POSTS (Con.)

PA.—Mechanicsburg
Comstock, Geo. S. (Hitching) C
Wilcox Mfg. Co., D. (Bicycle Seat) ....A
PA.—Nazareth
Nazareth Foundry & Mach. Co. (Hitching; Mooring) ....B
PA.—Philadelphia
Blatchley, C. G. (Newel; Hydrant) ....B
Creswell Iron Wks., S. J., 23d & Cherry (Lamp) ...B
Darby & Sons, Edward (Hitching) C
Gaumer Co., Jno. L., 19th & Hamilton (Lamp)....C
Kitson Hydro-Carbon Heating & Incan. Ltg. Co., 8th & Willow (Lamp) ......A
Partrick, Carter & Wilkins 1231 Callowhill (Binding) ....B
Penna. Globe Gas Light Co., Broad & Arch (Lamp)..A
Wood & Co., R. D. (Lamp) ....AAAA
PA.—Pittsburg
National Tube Co., Frick Bldg. (Arc Lamp)..AAAA
Phoenix Steel Construction Co., Penn. Av. & 3d (Iron; Steel Fence) ....D
PA.—Reading
Reading Foundry Co. (Lamp) X
PA.—So. Bethlehem
Bethlehem Foundry & Mach. Co. (Hitching; Lamp; Mooring) C
PA.—Tamaqua
Tamaqua Mfg. Co. (Hitching) ....B
R. I.—Providence
Builders' Iron Foundry (Lamp) ....AA
S. C.—Spartanburg
Morgan Wood & Iron Wks. (Newel) ....D
TENN.—Nashville
Prewitt, Spurr Mfg. Co. (Cedar) ....A
VA.—Norfolk
Roper Lumber Co., Jno. L. (Cedar) ....AAA
Whitehurst Co., R. W. (Mooring) ....B
WIS.—Milwaukee
Bailey & Sons, Wm. (Lamp) X
League Cycle Wks. (Bicycle Seat) ....D
Schwab Sons Co., R. J. (Iron; Steel Fence)...AA
Willer Mfg. Co. (Newel).A
WIS.—Racine
Freeman & Sons, S. (Lamp) ....A
Racine Malleable & Wrought Iron Co. (Bicycle Seat).A
WIS.—So. Milwaukee
Stowell Mfg. & Foundry Co. (Car Bumping; Iron; Steel Fence) ....A

POTASH

ILL.—Chicago
Brookman Bros., 149 Huron ....E
Brookman Mfg. Co., 79 La Salle Av ....D
MD.—Baltimore
Balto Chrome Wks. (Bichromate) ....AA
Hoefner & Sons, A., 403 Exchange Pl............AA
MASS.—Boston
Billings Clapp & Co. (Caustic) ....B
Fort Hill Chemical Co., 84 State (Chlorate).......A
Linder & Meyer (Chlorate) ....A
MASS.—Montague
Mann, Jason ....D
MICH.—Bay City
Michigan Chemical Co. AAA
North American Chemical Co. (Chlorate) ....A

POTASH (Con.)

MICH.—Saginaw
Passolt, H. (Crude) ......B

MO.—St. Louis
Herf & Frerichs Chemical
Co. (Iodide) ....A
Myers Lye Co., E. 3rd &
Clark Av..............B

N. J.—Newark
Carhuff & Son Co., E. R.
(Prussiate) ....B
Hanson & Van Winkle Co.
(Cyanide of) ....AA

N. Y.—Albany
Mendleson & Sons (Ball) ..A

N. Y.—Brooklyn
Wiarda & Co., Jno. C. (Cyanide; Carbonate)......AA

N. Y.—Buffalo
Hoefner & Sons, A., 170
Van Ressno ....A
Schoelkopf, Hartford &
Hanna Co. (Carbonate;
Chlorate) ....AAA

New York City
Anthony Co., H. M., 48
B'way ....B
Babbitt, B. T., 82 Greenwich ....AAAA
Battelle & Renwick, 163
Front (Muriate) ......AA
Beggs & Co., E. J., 101
Beekman (Dry Bisulphite) ....D
Brookman Mfg. Co., 193
Front ....D
Brower & Co., J., 16 Water
A
Champion Chemical Wks.,
177 Franklin ....B
Fuerst Bros. & Co. (Carbonate; Chlorate) ......D
Hall, E. N., 396 B'way (Ammoniated) ....
Hill's Sons Co., Edw. (Caustic; Carbonate) ......A
Hirsh & Son, Leon, 368
Greenwich (Pearl Ash) D
Jones Chemical Co., Enos.
F., 51 Jay (Pearl Ash;
White Crystal) ....B
Klipstein & Co., A. (Carbonate; Chlorate) .....AA
Kuttroff-Pickhard & Co.
(Carbonate Chlorite)..A
Lee & Co., James (Carbonate) ....A
New York Chemical Wks.,
48 W. B'way ....D
Phair, R. W. (Chlorate) F
Riker, J. L. & O. S. (Chlorate) ....A
Roessler & Hasslacher Chemical Co. (Bi-Chromate;
Cyanide of; Carbonate;
Chlorate) ....AA
Rogers & Pyatt (Chlorate)
A
Selling Co., The (Bichromate) C
Wing & Evans (Pearl Ash)
AAA

N. Y.—Niagara Falls
National Electrolytic Co.
A

N. Y.—Syracuse
Solvay Process Co. (Caustic)
AAAA

OHIO—Cincinnati
Babbitt, B. T., 804 Race
AAAA
Winkler & Co., Isaac (Carbonate) ....AA

OHIO—Defiance
Dietrick, D..............H

PA.—Philadelphia
Ferguson Bros. (Carbonate;
Chlorate; Bi-Chromate) A
Kalion Chemical Co. (Bi-Chromate) ....AA
Penna Chemical Wks. AAAA
Pennsylvania Salt Mfg. Co.
AAAA
Powers-Weightman - Rosengarten Co. (Bi-Chromate;
Caustic) ....AAAA

R. I.—Pawtucket
Draper & Co., Jas. O. (Ammoniated) ....B

VA.—Richmond
Virginia Carolina Chemical
Co. (Caustic) ......AAAA

POTASH (Con.)

WIS.—Milwaukee
Eagle Lye Wks. (Caustic)
A

POTS

See also Earthenware;
Chinaware; Silverware;
Enamelled Ware; Tinware

CONN.—Bridgeport
Amer. Tube & Stamping Co.
(Tallow) ....AAAA

CONN.—Elmwood
Goodwin Bros. Pottery Co.
(Flower) ....B

CONN.—Meriden
Manning, Bowman & Co.
(Coffee; Tea) ....AA

CONN.—New Britain
Landers, Frary & Clark
(Glue) ....AAA

CONN.—Wallingford
Wallace & Sons Mfg. Co.,
R. (Coffee; Tea) ..AAAA

ILL.—Chicago
Allis-Chalmers Co. (Slag)..
AAAA
Illinois Malleable Iron Co.
(Soldering) ....AAAA

ILL.—Paxton
Paxton Hardware Mfg. Co.
(Coffee; Tea) X

ILL.—Quincy
Modern Iron Wks. (Soldering) ....B

ILL.—St. Charles
Glen Mfg. Co. (Melting;
Soldering) ....D

IOWA—Fort Dodge
Fort Dodge Stoneware Co.
(Bean) C

MASS.—Boston
Contractors Plant Co., 8 Oliver (Lead Melting) ....E

MASS.—Cambridge
Hewes & Co., A.H. (Flower)
A

MASS.—Worcester
Wheeler Foundry Co. (Annealing) ....D

MICH.—Detroit
Amer. Electrical Heater Co.
(Electric Soldering) ..B
Byram & Co. (Iron; Melting)
D

MO.—St. Louis
Kupferle, John C. (Solder)
AA
St. Louis Stamping Co.
(Coffee; Tea; Sauce)....
AAAA

N. J.—Burlington
Lindsay & Co., J. C. (Lead;
Melting) ....D

N. J.—Newark
Bernz, Otto, S. 13th cor. S.
Orange Av. (Soldering) B

N. J.—Trenton
MacKenzie Co. Duncan (Annealing) ....A

N. Y.—Brooklyn
Graham Chemical Pottery
Wks., Chas., 1018 Met.
Av. (Stoneware Mixing)
D
Sweeney Mfg. Co., W. H.
(Coffee; Tea) ....A
Vogel & Bros., Wm. (Watering) ....AA

N. Y.—Buffalo
Aldrich Mfg. Co. (Coffee;
Tea) ....A
Buffalo Dental Mfg. Co.
(Soldering) ....B
Household Mfg. Co., 18
Pearl (Coffee) ......E
Shepard & Co., Sidney
(Coffee; Tea; Watering;
Glue) ....AAAA

New York City
Central Stamping Co. (Beer;
Soup Stock;Stove) ..AA
Cornell Co., J. B. & J. M.,
26th & 11th Av. (Annealing) ....AA
Crane Co., Wm. M., 1133
B'way (Melting) ......A
International Silver Co.
(Chocolate; Coffee; Tea,
&c.) ....AAAA
Iron Clad Mfg. Co., 2 Cliff

POTS (Con.)

(Watering) ....A
Koven & Bros., L. O. (Melting) ....A
Lalance & Grosjean Mfg. Co. (Beer; Coffee; Tea; Cooking; Soup Stock; Glue; Stove) ....AAAA
Nichthauser & Levy, 96 Beekman (Watering)....C
Reilley Bros., 322 W. 41st (Knife Edge; Painters') ....D
Stoutenborough, X. (Cooking; Sauce; Soup Stock; Stove) ....D
N. Y.—Rochester
Castle & Co., Wilmot (Coffee; Tea) ....B
N. Y.—Rome
Rome Mfg. Co. (Coffee; Tea) ....B
N. Y.—Troy
Troy Stamping Wks. (Coffee; Tea; Watering) .... AAAA
OHIO—Cincinnati
Blymyer Iron Wks. Co. (Iron) ....B
Obermayer Co., S. (Glue; Watering) ....AA
OHIO—Cleveland
Fanner Mfg. Co. (Glue) A
Riverside Foundry Co. (Annealing) ....B
OHIO—Cuyahoga Falls
Turner, Vaughn & Taylor Co. (Annealing) ....B
OHIO—Findlay
Findlay Clay Pot Co. (Clay) A
OHIO—Hamilton
Kahn Bros., F. & L. (Iron) A
OHIO—Steubenville
Ohio Valley Clay Co. (Glass) A
OHIO—Youngstown
Pollock Co., Wm. B. (Annealing; Slag) ....AA
PA.—Allegheny
Pittsburg Clay Pot Co. (Glass) ....AA
PA.—Erie
Griswold Mfg. Co. (Soldering) ....A
Holland Mfg. Co. (Melting) B
PA.—Harrisburg
Hickok Mfg. Co., W. O. (Glue) ....AA
PA.—Mooresburg
Ack, J. F. (Earthen Flower) X
PA.—New Brighton
Pittsburg Clay Mfg. Co. (Bean; Flower) ....AAAA
PA.—New Castle
Pennsylvania Engineering Wrks. (Slag) ....AA
PA.—Philadelphia
Philadelphia Scoop Co. (Coffee; Tea) X
PA.—Pittsburg
McCullough-Dalzell Crucible Co. (Teeming) ....A
Standard Mfg. Co. (Cooking) AA
Willetts Co. (Glass House) B
PA.—Rochester
Rochester Clay Pot Co. (Clay) C
VT.—Rutland
Rutland Fire Clay Co. (Watering) ....B
WIS.—Milwaukee
Allis-Chalmers Co. (Slag) AAAA

POTTERY

See also Stoneware; Earthenware; Chinaware

CAL.—Los Angeles
Los Angeles Stoneware Co. D
CONN.—Elmwood
Goodwin Bros. Pottery Co. (Artistic) ....B
ILL.—Chicago
Chicago Pottery Co. C
ILL.—Peoria
Peoria Pottery Co. ......A

POTTERY (Con.)

KY.—Paducah
Bauer, J. A. ....B
MAINE—Bangor
Bangor Stoneware Co. ...E
MD.—Baltimore
Bennett Pottery Co., E. 1301 Canton Av ....B
Chesapeake Glass Co. (Druggists) ....D
Perine & Sons, M., 1009 W. Baltimore (Druggists)..B
MASS.—Taunton
Wright & Son, F. ....H
MO.—St. Louis
Monmouth Pottery Co.. 1302 N. Main ....D
N. H.—Keene
Taft & Co., J. S. (Artistic) B
N. J.—Flemington
Fulper Pottery Co. (Stone Liquor Jugs) ....D
N. J.—Trenton
Ceramic Art Co. (Artistic) B
Cook Pottery Co. (Art) ..A
Monument Pottery Co. (Majolica) ....A
Morris & Wilmore Co. (Majolica) X
Willets Mfg. Co. (Artistic) A
N. Y.—Brooklyn
Graham Chemical Pottery Wks., 1018 Met. Av. (Acid Proof Chem.) ....D
N. Y.—Elmira
Farrington, E. W. C
New York City
Ahrenfeldt & Son, Chas., 50 Murray (Art) ....B
Bawo & Dotter, 26 Barclay (Art) ....AA
Bing & Co., Ferd., 10 Wash. Pl. (Art) ....A
Borgfeldt & Co., Geo., 48 W. 4th (Art) ......AAAA
Davison Bros., 12 Barclay (English) ....B
Dwenger, C. L., 35 Park Pl. (Art) ....D
Glaenzer Freres & Rheinboldt, 26 Washn. (Art) .A
Lazarus, Rosenfeld & Lehmann, 62 Murray (Art) B
Hospital Supply Co. (Hospital) ....A
Levy & Co., L. W., 194 Bway. (Art) ....D
Owens Pottery Co., Jos., 70 W. Bway. (Art) X
Straus & Sons, L., 42 Warren (Art) ....AAAA
Vantine & Co., A. A., 20 E. 18th (Art) ....AAA
N. Y.—Syracuse
Syracuse Stoneware Co. AA
OHIO—Akron
Akron Pottery Co. C
OHIO—Buckeye Cottage
Buckeye Stoneware Co. ...F
OHIO—Cincinnati
Rockwood Pottery Co. (Am. Faience; Druggists') ..B
OHIO—East Liverpool
Cartwright Bros. Co. (Druggists') ....A
OHIO—Sebring
Sebring Pottery Co. (Barroom) ....AA
OHIO—Zanesville
Ohio Pottery Co. (Ewers) .C
Owins Pottery Co., J. B. (Am. Faience; Art) ...A
Weller, S. A. (Faience) AA
Zanesville Art Pottery Co. (Pitchers) ....B
Zanesville Stoneware Co. (Tableware) C
W. VA.—Wheeling
Wheeling Potteries Co. (Tableware) ....AAA

POUCHES

CONN.—Waterbury
Waterbury Brass Co. (Shot) AAAA
D. C.—Washington
Peerless Pouch Co. ......H
ILL.—Chicago
Nicol & Co. (Coin; Tobacco) D
Shafer Co., F. L., 263 Dear-

POUCHES (Con.)
born (Leather Coin) ....D
MASS.—Andover
Tyer Rubber Co. (Rubber)
................AA
MASS.—Boston
Davidson Rubber Co.
(Tobacco) ....A
N. Y.—Gloversville
Mills, Fred S. (Tobacco) ..D
Wilkins Co., E. J. (Tobacco)
................B
New York City
Spalding & Bros., A. G.
(Shot) ....,......AAAA
OHIO—Akron
Faultless Rubber Co. (Rub-
ber) ....AA
Goodrich Co., B. F. (Rubber)
................AAAA
OHIO—Barberton
Pure Gum Specialty Co.
(Rubber) C
PA.—Blue Ball
Shirk, P. E. (Metal) ....D

POUNCE

New York City
Davids Co., Thaddeus, 127
William C
Stafford, S. S. ....B

POUNDERS

CONN.—New Britain
Landers, Frary & Clark
(Steak) ....AAA
Stanley Rule & Level Co.
(Steak) ....AAA
CONN.—New Haven
Brown & Co., R. H. (Steak)
................B
ILL.—Freeport
Stover Mfg. Co. (Steak) AA
MASS.—North Hadley
Dickinson & Son, C. D.
(Broom) ....D
MASS.—Worcester
Parker Wire Goods Co.
(Steak) ....D
New York City
Burns & Sons, Jabez (Spice;
Drug) ....B
Peck, Stow & Wilcox Co.
(Steak) ....AAAA
OHIO—Cleveland
Fanner Mfg. Co. (Steak) ..A
OHIO—Ravenna
Williams, A. C. (Steak) ..A
PA.—Wrightsville
Wrightsville Hardware Co.
(Steak) ....B

POWDER

See also Gunpowder

ARK.—Little Rock
Fletcher Coffee & Spice Co.
(Baking) ....D
CAL.—Los Angeles
Southern Calif. Supply Co.
(Baking) ....B
CAL.—Petaluma
Petaluma Incubator Co.
(Insect) ....B
CAL.—San Francisco
Amer. Cream Tartar Co.
(Baking) ....A
California Powder Wks. (Ex-
plosive; Blasting; Gun) A
California Vigorit Powder
Co., 208 California (Ex-
plosive) ....A
Guitard Mfg. Co., 119 Front
(Baking) ....E
San Francisco Candle Co.
(Soap) ....A
CAL.—Stockton
Buhach Producing & Mfg.
Co. (Insect) ....AA
CONN.—Derby
U. S. Rapid Fire Gun &
Powder Co. (Explosive)AA
CONN.—Hartford
Sturtevant Corporation, F. C.
(Insect) ....D
DEL.—Wilmington
Dupont Co., E. I. (Smoke-
less; Gun, etc.) ..AAAA
FLA.—Pensacola
Buffalo Mfg. Co. (Baking)G

POWDER (Con.)
GA.—Brunswick
Downing Co. (Baking) ..AA
GA.—Savannah
Imperial Baking Powder Co.
(Baking) ....B
ILL.—Bloomington
Ela Mfg. Co. (Baking) ....F
Waldorf, W. A. (Baking) E
ILL.—Chicago
Aetna Powder Co., 143 Dear-
born (Dynamite; Gelatine;
Blasting; Gun) ......AA
Allen & Co., J. W., 210
Washn. Bould. (Baking) B
Armour Soap Wks. (Soap)
................AAAA
Arnstein, Eugene, 35th &
Shields Av. (Bronze) ..A
Atwood & Steele, 18 River
(Baking; Insect) C
Barrett & Co., M. L., 219
Lake (Aluminum) .....A
Bear Bros., 69 So. Water
(Baking) C
Benjamin, M. A. (Pure Food
Baking Powder Co.) 112
W. Washn. (Baking) ..F
Calumet Baking Powder Co.,
St. Clair & Ohio (Baking)
................D
Chapman & Davison Co., 59
W. Washn. (Baking) ..C
Chapman & Smith Co., 187
W. Randolph (Baking;
Almond Macaroon; Yeast)
................A
Dieter Co., J. P. (The)
(Baking) C
Field-Collins Mfg. Co., 39
W. Washn. (Baking) ..D
Gillett, E. W., 99 Erie
(Baking) ....AAAA
Grant Hygienic Baking Pow-
der Co., 25 So. Desplaines
(Baking) ....B
Independent Baking Powder
Co., 42 River (Baking) E
Jaques Mfg. Co., 244 John-
son (Baking) ......AAA
Krembs & Co. (Insect) ...C
Lewis & Co., Geo. A. (Bak-
ing) C
McMahon & Durlacher Co.
(Baking) ....D
Matchless Metal Polish Co.
(Metal Polishing) .....D
Price Baking Powder Co.,
186 Michigan (Baking)
................AAAA
Puhl-Webb Co., 119 W. Ran-
dolph (Baking) C
Purity Chemical Co., 279 E.
Madison (Baking) .....D
Raven & Co., L. A. (Horse;
Cattle, etc.) ....B
Reid, Murdock & Co., Lake
& Market (Baking) AAAA
Sherman Bros. & Co., 22 So.
Water (Baking) ......A
Stearns Electric Paste Co.
(Insect) ....F
Thompson & Taylor Spice
Co. (Baking) ......AA
ILL.—Decatur
Decatur Extract Co. (Bak-
ing) ....D
ILL.—East St. Louis
Layton Pure Food Co. (Bak-
ing) ....D
ILL.—Peoria
Allaire, Woodward & Co.
(Insect) ....A
Fisher & Co., Chas. (Baking)
................B
Miller Pure Food Co.
(Baking) ....F
ILL.—Plano
Cunningham & McCracken
(Baking) ....F
IND.—Evansville
Grocers' Chemical Wks.
(Baking) ....E
IND.—Indianapolis
Climax Coffee & Baking
Powder Co., 523½ E.
Washn. (Baking) .....A
Everitt, J. A. (Insect) ....B
Grocers' Supply Co., 128 So.
Penna. (Baking) C
IND.—Logansport
Kewanna Baking Powder Co.
(Baking) ....A

POWDER (*Con.*)

IND.—Richmond
Fouts, O. H. (Horse; Cattle) ....D
Ross Drug Co., W. H. (Baking) ....D

IND.—South Bend
Russ Co. (Baking) C
Victor Mfg. Co. (Baking) F

IND.—Terre Haute
Eureka Powder Co. (Explosive) ....D
Independent Powder Co. (Explosive) C
Indiana Powder Co. (Explosive) ....A
Northwestern Powder Co. (Explosive) ....B

IND.—Wabash
Wabash Baking Powder Co. (Baking) ....B

IOWA—Allerton
Allerton Caponizer Mfg. Co. (Insect) ....H

IOWA—Des Moines
Globe Baking Powder Co. (Baking) ....G

IOWA—Sioux City
Northwestern Mfg. Co. (Baking) ....E

KANS.—Topeka
Hygienic Mfg. Co. (Baking) F

KANS.—Wichita
Amer. Soda & Baking Powder Co. (Baking) .....F

KY.—Covington
Chemical Mfg. Co. (Talcum) E

KY.—Louisville
Ottenhimer & Son, E., 630 E. Market (Baking Powder) C
Robertson & Carrier Co. (Baking) ....D

KY.—Paducah
Paducah Vinegar Wks. (Baking) ....D

LA.—New Orleans
Gulf Mfg. Co., (F. W. Young, Prop.) 523 Natchez (Baking) ....B
Vermont Chemical Mfg. Co. (Ltd.) 206 Poydras (Baking) C

MD.—Baltimore
Foutz, D. E. (Horse; Cattle) B
Koehler & Son, J. (Insect) E
McCormick & Co. (Baby; Horse; Cattle; Insect) ..C
Parrish Bros., 115 E. Lombard (Baking) ....B
Read & Co., C., 113 So. Fred'k (Baking) C
Rolan Mfg. Co., (C. Read & Co., Prop.) 113 So. Fred'k (Baking) C
Sea Gull Spec. Co., (The) 509 E. Lombard (Baking) D
Thomsen Chemical Co. (Dover's) ....B

MASS.—Boston
Amer. Powder Mills, 233 State (Gun, etc.) ....AA
Anderson Bros., 100 Boylston (Putty) X
Boston Baking Powder Co., 234 State (Baking) ....D
Gary & Co., J. E. (Insect) A
Harrison Supply Co., 32 India Wharf (Putty) ..E
India Alkali Wks. (Compounds; Car Cleansing) C
Lincoln's Baking Powder Co. (Mrs. M. J.) 21 Commerce (Baking) ....D
Linder & Meyer (Bleaching) A
Slade Co., D. & L. (Imp. & Mfrs.) 13 India (Baking; Yeast) ....A
Wheeler, Asabel (Bronze) C

MASS.—Cambridge
Savena Mfg. Co. (Soap) ..B

MASS.—Newburyport
Eagle Chemical Co. (Soap)B

MICH.—Ann Arbor
Dean & Co. (Mfrs.) (Baking) ....A

MICH.—Detroit
Horton-Cato Mfg. Co., 25

POWDER (*Con.*)

Griswold (Baking; Curry) D
Ingram & Co., F. F., 50 10th (Baking; Horse; Cattle) B
Lafer Bros., 9 Cadillac Square (Baking) C
Murray, Edgar A., 71 Glendale Av. (Roach) .....H
Parke, Davis & Co. (Insect) ....AAAA
Regal Mfg. Co. (D. J. Smith) (Baking) ......D
Seely Mfg. Co. (Baby) ...C
Stevens, F. B. (Dentists' Polishing) ....A

MICH.—Grand Rapids
Jennings Flavoring Extract Co. (Baking) C

MICH.—Ishpeming
Anthony Powder Co. (Gun, etc.) C

MICH.—Jackson
Foote & Jencks (Inc.) (Face) ....D

MICH.—Lansing
Northrop, Robinson & Carrier Co. (Baking) ......B

MICH.—Marquette
Lake Superior Powder Co. (Explosive) ....A

MICH.—Midland
Dow Chemical Co. (Bleaching) ....AAA

MICH.—Muskegon
Puro Mfg. Co. (Baking) ..C

MICH.—Saginaw
Henderson & Co. (Baking) D

MINN.—Minneapolis
Hunt Perfect Baking Powder Co., 215 1st Av. No. (Baking) C
Strait Co., H. B., 106 2d Av. No. (Baking) ....B

MINN.—St. Paul
Kent, W. H., 9th & Jackson (Baking) C
Schmitz-Auss Co., 282 Jackson (Baking) ....D

MO.—Kansas City
Murdock Mfg. Co., C. A., 1225 Union Av. (Baking)A
Peet Bros. Mfg. Co. (Soap) AA

MO.—St. Louis
Amer. Supply Co., 900 No. Main (Baking) C
Aquart, A. D. (& Compounds; Car Cleansing; Varnish Renovator) ...E
Bain & Chapman Mfg. Co., 114 No. Main (Baking) C
Bayle, Geo. A., 113 So. 2nd (Baking; Curry) ......B
Blanke Tea & Coffee Co., C. F., Clark Av. & 7th (Baking) ....AA
Donnell Mfg. Co., 612 So. 6th (Baking) ....B
Eddy & Eddy, Main & Market (Baking) ....AA
Grant Chemical Co., J. C., 502 So. 7th (Baking) ...E
Live Stock Remedy Co. (Cattle) ....:....F
Metzenauer, E., 211 So. 3d (Baking) C
Perfect Baking Powder Mfg. Co., 22 No. Com'l (Baking) ....E
Pozzoni & Co., J. A. (Face) ....B
Shepard Baking Powder Co., 311 No. Main (Baking) .D
Taylor Baking Powder Co., 307 No. Main (Baking) E

NEBR.—Omaha
On Time Yeast Co. (Baking) C

N. J.—Red Bank
Keystone Baking Powder Co. (Baking) C

N. Y.—Albany
Moore Bros. (Horses; Cattle) ....B
Pure Baking Powder Co. (The) (Baking) ....D

N. Y.—Brooklyn
Columbia Chemical Wks. (Soap) ....B
Monarch Chemical Co., 18 Sackett (Baking) ....E
Wiards & Co., John C. (Putty) ....AA

POWDER (Con.)

POWDER (*Con.*)

Parian Mfg. Co. (Baking) C

OHIO—Canton

Bernower Baking Powder
Co. (Baking) ....E

OHIO—Cincinnati

American Chemical Co.
(Bleaching) C

Cincinnati Soap Co. (Soap)B

Freeman Perfume Co.
(Face) ....B

Howell Mfg. Co., 135 Sycamore (Baking) ....E

Jergens Co., Andrew (The)
(Talcum) ....AAA

Kenton Baking Powder Co.,
326 E. 3d (Baking) ....A

King Powder Co., cor. 5th
& Main (Gun, etc.) ..AAA

Marshall Chemical Co., 109
W. Front (Baking) C

Pure Food Co., 240 Main
(Baking) C

Winkler & Co., Isaac
(Bleaching) ....AA

OHIO—Cleveland

Austin Powder Co. (Gun,
Smokeless) ....AA

Clark Co., Fred. G. (Bleaching) ....A

Mattie Mitchell Co., 1925
Harvard (Baking) ....B

Schorndorfer & Eberhard
Co. (Baking) C

Zipp Mfg. Co. (The) 111
Woodland Av. (Baking) C

OHIO—Dayton

Dayton Spice Mills Co.
(Baking) ....A

Ware Coffee Co., C. F.
(Baking) ....A

OHIO—Findlay

Happer & Co., C. H.
(Baking) ....B

OHIO—Newark

Styron, Beggs & Co. (In-
sect; Horse; Cattle) ..A

OHIO—Springfield

United States Baking Pow-
der Wks. (Baking) ....D

OHIO—Toledo

Bour Co. (The) J. M. (Baking) ....B

Great Western Powder Co.
(Blasting) ....A

Lorenz Co., Geo. (Face) ..D

Woolson Spice Co. (Baking)
AAAA

OHIO—Troy

Pearson & Co., J. E. (Baking) ....A

OHIO—Urbana

Urbana Baking Powder Co.
(Baking) C

OHIO—Xenia

Miami Powder Co. (Explo-
sive; Blasting; Gun) ..AA

OHIO—Youngstown

Ohio Powder Co. (Explosive)
A

PA.—Allegheny City

Jones, G. W. (Insect) C

PA.—Ashland

Anthracite Powder Co. (Explosive) X

PA.—Bedford

Peerless Mfg. Co. (Horse;
Cattle) C

PA.—Bradford

Rock Glycerine Co.
(Smokeless) ....F

PA.—Easton

World Refining Co. (Horse;
Cattle; Baking) X

PA.—Emporium

Keystone Powder Mfg. Co.
(Explosive) ....B

PA.—Oliver Mills

Du Pont Co., E. I. (Explosive) ....AAAA

PA.—Philadelphia

Binswanger Co., B., 115 N.
4th (Bronze) ....D

Colburn Co., A., 110 N. 2nd
(Baking) ....AA

Fergusson Bros. (Bleaching)
A

French & Co., Samuel H.,
4th & Callowhill (Bronze)
AAA

Heinle Specialty Co., Chas.,
2731 Kens Av. (Baking)D

Hollingsworth & Peterson
(Bleaching) ....B

POWDER (*Con.*)

Jewel Mfg. Co., 202 Chan-
cellor (Baking) ....A

Krout Co., Alb., 66 N. Front
(Baking) C

Lucas & Co., John, 322
Race (Bronze) ....AAAA

McCollin & Co., Thos. H.
(Photographic Flash) ..H

Maurer & Son, D. (Insect)E

Tetlow Mfg. Co., 57 No.
Mascher (Baby; Bath;
Face) C

Vail Bros. (Face) C

White Dental Mfg. Co., S. S.
(Tooth) ....AAAA

PA.—Pittsburg

Banner Baking Powder Co.,
334 2d Av. (Baking) ..B

Hommel Co., O., 110 Mar-
ket (Bronze) ....H

Pittsburg Crushed Steel Co.,
61st & Butler (Putty) ..B

PA.—Pottsville

Cressona Powder Co. (Explosive) ....B

PA.—Scranton

Trager & Son, H. F. (Roach,
etc.) ....F

PA.—Shamokin

Beury Powder Mills (Explosive) ....B

Shamokin Powder Co.
(Explosive) C

PA.—Shenandoah

Lakeside Powder Co. (Ex-
plosive) C

Roberts Powder Co. (Explosive) C

Shenandoah Powder Co. (Explosive) X

PA.—West Fairview

Universal Baking Powder
Co. (Baking) ....B

PA.—York

Rockdale Powder Co. (Ex-
plosive) ....A

R. I.—Apponaug

Lambert, D. J. (Insect) ..F

R. I.—Pawtucket

Draper & Co., Jas. O.
(Soap) ....B

R. I.—Providence

Arnold, Hoffman & Co.
(Bleaching) ....AA

Kendall Mfg. Co. (Soap)
AAA

Rumford Chemical Wks.
(Baking; Yeast) ....AAA

TENN.—Chattanooga

Chattanooga Powder Co.
(Explosive) ....AA

Magic Food Co. (Horse;
Cattle) ....D

Steward Mfg. Co., D. M.
(Talc) ....B

TENN.—Knoxville

New South Baking Powder
Co. (Baking) ....G

TENN.—Nashville

Southern Soda Wks. (Bak-
ing) ....A

TEXAS—Dallas

Hughes Bros. Mfg. Co.
(Baking) ....A

Kitchen Queen Baking Pow-
der Co. (Baking) ......E

VT.—Swanton

Robin Hood Powder Co.
(Gun, Smokeless) .....A

VA.—Portsmouth

Virginia Chemical & Mfg.
Co. (Baking) ....B

VA.—Richmond

Amer. Baking Powder Co.
(Baking) ....AAA

Sauer Co., C. F. (Baking) C

Southern Mfg. Co. (Baking)
A

W. VA.—Glen Easton, P. O.

Moninger Poultry Powder
Co. (Horse; Cattle; Poul-
try) ....H

WIS.—Milwaukee

Forrest City Baking Powder
Co., 274 E. Water (Bak-
ing) C

Grossman & Co., W., 274 E.
Water (Baking) C

Jewett & Sherman Co., 289
Bway (Baking) ....A

POWERS

See also Agr. Imps

ILL.—Aurora
Amer. Well Wks. (Horse)..AA

ILL.—Batavia
Appleton Mfg. Co. (Horse)
....A

Challenge Wind Mill &
Feed Mill Co. (Horse) ...
....AAA
U. S. Wind Engine & Pump
Co. (Horse) ....AA
ILL.—Chicago
Creamery Package Mfg. Co.
(Churn) ....AAAA
Staver Carriage Co. (Horse)
....AA

ILL.—Freeport
Stover Mfg. Co. (Horse).AA
ILL.—Marseilles
Marseilles Mfg. Co. (Horse)
....A
ILL.—Moline
Deere & Mansur Co. (Horse)
....AAAA
ILL.—Ottawa
Porter Co., J. E. (Horse).A
ILL.—Rockford
Dobson Mfg. Co. (Animal) B
McDermaid, John (Churn) A
Palmer Co., H. H. (Churn)
....D

ILL.—Sandwich
Sandwich Mfg. Co. (Horse)
....AA

ILL.—Sterling
Keystone Co. (Horse)...AA
Sterling Mfg. Co. (Horse).A
IND.—Kendallville
Flint & Walling Mfg. Co.
(Horse) ....AA
IND.—Richmond
Gaar, Scott & Co. (Horse)..
....AAAA
Robinson & Co. (Horse).AA
IOWA—Waterloo
Kelly & Taneyhill Co.
(Horse) C
IOWA—Webster City
Litchfield Mfg. Co. (Horse)
....A
KANS.—Fort Scott
Fort Scott Foundry & Mach.
Co. (Horse) ....H
KANS.—Manhattan
Blue Valley Mfg. Co.
(Horse) ....F
MASS.—Boston
Ames Plow Co. (Horse)
....AAAA
MASS.—Greenfield
Goodell-Pratt Co. (Foot)..B
MICH.—Battle Creek
Advance Thresher Co.
(Horse) ....AAAA
MICH.—Kalamazoo
Smith & Pomeroy Windmill
Co. (Horse) ....B
MICH.—Monroe
Wilder-Strong Implement
Co. (Horse) ....B
MINN.—Mankato
Mankato Mfg. Co. (Horse)
....D

MINN.—Minneapolis
Howell & Co., R. R.
(Horse) ....B
Minneapolis Threshing Ma-
chine Co. (Horse)..AAAA
MO.—St. Louis
Kingsland Mfg. Co. (Horse)
....B
Whitman Agricultural Co.
(Horse) ....AA
N. Y.—Albany
Dedericks Son, P. K.
(Horse) ....A
N. Y.—Buffalo
Buffalo-Pitts Co. (Horse)
....AAAA
Squier Mfg. Co., Geo. L.
(Horse) ....AAA
N. Y.—Cobleskill
Harder Mfg. Co. (Dog
Tread) ....B
N. Y.—Greene
Lyon Iron Wks. (Animal)
....B
N. Y.—Ithaca
Williams Bros. (Horse).AA

POWERS *(Con.)*
New York City
Slotkin & Praglin (Foot)..B
N. Y.—Seneca Falls
Goulds Mfg. Co. (Horse)..
....AAA
N. C.—Winston-Salem
Salem Iron Wks. (Horse), A
OHIO—Ashland
Myers & Bro., F. E.
(Horse) ....AA
OHIO—Cincinnati
Blymyer Iron Wks. Co.
(Horse) ....B
OHIO—Cleveland
North Electric Co. (Board)
....A
OHIO—Lancaster
Eagle Machine Co. (Horse)
....A
Hocking Valley Mfg. Co.
(Horse) ....A
OHIO—Mansfield
Aultman & Taylor Machin-
ery Co. (Horse) ...AAAA
OHIO—Martin's Ferry
Spence & Son, L. (Horse).A
OHIO—Massillon
Russell & Co. (Horse).AAA
OHIO—Salem
Silver Mfg. Co. (Horse).AA
OHIO—Springfield
Foos Mfg. Co. (Horse)...A
PA.—Allegheny
Carlin's Sons, Thos. (Horse)
....A
PA.—Elizabethtown
Buch's Sons, A. (Horse).A
PA.—Lansdale
Heebner & Sons (Horse).A
PA.—Mechanicsburg
Comstock, Geo. S. (Horse)
....C
PA.—Monroeton
Booth & Co., O. N. (Churn)
....F
PA.—Tatamy
Messinger Mfg. Co. (Lever;
Churn; Dog) ....B
PA.—Waynesboro
Geiser Mfg. Co. (Horse) ..
....AAAA
TENN.—Memphis
Livermore Foundry & Mach.
Co. (Horse) ....A
VT.—Bellows Falls
Vermont Farm Mach. Co.
(Dog; Horse) C
VT.—Middletown Springs
Gray's Sons, A. W. (Horse)
....AA
VA.—Richmond
Cardwell Machine Co.
(Horse) ....A
WIS.—Manitowoc
Smalley Mfg. Co. (Horse) B
WIS.—Racine
Freeman & Sons Mfg. Co.,
S. (Horse) ....A
WIS.—Sheboygan
Stehn Mfg. Co. (Horse)..D

PRESERVA-
TIVES

See also Anti-Septics

CAL.—San Francisco
Preservaline Mfg. Co. (Br.
N. Y. City, N. Y.) (Fruit;
Food) ....A
CONN.—New Haven
Humiston Preservative Co.
(Fruit; Food) X
ILL.—Chicago
Heath & Milligan Mfg. Co.
(Paint) ....AAA
Heller & Co., B., 251 S. Jef-
ferson (Freezing Com-
pound) ....D
IND.—Indianapolis
Indianapolis Chemical Co.,
1442 Madison Av. (Wood)
....F
MAINE—Portland
Berlin Mills Co. (Wood)...
....AAAA
Egg Crystalline Mfg. Co.
(Egg) X
MD.—Baltimore
Germania Mills (Fruit;
Food) ....D

PRESERVATIVES Con.

MASS.—Boston
Cabot, Samuel (Brick; Stone; Wood) ....A
MICH.—Detroit
Chrysocolla Preservative Co. (Ltd.) (Fruit; Food)....X
MICH.—Pentwater
Congdon & Co., J. L. (Fruit; Food) ....B
MO.—St. Louis
Mallinckrodt C h e m i c a l Wks., 2nd & Mallinckrodt (Wood) ....AAAA
N. J.—Kearney
Cromwell-Walker Co. (Wood) C
N. Y.—Buffalo
Cling Surface Co. (Rope).D
New York City
Chemicals & Drug Co. of America (Fruit; Food).D
Electric Fire Proofing Co. (Wood) ....B
Lieber & Co., H. (Fruit; Food) C
Maas & Waldstein (Fruit; Food) ....A
Menzel & Son, Wm., 68 Broad (Wood) ....D
Preservaline Mfg. Co., 41 Warren (Beverages; Fruit; Food; Coating) ....A
Smith & Co., Edward (Coating) ....A
Standard Paint Co. (Paint; Coating) ....A
U. S. Wood Preserving Co., 29 B'way (Wood) .....B
Williamson & Co., D. D. (Fruit; Food) ....B
N. C.—Wilmington
Spirittine Chemical Co. (Wood) C
OHIO—Cincinnati
Pfaff Varnish & Stain Co., Jno., 1660 Central Av. (Wood) X
OHIO—Geneva
Forman Chemical Mfg. Co. (Fruit; Food) ....G
PA.—Philadelphia
Bean Co., Lewis U. (Coating) ....D
Lucas & Co., John (Paint) AAA
Protectus Co., North Amer. Bldg. (Wood) ....B
Rhoads & Son, J. E. (Coating) ....A
PA.—Pittsburg
Suydam Co., M. B., 61st & Butler (Wood) ....A
PA.—Williamsport
National Paint Wks. (Paint) ....B
R. I.—Providence
U. S. Gutta Percha Paint Co. (Paint) ....A
S. C.—Summerville
Summerville Fernoline Wks. (Coatings; Wood) .....F
TEXAS—Beaumont
International Creosoting & Construction Co. (Wood) AA
VA.—Norfolk
Atlantic Creosoting & Wood Preserving Wks. (Wood) A
Norfolk Creosoting Co. (Wood) ....A
WIS.—Milwaukee
Carbolineum Wood Preserving Co. (Wood) ....D
Milwaukee Wood Preserving Co. (Wood) ....E

PRESERVERS

DEL.—Wilmington
Drein & Son, Thos. (Life) B
N. Y.—Brooklyn
Kahn-Weilers Sons, David (Life) ....B
N. Y.—Buffalo
Cling Surface Co. (Belt)..D
N. Y.—Long Island City
Lane & De Groot Co. (Life) D

New York City
Armstrong Cork Co., 57

PRESERVERS (Con.)
Murray (Cork Life)AAAA
Colgan, Jas. B., 675 Hudson (Life) C
Hodgman Rubber Co., 806 B'way (Rubber Life).AA
N. C.—Wilmington
Spirittine Chemical Co. (Brick) C
PA.—Pittsburg
Banar & Wieland (Life)..C

PRESERVES
See Jams, etc.

PRESSES
See Mills; Machy; Tools; Agr. Imps, etc.

ALA.—Attalla
Attalla Foundry & Mach Co. (Cotton) C
ALA.—Montgomery
Janney & Co., A. A. (Cotton) ....A
ARK.—Little Rock
Thomas-Fordyce Mfg. Co. (Cotton) ....A
Wing & Stephens Co. (Cotton) X
CAL.—Chico
Bullard, Walter (Hay)....F
COLO.—Denver
Mine & Smelting Supply Co., Blake & 17th (Filter)... AAAA
CONN.—Ansonia
Cook Co., Henry C. (Power) ....D
Farrell Foundry & Mach Co. (Rubber Vulcanizing; Hydraulic) ....AAAA
CONN.—Bridgeport
Amer. Tube & Stamping Co. (Drop) ....AAAA
Automatic Machine Co. (Power) ....B
Coulter & McKenzie Mach. Co. (Drop) ....B
Nilson Machine Co., A. H. (Power) ....D
Schwerdtle Stamp Co. (Seal, all Kinds) ....F
CONN.—Derby
Birmingham Iron Foundry (Hydraulic; Heel) ....AA
Whitlock Printing Press Mfg. Co. (Cylinder; Pony) ....A
CONN.—Guilford
Spencer's Sons, J. S. (Tobacco) ....A
CONN.—Hartford
Bailey Mfg. Co. (Copying) C
Billings & Spencer Co. (Drop; Trimming) ..AA
Colt's Patent Fire Arms Co. (Job Printing; Foot Power; Embossing; Paper Box Cutter) ......AAAA
National Machine Co. (Embossing; Cutting; Breasting; Printing) ....A
Parker, T. M. (Seal)......G
Pratt & Whitney Co. (Blacksmiths' Drill; Broaching; Drawing; Drop; Power; Screw; Shearing; Trimming; Punching; Foot)... AAAA
CONN.—Higganum
Cutaway Harrow Co. (Tobacco) X
CONN.—Meriden
Kelsey Press Co. (Job; Card Printing) ....A
Merriman, A. H. (Drawing; Cutting; Punching; Stamping; Sheet Metal Power; Screw) C
Wheeler & Son, Frank (Power) C
CONN.—Milldale
Ellis & Son, F. L. (Foot; Power) ....E
CONN.—New Britain
Landers, Frary & Clark (Fruit; Meat; Lard; Tallow) ....AAA

PRESSES (*Con.*)

CONN.—New Haven

Eastern Machinery Co. (Brick) ....B

Griswold, Geo. M., 35 Union (Power) ....D

Miner & Peck Mfg. Co. (Drop; Power; Trimming; Blanking; Drawing; Stamping) X

Shuster Co., F. B. (Toggle; Double; Pendulum Lever Foot; Power; Screw; Lever) X

CONN.—New London

Babcock Printing Press Mfg. Co. (Cylinder Printing) C

Brown Cotton Gin Co. (Printing) ....AA

CONN.—Southington

Peck, Stow & Wilcox Co. (Blacksmiths' Drill; Foot; Hand; Power) ....AAAA

CONN.—Thompsonville

Bushnell Press Co. (Hay; Wine; Cider; Cotton Seed Oil; Hydraulic; Linseed Oil; Peanut Oil; Power; Screw; Veneer; Wood Pulp; Bookbinders'; Hand; Knuckle; Joint; Baling; Cloth; Drug; Emery Wheel; Fish Scrap; Hair; Hand Power; Hemp; Herb; Hide; Hop; Hydraulic Baling; Leather; Moss; Packing House; Rag; Wool; Yarn; Castor Bean; Clay Filter; Filter; Fruit; Lard; Oil; Hydraulic Oil; Oleomargerine; Paraffine; Oil; Wax; Tallow; Tincture; Varnish; Whitelead Filter; Standing Tankage; Butchers' Offal; Electrotype; Paper; Paper Box Cutter; Sewerpipe; Tile; Vulcanizing) ....A

CONN.—Tolland

Clough, R. M. (Foot; Power) ....D

CONN.—Waterbury

Blake & Johnson (Drawing; Drop; Foot; Power; Cutting) ....A

Cross & Speirs Mach. Co. (Drop; also Portable; Foot; Power) X

Draher, Jno. (Foot; Power) ....F

Manville Mach. Co., E. J. (Single Foot; Single; Double acting Power; Jewelers') C

Waterbury Farrel Foundry & Mach. Co. (Cotton; Drawing; Drop; Embossing; Foot; Forming; Hydraulic; Power; Screw; Shearing; Punching; Toggle Joint; Jewelers') .AA

Waterbury Mach. Co. (Power; Hydraulic; Gang Tool) ....B

DEL.—Wilmington

Betts Machine Co. (Hydraulic Wheel; Hydostatic Wheel; Hydraulic) ..AA

Hillis & Jones Co. (Power; Rail Straightening; Trimming) ....AAA

Pusey & Jones Co. (Cotton; Filter; Hydraulic) ..AAA

GA.—Atlanta

De Loach Mill Mfg. Co. (Baling; Hay) ....B

Van Winkle Gin & Mach Wks. (Cotton) .....AAA

Lombard Iron Wks. & Supply Co. (Cotton; Baling) ....A

GA.—Fort Valley

Miller, O. H. (Cotton) ..B

GA.—Macon

Schofield Sons Co., J. S. (Cotton) ....A

GA.—Newman

Cole Mfg. Co., R. D. (Cotton; Hydraulic) ......AA

GA.—West Point

West Point Iron Wks.

PRESSES (*Con.*)

(Cotton) ....B

ILL.—Batavia

Sperry & Co., D. R. (Filter) ....B

ILL.—Belleville

Belleville Pump & Skein Wks. (Copying) ....AA

ILL.—Bradley

Bradley Mfg. Co., David (Hay) ....AAA

ILL.—Carpentersville

Illinois Iron & Bolt Co. (Blacksmiths' Drill; Horizontal; Upright; Copying; Hydraulic) ....AA

ILL.—Chicago

Allbright-Well Co. (Filter) ....D

Allis-Chalmers Co., Home Ins. Bldg. (Filter) .AAAA

Amer. Can Co., Merchants' Loan & Trust Bldg. (Broaching; Drawing; Power; Screw; Trimming) ....AAAA

Barnhardt Bros. & Spindler (Job Printing) ......AA

Challenge Machinery Co. (Job; Newspaper Ptg.) ..A

Chicago Scale Co., 296 W. Jackson Boul. (Copying; Letter) ....A

Consolidated Press & Tool Co. (Blanking; Broaching; Drawing; Flanging; Foot; Forging; Power; Screw; Stamping) ....D

Creamery Package Co. (Cheese) ....AAAA

Drake Standard Mach. Wks. (Brick) ....B

Elmes Engineering Wks., Chas. F., cor. Fulton & N. Morgan (Filter; Hydraulic Flanging; Hydraulic Rubber Vulcanizing; Hydraulic Wheel) ....A

Goss Printing Press Co., 732 S. Paulina (Printing; Rotary; Newspaper Perfecting) ....A

Latham Machinery Co. (Job Printing; Monogram; Proof; Washington Hand; Embossing; Standing)..C

Miehle Printing Press & Mfg. Co., 75 N. Clinton (Cylinder; Job; Book Printing; Two Revolution) ....A

Perrin & Co., Wm. R., 46th & Loomis (Filter for Abattoirs; Hydraulic for Abattoirs; Knuckle Joint; Lever; Power; Screw, for Abattoirs) ....A

Pridmore, Henry E., 918 S. Rockwell (Automatic Copying) ....A

Rosback, F. P. (Monogram; Embossing) .....E

Schmedewind Co., Paul (Printers' Proof) X

Sharpless Co. (Gang Cheese) C

Sigwalt Mfg. Co. (Seal)...C

Vulcan Iron Wks., 63 Milwaukee Av. (Hand Power Hydraulic) ...AA

Whitman & Barnes Mfg. Co. (Blacksmiths' Drill; Wine; Cider) .....AAAA

Wold, Porrice & Co. (Can) C

Wolf Co., Fred. W. (Filter; Sugar Filtering)....AAA

ILL.—Decatur

Chambers - Bering - Quinlan Co. (Hay; Hand)...A

ILL.—De Kalb

Haish Wire & Implement Co. (Wine; Cider) .....B

ILL.—Galesburg

Colton & Co., G. D. (Hay; Broom Corn) C

ILL.—Moline

Williams, White & Co. (Drop; Riveting; Shearing; Punching; Tire Welding) ....AA

PRESSES (Con.)

ILL.—Ottawa
Porter Co., J. E. (Hand; Power) ....A

ILL.—Quincy
Adams Tobacco Press Co. (Tobacco; Plug Tobacco) ...D
Collins Plow Co. (Baling; Hay; Straw) ....A
Ertel Co., Geo. (Baling; Cotton; Hay; Moss; Wool) ...A

ILL.—Rockford
Barnes Co., B. F. (Screw; Drill) ....B

ILL.—Sandwich
Sandwich Mfg. Co. (Hay) ...AA

IND.—Anderson
Wooley Foundry & Mach. Wks. (Drop; Power) ...B

IND.—Aurora
Stedman Foundry & Mach. Wks. (Cotton) ....B

IND.—Cambridge City
Bretsch & Co. (Geared Punch, etc.; Power) ...D

IND.—East Chicago
Famous Mfg. Co. (Card Board; Metal Scrap; Cotton; Cotton Seed Hull; Baling; Hay; Paper Scrap; Shaving; Tin Scrap; Hop) ....A

IND.—Evansville
Grote Mfg. Co. (Tobacco) ...D

IND.—Goshen
Thomas - Allbright Co. (Wine; Cider; Hydraulic; Rasing) ....B

IND.—Indianapolis
Over, Ewald (Cider; Wine) ...C
Potts & Co., C. & A. (Inc.) (Brick) ....B

IND.—Kendallville
Flint & Walling Mfg. Co. (Baling) ....AA
Rumley Co., M. (Baling) ...AAA

IND.—Richmond
Robinson & Co. (Baling; Hay; Straw) ....AA

IOWA—Burlington
Murray Iron Wks. Co. (Lard; Tallow) ....A

IOWA—Davenport
Davenport Foundry & Mach. Co. (Hydraulic) X

IOWA—Ottumwa
Dain Mfg. Co. (Hay) ..AA

IOWA—Spencer
Maurer Co., F. X. (Cotton) ....F

KANS.—Fort Scott
Fort Scott Foundry & Mach. Co. (Filter; Sugar Filtering) ....H

KANS.—Leavenworth
Great Western Mfg. Co. (Plaster) ....AA

KY.—Louisville
Turney Dryer Co., Columbia Bldg. (Filter) X

LA.—Amite City
Gullett Gin Co. (Cotton; Cotton Seed Hull).....A

LA.—New Orleans
Coleman, H. Dudley (Hydraulic) ....D
Whitney Iron Wks. Co., 361 Tchoupitoulas (Filter) ....AA

MAINE—Portland
Lang Co., E. M. (Screw; Punching; Cutting; Can) ...C
Portland Co. (Hydraulic).. AA

MD.—Baltimore
Adt, John B. (Plug Tobacco) ....B
Dorman Co., J. F. W. (Job Printing) ....F
Sinclair-Scott Co. (Cotton; Baling; Hay; Rag; Fruit) ...E

MASS.—Athol
Athol Machine Co. (Domestic; Fruit; Meat) ......B

PRESSES (Con.)

MASS.—Boston
Ames Plow Co. (Cider; Wine; Lard) ......AAAA
Bartlett, E. E. (Arbor)..E
Beaudry & Co., 8 Oliver (Power; Forging) ......D
Boston Printing Press Mfg. Co., 176 Federal (Embossing; Half Tone; Wood Printing) X
Child Acme Cutter & Press Co. (Cylinder Printing).X
Empire Laundry Machinery Co. (Power; Shirt) C
Golding & Co. (Card Printing; Job Printing; Foot Power Job; Pad; Proof; Tablet) ....B
Hersey Mfg. Co. (Foot; Hand; Power; Sugar).AA
Holmes Mach. Co., Chas. (Tan) ....D
McLauthlin Co., Geo. T., 120 Fulton (Hydraulic), A
Marston & Co., J. M., 226 Ruggles (Arbor) ......D
Mead, A. G., 564 Atlantic Av. (Stationers' Embossing) ....H
Meisel Press & Mfg. Co. (Printing) C
Seelye Mfg. Co., 110 Lincoln (Die) C

MASS.—Bridgewater
Continental Cotton Gin Co. (Cotton) ....AAAA

MASS.—Brockton
Sweetser, Wm. A. (Bench; Power) X

MASS.—Fitchburg
Fitchburg Machine Wks. (Drill) ....B
Putnam Mach. Co. (Car Wheel) ....A

MASS.—Greenfield
Wells Bros. Co. (Blacksmiths' Drill) ....A
Wiley & Russell Mfg. Co. (Punching) ....AA

MASS.—Holyoke
Holyoke Mach. Co. (Hydraulic; Rotary Steam Cloth) ....AA

MASS.—Hyde Park
Robinson Co., John T. (Paper Box Cutter) X

MASS.—Lowell
Dennis & Co., Jno. (Baling; Hay; Hydraulic for Hot Pressing; Screw for Hot Pressing) ....E
Lowell Machine Shop (Hydraulic; Double Screw).. AAAA

MASS.—New Bedford
Morse Twist Drill & Machine Co. (Blacksmiths' Drill) ....AAA

MASS.—Northampton
Herrick, Chas. E. (Cotton) ...D

MASS.—Salem
Martin, Wm. F. (Tan) ..B

MASS.—Springfield
Smith Mfg. Co., R. H., 293 Main (Seal) C

MASS.—Taunton
Huber-Hodgman Printing Press Co. (Printing; Cylinder; Book Printing; Sheet Perfecting; Two Color; Zincographic) ..B
New Process Twist Drill Co. (Blacksmiths' Drill) ...X

MASS.—Webster
Prescott & Son, J. B. (Blacksmiths' Drill) ...B

MASS.—Worcester
Boynton & Plummer (Blacksmiths' Drill) ..B
Cleveland Machine Wks. (Hydraulic) ....A
Crompton & Knowles Loom Wks. (Screw) ....AAAA
Curtis & Marble Machine Co. (Rotary Steam; Cloth) ....A
Kidder, R. E., 2 Hermon (Copying; Envelope) ..E
Luther & Co., B. G. (Box Shook) ....E

PRESSES (Con.)

Morgan Construction Co.
(Hydraulic Forging) ..A
Reed Co., Francis (Blacksmiths' Drill) ....E
Whitcomb Mfg. Co. (Broaching; Copying; Shearing;
Punching; Power) ....B

MICH.—Alpena
Kline, Lewis T. (Veneer)
...............D

MICH.—Battle Creek
Duplex Printing Press Co.
(Book Printing; Newspaper; Stop Cylinder;
Web Perfecting; Stereotypers') ....B

MICH.—Grand Rapids
Fox Machine Co., 127 N.
Front (Arbor; Power;
Veneer; Sheet-Metal
Stamping) ....A
Wilmarth & Merman Co.
(Arbor) C

MICH.—Lansing
Lansing Wheelbarrow Co.
(Wine; Cider) ......AAA

MICH.—Morenci
Michigan Brick & Tile Machine Co. (Brick) ......D

MICH.—Owosso
Castree & Son (Hay; Steel
Case Hay) ....H

MICH.—Saginaw
Wickes Bros. (Hydraulic
Flanging; Forging) ..AAA

MINN.—Minneapolis
Kinnard-Haines Co. (Leather; Wool) ....B

MISS.—Corinth,
Adams Mach. Co. (Cotton)
..................AA

MISS.—Meridian
Southern Standard Press Co.
(Cotton; Cotton Seed
Hull) ....D

MO.—Carrollton
Farm Tool Mfg. Co.
(Hay) ....B

MO.—Kansas City
Eagle Mfg. Co. (Hay)....A
Eclipse Hay Press Co.
(Hay) ....D
Kansas City Hay Press Co.
(Baling; Hay) ....AA

MO.—St. Louis
Barnard Stamp Co. (Seal)
..................E
Gohlke, Theo., 12th & Locust (Power) X
Handlan-Buck Mfg. Co., 212
N. 3rd (Car; Seal) ..AA
Hiertz Metal Co., Theo.
(Car Seal) ....D
Kingsland Mfg. Co. (Steam
Cotton; Cotton Seed Hull;
Self Packing Cotton;
Wool) ....B
Pleuger & Henger Mfg. Co.,
11th & Hebert (Blacksmiths' Drill) ....A
Ross-Keller Triple Pressure Brick Machine Co.
(Brick) ....D
St. Louis Iron & Mach. Co.
(Cotton; Brick) ......AA
Swaine Co., F. J. (Bumping; Die; Drawing; Drop;
Sheet Metal Embossing;
Foot; Forming; Lever;
Punching; Power; Arch.
etc.; Screw; Sheet Metal
Stamping; Wiring) ....B
Whitman Agricultural Co.
(Wine; Cider; Cotton
Seed Hull; Baling; Hay)
..................AA
Zelnicker Supply Co., Walter A. (Portable Hydraulic Wheel) X

N. H.—Dover
Kidder Press Co. (Ticket
Printing; Tissue Paper
Printing) ....A

N. H.—Keene
Humphrey Mach. Co.
(Power; also Hand) ...C

N. H.—Nashua
Spence & Rideout (Hydraulic) ....D

N. J.—Bridgeton
Ferracute Machine Co.
(Bench; Cartridge Mak-

PRESSES (Con.)

ing; Disc Notching;
Drawing; Drop; Sheet
Metal Embossing; Foot;
Power; Riveting; Screw;
Car Wheel; Punching;
Cutting; Embossing; Coining) ....A

N. J.—Harrison
Greenfield, W. G. & G.
(Screw) X

N. J.—Newark
Burroughs Co., Chas., 141
Commerce (Bicycle Saddles; Screw) X
Crowell Mfg. Co., H. M.
(Hydraulic Stamping) ..G
Currier & Sons, Cyrus (Filter; Embossing) .....AA
Gould & Eberhardt (Drawing; Drop; Foot; Hydraulic; Lever; Power; Screw;
Toggle Joint; Bank Note)
..................A
Ohl & Co., Geo. A. (Power;
Drawing; Sheet; Metal;
Ceiling; Cornice; Leather
Embossing; Stamping) ..B
Standard Machine Wks.
(Filter; Foot; Hydraulic) X
Traud Co., Alex., 28 Maine
(Filter) ....A

N. J.—Plainfield
Pond's Machine Tool Co.
(Hydraulic Wheel) AAAA
Potter Printing Press Co.
(Cylinder Printing) ..AA
Scott & Co., Walter (Cylinder Printing; Book Printing; Lithographing; Newspaper; Web Perfecting) ..
..................AA

N. J.—Rahway
Gordon Press Wks (Job
Printing; Foot Power Job
Printing; Embossing) ...A

N. J.—Salem
Ayars Machine Co. (Foot,
for Can Making; Power,
for Can Making) ......B

N. J.—Smithville
Smith Mach. Co., H. B.
(Veneer) ....A

N. Y.—Albany
Dedericks Sons, P. K. (Hay;
Cotton; Cotton Seed Hull;
Hydraulic; Baling; Cloth;
Excelsior; Feed; Hair;
Hemp; Hide; Hop; Moss;
Rag; Straw; Wool) ...A

N. Y.—Auburn
Crane Foundry & Mach
Wks., W. W. (Trimming)
..................D

N. Y.—Brooklyn
Adriance Mach. Wks., 254
Van Brunt (Drawing;
Drop; Sheet Metal;
Leather; Paper; Embossing; Wire; Paper; Power;
Trimming) ....A
Bliss Co., E. W. (Ltd.)
(Auger; Bit Heading;
Bench; Broaching; Die;
Draw; Drop; Embossing;
Foot; Forming; Lever;
Perforating; Power;
Screw; Shearing; Trimming; Wiring; Punching;
Adjustable Incline; Pendulum; Toggle Joint;
Double Crank; Cutting;
Reducing; Stamping)
..................AAAA
Guild & Garrison, Kent Av.
& S. 10th (Filter) ....B
Hibbard Mfg. Co., 79 Washington (Drawing; Drop;
Embossing; Foot; Power;
Screw; Trimming) C
Houchin & Huber (Box
Printing) ....D
Jones, W. E., 14 Water
(Embossing; Foot; Power)
..................E
Leffler & Co., Chas., 63
Clymer (Sheet Metal;
Drawing; Sheet Metal
Drop; Toggle Lever;
Sheet Metal Foot; Pendulum for Jewelry; Brass;
Hardware; Wiring; Sheet

PRESSES (Con.)
Metal Power in 10 Sizes)
C
Merril Bros., 465 Kent Av.
(Trimming) ....A
Miller Co., W. P. (Cotton;
Hay; Hemp; Hide; Rag)D
Robertson & Co., John
(Hydraulic) ....AA
Simpson Foundry Co., 26
B'way (Filter; Foot;
Power) C
Taylor & Co., 417 Driggs
Av. (Hydraulic) .....D
N. Y.—Buffalo
Ashbery, Henry C., 16 Sen-
eca (Seal) ....G
Buffalo Forge Co. (Black-
smiths' Drill; Shearing)
AAA
East Mfg. Co. (Raisin Seed
Extracting) ....A
Holmes Machinery Co., E.
& B. (Wood Printing)..B
Howard Iron Wks. (Hydrau-
lic for Leather; Bookbind-
ers'; Hand; Lithographic;
Embossing; Standing)..A
Niagara Mach. & Tool Wks.
(Bench; Bending; Die;
Drop; Embossing; Foot;
Forming; Lever; Perforat-
ing; Power; Riveting;
Screw; Shearing; Trim-
ming; Wiring) ....A
Noye Mfg. Co., John T.
(Butchers' Offal) X
Oliver Mfg. Co., 1483 Niag-
ara (Jewelers' Drop;
Punching) C
Rogers & Co., S. C. (Book-
binders'; Embossing) ...C
Squier Mfg. Co., G. L.
(Sugar Filter) .....AAA
Union Mfg. & Specialty Co.
(Stamping) C
N. Y.—Gowanda
Gowanda Agricultural Wks.
Co. (Cheese) X
N. Y.—Grassy Point
Wiles Co., A. M. & W. H.
(Brick) ....B
N. Y.—Little Falls
Burrell & Co., D. H. (Ad-
justable Continuous Pres-
sure Gang Cheese; Hooks)
AAAA
N. Y.—Lockport
Trevor Mfg. Co. (Wood
Pulp) ....B
N. Y.—Lyons
Nagley Mfg. Co. (Tobacco)
D
N. Y.—Medina
Swett Iron Wks., A. L.
(Steel Spindle; Black-
smith's Drill) ....A
N. Y.—Middletown
Morgan & Wilcox Mfg. Co.
(Printers' Proof) C
N. Y.—Newburg
Coldwell-Wilcox Co. (Cot-
ton) ....B
New York City
Aluminum Press Co. (Ro-
tary Printing) X
Amer. Type Founders' Co.
(Foot Power Job).AAAA
Babcock Printing Press
Mfg. Co., 38 Park Row
(Cylinder Printing; Book
Printing; Lithographic;
Pony Printing; Two Rev-
olution) C
Behr & Co., Herman (Glass-
ware; Moulds) ....AA
Bender & Sons, Ph. J., 87
Frankfort (Foot; Power;
Screw) ....E
Campbell Printing Press &
Mfg. Co., 1 Madison Av.
(Printing Cylinder; Bag-
Book-Box-Printing; Cyl-
inder Job; Lithographic;
Newspaper; Pony Print-
ing; Two Color; Two Rev-
olution) C
Cook, Thos. W. G., 4 Reade
(Foot; Power; Screw;
Trimming) ....F
Cornell Co., J. B. & J. M.,
26th & 11th Av. (Cotton;

PRESSES (Con.)
Filter; Screw; Hydraulic)
AA
Cottrell & Sons Co., C. B.
(Cylinder; Rotary Print-
ing) ....AAA
Deeley & Co., Robert
(Sugar) ....AA
Dudgeon, Richard, 24 Co-
lumbia (Car Wheel;
Crank Pin; Hydraulic; Hy-
draulic Wheel) ....A
Fairbanks Co., 186 Elm
(Copying) ....AAAA
Garvin Machine Co. (Foot;
Power) ....AA
Hammacher, Schlemmer &
Co., 209 B'way (Veneer)
AAA
Hoe & Co., R., 504 Grand
(Rotary Newspaper;
Copying; Book Printing;
Card Printing; Cylinder
Printing; Job Printing;
Lithographic; Newspaper;
Lever Hand; Proof; Tick-
et Printing; Washington
Hand; Web Perfecting)
AAAA
Johnson & Co., Jno., 1
Franklin Sq. (Filter) ..D
Liberty Machine Co., 140
Nassau (Job Printing;
Card Printing; Cylinder;
Foot Power Job) ......E
Lovejoy Co. (Stereotypers')
B
Loyd Co., Jno., 562 Water
(Foot; Power; Screw)..B
Morrill, Chas. (Seal) ....D
Ness, Geo. M., Jr. (Seal).A
Niles-Bement-Pond Co., 111
B'way (Arbor; Black-
smiths' Drill; Drop; Foot;
Hydraulic Flanging;
Trimming; Power; Hy-
draulic Forging; Filter;
Screw; Hydraulic Wheel)
AAAA
Pollard-Alling Mfg. Co., 36
E. 20th (Printing) ....D
Russell & Erwin Mfg. Co.
(Cork) ....AAAA
Sargent & Co. (Cork)....
AAAA
Sheridan Co., T. W. & C.
B., 56 Duane (Bookbind-
ers' Die; Signature; Cut-
ting Power; Bookbinders'
Blocking; Embossing;
Smashing; Stamping; En-
velope Cutting) ....A
Shriver & Co., Thos., 335
E. 56th (Copying; Cotton
Seed Oil; Filter) ......A
Smith & Hemenway Co.
(Seal) ....D
Staubach, Baldwin, 652 E.
12th (Wine; Cider; Lin-
seed Oil; Hydraulic;
Power; Screw; Toggle
Joint; Baling; Hop Leath-
er; Lard; Oil Tankage).A
Stimpson & Son, Edwin B.,
31 Spruce (Punching; Per-
forating Leather; Foot;
Punching; Perforating
Power; Screw; Hand) ..B
Turl's Sons, John (Sugar)
D
Van Allens & Boughton, 59
Ann (Cylinder Printing)
AA
Watson-Stillman Co., 210
E. 43rd (Bending; Broach-
ing; Car Wheel; Crank
Pin; Die; Drawing; Em-
bossing; Gun Powder; Hy-
draulic; Forging; Power;
Shearing; Chilling; Lead;
Projectile; Punching;
Steam Plate; Lead Pen-
cil; Baling; Cylindrical
Bale Cotton; Drug; Leath-
er; Belting; Oil; Fish Oil;
Coppersmith's; Electro-
type; Jewelers'; Paper;
Wagon Wheel; Wire Ca-
ble Covering; Veneer)..A
Wesel Mfg. Co., F. (Proof;
Stereotypers'; Foot) ...X
Wood & Selick (Fruit) ..A

799

PRESSES (Con.)

N. Y.—Oswego
Oswego Tool Co. (Punching; Hand Power) .....B
N. Y.—Palmyra
Peerless Printing Press Co. (Printing) C
N. Y.—Pearl River
Braunsdorf, John H. (Job Printing) C
N. Y.—Rochester
Erdle & Schenck (Foot; Power) ....B
Schaffer Mfg. Co., J. T. (Arbor; Hydraulic Car Wheel; Crank Pin; Hydraulic Wheel; Platen).D
Streeter & Co., N. R. (Fruit) ....A
Yawman & Erbe Mfg. Co. (Copying) ....AA
N. Y.—Seneca Falls
Seneca Falls Mfg. Co. (Arbor) ....B
N. Y.—Syracuse
Boomer & Boschert Press Co. (Baling; Hay; Cheese; Wine; Cider; Cotton; Cotton Seed Oil; Filter; Hydraulic; Knuckle; Linseed Oil; Power Screw; Veneer; Wood Pulp; Cloth; Feed; Fertilizer; Hair; Herb; Knuckle Joint; Hide; Hop; Leather; Leather Belting; Paper Stock; Rag; Tobacco; Wool; Fruit; Lard; Oil; Hydraulic Oil; Oleomargerine; Paraffine Wax; Power Screw; Tallow; Tincture; Standing; Paraffine Oil; Chocolate; Tankage; Paper; Vulcanizing) ....A
N. Y.—Troy
Troy Laundry Machinery Co. (Ltd.) (Power; Shirt) ....AA
N. Y.—Utica
Utica Drop Forge & Tool Co. (Seal) ....B
N. Y.—Waterville
Waterville Foundry Mfg. Co. (Baling) ....F
N. C.—Charlotte
Liddell Co. (Inc.) (Cotton; Cotton Seed Hull) .....A
Mecklenburg Iron Wks. (Cotton) X
OHIO—Akron
Akron Foundry Co. (Hydraulic) ....B
Taplin, Rice & Co. (Sewer Pipe) ....B
Webster, Camp & Lane Machine Co. (Sewer Pipe)..AAAA
OHIO—Alliance
Alliance Mach. Co. (Bending; Crank Pin; Forming; Riveting; Shearing; Hydraulic Flanging; Forging; Armature Forging; Punching; Rail Straightening) ....AA
Morgan Engineering Co. (Hydraulic Flanging; Forging) ....AAAA
OHIO—Bucyrus
Amer. Clay Working Machine Co. (Brick; Sewer Pipe) X
OHIO—Cambridge
Crescent Seal & Stamp Co. (Seal) ....H
OHIO—Canton
Bonnot Co. (Filter) .....A
OHIO—Cincinnati
Amer. Laundry Machinery Co. (Power; Shirt) ...AA
Andrew & Co., M. L., 118 W. 2nd (Compo Molding) C
Blymyer Iron Wks. Co. (Filter) ....B
Cincinnati Punch & Shear Co. (Punching; Trimming) ....D
Day & Co. (Tincture) .....A
Francis & Bro., Chas. E., 425 E. 8th (Veneer)...B
Keene & Co., Geo. C., 502

PRESSES (Con.)

E. Front (Drop; Screw) ....F
Laidlow-Dunn-Gordon Co. (Hydraulic; Plug Tobacco) ....AAAA
Lodge & Shipley Mach. Tool Co. (Punching) .....AA
McGovan Co., John H. (Hydraulic; Tobacco; Plug Tobacco) ....A
Murdock, Jr., Co., Jas., 116 Longworth (Seal) C
Randall & Co. (Harness)..B
Robinson Mfg. Co., J. M., 2nd & Central Av. (Drop; Power; Screw; Hand)...C
Schriver & Co., O. P. (Wine; Cider) ....B
Tatum Co., Samuel C., 414 W. Water (Copying) ..B
Towsley Mfg. Co., John T., Evans, near Gest (Veneer) ....B
OHIO—Cleveland
Avery Stamping Co. (Drawing; Forging; Punching; Trimming) ....B
Cady Mach. Co. (Power)..X
Chandler & Price Co., 82 E. Prospect (Lever; Job Printing; Proof) ....A
Cleveland Punch & Shear Wks., 152 Case Av. (Hydraulic; Power) ....A
Cleveland Stamping & Tool Co. (Power; Blanking Stamping) ....A
Cott, C. M. (Pad) X
Dyer & Co., E. H., New England Bldg. (Filter)..AAA
Fanner Mfg. Co. (Fruit; Meat; Vegetable) .....A
Globe Machine & Stamping Co. (Screw) C
Standard Tool Co. (Blacksmiths' Drill) ....AA
Standish Mach. & Supply Co., 120 W. Spring (Screw) ....D
Strong, Carlisle & Hammond Co., 61 Frankfort (Power) ....A
OHIO—Cuyahoga Falls
Turner, Vaughan & Taylor Co. (Brick) ....B
OHIO—Dayton
Buckeye Iron & Brass Wks. (Peanut Oil) ....AA
Seybold Machine Co. (Die; Signature; Standing) ..A
OHIO—Defiance
Defiance Mach. Wks. (Hydraulic Hub; Flange; Hydraulic Wheel) ....A
OHIO—Galion
Freeze & Co.. E. M. (Sewer Pipe) ....A
OHIO—Hamilton
Advance Mfg. Co. (Cider) X
Long & Allstatter (Drop; Punching) ....AA
Niles Tool Wks. Co. (Hydraulic Wheel; Hydraulic) ....AAAa
OHIO—Lancaster
Eagle Machine Co. (Wine; Cider) ....A
Hocking Valley Mfg. Co. (Wine; Cider; Lard) ..A
OHIO—Mount Gilead
Hydraulic Press Mfg. Co. (Wine; Cider; Cotton; Embossing; Filter; Hydraulic; Hydraulic Rubber Vulcanizing; Linseed Oil; Power; Lard; Tobacco; Veneer) ....A
OHIO—New London
Arnold-Creager Co. (Brick) ....B
OHIO—Norwood
Cincinnati Tool Co. (Blacksmiths' Drill) ....B
OHIO—Ripley
Phoenix Foundry & Mfg. Co. (Tobacco) X
OHIO—Salem
Silver Mfg. Co. (Blacksmiths' Drill; Lard; Mandioca; Tallow) ....AA

OHIO—Sandusky
Klotz Mach. Co. (Geared Wine; Cider) C

OHIO—Springfield
Foos Mfg. Co. (Blacksmiths' Drill) ....A
Mast & Co., P. P. (Wine; Cider; Lard) ......AAAA
Springfield Mach. Tool Co. (Bench; Power) ......A

OHIO—Tiffin
National Machinery Co. (Punching; Shearing).AA

OHIO—Toledo
Baker Bros. (Drill) ....A
Toledo Mach. & Tool Co. (Drop; Foot; Embossing; Power; Riveting; Power Trimming; Wiring; Bicycle Chain; Horning; Cutting; Stamping; Automatic Feed; Power) ....A

OHIO—Warren
Denison Mfg. Co. (Raisin Seed Extracting) .....F

OHIO—Wellsville
Stevenson Co. (Sewer Pipe) . B

OHIO—Youngstown
Sennett Co., Geo. B. (Forging; Hydraulic; Power).B

PA.—Allentown
Allentown Foundry & Mach. Wks. Co. (Hydraulic)..A
Grammes & Sons, L. F. (Gold; Wood Embossing; Gilding; Stamping; Wood Printing; Box Board Printing) ....A

PA.—Avonmore
West Penn Foundry & Mach. Co. (Hydraulic)..X

PA.—Bloomsburg
Richards Mfg. Co. (Drawing; Power) ....B

PA.—Bradford
Caldwell & Co., E. R. (Hydraulic Car Wheel) ....B

PA.—Carbondale
Carbondale Mach. Co. (Filter; Hydraulic) ......AA
Hendrick Mfg. Co. (Ltd.) (Filter; Hydraulic)...AA

PA.—Chambersburg
Chambersburg Engineering Co. (Hydraulic Flanging) A

PA.—Chester
Vulcan Works (Steam; Hydraulic Cotton) ....B

PA.—Harrisburg
Hickok Mfg. Co., W. O. (Drawing; Embossing; Power; Bookbinders'; Toggle Joint; Lard; Tincture; Wine; Bookbinders' Blocks; Signature; Smashing; Stamping; Standing) ....AA

PA.—Lancaster
Champ Blower & Forge Co. (Blacksmiths' Drill)..AA

PA.—Mechanicsburg
Comstock, Geo. S. (Wine; Cider) C

PA.—Media
Wood, W. H. (Hydraulic) D

PA.—Philadelphia
Barnes & Erb Co. (Shirt Bosom) ....A
Bement, Niles & Co. (Hydrostatic Wheel; Drill; Hydraulic Baling).AAAA
Chambers Bros. Co. (Embossing; Stamping) ..AA
Enterprise Mfg. Co., 3rd & Dauphin (Raisin Seed Extracting; Wine; Cider; Cork; Tincture; Druggists'; Fruit; Lard; Domestic) ....AAAA
Hill Mfg. Co., B. B., 1020 New Market (Copying; Seal) ....B
Horn & Bros., Wm. H. (Tan) ....B
Johnson, Jr., & Co., Israel H. (Arbor; Drop; Foot; Screw) ....B
Kueny, Nicholas M. (Brick) X

Morris, Henry G. (Filter) B
Nazel Mach. Tool Wks., 1042 Ridge Av. (Lock Corner Die for Paste Board Folding Box Mchry.; Scorching) ....E
Nittinger, August (Lard; Tallow) ....A
Olsen, Tinius & Co., 500 N. 12th (Car Wheel; Crank Pin; Foot; Hydraulic; Power; Stamping; Hydrostatic Wheel) ....A
Penna. Iron Wks. Co., 51st & Lancaster Av. (Hydraulic; Special to order only) AAA
Phila. Novelty Mfg. Co. (Copying) ....D
Phila. Roll & Machry. Co., S. 23rd & Washington Av. (Hydraulic Forging; Hydraulic Wheel) ....A
Reid Creamery & Dairy Supply Co., 33rd & Market (Cheese) ....A
Riehle Bros. Testing Mach. Co., 1429 N. 9th (Hydraulic; Screw) .....B
Sellers & Co., Wm. (Inc.), 1600 Hamilton (Hydraulic Wheel Hydrostatic Wheel; Forging; Hand; Gun; Cotton) ......AAAA
Wood & Co., R. D., 400 Chestnut (Forging; Hydraulic) ....AAAA

PA.—Pittsburg •
Fischer Foundry & Machine Co. (Tile; Hydraulic).AA
Lewis Foundry & Machine Co. (Hydraulic) ....A
Phillips & McLaren (Brick) B
Scaife & Sons Co., Wm. B., 221 1st (Filter) ...AAA
Somerfield Mach. & Mfg. Co., 224 3rd Av. (Glass) B
United Engineering & Foundry Co. (Hydraulic) .... AAAA

PA.—Reading
Reading Iron Co. (Cotton) AAAA

PA.—So. Bethlehem
Bethlehem Foundry & Mach. Co. (Power; Hydraulic; Punching; Trimming) ..C
Bethlehem Steel Co. (Heavy Hydraulic; Flanging; Forging) ....AAAA

PA.—West Chester
Dairy Specialty Co. (Cheese) ....F

PA.—York
Farquhar Co., A. B. (Wine; Cider; Baling; Hay)... AAA
Hench & Drumgold Co. (Wine; Cider) ....B
Keystone Farm Mach. Co. (Wine; Cider) ....B

R. I.—Hope Valley
Nichols & Langworthy Mach. Co. (Printing)... AA

R. I.—Pawtucket
Bliss Mfg. Co., R. (Punching; Trimming) ..AAAA
Pawtucket Mfg. Co. (Trimming) ....A

R. I.—Providence
Builders Iron Foundry (Hydraulic) ....AA
Standard Machinery Co. (Blanking; Broaching; Drawing; Foot; Forging; Power; Punching; Trimming; Screw; Stamping) B

R. I.—Westerly
Cottrell & Sons Co., C. B. (Printing; Cylinder; Bag; Book Printing; Job; Lithographic; Newspaper; Rotary Printing; Stop Cylinder; Two Color; Two Revolutions) ....AAA

R. I.—Woonsocket
Woonsocket Mach. & Press

PRESSES (Con.)
Co. (Drawing; Lever;
Cloth; Rotary Steam;
Cloth) ....AA
S. C.—Charleston
Valk & Murdoch Iron Wks.
(Cotton; Cotton Seed
Hull) ....B
S. C.—Cheraw
Cheraw Hardware Supply
Co. (Cotton) ....F
TENN.—Chattanooga
Chattanooga Impl. & Mfg.
Co. (Hay) ....B
Copeland, Henry (Hay; Cot-
ton; Cotton Seed Hull)..G
TENN.—Jackson
Southern Engine & Boiler
Wks. (Cotton) ....AA
TENN.—Memphis
Chickasaw Iron Wks.
(Cotton) ....A
Livermore Foundry & Mach.
Co. (Cotton) ....A
TEXAS—Dallas
Murray Co. (Cotton; Cotton
Seed Hull) C
TEXAS—San Antonio
Collins Mfg. Co., F. F.
(Hay) ....B
VT.—Bellows Falls
Vermont Farm Machinery
Co. (Cheese) C
VT.—Bennington
Scott, Olin (Wood Pulp).A
Sibley, E. L. (Eyelet) ...D
VT.—Rutland
Stoddard Mfg. Co. (Cheese)
B
VA.—Danville
Westbrook Foundry & Ma-
chine Co. (Hydraulic ..F
VA.—Norfolk
Whitehurst Co., R. W.
(Wine; Cider; Cotton;
Cotton Seed Hull; Baling;
Hay; Hay Hand; Fruit)
B
VA.—Petersburg
Petersburg Iron Wks. Co.
(Hydraulic) ....D
VA.—Richmond
Cardwell Mach. Co. (Cot-
ton; Cotton Seed Hull;
Hydraulic; Foot; Baling;
Broom Corn; Hair; Hy-
draulic Baling; Wool;
Plug Tobacco) ....A
Talbott & Sons (Tobacco)
X
WIS.—Janesville
New Doty Mfg. Co. (Power;
Screw; Shearing; Punch-
ing; Trimming) ....D
WIS.—Milwaukee
Allis-Chalmers Co. (Filter)
AAAA
Filer & Stowell Co. (Hy-
draulic Wheel) ....AAA
WIS.—Racine
Racine Malleable &
Wrought Iron Co. (Copy-
ing) ....A
WIS.—Seymour
Dean Mfg. Co. (Cheese)..D

PRINTS

See Cotton Goods

PRICKERS

CONN.—Bridgeport
Knapp & Cowles Mfg. Co.
(Sailmakers') C

PRIMERS

CONN.—Bridgeport
Union Mercantile Cartridge
Co. (Friction; Cartridge)
AAA
CONN.—Waterbury
Waterbury Brass Co. (Fric-
tion; Cartridge) ..AAAA
New York City
Metallic Cap Mfg. Co., 271
B'way (Blasting) .....A
OHIO—Cincinnati
Peters' Cartridge Co. (Me-
tallic Cartridge) ..AAAA

PRISMS

ILL.—Chicago
American Luxfer Prism Co.,
346 Wabash Av. ......D
New York City
New York Prism Co., 473
W. B'way ....E

PRISONS

OHIO—Cleveland
Van Dorn Iron Wks. Co.
(Steelwork) ....AA

PRODUCERS

MASS.—Worcester
Morgan Construction Co.
(Gas) ....A
OHIO—Cleveland
Wellman-Seaver-Morgan
Co. (Gas) ....AAAA
OHIO—Youngstown
Pollock Co., Wm. B.
(Gas) ....AA
PA.—Philadelphia
Herrick, J. A. (Gas) ....D
Philadelphia Roll & Ma-
chine Co. (Gas) ....A
Wood Co., R. D. (Gas)...
AAAA
PA.—Pittsburg
Amer. Furnace & Machine
Co. (Gas) ....D
Amsler Engineering Co.
(Gas) ....D
Duff Patents Co. (Gas)..A
Laughlin & Co., Alex.
(Gas) ....A
McClure, Son & Co., G. W.
(Gas) ....D
Riter-Conley Mfg. Co. (Gas)
AAA
Smythe Co., S. R. (Gas)..B
Swindell & Bro., Wm.
(Gas) ....B
PA.—York
Broomell, Schmidt & Steacy
Co. (Gas) ....A

PRODUCTS

ILL.—Rock Island
Lewis Roofing Co. (Coal
Tar) ....B
MD.—Baltimore
Baltimore Roofing & Coal
Tar Co., 1211 Leadenhall
(Coal Tar) ....F
Foy & Co., Edw. L., 16 W.
Camden (Coal Tar) ....D
Noble & Co., H., 18 S. Gay
(Coal Tar) X
MASS.—Boston
Cabot, Samuel, 70 Kilby
(Coal Tar) ....A
Warren Bros. Co., 93 Fed-
eral (Coal Tar) ......AA
MASS.—Malden
Huggins & Son, Jas. (Coal
Tar) ....E
MICH.—Detroit
Parke, Davis & Co. (Beef;
Biological) ....AAAA
N. J.—Elizabeth
Rankin Co., Wm. H. (Coal
Tar) ....AA
N. Y.—Buffalo
Schoelikopf, Hartford &
Hanna Co. (Coal Tar)AAA
New York City
Mathewson & Co., Wm. J.
(Coal Tar) ....A
OHIO—Cleveland
Monitor Oil Co. (Coal Tar)C
PA.—Erie
Watson Co., H. F. (Coal
Tar) ....AAA
PA.—Philadelphia
Ammonia Co. of Phila.
(Ammonia) ....A
Barrett Mfg. Co., Land
Title Bldg. (Coal Tar)
AAAA
Garrett & Son Co., C. S., 21
Decatur (Coal Tar) ..AA
PA.—Pittsburg
McClintock & Irvine Co.
(Coal Tar) ....B
TENN.—Nashville
Nashville Chemical Co., 919
N. Front (Coal Tar) ...D

PROTECTORS (Con.)
(Check) ....B
Klemm & Co., 123 N. 5th
(Arc Lamp) C
Loeb, Lipper & Co. (Brush
Edge Skirt) ....A
Seeley, Isaac B. (Kidney) F
PA.—Pittsburg
Oliver Iron & Steel Co.
(Pole) ....AAAA
R. I.—Pawtucket
Fuller & Son Co., Geo. H.
(Watch) ....A
R. I.—Providence
D. & W. Fuse Co. (Tele-
phone) ....B

PROTRACTORS

MASS.—Athol
Athol Machine Co. (Bevel)B
Starrett Co., L. S. (Bevel;
Draughtman's Universal
Bevel, etc.) ....A
MASS.—Chicopee Falls
Stevens Arms & Tool Co., J.
(Bevel) ....AAA
MASS.—Fitchburg
Sawyer Tool Mfg. Co. ...C
MASS.—Greenfield
Massachusetts Tool Co. ...C
New York City
Keuffel & Esser Co., 127
Fulton ....AA
PA.—Philadelphia
Alteneder & Sons, Theo.
(Bevel) ....D
R. I.—Providence
Brown & Sharpe Mfg. Co.
..............AAAA

PROVERS

New York City
Amer. Meter Co., 561 W.
47th (Metal) ....B
PA.—Philadelphia
Harris Bros. & Co., 12th &
Brown (Metal) ....F

PRUNERS

CONN.—Hamden
Henry Mfg. Co., J. T.
(Tree) ....E
MICH.—Jackson
Novelty Mfg. Co. ....A
New York City
Peck, Stow & Wilcox Co.
..............AAAA
N. Y.—Rochester
Eichelman, C. W. (Tree) F
OHIO—Hamilton
Meyers Mfg. Co., Fred. J. B

PRUNES

CAL.—Fresno
Castle Bros. (Br. San Fran.)
..............AA
Griffin & Skelley Co. (Br.
San Fran) ....A
CAL.—Geyserville
Walden & Co. ....A
CAL.—Gilroy
Prune City Pack. Co. AAA
CAL.—Los Gatos
Rogers, Noah G. ....B
CAL.—San Francisco
Castle Bros., 463 Mission AA
Griffin & Skelley Co., 132
Mkt. ....A
Rosenberg Bros. & Co., 211
Calif. ....A
CAL.—San Jose
Castle Bros. ....AA
Griffin & Skelley Co. (Br.
San Fran.) ....A
CAL.—Visalia
Downing, Chas. C
New York City
Hartwig & Bennett, 61 N.
Moore ....
Higgins & Co., Wm. A., 374
Washn. (Dried) C
OREGON—Portland
Lanz & Co. (Ship.) .....AA
WASH.—Spokane
Shinn & Co., H. J. ....A

PUBLISHERS

CAL.—San Francisco
Payot, Upham & Co. (Belles-
Lettres) ....A

PUBLISHERS (Con.)
D. C.—Washington
Ellis & Co., Jno. F. (Musi-
cal) ....A
ILL.—Chicago
Conkey Co., W. B. (Belles-
Lettres) ....AAA
Hazlitt & Co., Geo. K.
(Technical) ....D
Law Publishing Co. (Legal)
..............F
Lyon & Healy (Musical)
..............AAAA
McClury & Co., A. C.
(Belles-Lettres; School)
..............AAA
MASS.—Boston
Estes, Dana & Co. (Art;
Belles-Lettres) ......AA
Ginn & Co. (School) AAAA
Houghton. Mifflin & Co.
(Belles-Lettres; Legal;
Medical; School; Techni-
cal) ....AAA
Little, Brown & Co.
(Legal) ....AA
N. J.—Paterson
Royle & Son, Jno. (Guide) A
N. Y.—Albany
Banks & Co. (Legal) ....A
New York City
American Bible Society
(Religious Publications)
..............AAA
American Tract Society
(Religious Publications)
..............AAA
Appleton & Co., D. (Art;
Belles-Lettres; . Medical;
School; Technical) .....B
Baker, Voorhis & Co.
(Legal) ....A
Benziger Bros. (Religious
Publications) ....A
Boericke & Tafel (Medical)
..............F
Christian Press Ass'n Pub-
lishing Co. (Religious
Publications) C
Comstock. Wm. T. (Archi-
tectural) ....F
Davidson Publishing Co.
(Textile) ....D
Dillingham Co., Geo. W.
(Belles-Lettres) ....B
Ditson & Co., C. H.
(Musical) ....B
Dodd, Mead & Co. (Belles-
Lettres) ....AA
Dutton & Co., E. P. (Belles-
Lettres; School) ....A
Fowler & Wells Co. (Belles-
Lettres) ....A
Funk & Wagnalls Co.
(Belles-Lettres) ....AAA
Harper & Bros. (Inc.)
(Belles-Lettres; Medical;
School; Scientific) .....B
Henley Pub. Co., Norman
W. (Scientific; Technical)
..............D
Holt & Co., Henry (Belles-
Lettres; School) ......AA
Methodist Book Concern
(Religious Publications)
..............AAAA
Munn & Co. (Inc.) (Scienti-
fic; Technical) ....A
Oil, Paint & Drug Pub. Co.
(Drug) ....B
Pond & Co., Wm. A. (Musi-
cal) ....D
Pustet & Co., Fdk. (Re-
ligious Publications) ..AA
Putnam's Sons (Inc.), G. P.
(Belles-Lettres; School)
..............AA
Schirmer, G. (Musical) ...B
Scribners' Sons, Chas. (Art;
Belles-Lettres Scientific;
Technical) ....AAA
Spencer Optical Co. (Scienti-
fic) C
Spon & Chamberlain (Techni-
cal) ....D
Thomas Publishing Co., 220
Bway. (Trade Directories)
..............A
Van Nostrand Co., D. (Scien-
tific; Technical) ......AA
Williams Co., David (Iron;
Steel) ....B
Wood & Co., Wm. (Medical)
..............AA

OHIO—Cincinnati
Church Co., Jno. (Musical)
.................................AAAA
Clarke Co., Robt. (Legal), B
PA.—Philadelphia
Amer. Baptist Pub. Society
(Religious Publications)
.................................AAAA
Baird & Co., Henry (Technical) ....A
Lea Bros. & Co. (Medical;
Scientific) ....AAA
Lippincott Co., J. B. (Belles-
Lettres; Historical; Medical; School; Scientific)
.................................AAA
Trades Pub. Co. (Carpet;
Upholstery) ....B

PUDDING

DEL.—Dover
Richardson & Robbins
(Plum) ....AAA
DEL.—Seaford
Greenbaum Bros. (Plum)..A
ILL.—Chicago
Libby, McNeill & Libby
(Plum) ....AAAA
IND.—Indianapolis
Van Camp Pack Co. (Plum)
.................................AA
MD.—Baltimore
Fruit Puddine Co. (Plum) A
N. J.—Jersey City
Home Cocoanut Co. (Plum)
.................................X
N. J.—Passaic
Amer. Compr. Food Co.
(Plum) C
N. Y.—Buffalo
Erie Preserving Co. (Plum)
.................................AAAA
New York City
Burnham & Co., E. S.
(Plum) ....B
N. Y.—Rochester
Curtice Bros. Co. (Plum)
.................................AA
PA.—Philadelphia
Atmore & Son (Plum) ....A

PULLERS

See also Machy; Agr. Imps

CONN.—Bridgeport
Bridgeport Hdw. Mfg. Co.,
481 Iraniston Av. (Nail;
Tack) ....B
Hurwood Mfg. Co. (Tack),
.................................C
CONN.—Danielson
Parkhurst, L. D. (Tack), G
CONN.—New Haven
Beldon Machine Co. (Nail) D
Kilborn & Bishop Co. (Nail)
.................................C
Scranton & Co. (Nail; Tack)
.................................C
Snow, L. T. (Nail) .....D
CONN.—Plantsville
Atwater Mfg. Co. (Nail), A
CONN.—Southport
Jelliff & Co., C. O. (Onion)
.................................B
ILL.—Batavia
Snow Mfg. Co. (Stump) ..E
ILL.—Canton
Parlin & Orendorff Co.
(Beet) ....AAAA
ILL.—Chicago
Borden & Selleck Co., 48
Lake (Car) ....B
Hoisting & Conveying
Mchry. Co., 44 N. Elizabeth (Car) ....E
Link Belt Mchry. Co., W.
39th & Stewart (Car) AAA
Nat'l Hoist & Mach. Co., 463
W. 22d (Stump) ....G
Webster Mfg. Co. (Power
Car) ....AA
ILL.—Downer's Grove
Dicke Tool Co. (Wire) C
ILL.—Freeport
Arcade Mfg. Co. (Cork) ..A
ILL.—Harvard
Hunt, Helm & Ferris (Staple) ....AA
ILL.—Moline
Barnard & Leas Mfg. Co.
(Car; Power Car) ....AA

Deere & Mansur Co. (Beet;
Onion) ....AAAA
ILL.—Monmouth
Milne Mfg. Co. (Stump) ..C
ILL.—Pekin
Duisdieker Fdry. & Mfg. Co.
(Stump) ....D
IND.—Evansville
Kratz Bros. (Stump) X
IND.—Indianapolis
Nordyke & Marmon Co.
(Car) ....AAA
Over, Ewald (Stump) C
IND.—Mishawaka
Dodge Mfg. Co. (Car)..AAA
IOWA—Burlington
Mohland & Co. (Stump) ..C
IOWA—Cresco
Caward, R. S. (Stump)....E
IOWA—Ft. Madison
Morrison Mfg. Co. (Beet)
.................................AA
IOWA—Lone Tree
Monarch Grubber Co.
(Stump) ....B
IOWA—Waterloo
Kelly & Taneyhill (Boulder)
.................................C
MASS.—Boston
Harvey, H. H., 608 Atlantic
Av. (Spike) ....D
Pearson Co., C., 64 Federal
(Spike) ....AAAA
Strater & Sons, Herman
(Cork) ....A
MASS.—Greenfield
Goodell-Pratt Co. (Nail) ..B
MASS.—Millers' Falls
Millers' Falls Co. (Nail)
.................................AA
MICH.—Almont
Lee, R. E. (Stump) ....F
MICH.—Grand Rapids
Butterworth & Lowe
(Stump) ....A
MICH.—Mt. Clements
Donaldson Bros. (Beet) ..A
MICH.—Saginaw
Hurtibise, Alex. (Stump), E
MINN.—Albert Lea
Edwards, C. D. (Stump)...D
MO.—Kansas City
Kansas City Hay Press Co.
(Stump) ....AA
N. J.—Grenloch
Bateman Mfg. Co. (Onion),
.................................A
N. J.—Newark
Williamson Wire Novelty
Co., C. T. (Cork) ....B
N. Y.—Canisteo
Carter, W. D. (Stump) ...X
N. Y.—Elmira
Cronk & Carrier Mfg. Co.
(Staple; Tack) ....B
New York City
Graham & Co., Jno. H.
(Cork) ....AA
Millers' Falls Co. (Nail), AA
Morrill, Chas. (Railroad
Spike) ....D
Reisinger, Hugo (Cork) AA
Sargent & Co. (Tack)
.................................AAAA
Smith & Hemenway Co., 296
Bway. (Nail; Staples;
Tack) ....D
Tower & Lyon Co., 95
Chambers (Nail) ....B
N. Y.—Olean
Chamberlain Mfg. Co.
(Stump) ....F
N. Y.—Troy
Hagen & Reid (Nail; Tack)
.................................X
N. Y.—Utica
Utica Drop Forge & Tool Co.
(Staple; Tack) ....B
OHIO—Bellevue
Ohio Cultivator Co. (Beet)
.................................AAA
OHIO—Cincinnati
Schriver & Co., O. P., 208
Elm (Staple) ....B
OHIO—Cleveland
Federal Mfg. Co. (Tack)
.................................AAAA
OHIO—Fremont
Lehr Agr'l Co. (Beet) ....B
OHIO—Ravenna
Williams, A. C. (Tack) ..A
OHIO—Warren
Denison Mfg. Co. (Nail;

PULLERS (Con.)

Tack)

...........F

OHIO—Westerville

Bennett & Co., H. L.
(Stump) ....E

PA.—Allentown

Grammes & Sons, L. F.
(Nail) ....A

PA.—Erie

Erie Specialty Co. (Self-
Pulling Cork) ....B

PA.—Indiana

Indiana Fdry. Co. (Stump) D

PA.—Lancaster

Clamp Window-Shade Pull
Co. (Window Shade)....F

PA.—Philadelphia

Enterprise Mfg. Co. (Cork)
A

PA.—Pittsburg

Pittsburg Tool & Drop Forge
Co., Arnott Bldg. (Spike)
D

PA.—Reading

Chandrell Tool Co. (Nail), B

PA.—Wrightsville

Wrightsville Hdw. Co.
(Tack) ....B

PA.—York

Farquhar Co. (Ltd.), A. B.
(Stump) ....AAA

VT.—St. Albans

St. Albans Fdry. & Imple-
ment Co. (Stump) .....B

WIS.—La Crosse

Smith Mfg. Co. (Stump) ..A

WIS.—Seymour

Dean Mfg. Co. (Stump) ..D

WIS.—Sparta

Sparta Iron Wks. Co.
(Stump) C

PULLEYS

CAL.—San Francisco

Henry Machine Wks., 38
Fremont (Cast Iron)..AA

Meese & Gottfried Co., 167
Fremont Wrought Steel
Rim) ....A

Risdon Iron & Locomotive
Wks., Steuart & Folsom
(Cast Iron) .....AAAA

CONN.—Bridgeport

Parsons Co., R. E. (Cast
Iron) ....D

Smith & Egge Mfg. Co.
(Sash) ....A

CONN.—Derby

Birmingham Iron Foundry
(Cast Iron Friction
Clutch) ....AA

CONN.—Hartford

Hartford Mach. Screw Co.
(Cone) ....AAAA

Pratt & Whitney Co. (Friction Clutch) .....AAAA

CONN.—Middletown

Palmer, I. E. (Awning; Curtain Screw Self-Adjusting;
Ceiling; Shade) ....AAA

Wilcox, Crittenden & Co.
(Awning, or Tackle)...A

CONN.—New Britain

Corbin, P. & F. (Sash)
AAAA

Russell & Erwin Mfg. Co.
(Sash; Screw) ....AAAA

CONN.—New Haven

Eastern Machinery Co. (Cast
Iron; Friction Clutch;
Shaft) ....B

Henn & Co., A. S. (Clothes
Line) ....F

McLagon Foundry Co. (Ma-
chine Moulded) C

New Haven Mfg. Co. (Fric-
tion Clutch) ....AA

CONN.—Rockfall

Smith, Otis A. (Wire Stitching) ....B

CONN.—Southington

Peck, Stow & Wilcox Co.
(Awning or Tackle; Hay
Fork; Sash; Screw; Dumb
Waiter; Side; Tackle;
Wagon Brakes) .....AAAA

CONN.—Stamford

Yale & Towne Mfg. Co.
(Screw) ....AAAA

CONN.—Tolland

Sumner Belting Co., Wm.
(Wooden) ....D

PULLEYS (Con.)

CONN.—Torrington

Union Hdw. Co. (Wooden)
AA

CONN.—Waterbury

Waterbury Farrell Foundry
& Mach. Co. (Cast Iron)
AA

DEL.—Wilmington

Pusey & Jones Co. (Fric-
tion Clutch) ....AAA

Remington Machine Co.
(Cast Iron) ....A

GA.—Columbus

Goldens' Fdy. & Mach. Co.
(Cast Iron) ....A

ILL.—Batavia

U. S. Wind Engine & Pump
Co. (Hay Fork) ......AA

ILL.—Chicago

Allis-Chalmers Co., Home
Ins. Bldg. (Cast Iron)
AAAA

Burton Son, A. G. (Dyna-
mometer) C

Caldwell & Son Co., H. W.,
Western Av. & 17th
(Friction Clutch; Sash;
Shaft) ....AA

Coleman Hdw. Co., 59 Dearborn (Sash) ....A

Fairbanks, Morse & Co.
(Friction Clutch) ..AAAA

Gardner Sash Balance Co.,
164 Dearborn (Ball Bear-
ing Sash; Ball-Bearing
Show Case) C

Janesville Hay Tool Co.,
122 Lake (Hay Fork)...E

Jones Fdy. & Mach. Co., W.
A., 143 W. North Av.
(Machine Moulded Cast
Iron; Friction Clutch)..A

Kaestner & Co. (Inc.), 241
S. Jefferson (Cast Iron)
A

Link Belt Machinery Co.,
W. 39th & Stewart Av.
(Cast Iron Balanced).AAA

Plamondon Mfg. Co., A., 57
S. Clinton (Cast Iron Friction Clutch) ....A

Webster Mfg. Co., 1075 W.
15th (Cast Iron) ....AA

ILL.—Freeport

Stover Mfg. Co. (Sash;
Screw) ....AA

ILL.—Galesburg

Frost Mfg. Co. (Cast Iron)
A

ILL.—Harvard

Hunt, Helm, Ferris Co.
(Rope; Hay Fork) ..AA

ILL.—Marseilles

Marseilles Mfg. Co. (Cast
Iron) ....A

ILL.—Moline

Barnard & Leas Mfg. Co.
(Friction Clutch; Wood
Split) ....AA

ILL.—Ottawa

Porter Co., J. E. (Hay
Fork) ....A

ILL.—Sterling

Charter Gas Engine Co.
(Friction Clutch; Shaft)
A

Lawrence Bros. (Cast Iron;
Hay Fork) ....AAA

IND.—Columbus

Reeves Pulley Co. (Wood
Split) ....AA

IND.—Eaton

Eaton Mfg. Co. (Wood,
Split; Shaft) ....B

IND.—Goshen

Goshen Mfg. Co. (Hay
Fork) ....B

IND.—Indianapolis

American Paper Pulley Co.
(Paper; Wooden) .....A

Atkins & Co., E. C. (Wood-
en; Wooden Split) .AAAA

Nordyke & Marmon Co.,
1101 W. Morris (Cast
Iron; Paper) ....AAA

Rockwood Mfg. Co. (Paper)
A

Speed Changing Pulley Co.
(Speed Changing) ....B

IND.—Mishawaka

Dodge Mfg. Co. (Cast Iron;

PULLEYS (Con.)

Cone; Flange; Friction Clutch Guide; Iron Split; Wood Rim; Wood Split; Dynamometer; Wooden) ....AAA

IND.—South Bend
South Bend Pulley Co. (Cast Iron; Wood Split) .....B

IOWA—Davenport
Davenport Fdy. & Machine Co. (Split Wrought Steel) X

IOWA—Fairfield
Louden Machinery Co. (Hay Fork) C

IOWA—Ottumwa
Johnston & Sharp Mfg. Co. (Ball Bearing Steel Sash) ....D

KANS.—Leavenworth
Great Western Mfg. Co. (Cast Iron; Friction Clutch; Grooved; Split) ....AA

KY.—Louisville
Caldwell Co., W. E., Brandeis Av. & Brook (Cast Iron) ....AA

KY.—Maysville
Ohio Valley Pulley Works (Wood Split) ....B

MAINE—Portland
Laughlin Co., Thos. (Awning, or Tackle) ......A
Portland Co. (Cast Iron; Grooved) ....AA

MAINE—South Portland
Marine Hdw. & Equipment Co. (Awning or Tackle) C

MD.—Baltimore
Poole Engineering & Mach. Co. (Cast Iron; Cone; Flange; Friction Clutch; Guide Shaft) ....AA
Sinclair-Scott Co., Wells & Patapsco (Clutch; Friction Clutch) ....E
Sloan & Co., Frank B., 10 S. Charles (Sash) .....D

MASS.—Boston
American Tool & Mach. Co., 109 Beach (Cast Iron; Friction Clutch; Centrifugal Clutch; Small Iron) ....AA
Austin & Eddy, 117 Broad (Sash) C
Boston Gear Works (Shaft) ....B
Sturtevant Co., B. F. (Shaft) ....AAA

MASS.—Fitchburg
Brown & Co., C. H. (Cast Iron) X
Cowdrey Mach. Wks., C. H. (Self-Oiling) ....D
Fitchburg Machine Works (Friction Clutch) ......B
Putnam Mach. Co. (Cast Iron; Friction Clutch)..A

MASS.—Greenfield
Wells Bros. Co. (Friction Clutch) ....A
Wiley & Russell Mfg. Co. (Friction Clutch) ....AA

MASS.—Lawrence
McCaffrey, Jno. (Shaft; Cast Iron) ....H

MASS.—North Adams
Hunter Mach. Co., James (Cast Iron; Friction Clutch; Guide; Clutch).A

MASS.—Orange
Hunt, Rodney Machine Co. (Friction Clutch; Clutch) ....A

MASS.—Pittsfield
Jones & Sons' Co., E. D. (Split) ....B

MASS.—Worcester
Burlingame Co., A. (Wood Split) ....D
Holyoke Mach. Co. (Cast Iron; Split) ....AA
Luther & Co., R. G., 91 Foster (Self-Oiling) ..E
Union Machine Co. (Cast Iron; Friction Clutch)..X

MICH.—Bay City
Garland Co., M. (Clutch).C

PULLEYS (Con.)

MICH.—Detroit
Buhl Malleable Co. (Split) ....A
Co-operative Fdy. Co. (Cast Iron; Iron Split) X
Detroit Wood Pulley Co., Bellevue & Kirby Av. (Wood Split) ♦........B
Wing & Co., J. T., Woodward Av. (Wood Split).C

MICH.—Grand Rapids
Fox Machine Co. (Sash)..A
Grand Rapids Hdw. Co. (Sash) ....B
Wilmarth & Marman Co. (Friction Clutch; Loose) C

MICH.—Saginaw
Saginaw Mfg. Co. (Wood Split) ....AA
Wickes Bros. (Cast Iron) ....AAA

MICH.—St. Johns
Mason & Co., F. C. (Hay Fork) C

MINN.—Minneapolis
Diamond Iron Works (Friction Clutch) ....B
Hoyt Mfg. Co. (Friction).E
Minnesota Steel & Machinery Co., Minnehaha & 29th (Cast Iron; Friction Clutch; Shaft; Split).AAA

MO.—St. Louis
Kupferle, Jno. C., cor. 2d & Mound (Iron & Wood Hay Fork; Sash) ....AA
Leschen & Sons Rope Co., A., 920 N. 1st (Cast Iron; Self-Oiling) ..AAA
Medart Patent Pulley Co. (Cast Iron; Friction Clutch; Wrought Rim; Clamp Hub; Clutch; Special; Split) ....AAA
Pleuger & Henger Mfg. Co., 11th & Hebert (Ceiling; Hay Fork) ....A
Standard Pulley & Fdy. Co., 1228 Collins (Machine Moulded Cast Iron) ....D
Williams Mfg. Co., Milton F., 2701 N. Broadway (Friction Clutch) ......B

N. H.—Dover
White Co., Jno. A. (Cast Iron) C

N. H.—Keene
Humphrey Machine Co. (Cast Iron) C

N. J.—Dover
Morris County Mach. & Iron Co. (Friction Clutch)...B

N. J.—Elizabeth
Brown Co., A. & F. (Cast Iron; Cone; Flange; Friction Clutch; Guide; Balanced; Clamp Hub; Dynamometer; Clutch; Split) ....B

N. J.—Garwood
Whitman Mfg. Co. (Friction Clutch, for Gas & Gasoline Engines) ....F

N. J.—Newark
Blayney, J. C. (Friction Clutch) X

N. J.—Raritan
Kenyon & Son, D. R. (Friction Clutch) ....B

N. J.—Smithville
Smith Mach. Co., H. B. (Cast Iron) ....A

N. Y.—Brooklyn
Bliss Co., E. W. 17 Adams (Friction Clutch) ..AAAA

N. Y.—Buffalo
Clark Mfg. Co., 260 Chandler (Sash) C
Howard Iron Works (Cast Iron) ....A

N. Y.—Elmira
Cronk & Carrier Mfg. Co. (Hay Fork) ....B

N. Y.—Horseheads
Weller Hdw. & Fdy. Co. (Hay Fork) ....D

N. Y.—Hudson
Gifford Bros. (Friction Clutch) ....A

PULLEYS (Con.)

N. Y.—Lockport
Boston & Lockport Block
Co. (Hay Fork & Sling).A
N. Y.—Long Island City
North American Metaline
Co., cor. West Av. & 3d
(Oilless Bearing Loose).C
N. Y.—Manlius
Cheney & Son, S. (Hay
Fork) ....A
N. Y.—Medina
Swett Iron Works, A. L.
(Hay Fork) ....A
New York City
American Wood Working
Machine Co. (Wooden)
...........AAAA
Creamer & Co., W. G., 96
John (Bell Cord) ......A
Fairbanks Co. (Friction
Clutch; Wooden) ..AAAA
Garvin Machine Co., Spring
and Varick (Friction
Clutch) ....AA
Grant Pulley & Hdw. Co.,
23 Warren (Overhead
Sash) ....F
Judd Co., H. L., 87 Chambers (Screw; Curtain;
Wedge Back) ....AA
Leonard & McCoy (Split)..B
Niles-Bement-Pond Co., 111
B'way (Cast Iron; Iron
Split) ....AAAA
Sargent & Co., 151 Leonard
(Ceiling; Clothes Line;
Dumb Waiter; Hothouse;
Sash; Screw; Side; Upright; Tackle; Wagon
Brake) ....AAAA
Singer Mfg. Co. (Sewing
Machine) ....AAAA
Tiebout, W. & J., 118 Chambers (Sash: Upright)...B
N. Y.—Oneida
Oneida Steel Pulley Co.
(Pressed Steel Split; Steel
Centre Wood Rim; Wood
Split) ....B
N. Y.—Rochester
Pullman Mfg. Co. (Sash).B
Ricker Mfg. Co. (Hay Fork)
.........................E
N. Y.—Sandy Hill
Friction Pulley & Machine
Co. (Noiseless Screen
Friction Clutch) ......B
Sandy Hill Iron & Brass
Works (Friction Clutch)
.........................A
N. Y.—Schenectady
General Electric Co. (Balanced) ....AAAA
N. Y.—Syracuse
Stearns & Co., E. C. (Awning; Curtain; Small Iron;
Swivel) ....AA
N. Y.—Troy
McMurray Co., Clarence F.
(Split) ....AA
Palmer Hdw. Mfg. Co.,
Green Island P. O. (Sash;
Screw; Side) ....D
N. C.—Statesville
Steele & Son, J. C. (Friction Clutch) ....B
OHIO—Akron
Whitman & Barnes Mfg.
Co. (Hay; Sling, &c.;
Self-Oiling) ......AAAA
OHIO—Ashland
Myers & Bro., F. E. (Hay
Fork) ....AAAA
OHIO—Canal Fulton
Fulton Mach. Co. (Cast
Iron) ....E
OHIO—Canton
Ney Mfg. Co. (Awning or
Tackle; Hay Fork; Screw;
Side) ....B
Ney Co., V. L. (Hay Fork)
.........................C
OHIO—Cincinnati
Bradford Belting Company
(Wooden Split) ....A
Fay. Egan Co., J. A., cor.
Front & John (Cast Iron)
...........AAAA
Greenwald Co., I. & E.
(Cast Iron) ....A
Kissinger-Ison Co. (Friction

PULLEYS (Con.)

Clutch) ....D
Lane & Bodley Co., cor.
John & Walter (Cast
Iron; Balanced) .....B
Oesterlein Mach. Co., Elam
& Garrard Av. (Friction
Clutch) ....B
Xylotite Product Co. (Fibre)
.........................B
OHIO—Cleveland
Brown Hoisting Machinery
Co. (Friction Clutch)
...........AAAA
Cleveland Block Co., 163
River (Hay Fork) .....B
Federal Mfg. Co., American
Trust Bldg. (Steel Face
Wood Rim; Steel Face,
Wood Centre, Wrought
Steel) ....AAAA
Hill Clutch Co., ft. Waverly
Pl. (Cast Iron; Friction
Clutch; Clutch) ....B
Standard Sewing Machine
Co. (Sewing Machine)
.........................AAA
Strong, Carlisle & Hammond, 61 Frankfort
(Wood Split; Wrought
Steel) ....A
OHIO—Columbus
Case Mfg. Co. (Friction
Clutch; Shaft; Split;
Wood Split; Steel Face)
.........................A
Jeffrey Mfg. Co. (Cast
Iron; Friction Clutch;
Shaft) ....AAAA
OHIO—Cuyahoga Falls
Falls Rivet & Machine Co.
(Cast Iron; Flange; Friction Clutch; Guide) ....A
OHIO—Dayton
Brownell & Co. (Wooden
Split) ....AAA
Dayton Globe Iron Works
Co., 833 S. Ludlow (Cast
Iron) ....B
OHIO—Defiance
Defiance Machine Works
(Balanced) ....A
OHIO—Marion
Ohio Pulley Co. (Wood
Split) ....A
OHIO—Massillon
Hess-Snyder Co. (Cast
Iron; Friction Clutch;
Clutch; Split; Shaft)..AA
OHIO—Mt. Gilead
Hydraulic Press Mfg. Co,
(Friction Clutch) ......A
OHIO—St. Mary's
St. Mary's Machine Co.
(Clutch, Cast Iron) ...A
OHIO—Sandusky
Klotz Mach. Co. (Cast Iron)
.........................C
OHIO—Shelby
Brightman Mfg. Co. (Friction Clutch) ....AA
OHIO—Springfield
Leffel & Co., James (Cast
Iron) ....AA
OHIO—Toledo
Baker Bros. (Cast Iron;
Wood Split) ....A
Keasey Pulley Co., Albion
& Bancroft (Malleable
Iron Centre, Wood Split)
.........................C
Toledo Fdy. & Machine Co.
(Cast Iron; Guide) ....B
OHIO—Wellsville
Stevenson Co. (Friction
Clutch) ....B
PA.—Allegheny
Enterprise Foundry Co., cor.
Nixon & Manhattan
(Sash) ....E
Porter Foundry & Machine
Co. (Cast Iron) ....A
PA.—Allentown
Allentown Foundry & Machine Wks. (Clutch)...A
Kline & Co., D. R. (Sash)
.........................B
PA.—Berlin
Eclipse Wood Pulley Co.
(Wood Split) ....B
PA.—Chambersburg
Wolf Co. (Cast Iron; Fric-

PULLEYS (*Con.*)

tion Clutch; Shaft) ..AA
Woods' Sons, T. B. (Cast Iron; Friction Clutch) .A
PA.—Erie
Taper Sleeve Pulley Works (Friction Clutch; Wooden; Wooden Split) C
PA.—Muncy
Sprout, Waldron & Co. (Cast Iron) ....A
PA.—Philadelphia
American Pulley Co., 29th & Bristol (Cast Iron; Split Wrought Steel; Steel Rim; Pressed Steel) ....A
Box & Co., Alfred (Traveling) ....B
Brill Co., J. G. (Bell Cord; also Register Cord).AAAA
Cresson Co., Geo. V., 18th & Allegheny Av. (Cast Iron; Cone; Flange; Friction Clutch; Guide; Clamp Hub; Split) ..AA
Link Belt Engineering Co. (Friction Clutch) ....AA
Moore & White Co., 15th & Lehigh Av. (Friction Clutch) ....AA
Sellers & Co. (Inc.), Wm., 1600 Hamilton (Cast Iron; Friction Clutch) AAAA
Yocom & Son, James, 145 N. 2d (Friction Clutch) ....B
PA.—Pittsburg
Columbia Bridge Company (Shaft) ....AA
Fischer Fdy. & Mach. Co., S. 21st & Mary (Cast Iron) ....AA
Jones & Laughlin Steel Co. (Cast Iron; Flange; Friction Clutch; Guide; Grooved) ....AAAA
Pittsburg Pulley Co., Frick Bldg. (Cast Iron, in the rough. etc.; Flange; Friction Clutch) ....B
Scaife Fdy. & Machine Co. (Cast Iron) ....B
PA.—Pittston
Exeter Machine Wks. (Friction Clutch) ....AA
PA.—Reading
Penna. Hdw. Co. (Awning or Tackle; Ceiling; Hay Fork; Sash; Screw)..AA
Reading Hdw. Co. (Awning or Tackle; Ceiling; Hay Fork; Ball or Roller Bearing Sash; Screw; Dumb Waiter; Hot House; Side; Upright; Wagon Brake) AAAA
Reading Wood Pulley Co. (Iron & Wood Centre. Wood Split) C
PA.—Warren
Jacobson Mach. Mfg. Co. (Clutch Cast Iron; Friction Clutch) C
PA.—Waynesboro
Frick Co. (Cast Iron, Split) AAAA
PA.—Wilkesbarre
Vulcan Iron Works (Balanced; Clutch; Friction Clutch; Split) ....AAAA
PA.—Williamsport
Valley Iron Works (Cast Iron; Paper; Friction Clutch; Split; Wooden).A
Williamsport Clutch & Pulley Co. (Cast Iron; Friction Clutch) ....B
PA.—Wrightsville
Dissinger & Bro., C. H. A. (Safety Clutch Hay Fork) D
Susquehanna Casting Co. (Sash; Hay Fork; Sling) AA
Wrightsville Hdw. Co. (Hay Fork; Sash, for Auger Mortises; Frame)...B
R. I.—Pawtucket
Fales & Jenks Mach. Co. (Cast Iron) ....AAA

PULLEYS (*Con.*)

R. I.—Providence
Brown & Sharpe Mfg. Co. (Friction Clutch; Clutch) AAAA
Chase Pulley Co. (Iron Hub & Arms, Wood Rim; Wooden Split) ....B
R. I.—Woonsocket
Woonsocket Mach. & Press Co. (Cast Iron; Cone; Balanced; Clamp Hub; Dynamometer; Grooved; Guide; Split; Wooden).AA
S. C.—Charleston
Valk & Murdoch Iron Wks. (Balanced) ....B
TENN.—Jackson
Southern Engine & Boiler Works (Inc.) (Cast Iron) AA
VT.—Montpelier
Lane Mfg. Co. (Cast Iron; Cone; Split; Wooden; Wooden Split) ....A
VT.—Rutland
Patch Mfg. Co., F. R. (Cast Iron) ....B
WIS.—Beloit
Beloit Iron Works (Friction Clutch) ....A
WIS.—Eau Claire
McDonough Mfg. Co. (Sash) A
WIS.—Janesville
Rock River Mach. Co. (Hay Fork) ....D
WIS.—Menasha
Menasha Wood Split Pulley Co. (Wood Split) ....D
WIS.—Milwaukee
Brodesser Elevator Mfg. Co. (Friction Clutch)..X
Filer & Stowell Co. (Cast Iron; Friction Clutch; Guide Shaft) ......AAA
Milwaukee Hay Tool Co. (Hay Fork) ....A
WIS.—Racine
Freeman & Sons' Mfg. Co., S. (Cast Iron) ....A
WIS.—South Milwaukee
Stowell Mfg. & Foundry Co. (Ceiling; Hay Fork; Dumb Waiter) ....A

PULLS

CONN.—Bridgeport
Bridgeport Brass Company (Drawer) ....AAA
Smith & Egge Mfg. Co. (Wood Closet; Door Drawer) ....A
CONN.—Bristol
Warner & Co., A. H. (Water Closet) X
CONN.—Chester
Brooks & Sons, M. S. (Screen Door; also Ring Shade) ....B
CONN.—Deep River
Williams & Marvin Mfg. Co. (Wood Closet) ....D
CONN.—Meriden
Bradley & Hubbard Mfg. Co. (Drawer) .....AAAA
Foster, Merriam & Co. (Drawer) ....AA
Meriden Curtain Fixture Co. (Shade) ....B
Rogers & Bros. Co. (Drawer) ....AAAA
CONN.—New Britain
Corbin, P. & F. (Door; Drawer) ....AAAA
Russell & Erwin Mfg. Co. (Door; Bell; Drawer; Window) ....AAAA
Stanley Works (Drawer) AAA
CONN.—New Haven
Mallory, Wheeler Co. (Door; Sliding Door) ....AA
Sargent & Co. (Door; Bell; Drawer; Screen; Window) AAAA
CONN.—Southington
Peck, Stow & Wilcox Co. (Drawer; Bell; Door; Screen) ....AAAA
CONN.—South Norwalk
Norwalk Lock Co. (Door).A

PULLS (Con.)

CONN.—Stamford
Yale & Towne Mfg. Co.
(Door; Bell; Sliding Door;
Drawer) ....AAAA
CONN.—Torrington
Turner & Seymour Mfg. Co.
(Shade) ....
Union Hdw. Co. (Bell)..AA
CONN.—Waterbury
American Ring Co. (Shade;
Drawer; Escutcheon) ..A
Benedict & Burnham Mfg.
Co. (Drawer) ......AAAA
Plume & Atwood Mfg. Co.
(Shade; Drawer) ...AAA
ILL.—Aurora
Wilcox Mfg. Co. (Door)..B
ILL.—Chicago
Barbee Wire & Iron Works
(Door) ....B
Chicago Spring Butt Co.,
491 Carroll Av. (Door).B
ILL.—Decatur
Mueller Mfg. Co., H. (Wood
Closet) ....AAA
ILL.—Freeport
Arcade Mfg. Co. (Drawer;
Door) ....A
Stover Mfg. Co. (Door;
Drawer; Screen Door).AA
ILL.—Sterling
National Mfg. Co. (Door).C
MASS.—Boston
Grundy Brass Works, 50
Sudbury (Closet) ....F
Young, Jos. H., 224 Frank-
lin (Closet) ....D
MASS.—Cambridge
Standard Turning Works
(Water Closet) C
MASS.—Worcester
Wire Goods Co. (Door;
Drawer) ....
MICH.—Detroit
Ideal Mfg. Co. (Wood
Closet) ....A
Ireland & Matthews Mfg.
Co. (Closet) ....A
MICH.—Grand Rapids
Grand Rapids Brass Co.
(Drawer; Escutcheon) .A
MINN.—St. Paul
Union Brass & Metal Mfg.
Co. (Wood Closet) ....A
N. J.—Newark
Bernz, Otto, S. 13th & S.
Orange Av. (Closet)....B
N. J.—Trenton
Maddock & Sons, Thos.
(Porcelain Closet) ...AA
Trenton Potteries Company
(Porcelain Closet) ..AAA
N. Y.—Albany
Troy Nickel Works (Jno.
E. Gaitley, Prop.) (Screen
Door) C
N. Y.—Elmira
Cronk & Carrier Mfg. Co.
(Door) ....B
N. Y.—Horseheads
Weller Hdw. & Fdy. Co.
(Door) ....D
New York City
Bardsley, Joseph (Drawer)
B
Emery, Wm. S., 94 Beek-
man (Wood Closet) ..B
Judd & Co., H. L. (Cur-
tain Chain; Shade)..AA
Kroder, John & Henry Reu-
bel Co. (Shade) ....A
Mott Iron Works, J. L., 88
Beekman (Porcelain
Closet) ....AA
Ostrander & Co., W. R., 22
Dey (Bell) ....D
Peck, Stow & Wilcox Co.,
27 Murray (Bell Box)
AAAA
Russell & Erwin Mfg. Co.,
43 Chambers (Bell)
AAAA
Sargent & Co., 151 Leonard
(Bell Box) ....AAAA
Tiebout, W. & J., 118
Chambers (Bell; Door).B
N. Y.—Syracuse
Stearns & Co., E. C. (Door)
AA
OHIO—Canton
Ney Mfg. Co. (Door) ....B

PULLS (Con.)

OHIO—Cincinnati
Vanduzen Co., E. W. (Bell)
B
OHIO—Cleveland
Chamberlain Cartridge &
Target Co. (Target;
Trap) ....A
Columbian Hdw. Co. (Door)
AA
Globe Machine & Stamping
Co. (Drawer) C
Taylor & Boggis Fdy. Co.
(Drawer) ....AA
OHIO—Piqua
Piqua Handle & Mfg. Co.
(Drawer) ....A
OHIO—Ravenna
Williams, A. C. (Drawer)
A
OHIO—Shelby
Shelby Spring Hinge Co.
(Drawer) ....B
PA.—Erie
Griffin Mfg. Co. (Drawer)
A
PA.—Philadelphia
Boekel & Co., Wm., 518
Vine (Closet) ....A
Stortz & Son, Jno., 210 Vine
(Closet) ....E
PA.—Reading
Penn. ; Hdw. Co. (Door)
Drawer) ....AA
Reading Hdw. Co. (Door;
Bell; Drawer; Screen;
Window) ....AAAA
PA.—Wrightsville
Wrightsville Hdw. Co.
(Drawer) ....B

PULP & FIBRE

CAL.—Floriston
Floriston Pulp & Paper Co.
(Ground Wood Pulp &
Sulphite Fibre, also Pa-
per) ....AA
CAL.—Towle
Pioneer Pulp Co. (Wood
Flour for Dynamite).AAA
COLO.—Denver
Rocky Mountain Paper Co.
(Sulphite Fibre) .....E
CONN.—Comstock's Bridge
Brown Bros. (Wood).....A
DEL.—Wilmington
Jessup & Moore Paper Co.
(Soda Fibre) .....AAAA
GA.—Marietta
Marietta Paper Mfg. Co.
(Wood) ....A
IND.—Hartford City
Hartford City Paper Co.
(Ground Wood, dry)...A
IND.—Marion
Marion Pulp Co. (Ground
Wood, dry) ....D
United Box Board & Paper
Co. (Ground Wood, dry)
AAAA
IND.—Muncie
Muncie Pulp Co. (Bleached
Soda Fibre) ....AA
MAINE—Augusta
Cushnox Paper Co. (Wood)
A
MAINE—Bangor
Orono Pulp & Paper Co.
(Wood) ....AA
MAINE—Enfield
International Paper Co.
(Ground Wood, dry)
AAAA
MAINE—Fairfield
United Box Board & Paper
Co. (Ground Wood)
AAAA
MAINE—Great Works
Penobscot Chemical Fibre
Co. (Soda Fibre, dry)..A
MAINE—Howland
Howland Pulp Co., The
(Sulphite Fibre) ....A
MAINE—Jay
International Paper Co.
(Ground Wood, dry)
AAAA
MAINE—Lincoln
Katahdin Pulp & Paper Co.
(Sulphite Fibre, dry)..A

PULP (*Con.*)

MAINE—Oldtown

Nekonegon Paper Co. (Ground Wood) C

MAINE—Portland

Androscoggin Pulp Co. (Wood) ....AA

Berlin Mills Co. (Paper) AAAA

MAINE—Riley

International Paper Co. (Ground Wood; also Paper) ....AAAA

MAINE—Rumford Falls

International Paper Co. (Soda & Sulphite Fibre; also Paper) ......AAAA

Oxford Paper Co. (Soda & Sulphite Fibre; also Paper) ....AAAA

MAINE—Shawmut

Lawrence, Newhall & Page Co. (Soda & Sulphite Fibre) ....A

MAINE—Skowhegan

Skowhegan Pulp Company (Ground Wood) ....D

MAINE—Solon

International Paper Co. (Ground Wood, dry) AAAA

MAINE—South Brewer

Eastern Mfg. Co. (Sulphite Fibre; Ground Wood; also Paper) ....A

MAINE—South Gardiner

International Paper Co. (Sulphite Fibre) ..AAAA

MAINE—South Windham

Androscoggin Pulp Company (Ground Wood) ......AA

MAINE—Winslow

Hollingsworth & Whitney Co. (Sulphite Fibre; also Paper) ....AAAA

MAINE—Yarmouthville

Forrest Paper Co. (S. D. Warren & Co., Boston, Mass Props) (Soda Fibre) AAAA

MD.—Elkton

Kenmore Pulp & Paper Co. (Soda Fibre) C

MD.—Luke

West Virginia Pulp & Paper Co. (Bleached Soda Fibre) AAAA

MASS.—Boston

Train, Smith &Co. (Wood) B

Wilder & Co. (Wood)...AA

MASS.—Farley

Farley Paper Co. (Ground Wood, dry) ....B

MASS.—Lawrence

Champion-International Co. (Soda & Sulphite Fibre) AAA

MASS.—Monroe

Ramage Paper Co., James (Wood) ....A

MASS.—Mt. Tom

Mt. Tom Sulphite Pulp Co. (Bleached Sulphite Fibre) A

MASS.—Turner's Falls

International Paper Co. (Ground Wood) ...AAAA

MICH.—Alpena

Fletcher Paper Co. (Ground Wood & Sulphite Fibre) AA

MICH.—Cheboygan

Cheboygan Paper Company (Ground Wood) ......AA

MICH.—Detroit

Detroit Sulphite Fibre Co. (Sulphite Fibre, dry)...A

MICH.—Jackson

Jackson Pulp Co. (Soda Fibre) ....A

MICH.—Menominee

Marinette & Menominee Paper Co. (Ground Wood, dry) ....AAA

MICH.—Munising

Munising Paper Co. (Sulphite Fibre) ....B

MICH.—Muskegon

Central Paper Co. (Sulphite Fibre; also Paper) ....A

MICH —Petoskey

Petoskey Fibre **Paper** Co.

PULP (*Con.*)

(Sulphite Fibre) ....A

MICH.—Port Huron

Michigan Sulphite Fibre Co. (Mitscherlich Process Sulphite Fibre) ....H

MINN.—Cloquet

Northwest Paper Company (Ground Wood) ....AAA

MINN.—Little Falls

Hennepin Paper Co. (Ground Wood) ....B

MINN.—Ypsilanti

Ypsilanti Paper Co. (Wood) B

N. H.—Berlin

Berlin Mills Co. (Ground Wood, dry) ......AAAA

Burgess Sulphite Fibre Co. (Bleached & Unbleached Sulphite Fibre, dry) AAAA

International Paper Co. (Sulphite Fibre) ......AAAA

N. H.—Bristol

Mason-Perkins Paper Co. (Ground Wood) ......A

N. H.—Franklin

International Paper Company (Ground Wood) AAAA

N. H.—Gorham

Berlin Mills Co. (Ground Wood; also Paper).AAAA

N. H.—Groveton

Odell Mfg. Co. (Sulphite Fibre; also Paper) ....A

N. H.—Lincoln

Henry & Son, J. E. (Sulphite Fibre) ....AAAA

N. H.—Plymouth

Livermore Falls Pulp Co. (Ground Wood, dry) AAAA

N. Y.—Ausable Chasm

Alice Falls Co. (Ground Wood, dry) ......AAAA

N. Y.—Ausable Fork

Rogers Co., J. & J. (Ground Wood & Sulphite) ..AAA

N. Y.—Ballston Spa

Union Bag & Paper Co. (Sulphite Fibre; also Paper) ....AAAA

N. Y.—Beaver Falls

Lewis Co., J. P. (Inc.) (Ground Wood; also Paper) ....B

Lewis, Slocum & Lefevre (Ground Wood) ....B

N. Y.—Binghamton

Bayless Pulp & Paper Co. (Paper) ....AA

N. Y.—Black River

Jefferson Paper Co. (Ground Wood, dry) ....A

Remington & Son Pulp & Paper Co., H. (Ground Wood) ....B

N. Y.—Brown's Station

Hudson River Wood Pulp Mfg. Co. (Ground Wood; Wood Flour for Dynamite, Linoleum, &c.)...D

N. Y.—Brownville

Brownville Paper Company (Ground Wood, dry)....B

Harmon Paper Co. (Ground Wood; also Paper) C

N. Y.—Cadyville

Internatl. Paper Company (Ground Wood) ...AAAA

N. Y.—Carthage

Carthage Sulphite Pulp Co. (Sulphite Fibre) ......B

Champion Paper Company (Ground Wood; also Paper) ....B

Island Paper Co. (Ground Wood, dry) ....B

N. Y.—Chateaugay

Chateaugay Pulp Company (Ground Wood) ....D

High Falls Pulp Co. (Ground Wood, dry)....B

N. Y.—Colton

Raquette River Pulp Co. (Ground Wood, dry) C

N. Y.—Deferiett

St. Regis Paper Co. (Ground Wood, dry; Sulphite Fibre; also Paper) .AAA

PULP (Con.)
N. Y.—Dexter
Dexter Sulphite Pulp & Paper Co. (Ground Wood) AA

N. Y.—Emeryville
Gouverneur Wood Pulp Co. (Ground Wood, dry)...B
N. Y.—Felts Mills
Taggarte Paper Co. (Ground Wood; also Paper) ....A
N. Y.—Fort Ann
Kanes Falls Pulp Company (Ground Wood, dry)...AA
N. Y.—Fort Edward
International Paper Co. (Ground Wood; Sulphite Fibre; also Paper).AAAA
N. Y.—Fort Miller
Fort Miller Pulp & Paper Co. (Ground Wood, dry; also Paper) ....B
N. Y.—Fullerville
Union Talc. Co. (Ground Wood, dry) ....AAA
N. Y.—Fulton
Battle Island Paper Co. (Sulphite Fibre, dry)...A
Fulton Paper Co. (Ground Wood, dry) C
United Box Board & Paper Co. (Ground Wood; Dry; also Paper) ....AAAA
N. Y.—Glens Falls
International Paper Co. (Ground Wood; also Paper) ....AAAA
N. Y.—Gouverneur
Gouverneur Wood Pulp Co. (Wood) ....B
N. Y.—Great Bend
Taggarts Paper Co. (Ground Wood, dry; also Paper).A
N. Y.—Hadley
Union Bag & Paper Co. (Ground Wood; also Paper) ....AAAA
N. Y.—Herring
Jefferson Power Co. (Sulphite Fibre) ....AA
N. Y.—Hinckley
Hinckley Fibre Co. (Sulphite Fibre) ....A
N. Y.—Lockport
United Box Board & Paper Co. (Ground Wood, dry; Sulphite Fibre; also Paper) ....AAAA
United Indurated Fibre Co. of N. J. (Ground Wood, dry) ....AA
N. Y.—Lyon Falls
Gould Paper Co. (Ground Wood) ....AAA
N. Y.—Lyonsdale
International Paper Co. (Ground Wood) ..AAAA
Moyer & Platt (Ground Wood, dry) ....E
N. Y.—Malone
Malone Paper Co. (Sulphite Fibre, wet) ....B
N. Y.—Mechanicsville
Duncan Co. (Sulphite Fibre; also Paper) ......AAAA
N. Y.—Napanoch
Napanoch Mfg. Co. (Wood Flour) ....D
N. Y.—Natural Dam
Aldrich Paper Co. (Ground Wood; Sulphite Fibre; also Paper) ....AA
N. Y.—Lyon Falls
Gould Paper Co. (Wood) AAA
N. Y.—Newton Falls
Newton Falls Paper Co. (Wood; Sulphite Fibre; Paper) ....A
New York City
Hudson River Wood Pulp Mfg. Co. (Wood) ....D
International Pulp Co., Times Bldg. (Asbestine) AAA
New York & Penna. Co. (Wood) ....AAAA
Perkins, Goodwin & Co. (Paper) ....AAA
Standard Pulp Co. (Wood) A
West Virginia Pulp & Paper

PULP (Con.)
Co. (Wood) ......AAAA
N. Y.—Niagara Falls
Cliff Paper Co. (Ground Wood, dry) ....AA
By-Products Paper Co. (Flax & Cotton Fibres).A
International Paper Co. (Sulphite Fibre; also Paper) ....AAAA
Pettebone-Cataract Paper Co. (Ground Wood, dry; also Paper) ......AAAA
N. Y.—Norfolk
Remington-Martin Co. (Sulphite Fibre; also Paper) A
N. Y.—Oswegatchie
Standard Pulp Co. (Ground Wood, dry) ....D
N. Y.—Palmer
International Paper Co. (Ground Wood; Sulphite Fibre) ....AAAA
N. Y.—Piercefield
International Paper Co. (Ground Wood; Sulphite Fibre; also Paper).AAAA
N. Y.—Potsdam
Racquette River Paper Co. AA
N. Y.—Pyrites
De Grasse River Paper Co. (Ground Wood; Sulphite Fibre) ....A
N. Y.—Rochester
Genesee Paper Co. (Ground Wood, Dry; also Paper), B
N. Y.—Sandy Hill
Allen Bros. Co. (Ground Wood; also Paper) ....A
Union Bag & Paper Co. (Sulphite Fibre; Paper Pulp) ....AAA
N. Y.—Schuylerville
United Box Board & Paper Co. (Ground Wood; also Paper) ....AAAA
N. Y.—South Edward
Carthage Tissue Paper Mills (Ground Wood, dry) ...B
N. Y.—Ticonderoga
International Paper Co. (Ground Wood, dry; also Paper) ....AAAA
Ticonderoga Pulp & Paper Co. (Soda Fibre; also Paper) ....AAA
N. Y.—Troy
Manning Paper Co., John A. (Wood) ....AA
Orr Co. (Wood) ....AA
N. Y.—Warrensburg
Schroon River Pulp & Paper Co. (Ground Wood, dry) ....A
N. Y.—Watertown
International Paper Co. (Ground Wood; Sulphite Fibre; also Paper).AAAA
Remington-Martin Company (Wood) ....AA
Taggart Bros. Co. (Wood) AA
N. Y.—Willsboro
N. Y. & Pa. Co. (Soda Fibre; also Paper) ..AAA
OHIO—Cleveland
Cleveland Paper Mfg. Co. (Ground Wood; also Paper) ....B
OHIO—Miamisburg
Ohio Paper Co. (Straw)..A
OHIO—Steubenville
Hartje Paper Mfg. Co. (Ground Wood; Sulphite Fibre; also Paper)..AAA
OHIO—West Carrellton
Friend Paper & Tablet Co. (Sulphite Fibre) ....AAA
OREGON—Oregon City
Crown Paper Co. (Sulphite Fibre) ....A
Williamette Pulp & Paper Co. (Sulphite Fibre; also Paper) ....AAA
PA.—Austin
Bayless Pulp & Paper Co. (Ground Wood; Sulphite Fibre; also Paper) ....AA
PA.—Catawissa
Penna. Paper Mills (Ground

PULP (Con.)

Wood; also Paper) .....B

PA.—Easton
Wagener & Co., Jno. O. (Mineral) ....A
Williams & Co., C. K. (Mineral) ....A

PA.—Erie
Hammermill Paper Co. (Sulphite Fibre; also Paper) ....AAA
Watson Co., H. F. (Ground Wood; also Paper).AAAA

PA.—Johnsonburgh
Highland Paper Co. (Soda Fibre) ....A
N. Y. & Pa. Co. (Bleached Sulphite) ....AAAA

PA.—Lock Haven
N. Y. & Pa. Co. (Soda Fibre; also Paper).AAAA

PA.—Philadelphia
Dill & Collins (Soda Fibre; also Paper) ....AAA
Nixon Paper Co., Martin & Wm. H. (Soda Fibre; also Paper) ....AAAA

PA.—Roaring Spring
Bare & Co. D. M. (Soda Fibre; also Paper).....A

PA.—Spring Forge
Glatfelter, P. H. (Soda Fibre; also Paper)..AAA

PA.—Williamsburg
Williamsburg Paper Mfg. Co. (Soda Fibre; also Paper) ....A

PA.—York Haven
York Haven Paper Co. (Ground Wood dry; Sulphite Fibre dry; also Paper) ....AA

S. C.—Hartsville
Carolina Fibre Co. (Ground Wood dry; Sulphite Fibre; also Paper).....A

TENN.—Memphis
Tenn. Fibre Co. (Cotton Hull Fibre, dry) ......D

TEXAS—Orange
Orange Paper Co. (Soda Fibre; also Paper) ....D

VT.—Bellows Falls
International Paper Co. (Ground Wood; Sulphite Fibre; also Paper).AAAA

VT.—Fitzdale
Dalton Paper Mills (Ground Wood; also Paper) ....A

VT.—Middlebury
Green Mountain Pulp Co. (Ground Wood, dry)....B

VT.—Milton
International Paper Co. (Ground Wood) ...AAAA

VT.—Readsboro
National Metal Edge Box Co. (Ground Wood; also Paper) ....A

VT.—Sheldon Springs
Missisquoi Pulp Company (Ground Wood, dry)....C

VT.—South Lunenburg
Dalton Paper Mills (Ground Wood, dry) ....A

VT.—West Derby
Spaulding Bros. (Wood)..B

VT.—Wilder
International Paper Co. (Ground Wood; also Paper) ....AAAA

VT.—Wilmington
Deerfield River Co. (Ground Wood, wet) ....B

VA.—Big Island
Bedford Pulp & Paper Co. (Ground Wood, dry)....B

VA.—Buena Vista
Columbia Paper Co. (Soda Fibre) ....AAA

VA.—Covington
West Virginia Pulp & Paper Co. (Bleached Sulphite Fibre) ......AAAA

WASH.—Camas
Columbia River Paper Co. (Wood) ....AA

WASH.—Everett
Everett Pulp & Paper Co. (Soda Fibre) ......AAA

W. VA.—Davis
West Virginia Pulp & Pa-

PULP (Con.)

per Co. (Bleached Sulphite Fibre) ....AAAA

W. VA.—Harpers Ferry
Harpers Ferry Paper Co. (Ground Wood, dry)....B
Shenandoah Pulp Company (Ground Wood, dry)....B

W. VA.—Parsons
Parsons Pulp & Paper Co. (Bleached & Unbleached Sulphite) ....B

WIS.—Appleton
Fox River Paper Co. (Wood) AA
Interlake Pulp & Paper Co. (Ground Wood) ......A
Marshall Paper Co. (Wood) B
Patten Paper Co. (Wood) A
Riverside Fibre & Paper Co. (Bleached & Unbleached Sulphite Fibre; also Paper) ....D
Wisconsin Tissue Paper Co. (Wood) ....B

WIS.—Ashland
Ashland Sulphite Fibre Co. (Sulphite Fibre) ....D

WIS.—Brokaw
Wausau Paper Mills Co. (Ground Wood; Sulphite Fibre) ....A

WIS.—Centralia
Centralia Pulp & Water Power Co. (Ground Wood, dry) ....A

WIS.—Combined Locks
Combined Locks Paper Co. (Sulphite Fibre)....AAA

WIS.—Eau Claire
Dells Paper & Pulp Co. (Sulphite Fibre)....AAA

WIS.—Grand Rapids
Centralia Pulp & Water Power Co. (Wood) .....A
Consolidated Water Power & Paper Co. (Ground Wood; also Paper) ...AA
Grand Rapids Pulp & Paper Co. (Ground Wood, dry; also Paper) ....A
Pioneer Wood Pulp Co. (Ground Wood; also Paper) ....D

WIS.—Green Bay
Green Bay Paper Co. (Sulphite Fibre) ....B

WIS.—Kaukuna
Kaukuna Fibre Co. (Sulphite Fibre, dry)......C
Lindauer Pulp Co. (Ground Wood) ....E
Owtagamie Paper Company (Ground Wood) ......A
Thilmany Pulp & Paper Co. (Ground Wood) ....A
Union Bag & Paper Co. (Ground Wood) ...AAAA

WIS.—Kimberly
Kimberly & Clark Co. (Sulphite Fibre) ......AAAA

WIS.—Ladysmith
Menasha Paper Co. (Ground Wood; also Paper) ....A

WIS.—Marinette
Marinette & Menominee Paper Co. (Wood; Sulphite Fibre) ....AAA

WIS.—Menasha
Howard Co., C. W. (Sulphite Fibre; also Paper) A

WIS.—Neenah
Atlas Paper Co. (Paper) AA
Kimberly & Clark Co. (Wood) ....AAAA
Telulah Paper Co. (Wood) AA

WIS.—Nekoosa
Nekoosa Paper Co. (Ground Wood; Sulphite Fibre) AA

WIS.—Oconto Falls
Falls Mfg. Co. (Sulphite Fibre, dry) ....A
Union Mfg. Co. (Ground Wood) ....D

WIS.—Park Falls
Flambeau Paper Company

PULP (Con.)
(Ground Wood; also Paper) ....A
WIS.—Fort Edwards
Edwards Mfg. Co., John (Spruce & Poplar Ground Wood; also Paper).....A
WIS.—Shawano
Wolf River Paper & Fibre Co. (Sulphite Fibre, dry; also Paper) ....A
WIS.—Stevens Point
Wisconsin River Paper & Pulp Co. (Ground Wood, dry; also Paper) ......A

PULPERS

See also Machy

N. Y.—Buffalo
Squier Mfg. Co., Geo. L. (Coffee) ....AAA
N. C.—Winston-Salem
Salem Iron Works (Coffee) A
OHIO—Cincinnati
Blymyer Iron Works Co. (Coffee) ....B
WIS.—Manitowoc
Smalley Mfg. Co. (Vegetable) ....B

PULPITS

See also Furniture

MASS.—Boston
Davenport Co., Albert H. AA
MICH.—Detroit
Amos & Co., Chas. A., 94 W. Larned (Brass)....E
MO.—Lexington
Winkler Furniture Co.....D
MO.—St. Louis
Prufrock, Wm., 1441 N. 6th ....A
New York City
Church Art Work Co., 253 4th Av. X
Masset, A., 78 E. 10th (Brass) ....D
Stoltzenberg Co. ....B

PULVERIZERS

See also Crushers; Mills; Machy; Agr. Imps

DEL.—Wilmington
Walker & Elliot ....B
ILL.—Chicago
Allis-Chalmers Co., Home Ins. Bldg. (Ore; Clay) AAAA
Kaestner & Co. (Drug; Stone, &c.) ....A
Raymond Bros. Impact Pulverizer Co. (Drug; Stone, &c.) ....D
IND.—Aurora
Stedman Fdy. & Mach. Works ....B
IND.—Indianapolis
Over, Ewald C
KANS.—Ft. Scott
Ft. Scott Fdy. & Mach. Co. H
MASS.—Boston
Bradley Pulverizer Co. (Mining) X
Sturtevant Co., B. F. (Grinding) ....AAA
MINN.—Minneapolis
Schultz-O'Neil Co. (Coffee; Sugar; Spice) C
N. Y.—Brooklyn
Hoachin & Huber.........D
Simpson, J. S. & G. F. (Grinding) ....A
N. Y.—Buffalo
Squier Mfg. Co., Geo. L. (Sugar) ....AAA
N. Y.—Newburgh
Coldwell-Wilcox Co. (Asphalt) ....B
New York City
Abbe Engineering Co. (Drug; Stone, etc.) .....D
Alsing & Co., J. R. (Drug; Stone, etc.). X

PULVERIZERS (Con.)
OHIO—Canton
Bucher-Gibbs Plow Co...AA
OHIO—Cleveland
Bartlett & Snow Co., C. O. (Drug; Stone, etc.) ....A
OHIO—Cuyahoya Falls
Turner, Vaughn & Taylor Co. (Ore; Clay).......B
OHIO—Fremont
Lehr Agrl. Co. ....B
OHIO—Hamilton
Deuscher Co., H. P......A
OHIO—Springfield
Foos Mfg. Co..............A
PA.—Philadelphia
Campbell, P. F. (Drug; Stone, etc.) ....D
PA.—Pittsburg
Garrison Fdry. Co., A. (Ore; Clay; Priming) ....AAA
S. C.—Charleston
Valk & Murdock Iron Wks. (Grinding) C
WIS.—Beloit
Thompson & Sons Mfg. Co., J. ....AA
WIS.—Janesville
Janesville Mach. Co. (Rotary Disk) ....AA
WIS.—Milwaukee
Allis-Chalmers Co....AAAF

PUMICE

ILL.—Chicago
Rhodes & Co., Jas. H.....C
Thurston & Co., F. W..A
New York City
Behr & Co., Herman, 75 Beekman (Stone).....AA
Waddell & Co., R. J....AA
Wetmore Co., S. H., 240 Pearl (Toilet) ....D
PA.—Eaton
Williams & Co., C. K. (Pulverized) ....A
PA.—Pittsburg
Finkell-Hachmeister Chemical Co. ....D

PUMPKIN

See Canned Goods

PUMPS

See also Machy

CAL.—Los Angeles
Luitwieler Pumping Engine Co. (Non-Pulsating Balanced Artesian Well; Centrifugal; Deep Well; Non-Pulsating Balanced Electric; Elevator; Non-Pulsating Mining; Non-Pulsating Tank; Non-Pulsating Water Works)......D
CAL.—San Francisco
Dow Pumping Engine Co., Geo. E., 179 1st (Air; Electric; Irrigating; Mining; Steam) ....AA
Evans & Co., C. H. (Deep Well; Power; Steam)..C
Garratt & Co., W. T., 138 Fremont (Air; Centrifugal; Deep Well; Electric; Elevator; Mining; Steam) AA
Hendy Machine Wks., Josh. 38 Fremont (Cornish; Sinking; Steam)......AA
Jackson Machine Wks., Byron, 411 Market (Centrifugal; Sand; Dredging; Steam) ....A
Krogh Mfg. Co. (Wind Mill) ....A
Moore &Co., Chas. C., 32 1st (Steam) ....AA
Pacafic Pump & Windmill Co. (Windmill) C
Risdon Iron & Locomotive Wks. (Centrifugal; Ship; Hydraulic) ....AAAA
San Francisco Tool Wks. (Centrifugal; Irrigating) E
Union Iron Wks., 222 Market (Air; Condenser;

PUMPS (Con.)

Cornish; Steam) X
Wood & Little (Windmill)
.............................A
Yeatman & Co., Jno. A., 13
1st (Centrifugal; Sand;
Dredging) X

CAL.—San Jose
Bean Spray Pump Co.
(Spray; Chain) ....D

COLO.—Denver
Mine & Smelter Supply Co.
(Mining; Sinking).AAAA
Stearns-Rogers Mfg. Co.
(Electric) ....A

CONN.—Ansonia
Farrell Fdry. & Machine Co.
(Hydraulic) ....AAAA

CONN.—Bridgeport
Bridgeport Brass Co. (Bi-
cycle; Brass) ....AAA
Bridgeport Gun Implement
Co. (Bicycle) ....AA

CONN.—Bristol
New Departure Mfg. Co.
(Bicycle) ....AAA

CONN.—Collinsville
Hartigan, Wm. R. (Bi-
cycle) ....H

CONN.—Derby
Birmingham Iron Fdry.
(Hydraulic) ....AA

CONN.—Hartford
Davis & Son, I. B. (Boiler
Feed; Power; Plumbers'
.............................A
Hartford Mach. Screw Co.
(Rotary) ....AAAA
Noppel Pump Co. (Plumb-
ers' Force) ....D
Rhodes, L. E., 28 High (Air
Lift; Automatic; Cistern;
Pneumatic) ....F

CONN.—Midletown
Douglas, W. & B. (Air;
Boiler Feed; Boiler Test-
ing; Brass; Centrifugal;
Cistern; Contractors' for
Sewers; Foundations;
Electric; Elevator; Force;
Lift; Hydraulic; Mining;
Plumbers'; Spray; Steam;
Sugar House; Windmill;
Wrecking; Anti-Freezing;
Beer; Ale; Brewery; Cel-
lar; Chain; Greenhouse
Force; Hand; Porcelain-
Lined; High Pressure;
Horse Power; Bilge;
Boat; Ship; Molasses;
Stuff; Hand Section; Ar-
tesian Well; Drive Well)
.............................A

CONN.—New Britain
Union Mfg. Co. (Brass;
Centrifugal; Chain; Cis-
tern; Copper; Force; Lift;
Plumbers'; Barrel; Beer;
Ale; Hand; Boiler Feed;
Garden; Iron; Power; Ro-
tary; Well; Drive Well;
Windmill) ....AA

CONN.—New Haven
Foskett & Bishop Co. (Cop-
per; Force; Lift) ......B
Peck Bros. & Co. (Beer;
Ale; Plumbers') ......AA

CONN.—Norwich
Norwich Belt Mfg. Co.
(Hydraulic Test) ......A

CONN.—South Norwalk
Norwalk Iron Wks. Co. (Air
Lift; Natural Gas; Com-
pressing; Steam)....AAA

CONN.—Thompsonville
Bushnell Press Co., G. H.
(Hydraulic; Steam) ...A

CONN.—Torrington
Union Hdw. Co. (Contrac-
tors, for Sewers; Founda-
tions by Hand Power;
Diaphragm; Hand Suc-
tion) ....AA

CONN.—Waterbury
Scovill Mfg. Co. (Boiler
Testing; Bicycle).AAAA
Waterbury Farrell Fdry.
Machine Co. (Power)..AA

CONN.—Windsor Locks
Windsor Locks Machine Co.
(Stuff) ....E

PUMPS (Con.)

DEL.—Wilmington
Henderer's Sons, A. L.
(Boiler Testing) ....E

D. C.—Washington
Emerson Steam Pump Co.,
Mertz Bldg. (Steam Va-
cuum) X

GA.—Savannah
Kehoe & Sons, Wm.
(Steam) ....A

ILL.—Aurora
Amer. Well Wks. (Deep
Well; Mining; Steam;
Windmill; Artesian Well)
.............................AA

ILL.—Batavia
Appleton Mfg. Co. (Irri-
gating) ....A
Challenge Windmill & Feed
Mill Co. (Irrigating;
Tank; Wooden; Windmill)
.............................AAA
Snow Mfg. Co. (Wind-
mill) ....E
U. S. Wind Engine & Pump
Co. (Artesian Well; Cis-
tern; Irrigating; Tank;
Windmill; Drainage;
Hand Lawn Force; Hand;
Brass; Iron; Porcelain-
Lined; Wooden; Horse
Power; Low Pressure;
Plantation; Power; Hand
Suction; Quarry; Deep
Well; Well Force)....AA

ILL.—Bushnell
Bushnell Pump Co. (Tank;
Hand) ....B

ILL.—Chicago
Allis-Chalmers Co., Home
Ins. Bldg. (Air; Cornish;
Irrigating; Mining; Boiler
Feed; Steam) ....AAAA
Austin Mfg. Co., Manhattan
Bldg. (Steam) ......AAA
Baragwanath & Son, Wm.,
52 W. Division (Boiler
Feed; Steam Boiler Feed)
.............................C
Barber & Co., A. H. (Com-
bined; Creamery Engine)
.............................A
Brewers' & Bottlers' Machy.
Wks. (Beer) ....G
Burdett-Rountree Mfg. Co.,
85 W. Jackson Boul.
(Electric Air) ....B
Contractors Supply & Equip-
ment Co., 232 5th Av.
(Quarry) ....B
Crane Co. (Centrifugal)
.............................AAAA
Davis-Johnson Co., 41 W.
Randolph (Centrifugal;
Rotary) ....D
Elmes Engineering Wks.,
Chas. F., cor. N. Morgan
& Fulton (Hydraulic)...A
Erwin & Co., 35 S. Canal
(Automatic; Electric)..B
Fairbanks, Morse & Co.,
Franklin & Monroe (Air;
Belt-Driven; Bilge; Boiler
Feed; Centrifugal; Arte-
sian Well; Cistern; Deep
Well; Elevator; Filter
Press; Hydraulic; Irrigat-
ing; Mining; Power;
Quarry; Steam; Sugar
House; Tank; Tar; Va-
cuum; Water Works;
Windmill; Anti-Freezing;
Drainage; Greenhouse
Force; Iron; Pitcher; Ro-
tary; Hand Suction; Drive
Well) ....AAAA
Goetz & Flodin Mfg. Co.
(Beer) ....A
Goodman Mfg. Co., 39th &
Stewart Av. (Electric;
Elevator) ....AA
Illinois Malleable Iron Co.,
30 W. Monroe (Brass)..
.............................A 'AA
Kaestner & Co., (Rotary;
Air; Beer; Pressur)...A
Laubenheimer Co., Geo. H.
(Beer) ....D
Lindgren, Mahan Fire Ap-
paratus Wks. (Fire)....X
Liquid Carbonic Acid Mfg.

PUMPS (*Con.*)
Co. (Beer; Ale) ..AAAA
Marsh & Co., James P.
(Hydraulic Test) ......B
Nye Steam Pump & Mach.
Co., 70 W. Washn.
(Wrecking) X
Perrin & Co., Wm. R., 1500
46th (Hydraulic; Rotary)
..........................A
Scott Valve Co., 32 W.
Randolph (Air; Steam).D
Shaw, Willis, N. Y. Life
Bldg. (Centrifugal) ....E
Stier Mfg. Co., Herman
(Beer) ....D
Temple Pump Co. (Chain;
Windmill; Wooden; Puri-
fying; Rubber Bucket), A
Trenkhorst, Frank (Beer).F
Union Elevator & Mach. Co.
144 Ontario (Centrifugal;
Contractors' for Sewers;
Foundations; Diaphragms)
..........................C
Weir & Craig Mfg. Co.,
2439 Wallace (Boiler Feed
Creamery Hydraulic; Min-
ing; Steam) ....D
Wells Steam Pump Wks.,
F. C., 116 S. Clinton (Air;
Acid; Steam Boiler Feed;
Hydraulic; Mining; Sugar
House; Steam; Tank;
Water Works; Gas
Works; Brewery; Circu-
lating; Combined Air Cir-
culating; Combined Boiler
Pump; Combined Vaccum
Water; Distillery Drain-
age; Fire; Hotel; Hy-
draulic Pressure; Irrigat-
ing; Lard; Locomotive;
Low Pressure; Marine;
Oil; Oil Line; Quarry;
Soap; Plunger; Hand Suc-
tion; Tannery; Vacuum;
Vinegar; Wrecking)..AA
Wilson & Co., F. Cortez
(Galvanized; Brass; Cop-
per; Measuring; Oil; Tin)
..........................B
Wolf Co., Fred W. (Ice
Manufacturing; Sugar
House) ....AAA
ILL.—Decatur
Decatur Lumber & Mfg. Co.
(Wooden) ....B
Oakes, Wm. L. (Steam)..D
ILL.—Du Quoin
Blakeslee Mfg. Co. (Inc.)
(Air; Bilge; Boiler Feed;
Elevator; Hydraulic; Irri-
gating; Mining; Steam;
Tank; Vacuum; Wreck-
ing; Acid; Brewery; Fire;
Jet; Marine; Oil; Quarry;
Sugar House; Tannery;
Duplex Steam) ....B
ILL.—Elgin
Elgin Wind Power & Pump
Co. (Windmill) ....B
ILL.—Evanston
Comstock, A. S. (Motor-
Driven Air) C
ILL.—Freeport
Stover Mfg. Co. (Irrigat-
ing) ....AA
Woodmanse Mfg. Co.
(Hand) ....A
ILL.—Galesburg
Frost Mfg. Co. (Steam)..B
May Bros. (Force) ......B
ILL.—Galva
Hayes Pump & Planter Co.
(Cistern; House; Wind-
mill; Force; Lift; Tank;
Chain; Rotary Force)..A
ILL.—Grafton
Rippley Hdw. Co. (Spray-
ers) C
ILL.—Harvey
Austin Mfg. Co., F. C.
(Hand; Steam; Irrigat-
ing) ....AAA
ILL.—Kewanee
Peters Pump Co. (Tank;
Windmill) ....A
ILL.—Moline
Moline Pump Co. (Hand
Power Feed; Cistern;
Force; Lift; Windmill;

PUMPS (*Con.*)
Chain; Wooden; Hand
Suction) ....A
ILL.—Ottawa
Porter Co., J. E. (Force;
Lift; Spray; Tank)....A
ILL.—Peoria
Avery Planter Co. (Hand)
......................AAA
ILL.—Quincy
Gardner Governor Co. (Boil-
er Feed; Elevator; Tank;
Steam) ....AA
ILL.—Rockford
Love Mfg. Co., M. A.
(Tank) ....B
Trahern Pump Co. (Force;
Lift; Spray; Tank; Iron)
..........................A
Ward Pump Co. (Irrigating;
Tank) ....B
ILL.—Sandwich
Sandwich Mfg. Co. (Spray;
Hand Force; Iron; Wind-
mill) ....AA
ILL.—Springfield
Aetna Fdry. & Mach. Co.
(Boiler Feed; Steam)..B
ILL.—Sterling
Charter Gas Engine Co.
(Irrigating) ....A
Novelty Iron Wks. (Force;
Lift) ....E
IND.—Anderson
Hill Machine Co. (Boiler
Feed; Deep Well; Juice;
Mining; Power; Steam;
Hand Force; Hydraulic
Pressure; Tank; Water
Motor) ....E
IND.—Brazil
Crawford & McCrimmon Co.
(Boiler Feed; Mining;
Steam) ....A
IND.—Butler
Butler Co. (Windmill)....B
ND.—Connersville
Connersville Blower Co.
(Rotary Force) ....A
Roots Co., P. H. & F. M.
(Boiler Feed; Electric;
Elevator; Irrigating; Min-
ing; Pneumatic; Force
Rotary; Steam; Sugar
House; Tank; Water
Works; Wrecking; Air;
Air Pressure; Rotary
Fire; Gas; Rotary)..AA
IND.—Fort Wayne
Bowser Co., S. F. (Varnish;
Paint; Oil) ....A
Wayne Mfg. Co., Anthony
(Oil) X
IND.—Goshen
I. X. L. & Goshen Pump
Co. (Chain; Wooden; Por-
celain-Lined) ....B
Kelly Fdry. & Machine Co.
(Tank) ....A
IND.—Green Castle
Cole Bros. Lightning Rod
Co. (Wooden) ....A
IND.—Indianapolis
Armstrong & Co., Wm. H.
(Stomach) ....B
Commercial Electric Co.
(Electric) ....A
Dean Bros. Steam Pump
Wks. (Twin Cylinder Air;
Boiler Feed; Elevator;
Mining; Steam; Sugar
House; Vacuum; Wreck-
ing; Brewery; Circulating
Combined; Boiler; Pump;
Distillery; Duplex Fly-
wheel; Fire; Duplex
Steam; Plunger; Tank;
Well; Artesian; Deep
Well) ....AA
Everett, J. A. (Sprayers;
Power Distributors)....B
IND.—Kendallville
Flint & Walling Mfg. Co.
(Artesian Well; Cistern;
Force; Lift; Irrigating;
Orchard Spray; Tank;
Windmill; Hand Brass;
Iron; Mining; Pitcher;
Power; Rotary; Hand
Suction; Well; Deep
Well) ....AA

PUMPS (Con.)

IND.—Lafayette
Biggs Pump Co., B. F. (Chain; Hand; Wooden) ....A

IND.—Lowrenceburg
Cook, A. D. (Artesian Well; Steam; Hand Suction; Tank) ....B

IND.—Mishawaka
Perkins Windmill Co. (Windmill) ....A

IOWA—Burlington
Murray Iron Wks. Co. (Steam) ....A

IOWA—Cedar Falls
Harris & Cole Bros. (Wooden) ....AA

IOWA—Cedar Rapids
Cedar Rapids Pump Co. (Chain; Cistern; Spray; Tank) ....AA
Chandler Pump Co. (Windmill) ....AA
Cherry Co., J. G. (Combined; Creamery Engine)

IOWA—Davenport
Red Jacket Mfg. Co. (Force; Lift; Irrigating; Spray; Tank; Rubber Bucket Chain; Hand; Windmill) ....A

IOWA—Des Moines
Dempster Mfg. Co. (Tank; Windmill) .... B
Globe Machy. & Supply Co. 418 W. Court Av. (Steam) B

IOWA—Dubuque
McDonald & Morrison Mfg. Co., A. Y. (Brass; Chain; Force; Lift; Spray; Tank; Cistern; Wooden; Pitcher; Well; Windmill) AA
Smedley Steam Pump Co. (Steam) ....B

KANS.—Enterprise
Ehrsam & Sons Mfg. Co., J. B. (Hand) ....B

KANS.—Fort Scott
Fort Scott Fdry. & Machine Co. (Elevator; Horse Power) ....H

KANS.—Leavenworth
Great Western Mfg. Co. (Rotary Force; Power; Irrigating; Mining; Rotary) ....AA

KY.—Louisville
Natl. Fdry. & Mach. Co. (Acid; Air; Ammonia; Artesian Well; Boiler Feed; Deep Well; Elevator; Gas Compressing; Hydraulic; Irrigating; Mining; Steam; Sugar House; Tank; Vacuum; Water Works; Wrecking) A

LA.—New Orleans
Coleman, H. Dudley (Cellar; Centrifugal; Steam) ..D

MD.—Baltimore
Crook-Horner & Co., 303 N. Howard (Brass; Force; Lift) ....A
Regester & Sons, J. (Steam Boiler Feed) ....A

MASS.—Andover
Tyer Rubber Co. (Breast) AA

MASS.—Athol
Athol Pump Co. (Cistern; Copper; Force; Lift)...H

MASS.—Boston
Ashton Valve Co. (Hydraulic Test) ....A
Boston & Lockport Block Co., 142 Commercial (Ship; Diaphragm; Rubber Diaphragm) ....A
Crosby Steam Gauge & Valve Co., 95 Oliver (Boiler Testing; Air; Steam Boiler Feed; Railway; Hydraulic Test) .AA
Davidson Rubber Co. (Breast) ....A
Edson Mfg. Co., 257 Atlantic Av. (Contractors' for Sewers; Foundations;

PUMPS (Con.)

Force; Lift; Diaphragm; Manhole; Mine Sinking; Mining; Prospecting; Ship Deck; Drainage Hand Hand Force; Marine Bilge Boat; Hand Suction; Tannery; Trench; Odorless Vault; Cesspool) ......B
Hersey Mfg. Co., 314 W. 2d (Soap Rotary; Acid; Beer; Ale; Brewery; Distillery; Force; Rotary Force; Iron; Lard; Molasses; Oil Refinery; Plantation; Power; Juice; Rotary; Sugar House; Syrup; Tannery)......AA
Mason Regulator Co., 6th & Olive (Air; Boiler Feed; Steam) ....A
Morse & Son, Andrew J. (Fire) ....B
Strater & Sons, Herman (Air; Beer; Ale).......A
Walworth Mfg. Co., 132 Federal (Steam; Steam Boiler Fed) ....AAAA

MASS.—Fitchburg
Blake Steam Pump Co., W. H. (Boiler Feed; Steam; Tank) X

MASS.—Florence
Norwood Engineering Co. (Steam Boiler Feed)...B

—Haydenville
Haydenville Co. (Brass; Force; Lift; Beer; Ale; Hand Suction) ....A

MASS.—Holliston
Wilder & Co., Sidney (Air Chamber; Cistern; Copper; Deep Well; Force; Lift; Hand) ....E

MASS.—Holyoke
Deane Steam Pump Co. (Acid; Admiralty; Air; Ammonia; Beer; Ale; Bleaching; Steam Boiler Feed; Brewery; Circulating; Cistern; Combined Boilers; Pumps; Combined Vacuum; Water; Crank; Distillery; Mash; Drainage; Duplex Flywheel; Electric; Elevator.. Filter Press; Steam Force; Fire; Fountain; High Pressure; Hydraulic; Ice Manufacturing; Irrigating; Lard; Low Pressure; Marine; Bilge; Boat; Ship; Mining; Sinking; Molasses; Oil Line; Oil; Oil Refinery; Oil Tank; Paper Mill; Plantation; Pulp Mill; Quarry; Sewerage; Steam; Stuff; Compound Steam; Plunger; Duplex Steam; Sugar House; Tank; Tannery; Syrup; Vacuum; Vinegar; Well; Artesian; Deep Well; Windmill; Wrecking; Soap) ....AAAA
Holyoke Machine Co. (Hydraulic; Rotary; Fire; Rotary; Power; Size)....AA

MASS.—Lawrence
Emerson Mfg. Co. (Centrifugal) C
Lawrence Machine Co. (Centrifugal; Contractors' for Sewers; Foundations; Electric; Sand; Dredging; Steam; Acid; Steam Boiler Feed; Brewery; Irrigating; Mining; Tank) X
Lowell Machine Shop (Hydraulic) ....AAAA

MASS.—Newburyport
Russell & Sons, Albert (Fire; Marine; Sewerage) C

MASS.—Orange
Hunt-Rodney Mach. Co. (Rotary; Rotary Fire).A

MASS.—Pittsfield
Jones & Son Co., E. D. (Steam Boiler Feed; Fire; Rotary Fire; Ro-

PUMPS (Con.)
draulic; High Duty Hy-
draulic Elevator Service)
..................B
Mattson Rubber Co.
(Breast) ....E
Mietz, August, 128 Mott
(Force & Lift) ....A
Nason Mfg. Co., 71 Bleek-
man (Boiler Feed; Brass;
Force & Lift; Combined
Heater & Boiler; Siphon)
..................B
New York Air Brake Co.,
66 B'way (Air; Electric;
Vacuum) ....AAAA
New York Safety Steam
Power Co. (Combined
Boiler & Heater) ......B
Pierce Well Engineering &
Supply Co., 136 Liberty
(Well; Windmill; Deep
Well; Artesian Well)..D
Power Specialty Co., 126
Liberty Irrigation) .....E
Pulsometer Steam Pump
Co., 135 Greenwich (Min-
ing; Steam; Contractors';
for Sewers & Founda-
tions) ....D
Quimby, W. E., (Inc.))141
B'way (Automatic; Belt-
Driven; Direct Connected
Electric; Elevator; Oil;
Power; Sinking; Sugar
House; Tank) ....B
Rand Drill Co., 128 B'way
(Air Lift) ......AAAA
Reilley Bros. (Painters'
Oil) ....D
Reynolds Plumbers' Supply
Co., M., 25 Centre (Brass;
Force & Lift) ....B
Sands & Son, Alfred B., 134
Bleekman (Copper; Ship
& Dek; Brass; Bilge) .D
Schneible Co., Jos. (Brew-
ers' Air; Pressure) .....B
Steeger, Henry (Gas Main
Foring) ....A
Stoutenborough, X. (Cellar;
Boat; Tin) ....D
Toombs, Samuel (Beer &
Ale) ....A
Trageser Steam Copper
Wks., Jno (Bicycle) ..B
Watson-Stillman Co., 210
E. 43d (Hydraulic;
Steam; Hydrostatic Press)
..................A
Wheeler Condenser & En-
gineering Co., 120 Liber-
ty (Air for Marine En-
gines; Improved Centrifu-
gal; Steam) ....A
Worthington Pumping En-
gine Co. (Acid; Air; Ad-
miralty; Duplex Air; Am-
monia; Bleaching; Steam,
Boiler Feed; Brewery; Air
Pressure; Circulating;
Cistern; Combined Air &
Boiler Feed; Combined
Air & Circulating; Com-
bined Boilers & Pumps;
Combined Injection & Re-
frigerators; Combined
Vacuum & Water; Cooler;
Cotton Press; Crank;
Diaphragm; Distillery;
Mash; Drainage; Duplex;
Elevator; Fire; Rotary
Fire Steam Force; High
Pressure; Hydraulic Ice
Manufacturing; Irriga-
ting; Lard; Low Press-
ure; Marine; Bilge; Ship;
Mining; Sinking; Oil
Line; Oil Refiery; Oil
Tank; Power; Juice; Sew-
erage; Salt Water; Com-
pound; Duplex & Vertical
Steam; Sugar House;
Tank; Tannery; Syrup;
Hydraulic Test; Vacuum;
Wrecking) ......AAAA
N. Y.—Niagara Falls
Dobbie Fdry. & Mach. Co.
(Centrifugal) ....D
N. Y.—North Tonawanda
Buffalo Steam Pump Co.
(Power; Steam; Tank) A

PUMPS (Con.)
N. Y.—Oswego
Kingsford Fdry. & Mach.
Wks. (Centrifugal; Steam
Wrecking) ....AAAA
N. Y.—Rochester
Clark Novelty Co. (Va-
cuum) ....D
Sargent & Greenleaf Co.
Vacuum) ....AA
N. Y.—Rome
Rome Mfg. Co. (Bicycle &
Auto) ....B
N. Y.—Sandy Hill
Friction Pulley & Mach.
Co. (Centrifugal for Pap-
er Mills, etc.; Stuff) ..B
Sandy Hill Iron & Brass
Wks. (Fan; Stuff) ....A
N. Y.—Schenectady
General Electric Co. (Elec-
tric) ....AAAA
N. Y.—Seneca Falls
Amer.-La rrance Fire En-
gine Co. (Fire; Piston &
Rotary Fire; Rotary
Force; Garden Sprink-
ling; Power; Quarry;
Wrecking) ....B
Gleason-Bailey & Sciple
Mfg. Co. (Ltd.) (Boiler
Feed; Cistern; Force; Hy-
draulic; Anti-Freezing;
Beer & Ale; Centrifugal;
Chain; Hydraulic Press-
ure) ....D
Goulds Mfg. Co. (Air; Boil-
er Feed; Boiler Testing;
Brass; Centrifugal; Cis-
tern; Cornish; Deep Well;
Electric; Elevator.. Lift;
Force; Hydraulic; Irrigat-
ing; Mining; Plumbers';
Rotary; Ship; Deck;
Spray Steam; Sugar
House; Tank; Hydraulic
Test; Vacuum; Windmill;
Ammonia; Centrifugal;
Fire; Rotary Force; Gar-
den Sprinkling; Gas En-
gine; Power; Vertical
Steam; Hand Suction)....
..................AAA
Rumsey & Co. (Ltd.) (Inc.)
(Air; Boiler Feed; Dia-
phragm; Electric; Eleva-
tor; Force & Lift; Hy-
draulic; Irrigating; Min-
ing; Plumber's; Ship &
Deck; Steam; Sugar
House; Tank; Windmill;
Ammonia; Anti-Freezing;
Beer & Ale; Hand Boiler
Feed; Fire; Rotary Fire;
Hand Rotary Force;
Fountain; Garden Sprink-
ling; Portable, Orchard
Force; Spray and Sprink-
ling; Gas Drp; Green-
house; Ham; Hand Brass
& Iron; Horse Power;
Hydraulic Pressure;
Bilge & Ship; Molasses;
Oil; Pitcher; Power &
Pulp Mill; Rotary; Hand
Suction; Hydraulic Test;
Well; Well Force &
Drive Well) ....A
N. Y.—Syracuse
Baldwinsville Centrifugal
Pump Wks., 715 W. Fay-
ette (Electric; Belt-
Driven; Boiler Feed; Cen-
trifugal; Contractors' for
Sewers; Foundations;
Creamery; Deep Well;
Gas Engine Starting; Hy-
draulic Dredging; Irrigat-
ing; Sand; Dredging;
Steam; Wrecking; Bleach-
ing; Circulating; Com-
bined; Mash; Elevator;
Filter Press; Brass; Min-
ing; Power; Paper Mill;
Quarry.. Salt Water;
Sewerage; Plunger; Tan-
nery; Triplex; Artesian
Well; Deep Well) C
Boomer & Boschert Press
Co. (Hydraulic) ....A
Howard & Jennings (Rub-
ber Bucket; Chain; Wood-
en) ....D

PUMPS (Con.)

Van Wie, Irvin (Suction).C

N. Y.—Troy

Bernard Co., E. G. (Elevtric) ....D

Knowleson & Kelly (Steam) B

N. Y.—Utica

Childs & Co., Chas. H. (Electric Spray) ....A

Eureka Mower Co. (Atomizers) ....A

Millar & Son Co., Chas. (Force; Lift) ....AA

Smith & Co., D. B. (Bicycle; Spray) .....B

N. Y.—Watertown

Bagley & Sewell Co. (Rotary & Reciprocating Stuff) ....AA

N. C.—Charlotte

Mecklenburg Iron Wrks. (Mining) X

N. C.—Hickory

Latta-Martin Pump Co. (Pneumatic) ....D

OHIO—Akron

Webster Camp & Lane Mach. Co. (Mining) ....AAAA

Whitman & Barnes Mfg. Co. (Spray; Tank) ....AAAA

OHIO—Alliance

Morgan Engineering Co. (Hydraulic) ....AAAA

OHIO—Ashland

Myers & Bro., F. E. (Boiler Feed; Cistern; Deep Well; Force; Lift; Irrigating; Power; Spray; Syphon; Tank; Windmill; Hand Suction) ....AAAA

OHIO—Canton

Berger Mfg. Co. (Spray; Orchard Spray; Lift)..AA

Canton Pump Co. (Boiler Feed; Elevator; Hydraulic; Steam) ....B

Gibbs Mfg. Co. (Measuring) A

Hurst Mfg. Co., H. L. (Spray) ....F

Kohler & Co., F. E. (Spray) B

OHIO—Cincinnati

Blymyer Iron Wrks. Co. (Hand or Power Juice) B

Fritch Mfg. Co., Francis, 223 W. McMicken Av. (Air) X

Kirkup & Co., Robt., 620 Lodge (Brass; Force; Lift; Plumbers') C

Laidlaw-Dunn-Gordon Co. (Acid; Air; Duplex Air; Ammonia; Beer; Ale; Steam; Boiler Feed; Brewery; Circulating; Combined Air; Circulating; Combined Boilers; Pumps; Combined Vacuum; Water; Crank; Distilling; Mash; Drainage; Elevator; Filter Press; Fire; Steam; Force; Gas Works; High Pressure; Hydraulic; Irigating; Low Pressure; Marine; Bilge; Ship; Mining; Sinking; Oil Line; Oil Refinery; Plantation; Power; Quarry; Salt Water; Sewerage; Compound; Duplex; Steam; Plunger; Vertical Steam; Stuff; Handy Suction; Sugar House; Syrup; Tank; Tannery; Vacuum; Artesian; Deep Well; Wrecking) ....AAAA

McGowan Co., Jno. H., 56 Central Av. (Boiler Feed; Cistern; Deep Well; Electric; Elevator; Force; Lift; Hydraulic; Irrigating; Mining; Steam; Tank; Water Works; Vertical Steam) ....A

Macleod & Co., Walter, 463 E. Front (Contractors'; for Sewers; Foundations) B

Murdock & Co., J. G., 428 Plum (Brass; Force; Lift;

PUMPS (Con.)

Plumbers) ....A

Powell Co., Wm., 2525 Spring Grove Av. (Force; Lift; Plumbers'; Oil) ..A

Vanduzen Co., E. W., 428 E. 2d (Ship; Deck; Steam) D

OHIO—Cleveland

Bishop & Babcock Co. (Bicycle; Vacuum Hydraulic; Beer; Ale) ....AAA

Burton & Johnson, 107 W. Centre (Air; Mining; Steam) ....F

Cleveland Faucet Co. (Beer; Ale) ....AAA

Cleveland Steam Gauge Co., 106 Mervine (Boiler Testing) C

Loew Supply & Mfg. Co. (Brewers' Air; Pressure; Beer) ....B

Snider-Hughes Co., Coe cor. Hamilton (Air; Elevator; Boiler Feed; Hydraulic; Mining Power; Sinking; Steam; Sugar House; Vacuum; Wrecking) .....B

OHIO—Columbiana

Columbiana Pump Co. (Force; Lift; Spray; Hand; Iron) ....B

OHIO—Columbus

Chase Fdry. & Mfg. Co. (Deep Well) C

Jeffrey Mfg. Co. (Electric) AAAA

Ohio Pump & Brass Co., 18th & Oak (Physicians'; Surgeons' Hydraulic Air) ..C

Pulling & Co., James G. (Air; Boiler Feed; Deep Well; Hydraulic; Mining; Power; Steam; Vacuum; Acid; Brewery; Centrifugal; Circulating; Combined Boilers; Pumps; Distillery; Elevator; Fire; Irrigating; Lard; Pow Pressure; Molasses; Oil; Oil Line; Oil Refinery; Plantation; Plumbers; Quarry; Sewerage; Vertical Steam; Artesian Well) ....B

OHIO—Dayton

Buckeye Iron & Brass Wrks. (Hydraulic) ....AA

Roberts Co., Geo. J. (Boiler Feed; Mining; Steam) ..A

OHIO—Genoa

Genoa Mfg. Co. (Windmill) ....D

OHIO—Greenville

Lucas & Co., C. O. (Boiler Feed; Power; Tank) .F

OHIO—Hamilton

Black-Clawson Co. (Fan; Steam; Stuff)) ....AAA

OHIO—Kenton

Champion Iron Co. (Hand Force; Iron) ....AA

OHIO—Mansfield

Barnes Mfg. Co. (Brass; Centrifugal; Cistern; Diaphragm; Force; Lift; Irrigating; Plumbers'; Rotary; Ship; Deck; Spray; Tank; Windmill; Pitcher; Artesian Well; Boiler Feed) ....A

Humphreys Mfg. Co. (Brass; Centrifugal; Force; Lift; Plumbers' Ship; Deck; Spray; Syphon; Tank; Windmill; Hand Iron; Boiler Feed) ....B

Mansfield Machine Wrks. (Steam; Boiler Feed; Steam) X

Phoenix Electric Mfg. Co. (Electric) ....B

OHIO—Marietta

Pattin Bros. Co. (Air; Boiler Feed; Steam) ....B

OHIO—Massillon

Hess, Snyder & Co. (Hand Air; Cistern; Deep Well; Force; Lift; Orchard Spray; Hand; Hand Suction; Tank; Well; Windmill) ....AA

OHIO—Mt. Gilead

Hydraulic Press Mfg. Co.

PUMPS (*Con.*)
(Hand; Power; Hydraulic)
A

OHIO—Salem
Deming Co. (Air; Steam; Hand Boiler Feed; Boiler Testing; Brass; Centrifugal Cistern; Electric; Force; Lift; Pressure Hydraulic; Irrigating; Mining; Plumbers'; Power; Rotary; Ship; Deck; Spray; Tank; Windmill; Barrel; Air Pressure; Cellar; Fire; Rotary Force; Garden; Greenhouse Force; Ham; Molasses; Pitcher; Soap; Quarry; Sewerage; Hand Suction; Vacuum; Well; Deep Well; Well Force) ....AA
Silver Mfg. Co. (Ham) ..AA
OHIO—Sandusky
Klotz Machine Co. (Oscillating Force) C
OHIO—Springfield
Mast, Foos & Co. (Force; Lift; Irrigating; Spray; Tank; Windmill; Hand; Hand Suction) ....AA
Thomas Mfg. Co. (Hand; Iron) ....AAA
OHIO—Toledo
Amer. Pump & Supply Co. (Chain) C
Heartley, Geo. W. (Drop; Embossing; Foot; Power; Riveting; Trimming; Wiring) ....D
Toledo Fdry. & Mach. Co. (Centrifugal) ....B
OHIO—Upper Sandusky
Nat'l Steam Pump Co. (Ammonia; Artesian Well; Boiler Feed; Deep Well; Electric; Hydraulic; Mining; Power; Sinking; Steam; Low Duty Tank; Water Works) ....B
OHIO—Youngstown
Tod & Co., W. (Water Works) ....AA
OHIO—Zanesville
Griffith & Wedge Co. (Cornish) ....A
OREGON—Portland
Simonds Mfg. Co. (Steam) ....AAA
Willamette Iron & Steel Wrks. (Steam) ....A
PA.—Allegheny
Carlin Mchry. & Supply Co., 103 Lacock (Centrifugal) ....B
Hall' Steam Pump Co. (Air Lift; Boiler Feed; Deep Well; Elevator; Hydraulic; Mining; Sinking; Steam; Combined Air; Boiler Feed; Combined Boilers; Pumps; Low Pressure; Power; Duplex; Vertical Steam; Artisian Well) ....A
PA.—Allentown
Allentown Fdry. & Mach. Wrks. (Hydraulic) ....A
Allentown Rolling Mills (Boiler Feed) ....AAA
PA.—Ashland
Goyne Steam Pump Co. (Goyne Bros., Props.) (Mining; Steam) ......B
PA.—Beaver Falls
Keystone Driller Co. (Artesian Well) ....A
PA.—Birdsboro
Diamond Drill & Machine Co. (Deep Well) ......A
PA.—Bradford
Caldwell & Co., E. R. (Gas Engine Starting) ......B
PA.—Bridgeport
Wilkinson Mfg. Co. (Steam) B
PA.—Carbondale
Carbondale Mach. Co. (Belt-Driven) ....AA
Hendrick Mfg. Co. (Ltd.) (Power) ....AA
PA.—Chester
Wetherill & Co. (Steam; Boiler Feed) ......AAAA

PUMPS (*Con.*)
PA.—Connellsville
Boyts, Porter & Co. (Special Boiler Feed; Electric; Vertical Deep Well; Hydraulic Mining; Sinking; Steam; Tank; Brass) ..B
Connellsville Mach. & Car Co. (Mining) ....A
PA.—Corry
Ajax Iron Wrks. (Steam; Tanners') ....A
PA.—Downieville
Downieville Pump Co. (Deep Well; Steam) ....B
PA.—Downingtown
Downingtown Mfg. Co. (Ltd.) (Centrifugal; Stuff; Hand Suction) ....A
PA.—Erie
Erie Pump & Engine Co. (Centrifugal Contractors'; for Sewers; Foundations) C
Jarechi Mfg. Co. (Artesian Well; Brass) ......AAAA
Lake City Engineering Co. (Centrifugal; Sand; Hydraulic; Hydraulic Dredging; Wrecking) X
Watson, N. A. (Steam Jet) A
PA.—Grove City
Bessemer Gas Engine Co. (Power) ....A
PA.—Harrisburg
Harrisburg Mfg. & Boiler Co. (Force; Lift) ......A
PA.—Lancaster
Eureka Bark Mill Co. (Centrifugal) ....B
PA.—Mahanoy City
Grant Iron Wrks. (Steam) D
PA.—Middletown
Raymond Mfg. Co. (Steam) X
PA.—Philadelphia
Barr Pump Co. (Air; Boiler Feed; Hydraulic; Steam; Circulating; Fire; Hydraulic Pressure; Marine Mining; Duplex Steam; Tank; Tannery; Vacuum) A
Belfield & Co., H., 433 N. Broad (Test) ....AA
Blatchley, C. G. (Chain; Wooden Force; Wooden) B
Boekel & Co., Wm., 518 Vine (Inclined Air Plumbers'; Force; Gasfitters Test) .A
Dallett Co., Thos. H. (Electric) ....B
Eccles, James, 2424 Ambler (Force; Lift) ....B
Enterprise Mfg. Co., 3d & Dauphin (Measuring; Self Priming) ....AAAA
Eynon-Evans Mfg. Co., 1519 Clearfield (Syphon) ....A
Johnson, Jr., & Co., Israel H., 1422 Callowhill (Gas Compressing; Hydraulic Proving) ....A
Kensington Engine Wks., Beach & Vienna (Steam; Steam Boiler Feed) ...A
Lonergan & Co., J. E. (Oil) ....AA
Nittinger, August (Ham) .A
Noppel, Emil, 803 Callowhill (Plumbers' Force) .H
Olsen, Tinius & Co., 500 N. 12th (Hydraulic) .....A
Perks, Chas., 625 Arch (Plumbers' Force; Test) B
Riehle Bros. Testing Mach. Co., 1424 N. 9th (Hydraulic) ....B
Schutte & Koerting Co., 1251 N. 12th (Syphon; Test; Vacuum) ....A
Southwark Fdry. & Mach. Co., Washington Av. & 5th (Steam; Centrifugal; Hydraulic; Rotary; High Pressure) ....AAA
Ware Co., Walter F. (Breast) ....B
Wilbraham - Baker Blower Co., 2518 Frankford Av.

PUMPS (Con.)
(Rotary) ....B
Wood & Co., R. D., 400
Chestnut (Centrifugal;
Steam; Hydraulic; Water
Works) ....AAAA
PA.—Pittsburg
Chaplin-Fulton Mfg. Co.
(Inc.) (Syphon) ......A
Epping-Carpenter Co., 41st
& A. V. Ry. (Direct Act-
ing Altesian Well; Beer;
Bilge; Boiler Feed; Brew-
ers' Ale; Deep Well; Ele-
vator; Hydraulic; Mining;
Steam; Sugar House;
Tank; Vacuum; Water
Works; Wrecking; Air;
Duplex Fly Wheel; Hy-
draulic Pressure) .....AA
Harris Pump & Supply Co.,
320 2nd (Brass) ......B
Heisler Pumping Engine
Co., Westinghouse Bldg.
(Boiler Feed; Steam) ...B
Pittsburg Valve, Fdry. &
Cons. Co. (Steam)..AAA
Scaife & Sons Co., Wm. B.,
221 1st Av. (Boiler Feed)
AAAA
Rees & Sons Co., James
(Steam) ....AA
Tranter Mfg. Co., 105 Water
(Hydraulic) ....B
Wilson-Snyder Mfg. Co.,
Ross & Water (Boiler
Feed; Hydraulic; Mining;
Steam; Wrecking) ...AA
PA.—Reading
Seibert, Jno. H., 116 Wash.
(Steam) ....E
PA.—Scranton
Scranton Steam Pump Co.
(Boiler Feed; Power;
Steam) ....A
PA.—Shamokin
Mullen & Son, Jno. (Min-
ing; Steam) ....AA
PA.—Sheffield
Woods' Sons, G. R.
(Wooden) ....D
PA.—Titusville
Smith Pump Co. (Steam)..
AA
Titusville Iron Co. (Steam)
AAA
PA.—Waynesboro
Frick Co. (Steam; Boiler
Feed) ....AAAA
PA.—Wilkesbarre
Vulcan Iron Wks. (Cornish;
Steam; Boiler Feed;
Steam Force; High Press-
ure; Mining; Salt Water;
Duplex Steam; Steam)
AAAA
PA.—Williamsport
Darling Pump & Mfg. Co.
(Ltd.) (Artesian Well;
Boiler Testing; Brass;
Deep Well; Oil)......B
PA.—York
Motter & Sons, Geo. F.,
(Air Boiler Feed; Air
Pressure; Power) C
Smith Co., S. Morgan (Ro-
tary Fire) ....AAA
York Mfg. Co. (Ltd.)
(Steam) ....AAA
R. I.—Pawtucket
Fales & Jenks Machine Co.
(Rotary) ....AAA
R. I.—Providence
Brown & Sharpe Mfg. Co.
(Centrifugal; Water Tank
Geared; Oil; Water for
Milling; Gear; Chucking
Machines, etc.) ....AAAA
Builders' Iron Fdry. (Irri-
gation) ....AA
Davol Rubber Co. (Breast)
AA
Harris Steam Engine Co.,
Wm. A. (Steam; Boiler
Feed) ....B
S. C.—Charleston
Charleston Iron Wks. (Cen-
trifugal) ....D
TENN.—Memphis
Electric Novelty Co., 43
Monroe (Cistern) ....F
TEXAS—San Antonio
Collins Mfg. Co., F. F.

PUMPS (Con.)
(Well) ....B
Gunther Fdry. Mach. &
Supply Co. (Irrigating)..
X
VT.—Randolph
Brooks, Edw. E. (Garden
Sprinkling) ....E
VT.—Rutland
Frenier, J. H., Cleveland
Av. N. (Mining; Sand
Feed Stone - Sawing;
Slime Tailings) ......D
VA.—Richmond
Cameron Tennant Mach.
Wks. (Boiler Feed; Pow-
er) ....D
Cardwell Machine Co. (Hy-
draulic; Underwriter
Fire; Hydraulic Pressure;
Stuff) ....A
Sydnor Pump & Well Co.,
1326 E. Main (Centrifu-
gal; Steam) C
W. VA.—Charleston
Ward, Chas. (Aciu).....B
Wis.—Beloit
Beloit Iron Wks. (Centrifu-
gal; Fan) ....A
WIS.—Evansville
Baker Mfg. Co. (Force &
Lift; Brass; Iron)....AA
WIS.—Janesville
Rock River Machine Co.
(Boiler Feed) ....D
WIS.—Madison
Northern Electric Mfg. Co.
(Electric) ....AAAA
WIS.—Milwaukee
Allis-Chalmers Co. (Steam
Power Air; Steam Boiler
Feed; Sewerage; Vacu-
um) ....AAAA
Cutler-Hammer Mfg. Co.,
12th cor. St. Paul Av.
(Electric) ....AAA
Filer & Stowell Co. (Air;
Ammonia; Power; Steam;
Boiler Feed; Brewery;
Air Pressure; Steam;
Plunger; Compound; Du-
plex, Steam) ....AAA
Prescott Steam Pump Co.,
Fred M., (Boiler Feed;
Elevator; Steam) ...AA
Vilter Mfg. Co. (Brewers'
Air; Combined Creamery
Engines; Cooler) ....AA
WIS.—Racine
Case Threshing Mach. Co.,
J. I. (Tank) ......AAAA
Freeman & Sons Mfg. Co.,
S. (Windmill) ....A
Winship Mfg. Co. (Wooden)
E
WIS.—South Milwaukee
Bucyrus Co. (Dredging;
Centrifugal) ......AAA
WIS.—Superior
Duplex Mfg. Co. (Force &
Lift; Windmill Iron) AA
WIS.—Waupun
Althaus-Wheeler Co.
(Hand; Well; Windmill)
A

PUNCHES

See also Machy; Tools

CONN.—Bridgeport
Bridgeport Hardware Mfg.
Corporation (Conductors
Ticket Belt) ....B
Hurwood Mfg. Co. (Drive) C
Smith & Egge Mfg. Co. (Re-
volving Spring Belt; Con-
ductors' Ticket, etc.;
Spring) ....A
CONN.—Hartford
Cushman Chuck Co. (Center;
Prick) ....AA
Pratt & Whiting Co. (Hand;
Power; Spiral Shear)
AAAA
Sigourney Tool Co. (Hand;
Power) ....A
CONN.—Middletown
Wilcox, Crittenden & Co.
(Drive) ....A
CONN.—New Britain
Humason & Beckley Mfg.
Co. (Bull; Belt) ......A

PUNCHES (Con.)
Wks. (Blacksmiths'; Center; Prick; Hand; Lever)
.... A
Union Mfg. & Specialty Co.
(Hand; Power) C
N. Y.—Elmira
Cronk & Carrier Mfg. Co.
(Drive) .... B
New York City
Amer. Railway Supply Co.,
24 Park Place (Conductors' Ticket) X
Dudgeon, Richard, 24 Columbia (Hand; Power; Hydraulic) .... D
Eckstein, Chas. G., 249 Center (Hand) .... D
Graham & Co., J. H., 113
Chambers (Spring) ...AA
Jennings & Co., C. E., 79
Reade (Center; Prick) ..B
Kinsman Electric & Railway
Supply Co., 61 Liberty
(Hand) .... E
Loyd Co., Jno., 558 Water
(Hand; Power) .... B
McDougall & Potter Co., 602
W. 55th (Hand; Power) D
Morrill, Chas., 277 Bway.
(Belt; Hand; Power; Paper) .... D
New York Stencil Wks.
(Conductors' Ticket) ..C
Niles-Bement-Pond Co., 111
B'way (Hand).....AAAA
Pels & Co., Henry, 66 Broad
(Hand; Power) C
Smith & Hemenway Co., 296
Bway. (Belt) .... D
Stimpson & Son, Edwin B.
(Leather) .... B
Tower & Lyon Co., 95 Chambers (Conductors' Ticket;
Round; Saddlers') .....B
Watson-Stillman Co., 210 E.
43d (Hand; Hydraulic
Track; Power; Shears) ..A
Weiss & Co., H., 20 Cliff
(Hand) .... F
N. Y.—Rochester
Erdle & Schenck (Hand;
Power) .... B
N. Y.—Syracuse
Syracuse Twist Drill Co.
(Center; Prick) .... B
OHIO—Akron
Akron Machine Co. (Hand)
.... X
Whitman & Barnes Mfg. Co.
(Steel) ....AAAA
OHIO—Alliance
Alliance Machine Co. (Hand;
Power; Hydraulic) ...AA
Transue & Williams Co.
(Drive) .... A
OHIO—Canton
Ney Mfg. Co. (Drive) ....B
OHIO—Cincinnati
Cincinnati Mfg. Co. (Conductors' Ticket)........B
Cincinnati Punch & Shear
Co. (Hand; Power; Tube;
Manhole; Multiple) .....B
Keene & Co., Geo. C., 502 E.
Front (Hand) .... F
OHIO—Cleveland
Cleveland Punch & Shear
Wks. Co. (Hand; Power;
Tube; Manhole; Multiple)
.... A
Globe Machine & Stamping
Co. (Hand; Power) C
Konigslow Stamping & Tool
Wks. (Hand; Power) ..D
OHIO—Columbus
Ohio Tool Co. (Coopers), AA
OHIO—Hamilton
Long & Allstatter Co.
(Hand; Tube Hole; Hydraulic; Power; Shears)
.... AA
Meyers Mfg. Co., Fred. J.
(Conductors' Ticket;
Spring; Leather; Cattle) B
Niles Tool Wks. Co. (Power;
Shears) ....AAAA
OHIO—Tiffin
National Machinery Co.
(Power; Shears) ......AA
OHIO—Toledo
Heartley, G. W. (Hand) ..D
Toledo Machine & Tool Co.
(Deep Gap; Power;

PUNCHES (Con.)
Shears; Tinners') ......A
OHIO—Youngstown
Sennett Co., G. B. (Hand;
Power; Hydraulic) .....B
PA.—Bellefonte
Lingle, J. H. (Hand; Power)
.... D
PA.—Danville
Curry & Co. (Hydraulic) ..B
PA.—Philadelphia
Bement, Niles & Co. (Power; Shears) ....AAAA
Disston & Sons, Henry
(Saw) ....AAAA
Horn & Bros., Wm. H.
(Leather) .... B
Pedrick & Ayer Co., 1001
Hamilton (R. R. Track) A
Phila. Roll & Mach. Co.
(Power; Shears) .... A
Sellers & Co., Wm. (Inc.)
(Power; Shears; Multiple)
.... AAAA
Stortz & Son, Jno., 210 Vine
(Center; Prick) .... B
Wood & Co., R. D. (Hand;
Power; Hydraulic), AAAA.
PA.—Pittsburg
Fischer Foundry & Mach. Co.
(Hydraulic) ....AA
Iron City Tool Wks. (Ltd.),
32d & Smallman (Blacksmiths'; R. R. Track) ..A
Klein-Logan Co., So. 13th &
Breed (Blacksmiths'; R.
R. Track) .... A
Pittsburg Mfg. Co. (Hand;
Power) .... .A
Pittsburg Tool & Drop Forge
Co. (Driving Tie Plate), D
United Engineering & Foundry Co. (Hydraulic) AAAA
PA.—Royersford
Royersford Foundry & Machine Co. (Hand; Power)
.... D
PA.—So. Bethlehem
Bethlehem Foundry & Mach.
Co. (Hand; Power; Hydraulic; Screw) C
Bethlehem Steel Co. (Hydraulic) ....AAAA
R. I.—Pawtucket
Haskell Mfg. Co., Wm. H.
(Hand; Power) ....AA
R. I.—Providence
Standard Machinery Co.
(Hand; Power) .... B
WIS.—Janesville
Bicknell Hardware Co.
(Blacksmiths'; Hand;
Power) .... E
New Doty Mfg. Co. (Hand;
Tube Hole; Belt; Power;
Shears; Multiple) ......D
Rock River Machine Co.
(Hand; Power) .... D

PURATYLENE

New York City
Roessler & Hasslacher Chemical Co., 100 William (for
purifying Acetylene) ..AA

PURIFIERS

CONN.—Hartford
Whitlock Coil Pipe Co.
(Feed Water) .... A
CONN.—New Haven
Harrison, Leonard D. (Middlings) .... H
National Pipe Bending Co.
(Feed Water) .... B
ILL.—Chicago
Baragwanath & Son, Wm.
(Live Steam) C
Wolf Co., Fred. W., 139
Rees (Ammonia) ....AAA
ILL.—Moline
Barnard & Leas Mfg. Co.
(Middlings) ....AA
IND.—Fort Wayne
Kerr-Murray Mfg. Co. (Gas)
.... A
Nordyke & Marmon Co.
(Corn Meal; Middlings)
.... AAA
IND.—Wishawka
Dodge Mfg. Co. (Feed Water) ....AAA

825

PURIFIERS (Con.)

IND.—Richmond
Richmond City Mill Wks.
(Middlings). ....B
IOWA—Dubuque
Dubuque Turbine & Roller
Mill Co. (Middlings)....B
KANS.—Leavenworth
Great Western Mfg. Co.
(Corn Meal; Aspirators;
Middlings) ....AA
MD.—Baltimore
Bartlett Hayward & Co.
(Gas) ....B
MASS.—Boston
Walworth Mfg. Co. (Feed
Water) ....AAAA
MICH.—Detroit
Lloyd Construction Co. (Gas)
........................C
MICH.—Saginaw
Wickes Bros. (Feed Water)
........................AAA
N. J.—Camden
Webster & Co., Warren
(Feed Water) ....AA
N. J.—Garwood
Beckley & Co., A. J. (Sand)
........................D
N. Y.—Brooklyn
Continental Iron Wks. West
& Cayler (Gas) ....A
N. Y.—Buffalo
Noye Mfg. Co., John T.
(Corn Meal; Corn Meal Aspirators; Middlings) X
New York City
Patterson & Co., F. L., 26
Cortlandt (Feed Water), E
Strauss & Co., 55 Broad
(Water) ....E
N. Y.—Silver Creek
Huntley Mfg. Co. (Corn
Meal) ....A
OHIO—Columbus
Case Mfg. Co. (Corn Meal;
Aspirators; Middlings)..A
OHIO—Springfield
Hopper Mfg. Co. (Live
Steam) ....A
PA.—Harrisburg
Harrisburg Pipe & Pipe
Bending Co. (Feed Water)
........................AAA
PA.—Irwin
Irwin Flour Mill Co. (Middlings) ....B
PA.—Muncy
Sprout, Waldron & Co.
(Middlings) ....A
PA.—Philadelphia
Harrison Safety Boiler
Wrks. (Feed Water) ...A
Wood & Co., R. D., 400
Chestnut (Gas) ....AAAA
PA.—Pittsburg
Bonar & Co. , Jas. (Live
Steam) ....A
Scaife & Sons Co., Wm. B.
(Feed Water) ......AAA
WIS.—Milwaukee
Allis-Chalmers Co. (Middlings) ....AAAA

PURSES

See also Leather Goods; Jewelry

ILL.—Chicago
Webster, Geo. A., 64 Wabash Av. (Coin) C
Western Leather Mfg. Co.
........................D
MASS.—Athol
Bates Bros. Co. ....B
MASS.—Attleboro
Blake Co., James E. (Metal)
........................A
Eden Co.. C. H. (Metal) ..A
Regnell, Bigney & Co. (Metal) C
MASS.—Ayer
Sigsbee Co. (Coin) ......D
MASS.—North Attleboro
Blackington & Co., R.
(Metal) ....A
MASS.—South Deerfield
Arms. Mfg. Co. ....B
MASS.—Worcester
Warren Leather Goods Co.
........................B
N. J.—Hoboken
Lehman & Co. ....A

PURSES (Con.)

N. Y.—Gloversville
Wilkins Co.., E. J. (Coin)
........................B
New York City
Culbert & Co. X
Fischman Leather Goods Co.,
95 5th Av. (Leather) ..D
Maas, Blum & Co. ......AA
Scheuer & Bro., 79 Walker
........................X
PA.—Philadelphia
Rumpp & Sons, C. F. .AAA

PUSHERS

ILL.—Chicago
Fairbanks, Morse & Co.,
(Car) ....AAAA
Webster Mfg. Co., 1075 W.
15th (Car) ....AA
ILL.—Moline
Barnard & Leas Mfg. Co.
..(Car) ....AA
MASS.—Boston
Boston & Lockport Block
Co., 160 Commercial (Car)
........................A
Woodman Mfg. Supply Co.,
3 Oliver (Car) ....F
MICH.—Detroit
Buhl Malleable Co. (Car)
........................A
MO.—St. Louis
Zenicker Supply Co., Walter
A., 408 N. 4th (Car) ..X
N.Y.—New York City
Motley, Green & Co., 12
John (Car) X
Thomas, Theodore, 11 B'way
(Car) ....D
OHIO—Cleveland
Brown Hoisting Machinery
Co. (Coke Oven) ..AAAA
Osborn Mfg. Co. (Car) ..B
OHIO—Dayton
Boyer & Radford Mfg. Co.
(Car) C
PA.—Pittsburg
Verona Tool Wrks., Murtland Bldg. (Car) ......A
R. I.—Pawtucket
Fuller & Son Co., Geo. H.
(Watch) ....A

PUSHES

CONN.—Collinsville
Hartigan, W. R. (Electric
Bell) ....H
PA.—Reading
Reading Hardware Co.
(Electric Bell) ....AAAA

PUTTY

COLO.—Denver
James Mercantile & Mfg.
Co., B. L. ....B
ILL.—Chicago
Chicago White Lead & Oil
Co. ....AA
Chicago Wood Finishing Co.
259 Elston Av. ....A
Heath & Milligan Mfg. Co.
........................AAA
Rubber Paint Co. ....A
KY.—Louisville
Caron Stone Co. (Stone Polishing) ....D
Hughes & Sons Co., W. J.
........................B
LA.—New Orleans
McWilliams. R. (Ltd.) ..X
MAINE—Hallowell
Fuller Sons, Geo. C
MASS.—Boston
Briggs & Co., John, 33 Batterymarch ....D
MICH.—Detroit
Acme White Lead & Color
Wrks. ....AAA
Boydell Bros. White Lead &
Color Wrks. ....AA
Detroit White Lead Wrks.
........................AAA
MINN.—St. Paul
St. Paul White Lead & Oil
Co., ...B
MO.—St. Louis
Kent & Purdy Paint Co.,
701 N. 2d C

PUTTY (*Con.*)

N. J.—Jersey City
Baker, Wm. T., 35 Suydam
  D
Dixon Crucible Co., Joseph
  (Stove) ....AAA
Woolsey Paint & Color Co.,
  C. A. ....A
N. Y.—Brooklyn
Phillips, John B. X
Wiarda & Co., John C. (Pow-
  der) ....AA
New York City
Amer. Whiting & Putty
  Mfg. Co., 200 Water ..B
Belknap, McSherry & Moran
  Co., E. S., 286 Monroe
  C
Devoe, F. W. & C. T. Ray-
  nolds Co., 103 Fulton
  AAAA
Grote, Geo. W., 605 W. 39th
  D
Jacob & Sons, S., 424 E.
  102d ....D
Mark, Jacob, 7 Worth
  (Blue) ....D
Tieman & Co., D. F. .....A
Tucker Mfg. Co., Wm. G.,
  foot E. 116th X
N. Y.—Troy
Connors Paint Mfg. Co.,
  Wm. (Stove; Glaziers) .A
OHIO—Cincinnati
Obermayer & Co., S. (Stove)
  AA
OHIO—Cleveland
Billings-Chapin Co. ....A
Cleveland Stone Co., Hickok
  Bldg. (Stone) ....AAAA
Smith Foundry Supply Co.,
  J. D. (Stove) ....D
Ullman & Philpott Mfg. Co.,
  95 Merwin ....B
OHIO—Dayton
Dicks & Wiggin Co. (Fruit
  Jar Sealing) C
OHIO—Piqua
Piqua Paint & Putty Co.
  D
PA.—Allentown
Allentown Mfg. Co. ....A
PA.—Philadelphia
Butterworth & Co., C. H.,
  125 Market ....B
Felton, Sibley & Co., 136 N.
  4th ....AAA
French & Co., Samuel H.,
  4th & Callowhill (Roof)
  B
Howell & Co., C. H. ...B
Lucas & Co., Jno., 322 Race
  (Glaziers) ....AAA
Nice, Eugene E. (Glazier)
  A
Waterall & Co., Wm., 4th &
  Race ....A
PA.—Pittsburg
Lawrence & Co., W. W.
  (Inc.) ....AA
PA.—Reading
Wilhelm Co., A. ....AA
VT.—Rutland
Rutland Fire Clay Co...B

PUZZLES

MASS.—Springfield
Bradley Co., Milton .....A
N. Y.—New York City
McLoughlin Bros. ...AAA
Tablet & Ticket Co., 381
  B'way ....B
N. Y.—Senaca Falls
Wescott-Jewell Co. ......D
WIS.—Casco
Casco Novelty Co. C

PYRITES

PA.—Philadelphia
Penn. Salt Mfg. Co. (Kryo-
  lith) ....AAAA

PYROMETERS

CONN.—Waterbury
Bristol Co. ....D
ILL.—Chicago
Hubbard Portable Oven Co.,
  112 Michigan C
Marsh & Co., Jas. P., 224
  Wash'n ....B
Weiskopf, Abraham, 69 S.

PYROMETERS (*Con.*)

Canal ....E
MASS.—Boston
Amer. Steam Gauge & Valve
  Mfg. Co. ....A
Ashton Valve Co., 271
  Franklin ....A
Crosby Steam Gauge &
  Valve Co., 93 Oliver ..AA
N. J.—Passaic
Mehling-Decker- Co. (Re-
  cording) ....B
N. Y.—Brooklyn
Schaffer & Budenburg, 25
  Bedford Av. ....D
New York City
Ashcroft Mfg. Co. ......A
Elmer & Amend, 211 3d Av.
  A
Globe Machine & Stamping
  J., 53 Fulton ....A
Tagliabue, Guiseppe, 302
  Pearl ....B
N. Y.—Rochester
Hohmann & Maurer Mfg. Co.
  B
N. Y.—Watertown
Watertown Thermometer Co.
  C
PA.—Philadelphia
Brown, Edward, 313 Walnut
  (all Kinds) ....B

PYROZONE

N. Y.—New York City
McKesson & Robbins
  AAAA

QUADRANTS

N. Y.—New York City ...
Tiebout, W. & J., 118 Chambers (Brass Skylight) ..B

QUADS

See also Type

R. I.—Providence .. ..
Hammond Printers Supply
  Co. X

QUARTZ

CONN.—New Milford
Bridgeport Wood Finishing
  Co. (Ground) ....AA
ILL.—Chicago
Garden City Sand Co., 188
  Madison ....A
N. Y.—Brooklyn
Wiarda & Co., John C.
  (Ground) ....AA
PA.—Philadelphia
Baeder, Adamson & Co.
  (Ground) ....AAAA
VT.—Bennington
Adams & Co., Enos (Crys-
  talized) ....D

QUEENSWARE

ARK.—Pine Bluff
Ryland Queensware Co.,..E
KANS.—Pittsburg
Peck-Houston Queensware
  Co. ....F
MO.—St. Louis
Blankenmeister & Son, F.
  H., 721 N. 11th ....B
Fenckel, A., 805 Lucas Av.
  X
Missouri Glass Co., 908
  Clark Av. ....A
St. Louis Glass & Queens-
  ware Co., 9th & Spruce
  A
W. VA.—Wheeling
Warwick China Co. ......A

QUICKSILVER

See also Mercury

CAL.—Los Angeles
Braun Co., F. W. ....AAA

QUILLERS

See also Machy

CONN.—Stonington
Atwood, Morrison Co. ..AA

QUILLERS (Con.)
IND.—Evansville
Horster, Henry (Feather)
...................F
MASS.—Whitinsville
Whitin Machine Wrks.
...................AAAA
MASS.—Worcester
Crompton & Knowles Loom
Wrks. ....AAAA
Steele & Bro., A. H. 54
Hermon ....D
N. J.—Paterson
Atherton Machine Co. ....B
Eastwood Co., Benj. ......A
Paterson Machine Wrks., 46
Warren ....F
Royle & Sons, Jno. ......A
PA.—Philadelphia
Altemus, Jacob K., 2824 N.
4th C
R. I.—Pawtucket
Payne Co., G. W. (Upright)
...................D
R. I.—Providence
Franklin Machine Co. ....A
Rhode Island Braiding Mach.
Co. C

QUILLS

N. J.—Paterson
Dempwolf, Jr., Chas. ..X
Ferrary & Schauble Co. ..D
Frost & Sons, Geo. T. ..A
Hall & Co., I. A. ....A
Van Riper Mfg. Co. ....B
Ulrich & Co. ....F

QUILTERS

CONN.—New Haven
Brown & Co., Ruben H...B

QUILTS

See Bedding

QUININE

MD.—Baltimore
McCormick & Co. ....D
MO.—St. Louis
Mallinckrodt Chemical
Works ....AAAA
N. J.—Newark
Styron, Beggs Co. ....A
N. Y.—New York City
Boehringer & Soehne, C. F.,
7 Cedar ....A
Fuerst Bros. & Co., 2 Stone
...................D
Merck & Co. ....AAA
New York Quinine & Chem-
ical Wrks., 114 William
...................A
Phair, R. W. ....F
PA.—Philadelphia
Powers-Weightman - Rosen-
garten Co. ....AAAA

QUOINS

ILL.—Chicago ... .
Wanner Co., A. F., 298 Dear-
born (Printers') C
MASS.—Boston
Golding & Co. ....B
Hansen, H. C. ....B
Wickersham Quoin Co.
(Printers') 174 Fort Hill
Sq. ....G
N. Y.—Buffalo
Hempel & Dingens, 594
Washington C
New York City
Amer. Type Founders Co.
...................AAAA
Hoe & Co., R. ....AAAA
Moore & Warren ....B
N. Y.—Senaca Falls
Wescott-Jewell Co. ......D
WIS.—Clinton
Smith & Holum Mfg. Co.
(Printers') ....F
WIS.—Two Rivers
Hamilton Mfg. Co. ...,...AA

QUOITS

ILL.—Freeport
Arcade Mfg. Co. ....A

QUOITS (Con.)
MO.—St. Louis
Kupferle, John C. ......AA
Pleuger & Henger Mfg. Co.
...................A
N. H.—Keene
Wilkins Toy Co. ......AAA
OHIO—Cincinnati
Tatum Co., Samuel C...B
OHIO—Ravenna
Williams, A. C. ....A
PA.—Nazareth
Nazareth Foundry & Mach.
Co. ....B
PA.—Reading
Reading Hardware Co.
...................AAAA
TENN.—South Pittsburg
Blacklock Foundry C

RABBITS

ILL.—Chicago
Barbee Wire & Iron Wrks.
...................B

RACKETS

N. Y.—New York City
Dayton & Co., G. S., 76 Nassau ....E

RACKS

See also Furniture; Cases

CONN.—East River
Munger & Son (Chalk) ..C
CONN.—Essex
Essex Wood Turning Co.
(Book) X
CONN.—Georgetown
Gilbert & Bennett Mfg. Co.
(Hay) ....AAA
CONN.—Meriden
Bradley & Hubbard Mfg. Co.
(Book; Hat; Coat; Pen)
...................AAAA
Foster, Merriam & Co.
(Towell; Brass Towell)
...................AA
Landers, Frary & Clark
(Hat; Coat; Card) ..AAA
Meriden Britannia Co.
(Toast) ....AAAA
CONN.—New Britain
New Britain Mach. Co.
(Tool) ....A
Taplin Mfg. Co. (Towel) ..D
CONN.—New Haven
Henn & Co., A. S. (Towel)
...................F
CONN.—Torrington
Turner & Seymour Mfg. Co.
(Hat; Coat; Towel; Brass)
...................A
CONN.—Wallingford
Wallace & Sons Mfg. Co., R.
(Toast) ....AAAA
ILL.—Chicago
Adams & Westlake (Bag-
age) ....AAAA
Allen Mfg. Co., W. D., 151
Lake (Fire Hose) ......A
Barbee Wire & Iron Wrks.
(Canning; Hay; Iron;
Sponge; Newspaper; Por-
table Pie; Whip) ......B
Ehnborn & Co., C. (Hat;
Coat) ....G
Gould Co., 24 N. North Ca-
nal (Bicycle) ....B
Nicol & Co. (Broom) ....D
Parsons & Co., W. R. (Tow-
el; Coat; Hat; Display)
...................D
ILL.—Peoria
Van Epps, Henry R. (Card)
...................F
IND.—Indianapolis
Tucker & Dorsey Mfg. Co.
(Hat; Coat; Folding Hat;
Coat; Towel) ....A
Udell Wrks. (Hat; Coat)
...................A
Western Furniture Co. (Hat;
Coat) ....A
IOWA—Fort Madison
Iowa Farming Tool Co.
(Garden Tool; Steel
Goods)) ....A
MAINE—Portland
Portland Co. (Cast) ....AA
MASS.—Boston
Allen Totman Co. (Umbrel-

RACKS (Con.)

la) ....F
Boston Gear Wrks. (Brass)
.....................B
Bramer, A. D., 21 S. Market
(Bicycle) ....F
Golding & Co. (Printers)
.....................B
Revere Rubber Co., 63
Franklin (Fire Hose)
....................AAAA

MASS.—Cambridge
Barbour-Stockwell Co. (Bak-
ers' Pie) ....A
MASS.—Gardner
Heywood Bros. & Wakefield
Co. (Rattan Towel)
....................AAAA
MASS.—Holyoke
Holyoke Machine Co. (Cast)
.....................AA
MASS.—Lawrence
Lawrence Machine Co.
(Cast) X
MASS.—Lowell
Woods, Sherwood Co.
(Toast; Portable Pie) ..E
MASS.—Pittsfield
Jones & Sons Co., E. D.
(Cast) ....
MASS.—Worcester
Hill, Dryer Co. (Clothes) ..D
National Mfg. Co. (Toast;
Portable Pie) ....A
Parker Wire Goods Co.
(Bakery; Card; Book; Pa-
per) ....D
Spencer Wire Co. (Towel)
.....................A
Wire Goods Co. (Towel;
Portable Pie; Bakery) ..A
MICH.—Detroit
Barnum Wire & Iron Wrks.,
E. T. (Hay) ....B
MICH.—Fenton
Phillips Co., A. J. (Towel;
Clothes) ....A
MICH.—Galien
Montross, Richard W. (Bi-
cycle Cleaning) ....B
MICH.—Grand Rapids
Nelson Matter Furniture Co.
(Hat; Coat) ....AA
Oriel Cabinet Co. (Towel)
.....................AA
MICH.—Jackson
Walcott & Son, Geo. D.
(Cut) C
MO.—St. Louis
Ludlow-Saylor Wire Co.
(Pew) ....AA
Pleuger & Henger Mfg. Co.
(Towel) ....A
N. H.—Nashua
Fletcher & Webster Furni-
ture Co. (Hat; Coat;
Brass Hat; Coat; Towel)
.....................C
N. J.—Burlington
Stewart & Peterson Co.
(Hay) ....A
N. J.—Newark
Searls Mfg. Co. (Towel) ..B
N. Y.—Buffalo
Shepard & Co. Sidney (Fruit
Steaming). ....AAAA
Western Wire Goods Co.
(Towel; Card; Book; Pa-
per) ....D
N. Y.—Cato
Dutton & Co., E. Q. (Cor-
ner Hay) ....E
N. Y.—Herkimer
Quackenbush, H. M. (Desk)
.....................A
N. Y.—Jamestown
Fenton Metallic Mfg. Co.
(Postal Car) ....A
New York City
Amer. Type Founders Co.
(Printers') ....AAAA
Brunswick-Balke- Collender
Co. (Desk) ....AAAA
Farmer & Son Type Found-
ing Co., A. D. (Printers')
....
Fiske Iron Wrks., J. W.
(Hat; Coat; Towel; Hay;
Whip) ....B
Hale Co. (Folding Hat;
Coat) ....A
Hoe & Co., R. (Printers')
....................AAAA
Homan Co., Andrew (Hat;

RACKS (Con.)
.....................D
Coat) ....D
Howard & Morse (Hay) ..D
Judd & Co., H. L. (Inc.)
(Brass; Hat; Coat; Pen)
.....................AA
Mace & Co., L. H. Hat;
Coat; Hanging) ....B
Manning, Maxwell & Moore,
85 Liberty (Brass) ....AA
Mason & Co., J. W. (Fold-
ing Hat; Coat) ....D
Maurer & Son, Henry, 420
E. 23d (Bottle; Hollow
Tile) ....H
Mohr & Co., Fred. (Hat;
Coat) ....A
Palmer & Embury Mfg. Co.
(Hat; Coat) ....A
Peck, Stow & Wilcox Co.,
27 Murray (Card; Book;
Paper) ....AAAA
Schloss & Co., E. (Hat;
Coat) ....A
Spencerian Pen Co. (Pen)
.....................AA
Swain & Son, H. C. (Fold-
ing Hat; Coat) ....D
Vogel & Co., F. (Hat; Coat)
.....................X
N. Y.—Rochester
Copeland & Durgin Co.
(Hat; Coat; Towel) ....A
N. Y.—Senaca Falls
Wescott-Jewell Co. (Adjus-
table Book) ....D
N. Y.—Syracuse
Brown Furniture Co., C. G.
(Hat; Coat) ....B
Stearns & Co., E. C. (Hay)
.....................AA
Wells Mfg. Co., A. J.
(Book) X
N. Y.—Troy
Kellogg, Wm. P. (Whip), X
Kilbourne Mfg. Co. (Towel;
Hat; Coat) C
OHIO—Bryan
Bryan Novelty Mfg. Co.
(Biscuit Can Display) ..E
OHIO—Cincinnati
Sextro Furniture Mfg. Co.
(Hat; Coat) ....B
Tatum Co., Samuel C.
(Book; Card; Pen) ....B
OHIO—Cleveland
Amer. Fork & Hoe Co. (Inc.)
(Steel Goods) ....AAAA
Federal Mfg. Co. (Towel;
Clothes) ....AAAA
Van Dorn Iron Works Co.
(Bakery). ....AA
OHIO—Dayton
City Forge & Iron Wrks.
.....................D
OHIO—Norwalk
Gregory, Giles R. (Bicycle)
.....................F
OHIO—Salem
Clark Co., W. J. (Hat;
Coat) ....A
OHIO—Warren
Eureka Mfg. Co. (Furniture
Display; Table Couch;
Chair) ....G
PA.—Allegheny
Pittsburg Lamp, Brass &
Glass Co. (Brass Towel)
....................AAAA
PA.—Beaver Falls
Standard Steel Gauge Co.
(Finished Cut) ....A
PA.—Brownsville
Herbertsons' Sons, J. (Hay)
.....................D
PA.—Corry
Raymond Mfg. Co. (Hat;
Coat; Towel) ....B
PA.—Lebanon
Hauck, Adam (Hat; Coat))
.....................D
PA.—North East
Fernald Mfg. Co. (Hanging)
.....................D
PA.—Philadelphia
Cresson Co., Geo. W. (Cast)
.....................AA
McCambridge & Co. (Ltd.)
(Brass Towel) ....B
Phila. Novelty Mfg. Co.
(Towel; Pen) ....D
PA.—Pittsburg
Nuttal Co., R. D. (Cut) ..A
Simonds Mfg. Co. (Cut) ..B

829

RACKS (Con.)
R. I.—Pawtucket
Bliss Mfg. Co., R. (Book)
........................AAAA
Thayer's Son, Ellis (Book)
................................X
R. I.—Providence
Towel Rack & Novelty Mfg.
Co. (Towel; Hat; &c.)..F
TENN.—Chattanooga
Chattanooga Furniture Co.
(Hat; Coat) ....A
VT.—North Bennington
Cushman Mfg. Co., Henry T.
(Book; Hat; Coat) C
VT.—Springfield
Fellows Gear Shaper Co.
(Cut) ....A
WIS.—Fond-du-Lac
Harrison Postal Bag Rack
Co. (Postal Car) ......D
WIS.—Marsfield
Roddis Lumber & Veneer
Co. (Glass) ....A
WIS.—Milwaukee
Meinecke & Son, A. (Hang-
ing) ....AA
WIS.—Racine
Winship Mfg. Co. (Shoe)..E
WIS.—Sheboygan
Mattoon Mfg. Co. (Book)..A
WIS.—Two Rivers
Hamilton Mfg. Co. (Print-
ers' ....AA

RADIATORS

CONN.—Hartford
Whitlock Coil Pipe Co.
(Disc for Automobiles)..A
CONN.—New Haven
National Pipe Bending Co.
(Car Seat) ....B
CONN.—New London
Hopson & Chapin Mfg. Co.
(Hot Water; Steam) ..B
CONN.—Norwich
Page Boiler Co., W. H.
(Hot Water; Steam) . D
ILL.—Chicago
Amer. Radiator Co., cor.
Lake & Dearborn (Hot
Water; Steam; Cast Iron;
Pin) ....AAAA
Amer. Stove Co., 479 Case
Av. & 62 So. Canal (Gas;
Oil) ....AAAA
Kellogg-Mackey-Cameron Co.
222 Lake (Hot Water;
Steam) ....AA
ILL.—Gibson City
Gibson Iron Wks. (Hot
Water & Steam) C
ILL.—Kewanee
Western Tube Co.
(Staggered Tube Circular,
Coil, etc.) ....AAA
IND.—Indianapolis
Shirley Radiator & F'dry
Co. (Hot Water & Steam)
B
IND.—Terre Haute
Prox & Brinkman Mfg. Co.
(Hot Water; Steam) ..A
IOWA—Webster City
Webster City Steel Radiator
Co. (Hot Water; Steam)
D
KY.—Louisville
Peerless Mfg. Co. (Gas)
AA
MD.—Baltimore
Weiskittel & Son, A.,
Aliceanna & Wash'n
(Gas) ....AA
MASS.—Boston
Gurney Heater Mfg. Co.,
74 Franklin (Hot Water;
Steam; Cast Iron) .....B
Ingalls & Kendricken (Cast
Iron; Vertical Tube; Pin)
A
Walker & Pratt Mfg. Co.,
33 Union (Hot Water;
Steam) ....AA
Walworth Mfg. Co., 132
Federal (Hot Water;
Steam) ....AAAA
MICH.—Detroit
Detroit Heating & Lighting
Co., 335 Wight (Gas; Hot
Water) ....B
Detroit Lubricator Co.

RADIATORS (Con.)
(Steam) ....AA
Detroit Stove Wks. (Gas)
........................AAAA
MINN.—St. Paul
South Park Fdry & Machine
Co. (Hot Water; Steam)
B
MO.—St. Louis
Ringen Stove Co. (Gas)
........................AAAA
Sodemann Heat & Power
Co., 412 N. 6th (Hot
Water; Steam) ......B
NEBR.—Omaha
Crane Co. (Steam) .....A
N. H.—Exeter
Exeter Machine Wks. (Hot
Water; Steam) ....B
N. Y.—Buffalo
Niagara Radiator Co. (Hot
Water; Steam) ....A
N. Y.—Newburgh
Ross Radiator Co. (Smoke-
pipe) ....B
New York City
Crane Co., Wm. M., 1131
B'way (Gas; Oil) .....A
Criterion Gas Stove Mfg.
Co., 447 Greenwich (Gas)
X
Eaton, Cole & Burnham Co.
(Steam) ....AAAA
Griffing Iron Co., A. A.
(Cast Iron; Hot Water
Pin; Vertical Tube) ..AA
Mott Iron Wks, J. L., 84
Beekman (Hot Water;
Steam) ....AA
Nason Mfg. Co., 71 Beek-
man (Hot Water; Steam;
Vertical Tube) ....B
Smith Co., H. B., 133
Centre (Hot Water;
Steam; Pin) ....AA
Southard-Robertson Co., 257
Water (Gas) ....B
Union Stove Wks, 70 Beek-
man (Gas) ....AA
N. Y.—Rochester
Castle & Co., Wilmot (Hot
Air; Steam) ....B
Rochester Radiator Co., 268
State (Stove Pipe) ....E
N. Y.—Syracuse
Pierce, Butler & Pierce Mfg
Co. (Hot Water; Steam)
AAA
OHIO—Ashtabula
Barber Mfg. Co. (Stove
Pipe) C
OHIO—Canton
Aultman Co. (Automobile)
AAAA
McLain Co., J. H. (Hot
Water; Steam) ......AA
Novelty Iron Co. (Hot
Water; Steam) ....A
OHIO—Cleveland
Dangler Stove & Mfg. Co.
(Br. Amer. Stove Co.)
(Gas; Oil) ....AAAA
OHIO—Columbus
Elk Heater Mfg. Co.
(Natural Gas) ......F
PA.—Erie
Jarecki Mfg. Co. (Hot
Water; Steam) ....AAAA
PA.—Johnstown
National Radiator Co. (Hot
Water; Steam) ......A
PA.—Lancaster
Best Engine & Boiler Wks.
(Hot Water; Steam)....B
PA.—Lansdale
Heebner & Sons (Hot
Water; Steam) ......A
PA.—Philadelphia
Devlin Mfg. Co., Thos. (Gas;
Hot Water; Steam) ..AA
Fowler & Wolfe Mfg. Co.
(Phila. Bourse) (Hot
Water; Steam) ......A
Phila. Hdw. & Malleable
Iron Wks. (Inc) 9th &
Jeff'n (Hot Water;
Steam) ....A
PA.—Reading
Reading Radiator Co. (Hot
Water; Steam) ......D
PA.—West Newton
U. S. Radiator Co. (Hot
Water; Steam) ......A

RADIATORS (Con.)

PA.—Williamsport
Steel & Robinson Co. (Hot
Water; Steam) X
PA.—York
Broomell, Schmidt & Steacy
Co. (Steam) ....A
WIS.—Milwaukee
Fuller-Warren Co. (Hot
Water; Steam) ......AAA
Milwaukee Gas Stove Co.,
139 Burrell (Gas) .....D

RADISH:
HORSE

See Condiments

RAFTS

DEL.—Wilmington
Drein & Son, Thos. (Metallic
Life) ....B
N. Y.—Brooklyn
Kahnweiler's Sons & Co.,
David (Life)..........B
New York City
Smith, John T. (Life) ....E

RAGS, PAPER
STOCK, ETC.

ALA.—Mobile
Piser & Co., Henry ......B
CONN.—Bridgeport
Gledhill & Co. C
CONN.—Hartford
Garvan, Patrick ....A
Tuckers' Sons E. C
D. C.—Washington
Broderick Bros. ....B
ILL.—Chicago
Birkenstein & Son, S., 48
Michigan ....B
Chicago Paper Stock Co.,
248 W. Randolph C
Doppelt, Jacob, 79 Market
C
Kaufmann, Moses, 200
Mich. Av. C
Loewenthal Bros. & Co., B.,
515 S. Canal ......AAAA
Pioneer Paper Stock Co.,
318-324 S. Desplaines &
105-107 Law Av. C
Sleph & Jaffe, 653 S. Canal
C
Standard Paper Stock Co.
C
IND.—Anderson
Ziegler, J. C
IND.—Ft. Wayne
Bash & Co., S. C
Weil Bros. ....A
IND.—Goshen
Blumenberg & Tobias C
IND.—Terre Haute
Duncan & Kingsolver ....B
IOWA—Davenport
Raphael, Jacob C
MAINE—Waterville
Buxton & Son Co., The E.
C
MD.—Baltimore
Fenton & Co., M. C., 18 W.
Pratt ....B
Hoopes & Radford, 1018
Ashland ....B
Tyler, Armenius, 500 Light
C
Winternitz, Hiram, 221 S.
Howard C
Winternitz, Samuel G., 214
S. Howard ....A
Woolford, N. B., 916 S.
B'way ....B
MASS.—Boston
Bishop, Robt. (Est of), 157
W. 6th ....B
Butterworth & Co., Edwin,
58 Federal ....A
Carter, Rice & Co., 246
Devonshire ....AA
Corbett & Co., W. J., A near
Binford ....A
Emerson & Co., A., 683
Atlantic Av. C
Hill & Cutler, 567-569
Atlantic Av. ....B
Lodge & Co., J. T., 555
Atlantic Av. ....B

RAGS (Con.)

Remick & Co., T., 489
Atlantic Av. ....A
Train-Smith Co., 24 Federal
C
MASS.—Fall River
Massasoit Mfg. Co. ......A
MASS.—New Bedford
McCullough, John C
MASS.—Springfield
Castle, Gottheil & Overton
B
Mayo & Co., A. N. ......A
MICH.—Detroit
American Paper Stock Co.
C
MO.—St. Louis
Columbia Paper Stock Co.
C
Graham Paper Co. ....AA
N. Y.—Albany
Albany Waste & Metal Co.
A
N. Y.—Brooklyn
Hughes, Lawrence, 229
Union Av. ....B
Hughes, Wm., 84 Metropoli-
tan Av. ....B
Shaw, Wm C., 59 Sedgwick
C
N. Y.—Buffalo
Hayman & Co., M. .....B
Hofeller & Co., Theo. ....B
Ullmans' Sons, D. ....B
New York City
Buterworth & Co., Edwin,
132 Nassau ....AAA
Castle, Gottheil & Overton,
Times Bldg. ....B
Lamport Mfrs. Supply Co.,
92 Walker C
Libmann & Co., Jos., 351
B'way ....B
Lyon & Co., John H., 176
Duane ....A
McGuire, Michael, 102 10th
Av. & 361 W. 16th ....B
Mitchell, Michael, 42 Watts
B
Rawitser & Co., S., 287 W.
Bway. ....AA
Samuel & Sons, M., 760
Washington ....A
Schofield & Co., Geo., 12
Lispenard ....B
N. Y.—Oneonta
Moody & Gould ....B
N. Y.—Rochester
Hey & Co. C
N. Y.—Syracuse
Garrett, J. & F. B. .....B
N. Y.—Troy
Troy Waste Mfg. Co. .....A
OHIO—Columbus
Basch Bros. C
OHIO—Dayton
Blau Bros. C
Israel Bros. C
OHIO—Cincinnati
Bowen. E., 120 E. 6th ....B
PA.—Allentown
Sofransky & Son. H. C
PA.—Philadelphia
Badger, Evan, 916 Cherry C

RAILINGS

See also Fixtures

CAL.—Los Angeles
Biescar, Henry, 118 S. An-
derson (Bank; Office) .C
CAL.—San Francisco
Brunswick - Balke - Collen-
der Co., 655 Market
(Bank; Office) ..AAAA
Calif. Artistic Metal & Wire
Co. (Bank; Office) ....D
Garrett & Co., W. S., 138
Fremont (Bank; Office)
AA
Ralston Iron Wks. 222 How-
ard (Bank; Office) C
San Francisco Novelty &
Plating Wks. (Bank; Of-
fice) ....B
COLO.—Denver
Denver Wire & Iron Wks.,
1403 Market (Bank; Of-
fice) ....D
Richter Iron Wks., 1521
Stout (Bank; Office) ..H

RAILINGS (Con.)

CONN.—Bridgeport
Barnes, T. M., 151 Middle
(Bank; Office) ....A
CONN.—Georgetown
Gilbert & Bennett Mfg. Co.
(Wire) ....AAA
CONN.—Hartford
Howard & Co., Jas. L.
(Bank; Office) ....A
CONN.—Meriden
Bradley & Hubbard Mfg. Co.
(Bank; Office) ....AAAA
CONN.—New Haven
Smith & Co., Edw. F., 23
Center (Bank; Office,
etc.) ....A
CONN.—Norwich
Norwich Nickel & Brass Co.
(Bank; Office; Plated
Counter; Brass Desk) ..B
CONN.—West Haven
Yale Safe & Iron Co., 16
Richards (Bank; Office,
etc.) ....D
GA.—Atlanta
Atlanta Wire & Iron Wks.
(Bridge; Cemetery) ...F
GA.—Dalton
Manly Machine Co. (Bal-
cony) X
GA.—Savannah
Kehoe & Co., Wm. (Iron) A
ILL.—Chicago
Barbee Wire & Iron Wks.
(Church; Theatre; Floor;
Iron; Bank; Office; Coun-
ter; Wire; Boat) ......B
Booth, John. 116 Lake
(Bank; Office, etc.) ...B
Braumoeller & Sons, Hy.
(Balcony, Iron) ....B
Chicago Ornamental Iron Co.
(Bank; Office; Bronze;
Architectural, etc.) C
Gilbert & Bennett Mfg. Co.,
153 Lake (Bank; Office,
etc.) ....AAA
Globe Iron Wks. (Iron) ..B
Hickey Wire & Iron Wks.,
M. H., 54 Dearborn (Ceme-
tery) ....F
Smith Wire & Iron Wks., F.
P., 100 Lake (Bank; Of-
fice; Cemetery) ....B
Snead Architectural Iron
Wks., 10th & Hill (Bank;
Office) C
Turner Brass Wks. (Bank;
Office, etc.) ....D
Winslow Bros. Co., 368 Car-
rol Av. (Bank; Office;
Iron; Bronze; Brass) ..AA
ILL.—Edwardsville
Edwardsville Brass Co.
(Bank; Office) ....B
ILL.—Rockford
Andrews Wire & Iron Wks.
(Bank; Office) ....D
IND.—Evansville
Mesker & Co., Geo. L.
(Bank; Office) ......AA
IOWA—Dubuque
Carr, Ryder & Adams Co.,
Jackson, 9th & 10th
(Bank; Office) ....A
KY.—Louisville
Dow Wire Wks. Co., 730 W.
Market (Bank; Office) ..D
MAINE—Portland
Megquire & Jones Co., 33
Pearl (Bank; Office) B
MD.—Baltimore
Balderston & Son, H., 119
Light (Bank; Office) ..D
Dufur & Co., 311 N. How-
ard (Bank; Office; Ceme-
tery) ....B
MASS.—Boston
Bay State Brass Foundry,
155 A. (Bank; Office) ..D
Chelmsford Foundry Co.
(Bank; Office) ....B
Jones & Co., M. D., 71 Port-
land (Cemetery) ....F
Morse & Whyte, 75 Cornhill
(Bank; Office) ....A
Murdock Parlor Grate Co.,
156 Boylston (Bank; Of-
fice) ....B
National Mfg. Co., 72 Equi-
table Bldg. (Bank; Office)
B

RAILINGS (Con.)

MASS.—Clinton
Clinton Wire Cloth Co. (Of-
fice Fixtures) ......AAA
MASS.—Lowell
Rice & Co., 251 Mount Ver-
non (Bank; Office) ....D
MASS.—Springfield
Bigelow-Cheney Wire Wks.
(Bank; Office) ....A
Chapman & Co., J. B.
(Brass) ....E
Emery Mfg. Co., P. P., 48
Hampden (Bank; Office)
C
Springfield Iron Wks., 108
Taylor (Bank; Office) D
MASS.—Worcester
Dean & Co., H. E., 180 Aus-
tin (Bank; Office) ....D
Eastern Bridge & Structural
Co. (Bridge) ....B
National Mfg. Co. (Wire) A
Wright Wire Co. (Bank;
Office) ....AA
MICH.—Detroit
Acme Fancy Wire Wks.
(Balcony; Boat) ....D
Amos & Co., Chas., 94 W.
Larned (Cemetery) .....E
Barnum Wire & Iron Wks.,
E. T., 103 Shelby (Bank;
Office; Cemetery) .....B
Bolles Iron & Wire Wks., J.
E. (Balcony; Bank; Of-
fice; Counter; Wire) ...X
Inglis Iron & Wire Wks., 59
Woodbridge (Bank; Of-
fice) ....D
Vulcan Co. (Cemetery) ..F
MICH.—Grand Rapids
Grand Rapids Co. (Bank;
Office; Church; Theatre)
A
MINN.—Minneapolis
Crown Iron Wks. Co., 113
Second Av. S. E. (Bridge)
B
Flour City Ornamental Iron
Wks., 27th Av. & 27th
(Bank; Office, etc.) ...C
MINN.—St. Paul
Herzog Iron Wks. (Bank;
Office, etc.) ....D
Perkins Mfg. Co., 1121 E.
7th (Bank; Office, etc.) D
MO.—Kansas City
Kansas City Wire & Iron
Wks. (Bank; Office;
Wire) ....B
MO.—St. Louis
Globe Iron & Foundry Co.,
9th & Victor (Bank; Of-
fice, etc.) ....B
Koken Iron Wks., Koken
Bldg. (Bank; Office, etc.)
AA
Ludlow, Saylor Wire Co.,
4th & Elm (Bank; Office,
etc.) ....A
St. Louis Wire & Iron Co.,
520 Chouteau Av. (Bank;
Office, etc.) ....E
Union Iron & Foundry Co.,
1458 S. 2nd (Bank; Office,
etc.) ....B
NEBR.—Omaha
Champion Wire & Iron Wks.
617 S. 16th (Bank; Office,
etc.) ....F
N. J.—Belleville
De Witt Wire Cloth Co.
(Bank; Office, etc.) ..A
N. J.—Boonton
Lincoln Iron Wks. (Iron) A
N. Y.—Binghamton
Titchener & Co., E. H., 8
Spring (Bank; Office,
etc.) ....B
N. Y.—Brooklyn
Durst, Wm., 135 Front
(Bank; Office, etc.) ...D
Hecla Iron Wks. (Iron;
Wire) ....AA
Lister & Fee, 35 S. 5th
(Cemetery) ....F
McMurray, Wm. H., 365
Harman (Bank; Office;
etc.) ....D
N. Y.—Buffalo
Sanford, Thos. F., 198 Sene-
ca (Bank; Office, etc.) D
N. Y.—Marathon
Climax Road Machine Co.

RAILINGS (Con.)
(Bridge) ....B

New York City

Bayer, Gardiner & Himes, 157 W. 29th (Bank; Office, etc.) ....D

Cabaret, Paul E., 342 W. 14th (Bank; Office, etc.)D

Cabble, Wm., 43 Fulton (Bank; Office, etc.) ....B

Clinton Wire Cloth Co., 33 Park Pl. (Bank; Office, etc.) ....A

Cornell Co., J. B. & J. M. (Iron) ....AA

De Witt Wire Cloth Co., 17 Warren (Bank; Office, etc.) ....A

Fiske Iron Wks., J. W., 39 Park Pl. (Bank; Office, etc.) ....A

Gould's Son & Co., M., 83 Reade (Brass; Bronze; Bank; Office, etc.) ..A

Hopkins & Co., 198 W. Bway. (Bank; Office, etc.) C

Howard & Morse, 45 Fulton (Balcony; Bank; Office; Brass; Cemetery; Counter; Iron; Wire) ....D

Jackson Co., W. H. (Bank; Office, etc.) C

Judd & Co., H. L. (Plated Counter; Brass, Desk) AA

Lobel-Andrews Co., 531 W. 55th (Bank; Office, etc.)A

McLean, John, 298 Monroe (Cemetery) ....D

Manhattan Brass Co., 334 E. 28th (Bank; Office, etc.) ....AA

Mott Iron Wks., J. L. (Iron) ....AA

New York Brass & Wire Wks. Co., 177 Grand (Bank; Office, etc.) ..D

Pitt Composite Iron Wks., Wm. R., 111 Fifth Av. (Bank; Office; Bridge, etc.) ....D

Tyler Co., W. S., 11 Bway. (Bank; Office, etc.) AAA

Union Equipment & Bronze Co. (Altar) ....D

Westervelt, A. B. & W. T., 102 Chambers (Bank; Office, etc.) ....B

Williams, John, 556 W. 27th (Bank; Office, etc.) ..B

Williams & Sons, Geo. A., 85 Fulton (Bank; Office, etc.) ....B

N. Y.—Rochester

Snow Wire Wks. Co., 76 Exchange (Bank; Office; Brass, etc.) ....D

N. Y.—Troy

Mahoney Mfg. Co. (Iron) B

OHIO—Cincinnati

Art Metal Construction Co. (Bank; Office, etc.) ..A

Bromwell Brush & Wire Goods Co. (Bank; Office) ....AA

Kinsley, Jno. R., 115 E. 6th (Bank; Office, etc) ....A

Michaels, Lewis, 216 W. Pearl (Bank; Office, etc.) ....D

Stewart Iron Wks., 714 E. 3d (Cemetery) ....A

OHIO—Cleveland

Cleveland Ornamental Fixture Co., 60 High (Bank; Office, etc.) C

Forest City Steel & Iron Co., 10 Ramsey (Bank; Office, etc.) ....A

Van Dorn Iron Wks. Co. 1793 E. Madison Av. (Bank; Office, etc.) ....A

OHIO—Columbus

Columbus Brass Co., 94 N. 6th (Bank; Office, etc.) B

Kinkade & Liggett, Jeff. & Curtis Av. (Bank; Office) ....D

OHIO—Dayton

City Forge & Iron Wks. (Office Fixtures) ......D

OHIO—Hamilton

Meyer's Mfg. Co.. F. T.

RAILINGS (Con.)
(Balcony; Bank; Office; Cemetery; Counter; Wire) ....B

OHIO—Kenton

Champion Iron Co. (Balcony; Cemetery; Iron) ......AA

OHIO—Springfield

Rogers Iron Co. (Bank; Office; Bridge) C

OHIO—Toledo

Donovan Wire & Iron Wks. (Bank; Office) C

PA.—Allegheny

Albree Iron Wks. Co., Chester B., 1115 Market (Bridge) ....A

PA.—Mont Clare

Hallman, Oliver (Bridge) F

PA.—Philadelphia

Belmont Iron Wks., 22nd & Washn. Av. (Bank; Office; Bridge) ....A

Darby & Sons, Edw. (Bank; Office; Iron) ....A

De Witt Wire Cloth Co., 703 Market (Bank; Office) A

Gaumer Co., John L. (Brass) C

Gensel & Co., Fred. (Bank; Office) ....D

Giese & Goodyear Co., 1021 Ridge Av. (Bank; Office)

Halstead & Co., 1129 Cherry (Bank; Office) ....D

Jackson & Cook, 318 Market (Bank; Office) ....A

Merritt & Co., 1024 Ridge Av. (Bridge; Cemetery) E

Remppis Co., Wm. F., Witherspoon Bldg. (Bank; Office) C

PA.—Pittsburg

Marshall Bros. (Iron) ...AA

Phoenix Steel Construction Co., Penna. & 3d (Bridge) ....G

Pittsburg Brass Mfg. Co., 107 Wood (Bank; Office) ....D

Vilsack Co., Martin, 3230 Penn Av. (Bridge) ....E

PA.—South Bethlehem

Bethlehem Foundry & Machine Co. (Bridge) C

TENN.—Chattanooga

Ornamental Iron & Wire Co. (Bank; Office) ....B

VA.—Norfolk

Roper Lumber Co., Jno. L. (Cedar) ....AAA

WIS.—Milwaukee

Bayley & Sons Co., Wm. (Bank; Office; Cemetery) ....A

Loeffelholz & Co., 170 Clinton (Bank; Office) ....A

Wagner, A. F., 514 Market (Bank; Office) ....D

Wisconsin Iron & Wire Wks. 186 E. Water (Bank; Office) ....D

RAILS

See also Hardware; Carriage

COLO.—Denver

Colorado Fuel & Iron Co. (Light Steel) ....B

CONN.—Bridgeport

Bridgeport Brass Co. (Brass Door; Door; Barn Door) ....AAA

CONN.—Derby

Burmingham Iron Fdry. (Iron) ....AA

CONN.—Mount Carmel

Woodruff & Sons, Walter W. (Dash) ....A

CONN.—New Britain

Russell & Erwin Mfg. Co. (Door; Barn Door) AAAA

Stanley Works (Door; Barn Door) ....AAA

Union Mfg. Co. (Barn Door; Door) ....AA

CONN.—New Haven

Dann Bros. & Co. (Best Wood Seat) .,........B

CONN.—Norwich

Norwich Nickel & Brass Co.

RAILS (Con.)
(Plated Counter) ......B
CONN.—Plantsville
Blakeslee Forging Co.
(Spindle) ....B
CONN.—Southington
Peck, Stow & Wilcox Co.
(Door; Barn Door) AAAA
CONN.—Stamford
Yale & Towne Mfg. Co.
(Sliding Door) ....AAAA
CONN.—Waterbury
Benedict & Burnham Mfg.
Co. (Door) ....AAAA
Holmes, Booth & Hayden
Co. (Door; Brass Door)
..................AAAA
Plume & Atwood Mfg. Co.
(Door; Brass Door) AAA
Scovill Mfg. Co. (Door;
Barn Door) ....AAAA
Waterbury Brass Co. (Door)
..................AAAA
ILL.—Aurora
Richards Mfg. Co. (Door;
Barn Door) ....A
Wilcox Mfg. Co. (Sliding
Door; Barn Door) ......B
ILL.—Chicago
Chicago Spring Butt. Co.
(Door; Barn Door) ....B
Illinois Steel Co. (The Rook-
ery) Light Steel) ..AAAA
Morden Frog & Crossing
Works (Guard) ....A
Republic Iron & Steel Co.
(Light Steel) ....AAAA
ILL.—Chicago Heights
Inland Steel Co. (Light)
..................AAAA
ILL.—De Kalb
De Kalb Fence Co. (Steel)
.....................AA
ILL.—Harvard
Hunt, Helm, Ferris & Co.
(Barn Door) ....AA
ILL.—Ottawa
Porter Co., J. E. (Door;
Barn Door) ....A
ILL.—Sterling
Lawrence Bros. (Barn Door)
..................AAA
National Mfg. Co. (Door;
Barn Door) C
MD.—Cumberland
Maryland Rail Co. (Steel,
Light, 12 to 35 lbs.) ...B
MASS.—Boston
Harrington, Robinson &
Co. (Second Hand) ....D
MASS.—Cambridge
Barbour Stockwell Co. (Iron;
Girder; Steel) ....A
MICH.—Albion
Prouty Co., (Ltd.) T. C.
(Barn Door) ....B
MICH.—Detroit
Amos & Co., Chas. A., 94 W.
Larned (Brass Altar) ...E
Detroit Shipbuilding Co.
(Brass Dept. — Hand;
Foot) ....AAAA
MO.—St. Louis
Harry Steel Works, O. K.
(Light T.) ....B
Kupferle, Jno. C. (Door;
Barn; Sliding Door, etc.)
.....................AA
N. J.—Harrison
Atha Steel Co. (Mine)AAAA
N. J.—Newark
Searles Mfg. Co. (Dash) .B
N. J.—Trenton
Trenton Iron Co. (Sus-
pended) ....A
N. Y.—Auburn
Clapp Mfg. Co., E. D.
(Shifting) ....B
N. Y.—Binghamton
Crandal Stone & Co.
(Shifting) ....A
N. Y.—Brooklyn
Logan Iron Works (Light
T.) ....B
N. Y.—Buffalo
Lackawanna Steel Co.
(Light Steel) ....AAAA
Pratt & Letchworth Co.
(Shifting) ....AAA
N. Y.—Elmira
Crook & Carrier Mfg. Co.
(Sliding Door; Door; Barn
Door) ....B

RAILS (Con.)
N. Y.—Long Island City
Steubner, G. L. (Steel) ..C
New York City
Ansonia Brass & Copper Co.
(Brass Door) ....AAAA
Carey, Geo. H. (Iron; Sec-
ond Hand) ....D
Church Art Work Co., 253
Fourth Av. (Brass Altar)
.....................X
Judd & Co., H. L. (Plated
Counter) ....AA
Koppel, Arthur, 68 Broad
(Steel) ....A
Leavitt & Co., C. W., 15
Cortlandt (Steel) .....D
McCabe Hanger Mfg. Co.
(Sliding Door) ....B
Metal Stamping Co.
(Shifting) ....A
Steel Rail Supply Co. (Sec-
ond Hand) ....A
N. Y.—Poughkeepsie
Lane Bros. Co. (Door; Barn
Door) ....A
N. Y.—Rome
Rome Brass & Copper Co.
(Door) ....AAAA
N. Y.—Syracuse
Stearns & Co., E. C.
(Door) ....AA
N. Y.—Tonawanda
Buffalo Steel Co. (Light)AA
OHIO—Ashland
Safety Door Hanger Co.
(Door; Barn Door) ....D
OHIO—Cambridge
Cambridge Rolling Mill Co.
(Light) ....B
OHIO—Canton
Wey Mfg. Co. (Suspended;
Door; Barn Door) ....B
OHIO—Cincinnati
Corcoran's Sons, Thos. H.
(Dash) ....B
OHIO—Cleveland
Atlas Car & Mfg. Co. (Light
Steel) ....AA
Chisholm & Moore Mfg. Co.
(Door; Barn Door) ....AA
Fulton Foundry Co. (Curved;
Iron; Steel; Street) ..C
OHIO—Columbus
Peters & Herrin Dash Co.
(Dash) C
OHIO—Dayton
Dayton Mfg. Co. (Car Plat-
form) ....A
PA.—Allegheny
McKinney Mfg. Co. (Door;
Barn Door) ....AAA
PA.—Allentown
Allentown Rolling Mills
(Iron; Steel) ......AAA
PA.—Erie
Griffin Mfg. Co. (Door;
Barn Door) ....A
PA.—Hollidaysburg
Hollidaysburg Iron & Nail
Co. (Light) ....A
PA.—Philadelphia
Cambria Steel Co. ....AAAA
Camden Iron Works (Iron;
Light T.; Steel Street;
Sliding Door) ....A
Conard, T. P., 119 S. 4th
(Steel) C
Donaldson & Newton, 421
Chestnut (Light. Steel) D
Frankford Steel & Forging
Co. (Steel) X
Harrington, Son & Co., Ed-
win, 1515 Penna. Av. (Sus-
pended) ....AA
Wharton & Co., Wm. Jr.
(Inc.) (Curved; Steel;
Street) ....AAA
PA.—Pittsburg
Baumgarten & Bros., A. F.,
Farmers Bank Bldg.
(Light) C
Carnegie Steel Co. (Ltd.)
Carnegie Bldg. (Steel;
Iron; Light T.) ....AAAA
Jones & Laughlins Steel Co.
(Ltd.) (Light up to 40
lb.; Steel; Mine) AAAA
McKenna Bros. Brass Co.
(Door; Barn Door) ....A
Standard Chain Co. (Light
12 to 14 lbs.) ....AAAA

884

RAILS (Con.)

PA.—Reading
Penn Hardware Co. (Sliding Door) ....AA
Reading Hardware Co. (Door; Barn Door) AAAA
Reading Iron Co. (Light Steel) ....AAAA

PA.—South Bethlehem
Bethlehem Iron Co. (Iron; Steel) ....AAAA

PA.—Steelton
Pennsylvania Steel Co. (Light; Sliding Door; Steel; Curved; Guard; Light T.; Mine; Street; Garden) ....AAAA

PA.—Tamaqua
Tamaqua Mfg. Co. (Stool)B

R. I.—Providence
New England Butt Co. (Barn Door) ....AA

TENN.—Knoxville
Knoxville Iron Co. (Light T.) ....AA

W. VA.—Fairmont
Fairmont Steel Co. (Light) B

W. VA.—Huntington
Union Rail Co. (Light) ..X

WIS.—South Milwaukee
Stowell Mfg. & Foundry Co. (Barn Door; Steel Door) A

RAILWAYS

ILL.—Chicago
Hoisting & Conveying Machine Co., 44 N. Elizabeth (Industrial) ....E

ILL.—Harvey
Whiting Foundry Equipment Co. (Industrial) ......AA

IND.—Mishawaka
Dodge Mfg. Co. (Industrial) AAA

MD.—Baltimore
Poole Engineering & Machine Co. (Marine) ..AA

MASS.—Boston
Sturtevant Co., B. F. (Industrial) ....AAA

MICH.—Detroit
Russell Wheel & Foundry Co. (Industrial) ......AA

MINN.—Minneapolis
Peteler Portable Railway Mfg. Co. (Portable) ...C

N. J.—Trenton
Trenton Iron Co. (Elevated) A

New York City
Koppel, Arthur (Industrial; Portable) ....A
Krajewski, Pesant & Co. (Marine) ....AA
N. Jersey Foundry & Machine Co. (Industrial) B
Turls Sons, John (Plantaion Portable) ....D

N. Y.—North Tonawanda
Armitage - Herschell Co. (Miniature, Steam; Mountain) C

N. Y.—West New Brighton
Hunt Co., C. W. (Industrial) AA

OHIO—Cincinnati
Creaghead Engineering Co. (Electric) ....D

OHIO—Cleveland
Atlas Car & Mfg. Co. (Industrial) ....AA
King Bridge Co. (Elevated) AAAA

PA.—Philadelphia
Pennsylvania Steel Co. (Elevated; Portable) ..AAAA
Phoenix Bridge Co. (Elevated) ....A
Wharton Jr. & Co., Wm. (Portable; Mine; Electric) AAA

PA.—Pittsburg
Westinghouse Electric & Mfg. Co. (Electric) AAAA

RAIN COATS

See Clothing: Men's

RAISERS

CONN.—Norwich

RAISERS (Con.)
Rogers & Co., C. B. (Panel) AAAA

ILL.—Chicago
Boyd, Jno. (Cream) ......B

ILL.—Rockford
Palmer Co., H. H. (Cream) D

IOWA—Clinton
Moseley & Pritchard Mfg. Co. (Cream) ....D

MICH.—Flint
Flint Cabinet Creamery Co. (Cream) ....E

MICH.—Grand Rapids
Grand Rapids Refrigerator Co. (Cream) ....A

N. J.—Smithville
Smith Machine Co., H. B. (Panel) ....A

New York City
American Wood Working Machine Co. (Panel)AAAA

N. Y.—Syracuse
Gowing, D. H. (Cream) ...C

N. Y.—Utica
Jones, Frank L. (Cream) C

OHIO—Cincinnati
Fay, J. A. & Egan Co. (Panel) ....AAAA

PA.—Philadelphia
Colladay, Jos. O. (Panel) B
Power & Co., C. L. (Panel)A

VT.—Bellows Falls
Vermont Farm Machine Co. (Cream) C

VT.—Rutland
Stoddard Mfg. Co. (Cream) B

WIS.—Beloit
Berlin Machine Works (Panel) ....AAAA

WIS.—Fort Atkinson
Cornish, Curtis & Greene Mfg. Co. (Cream) ....A
Hoard, A. R. (Cream) ....A

WIS.—Whitewater
Billett & Marshall (Cream) B

RAISINS

CAL.—Armona
Armsby Co., J. K. (Br. Chicago) ....A
Downing, Chas. C

CAL.—Fowler
Chaddock & Co. ....A
Phoenix Raisin Seeding & Pack. Co. ....B

CAL.—Fresno
Bonner Vineyard Co. ....B
Calif. Raisin Growers' Assn. A
Castle Bros. (Br. San Fran.) AA
Co-operative Packers Assn. B
Forsyth Seeded Raisin Co. B
Griffin & Skelley Co. (Br. San Fran.) ......A
Inderrieden & Co., J. B. AA
Phoenix Raisin Seeding & Pack. Co. ....B
Producers Raisin Packing Co. ....B
St. George Vineyard ......B

CAL.—Kingsburg
Kingsburg Co-op. Pack. Assn. C

CAL.—Los Angeles
Germain Fruit Co. ......A
Simpson & Hack Fruit Co. (Inc.) C

CAL.—Madera
Sayre, A. L. ....B

CAL.—Modesto
McHenry Seeded Raisin Co. AA

CAL.—Oleander
Oleander Pack Co. C

CAL.—Riverside
Pattee & Lett Co. ....AAAA

CAL.—San Francisco
Armsby Co., J. K. ......A
Castle Bros., 413 Mission AA
Eggers Vineyard Co., 214 Calif. ....A
Guggenhime & Co., 118 Davis ....A
Phoenix Raisin Seeding & Pack. Co. ....B
Rosenberg Bros. Co., 211 Calif. ....A

RAISINS (Con.)
CAL.—San Jose
Castle Bros ....AA
Griffin & Skelley Co. ....A
Phoenix Raisin Seeding &
Pack. Co. ....B
CAL.—Selma
Matthews & Jones C
CAL.—Visalia
Downing, Charles C
New York City
Hartwig & Bennett, 61 N.
Moore ....A
Higgins & Co., W. A., 374
Washn. ....B

RAKES

See also Agr. Imps

CAL.—San Francisco
Jackson - Bryan Machine
Works, 411 Market
(Hand Hay; Horse Hay)
........................A
CONN.—Higganum
Scovill, D. & H. (Iron
Hand) ....A
CONN.—New Hartford
Rogers Rake Co. (Wooden
Hand; Hand Hay) .....E
ILL.—Belleville
Sucker State Drill Co.
(Sulky; Hay) =........A
ILL.—Bradley
Bradley Mfg. Co., David
(Horse Hay; Sulky Hay)
.....................AAA
ILL.—Chicago
International Harvester Co.
(Horse; Sulky Hay) ....
.....................AAAA
ILL.—Decatur
Chambers - Bering - Quin-
lan Co. (Side Delivery
Hay) ....A
ILL.—Dixon
Grand Detour Plow Co.
(Sulky Hay) ....AA
ILL.—Lincoln
Sheer, Eugene (Stalk) ...D
ILL.—Moline
Deere & Mansur Co. (Hand
Hay; Side Delivery Hay;
Horse Hay; Sulky Hay) ..
.....................AAAA
Moline Plow Co. (Sulky
Hay) ....AAAA
ILL.—Peoria
Luthy & Co. (Stalk) ....A
ILL.—Rockford
Emerson Mfg. Co. (Inc.)
(Horse Hay; Sulky Hay)
.....................AAA
ILL.—Rock Island
Rock Island Plow Co.
(Steel) ....AAAA
ILL.—Sandwich
Sandwich Mfg. Co. (Horse
Hay) ....AA
ILL.—Sterling
Keystone Co. (Side Delivery
Hay; Drag; Horse Hay)
.....................AA
Sterling Mfg. Co. (Revolv-
ing Hay; Side Delivery;
Hay; Horse; Sulky Hay)
........................A
ILL.—Liberty
Rude Bros. Mfg. Co. (Sul-
ky; Hay) ....A
IND.—Richmond
Wayne Works (Wooden;
Hay) ....=..........A
IND.—Terre Haute
Terre Haute Shovel & Tool
Co. (Iron Hand) ......A
IND.—Vernon
Reed & Rogers Mfg. Co.
(Revolving Hay) .....E
IOWA—Fort Madison
Iowa Farming Tool Co.
(Garden or Lawn Hand;
Hay) ....AA
IOWA—Ottumwa
Dain Mfg. Co. (Side Deliv-
ery Hay) ....AA
MASS.—Chicopee Falls
Belcher & Taylor Agricul-
tural Tool Co. (Horse;
Hay; Sulky Hay) .....A
MASS.—Greenfield
Rugg Mfg. Co. (Wooden

RAKES (Con.)
Hand; Drag; Hand Hay)
........................E
MASS.—Tyringham
Garfield, D. M. (Hand
Hay) ....F
MASS.—Winchendon
Streeter, Alvin (Coal;
Ballast) ....A
MICH.—Charlotte
Benton Mfg. Co. (Wooden
Hand; Wooden Hay;
Horse Hay) ....A
MICH.—Jackson
Withington & Cooley Mfg.
Co. (Garden or Lawn;
Steel; Clam; Gravel; As-
phalt; Ballast) ......AA
MICH.—Kalamazoo
Reed Mfg. Co. (Hay)...D
MINN.—Minneapolis
Howell & Co., R. R.
(Sulky Hay) ....B
N. H.—Marlow
Phelps, F. (Wooden Hand)
........................G
N. H.—South Tamworth
Bartlett & Son, L. B.
(Wooden Hand) ....E
N. H.—Sunapee
Alexander & Perkins (Gar-
den or Lawn) ....F
Sleeper, B. R. (Garden or
Lawn) ....G
N. Y.—Auburn
Osborn & Co., D. M. (Spring
Tooth; Horse Hay).....
.....................AAAA
N. Y.—Buffalo
Buffalo-Pitts. Co. (Hay)...
.....................AAAA
N. Y.—Canastota
Patton & Stafford (Wooden
Hand; Sulky Hay) ....A
N. Y.—Elmira
Cronk & Carrier Mfg. Co.
(Brace - Wrought Steel;
Malleable Iron; Garden
or Lawn) ....B
N. Y.—Frankfort
Continental Tool Co. (Solid
Steel; also Malleable Gar-
den or Lawn Ban) .....A
N. Y.—Hoosick Falls
Wood Mowing & Reaping
Machine Co. (Horse; Sul-
ky Hay) ....AAAA
N. Y.—Ithaca
Williams Bros. (Horse;
Sulky Hay) ....AA
N. Y.—Napanoch
Whiteley, W. W. (Wooden
Hand) =..............H
N. Y.—Newburgh
Coldwell Lawn Mower Co.
(Lawn) ....A
N. Y.—Troy
Lane & Gale (Iron; Hand)
........................A
N. Y.—Union
Heath, M. (Wooden Hand)
........................F
OHIO—Burton
Burton Handle Co. (Wooden
Hand; Revolving Hay)..B
OHIO—Canfield
Canfield Mfg. & Novelty
Co. (Wooden Hand) ...E
OHIO—Canton
Gibbs Mfg. Co. (Iron Hand;
Garden; Lawn) ....A
Kohler & Co., F. E. (Gar-
den or Lawn) ....A
Ney Mfg. Co. (Automatic
Self-Cleaning Lawn)....B
OHIO—Cleveland
American Fork & Hoe Co.
(Asphalt; Garden; Lawn;
Wood; Ballast; Gravel)..
.....................AAAA
Avery Stamping Co. (Steel)
........................B
OHIO—Columbus
Brown, Hinman & Hunting-
ton Co.* (Steel; Malleable
Iron; Road; Potato, etc.)
U. S. Hoe & Tool Co. (Iron
Garden, etc.) ....A
OHIO—Dayton
Ohio Rake Co. (Revolving
Hay; Horse Hay) ....AA
Stoddard Mfg. Co. (Hand
Hay; Sulky Hay) ...AAA

836

RAKES (Con.)

OHIO—Galena
Hughes & Smythe (Revolving Hay) C
OHIO—Hamilton
Deuscher Co., H. P. (Horse Hay; Sulky Hay) .....A
Long & Allstatter Co. (Horse Hay; Sulky Hay) ....AA
OHIO—Lancaster
Hocking Valley Mfg. Co. (Sulky Hay) ....A
OHIO—Piqua
Piqua Handle & Mfg. Co. (Steel; Weldless; Malleable Iron; Garden or Lawn) ....A
OHIO—Shenandoah
McClain, J. K. (Wooden Hand) ....E
OHIO—Springfield
Mast & Co., P. P. (Horse Hay) ....AAAA
Thomas Mfg. Co. (Hand Hay; Sulky Hay; Horse Hay) ....AAA
OHIO—Tippecanoe
Miller, Jos. W. (Wooden Hand) ....G
OHIO—Trail
Brandt, G. (Wooden Hand) G
PA.—Bellefonte
Howard Iron & Tool Co. (Weldless; Steel Garden or Lawn) ....B
PA.—Elizabethtown
Buch's Sons, A. (Hay)...A
PA.—Mechanicsburg
Comstock, Geo. S. (Horse Hay; Hand Hay) C
PA.—Mifflinsburg
Allbright & Sons, J. H. (Wooden Hand) C
PA.—Morrell
Union Furnace Mfg. Co. (Malleable Iron; Garden or Lawn) ....A
PA.—Oakford
Van Sant, Edw. (Wooden Hand) ....G
PA.—Philadelphia
Myers & Ervien Co. (Iron; Hand) ....=........B
PA.—Tatamy
Messinger Mfg. Co. (Horse Hay) ....B
PA.—York
Farquhar Co., A. B. (Ltd.) (Horse Hay; Sulky Hay) AAA
Keystone Farm Machine Co. (Weeder) ....B
TENN.—Harriman
Harriman Hoe & Tool Co. (Iron; Hand) ....A
VT.—Bellows Falls
Derby & Ball (Garden or Lawn) ....B
VT.—Brookfield
Peck, Clark & Co. (Iron Hand) ....B
VT.—East Johnson
Stearns, W. H. (Wood Hand) ....D
VT.—Hartford
French, Watson & Co.(Iron; Hand) C
VT.—St. Johnsbury
Ely Hoe & Fork Co. (Iron; Hand) ....B
VT.—Wallingford
Batcheller & Sons Co. (Iron; Hand) ....A
VT.—Westminster
Wellman, H. E. (Wood Hand) ....F
W. VA.—Wheeling
Warwood Tool Co. (Iron Hand) ....A
WIS.—Beaver Dam
Rowell Mfg. Co., J. S. (Sulky; Hay) ....=A
WIS.—Beloit
Thompson & Sons Mfg. Co., J. (Stalk; Hand Hay; Horse Hay) ....AA
WIS.—Horicon
Van Brunt Mfg. Co. (Sulky Hay) ....AA
WIS.—Madison
Fuller & Johnson Mfg. Co.

RAKES (Con.)
(Hand Hay; Horse Hay; Sulky Hay) ....AAA
WIS.—Racine
Foster & Williams Mfg. Co. (Drag; Hay) ....B

RAMMERS

ILL.—Chicago
Chicago Pneumatic Tool Co. Fisher Bldg. (Foundry) AAAA
Union Elevator & Machine Co., 144 Ontario (Foundry) C
MICH.—Detroit
Anderson & Sons, W. H. (Paving) C
MO.—St. Louis
Standard Railway Equipment Co., Union Trust Bldg. (Pneumatic Foundry) ....G
OHIO—Cincinnati
Obermayer & Co., S. (Moulders'; Floor; Foundry) ....AA
OHIO—Cleveland
Osborn Mfg. Co. (Foundry) B
Smith Fdry. Supply Co. (Wood) ....D
OHIO—Piqua
Piqua Handle & Mfg. Co. (Foundry; also Moulders' Bench; Moulders' Floor) A
OHIO—Sandusky
Sandusky Tool Co., J. W. (Sandusky) ....AA
PA.—Philadelphia
Philadelphia Pneumatic Tool Co. 21st & Allegheny Av. (Foundry)...B
R. I.—Providence
Brown & Sharpe Mfg. Co. (Foundry) ....AAAA

RAMS

CAL.—San Francisco
Garratt & Co., W. T.(Inc.), 142 Fremont (Hydraulic) AA
Pelton Water Mill Co., 127 Main (Hydraulic) ...AA
CONN.—New Britain
Union Mfg. Co. (Hydraulic) AA
DEL.—Wilmington
Gawthrop, Jr., Allen, 100 W. 4th (Hydraulic) ...E
ILL.—Chicago
Fairbanks, Morse & Co., Franklin & Monroe (Hydraulic) ....AAAA
ILL.—Rockford
Trahen Pump Co. (Hydraulic) ....A
Ward Pump Co. (Hydraulic) ....B
New York City
Douglas, F. & B., 83 John (Hydraulic) .....A
Hanson & Rhodes, 157 W. 29th (Hydraulic) ....F
Power Specialty Co., 126 Liberty (Hydraulic) ...E
Watson-Stillman Co. (Hydraulic) ....A
N. Y.—Seneca Falls
Gleason-Bailey-Sciple Mfg. Co. (Hydraulic) ....D
Goulds Mfg. Co. (Hydraulic) ....AAA
Rumsey & Co. (Ltd.) (Inc.) (Hydraulic) .....A
N. Y.—Utica
Millar & Son, Chas. (Hydraulic) ....AA
OHIO—Ashland
Myers & Bros., F. E. (Hydraulic) ....AAAA
OHIO—Columbiana
Columbiana Pump Co. (Hydraulic) ....B
OHIO—Mansfield
Barnes Mfg. Co. (Hydraulic) ....A
Humphreys Mfg. Co. (Hydraulic) ....B

RAMS *(Con.)*
OHIO—Salem
Deming Co. (Hydraulic).AA
PA.—Beavertown
Kline, Jas. M. (Hydraulic)
......F
PA.—Chester
Niagara Hydraulic Engine
Co. (Hydraulic) ......B
PA.—Philadelphia
Wood & Co., R. D., 400
Chestnut (Hydraulic)....
AAAA
VA.—Waynesboro
Rife & Schoppert Co.
(Hydraulic) ....E

RANGES.

See Stoves

RASPS

See also Files

N. J.—Newark
Heller Bros. Co., 879 Mt.
Prospect Av. (Horse
Tooth) ....AA
N. Y.—Troy
Troy File Works ....D
PA.—Philadelphia
Barnett Co., G. & H......X
Disston & Sons Co., Hy.
(Horse Tooth) ....AAAA
Horn & Bros., Wm. H.
(Horse) ....B
McCaffrey File Co., 5th &
Berks ....AA
PA.—Reading
Carpenter Steel Co.
(Steel) ....B
Tragle Mfg. Co. (Veterin-
ary) ....F
R. I.—Providence
Chatterton File Works
(Horse) X
Nicholson File Co. (Horse
Tooth) ....AAAA
WIS.—Milwaukee
Milwaukee File Wks.
(Horse) ....B
Westfahl & Co., F. C

RATCHETS

CONN.—Hartford
Pratt & Whitney Co..AAAA
ILL.—Chicago
Adams & Westlake Co., On-
tario, cor. N. Franklin
(Desk Sash) ......AAA
Armstrong Bros. Tool Co.,
617 Austin Av. (Univer-
sal) ....B
Lovejoy, T. H., 90 Ohio
(Packer) ....D
ILL.—Sterling
Chain Stay Fence Co.
(Fence) ....E
MASS.—Boston
Walworth Mfg. Co...AAAA
MICH.—Jackson
Electric Oil Stove Co.
(Fence) ....B
N. Y.—Buffalo
Keystone Mfg. Co. ......B
OHIO—Cleveland
Cleveland Hardware Co.
(Wagon Brake) ......AA
OHIO—Dayton
Dayton Mfg. Co. (Desk;
Sash) ....A

RATTAN
GOODS

See Furniture

RATTAN

IND.—Indianapolis
Capital Rattan Co.......D
IND.—Michigan City
Western Cane Seating Co.
B
MASS.—Gardner
Heywood Bros. & Wakefield
Co. ....AAAA
N. Y.—Brooklyn
American Rattan & Reed
Mfg. Co., 18 Guernsey ..A

RATTAN *(Con.)*
New York City
Hale & Kilburn Mfg. Co.
(Woven) ....AAAA
Rattan & Cane Co., 66 W.
B'way ....B

RATTLERS

See also Hardware; Carriage

CONN.—Bristol
Dunbar Bros. (Anti-Shaft)
B
CONN.—Collinsville
Hartigan, Wm. R. (Anti-
Shaft) ....A
IOWA—Marshalltown
Argis Co. (Anti-Shaft)....X
MASS.—Boston
Boston Belting Co. (Anti-
Carriage; Anti-Shaft;
Window; Thill) ...AAAA
MASS.—Bridgewater
Miller's Sons, H. J. (Mail)
D
Perkins Co., Henry (Nail)
B
N. J.—Jersey City
New Jersey Car Spring &
Rubber Co. (Anti-Rubber
Shaft) ....AA
N. J.—Newark
Searls Mfg. Co. (Anti-
Shaft) ....B
N. J.—Trenton
Empire Rubber Mfg. Co.
(Anti-Shaft) ....AA
Home Rubber Co. (Anti-
Shaft) ....AA
Trenton Rubber Mfg. Co.
(Anti-Shaft) ....A
United Rubber Co. (Anti-
Window) ....AAAA
New York City
Goodyear Rubber Co. (Anti-
Shaft) ....AAAA
Gutta Percha & Rubber
Mfg. Co. (Anti-Shaft)...
AAAA
Metal Stamping Co., 468
W. B'way (Anti-Window;
Shaft) ....A
New York Belting & Pack-
ing Co. (Anti-Shaft) ...
AAA
Rubber Goods Mfg. Co., 253
B'way (Anti - Rubber
Shaft) ....AAAA
OHIO—Canton
Kohler & Co., F. E. (Anti-
Window; Carriage; Thill;
Anti-Shaft) ....B
OHIO—Cincinnati
Monarch Carriage Goods Co.
(Anti-Shaft) ....B
OHIO—Cleveland
Garry Iron & Steel Co.
(Anti-Shaft) ....A
PA.—Corry
Raymond Mfg. Co. (Ltd.)
(Anti-Shaft) ....B
PA.—North East
Fernald Mfg. Co. (Anti-
Steel Shaft) ....D
R. I.—Providence
Browne & Sharpe Mfg. Co.
AAAA

RATTLES

See also Toys

CONN.—Middletown
Kirby Mfg. Co. (Babies').B
N. J.—Newark
Celluloid Co. (Toy) ......B
N. Y.—Buffalo
Shepard & Co., Sidney
(Toy) ....AAAA
New York City
Goodyear Rubber Co. (Toy)
AAAA
Grote & Co., F. (Ivory)...D
Hodgman Rubber Co. (Toy)
A'A

RAVELERS

N. Y.—Philmont
American Raveler Co. ...X

RAWBONE

CONN.—Middletown
Rogers & Hubbard Co.
(Granulated) ....A
New York City
Coopers Glue Factory, Peter
13 Burling Slip (Boiled)
.........AA
Lister Agricultural & Chemical Wks., 26 B'way
(Granulated) ......AAAA
Taylor, Geo. F., 80 Pine
(Granulated) ....F
PA.—Carbondale
Carbondale Chemical Co.
(Granulated) ....E
PA.—York
York Chemical Wks. (Granulated) ....A

RAWHIDE

ILL.—Chicago
Chicago Rawhide Mfg. Co.
.........A
MASS.—South Attleboro
Coupe & Co., Wm. X
MICH.—Niles
National Rawhide & Belting
Co. C
N. J.—Newark
Whiting & Co., C. R.
(Trunk Binding) ....D
New York City
Neumann & Co., R.......A
Rahmann & Co., Geo. C
United States Leather Co..
.........AAAA
N. Y.—Rochester
Riggs, L. F. & G. B. ....E
OHIO—Cincinnati
Trautmont Co., C. ......A
PA.—Philadelphia
Janney & Sons, E. K..AAA

RAZORS

CONN.—Bridgeport
Challenge Cutlery Corpn..A
CONN.—Southington
Southington Cutlery Co..AA
CONN.—Wallingford
Wallace Sons Mfg. Co., R.
.........AAAA
CONN.—West Winsted
Empire Knife Co. ....B
ILL.—Chicago
Gillette Sales Co., Man
Bldg. (Safety) ....B
IOWA—Dubuque
Fox Cutlery Co. ....D
MASS.—Boston
Gillette Safety Razor Co.,
394 Atlantic Av. (Safety)
.........D
MASS.—Millbury
Buck, Charles............B
Buck Bros. ....A
MASS.—Worcester
Torrey & Co., J. R.......A
N. Y.—Geneva
Geneva Cutlery Co. ......D
N. Y.—Little Falls
Korn Razor Mfg. Co., G.
W. ....D
New York City
Kampfe Bros. (Safety)....D
Pall Mall Electric Association, 870 B'way (Safety)
.........F
Silberstein, A. L., 459
B'way (Safety) ....A
Smith & Hemenway Co., 296
B'way ....D
Wiebusch & Hilger, 9 Murray ....A
N. Y.—Rochester
Robeson Cutlery Co. .....A
N. Y.—Syracuse
Clinton Knitting Co.
(Safety) =............X
PA.—Philadelphia
Hessenbrush, H. ....A
PA.—Titusville
Schatt & Morgan Cutlery
Co. ....B

REAMERS

CONN.—Bridgeport
Bridgeport Hdw. Mfg. Co.
(Belt) ....B

REAMERS (Con.)

CONN.—Hamden
Hamden Mfg. Co. (Lead
Pipe) ....E
CONN.—Hartford
Billings & Spencer Co.
(Belt) ....AA
Pratt & Whitney Co. (Center; Chucking; Hand;
Shell; Taper; Pipe) ....
.........AAAA
CONN.—Tolland
Clough, R. M. (Shell;
Hand; Adjustable; Chucking; Expansion) ....D
ILL.—Chicago
Chicago Pneumatic Tool Co.,
Fisher Bld. (Pneumatic)
.........AAAA
Chicago Screw Co., 2 N.
Canal (Taper Pen), AAA
Crane Co. ....AAAA
Federal Co., Old Colony
Bldg. (Pipe) ....A
Standard Screw Co., 2 N.
Canal (Taper Pin)....AAA
Vaughan & Bushnell Mfg.
Co., 877 Carroll Av.
(Square) ....A
ILL.—Decatur
Mueller Mfg. Co. H. (Pipe)
.........AAA
MD.—Baltimore
Mergenthaler-Ott Co., Cor.
Claggett & Allen (Adjustable Blade) ....B
MASS.—Athol
Gay & Ward ....A
MASS.—Boston
Lapointe Machine Tool Co.,
36 Hartford (Adjustable)
.........D
Walworth Mfg. Co., 132
Federal (Pipe) ....AAAA
MASS.—Brockton
Tuck Mfg. Co. ....E
MASS.—Fitchburg
Putnam Machine Co. (Locomotive Work; Sheel;
Pipe) ....A
MASS.—Greenfield
Wells Bros. Co. (Bit Brace
Pipe) ....A
Reece Co., E. F. ....D
Wiley & Russell Mfg. Co.
(Bit Brace; Bridge; Center; Chucking; Hand;
Shell; Taper; Pipe) ..AA
MASS.—Mansfield
Card Mfg. Co., S. W. (Center; Pipe; Expansion)...B
MASS.—Millbury
Buck, Chas ....B
Buck Bros (Square) .....A
MASS.—New Bedford
Morse Twist Drill & Machine Co. (Adjustable;
Bit; Brace; Bridge; Center; Chucking; Expansion; Hand; Shell; Taper;
Pipe; Locomotive Work)
.........AAA
MASS.—Shelburne Falls
Mayhew Co., H. H. (Bit
Brace) ....D
MASS.—Taunton
New Process Twist Drill
Co. (Chucking) X
MASS.—Wrentham
Winter Bros Co. (Pipe)..E
MICH.—Detroit
Detroit Twist Drill Co....C
MO.—St. Louis
St. Louis Screw Co., 3017
N. 13th (Pipe) ....A
Standard Railway Equipment Co., Union Trust
Bldg. (Pneumatic) ....G
N. H.—Portsmouth
Chadwick & Co., G. B.
(Expansion) ....E
N. J.—Elizabeth
Braunsdorf-Mueller Co...D
N. J.—Gloucester City
Rogers Boat Gauge & Drill
Wks., Jno. M. (Adjustable Chucking; Solid; Adjustable Taper; Machine)
.........A
N. J.—Newark
Bernz, Otto (Lead Pipe)..B
Lowentraut Mfg. Co. (Lead
Pipe) ....A

REAMERS (Con.)

Osborn & Co., C. S. (Lead
Pipe) ....**B**
Gould & Elberhardt (Adjus-
table; Taper) ....**A**
Kraeuter & Co., 577 18th
Av. (Bit Brace; Hand).**X**

New York City

American Axe & Tool Co.,
253 B'way (Adjustable)..
................**AAAA**
Ashcroft Mfg. Co., 85 Lib-
erty (Pipe) ....**A**
Bramberg, Charles, 91 Cliff
(Bit Brace Center) ...**A**
Etna Mfg. Co., 253 B'way
(Pipe) ....**D**
Jennings & Co., C. E., 79
Reade (Lead Pipe) ...**B**
McNab & Harlan Mfg. Co.,
56 John (Pipe) ....**AAA**
Nile s- Bement - Pond Co.,
111 Bway. ....**AAAA**

N. Y.—Orangeburg

Empire Engine & Motor Co.
(Pneumatic) ....**B**

N. Y.—Oswego

Oswego Tool Co. (Pipe)..**B**

N. Y.—Waterford

Holroyd & Co. (Bit Brace
Pipe) ....**A**
King & Co. (Pipe) .....**A**

N. Y.—Yonkers

Saunders' Sons, D. (Pipe;
Hand; Machine) .....**A**

OHIO—Akron

Whitman & Barnes Mfg.
Co. (Bit; Brace; Center
Chucking; Shell; Taper;
Pipe) ....**AAAA**

OHIO—Cincinnati

Cincinnati Screw & Tap Co.,
2442 Beekman (Taper
Pin; Pipe) ....**A**
National Machine Tool Co.,
208 Lawrence (Hand)..**E**
Shepard Lathe Co., 129 W.
2nd (Hand) ....**F**

OHIO—Cleveland

Cleveland Twist Drill Co.
(Center; Chucking; Ex-
pansion; Shell Taper;
Pipe) ....**A**
Grabler Mfg. Co. (Pipe)..**D**
Hart Mfg. Co., 22 Wood
(Pipe) ....**B**
Standard Tool Co. (Adjus-
table; Bit; Brace; Cen-
ter; Chucking; Hand;
Shell; Taper; Pipe; Ex-
tension; Locomotive
Work) ....**AA**

OHIO—Elyria

Western Automatic Ma-
chinery Screw Co. (Taper
Pin) ....**AA**

PA.—Erie

Reed Mfg. Co. (Pipe) ....**A**

PA.—Meadville

Lord Co., L. L. (Pipe)...**C**

PA.—Millersburg

Polk & Son, A. I. (Fluted
,Chucking; Hand Shell;
Taper; also for Bit
Brace; Pipe) ....**C**

PA.—Philadelphia

Stow Flexible Shaft Co., N.
26th & Buttonwood (Long
Taper) ....**B**

PA.—Pittsburg

Baird Machinery Co. ...**B**

PA.—Reading

Reading Standard Cycle
Mfg. Co. (W. F. Remppis.
Prop.) (Adjustable; Rose
Chucking) ....**B**

R. I.—Pawtucket

Carpenter Tap & Die Co., J.
M. (Pipe) ....**C**

R. I.—Providence

Brown & Sharpe Mfg. Co.
................**AAAA**

VT.—Derby Line

Butterfield & Co. (Taper
Pipe) ....**A**

REAPERS

See Agr. Imps

RECEIVERS

COLO.—Denver

RECEIVERS (Con.)

Leyner Engineering Works
Co., J. Geo. (Air) .....**C**

CONN.—Meriden

Meriden Brittania Co.
(Silver Cord) ....**AAAA**
Wilcox Silver Plate Co.
(Silver Cord) ....**AAAA**

CONN.—New Britain

Taplen Mfg. Co. (Ash)...**D**

ILL.—Chicago

Allis-Chalmers Co. (Air)...
................**AAAA**
American Electric Telephone
Co. (Telephone) ......**B**
Chicago Pneumatic Tool Co.
Fisher Bldg. ......**AAAA**
Fisher, A. J. (Air) .....**F**
Western Telephone Mfg.
Co. (Telephone) ......**B**

MASS.—Boston

Mason Regulator Co. (Automatic Cotton) ....**A**

MICH.—Detroit

Northern Engineering
Works (Air) ....**A**

N. Y.—Brooklyn

American Air Compressor
Works (Air) ....**G**

New York City

Gorham Mfg. Co. (Silver
Card) ....**AAAA**
Ingersoll Drill Co., 26 Cort-
landt (Air) ....**AAAA**
Judd & Co., H. L. (Cord)
................**AA**
Kooen & Bros., L. O., 50
Cliff (Air) ....**A**
McKiernan Drill Co., 159
Liberty (Air) ....**X**
Pedrick & Ayer Co., 87
Liberty (Air) ....**A**
Rand Drill Co. (Air)......
................**AAAA**
Tiffany & Co. (Inc.), 15th
& B'way (Silver Card)..
................**AAAA**

N. Y.—Rochester

Bradley & Co., E. C. (Telephone) ....**H**

OHIO—Cleveland

Williams-Abbott Electric
Co. (Telephone) ......**B**

OHIO—Youngstown

Polloch Co., W. B. (Air)
................**AA**

PA.—Erie

Herron & Bury Mfg. Co.
(Air) ....**C**

PA.—Harrisburg

Harrisburg Pipe & Pipe
Belting Co. (Ltd.) (Am-
monia) ....**AAA**

PA.—Philadelphia

Underwood & Co., H. B.,
1025 Hamilton (Air) ...**B**

PA.—Pittsburg

Riter-Conley Mfg. Co. (Gas)
................**AAA**
Scaife & Sons Co., Wm. B.,
221 First Av. (Air).....**A**

PA.—Washington

Petroleum Iron Works Co.
(Air) ....**C**

PA.—Wilkesbarre

Vulcan Iron Works (Air)..
................**AAAA**

RECEPTACLES

DEL.—Wilmington

Morris Electric Co. ......**X**

IND.—Peru

Peru Electric Mfg. Co.
(Electrical) ....**A**

MASS.—Boston

Marshall Electric Mfg. Co.,
303 Congress ....**B**

N. J.—Newark

Electric Motor & Equip-
ment Co., 13 Beaver ...**C**

N. Y.—Rochester

Crescent Electrical Mfg. Co.
(Electric Sign; Wall)..**F**

N. Y.—Syracuse

Pass & Seymour (Electrical)
................**A**

PA.—Philadelphia

Pringle, Wm. T. (Electric)
................**D**

RECKONERS

MINN.—St. Paul

RECKONERS (Con.)
Christadoro, Charles (Box)
X

RECORDERS

See also Clocks; Indicators

CONN.—Waterbury
Bristol Co. (Electrical)...D
ILL.—Chicago
Chicago Pneumatic Tool Co.,
Fisher Bldg. (Railway
Speed) ....AAAA
MD.—Baltimore
Friez, Julian P., 1230 E.
Baltimore (Electrical)..E
MASS.—Boston
Crosby Steam Gauge &
Valve Co. (Speed).....AA
Sturtevant Co., B. F., 34
Oliver (Mechanical Draft)
AAA
MASS.—Brookline
Holtzer-Cabot Electric Co.
(Time) ....A
MASS.—Gardner
Simplex Time Recorder Co.
(Time) ....B
MASS.—Indian Orchard
Hough Cash Recorder Co.
(Cash Autograph) .....B
N. Y.—Binghamton
International Time Record-
ing Co. (Time) ....A
New York City
American Watchman's Time
Detector Co. (J. E.
Morse, Treasr.), 234
B'way (Time) X
A
Aschroft Mfg. Co. (Speed)
A
General Watchman's Time
Detector Co., 49 Dey
(Time) ....G
Herzog Telephone Co., 51
W. 24th (Time) ......D
Imhauser & Co., E., 202
B'way (Time) C
Nanz & Co., 127 Duane
(Time) ....F
N. Y.—Syracuse
Dey Time Register Co., 305
N. State (Time) .....AA
OHIO—Columbus
Pneumatic Watchman Check
Co. (Watchmens'; Em-
ployees' Time) ....E
PA.—Philadelphia
Riggs & Bro., 310 Market
(Time) ....B

RECORDS

CONN.—Bridgeport
Burt Co. (Graphophone) ..A
N. J.—Orange
National Phonograph Co.
(Phonograph) ......AAA
New York City
Leeds & Catlin Co., 53
E. 11th (Phonograph)..A
PA.—Philadelphia
Hawthorne & Sheble Mfg.
Co., Mascher & Oxford
(Talking Machine) ....B

REDUCERS

ILL.—Chicago
Illinois Malleable Iron Co.,
30 W. Monroe (Hose)...
AAAA
MO.—St. Louis
Kupferle, John C., 2nd &
Mound (Hose) ....A
Pleuger & Henger Mfg. Co.,
1015 Herbert (Hose)....A
New York City
McNab & Harlin Mfg. Co.,
56 John (Hose) ......AA
OHIO—Canton
Kohler & Co., F. E. (Hose)
C

REDWOOD

See Lumber

REED
FURNITURE

See Furniture

REEDS

CONN.—Bethel
Shepard & Sons Co., Geo.
A. ....F
CONN.—New Haven
Cowles Co., C. (Inc.) (Sad-
dle) ....A
ILL.—Chicago
Piano & Organ Supply Co.,
125 Racine Av. (Organ)
AA
Street & Co., R. R., 184-186
Washington ....A
MAINE—Lewiston
Craig & Scott ....:.F
MAINE—Saco
Littlefield & Sawyer ....F
MASS.—Fall River
Berry & Johnston .....E
Luther Reed Mfg. Co. ...D
McGregor & Sons ......F
MASS.—Gardner
Heywood Bros. & Wakefield
Co. (Hat) ....AAAA
MASS.—Hopedale
Draper Co. ......AAAA
MASS.—Lawrence
Emmons Loom Harness Co.
A
MASS.—Lowell
Carruthers, Robt. (Silk;
Cotton; Woolen; Carpet;
Wire; Hair Cloth) ....B
Harris, Geo. W. (Loom).B
MASS.—New Bedford
New Bedford Reed Co. ...F
MASS.—Springfield
Tilley, Norris, 49 Taylor.D
MASS.—Worcester
Hammond Reed Co. (Organ)
A
Whittaker Reed Co., Jno..E
Worcester Loom Co.
(Loom) ....E
N. H.—Manchester
Baldwin Co., Jas. ..AAAA
N. J.—Newark
Crabb & Co., William ...A
Peters Harness & Saddlery
Co. (Saddle) C
N. J.—Paterson
Hall & Co., I. A., 30 Ham-
ilton ....A
Paterson Reed & Harness
Co. (Loom) ....B
Ulrich & Co. ....F
Walden, J. ....AA
N. Y.—Utica
Williams Co., J. H. .....A
PA.—Philadelphia
Fitzgerald Loom Reed Co.,
N. 2nd & Diamond.....X
Stewart & Sons, 312 Mas-
ter X
R. I.—Pawtucket
Blackstone Reed & Harness
Co. ....F
Excelsior Loom Reed Wks.-
E
American Supply Co....AA
Gowdey Reed & Harness
Mfg. Co., J. A........F
R. I.—Providence
Gowdey Reed & Harness
Mfg. Co. (Loom) .....F
R. I.—Woonsocket
Wilkins Mfg. Co., 14 S.
Main X
Woonsocket Reed & Shuttle
Works ....E
TENN.—Newport
American Oak & Hickory
Reed Co. (Furniture)...C

REEFERS

See Clothing: Men's

REELS

See also Fish Tackle

CONN.—Bridgeport
Automatic Machine Co.
(Wire) ....B
CONN.—Collinsville
Hartigan, W. R. (Chalk
Line) ....H
CONN.—New Britain
Stanley Rule & Level Co.
(Chalk Line) ......AAA

REELS (*Con.*)

CONN.—New Haven
Hendryx & Co., Andrew B.
(Fishing) ....A
Shuster Co., F. B. (Adjustable Wire) X
CONN.—Torrington
Union Hardware Co. (Chalk Line) ....AA
CONN.—Waterbury
Blake & Johnson (Wire) .A
D. C.—Washington
Howard, H. J. M., 113 4½
S. W. (Fire Hose) .....H
ILL.—Carpentersville
Illinois Iron & Bolt Co.
(Clothes) ....AA
ILL.—Chicago
Allen Mfg. Co., W. D., 151
Lake (Fire Hose) ......A
Bosley Co., D. W., Fulton & May (Wire) ....B
Klein & Son, Mathias, 87 W.
Van Buren (Payout) ..B
Noblett & Co., E. J., 898
35th (Payout) C
ILL.—Downer's Grove
Dicke Tool Co. (Payout) ..C
ILL.—Freeport
Hoefer Mfg. Co. (Wire) ..C
ILL.—Moline
Barnard & Leas Mfg. Co.
(Rice; Centrifugal) ..AA
ILL.—Monmouth
Milne Mfg. Co. (Clothes) U
ILL.—Sterling
Novelty Iron Works (Clothes Line) ....E
IND.—Evansville
Evansville Tool Works
(Chalk Line) ....A
IND.—Indianapolis
Nordyke & Marmon Co.
(Round, Centrifugal) AAA
Udell Works (Rope) ......A
IND.—Richmond
Richmond Safety Gate Co.
(Wire) C
IOWA—Dubuque
Adams Co. (Clothes Line) A
KANS.—Leavenworth
Great Western Mfg. Co.
(Round, Centrifugal) AA
KY.—Frankfort
Millam & Son, B. C. (Fishing) ....E
MASS.—Boston
Firth Co., Wm., 150 Devonshire (Yarn) ....D
Mason Regulator Co. (Wire)
A
MASS.—Cambridge
Boston Woven Hose & Rubber Co. (Hose) ....AAAA
MASS.—Hopedale
Draper Co. (Yarn) ..AAAA
MASS.—Lowell
Lowell Machine Shop (Yarn;
Cotton Yarn) ......AAAA
MASS.—Newton Upper Falls
Saco & Pettee Machine Shop
(Yarn; Cotton Yarn)AAA
MASS.—Springfield
Blair Mfg. Co. (Hose) ...B
MASS.—Whitinsville
Whitin Machine Wks.
(Yarn; Cotton Yarn)
AAAA
MASS.—Worcester
American Card Clothing Co.
(Wooden Yarn) ....AAA
Cleveland Machine Works
(Yarn, Dresser) ......A
Morgan Construction Co.
(Wire) ....A
Wright Wire Co. (Wire) AA
MICH.—Bay City
Vance Box Co., E. J. (Ltd.)
(Barb Wire; Lead Pipe;
Wooden for Insulated Wire) ....B
MICH.—Detroit
Anderson & Sons, W. H.
(Payout) C
MICH.—Hastings
Hastings Woodworking Co.
(Ltd.) (Garden Hose) F
MICH.—Northville
Dubuar Mfg. Co., J. A.
(Garden Hose) X
MICH.—Ypsilanti
Ypsilanti Machine Works
(Round. Centrifugal) ..D

REELS (*Con.*)

MINN.—Minneapolis
Minneapolis Electric & Construction Co., 17 So.
4th (Payout) ....F
Therien, J. O., 116 1st Av.
(Payout) ....:..F
MO.—Nevada
Talbot Reel Co., W. H.
(Fishing) C
MO.—St. Louis
Kupferle, J. C. (Clothes Line) ....AA
Pleuger & Henger Mfg. Co.
(Clothes Line) ....A
N. H.—Manchester
Moulton, W. F. (Chalk Line) ....H
N. J.—Newark
Meisselbach & Bro., A. F.
(Chalk Line) C
Sommer's Son, John (Rope;
Clothes Line; Fishing) A
N. J.—Paterson
Sipp Electric & Machine Co.
1 Mill ....D
N. J.—Trenton
Empire Rubber Mfg. Co.
(Hose) ....AA
N. Y.—Buffalo
Noye Mfg. Co., Jno. T.
(Round, Centrifugal; Cylindrical Flour) X
Squier Mfg. Co., Geo. L.
(Coffee; Rice) ......AAA
N. Y.—Fulton
Dilts Machine Co.
(Revolving) ....B
New York City
Abbey & Imbrie (Fishing) A
Cliff & Gilbert Co., 198 W.
Bway. (Fire Hose) ....D
Empire Rubber Mfg. Co., 88
Reade (Hose) ....AA
Estes & Sons, E. B., 45
John (Wooden) .....AA
Gutta Percha & Rubber Mfg.
Co., 126 Duane (Hose)
AAAA
Haydenville Co., 150 Nassau
(Hose) ....A
Jones & Son, J., 64 Cortlandt (Wire) ....F
Manhattan Rubber Mfg. Co.,
18 Vesey (Swinging Hose)
AA
Mineralized Rubber Co., 18
Cliff (Fire Hose) ......A
New York Agricultural Co.,
51 Cliff (Hose) X
Stokes & Co., Wm. A., 30
Warren (Rope) ....D
Vom Hofe, Edward (Fishing) ....D
N. Y.—Peekskill
Anderson, Homer (Blasting Cable) ....H
N. Y.—Rochester
Caldwell Mfg. Co. (Hose) C
Yawman & Erbe Mfg. Co.
(Fishing) ....AA
N. Y.—Syracuse
Stearns & Co., E. C. (Clothes Line; Clothes) ......AA
OHIO—Cincinnati
Nuhring, Chas., 907 Walnut
(Swinging; Automatic Fire Hose) ....G
OHIO—Columbus
Case Mfg. Co. (Round; Centrifugal) ....A
Jeffrey Mfg. Co. (Cylindrical Flour) ....AAAA
Ohio Tool Co. (Chalk Line)
AA
OHIO—Cuyahoga Falls
Turner, Vaughan & Taylor
Co. (Wire) ....B
OHIO—Hamilton
Black & Clawson Co. (Revolving; Stack) ....AAA
OHIO—New Philadelphia
Spicer Mfg. Co. (Wire) ...C
OHIO—Piqua
Piqua Handle & Mfg. Co.
(Chalk Line) ....A
OHIO—Reading
Reading Fire Apparatus
Works (Hose) ....H
(Hose) ....H
OHIO—Sandusky
Sandusky Tool Co. (Chalk Line) ....A

REELS (Con.)

OHIO—Toledo
Nagel Electric Co., W. G.
(Payout) ....B

PA.—Downingtown
Downingtown Mfg. Co.
(Ltd.) (Revolving) ....A

PA.—Erie
Hollands Mfg. Co. (Hose) B

PA.—Philadelphia
Altemus, Jacob K., 2824 N.
4th C
Clay, Jno. H., 1320 Ridge
Av. (Swinging Hose) ..B
Diamond Textile Machine
Works, 2nd & Diamond
(Yarn) ....E
Smith Woolen Mchry. Co.,
Jas., 411 Race (Yarn) AAA
Wirt & Knox Mfg. Co., 21 N.
4th (Fire Hose) ....D
Woodason, Thos. (Galva-
nized Garden Line) ....F

R. I.—Pawtucket
Bliss Mfg. Co., R. (Chalk
Line) ....AAAA
Carpenter, Orville ......F
Luther & Co., Chas. A.
(Yarn; Thread) C

R. I.—Providence
Brown & Sharpe Mfg. Co.
(Yarn) ....AAAA
Rhode Island Braiding Ma-
chine Co. (Skeining;
Measuring) C
Standard Machinery Co.
(Wire) ....B

R. I.—Woonsocket
Woonsocket Shuttle Co.
(Payout) X

VT.—Post Mills
Chubb Rod Co., T. H.
(Fishing) ....A

VA.—Norfolk
Whitehurst & Co., R. W.
(Fire Hose) ....D

WIS.—Beloit
Beloit Iron Works (Revolving; Stock) ....A

WIS.—Milwaukee
Allis-Chalmers Co. (Centrifugal) ....AAAA

WIS.—Racine
Winship Mfg. Co. (Hose) .E

REFINERS

PA.—Pittsburg
Riter-Conley Mfg. Co. (Oil)
AAA

REFLECTORS

CONN.—Meriden
Miller & Co., Edward (for
Churches, Halls, etc.)...
AAAA

CONN.—Waterbury
Plume & Atwood Mfg. Co.
(Lamp) ....AAA
Waterbury Brass Co.
(Locomotive) .....AAAA

ILL.—Chicago
American Reflector &
Lighting Co., 271 Frank-
lin (for Churches, Halls,
etc.) ....D
Chicago Lamp & Reflector
Co., 77 Blue Island Av.
(Acetylene) ....G
Electric Appliance Co., 92
W. Van Buren (Electric)
.......B
Western Electric Co. (for
Churches, Halls, etc.)..
AAAA

ILL.—Decatur
Faries Mfg. Co. (Electric
Light) ....B

MASS.—Boston
Wheeler Reflector Co., 156
Pearl (for Churches,
Halls, etc.; Daylight;
Enamelled; Electric; Gas;
Lamp Light; Mirror;
Plate; Silvered Glass) .C

MO.—St. Louis
Kraushaar Brass Mfg. Co.
(for Churches, Halls,
etc.) ....A

N. Y.—Brooklyn
Sunlight Reflector Co., 141
Court (for Churches,
Halls, etc.) ....E

REFLECTORS (Con.)

New York City
Frink, Isaac P., 551 Pearl
(for Art Galleries,
Churches, Halls, etc.;
Daylight; Arc Lamp;
Window; Cluster Section-
al Glass; Electric Light;
Gas Light; Mirror Plate)
AA
Gleason Mfg. Co., E. P.,
20 W. Houston (for
Churches, Halls, etc.)..B
Holophone Glass Co. (Pris-
matic Glass Gas Shade).D
Manhattan Brass Co.
(Lamp) ....A
Mitchell-Vance Co., 836
B'way (for Churches,
Halls, etc.) ....AA
Universal Electric Stage
Lighting Co. ....D

OHIO—Dayton
Dayton Mfg. Co. (for
Churches, Halls, etc.;
Lamps) ....A

OHIO—Steubenville
Gill Bros. & Co. (Silvered
for Churches, Halls, etc.;
Lamp; Mirror Plate) .AA

PA.—Philadelphia
Gaumer Co., Jno. L., 19th
& Hamilton (for
Churches, Halls, etc.)..C
Gillinder & Sons (Inc.), 135
Oxford (Glass for
Churches, Halls, etc.;
Lamp) ....A
Klemm & Co., 5th & Cherry
(for Churches, Halls,
etc., Daylight; Electric;
Gas & Lamplight) C

PA.—Pittsburg
Bailey Reflector Co., 208
Smithfield (for Churches,
Halls, &c.) ....D
Macbeth-Evans Glass Co.
(Silvered Glass) ..AAAA

REFRIGERA-
TORS

ILL.—Chicago
Belding-Hall Mfg. Co., 196
Monroe ....AA

ILL.—Morrison
Illinois Refrigerator Co....C

IND.—Anderson
Wilke Mfg. Co. (Glass;
Porcelain Lined) ......B

IND.—Indianapolis
Eureka Refrigerator Co...C

IND.—Kendallville
McCray Refrigerator Co.
(Tile Lined; also Opal
Tile Lined) ....A

IOWA—Cedar Rapids
Cherry Co., J. G. (Cream-
ery) ....A

KANS.—Kansas City
Herrick Refrigerator Mfg.
Co., 4th & Oakland Av.
(Glass Lined; Tile Lined)
X

MASS.—Boston
Eddy & Sons, D. C
Hall & Son, A. D........C
Holmes, C. D. 20 Creek
Sq. ....F

MICH.—Belding
Belding-Hall Mfg. Co.
(Butchers'; Grocers) ..AA

MICH.—Grand Haven
Challenge Refrigerator Co.,
A

MICH.—Grand Rapids
Grand Rapids Refrigerator
Co. (Grocers') ....A
Leonard Mfg. Co. ....A
Michigan Barrel Co. (White
Enamel) ....A
Northern Refrigerator Co..A

MICH.—Greenville
Ranney Refrigerator Co.
(Grocers') ....A

MICH.—Muskegon
Alaska Refrigerator Co.
(Inc.) ....A

MINN.—Duluth
Hurd Refrigerator Co.
(Butchers') C

MINN.—St. Paul

REFRIGERATORS Con.
Perkins Mfg. Co., 1121 E.
  7th ....D
White Enamel Refrigerator
  Co. (for Refrigerators &
  Dining Cars) ....AA
MO.—St. Louis
Brecht Butchers' Supply
  Co., G. V., 1201 Cass Av.
  (Butchers') ....AAA
N. H.—Nashua
Maine Mfg. Co. ....A
N. J.—Trenton
Hill & Co., C. V. (Butch-
  ers') ....D
N. Y.—Brooklyn
Cooper & McKee ....B
N. Y.—Buffalo
Heinz & Munschauer .....A
Jewett Refrigerator Co., 27
  Chandler (Glass Lined;
  Tile Lined) ....B
Vogt, Peter A. ....B
N. Y.—Cohoes
Standard Refrigerator Co.
                          C
New York City
Brunswick, Balke, Collen-
  der Co., 229 4th Av.
  (Butchers'; Grocers)
                       AAAA
Fritts Refrigerator Con-
  struction Co., 150 5th Av.
  (Glass Lined; Tile Lined)
                          F
Herrmann Furniture &
  Plumbers' Cabinet Wks.
                          A
Keil & Son, Francis (Butch-
  ers') ....AA
Lorillard Refrigerator Co.,
  23 W. 34th (Glass Lined)
                          X
Mace & Co., L. H.......A
Morgan & Cornell, 211
  Duane (Grocers') X
Page, Dennis & Co., 341
  B'way ....B
OHIO—Lockland
Monroe Refrigerator Co...A
OHIO—Toledo
Stevens, B. A. (Butchers')
                          A
PA.—Philadelphia
Fries' Sons, Geo., 909 Fil-
  bert (Nursery) ....D
Knoell, John ....A
Ridgway Refrigerator Co.,
  707 N. Broad ....F
Wotherspoon, James R., 430
  Race (Nursery) ....E
PA.—Pittsburg
Gloeckler, Bernard (Butch-
  ers') ....AA
PA.—Tamaqua
Weaver & Son, Daniel....B
TENN.—Chattanooga
Keyser Mfg. Co. C
VT.—Burlington
Baldwin Refrigerator Co.
                          A
WIS.—Eau Claire
Wisconsin Refrigerator Co.
                          C
WIS.—Fond du Lac
Bowen Mfg. Co. ....B
Gurney Refrigerator Co..AA
WIS.—Racine
Racine Refrigerator & Fix-
  ture Co. ....D
WIS.—Rhinelander
Rhinelander Mfg. Co. ....E
WIS.—Sheboygan
Dillingham Mfg. Co. .....B

REGALIAS

CAL.—San Francisco
Pasquale Co., B. ....B
ILL.—Chicago
Armstrong Mfg. Co., E. A.,
  315 Wabash Av. (Secret
  Society) ....A
Foster, Son & Co., G. F...D
MD.—Baltimore
Sisco Bros. ....E
MO.—St. Louis
Parson & Co., 1010 Pine
  (Society) ....E
New York City
Benziger Bros. ....A
OHIO—Cincinnati
Pettibone Bros. Mfg. Co...A

REGALIAS (Con.)
OHIO—Columbus
Lilley & Co., M. C....AAAA
PA.—Philadelphia
Horstman Co., Wm. H.
                       AAAA
W. VA.—Huntington
Floding, Geo. A.........E

REGISTERS

CONN.—Bridgeport
Smith & Egge Mfg. Co.
  (Car Fare) ....A
CONN.—Bristol
Root, C. J. (Hand Tally-
  ing) C
CONN.—Hartford
Pratt & Whitney Co. (Hand
  Tallying) ....AAAA
CONN.—New Britain
Hart & Cooley Co. (Wrought
  Steel Hot Air) ....A
CONN.—Waterbury
Bristol Co. (Electric) ....D
ILL.—Chicago
Baird Mfg. Co. (Telephone
  Call) C
Chicago Sewing Machine Co.
  (Hot Air) ....A
Excelsior Steel Furnace Co.,
  40 W. Monroe (Hot Air)
                          A
International Register Co.,
  118 W. Jackson Boul.
  (Car Fare; Single &
  Double) ....A
Tuckhorn & Co., H., 217
  Madison (Cash) C
Western Electric Co. (Elec-
  tric) ....AAAA
ILL.—Freeport
Arcade Mfg. Co. ....A
Stover Mfg. Co. (Hot Air)
                         AA
ILL.—Peoria
Rooke Register Co. (Car
  Fare) ....E
ILL.—Sterling
Novelty Iron Wks. (Stone
  Pipe) ....E
IND.—Indianapolis
Nordyke & Marmon Co.
  (Grain) ....AAA
IND.—Wabash
Standard Cash Register Co.
  (Cash) ....B
IOWA—Dubuque
Adams Co. (Stove Pipe)...A
Schreiber & Conchar Mfg.
  Co. (Hot Air) ....A
MASS.—Boston
Barney Ventilating Fan
  Works (Hot Air)....X
Groom & Co., Thos. (Hotel)
                          B
Tufts Meter Co., Nathaniel
  (Gas Pressure) ....A
Woodman Mfg. & Supply
  Co., R. (Hand Tally)...F
MASS.—Indian Orchard
Hough Cash Recorder Co.
  (Cash) ....B
MASS.—Worcester
Maynard-Gough Co. (Hotel;
  Photographers) ....E
MICH.—Battle Creek
Advance Thresher Co.
  (Grain) ....AAAA
Nichols & Shepard Co.
  (Grain) ....AAAA
United States Register Co.
  (Side Wall Hot Air)...D
MICH.—Detroit
Century Cash Register Co.
  (Cash) ....F
MICH.—Jackson
Novelty Mfg. Co. (Hot Air)
                          A
MICH.—Northville
American Bell & Foundry
  Co. (Hot Air) ....D
MICH.—Port Huron
Port Huron Engine &
  Thresher Co. (Grain).AAA
MINN.—Minneapolis
Howell & Co., R. R.
  (Grain) ....B
MO.—St. Louis
Pleuger & Henger Mfg. Co.
                          A
Stockhoff Supply Co. (Hot

REGISTERS (Con.)
Air) ....E
Western Electrical Supply
Co. (Car Fare) X
N. H.—Nashua
Highton & Sons, Wm. (Hot
Air) ....B
N. J.—Newark
Sterling-Meaker Co., 420
Ogden (Car Fare) .....D
N. Y.—Albany
McDonald & Co., D. (Gas;
Vacuum Pressure) .....A
N. Y.—Manlius
Cheney & Son, S. ....A
New York City
American Mechanical Cash-
ier Co., 40 Wall (Cash)
D
American Watchman's Time
Detector Co. (Electric).X
Benton Mfg. Co., 8 Abing-
don Sq. (Hand Tallying)
E
Bunnell & Co., J. H. (Elec-
tric) ....B
Creamer & Co., W. G., 96
John (Hot Air) ....A
Griffing Iron Co., A. A.
(Hot Air) ....AA
Hunt Co., C. W. (Coal
Counting) ....AA
National Meter Co. (Gas;
Vacuum Pressure) .....A
Peck, Stow & Wilcox Co.,
27 Murray ......AAAA
Tuttle & Bailey Mfg. Co.,
83 Beekman (Hot Air)
AA
N. Y.—Olean
Enterprise Foundry Co., 48
Orlean (Hot Air) ......B
N. Y.—Syracuse
Dey Time Register Co.
(Time) ....AA
Stearns & Co., E. C. (Hot
Air) ....AA
N. Y.—Troy
Gurley, W. & L. E. (Elec-
tric) ....A
OHIO—Akron
American Castings Co. (Hot
Air) ....H
OHIO—Ashtabula
Barber Mfg. Co. (Hot Air)
C
OHIO—Canton
Canton Steel Roofing Co...A
OHIO—Cleveland
Cleveland Foundry Co. (Hot
Air) ....A
Columbian Hardware Co.
A
Fanner Mfg. Co. (Hot Air)
Ferrosteel Co., 34 Michigan
(Hot Air) ....B
Independent Register Co.,
156 Champion (Hot Air)
F
OHIO—Columbus
Sun Mfg. Co. (Cash) ....A
OHIO—Dayton
Bates & Bros. Co., D. L.
(Car Fare) ....D
National Cash Register Co.
(Cash) ....AAAA
Ohmer Fare Register Co.
(Car Fare) ....A
OHIO—Marion
Huber Mfg. Co. (Grain)
AAA
OHIO—Massillon
Hess-Snyder Co. ....AA
OHIO—Orrville
Champion Thresher Co.
(Grain) ....B
OHIO—Springfield
Robbins & Myers Co. (Hot
Air) ....A
PA.—Lancaster
Eureka Cash & Credit Reg-
ister Co. (Cash) X
PA.—Meyersdale
Miller, Wm. S. (Grain)..F
PA.—Philadelphia
Brill Co., J. G. (Car Fare)
AAAA
Devlin Mfg. Co., Thomas
(Hot Air) ....AA
Helme & McIlhenny (Gas
Pressure) ....AA
Mayer & England Co. (Car
Fare) ....A

REGISTERS (Con.)
Partrick, Carter & Wilkens
(Electric) ....B
PA.—Reading
Mount Penn Stove Works
(Hot Air) ....A
Reading Hardware Co. (Hot
Air) ....AAAA
WIS.—Milwaukee
Erwin Hydraulic Machinery
Co. (Hot Air) ....D
WIS.—South Milwaukee
Stowell Mfg. & Foundry Co.
(Hot Air) ....A

REGLETS

MASS.—Boston
Hansen, H. C. ....B
MICH.—Ludington
Tubbs Mfg. Co. (Printers')
B
N. Y.—Brooklyn
Wesel Mfg. Co., F.........A
N. Y.—Middletown
Hamilton Mfg. Co. .....AA
New York City
American Type Founders
Co. ....AAAA
N. Y.—Seneca Falls
Westcott-Jewell Co. ......D
WIS.—Two Rivers
Hamilton Mfg. Co. ....AA

REGULATORS

See also Governors

CAL.—San Francisco
Dow Pumping Engine Co.,
Geo. E., 179 1st (Pres-
sure) ....AA
CONN.—Bridgeport
Hurwood Mfg. Co. (Uphol-
sterers') C
Weld Mfg. Co. (Hot Air).D
CONN.—New Haven
Foskett & Bishop Co.
(Damper) ....B
New Haven Clock Co.
(Watchmakers') .....AAA
CONN.—Waterbury
Standard Electric Time Co.
(Electric) ....D
Waterbury Electric Co.
(Electric Heat) ......F
ILL.—Batavia
Batavia Windmill Co.
(Windmill) ....B
Challenge Windmill & Feed
Mill Co. (Windmill).AAA
U. S. Wind Engine & Pump
Co. (Windmill) ......AA
ILL.—Bushnell
Bushnell Pump Co. (Wind-
mill) ....B
ILL.—Chicago
Clow & Sons, Jos. B., 344
Franklin (Water Pres-
sure) ....AAA
Davis Co., Jno., 22d & Hal-
sted (Gas Pressure; Pump
& Damper) ....AA
Davis Regulator Co., Geo.
M., 145 Milwaukee Av.
(Damper; Fan Engine;
Pressure; Water Pres-
sure) C
Fairbanks, Morse & Co.,
Franklin & Monroe
(Windmill) ......AAAA
Johnson Temperature Con-
trolling Co., 152 Lake
(Heat) ....AAA
Klipfel & Thomas Co., 74
W. Lake (Pressure;
Pump) X
Morgan & Co., 40 Dearborn
(Damper for Steam & Hot
Water Boilers) X
Powers Regulator Co., 145
Dearborn (Damper; Nat-
ural Gas Pressure; Heat;
Water Pressure) .....B
Scott Valve Co., 32 West
Randolph (Pump) .....D
Wilson & Co., F. Cortez,
239 Lake (Gas Pressure)
B
ILL.—Decatur
Mueller Mfg. Co., H. (Dam-
per; Water Pressure)
AAA

REGULATORS (Con.)

ILL.—Freeport
Stover Mfg. Co., 165 River (Windmill) ....AA
ILL.—Harvard
Hunt, Helm, Ferris & Co. (Windmill) ....AA
ILL.—Kewanee
Western Tube Co. (Damper) ....AAA
ILL.—Ottawa
Porter Co., J. E. (Windmill) ....A
ILL.—Quincy
Gardner Governor Company (Steam) ....AA
ILL.—Waukegan
Thomas Brass & Iron Co. (Fan Engine; Water Pressure) ....A
IND.—Anderson
Johnson-Reynolds Co. (Gas Pressure) ....E
IND.—Auburn
Zimmerman Mfg. Company (Windmill) ....B
IND.—Indianapolis
Aneshaensel & Co., C. (Water Pressure) ....D
Jenney Electric Mfg. Co. (Motor Speed) ....A
IND.—Kendallville
Flint & Walling Mfg. Co. (Windmill) ....AA
IND.—Lapel
Wright, George (Gas Pressure) ....E
IOWA—Davenport
Red Jacket Mfg. Co. (Windmill) ....A
IOWA—Des Moines
Dempster Mfg. Co. (Windmill) ....B
IOWA—Keokuk
Garton-Daniels Co. (Controller, Electric Railway) ....D
IOWA—Marshalltown
Fisher Governor Co. (Water Pressure) ....D
LA.—New Orleans
Buckel Machine Wks. (Pressure for Cane Mills)....X
MAINE—Portland
Portland Co. (Voltage).AA
MD.—Baltimore
Patterson Regulator Co., 14 W. Barre (Hydraulic)..X
MASS.—Boston
Crosby Steam Gauge & Valve Co., 95 Oliver (Pressure; Water Pressure; Feed Water)....AA
D'Este Co., Julian, 24 Canal (Damper; Water Pressure; Pump; Air Pressure; Heat; Temperature)...B
Gilchrist Co., Geo. E., 106 High (Pressure) ......B
Howard Clock Co., E. (Watchmakers' Clock)..A
McLaughlin Mfg. Co., Geo. G., 812 E. 6th (Gas Pressure) X
Mason Regulator Co., 158 Summer (Damper; Pressure; Pump; Steam; Air Pressure; Elevator Pressure; Water Pressure; Air Brake; Rheostat)..A
Noyes Mfg. Co., 47 India (Gas Pressure) ....H
Ridgeway Furnace Co., 6 Portland (Furnace) ....E
Rowe, L. L., 24 Portland (Furnace) ....F
Starr Brass Mfg. Co., 108 E. Dedham (Fan Engine Pressure) ....A
Stroter & Sons, Herman (Water Pressure) ......A
Trask Co., H. D., 74 Portland (Fan Engine; Pressure) ....F
Walworth Mfg. Co. (Damper Feed Water) .AAAA
White & Co., C. H., 22 Bowker (Automatic Furnace) X
MASS.—Brockton
Tuck Mfg. Co. (Upholsterers') ....E

REGULATORS (Con.)

MASS.—Everett
Waters Governor Co. (Fan Engine; Hydraulic; Pressure) C
MASS.—Holyoke
Deane Steam Pump Co. (Pump) ....AAAA
MASS.—Indian Orchard
Chapman Valve Mfg. Co. (Pressure) ....AAA
MASS.—Lawrence
Watts Regulator Co. (Fan Engine; Damper; Water Pressure; Pump) X
MASS.—Salem
Locke Regulator Co. (Steam Damper; Water Pressure; Boiler Feed Pump) ....A
Spencer Regulator Co. (Damper) C
MASS.—Worcester
Crompton & Knowles Loom Works (Damper)..AAAA
Rice, Barton & Fales Machine Co. (Fan; Engine; Pressure) ....AA
Union Water Meter Co. (Damper; Fan Engine; Gas Pressure; Pump; Water Pressure) ......B
MICH.—Detroit
Detroit Heating & Lighting Co., 335 Wight (Heat).B
MINN.—Minneapolis
Electric Heat Regulator Co. (Automatic Heat) .....E
MO.—St. Louis
Johnson Heating & Regulating Co., 205 N. 10th (Heat) ....D
St. Louis Steam Engine Co., 16 S. Commercial (Fan Engine; Pressure) .....D
N. J.—Jersey City
Griffing Iron Co., A. A., 449 Communipaw Av. (Heat; Pressure) ....AA
N. J.—Newark
Foster Engineering Co. (Automatic Damper; Fan Engine; Pressure; Pump).A
N. Y.—Brooklyn
Acton, Jno., 118 John (Damper) ....D
Schaffer & Budenberg Mfg. Co., 10 Division (Pump) ....D
N. Y.—Buffalo
Electric Service Co., Bank Bldg. (Heat) ......AAA
N. Y.—Frankfort
Utica Steam Gauge Co. (Heat) X
N. Y.—Jamestown
Engineering & Power Co. (Damper) ....AA
N. Y.—Lockport
American District Steam Co. (Steam Pressure) ..AAA
N. Y.—Monroe
Newburg Mfg. Co. (Low Pressure Damper) .....D
N. Y.—Newburgh
Chadborn Mfg. Co. (Heat) X
New York City
Ansonia Clock Co. (Watchmakers') ....AAAA
Baylis Co., 140 Greenwich (Gas Pressure) ....D
Blake & Williams, 211 W. 20th (Damper) ....B
Boyce, Myron J., 584 Hudson (Gas Pressure) ....B
Bushnell Co., Jno. S., 120 Liberty (Damper) ......E
Cobb, Chas. C., 71 Gold (Furnace) ....H
Crane Co., Wm. M., 1133 B'way (Gas Pressure)..A
Ford Co., Thos. P., 81 Centre (Damper; Steam & Electric Pump; Rheostat; Water Pressure) ......D
Gleason Mfg. Co., E. P., 20 W. Houston (Gas Pressure) ....B
Harlem Mfg. Co., 42 W. 67th (Pressure) ....F
Haydenville Co., 150 Nassau (Water Pressure; Steam; Gas) ....A
Homan, J. & E., 378 W.

846

REGULATORS (Con.)

B'way (Heat) ....D

Jenkins Bros., 71 John (Damper) ....A

Johnson Temperature Regulating Co., 240 4th Av. (Heat) ....AAA

Kiely & Mueller, 7 W. 13th (Improved Damper; Steam Pressure Pump; Water Pressure) ....B

Lawler Water Feed & Damper Regulator Co., 181 Mercer (Hot Water Damper; Furnace; Heat; Hot Water; Pressure)..F

McNab & Harlan Mfg. Co., 56 John (Damper)...AAA

Monash-Younker Co. (Pressure Pump) ....D

Nason Mfg. Co., 71 Beekman (Damper; Fan Engine; Hot Water; Water Pressure; Pump) .....B

Puffer & Sons, W. E., 118 Beekman (Automatic Furnace) ....D

Quimby, Wm. E. (Inc.), 141 B'way (Pump) ....B

Roberts & Bros., Geo. I., 473 4th Av. (Pump) ...A

Robertson & Sons, Jas. L., 204 Fulton (Damper; Pump) ....D

Rutzler Co., E., 178 Centre (Damper) ....A

Schneible Co., Jos. (Beer Pressure) ....B

Standard Steam Specialty Co., 111 5th Av. (Damper) ....D

Thompson & Co., Richard, 126 Liberty (High & Low Pressure Damper) ....F

Wittemann Bros. (Beer Pressure) ....A

Worthington Pumping Engine Co. (Steam; Water Pressure) ....AAAA

N. Y.—Ossining

Kipp, Jr., A. (Damper; Pressure) ....E

N. Y.—Oswego

Howard Thermostat Co. (Damper; Heat) .....F

Kitts Mfg. Co. (Damper for Steam Boilers; Pressure Pump; Water Pressure) D

N. Y.—Rochester

Beers Bros. Thermostat Co., 20 Elm (Heat) ....D

Falls, Frank H., 272 State (Heat) ....D

Rochester Bunging Apparatus Co. (Beer Pressure) B

Taylor Bros. Co., 29 Elizabeth (Heat) ....AA

N. Y.—Troy

Ross Valve Co. (Fan Engine; Pressure; Pump; Steam; Air, Gas & Water Pressure) C

N. Y.—Utica

International Heater Co. (Heat) ....AAA

N. Y.—Yonkers

Van Auken-Clevaue Co. (Damper; Fan Engine; Heat; Hot Water; Pressure; Pump) ....E

OHIO—Ashland

Myers & Bros., F. E. (Windmill) ......AAAA

OHIO—Cincinnati

Lunkenheimer Co. (Pressure Pump) ....AA

Steigert, Leopold, Elder & Logan (Automatic Feed Water; Automatic Pump) F

OHIO—Cleveland

Bishop & Babcock Co., Hamilton, cor. Kirtland (Carbonic Acid; Gas Pressure; Water Pressure) AAA

Burton & Johnson, 107 W. Center (Pump) ....F

Cleveland Faucet Co. (Carbonic Acid Gas) ...AAA

REGULATORS (Con.)

Strong, Carlisle & Hammond Co., 61 Frankfort (Feed Water; Pump)...A

OHIO—Dayton

Thresher Electric Co. (Motor Speed) X

OHIO—Napoleon

Heller, Aller & Co. (Hydraulic Windmill) .....A

OHIO—Salem

Deming Co. (Windmill).AA

OHIO—Springfield

Mast, Foos & Co. (Windmill) ....AA

PA.—Bridgeport

Wilkinson Mfg. Co. (Damper) ....B

PA.—Butler

Evans Mfg. Co. (Gas Pressure) ....B

PA.—Conshohocken

Collins Mfg. Co. (Automatic Damper; Automatic Pump) X

PA.—East Pittsburg

Pittsburg Meter Co. (Gas Pressure) ....AA

PA.—Harrisburg

Harrisburg Mfg. & Boiler Co. (Damper) ....A

PA.—Lancaster

Central Machine Works (Damper) ....E

PA.—Philadelphia

Belfield & Co., H., 435 N. Broad (Pressure; Pump; Damper) ....AA

Eynon-Evans Mfg. Co., 1519 Clearfield (Pump) .....A

Haines Co., Wm. S. (Gas; Heat) X

Hess & Barker Co., 810 Sansom (Improved Damper) E

Lonergan & Co., J. E. (Damper) ....AA

Phila. Electric Service Co., 1109 Arch (Heat) .AAA

Thompson & Co., J., cor. Van Horn & Sophia (Water; Pressure) ....A

Watson & McDaniel Co., 146 N. 7th (Fan Engine for Steam, Water & Air; Pressure, for Steam, Water & Air) C

PA.—Pittsburg

Chaplin-Fulton Mfg. Co., 28 Penn. Av. (Water Pressure) ....A

Equitable Meter Co., 225 1st Av. (Gas Pressure).B

Kelly & Jones Co., 135 Water (Damper; Pressure Pump) ....AA

Oil Well Supply Co., 213 Water (Gas Pressure) AAAA

Pittsburg Supply Co. (Ltd.) (Gas) ....A

Westinghouse Electric & Mfg. Co. (Electric).AAAA

PA.—Scranton

Wilson & Warman (Laundry Water) ....B

PA.—Warren

Jacobson Machine Mfg. Co. (Gas Pressure) C

PA.—Williamsport

Valley Iron Wks. (Pump) A

PA.—York

Burrows Mfg. Co. (Automatic Damper; Pressure; Automatic Pumps) ....E

Spangler Mfg. Co. (Grain Drill) C

WIS.—Evansville

Baker Mfg. Co. (Windmill) AA

WIS.—Milwaukee

Erwin Hydraulic Machinery Co., 204 Grand (Water Pressure) ....D

Johnson Service Co. (Heat; Pressure; for Branch Offices) ....AAA

WIS.—Waupun

Althouse, Wheeler Company (Windmill) ....A

REHEATERS

CONN.—Hartford
Whitlock Coil Pipe Co....A

RELISHES

See Condiments & Relishes

REMEDIES

CONN.—Hartford
Sturtevant, F. C. (Horse)
............................D
ILL.—Chicago
Burch & Co., F. S. (Horse)
............................D
Campbell & Co., James B.
(Horse) X
Emmert Proprietary Co.
(Horse) ....E
N. H.—Keene
Lesure, J. G. (Horse)....C
MASS.—Boston
Egyptian Chemical Co.
(Horse) X
NEBR.—Omaha
Lee & Co., G. H. (Horse;
Dog) ....B
VT.—Enosburgh Falls
Kendall Co., Dr. B. T.
(Horse) ....A

REMOVERS

See also Solvent

CONN.—New Milford
Bridgeport Wood Finishing
Co. (Varnish) ....AA
N. Y.—Buffalo
Pierce Co., Wm. B., 327
Washn. (Scale) ....D
New York City
Watson-Stillman Co. (Pis-
ton Rod) ....A
N. Y.—Rochester
Yawman & Erbe Mfg. Co.
(Battle; Tin Foil) ...AA
PA.—Allegheny
Ball Chemical Co. (Varnish;
Stairs; Paint) ....F
PA.—Philadelphia
Henshaw, Jno. B., German-
town (Wall Paper) ...H
WIS.—Racine
Johnson & Son, S. C.
(Paint) ....D

RENNET

ILL.—Chicago
Creamery Package Mfg. Co.
(Liquid) ....AAAA
N. Y.—Little Falls
Hansens Lab. Chr. (Junket
Tablets) ....B
N. Y.—Syracuse
American Rennet Ext. Co.
............................D
Gowing, D. H. (Ext.)....C
PA.—Philadelphia
Blair, H. C., Walnut & 8th
............................C
Favorite Mfg. Co., 201 N.
Front C

RENOVATORS

ILL.—Chicago
Jewel Mfg. Co., 515 Holden
Pl. (Carpet) ....F
MASS.—Worcester
Curtis & Marble Machine
Co. (Flock) ....A
N. Y.—Brooklyn
Houchin & Huber (Feather)
............................D

REPEATERS

N. J.—Paterson
Royle & Sons, Jno. (Jac-
quard Card; French In-
dex; Fine Scale) ......A
New York City
Bunnell & Co., J. H., 20
Park Pl. (Automatic)..B
PA.—Philadelphia
Schaum & Uhlinger (Jac-
quard Card) ....AAA

REPELLERS

CONN.—New Haven

REPELLERS (Con.)

Marlin Fire Arms Co.
(Rust) ....AA

REPLACERS

ILL.—Chicago
Handy Car Equipment Co.,
Old Colony Bldg. (Car).D
Railway Appliance Co., Old
Colony Bldg. (Car; Loco-
motive) ....A
Tilden Co., B. E., Monad-
nock Bldg. (Car) ......D
ILL.—Harvey
Buda Foundry & Mfg. Co.
(Car; Locomotive) .....A
MASS.—Boston
Laconia Car Co., 50 State
(Car) ....AA
MICH.—Kalamazoo
Kalamazoo Railway Supply
Co. (Car) C
N. Y.—Utica
Kline, August (Car) ....F
OHIO—Portsmouth
Portsmouth Pressed Steel
Co. (Pressed Steel) ....D
PA.—Scranton
Alexander Car Replacer
Mfg. Co., Mears Bldg.
(Car; Locomotive) .....D

RE-PRESSERS

MICH.—Morenci
Michigan Brick & Tile Ma-
chine Co. (Brick; Terra
Cotta) ....D
N. C.—Statesville
Steele & Sons, J. C. (Brick)
............................B
OHIO—Bucyrus
American Clay Working Ma-
chine Co. (Brick) X
OHIO—Middleport
Ohio Machine Co. (Brick).C
PA.—Lancaster
Martin Brick Machine Mfg.
Co., Henry (Brick) ....B

REPRO-
DUCTIONS

See also Furniture

MASS.—Boston
Soule Art Co. (Photograph)
............................X
MASS.—Springfield
Taber-Prang Art Co. (Pho-
tograph) ....AA

RE-SAWS

ILL.—Chicago
Preble Machine Works Co.
(Bond) ....D
MASS.—Orange
Chase Turbine Mfg. Co.
(Automatic) ....A
MICH.—Saginaw
Mershon & Co., Wm. B...A
Saginaw Mfg. Co. (Band)
............................AA
MINN.—Minneapolis
Mercen, Arno, 44th & Lyn-
dale (Horizontal Box)..X
N. J.—Smithville
Smith Machine Co., H. B.
(Circular) ....A
N. Y.—Belmont
Clark Bros. Co. (Band)...A
N. Y.—Buffalo
Frank Machinery Co. (Cir-
cular) C
N. Y.—Rochester
Connell & Dengler Machine
Co. ....B
OHIO—Cincinnati
Cordesman Machine Co.
(Band) X
Fay & Egan Co., J. A.
(Band) ....AAAA
WIS.—Beloit
Berlin Machine Wks..AAAA
WIS.—Eau Claire
McDonough Mfg. Co. ....A

RESERVOIRS

ILL.—Chicago

RESERVOIRS (Con.)
Cribben & Sexton Co., 54
  Erie (Enamelled Stove)
  ....AA
IND.—Jeffersonville
Indiana Mfg. Co. (Stove).A
PA.—Erie
Erie Stamping & Mfg. Co.
  (Oil) ....D
WIS.—Milwaukee
Pressed Steel Tank Co. (Air
  Brake) ....B

RESINOIDS

ILL.—Chicago
Baker & Co., Chas. S.....C
MD.—Baltimore
Sharp & Dohme ....AAA
MASS.—Cambridge
Thayer & Co., Henry ....A
MICH.—Detroit
Parke, Davis & Co...AAAA
New York City
Keith & Co., B.........F
PA.—Philadelphia
Hance Bros. & White..AA

RESORCINE

New York City
Boehringer & Soehne, C. F.
  ....A

RESPIRATORS

IND.—South Bend
Cover, H. S. C

RESTS

See also Furniture

CONN.—Meriden
Bradley & Hubbard Mfg.
  Co. (Music) .....AAAA
Foster, Merrimon & Co.
  (Music) ....AA
CONN.—New Britain
Taplin Mfg. Co. (Cigar).D
CONN.—New Haven
New Haven Mfg. Co.
  (Shafting) ....AA
CONN.—Torrington
Hendey Machine Co.
  (Slide) ....AA
ILL.—Chicago
Chicago Chair & Wheel Co.
  (Back) ....A
Chicago Spring Butt. Co.,
  491 Carroll Av. (Shoe
  Blacking) C
Nicol & Co. (Shoe).....D
ILL.—Freeport
Stover Mfg. Co. (Book).AA
MD.—Baltimore
Kerr & Son Co., Samuel
  (Arm) ....
MASS.—Boston
American Tool & Machine
  Co. (Slide) ....AA
MASS.—Everett
Blount & Co., J. G. (Slide)
  ....D
MASS.—Fitchburg
Fitchburg Machine Works
  (Shafting) ....B
Putnam Machine Co.
  (Shafting) ....A
MASS.—Lowell
Woods, Sherwood Co.
  (Wire; Knife) ....E
MASS.—Worcester
Cleveland Machine Works
  (Slide) ....A
Draper Machine Tool Co.
  (Shafting) ....B
National Mfg. Co. (Wire
  Knife) ....A
Reed Co., F. E. (Slide) .A
MICH.—Muskegon
Sargent Mfg. Co. (Book)
  ....B
MINN.—Minneapolis
McLeod & Smith (Foot)).B
MO.—St. Louis
Brauer, A. G. (Stove;
  Foot) C
Kupferle, Jno. C. (Shoe
  Blacking) ....AA
Pleuger & Henger Mfg. Co.
  (Shoe Blacking) .....
N. H.—Nashua
Fletcher & Webster Furni-

RESTS (Con.)
  ture Co. (Foot) C
N. J.—Newark
Chase, Edward O. (Slide)D
Sacks, Louis (Foot; Shoe
  Blacking) ....A
N. Y.—Binghamton
Crescent Co. (Body)......F
N. Y.—Buffalo
Aldrich Mfg. Co. (Stove;
  Foot) ....A
Oliver Mfg. Co., W. W.
  (Slide) C
N. Y.—Jamestown
Jamestown Lounge Co.
  (Foot) ....AA
New York City
Aeolian Co. (Music).AAAA
Denzi & Phillips (Foot).C
Carvin Machine Co. (Slide)
  ....AA
Gould-Mersereau Co.
  (Music) ....B
Johns, H. W. & Manville
  Co, (Asbestos; Iron)
  ....AAAA
Mace & Co., L. H. (Back;
  Invalid) ....B
Mason & Co., J. W. (Inva-
  lid; Back) ....D
Sargent Co., Geo. F.
  (Invalid; Back) X
Stove Mfrs. Repair Asso-
  ciation (Stove; Foot)...E
N. Y.—Seneca Falls
Westcott-Jewell Co. (Arm;
  Book; Bookeepers' Arm)
  ....D
OHIO—Cincinnati
Globe-Wernicke Co. (Arm)
  ....AAAA
Lodge & Shipley Machine
  Tool Co. (Slide)......AA
OHIO—Cleveland
Chandler & Price Co.
  (Galley) ....A
Tanner Mfg. Co. (Stove
  Leg) ....A
PA.—Allegheny
Pittsburg, Brass & Glass
  Co. (Music) .....AAAA
Superior Mfg. Co. (Gas
  Log) C
PA.—Philadelphia
Johnson & Lund (Head)AA
PA.—Reading
Reading Hardware Co.
  (Shoe Blacking; Foot)
  ....AAAA
PA.—Wrightsville
Wrightsville Hardware Co.
  (Foot; Shoe Blacking).B

RETAINERS

See also Hardware; Carriage

IOWA—Fort Dodge
Fort Dodge Stoneware Co.
  (Extract) C
MASS.—Springfield
Young, W. T. (Hoof Pad)
  ....D
New York City
Osmer's Co., Frank C., 15
  W. 27th (Tie) ....E
N. Y.—Rochester
Pullman Mfg. Co. (Plaster)
  ....B
PA.—Pittsburg
Alpine Mfg. Co. (Skirt).B
R. I.—Providence
Cory & Reynolds Co.
  (Necktie) C
VA.—Richmond
Richmond Woodworking
  Co. (Tobacco) ....B

RETARDERS

New York City
Hoyt, Arthur S. (Plaster).B
Reilly Repair & Supply
  Co., 229 West (Boiler
  Tube) ....AA
OHIO—Port Clinton
Ohio Retarder Co. (Stucco)
  ....D
OHIO—Uhrichsville
Binns Stucco Retarder Co.
  (Stucco) ....E

RETICULES

WIS.—Milwaukee
Meinecke & Son, A.....AA

RETOOTHERS

MICH.—Grand Rapids
Baldwin, Tuthill & Bolton
               B

RETORTS

See also Clay

.—Denver
Denver Fire Clay Co.
  (Mining) ....AA
ILL.—Batavia
Sperry & Co., D. R. (Amalgam; Condensers) .....B
ILL.—Chicago
Allis-Chalmers Co. (Amalgam; Condensers; Mining) ....AAAA
Chicago Retort & Fire
  Brick Co., 45th & Clark
  (Gas) ....A
KY.—Louisville
Louisville Fire Brick
  Works (Gas) ....A
MD.—Baltimore
Baltimore Retort & Fire
  Brick Co., Nicholson Cor.
  Hall (Gas; Clay) ......B
Bartlett, Hayward & Co.
  (Gas) ....B
MASS.—Boston
Boston Fire Brick Co.,
  (Geo. M. Fiske, Mgr.),
  164 Devonshire (Gas) ...A
MASS.—Taunton
Taunton Crucible Co.
  (Plumbago) ....B
MASS.—Worcester
Arcade Malleable Iron Co.
  (Gas; Iron) ....A
MO.—St. Louis
Laclede Fire Brick Mfg.
  Co., 105 N. 7th (Gas Canning) ....AAAA
Missouri Fire Brick Co.
  (Gas) ....B
Parker-Russell Mining &
  Mfg. Co. (Clay)....AAA
N. J.—Garwood
Beckley & Son, A. J.
  (Amalgam; Condensers)
              D
N. J.—Jersey City
Gautier Co., J. H., Greene
  & Essex (Gas; Clay)..AA
N. J.—Phillipsburg
Warren Fdry. & Machine
  Co. (Cast Iron) .....AA
N. Y.—Brooklyn
Brooklyn Fire Brick
  Works, 88 Van Dyke
  (Gas; Clay) ....A
N. Y.—Buffalo
Trout, H. G. (Chemical).B
New York City
Kreischer Brick Mfg. Co.,
  119 E. 23rd (Gas; Canning; Clay) ....B
Maurer & Son, Henry, 420
  E. 23rd (Gas; Clay)..AA
Weber's Sons, Adam, 15
  Park Row (Gas; Canning) ....AA
OHIO—Zanesville
Griffith & Wedge Co.
  (Amalgam; Condensers)
              A
PA.—New Brighton
Pittsburg Clay Mfg. Co.
  (Chemical) ......AAAA
PA.—Philadelphia
Borgner Co., Cyrus, 23rd &
  Race (Gas; Clay) ....B
Gillinder & Sons (Inc.)
  (Chemist's Glass) ......A
Philadelphia Fire Brick
  Works, 2306 Vine (Gas)
Wood Co., R. D. (Canning)
             AAAA
PA.—Pittsburg
Gardner, Co., James Jr.,
  Hamilton Bldg. (Gas;
  Canning; Clay) .....B
PA.—Warren
Struthers, Walls Co.
  (Chemial for Wood Al-

RETORTS (Con.)
  cohol Wks.) ....AA
PA.—Williamsport
Keeler Co., E. (For Wood
  Alcohol Wks.) ....A

RETRACTORS

OHIO—Cleveland
Federal Mfg. Co. (Trolley)
             AAAA

REVOLVERS

See Fire-Arms

REWINDERS

N. Y.—Rochester
Knowlton Co., M. D.
  (Paper) ....AA

RHEOSTATS

ILL.—Chicago
Badt & Co., F. B., Monadnock Blk. (Mfr's Agents)
              F
McGuire Cummings Mfg.
  Co., 122 N. Sangamon
  (Carbon Elec.) ......AA
McIntosh Battery & Optical Co., 39 W. Randolph
  (Cauterycet) ....D
Roth Bros. & Co. (Dynamos; Field) ....B
Western Electric Co., 257
  So. Clinton (Stage Dimming) ....AAAA
ILL.—Peoria
Diamond Meter Co., 926 So.
  Adams C
IND.—Fort Wayne
Fort Wayne Electric W'ks.
  (Motor Starting) ...AAA
IND.—Indianapolis
Jenney Electric Mfg. Co.
  (Motor Starting) .....A
MASS.—Boston
Gilmore Electric Co.....AA
Mason Regulator Co......A
Simplex Electrical Co..AAA
Zeigler Apparatus Co., 200
  Summer (Stage Dimming, etc.) X
MASS.—Springfield
Elektron Mfg. Co.
  (Automatic) ....A
MICH.—Detroit
Muir & Son, Thos., Union
  Trust Bldg. ....H
N. Y.—Bronxville
Ward Electric Co., Leopold
  (Automatic; Dynamo
  Field; Motor Speed Regulating; Motor Starting)
              A
New York City
Darrin Co., D. H., 126
  Liberty ....D
Gordon Battery Co. (Water) ....D
Zucker, Levett & Loeb Co.,
  526 W. 25th ....A
N. Y.—Schenectady
General Electric Co. (For
  Generators; Motors; Projectors) ....AAAA
N. Y.—Troy
Bernard Co., Ely (Dynamo
  Field) ....D
OHIO—Cleveland
Electric Controller & Supply Co., 31 Michigan...A
Lincoln Electric Co., 71
  Ontario ....D
OHIO—Troy
Hobart Electric Mfg. Co.
  (Dynamo) ....B
Ohio Elec. Specialty Mfg.
  Co. (Dynamo Field; Motor Speed Regulating;
  Motor Starting) ......G
PA.—Philadelphia
Cutler Electrical & Mfg.
  Co., 1112 Sansom (Motor Starting) ....A
Quaker City Electric Co.,
  237 Dock ....D
Wirt Electric Co., 4523
  Tacony (Dynamos;
  Field) ....D

RHEOSTATS (Con.)
PA.—Pittsburg
Westinghouse Electric &
Mfg. Co., Westinghouse
Bldg. ....AAAA
W. Va.—Wheeling
Mutual Electric Machine
Co. (Charging) C
WIS.—La Crosse
Benton & Son, Thos. P...E

RIBBONS

See also Silk Goods

ILL.—Chicago
Am. Steel & Wire Co.,
The Rookery (Sash)
AAAA
Gardner Sash Balance Co.,
164 Dearborn (Sash)...C
Wood & Co., Chas. H.
(Typewriter) ....F
MASS.—Boston
Carters' Ink Co. (Type-
writer) ....A
Webster Co., F. L.
(Typewriter) ....AA
MASS.—Springfield
Smith Mfg. Co., R. H.
(Stamp) C
N. J.—Paterson
Pelgram & Meyer (Cigar)
AAAA
New York City
Clark & Zugalla, 98 Gold
(Typewriter) ....D
Gerber Co., Henry (Type-
writer) ....D
N. Y. Carbon & Transfer
Paper Co. (Typewriter).X
N. Y. Stencil Wks. (Stamp)
D
Underwood Typewriter Co.
(Typewriter) .....AAA
Wicke Ribbon Co., Wm.
(Cigar) ....A
Wolff & Co., Chas. (Cigar)
A
N. Y.—Rochester
American Ribbon & Carbon
Co. (Typewriter) ......D
Caldwell Mfg. Co. (Sash)
C
Little, A. P. (Typewriter)
AA
Pullman Mfg. Co. (Sash).B
OHIO—Cleveland
Donovan & Straus, 58
Frankfort (Typewriter)F
OHIO—Toledo
Newton-Rotherick Mfg. Co.
(Typewriter) ....D
PA.—Philadelphia
U. S. Typewriter Ribbon
Mfg. Co., 805 Walnut
(Typewriter) X

RICE

CAL.—San Francisco
Brandenstein & Co., M. J.,
118 Market ......AAAA
Parrott & Co., 306 Calif..A
Siegfried & Co., J. C.
(Imp. Japan) ....A
GA.—Savannah
Planters' Rice Mill Co..A
GA.—Woodbine
Bedell, J. K............C
ILL.—Chicago
Siegfried & Co., J. C., 5
Lake (Imp. Japan)....A
KANS.—Oswego
Indian Rice Mills Co.....C
LA.—Abbeville
Abbeville Rice Mill......C
Hunter Bros. Canal Co...C
Planters' Rice Milling Co.
B
LA.—Crowley
Columbia Rice Packing Co.
(Ltd.) ....B
Crowley Rice Milling Co..B
Gueydan Rice Mill........B
Hunter Rice Milling Co..B
Jones Bros. Rice Milling
Co. C
Marks' Rice Milling Co..C
Peoples' Independent Rice
Mills Co. ....B
Platt, J. E. ....B
Star Rice Milling Co....B

RICE (Con.)
Union Rice Milling Co...B
LA.—Donaldsonville
Donaldsonville Rice Mill...A
LA.—Estherwood
Eureka Rice Mill........B
LA.—Gueydan
Gueydan Rice Mill Co....B
Mutual Rice Mill Co (Ltd.)
C
LA.—Iota
Iota Rice Milling Co.....B
LA.—Jeanerette
Jeanerette Rice Milling
Co. C
LA.—Jennings
Louisiana Rice Milling Co.
B
Riverside Irrigating Co. &
Rice Mill ....B
LA.—Kinder
Kinder Rice Milling Co.
(Ltd.) C
LA.—Lake Charles
Lake Charles Rice Mills
Co. ....A
Wall Rice Milling Co....B
LA.—Mermenton
Pelican Rice Milling &
Warehouse Co. ....B
LA.—Morse
Morse Rice Milling Co...B
White Swan Rice Mill Co.
B
LA.—New Orleans
Barkley & Co., J., 219 N.
Peters ....A
Breaux, S. L. 808 Perdido
C
Brierre,s Sons, Theo., 217
N. Peters C
Cormier Rice Co., C., 209
N. Peters C
Crescent City Rice Mills,
527 Toulane ....A
Del Bondio, E. F., 300
Poydras ....AA
Drane & Garic, 217 N.
Peters C
Guerard & Hassinger, 223
N. Peters C
Henderson, T. J., 235 N.
Peters C
Hobart & Co., Hy. L., 307
N. Front ....B
Israel Leon, 407 Poydras..B
Levy, Isaac, 400 Julia...A
La. Molasses Co., 414 St.
Jos. ....A
Mc Dermott, Thos., 225 N.
Peters ....A
Nat'l Rice Milling Co., 542
Montegut C
Orleans Rice Mills (J.
Foerster, Prop.), 730
Magazine ....B
Orme & Sutton Rice Co.,
209 N. Peters........C
Rickert, F. Jr., 700
Fulton C
St. Louis Rice Mill Co.,
520 St. Louis C
Socolo, A., 600 Decatur..A
Talmadge, John S., 237 N.
Peters ....A
Trautman & Co., Jac., 401
Magazine ....A
Westerfield, J. R., 235 N.
Peters C
Wynne, Martin J., 213 N.
Peters ....A
LA.—Rayne
Acadia Rice Milling Co..C
Rayne Rice Milling Co...C
LA.—Roanoke
Roanoke Rice Milling Co..C
LA.—Welsh
Daniels, P. W...........A
Welch Rice Milling Co.
(Ltd.) C
MD.—Baltimore
Wagner & Co., H. M., 115
Com. ....A
MISS.—Natchez
Natchez Molasses & Vine-
gar Co. ....AA
N. J.—Matawan
Amer. Rice Food & Mfg.
Co. (Flaked Rice)....AA
N. Y.—Brooklyn
Atlantic Rice Mills Co..AA
New York City
Adler & Hirsch, 19 White-

RICE (Con.)

hall (Imp. Brewers)...B
Atlantic Rice Mills (G. A. Jahn & Co., Prop.), 98 Wall ....B
Brandenstein & Co., M. J., 96 Wall ....AAAA
Cook & Co., W. P., 100 Wall ....B
Crooks & Co., 136 Front.AA
Davis, A., 90 Wall......A
Hobart & Co., H. L., 120 Front ....A
Israel, Leon, 113 Wall..B
Larendon, M. W., 138 Front ....B
Reisinger, H., 11 B'way (Imp. Brewers') ......A
Starace, Achille, 76 Pearl B

N. C.—Goldsboro
Carolina Rice Mills......B
N. C.—Wilmington
Carolina Rice Mills ....B
OREGON—Portland
Portland Rice Mills Co...C
PA.—Philadelphia
Rogers, Holloway & Co., 131 S. 4th ....A
S. C.—Charleston
Atlantic Rice Mills .....B
Bennett's Rice Mill....AA
Charleston Import & Export Co. ....A
Melchers & Co. ....A
O'Neill & Sons, Bernhard AA
Ravenel & Co. C
Talmage, Dan ....A
West Point Mill Co......A
S. C.—Georgetown
Georgetown Rice Milling Co. C
Guendalos Rice Co. (Planters) C
Santee Rice Planting Co. (Planters) C
S. C.—Waverly Mills
Lachicotte & Sons, P. R..C

S. C.—Whithall
Hayward, D. C., (Planters) C
TEXAS—Bay City
Bay City Rice Milling Co. B
Colo. Valley Rice Milling Co. ....B
TEXAS—Beaumont
Beaumont Rice Mills.....A
Hinz Rice Milling Co....A
McFaddin-Wiess--Kyle Rice Milling Co.........AA
San Jacinto Rice Co....AA
TEXAS—Brownsville
Merchants' & Planters' Rice Mill ....A
TEXAS—Eagle Lake
Eagle Lake Rice Milling Co. ....B
TEXAS—El Campo
El Campo Rice Milling Co. B
TEXAS—Galveston
Seaboard Rice Milling Co. A
Texas Star Rice Mills.AA
TEXAS—Houston
Chafee Rice Mill & Irrigation Co. ....AAA
Dunovant, Wm. ......AA
Houston Rice Milling Co. B
Lane City Rice Milling Co. B
Matagorda Rice Mills....B
Talmage, Dan ....A
Thompson Milling Co., T. G. C
TEXAS—Lakeside
Dunovant, Wm. ....AA
TEXAS—Orange
Orange Rice Mill Co.....A
TEXAS—Port Arthur
Port Arthur Milling Co...A
Raywood Rice, Canal & Milling Co. ....AA

RIDDLES

CONN.—Georgetown
Gilbert & Bennett Mfg. Co. (Foundry) ....AAA

RIDDLES (Con.)

CONN.—Southport
Jolleff Co. Mfg. Corpn. (Bakers' Foundry) C
ILL.—Chicago
Barbee Wire & Iron Works (Brass; Foundry; Grain; Miners') ....B
Brand & Co., S. H., 99 West Monroe (Nickel Plate) ....E
Smith Wire & Iron Works, F. P., 100 Lake (Foundry) ....AA
MASS.—Springfield
Bigelow-Cheney Wire Works (Foundry Galvanized)...A
MASS.—Worcester
National Mfg. Co. (Foundry) ....A
Wright Wire Co. (Foundry Galvanized; Miners').AA
MICH.—Detroit
Phoenix Wire Works, 68 Champlain ....D
MO.—St. Louis
Ludlow-Saylor Wire Co. (Farmers' Foundry; Miners') ....AA
N. Y.—Buffalo
Buffalo Wire Works Co..D
New York City
Cabble Excelsior Wire Mfg. Co., Wm. (Galvanized).B
Estey Wire Works Co., 59 Fulton ....D
Gilbert & Bennett Mfg. Co., 277 B'way (Coal; Foundry; Grain; Miners') AAA
Howard & Morse, 45 Fulton (Foundry; Galvanized) D
OHIO—Cincinnati
Bromwell Brush & Wire Goods Co. (Coal; Foundry) ....AA
Obermayer Co., S. (Foundry) ....AA
OHIO—Cleveland
Forest City Steel & Iron Co. ....A
Osborn Mfg. Co., 1331 Hamilton ....B
Smith Foundry Supply Co.. J. D., 40 So. Water ....D
Tyler Co., W. S., 1150 St. Clair (Foundry) ..AAAA
OHIO—Hamilton
Meyers' Mfg. Co., Fred J. (Coal; Foundry) ......B
PA.—Philadelphia
Darby & Sons, Edward, 233 Arch ....A
Paxson Co., J. W., 1021 N. Delaware Av. (Coal; Foundry) ....AA

RIDGERS

MASS.—Chicopee Falls
Belcher & Taylor Agr. Tool Co. (Horse) ....A
N. J.—Grenloch
Bateman Mfg. Co. (Horse) A

RIDGING

ILL.—Warren
Warren Steel Co.(Ornamental) ....D
N. Y.—Troy
Globe Ventilator Co., 203 River (Globe Ventilator) C
OHIO—Canton
Berger Mfg. Co. (Iron)..AA
OHIO—Cleveland
Garry Iron & Steel Co. (Iron) ....A
PA.—Philadelphia
Merchant & Co., 517 Arch (Iron) ....AA

RIFFLERS

PA.—Philadelphia
Disston & Sons, Henry (Bent) ....AAAA
R. I.—Providence
Nicholson File Co. (Bent) AAAA

RIFLES
See Fire-Arms

RIGGING
MASS.—Boston
Durable Wire Rope Co.
(Ships; Wire) ....D
MO.—St. Louis
Leschen & Sons Rope Co.,
A. (Ships) ....AA
New York City
Moseley Iron Bridge &
Roof Co., 39 Cortlandt
(Iron) ....B
N. Y.—Troy
Globe Ventilator Co......C
OHIO—Cleveland
Garry Iron & Steel Co.
(Iron) ....A
OHIO—Salem
Mullins, W. H. (Iron)...A
PA.—Philadelphia
Merchant & Co., 517 Arch
(Iron) ....AA

RIMS
For Wagon Rims see Woodwork

CONN.—Bridgeport
American Tube & Stamping
Co. (Automobile) .AAAA
CONN.—New Haven
Dann Bros. & Co. (Bicycle;
Vehicles) ....B
Shepard & Sons, H. G.
(Bicycle) ....B
CONN.—Torrington
Eagle Bicycle Mfg. Co.
(Bicycle) ....A
ILL.—Chicago
Chicago Screw Co. (Bicycle
Pedal) ....AAA
IND.—Fort Wayne
Olds' Wagon Works
(Bicycle) X
Rastetter & Son, L.
(Bicycle) ....B
IND.—Indianapolis
Gillett & Co., C. H. (Vehicle) C
Lauter, H. (Bicycle).....B
Parry Mfg. Co. (Vehicle)
AAAA
IND.—La Porte
Niles & Scott Co. (Vehicle)
AA
NE—West Falmouth
West Falmouth Mfg. Co.
(Vehicle) ....E
MD.—Baltimore
Stinson, John (Barrel)...C
Stinson Mfg. Co., E.
(Vehicle) ....A
MASS.—Boston
Pope Mfg. Co. (Bicycle)
AAAA
MICH.—Grand Rapids
Michigan Barrel Co. (Barrel; Riddle; Sieve)...A
N. H.—Concord
Holt Bros. Mfg. Co.
(Vehicle) ....B
N. J.—Newark
Jones & Co., Phineas
(Vehicle) ....A
N. J.—Sussex
Little, Owen J. (Automatic
Rifle) ....F
N. Y.—Buffalo
Buffalo Weaving & Belting Co. (Web).......A
Forsyth Mfg. Co. (Vehicle)
C
OHIO—Cleveland
Federal Mfg. Co. (Automobile) ....AAAA
Standard Welding Co.
(Automobile) ....AA
OHIO—Defiance
Turnbull Wagon Co.
(Vehicle) ....AA
OHIO—Hicksville
Kerr Bros. Mfg. Co.
(Bicycle) C
OHIO—Hudson
Shield, E. B. (Bicycle)..F
OHIO—Toledo
Toledo Carriage Woodwork
Co. (Vehicle) ....A

RIMS (Con.)
OHIO—Van Wert
Gleason Lumber Co. (Vehicle) ....A
PA.—Mechanicsburg
Koller & Co., J. B.
(Barrel) C
PA.—Reading
Leippe's Sons, Jacob A.
(Vehicle) ....A
PA.—West Chester
Hooper Bros. & Darlington
(Vehicle) ....AA

RINCERS
MASS.—Boston
Blue Seal Supply Co., 12
Portland (Bottle) C

RINGERS
ILL.—Chicago
Chicago Pneumatic Tool Co.
Fisher Bldg. (Pneumatic;
Locomotive Bell) .AAAA
Pratt Mfg. Co., 91 Lake
(Hog) ....B
Roth Bros. Co., 27 S.
Clinton (Telephone)....B
ILL.—Decatur
Chambers-Bering-Quinlan,
Co. (Hog) ....A
IOWA—Dubuque
Smedley Steam Pump Co.
(Automatic Locomotive
Bell) ....B
MD.—Baltimore
Adt, Jno. B. (Tobacco)..A
MICH.—Saginaw
Heginbottom, S. H. (Automatic Locomotive Bell)F
MO.—St. Louis
Western Railway Equipment Co., Union Trust
Bldg. (Locomotive Bell)
A
New York City
Edward & Co. (Pneumatic
Bell) ....D
N. Y.—Troy
Hammett, Hiram Co.
(Locomotive Bell) .....D
OHIO—Canton
Kohler & Co., F. E. (Hog)
B
OHIO—Cincinnati
Van Duzen Co., 428 E. 2nd
(Locomotive Bell) ....B
PA.—Cheswick
Cheswick Mfg. Co. (Locomotive Bell) X
PA.—Philadelphia
United States Metallic
Packing Co., 427 N. 13th
(Locomotive Bell) ....B

RINGS
See also Rubber Goods; Jewelry
CONN.—Bridgeport
Canfield Co., H. O. (Umbrella) ....B
Smith & Egge Mfg. Co.
(Napkin; Key) ....A
CONN.—Hartford
Billings & Spencer Co. (Key)
AA
CONN.—Meriden
Foster, Merriment & Co.
(Caster) ....AA
Manning, Bowman & Co.
(Napkin) ....AA
Meriden Brittania Co. (Napkin) ....AAAA
CONN.—Mt. Carmel
Woodruff & Sons, Walter W.
(Apron) ....A
CONN.—New Britain
Corbin P. & F. (Locker;
Hitching) ....AAAA
Humason & Beckley Mfg.
Co. (Bull; Hog; Wrought
Iron) ....A
North & Judd Mfg. Co. (Halter; Breeching; Harness;
Iron; Brass; Steel) ...AA
CONN.—New Haven
Cowles & Co., C. (Inc.)
(Apron) ....A
Headey & Co., Andrew B.
(Brass) ....A
North & Co., O. B. (Har-

RINGS (Con.)
OHIO—Akron
Goodrich Co., B. F.
  (Harness; Rubber; Um-
  brella; Fruit Jar; Teeth-
  ing) ....AAAA
Whitman & Barnes Mfg. Co.
  (Fruit Jar; Flush). AAAA
OHIO—Canton
Elbel & Co. (Harness;
  Lariat; Lasso) ....A
Ney Mfg. Co. (Hitching)..B
OHIO—Cincinnati
Glenny Glass Co., W. (Fruit
  Jars, etc.) ....A
OHIO—Cleveland
Crucible Steel Forge Co., 83
  Lake (Welders) X
Standard Welding Co.
  (Steel) ....AA
OHIO—Piqua
Piqua Handle & Mfg. Co.
  (Wood Curtain Pole) ..A
OHIO—Plymouth
Root Bros. Co. (Brass)...B
PA.—Allegheny
Carlin's Sons, Thomas (Pile)
  A
PA.—Allentown
Grammes & Sons, L. F.
  (Brass) ....A
PA.—Erie
Continental Rubber Works
  (Rubber) ....A
PA.—Lebanon
Amer. Iron & Steel Mfg. Co.
  (Pole) ....AAAA
Coldren Rubber Co. (Rubber
  Fruit Jar) ....D
PA.—Philadelphia
Bingham, James (Galvanic))
  A
Latrobe Steel Co. Girard
  Bldg. (Rock Crusher)
  AAAA
Randolph, W. C. (Bone;
  Harness) ....E
PA.—Pittsburg
Lanz & Son, M. (Pole) ..AA
Oliver Iron & Steel Co.
  (Pole) ....AAAA
Standard Chain Co. (Iron;
  Lap) ....AAAA
PA.—Reading
Reading Hardware Co.
  (Flush) ....AAAA
R. I.—Pawtucket
Haskell Mfg. Co., Wm. H.
  (Clinch) ....AA
Jenckes Mfg. Co., E. (Spin-
  ning) ....AA
Pawtucket Spinning Ring
  Co. (Spinning) ....D
R. I.—Providence
American Supply Co. (Spin-
  ning) ....AA
Brown Bros. Co. (Spinning)
  AA
Davol Rubber Co. (Teeth-
  ing) ....AA
  AA
Rhode Island Tool Co.
  (Clinch) ....AAA
Waite-Thresher Co. (Gold) A
Wall & Co., A. T. (Spring;
  Key) C
WIS.—South Milwaukee
Stowell Mfg. & Foundry Co.
  (Reducing) ....A

RINKS
WIS.—Milwaukee
Vilter Mfg. Co. (Ice Skat-
  ing) ....AA

RIPPERS
See also Machy

MAINE—Bangor
Union Iron Wks. (Gang), A
MASS.—Somerville
Underhill Chas. L. (Shingle)
  E
MICH.—Bay City
Garland Co., M. (Gang) ..C
New York City
Amer. Woodworking Ma-
  chine Co., 136 Liberty
  (Gang) ....AAAA
PA.—Easton
Bangor Excelsior Slate Co.
  (Slaters) ....A

RIPPERS (Con.)
PA.—Erie
Standard Saw Mill Mchry.
  Co. (Gang) ....B
WIS.—Milwaukee
Filer & Stowell Co. (Gang)
  AAA

RIVETERS
See also Machy

CONN.—New Haven
Shuster, F. B. Co. (Bicycle
  Chain; Rotary Blow) ..X
ILL.—Chicago
Hanna Engineering Wks.,
  820 Elston Av. (Compres-
  sion) ....B
Railway Appliances Co.
  (Pneumatic). ....A
Smith, F. H. Mfg. Co., 18
  W. Randolph (Hand)....D
ILL.—Freport
Arcade Mfg. Co. (Belting;
  Harness Repairing, etc.)
  A
MICH.—Saginaw
Wickes Bros. (Hydraulic)
  AAA
N. Y.—Dunkirk
American Air Tool Co. (Com-
  pression). ....A
New York City
McCabe Hanger Mfg. Co.,
  533 W. 22d (Bicycle
  Chain) ....B
Niles-Bement-Pond Co., 136
  Liberty (Hydraulic; Port-
  able; Steam) ......AAAA
Pedrick & Ayer Co., 87 Lib-
  erty (Pneumatic) .....A
Rand Drill Co., 128 Bway.
  (Pneumatic; .....AAAA
Watson Stillman Co., 204 E.
  43d (Hydraulic; Portable)
  A
OHIO—Alliance
Alliance Machine Co. (Hy-
  draulic; Portable; Steam)
  AA
Morgan Engineering Co.
  (Hydraulic) ....AAAA
OHIO—Cleveland
Oram, John S., 1 N. Coe
  (Hoop) ....A
OHIO—Plymouth
Root Bros. Co. (Hand) ....B
OHIO—Ravenna
Williams, A. Co. (Hand) ..A
PA.—Chambersburg
Chambersburg Engineering
  Co. (Hydraulic) ......A
PA.—Philadelphia
Bement, Niles & Co. (Hy-
  draulic) ....AAAA
Phila. Pneumatic Tool Co.,
  1038 Ridge Av. (Pneuma-
  tic) ....B
Phila. Roll & Machine Co.
  23d & Wash. Av. (Hydrau-
  lic) ....A
Sellers & Co., Wm. (Inc.)
  (Hydraulic; Pneumatic;
  Portable). ....AAAA
Wood Co., R. D., 400 Chest-
  nut (Hydraulic) ...AAAA
PA.—Pittsburg
Fischer Fdy. & Machine Co.
  (Hydraulic) ....AA
PA.—So. Bethlehem
Bethlehem Fdy. & Machine
  Co. (Pneumatic; Portable;
  Steam) C

RIVETS
See also Bolts; Hardware;
  Carriage

CONN.—Bridgeport
Bridgeport Brass Co. (Belt;
  Hose; Brass; Copper)
  AAA
CONN.—Derby
Birmingham Brass Co.
  (Brass) ....AA
CONN.—Milldale
Clark Bros. Bolt Co. (Iron;
  Steel) ....A
CONN.—New Haven
Cowles & Co., C. (Inc.)
  (Iron) ....A
Grilley Co. (Hame) C
National Rivet Wks. (Chas.

RIVETS (Con.)

E. Brown) (Barrel; Belt; Hose; Coopers; Norway Iron; Stove; Tinners) ..B
Reves Mfg. Co. (Brass; Copper) C

CONN.—Torrington
Coe Brass Mfg. Co. (Belt; Hose; Brass; Copper) AAAA
Progressive Mfg. Co. (Brass; Copper; German Silver; Iron; Steel) ....A
Turner & Seymour Mfg. Co. (Iron) ....A

CONN.—Unionville
Upson Nut Co. (Boiler; Tank; Bridge; Structural; Norway Iron; Tinners; Steel) ....AAAA

CONN.—Waterbury
Benedict & Burnham Mfg. Co. (Brass; Copper; Belt; Hose) ....AAAA
Blake & Johnson (Aluminum; Brass; Copper; German Silver; Braziers; Iron; Steel) ....A
Holmes, Booth & Haydens Co. (Belt; Hose; Brass; Copper) ....AAA
Patent Button Co. (Rubber Shoe) ....A
Plume & Atwood Mfg. Co. (Belt; Hose; Brass Copper; Bronze; Braziers) AAA
Scovill Mfg. Co. (Brass; Copper; Braziers) ....AAAA
Steele & Johnson Mfg. Co. (Brass) ....A
Waterbury Mfg. Co. (Brass; Boiler; Tank; Copper; Coppersmiths) ....AAAA

CONN.—Winsted
Moore, Franklin Co. (Cone; Truss; Oval; Round Headed; Norway Iron; Steel Carriage) ....A

DEL.—Wilmington
Diamond State Steel Co. (Boiler; Tank; Bridge; Structural; Norway Iron; Ship; Black Tinners; Steel) X

ILL.—Chicago
American Steel & Wire Co., The Rookery (Barrel; Belt; Hose; Boiler; Tank; Brass; Copper; Coopers; Norway Iron; Shovel; Stove; Tinners) ....AAAA
Besly, Chas. H. & Co., 15 Clinton (Iron; Steel), AA
Braun, J. G., 232 So. Pauline (Ornamental Steel) ....A
Continental Bolt & Iron Wks., 22d & Union (Bridge; Structural) ...A
Grand Crossing Track Co., So. Chicago Av. & 79th (Belt; Hose; Tinners; Copper; Clinch; Hinge; Iron; Steel) ....AAA
Republic Iron & Steel Co., Stock Exchange Bldg., (Boiler; Tank; Bridge; Structural; Car; Norway Iron; Ship; Steel), AAAA

ILL.—Freeport
Stover Mfg. Co. (Braziers) AA

IND.—Indianapolis
Parkhurst Mfg. Co. (Bridge; Structural) C

IND.—Madison
Tower Mfg. Co. (Tinned; Coppered; Iron; Burrs; Belt; Hose; Countersunk; Coopers; Tinners) C

MASS.—Boston
Boston Bolt Co., 33 Purchase (Boiler; Tank; Norway Iron; Ship; Tinners) C
New England Bolt & Nut Co., 253 Atlantic Av. (Boiler; Tank; Bridge; Structural ;Ship) ......B
Standard Rivet Co., 41 Lincoln (Belt; Hose, for Leather, Cloth; & other Fabrics; Bifurcated; Rubber Shoe; Shoe; Tinned;

RIVETS (Con.)
Pronged) ....B
Tubular Rivet & Stud Co. (Bevel Pointed; Tubular; Leather; Harness; Shoe; Pronged) ....AAA

MASS.—Fairhaven
Atlas Tack Co. (Copper; Belt; Hose; Boiler; Tank; Brass, also Brass; Copper; Burrs; Tinners; Carriage; Iron; Rubber Shoe; Wagon; Tinned; Stove; Trunk; Hame) ....AAAA

MASS.—Plymouth
Cobb & Drew (Brass; Copper; Iron; Steel) ......AA
Plymouth Mills (Inc.) (Iron; Steel) ....B

MASS.—Taunton
Taunton Rivet Co. (Copper, also Burrs, Tinners) X

MASS.—Waltham
Thomson Mfg. Co., Judson L. (Bifurcated) ....A

MASS.—Winchenron
Townsend, G. G. (Barrel) X

MASS.—Worcester
Reed & Prince Mf. Co. (Brass; Copper; Norway Iron; Shovel; Tinners) ..B
Wright Wire Co. (Wire) AA

MICH.—Detroit
Detroit Copper & Brass Rolling Mills (Belt; Hose; Brass; Copper; Wire; German; Silver) ....AAAA
Michigan Bolt & Nut Wks. Ft. Meldrum Av. (Boiler; Tank; Bridge; Structural; Car; Norway Iron; Ship) AA

MO.—Kansas City
Kansas City Bolt & Nut Co. (Boiler; Tank; Bridge; Structural; Car; Ship) ..A

MO.—St. Louis
Moran Bolt & Nut Mfg. Co. (Boiler; Tank; Bridge; Structural; Car) ....A

N. J.—Boonton
Lincoln Iron Works (Bridge) B

N. J.—Dover
Ulster Iron Wks. (Boiler; Tank) ....AA

N. J.—Newark
Gould's Son & Co., M. (Trunk) ....A
Jenkenson, R. C. & Co.(Iron; Steel) ....AA
Newark Rivet Works (Brass; Copper; Black Coppered; Tinned; Norway Iron) ....AA

N. J.—Trenton
Trenton Iron Co. (Iron) ...A

N. Y.—Brooklyn
Upham & Bros., N. B., 30 Hudson Av. (Aluminum; Brass; Copper; Bridge; German Silver) X

New York City
Amer. Steel & Wire Co., 71 Bway. (Belt; Hose; Boiler; Tank; Brass; Copper; Norway Iron; Shovel; Stove; Tinners) ....AAAA
Fuller Bros. & Co., 139 Greenwich (Mfrs. Agents) (Boiler; Tank; Bridge; Structural) ....D
Greenlie, Wyatt & Co., 499 Water (Bridge; Structural) ....B
Hassall, Jno., 169 Elm (Brass; Copper; German Silver; Norway Iron) ...B
Hendricks Bros., 49 Cliff (Copper) ....AAAA
Hungerford Brass & Copper Co., U. T., 497 Pearl (Belt; Hose; Brass; Copper; Coopers) ....AA
Hose; Brass; Copper; Coopers) ....AA
Iron Clad Mfg. Co., 24 Cliff (Tinners') ....AAA
Russell & Erwin Mfg. Co., 43 Chambers (Iron; Steel) AAAA
Sargeant & Co., 151 Leonard (Hinge) ....AAAA
Stimpson & Son, Edwin B.,

RIVETS (Con.)

31 Spruce (Belt; Hose; Tubular) ....A
Tiebout, W. & J., 118 Chambers (Oyster) ....B
N. Y.—Portchestr
Russell, Burdsall & Ward Bolt & Nut Co. (Iron; Steel) ....AAAA
N. Y.—Rome
Rome Brass & Copper Co. (Belt; Hose; Brass; Copper) ....AAAA
N. Y.—Troy
Burden Iron Co. (Boiler; Tank; Iron Steel) .AAAA
OHIO—Cincinnati
Robertson Steel & Iron Co., Cor. Front & Elm (Steel) ....A
OHIO—Cleveland
Atlas Car & Mfg. Co. (Iron; Steel) ....AA
Bassett-Presley Co. (Bridge; Structural) ....AA
Bourne & Knowles Mfg. Co. 8 Main (Iron) ....A
Champion Rivet Co., Union at Erie R. R. (Boiler; Tank; Bridge; Structural; Ship; Boat; Iron Steel) ..A
Forest City Steel & Iron Co. (Iron; Steel) ....A
Lamson & Sessons Co., 412 Scranton Av. (Car; Coopers; Stove) ....AA
National Screw & Tack Co. (Coopers; Tinners) ....AA
Vulcanus Forging Co. (Forged; Boiler; Tank; Forged Bridge; Structural; Forged Ship) ....B
OHIO—Columbus
Berry Bros. ....B
Columbus Bolt Works (Iron) AA
OHIO—Youngstown
Youngstown Mfg. Co. (Boiler; Tank) ....AA
PA.—Allentown
Allentown Rolling Mills (Iron) ....AAA
PA.—Lancaster
Penn. Iron Co. (Bridge; Structural; Car; Ship) ..A
PA.—Lebanon
American Iron & Steel Mfg. Co. (Boiler; Tank; Bridge; Structural; Car; Norway Iron; Ship) ....AAAA
PA.—New Brighton
Townsend. C. C. & E. P. (Tinners; Copper; Iron; Steel) ....AAA
PA.—New Castle
New Castle Forge & Bolt Co. (Boiler; Tank; Bridge; Structural; Ship; Iron; Steel) ....AA
PA.—Norristown
Reading Screw Co. (Iron; Steel) ....A
PA.—Philadelphia
Hoopes & Townsend Co., 1330 Buttonwood (Barrel; Boiler; Tank; Bridge; Structural; Car; Coopers; Norway Iron; Ship; Flat) AAA
Phoenix Bridge Co. (Iron) A
PA.—Pittsburg
Carroll-Porter Boiler & Tank Co. (Iron; Steel) .....A
Dowerman Rivet & Bolt Mfg. Co.. 32d & Penn Av. (Bridge; Structural)....E
Fort Pitt Forge Co.. (Boat; Iron; Steel) ......AAA
Garland Chain Co., Frick Bldg. (Tinners) ....AAA
Hussey & Co., C. G., 2850 2d Av. (Copper) .....AAA
Jones & Laughlin Steel Co. (Boiler; Tank; Bridge; Structural; Norway Iron) AAAA
Lamz & Sons, Mathew, 101 S. 29th (Bridge; Structural; Car; Iron; Steel) AA
Oliver Iron & Steel Co. (Boiler; Tank; Bridge; Structural; Car; Ship) AAAA

RIVETS (Con.)

Pittsburg Forge & Iron Co. (Iron) ....A
Pittsburg Mfg. Co., 28th & R. R. (Boiler; Tank; Iron; Steel) ....A
Pittsburg Screw & Bolt Co. (Boiler; Tank; Bridge; Structural) ....A
Scaife & Sons, Wm. B., 221 1st Av. (Belt; Hose; Boiler; Tank; Bridge; Structural; Iron; Steel) ....AAA
Severance Mfg. Co., S., Murtland Bldg. (Boiler; Tank; Bridge; Structural; Norway Iron; Ship) ....B
PA.—Scranton
Scranton Bolt & Nut Co. (Bridge; Structural) ..AA
R. I.—Providence
American Screw Co. (Belt; Hose; Tinners; Carriage; Iron Trimmers; Hame; Steel) ....AAAA
TENN.—Memphis
Livermore Foundry & Machine Co. (Iron) ....A
VA.—Richmond
Old Dominion Iron & Nail Wks. Co. (Boiler; Tank; Bridge; Structural; Ship) AA

ROADS

MICH.—Grand Rapids
Butterworth & Lowe (Pole; Legging) ....A

ROASTERS

COLO.—Denver
Denver Engineering Wks. Co. (Mechanical) ....A
ILL.—Chicago
Crestors & Co., C. (Peanut) E
ILL.—Paxton
Paxton Hdw. Mfg. Co. (Coffee) X
MASS.—Attleboro
Carter, Quarnstrom & Remington (Coffee) C
MASS.—Worcester
Hamblin & Russell Mfg. Co. (Wire Turkey) ....B
N. J.—Burlington
Stuart & Peterson Co. (Peanut) ....A
New York City
Bramhall-Deane Co. (Coffee) B
Burns & Sons, Jabez, 542 Greenwich (Coffee) ..B
Crandall & Godley Co. (Peanut) ....AA
Fraser Mfg. Co., 26 Cortlandt (Coffee) ....D
Hungerford Bros. & Co. (Coffee) ....B
N. Y.—Poughkeepsie
Lane Bros. Co. (Coffee) ..A
N. Y.—Silver Creek
Howes Co., S. (Coffee) ..A
OHIO—Cincinnati
Hilbert Machine Co. (Peanut) ....D
Kingery Mfg. Co. (Peanut; Coffee) C
Lee. Thos. (Peanut) C
OHIO—Troy
Royal Polished Steel Roaster Co. (Steel) ....D
PA.—Hazleton
Koenig. M. F. (Coffee) ...X
PA.—Philadelphia
Mills & Bro. Thos., 1301 N. 8th (Peanut)...........A

ROBES

CAL.—Napa
Napa Woolen Mill (Lap), C
CAL.—Oakland
Keller Co.. M. J. (Night) A
CAL.—San Francisco
Golden Gate Woolen Mfg. Co., Cor. Bryant & 19th (Carriage) ....A
Ulman, Seeligsohn & Brown (Night) ....B
CAL.—Santa Rosa
Santa Rosa Woolen Mills

ROBES (Con.)
(Fancy; Woolen) C
ILL.—Chicago
Chase & Co., L. C. (Common) ....AA
Freytag, M. (Fur) ......B
Kimball & Co., C. P. (Carriage) ....AA
ILL.—Mattoon
Buck Mfg. Co., Geo. N. (Night) ....B
ILL.—Sterling
Rock Falls Mfg. Co. (Burial) ....A
IND.—Crawfordsville
Crawfordsville Casket Co. (Burial) ....B
IND.—La Grange
La Grange Robe & Fur Co. (Fur) ....H
IOWA—Dubuque
Glover Co., H. B. (Flannelette Night) ....A
Rider Wallis Co. (Night) ....AA
MAINE—Lewiston
Bates Street Shirt Co. ...C
MAINE—Sanford
Sanford Mills (Carriage; Plush; Wool) .....AAA
MAINE—South Berwick
Newichawanick Co. (Carriage) ....A
MD.—Baltimore
Day, Son & Co., O. Y. (Carriage) C
North Bros. & Strauss (Night) ....A
MASS.—Boston
Chase & Co., L. C. (Common) ....AA
Macullar-Parker Co. (Bath) ....AA
Richardson & Co., Wm. H. (Bath) ....B
Sasconville Mills (Carriage) ....AAAA
MASS.—Leominster
Wachusetts Shirt Co. (Night) ....A
MASS.—Pittsfield
Pontoosuc Woolen Mfg. Co. (Carriage; Lap) ......AA
MICH.—Coronna
U. S. Robe Co. (Knit) ..C
MICH.—Detroit
Pioneer Woolen Mills (Carriage) ....D
MICH.—Grand Rapids
Powers & Walker Casket Co. (Burial) ....A
MICH.—Wyandotte
Bishop Co., J. H. (Carriage; Fur) ....A
MINN.—Minneapolis
North Star Woolen Mill Co. (Carriage) ....AA
MO.—St. Joseph
Buell Mfg. Co. (Carriage) ......A
MO.—St. Louis
Mound Coffin Co. (Burial) ....A
N. J.—Newark
Peters Harness & Saddlery Co. (Lap) C
N. J.—Passaic
Algonquin Co. (Carriage; Lap) ....AA
N. Y.—Albany
Munson, S. L. (Night) ..AA
N. Y.—Brooklyn
Kenyon Co., C. (Bath) ..AA
N. Y.—Buffalo
Amer. Buffalo Robe Co. (Carriage; Plush; Lap; Automobile; Baby Carriage) ....A
N. Y.—Gloversville
Leak Fur Mfg. Co. (Fur) ....D
Steele Bros. (Fur) ......D
N. Y.—Lockport
Dumville & Co. (Night)..D
N. Y.—Mattewan
Mattewan Mfg. Co. (Fur Lap) ....A
N. Y.—Milton
Bell's Sons Co., Henry H. (Men's Bath) ....B
N. Y.—Newburg
Stroock Plush Co. (Lap).B
New York City
Benjamin & Co., Alfred

ROBES (Con.)
(Bath) ....AAA
Cooper, Michael (Ladies' Bath) ....AAAA
Goodyear Rubber Co. (Lap) ....A
Heller, Rothschild & Lang (Bath) ....A
Kelsey, Albert (Lap) ....B
Rogers, Peet & Co., 13th & B'way (Bath) ...AAAA
Steiner & Son (Women's Night) ....A
Strook & Co., S. (Carriage; Plush) ....A
Taylor & Co., H. E., 510 E. 72d (Burial) ....A
N. Y.—Rochester
National Casket Co. (Burial) ....AAAA
N. Y.—Troy
United Shirt & Collar Co. (Night; Bath) ....AAAA
OHIO—Cincinnati
Crane & Breed Mfg. Co. (Burial) ....AA
Sturn & Sons, G. (Bath) ....B
OHIO—Cleveland
Beckman Co. (Carriage; Lap; Woolen) ....AA
OHIO—Columbus
Columbus Coffin Co. (Burial) ....A
OHIO—Zanesville
Muskingham Coffin Co. (Burial) ....A
OREGON—Eugene
Williamette Valley Woolen Mfg. Co. (Woolen) C
OREGON—Oregon City
Oregon City Mfg. Co. (Carriages) ....A
PA.—Philadelphia
Ayres & Sons, Wm. (Lap) ....AA
Brownstein, Segall & Co. (Night) ....D
Hanifer & Co., J. E. (Eiderdown) ....B
Kennedy, Willing & Co. (Lap) ....A
Lane's Sons, D. M. (Carriage) ....D
Leicester & Continental Mills Co. (Bath) ......A
Riley & Co., Wm. B. (Carriage; Lap) ....A
Sumner & Co., T. (Lap) ..D
Star & Crescent Mills Co. (Bath) ....A
Stern, David & Co. ....A
Tutelman Bros. & Faggen (Night) ....A
WIS.—Milwaukee
Gem Hammond & Fly Net Co. (Fur) ....A
Hansen's Empire Fur Factory (Fur) ....A

ROCKAWAYS
See also Carriages & Wagons

CONN.—New Haven
Goodrich & Co., J. F. ..AA
ILL.—Chicago
Kimball & Co., C. P. ....AA
IND.—South Bend
Studebaker Bros. Mfg. Co. ....AAAA
IOWA—Dubuque
Connolly, Tom ....A
MASS.—Amesbury
Biddle & Smart Co. ......B
Feltsch & Co., E. S. C
MASS.—Boston
French & Co., Ferd. F. (Ltd.) ....D
MASS.—Merrimac
Pease & Son, S. C. C
N. J.—Newark
Quimby & Co., J. ....A
N. Y.—Albany
Goold Co., James ....B
New York City
Brewster & Co., J. B. ..B
Stivers, Rufus M. ....B
N. Y.—Troy
Troy Carriage Wrks. ....B
N. Y.—Watertown
Babcock Co., H. H. ..AA

ROCKAWAYS (Con.)
OHIO--Columbus
Buckeye Buggy Co. ....AAA

ROCKERS
See Furniture

RODS
See also Fish Tackle; Iron & Steel
ALA.—Ensley
Alabama Steel & Wire Co. (Wire) ....AAAA
CAL.—San Francisco
Paynes Bolt Wrks., 121 Howard (Bridge; Roof) A
COLO.—Denver
Colorado Fuel & Iron Co. (Wire) ....D
CONN.—Ansonia
Ansonia Brass & Copper Co. (Brass; Copper; Stair) AAAA
CONN.—Berlin
Berlin Construction Co. (Tie) ....A
CONN.—Bridgeport
Amer. Tube & Stamping Co. (Lightning) .....AAAA
Bridgeport Brass Co. (Brass; Copper; Bronze; German Silver) ....AAA
CONN.—Bristol
Bristol Brass Co. (Brass; German Silver) ....AAA
Horton Mfg. Co. (Fishing; Steel Fishing) ....B
CONN.—Clinton
Kelsey, Horatio (Gun) ..E
CONN.—Collinsville
Hartegan, W. R. (Gun; Rifle Cleaning) ....H
CONN.—Hartford
Pratt & Whitney Co. (Measuring) ....AAAA
CONN.—Meriden
Parker Co., Chas. (Saw) AAA
CONN.—Milldale
Clark Bros Bolt Co. (ron)..B
CONN.—Mt. Carmel
Mt. Carmel Bolt Co. (Stove) B
CONN.—New Britain
Corbin, P. & F. (Stove) AAAA
Stanley Rule & Level Co. (Gauging) ....AAA
CONN.—New Haven
Dann Bros. & Co. (Dowel, Carpet) ....B
English & Mersick Co. (Carpet) ....B
Goodrich & Co., J. F. (Wagon Box) ....AA
National Steel & Wire Co. (Bessemer Coppered; Brace; Bracket Pump; Saw Wire) .. ....AAAA
National Wire Corpn. (Bessemer Coppered Machine Screw; Curtain; Gun Screw; Nail; Rivet; Screw; Wire) ....AA
CONN.—Norwich
Norwich Nickel & Brass Co. (Nickel; Plated Window) B
CONN.—Pine Meadow
Chapin-Stephens Co. (Gauging) ....A
CONN.—Seymour
Seymour Mfg. Co. (German Silver) ....AAA
CONN.—Torrington
Coe Brass Mfg. Co. (Brass; Copper) ....AAAA
Turner & Seymour Mfg. Co. (Banner) ....A
CONN.—Unionville
Upson Nut Co. (Stove; Gauging) ....AAAA
CONN.—Waterbury
American Pin Co. (Banner) AA
Benedict & Burnham Mfg. Co. (Brass; Copper) AAAA
Chase Rolling Mill Co. (Brass; Copper) ..AAAA
Holmes Booth & Hayden

RODS (Con.)
Co. (Brass; Copper; German Silver) ......AAAA
Plume & Alwood Mfg. Co. (Brass; Copper; German Silver; Bronze) .....AAA
Randolph-Clowes Co. (Brass; Copper) ....AAA
Scovell Mfg. Co. (Alnuminum; German Silver; Brass) ....AAAA
Waterbury Brass Co. (Brass; Copper; German Silver; Bronze) ....AAAA
DEL.—Elsmere
Diamond State Fibre Co. (Hard Fibre) ....B
DEL.—Wilmington
Amer. Vulcanized Fibre Co. (Hard Fibre) .....AAAA
Delaware Electric & Supply Co. (Lightning) ....B
Delaware Hard Fibre Co. (Hard Fibre) ....A
Diamond State Steel Co. (Bridge; Roof; Tie; Upset) X
ILL.—Batavia
U. S. Wind Engine & Pump Co. (Pump; Sucker) AA
ILL.—Chicago
American Steel & Wire Co., The. Rookery (Awning; Bessemer Coppered Brace; Brass; Copper; Drill; Eye; Pump; Rake; Roller Bearing Screw; Polished Steel Stove Wire) ....AAAA
Continental Bolt & Iron Wrks., 22d & Union (Dock: Upset) ....A
Grand Crossing Tack So. Chicago & 19th (Bessemer; Open Hearth Wire) ....AAA
Illinois Steel Co., The Rookery (Wire) ....AAAA
Klein & Son, Mathias, 87 W. Van Buren (Anchor; for Guy Wires)......B
Kropp & Co., A., 52 Law Av. (Bridge; Roof; Dock) E
McGuire, Cummings Mfg. Co. (Brake) ....AA
Morden, Frog & Crossing Wrks. (Connecting) ..A
Morgan & Wright, 333 W. Lake (Rubber) ....AA
O'Leary & Son Co., Arthur J., 103 Lake (Upset)..B
Republic Iron & Steel Co., Stock Exchange Bldg. (Anchor; Bridge; Roof; Eye; Tie) ....AAAA
Sturm Co., Adolph, 51 W. Wash. (Dowel) .....D
Union Drop Forge Co., 66 E. Ohio (Connecting) ..A
ILL.—Decatur
Faries Mfg. Co. (Gun Cleaning) ....A
ILL.—Galesburg
Smith, J. W. (Lightning) D
ILL.—Peoria
Struthers, R. F. (Lightning) F
ILL.—Sterling
Dillon-Griswold Wire Co. (Copper; Steel; Iron Wire) X
IND.—Greencastle
Cole Bros. Lightning Rod Co. (Lightning) ......A
IND.—Indianapolis
Atkins & Co., E. C. (Saw) AAAA
IND.—South Bend
Bowsher Co., N. P. (Banner) ....B
Kuntz, Jacob E. (Dowel) E
IOWA—Burlington
Kriechbaum, Geo. (Lightning) ....E
IOWA—Cedar Falls
Harris & Cole Bros. (Poplar; Oak; Yellow Pine) ..AA
OHIO—Des Moines
Dodd & Struthers (Lightning) ....A

RODS (Con.)

OHIO—Dubuque
Adams Co. (Stove) ......A
KANS.—Wichita
Wichita Mfg. Co. (Bridge; Roof) C
KY.—Ashland
Ashland Steel Co. (Wire) AAA
MAINE—Bangor
Gerrish, Evan H. (Fishing; Split Bamboo Fishing) G
MAINE—Greenville
Greenville Mfg. & Veneer Co. (Dowel) C
MAINE—Kennebunk
Leatheroid Mfg. Co. (Hard Fibre) ....A
National Fibre Board Co. (Horn Fibre) ....A
MAINE—Lewiston
Keyes & Co., O. P. (Lightning) X
MD.—Baltimore
Baltimore Lightning Rod Works (J. A. Ruth, Prop.) 341 S. Woodyear (Lightning) ....G
Dietrich Bros., 344 North (Bridge; Roof) ....B
National Supply Co., 7 W. Lombard (Bridge; Roof; Connecting; Eye; Stove; Tie) ....B
MASS.—Boston
Boston Bolt Co. (Bridge; Roof) C
Boston Lightning Rod Co., 28 Beach (Lightning) ..G
Broad Gauge Iron Stall Works, 53 Elm (Lightning) ....D
Brown-Wales Co. (Machine Screw) ....A
Dame, Stoddard & Co. (Fishing) ....A
Jones & Co., B. M., 81 Milk (Iron Piston) ....A
New England Bolt & Nut Co., 253 Atlantic Av. (Bridge; Roof) ....B
Snow & Co., W. A., 19 Portland (Lightning) ...C
Preble, Edward, 103 Summer, E. B. (Bridge; Roof) ....F
Boston Forge Co., 340 Maverick, E. B. (Connecting; Steel Piston) ....A
MASS.—Canton
Kinsley Iron & Mach. Co. (Bridge; Roof) ......AA
MASS.—Chicopee Falls
Stevens Arms & Tool Co., J. (Gun & Rifle Cleaning) AAA
MASS.—Fall River
Berry & Johnston, 209 Bedford (Lease) ....E
MASS.—Fitchburg
Simonds Mfg. Co. (Saw) AAA
MASS.—Greenfield
Warner Mfg. Co. (Baby Carriage) C
MASS.—Lowell
Woods, Sherwood Co. (Banner) ....E
MASS.—Montague City
Montague City Rod Co. (Fishing) ....A
MASS.—New Bedford
Taunton-New Bedford Copper Co. (Copper; Yellow Metal; Piston Pump) AAA
MASS.—Springfield
Hawkins Iron Works. R. F. (Bolt Bridge) ....E
MASS.—Worcester
Morgan Spring Co. (Wire) A
Parker Wire Goods Co. (Curtain) ....D
Reed & Prince Mfg. Co. (Stove) C
Smith & Co., Thos. (Anchor; Bridge; Roof)....C
Spencer Wire Co. (Curtain) A
Wire Goods Co. (Curtain) .A

RODS (Con.)

Wright Wire Co. (Curtain) AA
MICH.—Detroit
Anderson & Sons, W. H. (Eye) C
Detroit Copper & Brass Rolling Mills (Brass; Copper) ....AAAA
Michigan Bolt & Nut Wks. ft. Meldrum Av. (Anchor; Bridge; Roof; Eye; Stove; Tie; Upset)..AA
MO.—Kansas City
Kansas City Bolt & Nut Co. (Anchor; Bridge; Roof; Eye; Tie; Threaded)..A
MO.—St. Louis
Bajohr Lightning Rod Wks., Carl, 4051 Keokuk (Lightning) ....D
Cole Bros. Lightning Rod Co. (Inc.) (Lightning)..A
Helmbacker Forge & Rolling Mill Co., Wainwright Bldg. (Piston; Side)..AA
Ludlow-Saylor Wire Co. (Curtain) ....AA
Moran Bolt & Nut Mfg. Co. (Anchor; Bridge; Roof; Eye; Stove; Tie) .....A
St. Louis Lightning Rod Co., 1901 S. 3d (Lightning) ....B
St. Louis Wire & Iron Co. (Wire) ....B
N. J.—Boonton
Lincoln Iron Works (Tie; Truss) ....B
N. J.—Jersey City
Dixon Crucible Co., Joseph (Resistance; Electric) AAA
N. J.—Newark
Duranoid Mfg. Co. (Hard Fibre) ....B
Lyon & Son. C. R., 213 N. 13th (Lightning)...H
Meisselbach & Bros. Aug. F. (Fishing; Bamboo & Split Bamboo Fishing)..B
National Saw Co. (Mitre Saw) ....B
Walker Mfg. Co., D. (Stair Carpet) ....E
N. J.—Paterson
Demuwolf, Jr., Charles (Glass) X
N. J.—Smithville
Smith Machine Co., H. P. (Sash) ....A
N. J.—Trenton
Roebling's Sons Co., Jno. A. (Wire) ....AAAA
Trenton Iron Co. (Wire; Nail) ....A
N. Y.—Albany
Troy Nickel Wks. (Stove) C
N. Y.—Brooklyn
Brass Goods Mfg. Co. (Stair) ....B
N. Y.—Buffalo
Pratt & Letchworth Co. (Connecting) ....AAA
N. Y.—Cortlandt
Wickwire Bros. (Wire) AAAA
N. Y.—Herkimer
Quackenbush, H. M. (Stair) A
New York City
Abbey & Imbrie (Fishing) A
Barron & Co., Jas. S., 290 B'way (Duct; Conduit Wiring) ....A
Bishop Gutta Percha Co. (Gutta Percha) ....B
Columbia Shade Cloth Co. (Shade) ....B
Dorendorf, Dederick, 44 Centre (Lightning) ...H
Estes & Sons. E. B., 45 John (Dowel) ....AA
Gould-Mersereau Co. (Carpet; Banner Nickel)....B
Gould's Son & Co., M. 83 Reade (Brass & Bronze Stair; Banner) ....A
Hall's Sons. Samuel. 229 W. 10th (Tie) ....A
Hendricks Bros., 49 Cliff

RODS (Con.)

(Copper) ....AAAA
Howard & Morse, 45 Fulton
  (Lightning) ....D
Hungerford Brass & Copper
  Co., U. T., 497 Pearl
  (Brass; Copper; Light-
  ning; Stair) ....AA
Johnson, Charles, 52 John
  (Lightning) ....F
Jones, T. W., 18 Fletcher
  (Lightning) ....E
Judd & Co., H. L. (Brass;
  Nickel; Brass Picture;
  Plated Window; Stair)
  ....AA
Keupfel & Esser Co., 127
  Fulton (Measuring; Level-
  ing) ....AA
Kroder, John, & Henry Reu-
  bel Co. (Stair) ......B
Lamb, J. & R. (Banner)..D
Manhattan Brass Co., 338
  E. 28th (Brass; Copper;
  Lightning) ....A
Mitchell-Bissell Co., 38 Mur-
  ray (Glass, for Looms)
 X
Ogilvy, Ribert (Fishing).D
Patriarche & Bell, 215 Pearl
  (Coppered Steel) .....A
Peck, Stow & Wilcox Co.,
  27 Murray (Saw) .AAAA
Pierce Well Engine & Sup-
  ply Co. (Sucker) .....D
Plath & Son, Chas. (Fish-
  ing) ....F
Plume & Atwood Mfg. Co.,
  29 Murray (Brass Wire;
  German Silver) ....AAA
Pope Mfg. Co., 21 Park
  Row (Baby Carriage)
  ....AAAA
Remington Arms Co. (Gun)
  ....B
Sargeant & Co., 151 Leonard
  (Saw) ....AAAA
Soltmann, E. G., 125 E.
  42d (Measuring) .....B
Spalding & Bros., A. G.
  (Inc.) (Fishing; Bamboo)
  ....AAAA
Waclark Wire Co. (Copper)
  ....A
Wardlow & Co., S., 95 John
  (Wire) ....A
Washburne & Co., Edw. G.,
  46 Cortlandt (Copper;
  Lightning) ....E
Wemple Co., James C.
  (Shade) ....AA
Westervelt, A. B. & W. T.,
  102 Chambers (Lightning)
  ....B

N. Y.—Portchester
Russel, Burdsall & Ward
  Bolt & Nut Co. (Stove)
  ....AAAA

N. Y.—Rome
Rome Brass & Copper Co.
  (Brass; Copper) .AAAA

N. Y.—Utica
Clark-Horrocks Co. (Fish-
  ing) ....A

N. C.—Greensboro
Southern Bobbin Co. (Dow-
  el; Enameled Case) ....D

OHIO—Akron
Kile Mfg. Co. (Sucker, for
  Wells) C

OHIO—Alliance
Transue & Williams Co.
  (Drop Forged Connecting)
  ....A

OHIO—Carthage
Bloch-Pollak Iron Co. (Connecting) ....AAA

OHIO—Cincinnati
Bishop & Co., Geo. H.
  (Saw) ....A
Foy & Co., Edw. A., 640
  Main (Lightning) C

OHIO—Cleveland
Atlas Bolt & Screw Co.
  (Stove) ....AA
Bacon & Co., 309 Prospect
  (Lightning) X
Cleveland Hardware Co.
  (Wagon Box) ....AA
Cleveland Wire Spring Co.
  (Machine Screw; Gun
  Screw) ....AA
Fanner Mfg. Co. (Stove).A

RODS (Con.)

Forest City Steel & Iron
  Co. (Awning) ....A
Kirk-Latty Mfg. Co. (Stove)
  ....A
Lake Erie Iron Co., 155
  St. Clair (Bridge; Roof)
  ....AAA
Lamson & Sessions Co.
  (Stove) ....AA
National Carbon Co. (Car-
  bon) ....AAAA
National Screw & Tack Co.
  (Stove) ....AA
Otis Steel Co., Lake, cor.
  Lawrence (Connecting).A
Union Rolling Mill Co.
  (Nut) ....AA
Vulcanis Forging Co. (Con-
  necting; Upset) ....B

OHIO—Columbus
Berry Bros. (Stove; Seat)
  ....A
Columbus Bolt Works
  (Bridge; Roof) ......AA

OHIO—Elyria
Topliff & Ely Co. (Connecting) ....B

OHIO—Findlay
Findlay Sucker Rod Co.
  (Sucker) ....D

OHIO—Kenton
Champion Iron Co. (Beam
  Tie) ....AA

OHIO—Lima
Coss & Stinebough (Sucker)
  ....E

OHIO—Toledo
Bissell Co., F. (Duct; Con-
  duit Wiring) ....A
Nagel Electric Co., W. G.
  Duct; Conduit Wiring).B

OHIO—Youngstown
Finished Steel Co. (Polished
  Steel Piston; Polished
  Steel Pump; Screw)....A

PA.—Aliquippa
Vulcan Crucible Steel Co.
  (Wire) ....B

PA.—Allegheny
Graham Nut Co., 755 Re-
  becca (Anchor; Bridge;
  Roof; Connecting) ....B

PA.—Beaver Falls
Standard Connecting Rod
  Co. (Connecting) .....D
Standard Gauge Steel Co.
  (Piston Pump) ....A
Union Drawn Steel Co. (Pis-
  ton; Pump) ....A

PA.—Bradford
Dresser, S. R. (Sucker).AA

PA.—Braeburn
Braeburn Steel Co. (Steel
  Piston) ....A

PA.—Burnham
Logan Iron & Steel Co.
  (Drill) ....AA

PA.—Eddystone
Tindel-Morris Co. (Connecting) ....AA

PA.—Harrisburg
Hickok Mfg. Co., W. O.
  (Machinery Joint) ....AA

PA.—Johnstown
Cambria Steel Co. (Connecting Piston) ......AAAA

PA.—Lancaster
Penna. Iron Wks. (Tie)..A

PA.—Lebanon
American Iron & Steel Mfg.
  Co. (Anchor; Bracket;
  Brake Lever Connecting;
  Bridge; Roof; Eye; Tie;
  Upset) ....AAAA

PA.—McKees Rocks
Kidd Bros. & Burgher Steel
  Wire Co. (Polished Drill;
  Roller Bearing; Polished
  Steel Wire; Black Steel;
  Dental Octagon; Screw
  Drivers, Steel; Steel
  Drill; Tap; Reamer) ..B
Lockhart Iron & Steel Co.
  (Piston) ....AA

PA.—Milesburg
McCoy-Linn Iron Co. (Wire,
  from Charcoal Iron)...D

PA.—Monaca
Pittsburg Tool Steel Wire
  Co. (Drill; Dental Octa-
  gon; Roller Bearing;
  Steel Drill; Tap; Ream-

RODS (Con.)

er) C
PA.—Monessen
Page Woven Wire Fence Co.
(Wire) ....A
PA.—New Castle
New Castle Forge & Bolt
Co. (Anchor; Bridge;
Roof; Eye; Upset) ..AA
PA.—Norristown
Reading Screw Co. (Screw)
A

PA.—Philadelphia
Brill Co., J. G. (Brake)
AAAA
Chester Steel Castings Co.
(Connecting) ....AA
Damascus Nickel Steel Co.,
Bullitt Bldg. (Drills)..D
De Witt Wire Cloth Co.,
703 Market (Lightning)
A
Disston & Sons (Inc.), Hy.
(Wood Saw) .....AAAA
Duncannon Iron Co. (Spike)
AA
Ivins, Elwood (Steel Um-
brella) ....F
Goodwin, Fredk. O.. 53d &
Wyalusing (Lightning).D
Hoopes & Townsend Co.,
1330 Buttonwood (Bridge;
Roof; Upset) ......AAA
Jackson & Cook, 318 Mar-
ket (Lightning) ......B
Merchant & Co., 517 Arch
(Brass; Copper) .....AA
Midvale Steel Co., Nicetown
(Connecting Piston)
AAAA
Phoenix Bridge Co. (Bridge)
A
Phosphor Bronze Smelting
Co. (Ltd.) 2204 Washn.
Av. (Phosphor Bronze Pis-
ton; Pump) ....A
Reeves & Son, Paul S., 1415
Catharine (Phosphor &
Manganese Bronze) ...B
Reyburn, Hunter & Co., 488
N. American (Lightning)
AAAA
Rowland, Wm. & Harvey
(Inc.) (Nail) ....B
Shipley, Malcolm A. (Fish-
ing) ....D
Standard Steel Works, Har-
rison Bldg. (Piston; Side)
AAAA
Stubbs Steel Co., 17 N. 5th
(Drill) ....E
PA.—Pittsburg
Carbon Steel Co. (Piston;
Side) ....A
Carnegie Steel Co. (Ltd.)
(Connecting Piston)
AAAA
Columbia Bridge Co., Park
Bldg. (Piston; Pump;
Key; Screw; Wire) ..AA
Crucible Steel Co. of Amer-
ica, Frick Bldg. (Connect-
ing Drill; Piston)..AAAA
Fort Pitt Forge Co., 26th &
Liberty (Iron; Steel; Up-
set; Tie) ....B
Hum & Leatherman, 320 3d
Av. (Lightning) ....B
Hussey & Co., C. G. (Brass;
Copper) ....AAA
Jones & Laughlin Steel Co.
(Connecting; Piston)
AAAA
Lanz & Sons, Mathew, 101
S. 29th (Anchor; Bridge;
Guy; Tie) ....AA
Morris & Bailey Steel Co.
(Connecting) ....A
Oil Well Supply Co. (Suck-
er) ....AAAA
Oliver Iron & Steel Co.
(Anchor; Bridge; Roof;
Connecting; Eye; Tie; Up-
set) ....AAAA
Pittsburg Forge & Iron Co.
(Bridge; Roof) ....A
Pittsburg Mfg. Co., 28th
& R. R. (Connecting)...A
Pittsburg Reduction Co.,
Park Bldg. (Aluminum)
AAAA
Pittsburg Screw & Bolt Co.
(Upset) ....A

RODS (Con.)
Pittsburg Steel Co., Peoples
Sav. Bank Bldg. (Wire)
AAAA
Scaife & Sons' Co., Wm. B.,
221 1st Av. (Bridge;
Roof) ....AAA
PA.—Reading
Reading Iron Co. (Connect-
ing Piston) ....AAAA
PA.—Scranton
Scranton Bolt & Nut Co.
(Anchor; Bridge; Roof;
Eye; Tie) ....AA
PA.—Sharpsburg
Globe Wire Co. (Polished
Drill) ....A
PA.—South Bethlehem
Bethlehem Steel Co. (Con-
necting; Piston; Steel
Hammer) ....AAAA
PA.—Titusville
Titusville Forge Co. (Con-
necting Piston) ....A
PA.—Washington
Chapman Sucker Rod Co.
(Sucker) ....B
R. I.—Pawtucket
Pawtucket Mfg. Co. (An-
chor; Bridge; Roof; Tie)
A
R. I.—Phillipsdale
Washburn Wire Co. (Drill;
Rake; Roller Bearing;
Stove; Wire) .....AAAA
R. I.—Providence
American Enamel Co.
(Enameled Lease) .....B
American Screw Co. (Stove)
AAAA
Brown & Sharpe Mfg. Co.
(Measuring) ......AAAA
TENN.—Greeneville
Doughty, J. H. (Lightning)
AA
VT.—Bennington
Scott, Olin (Measuring)..A
VT.—Post Mills
Chubb Rod Co., T. H.
(Bamboo & Split Bamboo
Fishing) ....A
VA.—Richmond
Old Dominion Iron & Nail
Works (Bridge; Roof;
Tie; Upset; Bolt; Nut)
AA
WIS.—Kenosha
Chicago Brass Co. (Brass)
AA
WIS.—Racine
Racine Malleable &
Wrought Iron Co. (Wa-
gon Box) ....A

ROLL

See also Roofing

LA.—New Orleans
New Orleans Roofing &
Metal Works (Ridge) ..A

ROLLERS

See also Agr. Imps; Machy;
Rolls

CAL.—San Francisco
Shattuck Co., E. J. (Print-
ers') ....B
CONN.—Bridgeport
Bridgeport Brass Co. (Cop-
per) ....AAA
Smith & Egge Mfg. Co.
(Skate) ....A
Spring Perch Co. (Carriage
Curtain) ....B
CONN.—Bristol
Sessions & Son, J. H.
(Trunk) ....AA
CONN.—Guilford
Spencer Sons, J. S. (Sliding
Door) ....A
CONN.—Higganum
Cuttaway Harrow Company
(Land; Lawn) X
CONN.—Meriden
Meriden Curtain Fixture
Co. (Blind; Shade;
Spring) ....B
CONN.—New Haven
Hoggson & Pettis Mfg. Co.
(Hand; Stitchers) .....A
Mallory, Wheeler Co. (Barn

ROLLERS (*Con.*)

Door) ....AA
CONN.—Norwalk
Arnold Co. (Barn Door)..C
CONN.—Pine Meadow
Chapins, Stephens Co.
(Skate) ....A
CONN.—Southington
Peck, Stow & Wilcox Co.
(Trunk; Door; Sash;
Towel) ....AAAA
ILL.—Aurora
Richards Mfg. Co. (Stay).B
Wilcox Mfg. Co. (Stay)..B
ILL.—Bradley
Bradley Mfg. Co., David
(Lawn; Garden; Field;
Land) ....AAA
ILL.—Chicago
Austin Mfg. Co., Manhat-
tan Bldg. (Road Horse
Power; Road Steam).AAA
Chicago Spring Butt Co.
(Stay) ....B
Contractors' Supply &
Equipment Co., 232 5th
Av. (Road Horse Power;
Steam Road) ....B
Evans & Co., R. O., 210
Madison (Chart) ......A
National Drill & Mfg. Co.,
Pullman Bldg. (Riverside
Road) ....B
Opaque Shade Cloth Co.
(Shade) ....AA
ILL.—Chicago
Shaw, Willis, N. Y. Life
Bldg. (Steam Road)....E
Vulcan Iron Works, 59 Mil-
waukee Av. (Steam Road)
AA
ILL.—Decatur
Tait Mfg. Co., F. R.
(Land) ....A
ILL.—Rock Island
Rock Island Plow Co.
(Land) ....AAAA
ILL.—Sterling
Lawrence Bros. (Stay).AAA
Nat. Mfg. Co. (Stay)....C
IND.—Elkhart
Foster Novelty Co., C. A.
(Lawn; Garden).......F
IND.—Fort Wayne
Indiana Road Machine Co.
(Road; Horse Power;
Road Steam) ....A
IND.—Indianapolis
Over Ewald (Clod; Field)
C
Tucker & Dorsey Mfg. Co.
(Towel) ....A
IOWA—Fairfield
Louden Machy. Co. (Stay)
C
IOWA—Ottumua
Johnston & Sharp Mfg. Co.
(Ball Bearing) ....D
MD.—Baltimore
Adt, John B. (Tobacco
Steam) ....A
Sinclair Scott Co. (Clod).E
MASS.—Boston
Ames Plow Co. (Lawn;
Garden; Road; Horse
Power; Clod; Field)....
AAAA
Osgood Co., J. H. (Print-
ers') X
Wild & Stevens (Printers)
B
MASS.—Norwood
Winslow Bros. & Smith Co.
(Tanners' Calf)......AA
MASS.—Worcester
Wire Goods Co. (Towel)..A
MICH.—Bay City
Garland Co., M. (Log)..C
Michigan Box Co. (Shade)
AA
MICH.—Bellaire
Richardi & Bechtold
(Cake) ....B
MICH.—Detroit
Am. Harrow Co. (Road;
Horse Power) ....AA
Ranney, Wm. H. (Printers')
H
MICH.—Lansing
Lansing Wheelbarrow Co.
(Lawn; Garden; Field;
Land) ....AAA

ROLLERS (*Con.*)

MICH.—Monroe
Wilder-Strong Implement
Co. (Lawn; Garden; Clod;
Land) ....B
MICH.—Port Huron
Port Huron Engine &
Thresher Co. (Steam
Power; Road) ......AAA
MICH.—Saginaw
Morley Bros. (Door) ...AA
MO.—St. Louis
Union Iron & Foundry Co.,
1460 52d (Lawn; Garden)
A
Whitman Agricultural Co.
(Lawn; Garden) ......AA
N. J.—Newark
Hartshorn Stewart Co.
(Shade; Blind; Spring)..
AAA
N. Y.—Auburn
New Birdsall Co. (Steam
Road for Country Road)
AA
Osborne & Co., D. M.
(Clod) ....AAAA
N. Y.—Brooklyn
Pioneer Iron Works, 153
Williams (Road; Horse
Power; Steam Road)..A
Wesel Mfg. Co., F.
(Printers') X
N. Y.—Buffalo
Buffalo-Pitts Co. (Steam;
Asphalt; Road; Horse
Power; Steam Road)
Land) ....AAAA
Contracting Plant Mfg. Co.
(Guide) ....B
Iroquois Iron Works
(Steam Road) ....A
N. Y.—Canastota
Pattern & Stafford Co.
(Land) ....B
N. Y.—Corning
Allen Fdry. Co., E. R.
(Lawn; Garden; Land).E
N. Y.—Frankfort
Acme Road Machy. Co.
(Road; Horse Power;
Steam Road; Land)....B
N. Y.—Gowanda
Gowanda Agricultural Wks.
Co. (Lawn; Garden)...X
N. Y.—Ithaca
Williams Bros. (Field)..AA
N. Y.—Manlius
Cheney & Son, S. (Door).A
N. Y.—Marathon
Climax Road Machine Co.
(Reversible Road; Road;
Horse Power; Steam
Road) ....B
N. Y.—Minetto
Minetto Shade Cloth Co.
(Shade; Spring).....AAA
N. Y.—Mt. Morris
Genesee Valley Mfg. Co.
(Land) ....B
N. Y.—Munnsville
Munnsville Plow Co.
(Field) ....B
New York City
Amer. Road Roller Co., 156
5th Av. (Steam Road)..B
Columbia Shade Cloth Co.
(Spring) ....B
Haviland Shade Roller Co.,
307 W. B'way (Shade).B
Judd & Co., H. L. (Shade)
AA
Mace & Co., L. H. (Towel)
B
Mott Iron Wks., J. L., 88
Beekman (Lawn; Garden)
AA
Reilly Bros. (Paper Hang-
ers') ....D
Russell & Erwin Mfg. Co.
(Sliding Door; Sash)...
AAAA
Sargent & Co., 151 Leonard
(Door; Sash; Stay) AAAA
Scholl & Co., Julian, 126
Liberty (Road; Horse
Power; Steam Road)...C
Sheridan Co., T. W. & C.
B. (Paper Hangers')...A
Tiebout, W. & J., 118
Chambers (Sash) ......B
Wemple Co., Jay C. (Awn-

ROLLERS (Con.)

ing; Window; Shade;
Spring) ....AA
Westervelt, A. B. & W. T.,
102 Chambers (Lawn;
Garden) ....B
N. Y.—Poughkeepsie
Lane Bros. & Co. (Sliding
Door) ....A
N. Y.—Rochester
Knowlton Co., M. B.
(Mailing Tube) ....AA
N. Y.—Syracuse
Edwards Co., O. M. (Car
Window,etc., Shade) ...D
Stearns & Co., E. C.
(Sliding Door)........AA
N. Y.—Utica
Palmer, C. F. (Lawn;
Garden) C
Utica Drop Forge & Tool
Co. (Glass) ....B
OHIO—Berea
Dunham & Son. J. W.
(Lawn; Garden) .....B
OHIO—Canton
Aultman Co. (Road; Horse
Power) ....AAAA
Anchor & Gibbs Plow Co.
(Land) ....AA
Ney Mfg. Co. (Road; Stay)
B
OHIO—Cincinnati
Van Bibber Roller Co.
(Printers') ....D
OHIO—Cleveland
Chandler & Price Co.
(Printers' Proof) ......A
Van Dorn Iron Works Co.
(Lawn; Garden) ....AA
OHIO—Columbiana
Enterprise Mfg. Co. (Road;
Horse Power; Road
Steam) ....A
OHIO—Fremont
Lehr Agricultural Co.
(Land) ....B
OHIO—Hamilton
Deuscher Co., H. P.
(Clod) ....A
OHIO—Massillon
Russell & Co. (Steam
Road) ....AAA
OHIO—Piqua
Piqua Handle & Mfg. Co.
(Skate) ....A
OHIO—Springfield
Kelly Springfield Road Rol-
ler Co., O. S. (Steam
Road; Asphalt; Steam) A
Webster & Perks Tool Co.
(Paper Hangers' Seam).C
PA.—Allegheny
Carlin's Sons, Thomas
(Road; Horse Power)..A
PA.—Bausman
Bausman, D. H. (Lawn;
Garden) C
PA.—Elizabethtown
Buch's Sons Co., A. (Field;
Garden; Land; Road)..A
PA.—Erie
Erie Machine Shops, (Steam
Road) ....B
PA.—Harrisburg
Harrisburg Fdry. & Machine
Works(Steam Road)..AA
PA.—Kennett Square
Am. Road Mach. Co.
(Lawn; Garden; Road;
Horse Power) ....AA
Good Roads Machy. Co.
(Road; Horse Power)..D
PA.—Lebanon
Hauck, A. R. (Towel) ..B
PA.—Mechanicsburg
Comstock. Geo. S. (Land).C
PA.—Philadelphia
Bendernagel & Co., (Print-
ers') X
Short & Son. Jno. (Paper
Hangers') ....E
PA.—Reading
Reading Hardware Co.
(Door; Sash) .....AAAA
PA.—South Bethlehem
Bethlehem Fdry. & Machine
Co. (Bogie) C
PA.—Tatamy
Messinger Mfg. Co. (Lawn;
Garden; Road; Steam;
Land) ....B

ROLLERS (Con.)

PA.—Wilkesbarre
Vulcan Iron Works (Guide;
Incline Plane) ....AAAA
PA.—Wrightsville
Wrightsville Hardware Co.
(Barn Door; Sliding Door)
B
PA.—York
Farquhar Co., A. B.
(Clod) ....AAA
Keystone Farm Mach. Co.,
Ltd. (Field; Land).....B
R. I.—Providence
New England Butt Co.
(Barn; Sliding Door).AA
VT.—Montpelier
Lane Mfg. Co. (Log)....A
VA.—Norfolk
Whitehurst Co., R. W.
(Clod; Lawn; Garden;
Field; Land; Road)....B
WIS.—Milwaukee
Allis-Chalmers Co. (Log)
AAAA
Filer & Stowell Co., Ltd.
AAA
WIS.—Racine
Johnston & Field Mfg. Co.
(Lawn; Garden; Field;
Land) ....F
WIS.—So. Milwaukee
Stowell Mfg. & Foundry Co.
(Door; Stay) ....A

ROLLS

COLO.—Denver
Colorado Iron Wks. Co.
(Crushing) ....AA
Davis Iron Works Co., F.
M. (Crushing) ....AA
Denver Engineering Works
Co., Blake & 30th (Crush-
ing without Springs)...A
Mine & Smelter Supply Co.,
Blake & 17th (Crushing)
AAAA
Stearns Roger Mfg. Co.,
1718 Cal. (Crushing;
Cornish) ....A
CONN.—Ansonia
Farrell Foundry & Mach.
Co. (Chilled Calender
Crushing; Chilled; Sand;
Paper; Flour Mill; Rub-
ber Machy.).......AAAA
CONN.—Derby
Birmingham Iron Foundry
(Sand; Chilled Engraved)
AA
CONN.—New Haven
Kilborn & Bishop Co.
(Forging) C
CONN.—Thompsonville
Bushnell Press Co., G. H.
(Crushing) ....A
CONN.—Waterbury
Blake & Johnson (Hard-
ened Steel; Chilled Iron;
Jewelers) ....A
Manville Machine Co., E.
J. (Jewelers') C
Waterbury Farrell Fdry.
Machine Co. (Sand;
Chilled; Steel; Jewelers'
Bending; Straightening).
AA
CONN.—Windsor Locks
Clark & Co., Geo. (Rubber
for Scouring)..........C
DEL.—Wilmington
Betts Machy. Co. (Bending;
Straightening) ......AA
Hilles & Jones Co. (Bend-
ing; Straightening Plate;
Bending Hand; Belt
Power) ....AAAA
Lobdell Car Wheel Co.
(Chilled Calender Sand;
Chilled Flour Mill; Ink
Mill; Rubber Machy.)...
AAAA
Poole Co., J. Morton
(Chilled Calender Paper
Mill; Grinding) ......AA
Pusey & Jones Co. (Chilled
Calender) ....AAA
ILL.—Chicago
Allis Chalmers Co., Home
Ins. Bldg. (Crushing;
Cornish) ....AAAA

ROLLS (Con.)

Chicago Rubber Brokerage Co. (Wringer) ....E

Davis & Nichols, 34 S. Clark (Painters' Graining) X

Western Leather Mfg. Co. (Music) ....D

ILL.—Moline

Williams. White & Co. (Bending; Straightening; Forging) ....AA

IND.—Aurora

Stedman Fdry. & Mach. Works (Crushing; Coal Breaking) ....B

IND.—Cambridge City

Bertsh & Co. (Angle Iron, etc.; Bending; Straightening; Crimping; Hand; Belt; Power) ....D

IND.—Indianapolis

Nordyke & Marmon Co. (Flour Mill) ....AA

IND.—Richmond

Richmond City Mill Works (Flour Mill) ....B

IND.—Davenport

Davenport Fdry. & Mach. Co. (Sand; Chilled)....X

KANS.—Fort Scott

Fort Scott Fdry. & Machine Co. (Cornish) ....H

MAINE—Portland

Portland Co. (Chilled Calender; Paper Calender)..AA

MD.—Baltimore

Marquette, Jno. N. (Crushing) X

MASS.—Boston

Boston Belting Co. (Rubber; Wringer; Rubber Covered) AAAA

Eastern Forge Co. of Mass., 70 Kilby (Bending; Straightening) ....B

Harvey, Henry H. (Stone Workers'; Wooden).....D

Hanwood & Son, Geo. S., 53 State (Card; Feed) .A

Revere Rubber Co. (Rubber Covered) ......AAAA

Riley & Co., C. E. (Fluted) ....A

Sewing Machine & Supplies Co. (Hard Rubber; Pinking) ....B

MASS.—Fall River

Fall River Fdry. & Mach. Co. (Card; Feed) .....F

Thurston & Son, A. G. (Fluted) ....E

MASS.—Florence

Norwood Engineering Co. (Paper; Calender) .....B

MASS.—Holyoke

Brown & Sellers Co. (Dandy) X

Buchanan & Bolt Wire Co. (Dandy) ....B

Holyoke Machy. Co. (Chilled Iron; Paper; Cotton; Husk; Calender)..AA

Perkins & Son, B. F. (Splined Paper Calender) A

Smith & Co., C. H. (Dandy) ....D

MASS.—Indian Orchard

Metallic Drawing Roll Co. (Metallic Drawing)....A

MASS.—Lawrence

Emerson Mfg. Co. (Chilled Calender) C

MASS.—Lowell

Adams, J. F. & M. J., 46 Leverett (Card; Feed).X

Kitson Mach. Co. (Chilled Calender) ....AAA

Lowell Machine Shop (Gun Metal Calender) ..AAAA

MASS.—Springfield

Bigelow-Cheney Wire Wks. (Dandy) ....A

Bullock Mfg. Co. (Jewelers') ....A

MASS.—Worcester

Arcade Malleable Iron Co. (Rolls, Sand; Chilled; Steel) ....A

Curtis & Marble Machy.

ROLLS (Con.)

Co. (Card; Feed) ......A

Rice, Barton & Fales Mach. & Iron Co. (Chilled Calender) ....AA

Warren Leather Goods Co. (Music) ....A

Whitcomb Mfg. Co. (Bending; Straightening; Hand Banding; Plate Bending) B

MICH.—Alpena

Kline, Lewis F. (Wood; Caster) ....D

MICH.—Grand Rapids

Grand Rapids Brass Co. (Sliding Door) ....A

MICH.—Kalamazoo

Hill & Co., W. E. (Live).B

MICH.—Saginaw

Wickes Bros. (Plate, etc.; Bending; Straightening; Hand; Belt; Power).AAA

MO.—St. Louis

Fritsch Fdry. & Mach. Co., Arthur, 216 Gratiot (Crushing) ....B

South St. Louis Fdry. Co., 7516-8 B'way (Crushing) C

N. J.—Belleville

Eastwood Wire Mfg. Co. (Dandy) ....A

N. J.—Bloomfield

Comb. Rubber & Belting Co. (Typewriter) ....A

N. J.—East Newark

Gleeson, Thomas E. (Dandy) C

N. J.—Garwood

Beckley Co., A. J. (Machy. Bending) ....D

N. J.—Harrison

Globe Wire Co. (Dandy).D

N. J.—High Bridge

Taylor Iron & Steel Co. (Coal Breaker) ......AAAA

N. J.—Jersey City

Krom Mach. Works (Crushing) X

New Jersey Car Spring & Rubber Co. (Rubber Wringer; Rubber Covered Typewriter).....AA

N. J.—Newark

Currier & Sons, Cyrus (Chilled Calender) ...AA

Ohl & Son, Geo. A. (Crimping; Hand; ....B

Stone, F. & G. M. (Calico Printers'; Embossing; Engraved) C

N. J.—Raritan

Kenyon & Son, D. R. (Card; Feed) ....B

N. J.—Rockaway

Hoagland Sons Co., M. (Crushing) ....A

N. J.—Trenton

Home Rubber Co. (Wringer; Rubber Covered) .....AA

N. Y.—Albany

Townsend Furn. & Mach Shop Co. (Soft; Chilled Sand) ....B

N. Y.—Brooklyn

Bliss & Co.. E. W., 17 Adams (Crimping) AAAA

Houchin & Huber (Ink Mill) ....D

Niagara Mach. & Tool Wks. (Bending; Straightening; Crimping; Fluted; Hand; Belt; Power; Sheet Metal Forming) ....A

N. Y.—Buffalo

Oliver Mfg. Co.. W. W. (Jewelers) C

N. Y.—Cohoes

Cohoes Iron Foundry & Machine Co. (Fluted).....B

N. Y.—Dansville

Gilman A. J. (Chilled Calender) X

N. Y.—Fulton

Dilts Machine Works (Iron) ....B

N. Y.—Newburgh

Coldwell, Wilcox Co. (Cornish) ....B

New York City

Cavagnaro, John, 215

ROLLS (Con.)
Centre (Paper) ....D
De Witte Wire Cloth Co.
(Dardy) ....A
Dickinson, John (Est. of),
64 Nassau (Granite;
Chocolate) ....B
Goodyear Rubber Co.
(Wringer) ....AAAA
Gutta Percha & Rubber
Mfg. Co. (Rubber; Rub-
ber Covered) .....AAAA
Manhattan Rubber Mfg. Co.
18 Vesey (Rubber) ...AA
New York Belting & Pack-
ing Co. (Rubber; Wring-
er) ....AAAA
New York Rubber Co.
(Rubber) ....AA
Niles-Bement-Pond Co., 136
Liberty (Hand; Belt;
Power; Bending; Straigh-
tening) ....AAAA
Peck, Stow & Wilcox Co.,
27 Murray (Bending
Straightening) ...AAAA
Spencer Optical Co.
(Music) C

N. Y.—Sandy Hill
Sandy Hill Iron & Brass
Works (Paper; Calender)
................A

OHIO—Akron
Goodrich Co., B. F. (Rub-
ber; Rubber Covered)...
................AAAA
OHIO—Alliance
Morgan Engineering Co.
(Plate, etc.; Bending;
Straightening) ....AAAA
OHIO—Canton
Bonnot Co. (Clay, etc.;
Crushing) ....A
Canton Roll & Machy Co.
(Sand; Chilled; Semi
Steel) ....B
OHIO—Cincinnati
Cinn. Punch & Shear Co.
(Power Driven; Bending;
Straightening; Hand;
Belt; Power) ....D
Keene & Co., Geo. C., 502
E. Front (Crimping) ..F
Robinson Mfg. Co., J. M.,
2d & Cent. Av. (Crimp-
ing) C
OHIO—Cleveland
Ajax Mfg. Co. (Forging)
................AA
Cleveland Punch & Shear
Works Co., 156 Case
(Plate Bending; Straight-
ening) ....A
Riverside Fdry. Co. (Sand;
Chilled; Steel) ....B
Wellman Seaver Morgan Co.
(Bending; Straightening)
................AAAA
OHIO—Columbus
Jeffrey Mfg. Co. (Coal
Breaker) ....AAAA
OHIO—Hamilton
Black & Clawson Co.
(Sand; Chilled; Steel;
Dandy) ....AAA
Niles Tool Works Co.
(Plate Bending) ...AAAA
OHIO—Youngstown
Republic Rubber Co.
(Rubber) ....AA
Youngstown Fdry. & Mach.
Co. (Sand; Chilled; Semi
Steel) ....A
OHIO—Zanesville
Griffith & Wedge Co.
(Cornish) ....B
PA.—Allegheny
Carlin's Sons, Thomas
(Crushing; Beam Bend-
ing; Straightening) ...A
PA.—Avonmore
West Penn. Fdry. & Mach.
Co. (Sand; Chilled; Semi
Steel) X
PA.—Birdsboro
Diamond Drill & Mach. Co.
(Bending; Straightening;
Crushing; Sand; Chilled;
Steel) ....A
PA.—Braddock
Braddock Machy. & Mfg.
Co. (Sand; Chilled).....A

ROLLS (Con.)
PA.—Chester
Wetherill & Co., Robert
(Sand; Chilled; Steel)..
................AAAA
PA.—Eddystone
Tindel Morris Co. (Sand;
Chilled; Steel) ....AA
PA.—Erie
Continental Rubber Works
(Rubber) ....A
Lovell Mfg. Co. (Blue
Print; for Mechaical
Work; Rubber; for
Laundress; Woolen Mills;
Tanneries, etc.) ......AA
Stearns Mfg. Co. (Live) ..B
PA.—Hyde Park
Hyde Park Fdry. & Machine
Co. (Sand; Chilled) C
PA.—Muncy
Sprout, Waldron & Co.
(Flour Mill) ....A
PA.—New Castle
Vulcan Foundry & Mach.
Co. (Train) ....A
PA.—Philadelphia
Bement Niles &Co. (Plate
Bending) ....AAAA
Butterworth & Sons Co.,
H. W. (Paper; Calender)
................A
Cresson Co., Geo. V., 18th
& Allegheny (Crushing).
................AA
Phila. Roll & Mach. Co.,
So. 23d & Wash. Av.
(Plate Bending; Straight-
ening; Sand; Chilled;
Steel; Crushing; Hand;
Belt; Power; Jewelers')
................A
Phila. Textile Machy. Co.,
Hancock & Somerset
(Card; Feed) ....A
Phillips & Sons Co., F.R.,
Penna. Bldg. (Sand;
Chilled; Steel) ....D
Sellers & Co., Wm.. Inc.
(Plate; Beam; Vertical
Bending; Hand; Belt;
Power) ....AAAA
Western & Wells Mfg. Co.
(Wire; Hair) ....B
Woodford Wood Tanks Mfg.
Co. (Wooden; Scouring)
................G
PA.—Pittsburg
Fischer Fdry. & Machine
Co. (Beam Bending)..AA
Garrison Fdry. Co., A.
(Chilled; Calender; Crush-
ing; Steel Bending;
Straightening) ....AAA
Heppinstall Forge & Knife
Co. (Hardened Forge)..B
Hogg Iron & Steel Fdry.
Co., Geo. A., 24th & R.
R. Av. (Train; Chilled;
Sand; Steel; Semi Steel)
................A
Lewis Fdry. & Machine Co.
(Bending; Straightening;
Sand; Chilled) ....A
Mesta Mach. Co., Lewis
Block (Sand; Chilled;
Steel; Dry Sand) ..AAAA
Pittsburg Mfg. Co., 28th &
R. R. (Bending; Straight-
ening) ....A
Pittsburg Steel Foundry Co.
(Sand; Chilled; Steel)..
................AA
Scaife Fdry. & Mach. Co.
(Crushing) ....B
Sermen Sleuth Co., 41st &
A. V. Ry. (Sand; Chilled)
................AA
Trethway & Co. (Ltd.),
Samuel, 47th. near Plum-
mers (Sand; Chilled;
Steel) ....F
United Engineering & Fdry.
Co. 54th & A. V. Ry.
(Bending; Straightening;
Crushing; Sand; Chilled;
Steel) ....AAAA
PA.—Rankin Station
Duquesne Forge Co. (Rough-
ing Bends Machy.) ...A
PA.—Reading
Reading Iron Co. (Sand;
Chilled; Steel) ....AAAA

866

ROLLS (Con.)

PA.—So. Bethlehem
Bethlehem Fdry. & Mach.
Co. (Bending; Straightening; Crimping; Hand;
Belt Power) C
Bethlehem Iron Co. (Cast
Steel; Hardened Forge;
Sand; Chilled Steel)
AAAA

PA.—Titusville
Titusville Forge Co. (Bending; Straightening)....A

PA.—Wilkesbarre
Vulcan Iron Works (Gray
Iron; Coal Breaker) AAAA

R. I.—Pawtucket
Atwood Crawford Co.
(Braid) ....B

R. I.—Providence
Franklin Machine Co.
(Fluted) ....A
New England Ventilating &
Heating Co. (Steaming) D
Providence Mach. Co.
(Fluted) ....AA
Standard Machy. Co.
(Hardened Forge; Jewelers') ....B
Textile Finishing Machy Co.
17 Exch. Place (Card;
Feed) ....AAA

W. VA.—Wheeling
Central Fdry. & Mach. Co.
(Sand) ....B
Wheeling Mold & Fdry. Co.
(Sand; Chilled) ....B

WIS.—Beloit
Beloit Iron Works (Gray
Iron) ....A

WIS.—Cudahy
Power & Mining Machy. Co.
(Straight Line; Crushing)
AAA

WIS.—Janesville
New Doty Mfg. Co. (Bending; Straightening; Plate
Bending; Crimping; Hand
Belt Power) ....D

WIS.—Milwaukee
Allis Chalmers Co. (Crushing; Cornish; Live) AAAA
Filer & Stowell Co., Ltd.
(Live) ....AAA

WIS.—Racine
Secor Trunk Co., M. M.
(Music) ....A

ROOFING

See also Iron & Steel;
Paper; Roofs

ALA.—Birmingham
East Birmingham Roofg. &
Corrogating Co. (Iron &
Steel) C

CAL.—Los Angeles
Densmore Stabler Refining
Co. (Asphalt Ready)...B
Pioneer Roll Paper Co.
(Ready Rock) ....B

GA.—Atlanta
Southern Roofing Co. (Iron
& Steel) ....D

ILL.—Chicago
Chicago Asbestos Mfg. Co.,
96 W. Lake (Asbestos)
E
Chicago-Cleveland Car Roofing Co., Old Colony Bldg.
(Car) ....A
Chicago Fire Proof Covering
Co., 18 N. Canal (Asbestos) ....E
Illinois Roofing & Supply
Co., 23 Lake (Iron &
Steel) ....B
Gale & Co., Julian L., The
Rookery (Torison; Proof;
Car) ....D

ILL.—East St. Louis
The Process Steel & Wire
Co. (Iron; Steel)......A

IND.—Anderson
Gedge Bros. Iron Roofing
Co. (Iron; Steel) C

IND.—Aurora
Excelsior Iron Roofong Co.
(Iron; Steel) ....H

IND.—Indianapolis
Indianapolis Steel Roofing
& Corrigating Co., 23 E.

ROOFING (Con.)

South (Iron; Steel)....C

IOWA—Des Moines
Steel Roofing & Stamping
Wks. (Iron; Steel)....C

IOWA—Vinton
Vinton Steel Wks. (Iron &
Steel) ....E

KY.—Louisville
Conner & Co., Chas. H.,
17th & Arbegust (Iron;
Steel) ....B

LA.—New Orleans
New Orleans Roofing &
Metal Wks. (Galvanized
Iron) ....A

MASS.—Boston
Bird & Co., J. A. & W., 34
India (Flint Kole)...AA
Boston Bridge Wks. (Iron;
Steel) ....AA
New England Felt Roofing
Wks. (Felt) ....A
Trainer Mfg. Co., C. W.,
89 Pearl (Asphalt Ready)
E
Van Norden & Co., E.
(Iron) C

MASS.—East Walpole
Bird & Son, F. W. (Car;
Paroid) ....AA

MASS.—Waltham
Davis & Farnum Mfg. Co.
(Iron) ....A

MASS.—Worcester
New England Steel Roofing
Co. (Iron; Steel)......F

MICH.—Detroit
Burton Co., W. J., 164
Larned (Iron; Steel)...C
Hutchins & Sons, C. B.,
Majestic Bldg. (Iron;
Plastic Car) ....D

MICH.—Saginaw
Asphalt Roofing Co. (Asphalt; Ready) ....D
Mershon & Co., Wm. B.
(Car) ....A

MINN.—Duluth
Duluth Corrugating & Roofing Co. (Iron; Steel)..B

MINN.—Minneapolis
Crittenden Roofing & Mfg.
Co., 704 S. 5th (Iron;
Steel) ....E
Minneapolis Paper Co.
(Asphalt; Ready) .....B

MINN.—St. Paul
St. Paul Roofing Cornice &
Ornamental Co. (Steel) B

MO.—Kansas City
Kansas City Roofing &
Corrug. Co., 416 Delaware
(Iron; Steel) ....B

MO.—Saint Louis
Ames Insulating Material
Mfg. Co., 213 N. 3d
(Ivoryoid Indestructible
Fire Proof) ....B
Asbestos Mfg. & Roofing
Co. (Asbestos) ....E
Asphalt Roofing Co., 808 S.
Theresa (Asbestos; Asphalt; Ready) X
Excelsior Car Roofing Co.,
Chemical Bldg. (Car)..D
Harry Steel Wks. O. K.
(Corrugated & Formed)
B
Meeker & Bro. (Slate) AA
Saint Louis Corrugating
Co., 117 Soulard (Iron;
Steel) C
Souther Iron Co., E. E.
(Iron; Steel) ....A
Standard Railway Equipment Co., Union Trust
Bldg. (Galvanized Iron
bar) C
Trundad Asphalt Mfg. Co.
(Abestos; Asphalt Ready)
A
Zelnicker Supply Co. (Prepared) X

N. J.—Camden
Fay Manilla Roofing Co.,
516 Point (Car) ......D
New Jersey Asbestos Co.,
117 N. Front (Asbestos)
AA

N. J.—Jersey City
New York Iron Roofing &
Corrug. Co. (Roofing)..C

867

ROOFING (Con.)

Stowell Mfg. Co., 114 to 134 Culver Av. (Asbestos; Asphalt Gravel; Asphalt Ready; Cork Mica; Slate) ....B

N.Y.—Brooklyn
Hatfield, Geo. E., 11 Claseon Av. (Slag) ......D

New York City
Amer. Bridge Co., 100 B'way (Iron; Steel)...A
Asbestos Felting Wks., 79 Maiden La. (Asbestos)..D
Asphalt Ready Roofing Co. (Asphalt; Cement; Prepared) ....B
Barrett Mfg. Co. (Asphalt; Felt; Gravel) ....AAAA
Eastern Granite Roofing Co., Chambers & W. B'way (Asphalt; Ready; Granite) ....A
Gast, Frank J., 26 Cortland (Asbestos) ....E
Johns Manville Co., H. W., 100 William (Asbestos).. AAAA
Lefferts Galvanzing Wks. (Corrugated; Formed)..C
Monarch Asbestos Co., 411 Washington (Asphalt; Ready) ....E
Moseley Iron Bridge & Roofing Co., 39 Cortland (Iron; Steel) ....B
N. Y. Metal Ceiling Co., 537 W. 24th (Iron; Steel)
Standard Paint Co. (Rubberoid; Car Prepared)..A
Warren Chemical & Mfg. Co. (Asphalt; Tarred).A

N. Y.—Tonawanda
National Roofing Co. (Asphalt) ....B

OHIO—Cambridge
Cambridge Roofing Co. (Iron; Steel) ....B

OHIO—Canton
Berger Mfg. Co. (Iron; Steel) ....AA
Canton Steel Roofing Co. Iron; Steel) ....A
Eller & Co., J. H., 94 E. 5th (Iron; Steel) ....A
Kanneberg Roofing & Ceiling Co. (Iron; Steel).B

OHIO—Cincinnati
Edwards Mfg. Co. (Iron; Steel) C
Globe Iron Roofing & Corrugating Co. (Iron; Steel)
Hyndman Steel Roofing Co. 318 E. 2d (Iron; Steel; Corrugated; Formed)...C
Porter Iron Roofing & Corrug. Co., 27 W. Front (Iron; Steel) ....D
Scott & Co., 234 E. Front Asphalt Ready; Iron; Steel) ....B

OHIO—Cleveland
Auld & Conger Co. (Slate) A
Brown Hoisting Machinery Co., 1345 St. Clair (Terroinclare; Fire Proof) AAAA
Drake & Wiers Co. (Asphalt Car) ....B
Garry Iron & Steel Co. (Iron; Steel; Cement Prepared) ....A

OHIO—Columbus
Consolidated Roofing Wks. (Seamless; Asphalt; Ready) C

OHIO—Forest
Dickelman Mfg. Co. (Iron; Steel) ....A

OHIO—Lockland
Carey Mfg. Co., Philip (Asbestos; Cement)..... AAA

OHIO—Mansfield
Bodine Roofing Co. (Wood Fibre) ....D

OHIO—Middletown
Ames Steel Roofing Co. (Iron; Steel) ....AA

ROOFING (Con.)

OHIO—Niles
Niles Iron & Steel Roofing Co. (Iron; Steel) .....B
Sheet Metal Mfg. Co. (Iron; Steel) C
Sykes Metal Lathing & Roofing Co. (Iron; Steel) B

OHIO—Youngstown
Youngstown Iron Sheet & Tube Co. (Puddled Iron Sheets a Specialty) AAAA
Youngstown Iron & Steel Roofing Co. (Iron; Steel) AA

OHIO—Zanesville
Muskingum Valley Steel Co. (Iron; Steel) ....A

PA.—Conschohocken
Little, Wm. (Slag)......C

PA.—Easton
Bangor Excelsior Slate Co. (Slate) ....B

PA.—Erie
Watson & Co., H. F. (Asbestos; Car Felt; Asphalt Tarred) ......AAA

PA.—Philadelphia
Buchanan Foster Co., Drexel Bldg. (Asphalt; Ready) ....A
Penn. Metal Ceiling & Roofing Co. (Ltd.) 23d & Hamilton (Iron; Steel)B
Vulcanite Paving Co., Fidelity Bldg. (Slag).AAA
Wood, Iron & Steel Co. Alan., 519 Arch (Iron; Steel) ....AAAA

PA.—Pittsburg
Goff, Horner & Co. (Ltd.) Frick Bldg. (Iron; Steel) A
Iron City Metal Ceiling Co., Schmidt Bldg. (Iron; Steel) ....D
McConnelly Asbestos & Covering Co., 239 Water (Asbestos) ....B
Scaife & Sons Co., Wm. B., 221 First Av. (Iron; Steel) ....AAA

PA.—Pittston
Pittston Iron Roofing Co. (Iron; Steel) ....D

PA.—Slatington
Statington, Bangor Slate Syndicate (Slate) .....D

TENN.—Chattanooga
Chattanooga Roofing & Foundry Co. (Iron; Steel) A
Montague & Co. (Tin)...A

TENN.—Memphis
Bartholomew Roofing Co. (Asbestos) ....B
Livermore Foundry & Machine Co. (Iron)......A

VT.—Poultney
Griffith & Nathaniel (Slate) ....B

VA.—Richmond
Armitage Mfg. Co. (Asphalt; Ready; Car)....B

W. VA.—Wheeling
Caldwell B. F. & Co. (Corrugated; Formed Steel).. D
Laughlin Nail Co. (Steel) AA
Wheeling Corrugated Co. (Iron; Steel; Painted Galv. Iron Steel)..AAAA

WIS.—Milwaukee
Milwaukee Corragting Co. (Iron; Steel) ....A

ROOFS

CONN.—New Haven
Dann Bros. & Co. (Coach) B

DEL.—Wilmington
Edge Moor Iron Co. (Iron) AAA

ILL.—Chicago
Globe Iron Wks. (Iron).B

KY.—Louisville
Conner & Co., Chas. H. (Inc.) ....B

ᴬ.—Baltimore
Bartlett Hayward & Co.

ROOFS (Con.)
(Iron) ....B
N. J.—Trenton
Trenton Iron Co. (Iron).A
N. Y.—Brooklyn
Continental Iron Wks.
(Iron) ....A
Helca Iron Wks. (Iron)AA
N. Y.—New York
Cornell, J. B. & J. M. Co.
(Iron; Iron Truss)..AA
Dimond Thos. (Iron).....A
Moseley Iron Bridge &
Roof Co. (Iron).......B
OHIO—Cincinnati
Stacey Mfg. Co. (Iron).AA
Walton Iron Co. (Iron)..C
PA.—Philadelphia
Phoenix Bridge Co. (Iron;
Iron Truss; Steel) ......A
Wood & Co., R. D. (Iron)
AAAA
PA.—Pittsburg
Carnegie Steel Co. (Ltd.)
(Steel) ....AAAA
Riter-Conley Mfg. Co. (Iron)
AAA
PA.—Steelton
Penna. Steel Co. (Iron;
Iron Truss; Steel).AAAA

ROOMS

ILL.—Chicago
Chicago Clothes Dryer Wks.
346 Wabash Av. (Dry-
ing) ....D
Steel Rod Machine Co., 142
Wash. Boul. (Drying).F
MASS.—Boston
Empire Laundry Machy Co.
(Drying; Laundry Dry)C
N. Y.—Troy
Adams Laundry Machy Co.
(Drying) ....B
Troy Laundry Machy Co.
(Laundry Drying) ...AA
OHIO—Cincinnati
Amer. Laundry Mach. Co.
(Drying) ....AA
Peck-Williamson Htg. &
Ventl. Co. (Drying)..AA
OHIO—Toledo
Stevens Benjamin, A.
(Cooling) ....A
PA.—Columbia
Wilson Laundry Machy. Co.
(Drying) ....A
PA.—Philadelphia
Barnes & Erb Co. (Laundry
Drying) ....A

ROOTS

See also Herbs

MD.—Baltimore
Sharp & Dohme (Pressed)
AAA
MICH.—Detroit
Parke, Davis & Co. (Press-
ed) ....AAAA
MINN.—Mineapolis
McMillan Fur & Wool Co.
(Pressed) X
New York City
Adams & Co., Walter
(Pressed) ....H
Hopkins & Co., J. C., 100
William (Aconite; Ar-
row) ....A
Lehn & Fink (Bleached
Calamus) ....AAA
McKesson & Robbins
(Rhubarb) ....AAAA
VT.—Burlington
Wells & Richardson Co.
(Pressed) ....AA
WIS.—Fond Du Lac
Huber & Fuhrman Drug
Mills (Pressed) ......B

ROPE

See also Cordage

CAL.—San Francisco
Hallidie-Painter Tramway
Co., 46 Fremont (Wire)D
Tubbs Cordage Co. (Jute
Manila: Sisal)....AAAA
CONN.—Middletown
Kirby Mfg. Co. (Jump)..B

ROPE (Con.)
Palmer, J. E. (Hammock;
Hitching) ....AAA
CONN.—New Haven
National Steel & Wire Co.
(Wire) ....AAAA
National Wire Corpn.
(Wire) ....AA
GA.—Athens
Princeton Mfg. Co. (Cot-
ton) ....AA
GA.—Banning
Hutchinson Mfg. Co. (Cot-
ton) ....A
GA.—Columbus
Eagle & Phoenix Mills
(Cotton) ....AAA
GA.—Macon
Bibb Mfg. Co. (Cotton)
AAAA
ILL.—Chicago
Amer. Steel & Wire Co.,
The Rookery (Wire)....
AAAA
Carpenter & Co., Geo. B.,
208 So. Water (Wire;
Braided Cotton; Linen;
Manila; Sisal; Jute &
Hemp, Transmission).AA
Chicago Rawhide Mfg. Co.,
75 E. Ohio (Rawhide).A
Macomber & Whyte Rope
Co. (Manilla; Sisal; Jute
& Hemp Wire) ....A
ILL.—Sterling
Charter Gas Engine Co.
(Wire) ....A
IND.—Mishawaka
Dodge Mfg. Co. (Transmis-
sion Manila; Sisal; Jute
& Hemp) ....AAA
IOWA—Cedar Rapids
Adams Mfg. Co., A. L.
(Hammock) ....E
KY.—Maysville
January & Wood Co. (Cot-
ton) ....A
MD.—Baltimore
Hooper & Sons., Wm. E.
(Cotton) ....AAAA
MASS.—Boston
Durable Wire Rope Co.. 228
Congress (Durable Wire)
D
Hinckley Bros. & Co., 58
Commercial (Flattened
Strand Wire) ....B
Samson Cordage Wks. (Bell
Braided: Cotton; Ham-
mock: Hitching) ......A
MASS.— Fall River
Small Bros. (Cotton) ....D'
MASS.—Holyoke
Prentiss & Co., Geo. W.
(Wire) ....AA
MASS.—New Bedford
New Bedford Cordage Co.
Bale: Derrick: Elevator:
Manila: Sisal: Tarred
Manila) X
MASS.—Newtonville
Silver Lake Co. (Braided
Cotton) ....
MASS.—Palmer
Wright Wire Co. (Wire)..
AA
MASS.—Plymouth
Plymouth Cordage Co. (Ma-
nila: Sisal; Rawhide)...
AAAA
MINN.—Minneapolis
Minneapolis Steel & Machy.
Co. (Transmission).AAA
MISS.—Wesson
Mississippi Mills (Cotton)
AAA
MO.—St. Louis
Broderick & Bascon Rope
Co.. 809 N. Main (Wire:
Transmission: Galvanized
Wire: Iron: Steel Wire:
Steel Switch: Manila:
Sisal: Jute: Hemp)....A
Leschen & Sons Rope Co..
A.. 920 N. 1st (Steel
Switching: Wire: Wreck-
ing: Braided Cotton; Ele-
vator: Manila: Sisal:
Galvanized Wire: Iron:
Steel Flat: Linen: Hay:
Hide: Jute: Hemp: Trans-
mission: Locomotive).AA
Ludlow-Saylor Wire Co.

ROPE (*Con.*)
(Wire) ....AA
St. Louis Cordage Co.
(Hide) ....AA
N. J.—Trenton
Roebling's Sons Co., Jno.
A. (Wire; Iron; Steel
Flat) ....AAAA
Trenton Iron Co. (Iron;
Steel Wire; Copper Wire;
Iron; Steel Flat; Wire)
A
N. Y.—Auburn
Columbian Cordage Co.
(Hay; Manila; Sisal;
Rawhide; Transmission)
AA
N. Y.—Buffalo
Contractors Plant Mfg. Co.
(Wire) ....B
New York City
American Mfg. Co., 63
Wall (Manila; Sisal;
Jute Hemp; Hammock;
Hitching; Transmission)
AAAA
Dewitt Wire Cloth Co.
(Copper Wire; Galvanized
Wire; Wire) ....A
Harzard Mfg. Co., 50 Dey
(Wire) ....AAAA
Jessop & Sons, Wm. (Ltd.)
95 John (Wire) ....AAA
Johns, H. W., Manville Co.
(Asbestos) ....AAAA
Lawrence Cordage Wks.
(Bale; Jute; Manila;
Sisal) ....A
Macomber-Whyte-Moon Co..
131 Worth (Wire) ....H
New Jersey Fdry. & Ma-
chine Co., 9 Murray
(Wire) ....D
Rahmann & Co., Geo. (Raw
Hide) C
Schieren & Co., Chas. A.
(Raw Hide) .....AAAA
Waterbury & Co., 69 South
(Manila; Sisal; Jute;
Hemp; Wire) ...AAAA
N. Y.—Unadilla
Tie Co. (Boat Anchor;
Transmission) ....D
N. Y.—Watervliet
Covert Mfg. Co. (Ham-
mock; Hitching) ......A
N. Y.—West New Brighton
Hunt Co., C. W. (Trans-
mission) ....AA
N. C.—Mountain Island
Catawba Elec. Light Co.
(Cotton) ....A
OHIO—Cincinnati
Cincinnati Railway Supply
Co., 13 E. 2nd (Mfrs.
Agts.) (Wire) ....A
Jacobs Cordage Co. (Bell;
Tarred; Manila) .....A
OHIO—Columbus
Case Mfg. Co. (Transmis-
sion) ....A
Ironsides Co. (Manila;
Sisal; Jute; Hemp;
Transmission) C
OHIO—Lockland
Carey Mfg. Co., Philip
(Asbestos) ....AAA
OHIO—Xenia
Kelly Co., R. A. (Hay;
Manila; Sisal; Raw
Hide) ....A
PA.—Allegheny
Carlins' Sons, Thos. (Ma-
nila; Sisal; Wire) ....A
PA.—Erie
Watson Co., H. F. (As-
bestos) ....AAAA
PA.—Harrisburg
Jackson Mfg. Co. (Wire) .B
PA.—Philadelphia
Hodson, John W. (Cotton)
C
Phosphor Bronze Smelting
Co. (Ltd.) (Phosphor;
Bronze Wire; Wire;
Transmisson) ....F
Schlichter Jute Cordage Co.
(Manila; Sisal) .....AA
PA.—Pittsburg
Frick & Lindsay Co.. 109
Wood (Mfrs Agts. Wire)
B
Milhollani Co., J. & J. B..

ROPE (*Con.*)
718 5th Av. (Wire) ....A
PA.—Reading
Jackson & Son, Thos. (Bale;
Cotton; Jute; Manila;
Sisal) ....AA
PA.—Wilkesbarre
Harzard Mfg. Co. (Locomo-
tive Switching; Galvan-
ized Wire; Iron; Steel
Flat; Wire) .....AAAA
PA.—Williamsport
Williamsport Wire Rope
Co. (Wire) ....A
R. I.—Pawkucket
Briggs & Co., H. A. (Cot-
ton) ....A
S. C.—Columbia
Columbia Mills Co. (Cot-
ton) X
TEXAS—Galveston
Galveston Rope Co. (Ma-
nila; Sisal) ....A
WIS.—Milwaukee
Allis Chalmers Co. (Trans-
mission) ....AAAA
Western Rawhide & Belt-
ing Co. (Raw Hide) ..A

ROSARIES

See Jewelry

ROSES

See Jewelry

ROSETTES

See also Pickets; Wood-
work

CONN.—Bridgeport
Bryant Eltric Co. (Electric
Light) ....A
Perkins Electric Switch
Mfg. Co. (Electric) ....A
CONN.—New Britain
North & Judd Mfg. Co.
CONN.—New Haven
Grelley Co. (Bridle) C
CONN.—Waterbury
Amer. Ring Co. (Bridle) ..A
Plume & Alwood Mfg. Co.
(Bridle) ....AAA
IND.—Peru
Peru Electric Mfg. Co.
(Electric) ....A
KY.—Covington
Ohio Scroll & Lumber Co.
(Vehicle) ....D
KY.—Louisville
Harbison & Gathright
(Bridle) ....AA
MASS.—Boston
Gilmore Electric Co. (Elec-
tric) ....AA
NEBR.—Lincoln
Harpham Bros. (Harness)
A
N. J.—Newark
Duramond Mfg. Co.
(Bridle) ....B
Greacen & Co., Walter
(Harness) ....E
Peters Harness & Saddlery
Co. (Bridle; Harness) ..C
N. Y.—Albany
Clark, Jno. W. (Iron) ...D
New York City
Eckstein, Chas. G., 249
Centre (Iron) ....D
N. Y.—Syracuse
Pass & Seymour (Electric)
A
OHIO—Akron
Enterprise Mfg. Co. (Har-
ness) ....A
PA.—Chester
Keystone Drop Forge Wks.
(Iron) ....B
PA.—So. Bethlehem
Bethlehem Foundry &
Mach. Co. (Iron) C
TENN.—Nashville
Nashville Saddlery Co. •
(Bridle) ....AA
WIS.—So. Milwaukee
Stowell Mfg & Foundry Co.
(Iron) ....A

ROSIN

GA.—Brunswick
Downing Co. ....AA
GA.—Savannah
Shotter Co., S. P.....AAAA
MASS.—Boston
Champman & Soden, 410
  Atlantic Av. ....A
New York City
Foote J. Howard, 33
  Maiden Lane X
Hayne, H. J., 142 Front.D
Longman & Martinez,
  AAA
N. C.—Wilmington
Martin & Co., W. A.....D
OHIO—Cincinnati
Ogiloy, D. J............B
PA.—Erie
Watson Co., H. F.....AAA

ROUGE

MICH.—Detroit
Detroit White Lead Wks.
  AAA
N. J.—Newark
Hanson & Van Winkle Co.
  (Ltd.) ....AA
N. Y.—Brooklyn
Wiarda & Co., John C..AA
New York City
Cooper & Co., Chas....AA
Ely, C. J., 35 Dey C
Wetmore Co., S. H......D
PA.—Pittsburg
Pittsburg Crushed Steel Co.
  (Ltd.) ....B

ROUGHERS

See also Machy

OHIO—Defiance
Defiance Mach. Wks.
  (Hub) ....A

ROUNDERS

CONN.—New Haven
Shuster Co., F. B. (Hoop)
  X
IND.—Indianapolis
Atkins & Co., E. C. (Saw)
  AAAA
MASS.—Fitchburg
Simonds Mfg. Co. (Saw) ..
  AAA
N. J.—Newark
Osborne & Co., C. S. (Sad-
  dlers' Rein) ....B
OHIO—Cincinnati
Randall & Co., (Saddlers'
  Rein) ....B
OHIO—Cleveland
Oram, John S. (Heading)
  A

ROUNDS

IND.—Frankfort
Frankfort Handle Mfg. Co.
  (Ladder) ....E
OHIO—Hicksville
Kerr Bros. Mfg. Co. (Lad-
  der) C
OHIO—Sandusky
Sandusky Tool Co. (Ladder)
  A
PA.—Beaver Falls
Union Drawn Steel Co.
  (Iron) ....A
VT.—Bridgewater Corners
Josselyn, L. F. (Chair) ..H
WIS.—Menasha
Menasha Woodware Co.
  (Ladder) ....AA

ROWERS

ILL.—Canton
Parlin & Orendorff Co.
  (Check) ....AAAA
ILL.—Decatur
Chambers. Bering, Quinlan
  Co. (Check) ....A
Haworth & Sons Mfg. Co.
  (Check) ....AA
Tait Mfg. Co., F. B. (Check)
  A
ILL.—Galesburg
Cotton & Co., G. D. (Inc.)
  (Check) C

ROWERS (Con.)

ILL.—Joliet
Joliet Mfg. Co. (Check) ..A
ILL.—Moline
Deere & Mansur Co (Check)
  AAAA
Moline Plow Co. (Check)
  AAAA
ILL.—Peoria
Avery Mfg. Co. (Check)
  AAA
ILL.—Rockford
Emerson Mfg. Co. (Check)
  AAA
ILL.—Sterling
Keystone Co. (Check)
  AA
OHIO—Hamilton
Denscher Co., H. P. (Check)
  A
OHIO—Mansfield
Lean Mfg. Co., Roderick
  (Check) ....AA
WIS.—Beloit
Thompson & Sons Mfg. Co.,
  J. (Check) ....AA
WIS.—Madison
Fuller & Johnson Mfg. Co.
  (Check) ....AAA

ROWLOCKS

N. Y.—Buffalo
Praw & Letchworth Co.
  AAA
New York City
Tiebout, W. & J., 118 Cham-
  bers ....B
Tower & Lyon ....B

RUBBER

N. J.—Lambertville
New Jersey Rubber Co. (Re-
  claimed) ....A
N. J.—Trenton
Home Rubber Co. (Sash)
  AA
N. Y.—New York City
Gutta Percha & Rubber Mfg.
  Co. (Corrugated) ..AAAA
Jenkins Bros. (Pump Valve)
  A
Kleinert Rubber Co., I. B.
  (Vulcanite) ....A
N. Y. Beeting & Packing
  Co. (Corrugated) ....AAA
N. Y. Rubber Co. (Corru-
  gated) ....AA
OHIO—Akron
Goodrich Co., B. F. (Sash)
  AAAA

RUBBER BOOTS

See Boots & Shoes; Rubber

RUBBER GOODS

CAL.—San Francisco
Bowers Rubber Co. (Mechan-
  ical) C
Eagle Rubber Co. (Mechani-
  cal) ....E
Gorham Rubber Co.......A
CONN.—Bridgeport
Canfield, H. O. (Mechani-
  cal) C
Canfield Rubber Co. .....AA
CONN.—Fairfield
Fairfield Rubber Co. (Car-
  riage and Colored Imita-
  tion of Leather, &c.)...C
CONN.—Hartford
Hartford Rubber Wrks. Co.
  Mechanical Rubber) ..A
Premier Mfg. Co. ....B
CONN.—Middletown
Omo Mfg. Co. (Dress
  Shields) ....A
CONN.—New Haven
Baumann Rubber Co. (Drug-
  gists) C
Candee. L. & Co. .AAAA
Seamless Rubber Co. (Drug-
  gists' Sundries; Surgical)
  A
CONN.—Seymour
Day. H. P. & E. Co. C
ILL.—Chicago
Chicago Rubber Brokerage

RUBBER GOODS (Con.)
Co. (Mechanical; Moulded)
E

Morgan & Wright (Mechanical Rubber) ....AA

IND.—Goshen
Western Rubber Co. (Mechanical) C
Kokoma Rubber Co. ....A

MD.—Baltimore
Baltimore Rubber Co. C

MASS.—Andover
Tyer Rubber Co. (Surgical) AA

MASS.—Boston
Bailey & Co., C. J. (Druggists) ....B
Boston Belting Co. (Mechanical) ....AAAA
Boston Woven Hose & Rubber Co. (All Kinds) AAAA
Clapp, E. H., Rubber Co. A
Conant Rubber Co. C
Davidson Rubber Co. (Druggists' Sundries) ....A
Franklin Rubber Co. (Rainproof Garments) C
Revere Rubber Co. (Mechanical) ....AAAA

MASS.—Cambridge
Boston Wooven Hose & Rubber Co. (Mechanical) AAAA

MASS.—Easthampton
Easthampton Rubber Thread Co. (Thread) ....AA

MASS.—Reading
Reading Rubber Mfg. Co. A

MASS.—Springfield
Dickinson Hard Rubber Co. (Composition G'ds. for Electrical Trade) C

MO.—St. Louis
Sanders Duck & Rubber Co. C

N. J.—Belleville
Hardman Rubber Co. (Druggists Sundries) ....B

N. J.—Butler
Pequanoc Rubber Co. ....B

N. J.—Jersey City
New Jersey Car Spring & Rubber Co. (Mechanical) AA
Voorhees Rubber Mfg. Co. (Hose; Belting; Packing; Valves; Mats) ....B

N. J.—Newark
Roberts, C., Rubber Co. ..A

N. J.—New Brunswick
United States Rubber Co. AAAA

N. J.—Trenton
Consolidated Rubber Co. (Belting; Hose; Fruit Jar Rubbers) ....B
Empire Rubber Mfg. Co. A
Eureka Rubber Mfg. Co. (Belting; Hose; Mechanical) ....B
Hamilton Rubber Mfg. Co. (Mechanical) ....B
Home Rubber Co. (Mechanical) ....AA
Stokes, Joseph, Rubber Co. (Hose; Mechanical) ...C
Trenton Rubber Mfg. Co. (Belting; Packing; Mechanical; Hose, &c.)...A
Union Rubber Co. (Mechanical) ....E
United & Globe Rubber Mfg. Co. ....A
United Mfg. & Supply Co. C

N. Y.—Batavia
Batavia Rubber Tire Co. B

N. Y.—College Point
American Hard Rubber Co. AAAA
Kleinert, I. B. Rubber Co. A

New York City
American Hard Rubber Co., 9 Mercer St. (Stationers') AAAA
Arkay Rubber Co., 35 Warren (Druggists') ......F

RUBBER GOODS (Con.)
Ballard, Stephen, Rubber Co. C

Ellis & Goltermann (Antomizers; Toilet Goods) C
Faber, Eberhard (Stationers') ......AAA
Gates, M. S. & Co. C
Gennert, G. (Photographic) B
Goodyear's India Rubber Glove Mfg. Co. (Mechanical; Druggists; &c.) AAAA
Goodyear Rubber Co., 155 B'way ....AAAA
Gutta Percha & Rubber Mfg. Co. (Hose; Belting; Packing; Mechanical; Vulcanized) ....AAAA
Hodgman Rubber Co. (Druggists) ....AA
Home Rubber Co. ....A
Imperial Rubber Co. C
India Rubber Co., 16 Warren (Druggists'; Photographic) ....AA
International Automobile & Vehicle Tire Co., 346 B'way (Mechanical)..B
Kleinert Rubber Co., I. B., 725 B'way (Sheeting)..A
Knapp Rubber Binding Co. (Binding; Nosings) ...B
Manhattan Rubber Mfg. Co. (Mechanical) ....AA
Matson Rubber Co., 26 W. B'way (Druggists' Sundries; Mechanical Rubber Co. (Druggists'; Moulded; Vulcanized; Stationers', etc.) ....AAAA
Meinecke & Co., 50 Park Place (Druggists') C
Mineralized Rubber Co. (Hose; Mechanical Goods) C
New York Belting & Packing Co. (Ltd.) (Hose; Belting; Mechanical; Packing, etc.) ....A
New York Gas Tubing Co. B
New York Rubber Co., 84 Reade (Mechanical; Vulcanized) ....AAA
Parker, Stearns & Sutton, 228 South (Surgical; Druggists' Stationers'; Atomizers, etc.; Electrical) AA
Peerless Rubber Mfg. Co., 16 Warren (Packing; Hose; Belting; Mechanical) ....A
Rubber Goods Mfg. Co., 253 B'way (Mechanical) ..... AAAA
United States Rubber Reclaiming Works, 127 Duane ....AA
Vulcanized Rubber Co....A

OHIO—Akron
American Hard Rubber Co. Hard; Insulite) ..AAAA
Diamond Rubber Co. (Mechanical) ....AAA
Firestone Tire & Rubber Co. B
Goodrich Co., B. F. (Akron Rubber Wks.) (Mechanical; Embalmers'; Druggists'; Hose; Belting; Drug; Sund; Matting)... AAAA
Goodyear Tire & Rubber Co. (Solid; Cushion; Carriage; Motor; Vehicle Tires).AA
Miller Rubber Mfg. Co. (Gloves; Surgical; Finger Cots) ....B
Rubber Specialty Co. (Surgical) X
Whitman & Barnes Mfg. Co. (Mechanical) .....AAAA

OHIO—Barberton
Alden Rubber Co.........A

PA.—Erie
Lake Shore Rubber Co. (Mechanical) C

PA.—Philadelphia
Bovd & Bro., Jas. (Belting; Hose; Packing) ....A

872

RUBBER GOODS (Con.)

Kendrick, James R. (Surgical) ....E
Manufactured Rubber Co. (Reclaimed) ....A
Philadelphia Rubber Works (Reclaimed) ....A
Restein, Clement & Co. (Mechanical) ....B
Sayen & Schultz (Mechanical) C
Town & Bro C

PA.—Pittsburg
Feick Bros. Co. (Surgical) ....D

R. I.—Bristol
National India Rubber Co. (Druggists'; Mechanical) ....AAAA

R. I.—Providence
Davol Rubber Co. (Surgical; Druggists'; Stationers').. AA

RUBBERS

See also Rings

N. J.—Trenton
Consolidated Rubber Co. (Fruit Jar) ....B
New York City
New York Rubber Co., 84 Reade (Square Packing) AA

OHIO—Akron
Faultless Rubber Co. (Sling Shot) ....AA
PA.—Erie
Continental Rubber Wks. (Fruit Jars) ....A
PA.—Philadelphia
Sayne & Schultz, 13th & Commerce (Fruit Jars) C

RUBIES

See Jewelry

RUBS

CONN.—Bridgeport
Bridgeport Safety Emery Wheel Co. (Emery for Foundry Use) ....F
ILL.—Chicago
Chicago Wheel & Mfg. Co. (Emery for Foundry Use) C
MASS.—Westfield
Vitrified Wheel Co. (Emery for Foundry Use) C
MASS.—Worcester
Norton Emery Wheel Co. (Emery Foundry) ....AA
OHIO—Tiffin
Sterling Emery Wheel Mfg. Co. (Emery for Foundry Use) ....A
PA.—Philadelphia
Abrasive Material Co., 72d & Upland (Emery) ....A
R. I.—Providence
American Emery Wheel Wrks. (Emery for Foundry Use) ....B

RUGS

See Carpets & Rugs

RULES

CONN.—Hartford
Billings & Spencer Co. (Scale; Shrinkage; Steel) AA
CONN.—New Britain
Russell & Irwin Mfg. Co. (Tinners) ....AAAA
Stanley Rule & Level Co. (Steel Metric; Ivory; Steel; Boxwood; Extention; Lumbermans') AAA
CONN.—Pine Meadow
Chapin-Stephens Co. (Caliper; Architect; Hickory Board; Boxwood; Freight; Ivory; Hickory Log; Combination; Scale; Shrinkage; Slide; Slope Level Try Square; School; Desk) A

RULES (Con.)

CONN.—Southington
Peck, Stow & Wilcox Co. (Steel; Tinners; Iron) AAAA
CONN.—Unionville
Union Nut & Bolt Co. (Boxwood) ....A
Upson Nut Co.. (Caliper; (Lumbermens' Boxwood; Ivory) ....AAAA
ILL.—Chicago
Dietzgen Co., Eugene (for Draughting Room) ....A
IOWA—Ottumwa
Nicholls Mfg. Co. (Steel Framing) ....D
MASS.—Athol
Athol Machine Co. (Caliper; Machinist Steel) ....B
Starrett Co., L. S. (Keyseat; Machinists'; Scale; Shrinkage; Steel; Desk; Blacksmiths'; Metric; Slide; Caliper) ....A
MASS.—Boston
Hanson, H. C. (Steel Perforating; Printers') ....B
Wyke & Co., Jno., 898 Saratoga (Machinist) ......D
MASS.—Chicopee Falls
Stevens Arms & Tool Co., J. (Machinist) ....AAA
MASS.—Fitchburg
Sawyer Tool Mfg. Co. (Steel; Steel Metric Key Seat; Machinists'. Desk; School) C
MASS.—Greenfield
Massachusetts Tool Co. (Tempered Steel) C
MICH.—Saginaw
Lufkin Rule Co. (Lumbermens' Machinists' Steel; Steel Metric; Tinners; Blacksmiths'; Hickory Board; Steel Board; Steel Folding; Freight; Hickory Log; Scale Shrinkage; Desk; School) ....AA
N. Y.—Keene
Humphrey Mach. Co. (Caliper) C
N. J.—Irvington
Belcher Bros. Co. (Boxwood; Caliper; Freight; Parallel; Plate Glass; Shrinkage; Saddlers' Glaziers'; Scale; Desk) ...X
N. J.—Newark
Smith, S O. (Counting House; Wood) ....D
N. Y.—Brooklyn
Eddy & Co., Geo. M. (For Surveyers', &c.) ....A
N. Y.—Jamestown
American Mfg Concern (Advertising) ....A
New York City
Faber, Eberhard (Desk; Boxwood) ....AAA
Goodyear India Rubber Glove Mfg. Co. (Desk) AAAA
Hammacher, Schlemmer & Co. Fourth Av. (Caliper; Extension; Key Seat; Lumbermens' Machinists') AAA
Hoe & Co., R. (Printers') AAAA
Jennings & Co., C. E., 42 Murray (Boxwood; Ivory; Machinists') ....B
Keuffel & Esser Co.. 127 Fulton (Extension; Scale; Shrinkage; Steel; Steel Metric; Boxwood; Combination; Slide) ......AA
Sargent & Co., 151 Leonard (Steel) ....AAAA
Solfmann, E. G., 125 E. 42d (Architects; Engineers; Slide; Caliper) ....B
Spencerian Pen Co. (Desk) AA
N. Y.—Seneca Falls
National Advertising Co. (Advertising) ....B
Westcott, Jewell Co. (Advertising Desk; Parallel; School) ....D
OHIO—Akron

RULES (Con.)
Goodrich Co., B. F. (Desk)
................AAAA

PA.—Philadelphia
Disston & Sons (Inc.) Henry
(Machinists'; Steel)
................AAAA

PA.—Williamsport
Andrews & Sons, E. (Nickel
Plated; Steel Board) ..D

R. I.—Providence
Brown & Sharpe Mfg. Co.
(Caliper; Key Seat; Ma-
chinists'; Scale; Shrink-
age; Steel; Steel Metric;
Boxwood; Iron; Metric)
................AAAA

RUM

See also Liquors

MASS.—Boston
Chapin, Trull & Co. (New
England) ....A
Felton & Son, 17 Broad
(New England) ....A
Lawrence & Sons, S.
(New England) ...AAAA

MASS.—Newburyport
Caldwell, A. & G. J.
(New England) .....AA

MO.—St Louis
Eddy & Eddy (Bay)......A

New York City
Caswell, Massey & Co.
(Bay) X
Chaskel Chemical Works
(Inc.), (Bay) X
Cook & Bernheimer Co., 150
Franklin ....AAA
Jones Chemical Co., Enos F.
(Bay) X
Rudkin Co., Wm. H. (Bay)
................D
Tyler & Finch Co. (Bay)
................B

OHIO—Cincinnati
Freiberg & Workum ..AAAA

PA.—Philadelphia
Penn. Chemical Works.
(Bay) ....AAA

RUMBLERS

See also Tumblers; Barrels

PA.—Philadelphia
Paxson Co., J. W. (Foun-
dry) ....AA

RUNABOUTS

See also Carriages & Wagons

MASS.—Amesbury
Hassett & Hodge ....A

MICH.—Flint
Durant-Dort Carriage Co.
................AAAA

MICH.—Pontiac
Pontiac Buggy Co. ......A

N. Y.—New York City
Goodrich & Co., J. F. ..AA
Stivers, R. M. ....B

OHIO—Columbus
Buckeye Buggy Co. ...AAA

WIS.—Racine
Racine-Sattley Co. ...AAAA

RUNGS

See Rounds

RUNNERS

See also Woodwork; Car-
riage

ILL.—Chicago
Wagner, Carl X

ILL.—Freeport
Schofield & Co. (Bob Sleigh)
................D

IND.—South Bend
South Bend Toy Mfg. Co.
(Childrens' Carriage) ..A

MICH.—Lansing
Lansing Wheelbarrow Co.
(Sleigh) ....AAA

MICH.—Traverse City
Peteryl, Victor (Sleigh)
................D

MASS.—Boston
Kimball Bros. Co. (Hub) ..B

RUNNERS (Con.)
New York City
Tagliabue, Chas. J.......A
Tagliabue, Guiseppe, 302
Pearl ....B

OHIO—Canton
Elbel Co. (Gag) ....A

OHIO—Cincinnati
Shelt Co. (Sled & Sleigh)
................A

OHIO—Cleveland
Eberhard Mfg. Co. (Gag)
................AA

SACCHARINE

See Sweeteners

SACCHARO-METERS

CAL.—San Francisco
Neville & Co. (Inc.).....A

SACKS: FLOUR

See also Bags

GA.—Atlanta
Atlanta Paper Co........A

ILL.—Chicago
Neahr & Co., M. J......AA

IOWA—Davenport
Davenport Bag & Paper
Co. ....B

MINN.—Minneapolis
Hardwood Mfg. Co.....AA

MO.—St. Louis
Bemis Bros. Bag Co.AAAA
Chase Bag Co., H. & L.
................AA

N. Y.—Canajoharie
Arkell & Smiths ....A

New York City
Halsted & Co., E. S. ...A

OHIO—Cleveland
Adams Bag Co. ....A

PA.—Philadelphia
Bailey & Co., John T.
................AAAA

PA.—Pittsburg
Tarentum Paper Mills....X

WIS.—Milwaukee
Milwaukee Bag Co.......A

SACQUES

See Clothing: Ladies'

SADDLERY & HARNESS

ARK.—Ft. Smith
Murphy, W. J...........B

CAL.—Los Angeles
Hayden & Lewis Co......B

CAL.—Sacramento
Van Voorhees & Co., A. A.
................A

CAL.—San Francisco
Davis & Son, W........,B
Johnson & Co., J. C.....AA
Main & Winchester..AAAA
Stone & Co., L. D......B

COLO.—Denver
Colorado Saddlery Co.....C

CONN.—Hartford
Smith, Bourn & Co......A

CONN.—Middletown
Russell Mfg. Co. (Halters)
................AAAA

GA.—Atlanta
Georgia Tanning & Mfg.
Co. C

GA.—Augusta
Day & Tannahill.........A

GA.—Buford
Allen Bona (Collars).....A

GA.—East Point
Couch Bros. & J. J. Eagan
Co. (Collars) C

GA.—Fairburn
McCurry & Inman Harness
Mfg. Co. C

GA.—Macon
Berud & Co., G..........C

GA.—Valdosta
Roberts, Crawford Dasher
Co. C

ILL.—Benton
Jackson Saddlery Co., A.
D. C
ILL.—Bloomington
Green & Co., B. S.........C
ILL.—Champaign
Miller Harness Co.........C
ILL.—Chicago
Chicago Horse Collar Co.
(Collars) ....F
Chicago Raw Hide Mfg.
Co. (Leather Halters)..A
Kiper & Sons, L. ......AA
Morley Bros. Sadd. Co. ..A
Oberne & Co., Geo. ......E
Starr & Sons Harness Co.,
J. G. ....B
Staver Carriage Co. ....AA
ILL.—Elgin
Elgin Saddlery & Harness
Co. C
ILL.—Galesburg
Adams & Johnson Co. ....B
ILL.—Ottawa
Bach & Co., M. W. C
ILL.—Peoria
Case & Kroenlein.........B
ILL.—Quincy
Schott Saddlery Co., J. B.
(Bridles) ....B
ILL.—Rockford
Hess & Hopkins Leather Co.
A
ILL.—Sterling
Harpham & Son, John C
IND.—Columbus
Mooney & Sons, W. W...AA
IND.—Elkhart
Elkhart Carriage & Har-
ness Co. ....B
IND.—Evansville
Britz Bros. & Co. ....A
Flickner & Sons, J. O.....C
IND.—Ft. Wayne
Bayer, John (Collars) C
Ft. Wayne Sadd. Co. C
Johns & Co., A. L. C
IND.—Indianapolis
Holliday & Wyon Co......A
Indianapolis Sadd. Co....A
IND.—Kokomo
Ulrich Harness Mfg. Co...E
IND.—Lafayette
Jamieson Bros. ....D
IND.—Laporte
Lonn & Sons Co., J.......E
IND.—Monticello
Gustavel Co., L. G. .....D
IND.—Terre Haute
Miller & Co., P. (Collars).D
IOWA—Burlington
McConnell, S. R. & I. C...
AA
IOWA—Clinton
Clinton Sadd. Co. C
IOWA—Davenport
Sears-Frizzell Co. C
IOWA—Des Moines
Des Moines Sadd. Co. .....B
IOWA—Dubuque
Dubuque Harness & Sadd.
Co. (Bridles; Leather Hal-
ters) C
IOWA—Muscatine
Van Nostrand Sadd. Co...B
IOWA—Sioux City
Meyer Bros. ....B
IOWA—Waterloo
Iowa Saddlery Co. C
Waterloo Sadd. Co. C
KANS.—Atchison
Atchison Sadd. Co. ......B
KANS.—Ft. Scott
Glunz, Jno. ....B
KANS.—Lawrence
Herrman, Jno. (Collars)..C
KANS.—Leavenworth
Ackenhausen Bros. C
KANS.—Wichita
Hays Sadd. & Leather Co.,
L. C
KY.—Louisville
Floyd & Bohr C
Harbison & Gathright ....A
Kreiger & Miller C
Louisville Girth & Blanket
Mills (Girths) C
Louisville Sadd. Co. C
KY.—Paducah
Rehkopf Sadd. Co., E.....B
LA.—New Orleans
Rice & Co., Louis P. .....B

MAINE—Portland
Whitney-Sloo Co. ....B
Bailey Co., The Jas.. C
MD.—Baltimore
Day & Son Co., O. F
(Bridles) C
Lerch Bros ....A
McCauley, J. C. (Collars).D
O'Connor, T. J. C
Rose & Sons, P. ....B
Wilkins & Sons, B. ......B
MASS.—Concord Junction
Boston Harness Co. ......A
MASS.—Holyoke
Holyoke Belting Co.
(Leather Halters) C
MASS.—North Adams
Dowlin, R. M. C
MASS.—Waltham
Thompson Mfg. Co., J....A
MICH.—Albion
Manning Harness Co. ....E
MICH.—Detroit
Armstrong & Graham ....A
Pierson & Hough ....B
MICH.—Saginaw
Morley Bros. ....AA
MINN.—Minneapolis
Dodson-Fisher-Brockmann
Co. ....A
MINN.—St. Paul
Hardenburgh & Co., P. R.
L. ....A
Konantz Sadd. Co. ....A
MO.—Carrollton
Lindsay Bros. C
MO.—Kansas City
Buford & George Mfg. Co.
C
MO.—St. Joseph
Myeth Hdw. & Mfg. Co...AA
MO.—St. Louis
Hayden Saddlery Hdw. Co.,
P. (Riding Bridles; Hal-
ters) ....A
Holthaus Sadd. Co., A. ..C
Homann Sadd. Co., W.
(Riding Bridles) ....B
Loeblein Collar & Whip Co.,
B. (Collars) ....B
Meyer, Bannerman & Co.
(Bridles; Halters).AAAA
Sickles Sadd. Co., J. B....B
Sommers Bros. Mfg. Co.
(Collars) ....B
Strauss Sadd. Co., J. D.
(Halters) ....A
MO.—Springfield
Herman Sadd. Co., F. C...C
Lovan Sadd. Co. ....B
NEBR.—Fremont
Fremont Sadd. Co. ....D
NEBR.—Hastings
Haney & Co., J. H. .....B
NEBR.—Lincoln
Buckstaff Bros. Mfg. Co...
AAA
Harpham Bros. Co. C
Wittman & Co., H. C
NEBR.—Omaha
Marks Bros. Sadd. Co. ...B
N. H.—Manchester
Ranno & Son. H. C. .....D
N. J.—Newark
Crabbe Harness Co. .....D
Peters Harness & Sadd. Co.
(Riding Bridles; Bridle
Leather; Web Halters).C
Tompkins & Mandeville...B
N. Y.—Bath
Bath Harness & Collar Co.
D
N. Y.—Binghamton
Persels & Mack C
N. Y.—Buffalo
Buffalo Weaving & Belt-
ing Co. (Web Bridles;
Web Halters) ....A
Smith & Son, J. H. (Collars)
N. Y.—Clyde
Brown Harness Wks., G. A.
E
N. Y.—Glens Falls
Peysers Collar Co. (Collars)
B
N. Y.—Oswego
King Harness Co. C
N. Y.—Rochester
Neidhardt & Co., C. C
Peters Bros. (Collars) ...D
N. Y.—Rome

Barnard, Edward (Leather; Web Halters) C
Bingham Harness Co. ....D
N. Y.—Syracuse
Fraser & Jones Co. (Leather Halters) ....AA
N. Y.—Troy
Curtis & Co., M. G. .....D
Troy Harness Mfg. Co.....E
N. Y.—Utica
Windheim, Geo. C
N. Y.—Watervleit
Covert Mfg. Co. (Leather; Rope; Web Halters) ...A
N. C.—Charlotte
Shaw Harness Co. C
N. DAK.—Fargo
Bristol & Sweet Co. C
North Dak. Harness Co...D
OHIO—Canton
Elbel Co. (Bridle; Halters) A
OHIO—Cincinnati
Engelke Sadd. Co. C
Graf, Morsbach & Co. ..A
Grossman & Hove Sadd. Co. A
Perkins-Campbell Co. (The) (Riding Bridles) ....A
OHIO—Columbus
Buckeye Sadd. Co. C
Columbus Carriage & Harness Co. C
Meek & Co., J. W. ....B
Sells Co., J. H. & F. A...C
OHIO—New Berlin
Hoover, W. H. (Collars).B
OHIO—New Philadelphia
Diffenbacher, Jno. T. (Collars) C
OHIO—Marietta
Strecker Bros. & Co. .....A
OHIO—Sidney
Given & Son, R. (Collars) B
OHIO—Stryker
Stryker Mfg. Co. C
OHIO—Toledo
Quinn, J. E. (Collars)....C
OREGON—Portland
Lawrence Co., Geo. C.....C
Sharkey Co., Jno. P. .....D
PA.—Canton
Gleckner & Sons Co., W. W. D
PA.—Easton
Sage & Co., H. A. C
PA.—Quakertown
Harley, J. S. ....A
PA.—Philadelphia
Keim Sadd. Co., Geo. De B. A
Kiehl, M. (Collars) C
PA.—Pittsburgh
Pittsburgh Harness Supply Co. C
R. I.—Providence
Rounds & Co., T. W. ....D
S. DAK.—Aberdeen
Foster, W. H. C
TENN.—Chattanooga
Southern Sadd. Co. ....A
TENN.—Knoxville
Karnes, J. Howard C
TENN.—Memphis
Bruce & Co., W. S. .....A
Hart Mfg. Co. ....B
Smith Sadd. Co., J. T. ...F
TENN.—Nashville
Buford Bros. ....A
Montgomery, Moore & Co..B
Nashville Sadd. Co. (Riding Bridles) ....AA
Tenn. Harness Co. ....D
TEXAS—Dallas
Dodson Sadd. Co., E. C. ..D
Schoelkopf, G. H. ....A
Tenison Bros. Sadd. Co....A
TEXAS—Ft. Worth
James & Sons, T. R. .....B
Kellner-Durrett Sadd. Co..C
UTAH—Salt Lake City
Salt Lake Sadd. Co. .....D
VA.—Richmond
Cottrell Sadd. Co. ....E
Crump & Co., Benj. T.....D
WASH.—Seattle
Seattle Harness & Sadd. Co. D
W. VA.—Moundsville
Bardall & Co., J. C. (Web Halters) ....B

W. VA.—Parkersburg
Woodward Mfg. Co. .....D
WIS.—La Crosse
Medary Sadd. Co., J. S....C
WIS.—Madison
Madison Sadd. Co. ....D
WIS.—Milwaukee
Dyer Sadd. Co. C
Gem Hammock & Fly Net Co. (Rope Halters) ....A
Wallace, Smith & Co. ...A
Young Sadd. Co., Benj...B

SADDLES

See also Saddlery

CONN.—Bridgeport
Bridgeport Gun Implement Co. (Bicycle) ....AA
CONN.—E. Hampton
Climax Mfg. Co. (Spring Wire) ....G
CONN.—Hartford
Jewell Pad Co. (Express Gig) ....AAA
CONN.—New Haven
Goodrich & Co., J. F. (Riding Side) ....AA
ILL.—Chicago
Barber Mfg. Co., A. C. 104 Lake (Bicycle) C
Beckley-Ralston Co., 161 Lake (Bicycle) C
Bunker Saddle & Specialty Co. (Bicycle) ....F
Haussmann & Dunn (Bicycle) C
Illinois Malleable Iron Co. (Pipe) ....AAAA
Kiper & Sons, L. Congress & Peoria (Bicycle) ...AA
Plew, James E. (Bicycle).B
Sturgis & Burn Mfg. Co. (Bicycle) ....A
Western Leather Mfg. Co., 75 Wabash (Bicycle) ..D
ILL.—Freeport
Stover Mfg. Co. (Saddle).. AA
ILL.—Quincy
Schott Saddlery Co. (Gig; Riding) ....AAA
IND.—Indianapolis
Holliday & Wyon Co. (Cart; Coupe; Express; Gig)..A
IND.—Kokomo
Ulrich Mfg. Co. (Lace; Strap) ....E
IND.—Laporte
Lonn & Sons Co., J. (Bicycle) ....A
IND.—South Bend
Studebaker Bros. Mfg. Co. (Coupe; Express; Gig; Track) ....AAAA
IOWA—Des Moines
Des Moines Saddlery Co. (Riding Side) ....A
KY.—Louisville
Harbison & Gathright (Riding) ....AA
MASS.—Springfield
Brown, Henry A. (Bicycle) X
MASS.—Westboro
Hunt Leather Goods Co. (Bicycle) ....B
MICH.—Buchanan
Zinc Collar Pad Co. (Bicycle) ....D
MICH.—Detroit
Wheeler Mfg. Co. (Bicycle) D
MO.—St. Louis
Meyer, Bannermann & Co. (Express; Gig; Riding; Side) ....AAA
Straus Saddlery Co., Jacob (Express; Gig; Riding).A
N. H.—Nashua
Nashua Saddlery Hdw. Co. (Express; Gig) ....B
N. J.—Newark
Meisselbach & Bro., A. F. (Bicycle) C
Newark Cycle Specialty Co. (Bicycle) X
Peters Harness Saddlery Co. (Cart; Coupe; Express; Gig; Hard Rubber Gig; Mexican; Side; Track)..C

SADDLES (*Con.*)

Rubber & Celluloid Harness Trimming Co. (Coupe; Express; Gig) ....AA
Sargent Mfg. Co. (Hard Rubber Gig) ....A
Smith Bros. (Express; Riding) ....F

N. Y.—Buffalo
Scamber & Sons, S. (Express) ....F

New York City
Abercrombie & Fitch, 314 B'way (Pack) C
Cole & Co., G. W., 141 B'way (Bicycle) ......D
Luqueer Co., R. S. (Riding) ....B
Mesinger Bicycle Saddle Co., 1318 Av. A. (Bicycle) X
Smith, Worthington & Co. (Riding) ....B

N. Y.—Rochester
Sager Gear Co. (Bicycle)..X

N. Y.—Syracuse
Frazer & Jones Co. (Express; Gig) ....AA

OHIO—Canton
Gilliam Mfg. Co. (Coupe; Express; Gig; Strap Bicycle) ....A

OHIO—Cincinnati
Graf, Morsebach & Co. (Riding Side) ....AA
Perkins-Campbell Co. (Riding) ....AA

OHIO—Cleveland
Federal Mfg. Co. (Bicycle) ....AAAA

OHIO—Dayton
Dayton Malleable Iron Co. (Malleable Iron Car Roof for Running Board)..AAA

OHIO—Elyria
Topliff & Ely Co. (Bicycle) ....D

OHIO—New Berlin
Hoover, W. H. (Cart; Coupe; Express; Gig; Riding; Strap; Track).....A

OHIO—Sabina
Tener Mfg. Co., J. B. (Express) ....F

OHIO—Springfield
Kirkpatrick Saddle Co. (Bicycle) X

OHIO—Toledo
Harris Toy Co. (Bicycle)..B

OHIO—Wooster
Standard Coach Pad Co. Cart; Coupe; Express; Gig) C

PA.—Erie
Reed Mfg. Co. (Pipe)....A

PA.—Philadelphia
Berger Bros. & Co., 231 Arch (Extension) .....A
Rosenblatt & Co., H. M., 22nd & Oxford (Bicycle) ....A

PA.—Pittsburg
Best Mfg. Co. (Pipe) ..AA
Kelly & Jones Co., 135 Water (Pipe) ....AA

PA.—Quakertown
Harley, J. S. (Gig) ...AA

R. I.—Bristol
Dixon Lubricating Saddle Co. ....B

TENN.—Nashville
Nashville Saddlery Co. (Express; Riding) ...AA

SAFEGUARDS: SHAFT

ILL.—Chicago
Allis-Chalmers Co....AAAA

PA.—Wilkesbarre
Vulcan Iron Wks. ...AAAA

SAFES

See also Vaults; Furniture

CONN.—Waterbury
Scovill Mfg. Co. (Match).. AAAA

ILL.—Chicago
Chicago Scale Co., 292 Jack-

SAFES (*Con.*)

son (Fire; Burglar Proof) ....A
National Recording Safe Co., 197 Wabash Av....E

MO.—Kansas City
Kansas City Furniture Co., 9th & Walnut (Fire; Burglar Proof; Screw, Round Door Bank) C

N. Y.—Brooklyn
New York Stamping Co. (Match) ....A

N. Y.—Buffalo
Shepard & Co., Sidney (Match) ....AAAA

New York City
Herring-Hall-Marvin Safe Co., 400 B'way (Fire; Burglar Proof) ....B
Howard & Morse, 45 Fulton (Provisions) .....D
Peck, Stow & Wilcox Co., 27 Murray (Match)...... AAAA
Remington & Sherman Co., 23 Park Place (Fire; Burglar Proof) ......AA
Russell & Erwin Mfg. Co., 43 Chambers (Match) .... AAAA
Sargent & Co., 151 Leonard (Match) ....AAAA

OHIO—Canton
Diebold Safe & Lock Co. (Fire; Burglar Proof) ....AAA

OHIO—Cincinnati
Halls' Safe Co., Spring Grove Av. (Fire; Burglar Proof; Bank; Patent Screw Door; Vault) ..A
Littleford Bros., 453 E. Pearl (Receiving) ....B
Victor Safe & Lock Co., 9th & B'way (Fire; Burglar Proof) ....A

OHIO—Cleveland
National Safe & Lock Co., Craw Av. & C. & P. R. R. (Fire; Burglar Proof)...A

OHIO—Hamilton
Mosler Safe Co. (Fire; Burglar Proof) ....AAAA

OHIO—Ravenna
Williams, A. C. (Match)..A

PA.—Pittsburg
Barnes Safe & Lock Co., 325 3rd Av. (Fire; Burglar Proof) X

PA.—Reading
Reading Hdw. Co. (Match) AAAA

SAFFRON

New York City
Lehn & Fink (Valencia)... AAA
Schieffelin & Co. (Spanish) AA

SAGO

New York City
Androvette, E. E., 250 Front ....D
Archibald & Lewis, 193 Front C
Fuerst Bros. & Co., 2 Stone ....D
Pulsford, A. J., 97 Water.F

SAILS

CAL.—San Francisco
Ames & Harris (Inc.) ...A
Braun & Prior C
Doyle, J. J. C
Henrix. C. C

ILL.—Chicago
Carpenter & Co., Geo. B. (Yacht) ....AA
Channon & Co., H., Market & Randolph ....AA

LA.—New Orleans
Gerdes & Bro., A. X

MAINE—Bangor
Currier & Hook ....F

MAINE—Portland
Fowler, J. & J. ....E
Lincoln & Allen ....D

MAINE—Thomaston

SAILS (Con.)
Dunn & Elliott Co. .....B
MD.—Baltimore
Hooper & Co. ....B
Mitchell & Co., Z. ......E
Nicholson & Son, Jas. A..C
Sisco Bros. C
Stevenson & McGee (Yacht)
.......F
MASS.—Boston
Cousens & Pratt (Yacht).F
Lamprell & Marble ......F
Matthews & Co., Geo. ...C
Wilson & Silsby (Yacht)..C
MASS.—Fall River
Gifford, John B. (Yacht).E
McClellan, Chas. P. (Yacht)
.......F
MASS.—Gloucester
Rowe & Son, E. L. .....D
MASS.—Newburyport
Davis, Benj. G. ....A
MICH.—Detroit
Goss & Co., J. C. (Yacht).C
MO.—St. Joseph
Kloss Mfg. Co. C
MO.—St. Louis
Zittlosen Mfg. Co. ......B
New York City
De Grauw, Aymar & Co.
(Canoe) ....AA
Harrison, John (Yacht)...D
Hemmenway & Son, S.
(Yacht; Canoe) C
Holly & Son, N. (Canoe)..F
Hopkins & Co., John C...C
Hutchings Bros. ....B
Magee & Son, M. C
Sawyers & Sons, John M..C
Shaw Co. C
Wilson & Griffin (Yacht).D
N. Y.—Port Jefferson
Wilson, F. M. (Yacht)....F
N. Y.—Rochester
Bickford Bros. C
Field Co., James ....B
OHIO—Cincinnati
Ryling & Son, John C
OHIO—Cleveland
Upson-Walton Co. (Yacht;
Canoe) ....A
OHIO—Toledo
Hettick Bros. Co........A
Wilson Co., M. I. ....A
OREGON—Portland
Noon-Bay Co., W. C. ...B
R. I.—Providence
Pease Co., L. F. (Yacht)..E
WIS.—Milwaukee
Jays Bros. & Co. ....B

SALACIN
New York City
Boehringer & Soehne, C. F.
......A

SALAMANDO-RITE
New York City
Johns-Manville Co., H. W.,
100 William (a new fire-
proof paneling for interior
decorative work)...AAAA

SAL-AMMONIAC
N. Y.—Brooklyn
Wiarda & Co., Jno. C....AA
N. Y.—Buffalo
Schoelkoff, Hartford & Han-
na ....AAA
New York City
Fuerst Bros. & Co. ......D
Graselli Chemical Co.
.........AAAA
Klipstein & Co., A. ....AA
Phair, R. W. ....F
Roessler & Hasslacher
Chemical Co. ....AA
PA.—Philadelphia
Jordan, W. H. & F., Jr., 127
N. Water ....AA

SALASEE
New York City
Weeks & Bro., Chas. R.,
542 W. 14th ....Σ

SAL-EMIXUM
New York City
Church & Dwight Co..AAAA
General Chem. Co. ...AAAA
Jones Chem. Co., Enos F..B

SALERATUS
See Soda

SALINO-METERS
MASS.—Boston
Amer. Steam Gauge & Valve
Mfg. Co. ....A
New York City
Ashcroft Mfg. Co. ....A

SALMON
See Canned Goods; Fish

SALT
For Celery Salt see Con-
diments

CAL.—Haywards
Haywards Lumber Co. ...A
CAL.—San Diego
Western Salt Co. ....A
CAL.—San Francisco
Amalgamated Salt Co.,
Mills Bldg. ....B
Continental Salt & Chemical
Co., Mills Bldg. ....B
Dairymen's Union of Calif.,
124 Davis ....A
Federal Salt Co., Mills
Bldg. ....A
Getz Bros. & Co., 111 Cali-
fornia ....AAAA
Kittle & Co., 202 Califor-
nia ....AAA
Rhodes Salt & Borax Co.,
Mills Bldg. ....B
DEL.—Wilmington
Philips-Thompson Co.
(Mfrs.' Agts.) ....B
ILL.—Bement
Camp, J. M. ....B
ILL.—Bloomington
Eardice, J. M............B
Parker Bros. ....A
ILL.—Cairo
Halliday, W. B. (Est.)..
AAAA
ILL.—Chicago
International Salt Co., Pier
No. 1 ....AA
Kingman Salt Mining Co.,
35 S. Water ....A
Moulton & Co., F. D., 169
Jackson Boul. ....A
United Salt Co., 84 Adams
AAA
ILL.—Quincy
Williamson, H. A. ....A
ILL.—St. John
Ill. Central Coal & Salt Co.
A
KANS.—Hutchinson
Hutchinson Kansas Salt Co.
AA
Morton Salt Co. ....A
Union Ice & Salt Co. ...B
KANS.—Kingman
Easley Salt Co. C
Kingman Salt Mining Co.
A
KANS.—Sterling
Sterling Salt Co. ....B
KY.—Louisville
Jefferson & Co., 101 W.
Main ....A
Speed & Co., J. B. ...AAA
LA.—New Orleans
Jackson & Kilpatrick ..AAA
Manson Bros., 111 Tchoup
AA
Myles Salt Co., 100 Com-
mon ....AAA
LA.—Weeks Island
Myles Salt Co. ......AAA
MAINE—Bath
Houghton Bros. ....A
MAINE—Portland
Bearce & Co., S. F., 118

878

SALT (Con.)

Coml. C
Norton-Chapman Co. .....B
MD.—Baltimore
Bonday & Co., Jas. Jr.,
304 Mcht. Bk. Bldg....A
Kerr Bros. & Co., 303 Exch.
Place ....AAA
MASS.—Boston
Eastern Salt Co., 186 State
B
Lyon, Dupuy & Co., Carle-
ton Wharf ....AA
MASS.—Gloucester
Perkins & Son, Geo. ......A
Pew & Son, J. ....AAA
MICH.—Algonac
Walton Salt Association
(Ltd.) ....B
MICH.—Bay City
Eddy Bros. & Co ......AAAA
Michigan Salt Assn. .....A
North American Chemical
Co. ....AAAA
Peters, Wm. ....AAAA
Rouse, W. B. C
Woodworth & Co., F. F. ..C
MICH.—Buttersville
Butters Salt & Lumber Co.
A
MICH.—Delray
Delray Salt Co. ....A
MICH.—Detroit
Brownlee & Co. ....A
Detroit Salt Co., Butler
Bldg. ....B
Hiawatha Salt Co., Campau
Bldg. ....B
Peninsular Salt Co., Ham-
mond Bldg. ....B
River Rouge Salt Co., Mof-
fat Bldg. C
Walton Salt Assn. (Ltd.),
Hammond Bldg. ......B
MICH.—Ecorse
Tecumseh Salt Co. ....A
MICH.—Filer City
Filer & Sons ....AAAA
MICH.—Manistee
Canfield Salt & Lumber Co.
AA
Union Lumber & Salt Co...C
MICH.—Marine City
Crystal Lake Salt Co. ...C
MICH.—Menominee
Carpenter, Cook & Co....
AAAA
MICH.—Port Huron
Port Huron Salt Co. .....B
MICH.—River Rouge
Brownlee & Co. ....A
Salliate & Furgason .....A
MICH.—Saginaw
Bliss, A. T. ....AA
Bliss & Van Aukin ..AAAA
Brand & Hardin ....B
Central Lumber Co. ......A
Eddy & Sons, C. K....AAA
Hardin Co., D. C
Merrill & Co., C. ....AAAA
Merrill, Ring & Co. ....AA
Mershon, Schuette, Parker
& Co. ....AAA
Michigan Salt Assn. ......A
Saginaw Lumber & Salt Co.
AA
MICH.—St. Clair
Diamond Crystal Salt Co..B
Thompson Bros. ....B
MICH.—Trenton
Kelly, W. N. ....B
MICH.—West Bay City
Kern Mfg. Co. C
North Amer. Chemical Co.
C
MO.—Boonville
Meierhoffer, C. C
MO.—St. Louis
Bevis Rock Salt Co., 421
Olive ....B
Ewing Salt Co., J. F., Cham.
of Commerce ....B
Haase & Sons, A. C. L., 415
N. 2nd ....A
NEV.—White Plains
Crystal Salt Co. C
N. Y.—Albany
Wooster, S. C. ....B
N. Y.—Alfred
Reynolds, C. D. ....A
N. Y.—Brooklyn
Bursch, F. J. W., 431
Hamilton ....B

SALT (Con.)

Hoag, Werner & Co., 2
Taylor C
N. Y.—Buffalo
Baker & Co., H. H., 18
Terrace ....B
Iroquois Salt Co., Pruden-
tial Bldg. C
N. Y.—Ithaca
National Salt Co. ...AAAA
N. Y.—Le Roy
Empire State Salt Co......B
N. Y.—Livonia Station
Retsof Mining Co. ...AAAA
New York City
Ferris & Co., E., 185. Wash-
ington ....B
Genesee Salt Co., 6 Harrison
A
Hansen & Dieckmann, 368
Washington ....AA
Mattlage & Sons, C. F., 335
Greenwich ....AAA
OHIO—Cincinnati
Creasey's Sons, W. D. ...C
OHIO—Cleveland
Cleveland Salt Co., 2nd &
Central Av ....B
Colonial Salt Co., 480 Arcade
A
Union Elevator Co., 197
Merwin ....B
OHIO—Columbus
Mich. Salt Assn., Clinton
Bldg. ....A
OHIO—Pomeroy
Coal Ridge Salt Co. C
OHIO—Wadsworth
Ohio Salt Co. ....A
Wadsworth Salt Co. .....B
PA.—Allegheny
Beck & Co., J. A. ....A
PA.—Altoona
Hauser & Son, C. ......B
PA.—Lancaster
Weill, H. ....B
PA.—Natrona
Pa. Salt Mfg. Co. ...AAAA
PA.—Parkersburg
Walter, B. ....B
PA.—Philadelphia
Kerr Bros. & Co., Alex., 516
N. Del. Av. ....AAA
Pa. Salt Mfg. Co., 332 S.
Del. Av. ....AAAA
Somers, H. S., 40 N. Del-
Av. ....B
PA.—Pittsburg
Pa. Salt Mfg. Co., 223
Water ....AAAA
PA.—Scranton
Retsof Mining Co., Common-
wealth Bldg. .....AAAA
R. I.—Providence
Andrews & Son, S. D....B
Reliance Mill Co. ....AA
Sweet, J. H. & J. B....C
TENN.—Memphis
Speed & Co., J. K........B
TEXAS—Colorado
Colorado Salt Co. ....D
Lone Star Salt Co. ....A
TEXAS—Galveston
Parr & Co., W. ....A
TEXAS—Grand Saline
Fielder Salt Co. ....B
Grand Saline Salt Wks...A
Lone Star Salt Co........A
UTAH—Salt Lake City
Inland Crystal Salt Co.
(Impts.) ....B
W. VA.—Hartford
Hartford City Salt Co....C
W. VA.—Malden
Dickinson & Co., J. Q....AA
WIS.—Green Bay
Hurlbut, Frederick ......B
WIS.—Manitowoc
Manitowoc Land & Salt Co.
B
WIS.—Milwaukee
Ludington Salt Co., Wells
Bldg. ....B
WIS.—Stevens Point
Copps, E. M. ....A
WIS.—Watertown
Gorden Co., W. C

SALTERS;
STOCK

IOWA—Lone Tree

SALTPETRE

ILL.—Chicago
Chicago Hydraulic Press
Brick Co. ....B
MD.—Baltimore
McCormick & Co. ....D
Sonneborn Sons, L., 801 S.
Wolfe (Refined) C
New York City
Archibald & Lewis, 193
Front C
Baker & Bro., H. J., 100
William ....AA
Battelle & Renwick, 163
Front ....AAAA
Croton Chem. Co., 20 Cedar
A
Jones Chemical Co., Enos F.,
51 Jay C
Knowles Bros. Co., 181
Pearl (Crystal; Granu-
lated; Pulverized) .....D
OHIO—Newark
Styron. Beggs & Co......A
PA.—Philadelphia
Jordan, W. H. & F., Jr., 127
N. Water (Refined) ..AA

SALTS

CAL.—San Francisco
Selby Smelting & Lead Co.
(Copper) ....AAA
COLO.—Denver
Western Chem. Mfg. Co.
(Lime; Medicinal; So-
dium)) ....AA
DEL.—Wilmington
Atlantic Dynamite Co.
(Ammonia) ....AAA
D. C.—Washington
Neely Electric Construction
Supply Co. (Soldering)..X
ILL.—Aurora
Jobbins, Wm. F. (Glaubers)
A
ILL.—Chicago
Crescent Co., 134 Van
Buren (Soldering) ....F
Grant Hygienic Baking Pow-
der Co., 25 S. Desplaines
(Sodium) ....B
Hutchinson & Son, W. H.
(Inc.) (Magnesium; Med-
icinal; Sodium) ....A
Kester Electric Mfg. Co.,
251 S. Jefferson (Solder;
Self-Fluxing; Drop or
Stick) ....D
Liquid Carbon Acid Mfg.
Co. (Mineral Water).....
AAAA
MD.—Baltimore
Davison & Co., Wm. (Medi-
cinal; Potassium) C
Schultz & Co., 1016 E. Bal-
to, (Fluid Soldering) ..A
Sharp & Dohme (Medicinal)
AAA
Sonneborn's Sons, L., 801 S.
Wolfe (Glaubers) C
Thomsen Chemical Co.
(Glaubers; Epsom) ....B
MASS.—Boston
Ashley & Co., T. C., 145
Milk (Soldering) X
Billings, Clapp & Co. (Am-
monia; Ammonium; Anti-
mony; Copper; Iron;
Lead; Lime; Magnesium;
Manganese; Lithium; So-
dium; Zinc; Platinum; Po-
tassium) ....B
Cochrane Chemical Co., 640
Carr (Glaubers) .....AA
MASS.—Chelsea
Hecla Compressed Gas Co.
(Barium; Magnesium;
Zinc) ....E
MASS.—New Bedford
Davis Chem Wks., Henry
V. (Potassium) ....F
MICH.—Detroit
Acme White Lead & Color
Wks. (Lime) ......AAA
Michigan Ammonia Wks.
(Ammonia) ....A
Michigan Carbon Wks. (Am-
monia; Lime) .. ..AAAA

SALTS (Con.)
Parke, Davis & Co.
(Medicinal) ....AAAA
Seely Mfg. Co. (Mineral
Water; Smelling) C
Thompson & Co., F. A. (Hy-
drastine; Barberine) ..B
MO.—St. Louis
Chisholm & Co., A., 2472
Madison (Fluid Soldering)
F
Herf & Frerichs Chem. Co.
(Mercury; Strontium;
Platinum) ....A
Larkin & Scheffer Chem.
Co. (Potassium) ....A
Mallinckrodt Chem. Wks.
(Ammonia; Ammonium;
Antimony; Barium; Bis-
muth; Cadium; Calcium;
Iron; Lead; Lime; Lith-
ium; Manganese; Mer-
cury; Strontium; Silver;
Zinc; Platinum; Potass-
ium) ....AAAA
Pope Chemical Co., Wm. C.
(Effervescent) ....D
N. J.—Newark
Butterworth & Judson Co.
Copper; Iron; Tin) ....B
Hanson & Van Winkle Co.
(Nickel) ....AA
Listers Agr. Chem. Works
(Ammonia) ....AAAA
Schneider, Emil, 541 Riv-
erside Av. (Soldering)..E
N. Y.—Binghamton
Bayless & Berkalew (Lime)
AA
N. Y.—Brooklyn
Columbia Chem. Wks.
(Ammonia) ....B
Wiarda & Co., John C.
(Ammonia; Antimony;
Barium; Calsium;
Chrome; Cobalt; Copper;
Iron; Lead; Lime; Nickel;
Manganese; Silver; So-
dium; Tin; Zinc; Potass-
ium) ....AA
N. Y.—Buffalo
Larkin Soap Mfg. Co.
(Smelling) ....AAAA
N. Y.—Hudson
Benson, A. R. (Smelling).F
New York City
Baker & Bro., H. J.
(Potassium) ....AA
Battelle & Renwick
(Potassium) ....AA
Berlin Aniline Wks., 213
Water (Aniline) ....B
Boehringer & Sons, C. F.
(Quinine) ....A
Callahan & Co., Geo., 218
Front (Fluid Soldering).F
Chaskel Chem. Wks. (Inc.)
(Medicinal) X
Church & Dwight Co.
(Sodium) ....AAAA
Cooper & Co., Chas. (Am-
monium; Antimony; Cad-
mium; Calcium; Ethyl;
Copper; Iron; Lead; Mag-
nesium; Nickel. Medicin-
al; Silver; Sodium; Tin;
Platinum; Potassium) AA
De Ronde & Co., Abraham
(Antimony; Copper; Iron;
Lead; Sodium; Tin; Zinc)
A
Durkee & Co., E. R.
(Potassium) ....AA
Feuchtwanger & Co., L.
(Barium; Copper; Lime;
Manganese; Mercury;
Nickel; Silver; Sodium;
Potassium) ....B
General Chemical Co., 25
Broad (Solutions); Solder-
ing; Ammonia; Antimony;
Copper; Iron; Lime; Medi-
cinal; Sodium; Tin; Zinc)
AAAA
Heller, Hirsh & Co. (Double
Manure) ....AA
Jones Chem. Wks., E. F.
(Lime; Potassium) ....B
Klipstein & Co., A.
(Chrome) ....AA
McKesson & Robbins (Am-
monia; Lead; Magnesium;
Medicinal; Quinine; Po-

SALTS (Con.)
tassium) ....AAAA
Manhattan Electrical Supply
Co., 38 Cortlandt (Solder-
ing) ....AA
Matheson & Co., Wm. J.
(Ltd.) (Sodium) ......A
N. Y. Quinine & Chem.
Wks. (Ltd.) (Iron; So-
dium; Quinine; Potass-
ium) ....A
Pfizer & Co., Chas. (Mer-
cury; Medicinal) .AAAA
Reade Mfg. Co. 542 W.
22nd (Fluid Soldering) .X
Ricksecker Co.. Theo.
(Smelling; Medicinal)..C
Roessler & Hasslacker
Chem. Co. (Sodium; Qui-
nine; Potassium) ....AA
Salmon & Co.. H. H.
(Double Manure) ....AA
Schieffelin & Co., W. H.
(Medicinal; Potassium;
Quinine) ....AA
Schultze Co., A. H., 198
W. B'way (Mineral Wa-
ter) X
Sholes Co., C. E.
(Glaubers) X
U. S. Electro-Chemical Co.,
80 Elm (Electro-Plating)
F
Williamson & Co., D. D.
(Lime; Sodium) ....B
Wing & Evans (Sodium)..
AAA
Zucker, Levett & Loeb Co.
(Potassium) ....A
N. Y.—Rochester
Standard Electric Construc-
tion Co., 14 N. Water
(Paste; Soldering) .....F
N. Y.—Syracuse
Solvey Process Co. (Cal-
cium; Sodium) ...AAAA
OHIO—Butler
Hubbs Mfg. Co. (Soldering
Paste) ....G
OHIO—Cincinnati
American Chemical Co.
(Glaubers) C
OHIO—Cleveland
Grasselli Chemical Co., 184
Arcade (Soldering; Am-
monium; Copper; Iron;
Medicinal; Sodium; Zinc)
AAAA
Lennox Chemical Co.
(Epsom) ....B
Paragon Insulating Co.,
Erie R. R., near Forest
(Soldering) X
OHIO—Dayton
Sachs-Pruden Ginger Ale
Co. (Mineral Water) ..D
OHIO—Hamilton
Meyers Mfg. Co., Fred. J.
(Shaker) ....B
OHIO—Newark
Stryon-Beggs Co. (Head-
ache) ....A
PA.—Ambler
Keasby & Mattison Co.
(Magnesium; Medicinal)..
AAAA
PA.—Connellsville
Highland Electro-Chem.
Mfg. Co. (Insulating; Sol-
dering; Paste) X
PA.—Easton
Baker & Adamson Chemical
Co. (Ammonium; Barium;
Bismuth; Cadmium; Cal-
cium; Chrome; Cobalt;
Copper; Iron; Lead; Mag-
nesium; Manganese; Mer-
cury; Nickel; Silver; So-
dium; Tin; Zinc; Potass-
ium) ....A
PA.—Erie
Watson Co., H. F. (Ammo-
nium) ....AAA
PA.—Philadelphia
Ammonia Co. of Phila.
(Tin; Potassium) ......A
Drueding Bros. Co. (Mag-
nesium; Medicinal) ..AA
Hance Bros. & White
(Magnesium) ....AA
Husband, Thos. J., Jr.
(Magnesium) ....B
Kalion Chem. Co. (Sodium;

SALTS (Con.)
Potassium) ....AA
Penna. Salt Mfg. Co. (Cop-
per; Iron; Manganese;
Medicinal; Sodium; Zinc)
AAAA
Phila. Quartz Co. (Sodium)
AA
Philips & Jacob (Silver)..A
Powers - Weightman - Ros-
engarten Co. (Ammonia;
Ammonium; Antimony;
Barium; Calcium; Copper;
Ethyl; Glaubers; Iron;
Lead; Lithium; Magne-
sium; Mercury; Manga-
nese; Medicinal; Silver
Sodium; Tin; Zinc; Po-
tassium; Bismuth; Qui-
nine) ....AAAA
Savage, Mahlon L. (Medi-
cinal; Sodium) ....E
Twitchell C. S. (Ammo-
niuh) ....A
Vail Bros. (Medicinal) ...C
UTAH—Salt Lake City
Western Drug & Mfg. Co.
(Effervescent) ....E

SALVE

MINN.—Minneapolis
Chemical Mfg. Co. (Animal)
X
OHIO—Tiffin
Flack, J. J. (Corn) ......B
TEXAS—Dallas
Patton-Worsham Drug Co.
(Eye) ....A
WIS.—Berlin
Hawley. C. D. (Corn) ...D
WIS.—Black River Falls
Cole & Co., J. W. (Carbolic)
B

SAMPLERS: GRAIN

New York City
Kohlbusch, Herman ......B
Russell & Erwin Mfg. Co.
AAAA

SAND

DEL.—Wilmington
Warner Co., Chas. (Silica)
AA
ILL.—Chicago
Garden City Sand Co., 188
Madison (Moulding or
Foundry; Silica; also
White; Standard for Ce-
ment Testing) ....A
Lake Shore Sand Co., 138
Washington (Moulding;
Foundry) ....B
Preston & Co., D. H., 4 W.
Harrison (Moulding;
Foundry) ....B
U. S. Silica Co., The Rook-
ery (Silica) ....B
ILL.—Ottawa
Ottawa Silica Co. (Foundry;
Glass) ....B
IND.—Terre Haute
American Asbestos Co.
(Asbestos) ....D
KY.—Newport
Newport Sand Bank Co.
(Moulding; Foundry)...X
MASS.—Boston
Presbrey Stove Lining Co.
(Fire) ....B
Waldo Bros., 102 Milk
(Moulding; Foundry)AAA
N. J.—Bridgeton
Crystal Sand Co. (Glass-
makers') ....B
Vineland Glass Sand Co.
(Glassmakers') ....G
N. J.—Jersey City
Gautier & Co., J. H. (Fire)
AA
N. J.—So. Vineland
Bidwell, R. O. (Glass-
makers') ....E
N. Y.—Brooklyn
New York Sand & Facing
Co. (Moulding; Foundry).
D
Wiarda & Co., John C.
(Glassmakers') ......AA

SAND (Con.)

New York City
Maurer & Son, Henry, 420 E. 23rd (Fire) ......AA
Whitehead Bros. Co., 537 W. 27th (Moulding; Foundry) ....AA
N. Y.—Troy
Ostrander Fire Brick Co. (Fire) ....A
N. Y.—Waterford
Evers, Jno. (Moulding; Foundry) ....E
OHIO—Cincinnati
Obermeyer Co., S., 647 Evans (Moulding; Foundry; Fire) ....AA
Tygart Fire Brick Co., 406 Burns (Fire) C
OHIO—Cleveland
Shepard, J. J., 35 River (Fire) ....A
Smith Foundry Supply Co., J. D., 40 S. Water (Moulding; Foundry; Fire) ....D
Standard Sand & Mach. Co., 1434 Superior (Moulding; Foundry) C
OHIO—Conneaut
Gordon, F. E. (Moulding; Foundry) ....D
PA.—Danville
Keystone Moulding Sand Co. (Moulding; Foundry) ....A
PA.—Philadelphia
Haedrick, E. M., Mariner & Merchants' Bldg. (Moulding; Foundry; Silica; Fire) X
Paxson Co., J. W., 1021 N. Del. Av. (Moulding; Foundry; Fire) ....AA
PA.—Pittsburg
Harbison-Walker Refractories Co., Farmers' Bk. Bldg. (Fire) .....AAAA
Pa. Glass Sand Co., 341 4th Av. (Glassmakers'; White Rock Silica) ....AAA
PA.—Reading
Temple Sand Co. (Silica).D
PA.—Valley Forge
Bean, Francis M. (Silica for Furnaces, etc.).....H

SANDERS

MD.—Baltimore
Economy Locomotive Sander Co., 15 S. Charles (Locomotive) X
MASS.—Boston
Austin & Eddy, 117 Broad (Moulding) C
MO.—St. Louis
Western Railway Equipment Co., Union Trust Bldg. (Mudd; Pneumatic; Locomotive; Track) ....A
New York City
Reilly Bros. (Painters')..D
OHIO—Cincinnati
Powell Co., Wm., 2529 Spring Grove Av. (Locomotive) ....A

SANDSTONE

COLO.—Denver
American Granite & Sandstone Co. X
N. H.—Pike
Pike Mfg. Co. ....A
OHIO—Toledo
Toledo Stone & Glass Sand Co. X
PA.—Ridgway
Ridgway Sandstone Co....B

SANTONIN

MASS.—Boston
Billings, Clapp & Co.....B
MO.—St. Louis
Larkin & Scheffer Chemical Co. ....A
Mallinckrodt Chem. Wks...AAAA
New York City
N. Y. Quinine & Chemical Wks. (Ltd.) ....A

SAPPERS

MICH.—Kalamazoo
Hill & Co., W. E. (Shingle) ....D
N. Y.—Lockport
Trevor Mfg. Co. (Shingle).B
VT.—Montpelier
Lane Mfg. Co. (Shingle)..A
WIS.—Eau Claire
Phoenix Mfg. Co. (Shingle) ....A
WIS.—Milwaukee
Filer & Stowell Co. (Ltd.) (Shingle) ....AAA

SAPPHIRES

See Jewelry

SARDINES

See Canned Goods; Fish

SARSA-PARILLA

CONN.—Seymour
Arethusa Spring Water Co. ....AA
MAINE—Bangor
Warren, Ara X
MASS.—Lowell
Ayer Co., J. C. (Medicinal) ....AA
Hood & Co., Chas. J. .....B
New York City
Lanman & Kemp .....AAA
Riker & Son Co., Wm. B. ....AA
Seelys' Son, G. B. ....B
Tutt Mfg. Co., Dr........B

SASH

See also Woodwork

ILL.—Chicago
Chicago Metallic Sash Wks., 21 Mohawk (Metallic)..D
Knisley Bros., 28th & 5th Av. (Metallic Window).A
Miller & Bro., Jas. A., 129 S. Clinton (Metallic Window) ....A
MASS.—Boston
Badger & Sons Co., E., 63 Pitt (Metallic Window) ....B
Hicks & Sons, S. D., 9 Bowker (Metallic Window) ....A
Smith-Warren Co., 93 Federal (Metallic Window) ....D
N. J.—Newark
Tabor Sash Co., 69 Polk (Reversible Window)...D
N. Y.—Irvington
Lord & Burnham Co. (Hot Bed) ....A
New York City
Hayes & Co., Geo., 71 8th Av. (Metallic Window).B
WIS.—Milwaukee
Biersach & Niedermeyer Co. (Metallic Window) ....B

SATCHELS

See also Leather Goods

ILL.—Chicago
Fitzgerald Trunk Co......A
Haskell Bros. ....A
Wilt, Chas. F. ....B
N. J.—Harrison
Headley & Farmer Co.....A
N. J.—Newark
Cailly Co., P. ....D
Goldsmith & Son, L. ...AA
Hager & Co. ....H
Peddie & Co., T. B......AA
New York City
Breidenback, Philip .....D
Hahn & Co., A. ....B
Lissa & Co., Henry ......B
McHugh, John F. C
Scheuer & Bro............X
PA.—Philadelphia
Rumpp & Sons, C. F...AAA

SATCHELS (Con.)

VA.—Petersburg
Seward Trunk & Bag Co.. AA
WIS.—Milwaukee
Abel & Bach Co. ....AA
WIS.—Racine
Secor Trunk Co., M. M....A

SATEENS

See Cotton Goods

SATIN

See Silk

SATINETS

See Woolen Goods

SAUCERS

See Chinaware; Glassware;
Earthenware

New York City
Cordley & Hayes (Flower
Pot) ....A

SAUCES

See also Condiments

COLO.—Denver
Kuner Pickle Co. (Table) A
ILL.—Chicago
Henning Co., Wilhelm, 113
E. North Av. ....A
IOWA—Keokuk
Keokuk Pickle Co. (Pepper,
Table) ....B
KY.—Paducah
Paducah Vinegar Wks.
(Pepper) ....D
MO.—St. Louis
Bayle, Geo. A. (Table) ...B
N. Y.—Buffalo
Erie Preserving Co. (Apple) AAA
New York City
Alart & McGuire, 68 Madison ....AA
Burnham Co., E. S., 61 Gansevoort ....A
Cohen & Co., Wm. H.
(Table) X
Durkee & Co., E. R. (Table) AA
Falcon Packing Co. (Pepper) B
Gordon & Dilworth, 561
Greenwich (Table) .....A
Gulden, Chas. (Fish, Table) AA
Hazard & Co., E. C. (Pepper,
Table) ....AA
OHIO—Cincinnati
Snider Preserve Co., T. A. A
Weller Co., J. (Table) ....A
PA.—Meadville
Soyer Sauce Co. (Table) ..F
PA.—Philadelphia
Phila. Pickling Co. (Table) C
Ritter Conserve Co., Philip
J. ....A
PA.—Pittsburg
Heinz Co., H. J. (Table) AAAA
VT.—Brattleboro
Brattleboro Jelly Co.
(Apple) ....D
W. VA.—Wheeling
McMechan & Son Co., Geo.
K. ....B

SAUERKRAUT

See Cider; Vinegar; &c.

SAUSAGE

See Meat Packer

SAVERS

OHIO—Salem
Clark Co., W. J. (Galvanized Steel, Oil) ......A

SAWS

ALA.—Birmingham
Birmingham Saw Wks. ..H
ALA.—Huntsville
Huntsville Fdy. & Mach.
Wks. (Nolan & Jones,
Prop.) (Swing) ....B
CAL.—San Francisco
California Saw Wks., 208
Mission ....A
Pacific Saw Mfg. Co., 110
Beale (Cross-Cut; Hand;
Pit; Wood; Circular; Mill;
Mulay; Shingle; Butchers;
Pruning) X
Simonds Saw Co., 33 Market
C
CONN.—Ansonia
Farrell Fdry. & Mach. Co.
(Diamond) ....AAAA
CONN.—Branchville
Branchville Ice Tool. Wks.
(G. G. Grunnan, Prop.) . F
CONN.—Bridgeport
Bridgeport Hdw. Mfg. Co.,
481 Iranistan Av. (Hack;
Compass; Coping; Fret;
Jig) ....B
CONN.—Bristol
Penfield Saw Wks. C
CONN.—Hartford
Pratt & Whitney Co. (Metal
Slitting) ....AAAA
CONN.—New Haven
Barnes Tool Co. (Band; Circular) ....B
Thompson's Son Co., Henry
G. (Band; Hack; Hack
Power; Kitchen) ......B
West Haven Mfg. Co.
(Hack; Hack Power
Plumbers') ....B
CONN.—Norwich
Roegers & Co., C. B. (Swing
Cut-off; Cut-off; Re-Sawing; Gang Rip; Self Feeding Rip; Scroll) ..AAAA
CONN.—Pine Meadow
Chapin-Stephens Co. (Turning) ....A
CONN.—South Norwalk
Le Count, Wm. G. (Metal
Top Slitting) ....D
CONN.—Waterbury
Waterbury Farrell Fdry. &
Mach. Co. (Tube) .....AA
Waterbury Machine Co.
(Wire Scarfing) ......B
DEL.—Wilmington
Trump Bros. Mach. Co.
(Scroll) ....A
GA.—Atlanta
De Loach Mill Mfg. Co.
(Drag) ....B
Southern Saw Wks. (Band;
Circular; Concave; Gang;
Inserted Tooth Circular;
Shingle) ....B
ILL.—Batavia
Appleton Mfg. Co. (Circular)
A
U. S. Wind Engine & Pump
Co. (Swing; Swing Cutoff; Circular) ....AA
ILL.—Chicago
Allis-Chalmers Co., Home
Ins. Bldg. (Band; Circular) ....AAAA
Born Packers Supply Co., H.
A. (Butchers) ....P
Curtis & Co., Mfg. Co., 42 S.
Canal (Band; Circular;
Cross-Cut; Drag; Gang;
Insulated Circular) C
Goes & Co., Oscar, 18 So.
Canal ....D
Greenlie Bros. & Co. (Self
Feeding Rip) ....AA
Hiles & Co., C., 336 Carroll
Av. C
Perrin & Co., W. R.
(Butchers) ....A
ILL.—Freeport
Arcade Mfg. Co. (Hack;
Hack Power) ....A
Hoefer Mfg. Co. (Hack Power) C
Stover Mfg. Co. (Wood) AA
ILL.—Marseilles
Marseilles Mfg. Co. (Wood)
A

ILL.—Rockford

Barnes Co., W. F. & John
(Foot Power Circular;
Hand Rip; Scroll; Ama-
teur Scroll; Dehorning)
..............................AAA

ILL.—Rock Island

Donaldson Bros. (Band; Circular; Gang; Segment) C

ILL.—Sandwich

Sandwich Mfg. Co. (Wood)
..............................AA

IND.—Indianapolis

Atkins & Co., E. C., 402 So.
Illinois (All Kinds)AAAA

Barry Saw Co., 228 So. Penn
(All Kinds) C

Chandler & Taylor Co.
(Swing; Swing Cut-off;
Mulay) ....AA

Rockwood Mfg. Co., 1801
English Av. (Bolting;
Swing Cut-off) ....A

Sinker-Davis Co. (Cut-off;
Iron Frame Ripping) ..B

IND.—Lawrenceburg

Bishop & Co., G. H. (Band;
Circular; Hand; Butcher;
Kitchen; Compass; De-
horning; Ice; Pruning;
Wood; Ice; Veneer) ....A

IND.—New Albany

New Albany Mfg. Co.
(Stone; Slate Gang) ...C

MAINE—Bangor

Schwartz Sons, M. ....D

Union Iron Wks. (Swing) A

MD.—Baltimore

Toland & Son, Front & Low
(Band) C

MASS.—Arlington

Wood & Co., W. T. (Ice) A

MASS.—Athol

Athol Machine Co. (Hack)B

Starrett Co., L. S. (Hack;
Metal; Slotting) ....A

MASS.—Boston

Hawkins Mfg. Co., 591 At-
lantic Av. (Jig) ......H

Marston & Co., J. M. (Foot
Power Band; Foot Power
Circular; Grooving) ...D

Woods Machine Co., S. A.
(Foot Power Circular;
Self Feeding Rip; Band)
..............................AA

MASS.—Fitchburg

Fitchburg File Wks. (Band;
Hack) ....D

Putnam Mach. Co. (Pattern
Makers Dimension) ...A

Simonds Mfg. Co. (All
Kinds) ....AAA

MASS.—Greenfield

Goodell-Pratt Co. (Hack;
Butchers; Kitchen; Circu-
lar) ....B

MASS.—Millers Falls

Millers Falls Co. (Butchers;
Jewelers) ....AA

MASS.—Natick

Ambler Saw Mfg. Co.
(Band) ....F

Hall Co., Frank H. X

MASS.—New Bedford

Morse Twist Drill & Mach.
Co. (Metal Slitting) AAA

MASS.—Taunton

Stranges Mach. Wks. (Cir-
cular) ....E

MASS.—Worcester

Cunningham, E. E., 23
Hudson (Band) ....H

Kidder, R. E. (Circular) ..E

Luther & Co., B. G., 91 Foster ....E

Wright Wire Co. (Power
Hack) ....AA

MICH.—Bay City

Garland Co., M. (Bolting;
Cut-off) C

Industrial Works (Rail) AA

Ward, Wm. ....F

MICH.—Grand Rapids

Butterworth & Lowe (Band,
Cut-off) ....A

Porter, C. O. & A. D.
(Swing) C

Edge & Co., Frank (Band;
Scroll) ....E

Porter, C. O. & A. D.
(Swing) C

MICH.—Manistee

Batty, Wm. (Circular) ....F

Broadhead, Jos. X

MICH.—Muskegon

Barcus Bros. (Circular) ..C

MICH.—Port Huron

Port Huron Saw Co. (Ltd.)
(Band; Circular for Metal;
Concave; Cross-Cut; Drag;
Gang; Grooving; Ice; Jig;
Metal Slitting; Scroll;
Swing) C

MICH.—Saginaw

Mershon & Co., Wm. B. (Re-
Sawing) ....A

Michigan Saw Co. (Ice) ...B

Wickes Bros. (Swing; Swing
Cut-off; Circular) ..AAA

MINN.—Minneapolis

Howell & Co., R. R. (Swing,
Cut-off) ....B

MO.—St. Louis

Branch Saw Co., 817 N. 2nd
(Cross-Cut Turning) ..B

Brecht Butchers Supply Co.,
G. V., 1201 Cass Av.
(Butchers) ....AAA

N. H.—Dover

White Co., Jno. A. (Swing)C

N. J.—Hasbrouck Heights

Olmstead, L. H. (Hack
Power) ....B

N. J.—Newark

Bernz, Otto, So. 13th cor.
Orange Av. (Hack; Plumb-
ers') ....B

Hastings & Co., Arthur J.,
Railroad Pl. ....B

National Saw Co., 15 River
(All Kinds) ....B

Seymour & Whitlock, 43
Lawrence (Swing) .....B

N. J.—Paterson

Royle & Sons (Inc.) Jno.
Straight & Essex (Jig for
Metal Mortising) ......A

N. J.—Smithville

Smith Mach. Co., H. B.
(Swing; Swing Cut-off;
Self Feeding Rip; Scroll)A

N. Y.—Albany

Decker, E. F. ....D

N. Y.—Brooklyn

Mack & Winkle, 172 Skill-
man Av. ....F

Oldham & Sons, Joshua, 26th
& 3rd Av. (Band; Circu-
lar; Concave; Grooving;
Ice; Mill) ....D

N. Y.—Buffalo

Buffalo Scale Co. (Butchers)
..............................AA

Diamond Saw & Stamping
Co. (Hack; Hack Power;
Butcher; Kitchen) .....D

Frank Mchry. Co. (Swing;
Swing Cut-off; Scroll)..C

Holmes Mchry. Co., E. & B.
(Swing; Swing Cut-off;
Bolting; Foot Power Cir-
cular; Segment; Gang
Rip; Self Feeding Rip;
Variable Feed Rip; Box
Board Cut-off) ....B

Robertson Mfg. Co. (Hack)E

N. Y.—Elmira

Elmira Saw & Mach. Wks. X

N. Y.—Lockport

Cocker, Wm. ....D

Trevor Mfg. Co. (Shingle) B

N. Y.—Long Island City

Meyers, W. F. (Circular;
Stone; Diamond) ......E

N. Y.—Malone

Hinds, Thos. (Stone; Slate
Gang) ....D

N. Y.—Middletown

Clemsen Bros. (Band; Cir-
cular; Cross-Cut; Hand;
Ice) ....AAAA

New York City

Amer. Woodworking Mach.
Co., 136 Liberty (Blind
Slat; Swing; Bolting;
Splitting; Swing Cut-off;
Circular; Grooving; In-
serted Tooth Circular; Seg-
ment; Self Feeding Rip;
Gang Rip; Scroll; Box
Board Cut-off; Edging)
..............................AAAA

Chatillon Sons, John, 85

SAWS (Con.)

Cliff (Butcher; Kitchen) A
Etna Mfg. Co., 253 Bway.
  (Hack; Slitting) X
Fairbanks Co., 416 Broome
  (Hack; Hack Power)
  ....AAAA
Hammacher, Schlemmer &
  Co., 4th Av. near 13th
  (Bands) ....AAA
Hoe & Co., R., 504 Grand
  Band; Circular; Drag;
  Gang; Grooving; Ice; Pit;
  Inserted Tooth Circular;
  Mill; Mulay; Shingle;
  Veneering; Printers') ..
  ....AAAA
Jennings & Co., C. E., 42
  Murray (All Kinds) ....B
Miller's Falls Co., 28 War-
  ren (Hack Power; Scroll;
  Kitchen; Butchers'; De-
  horning; Jewelers') ..AA
Moss & Graham, Centre &
  Grand (Band; Circular). F
Reichhelm & Co., E. P.
  (Jewelers) ....A
Slotkin & Praglin, 210 Ca-
  nal (Circular) ....B
Stone-Working Mach. Co.,
  41 Wall (Stone; Slate
  Gang) ....F
Tower & Lyon (Compass;
  Hack) ....B
N. Y.—Rochester
Huther Bros., 229 Mill
  (Band; Circular for Metal;
  Concave) ....B
N. Y.—Seneca Falls
Seneca Falls Mfg. Co.
  (Foot Power Circular; Cir-
  cular; Scroll; Amateur
  Scroll) ....B
OHIO—Canton
Canton Saw Co. (Band; Cir-
  cular; Concave; Drag;
  Gang) C
Knight Mfg. Co. (Swing). B
OHIO—Cincinnati
Cordesman Mach. Co.
  (Swing Scroll) X
Cordesman, Meyers & Co.
  (Scroll) ....B
Fay, J. A. & Egan Co., Cor.
  Front & John (Blind Slat;
  Swing; Swing Cut-off;
  Cut-off; Bevel; Mitre Rip-
  ping; Double Revolving
  Ripping; Iron Frame Rip-
  ping; Self Feeding Rip;
  Scroll; Band) ....AAA
Greaves, Klusman & Co.,
  Cor. Cook & Alfred
  (Swing; Band; Scroll; Cut-
  off) ....B
Lane & Bodley Co., Cor. John
  & Water (Swing) ......B
Rowe & Trunell, 123 W. 2d
  (Circular) ....E
OHIO—Cleveland
Gerlach & Co., Peter, 28 Col-
  umbus (Band; Circular;
  Ice; Mill) ....A
Strong, Carlisle & Ham-
  mond Co. (Power Hack) A
OHIO—Columbus
Buckeye Saw Mfg. Co. (Cir-
  cular; Gang; Mill) .....D
Ohlen & Sons Saw Mfg. Co.,
  J., Buttles Av. ....A
OHIO—Dayton
Patterson Tool & Supply Co.
  (Power Hack) ....A
Siebler, Geo., E. (Circular)
  ....H
OHIO—Defiance
Defiance Machine Wks.
  (Bolting; Self Feeding;
  Rip) ....A
OHIO—Leetonia
Crescent Mach. Co. (Power;
  Foot Band) ....D
OHIO—Salem
Silver Mfg. Co. (Band) AA
OHIO—Toledo
Toledo Saw Co., Water Cor.
  Monroe (Circular) C
PA.—Allentown
Grammes & Sons, L. F. (Cut-
  off) ....A
PA.—Bangor
Flory Mfg. Co., S. (Stone;
  Slate Gang) ....A

SAWS (Con.)

PA.—Beaver Falls
Champion Saw & Gas Engine
  Co. (Circular; Concave;
  Gang; Grooving) X
Emerson, Smith & Co., Ltd.
  (Band; Circular; Concave;
  Drag; Gang; Scroll; Cross
  Cut; Mitre Box; Concave
  Circular; Grooving; Insert-
  ed Tooth Circular; Edger;
  Mill; Mulay; Re-Sawing;
  Shingle; Slate) ....A
PA.—Bradford
Standard Saw Co. (Band;
  Cut-off; Circular; Groov-
  ing; Segment; Veneering)
  ....A
PA.—Eddystone
Tindel-Morris Co. (Inserted
  Tooth for Cold Cutting)
  ....AA
PA.—Eldred
Prouty & Co., C. (Cross Cut)
  ....B
PA.—Erie
Standard Saw Mill Mchry.
  Co. (Swing; Cut-off) ...B
Stearns Mfg. Co. (Cut-off) B
PA.—Kane
United Saw Mfg. Co. ....D
PA.—Philadelphia
Atlantic Wks. (Inc.), 23d &
  Arch (Blind; Slat; Swing)
  ....B
Disston & Sons (Inc.), Henry
  (All Kinds) ....AAAA
Espen-Lucas Machine Wks.,
  Broad & Noble (Bar Cold;
  Metal Cutting; Rail) ...D
Kennedy, Ralph M., 111 N.
  7th (Band; Circular) ...X
McNiece & Son, Wm., 515
  Cherry (Imptd. Band; Cir-
  cular) C
Nicholls, Harry, 212 Pine. F
Nittinger, August (Butch-
  ers) ....A
Phila. Roll & Machine Co.,
  2d & Wash. Av. (Hot
  Metal) ....A
Power & Co., L. (Re-Saw-
  ing; Gang; Rip.) ....A
PA.—So. Bethlehem
Bethlehem Fdy. & Machine
  Co. (Band) C
PA.—Williamsport
Andrews & Sons, E. (Solid;
  Inserted Brick; Circular;
  Hand) ....D
Foucart, J. E. (Circular;
  Gang) ....D
U. S. Machine Co. (Iron
  Frame; Swing) ....D
PA.—York
Farquhar Co. (Ltd.), A. B.
  (Swing) ....AAA
R. I.—Providence
Brown & Sharpe Mfg. Co.
  (Metal Slitting) ...AAAA
Thurston Mfg. Co. (Jewel-
  ers; Metal Slitting) C
TENN.—Chattanooga
Chattanooga Saw Wks.
  (Solid Tooth Circular) ..D
Wheland Machine Wks.
  (Swing) ....A
TENN.—Jackson
Southern Engine & Boiler
  Wks. (Swing; Cut-off;
  Swing Cut-off) ....AA
VT.—Bennington
Scott, Olin (Stone) ......A
VT.—Montpelier
Lane Mfg. Co. (Bolting;
  Swing Cut-off; Cut-off;
  Drag) ....A
VT.—Rutland
Lincoln Iron Wks. (Circular,
  for Soft Stone; Stone;
  Slate Gang) ....D
WASH.—Seattle
Fox Saw Wks. (Inc.), J. E.
 C
WIS.—Beloit
Berlin Machine Wks. (Cut-
  off; Self-Feeding Rip.)
  ....AAAA
WIS.—Evansville
Baker Mfg. Co. (Wood), AA
WIS.—Milwaukee
Filer & Stowell Co. (Swing;

885

SAWS (*Con.*)
Cut-off; Band; Circular)
........................AAA
WIS.—Oshkosh
Hayes Mach. Co., E. B.
(Blind Slat) ....B
WIS.—Racine
Freeman & Sons Mfg. Co.,
S. (Wood) ....A
WIS.—Wausau
Murray Mfg. Co., D. J.
(Swing) ....A

SCABBARDS

Dobson-Fisher-Brockman Co.
(Leather Rifle); ......AA
MO.—St. Joseph
Wyeth Hdw. & Mfg. Co.
(Carbine) ....AAA
MO.—St. Louis
Brauer Bros. Mfg. Co. ....E
Straus Saddlery Co., Jacob
D. (Hinge) ....A
New York City
Spalding, A. G. & Bros.,
Inc. (Knife) ......AAA
OHIO—Cleveland
Standard Welding Co.
(Sword) ....AA
TEXAS—El Paso
Jackson-Hughes Co. ......B

SCAFFOLDS

New York City
Chesebro, Whitman & Co.,
1167 1st Av. ....B
McCabe Hanger Mfg. Co.,
532 W. 22d ....A
New York Ladder Co., 580
Hudson (Builders') ....E
Reilley Bros., 322 W. 41st
(Painters') ....D

SCALDERS

IND.—Goshen
Kelly Fdy. & Machine Co.
(Hog) ....A
MD.—Baltimore
Sinclair-Scott Co. (Tomato)
........................E
N. Y.—Baldwinsville
Fancher Machine Co. (Toma-
to) ....G
N. J.—Bridgeton
Cox Bros. (Tomato) ......D
PA.—Bausman
Bausman, D. H. (Hog) ...C

SCALERS

New York City
Chatillons, John Sons, 85
Cliff (Fish) ....A
Dickinson, John (Est. of),
64 Nassau (Steel) ......A
Fairbanks Co., 416 Broome
(Fish) ....AAAA
OHIO—Ravenna
Williams, A. C. (Fish)....A
PA.—Reading
Reading Hdw. Co. (Fish)
....................AAAA
PA.—Wrightsville
Wrightsville Hdw. Co.
(Fish) ....B

SCALES

**See also Beams
Balances**

CAL.—San Francisco
Beck & Co., E. B., 122
Market ....F
COLO.—Denver
Ainsworth & Sons. Wm.
(Precision; Weights;
Chemists; Druggists)...B
CONN.—Guilford
Spencer's Sons, I. S. (Coun-
ter; Family; Heavy; Can-
dy; Grocers; Spring)....A
CONN.—Hartford
Pratt & Whitney Co.
(Grain) Automatic; Ele-
vator) ....AAAA
CONN.—New Britain
Landers, Frary & Clark
(Letter; Balances; Coun-
ter; Family; Candy; Gro-

SCALES (*Con.*)
cers; Fish; Spring) ..AAA
CONN.—Saugatuck
Computing Scale Co. (Com-
puting) ....A
ILL.—Chicago
American Cutlery Co.
(Family; Heavy) ....AA
Borden & Sellick Co. .....B
Chicago Computing Scale
Co, 237 5th Av........E
Chicago Scale Co., 292 W.
Jackson Boul. (All Kinds)
........................A
Fairbanks Morse & Co. (Au-
tomatic; Counter; Gold;
Silver; Market) ...AAAA
Pelouze Scale & Mfg. Co.,
182 W. Jack. Boul. (Con-
sulting; Counter; Grocers;
Family; Hopper; Ice;
Postal; Letter; Balances;
Market) C
Streeter-Amet. Weighing &
Recording Co., 140 Dear-
born (Automatic) ......B
Union Scale & Mfg. Co. (Au-
tomatic; Coffee; Cereal,
etc.).................D
ILL.—Moline
Moline Pump Co. (Platform
or Wagon) ....A
Moline Scale Co. (Platform
or Wagon) ....B
ILL.—Peoria
Selby, Starr & Co. (Grain) X
ILL.—Peru
Brunner, Chas. (Hopper;
Stock; Platform or Wag-
on; Track) ....A
ILL.—Waukegan
Chicago Recording Scale Co.
........................C
IND.—Anderson
Anderson Computing Scale
Co. (Computing) ......A
IND.—Elkhart
Stimpson Computing Scale
Co. ....A
IND.—Indianapolis
Nordyke & Marmon Co.
(Grain Testing; Heavy;
Platform or Wagon)
........................AAA
IND.—Terre Haute
U. S. Scale Co. (Stock; Wag-
on) ....B
IOWA—Council Bluffs
Kimball Bros. Co. (Platform
or Wagon) ....A
IOWA—Des Moines
Beckman Bros. (Platform or
Wagon; Track) ....B
IOWA—Lone Tree
Monarch Grubber Co. (Plat-
form or Wagon) ....B
KANS.—Kansas City
Strait Mfg. Co., H. N.
(Platform or Wagon). AA
MD.—Baltimore
Marden, Jesse (Est. of)
(Fine; Heavy)..........X
MASS.—Arlington
Wood & Co..Wm. T. (Ice) A
MASS.—Athol
Starrett Co., L. S. (Drafts-
mens; Graduated) ......A
MASS.—Boston
Cutter Tower Co. (Letter;
Balances) ....B
MASS.—Lowell
Knowles Scale Wks. (Heavy;
Light; Counter; Plat-
form) ....D
Lowell Scale Co. (Platform
or Wagon; Counter;
Dairy; Platform) ......D
Pneumatic Scale Corporation
........................X
MICH.—Battle Creek
Advance Thresher Co.
(Grain; Automatic) AAAA
Nichols & Shepard Co.
(Grain) ....AAAA
MICH.—Detroit
Standard Computing Scale
Co. (Computing) ......D
Stimpson Co., W. F., 24 An-
tietian (Computing) ...A
MICH.—Grand Rapids
Grand Rapids Scale Wks.
(Platform or Wagon)...C
Hartman & Co., F. (Plat-

SCALES (Con.)
form; Wagon) ....D
MICH.—Kalamazoo
Michigan Scale Co.........C
MO.—Kansas City
Kansas City Hay Press Co.
(Hopper; Platform or
Wagon; Track) ......AA
MO.—Pleasant Hill
McDonald Bros. (Wagon;
Stock) ....,.......B
MO.—St. Louis
Pope, J. William (Auto-
matic for Package)...AA
N. J.—Jersey City
Automatic Weighing Mach.
Co. (Auto. Weighing for
Packages) ....B
Snead & Co., Iron Wks.
(Hopper) ....A
N. J.—Newark
Meyer Scale & Hdw. Co., 15
Canfield (Platform or
Wagon) X
Willmore Computing Scale
Co. (Computing) X
N. Y.—Albany
Fairbanks Co. ......AAAA
N. Y.—Binghamton
Jones of Binghamton (Inc.)
A
Osgood Scale Co. (All Kinds)
B
N. Y.—Buffalo
Buffalo Scale Co. (All
Kinds) ....AA
Holmes Machinery Co., E.
& B. (Knife Balancing) B
Weeks Scale Wks. (Plat-
form) C
N. Y.—Cohoes
Sweet & Doyle (Yarn) C
N. Y.—New Rochelle
Becker Christian (Precision;
Weights; Chemists'; Drug-
gists; Gold; Silver) ....D
New York City
Automatic Scale Co., 16 Park
Row (Auto. Rice, Cereal,
etc.) X
Becker, Christian (Precision;
Weights; Chemists';
gists'; Gold; Silver) ....D
Century Machine Co., 576 W.
Bway. (Light) X
Chatillon & Sons, John (All
Kinds) ....A
Hunt Co., C. W., 45 Bway.
(Hopper; Platform or
Wagon, for Railways;
Boiler Rooms; Track), AA
Hurd & Co., 576 W. Bway.
(Postal) ....D
International Silver Co., 9
Maiden Lane (Postal)
AAAA
Keuffel & Esser Co., 127
Fulton (Computing;
Draftsmens'; Graduated)
AA
Kohlbusch, Herman, 194
Bway. (All Kinds) ....B
McCoy Co., Jos. F., 157
Chambers (Suspension) ..B
Maris & Co., John M., 219
Fulton (Light) ....B
Mead Mfg. Co., Jno. A., 11
Bway. (Hopper; Track)
AA
Page, Dennis & Co. (Auto-
matic; Heavy; Counter) B
Peck, Stow & Wilcox Co., 27
Murray (Counter; Grocers)
AAAA
Pneumatic Scale Corp (Auto-
matic for Packages) X
Richardson Scale Co., 15
Park Row (Hopper) ....D
Union Computing Machine
Co., 1 Union Sq. West
(Computing) ....B
N. Y.—Niagara Falls
Canning & Co., A. H. (Auto.
for Package Goods) X
N. Y.—Palmyra
Allen, J. ....,...E
N. Y.—Palmer
Cochran, B. S.............H
N. Y.—Troy
Kundson Scale Wks. ......E
Micrometer Balance Scale
Co. ....D

SCALES (Con.)
OHIO—Cincinnati
Cinn. Scale Mfg. Co., 212
Walnut (Grain Testing;
Hopper; Platform or Wag-
on; Track) C
Tatum Co., Saml. C., 414 W.
Water (Postal) ....B
OHIO—Columbus
Case Mfg. Co. (Automatic;
Grain; Automatic) .....A
OHIO—Dayton
Computing Scale Co. ......A
OHIO—Toledo
Toledo Computing Scale Co.
(Computing) ....A
PA.—Beaver Falls
Keystone Store Service Co.
D
PA.—Erie
Reed Mfg. Co. **(Computing)**
A
PA.—Philadelphia
Alteneder & Sons, Theo.
(Boxwood) ....D
North Bros. Mfg. Co.
(Family) ....AA
Olsen & Co., Tinuis, 500 N.
12th (Heavy) ....A
Troemner, Henry (Chemists;
Druggists; Counter; Dia-
mond; Gold; Silver)
AAA
PA.—Pittsburg
Standard Scale & Supply Co.,
211 Wood (All Kinds) ..B
PA.—Reading
Reading Hdw. Co. (Counter;
Grocers) ....AAAA
PA.—Waynesboro
Geiser Mfg. Co. (Grain;
Grain Automatic; Heavy)
AAAA
PA.—Wrightsville
Wrightsville Hdw. Co.
(Fish) ....B
R. I.—Providence
Browne & Sharpe Mfg. Co.
(Sample Weighing-Letter;
Balances; Draftsmen's;
Graduated; Yarn) ..AAAA
TENN.—Chattanooga
Arithmetical Scale Co. (Com-
puting) ....,.........B
VT.—Rutland
Howe Scale Co. (Grain Test-
ing; Hopper; Platform or
Wagon; Track; Letter;
Balances; Counter) AAAA
VT.—St. Johnsbury
Fairbanks & Co., E. & T.
(Grain Testing; Hopper;
Platform or Wagon)
AAAA
VA.—Richmond
Randolph Paper Box Co.
(Prescription; Pocket), A
WIS.—Beloit
Gaston's Sons Co., N. B.
(Platform or Wagon) ...C

SCALPERS

ILL.—Moline
Bernard & Leas Mfg. Co.
AA
IND.—Indianapolis
Nordyke & Marmon Co..AAA
KANS.—Enterprise
Ehrsam & Sons' Mfg. Co.,
J. B. ....B
KANS.—Leavenworth
Great Western Mfg. Co.
(Elevators) ....AA
MINN.—Minneapolis
Willford Mfg. Co. C
N. Y.—Buffalo
Nore Mfg. Co., John T.
(Elevator) X
OHIO—Columbus
Case Mfg. Co. ....A

SCARFS; PIANO

See Neckties for Scarfs

New York City
Tonk & Bro., Wm. (Inc.),
452 10th Av. (Piano)....C

SCISSORS

See also Shears

SCISSORS (Con.)

CONN.—Bridgeport
Acme Shear Co. (Pocket)..B
Bridgeport Hdw. Mfg. Co.
 (Button Hole; Kindergarten; Pocket) ....B
Jennings Bros. Mfg. Co.
 (Silver Mounted) .....AA
CONN.—Bristol
Clayton Bros. ....D
CONN.—New Haven
Schollhorn Co., Wm. (Barbers'; Buttonhole; Embroidery; Manicure; Pocket) ....A
CONN.—Wallingford
Wallace Sons' Mfg. Co., R.
 (Buttonhole; Embroidery;
 Folding; Ladies'; Manicure; Pocket) .....AAAA
MASS.—Mansfield
Spaulding, D. S. (Silver
 Mounted) ....B
MASS.—North Attleboro
Codding & Heilborn Co.
 (Silver Mounted) ......A
N. J.—Newark
Heinisch's Sons Co., R.
 (Pocket) ....A
Wiss & Sons, J. (Barbers';
 Buttonhole; Pocket) ..A
New York City
Gorham Mfg. Co., B'way &
 19th (Silver Mounted)
 ....AAAA
Wiebusch & Hilger (Ltd.)
 (Bent; Buttonhole; Embroidery; Pocket) ......A
OHIO—Fremont
Clauss Shear Co. ......AAA
International Cutlery Co.
 ....AAA
PA.—Mount Pleasant
Mt. Pleasant Tool Co. (Pocket) ....D
PA.—Philadelphia
National Cutlery Co., 3d &
 Lehigh Av. (Pocket)...C
PA.—Titusville
Schatt & Morgan Cutlery
 Co. (Buttonhole) ......B
R. I.—Providence
Bens Co., Wm. (Silver
 Mounted) C
Foster & Bro. Co., Theo. W.
 (Silver) ....AA

SCONCES.

CONN.—Meriden
Bradley & Hubbard Mfg. Co.
 (Brass; Bronze) ..AAAA
Meriden Britannia Company
 (Plated) ....AAAA
N. J.—New Brunswick
N. J. Lamp & Bronze Wks.
 (Bronze) ....AA
New York City
Gould Mersereau Co. (Brass)
 ....B
Judd & Co., H. L. (Brass)
 ....AA

SCOOPS

CONN.—Meriden
International Silver Co.
 (Silver Plated Cheese)
 ....AAAA
Meriden Cutlery Company
 (Cheese) ....AA
CONN.—New Britain
Landers, Frary & Clark
 (Cheese) ....AAA
Stanley Rule & Level Co.
 (Veneer) ....AAA
CONN.—New Haven
Harrison, Leonard D. (Aluminum) ....H
CONN.—Pine Meadow
Chapins-Stephens Co. (Veneer) ....A
CONN.—Wallingford
Wallace Sons' Mfg. Co., R.
 (Cheese) ....AAAA
ILL.—Chicago
American Cutlery Company
 (Cheese) ....AA
McMorran & Co., E. E., 15
 N. Clinton ....D
Radecke Mfg. Co., 84 S.
 Clark ....E
Vaughan & Bushnell Mfg.

SCOOPS (Con.)
 Co. (Veneer) ....A
IND.—Elgin
Elgin Mfg. Co. (Gravel)..F
IND.—Montpelier
Jackson Shovel & Tool Co.
 (Coal) ....B
IND.—Vincennes
Star Shovel & Range Co.
 (Coal; Grain) C
MASS.—Kingston
Drew & Co., C. (Veneer).C
MASS.—Shelburne Falls
Lamson & Goodnow Mfg. Co.
 (Cheese) ....A
MASS.—Turner's Falls
Russell Cutlery Co., John
 (Cheese) ....AA
MICH.—Milford
Bissell. E. J. (Potato)...C
MO.—St. Louis
National Enameling &
 Stamping Co., Cass Av.
 & 2d (Coal) ......AAAA
St. Louis Shovel Co. (Grain)
 ....B
St. Louis Stamping Co.
 (Thumb; Grocers'; Coal)
 ....AAAA
N. J.—Hoboken
Woodman, Joel H. (Veneer)
 ....A
N. J.—Newark
Osborne & Co., C. S.
 (Cheese) ....B
Sommers' Son, John (Wood)
 ....A
N. Y.—Brooklyn
Pollard, Jos. G., 141 Raymond (Tunneling) ......F
New York City
Central Stamping Co., 4
 Cliff (Coal; Thumb)..AA
Chatillon Sons', John, 85
 Cliff ....A
Crandall & Godley Co.
 (Grocers') ....AA
Jennings & Co., C. E. (Veneer) ....B
Lalance & Grosjean Mfg. Co.
 (Grocers'; Coal) ..AAAA
Stoutenborough, X., 277
 Pearl (Coal) ....D
OHIO—Canton
Kohler Co., F. E. (Furnace)
C
OHIO—Cleveland
Avery Stamping Co. (Steel;
 Coal; Grain) ....B
Chisholm & Sons, Wm.
 (Steel) ....AAA
Cleveland Lock Co. (Wire
 Fruit; Wire Vegetable)
 ....D
OHIO—Piqua
Wood Shovel & Tool Co.
 (Coke; Furnace) C
PA.—Mt. Pleasant
Mt. Pleasant Tool Co. (Coal;
 Grain) ....D
PA.—Philadelphia
Griffiths Co., George (Steel)
 ....AAAA
Phila. Scoop Co. (Grocers';
 Candy; Grain; Scale)...F
PA.—Pittsburg
Hubbard & Co., Murtland
 Bldg. (Coal) ....AA
Hussey. Binns Shovel Co.,
 541 Wood (Coal; Grain;
 Locomotive) ....A
Pittsburg Shovel Co., Frick
 Bldg. (Coal) ....B
PA.—Wyoming
Wyoming Shovel Works
 (Furnace; Grain) ......A

SCOURERS

ILL.—Moline
Barnard & Leas Mfg. Co.
 Buckwheat; Wheat;
 Rice) ....AA
IND.—Indianapolis
Nordyke & Marmon Co.
 (Buckwheat) ....AAA
MAINE—Portland
Conant Co., R. O. (Corn).F
MASS.—Boston
Riley & Co., C. E. (Wool)
 ....A
United Shoe Machinery Co.
 (Heel) ....AAAA

SCOURERS (Con.)

MASS.—North Adams
Hunter Machine Co., James (Wool) ....A

N. Y.—Buffalo
Squire Mfg. Co., Geo. L. (Rice) ....AAA

N. Y.—Lockport
Richmond Mfg. Co. (Grain) A

N. Y.—Silver Creek
Howes Co., S. (Wheat; Grain) ....A
Huntley Mfg. Co. (Wheat) A

PA.—Muncy
Sprout, Waldron & Co. (Wheat; Grain; Buckwheat) ....A

PA.—Philadelphia
Eavenson & Sons, J. (Wool) A
Link-Belt Engineering Co. (Wheat) ....AA

SCRAPERS

See also Agricultural Implements

CAL.—Benicia
Benicia Agricultural Wks. (Drag; Road) ......AAA

CAL.—Stockton
Holt Mfg. Co. (Drag; Road) AA

CONN.—Bridgeport
Bridgeport Hdw. Mfg. Co. (Wall) ....B
Knapp & Cowles Mfg. Co. (Box; Ship; Sidewalk)..C

CONN.—Georgetown
Gilbert & Bennett Mfg. Co. (Stove) ....AA

CONN.—Meriden
Nickel Plate Mfg. Co. (Kettle) X

CONN.—New Britain
Humason & Beckley Mfg. Co. (Box) ....A
Stanley Rule & Level Co. (Cabinet; Veneer; Box) AAA

CONN.—Pine Meadow
Chapin-Stephens Co. (Ship; Box) ....A

CONN.—Southington
Peck, Stow & Wilcox Co. (Box Foot; Plumbers'; Hog) ....AAAA

CONN.—Westport
Bradley's Sons, G. W. (Box; Plumbers') ....D

GA.—Columbus
Southern Plow Co. (Cotton) AA

ILL.—Aurora
Richards Mfg. Co. (Foot).B
Western Wheeled Scraper Co. (Wheeled Road; Drag) ....AA
Wilcox Mfg. Co. (Steel; Foot) ....B

ILL.—Bradley
Bradley Mfg. Co., David (Drag; Road; Wheeled Road) ....AAA

ILL.—Chicago
Austin Mfg. Co., 315 Dearborn (Drag; Wheel Road) AAA
Fairbanks, Morse & Co., Franklin & Monroe (Drag; Road) ....AAAA
Gould Co. (Drag; Road)...A
National Drill & Mfg. Co. (Pullman Mfg.) (Drag; Wheel) ....B
Pratt Mfg. Co., Wm. E., 91 Lake (Steel Foot)....B
Shaw, Willis, N. Y. Life Bldg. (Drag; Wheeled Road) ....D
Vaughan & Bushnell Mfg. Co. (Ship; Block; Hog) B

ILL.—Decatur
Fairies Mfg. Co. (Boiler Tube; Flue) ....A

ILL.—Downer's Grove
Dicke Tool Co. (Box; Plumbers') C

SCRAPERS (Con.)

ILL.—Freeport
Arcade Mfg. Co. (Foot; Shovel) ....A

ILL.—Galesburg
Stover Mfg. Co. (Foot).AA

ILL.—Galesburg
Colton & Co., G. D. (Broom Corn) ....D

ILL.—Harvey
Austin Mfg. Co., F. C. (Drag; Road; Wheeled Road) ....AA

ILL.—Moline
Moline Plow Co. (Road) AAAA

ILL.—Peoria
Herchell Mfg. Co., R. (Drag; Wheeled Road).A

ILL.—Rock Island
Rock Island Plow Co. (Cotton) ....AA

ILL.—Sterling
Sterling Mfg. Co. (Cornstalk; Shredders) ......A

IND.—Anderson
American Bridge & Scraper Co. (Drag; Wheel Road) D

IND.—Evansville
Blount, Henry F. (Cotton) AAAA

IND.—Fort Wayne
Indiana Road Machine Co. (Drag; Wheel) ....B

IND.—Indianapolis
Adams & Co., J. D. (Drag) C

IND.—Indianapolis
Atkins & Co., E. C. (Box; Cabinet; Bench; Plumber's) ....AAAA

IND.—Logansport
Dorner Truck & Foundry Co. (Track) X

IND.—Montpelier
Jackson Shovel & Tool Co. (Steel Sidewalk) ......B

IOWA—Fort Madison
Iowa Farming Tool Co. (Walk; Street) ....A
Morrison Mfg. Co. (Drag).A

IOWA—Ottumwa
Hardsocg Mfg. Co. (Miners') B

IOWA—Washington
Stewart, Frank (Drag; Road) ....B

KY.—Louisville
Avery & Sons, B. F. (Cotton) ....AAA
Brennan & Co. (Drag) ....A

KY.—Maysville
Hall Plow Co., Jos. H. (Cotton) ....AA

MASS.—Athol
Starrett Co., L. S. (Block; Floor) ....A

MASS.—Boston
Ames Plow Co. (Drag; Road) ....AAAA
Burbank Mfg. Co., 34 High (Box). ....D
Dame, Stoddard & Co. (Plumbers') ....A

MASS.—Cambridge
Barbour-Stockwell Co. (Bakers'; Confectioners'; Track) ....A

MASS.—Chicopee Falls
Belcher & Taylor Agricultural Tool Co. (Road)..A

MASS.—Fitchburg
Simonds Mfg. Co. (Butchers' Block; Cabinet; Bench; Wall) ....AAA

MASS.—Kingston
Drew & Co., C. (Plumbers'; Box) C

MASS.—Winchendon
Whitney, Baxter D. (Box) A

MASS.—Worcester
Wire Goods Co. (Kettle)..A

MICH.—Detroit
Anderson & Sons. W. H. (Drag; Wheeled Road).C

MICH.—Fenton
Phillips Co., A. J. (Snow; Stable; Sidewalk) .....A

MICH.—Jackson
Jackson Flue Scraper Co. (Flue; Drag) C

MICH.—Kalamazoo
Kalamazoo Railway Supply

SCRAPERS (Con.)

Co. (Drag; Wheeled Road)
  B

Root, Fred M. (Track)...D

MICH.—Lansing

Bement's Sons, E. (Drag;
  Road) ....AAA

Lansing Wheel Barrow Co.
  (Drag; Wheel Road).AAA

MICH.—Monroe

Wilder Sons', J. K. (Drag;
  Road) ....B

MICH.—Mount Clemens

Donaldson Bros. (Drag;
  Road) ....A

JH.—Owosso

Castree & Shaw Co. (Steel)
  H

MO.—Kansas City

Smith & Sons Mfg. Co.
  (Drag; Wheel Road)..AA

MO.—St. Louis

Brecht Butchers' Supply
  Co., G. V., 1201 Cass Av.
  (Butchers' Block; Box)
  AAA

Kupferle, John C. (Foot)
  AA

Pleuger & Henger Mfg. Co.
  (Foot) ....A

Whitman Agricultural Co.
  (Road) ....A

N. H.—Concord

Ford & Co., Wm. P. (Drag)
  A

N. J.—Elizabeth

Braunsdorf-Mueller Co.
  (Box Plumbers') .....D

N. J.—Newark

Bernz, Otto, S. 13th, cor.
  S. Orange Av. (Plumbers';
  Box) ....B

Kraeuter & Co., 577 18th
  Av. (Box; Plumbers')'..E

National Saw Co. (Cabinet;
  Block; Box; Wall; Bench)
  B

Osborn & Co., C. S. (Bar-
  rel) ....D

Sayre & Co., L. A. (Box).B

Wiener & Co. (Box) C

N. Y.—Albany

Stephenson Mfg. Co. (Boiler
  Tube) ....D

N. Y.—Buffalo

Case & Son, W. A. (Boiler
  Tube) ....AA

Sherwood Mfg. Co. (Flue;
  Boiler Tube) ....B

White Co., L. & I. J.
  (Ship Deck; Block; Hog)
  A

N. Y.—Cleron

Celeron Steel Co. (Cold
  Pressed Steel; Drag;
  Road) ....D

N. Y.—Coxsackie

Gates, Elias (Sidewalk)...E

N. Y.—Frankfort

Acme Road Machinery Co.
  (Drag; Wheel Road) ...C

N. Y.—Gowanda

Gowanda Agricultural Wks.
  Co. (Drag; Road) .....B

N. Y.—Greenwich

Eddy Plow Co., W. (Drag)
  B

N. Y.—Horseheads

Weller Hdw. & Foundry Co.
  (Cast Foot) ....D

N. Y.—Marathon

Climax Road Machine Co.
  (Drag; Wheel Road)....B

New York City

Chatillon & Sons, John, 85
  Cliff (Butcher Block;
  Hog) ....A

Fiske, J. W. Ironworks
  (Foot) ....A

Jennings Co., C. E., 42 Murray (Bench; Cabinet;
  Wall) ....D

Lidgerwood Mfg. Co., 96
  Liberty (Self-Filling)
  AAA

New York Agricultural Co.,
  51 Cliff (Drag) X

Reilley Bros. (Wall) ....D

Sargeant & Co., 151 Leonard
  (Foot) ....AAAA

Smith & Hemenway Co., 296
  B'way (Hog) ....D

SCRAPERS (Con.)

N. Y.—Rome

Adams & Sons, S. (Drag).C

N. Y.—Schenectady

Dakin, John H. (Broom
  Corn) ....D

Westinghouse Co. (Broom
  Corn) ....A

N. Y.—Syracuse

Smiths & Powell Co. (Foot)
  X

Stearns Co., E. C. (Box;
  Foot) ....AA

Syracuse Chilled Plow Co.
  (Drag; Wheel Road)..AA

OHIO—Akron

Whitman & Barnes Mfg. Co.
  (Drag; Road) ......AAAA

OHIO—Canton

Kohler & Co., F. E. (Flue;
  Sidewalk; Kettle) C

OHIO—Cincinnati

Bishop Co., Geo. H. (Cabinet; Bench) ....A

Haven Co., Jas. L. (Drag;
  Foot) X

Schriver & Co., O. P. (Sidewalk) C

Tatum Co., Samuel C. (Box;
  Cabinet) ....B

OHIO—Cleveland

American Fork & Hoe Co.
  (Walk; Street)....AAAA

Empire Plow Co. (Drag;
  Road) ....A

Lamson & Sessions Co.
  (Stove) ....AA

Osborn Mfg. Co. (Floor)...A

OHIO—Columbus

Kilbourne & Jacobs Mfg.
  Co. (Drag; Road; Ditch-
  ing; Wheeled) ......AA

OHIO—Fremont

Lehr Agricultural Company
  (Drag; Road) ....B

OHIO—Lancaster

Hocking Valley Mfg. Co.
  (Drag) ....A

OHIO—Mansfield

Monarch Stove & Mfg. Co.
  (Track; Street Railway)
  B

OHIO—Plymouth

Root Bros. Co. (Foot)....B

OHIO—Ravenna

Williams, A. C. (Foot)....A

OHIO—Salem

Clarke Co., W. J. (Hog)..B

OHIO—Sidney

American Steel Scraper Co.
  (Drag; Wheeled Road;
  Drag Revolving) ....A

Sidney Steel Scraper Co.
  (Drag; Wheeled Road;
  Ditching; Road) ....B

Slusser-McLean Scraper Co.
  (Drag; Wheeled Road).C

OHIO—Springfield

Ridgely Trimmer Co. (Paper
  Hangers') ....B

PA.—Chester

Black & Co., H. S. (Box)
  AA

PA.—Howard

Howard Iron & Tool Co.
  (Coke Oven) ....B

PA.—Kennett Square

American Road Machine Co.
  (Drag; Wheeled Road)
  AA

Good Roads Machinery Co.
  (Drag; Wheeled Road)..D

PA.—Mechanicsburg

Comstock, Geo. S. (Drag;
  Road) ....D

PA.—Mount Joy

Gray Iron Casting Co. (Ltd.)
  (Foot) ....AAA

PA.—Philadelphia

Bonney Vise & Tool Wks.,
  3015 Chestnut (Wall)...C

Brill Co., J. G. (Track;
  Street Railway) ....AAA

Disston & Sons, Henry
  (Cabinet; Steel; Bench;
  Machinists'; Wall).AAAA

Stortz & Son, Jno., 210 Vine
  (Box; Plumbers'; Burning-
  off; Shop; Painters';
  Wall) ....F

PA.—Pittsburg

Lippert, E. T. (Wall)....X

SCRAPERS (Con.)

PA.—Reading
Reading Hdw. Co. (Foot)
AAAA

PA.—Scottdale
Kenney & Co. (Coke Oven)
A

PA. —South Bethlehem
Bethlehem Fdy. & Machine
Co. (Foot; Road) C

PA.—Washington
Petroleum Iron Works Co.
(Pipe Line) ....B

PA.—Williamsport
Darling Pump & Mfg. Co.
(Boiler Tube) ....B

R. I.—Providence
Nicholson File Co. (Machinists') ....AAA

W. VA.—Wheeling
Wheeling Hinge Co. (Stove)
AA

WIS.—Beloit
Thompson & Sons' Mfg. Co.,
J. (Drag; Road) ......AA

WIS.—Manitowoc
Smalley Mfg. Co. (Road) ..B

SCREENINGS

OHIO—Youngstown
Bessemer Limestone Co.
(Stone) ....A

PA.—Harrisburg
Walton Quarries (Stone) ..E

PA.—Philadelphia
Shanley Co., B. M. & J. F.,
14 S. Broad (Stone) ....F

PA.—Pittsburg
Blair & Co., Reed F., Frick
Bldg. (Limestone) C
Winfield Sand Co., 421
Wood (Stone) ....B

SCREENS

**See also Furniture also
Cloth; Wire**

ARK.—Pine Bluff
Bluff City Lumber Co. (Window; Door) ....AAA

CAL.—San Francisco
Calif. Perforating Screen
Co., 147 Beale (Mining;
Sand; Coal; Gravel) ....D
Pacific Tank Co., 35 Beale
(Revolving; Shaking) ..A
Union Iron Works, 222 Market (Revolving; Shaking)
X

COLO.—Denver
Colorado Iron Works Co.
(Mining) ....AA
Davis Iron Works Co., F.
M., 8th & Larimer (Mining) ....AA
Denver Eng. Works Co.
(Mining) ....A
Mine & Smelter Supply Co.,
Blake & 17th (Mining)
AAAA

CONN.—Georgetown
Gilbert & Bennett Mfg. Co.
(Sand; Coal; Gravel) .AAA

CONN.—Meriden
Bradley & Hubbard Mfg.
Co. (Fire) ....AAA

CONN.—Mt. Carmel
Woodruff & Sons, Walter
W. (Dash) ....A

CONN.—New Haven
Hendryx Co., Andrew B.
(Cage; Guards) ....A

CONN.—Southport
Jelliff & Co., C. O. (Coal)
D

DEL.—Wilmington
Pusey & Jones Co. (Pulp
Mill) ....AAA
Walker & Elliott (Rolling)
B

GA.—Atlanta
Atlanta Wire & Iron Works
(Mining; Sand; Coal;
Gravel; Window; Door) .F

ILL.—Aurora
Western Wheeled Scraper
Co. (Revolving; Shaking)
AA

ILL.—Bloomington
Dunlap Mfg. Co. (Clay; Cement) ....D

SCREENS (Con.)

ILL.—Chicago
Atchinson Perforated Metal Co., Robert, 303 Dearborn (Mining; Sand; Coal;
Gravel; Flax) X
Allis-Chalmers Co., Home
Ins. Bldg. (Mining; Revolving; Shaking; Coal;
Iron; Gravel; Sand; Perforated Metal) .....AAAA
Barbee Wire & Iron Works,
44 Dearborn (Sand; Coal;
Gravel; Revolving; Steel;
Window; Wire) ....B
Borden & Selleck Co., 48
Lake (Sand; Coal) .....B
Caldwell & Son Co., H. W.,
Western Av. & 17th (Revolving; Sand; Coal) ..AA
Dodge & Co., H. B., 108
La Salle (Window; Door)
D
Harrington & King Perforating Co., 224 N. Union
(Mining; Revolving; Perforated Metal; Shaking;
Sand; Coal; Gravel; Rice;
Coffee; Grain) ....A
Hoisting & Conveying Machinery Co., 44 N. Elizabeth (Mining; Revolving;
Shaking) ....E
Hubbell & Son, 169 E. 39th
(Window; Door) ......H
Murphy & Co., Christopher,
204 Dearborn (Portable;
Pneumatic; Revolving;
Shaking) ....B
Winslow Bros. Co., 368 Carroll Av. (Iron; Brass;
Bronze; Ornamental Radiator; Fire) ....AA

ILL.—Decatur
Mueller Mfg. Co., H. (Sand)
AAA

ILL.—Geneva
Wheeler Screen Co. (Window; Door) C

ILL.—Harvey
Whiting Foundry Equipment
Co. (Sand) ....AA

ILL.—Kankakee
Sheldon Novelty Co. (Folding) ....A

ILL.—Peoria
Lucas & Sons, A. (Coal Mine
Shaking) ....B

ILL.—Quincy
Menke & Grimm Planing
Mill Co. (Window; Door)
C

ILL.—Rockford
Rockford Screen Co. (Window; Door) ....F

IND.—Goshen
I. X. L. & Goshen Pump Co.
(Extension, &c.; Window;
Door) ....B

IND.—Lafayette
Barbee Wire & Iron Works
(Mining; Fire; Coal) ...B

IND.—Terre Haute
Eagle Iron Works (Shaking, &c.; Mining, &c.; Revolving; Shaking) C
Prox & Brinkman Mfg. Co.
(Mining; Coal; Revolving)
A

IOWA—Clinton
Curtis Bros. & Co. (Door;
Window) ....AAA

IOWA—Des Moines
Carr & Adams Co. (Window; Door) ....B

IOWA—Muscatine
Roach & Musser Sash &
Door Co. (Window; Door)
AAA

IOWA—Ottumwa
Ottumwa Iron Works (Coal;
Elevators) ....B

KANS.—Fort Scott
Fort Scott Foundry & Machine Co. (Ore) ....H

KANS.—Leavenworth
Great Western Mfg. Co.
(Gravel; Rolling) ..AA

KY.—Bowling Green
Hartman Sliding Blind Co.
(Window; Door) ......D

KY.—Louisville
Dow Wire Works Co., 730

SCREENS (Con.)

W. Market (Window; Door) ....D
KY.—Newport
Higgin Mfg. Co. (Window; Door; Metal Frame) ...A
MAINE—Portland
Burrowes Co., E. F. (Window; Doors; also Wire Insect; Fly; Wire Partition) ....AA
MASS.—Boston
Coffin Valve Co. (Copper Wire) ....D
Howes Co., S. M. (Fire Folding) ....B
May & Freeman, 178 Devonshire (Sliding Window; Door) ....E
Steel Cable Engineering Co., 92 State (Revolving) ....B
MASS.—Brookline
American Screen Co. (Window; Metal Frame; Door) D
MASS.—Clinton
Clinton Wire Cloth Co. (Mining; Sand; Coal; Gravel) ....AAA
MASS.—Fitchburg
Union Machine Co. (Pulp Mill) ....B
MASS.—Gardner
Heywood Bros. & Wakefield Co. (Folding; Reed; Rattan) ....AAAA
MASS.—Quincy Hall
Ames Plow Co. (Sand; Coal; Gravel) ....AAAA
MASS.—South Easton
Purinton Co., C. F. (Rolling Window) ....F
MASS.—Springfield
Bigelow-Cheney Wire Wks. (Sand; Coal; Gravel) ...A
MASS.—Worcester
Wright Wire Co. (Sand; Coal; Revolving; White Mortar) ....A
MICH.—Detroit
Acme Fancy Wire Works, Canfield Av. & Moran (Ornamental Radiator) ...D
Barnum Wire & Iron Wks., E. T. (Sand; Gravel; Coal) ....B
Huebner Screen Door Co., Farnsworth Av. & Dequinare (Window; Door) ...C
Michigan Wire Cloth Co., 501 Howard (Mining; Revolving; Shaking; Sand; Coal; Gravel; Window; Door) ....AA
Phoenix Wire Works (Sand; Coal; Gravel) ....D
Vulcan Co. (Bank Counter) F
MICH.—Fenton
Phillips Co., A. J. (Window; Door) ....A
MICH.—Grand Rapids
Fuller & Rice Lumber & Mfg. Co. (Window; Door) AA
Royal Furniture Co. ......A
MICH.—Muskegan
Langeland Mfg. Co. (Window; Door) C
McGraft & Son, N. (Window; Door) ....A
MICH.—Northville
Dubuar Mfg. Co., J. A. (Door; Window) X
MICH.—Owosso
Owosso Mfg. Co. (Window; Door) ....AA
Screen Door & Window Co. (Window; Door) C
MO.—Kansas City
Kansas City Wire & Iron Works (Fly) ....A
Urie Boiler & Machine Co. (Mining) ....B
MO.—St. Louis
Ludlow-Saylor Wire Co. (Coal; Sand; Ore; Radiator) ....AA
South St. Louis Fdy. Co., 7516 S. B'way (Mining) C
Webber Moulding Co., J. R. F

SCREENS (Con.)

Williams Mfg. Co., Milton F. (Clay) ....B
N. H.—Keene
Fish & Co., A. E. (Window; Door) ....E
N. J.—High Bridge
Taylor Iron & Steel Co. (Revolving; Shaking) .AAAA
N. J.—Hoboken
Ferguson Bros. Mfg. Co. (Folding) ....A
N. J.—Jersey City
Krom Machine Wks. (Revolving; Shaking) ......D
Steele & Condict, Pearl & Steuben (Revolving; Shaking) ....B
N. Y.—Bainbridge
American Separator Co. (Cream) ....B
N. Y.—Brooklyn
Hecla Iron Works, N. 11th & Berry (Ornamental Radiator) ....AA
N. Y.—Buffalo
Buffalo Wire Works Co. (Sand; Coal) ....D
Churchyard, Joseph J. (Window) X
Noye Mfg. Co., John T. (Rolling) X
N. Y.—Cortland
Cortland Door & Window Screen Co. (Window; Door) C
Wickwire Bros. (Sand; Coal; Gravel) ....AAAA
N. Y.—Frankfort
Acme Road Machinery Co. (Revolving; Shaking)..B
N. Y.—Fulton
Dilts Machine Wks. (Pulp Mill) ....B
N. Y.—Horseheads
Horseheads Screen Door Co. (Window; Door) X
N. Y.—Jamestown
Fenton Metallic Mfg. Co. (Counter Metallic) .....A
Watson Mfg. Co. (Window; Door; Made to Order)...D
New York City
Bacon, Earle C., 26 Cortlandt (Revolving; Shaking) ....B
Cabble Excelsior Wire Mfg. Co., Wm. (Coal; Sand)..B
Denzi & Phillips (Stained Glass) C
Estey Wire Works, 59 Fulton (Sand; Coal; Gravel) D
Homan Co., Andrew, 446 Water (Folding) ....D
Howard & Morse, 45 Fulton (Mining; Revolving; Window; Door; Iron; White Mortar; Shaking; Sand; Coal; Gravel) ....D
Hunt Co., C. W., 45 B'way (Sand; Coal; Gravel) .AA
Jackson Co., Wm. H., 29 E. 17th (Bank Counter a Specialty; Fire) ....A
Judd & Co., H. L. (Fire; Brass) ....AA
Lamb, J. & R. (Fire; Fire Brass; Stained Glass)...D
Manhattan Perforated Metal Co., 237 Centre (Brass Perforated) ....F
Maxwell's Son, John (Cage; Guard) X
Mundt & Sons, Chas., 441 Pearl (Mining; Revolving; Sand; Shaking; Coal; Gravel) ....B
Patent Metallic Weather Strip Co., 133 W. 23d (Window; Door) ......E
Roebuck Weather Strip & Wire Screen Co. (Door; Window) X
Schloss & Co., E. (Hand Painted) ....A
Williams & Sons, G. A. (Window) X
Wilson Mfg. Co., Jas. G., 3 W. 29th (Window; Door) ....A
N. Y.—Sandy Hill
Sandy Hill Iron & Brass

SCREENS (Con.)
Works (Pulp Mill) ....A
N. Y.—Syracuse
Stearns & Co., E. C. (Door;
Window) ....AA
Syracuse Wire Works, 315
E. Water (Sand; Coal;
Gravel) ....D
N. C.—Charlotte
Mecklenburg Iron Works
(Mining) X
OHIO—Bucyrus
American Clay Working Machinery Co. (Clay; Cement) X
OHIO—Canton
Aultman Co. (Mining; Revolving; Shaking) X
Bonnot Co. (Clay Working;
Revolving; Shaking) ...A
OHIO—Cincinnati
Bromwell Brush & Wire
Goods Co. (Coal; Gravel;
Sand) ....AA
Cincinnati Mfg. Co., 512
Main (Sand; Coal; Gravel)
B
Day Co., J. H. (Sand; Clay,
&c.; Revolving; Shaking)
A
Littleford Bros., 453 E.
Pearl (Mining; Revolving;
Shaking; Sand; Gravel;
Coal) ....B
OHIO—Cleveland
Osborn Mfg. Co. (Coal;
Sand) ....B
Standard Sand & Mach. Co.
(Power; Hand Fdy.)....C
Taylor & Boggis Fdy. Co.
(Door; Window) .....AA
Tyler Co., W. S., 1150 St.
Clair (Mining; Sand; Revolving; Coal; Gravel)
AAAA
OHIO—Columbus
Jeffrey Mfg. Co. (Clay;
Coal; Cement; Revolving;
Sand; Vibrating) ..AAAA
OHIO—Cuyahoga Falls
Turner, Vaughan & Taylor
Co. (Sand; Coal; Gravel)
B
OHIO—Dayton
Raymond Co., C. W. (Clay;
Cement) ....A
OHIO—Greenville
Hart Mfg. Co. (Window;
Door) X
OHIO—Hamilton
Black-Clawson Co. (Pulp
Mill) ....AAA
Meyers Mfg. Co., Fred. J.
(Lime; Revolving; Sand;
Window; Coal; Gravel).B
OHIO—Lancaster
Eagle Machine Co. (Window) ....A
Martin Brick Mfg. Co., C.
(Clay) ....B
OHIO—Lima
Monroe Screen, Blind & Partition Co. (Window; Door)
H
OHIO—Marietta
Introstyle Novelty Mfg. Co.
(Window; Door) ......F
OHIO—Nelsonville
Nelsonville Fdy. & Machine
Co. (Revolving; Shaking)
B
OHIO—Niles
Niles Mine & Mill Supply
Co. (Mining) ....B
OHIO—Norwalk
Bostwick-Godell Co. (Window; Door) C
OHIO—Toledo
Maclaren & Sprague Lumber Co. (Window; Door)
A
PA.—Allegheny
Carlin's Sons, Thos. (Revolving) ....A
Pittsburg Lamp, Brass &
Glass Co. (Fire Brass)
AAAA
PA.—Carbondale
Carbondale Machine Co.
(Mining; Sand; Coal; Revolving; Gravel; Vibrating) ....AA
Hendrick Mfg. Co. (Ltd.)

SCREENS (Con.)
(Coal; Ore; Sand) ...AA
PA.—Connellsville
Connellsville Machine &
Car Co. (Mining) ......A
PA.—Ellwood City
Glen Mfg. Co. (Coal; Sand)
C
PA.—Kennett Square
American Road Machine Co.
(Revolving; Shaking) .AA
PA.—Lancaster
Martin Brick Machine Mfg.
Co., Henry (Clay) .....B
PA.—Monongahela
Monongahela Mfg. Co. (Revolving; Shaking) .....B
PA.—Philadelphia
American Parquetry Floor
Co., 143 S. 13th (Window;
Door) C
Cresson Co., Geo. V., 18th
& Allegheny Av. (Coal;
Sand) ....AA
Darby & Sons' Co., Edward,
233 Arch (Sand; Door;
Coal; Gravel; Window).A
De Witt Wire Cloth Co.,
703 Market (Window;
Door) ....A
Merritt & Co., 1024 Ridge
Av. (Mining) ....B
Paxon Co., J. W. (Coal;
Sand) ....AA
Phila. Screen Mfg. Co.
(Window; Door) ......A
PA.—Pittsburg
Mesta Machine Co. (Ash;
Crusher) ....AAAA
Phillips Mine & Mill Supply
Co. (Shaking; Sand; Coal;
Gravel) ....AA
PA.—Pittston
Exeter Machine Works (Revolving; Shaking) ....AA
PA.—White Haven
Wallace, Samuel (Revolving; Shaking) ....D
PA.—Wilkesbarre
Vulcan Iron Works (Mining;
Revolving; Shaking; Coal;
Sand; Gravel; Perforated
Metal) ....AAAA
R. I.—Providence
N. E. Ventilating & Heating
Co. (Card) ....D
What Cheer Wire Works
(Sand; Coal; Gravel)....F
TEXAS—Dallas
Dallas Screen Co. (Window;
Door) ....F
Hatch Mfg. Co. (Window;
Door) X
VT.—Bennington
Scott, Olin (Pulp Mill)...A
VT.—Burlington
Burlington Venetian Blind
Co. (Door; Fly; Window)
A
Porter Screen Mfg. Co. (Fly;
Window; Door; Extension) C
Queen Anne Screen Co.
(Fly; Window; Door; Extension) ....A
WIS.—Appleton
Valley Iron Wks. Co. (Pulp
Mill) C
WIS.—Cudahy
Power Mining & Machinery
Co. (Mining) ......AAA
WIS.—Milwaukee
Meinecke & Son, A. (Bamboo) ....AA
Phoenix Mfg. Co. (Window)
F
Willer Mfg. Co. (Window;
Door; Border only) ....A
Wisconsin Iron & Wire
Works, 186 E. Water
(Sand; Coal; Gravel)...D
WIS.—Oshkosh
McMillan Co., R. (Window;
Door) ....A
WIS.—Wausau
Curtis & Yale Co. (Window;
Door) ....AA

SCREWS
See also Corkscrews

SCREWS (*Con.*)

CAL.—San Francisco

Payne Bolt Works, 121 Howard (Cap; Set)........AA

CONN.—Bridgeport

Bridgeport Brass Co. (Brass; Copper; Bronze; Oil) AAA

Bridgeport Gun Implement Co., 219 Elm (Wood), AA

Gaynor & Mitchell Mfg. Co. (Brass for Steam; Gas; Water Fittings) C

Hubbell Harvey (Brass; Brass Machine Plumbers; Special; Cap, Set) C

CONN.—Chester

Brooks & Sons, M. S. (Dowel; Wing Wood) ....B

CONN.—Derby

Shelton Co. (Bed; Couch; Lag) ....A

CONN.—Forestville

Young Bros. (Brass Machine Cap; Set; Machine from Sample only) ....F

CONN.—Hartford

Atlantic Screw Wks. (David Fitton, Prop.) (Machine; Wood) ....AA

Billings & Spencer Co. (Thumb) ....AA

Cook C., Asa S. (Coach; Lag) ....G

Hartford Machine Screw Co. (Bicycle; Gib; Machine; Cap; Clock; Watch; Collar; Eye Glass; Gun; Knurled Head Thumb; Optical; Set; Sewing Machine; Special; Thumb) ....AAAA

Spencer Automatic Machine Screw Co. (Brass; Copper; Bronze Machine; Cap; Set) **X**

CONN.—Meriden

Foster Merriam & Co. (Wood) ....AA

Miller & Co., Edward (Oil) ....AAAA

Parker, Chas. Co. (Couch; Lac; Wood) ....AAA

CONN.—Milldale

Clarke Bros. Bolt Co. (Cap; Set; Coach; Lag) ....A

CONN.—Mt. Carmel

Mt. Carmel Bolt Co. (Brass; Copper; Bronze; Machine; Flathead; Wood; Nickel; Silver) ....B

Woodruff & Sons Co., Walter W. (Brass Plated; Brass, Silver Capped) ...A

CONN.—New Britain

Corbin, P. & F. (Brass Machine; Caps; Set; Coach; Lag; Collar; Hand Rail; Hand Saw; Machine Wood Dowel; Knob) .....AAAA

Humason & Beckley Mfg. Co. (Wood) ....A

North & Judd Mfg. Co. (Pad) ....AA

Russell & Erwin Mfg. Co. (Brass Machine; Shutter; Wood; Machine; Knob) ....AAAA

CONN.—New Haven

Cowles & Co., C. (Inc.) (Wood) ....A

Grilley Co. (Brass; Copper; Bronze; German Silver; Cap; Plated; Pad) C

North & Co., O. B. (Pad) ....AA

Reeves Mfg. Co. (Brass Machine) C

Reynolds & Co. (Brass Machine; Square; Round; Hex Head; Coach; Lag; Gib; Set; Machine; Stud; Cap) ....

Sargeant & Co. (Hand Rail; Hand Saw; Shutter; Wood; Bench; Looking Glass Piano Stool; Window Stop) ....AAAA

CONN.—Pine Meadow

Chapin-Stephens Co. (Hand; Bench) ....

CONN.—Southington

Peck, Stow & Wilcox Co. (Hand; Shutter; Jack; Bench) ....AAAA

SCREWS (*Con.*)

Southington Cutlery Co. (Wood; Brass) ....AA

CONN.—Stamford

Yale & Towne Mfg. Co. (Gib) ....AAAA

CONN.—Torrington

Progressive Mfg. Co. (Brass Machine; Piano Hardware; Special) ....A

CONN.—Unionville

Upson Nut Co., (Cap; Wood; Coach; Lag; Set; Bed; Hanger) ....AAAA

CONN.—Waterbury

American Pin Co. (Brass; Plumbers) ....AA

American Ring Co. (Mirror; Picture Hanging) .....A

Blake & Johnson (Brass; Bronze; German Silver; Copper; Machine Special) ....

Steele & Johnson Mfg. Co. (Bibb; Brass; Copper; Bronze; Brass; Machine; Plumbers; Thumb) .....A

CONN.—Winsted

Browne Machine Co. (Chair; Piano Stool; Wood) X

Moore, Franklin Co. (Wood) ....A

DEL.—Wilmington

Diamond State Steel Co. (Coach; Lag; Wood)....X

GA.—Augusta

Lombard Iron Works & Supply Co. (Jack) ....A

ILL.—Belleville

Belleville Pump & Skein Works (Building Movers; Jack) ....AA

ILL.—Carpentersville

Illinois Iron & Bolt Co. (Jack; House Raising; Locomotive; Track; Press) ....AA

ILL.—Chicago

Acorn Brass Mfg. Co., 206 Fulton (Special) ....D

Besley & Co., Chas. H., 10 N. Canal (Special; Thumb) ....AA

Columbia Screw Co. (Gimlet Pointed; Brass; Copper; Bronze; Gimlet Pointed Collar; German Silver; Handrail; Hanger; Machine; Plumbers; Wood) B

Illinois Malleable Iron Co., 30 W. Monroe (Piano Stool) ....AAAA

Read Co., A. P., 16 N. Canal (Window Stop) X

Republic Iron & Steel Co. (Coach; Lag; Gimlet Pointed; Hanger; Skein; Stud) ....AAAA

Smith Mfg. Co., F. N., 18 W. Randolph (Special) ....D

Standard Screw Co., 2 W. Canal (Bed; Iron; Brass; Machine; Stud; Thumb; Wood; Cap; Brass Bicycle; Collar; Set) ....AAA

Walker & Ehrman Mfg. Co. 127 W. Wash. (Cap; Set; Collar; Machine; Thumb) ....A

Whitman & Barnes Mfg. Co. (Wood)........AAAA

ILL.—Edwardsville

Edwardsville Brass Co. (Plumbers, also Floor) ..B

ILL.—Harvey

Buda Foundry & Mfg. Co. (Jack; Track) ....AA

ILL.—Rockford

Barnes Co., W. F. & John (Press) ....AA

Rockford Bolt Works (Cap; Coach; Collar; Hanger; Machine; Skein; Thumb; Set; Lag) X

IND.—Mishawaka

Dodge Mfg. Co. (Hand; Bench) ....AAA

MD.—Baltimore

Dietrich Bros. (Coach; Lag) ....B

National Supply Co. (Coach; Gimlet Point; Skein) ...B

SCREWS (Con.)

MASS.—Boston
Boston Bolt Co., 33 Purchase (Building Movers; Coach; Lag; Hangers) C
Dame, Stoddard & Co. (Cork) ....A
New England Screw Co. (Plumbers) ....E
Narton, A. O. (Track; Locomotive Jack) ....AA
Welch & Co., F. F., 65 Sudbury (Brass; Copper; Bronze; Brass Thumb) ..D

MASS.—Canton
Kingsley Iron & Machine Co. (Building Movers) ...AA

MASS.—Fitchburg
Parker, C. U. (Wood)....X
Simonds Mfg. Co. (Saw) AAA

MASS.—Hopedale
Draper Co. (Machine) AAAA

MASS.—Lowell
Aldrich, William K., 587 Dutton (Hand; Bench Wood; Wooden) ......F
Hope & Co., Wm. H. (Cap; Set; Milled Machine) ...X
Turner, John D. (Machine) D

MASS.—Millers Falls
Millers Falls Co. (Jack), AA

MASS.—Shelbourne Falls
Mayhew Co., H. H. (Wood) D

MASS.—Springfield
Bemis & Call Hdw & Tool Co. (Wood) ....A

MASS.—Worcester
Draper Machine Tool Co. (Machine) ....B
McCloud, Crane & Winter Co. (Brass; Copper; Bronze; Brass Machine; Caps; Set; Collar; Gib; Hanger; Machine; Stud) X
Parker Wire Goods Co. (Hand Rail) ....D
Reed & Curtis Mach. Screw Co. (Machine)..........D
Reed & Prince Mfg. Co. (Brass; Copper; Bronze; Wood) ....B
Wilson & Smith (Coach; Lag) ....E
Wire Goods Co. (Hand Rail; Dowel; Thumb) ....A
Worcester Machine Screw Co. (Cap; Collar; Machine Set) ....AAA
Wright Wire Co. (Wood; Brass) ....AA

MICH.—Detroit
Detroit Screw Works (Cap; Set; Iron Hand; Bench with Metal Bearings; Machine; Thumb) ....A
Michigan Bolt & Nut Works, ft. Meldrum Av. (Coach; Lag Hanger; Skein) ..AA

MICH.—Grand Rapids
Grand Rapids Brass Co. (Brass; Special) ....A
Grand Rapids Hand Screw Co. (Hand; Bench) .....B

MICH.—Port Huron
Port Huron Steel & Screw Co., Ltd. (Cap; Set) ...X

MINN.—Minneapolis
Howell & Co., R. R. (Jack) B

MO.—Kansas City
Kansas City Bolt & Nut Co. (Bed; Cap; Set; Coach; Hanger; Skein) ....A

MO.—St. Louis
Moran Bolt & Nut Mfg. Co., Cor. Florida & Main (Lag; Coach; Hanger; Hook; Eye; Skein)...........A
St. Louis Screw Co., 3014 N. 13th (Cap; Collar; Gib; Special; Thumb; Bicycle; Brass; Copper; Bronze; Brass; Machine; Set; Stud) ....A

N. H.—Alton
Rockwell Clough Co. (Cork) E

N. H.—Milford
Pierce & Co., W. E. (Wooden) ....D

SCREWS (Con.)

N. J.—Jersey City
Mack Mfg. Co., Thos. A. (Special Machine) X

N. J.—Newark
National Saw Co. (Saw) ..B
Williamson Wire Novelty Co., C. F. (Cork) ....B

N. Y.—Brooklyn
Taylor & Co., (Inc.) (Jack) D
Williams & Co., J. H. (Thumb) ....AA

N. Y.—Buffalo
Buffalo Bolt Co. (Brass; Mirror; Picture Hanging) AA
Buffalo Last Works (Crimping) ....B
Contractors Plant Mfg. Co. (Jack) ....B
Niagara Screw Co. (Cap; Set; Collar) X
Pratt & Letchworth Co. (Pad) ....AAA

N. Y.—Munnsville
Munnsville Plow Co. (Jack) B

New York City
Dunlap Machinery Co. (Crimping) ....F
Greenlie, Wyatt & Co., 499 Water (Cap; Set; Coach; Lag) ....A
Hungerford Brass & Copper Co., U. T., 497 Pearl (Brass; Copper; Bronze) AA
Olney & Warrin, 38 Dey (Cap; Set) ....D
Smith & Hemenway Co., 296 Bway. (Cork) ....D
Tiebout, W. & J., 118 Chambers (Hook; Eye) ......B
Watson-Stillman Co. (Jack) A

N. Y.—Portchester
Russell, Burdsell & Ward, Bolt & Nut Co. (Cap; Set) AAAA

N. Y.—Rochester
Rochester Machine Screw Co. (Bicycle; Brass; Copper; Bronze; Cap; Set; Machine; Stud; Thumb) ...B

N. Y.—Seneca Falls
Gould's Mfg. Co. (Jack) AAA
Rumsey & Co., (Ltd.) (Jack; Press) ....A

N. Y.—Syracuse
Central City Bolt Co. (Coach; Lag) C
Stearns & Co., E. C. (Bench; Jack) ....AA

OHIO—Canton
Elbel & Co. (Pad) ....A
Gilligan Mfg. Co. (Brass), A

OHIO—Cincinnati
Bishop, Geo. H. & Co. (Saw) A
Cinn. Screw & Tap Co. (Cap Collar; Machine; Thumb; Coach; Lag; Set; Special; Wood) ....A
Haven Co., James L. (Bench) X
Queen City Supply Co. (Machine) ....A

OHIO—Cleveland
Atlas Bolt & Screw Co. (Machine) ....AA
Cleveland Automatic Mach. Co., 131 2d Av. (Hanger) AAA
Cleveland Cap Screw Co., 66 Clarkewood Av. (Cap; Set) A
Kirk-Latty Mfg. Co. (Machine) ....A
Lake Erie Iron Co. (Coach; Lag; also Gimlet Pointed Coach) ....AAA
Lamson & Sessions Co., 412 Scranton Av. (Coach; Lag; Skein) ....AA
National-Acme Mfg. Co. (Cap; Set; Machine) ..AA
National Screw & Tack Co. (Bicycle; Brass; Copper; Bronze; Brass Machine; Cap; Set; Coach; Lag; Hanger; Wood) ......AA

895

SCREWS (Con.)

Sanitary Co. (Plumbers) ..B

Union Steel Screw Co. (Brass; Copper ;Bronze Wood) ....AAA

Vulcanus Forging Co. (Forged Coach; Lag) ....B

OHIO—Columbus

Columbus Bolt Works (Coach; Lag) ....AA

Ohio Tool Co. (Iron; Bench; Wood; Hand) ....AA

OHIO—Dayton

Joyce Cridland Co. (Locomotive; Track; Traversing) ....B

OHIO—Elyria

Western Automatic Machine Screw Co. (All Kinds) ....AA

OHIO—Sandusky

Sandusky Tool Co. (Wood; Hand; Bench) ....A

PA.—Erie

Campbell Brass Works, J. B. (Trap) ....A

Erie Specialty Co. (Cork) ....B

PA.—Lebanon

American Iron & Steel Mfg. Co. (Caps; Coach; Hanger; Hook; Eye; Skein; Wood; Drive; Ore Washer; Set; Lag; Special) ....AAAA

PA.—Mechanicsburg

Wilcox Mfg. Co., D. (Drop Forged Thumb) ....A

PA.—Milton

Milton Mfg. Co. (Cap; Set; Coach; Lag) ....AA

PA.—New Castle

New Castle Forge & Bolt Co. (Coach; Lag) ....AA

PA.—Norristown

Reading Screw Co. (Wood; achine; Coach; Lag: Hanger; Knob; Saw; Special; Wing) ....A

PA.—Philadelphia

Disston & Sons, Henry (Inc.) (Saw; Wood) ....AAAA

Hoopes & Townsend Co. Cap; Set; Couch; Lag; Machine; Wood) ....AAA

Miles, Franklin S. (Cap; German Silver; Machine; Wood; Set; Special; Thumb) ....F

Philadelphia Machine Screw Works, 624 Race (Machine; Special) C

Phosphor Bronze Smelting Co. (Ltd.) (Phosphor Bronze) ....A

Scott & Williams, 2079 Cumberland (Machine) ....A

Steward & Romaine Mfg. Co. Cap; Set; Machine) ....B

PA.—Pittsburg

Lanz & Sons, J. W.. 101 S. 29th (Lay; Coach) ....AA

Oliver Iron & Steel Co. (Coach; Lag; Gimlet Pointed; &c.) ......AAAA

Pittsburg Mfg. Co.. 28th & R. R. (Coach; Lag) ....A

Pittsburg Screw & Bolt Co. (Brass; Machine; Cap; Coach; Collar; Machine; Lag; Set) ....A

PA.—Reading

Penn. Hdw. Co. (Inc.) Cap; Set; Wood) ....AA

Reading Hdw. Co. (Brass; Bronze; Hand; Shutter; Wood; Copper Bench) .. ..AAAA

PA.—Scranton

Scranton Bolt & Nut Co. (Coach; Lag) ....AA

R. I.—Pawtucket

Bliss Mfg. Co., R. (Hand; Wood; Bench; Guitar; Violin Clamp) ....AAA

Haskell Mfg. Co., Wm. H. (All Kinds) ....AA

Pawtucket Mfg. Co. (Cap; Set; Coach:: Lag; Gimlet Point; Collar; Hanger

SCREWS (Con.)

Machine) ....A

R. I.—Providence

American Screw Co. (Brass; Bronze; Brass Machine; Hand Rail; Wood; Dowel; Lock Caps; Plated; Special; Wood Copper Knob) ....AAAA

Eastern Bolt & Nut Co. (Caps; Set; Coach; Lag; Collar; Hanger; Special Thumb) ....A

Rhode Island Tool Co. (Cap; Set; Coach; Lag; Thumb) ....AAA

TENN.—Memphis

Chickasaw Iron Works (Press) ....A

VT.—E. Arlington

Judson, J. R. (Brushmakers) ....B

VA.—Richmond

Old Dominion Iron & Nail Works Co. (Hanger) .AA

WIS.—Evansville

Baker Mfg. Co. (Jack) .AA

SCRIBERS

MASS.—Athol

Starrett Co., L. S. (Adjustable; Metal) ....A

MASS.—Chicopee Falls

Stevens Arms & Tool Co., J. (Metal) ....AAA

MASS.—Fitchburg

Sawyer Tool Mfg. Co. (Metal) C

MASS.—Springfield

Bemis & Call Hardware Tool Co. (Adjustable) ..A

SCRIBES

MASS.—Springfield

Bemis & Call Hdw. & Tool Co. (Adjustable) ......A

Co. (Timber) ....A

SCROLLS: TRANSFER

ILL.—Chicago

Meyercord Co. ....A

New York City

Palm, Fechteler & Co., 80 5th Av. ....A

OHIO—Cincinnati

Palm Bros. & Co. ....A

PA.—Philadelphia

National Decalcomania Co. ....F

SCRUBBERS

ILL.—Chicago

Bosley Co., D. W., 311 Fulton (Floor) ....B

IND.—Fort Wayne

Kerr-Murray Mfg. Co. (Gas) ....A

MD.—Baltimore

Bartlett. Hayward & Co. (Gas Works) ....B

N. Y.—Brooklyn

Continental Iron Wks. (Gas Works) ....A

N. Y.—Homer

Phoenix Hardware Mfg. Co. (Floor) ....D

New York City

Martin's Sons, J. M. C. (Floor) ....A

PA.—Minersville

Anthracite Machine Works (Keg) ....D

PA.—Philadelphia

Wood & Co.. R. D. (Gas Works) ....AAAA

SCYTHES

CONN.—Collinsville

Collins Co. (Bush; Lawn) ....AAAA

CONN.—Westport

Bradleys' Son, G. W.....B

CONN.—Winsted

Winsted Mfg. Co. ...AAAA

MAINE—Hallowell

North Wayne Tool Co.....B

SCYTHES (Con.)

MAINE—Oakland
Dunn Edge Tool Co. ....AA
Emerson Stevens Mfg. Co.
D
MAINE—Skowhegan
Nolin Mfg. Co. (Lawn)...C
N. H.—East Lebanon
Emerson Edge Tool Co.
(Weed) X
N. H.—North Newport
Sibley Scythe Co. C
N. Y.—Auburn
Wadsworth & Son, David
(Bush; Lawn) ....A
N. Y.—Elmira
Cronk & Carrier Mfg. Co.
(Bush) ....B
New York City
American Axe & Tool Co.,
253 B'way (Bush; Grain;
Lawn) ....AAAA
Wiebusch & Hilger, 9 Murray ....A
VT.—East Highgate
Rixford Mfg. Co. (Bush)..B

SEAL

See Leather; Plushes; Silk
Goods; Velvet

SEALERS

ILL.—Chicago
Board, Crosby & Co., 176
S. Clinton (Automatic)..X
N. J.—Salem
Ayars Machine Co. (Can
Body) ....B
New York City
Cushman & Denison, 240 W.
23d (Envelope) C

SEALS

See also Jewelry

CONN.—Bridgeport
Schwerdtle Stamp Co. (Notary) ....F
CONN.—New Haven
Hoggson & Pettis Mfg. Co.
(Notary) ....A
D. C.—Washington
Grant Mfg. Co., 809 Water
S. W. (All Lead or Tin;
Coppered Car) ....D
ILL.—Chicago
Chicago Car Seal & Mfg.
Co., cor. Knight & Green
(Car) ....B
Edgarton, A. Lewis (Notarial) ....B
Miller Car Lock & Seal Co.,
16 S. Canal (One Piece
Interlocking Car) .....D
Sigwalt Mfg. Co., Security
Bldg. (Car) C
MD.—Baltimore
Bartlett, Hayward & Co.
(Gas Works) ....B
Baumgarten & Co. (Wax).E
MASS.—Attleboro
Bliss Bros. Co. (Watch)..A
MASS.—Boston
Dennison Mfg. Co. (Notarial) ....AAAA
G. & P. Engraving Co., 185
Franklin (Car) X
Woodman Mfg. & Supply
Co., 63 Oliver (Lead Car)
D
MASS.—Springfield
Smith Mfg. Co., R. H., 293
Main (also Wax; Hand
Stamps, &c.; Car)......C
MICH.—Detroit
Detroit Car Seal Co., 232
Randolph (Car) ....D
MICH.—Hastings
International Seal & Lock
Co. (Car) ....B
MO.—St. Louis
Barnard Stamp Co., 311
Olive (Car) ....F
Handlan-Buck Mfg. Co., 212
N. 3d (Car) ....AA
Hiertz Metal Co., Theodore
(Lead Car) ....D
NEBR.—Omaha
Lehmer, Jos. R., 1212 Farnam (Car) C

SEALS (Con.)

N. J.—Irvington
Howlett & Co., J. (Express
Company Lead) ....F
N. J.—Jersey City
Williams & Son, E. A. (Car)
AA
N. J.—Newark
Reeves & Browne (Watch)
B
N. Y.—Buffalo
Buffalo Seal & Press Co.
(Car) X
New York City
American Railway Supply
Co., 24 Park Pl. (Car)..X
Brooks & Co., E. J., 51 Dey
(Car) ....B
Cary Mfg. Co., 19 Roosevelt (Strap; Box) ......B
Davids Co., Thaddeus (Notarial) C
Force & Co., Wm. A., 50
Beekman (Wax) ......B
Keystone Seal & Press Co.,
39 Cortlandt (Car) .....D
Larter & Sons (Watch) ..A
New York Stencil Works,
100 Nassau (Car) .....D
Richards & Co., E. Ira
(Watch) ....AAA
Sloan & Co. (Inc.) (Watch)
B
Standard Metal Strap Co.,
336 E. 38th (Box) .....F
Street & Sons, Geo. O.
(Watch) ....B
OHIO—Columbus
Saurbrey, Geo. J., 250 Livingston Av. (Car) ......G
OHIO—Dayton
Dayton Malleable Iron Co.
(Car) ....AAA
OHIO—Hamilton
National Car Seal Co. (Car;
Tin) ....D
PA.—Philadelphia
Hill Mfg. Co., B. B., 1020
New Market (Car; Wax)
B
R. I.—Providence
Snow & Westcott (Watch)
A
WIS.—Milwaukee
Schwaab Stamp & Seal Co.
(Lead; Wax) C

SEARCH-LIGHTS

IND.—Fort Wayne
Fort Wayne Electric Wks.
(Inc.) ....AAA
New York City
Bogue, Chas. J., 213 Centre
C
Colt Co., J. B., 408 E. 32d
(Acetylene) ....B
N. Y.—Schenectady
General Electric Co. .AAAA
OHIO—Cincinnati
Carlisle & Finch Co., 231
E. Clifton Av. ....B
Creaghead Engineering Co.
D
Macleod & Co., Walter, 463
E. Front (Acetylene) ..B
WIS.—La Crosse
Benton & Son, Thos. P...E

SEATINGS

See also Woodwork; Carriage; Veneers; Furniture

ILL.—Chicago
Ford, Johnson & Co. (Veneer) ....AAA
MASS.—Gardner
Heywood Bros. & Wakefield
Co. (Rattan) ....AAAA
MO.—St. Louis
Scarritt-Comstock Furniture
Co. (Rattan; Veneer)...A
N. J.—Hoboken
Woodman, Joel H. (Veneer;
Perforated Veneer) ...A
N. J.—Jersey City
American Veneer Co. (Veneer Settees) ....D
N. Y.—Brooklyn
Adler Veneer Seat Co. (Ve-

SEATINGS (Con.)
neer) C
New York City
Frost Veneer Seating Co.,
208 Canal (Rattan; Ve-
neer) X
PA.—Philadelphia
Hale & Kilburn Mfg. Co.
(Rattan) ....AAAA
R. I.—Pawtucket
American Hair Cloth Co.
(Hair) ....AA
WIS.—Sheboygan
Frost Veneer Seating Co.
(Veneer) ....B

SEATS

See also Woodwork; Car-
riage; Wagon

CONN.—Bristol
Warner & Co., A. H. (Bath
Tub) X
CONN.—New Haven
Dann Bros. & Co. (Carriage;
Wagon) ....B
ILL.—Chicago
Adams & Westlake Co., On-
tario & Franklin (Car)
AAAA
Sherwood Co. (School)....D
IND.—Evansville
Never Split Seat Co.
(Closet) ....B
MD.—Baltimore
Hutton & Co., G. H. (Car-
riage) ....F
MASS.—Boston
Grimmons & Co., Chas. A.
(Chair; Leather Board).B
MASS.—Gardner
Heywood Bros. & Wakefield
Co. (Car; Street Car;
Cane; Woven) .....AAAA
MICH.—Muskegon
Heap & Son, Wm. (Water
Closet; Complete) .....D
MINN.—St. Paul
Union Brass Metal Mfg. Co.
(Closet) ....A
MO.—St. Louis
Nelson Mfg. Co., N. O.
(Bath Tub; Water Closet,
Complete) ....AAA
Scarritt-Comstock Furniture
Co., 318 N. B'way (Car)
A
N. Y.—Brooklyn
Adler Veneer Seat Co. (Per-
forated Veneer) C
American Car Seat Co., 18
Guernsey (Car; Rattan)
D
Brooklyn Furniture Co.
(Church) ....A
N. Y.—Buffalo
Buffalo Specialty Mfg. Co.,
375 Elliott (Adjustable
Bath Tub) ....B
Pratt & Letchworth Co.
(Truck) ....AAA
N. Y.—Cobleskill
Hallenbeck, Chas. (Wagon)
H
New York City
Frost Veneer Seating Co.,
206 Canal (Car) ......AA
Lamb, J. & R. (Church)..D
Vogel & Co., F. (Hall)...X
N. Y.—Oswego
Cowmeadow Mfg. Co., John
(Water Closet, Complete)
D
N. Y.—Syracuse
Brown Furniture Co., C. G.
(Hall) ....B
OHIO—Cincinnati
Shelt Co. (Third Passenger
Adjustable) ....A
OHIO—Cleveland
Avery Stamping Co. (Agri-
cultural Implement; Steel
for Implements; Pressed
Steel) ....B
Federal Mfg. Co. (Ball
Valve) ....AAAA
Ohio Spring Bed Co. (Wire
Automobile) ....A
Van Dorn Iron Works Co.
(Steel Lawn) ....AA
OHIO—Columbus
Excelsior Seat Co. (Car-

SEATS (Con.)
riage) ....B
OHIO—Dayton
Dayton Mfg. Co. (Street
Car; Car) ....A
Ohio Rake Co. (School).AA
OHIO—Toledo
Kroh Mfg. Co., C. Z. (Car-
riage) ....E
Toledo Carriage Woodwork
Co. (Wagon) ....A
PA.—Cheswick
Cheswick Mfg. Co. (Pressed
Steel) X
PA.—Johnstown
Cambria Steel Co. (Agricul-
tural Implement)..AAAA
PA.—Philadelphia
Brill Co., J. G., 62d &
Woodland Av. (Reversible
Car, for open or closed
cars; Street) .....AAAA
Hale & Kilburn Mfg. Co.,
48 N. 6th (Car, Steam &
Electric; Street) .AAAA
PA.—Pittsburg
Standard Mfg. Co. (Bath
Tub; Water Closet, Com-
plete) ....AA
PA.—Titusville
Titusville Elastic Chair Co.
(Ltd.) (Church) C
WIS.—Algoma
Ahnapee Veneer & Seating
Co. (Chair) ....A
WIS.—Milwaukee
Milwaukee Chair Co. (Hall)
A
WIS.—Racine
Racine General Mfg. Co.
(Carriage) ....E

SECRETARIES
See Furniture

SECTIONAL
BOOK CASES
See Furniture

SEED
See also Seeds

ILL.—Chicago
Dickinson Co., Albert (Flax)
AA
Trilling & Co., H. (Flax)
E
IOWA—Sioux City
Sioux City Oil Wks. (Flax)
B
MD.—Baltimore
McCormick & Co. (Mustard)
D
MISS.—Vicksburg
Advance Gin & Mill Co.
(Cotton) ....B
N. Y.—Buffalo
Mann Bros. Co. (Ground
Flax) ....A
New York City
American Linseed Co. (Flax)
B
Hopkins & Co., J. C. (Card-
amon; Fennel) ....A
Schieffelin & Co. (Colchi-
cum) ....AA

SEED: BIRD
ILL.—Chicago
Atwood & Steele, 18 River
C
Brookman Bros., 149 Huron
(Columbia Chem. Works)
E
Brookman Mfg. Co., 79 La-
Salle Av. ....D
Dickinson Co., Albert, W.
Taylor & the River ..AA
Puhl-Webb Co., 119 W.
Randolph C
Vosbrink Merc. Co., 139
Mich. ....E
MASS.—Boston
Breck & Sons, Jos. (Corpn.)
A
N. Y.—Brooklyn
Fitzimmons,M., 81 9th..::C
New York City

SEED; BIRD (Con.)

Brookman Mfg. Co., 193
  Front ....D
Durkee & Co., E. R., 534
  Washington ....AA
Hirsh & Son, Leon, 368
  G'wich C
McAllister, A., 21 Fulton.F
McAllister, M. A., 69 Cort-
  landt (Food) ....F
Rosenstein Co., C., 373
  Washn. ....D
WIS.—Milwaukee
Pahl & Co., E. R., 294
  B'way ....D

SEEDERS

See also Agricultural Implements

CONN.—Higganum
Cutaway Harrow Co.
  (Broadcast) X
CONN.—Southport
Jelliff Co., C. O. (Hand).A
ILL.—Batavia
Appleton Mfg. Co. ......A
ILL.—Canton
Partino & Orendorff Co.
  (Harrows Combined)
  AAAA
ILL.—Chicago
Bristol & Gale Co. (End
  Gate) ....B
Pratt Mfg. Co., Wm. E.,
  91 Lake (Hand).......B
Whitman & Barnes Mfg. Co.
  (Hand) ....AAAA
ILL.—Decatur
Chambers, Bering Quinlan
  Co. (End Gate) ....A
Lait Mfg. Co., F. B. (Force
  Feed; End Gate; also
  Clover Seed Attachment)
  A
ILL.—Joliet
Humphrey & Sons (Broad-
  cast Hand) ....A
Stevens Mfg. Co. (Broad-
  cast Hand) ....E
ILL.—Moline
Deere & Mansur Co. (Broad-
  cast; also Gress Seeder
  Attachment; Cultivators
  Combined) ....AAAA
Deere & Co (Cultivators
  Combined) ....AAAA
ILL.—Peoria
Luthy & Co. (End Gate;
  Sowers; also Grass Seeder
  Attachment) ....A
Selby-Starr & Co.........X
ILL.—Rockford
Rockford Well Drill Co...E
ILL.—Rock Island
Rock Island Plow Co.
  AAAA
ILL.—Sterling
Keystone Co. (Broadcast)
  AA
Sterling Mfg. Co. (Disc
  Harrows, etc.) ....A
IND.—Indianapolis
Everett, J. A. (Broadcast
  Hand) ....B
IND.—Liberty
Rude Bros. Mfg. Co. (Grass)
  A
IND.—Richmond
Hoosier Drill Co. (Broad-
  cast) ....AAAA
Wayne Wks. ....A
IND.—South Bend
Trojan Mfg. Co. (Broadcast;
  Hand) ....F
IND.—Urbana
Cyclone Seeder Co.......D
Speicher, D. E. (Hand)..F
MASS.—Boston
Ames Plow Co. (Hand)....
  AAAA
MASS.—Chicopee Falls
Belcher & Taylor Agricul-
  tural Tool Co. ....A
MICH.—Albion
Gale Mfg. Co. (Broadcast)
  AA
MICH.—Dowagiac
Dowagiac Mfg. Co ....A
MICH.—Grand Rapids
Goshen Sweeper Co. (Hand)
  D

SEEDERS (Con.)

MICH.—Homer
Seeder Mfg. Co. (Wheel-
  barrow; Grass) ....F
MICH.—Kalamazoo
Reed Mfg. Co. (& Sowers;
  Broadcast) ....D
MICH.—Saginaw
Saginaw Hardware Co.
  (Grass) ....A
MICH.—Ypsilanti
Thompson & Son, O. E.
  (Wheelbarrow; Grass) ..B
MINN.—Minneapolis
Howell & Co., R. R. (With
  Cultivator) ....B
Monitor Mfg. Co. (Broad-
  cast) ....A
MINN.—Owatonna
Owatonna Mfg. Co. (&
  Sowers) ....B
MO.—St. Louis
Christen & Son, F. (Broad-
  cast; Hand) ....B
Whitman Agr'l Co. (Broad-
  cast) ....AA
N. H.—Antrim
Goodell Co. (Broadcast
  Hand) ....A
N. Y.—Batavia
Johnstone Harvester Co.
  (Disc) ....AAAA
N. Y.—Buffalo
Buffalo Specialty Mfg. Co.,
  375 Ellicott (Raisin)....B
Union Mfg. & Specialty Co.
  (Raisin) C
N. Y.—Ithaca
Williams Bros. (Broadcast)
  AA
N. Y.—Phelps
Crown Mfg. Co. (Wheel-
  barrow; Grass) ....B
N. Y.—Poughkeepsie
Chapinville Wheel Co. (&
  Sowers) ....D
N. Y.—Shortsville
Star Seeder Co. (Wheel-
  barrow; Grass) ....F
OHIO—Canton
Parlin & Orendorff Co.
  AAAA
OHIO—Dayton
Ohio Rake Co. (for Disc
  Harrows) ....AA
Stoddard Mfg. Co. (& Sow-
  ers; Broadcast) .....AAA
OHIO—Middletown
McSherry Mfg. Co.........A
OHIO—Ravenna
Williams, A. C. (Raisin).A
OHIO—Springfield
Amer. Seeding Mach. Co.
  AAAA
Mast & Co., P. P. (Broad-
  cast) ....AAAA
PA.—Philadelphia
Allen & Co., S. L., 1017
  Market (Bean; Pea, &c)
  AA
Enterprise Mfg. Co., 3rd &
  Dauphin (Raisin) .AAAA
PA.—York
Hench & Dromgold Co....B
VA.—Richmond
Cardwell Machine Co......A
WIS.—Beaver Dam
Rowell Mfg. Co., J. S. (also
  Combined Seeders & Drill)
  A
WIS.—Beloit
Thompson & Sons Mfg. Co.
  J. ....AA
WIS.—Fond du Lac
Fond du Lac Implement Co.
  D
WIS.—Horicon
Van Brunt Mfg. Co. (also
  Seeder & Cultivator Com-
  bined) ....AA
WIS.—La Crosse
La Crosse Plow Co. (also
  Grass Seeder Attach-
  ments) ....AAA
WIS.—Madison
Fuller & Johnson Mfg. Co.
  (& Harrows Combined)
  AAA
WIS.—Racine
Foster & Williams Mfg. Co.
  (End Gate Grass)......B
Freeman & Sons Mfg. Co.,
  S. ....A
Johnson & Field Mfg. Co.

Cortlandt ....AA
Jacob & Mullen, 1 Water.C
Mapes, J. D., 1920 W.
Farms Rd. ....B
Nungesser & Co., H., 65
Pearl ....A
Thompson, G. H., 107 Hudson ....B
Thorburn & Co., 36 Cortlandt ....AA
Taft Bros., 227 Pearl (Mustard) C
Tyler & Finch Co., 13 Gold
(Mustard) ....A
Vaughan, J. C., 14 Barclay
(Garden) ....B
N. Y.—Perrysburg
Hall, W. R. C
N. Y.—Richmondville
Harroway, M. W. ....B
N. Y.—Rochester
Crossman Bros. (Garden)..B
Cushman & Co., M.
(Garden) ....F
Mandeville & King .....B
N. Y.—Rose Hill
Mills, F. B. ....B
N. Y.—Syracuse
Saul, Chas. F. (Garden)...A
N. Y.—Watertown
Herrick & Son, A. H......B
OHIO—Chillicothe
Sears & Nichols Co., The
(Garden) ....A
OHIO—Cincinnati
Holden & Co., R. A., 46
Main (Field) ....B
Patterson & Evans, 52 Vine
B
OHIO—Findlay
Davis & Dukes ....A
OHIO—Mansfield
Lanehart & Co. C
OHIO—St. Mary's
Jay Grain Co............B
OHIO—Steubenville
Mc Gowan Bros. Gro. Co.
(Field) ....A
OHIO—Wakeman
Clark, C. S. ....B
OHIO—Wauseon
Eager & Green..........B
Smallman, F. R.........C
PA.—Fallington
Parsons, A. M..........B
PA.—Harrisburg
Holmes Seed Co. (Garden).C
PA.—Penn Valley
Parsons, A. B..........B
PA.—Philadelphia
Burpee & Co., W. A., 475
N. 5th ....AA
Johnson & Stokes (Garden)
A
Landreth & Sons, D., 1217
Market ....AA
Maule, W. H., 1711 Filbert
A
Weikel & Smith Spice Co.
129 N. Front...........A
PA.—Scranton
Clark & Co., G. R.......B
R. I.—Providence
Barrett Co., W. E.......B
S. C.—Charleston
Mc Intosh & Sons, W....B
S. C.—Columbia
Lorick & Lowrance ......B
TEXAS—Ft. Worth
Drumm Seed & Floral Co..C
TEXAS—Quanah
Callaway, John S......B
VA.—Independence
Dickey, Davis & Co......C
VA.—Richmond
Wood & Sons. T. W.......B
WASH.—Seattle
Bowen, E. J.............A
WIS.—La Crosse
Salzer Seed Co., J. A. (Garden) ....A
WIS.—Manitowoc
Landreth, A. C. (Garden).B
Madison Seed Co. (Garden)
C
Manitowoc Seed Co. (Garden) C
WIS.—Milwaukee
Courteen. S. G. (Garden)..A
Teweles & Co., L., 113 Clybourne C

WIS.—Sturgeon Bay ..
Teweles & Brandeis (Garden) C

SEERSUCKERS

See Cotton Goods

SEINES

See also Nets: Fish

ILL.—Chicago
Cook & Bro., E. C.........A
MASS.—Boston
American Net & Twine Co.
AAAA
Gloucester Net & Twine Co.
A
Lord Co., H. & G. W.....A
MASS.—Gloucester
Gloucester Net & Twine Co.
(Fish) ....A
N. Y.—New York City
United States Twine & Net
Co., 96 Franklin........B

SEMAPHORES

OHIO—Dayton
Barney & Smith Car Co.
(Train Order) .....AAAA

SEPARATORS

See also Agricultural Implements

CONN.—Elmwood
Whitlock Coil Pipe Co.
(Oil Steam) ....AA
CONN.—New Haven
Elm City Engineering Co.
(Electric Metal; Electric
to Separate Brass from
Iron Chips) C
CONN.—Thompsonville
Bushnell Press Co., G. H.
(Cotton Seed) ....A
ILL.—Belleville
Harrison Machine Wks.
(Grain) ....AA
ILL.—Chicago
Colles & Co., E. G. T., 34
So. Canal (Steam; Oil).B
Davis Co., Jno., 22nd & Halsted (Steam; Oil) ....AA
Monash-Younker Co., 203 So.
Canal (Steam; Oil) ....B
Sharples Co. (Cream) C
ILL.—Decatur
Union Iron Wks. (Wheat)
A
ILL.—Joliet
Bates Machine Co. (Steam;
Oil) ....AA
ILL.—Maywood
Stephens & Westcott Co.
(Steam; Oil) X
ILL.—Moline
Barnard & Leas Mfg. Co.
(Magnetic; Dustless;
Grain; Elevator Grain;
Screening; Wheat; Rice)
AA
ILL.—Peoria
Avery Mfg. Co. (Grain)....
AAA
ILL.—Quincy
Gardner Govenor C. (Steam;
Oil) ....AA
IND.—Frankfort
Wallace Mfg. Co. (Stone).C
IND.—Indianapolis
Nordyke & Marmon Co.
(Double Receiving Hominy; Magnetic; Screening
Grain) ....AAA
IND.—Lafayette
Polar Creamery Co.
(Cream) ....D
IND.—New Castle
Hoosier Mfg. Co.
(Grain) C
IND.—Richmond
Robinson & Co. (Grain).AA
IOWA—Clinton
Moseley & Pritchard Mfg.
Co. (Cream) ....D
IOWA—Webster City
Closz & Howard Mfg. Co.
(Grain) ....D

SEPARATORS (Con.)

KAN.—Leavenworth
Great Western Mfg. Co.
(for Separating Stone &
Gravel from Wheat)..AA
KY.—Louisville
Avery & Sons., B. F.
Bean) ....AAA
MD.—Baltimore
Adt., John B. (Stem)...A
Sinclair-Scott Co. (Pea)..E
MASS.—Boston
Amer Tool & Mach. Co., 109
Beach (Centrifugals for
Separating Oil from Metal
Chips; Turning)......AA
D'Este Co., Julian, 24 Canal
(Steam; Oil) ....B
MASS.—Hopedale
Draper Co. (Loom)..AAAA
MASS.—Worcester
Compton & Knowles Loom
Wks. (Loom) ....AAAA
Sawyer, Ezra, 31 Hermon
(Magnetic) ....E
Wire Goods Co. (Egg)....A
MICH.—Battle Creek
Nichols & Shepard Co.
(Small Seed; Grain)AAAA
MICH.—Breckenridge
Stone Bros. (Cream).....E
MICH.—Detroit
Austin Separator Co.,99
Woodbridge (Steamer;
Oil) ....E
Detroit Separator Co.
(Steam; Oil) ....F
Superior Fence Machine Co.
(Cream) ....F
Wright Mfg. Co., 57 W.
Woodbridge (Steam; Oil)
B
MICH.—Lansing
Monitor Water Purifier Co.
(Oil) X
MICH.—Pontiac
Bacon Mfg. Co. (Bean)..X
MICH.—Tecumseh
Brewer & Co., H. (Stone).B
MINN.—Minneapolis
Owens Co., J. L. (Grain; al-
so Flax; Cockle) ......A
MINN.—Winona
New Winona Mfg. Co.
(Cotton Seed) ....A
MO.—Joplin
Amer. Concentrator Co.
(Magnetic) ....D
NEBR.—Nebraska City
King Drill Mfg. Co.
(Cream) ....D
N. J.—Bloomfield
Empire Cream Separator
Co. (Grain) ....AAA
N. J.—Camden
Webster Warren & Co.
(Steam; Oil) ....AA
N. J.—Jersey City
Griffing Iron Co., A. A.
(Steam; Oil) ....AA
N. J.—Newark
National Dairy Machine Co.
(Centrifugal Cream)...B
N. Y.—Brooklyn
Acton, Jno., 188 John
(Steam; Oil) ....D
N. Y.—Buffalo
Noye Mfg. Co., John T.
(Gravity Grain) X
Squier Mfg. Co., Geo. L.
(Coffee; Rice) .....AAA
Stewart Heater Co. (Puri-
fier Combined; Steam;
Oil) ....D
N. Y.—Cato
Doty Mfg. Co. (Cream)..F
N. Y.—Little Falls
Burrell & Co., D. H. (Cen-
trifugal Hand Power)....
AAAA
N. Y.—Lockport
Amer. District Steam Co.
(Mud) ....AAA
Richmond Mfg. Co. (Grain)
A
N. Y.—Newburgh
Coldwell-Wilcox Co. (As-
phalt; Steam; Oil)....B
New York City
Burns & Sons, Jabez
(Coffee) ....B
Bushnell & Co., Jno. S., 124
Liberty (Steam; Oil) ..F

SEPARATORS (Con.)

De Laval Separator Co., 74
Cortland (Cream)..AAAA
Goubert Mfg. Co., 85 Liberty
(Live Steam) ....B
National Enameling &
Stamping Co., 80 Beek-
man (Cream) .....AAAA
Niles-Bement-Pond Co., 111
Broadway (Oil) ..AAAA
Patterson & Co., Frank L.,
26 Cortlandt (Oil; Steam)
E
Potter Separator Co., 43
Cortlandt (Steam; Oil)F
Power Specialty Co., 126
Liberty (Steam; Oil)..E
Roberts & Bros., Geo. I.,
473 4th Av. (Steam; Oil)
A
Robertson & Sons, Jas. L.,
204 Fulton (Steam; Oil)D
Standard Steam Specialty
Co., 111 5th Av. (Steam;
Oil) ....D
Thompson & Co., Richard,
126 Liberty (Steam; Oil)
F
Westinghouse Machine Co.
(Steam) ....AAAA
Wheeler Condenser & En-
gineering Co., 120 Lib-
erty (Steam; Oil) ....A
N. Y.—Phelps
Lawrence Bostwick Mfg. Co.
(Cream) ....D
N. Y.—Schenectady
General Electric Co. (Mag-
netic) ....AAAA
N. Y.—Silver Creek
Howes Co., S. (Grain; Mag-
netic; Aspirating; Double
Receiving; Elevator; Hull-
ed bat; Magnetic; Screen-
ing; Single Receiving;
Warehouse; Coffee; Mill-
ing; Rice) ....A
Huntley Mfg. Co. (Grain;
Dustless) ....A
Invincible Grain Cleaner Co.
(Grain; Dustless)......A
N. Y.—Syracuse
Direct Separator Co., 218
Geddes (Steam; Oil)....C
Engelberg Huller Co.
Coffee) ....D
Wheeler Gravity Cream Sep-
arator Co. (Cream) ....E
N. Y.—Utica
Jones, Frank L. (Cream).C
N. Y.——Yonkers
Van Auken-Clevauc Co.
(Steam; Oil) ....E
OHIO—Akron
Burt Mfg. Co. (Oil) C
OHIO—Bluffton
Bluffton Cream Separator
Co. (Cream) ....D
Ohio Cream Separator Co.
(Cream) ....E
Sanitary Cream Separator
Co. (Cream) ....E
OHIO—Bucyrus
Amer. Clay Working Machy.
Co. (Stone) X
OHIO—Cincinnati
Amer. Tool Wks. Co., 6th &
Eggleston Av. (Steam;
Oil) ....AA
OHIO—Cleveland
Reliance Gauge Column Co.,
76 E. Prospect (Steam;
Oil) ....D
OHIO—Columbus
Jeffrey Mfg. Co. (Cement;
Plaster; &c).....AAAA
OHIO—Lima
Dairy Implement Co.
(Cream) ....D
OHIO—Springfield
Hoppes Mfg. Co. (Steam;
Oil) ....A
OHIO—Toledo
Lawrence Mfg. Co. (Cream)
D
PA.—Allentown
Lindstrom, Jno. T. (Steam;
Oil) ....E
PA.—Erie
Chapman Cream Separator
Wks., C. L. (Cream)...D
Sims Co. (Steam; Oil) ..D

SEPARATORS (Con.)

PA.—Harrisburg
Central Iron & Steel Co.....
........................AAAA
PA.—Lancaster
International Cream Separator Co. (Cream).....D
Martin Brick Mach. Mfg. Co., Henry (Stone) ....B
PA.—Muncy
Sprout Waldron & Co. (Grain Magnetic) .....A
PA.—Nazareth
Nazareth Fdry. & Mach. Co. (Steam) ....B
PA.—Philadelphia
Cresson Co., Geo. V., 18th & Allegheny Av. (Magnetic) ....AA
Etting, Edw. J., Land Title Bldg. (Magnetic) .....B
Kensington Engine Wks. (Ltd.) 245 N. Broad (Steam; Oil) ....A
Kutztown Fdry. & Mach. Co., Fidelity Bldg. (Compound for Steam Boilers) A
Paxson Co., J. W. (Magnetic) ....AA
Reid Creamery & Dairy Supply Co., A. H., 33rd & Market (Cream) ....A
Watson & McDaniel Co., 146 N. 7th (Steam; Oil)C
PA.—Pittsburg
Bonar & Co., Jas. Carnegie Bldg. (Steam; Oil).....B
McCormick, J. S. 25th & A. V. Ry. (Iron; Brass)..B
Riter-Conley Mfg Co. (Gas; Steam) ....AAA
PA.—Scranton
Union Steam Specialty Co. (Steam; Oil) ....A
PA.—Tatamy
Messinger Mfg. Co. (Grain) B
PA.—Washington
Petroleum Iron Wks. Co. (Automatic Gas; Steam) A
PA.—Waynesboro
Geiser Mfg. Co. (Grain) AAAA
PA.—West Chester
Sharples, Philip M. (Cream) ....AAAA
PA.—York
Dempwolf & Co., C. H. (Magnetic) ....A
Farquhar Co., A. B. (Ltd.) (Grain) ....AAA
Hench & Dromgold Co. (Lime; Ash) ....B
Spangler Mfg. Co. (Lime; Ash) C
VT.—Bellows Falls
Vermont Farm Machine Co. (Cream) ....A
VT.—St. Albans
St. Albans Fdry. & Implement Co. (Grain).....D
VT.—Windsor
Windsor Machine Co. (Steam; Oil) X
WIS.—Milwaukee
Dings Electro Magnetic Separator Co. 103 So. B'way (Magnetic) .....E
Prinz & Rau Mfg. Co. (Cockle) ....A
Steam Appliance Co., 577 Grove (Steam; Oil)....D
WIS.—Racine
Case Threshing Machine Co., J. I. (Grain).AAAA
Johnson & Field Mfg. Co. (Dustless; Grain; Elevator; Warehouse; Wheat; Coffee, Rice) ....F

SERGES

See Woolen Goods; Silk Goods

SERUMS

MICH.—Detroit
Parke, Davis & Co. (Biological) ....AAAA

SERVERS

ILL.—Chicago
Amerian Cutlery Co. (Salad) ....AA

SERVICES

CONN.—Meriden
Meriden Brittania Co. (Communion) .....AAAA
Wilcox Silver Plate Co. (Communion) ....AAAA
CONN.—Middletown
Middletown Silver Co. (Communion) ....E
CONN.—Wallingford
Simpson Hall, Miller Co. (Communion) ....AAAA
Wallace & Sons Mfg. Co., R. (Communion) ..AAAA
MASS.—New Bedford
Pairpoint Corpn. (Communion) ....AA
MASS.—Taunton
Reed & Barton Corporation (Communion) ......AAA
N. Y.—Brooklyn
Webster & Son, E. G. (Communion) ....AA
New York City
Gorham Mfg. Co. (Communion) ....AAAA
Lamb, J. & R. (Communion; Pocket Communion) ....D
Tiffany & Co. (Inc.) B'way & 15th (Communion)....
........................AAAA

SETS

CONN.—Bridgeport
Fray & Co., John S. (Screw Driver; Tool; Hollow Handle Tool) ....A
Hurwood Mfg. Co. (Nail)C
CONN.—Bristol
Barrett, W. L. (Soldering) D
CONN.—Chester
Bates, C. J. (Manicure)..D
CONN.—Derby
O. K. Tool Holder Co. (Lathe Tool; Fixture)..F
CONN.—Essex
Tiley-Pratt Co. (Manicure) D
CONN.—Hartford
Rogers Co., S. L. & G. H. (Carving) ....A
CONN.—Meriden
Bradley & Hubbard Mfg. Co. (Fire Brass; Fire Smokers Brass) .AAAA
Meriden Brittania Co.
Meriden Brittania Co. (Manicure; Carving) ..AAAA
CONN.—Naubuc
Williams Bros. Mfg. Co. (Carving) ....A
CONN.—New Britain
Humason & Beckley Mfg. Co. (Nail; Saw) .....A
Landers, Frary & Clark (Carving) ....AAA
Stanley Rule & Level Co. (Hollow Handle Steel)..
........................AAA
CONN.—New Haven
Kilborn & Bishop Co. (Saw) C
Sargent & Co. (Fire Brass; Sliding Door; Saw: Hollow Handle Tool).AAAA
CONN.—Oakville
Smith & Son, Seymour (Saw) ....D
CONN.—Plainville
Clark & Son, A. R. (Manicure) ....B
CONN.—Southington
Peck, Stow & Wilcox Co. (Fire; Saw; Nail; Rivet; Screw Driver; Tool; Soldering) ....AAAA
CONN.—Wallingford
Simpson Hall Miller & Co. (Carvers) ....AAAA
Wallace & Sons Mfg. Co., R. (Manicure; Carvers)..
........................AAAA
CONN.—Waterbury
Plume & Atwood Mfg Co.

SETS (Con.)

(Smokers Brass; Smokers Copper) ....AAA
Scovill Mfg. Co. (Smokers Brass) ....AAAA

ILL.—Chicago
Bentley-Ralston Co. (Frame Bicycle) C
Western Electric Co. (Repeating) ....AAAA

ILL.—Freeport
Arcade Mfg. Co. (Garden Tool; Soldering) ....AA
Stover Mfg. Co. (Soldering) AA

ILL.—Sterling
National Mfg. Co. (Door; Screen; Storm) C

IND.—Indianapolis
Atkins & Co., E. C. (Saw) ....AAAA

IND.—Marion
Canton Glass Co. (Water)H

IOWA—Fort Madison
Iowa Farming Tool Co. (Garden Tool) ....A

MD.—Baltimore
Chloride & Silver Dry-Cell Battery Co. (Electrical Testing) ....B

MASS.—Athol
Starrett Co., L. S. (Nail; Lathe Tool; Fixture; Combination) ....A

MASS.—Attleboro
Daggett & Clap Co. (Jewelry Ladies) ....A
Horton-Angell Co. (Jewelry; Combination) ....A

MASS.—Attleboro Falls
Mason-Ruggles Co. (Jewelry Combination) X

MASS.—Boston
Bailey & Co., C. J. (Manicure) ....B
Eyelet Tool Co. (Hook; Rivet) X
Standard Rivet Co. (Rivet; Self-feeding; Tubular)..B
Sturtevant Co. B. F. (Generating) ....AAA
Tubular Rivet & Stud Co. (Rivet; Self-Feeding Tubular) ....AAA

MASS.—Brockton
Tuck Mfg. Co. (Nail)....E

MASS.—Chartley
Freeman, Donghaday & Co. (Jewelry Combination).C

MASS.—Fiskale
Snell Mfg. Co. (Nail)....A

MASS.—Fitchburg
Sawyer Tool Mfg. Co. (Nail) C
Simonds Mfg. Co. (Saw).. AAA

MASS.—Florence
Florence Mfg. Co. (Manicure) ....A

MASS.—Greenfield
Goodell-Pratt Co. (Nail; Screw Driver; Tool) ..B

MASS.—Kingston
Drew & Co.. C. (Rivet; Rivet Self-Feeding Tubular; Brick) C

MASS.—Millbury
Buck, Chas. (Nail) .....B
Buck Bros. (Nail)......A

MASS.—Northampton
Northampton Cutlery Co. (Carvers) ....A

MASS.—Shelburne Falls
Mayhew Co. H. H. (Nail) D

MASS.—Springfield
Bemis & Call Hardware & Tool Co. (Saw).......A

MASS.—Turners Falls
Russell Cutlery Co., John (Carvers) ....AA

MASS.—Worcester
Warren Leather Goods Co. (Manicure) ....B

MICH.—Detroit
Strelinger Co., Chas. A. (Saw) ....B

MICH.—Grand Rapids
Baldwin, Tuthill & Bolton (Saw) ....B

MICH.—Jackson
Withington & Cooley Mfg. Co. (Garden Tool) ...AA

SETS (Con.)

N. J.—Elizabeth
Braunsdorf-Mueller Co. (Grommet; Nail; Rivet)D

N. J.—Newark
Atha Tool Co. (Button)..A
Bannister & Co., A. F. (Manicure) ....A
Celluloid Co. (Manicure).B
Johnson Wm. (Nail; Rivet) D
Kraeuter & Co. (Rivet)..X
National Saw Co. (Saw).B
Osborne Co., C. S. (Rivet) B
Storm Mfg. Co. (Nail)..B

N. J.—New Brunswick
New Jersey Lamp & Bronze Wks. (Smokers Bronze) AA

N. J.—Paterson
Royle & Sons', John (Rivet; Self Feeding Tubular)..A

N. Y.—Buffalo
Jewett & Co. (Fire) ....A
Keystone Mfg. Co. (Nail)B

N. Y.—East Syracuse
Benedict Mfg. Co., M. S. (Carving) ....AA

New York City
Bunnell & Co., J. H. (Repeating) ....B
Graham & Co., John H. 113 Chambers (Saw)..AA
Gould-Mersereau Co., (Fire Brass; Smokers Brass)B
Grote & Co.. F. (Smokers Ivory; Manicure) ......D
International Silver Co. 9 Maiden Lane (Silver Plaited Communion; Tea; Coffee; Curling; Manicure; Smokers) ...AAAA
Jackson & Co., Wm. H. (Fire; Brass) ....A
Jennings & Co.. C.E. (Nail; Hollow Handle Tool)..B
Judd & Co., H. L. (Fire; Brass; Smokers Brass)... AA
Lalance & Grosjean Mfg. Co. (Fire) .....AAAA
Millers Falls Co., 28 Warren (Screw Drivers; Tool; Soldering; Hollow Handle Tool) ....AA
Morrill. Chas., 277 B'way (Saw) ....D
Mott Iron Wks., J. L. (Fire Brass; Fire Steel) ..AA
Smith & Hemenway Co., 296 B'way (Saw; Shaving; Soldering) ....D
Taintor Mfg. Co., H. F. 113 Chambers (Saw)..B
Tower & Lyon (Screw Driver) ....B

N. Y.—Rochester
Robeson Cutlery Co. (Carving) ....A

N. Y.—Schenectady
General Electric Co. (Repeating) ....AAAA

N. Y.—Syracuse
Syracuse Twist Drill Co. (Nail) ....B

OHIO—Canton
Kohler & Co., F. E. (Saw) B

OHIO—Cincinnati
Eureka Foundry Co. (Fire Brass) ....A

OHIO—Cleveland
American Fork & Hoe Co. (Garden Tool) ....AAAA

OHIO—Columbus
Ohio Tool Co. (Nail; Rivet) AA

OHIO—Hamilton
Meyers Mfg. Co., F. J. (Saw) ....B

OHIO—Wilmington
Irwin Augur Bit Co. (Nail) B

PA.—Allegheny
Pittsburg Lamp, Brass & Glass Co. (Smokers; Brass) ....AAAA

PA.—Beaver Falls
Co-operative Flint Glass Co. (Ltd.) (Water)....A

PA.—Philadelphia
Disston & Sons, Henry

SETS (Con.)

..... (Saw) ....AAAA
Horn & Brother, Wm. H.
 (Eyelet) ....B
Plumb, Fayette R. Tucker
 & James (Blacksmiths'
 Fire) ....AA
Rumpp & Sons, C. F.
 (Manicure) ....AAA
PA.—Pittsburg
McKee Glass Co., S.
 (Water) ....D
U. S. Glass Co. (Water)...
 AAAA
PA.—Wilkesbarre
Nicholson & Co., W. H.
 (Nail) C
PA.—Wrightsville
Wrightsville Hdw. Co.
 (Garden Tool) ....B
R. I.—Pawtucket
Bliss Mfg. Co., R. (Cro-
 quet) ....AAAA
R. I.—Providence ...
Foster & Bro. Co., Theo.
 W. (Manicure) ......AA
Hancock & Co., Chas. E.
 (Jewelry; Combination;
 Shirt Waist) ....B
New England Pearl Co.
 (Shirt Waist) ....F
Vose Mfg Co., Geo. L.
 (Shirt Waist) ....B
Waite, Mathewson & Co.
 (Jewelry; Combination)B
W. VA.—Wellsburg
Riverside Glass Co.
 (Water) C
W. VA.—Wheeling
Central Glass Wks.
 (Water) ....A
WIS.—Milwaukee
Filer & Stowell Co. (Saw)
 AAA

SETTEES

See also Furniture

CONN.—Derby
Derby Silver Co.....AAAA
CONN.—Georgetown
Gilbert & Bennett Mfg. Co.
 (Wire) ....AAA
ILL.—Chicago
Barbee Wire & Iron Wks.,
 44 Dearborn (Iron; Lawn;
 Wire) ....B
IND.—Indianapolis
Over, Ewald (Lawn) C
IND.—Laporte
Michael Mfg. Co., Chas. H.
 (Wood; Lawn) C
IOWA—Dubuque
Adams Co. (Lawn) ......A
MD.—Baltimore
Smysers' Sons Co., Ely, 4
 Light (Iron) ....A
MASS.—Chicopee Falls
Belcher & Taylor Agrl.
 Tool Co. (Lawn) .....A
MASS.—Gardner
Bent & Bros., S. (Lawn).A
Haywood Bros. & Wake-
 field Co. (Rattan)AAAA
MASS.—Middleboro
Le Baron Fdry. Co. (Iron)
 D
MICH.—Detroit
Amos & Co., Chas. 94 W.
 Larned (Iron) ....F
MICH.—Grand Rapids
Haney School Furniture Co.
 B
MICH.—Kalamazoo
Kalamazoo Sled Co. (Lawn)
 A
MO.—St. Louis
Ludlow Saylor Wire Co.,
 4th & Elm (Iron) ...AA
Scarritt-Comstock Furniture
 Co. (Shoe Store) .....A
N. H.—Nashua
Fletcher & Webster Furn.
 Co. (Lawn) C
Nashua Novelty Wks.
 (Lawn) ....B
N. Y.—Buffalo
Ginther's Sons, J., 417
 B'way (Iron) ....A
New York City
Fiske Iron Wks., J. W., 39
 Park Place (Iron; Lawn)
 B

SETTEES (Con.)

Mace & Co., L. H., 117 E.
 Houston (Lawn) .....B
Mott Iron Wks., J. L., 88
 Beekman (Iron; Wood;
 Iron Frame Lawn) ..AA
Sperling, Albert (Rattan)F
Westervelt, A. B. & W. T.,
 102 Chambers (Iron)..B
N. Y.—Utica
Palmer, C. F. (Iron; Iron
 & Wood with Iron
 Frames; Lawn) C
OHIO—Cincinnati
Bromwell Brush & Wire
 Goods. Co. (Wire).....AA
Mitchell Furn. Co., Robt.
 624 Race (Lawn) ....AA
Stewart Iron Wks., 3rd &
 Culvert (Iron) ....A
OHIO—Cleveland
Van Dorn Iron Wks. Co.,
 1793 E. Madison Av.
 (Iron) ....AA
OHIO—Columbus
Sun Mfg. Co. ....A
OHIO—Dayton
Ohio Rake Co. (Lawn).AA
OHIO—Delaware
Delaware Chair Co. (Hall)
 A
OHIO—Hamilton
Meyers Mfg. Co., Fred J.
 (Wire) ....B
OHIO—Kenton
Champion Iron Co. (Iron)
 AA
OHIO—Springfield
Rogers Iron Wks. (Iron).B
PA.—Bausman
Bausman, D. H. (Iron;
 Wood; Iron Frame Lawn)
 C
PA.—Philadelphia
Darby & Sons, Edward
 (Wire) ....AA
Merritt & Co., 1024 Ridge
 Av. (Iron) ....B
PA.—South Bethlehem
Bethlehem Fdry. & Mach.
 Co. (Bench; Iron)......C
PA.—York
Farquhar Co., A. B.
 (Lawn) ....AAA
Keystone Farm Mach. Co.
 (Iron Lawn) ....B
VT.—Burlington
Champlain Mfg. Co. (Wood;
 Iron Frame Lawn)....B
VT.—Readsboro
Readsboro Chair Mfg. Co.
 (Folding; Opera Porta-
 ble) ....B
VA.—Norfolk
Whitehurst & Co., R. W.
 (Lawn) ....B
WIS.—Milwaukee
Wisconsin Iron & Wire
 Wks. 186 E. Water
 (Iron) ....D
WIS.—Oshkosh
Buckstaff- Edwards Co.
 (Lawn) ....AA
WIS.—Racine
Gold Medal Camp Furn.
 Mfg. Co. (Lawn) .....B
Racine Hardware Co......X
WIS.—Sheboygan
Crocker Chair Co. (Lawn)
 AAA

SETTERS

ILL.—Chicago
Masters Planter Co., (To-
 mato Plant) ....D
IOWA—Keokuk
National Machine Co. (Hy-
 draulic Tire) X
Standard Tire Setter Co.
 (Hand Power Tire) ...E
MASS.—Boston
Wood Machine Co., S. A.
 (Bit) ....AA
MASS.—Greenfield
Wells Bros. Co. (Axle)..A
MO.—St. Louis
Mac Gowan & Finnigan
 Fdry. & Machy. Co., Gay
 Bldg (House Cold Tire)B
N. Y.—Rochester
West Tire Setter Co. (Tire;
 Hub Band) C

SHADES *(Con.)*
Machine Made) C
Utility Shade Co. (Electric
Light) ....F
N. Y.—Brooklyn
Wemple Co., Jay C. (Window) ....A
N. Y.—Minetto
Minetto Shade Cloth Co.
(Window) ....AAA
New York City
Amer.-Belgian Lamp Co.
(Lamp Metal; Lamp Piano) ....D
Berndt, Joseph (Window)
C
Bloch & Co., L. D. (Lamp
Lace; Lamp Silk) .....A
Block Light Co., 17 Park Pl.
(Incand. Gas Light) ..A
Boston Artificial Leather
Co., 12 E. 18th (Car Window) ....D
Columbia Shade Cloth Co.
(Window) ....A
Cullen, Richard J. (Window)
C
Dale Co., 13th & 9th Av.
(Aluminum; Electric
Light) ....B
Frink, Isaac P., 551 Pearl
(Mirror Lined; Silk; Electric; Light; Billiard;
Lamp; Lace; Lamp Metal;
Lamp Mirror; Lamp Silk;
Half; Window ....A
Gage, John S. (Window) ..E
Gleason Mfg. Co., 20 W.
Houston (Electric Light;
Gas; Opal; Lamp) ....B
Gleason-Tiebout Glass Co.,
37 Murray (Gas) X
Houchin Co., Thos. W. (Gas)
D
Husted, Henry, 74 Murray
(Glass) ....F
James & Co., T. M. (Window) C
Kloes, F. G. (Window) ..F
Masten & Hund (Window)
C
Moore Bronze & Plate Co.,
M. E., 546 W. 23d (Silk
Lamp) ....D
Pantasote Leather Co., 29
B'way (Car Window) .AA
Phoenix Glass Co. (Gas
Light) ....A
Pratt Mfg. Co. (Electric
Light) X
Rochester Lamp Co. (Lamp)
X
Spencer Optical Co. (Eye)
C
Weiss & Krau Co. (Window)
C
Wemple & Co., Jay C. (Window; Window Decorated)
AA
Wetmore Co., S. H., 240
Pearl (Eye) ....D
Whaley & Co., J. A., 318
6th Av. (Art Lamp) ..E
N. Y.—Owego
Storrs Mica Co. (Mica
Lamp) C
N. Y.—Syracuse
Will & Baumer Co. (Candle) ....AA
OHIO—Columbus
Schroth & Potter (Window;
Window Decorated) ....B
OHIO—Dayton
Dayton Mfg. Co. (Car Window) ....A
PA.—Meadville
Shyrock, John J. (Window)
C
PA.—Philadelphia
Gill & Co. (Inc.) (Electric
Light; Gas; Glass; Glass
Fancy Glass Opal) .....A
Gillinder & Sons (Gas) ..A
Green & Co., Henry W.
(All Kinds; Window) ..A
Hale & Kilburn Mfg. Co.,
48 N. 6th (Car Window)
AAAA
Hall & Carpenter, 518 Race
(Electric Light; Gas;
Lamp) ....AA
Klemm & Co., 132 N. 5th
(Tin) C

SHADES *(Con.)*
McMaster, Eldridge & Naugle Co. (Window) ....D
Murray Co., J. J. (Electric
Light; Gas; Glass; Glass
Fancy; Lamp; Lamp Decorated) ....A
Pabst & Co. (Window) ...C
PA.—Pittsburg
Evans Co., Thos. (Gas
Lamp) ....D
Phoenix Glass Co. (Glass;
Porcelain; Candle; Electric Light; Gas; Lamp)
A
Pittsburg Dry Goods Co.
(Window) ....AAA
United States Glass Co.,
Bingham & S. 9th (Glass;
Pressed or Blown) .AAAA
PA.—Reading
National Brass & Iron
Wrks. (Candle) .....A
R. I.—Coventry
Interlaken Mills (Holland
Linen) ....AAA
WASH.—Tacoma
Harmon & Co., F. S. (Window) ....B
W. VA.—Hartford
Newton & Donnally (Electric Light) C
WIS.—Janesville
Hough Shade Corpn. (Window; Porch) ....B
WIS.—LaCrosse
Pacific Electric Co. (Electric Light) X

SHAFTING

See also Woodwork: Carriage

CAL.—San Francisco
Judson Mfg. Co. (Key
Seating) ....AA
CONN.—Ansonia
Farrell Fdry. & Machine Co.
(Heavy) ....AAAA
ILL.—Chicago
Allis-Chalmers Co., Home
Ins. Bldg. ......AAAA
American Steel & Wire Co.
The Rookery (Cold Drawn
Steel; Polished Steel)
AAAA
Borden & Selleck Co., 48
Lake ....B
Chicago Flexible Shaft Co.,
La Salle Av. (Flexible)
B
Link Belt Engineering Co.
(Iron; Cold Rolled) ..A
Republic Iron & Steel Co.
Cold Drawn Steel; Polished Steel; Key Seating)
AAAA
ILL.—Harvey
Bliss & Laughlin (Key Seated; Fitted with Couplings; Polished Steel)..B
IND.—Indianapolis
Nordyke & Marmon Co.
(Steel) ....AAA
KY.—Covington
Lukens Rolling Mill Co.
(Key Seating) ......:..B
MD.—Baltimore
Poole's Son & Co., Robert
(Iron, Cold Rolled; Steel,
Cold Rolled; Iron Hammered; Steel Hammered)
A
MASS.—Boston
Amer. Tool & Mach. Co.,
109 Beach (Iron Turned)
AA
Compressed Steel Shafting
Wrks., 393 Dorchester Av.
(Polished Steel) ......D
Ward & Sons, E. T. ....B
MASS.—Worcester
Coates Clipper Mfg. Co.
(Flexible) ....D
MICH.—Detroit
Buhl Malleable Co. ......A
MICH.—Port Huron
Port Huron Steel & Screw
Co. (Ltd.) (Cold Drawn
Steel; Polished Steel)..B

SHAFTING (*Con.*)

MINN.—Minneapolis
Minneapolis Steel & Machine
Co. ....A
MO.—St. Louis
Helmbacher Forge & Rolling
Mills Co. (Crank) ....AA
Medart Patent Pulley Co.,
3500 DeKalb (Cold Drawn
Steel; Polished Steel;
Steel, Turned) ......AA
N. J.—Perth Amboy
Pardee Works Co. (Plani-
shed Key Seating)..AAA
N. Y.—Binghamton
Stow Mfg. Co. (Flexible)
B
N. Y.—Buffalo
Buffalo Steel Shafting Co.,
ft. Baitz Av. (Polished
Steel) ....B
Howard Iron Wrks. ....AA
Noye Mfg. Co., John T.
(Steel) ....D
N. Y.—Schenectady
General Electric Co. (Iron,
Cold Rolled) .....AAAA
N. Y.—Warsaw
Warsaw Elevator Co. ....B
OHIO—Cincinnati
Lane & Bodley Co. (Iron,
Cold Rolled) ....A
OHIO—Cleveland
Cleveland City Forge &
Iron Co. (Crank ...AA
Dyson & Sons, Jos. ....A
Fitzsimons & Co., 626
B'way (Polished Steel)
D
Strong, Carlisle & Ham-
mond Co., 61 Frankfort
(Cold Drawn Steel) ....A
Union Rolling Mill Co.
(Steel) ....AAAA
OHIO—Columbus
Case Mfg. Co. ....A
Jeffrey Mfg. Co. ....AAAA
OHIO—Cuyahoga Falls
Falls Rivet & Machine Co.
(Cold Drawn Steel) ....A
OHIO—Shelby
Brightman Mfg. Co. (Pol-
ished Steel; Agricultural;
Polished) ....AA
OHIO—Toledo
Baker Bros. ....A
OHIO—Youngstown
Finished Steel Co. (Polish-
ed Steel) ....B
PA.—Beaver Falls
Standard Gauge Steel Co.
(Polished Steel; Turned;
Key Seating) ....B
Union Drawn Steel Co.
(Cold Drawn Steel; Pol-
ished Steel; Key Seating;
Iron; Cold Rolled Steel;
Cold Rolled) ....A
PA.—Braddock
Pittsburg Steel Shafting
Co (Key Seating).....X
PA.—Eddystone
Tindel-Morris Co. ......A
PA.—Ellwood City
Standard Seamless Tube Co.
(Hollow Seamless Steel)
B
PA.—Lancaster
Penn Iron Co. (Iron; Key
Seating) ....A
PA.—McKees Rocks
Lockhart Iron & Steel Co.
(Key Seating) ....AA
PA.—Philadelphia
Cambria Steel Co., Arcade
Bldg. (Cold Drawn Steel)
AAAA
Cresson Co., Geo. V., 18th
& Allegheny Av. (Cold
Drawn Steel) ....AA
Houston & Co., C. B., Gi-
rard Bldg. ....A
Sellers & Co., Wm. ..AAAA
Stow Flexible Shaft Co.
(Flexible) ....B
White Dental Mfg. Co., S.
S., 12th and Chester
Branches at New York,
Chicago, Boston, Atlanta
(Flexible) ....AAAA
Wolf Co., 523 No. 23d..AA

SHAFTING (*Con.*)

PA.—Pittsburg
Carnegie Steel Co. (Crank)
AAAA
Columbia Bridge Co., Park
Bldg. (Steel; Agricultur-
al; Polished) C
Crucible Steel Co., of Amer-
ica Frick Bldg. (Cold
Drawn Steel; Polished
(Steel) ....AAAA
Everson, B. M C
Gem Mfg. Co. (Flexible)
D
Jones & Laughlin Steel Co.
(Crank; Cold Drawn
Steel; Polished Steel;
Iron; Cold Rolled Steel;
Cold Rolled) ......AAAA
PA.—Rankin
Duquesne Forge Co. (Steel)
A
PA.—Reading
Reading Iron Co. (Polished
Steel; Key Seating)
AAAA
PA.—Titusville
Titusville Forge Co. (Forged
10 lbs. to 20 Tons) ....B
PA.—Wilkesbarre
Vulcan Iron Wrks. (Iron
Hammered; Steel Ham-
mered) ....AAAA
S. C.—Charleston
Valk & Murdock Iron Wrks.
(Iron, Cold Rolled) ....B
TENN.—Jackson
Southern Engine & Boiler
Wrks. ....A
VT.—Rutland
Patch Mfg. Co., F. R...A

SHAKERS

CONN.—Hartford
Rogers Co., S. L. & Geo. H.
(Pepper) ....A
ILL.—Chicago
Johnston & Chapman Co.
(Coal) ....D
N. J.—Newark
Williamson Wire Novelty
Co. (Soap) ....B
N. Y.—Manlius
Cheney & Son, S. (Stove)
A
N. Y.—Rochester
Rochester Stamping Co.
(Lemonade; Pepper)
AAA
OHIO—Cincinnati
Bromwell Brush & Wire
Goods Co. (Soap) ......A
OHIO—Dayton
Bates & Bros., D. L. (Milk)
B
PA.—Erie
Erie Specialty Co. (Milk;
Drink) ....B
PA.—Philadelphia
Coles Mfg. Co.,1615 N. 23d
(Milk) ....AAAA
Whitall Tatum & Co. (Milk)
AAAA
W. VA.—Wellsburg
Eagle Glass & Mfg. Co.
(Glass Salt; Pepper) ..A

SHAMPOOS

ILL.—Edwardsville
Edwardsville Brass Co...AA
ILL.—Peoria
Mexican Amole Soap Co.
C
New York City
Mott Iron Works, J. L.
AA

SHAMS

See Bedding

SHANKS

CONN.—Plantsville
Smith & Co., H. D. (Step)
AA
MAINE—Portland
Cox & Son, A. F. (Steel;
Shoe) ....A
MASS.—Boston
Fuller, F. T., 16 Lincoln
(Shoe) C

SHAPERS (Con.)

Co. (Machine) ....A
WIS.—Oshkosh
Hayes Machine Co., E. B.
(Machine; Double End;
Wood) ....E
WIS.—Racine
Racine Hardware Co.
(Wood) X

SHAPES

ILL.—Chicago
Republic Iron & Steel Co.
(Agricultural) .....AAAA
MICH.—Kalamazoo
Harrow Spring Co. (Agri-
cultural) ....B
N. J.—Newark
Jenkinson & Co., R. C.
(Sheet Steel) ....A
OHIO—Cleveland
Avery Stamping Co. (Sheet
Steel) ....A
PA.—Aliquippa
Kidd Bros. & Burger Steel
Wire Co. (Cold Drawn)
B
Vulcan Crucible Steel Co.
(Crucible Steel) .....B
PA.—Cheswick
Cheswick Mfg. Co. (Agricul-
tural; Special; High Car-
bon Steel) ....D
PA.—Dunbar
Dunbar Fire Brick Co. (Bo-
iler) ....B
PA.—Elizabethtown
Buchs Sons Co., A. (Pressed
Steel) ....B
PA.—Philadelphia
Janney, Steinmetz & Co.,
741 Drexel Bldg. (Sheet
Steel) ....D
Standard Pressed Steel Co.,
20th & Clearfield (Pressed
Steel) C
PA.—Pittsburg
American Steel Hoop Co.
(Agricultural; Special
Rolled) ....AAAA
(Plow) ....B
Columbia Bridge Co. (Cold
Drawn ; Polished) ...C
Jones & Laughlin Steel Co.
(Agricultural) ....AAAA

SHARES

ILL.—Carpentersville
Star Mfg. Co. (Plow) ...A
ILL.—Havana
Havana Metal Wheel Co.
Plow ....B
ILL.—Rockford
Weyburn Co. (Plow; Sister)
C

SHARPENERS

CONN.—Higganum
Cutaway Harrow Co. (Mow-
er Knife) X
CONN.—New Britain
Stanley Rule & Level Co.
(Dowel) ....AAA
ILL.—Aurora
Wilcox Mfg. Co. (Lawn
Mower) ....B
ILL.—Chicago
Bartlett & Son Co., M. J.,
196 So. Clark (Disc. Har-
row) ....F
Cassady-Fairbank Mfg. Co.
(Knife) C
Chicago Wheel & Mfg. Co.
(Disc; Lawn Mower;
Knife; Saw) C
Covel Mfg. Co. (Band Saw;
&c.) ....AA
Dick Co., A. B. (Pencil)
AA
Olcott Mfg. Co., 115 Dear-
born (Pencil) X
ILL.—Freeport
Schofield & Co. (Disc) D
ILL.—Moline
Clark Mfg. Co. (Disc) ..G
Deere & Mansur Co. (Disc)
AAAA
ILL.—Peoria
Herschel Mfg. Co., R.
(Disc) ....A

SHARPENERS (Con.)

ILL.—Rock Island
Rock Island Plow Co.
(Disc) ....AAAA
IND.—Indianapolis
Atkins & Co., E. C., 402
So. Illinois (Saw) ..AAAA
IND.—Plymouth
Clizbe Bros. Mfg. Co.
(Disc; Lawn Mower) ..D
IOWA—Davenport
B. B. Mfg. Co. (Disc) ..D
MASS.—Boston
Cutter Tower Co. (Pencil)
B
Cutter, Wood & Stevens Co.
(Saw) ....B
Frost Co., George (Pencil)
A
New England Novelty Mfg.
Co. (Knife) ....A
Webster Co., F. S. (Pencil)
AA
MASS.—Turner's Falls
Russell Cuttlery Co., John
(Knife) ....AA
MASS.—Worcester
Walker & Co., Oakley S.
(Tool) ....E
Winston, Samuel, Skate
Mfg. Co. (Skate) .....A
MICH.—Grand Rapids
Aldine Grate & Mantel Co.
(Shear) C
Baldwin, Tuthill & Bolton
(Knife) ....B
MICH.—Saginaw
Wickes Bros. (Saw) AAA
N. H.—Antrim
Goodell Co. (Pencil) ....A
N. H.—Pike
Pike Mfg. Co. (Knife;
Skate) ....A
N. J.—Jersey City
Dixon Crucible Co., Jos.
(Pencil) ....AAA
N. J.—Newark
Sacks Iron Fdy., Louis
(Knife) ....A
N. Y.—Buffalo
Rogers & Co., S. C. (Saw)
C
New York City
American Book Co. (Pencil)
AAAA
Amer. Lead Pencil Co.
(Pencil) ....AA
Bainbridge & Co., Henry
(Pencil) ....A
Faber, Eberhard (Pencil)
AA
Keuffel & Esser (Pencil)
AA
Millers Falls Co., 28 War-
ren (Knife) ....AA
N. Y.—Troy
Troy File Works (Skate)
D
OHIO—Cleveland
Osborn Mfg. Co. (Skate)
B
OHIO—Tiffin
Sterling Emery Wheel Mfg.
Co. (Knife) ....A
OHIO—Toledo
Ohio Steam Cooker Co.
(Knife) ....E
PA.—Carnegie
Carnegie Plow & Mfg. Co.
(Horse Shoe) ....D
PA.—Philadelphia
Disston & Sons (Inc.) Hen-
ry, Broad & Noble (Saw;
File) ....AAAA
Espen Lucas Machine
Works (Auto; Saw)....D
Royal Mfg. Co., 408 Com-
merce (Lawn Mower) .X
R. I.—Central Falls
Mossberg Wrench Co.
(Knife) C
R. I.—Providence
American Emery Wheel
Works (Knife) ....B
Diamond Machine Co. (Saw)
B
WIS.—Milwaukee
Filer & Stowell Co. Saw)
AAA

SHAVERS

CONN.—New Britain
Landers, Frary & Clark

SHAVERS (Con.)

(Tobacco) ....AAA
Stanley Rule & Level Co.
(Iron; Spoke) .....AAA
Union Mfg. Co. (Spoke)
AA
CONN.—Oakville
Smith & Son, Seymour
(Spoke) ....D
CONN.—Pine Meadow
Chapin-Stephins Co. (Iron
Spoke) ....A
ILL.—Chicago
Nicol & Co. (Ice) ....D
ILL.—Freeport
Arcade Mfg. Co. (Ice) ..A
Stover Mfg. Co. (Ice) .AA
ILL.—Downers Grove
Dickie Tool Co. (Ice) C
MASS.—Brockton
Snell & Atherton (Heel)..C
MASS.—Greenfield
Goodell Pratt Co .(Spoke)
B
N. J.—Flagtown
Clawson, C. C. (Ice) X
N. J.—Newark
Johnson, William (Spoke).D
N. Y.—Buffalo
White, L. & I. J. (Ice;
Spoke) ....A
New York City
Jennings Co., C. E., 42 Mur-
ray (Spoke) ....B
Millers Fall Co., 28 Warren
(Spoke) ....AA
N. Y.—Syracuse
Stearns & Co., E. C. (Iron;
Spoke) ....AA
OHIO—Cincinnati
Tatum Co., Samuel C.
(Spoke) ....B
OHIO—Dayton
Bates & Bros., D. L. (Ice)D
OHIO—Norwood
Cincinnati Tool Co. (Coop-
ers') ....B
OHIO—Ravenna
Williams, A. C. (Ice) ....A
OHIO—Tiffin
National Machinery Co.
(Bolt Head) ....AA
PA.—Erie
Erie Specialty Co. (Ice) ..B
PA.—Philadelphia
Enterprise Mfg. Co., 3d &
Dauphin (Ice; Smoked
Beef) ....AAAA
North Bros. Mfg. Co., Le-
high Av. & American (To-
bacco; Ice) ....AA
Stortz & Son, John, 210 Vine
(Ice) ....E

SHAVINGS

CAL.—Los Angeles
Calkins Co. (Zinc) ......E
CAL.—San Francisco
Pacific Tank Co. (Zinc) A
COLO.—Denver
Denver Fire Clay Co. (Zinc)
AA
ILL.—Chicago
Chicago Cork Works Co., 167
Plymouth Ct. (Cork) ..F
Kelso & Co., 209 S. Clinton
(Brewers') ....E
Redlich Mfg. Co. (Clarify-
ing; Brewers'; Vinegar;
Cider) ....B
MASS.—Barre Plains
Rich Co., T. E. (Baled) ..F
MASS.—Fall River
Varney & Sons, Isaac
(Baled) C
New York City
American Steel Wool Mfg.
Co., 451 Greenwich (Steel)
D
Cahn & Co., Hugo (Cork) A
N. Y.—Tonawanda
Alliger, F. I. (Baled) ....A
PA.—Pittsburg
Armstrong Cork Co. (Cork)
AAAA

SHAWLS

MAINE—Hartland
Linn Woolen Co. (Woolen)A
MAINE—Lisbon Falls
Worumbo Mfg. Co.
(Woolen) C

SHAWLS (Con.)

MASS.—Boston
Wendell, Fay & Co. (Com.)
A
MASS.—Dudley
Merrimack Woolen Co.
(Woolen) ....A
N. J.—Jersey City
Zimmerman & Sons Co.
(Knit) ....D
New York City
Abegg & Rusch (Com.)
AAAA
Converse, Stanton & Co.,
(Com.) ....AAA
Economy Hand Knit Wks. D
Greenblatt & Son, Louis
(Woolen) C
Libby & Co., H. J. (Com.) B
Masters & Co., Francis R.
(Com.) ....B
Patterson & Greenough
(Com.) ....B
Schefer, Schramm & Vogel
(Com.) ....AAAA
N. Y.—Waterloo
Waterloo Woolen Mfg. Co.
(Woolen) ....A
OHIO—Cleveland
Bamber & Neuman C
OHIO—Toledo
Ohio Knitting Mills Co.
(Fancy Knit) ....D
Peerless Knitting Mills Co.D
OREGON—Oregon City
Oregon City Mfg. Co. ...A
PA.—Philadelphia
Erskine, Alexander ......B
Koch, Justus (Shetland) B
Stringthorpe, Isaac (Wool-
en) C
R. I.—South Kingston
Peace Dale Mfg. Co. AAAA
UTAH—Manti
Hoggan, James E. (Cotton)C
UTAH—Provo City
Provo Woolen Mills Co.
(Woolen) ....B

SHEARS

**See also Machinery; Scis-
sors; Tools**

CONN.—Ansonia
Farrell Foundry & Machine
Co. (Allegator; Metal)...
AAAA
Acme Shear Co. (Grape;
Flower; Metal; Pruning;
Tinners; Button Hole).B
Bridgeport Hdw. Mfg. Co.
(Turners; Bankers; Pap-
er Hangers; Barbers)..B
Knapp & Cowles Mfg. Co.
(Pruning) C
Smith & Egge Mfg. Co.
(Hand for Cutting Wire
Rods; Strip Metal).....A
CONN.—Derby
Birmingham Iron Foundry
(Allegator) ....A
CONN.—Hamden
Henry Mfg. Co. Jno. T.
(Pruning) ....E
CONN.—Hartford
Pratt & Whitney Co.
(Power) ....AAAA
CONN.—Meriden
Meriden Brittania Co.
(Grape; Flower)..AAAA
Merriman, A. H. (Armlar)
C
CONN.—New Haven
Mersick & Co. C. S. (Com-
pound Levers; Pinion
Slitting; Metal).......A
Schallhorn & Co., Wm. (La-
dies; Pruning; Tailors)B
CONN.—Oakville
Smith & Son, Seymour
(Pruning; Hedge) ....D
CONN.—Waterbury
Waterbury-Farrell Foundry
& Machine Co. (Circle;
Power; Squaring; Hand;
Circulars; Metal) ....AA
DEL.—Wilmington
Diamond Shear Co. (Sheep;
Grass; Lawn; Hedge).F
Hilles & Jones Co., 900
Church (Beveling; Ro-

SHEARS (Con.)
tary; Channel; Metal)..
AA

ILL.—Chicago
Braun, J. G., 322 So. Paulina (For Heavy Boiler Plates, &c; For Sheet Metal Work) ....B
Consolidated Press & Tool Co., 96 N. Clinton (Metal; Rotary; Rotary Circle Cutting; Slitting) ....D
Scully Steel & Iron Co., 136 Fulton (Spitting; Rotary) ....A

ILL.—Moline
Williams White & Co. (Power; Bean; Channel; Beveling; Metal) ....A

IND.—Cambridge City
Bertsch & Co. (Hand; Hydraulic; Lever; Plate Splitting; Power; Slitting; Squaring; Bean; Channel; Metal) .....D

IOWA—Marshalltown
Lennox Machine Co. (Beveling; Plate Splitting; Beveling; Splitting Rotary) C

MAINE—Augusta
Gay, Geo. E. (Grass) ....E

MD.—Baltimore
Detrick & Harvey Mach. Co. (Slitting; Rotary)AA

MD.—Sparrows Point
Maryland Steel Co. (Hydraulic) ....AAAA

MASS.—Boston
Beaudry & Co. (Metal)...D
Chandler & Farquhar (Metal) ....A
Eyelet Tool Co., 40 Lincoln (Button Hole Cutting) X

MASS.—North Easton
New England Specialty Co. (Pruning) ....F

MASS.—South Boston
Perkins Machine Co., below E. 1st (Gate; Guillotine) H

MASS.—Springfield
Bullock Mfg. Co. (Jewelers Shears) ....

MASS.—Worcester
'dler, R. E. (Metal)...E
Morgan Construction Co. (Billet; Hydraulic; Bloom; Metal) ....A
Whitcomb Mfg. Co. (Power; Hand; Bench ....
Yong Mfg. Co., W. C. (Power) ....D

'''ICH.—Detroit
National Fulton Brass Mfg. Co. (Metal) ....AA

MICH.—Grand Rapids
Fox Machine Co. (Power) A
Wilmarth & Mormon Co. (Metal) C

MICH.—Saginaw
Wickes Bros. (Metal).AAA

MICH.—Saugatuck
Little Giant Mfg. Co. (Pruning) ....E

MINN.—Albert Lea
Edwards, C. D. (Lever) ..E

MO.—St. Louis
St. Louis Machine Tool Co., 1114 So. 8th (Slitting) X

N. J.—Grenloch
Bateman Mfg. Co. (Pruning) ....A

N. J.—Newark
Gould & Eberhardt (Circular; Metal) ....A
Heinischs Sons Co., R. (Tanners; Bankers; Paper Hangers'; Barbers'; Candy; Glass; Tailors; Button Hole Cutting) ....A
Ohl & Co., Geo. A. (Scroll; Squaring; Metal; Rotary; Slitting) ....A
Wiss & Sons Co., J. (Pruning) ....A

N. J.—Plainfield
Pond Machine Tool Co. (Hand) ....AAAA

N. J.—Salem
Ayars Machine Co. (Squar-

SHEARS (Con.)
ing; for Can Making etc.)
B

N. Y.—Auburn
Crane Fdry. & Machine Wks., W. W. (Allegator) D
Henry & Allen (Pruning Knives) ....A

N. Y.—Brooklyn
Adriance Machine Works (Metal) ....A
Bliss Co., E. W., 19 Adams (Power; Rotary; Slitting; Squaring; Metal; Foot; Circular) ....AAAA
Leffler & Co., Chas. (Metal; Rotary) ....D

N. Y.—Buffalo
Buffalo Forge Co. (Metal) AA
Niagara Machine & Tool Works. (Angle Iron; Bar & Plate; Bench; Beveling; Hand, Lever; Plate Slitting; Power; Rotary; Slitting; Squaring; Circular; Tinners'; Metal) ...AAA
Oliver Mfg. Co., W. W., 1483 Niagara (Jewelers' Bench) C
West Mfg. Co., 374 7th (Circle; Power; Rotary; Slitting; Squaring; Circular; Scroll) ....D

N. Y.—Elmira
Cronk & Carrier Mfg. Co. (Grass; Pruning; Grape)B
Field Force Pump Co. (Pruning) ....G

N. Y.—Lyons
Nagley Mfg. Co. (Pruning; Tobacco) C

New York City
Eckstein, Chas. G., 249 Centre (Sheet Iron Hand; Metal) ....D
Graham & Co.. John H.. 113 Chambers (Pruning) ..AA
McDougall & Potter Co., 602 W. 55th (Metal) ....D
Niles-Bement-Pond Co., 111 B'way (Beveling; Beam; Hydraulic; Power; Channel; Metal; Rotary)AAAA
Pels & Co., Henry, 66 Broad (Beam; Power; Channel; Metal; Rotary) C
Russell & Erwin Mfg. Co. (Hedge) ....AAAA
Sheridan, T. W. & C. B. (Boxmakers') ....A
Silberstein, A. L., 459 Bway. (Bankers'; Paper Hangers'; Barbers'; Button Hole; Electricians) ....B
Smith & Hemenway Co. 296 Bway. (Tinners'; Bankers'; Paper Hangers'; Barbers'; Electricians'; Garden; Grape; Mill; Pruning; Rubber; Leather) ....D
Watson-Stillman Co., 210 E. 43d (Beam; Hydraulic; Power; Hand; Channel; Metal; Rotary) ....A
Wiebusch & Hilger, 9 Murray (Dental; Tinners'; Bankers'; Paper Hangers'; Barbers'; Candy; Garden; Pruning; Sheep; Tailors) ....A

N. Y.—Rochester
Eichelman, C. W. (Pruning) F

N. Y.—Waterford
King & Co., J. M. (Wire) A

OHIO—Akron
Taplin, Riec Co. (Metal).A

OHIO—Alliance
Alliance Machine Co. (Angle Iron; Bar & Plate; Beam; Billet; Bloom; Gate & Guillotine; Hydraulic; Plate Splitting; Power; Channel; Metal) ....A
Morgan Engineering Co. (Rolling Mill Billet & Bloom; Hydraulic; Power; Squaring) ....AA

OHIO—Cincinnati
Cincinnati Punch & Shear

SHEARS (Con.)

Co. (Beam; Channel; Beveling; Metal) ....B
Keene & Co., Geo. C., 502 E. Front (Slitting; Squaring) ....F
Robinson Mfg. Co., J. M., 2d & Central Av. (Lever; Metal) ....B

OHIO—Cleveland
Cleveland Hardware Co. (Hand) ....A
Cleveland Punch & Shear Wks. Co., 156 Case Av. (Bar & Plate; Beveling; Billet & Bloom; Slitting; Beam; Channel; Metal) A
Reade Machinery Co. (Alligator; Double Angle Iron; Bar; Beam; Channel; Throat) ....D
Walker Co. (Metal) ....F

OHIO—Clyde
Clyde Cutlery Co. (Hedge, etc.; Pruning) ....D

OHIO—Dayton
Seybold Machine Co. (Guage Table) ....A

OHIO—Fremont
Clauss Shear Co. (Button Hole Cutting) ......AAA
International Cutlery Co. (Pruning) ....AAA

OHIO—Hamilton
Long & Allstatter Co. (Angle Iron; Bar; Beveling; Bar; Billet Bloom; Gate & Guillotine; Plate Splitting; Beam; Channel; Metal) ....AA
Niles Tool Works Co. (Power) ....AAAA

OHIO—Piqua
Poorman Mfg. Co. (Circle; Power; Rotary; Slitting; Squaring) ....E

OHIO—Tiffin
National Machinery Co. (Alligator; Power; Rotary; Vertical; Metal; Foot) AA

OHIO—Toledo
Heartley, G. W. (Alligator; Lever; Rotary) ....D
Toledo Machine & Tool Co. (Rotary; Power; Squaring) ....A

OHIO—Warren
Aetna Foundry & Machine Co. (Doubling Plate & Sheet Mill; Squaring)B
Denison Mfg. Co. (Pruning) C

OHIO—Youngstown
Sennett Co., Geo. B. (Metal) A

PA.—Allegheny
Carlin's Sons, Thos. (Metal; Alligator; Power) ......A

PA.—Allentown
Grammes & Sons, L. F. (Boxmakers') ....A

PA.—Bellefonte
Lingle, J. H. (Metal) ....D

PA.—Columbia
Columbia Grey Iron Casting Co. (Fruit; Flower Gathering) C

PA.—Harrisburg
Hickok Mfg. Co., W. O. (Boxmakers'; Guage Table) ....AA

PA.—Media
Wood, Wm. H. (Hydraulic) B

PA.—New Castle
Vulcan Fdy. & Mach. Co. (Bar & Plate; Doubling Plate; Sheet Mill; Rolling Mill; Lever; Squaring) .B

PA.—Norristown
Newbold & Son Co., R. S. (Bar Plate; Rotary; Rotary Pipe Cutting) .....A

PA.—Philadelphia
Evans Sons, Jno., 13th & Buttonwood (Crocodile) B
Johnson Co., Israel H. Jr., 1422 Callowhill (Squaring) ....A
National Cutlery Co., 3d & Lehigh Av. (Dental; Tinners'; Bankers'; Paper Hangers'; Barbers'; Pruning; Rotary; Rubber; Lea-

SHEARS (Con.)

ther; Tailors') C
Phila. Roll & Machine Co., (Inc.) cor. So. 23d & Washington Av. (Hydraulic; Beam; Channel; Metal) ....A
Phillips Sons Co., F. R., Penna. Bldg. (Rotary) C
Sellers Co., Wm. (Inc.) 1600 Hamilton (Beam; Beveling; Hydraulic; Power; Metal; Channel) ..AAAA
Smith Co., J. Barton, N. 4th & Somerset (Horse; Mule; Sheep; Grass; Lawn; Hedge) ....AA
Southwark Fdry. & Machine Co., 5th & Washington Av. (Hydraulic) ....AAA
Stortz & Son, Jno., 210 Vine (Paper Hangers') .....F
Wood & Co., R. D., 400 Chestnut (Gate; Guillotine; Hydraulic; Metal) AAAA

PA.—Pittsburg
Fischer Foundry & Machine Co. (Beam; Channel; Hydraulic; Metal) ....A
Garrison Fdy. Co., A. (Beam; Channel; Hydraulic; Metal) ....AAA
Heppenstall Forge & Knife Co. (Metal; Rotary) ...B
Hogg Iron & Steel Fdry. Co., Geo. A. 24th & R. R. (Bar & Plate; Beam; Doubling Plate; Sheet Mill; Upright Hydraulic; Heavy Scrap; Trimming; Channel; Metal) .....A
Lewis Fdry. & Machine Co., 1001 Bingham (Billet & Bloom; Doubling Plate; Sheet Mill; Rolling Mill Lever; Slitting; Squaring; Vertical) ....A
Macintosh, Hemphill & Co., ft. of 12th (Power; Metal) AAA
Mesta Machine Co., Lewis Block (Bar & Plate; Billet & Bloom; Doubling Plate; Sheet Mill; Hydraulic; Power; Squaring; Metal) ....AAA
Phillips & McLaren, 24th & Smallman (Bar & Plate; Billet & Bloom; Doubling Plate; Sheet Mills; Squaring; Vertical) ....B
Union Fdry. & Machine Co., West Carson (Doubling Plate; Sheet Mill; Slitting; Squaring) ....B
United Engineering & Fdry. Co. (Bar & Plate; Billet & Bloom; Doubling Plate; Sheet Mill; Hydraulic; Lever; Power; Squaring; Vertical; Beam; Channel; Metal) ....AAAA

PA.—Reading
Wilkinson Shear Co. (Border; Horse; Mule; Pruning; Weavers') ....D

PA.—Royersford
Royersford Fdry. & Machine Co. (Power; Beam; Channel; Metal) C

PA.—South Bethlehem
Bethlehem Fdry. & Machine Co. (Rotary; Metal) C
Bethlehem Steel Co. (Beam; Channel; Beveling; Hydraulic; Metal) ....AAAA

PA.—Titusville
Schatt & Morgan Cutlery Co. (Bankers; Paper Hangers'; Barbers') ..C

R. I.—Pawtucket
Pawtucket Mfg. Co. (Lever; Slitting; Vertical) ....A

R. I.—Providence
Standard Machinery Co. (Rotary) ....A

VT.—Springfield
Gilman & Son (Rotary) ..D

WIS.—Janesville
Bicknell Hardware Co. (Metal) ....E
New Doty Mfg. Co. (Angle; Iron; Beam; Beveling;

SHEARS (Con.)
Power; Hand; Channel;
Metal) ....B
Rock River Machine Co.
(Beveling; Metal) ....D
WIS.—Madison
King & Walker Co. (Lever;
Power; Slitting) ......B
WIS.—Oshkosh
Oshkosh Logging Tool Co.
(Pruning) C

SHEATHING

See also Paper

CONN.—Ansonia
Ansonia Brass & Copper Co.
(Copper) ....AAAA
CONN.—Manchester
Lydall & Foulds Paper Co.
(Paper) ....B
CONN.—Seymour
New Haven Copper Co.
(Copper) ....AA
CONN.—Waterbury
Holmes, Booth & Haydens
Co. (Copper; Yellow
Metal) ....AAAA
Randolph-Clowes Co.
(Metal) ....AAA
ILL.—Chicago
Barrett Mfg. Co. (Felt
Building) ....AAAA
Chicago Fire Proof Covering
Co., 18 No. Canal (Build-
ing; Asbestos) ....E
Hopkins, H. H., 50 Dear-
born (Building; Asbestos)
B
KY.—Henderson
Henderson Cotton Mills
(Wool) ....AAA
MD.—Baltimore
Baltimore Copper Smelting
& Rolling Co. (Copper)
AAA
MASS.—Boston
Chapman & Soden, 410 At-
lantic Av. (Building; As-
bestos) ....A
MASS.—East Walpole
Bird & Son, F. W. (Paper;
Paper Waterproof) ...AA
MO.—Kansas City
Midland Asbestos Mfg. Co.
(Building) ....E
MO.—St. Louis
Libby & Williams Co.
(Building; Asbestos) ..A
N. J.—Camden
Fay Manilla Roofing Co.
(Paper) ....D
N. Y.—Marcellus Falls
Lawless & Co., M. J.
(Paper) C
New York City
Asbestos Felting Works, 79
Maiden Lane (Building,
Asbestos) ....D
Gilmour Mfg. Co., Robt. M.
(Building, Asbestos) ...X
Hammerschlag Mfg. Co.
(Paper Waterproof) ...F
Hendricks Bros., 49 Cliff
(Copper) ....AAAA
Johns-Manville Co., H. W.,
100 William (Building,
Asbestos) ....AAAA
Standard Paint Co. (Paper)
A
N. Y.—Ravenswood
New York Asbestos Mfg.
Co. (Building) C
N. C.—Ramseur
Columbia Mfg. Co. (Cotton)
AA
OHIO—Lockland
Carey Mfg. Co., Philip
(Building, Asbestos) AAA
PA.—Ambler
Keasbey & Mattison Co.
(Building, Asbestos)
AAAA
PA.—Erie
Watson Co. H. F. (Build-
ing; Asbestos;; Paper;
Waterproof) ....AAA
PA.—Philadelphia
Asbestos Mfg. Co., 426 Mar-
ket (Building, Asbestos) A
Merchant & Co. (Copper) AA
PA.—Pittsburg
Hussey & Co., C. G.

SHEATHING (Con.)
(Copper) ....AAA
McConnell Co., Jno. A., 239
Water (Building, Asbes-
tos) ....B

SHEAVES

See also Blocks

COLO.—Denver
Davis Iron Wks. Co., M.
8th & Larimer (Wire;
Manilla Rope) ....AA
Mine & Smelter Supply Co.
(Wire; Manilla Rope)
AAAA
CONN.—Middletown
Wilcox, Crittenden & Co.
(Tackle Block) ....A
CONN.—New Britain
Corbin, P. & F. (Block)
AAAA
Russell & Erwin Mfg. Co.
(Door; Shutter; Sash)
AAAA
CONN.—New Haven
Sargent & Co. (Door; Shut-
ter; Sash) ......AAAA
CONN.—Southington
Peck, Stow & Wilcox Co.
(Door; Shutter) ..AAAA
CONN.—Torrington
Union Hardware Co. (Tackle
Block) ....AA
ILL.—Chicago
Caldwell & Son, H. W.,
Western Av. & 17th (Pow-
er Transmission) ....AA
Caldwell & Son Co., H. W.
Dearborn (Ball-Bearing
Show Case) ....E
Jones Fdry. & Machine Co.,
W. A., 143 W. North Av.
(Wire; Manilla Rope) ..A
Link Belt Mchry. Co., W.
3d & Stewart Av. (Wire;
Manilla Rope) .....AAA
Macomber & Whyte Rope
Co., 19 So. Canal (Power
Transmission; Wire Rope;
Manilla Rope) ....A
Nicol & Co., 57 W. Washn
(Door) ....D
Skillin & Richards Mfg. Co.,
147 Fulton (Rope) C
Thornburgh-Crell Co. (Rope)
X
Webster Mfg. Co., 1075 W.
15th (Wire; Manilla
Rope) ....AA
ILL.—Joliet
Bates Machine Co. (Wire;
Manilla Rope) ......AA
ILL.—Marseilles
Marseilles Mfg. Co. (Wire;
Manilla Rope) ....A
ILL.—Sterling
Charter Gas Engine Co.
(Block) ....A
ILL.—Sycamore
Patten Co., F. C. (Wooden)
A
IND.—Brazil
Crawford & McCrimmon Co.
(Wrought Iron Spoke
Rope) ....A
IND.—Indianapolis
Nordyke & Marmon Co.
(Wire Rope) ......AAA
IND.—Mishawaka
Dodge Mfg. Co. (Power
Transmission; Wire Rope;
Manilla Rope; Wood
Split) ....AAA
IOWA—Ottumwa
Johnston & Sharp Mfg. Co.
(Ball-Bearing) ....D
KANS.—Leavenworth
Great Western Mfg. Co.
(Wire; Manilla Rope) AA
KY.—Louisville
Caldwell Co., W. E., Bran-
deis Av. & Brook (Wire;
Manilla Rope) ......AA
MAINE—Portland
Laughlin Co., Thos. (Tackle
Block. Rope) ....A
Portland Co. (Rope) ...AA
MAINE—South Portland
Marine Hdw. & Equipment
Co. (Tackle Block) ...C

SHEAVES (Con.)

MD.—Baltimore
Poole Engineering & Machine Co. (Wire; Manilla Rope) ....AA

MASS.—Boston
Boston & Lockport Block Co., 160 Commercial (Tackle Block; Rope; Wire Rope; Hoisting) A

MASS.—Chicopee Falls
Spencers Sons, I. S. (Door) X

MICH.—Bay City
Garland Co., M. (Wire; Manilla Rope) C

MICH.—Marquette
Lake Shore Engine Wks. (Wire; Manilla Rope) ..A

MICH.—Northville
Dubuar Mfg. Co., J. A. (Tackle Block) X

MICH.—Saginaw
Saginaw Mfg. Co. (Wood Split) ....AA

MINN.—Minneapolis
Minneapolis Steel & Mchry. Co. (Wire; Manilla Rope; Power Transmission) AAA

MISS.—Meridian
Soule Steam Feed Wks. (Power Transmission) ..C

MO.—St. Louis
Broderick & Bascom Rope Co., 809 N. Main (Wire Rope; Hoisting; Power Transmission) ....AA
Kupferle, John C., cor. 2d & Mound (Sliding Door) AA
Leschen & Sons Rope Co., A., 920 No. 1st (Hoisting; Wire Rope; Manilla Rope; Power Transmission; Tackle Block) .....AAA
Medart Patent Pulley Co., 3500 De Kalb Av. (Wire; Manilla Rope) ......AAA

N. J.—High Bridge
Taylor Iron & Steel Co. (Rope) ....AAAA

N. J.—Trenton
Trenton Iron Co. (Wire; Manilla Rope; Power Transmission) ....A

N. Y.—Buffalo
Contractors Plant Mfg. Co., 129 Erie (Tackle Block; Wire; Manilla Rope) ..B

N. Y.—Lockport
Western Block Co. (Rope) U

New York City
Brown Co., A. & F., 25 Dey (Wire; Manilla Rope) ..B
Fairbanks Co., 416 Broome (Power Transmission) ....AAAA
Lidgerwood Mfg. Co. (Rope) ....AAA
Mead & Co., Jno. A., 11 Bway. (Wire; Manilla Rope) ....AA
N. J. Fdry. & Machine Co., 9 Murray (Wire; Manilla Rope) ....D
Tiebout, W. & J., 118 Chambers (Door; Tackle; Block) ....B

N. Y.—Niagara Falls
Dobbie Fdry. & Machine Co. (Hoisting) ....D

N. Y.—Syracuse
Stearns & Co., E. C. (Block) ....AA

OHIO—Canton
Aultman Co. (Wire; Manilla Rope) ......AAAA

OHIO—Cincinnati
Greenwald Co., I. & E. (Power Transmission) ..A

OHIO—Cleveland
Bartlett, C. O. & Snow Co. (Power Transmission) ..A
Cleveland Block Co., 163 River (Tackle Block) ...B
Hill Clutch Co., ft. Waverley Av. (Wire; Manilla Rope) ....B
Walker & Co. (Rope) X
Wellman-Seaver-Morgan Co. (Hoisting) ....AAAA

OHIO—Columbus
Case Mfg. Co. (Hoisting; Power Transmission) ..A
Jeffrey Mfg. Co. (Power

SHEAVES (Con.)

Transmission) ....AAAA

OHIO—Cuyahoga Falls
Falls Rivet & Machine Co. (Wire; Manilla Rope) ..A

OHIO—Nelsonville
Nelsonville Foundry & Machine Co. (Rope) ......B

OHIO—Piqua
Piqua Handle & Mfg. Co. (Block; Pulley) ......A

PA.—Allegheny
Carlin's Son, Thos. (Block; Power Transmission) ...A

PA.—Bellwood
Bellwood Mfg. Co. (Rope)D

PA.—Chambersburg
Wood's Sons, T. B. (Wire; Manilla Rope) ....A

PA.—Monongahela
Monongahela Mfg. Co. (Track, Vertical) ......B
Robinson Machine Co. (Wire; Manilla Rope) ..B

PA.—Nazareth
Nazareth Fdy. & Mach. Co. (Hoisting; Power Transmission) ....B

PA.—New Castle
Pennsylvania Engineering Wks. (Hoisting; Power Transmission) ....AA

PA.—Philadelphia
Cresson & Co., Geo. V., 18th & Allegheny Av. (Power Transmission; Wire Rope; Manilla Rope) ......AA
Link Belt Engineering Co. (Power Transmission; Wire Rope; Manilla Rope) ....AA
Sellers & Co., (Inc.) Wm. (Rope; Power Transmission) ....AAAA

PA.—Pittsburg
Jones & Laughlin Steel Co. (Power Transmission; Wire Rope; Manilla Rope) ....AAAA
Pittsburg Pulley Co., Frick Bldg. (Wire; Manilla Rope) ....B
Union Fdry. & Mach. Co. (Wire; Manilla Rope) B

PA.—Pittston
Exeter Machine Wks. (Wire Rope; Manilla Rope) AA

PA.—Reading
Penn. Hdw. Co. (Door) AA
Reading Hdw. Co. (Door; Shutter; Sash) ....AAAA

PA.—South Bethlehem
Bethlehem Fdy. & Machine Co. (Power Transmission) C

PA.—Tamaqua
Tamaqua Mfg. Co. (Rope)B

PA.—Wilkesbarre
Hazard Mfg. Co. (Wire; Manilla Rope) ....AAAA
Vulcan Iron Wks. (Wire; Manilla Rope) ....AAAA

PA.—Wrightsville
Wrightsville Hdw. Co. (Door; Sliding Door) ..B

WIS.—Milwaukee
Allis-Chalmers Co. (Rope) ....AAAA
Filer & Stowell Co. (Ltd.) (Rope; Wire Rope) AAA

WIS.—South Milwaukee
Stowell Mfg. & Fdry. Co. (Door) ....A

SHEDDERS

ILL.—Batavia
Appleton Mfg. Co. (Fodder) A

ILL.—Sterling
Keystone Mfg. Co. (Fodder) AA

OHIO—Canton
Dick Agricultural Wks., Jos. (Fodder) ....A

SHEDS

IOWA—Clinton
Clinton Bridge & Iron Wks. (Train) ....AA

MO.—St. Louis
Christopher & Simpson Arch Iron & Fdy. Co. (Steel

SHEDS (Con.)
Frame) ....AA
PA.—Steelton
Pennslyvania Steel Co.
(Iron Train) ......AAAA

SHEEP LINED COATS

See Clothing: Men's

SHEEPSKINS

See also Leather

CAL.—Napa
Sawyer Tanning Co. ....A
CAL.—San Francisco
Norton Tanning Co. .....A
ILL.—Chicago
Weil, J. M. & V. .....A
MASS.—Boston
Leviseur & Conway ....AA
Winslow Bros. & Smith Co.
..................AA
MASS.—Lynn
Hoffman & Son, A. B. ...A
MASS.—Peabody
Southwick & Co., L. B. ..A
MICH.—Detroit
Schmidt, Traugott & Sons
(Inc.) ....AA
N. J.—Newark
Mahon Leather Co., Mark
W. X
Ziegel, Eisman & Co. ....A
N. Y.—Buffalo
Schoelkopf & Co.........AA
New York City
Garnar & Co., Thos. ....AA
Neumann & Co., R. .....A
U. S. Leather Co. ....AAAA
Young Co., Richard ....AA
OHIO—Cincinnati
Trautmann & Co., C. ....A
PA.—Philadelphia
Holmes, Henry ....A
McAdoo & Allen C
VT.—Hyde Park
Page, Carroll S. (Pickled)A

SHEETINGS

See Cotton Goods

SHEETS

See also Cotton Goods; Iron; Steel

CONN.—Bridgeport
American Tube & Stamp-
ing Co. (Iron; Steel;
Cold Rolled Steel) AAAA
CONN.—Hartford
Bailey Mfg. Co. (Copying)
..................C
CONN.—Seymour
Seymour Mfg. Co. (German
Silver) ....AAA
CONN.—Waterbury
Benedict & Burnham Mfg.
Co. (German Silver)AAAA
Plume & Atwood Mfg. Co.
(German Silver) ..AAA
Scovill Mfg. Co. (Alumi-
num; German Silver)
..................AAAA
Waterbury Brass Co. (Ger-
man Silver) ......AAAA
DEL.—Wilmington
McCullough Iron Co. (Gal-
vanized Iron; Steel Roof-
ing) ....AA
ILL.—Chicago
Eureka Blotter Bath Co.
(Copying Cloth) ......E
Republic Iron & Steel Co.
(Galvanized Iron; Steel)
..................AAAA
ILL.—Peru
American Nickeloid & Mfg.
Co. (Nickelized; Nickel-
ized Zinc) ....A
N. J.—Newark
Ohl & Co., Geo. A. (Corru-
gating Machinery) .....B
N. Y.—Buffalo
Niagara Machine & Tool
Wks. (Corrugating Ma-
chinery) ....A

SHEETS (Con.)
New York City
Ansonia Brass & Copper Co.,
99 John (Galley) AAAA
Boker & Co., Herman, 101
Duane ..(Nickel; Steel,
Nickel Covered) ...AAA
Goodyear India Rubber
Glove Mfg. Co. (Copying)
..................AAAA
Johns-Manville Co., H. W.
100 William (Asbestos
Packing) ....AAAA
Hobson, Houghton & Co.,
98 John (Hot Rolled
Steel) ....B
Jessop & Sons, Wm., 91
John (Iron; Steel; Cold &
Hot Rolled Steel) ...AAA
New York Silicate Book
Slate Co. (Black; White
Silicate) ....D
Wardlow, S. & C., 95 John
(Iron; Steel; Cold & Hot
Rolled Steel) ....A
OHIO—Cleveland
Federal Mfg. Co. (Cold
Rolled Steel) ....AAAA
Garry Iron & Steel Co.
(Curved Currogated; Dou-
ble Refined Puddled Iron;
Galvanized Iron; Steel;
Roofing; Cold & Hot
Rolled Steel) ....A
OHIO—Elyria
Columbia Steel Wks. (Fed-
eral Mfg. Co. Owners)
(Steel, Planished & Pol-
ished) ....AAAA
OHIO—Niles
Empire Iron & Steel Co.
(Steel, Bow Socket) ...A
OHIO—Youngstown
Youngstown Iron Sheet &
Tube Co. (Double Refined
Puddled Iron; Electrical;
Galvanized Iron & Steel;
Polished Steel; Range;
Roofing, Cold & Hot
Rolled Steel) ....AAAA
Youngstown Iron & Steel
Roofing Co. (Double Re-
fined Puddled Iron; Gal-
vanized Iron & Steel;
Stove; Body; Cold & Hot
Rolled Steel) ....AA
PA.—Conshohocken
Wood & Bros. Co. (Electri-
cal Iron & Steel; Loco-
motive Jacket Steel) AA
PA.—New Castle
Elliott-Blair Steel Co. (Cold
Rolled Steel) ....A
PA.—Philadelphia
Disston & Sons, Henry
(Iron; Steel; Cold & Hot
Rolled Steel) ....AAAA
Hill Mfg. Co., B. B.
(Copying) ....B
Janney Steinmetz & Co.,
Drexel Bldg. (Iron; Steel)
..................D
Phosphor-Bronze Smelting
Co., 2200 Wash. Av.
(Phosphor Bronze) ....A
Reeve & Son, Paul S.
(Phosphor Bronze) ....B
Wood Iron & Steel Co.,
Alan (Iron, Steel, Roof-
ing) ....AAAA
PA.—Pittsburg
Allegheny Steel & Iron Co.
(Electrical, Iron; Steel;
Steel for Electroplating;
Steel Stamping) ....AAA
American Steel & Tin Plate
Co. (Bicycle Tube;
Curved; Corrugated; Elec-
trical; Enameling Steel;
Milk Can Body; Polished
Steel; Range; Roofing;
Stove Body; Cold Rolled
Steel; Hot Rolled Steel;
Tinned Dairy) ....AAAA
Goff, Horner & Co. (Ltd.)
(Electrical, Iron; Steel;
Open Hearth Steel; Roof-
ing; Cold Rolled Steel) A
Pittsburg Reduction Co.,
Park Bldg. (Aluminum)
..................AAAA
Scaife & Sons Co., Wm. B.
(Curved Corrugated; Gal-

SHEETS (Con.)
vaulzed; Iron; Steel;
Roofing) ....AAA
Zug & Co. (Ltd.) (Galva-
nized Iron; Steel) AAAA
VA.—Norfolk
Norfolk Creosoting Co.
(Piling) ....A
WIS.—Kenosha
Chicago Brass Co. (German
Silver) ....AA
WIS.—Milwaukee
Pressed Steel Tank Co.
(Steel, Cylinder; Tank)B

SHELLACS

IOWA—Sioux City
Warner, Freiday & Co.
(Bowling Alley) C
MICH.—Detroit
Berry Bros. (Ltd.) AAAA
Detroit White Lead Works
AAA
N. J.—Newark
Murphy Varnish Co. AAAA
New York City
Feigel & Bro., M., 149 Mer-
cer (Bleached) ....B
Gillespie Sons., L. C. ..AA
Hooper & Androvette, 218
Fulton (Bleached) .AAA
Kasebier & Co., E. .....D
Longman & Martinez. AAA
Marx & Rawolle ....AA
Mayor & Loewenstein AAA
New York Shellac Co.,
AAAA
Pratt & Lambert........B
Rogers & Pyatt, 78 Maiden
Lane (Bleached) .....A
Zinsser & Co., W., 197 Will-
iam (White Gum) .....A
OHIO—Cleveland
Cleveland Varnish Co. ..AA
Glidden Varnish Co.....AA
PA.—Philadelphia
Felton, Sibley & Co., 136
No. 4th ....AAA
R. I.—Providence
U. S. Gutta Percha Paint
Co. ....A

SHELLERS

**See also Agricultural Imple-
ments**

CONN.—New Britain
Landers, Frary & Clark
(Pea) ....AAA
CONN.—New Haven
Harrison, Leonard D. (Corn)
H
ILL.—Batavia
Appleton Mfg. Co.(Corn)..A
Batavia Windmill Co. (Corn)
B
Challenge Windmill & Feed
Mill Co. (Corn) ....AAA
U. S. Wind Engine &
Pump Co. (Corn; Corn
Power) ....AA
ILL.—Chicago
Bristol & Gale Co., 110 W.
Washington (Corn) ...B
Henion & Hubbell (Corn).A
ILL.—Decatur
Tait Mfg. Co., F. B. (Corn)
A
Union Iron Wks. (Power
Corn) ....A
ILL.—Elgin
Elgin Wind Power & Pump
Co. (Corn) ....B
ILL.—Freeport
Stover Mfg. Co. (Corn).AA
ILL.—Joliet
Joliet Mfg. Co. (Corn; Corn
Power) ....A
ILL.—Marseilles
Marseilles Mfg. Co. (Cy-
clone Spring Power; Hand
(Corn) ....AA
ILL.—Moline
Barnard & Leas Mfg. Co.
(Corn) ....AA
Deere & Mansur Co. (Power
Corn) ....AAAA
ILL.—Ottawa
King & Hamilton Co. (Corn;
Corn Power) ....AA

SHELLERS (Con.)
ILL.—Peoria
Kingman & Co. (Corn) AAA
Luthy & Co. (Corn) ......A
ILL.—Sandwich
Sandwich Mfg. Co. (Horse
and Steam Power; Centri-
fugal Corn) ....:..AA
ILL.—Sterling
Keystone Co. (Power and
Hand Corn) ....AA
IND.—Butler
Butler Co. (Corn) ....B
IND.—Evansville
Kratz Bros (Corn) X
IND.—Indianapolis
Nordyke & Marmon Co.
(Hand and Power Corn)
AAA
IND.—Lafayette
McGrath, R. H. (Corn for
Warehouse) ....E
IND.—Richmond
Richmond City Mill Wks.
(Corn) ....B
IOWA—Dubuque
Schrieber & Couchar Mfg.
Co. (Corn) ....A
IOWA—Webster City
Litchfield Mfg. Co. (Corn)
A
KANS.—Leavenworth
Great Western Mfg. Co.
(Corn; Cleaners; Corn
Power) ....AA
MD.—Baltimore
Sinclair-Scott Co. (Corn
Power; Pea) ....E
MASS.—Boston
Ames Plow Co. (Corn)
AAAA
MASS.—Chicopee Falls
Belcher & Taylor Agr. Tool
Co. (Corn) ....A
MASS.—Millford
Mann Co., F. W. (Ball
Bearing Corn) ....A
MICH.—Grand Ledge
Streeter, Hiram, R. (Corn)
F
MICH.—Mount Clemens
Donaldson Bros. (Corn)..A
MICH.—Port Huron
Port Huron Engine & Thre-
sher Co. (Power Corn)
AAA
MINN.—Minneapolis
Howell & Co., R. R. (Corn)
B
Minneapolis Threshing Ma-
chine Co. (Corn) AAAA
MINN.—Winona
New Winona Mfg. Co.
(Corn) A
MO.—Kansas City
Kansas City Hay Press Co.
(Hand Cylinder; Spring
Belt Corn) ....AA
MO.—St Louis
Kingsland Mfg. Co. (Corn)
B
Rumsey Mfg. Co., L. M.
(Corn) ....AAA
Whitman Agr. Co., 6900 So.
B'way (Corn) ....AA
N. Y.—Buffalo
Noye Mfg. Co (Corn; Corn
Power) X
N. Y.—Mount Morris
Genesee Valley Mfg. Co.
(Hand and Power Corn)
B
N. Y.—Seneca Falls
Gould's Mfg. Co. (Corn)
AAA
Rumsey & Co. (Corn; Corn
Separators) ....A
N. Y.—Silver Greek
Huntley Mfg. Co. (Corn).A
N. Y.—Syracuse
Engelberg Huller Co. (Rice)
D
N. Y.—Utica
Standard Harrow Co. (Corn)
A
N. C.—Winston Salem
Salem Iron Wks. (Corn) .A
OHIO—Akron
Whitman & Barnes Mfg. Co.
(Corn) ....AAAA
OHIO—Berea
Dunham & Son, J. W.
(Corn) ....B

SHELLERS (Con.)

OHIO—Cincinnati
Straub Machinery Co. (Corn)
.............................B

OHIO—Cleveland
Bartlett & Snow Co., C. O.
(Corn) ....A
Garry Iron & Steel Co.
(Corn) ....A
OHIO—Columbus
Case Mfg. Co. (Corn;
Separaters) ....A
OHIO—Dayton
Ohio Rake Co. (Corn) ..A
OHIO—Fremont
Lehr Agricultural Co. (Corn)
.............................B
OHIO—Lancaster
Eagle Machine Co. (Corn;
Corn Power) ....A
Hocking Valley Mfg. Co.
(Corn) ....A
OHIO—Middletown
McSherry Mfg. Co (Corn) A
OHIO—New Lexington
Star Mfg. Co. (Corn) ....B
OHIO—Plymouth
Root Bros. Co. (Corn) ...B
OHIO—Sandusky
Klotz Machine Co. (Corn).C
OHIO—Springfield
Foos Mfg. Co. (Corn) ...A
Rogers Iron Co. (Corn) ..B
Ross Co., E. W. (Corn) ..A
OHIO—Tiffin
Tiffin Wagon Co. (Corn) AA
PA.—Elizabethtown
Buch's Sons Co., A. (Corn)
.............................A
PA.—Marietta
Penna. Electric Co. (Corn)
.............................C
PA.—Mountville
Mountville Mfg. Co. (Corn)
.............................C
PA.—Muncy
Sprout, Waldron & Co.
(Corn) ....A
PA.—Tatamy
Messinger Mfg. Co. (Power
and Hand Corn) ......B
PA.—York
Farquhar Co., A. B. (Corn)
.............................AAA
Hench & Dromgold Co.,
(Corn) ....B
Keystone Farm Machine Co.
(Corn; Corn Power) ...B
Spangler Mfg. Co. (Corn)
.............................C
TENN.—Clarksville
Patch, A. H. (Hand Corn)
.............................B
VT.—Derby Line
Butterfield & Co. (Corn .A
VA.—Norfolk
Billups Son & Co., C. (Corn)
.............................A
White & Bros. S. R. (Corn)
.............................A
Whitehurst Co., R. W. (Corn
and Corn Separators)..B
VA.—Richmond
Cardwell Machine Co. (Corn;
Corn Power) ....A
WIS.—Janesville
Rock River Machine Co.
(Hand Corn) ....D
WIS.—Manitowoc
Smalley Mfg. Co. (Corn) .B
WIS.—Marinette
Stevens Co., A. W. (Power
Corn) ....AA
WIS.—Racine
Freeman & Sons Mfg. Co.,
S. (Hand Corn) ......A
WIS.—West Bend
Silberzahn Bros. (Hand
Corn) C

SHELLS

See also Cartridges

CONN.—Bridgeport
Union Metallic Cartridge Co.
(Paper and Brass Car-
tridge; Brass Shot; Paper
Shot; Loaded Paper; Shot
Gun) ....AAA
CONN.—New Haven
Winchester Metal Cartridge

SHELLS (Con.)

Co. (Shot Gun; etc.)
.............................AAAA
CONN.—Torrington
Union Hardware Co. (Push
Button) ....AA
CONN.—Waterbury
Randolph Clowes Co. (Seam-
less Brass; Copper) AAA
Scovill Mfg. Co. (Brass)
.............................AAAA
Waterbury Brass Co. (Brass
Shot; Paper Shot) AAAA
ILL.—Alton
Western Cartridge Co. (Shot
Gun; etc.) ....A
MASS.—Boston
Baker & Co., Walter
(Cocoa) ....AAAA
MASS.—Chicopee Falls
Stevens Arms & Tool Co., J.
(Rifled Bullet) ....AAA
MASS.—Lowell
United States Cartridge Co.
(Shot Gun; etc.) ....AA
N. J.—High Bridge
Taylor Iron & Steel Co.,
(Roll) ....AAAA
New York City
Tower & Lyon Co., 95
Chambers (Loaded Paper)
.............................B
OHIO—Cincinnati
Peters Cartridge Co.
(Loaded Paper; Paper
Shot; Shot Gun; etc.)
.............................AAAA
PA.—Lancaster
Hershey Chocolate Co.
(Cocoa) ....AAAA
PA.—Philadelphia
Chester Steel Castings Co.
(Roll) ....AA
Janney, Steinmetz & Co.,
Drexel Bldg. (Automobile;
Marine Boiler; Seamless
Ordinance) ....D
Latrobe Steel Co., Girard
Bldg. (Rock Crusher Roll)
.............................AAAA
Wilbur & Sons, H. O.
(Cocoa) ....AAA
PA.—Pittsburg
Scaife & Sons Co., Wm. B.,
(Tank; Automobile; Ma-
rine Boiler) ....AAA
PA.—Washington
Petroleum Iron Wks. Co.
(Coke Oven) ....A
PA.—York
York Chemical Works
(Crushed; Flint) ......A
WIS.—Milwaukee
Pressed Steel Tank Co.
(Seamless Steel) ......B

SHELVES

See Furniture

CONN.—New Haven
Atlas Mfg. Co. (Detach-
able) ....F
ILL.—Edwardsville
Illinois Marble Co. (Slate
Refrigerator) C
ILL.—Sterling
Novelty Iron Works (Stove
Pipe) ....E
IND.—Indianapolis
Tucker & Dorsey Mfg. Co.
(Detachable) ....A
IOWA—Dubuque
Adams Co. (Stove Pipe)..A
MASS.—Boston
Matthews Consolidated
Slate Co., 199 Washn.
(Slate Refrigerator) ...X
MASS.—Worcester
National Mfg. Co. (Stove
Pipe) ....A
VT.—Poultney
Fleming Slate Co. (Slate
Bracket) C
WIS.—Milwaukee
Milwaukee Mirror & Art
Glass Wks. (Plate Glass)
.............................C

SHELVING

ALA.—Stanton
Dyer, W. C. (Store).....E

SHELVING (Con.)

ILL.—Chicago
Warren, Mfg. Co., J. D. Masonic Temple (Hardware Store) ....B

IOWA—Glidden
McNaught & Sons, G. W. (Store) ....D

MASS.—Boston
Library Bureau ....AA

MICH.—Grand Rapids
Grand Rapids Show Case Co. (Drug) ....A

OHIO—Canton
Berger Mfg. Co. (Steel Library) ....AA

SHIELDS

CONN.—Bridgeport
Canfield Rubber Co. (Dress) AA
Taylor, Thomas P. (Dress) A

CONN.—Middletown
Omo Mfg. Co. (Dress).....C

ILL.—Chicago
Andrews & Johnson Co., 260 Washington Boul. (Radiator) ....B
Monash-Younker Co., 201 S. Canal (Radiator) .....B
Prentice Co., L. H., 34 Sherman (Radiator) ...A

MD.—Baltimore
Brinkman & Co., A. H. (Dress) C

MASS.—Andover
Tyer Rubber Co. (Nipple)

MICH.—Detroit
Barnum Wire & Iron Works, E. T. (Radiator) ......B

N. J.—Newark
Transparent Cellulose Products Co. (Vaccination).D

N. Y.—Brooklyn
Rindskoff Bros. (Dress)..B
New York City
Frank & Gutman (Dress).B
Goodyear's India Rubber Glove Mfg. Co. (Dress; Nipple) ....AAAA
Goodyear Rubber Co. (Dress) ....AAAA
Hodgman Rubber Co. (Dress) ....AA
Kleinert Rubber Co., I. B. (Dress) ....AA
Mattson Rubber Co. (Dress; Breast; Nipple) ....B
Parker, Stearns & Sutton (Dress) ....AA
Rauh & Co., C. S. (Dress).D
Roche, Croll & Co. (Dress) D
Tutelman Bros. & Faggen (Men's) ....A
Warner Bros. Co. (Dress; Corset) ....AAAA

OHIO—Akron
Faultless Rubber Co. (Rubber Breast) ....AA
Goodrich & Co., B. F. (Dress) ....AAAA

OHIO—Columbus
Ironsides Co. (Gear)......C

OHIO—Cincinnati
Behrens & Co., F. D. (Buckle) ....F

PA.—Philadelphia
Pexson Co., J. W., 1021 No. Delaware Av. (Mica Eye) AA

R. I.—Providence
Davol Rubber Co. (Breast; Nipple) ....AA

SHIFTERS

See Hardware; Carriage

CONN.—Hartford
Pratt & Whitney Co. (Belt) AAAA

MASS.—Boston
Mason Regulator Co., 158 Summer (Belt Holder)..B

N. J.—Newark
Foster Engineering Co. (Belt) ....B
New York City
Brown Co., A. & F., 26 Cortlandt (Belt) .....A

SHIFTERS (Con.)

OHIO—Cuyahoga Falls
Falls Rivet & Machine Co. (Belt) ....A

PA.—Philadelphia
Cresson Co., Geo. V., 18th & Allegheny Av. (Belt) AA

R. I.—Providence
Builders Iron Foundry (Belt) ....AA

SHINGLES

See also Lumber

FLA.—Apalachicola
Cypress Lumber Co. (Wooden) ....AA

FLA.—Pensacola
Wright Co., W. B. (Wooden) ....AA

GA.—Darien
Hilton & Dodge Lumber Co. (Wooden) ....AAAA

GA.—Savannah
Southern Pine Co. of Georgia (Wooden) ......AAA

ILL.—Chicago
Palmer, Fuller & Co. (Inc.) (Wooden) ....A

ILL.—Moline
Dimock, Gould & Co. (Wooden) ....AA

ILL.—Rock Island
Rock Island Lumber & Mfg. Co. (Wooden) ....AA

IOWA—Davenport
Lindsay & Phelps Co. (Wooden) ....AAA

IOWA—Dubuque
Standard Lumber Co. (Wooden) ....AAAA

IOWA—Muscatine
Musser Lumber Co. (Wooden) ....AA

MAINE—Portland
Berlin Mills Co. (Wooden) AAAA

MICH.—Bay City
Ross & Son, W. M. (Wooden) ....B

MICH.—Cadillac
Cummer, Diggins & Co. (Wooden) ....AAAA
Mitchell Bros. Co. (Wooden) ....AAA

MICH.—Detroit
Burton Co., W. J., 164 Larned W. (Metallic)......C

MICH.—Hermansville
Wisconsin Land & Lumber Co. (Wooden) ....AAAA

MICH.—Ludington
Butters Salt & Lumber Co. (Wooden) ....A

MICH.—Manistee
Buckley & Douglas Lumber Co. (Wooden) ....AAAA
Sands, Louis (Wooden) AAAA

MICH.—Menominee
Lindsley Bros. Co. (Wooden) ....B

MICH.—Oscoda
Louds Sons Co., H. M. (Wooden) ....AA

MINN.—Anoka
Reed & Sherwood Mfg. Co. (Wooden) C

MINN.—Minneapolis
Nelson Tuthill Lumber Co. (Wooden) ....AA

N. J.—Camden
Montross Metal Shingle Co. (Metallic) ....D

N. J.—Jersey City
National Sheet Metal Roofing Co., 339 Grand (Metallic) C
Ringle & Son, Jacob, 85 Newark Av. (Metallic).A

N. Y.—Brooklyn
Miller & Doing, 83 Washington (Metallic) ......F

OHIO—Canton
Berger Mfg. Co. (Metallic) AA

OHIO—Cincinnati
Cincinnati Stamping Co. (Metallic) ....B
Hyndman Steel Roofing Co. (Metallic) C

SHINGLES (Con.)

OHIO—Cleveland
Garry Iron & Steel Co.
(Metallic) ....A

OHIO—Salem
Mullins, W. H. (Metallic)A

PA.—Philadelphia
Cortright Metal Roofing
Co., 50 W. 23d (Metallic)
................................B
Gara, McGinley & Co.
(Metallic) ....A
Merchant & Co., 517 Arch
(Metallic) ....AA
Penn Metal Ceiling & Roof-
ing Co., 23d & Hamilton
(Metallic) ....B

PA.—Pittsburg
Iron City Metal Ceiling Co.,
Schmidt Bldg. (Metallic)
................................D
Schuette Co., Wm. H.
(Wooden) ....A

TENN.—Chattanooga
Chattanooga Roofing & Fdy.
Co. (Metallic) ....A
Loomis & Hart Mfg. Co.
(Wooden) ....AA

TEXAS—Orange
Lutcher & Moore Lumber
Co. (Wooden) ....AAAA

VA.—Norfolk
Roper Lumber Co., John L.
(Wooden) ....AAA

W. VA.—Wheeling
Wheeling Corrugating Co.
(Galvanized; Tin) .AAAA

WIS.—Eau Claire
Shaw Lumber Co., Daniel
(Wooden) ....AA

WIS.—Green Bay
Murphy Lumber Co.
(Wooden) ....AAAA

WIS.—Hayward
North Wisconsin Lumber &
Mfg. Co. (Wooden) ..AA

WIS.—Mason
White River Lumber Co.
(Wooden) ....A

WIS.—Mosinee
Dessert Lumber Co., Joseph
(Wooden) ....AA

WIS.—Oshkosh
Gould Mfg. Co. (Wooden).A
Radford Bros. & Co.
(Wooden) ....A

WIS.—Rice Lake
Rice Lake Lumber Co.
(Wooden) ....AAA

WIS.—Stevens Point
Week Lumber Co., John
(Wooden) ....A

SHIPS

See also Boats & Vessels

CAL.—San Francisco
Union Iron Works (War)
(Steam) ....AAAA

DEL.—Wilmington
Harlan & Hollingsworth Co.
(Iron; Steel; (Steam)
................................AAAA
Pusey & Jones Co. (Iron;
Steel; Steam) ......AAA

ILL.—Chicago
Chicago Ship Building Co.
(Iron; Steel) ....AA

MAINE—Bath
Bath Iron Works (Iron;
Steel; War) ....AAAA
New England Co. (Steam)D
Sewall & Co., Arthur (Iron;
Steel) ....AA

MASS.—Boston
Atlantic Wks. (Steam)..AA

N. J.—Camden
Dialogue & Son, John H.
(Steam) ....AA

N. Y.—Brooklyn
Continental Iron Works
(Iron; Steel) ....A

New York City
American Bridge Co., 42
B'way ....A

OHIO—Cleveland
Globe Iron Wks. Co.
(Steam) ....AAAA

PA.—Chester
Delaware River Iron Ship
Building & Engine Wks.
(Steam) ....AAA

SHIPS (Con.)

PA.—Philadelphia
Cramp & Sons Ship & Eng.
Bldg. Co., Wm. (Iron;
Steel; War; Steam)
................................AAAA
Neafie & Levy Ship & En-
gine Bldg. Co. (Steam)
................................AAA

VA.—Newport News
Newport News Ship Bldg. &
Dry Dock Co. (War)
(Steam) ....AAAA

SHIRTINGS

See Cotton Goods

SHIRTS

See also Underwear

ALA.—Mobile
Pollock & Bernheimer
(Men's) ....AAA

CAL.—Los Angeles
Cohn, Goldwater & Co.
(Men's Canton Flannel).B

CAL.—Oakland
Eagleson & Co. (Br. of Eag-
leson-Hawkins Co. of San
Frans.) (Men's) ......A
Keller, M. J. C. (Men's)..A

CAL.—San Francisco
Atkins, Robert C. & Sons
(Men's) C
Dinkelspiel & Sons, L....A
Eagleson-Hawkins Co. (Pa-
cific Shirt Co.) (Men's)
................................A
Elkus, Brenner Co. (Men's)
................................B
Goldstone Bros. (Men's)..A
Greenebaum, Weil & Mich-
els (Men's) ......AAAA
Heynemann & Co. ....A
Heger, D. C. (Men's)....D
Hirsch, Leopold ....B
Lowenberg & Co. (Men's)
................................AAA
Neustadter Bros. (Men's
................................AAA
Strauss, Levi & Co. (Men's)
................................AAAA
Uhlman, Seeligsohn &
Brown (Men's) ....B

COLO.—Denver
Howe Allen & Kaull Merc.
Co. (Men's) C
Underhill Mfg. Co. (Men's)
................................B

CONN.—New Britain
Parker Shirt Co. (Men's
Dress; Negligee) C

CONN.—Norwalk
Hutchinson Pierce & Co.
(Men's) ....AAA

CONN.—Willimantic
Thread City Collar Co.....B

DEL.—Laurel
Fooks & Hastings (Men's;
Boys') ....A

D. C.—Washington
Hall, Philip T. (Men's)..C

FLA.—Jacksonville
Kahn, Furchgott Co.
(Men's) ....A

GA.—Atlanta
Loeb, Marcus & Co. (Men's)
................................B
Robinson Co., A. M.
(Men's) ....A
Wolf, H. (Men's) C

GA.—Columbus
Georgia Mfg. Co. (Men's).A

GA.—Dalton
Smith, M. D. & H. L.
(Work) ....D

GA.—Savannah
American Mfg. Co. (Men's)
................................B

ILL.—Chicago
Bartlett Lincoln Co.
(Men's) ....D
Bernstein, Cohn & Co.
(Men's) C
Blackman, C. S. (Men's)..D
Calumet Shirt Co. (Men's)
................................C
Castle Shirt Co. (Men's
White & Colored) ...D
Columbus Shirt Co. (Men's
White; Fancy; Flannel;

MASS.—Natick
Edwards, E. & Sons (Men's
Negligee) ....D
Randall Bros. (Men's)....D
MASS.—New Bedford
Denham, T. M. & Bros.
(Men's White; Night)..D
MASS.—Springfield
M. & M. Mfg. Co. (Rubber
Bosom) ....E
MASS.—Watertown
Elm City Mfg. Co. (Men's)
D
MASS.—West Newton
Martin Mfg. Co. (Men's)
D
MASS.—Worcester
Hildreth & Co., A. G.
(Work) C
Rowell, W. P. & Co.
(Men's Custom) ....D
Thayer & Co. (Men's)....D
MICH.—Ann Arbor
Mack & Co. (Men's)......C
MICH.—Detroit
Imerman Bros. C
Peerless Mfg. Co (Men's).B
Rosen & Co., A. D. (Men's)
B
Rosenfield Monroe Co.
(Men's) C
Stanton & Co., M. M.
(Men's) ....AAA
MICH.—Grand Rapids
Ideal Clothing Co. (Men's)
B
Kelly Shirt Co. (Men's
White; Colored) ......D
MICH.—Lansing
Flint Pantaloon Co.
(Men's) C
MICH.—Saginaw
Wylie Mfg. Co. (Men's)..C
MINN.—Duluth
Christensen, Mendenhall &
Graham (Men's) C
MINN.—Minneapolis
Belden & Evans (Men's
White; Colored; Flannel)
D
Plymouth Clothing House
(Men's) ....AA
Robitskik, Frank & Heller
(Men's) ....A
Wyman Partridge & Co.
(Men's) ....AAAA
MINN.—St. Paul
Finch, Young & Mc Conville
(Men's) ....AAA
Guitermann Bros. (Men's)A
Lindeke, Warner & Schur-
meier (Men's) ...AAAA
Sternberg, Weil & Co.
(Men's) ....B
MINN.—St. Peter
Johnson & Co.............B
MO.—Jefferson
Star Clothing Co. (Men's).C
MO.—Kansas City
Burnham-Munger Mfg. Co.
AAAA
Smith, McCord, Townsend
Dry Goods Co. (Men's)
AAA
Standard Mfg. Co. (Men's)
D
Swofford Bros. Dry Goods
Co. (Men's) ....AAA
Woolf Bros. Shirt Mfg. Co.
Dry Goods Co. (Men's)
D
MO.—St. Joseph
Brittain Dry Goods Co.,
John S. (Men's)......AA
Hundley Smith Dry Goods
Co. ....AA
Mc Donald & Co., R. L.
(Men's) ....AAA
Richardson Roberts Dry
Goods Co. (Men's)..AAA
Tootle Wheeler & Motter
Merc. Co. (Men's).AAAA
MO.—St. Louis
Bohm Bros. Furnishing
Goods Co. (Men's)......A
Boulevard hirt Mfg. Co.
(Men's) ....D
Boyd, T. B. & Co. (Men's)
C
Buckley Custom Shirt Mfg.
Co. (Men's Custom)....D

Casey, P. A. & Co. (Men's)
C
Ely & Walker Dry Goods
Co. (Men's) ......AAAA
Everett Mfg. Co. (Men's).D
Ferguson-Mc Kinney Dry
Goods Co. (Men's).AAAA
Gilbert Bros. (Men's)....C
Hargadine Mc Kittrick Dry
Goods Co. (Men's).AAAA
Lipshitz, M. & Co., (Men's)
C
New Era Mfg. Co. (Men's
Negligee) ....B
Premium Mfg. Co. (Men's)
AAAA
Red Diamond Clothing Co.
(Work) C
Rice Stix Dry Goods Co.
(Men's) ....AAAA
Weil Julius (Men's) C
Wolff, Paul E. Shirt Co.
(Men's) ....B
MO.—Sedalia
Lamy Mfg. Co., J. A.
(Men's) ....B
MONT.—Helena
Greenhood Benis Co.
(Men's) ....B
NEBR.—Lincoln
Herman Bros. Mfg. Co.
(Men's) ....A
Lincoln Overall & Shirt Co.
(Men's) ....D
NEBR.—Omaha
Byrne & Hammer Dry Goods
Co. (Men's) ....AAAA
King & Smead (Men's)...C
Smith, M. E. & Co. (Men's)
AA
N. H.—Canaan
Barney Bros. (Men's)....C
N. H.—Lebanon
Carter & Sons, H. W.
(Men's) ....B
Carter & Churchill Co.
(Men's) ....B
N. J.—Elizabeth
Rosenstein, S. & W. H.
(Men's) ....D
N. J.—Newark
Shiner, Alexander W.
(Men's) C
Smith-Linnett Shirt Co.
(Men's White; Colored).C
Sutphen, Co., C. Edgar
(Men's White; Fancy;
Negligee) C
N. J.—Paterson
Levi, Jacol & Co. (Men's).C
Manhattan Shirt Co.
(Men's) ....AAA
N. J.—South River
Herrmann, Aukam & Co.
(Men's) ....AAAA
N. J.—Trenton
Murray, Griffith & Messler
(Men's) ....B
N. Y.—Albany
Albany Garment Co.
(Men's) C
Munson, S. L. (Men's)....A
N. Y.—Amsterdam
Liddle Knitting Co. (Knit)
D
N. Y.—Binghamton
Bennet-Morgan Co. (Men's)
C
Mc Henry Shirt Co. (Men's
Custom) ....D
Smith, Crary & Davidge
(Men's) ....B
Smith, Kinney & Co.
(Men's) ....B
N. Y.—Brooklyn
Men's Wear Co. (Men's
Dress) ....D
N. Y.—Buffalo
Beyer Bros. (Men's)......B
Buffalo Shirt Co. (Men's;
Boys') ....D
Humburch, W. C. (Men's
Custom; Fancy; White).C
Kinne & Kinne Co. (Men's)
D
La Due, Tate Mfg. Co.
(Men's) ....B
Lepper & Ellwood (Men's)
D
Niagara Overall & Pants
Co. (Men's) ....D

SHIRTS (Con.)

N. Y.—Chatham
Chatham Shirt Co. (Men's
White; Colored; Night).B
N. Y.—Chestertown
Faxon Mfg. Co., C. H.
(Men's) ....A
N. Y.—Dansville
Hubertus, H. & Sons
(Men's) ....D
N. Y.—Dunkirk
Dunkirk Shirt Co. (Men's)
C
N. Y.—Ephratah
Yanney Levi (Men's) C
N. Y.—Glens Falls
Glens Falls Shirt Co.
(Men's) C
McMullen, Leavens Co.
(Men's White; Fancy)..C
Robertson, D. L. & Co.
(Men's) C
Weill, Haskell Co. (Men's;
Boys) ....AAA
N Y—Homer
Newton & Co. (Cotton;
Flannel) ....D
N. Y.—Jamestown
Logan, R. T. (Men's Cus-
tom) ....D
N. Y.—Lockport
Dumville & Co. (Men's
White; Colored) C
Sillesky, D. R. & Co. (Men's
White; Colored; Night)C
Tothill Shirt Co (Men's
White; Colored to order)D
N. Y.—Millerton
Eggleston Hanford & Co
(Men's Working) .....D
N. Y.—Newburgh
Sweet, Orr & Co. (Men's)..
AA
New York City
Abrams & Marcus (Men's)D
Ballin, M. & Sons (Men's)D
Ballin, J. H. & S. (Men's
White; Colored; Negligee;
Work; Blue; Fancy Flan-
nel) ....D
Bellamy, Geo. E. (Men's)C
Bernheim, Dryfoos & Herri-
man (Men's) ....B
Biermann, Henry (Men's)D
Broom & Meyer (Men's
Negligee; Stiff Bosoms)C
Carmichael, S. P. (Men's)D
Dreyfus, J & Sons (Men's)
A
Dubinsky, Louis (Men's).D
Duclos, D. E. (Men's
Custom) ....D
Eighmie Shirt Co. (Men's
Dress; White; Colored;
Negligee) ....B
Elias Bros & Co. (Men's).A
Fisk, Clark & Flagg
(Men's) ....A
Frank Lewis & Sons (Men's
Cassimere; Work; Flan-
nel; Outing) ....A
Freezer & Cohen (The
World Shirt Co.) (Men's
Negligee) ....D
Friend, Sol & Co. (Men's
Work; Negligee) .....B
Gittenstein, A. & Bro.
(Men's) C
Hauptner, Chas. & Co
(Men's Custom) C
Hutchinson, Pierce & Co.
(Men's) ....AAA
Jacobson & Gleitzman
(Men's) ....B
Kaplan, Joseph & Bro.
(Men's Shirts; Boys
Waists) C
Kaskel & Kaskel (Men's).B
Keep, H. V. Shirt Co.
(Men's) ....D
Keep Mfg. Co. (Men's Dress;
Negligee; Night) .....A
Kirker & Friedman (Men's)
C
Koblenzer, Morris ....B
Kommel, I. (Men's Negli-
gee; Work; Flannel) ..D
Lederer & Block (Men's).B
Levin & Zatulove (Men's)C
Liebovitz, S. & Son (Men's)
A
Loewy, J. & Co. (Men's)..C
Loewy, L. & Son (Men's).B
McLaughlin, W. A.

SHIRTS (Con.)
(Men's) ....B
Manheimer & Schwarz
(Men's Negligee; Flannel)
D
Meyerhoff, Sol. K. (Men's)
D
Michaelis & Rohman (Men's
Custom) ....D
Millen, E. & Co. (Men's
Dress; Negligee; Night)
A
New Columbia Shirt Co.
(Men's) C
Newell, E. A. (Men's) ..B
Noveck, S. & Co. (Men's
Negligee; Fancy; Flan-
nel) C
Rice, L. H. & Co. (Men's)C
Roggen & Eisenstein (Men's
White; Colored) ......A
Rosen, Morris H. & Co.
(Men's Negligee; Plain;
Fancy; Flannel) ......D
Rosenstein, S. & W. K.
(Men's) C
Rothschild, V Henry Co.
(Men's Colored; Negligee;
Laundered) ....B
Salant & Salant (Men's)..C
Samuels, I. A. & Co.
(Men's) C
Sapovit & Rosenthal (Apex
hirt Co) (Men's) ......D
Scharps & Simon (Men's)D
Schneer's Son & Co., Isaac
(Men's) ....B
Schmeidler, Rosen & Co.
Men's) C
Scriven, J. A. Co. (Men's)B
Shiner, Alex. W. (Men's)C
Silberstein Bros. (Men's)A
Simon, Julius (Men's Shirts;
also Flannel Night Shirts)
C
Stern & Son (Men's)......D
Sternburger, Samuel & Co.
(Men's) ....A
Werbin, S. & Son (Men's;
Boys) ....D
N. Y.—Oneonta
Buckley Bros. Co. (Men's)C
N. Y.—Peekskill
Janowitz-Maxwell Co.
(Men's Shirts; Boys
Waists) ....D
N. Y.—Petersburg
Reynolds C. W. & Co. (Pet-
ersburg Mfg. Co.) (Men's
Fancy; White) ....A
N. Y.—Plattsburg
Plattsburg Shirt Co.
(Men's) ....D
N. Y.—Port Chester
Simons Ernest Mfg. Co.
(Men's White; Night)..B
N. Y.—Salem
Manhattan Shirt Co.
(Men's) ....AAAA
N. Y.—Sandusky
Hayden Theo. (Men's
Flannel) C
N. Y.—Spring Valley
Falkenberg, Chas. (Men's)
B
N. Y.—Syracuse
Peters. C. A. (Men's)....D
Negligee) ....D
N. Y.—Troy
Cluett, Peabody & Co.
(Men's Linen) ......AAA
Curtis, H. C. & Co.
(Men's ....B
Earl & Wilson ....A
Fellows & Co. (White
Dress) ....B
Hall, Hartwell & Co.
(Men's White; Fancy).A
Ide, Geo. P. & Co (Men's
Shirts; Waists) ......A
International Shirt & Collar
Co. (Men's) ....
McClellan Co., C. H.
(White Dress; Colored;
Negligee) ....D
Miller-Hale Shirt & Collar
Co. (Men's) ....D
Tim & Co. (Men's White;
Colored) ....A
United Shirt & Collar Co.
(Men's) ....AAAA
Wilbur Campbell Stephens
Co. (Men's White; Fancy)
A

923

N. Y.—Utica
Riverside Mfg. Co. (Rathbun & Co.) (Work) ....A
N. Y.—Warrensburg
Empire Shirt Co. (Men's)
............................AAA
N. Y.—Waterford
American Shirt & Colar Co.
(Men's White) ....D
OHIO—Canton
Moore, M. (Men's Muslin;
Flannelette; Night also
Work) ....D
OHIO—Cincinnati
Eisenman & Co., Chas.
(Men's) ....A
Globe Overall Mfg. Co.
(Work) ....D
Gofton, Frank (Men's....D
Golde, Geo. & Co. (Men's
.........................D
Hanke Bros. (Men's).AAA
Levine Bros. (Men's) ...C
Lowmans' Sons (Men's
White; Fancy; Negligee)
.........................A
Martin, A., Jr. (Men's)..D
Rauh & Mack Shirt Co.
(Men's; all kinds) ....D
Reiter & Co., Peter (Men's
.........................D
Roth & Roth (Men's) ...C
Victor Shirt Co. (Men's).C
Wald Lewis & Co. (Men's;
Laundered; Fancy; Work)
.........................A
OHIO—Cleveland
Enterprise Mfg. Co. (Men's
.........................D
Fisher, B & Son (Men's) C
Halle Schwartz & Skall
Men's) ....A
Klein Lichtenstader & Co.
(Men's Work) ....A
Metropolitan Mfg. Co.
(Men's) ....D
Schwartz & Co. (Men's)..D
Steifel, Holstein & Falk
(Men's) ....D
OHIO—Columbus
Allen Mfg. Co. (Men's)..D
Capitol Mfg. Co. (Men's)D
Columbus Mdse Co. (Men's
.........................A
OHIO—Dayton
Gem Shirt Co. (Men's; all
kinds) ....A
Legler & Co. (Men's) ....A
OHIO—Hamilton
Sommers Mfg. Co., J. A.
(Men's) C
OHIO—Lisbon
Miller, Geo. L. (Men's)..D
OHIO—Toledo
Shaw & Welty Shirt Co.
(Men's: Negligee) C
OREGON—Portland
Fleischner, Mayer & Co.
(Men's) ....AAA
PA.—Allentown
Bittner, Hunsicker & Co.
(Men's) ....AA
PA.—Columbia
Triumph Embroidery Co.
Kinds) C
PA.—Dillsburg
Harrisburg Mfg. Co.
(Men's) ....D
PA.—Easton
Correll, J. W. (Men's) ..B
PA.—Glen Rock
Industrial Sewing Co.
(Men's) C
PA.—Hazleton
Gerhardt Jacob & Co.
(Men's Negligee, &c.)..B
PA.—Lebanon
Rauch & Bro. (Men's
Boy's) ....D
PA.—Mt. Wolf
Mt. Wolf Mfg. Co. (Men's:
Boy's) ....D
PA.—Norristown
Quaker City Shirt Mfg Co.
(Men's; Boy's; Negligee:
Stiff Bosom) C
Steppacher, W. M. & Bro.
(Men's) ....B
PA.—Philadelph..a
Baxter, Thos. F. & Co.
(Men's Negligee: Laundered) C
Brandes & Bro. (Men's)..B

Brownstein Segall & Co.
(Men's Shirts; Boy's
Waists) ....D
Brubaker & Son, E. (Men's)
.........................D
Eiseman, B. & W. (Men's)
.........................D
Eshleman & Craig Co.
(Men's Custom).......B
Feingold, S. & Co. (Men's
Shirts; Boy's Waists)..D
France, D. C. & Co. (Men's
Negligee) C
Gantert & Carpenter
(Men's ....D
Greenebaum Bros. (Men's)
.........................D
Gross & Raab (Men's Negligee; Dress) C
Hagedorn Merz Co. (Men's)
.........................A
Karr, Jacob A. & Co.
(Men's) ....D
Lang & Co., H. A. (Men's)
.........................C
Manifest Shirt Co. (Men's)
.........................D
Meyerhoff Son & Co. (Men's
Negligee only) ....B
Meyerhoff & Jacobs (Men's
Laundered; Unlaundered
Negligee) ....B
Miller, John P. (Men's
Custom) C
Miller, Jacob Sons & Co.
(Men's; all kinds)....AA
Miller Solomon & Co.
(Men's) ....A
Needles, L. & Co. (Men's
Negligee; Night)......D
Robbins, J. S. (Men's Negligee; Boy's Waists)..D
Roomberg Bros. (Men's).D
Shedaker, Chas. E. (Men's:
all kinds) ....B
Steppacher. W. M. & Bro.
(Men's Dress; Negligee)
.........................B
Sternberger, Samuel & Co.
(Men's) ....B
Tutelman Bros. & Faggen
Men's Negligee) ....A
Underdown, A. R. (Men's
.........................C
Weil. Bachrach & Co.
(Men's) ....B
PA.—Pittsburg
Arbuthnot Stephenson Co.
(Men's) ....AAA
Ferguson, Ferguson & Co.
(Men's) C
Hannah Bros. (Men's)..D
Mansmann Bros. (Men's)D
Pittsburg Dry Gds Co.
(Men's) ....AAA
Rauh Bros. & Co. (Men's)
.........................AAA
PA.—Pottsville
Phillips, M. & Son
(Men's) ....A
PA.—Reading
Brusstar, Jas. S. & Co.
Men's) C
Mercer, James R. (Men's)
.........................B
PA.—Scranton
White Mfg. Co., Theo. A.
(Men's) ....D
PA.—Shippensburg
Rummel Hines & Co.
(Men's) C
PA.—Telford
Godshall. Jacob G. (Men's
White: Fancy) ....D
PA.—Waynesboro
Waynesboro Mfg. Co.
(Work) ....D
PA.—York
Bear Mfg. Co. (Men's)..C
Williams. J. E. & Co.
(Men's Negligee) .....B
S. C.—Charleston
Wilbur & Son, T. A.
(Men's) ....A
TENN.—Knoxville
Briscoe Mfg. Co. (Men's)C
TENN.—Memphis
Loeb. Henry Shirt Co.
(Men's) ....B
National Woolen Co.
(Men's) ....B
TENN.—Nashville
Fish & Weil (Men's)....C

SHIRTS (Con.)
Frank & Co. (Men's Custom) C
O'Bryan Bros. (Work) ..A
TEXAS—Dallas
Rose Mfg. Co. (Men's) ..B
Sanger Bros. (Men's) ....AAAA
TEXAS—Galveston
Pierson, A. L. (Men's) ..C
VT.—Island Pond
Gane, G. A. Shirt Co. (Men's White) ......A
VA.—Norfolk
Hatch & Dean (Men's Custom; White; Fancy) ...D
Steels Union Overall Co. (Work) ....D
VA.—Urbana
Urbana Mfg. Co. (Men's Work) C
WASH.—Spokane ..
Spokane Dry Gds. Co. (Men's) ....A
W. VA.—Huntington
Biggs Watts & Co. (Men's) ....B
W. VA.—McMechen
McMechen Mfg. Co. (Men's Work) ....A
W. VA.—Parkersburg .
Case Mfg. Co. (Men's Cotton; Work; Flannel)D
WIS.—Appleton
Appleton Shirt & Pants Co. (Men's) C
WIS.—Fond Du Lac .
Fond Du Lac Shirt & Overall Co. (Men's Work).D
WIS.—Janesville .
Janesville Clothing Co. (Men's) ....D
WIS.—La Crosse
Martin Bros. Co. (Men's) C
WIS.—Milwaukee .
Fein Bros. & Co., S. (Men's) ....
Goll & Frank Co. (Men's).. ....AAAA
Landauer & Co. (Men's)AA
Mahler Allenberg & Co. (Men's) ....AA
Rice, J. H. & Friedmann Co. (Men's) ....A
WIS.—Racine
Alshuler Mfg Co.. Chas. (Men's) ....B

SHODDIES

See Woolen Goods

SHODDY

CONN.—Stafford Springs
Smith & Cooley ....B
N. Y.—Albany
Barret, Wm. ....B
N. Y.—Cohoes
United Waste Mfg. Co. ..B
OHIO—Cincinnati
Collings-Taylor Co. (All Wool) ....A
Hey & Co., Benj. ....A
OHIO—Cleveland
Acme Woolen Mill Co. (Wool) C
National Woolen Co. (Woolen) ....AA
PA.—Philadelphia
Adams & Co., Jos. M. (Wool) ....A
Hall & Co. (Cotton; Woolen) ....B
Kitchen & Co.. Jas. G....A
Simister & Son, Chas R...B
Spink, M. ....B
PA.—Upland
Wallworth & Sons, J. (Wool) ....B

SHOES

See also Boots; Shoes; Horse
Shoes

ALA.—Selma
Peacocks Iron Wks. (Brake) C
Union Iron Works (Brake) ....B
CAL.—San Francisco
Hendy Machine Wks, Joshua

SHOES (Con.)
(Stamp Mill) ....AA
COLO.—Denver
Colorado Iron Works Co., 721 17th (Stamp Mill) ....AA
Davis Iron Wks. Co., F. M., 8th & Larimer (Stamp Mill) ....AA
CONN.—Bristol
Sessions Fdy. Co. (Brake) ....AAA
Sessions & Son, J. H. (Trunk) ....AA
CONN.—Lime Rock
Barnum, Richardson Co. (Brake; Gun Metal).AAA
CONN.—Mt. Carmel
Woodruff & Sons' Co., W. W. (Horse; Ox; Mule)..X
CONN.—Plantsville
Atwater Mfg. Co. (Ox)..A
DEL.—Wilmington
Diamond State Steel Co. (Horse; Mule; Cowboy, &c.) X
ILL.—Chicago
Allen & Morrison Brake. Shoe Mfg. Co., Tacoma Bldg. (Brake) C
Allis-Chalmers Co., Home Ins. Bldg. (Stamp Mill; Ore Crushing; Dies) ....AAAA
McCord & Co.. Old Colony Bldg. (Brake) ....D
McGuire Cummings Mfg. Co., 122 N. Sangamon (Brake) ....A
Manufacturers' Railway Supply Co. (Brake; Driving; Interlocking) X
Spear & Miller Co., Monadnock Blk. (Brake) ...F
IND.—Logansport
Dorner Truck & Fdy. Co. (Brake) ....D
IND.—Montpelier
National Steel Casting Co. (Stamp Mill) X
MD.—Baltimore
Baltimore Car Wheel Co. (Brake) ....B
Diven-Deved Fdy. Co., 813 S. Howard (Brake) ....D
Levering Bros. (Brake)..C
MASS.—Boston
Neverslip Horseshoe Co. (Horse) ....D
Standard Horseshoe Co. (Horse; Mule) ....D
MASS.—Cambridge
Barbour Stockwell Company (Brake; Electric Railway) ....A
MASS.—Millers Falls
Millers Falls Co. (Ox)..AA
MASS.—Taunton
Taunton Locomotive Mfg. Co. (Brake) ....AA
MICH.—Detroit
Monarch Brake Beam Co. Wight & Leib (Brake).C
Pingree Co. (Plow) ..AA
Wheel Truing Brake Shoe Co., 106 Miami Av. (Brake) ....D
MICH.—Hancock
Portage Lake Fry. & Machine Co. (Stamp Mill).D
MO.—St. Louis
American Car & Fdy. Co., 706 Chestnut (Brake) ....AAAA
Kupferle, John C. (Sleigh; Wagon Lock) ....AA
Pleuger & Henger Mfg. Co. (Sleigh; Wagon Lock).A
Western Forge Co., 520 Olive (Stamp Mill) ....B
N. J.—High Bridge
Taylor Iron & Steel Co. (Stamp Mill; Ore Crushing; Dies) ....AAAA
N. J.—Hoboken
New York Switch & Crossing Co. (Brake) .....A
N. J.—New Brunswick
Neverslip Mfg. Co. (Horse) ....AA
N. J.—Phillipsburg
American Horse Shoe Co. (Horse; Jack; Mule)....B

SHOES (Con.)

N. Y.—Brooklyn
Pollard, Jos. G., 141 Raymond (Steel Plank) ....F
N. Y.—Buffalo
New York Car Wheel Wks., German Insurance Bldg. (Brake) ....AA
N. Y.—Hillburn
Ramapo Fdy. & Machine Wks. (Brake) .....AAA
N. Y.—Manlius
Cheney & Son, S. (Sleigh; Wagon Lock) ....A
N. Y.—Medina
Swett Iron Works, A. L. (Brake) ....A
New York City
American Brake Shoe & Fdy. Co., 170 Broadway (Brake) ....A
Bemis Car Truck Co., 120 Liberty (Brake) ......E
Corning Brake Shoe Co., 26 Cortlandt (Brake) ....H
Koppel, Arthur, 68 Broad (Stamp Mill) ....A
Wendell & McDuffie, 26 Cortlandt (Brake) ....B
N. Y.—Poughkeepsie
Phoenix Horse Shoe Co. (Horse; Mule) .....AAA
N. Y.—Troy
Burden Iron Co. (Horse; Mule) ....AAAA
Taylor Electric Truck Co. (Brake) ....B
OHIO—Akron
Goodyear Tire & Rubber Co. (Rubber; Horse) ......B
Whitman & Barnes Mfg. Co. (Horse; Rubber) AAAA
OHIO—Cambridge
Cambridge Fdy. Co. (Brake) F
OHIO—Cincinnati
Eureka Foundry Co. (Brake) A
Mowry Car Wheel Works, 2401 Eastern Av. (Brake) B
OHIO—Cleveland
Fulton Fdy. Co. (Brake)..F
Van Dorn & Dutton Co., 1796 E. Madison Av. (Brake) ....D
OHIO—Lima
Lima Locomotive & Machine Co. (Brake) ....AA
OHIO—Toledo
Vulcan Iron Wks. (Brake) A
PA.—Bellwood
Bellwood Mfg. Co. (Brake) C
PA.—Catasauqua
Bryden Horse Shoe Co. (Horse; Mule) ....AA
PA.—Fullerton
Lehigh Car Wheel & Axle Wks. (Brake) ....AAAA
PA.—Nazareth
Nazareth Fdy. & Machine Co. (Brake) ....B
PA.—Philadelphia
Brill Co., J. G., 62d & Woodland Av. (Brake) AAAA
Chester Steel Castings Co., 407 Sansom (Stamp Mill; Brake; Ore Crushing; Dies) ....AA
Janney, Steinmetz & Co., Drexel Bldg. (Pile) ....D
PA.—Philadelphia
Wharton, Jr. & Co., Wm., 25th & Washington Av. (Brake; Electric Railway) ....AAA
PA.—Pittsburg
Pittsburg Brake Shoe Co. Farmers' Bank Building (Brake) C
PA.—Scranton
Scranton Forging Co. (Ox) A
PA.—South Bethlehem
Bethlehem Fdy. & Machine Co. (Brake) C
PA.—York
Hench & Dromgold Co. (Plow) ....B

SHOES (Con.)

R. I.—Providence
Rhode Island Perkins Horse Shoe Co. (Horse; Mule) AAAA
TENN.—Bristol
Virginia Iron, Coal & Coke Co. (Horse; Mule) ...A
TENN.—Chattanooga
Ross-Meehan Fdy. Co.....A
TENN.—Memphis
Livermore Fdy. & Machine Co. (Mule) ....A
VA.—Richmond
Old Dominion Iron & Nail Wks. Co. (Horse; Mule) AA
Tredegar Co. (Horse; Mule) AAA
WIS.—Beloit
Thompson & Sons Mfg. Co., J. (Plow) ....AA
WIS.—Cudahy
Power & Mining Machinery Co. (Stamp Mill) AAA
WIS.—South Milwaukee
Eagle Horse Shoe Co. (Horse; Mule) ....B

SHOOFLYS

MASS.—Leominster
Whitney Reed Chair Co. AAAA
MO.—St. Louis
Great Western Planing Mill Co. ....B
WIS.—Milwaukee
Meinecke & Son, A. ....AA

SHOOKS

See also Boxes: Wooden

LA.—Patterson
Cypress Tank & Mfg. Co. (Tub; Bucket, &c.; for Washing Machines Ice Cream Freezers) ......B
MAINE—Bangor
Stewart & Co., T. J. (Box) X
MAINE—Eastport
Blanchard Mfg. & Canning Co. (Box) ....D
MD.—Baltimore
Canton Box Co. (Box, Cypress; Box, Poplar) ....B
MASS.—Carver
Bent, John (Box) ....D
MASS.—East Norton
Lincoln, Moses (Box)....F
MASS.—Worcester
Baker Co., Chas. (Box)..C
MICH.—Bay City
Vance Box Co., Ltd., E. J. (Box) ....B
MICH.—Bay Mills
Hall & Munson Co. (Box) X
MICH.—East Saginaw
Mershon & Co., Wm. B. (Box) ....A
N. J.—Jersey City
Dodge & Bliss Co. (Box) AA
N. Y.—Binghamton
Beman & Co. (Box) .....B
N. Y.—Buffalo
Buffalo Box Factory (Box) A
New York City
Estes & Sons, E. B. (Box) AA
Patterson, T. G. (Box)..AA
N. Y.—North Tonawanda
Butts & Co., Chas. G. (Box) D
OHIO—Cincinnati
Cincinnati Cooperage Co. (White Oak) ....AAA

SHOT

CAL.—San Francisco
Selby Smelting & Lead Co. (Drop; Chilled, &c; Lead; Buck) ....AAA
ILL.—Chicago
American Shot & Lead Co., 70 N. Clinton (Buck; Chilled) ....AAAA

SHOT (Con.)

Chicago Shot Tower Works .... AAAA

Raymond Lead Co., 55 W. Lake (See Amer. S. & L. Co.) (Buck; Chilled) .... AAAA

MD.—Baltimore

Robertson Mfg. Co., James, 30 Hanover .... A

MASS.—Boston

Harrison Supply Co., 32 India Wf. (Steel Chilled) .... E

MINN.—St. Paul

Northwestern Shot & Lead Works .... AAAA

MO.—St. Louis

American Shot & Lead Co. (Lead) .... AAAA

Collier Shot Tower Works, 319 N. 4th (See Amer. Shot & Lead Co.)..AAAA

N. J.—High Bridge

Taylor Iron & Steel Co. (Armor Piercing; Shell) .... AAAA

N. Y.—Buffalo

Shepard & Co., Sidney .... AAAA

N. Y.—Fishkill on Hudson

Hammond, Benj. (Slug)..D

New York City

American Shot & Lead Co., 71 B'way .... AAAA

Colwell Lead Co., 63 Centre (Buck; Lead; Chilled).AA

Leroy Shot & Lead Works, 261 Water (See Amer. Shot & Lead Co.).AAAA

Orford Copper Co., 74 B'way (Copper; Lead; Nickel) .... AAA

Tatham Bros., 82 Beekman (See Amer. Shot & Lead Co.) .... AAAA

OHIO—Cincinnati

Sportsman's Shot Works, Cor. Court & Harriet (See Amer. Shot & Lead Co.) .... AAAA

PA.—Philadelphia

Sparks, Thos. W., 121 Walnut (See Am. S. & L. Co.) .... AAAA

Tatham Bros. (See Amer Shot & Lead Co.)..AAAA

Tilghman, B. C. & R. A. (Chilled Iron) .... B

PA.—Pittsburg

Bailey, Farrel Mfg. Co., 615 Smithfield ...... AA

VA.—Austinville

Wythe Lead & Zinc Mine Co. (Buck) .... AA

SHOTS

ILL.—Chicago

Nicol & Co. (Sling) ...... D

SHOVELS

See also Machinery

COLO.—Denver

Montgomery Machinery Co., J. H. (Steam) C

CONN.—Collinsville

Collins Co. (Coal; Contractors') .... AAAA

CONN.—Southington

Peck, Stow & Wilcox Co. (Fire; Stove) ....AAAA

ILL.—Alton

Beall Shovel Co. .... A

ILL.—Bradley

Bradley Mfg. Co., David (Cultivator) .... AAA

ILL.—Canton

Parlin & Orendorff Co. (Cultivator) ......AAAA

ILL.—Carpentersville

Star Mfg. Co. (Cultivator) .... A

ILL.—Chicago

Caldwell & Son Co., H. W., Western Av. & 17th (Power; Grain) ...... A

Channon Co., H., Market & Randolph (Contractors') .... AA

Law Railway Equipment

SHOVELS (Con.)

Co., Western Union Bldg. (Steam; Second Hand).F

Shaw, Willis, N. Y. Life Bldg. (Steam; Second Hand Steam) .... D

Webster Mfg. Co. (Power; Grain) .... AA

ILL.—Freeport

Arcade Mfg. Co. (Ice)....A

Stover Mfg. Co. (Stove).AA

ILL.—Harvey

Austin Mfg. Co., F. C. (Steam) .... AA

ILL.—Havana

Havana Metal Wheel Co. (Cultivator) .... A

ILL.—Moline

Moline Plow Co. (Cultivator) .... AAAA

ILL.—Rockford

Weyburn Co. (Cultivator).B

ILL.—Streator

Iwan Bros. (Drain; Tiling) .... D

IND.—Anderson

Wright Shovel Co. (Hand Iron) .... B

IND.—Montpelier

Jackson Shovel & Tool Co. (Hand Iron) .... B

IND.—New Castle

Indiana Rolling Mill Co...A

IND.—South Bend

Sandage Steel Skein Co...X

IND.—Terre Haute

Terre Haute Shovel & Tool Co. (Coal; Coke Screening; Contractors'; Drain; Irrigating; Lime; Lipped; Mining; Moulders'; Sawdust; Round Point; 'Telegraph Line; Railroad; Mining; Machine) .....A

IND.—Vincennes

Star Shovel & Range Co. (Furnace; Tiling; Collier; Ore; Iron Hand) ......B

IOWA—Ft. Madison

Morrison Mfg. Co. (Cultivator) .... A

KANS.—Leavenworth

Great Western Mfg. Co. (Automatic Power Grain) .... AA

KY.—Louisville

Avery & Sons, B. F. (Cultivator) .... AAA

Louisville Shovel Co. ...C

MASS.—Boston

Ames Shovel & Tool Co., Ames Bldg. (Iron Hand) .... AAAA

Souther & Co., John (Steam) .... D

MASS.—Cambridge

Rawson & Morrison Mfg. Co. (Automatic Steam).B

MASS.—Greenfield

Rugg Mfg. Co. (Wood; Steel Snow) .... B

MASS.—Northampton

Maynard, C. A. X

MICH.—Albion

Gale Mfg. Co. (Cultivator) .... AA

MICH.—Charlotte

Benton Mfg. Co. (Snow)..A

MICH.—Detroit

Ireland & Matthews Mfg. Co. (Stove) .... A

Mitshkum Co., M., Chamber of Commerce (Steam, Second Hand) C

MICH.—Fenton

Phillips Co., A. J. (Wood Snow) .... A

MICH.—Kalamazoo

Harrow Spring Co. (Cultivator) .... B

Merrill-Stevens Mfg. Co. (Steel Snow) .... D

MICH.—Owosso

Owosso Mfg. Co. (Wood Snow) .... A

MICH.—St. Johns

Mason Co., F. C. (Cultivator) C

MINN.—Minneapolis

Howell & Co., R. R. (Power Grain) .... B

Kilgore Machine Company (Steam Railway Trac-

SHOVELS (*Con.*)
    tion; Mining) X
MO.—St. Louis
St. Louis Shovel Co. (Cof-
    fee; Contractors'; Lime;
    Mine; Sawdust; Tamping;
    Railroad) ....B
N. H.—Exeter
Lane, G. W. & C. A. (Au-
    tomatic Power Grain).D
N. J.—Newark
Lambert Hoisting Engine
    Co.   115-121   Poinier
    (Steam) C
Sommer's Son, John (Malt
    Wood) ....B
N. Y.—Albany
Kampf, Stephen (Malt)...E
Osgood Dredge Co., 37 State
    (Steam) ....A
Troy Nickel Works (Stove)
                        C
N. Y.—Brooklyn
New York Stamping Co.
    (Stove) ....A
Sweeney Mfg. Co., W. H.
    (Fire) ....B
N. Y.—Buffalo
Howard Iron Wks. (Grain)
                       AA
Shepard   &   Co.,   Sidney
    (Stove) ....AAAA
N. Y.—Ilion
Ross & Co., A. M. (Iron
    Hand; Snow) ....A
N. Y.—Lockport
Norman & Evans (Steam)
                        B
New York City
Davies, Frank, 68 Broad
    (Steam) X
Fairbanks Co., 416 Broome
    (Furnace; Tiling; Clay;
    Brick; Excavating; Irri-
    gating; Mining; Molders';
    Ore; Ox; Power Grain;
    Railroad; Tamping; Sew-
    er) ....AAAA
Floyd's Sons, Jas. R. (Coke
    Screening) ....A
Graf, Frank H., 322 7th
    Av. (Fireplace) ......D
Haiss Mfg. Co., 363 Rider
    Av. (Steam) ....D
Iron Clad Mfg. Co., 3 Cliff
    (Stove) ....AAA
Koppel, Arthur, 68 Broad
    (Steam) ....AA
Lalance & Grosjean Mfg.
    Co. (Fire) ......AAAA
Leavitt Co., C. W., 15 Cort-
    landt (Steam) ....D
Mead Mfg. Co., Jno. A., 11
    B'way (Automatic Steam)
                       AA
Russell & Erwin Mfg. Co.,
    43 Chambers (Stove)
                     AAAA
Sargent & Co., 151 Leonard
    (Stove) ....AAAA
N. Y.—Oswego
Kingsford Fdy. & Machine
    Wks. (Steam) ....AAAA
N. Y.—Troy
Troy Stamping Wks. (Con-
    tractors'; Fire) ..AAAA
N. Y.—West New Brighton
Hunt Co., C. W. (Auto-
    matic Steam) ....AA
OHIO—Akron
Akron Machine Co. (Culti-
    vator) C
Whitman & Barnes Mfg.
    Co. (Cultivator) ..AAAA
OHIO—Ashtabula
Rondberg & Co. X
OHIO—Bellevue
Ohio Cultivator Co. (Cul-
    tivator) ....AA
OHIO—Canton
Kohler & Co., F. E. (Fire;
    Snow; Steel Snow; Fur-
    nace) C
Ney Mfg. Co. (Tiling)..B
OHIO—Cincinnati
Males   Co.,   Aetna   Bldg.
    (Steam, Second Hand)..F
Obermayer Co., S. (Lipped.
    Moulders') ....A
OHIO—Cleveland
Avery Stamping Co. (Steel;
    Snow; Furnace; Boys';
    Tiling; Pole Hole; Brass;

SHOVELS (*Con.*)
    Bronze; Brick; Clay; Col-
    lier; Excavating; Irriga-
    tion; Mining; Ore; Rail-
    road Tamping; Sewer;
    Special; Tunnel) ......B
Chisholm & Sons, Wm., 358
    Case Av. (Iron Hand).AA
Osborn Mfg.   Co.,   16   S.
    Water (Molders') ......A
OHIO—Columbus
Kilbourne & Jacobs Mfg.
    Co. (Ox) ....AA
OHIO—Dayton
Dayton Malleable Iron Co.
    (Passenger   Coach   Fire)
                       AA
OHIO—Lorain
American Shovel & Stamp-
    ing   Co.   (Iron   Hand;
    Snow, &c.) ....B
Thew Automatic Shovel Co.
    (Automatic Steam) ..AA
OHIO—Marion
Fairbank's   Steam   Shovel
    Co. (Steam) ....B
Marion Steam Shovel Co.
    (Steam) ....AA
OHIO—Piqua
Wood Shovel & Tool Co.
    (Iron Hand) ....B
OHIO—Salem
Clark Co.,   W. J.   (Fire;
    Steel Garden; Stove).....A
OHIO—Toledo
Ohio   Steam   Shovel   Co.
    (Steam) ....D
Toledo Fdy. & Machine Co.,
    208-218 Cherry (Steam)
                        B
Union Mfg. Co. (Snow)..X
Vulcan   Iron   Works
    (Steam) ....A
OHIO—Youngstown
Pollock Co., Wm. B. (Ore)
                       AA
PA.—Beaver Falls
Meyers Co., H. M. (Iron
    Hand) ....AA
PA.—Corry
Penn   Shovel   Co.   (Iron
    Hand) C
PA.—Johnstown
Cambria   Fdy.   &   Machine
    Co. (Iron Hand) ......B
Cambria Steel Co. (Cultiva-
    tor) ....AAAA
PA.—Morrell
Union   Furnace   Mfg.   Co.
    (Iron Hand) ....D
PA.—Mifflinsburg
Albright & Sons, Jas. H.
    (Cultivator) ....D
PA.—Mt. Pleasant
Mt. Pleasant Tool Co. (Fur-
    nace Tiling; Pole Hole;
    Collier;   Lime;   Mining;
    Molders') ....B
PA.—Philadelphia
Allen & Co., S. L., 1017
    Market (Cultivator)..AA
Griffiths Co., Geo., 515 Lo-
    cust (Iron Hand) ......A
Pfeifer & Co. (Ltd.), Jno.,
    226 Race (Asphalt) ....A
Rowland, Maxwell & Co.
    (Inc.), 432 Market.....A
Standard Supply & Equip-
    ment Co., 1710 Market
    (Steam) ....D
PA.—Pittsburg
Carlin Co., W. J., 25th &
    Av. R. R. (Steam)....A
Hubbard & Co., Murtland
    Bldg. (Mining Machine)
                        A
Hussey, Binns & Co. (Ltd.),
    541 Wood (Contractors';
    Steel   Garden;   Mining;
    Railroad) ....AA
Klein, Logan & Co. (Iron
    Hand; Fire Place) ....A
Low & Co., Edgar S., Em-
    pire Bldg. (Steam, Sec-
    ond Hand) ....D
Patton & Co., J. R., (Steam,
    Second Hand) ....D
Pittsburg Shovel Co., Frick
    Bldg. (Iron Hand) .....B
Russell Shovel Co., J. C.
    (Iron Hand) ....B
PA.—Wyoming
Wyoming Shovel Co. (Iron

SHOVELS (Con.)
Hand) ....A
PA.—York
Hench & Dromgold Co. (Cultivator) ....A
VA.—Norfolk
White & Bro., S. R. (Cultivator) ....A
W. VA.—Wheeling
Laughlin Nail Co. (Iron Hand) ....AA
Wheeling Hinge Co. (Fire) AA
WIS.—Fort Atkinson
Hager, E. ....D
WIS.—Madison
Fuller & Johnson Mfg. Co. (Cultivator) ....AA
WIS.—Oshkosh
Jones, J. R. (Iron Hand).H
WIS.—South Milwaukee
Bucyrus Co. (Steam) ....B

SHOW CASES
See Cases: Show

SHOWERS
See also Baths

New York City
Trageser Steam Copper Wks., John (Copper)....B
PA.—Pittsburg
Standard Mfg. Co. (Brass) AA

SHREDDERS
See also Agricultural Implements

ILL.—Batavia
Appleton Mfg. Co. (Corn) A
ILL.—Harvard
Hunt, Helm, Ferris & Co. (Corn) ....AA
ILL.—Sterling
Keystone Co. ....AA
IND.—New Castle
Safety Shredder Co. (Corn) A
MICH.—Ann Arbor
Ann Arbor Machine Co. (Fodder) ....E
MICH.—Battle Creek
Advance Thresher Company (Corn) ....AAAA
MICH.—Monroe
Wilder-Strong Implement Co. (Fodder) ....B
N. J.—Newark
National Saw Co. (Vegetable) ....B
New York City
Newell Mfg. Co., 149 B'way D
OHIO—Lancaster
Eagle Machine Co. (Fodder) A
Hocking Valley Mfg. Co. A
OHIO—Salem
Silver Mfg. Co. (Dry Fodder) ....AA
PA.—Philadelphia
Disston & Sons, Henry (Vegetable) ......AAAA
VT.—St. Albans
St. Albans Fdy. & Implement Co. ....D
VT.—Wallingford
Wallingford Mfg. Company (Corn) X
WIS.—Marinette
Stevens Co., A. W. (Corn) AA
WIS.—Milwaukee
Milwaukee Hay Tool Co. (Corn) ....A

SHRIMP
See Canned Goods

SHRINKERS
ILL.—Carpentersville
Illinois Iron & Bolt Co. (Tire) ....AA
ILL.—Rockford
Weyburn Co. (Tire) C

SHRINKERS (Con.)
IND.—South Bend
Sandage Steel Skein Co. (Tire) X
MASS.—Greenfield
Wiley & Russell Mfg. Co. (Tire) ....AA
MASS.—Worcester
Boynton & Plumber (Tire) B
PA.—Lancaster
Champion Blower & Forge Co. (Tire) ....AA

SHUTES
See Chutes

SHUTTERS
See also Woodwork

ILL.—Chicago
Barbee Wire & Iron Works (Steel) ....B
Braumoeller & Son, Henry (Iron) ....B
Dodge & Co., H. B., 108 La Salle (Steel & Wood Rolling) ....D
Smith Wire & Iron Co., F. P., 100 Lake (Steel; Iron) AA
Variety Mfg. Co., 77 W. Lake (Steel Rolling) ..D
IND.—Evansville
Mesker & Co., George L. (Steel; also Iron Door) AA
IND.—Indianapolis
Indianapolis Steel Roofing & Corrugating Co. (Steel) A
IOWA—Des Moines
Steel Roofing & Stamping Works (Steel) C
MICH.—Detroit
Amos & Co., Charles (Steel) F
Barnum Wire & Iron Wks., E. T. (Steel) ....B
Bolles Iron & Wire Wks., J. E. (Iron) X
Vulcan Co. (Steel) ......E
MICH.—Kalamazoo
Michigan Photo. Shutter Co. (Photographic) ...H
MINN.—St. Paul
Perkins Mfg. Co., 1121 E. 7th (Steel) ....D
MO.—Kansas City
Swearingen Mfg. Co. (Steel; Automatic Steel Rolling) X
MO.—St. Louis
Christopher & Simpson Architectural Iron & Fdy. Co. (Iron) ....AA
N. H.—Milford
Pierce & Co., W. E. (Wood Rolling) ....D
N. J.—Boonton
Lincoln Iron Wks. (Iron) B
N. J.—Newark
Plumb, D. S. (Photographic) D
N. Y.—Binghamton
Roberson & Son, A. (Wooden) ....AA
N. Y.—Buffalo
Churchyard, Joseph J. (Sliding) X
New York City
Cornell Co., J. B. & J. M. (Iron, Rolling) ......AA
Dimond, Thomas (Iron Rolling) ....A
Fiske Iron Works, J. W. (Iron) ....B
Moseley Iron Bridge & Roof Co., 39 Cortlandt (Steel; Iron) ....B
Prosch Mfg. Co. (Photographic) ....F
Westervelt Co., A. B. & W. T. (Iron) ....B
Wilson Mfg. Co., Jas. G., 3 W. 29th (Steel; Iron; Wooden Rolling) ......A
N. Y.—Poughkeepsie
Lane Bros. Co. (Automatic Fire) ....A

SHUTTERS (Con.)

N. Y.—Rochester
Bausch & Lomb Optical Co.
(Photographic) ....AAA
Siddons Co., John (Steel)
B

OHIO—Cambridge
Cambridge Roofing Co.
(Steel) ....B

OHIO—Canton
Berger Mfg. Co. (Steel;
Iron) ....AA
Canton Steel Roofing Co.
(Steel) ....A
Eller & Co., J. H. (Steel)
A

OHIO—Cincinnati
Schreiber & Sons, L., 8th &
Eggleston Av. (Steel).AA

OHIO—Cleveland
Garry Iron & Steel
Co. (Iron) ....A
Van Dorn Iron Works Co.
(Iron) ....AA

OHIO—Columbus
Columbus Steel Rolling
Shutter Co. (Steel Roll-
ing) ....D
Kinnear Mfg. Co. (Steel;
Steel Rolling) ....AA

O..IO—Forest
Dickelman Mfg. Co. (St^el)
A

OHIO—Kenton
Champion Iron Co. (Iron)
AA

OHIO—Middletown
American Steel Roofing Co.
(Steel) ....A

OHIO—Niles
Sykes Metal Lath & Roof-
ing Co. (Steel) ....B

OHIO—Youngstown
Youngstown Iron & Steel
Roofing Co. (Steel) ..AA

PA.—Philadelphia
Darby & Sons, Edward
(Iron) ....AA
Gara, McGinley & Co., 23
S. 17th (Steel) ....A
Merritt & Co., 1024 Ridge
Av. (Steel) ....A
Pennsylvania Metal Ceiling
& Roofing Co. (Ltd.)
(Steel) ....B

R. I.—Providence
Clason Architectural Metal
Works (Inc.), 428 Kings-
ley Av. (Steel) C

TENN.—Chattanooga
Chattanooga Roofing & Fdy.
Co. (Iron) ....A

WIS.—Milwaukee
Willer Mfg. Co. (Wooden)
A

SHUTTLES

CONN.—Chester
Bates, C. J. (Bone Tatting)
D

CONN.—Hartford
Billings & Spencer Co.
(Sewing Machine) ...AA

MASS.—Lawrence
Sprague Co., L. .....AAAA
Union Shuttle Co. ....D

MASS.—Lowell
Lowell Shuttle Co. X
New England Shuttle Co..
64 Leverett X

MASS.—New Bedford
New Bedford Shuttle Co...B

MASS.—Southbridge
Litchfield Shuttle Co.....B

MASS.—Wilkinsonville
Dudley & Son Co., D. F.. X

N. H.—Nashua
Murray, Chas. O. X

N. J.—Paterson
Hall & Co., I. A.........A
Ulrich & Co. C

New York City
Domestic Sewing Machine
Co. (Sewing Machine)..X
Household Sewing Machine
Co. (Sewing Machine)..B
Kruse & Murphy Mfg. Co.
(Sewing Machine) ....D
New Home Sewing Machine
Co. (Sewing Machine)
AAAA
Singer Mfg. Co. (Sewing
Machine) ....AAAA

SHUTTLES (Con.)

N. Y.—Utica
Williams Co., J. H.......A

N. C.—Lincolnton
Grigg Mfg. Co. ....F

OHIO—Cleveland
Standard Sewing Machine
Co. (Sewing Machine)
AAA

PA.—Philadelphia
Billington Co., H. ....A
Sergeson Co., R., 1704 Tu-
lip (Loom) ....D

R. I.—Providence
American Supply Co.....AA
U. S. Bobbin & Shuttle Co.
AAAA

R. I.—Woonsocket
Coburn, Fred S. X
Woonsocket Reed & Shuttle
Works ....E
Woonsocket Shuttle Co...X

S. C.—Westminster
Southern Shuttle & Bobbin
Co. ....B

SICKLES

See also Scythes

ILL.—Peoria
Herschel Mfg. Co., R.
(Mower; Reaper) ......A

N. Y.—Auburn
Henry & Allen (Mower;
Reaper) ....A

New York City
American Axe & Tool Co.,
253 B'way ....AAAA

OHIO—Akron
Whitman & Barnes Mfg.
Co. (Mower; Reaper)
AAAA

SIDEWALKS

MASS.—Boston
Mathews Consolidated Slate
Co. (Slate) X

MO.—Kansas City
Kansas City Cement Side-
walk Co. (Cement) ...E

N. Y.—Brooklyn
American Metal Ceiling Co.,
215 Montague (Steel)..F
Brooklyn Metal Ceiling Co.
(Steel) C
Lyles & Mills Metal Ceiling
Co. (Steel) ....F

New York City
New York Metal Ceiling
Co., 537 W. 24th (Steel)
B

OHIO—Canton
Berger Mfg. Co. (Steel).AA

VT.—Poultney
Fleming Slate Co. (Slate).C

SIDEBOARDS

See Furniture

SIDES

**See also Woodwork: Car-
riage**

New York City
Hopkins Co. (Wagon)....C

OHIO—Cleveland
Standard Tool Co. (Fork;
Bicycle) ....AA

SIDING

**See also Roofing; Iron;
Steel, etc.**

LA.—Lake Charles
Bradley-Ramsay Lumber Co.
(Car) ....AAAA

MICH.—Saginaw
Mershon & Co., Wm. B.
(Car) ....A

MO.—St. Louis
Harry Steel Works, O. K.
(Brick Face; Rock Face)
B

N. Y.—Buffalo
Churchyard Jos. J. X

New York City
Sjoberg & Co., J. P. (Car)
D
Wheeling Corrugating Co.
(Metallic; Brick Steel;
Stone; Tin) ......AAAA

SIDING (Con.)

OHIO—Canton
Canton Steel Roofing Co.
(Metallic) ....A

OHIO—Cincinnati
Hyndman Steel Roofing Co.
(Metallic) C

OHIO—Cleveland
Garry Iron & Steel Co.
(Metallic) ....A

OHIO—Toledo
Smith Co., W. H. H. (Car)
.......................B

PA.—Philadelphia
Cortright Metal Roofing ...
Co. ....B

SIENNA
See also Colors

PA.—Easton
Williams & Co., C. K.....A

SIEVES
See Riddles

SIFTERS

CONN.—Georgetown
Gilbert & Bennett Mfg. Co.
(Ash; Flour; Coal; Drug-
gists') ....AAA

ILL.—Chicago
Aitchison Perforated Metal
Co., 303 Dearborn X
Barbee Wire & Iron Wks.
(Ash) ....B
Harrington & King Perfo-
rating Co., 224 N. Union
(Sand) ....A

ILL.—Harvey
Whiting Foundry Equip-
ment Co. (Rotary; Sand)
.......................AA

ILL.—Rockford
Clark Mfg. Co., J. L.
(Flour) ....D

IND.—Indianapolis
Nordyke & Marmon Co.
(Flour) ....AAA

IND.—Mishawaka
Dodge Mfg. Co. (Sand).AAA

IND.—Richmond
Richmond City Mill Works
(Flour) ....B

KANS.—Coffeyville
Pioneer Flint Glass Co.
(Glass; Sugar) C

MASS.—Amherst
Allen, L. H. (Ash) C

MASS.—Bridgewater
Perkins Co., Henry (Sand)
.......................B

MASS.—Cambridge
Barbour-Stockwell Company
(Sand) ....A

MASS.—Worcester
Hill Dryer Co. (Ash) ....D
National Mfg. Co. (Ash;
Flour; Coffee) ....A
Parker Wire Goods Co.
(Flour) ....D
Wire Goods Co. (Flour)..A
Wright Wire Co. (Ash).AA

MICH.—Detroit
Byram & Co. (Sand)......D
Colton, Arthur (Pharma-
ceutical) C
Northern Engineering Wks.
(Sand) ....A

MINN.—Minneapolis
Schutz-O'Neill Co. (Gyrator)
.......................C

MO.—St. Louis
Ludlow-Saylor Wire Co.
(Sand; Ash; Flour) ..AA

N. J.—Newark
Gould & Eberhardt (Sand)
.......................A

N. J.—Trenton
Crossley Mfg. Co. (Clay).B

N. Y.—Brooklyn
Ross & Son, Chas. (Coffee)
.......................D

N. Y.—Buffalo
Buffalo Wire Works Co..D
Noye Mfg. Co. (Mill)....X
Shepard & Co.,Sidney (Ash;
Flour) ....AAAA
Western Wire Goods Co.
(Flour) ....D

SIFTERS (Con.)

N. Y.—Cortland
Wickwire Bros. (Flour;
Coal; Ash) ....AAAA

New York City
Burns & Sons, Jabez (Cof-
fee) ....B
Estey Wire Works Co., 59
Fulton (Flour) ....D
Howard & Morse, 45 Fulton
(Druggists') ....D
Lalance & Grosjean Mfg. Co.
19 Cliff (Flour) ..AAAA
Mundt & Sons, Chas., 441
Pearl (Sand) ....B
Niles-Bement-Pond Co., 111
Broadway (Sand) .AAAA

N. Y.—Troy
Troy Stamping Works (Ash)
..................AAAA

OHIO—Cincinnati
Bromwell Brush & Wire
Goods Co. (Ash) ......AA
Day Co., J. H. (Flour)...A
Forest City Steel & Iron
Co. ....A
Obermeyer Co., S., 647
Evans (Sand) ....AA

OHIO—Cleveland
Osborn Mfg. Co., 1331 Ham-
ilton ....B
Smith Foundry Supply Co.,
J. D., 40 S. Water......D
Tyler Co., W. S. (Ash)
..................AAAA

OHIO—Hamilton
Meyers Mfg. Co., F. J.
(Ash; Flour; Coal; Foun-
dry) ....B

PA.—Muncy
Sprout, Waldron & Co.
(Flour) ....A

PA.—Philadelphia
Darby & Sons, E., 233 Arch
(Ash; Flour) ....A
Paxson Co., J. W. (Sand)
.......................AA

R. I.—Providence
Towel, Rack & Novelty Co.
(Ash; Automatic) .....F

SIGHTS

CONN.—Hartford
Colts Patent Fire Arms
Mfg. Co. (Firearm).AAAA

CONN.—Middlefield
Lyman Gun Sight Corpora-
tion (Firearm) ....A

CONN.—New Haven
Marlin Fire Arms Co. (Fire-
arm) ....AA
Winchester Repeating Arms
Co. (Firearm) ....AAAA

MASS.—Chicopee Falls
Stevens Arms & Tool Co.,
J. (Firearm; Gun; Rifle)
.......................AAA

N. Y.—Ilion
Remington Arms Co. (Fire-
arm) ....AAA

N. Y.—Utica
Savage Arms Co. (Firearm)
.......................A

SIGNALS

COLO.—Denver
Flint-Lomax Electric &
Mfg. Co. (Electric Mine)
.......................B

ILL.—Chicago
Adams & Westlake Co., On-
tario, cor. N. Franklin
(Telegraph Train Order)
..................AAAA
Burdett-Rountree Mfg. Co.,
76 W. Jackson Boul. (Ele-
vator) ....B
Elevator Supply & Repair
Co., 34 W. Monroe (Ele-
vator) ....B
Miller Signal Co., Monad-
nock Blk. (Railway Cross-
ing) ....D
Porter & Berg, 309 Dear-
born (Electric Railway)
.......................D
Rowell-Potter Safety Stop
Co., Rookery Bldg. (Au-
tomatic; Interlocking Sys-
tem) ....D

ILL.—Peoria
Acme Railway Signal &

SIGNALS (Con.)

Mfg. Co. (Railway Crossing) ....E

MD.—Baltimore
Baltimore Enamel & Novelty Co., cor. Allen & Clement (Enamelled Steel; Railway Crossing) ....B

MASS.—West Newton
United States Electric Signal Co. (Automatic Electric Railway) ....D

MICH.—Birmingham
Wilson Railway Gate Co. (Electric Railway; Railway Crossing) ....F

MICH.—Jackson
Parish Bros. (Block System for Electric Railroads; Railway Crossing) ....H

MO.—St. Louis
Handlan-Buck Mfg. Co., 212 N. 3rd (Railway Crossing) ....AA

N. Y.—Hillburn
Ramapo Iron Wks. (Railway Crossing; Switch; (Automatic) ....AAA

New York City
American Flag Co. (Code) ....A
Boyle & Co., John (Code) ....AA
Detwiller & Street Fireworks Mfg. Co. (Railway Fog) ....A
Hall Signal Co., 25 Broad (Electric Railway; Railway Crossing; Automatic) ....A
Herzog Teleseme Co., 51 W. 24th (Elevator) ...D
Jordan Bros. 74 Beekman (Electric Railway) ...D
Koster & Co., C. H. (Code).D

OHIO—Cincinnati
Vanduzen Co., E. W. (Fog) ....B
Weir Frog Co., cor. Front & Smith (Electric Railway) ....A

OHIO—Dayton
Barney & Smith Car Co. (Switch; Train Order; Railway) ....AAAA

PA.—Allentown
Allentown Rolling Mills (Block System; Interlocking System; Railway Crossing; Switch; Automatic; Mechanical; Junction; Station) ....AAA

PA.—Coatesville
Taite Railway Signal Co. (Railway Crossing) ...B

PA.—Pittsburg
Pittsburg Electrical & Machine Wks. (Mine; Electric) ....E
Union Switch & Signal Co. (Railway) ....AAAA
Westinghouse Electric & Mfg. Co. (Electric Railway) ....AAAA

PA.—Scranton
Everhart Brass Wks. (Mine; Pneumatic) ....A

PA.—Steelton
Penna. Steel Co. (Railway Crossing; Switch) .AAAA

PA.—Swissvale
Union Switch & Signal Co. (Block System; Electric Railway; Interlocking System; Pneumatic; Railway Crossing; Switch; Automatic; Mechanical; Junction) ....AAAA

SIGNS

For Electric Signs, see also Flashes

COLO.—Denver
Denver Novelty Work Mfg. Co. (Brass) ....D

CONN.—South Norwalk
McKibbin Mfg. Co., G. N. (Glass) ....B

ILL.—Chicago
Barbee Wire & Iron Wks. (Glass; Wire) ....B

SIGNS (Con.)

Gunning System (Enameled Iron) ....AAA
Marx Zero Sign Works (Enameled Iron Drug)..E
Meyercord Co., Chamber of Commerce Bldg. (Window Transparency) ....A
Rawson & Evans, 151 W. Washn. (Glass) C
Suess Ornamental Glass Co., 54 N. Clinton (Glass) .D
Tweed & Rau Co., 298 W. Madison (Glass) ......F
Western Sand Blast Co., cor. W. Jackson Boul. & S. Clinton (Glass) C
Winslow Bros. Co., 368 Carroll Av. (Bronze; also Brass & Iron) ....AA

ILL.—Joliet
Adams, W. J. (Wire)....D

IND.—Connersville
Roots & Heineman (Enameled Iron) ....A

IND.—Kokomo
Kokomo Fence Machine Co. (Wire) ....AAA

KY.—Louisville
Dow Wire Works Co. (Wire) ....D

MD.—Baltimore
Baltimore Enamel & Novelty Co., cor. Allen & Clement (Enameled Iron Station) ....B
Dorman Co., J. F. W. (Metal) ....F

MASS.—Waltham
O'Hara Waltham Dial Co. (Enameled) C

MICH.—Detroit
Barnum Wire & Iron Wks., E. T. (Wire) ....B
Bolles Iron & Wire Works, J. E. (Wire) X

MICH.—Grand Rapids
Leonard Mfg. Co. (Porcelain) X

MO.—St. Louis
Ludlow-Saylor Wire Co. (Wire) ....AA
Sentenne & Green (Enameled Iron) ....A

N. J.—Newark
Electric Motor & Equipment Co., 13 Beaver (Electrically Illuminated) C

N. Y.—Brooklyn
Union Porcelain Works (Porcelain) ....B

N. Y.—Buffalo
Buffalo Last Works (Boot; Shoe) ....B
Buffalo Wire Works Co. (Wire) ....A

New York City
Asbury Glass Sign Co., 43 John (Glass) ....F
Beck & Co. F. (Advertising) ....A
Caeser Bros., 112 Fulton (Enameled Iron; Glass; Advertising) ....D
Denzi & Phillips, 24 Dey (Glass; Advertising) ...C
Dorr, Wallie, 16 Reade (Enameled) ....E
Frink, I. P. (Illuminated) ....AA
Gleason Mfg. Co. E. P. (Illuminated) ....B
Gude Co., O. J. (Advertising) ....B
Herrlein & Henrich, 90 Hudson (Glass) ....D
Howard & Morse (Advertising) ....D
Hughes, Thomas, 51 E. 9th (Illuminating) ....D
Jackson Co., Wm. H., 29 E. 17th (Bronze) ....A
Jones & Co., Trevor F., 374 W. B'way (Bronze; also Silver; Metal) X
Kaufman & Strauss Co. (Tin) ....A
Mansfield & Co., 158 Chambers (Glass) ....F
Morris Electric Co., 15 Cortlandt (Car) ....D
Russell & Co., J. W. (Aluminum; Brass; Glass) ...E

SIGNS (Con.)

Spencer Optical Co. (Watch; Spectacle) C
Stafford, Nelson (Brass; Metal; Copper; Oxidized) F
Universal Electric Stage Lighting Co. (Illuminated) ....D
Upham & Co., Henry H. (Brass) C
Washburn & Co., E. G. (Emblematic; Watch; Spectacle) ....E
OHIO—Akron
Enterprise Mfg. Co. (Advertising; Luminous) ..A
OHIO—Cincinnati
Hunter Illuminated Car Sign Co. (Car) ....D
National Enameling Co. (Enameled) C
PA.—Beaver Falls
Ingram & Richardson Mfg. Co. (Enameled Iron)....D
PA.—Bethlehem
Strock & Co., L. W. (Metal) ....D
PA.—Ellwood City
Glen Mfg. Co. (Sheet Metal; Wire) C
PA.—Philadelphia
Brill Co., J. G., 62d & Woodland (Reversible Car) ....AAAA
Darby & Sons, Edward (Wrought Iron; Ornamental; Wire) ....A
Gaumer Co., John L.......C
Merritt & Co., 1024 Ridge Av. (Illuminating) ....B
WIS.—Milwaukee
American Sign Co., 51 Erie (Adv. of Cloth; Oil Cloth; Parchment Fibre; Paraffined Card Board) .....A

SILESIAS

See also Cotton Goods

SILEX

N. J.—Lincoln
Atlas Mineral & Machine Co.....................D
N. Y.—Brooklyn
Wiarda & Co., John C. (Ground) ....AA
New York City
Pettit Chemical Company (Ground) ....B
Salomon & Bros., L. A., 216 Pearl ....AA
OHIO—Piqua
Ohio Marble Co. ....D
PA.—Philadelphia
Nevins Co., Samuel, 109 S. 2d. ....D
Paxson C., J. W. (Ground) AA

SILICA

ILL.—Chicago
United States Silica Co...B
ILL.—Danville
Western Silica Co. (Glass) B
MICH.—Battle Creek
Silver Star Mfg. Co. C
OHIO—Cleveland
Grasselli Chemical Co.AAAA

SILICO

New York City
Dana & Co., 32 Broadway (Spiegel) ....A
Leavitt & Co., C. W., 15 Cortlandt (Spiegel).....D

SILICON

ALA.—Birmingham
Tennessee Coal, Iron & Railroad Co. (Ferro) AAAA
New York City
Roessler & Hasslacher Chemical Co., 100 William (Ferro) ....AA
N. Y.—Niagara Falls
Carborundum Co. (Carbide

SILICON (Con.)

of) ....A
PA.—Pittsburg
Carnegie Steel Co. (Ferro) AAAA
Hooker & Co., H. M. (Ferro) C

SILK

See also Silk Goods: Thread

CAL.—San Francisco
Carlson-Currier Co., 6 Sutter (Embroidery) ....B
MASS.—Athol
Adams, D. E. (Twist; Embroidery; Floss) ....B
MASS.—Canton
Eureka Silk Mfg. Co. (Embroidery; Floss; Twist).A
MICH.—Belding
Richardson Silk Co. (Embroidery; Twist, &c.) ..A
New York City
Beolchi, V. M. (Raw)....C
China & Japan Trading Co. (Raw) ....AAAA
Doherty & Wadsworth (Raw) ....AA
Eurasia Silk Importing Co. (Raw) X
Fraser & Co. (Raw).....X
Gerli & Co. (Raw) .....AA
Guerin, Vve & Fils (Raw) AAAA
Guichard & Co., A. (Raw) C
Hadden & Co. (Raw).AAAA
Hanssen, Herman J. (Raw) X
Jardine, Matheson & Co. (Raw) ....AAAA
Meyer & Co., Oscar R. (Raw) X
Morimura & Co., Arai (Raw) ....A
Murray, Russell & Co. (Raw) ....B
O'Donoghue & Co. (Raw).D
Paladini & Co., E. (Raw) A
Reimers & Co., Otto (Raw) A
Rosenthal & Co., A. S. (Imp. China & Japan)..A
Seabury & Johnson, 59 Maiden Lane (Oiled)..AA
Takai & Co. (Raw) .....A
Takata & Co. (Raw).....B
Vivanti Bros. (Raw) ...AA
Walker & Co. (Raw) ....F
Woodhouse & Bopp (Com.) A
PA.—Lansdowne
General Artificial Silk Co. (Artificial) ....B
PA.—Philadelphia
Wright. W. P., 1514 N. Marvine (Oiled) ....B

SILK GOODS

CONN.—Bridgeport
Salts' Textile Mfg. Co., The (Seal; Upholstery) A
Macfarlane, Jos. S. (Tram; Twist)................D
CONN.—New London
Brainerd & Armstrong Co. (Tailors' Silk Fabrics; Satins, etc.) ......AAA
CONN.—Putnam
Hammond, Knowlton & Co. (Dress) ....B
CONN.—Shelton
Specialty Weaving Co. (Ribbons) ....AA
CONN.—South Manchester .
Cheney Bros. (Silk; Satin Plushes; Velvets; Printed Silk Pongees; Ribbons; Fabric) ....AAAA
CONN.—Turnerville .
Turner & Co., P. W. (Ribbons) C
CONN.—Warehouse Point .
Warehouse Point Silk Co. (Art Silk) ....A
CONN.—Watertown
Heminway & Bartlett Silk Co. (Embroidery) C

CONN.—Winsted
Winsted Silk Co. (Knitting; Twist; Embroidery) ....A
DEL.—Dover
Post & Sheldon Silk Co. (Broad Goods) ....B
ILL.—Chicago
Baum & Co., C. F., 220 Madison (Dress; Cloak; Millinery Trimmings)....C
MD.—Ilchester
Thistle Mills Co. (Plain; Fancy) ....B
MASS.—Fitchburg ..
Cornforth & Marx (Dress; Tie) ....B
MASS.—Florence
Nonotuck Silk Co. (Embroidery; Twist, etc) AAA
MASS.—Holyoke
Goetz Silk Mfg. Co. (Linings; Serges) C
Skinner Mfg. Co., Wm...AA
MASS.—Northhampton
Belding Bros. & Co. (Satins; Serges; Sewing; Knitting) ....AAAA
MASS.—Worcester
Thayer Mfg. Co., L. D. (Ribbons) C
N. J.—Bloomfield
Underhill, Wm. K. (Dress Goods) ....B
N. J.—Carlstadt
Sharg Bros. (Dress Goods) D
N. J.—Hackettstown
Ashley & Shaw Silk Co. (Organzine) ....B
N. J.—Hoboken
Balas, Freres (Ribbons)..D
Hoboken Ribbon Co. (Ribbons) ....D
N. J.—Jersey City
Phalanx Silk Mill (Dress Goods) ....A
Schaefer, L. B. (Dress Goods) ....D
S'ohn's Sons, C. (Dress; Tie; Corset; Vestings; Shoe; Button) ....A
N. J.—Midland Park
De Gray & Co. (Dress; Tie) E
N. J.—Newton
Valentine & Bentley Silk Co. (Dress Goods) .....B
N. J.—Paterson
Altshuler Bros. (Satins; Taffetas) ....D
Anderson Bros. (Dress; Tie) ....B
Appel Bros. Mfg Co. (Tie; Silk) ....B
Aronson, Sam'l J. (Dress; Tie) ....I'
Ashley & Bailey Co. (Dress; Ribbons; Tie Goods) AAAA
Audiger & Meyer Silk Co. (Tie Silks) ....B
Augusta Silk Wks. (Ribbons) ....B
Baker & Schofield Co. (Broad) ....B
Ball. William (Ribbons)..C
Bamford Bros. Silk Mfg. Co. (Ribbons) ....A
Banner Silk Co. (Plain; Fancy Dress; Linings)..D
Becket Silk Co., David (Ribbons) ....D
Bentley Bros. (Lining; Neckwear; Dress; Trimming) C
Brandes Mfg. Co., Julius (Narrow Ribbons; Bindings) ....B
Bristow, Mc Collum & Port (Broad Silks) ....D
Cardinal & Becker (Broad Silks) ....B
Cardinal Silk Co. (Dress Goods; Linings) ......B
Cedar Cliff Silk Co. (Lining; Dress; Umbrella) AA
Clifton Silk Mills (Broad) AA
Clowes, Sothern Co. (Dress; Tie) C

Collinge & Nolan Co. (Ribbons) C
Columbia Ribbon Co. (Ribbons) C
Corbett, Reinhardt & Co. (Ribbons) ....B
Dexter, Lambert & Co. (Ribbons; Dress Goods) AAAA
Doherty & Wadsworth Co. (Broad; Ribbons; Silks) AA
Empire Silk Co (Dress; Tie Goods) ....A
Enterprise Silk Co. (Dress Goods) ....B
Fairhurst & Co. (Tie)....C
Frank & Dugan (Ribbons) AA
Grimshaw Bros. (Broad; Millinery; Tie).........C
Haemchen Bros. Silk Corp. (Linings; Furrier Goods; Tie; Umzrella) ....B
Hand & Sons, Jno. (Broad; Tie; Ribbon) ....A
Harris, Wm. (Ribbons)..D
Helvetia Silk Mill (Ribbons) ....A
Hollbach & Co., Jno. (Tie; Silks) C
Holmes Silk Co. (Dress Goods) ....B
Holzman Silk Mfg. Co. (Ribbons) C
Jansen & Pretzfeld (Dress Goods) C
John, Cowdin & Co. (Ribbons) ....AAA
Kattermann & Mitchell (Broad Goods) ....A
Laurel Silk Works (Dress Goods) ....B
Levey, A. & M. (Ribbons) AA
Little & Co., W. (Dress; Tie) C
Mason Silk Mills (Fancy Broad) ....AA
Mayhew Silk Mfg. Co. (Dress Goods) C
Meding Mfg. Co. (Ribbons) X
Meteor Silk Co..........D
Miesch Mfg. Co. (Ribbons) B
Miller & Ward Co. (Broad) D
Naef Bros. Co. (Broad Silks) ....B
National Ribbon Co (Ribbons) ....B
Neuberger-Phillips Silk Co. C
New Jersey Silk Co. (Dress Goods) ....AA
Paragon Silk Co. (Broad) B
Pelgram & Meyer (Broad Silks; Ribbons) ..AAAA
Phoenix Silk Mfg. Co. (Broad; Ribbons)..AAAA
Post & Sheldon Silk Co. (Broad) C
Potts Co., J. M.......B
Ramsey & Gore Mfg Co. (Tram; Organzine; Chiffon; Crepe-de-chine)....B
Reiling & Schoen, David (Dress; Tie) ....AA
Simon. R. H. (Dress Goods; Ribbons; Tie; Lining Silks) ....AAAA
Simpson & Co., Jas. (Fancy Dress Goods; Ribbons) AA
Standard Silk Co. (Taffetas; Gros-Grains; Failles; Satins; Surahs; Crepe-de-chines) ....A
Stern & Pohly (Broad Silks) C
Strange Co., Wm. (Dress Goods; Ribbons)....AAA
Threlfall & Steele (Tie)..C
Warner, Joseph (Ribbons) C
Westerhoff Bros. & Napier Co. (Dress; Tie; Organzine) ....B
N. J.—Stirling
Stirling Silk Mfg. Co. (Nov-

elties; Broad Goods)....A
N. J.—Summit
Summit Silk Mfg. Co. (Nov-
elties; Broad Goods)...A
N. J.—Town of Union
Simon, R. & H. (Ribbons)
AAAA
N. J.—Washington
Washington Silk Mills (Um-
brellas; Dress; Fancy)..B
N. Y.—West Hoboken
Givernand Bros. (Black;
Colored Dress) .....AAA
Schwarzenbach, Huber &
Co. (Dress; Necktie; Lin-
ing; Umbrella) ..AAAA
N. J.—West New York
North American Silk Co.
(Broad) ....D
N. Y.—Binghamton
Binghamton Silk Co.
(Broad) ....D
N. Y.—Brooklyn
Kaltenbach & Stephens
(Ribbons) ....B
N. Y.—Elmira
Read & Lovatt Mfg. Co..A
Stearns & Co., J. N.
(Broad Silks) .....AAA
N. Y.—Haverstraw
Home Silk Mills (Broad)..C
N. Y.—Hornellsville
Steuben Silk Co. (Broad).B
N. Y.—Kenwood
Oneida Community (Em-
broidery Silk) .....AAA
N. Y.—Long Island City
Astoria Silk W'ks. (Broad
Silks; Satins) ....AA
Migel & Co., M. C. (Broad
Dress Silks) ....B
N. Y.—Newburgh
Harrison & Gore Silk Co.
(Dress Goods; Pongees;
Tie Goods; Florentines)
C
New York City
Abegg & Rusch (Com.)
AAAA
Atlas Silk Co......AAAA
Auffmordt & Co., C. A.
(Com.; also Import)
AAAA
Bachmann, Emmerich &
Co. (Com.) ....B
Beckermann & Co.,
(Import) ....B
Bernhard & Son, B. (Im-
port) ....A
Bernstein, Mitchell B.
(Ribbons) ....B
Blum, J. A. (Import)...B
Boessneck, Broesel & Co.
(Com.) ....AAAA
Burgess & Co., W. H.
(Broad Goods) .....AAA
Caeser & Co., H. A. (Com.;
also Dress Goods)..AAA
Catoir Silk Co. (Broad
Silks) C
Cheney Bros. (Piece Goods;
Pongees; Ribbons) AAAA
Dazian & Son, D. W.
(Import) ....B
Derby & Co., W. E.
(Com.) ....A
Dexter, Lambert & Co.
(Dress Goods; Ribbons;
Trimmings) .....AAAA
Eisemann & Co., S.......X
Erskine & Co., J......B
Erstein & Bro. (Ribbons;
Dress Goods) ......AAA
Eureka Silk Mfg. Co...AA
Fithian & Co., J. H.
(Com.) ....A
Fleitmann & Co. (Com.;
Dress Silks) ......AAAA
Frank & Dugan (Ribbons)
AA
Gartner & Friedenheit (Rib-
bons) ....AAA
Givernaud Bros. (Broad
Goods) ....AAA
Gomprecht, M. (Ribbons).B
Graef & Co., Walter......A
Gumbinner Co., Paul...AAA
Hammond, Knowlton & Co.
(Twist) ....B
Hardt, von Bernuth & Co.
(Import; also Com.; Rib-
bons, etc.) ....AAAA

Heinsheimer Bros. (Rib-
bons) ....B
Hertlein, Chr. E. (Ribbons)
A
Hill Bros. (Ribbons)......B
Hoeninghause & Curtiss
(Com. Ribbons, etc.; also
Import) ....AA
Hyman, S. ....B
Iselin & Co., Wm. (Com.)
AAAA
Johnson, Cowdin & Co. (Rib-
bons) ....AA
Juilliard & Co., A. D.
(Com.) ....AAAA
Kahn, H. H. (Ribbons)..B
Klingenstein Bros. & Co.
(Import) ....AA
Krause & Son, R. (Ribbons)
C
Kridel Sons & Co., J.
(Ribbons) ....AAA
Levy, A. & M. (Ribbons)
AAA
Levy, E. & H. (Ribbons)
AA
Liberty Silk Co. (Broad
Silks & Satins) ....A
Loth & Co., Jos. (Ribbons)
AA
Lyon Silk Co. (Dress;
Tailors) C
Mason & Co., E. T. (Broad
Goods) ....AA
Mendelson & Co., H.....A
Menke & Co., Jno. (Broad
Goods) ....AA
Morrisania Silk Mills (Rib-
bons) ....AA
Oelbermann, Dommerich &
Co. (Com.) ....AAAA
Openhym & Sons, Wm. (Im-
port) ....AAAA
Passavant & Co. (Com.)
AAAA
Pearl, L. ....
Pelgram & Meyer (Broad;
Ribbons) ....AAAA
Poncet & Neeser (Ribbons)
B
Reiling & Schoen, David
(Dress; Tie) ....AA
Robertson, Wm. H. (Rib-
bons) ....B
Roessel & Co., Louis
(Broad Goods) ......A
Schefer, Schramm & Vogel
(Import; also Com.
Broad; Ribbons) ..AAAA
Schoolhouse & Son, Chas.
(Ribbons) ....A
Schroeder & Co., Wm.
(Dress Goods & Ribbons)
A
Schwarzenbach, Huber &
Co. (Import) ......AAAA
Simon & Co., J. R. (China;
Japanese) ....AAAA
Smith & Kaufman (Rib-
bons) ....AAA
Spielmann & Co. (also
Com.) ....AAA
Springarn Bros. (Ribbons)
B
Star Ribbon Mfg. Co.
(Ribbons) C
Stearns & Co., Jno. N.
AA
Steinfelder, Toplitz & Co.
B
Stieglitz & Sons, M. L.
(Linings) ....A
Strange Co., Wm. ....AA
Sullivan, Drew & Co....AA
Sundhemer Bros. (Ribbons)
B
Swan & Sons, Jos. (Rib-
bons) ....AA
Ulmann & Co., Bernhard
(Drapery) ....AAAA
Vietor & Achelis, Fred
(Com.) ....AAAA
Williams Silk Mfg. Co.
(Serges; Satins; de Chin-
es; Linings) ....B
Woodhouse, Bopp & Co.
(Plain; Fancy Dress)...A
Wright & Graham (Rib-
bons) ....B
N.Y.—Ogdensburg
Oswegatchie Mfg. Co.
AAAA

SILK GOODS (Con.)
N. Y.—Oneonta
Paragon Silk Co. (Broad)
................................B
N. Y.—Port Jervis
Kattermann & Mitchell Co.
................................A
N. Y.—Rochester
Caldwell Mfg. Co. (Ribbon) C
N. C.—Rockingham
Roberdel Mfg. Co..........A
OHIO—Marion
Susquehanna Silk Mills
(Broad Goods) ....B
PA.—Alburtis
Hartley Silk Mfg. Co.
(Broad; Tie) ....D
PA.—Allentown
Adelaide Silk Mill..AAAA
Allentown Silk Co. (Organzine; Ribbons) C
Givernaud Bros. (Broad)
..............................AAA
Lecha Silk Co. (Ribbons).D
Mack Silk Co., Jos. S...C
Palace Ribbon Mfg. Co.
(Ribbons) ....A
PA.—Altoona
Schwarzenbach, Huber &
Co. (Broad)......AAAA
PA.—Athens
Tioga Silk Co. (Dress; Lining Goods) ....D
PA—Avoca
Avoca Silk Co. (Dress; Linings) ....D
PA.—Bethlehem
Bethlehem Silk Co. (Organzine; Floss) ....A
Duplan Silk Co., (Piece
Dyed; Plain; Novelties)
..............................B
Fichter & Martin (Ribbons;
Broad Goods) ....A
Grube, Geo. W. (Ribbons)
..............................D
Lehigh Valley Silk Mills
(Broad Goods) C
Sauqoit Silk Mfg. Co.
Broad Goods) ...,AAAA
PA.—Bloomsburg
Bloomburg Silk Mill...AA
PA.—Butler
Butler Silk Mill (Broad
Goods) C
PA.—Carbondale
Empire Silk Co. (Broad).A
PA.—Catasauqua
Dery, D. G. (Dress Goods)
..............................A
PA.—Columbia
Ashley & Bailey Co.
(Dress & Tie) ....AAA
PA.—Danville
Colonial Spinning Mills...B
PA.—Dickson City
Bliss, Valentine ....B
PA.—East Greenville
Columbia Silk Mills (Ribbons) C
PA.—Easton
Phillipsburg Silk Mill Co.
(Broad Silks) ....D
Simon, R. & H. (Ribbons;
Broad Goods) ....AAAA
PA.—Emaus
Keystone Silk Mills (Dress)
..............................AAA
PA.—Ephrata
Westerhoff Bros. & Napier
Co. (Dress; Tie; Broad
Goods) ....B
PA.—Forest City
Harvey Silk Co., Alf.
(Organzine) ....B
PA.—Hamburg
Hamburg Silk Co. (Dress
Goods) ....D
PA.—Hanover
Hanover Silk Co. (Ribbons)
..............................A
PA.—Harrisburg
Pelgram & Meyer (Ribbon;
Broad Silks) ......AAA
PA.—Hawley
Bellmont Silk Mills (Tram;
Organzine; Dress; Ribbons) ....AAAA
PA.—Hazleton
Roessel & Co., Louis (Umbrella Silks) ....A
PA.—Honesdale
Dexter, Lambert & Co.

SILK GOODS (Con.)
(Dress Silks; Ribbons)..
..............................AAAA
PA.—Lansdale .
Lanza Silk Co. (Umbrella;
Dress) ....D
PA.—Lock Haven
Lock Haven Silk Co.
(Broad; Dress; Lining)A
PA.—Marietta .
Ashley & Bailey Co.....AA
PA.—Mauch Chuck .
Dery, D. G. (Dress Silks)
..............................A
PA.—Meadville
Meadville Silk Mfg. Co.
(Dress Goods) ....D
PA.—Newberry .
Holmes Silk Co. (Dress
Silks) ....A
PA.—New Hope .
Simpson & Co., Jas. (Dress
Silks) ....D
PA.—Philadelphia
Pine Tree Silk Mills Co.
(Ribbons; Broad Silks)C
Read, Wm. F.........AA
Scherr Bros (Broad Silks;
Ribbons) ....A
PA.—Phoenixville
Johnson, Cowdin & Co.
(Ribbons) ....AA
PA.—Pittston .
Frost & Van Ripper.....C
Valentine& Bentley Silk Co.
(Broad) ....B
PA.—Pottsville .
Tilt Silk Mill (Ribbons)..
..............................AAA
PA.—Quakertown .
Quakertown Silk Co.
(Broad) ....D
PA.—Reading .
Grimshaw Bros. (Broad).B
PA.—Scranton .
Ashley, Wm. H. ....B
Harvey Silk Co., Alfred
(Tram; Organzine) ...B
Reiling & Schoen, David
(Broad Goods) ......AA
Sauquoit Silk Mfg. Co.
(Broad; Dress Silks) ...
..............................AAAA
Simpson & Co., Jas.
(Dress Goods) ....D
PA.—Shamokin
Shamokin Silk Mills (Dress
Goods) ....A
PA.—Slatington
Slatington Textile Mfg. Co.
(Broad Silks) C
PA.—Sunbury
Susquehanna Silk Mills..A
PA.—Taylor
Taylor Worsted Co. (Dress)
..............................C
PA.—Titusville
Horn Silk Co., Chas. (Ribbons) ....B
PA.—Topton ...
Hartley Silk Mfg. Co.
(Broad Silks) ....D
PA.—Weatherly
Read & Lovatt Co. ......A
PA.—Wilkesbarre
Hess & Goldsmith Co.
Hess& Goldsmith Co.
(Broad) ....A
PA.—Williamsport .
Stearns & Co., Jno. N.
(Dress Silks; Ribbons)..
..............................AAA
PA.—York .
Monarch Silk Co. ......A
York Silk Mfg. Co........A
R. I.—Pawtucket .
Royal Weaving Co......AA
VA.—Norfolk ..
Norfolk Silk Co. (Dress).A

SILKERS
(CORN)

MD.—Baltimore
Maryland Mfg. & Construction Co. X
N. Y.—Syracuse
Hemingway Mfg. Co. ....A
Merrill-Soule Co. (Inc.) ..A

SILLS

See also Woodwork

SILVERWARE

CONN.—Berlin
Berlin Construction Co.
(Iron; Door; Window ..A
GA.—Savannah
Southern Pine Co. of Georgia (Car) ....AAA
LA.—Lake Charles
Bradley-Ramsey Lumber Co.
(Car) ....AAAA
N. Y.—Brooklyn
Hecla Iron Wrks. (Iron;
Door; Window) ......AA
New York City
Cornell Co., J. B. & J. M.
(Iron; Door; Window)AA
OHIO—Cleveland
Van Dorn Iron Krks. Co.
(Iron; Door; Window)
AA
OHIO—Kenton
Champion Iron Co. (Iron;
Door; Window) ......AA
PA.—Wilkesbarre
Vulcan Iron Wrks. (Iron;
Door; Window) ....AAAA

SILOS

KY.—Louisville
Caldwell Co., W. E. (Pine;
Cypress) ....AA
MASS.—Boston
Stearns Lumber Co., A. T.
(Building) ....AA
N. Y.—Cobleskill
Harder Mfg. Co. (Round)
B
N. Y.—Hamilton
Hamilton Lumber Co.
(Round) ....E
New York City
Elias & Bro., G........AA

SILVER

CAL.—San Francisco
Selby Smelting & Lead Co.
(Smelted) ....AAA
COLO.—Denver
Boston & Colorado Smelting
Co. (Smelted) ......AAA
CONN.—Bridgeport
Bridgeport Brass Co. (German) ....AAA
CONN.—Bristol
American Silver Co. (German Sheet) ....A
CONN.—Seymour
Seymour Mfg. Co. (German)
AAA
CONN.—Torrington
Coe Brass Mfg. Co. (German Sheet) ....AAAA
CONN.—Waterbury
Benedict & Burnham Mfg.
Co. (German Sheet)
AAAA
Holmes, Booth & Haydens
Co. (Inc.) (German
Sheet) ....AAAA
Plume & Atwood Mfg. Co.
(German Sheet) ....AAA
Scovill Mfg. Co. (German)
AAAA
Waterbury Brass Co. (German Sheet) ......AAAA
MICH.—Detroit
Detroit Copper & Brass
Rolling Mills (German
Sheet) ....AAAA
MONT.—Butte
Boston & Mont. Cons. Copper & Sil. Mine Co.
(Smelted) ....AAAA
N. J.—Newark
Balbach Smelting & Refining Co. ....AAA
N. J.—Riverside
Riverside Metal Co. (German) ....A
N. Y.—New York City
Ansonia Brass & Copper Co.
(German) ....AAAA
R. I.—Providence
Wall & Co., A. T. (Sheet)
C
UTAH—Salt Lake City
Centennial Eureka Mining
Co. (Smelted) ....B

CONN.—Bridgeport
Holmes & Edwards Silver
Co. (Sterling) .....AAAA
International Silver Co.
(Plated) ....AAAA
Jennings Bros. Mfg. Co.
(Plated) ....AA
Smith Silver Co., E. H. H.
(Plated) ....B
CONN.—Bristol
American Silver Co. (Plated; Sterling) ....A
CONN.—Danbury
Rogers Silver Plate Co.
(Plated) ....A
CONN.—Derby
International Silver Co.
(Plated) ....AAAA
CONN.—East Haddam
Boardman & Son, Luther
(Britannia; Plated) ..AA
CONN.—Hartford
Melrose Silver Co. (Plated;
Sterling) ....E
Rogers Co., Simon L. &
Geo. H. (Plated) ......A
CONN.—Meriden
International Silver Co.
(Britannia; Plated; Sterling) ....AAAA
Bliss Co., E. A. (Plated;
Novelties) ....B
Manning Bowman & Co.
(Plated Britannia Enameled; Hollow; Toilet)
AA
CONN.—Middletown
Middletown Silver Co. (Plated; Britannia) ....E
CONN.—Naubuc
Williams Bros. Mfg. Co.
(Plated) ....A
CONN.—Wallingford
International Silver Co.
(Plated) ....AAAA
Simpson, Hall, Miller &
Co. (Britannia) ..AAAA
Wallace & Sons Mfg. Co., R.
(Plated Sterling) .AAAA
Wallingford Co. (Plated)
D
Watrous Mfg. Co. (Sterling
Silver) ....AAAA
CONN.—Waterbury
Holmes, Booth & Haydens
Co. (Plated........AAAA
ILL.—Aurora
Aurora Silver Plate Mfg. Co.
(Plated) ....A
ILL.—Chicago
International Silver Co., 195
State (Plated) ....AAAA
Rogers Mfg. Co., W. F., 88
Wabash Av. (Plated)..D
Spaulding & Co. (Sterling)
AAA
Wendell & Co., 57 Washington (Sterling) ....B
ILL.—Rockford
Rockford Silver Plate Co.
(Plated) ....A
IND.—Muncie
Ontario Silver Co. (Plated)
A
MAINE—Portland
Colonial Silver Co. (Plated)
C
Woodman-Cook Co. (Plated)
B
MD.—Baltimore
Florence Silver Plate Co.
(Plated) ....D
Kann Bros. Silver Co.
(Plated) C
Kirk & Son, Samuel (Sterling Novelties) ....A
Klank & Sons Mfg. Co., C.
(Plated) ....E
MASS.—Attleboro
Attleboro Mfg. Co. (Sterling
Novelties) ....A
Blake Co., Jas. E. (Sterling
Novelties) ....A
Doggett & Clap Co. (Sterling
Novelties)............A
Fisher Co., J. M. (Sterling
Novelties) ....A
Marble. Forrester & Co.
(Sterling Novelties) ...C
Regnell. Bigney & Co. (Sterling Novelties) .....AA
Watson & Newell Co.

SILVERWARE (Con.)

Stern & Co., Louis (Sterling Novelties) ....B

Waite, Theresher Co. (Sterling Novelties) ....A

Williams Silver Co., Roger (Sterling) ....A

SINGLETREES: HAY

See also Woodwork: Carriage

ILL.—Ottawa
Porter Co., J. E. ....A

IOWA—Fairfield
Louden Mchry Co.........C

OHIO—Ashland
Myers & Bro., F. E. .AAAA

SINKERS

MICH.—Battle Creek
American Steam Pump Co. (Pump) ....AAA

MO.—St. Louis
Reliance Machine & Tool Co. (Pump) ....AAA

N. H.—Franklin
Franklin Needle Co. ....B

N. H.—Laconia
Mayo Machine Co.........D

OHIO—Akron
Enterprise Mfg. Co. (Adjustable) ....A

OHIO—Cincinnati
Vanduzen Co., E. W. (Pump) ....B

SINKS

ALA.—Anniston
Hercules Iron & Supply Co. (Br. Boston; Cast Iron) ....A

CONN.—Middletown
Douglas, W. & B. (Iron) ....A

ILL.—Chicago
Cribben, Sexton & Co. (Br. Stand. Sanitary Mfg. Co., Pittsburg, Pa.) (Enamelled) ....AAAA

Illinois Malleable Iron Co. (Iron) ....AAAA

Wolff Mfg. Co., L., 117 W. Lake (Cast Iron; Steel; Porcelain; Lined; Gray Enamelled; Slate; Soap stone) ....AAAA

ILL.—Edwardsville
Illinois Marble Co. (Slate) C

ILL.—Moline
Moline Pump Co. (Cast Iron; Steel) ....A

ILL.—Peoria
Culter & Proctor Stove Co. (Iron) ....A

ILL.—St. Charles
Glenn Mfg. Co. (Kitchen; Slop) ....D

MAINE—Bath
Monson Consolidated Slate Co. (Br. Monson, Me.) (Slate) ....B

MD.—Baltimore
Weiskittle & Son, A. Aliceanna & Washington (Enamelled) ....A

MASS.—Boston
Dalton-Ingersoll Co. (Iron; Steel) X

Magee Furnace Co. (Iron) ....AA

Murdock Corpn., 156 Boylston (Marble Composite) ....B

Sturtevant Co., B. F. (Cast) ....AAA

MASS.—Boston Highlands
Highland Foundry Co. (Iron) ....B

MICH.—Detroit
Northwestern Fdry. & Supply Co., Orleans & Grand Boul. (Cast Iron Slop) ..D

MO.—St. Louis
Evens & Howard Fire Brick Co., 920 Market (Earthenware) ....AAAA

N. J.—Burlington
Stuart & Peterson Co. (Iron;

SINKS (Con.)

Steel) ....A

N. J.—Perth Amboy
Perth Amboy Ceramic Co. (Ceramic) ....D

N. J.—Trenton
Brian Pottery Co. (Porcelain) ....D

Maddock & Sons, Thomas (Earthenware) ....AA

Monument Pottery Co. ..A

Trenton Potteries Co. (Earthenware; Solid Porcelain) ....AAA

N. Y.—Brooklyn
Graham Chemical Pottery Wrks., Chas., 1018 Metropolitan Av. (Earthenware) ....D

Minns Sink & Specialty Co., 349 Court (& Tubs Combined) ....F

Ronalds & Johnson Co., 51 Bourum Pl. (Copper).AA

N. Y.—Medina
Swett Iron Wrks., A. L. (Cast Iron) ....A

New York City
Alberene Stone Co., 393 Pearl (Soapstone) .....B

Central Fdry. Co., 116 Nassau (Cast Iron) ....AAA

Haydenville Co. (Iron)...A

Lalance & Grosjean Mfg. Co., 19 Cliff (Seamless Wrought; Steel Enamelled) ....AAAA

Mayer, Lane & Co., 128 White (Iron; Steel) ...A

Meyer-Sniffen Co. (Ltd.) (Earthenware) ....A

Mott Iron Wrks., J. L., 88 Beekman (Steel; Porcelain Enamelled; Iron Enamelled) ....AA

National Enamelling & Stamping Co., 81 Fulton (Iron; Steel) ......AAAA

New York Slate Wrks., 493 E. 138th (Slate) ......D

Steeger, Henry (Copper; Iron) ....A

Stein, Henry, 48 Cliff (Mfr. Agt. Enamelled Iron)..E

Trageser Steam Copper Wrks., Jno., 447 W. 26th (Copper) ....B

N. Y.—Rochester
Enterprise Fdry. Co., 48 Olean (Cast Iron) ....B

N. Y.—Rome
Rome Sanitary Wrks. ....B

N. Y.—Seneca Falls
Gleason & Bailey (Steel).B

Goulds Mfg. Co. (Iron) ....AAA

Rumsey & Co. (Ltd.) (Iron) ....A

N. Y.—Syracuse
Stearns & Co., E. C. (Iron; Steel) ....AA

OHIO.—Ashtabula
Barber Mfg. Co. (Cast Iron; White Enamelled; &c.).C

OHIO.—Cleveland
Auld & Conger Co., 262 Prospect (Soapstone) ..A

Cleveland Co-operative Stove Co. (Iron) ....A

Norcross Co. (Stone) .....A

OHIO.—Columbus
Kilbourne & Jacobs Mfg. Co. (Wrought Steel; Wrought Iron; Oval) ....AAAA

OHIO.—Mansfield
Barnes Mfg. Co. (Steel; Enamelled; Iron Enamelled; Cast) ....A

Humphreys Mfg. Co. (Cast) ....B

PA.—Braddock
McVay & Walker (Enamelled) ....A

PA.—Erie
Griswold Mfg. Co. (Iron).A

PA.—New Brighton
Amer. Porcelain Co. (Porcelain) C

PA.—Philadelphia
Blessing, C. A., 516 Montgomery Av. (Iron; Steel) ....AA

Cooper Brass Wrks., Wm. S. 437 N. 12th (Brass).B

SINKS (Con.)

Fleck Bros. Co., 44 5th (Iron; Steel) ....A

Horner Sanitary Mfg. Co., 121 & 123 N. 6th .....F

McCambridge & Co. (Ltd.) 525 Cherry (Copper; Iron; Steel) ....B

Sheppard & Co., Isaac A. 1801 N. 4th ....AAA

PA.—Pittsburg

Harris Pump & Supply Co., 320 2d Av. (Enamelled Iron) ....B

Iron City Sanitary Mfg. Co., German Nat'l Bank Bldg. (Enamelled Iron) ......A

Standard Sanitary Mfg. Co., Arrott Bldg. (Enamelled Iron) ....AAAA

United States Sanitary Mfg. Co., Arrot Bldg. (Enamelled Iron) ....A

PA.—Pittston

Pittson Stove Co. (Iron)..A

PA.—Reading

Reading Stove Wrks. (Iron) AA

PA.—So. Bethlehem

Bethlehem Fdy. & Mach. Co. (Cast) C

R. I.—Providence

Phillips Co., Thos. (Copper) C

TENN.—So. Pittsburg

Blacklock Fdy. Co. (Cast Iron; Stamped) C

VT.—Fair Haven

Allen's Sons. S. (Slate)..D

Fair Haven Marble & Marbleized Slate Co. (Slate) B

Pelkey, W. H. (Slate)....E

WIS.—Milwaukee

Rundle Mfg. Co. (Enamelled Iron) C

WIS.—Sheboygan

Kohler Sons Co., J. M. (Enamelled Iron) .....A

SIRENS

N. Y.—New York City

Brown Co., A. & F. ....A

SIZE

MASS.—Boston

Babcock & Co., John (Gold) B

Morrill & Co., Geo. H. (Gold) ....AA

MASS.—Lowell

Holt & Co., Jonathan ....D

MICH.—Detroit

Berry Bros. (Ltd.) (Gold) AAAA

N. Y.—Albany

Diamond Paste Co. (Vegetable) C

N. Y.—New Brighton

Muralo Co. ....:........A

New York City

Amer. Type Founders Co. (Gold) ....AAAA

Chase, John S. (Gold) ...D

Devoe, F. W. & C. T. Raynolds Co. ....AAAA

Fox & Co., M. E. 136th & Rider Av. (Paperhangers) D

Gillespie, L. C. (Gold) ..A

Hoyt, Arthur S. ....B

Longman & Martinez (Gold) AAA

Matheson & Co., Wm. J. (Ltd.) ....A

Mayer & Loewenstein (Gold) AAA

Pierce Co., F. O., 170 Fulton (Gold) ....A

Salamon & Bro., L A. (Gold) ....AA

OHIO—Cincinnati

Ault & Wiborg Co. (Gold) AAAA

OHIO—Cleveland

Cleveland Varnish Co. (Gold) ....AA

SIZERS

FLA.—De Land

Cairns, J. T. (Orange)....X

SIZERS (Con.)

ILL.—Chicago

Aitchison Perforated Metal Co., R. (Ore; Coal).....X

ILL.—Downers Grove

Dicke Tool Co. C

KANS.—Fort Scott

Fort Scott Fdy. & Mach. Co. (Ore; Coal) ....F

N. J.—Newark

Kraeuter & Co. (Wood Turners' ....E

N. Y.—New York City

Amer. Wood Working Mach. Co. (Timber) ......AAA

Tower & Lyon ....B

PA.—Carbondale

Hendrick Mfg. Co. (Lds.) (Ore; Coal) ....AA

PA.—Wilkesbarre

Vulcan Iron Wrks. (Ore; Coal) ....AAAA

SKATES

CONN.—Torrington

Union Hdw. Co. (Ice; Roller) ....AA

ILL.—Chicago

Richardson Ball Bearing Skate Co. (Roller) .....F

IND.—Richmond

Henley, M. C. (Ice Roller) A

MASS.—Springfield

Barney & Berry (Ice; Roller) ....A

MASS.—Worcester

Winslow Skate Mfg. Co., Saml. (Ice; Roller) ....A

N. J.—Newark

Lowentrant, P. (Ice; Roller) ....A

N. Y.—Buffalo

Crosby Co., (The) (Ice)..A

New York City

Cycle Skate Co., 123 Liberty (Roller) X

Graham & Co., John H. 113 Chambers (Ice) ..AA

Spaulding & Bros., A. G. (Ice; Roller) ......AAAA

OHIO—Cleveland

Avery Stamping Co. (Ice) B

PA.—Bloomsburg

Richard Mfg. Co. (Roller) B

SKEINS

See Hardware; Carriage

ILL.—Belleville

Belleville Pump & Skein Wrks. (Wagon) ....A

ILL.—Carpentersville

Illinois Iron & Bolt Co. (Wagon; Thimble; Thimble Steel) ....AA

IND.—South Bend

Sandage Steel Skein Co. (Wagon Steel) ....B

N. Y.—Utica

Giblin & Co. (Wagon)....B

OHIO—Cincinnati

Haven Co., Jas. L. (Thimble) ....B

OHIO—Defiance

Defiance Machine Wrks. (Wagon) ....A

OHIO—Ravenna

Williams, A. C. (Thimble) A

WIS.—Kenosha ..

Bain Wagon Co. (Wagon) AAA

SKELETONS

CONN.—Winsted

Empire Knife Co. (Steel) B

N. J.—Newark

Wiss & Sons Co., J. (Iron) A

WIS.—Milwaukee

Western Bottlers Supply Co. (Liquor Dealers) .....D

SKELP

See also Iron & Steel

SKELP (Con.)

DEL.—Wilmington
Seidel & Hastings Co. ....A
OHIO—Steubenville
La Belle Iron Works.AAAA
OHIO—Youngstown
Youngstown Iron Sheet &
Tube Co. ....AAAA
PA.—Harrisburg
Harrisburg Pipe & Pipe
Bending Co. ....AAA
PA.—Philadelphia
Houston & Co., C. B., Gi-
rard Bldg ....B

SKETCHES

New York City
Hickok & Pate (Water
Color) ....E

SKEWERS

CONN.—Meriden
Meriden Britannia Co.
AAAA
CONN.—New Britain
Landers, Frary & Clark
AAAA
GA.—Toccoa
Reeves Spool & Bobbin Co.
(Bobbin) ....D
IND.—Muncie
Weis & Lesh Mfg. Co.
(Butchers) ....A
MASS.—Lawrence
Hale, T. J. (Cop) ..AAAA
MASS.—Lowell
Parker, Frank (Cop).....F
MASS.—Winchendon
Winchendon Spool & Bobbin
Co. ....A
MASS.—Worcester
Hamblin & Russell Mfg. Co.
(Steel) ....B
Parker Wire Goods Co.
(Steel Butcher) ....D
N. Y.—New York City
Lalance & Grosjean Mfg. Co.
AAAA
PA.—Bradford
Union Dish Co. ....D
PA.—Philadelphia
Nittinger, August ....A
R. I.—Pawtucket
Payne & Co., Geo. W. (Cop)
D
S. C.—Greenville
Mallard Lumber & Bobbin
Co. C

SKIDS

ILL.—Chicago
Borden & Selleck Co., 48
Lake ....B
MASS.—Arlington
Wood & Co., Wm. T. (Ice)
A
MASS.—Boston
Boston & Lockport Block Co.
A
MICH.—Detroit
Anderson & Sons, W. H. C
MICH.—Lansing
Lansing Wheelbarrow Co.
AAA
N. Y.—New York City
Fairbanks Co., 186 Elm
AAAA
OHIO—Columbus
Kilbourne & Jacobs Mfg. Co.
AAAA

SKIFFS

See also Boats

N. Y.—New York City
Smith, John T. ....E
N. Y.—Ogdensburg
Spalding St. Lawrence Boat
Co. C
N. Y.—Skaneateles
Skaneateles Boat & Canoe
Co. C

SKILLETS

See also Holloware

ALA.—Mobile
Mobile Stove & Pulley Mfg.
Co. ....B

SKILLETS (Con.)

MO.—St. Louis
St. Louis Stamping Co.
AAAA
N. Y.—New York City
Central Stamping Co. ..AA
OHIO—Cleveland
Avery Stamping Co. ....B
OHIO—Toledo
Toledo Stamping Co. X
PA.—Erie
Griswold Mfg. Co. ......A

SKIMMERS

ILL.—Chicago
Barbee Wire & Iron Wks
B
MASS.—Worcester
National Mfg. Co. ....A
Wire Goods Co. (Wire) ..A
MO.—St. Louis
St. Louis Stamping Co.
AAAA
N. Y.—Buffalo
Shepard & Co., Sidney
AAAA
N. Y.—Cortland
Wickwire Bros. (Wire)
AAAA
New York City
Lalance & Grosjean Mfg. Co.
AAAA
Reilley Bros. (Tin Oil Float)
D
N. Y.—Troy
Troy Stamping Wks. (War-
ren & Co., J. M., Prop.)
AAAA
OHIO—Cleveland
Cleveland Stamping & Tool
Co. (Wire) ....A
PA.—Pittsburg
McCullough Dalzell Crucible
Co. ....A

SKINS

See also Hides

N. H.—Manchester
Kimball & Brown (Roller)
A
N. Y.—New York City
Young Co., Richard (Pig)
AA
PA.—Philadelphia
Drueding Bros. Co., 427 W.
Master (Chamois) ....AA
R. I.—Providence
Stone Co., C., Moulton
(Roller) ....B
VT.—Hyde Park
Page, Carroll S. (Calf; Deer;
Dog) ....A

SKIPS

CAL.—Stockton
Globe Iron Wrks. (Inc.)
(Ore; Water Mining) ..B
ILL.—Chicago
Allis-Chalmers Co., Home
Ins. Bldg. (Mining)AAAA
MICH.—Three Rivers
Sheffield Car Co. (Mine)
AA
OHIO—Zanesville
Griffith & Wedge Co.
(Mine) ....A
PA.—Pittsburg
Riter-Conley Mfg. Co.
(Mine) ....AAA
PA.—Wilkesbarre
Vulcan Iron Wrks. (Mine)
AAAA
WIS.—Cudahy
Power & Mining Machy Co.
(Mining) ....AAAA
WIS.—Milwaukee
Allis-Chalmers Co. (Mine)
AAAA

SKIRTINGS

See Cotton Goods
Woolen Goods

SKIRTS

See Clothing: Ladies'

SKIS

MAINE—South Paris
Paris Mfg. Co. ....A

SKIVERS

See also Leather

ILL.—Chicago
Eagle Tanning Wrks...AA
MASS.—Brockton
Tuck Mfg. Co. ....E
N. Y.—New York City
Garner & Co., Thos. (Oak;
Bark) ....AA
Neumann & Co., R. ....A
U. S. Leather Co. ....AAAA
Young Co., Richard ....AA
OHIO—Cincinnati
Trautman & Co., C ......A
WIS.—Milwaukee
Trostel & Sons, Albert
AAAA

SKYLIGHTS

CONN.—Bridgeport
Drouve Co., G. (Metal)....B
GA.—Atlanta
Dowman-Dozier Mfg. Co.
(Metal) ....D
ILL.—Chicago
Winslow Bros. Co., 368 Car-
roll Av. (Ornamental
Iron) ....AA
MD.—Baltimore
Valle & Young C
MASS.—Boston
Badger & Sons Co., E. B.
63 Pitts (Metal) .....B
Van Noorden Co., E., 944
Mass. Av. (Metal) C
MASS.—Lowell
Mack & Co., W. A. C
MO.—St. Louis
Southern Iron Co., E. E.
B
N. J.—Jersey City
National Steel Metal Roof-
ing Co. C
N. Y.—Brooklyn
Hecla Iron Wrks., N. 11th &
Berry (Ornamental Iron)
AA
N. Y.—New York City
Bickelhaupt Skylight Wrks.
Geo., 243 W. 47th (Or-
namental Iron) ....F
Hayes Co., Geo., 71 8th Av.
B
OHIO—Canton
Berger Mfg. Co. ....AA
Canton Steel Roofing Co.
A
OHIO—Cincinnati
Kiechler Mfg. Co. C
OHIO—Cleveland
Garry Iron & Steel Co.
(Metal) ....A
Shackleton Bros. ....F
OHIO—Salem
Mullins, W. H. .... A
PA.—Philadelphia
Gara, McGinley & Co., 23 S.
17th ....A
Luptons' Sons, David ..AAA
R. I.—Providence
Clason Architectural Metal
Co. C
TENN.—Chattanooga
Chattanooga Roofing & Fdy.
Co. ....A

SLABBERS: LOG

N. H.—Keene
Humphrey Machine Co. ..C
ILL.—Chicago
Olmstead & Co. (Marble) ..C
ILL.—Edwardsville
Illinois Marble Co. (Marble)
C

SLABS

KY.—Ashland
Ashland Steel Co. (Steel)
AAAA
MASS.—Boston
American Soda Fountain Co.
(Marble) ....AAAA
MO.—St. Louis
Nelson Mfg. Co., N. O.

SLABS (Con.)
(Marble) ....AAA
N. Y.—New York City
Sizer Forge Co. (Iron) ..A
Dana & Co., 32 B'way
(Steel) ....AA
Graf, Frank H., 322 7th
Av. (Soapstone) ......D
Leavitt & Co., C. W., 15
Cortland (Steel) ......D
Mayer, Lane & Co., 128
White (Marble) ....A
PA.—Allentown
Blue Valley Slate Co. (Uri-
nal Slate) ....B
PA.—Bangor
American Slate Co. (Urinal
Slate) ....AA
Bangor Crescent Slate Co.
(Urinal Slate) ....B
Bangor State Mining Co.
(Urinal Slate) ....B
PA.—Delta
Peerless Slate Co. (Urinal
Slate) ....B
PA.—Pen Argyl
Crown Slate Co. (Slate) C
PA.—Philadelphia
Pennsylvania Steel Co.
(Steel) ....AAAA
PA.—Pittsburg
Carnegie Steel Co. (Ltd.)
(Steel) ....AAAA
PA.—Pottstown
Potts Bros. Iron Co.
(Steel) ....A
PA.—Slatington
Slatington-Bangor Slate
Syndicate (Urinal Slate)D
VT.—Proctor
Vermont Marble Co. (Print-
ers Imposing; Plumbers')
AAAA
W. VA.—Wheeling
Laughlin Nail Co. (Inc.)
(Steel) ....AA
Portsmouth Steel Co.
(Steel) ....A

SLASHERS

ILL.—Chicago
Allis-Chalmers Co., Home
Ins. Bldg. (Saw) AAAA
MASS.—Boston
Riley & Co., C. E., 65
Franklin ....A
MASS.—Lowell
Entwistle Co., T. C. C
Lowell Mach. Shop ..AAAA
MICH.—Bay City
Garland Co., M. (Saw) ...C
N. Y.—Cohoes
Cohoes Iron & Fdry. &
Machine Co. ....A
PA.—Philadelphia
Bement-Niles-Pond Co.
AAAA
R. I.—Pawtucket
Howard & Bullough Amer.
Machine Co. (Ltd.) AA
R. I.—Providence
Textile Finishing Mchry.
Co., 17 Exchange Pl .AAA
WIS.—Milwaukee
Allis-Chalmers Co. (Slab)
AAAA
Filer & Stowell Co. (Saw
Slab) ....AAA

SLATE

ILL.—Chicago
Aitchison Perforated Metal
Co., R. (Roofing) X
ILL.—Edwardsville
Illinois Marble Co. (for
Electrical Purposes) ..C
MAINE—Bath
Monson Consolidated Slate
Co. (for Electrical Pur-
poses) ....B
MASS.—Boston
Mathews Consolidated Slate
Co., 199 Washn. (Decora-
tive; for Backing Litho-
graphic Stones; for Elec-
trical Purposes; Monu-
mental; Sculptural Unfad-
ing Purple) X
Munson Maine Slate Co.,
113 Devonshire (for Elec-
trical Purposes) X

SLATE (Con.)

MASS.—Lowell
Lowell Slate Co. (Roofing)
.....X

MASS.—Worcester
Algonquin Red Slate Co.
(for Electrical Purposes)B
Brownville Maine Slate Co.
(for Electrical Purposes;
Roofing) ....B

MO.—St. Louis
Mesker & Bro. (Roofing)AA

N J.—Lincoln
Atlas Mineral & Machine
Co. (Flour) X

N. Y.—Brooklyn
Wiarda & Co., John C.
(Ground) ....AA

N. Y.—Granville
Norton Bros. (Roofing) A

OHIO—Cleveland
Auld & Conger (Roofing) A

PA.—Allentown
Madoc Slate Co. (for Electrical Purposes) X

PA.—Bangor
Bangor Crescent Slate Co.
(for Electrical Purposes)B
Bangor Peerless Slate Co.
(Roofing) C
Bangor Slate Mining Co.
(for Electrical Purposes)B
North Bangor Slate Co. (Br.
Newark, N. J.) (For Elec-
trical Purposes) X

PA.—Danielsville
Hower. J. K. (Roofing; for
Electrical Purposes) ..B

PA.—Delta
Peerless Slate Co. (for
Electrical Purposes) ..B

PA.—East Bangor
East Bangor Consolidated
Slate Co. (Roofing) ..AA

PA.—Easton
Bangor Excelsior Slate Co.
(Roofing) ....A
Penna. Structural Slate Co.
(for Electrical Purposes)B
Williams & Co., C. K.
(Ground; Powdered) ...A

PA.—Lynnport
Ontalawaunee Slate Mfg.
Co (for Electrical Pur-
poses) C

PA.—Pen Argyl
Lobb's Sons, Wm. (Roof-
ing) C

PA.—Philadelphia
Emack, John D., S. Girard
Bldg. (Roofing) C
Kimes & Co., J. B., 1822
Filbert (Unfading Purple)
C

PA.—Slatington
Blue Mountain Slate Co.
(Roofing) ....B
Eureka Slate Mfg. Co.
(Roofing) ....E
McKenna. David (for Elec-
trical Purposes; School)E
Slatington Slate Co. (for
Electrical Purposes; Roof-
ing Purposes) ....B
Washington Slate Co. (for
Electrical Purposes) ..C

PA.—Wind Gap
Pelican Slate Mfg. Co. (for
Electrical Purposes) ...E

VT.—Fair Haven
Allen's Sons. S. (for Elec-
trical Purposes) ......D
Coulman & Westcott (for
Electrical Purposes) ..D
Fair Haven Marble & Mar-
bleized Slate Co. (for
Electrical Purposes) ..B
M'Namara Bros. (for Elec-
trical Purposes) ......D
Pelkey. W. H. (for Elec-
trical Purposes) ......E
Young. A. B. (for Elec-
trical Purposes) ......F

PA.—Poultney
Fleming Slate Co. (for Electrical Purposes) C
Griffith & Nathaniel (Roofing) ....B

SLATES

CONN.—East River
Munger & Son (Paper) ..C

SLATES (Con.)

ILL.—Chicago
Kane & Co., Thos. (Noise-
less) ....B

New York City
Gait & Sons, John (School)
A
New York Silicate Book
Slate Co. (Noiseless;
Book; Silicate) ....D

PA.—Bangor
Bangor Peerless Slate Co.
(School) C
Dernberger, Isaac D.
(School) ....D
Wise School Slate Co.
(School) ....D

PA.—Bethlehem
National School Slate Co.
(School) ....A

PA.—Portland
Gardner, John (School) ...F
Wise & Co., J. (School) B

PA.—Slatington
Blue Valley Slate Co.
(School) ....B

SLATING

CONN.—East River
Munger & Son (Blackboard,
Liquid) C

New York City
New York Silicate Book
Slate Co. (Blackboard,
Liquid) ....D

SLATS

MASS.—Athol
Tyler, Arthur F. (Blind) C

MICH.—Bay City
Vance Box Co., E. J.
(Ltd.) (Ash Can) .....B

MICH.—Mount Pleasant
Gorham Bros. Co. (Trunk)A

MICH.—New Lathrop
Hess & Prouty (Fence) ..A

MO.—St. Louis
St. Louis Basket & Box
Co. (Trunk) ....A

N. J.—Newark
Gould & Sons Co., M.
(Trunk) ....A

N. Y.—Poughkeepsie
Chapinville Wheel Co.
(Binder) ....A

OHIO—Youngstown
Youngstown Iron & Steel
Roofing Co. (Louver) AA

TENN.—Chattanooga
Heron Iron Bedstead Co.
(Iron Bed) ....D

VT.—Burlington
Vermont Shade Roller Co.
(Shade) ....A

VA.—Norfolk
Roper Lumber Co., John L.
(Bed) ....AAA

SLEDGES

See also Hammers

CONN.—Collinsville
Collins Co. ....AAAA

CONN.—Wallingford
Wallace & Sons Mfg. Co.,
R. ....AAAA

ILL.—Chicago
Union Drop Forge Co.. 66
E. Ohio (Drop Forged) .A

ILL.—Streator
Iwan Bros. C

IND.—Evansville
Evansville Tool Wks. (Coal;
Blacksmith's; Stone, etc.)
A

IOWA—Ottumwa
Hardsocg Mfg. Co. (Coal) B

MASS.—Boston
Harvey, H. H. (Stone) ...D

MICH.—Detroit
Anderson & Sons, W. H. C
Detroit Steel & Spring Co.
(Stone) ....B

N. J.—Mohawk
American Brake Shoe &
Fdy. Co. ....A

N. J.—Newark
Atha Tool Co. (Railroad
Stone) ....A
Heller Bros. Co., 879 Mt.

SLEDGES (Con.)

Prospect Av. ....AA

N. Y.—Norwich

Maydole Hammer Co.,
David (Stone) ....B

PA.—Frankford

Plumb, Fayette R. (Inc.)
(Stone) ....AA

PA.—Ogontz

Hammond & Son, C ....A

PA.—Pittsburg

Anderson, Du Puy & Co. X
Gerber & Sons, L. (Coal) D
Hubbard & Co., Murtland
Bldg. ....AA
Iron City Tool Wks., 32nd
& Smallman (Solid Cast
Steel; Railroad; Stone) A
Klein-Logan Co., So. 13th &
Broad ....A
Pittsburg Tool & Drop
Forge Co., Arrott Bldg.
(Miners'; Blacksmiths') D

W. VA.—Wheeling

Warwood Tool Co. ......B

SLEDS

See also Sleighs

ILL.—Bradley

Bradley Mfg. Co., David

ILL.—Chicago

Staver Carriage Co. (Bob)
AA
Weber Wagon Co. (Bob)AA

ILL.—Galesburg

Cotton & Co., G. D. (Bob)C

ILL.—Marseilles

Marseilles Mfg. Co. (Bob)
A

ILL.—Sterling

Sterling Mfg. Co. (Bob) A

IND.—Bremen

Wright, John J (Bob) ....B

IND.—Indianapolis

Over, Ewald (Bob) C

IND.—South Bend

Coguillard Wagon Wks.
(Bob) ....A

MAINE—South Paris

Paris Mfg. Co. (Childrens')

MASS.—Boston

Harvey, H. H. (Coasting) D

MICH.—Charlotte

Benton Mfg. Co. (Hand) A

MICH.—Kalamazoo

Kalamazoo Sled Co.
(Childrens') ....A

MICH.—Lansing

Bement & Sons, E. (Bob)X
Lansing Wagon Wks.
(Bob) ....A

MINN.—Minneapolis

Howell & Co., R. R. (Bob)
B

MINN.—Sauk Center

Keller Mfg. Co. (Bob) ..B

MINN.—Winona

Winona Wagon Co. (Bob)
AA

N. J.—Hightstown

Shangle, Serin & Son (Furrowing) ....A

New York City

Fellows & Lathrop Co., 104
Reade (Boys') ....D

N. Y.—Watertown

Union Carriage & Gear Co.
(Bob) ....B

OHIO—Ashtabula

Barber Mfg. Co. (Oscilla-
ting Bob) C

OHIO—Toledo

Hickox, Mull & Hill Co.
(Logging) ....A

PA.—Columbia

Columbia Wagon Co. (Bob)
A

PA.—Philadelphia

McHenry, W. J. (Chil-
drens') ....D

VT.—Brattleboro

Smith & Co., S. A. (Chil-
drens' Coasting) ..AAA

VT.—Hartford

Rugbee, Chas. L. (Bob) H

WASH—Tacoma

West Coast Wagon Co
(Log) ....E

WIS.—Boscobel

Ruka Bros. Mfg. Co. (Ltd.)
(Bob) C

SLEDS (Con.)

WIS.—Fon-du-Lac

Sweet Co., B. F. & H. L.
(Bob) ....A

WIS.—Fort Atkinson

Northwestern Mfg. Co.
(Bob) ....AA

WIS.—Madison

Fuller & Johnson Mfg. Co.
(Bob) ....AAA

WIS.—Racine

Dickey Mfg. Co., A. P.
(Bob) ....F

WIS.—Sheboygan

Garton Toy Co. (Coasting) A

WIS.—Stoughton

Stoughton Wagon Co. (Bob)
AA

WIS.—Whitewater

Weyher & Son, Theo. (Bob)
E

SLEEVES

MASS.—Cambridge

Boston Wooven Hose &
Rubber Co. (Rubber
Dredging) ....AAAA

MASS.—Chelsea

Carr & Co., J. H. (Iron) X

N. J.—Bloomfield

Combination Rubber Mfg.
Co. (Dredging) ......B

N. Y.—Buffalo

Keystone Mfg. Co. (Taper
Drill) X

OHIO—Akron

Faultless Rubber Co. (Rubber) ....AA

OHIO—Barberton

Pure Gum Specialty Co.
(Rubber) ....B

OHIO—Bucyrus

Blair Husking Glove Co.
(Corn Harvester) ......D

PA.—Bradford

Dresser, S. R. (Iron Pipe)
AA

PA.—Philadelphia

Pressed Steel Mfg. Co.,
Ridge Av. & Willow (Ball
Bearing Loose Pulleys) D

PA.—Pittsburg

McCullough-Datzell Crucible
Co. (Plumbago) ......A

SLEEVING: COTTON

PA.—Philadelphia

Moore, Alfred F., 202 N.
3rd ....AAAA

SLEIGHS

See also Sleds; Carriages

MAINE—South Paris

Paris Mfg. Co. (Childrens')
A

MICH.—Kalamazoo

Kalamazoo Sled Co. (Chil-
dren's) ....A

N. Y.—Buffalo

Heinz & Munschauer (Chil-
dren's) ....A

N. Y.—Cortland

Ellis Omnibus & Cab Co.
(Railroad) ....D

N. Y.—Nyack

Christie, A. E. & J. H.
(Russian) ....D

N. Y.—Rome

Bingham Harness Co.
(Pony) ....D

N. Y.—Troy

Troy Carriage Wks.
(Russian) ....B

VT.—Brattleboro

Smith & Co., S. A. (Chil-
dren's) ....AAA

WIS.—Milwaukee

Meinecke & Sons, A. (Children's, Perambulator) AA

SLICERS

CONN.—New Britain

Landers, Frary & Clark
(Bread; Cake; Potato)
AAA

SLICERS (Con.)

ILL.—Chicago
American Fdy. & Mchry. Co., Monadnock Bldg. (Beet) ....AA
IND.—Indianapolis
Atkins & Co., E. C. (Vegetable; Fruit) ....AAAA
Tucker & Dorsey Mfg. Co. (Bread; Vegetable; Fruit) A
MD.—Baltimore
Sinclair-Scott Co. (Pineapple) ....E
MASS.—Southbridge
Harrington Cutlery Co. (Beef) C
MASS.—Worcester
Parker Wire Goods Co. (Vegetable; Fruit) ..D
MICH.—Grand Ledge
Vanator Edge Tool Wks. (Ham) ....D
N. H.—Antrim
Goodell Co. (Potato) ....A
New York City
Houchin Co., Thos. W. (Revolving) ....D
Jennings Co., C. E., 42 Murray (Vegetable; Fruit) .B
Lalance & Grosjean Mfg. Co. (Egg) ....AAAA
Peck, Stow & Wilcox Co., 27 Murray (Vegetable; Fruit) ....AAAA
N. Y.—Rochester
Streeter & Co., N. R. (Fruit) ....A
N. Y.—Silver Creek
Howes Co., S. (Bean for Canners) ....A
OHIO—Clyde
Clyde Cutlery Co. (Ham) C
PA.—Lancaster
Eagle Machine Co. (Ear Corn) ....
National Mfg. Co. (Revolving) C
PA.—Philadelphia
Disston & Sons, Hy. (Vegetable; Fruit) ......AAAA
Enterprise Mfg. Co. of Penn. (Vegetable; Fruit) AAAA
TENN.—Johnson City
Johnson City Fdy. & Mach. Wks. (Veneer) ......D

SLICKERS

MASS.—Boston
Tower & Co., A. J. ....AA
MASS.—Cambridge
Sawyer & Son, H. M. ....B
N. J.—Newark
National Saw Co. ....B
N. Y.—Buffalo
White Co., L. & I. J. ....A
New York City
Standard Oiled Clothing Co., 152nd & Union Av. ......A

SLICKS

CONN.—Seymour
Swan Co., Jas. ....A
MASS.—Millbury
Buck Bros. (Carpenters') A
N. Y.—Buffalo
White Co., L. & I. J. (Carpenters') ....A
New York City
Peck, Stow & Wilcox Co., 27 Murray (Carpenters') AAAA

SLIDES

CONN.—New Britain
North & Judd Mfg. Co. (Blanket; Breast Strap; Rein) ....AA
Stanley Works (Desk) AAA
CONN.—Seymour
Matthews Mfg.Co., H. A. (Damper) ....B
ILL.—Chicago
McIntosh Stereopticon Co., 35 Randolph (Lantern) E
IND.—Wabash
Walter & Co., B. (Table) D
MASS.—Worcester
Hamblin & Russell Mfg. Co. (Wire, Oven) ....B

SLIDES (Con.)

MICH.—Detroit
Parke Davis & Co. (Microscopical) ....AAAA
MICH.—Grand Rapids
Grand Rapids Brass Co. (Desk) ....A
MICH.—Northville
Dubuar Mfg. Co., J. A. (Tent) X
MINN.—St. Paul
Ingersoll, T. W. (Lantern) D
New York City
Colt & Co., J. B. (Magic Lantern) ....B
Folmer & Schwing Mfg. Co. (Magic Lantern) ......B
McAllister, T. H. (Magic Lantern) ....B
N. Y.—Syracuse
Stearns & Co., E. C. (Breast Strap) ....AA
OHIO—Cleveland
Fanner Mfg. Co. (Hame Strap) ....A
OHIO—Dayton
Dayton Table Slide Co. (Table) C
OHIO—Youngstown
Finished Steel Co. (Elevator Shape) ....A
PA.—Philadelphia
Briggs, C. W. (Magic Lantern) ....E
PA.—Pittsburg
Ingersoll Construction Co., 307 4th Av. (Toboggan) B
WIS.—Watertown
Watertown Table Slide Co. (Table) ....E

SLINGS

ILL.—Harvard
Hunt, Helm Ferris & Co. (Hay) ....AA
ILL.—Ottawa
Porter Co., J. E. (Centre Trip Hay) ....A
IND.—Goshen
Goshen Mfg. Co. (Hay) ..B
IOWA—Fairfield
Louden Mchry. Co. (Hay) C
MICH.—Detroit
Byram & Co. (Chain) ....D
N. Y.—Rochester
Ricker Mfg. Co. (Hay) .E
OHIO—Akron
Whitman & Barnes Mfg. Co. (Hay) ....AAAA
OHIO—Ashland
Myers & Bro., F. E. (Hay) AAAA
OHIO—Canton
Ney Mfg. Co. (Hay) ....B
Ney Co., V. L. (Hay) C
PA.—Philadelphia
Paxson Co., J. W. (Rope for lifting Hasks) ......AA
TENN.—Memphis
Rodley Wagon Co. (Cane) A
WIS.—Janesville
Rock River Machine. Co. (Hay) ....D
WIS.—Milwaukee
Milwaukee Hay Tool Co. (Hay) ....A

SLIPPERS
See Boots & Shoes

SLITTERS
See also Machy

CONN.—Ansonia
Farrell Foundry & Machine Co (Rubber Belt) AAAA
CONN.—Derby
Birmingham Iron Foundry (Rubber Belt) ......AA
ILL.—Chicago
Board-Crosby Co., 176 So. Clinton (Power) X
MO.—St. Louis
Amer. Roll Paper Co. ....B
N. J.—Salem
Ayars Machine Co. (Can Body) ....B
N. Y.—Amsterdam
Inman & Amer. Box Machine Co. (Envelope Band) ....AA

SLITTERS (Con.)

N. Y.—Rochester
Knowlton Co., M. L. (Card-
board) ....AA
OHIO—Hamilton
Black & Clawson Co. AAA

SLOTTERS

See also Machy
CONN.—Bridgeport
Grant Mfg. & Machine Co.
(Bench, Screw) ......E

SLUGS

ILL.—Chicago
Barnhart Bros. & Spindler
(Printers') ....AA

SLUNG SHOTS

See Catapults

SMALTS

ILL.—Chicago
Central Commercial Co. ..C
N. Y.—Brooklyn
Wiarda & Co., John C. AA
New York City
Longman & Martinez..AAA
Tiemann & Co., D. F. ....A

SMELTERS

PA.—Allegheny
Pittsburg Clay Pot. Co.
(Enamel) ....AA

SMOKERS

CAL.—Petaluma
Petaluma Incubator Co.
(Bee) ....B
OHIO—Cincinnati
Muth, Mrs. Anna (Bee) ..F
IOWA—Red Oak
Kretchmer Mfg. Co. (Bee)C
MICH.—Farwell
Bingham, T. F. (Bee) ..A
OHIO—Medina
Root Co., A. I. (Bee) AA

SMOKESTACKS

See also Stacks

CAL.—Sacramento
Schaw-Batcher Co. ......A
IOWA—Waterloo
Tallerday Steel Pipe &
Tank Co. C
N. J.—Paterson
East Jersey Pipe Co. ....B
New York City
Koven & Bro., L. O., 50
Cliff ....A
PA.—Pittsburg
Scaife & Sons Co., Wm. B.
AAA

SMOOTHERS

MICH.—Detroit
Anderson & Sons, W. H.
(Asphalt) C
New York City
Sheridan, T. W. & C. B.
(Bookbinders' Case) ..A
PA.—Harrisburg
Hickok Mfg. Co., W. O.
(Bookbinders' Case) ..AA

SNAPS

CONN.—Bridgeport
Bridgeport Chain Co. (Hal-
ter Harness) ....A
CONN.—Hartford
Billings & Spencer Co.
(Halter Harness) ...AA
CONN.—New Britain
North & Judd Mfg. Co.
(Strap Buckle; Halter;
Harness) ....AA
MASS.—Westfield
Bay State Whip Co. (Br. U.
S. Whip Co.) (Whip)AAA
U. S. Whip Co. (Whip)AAA
MASS.—Worcester
Wire Goods Co. (Safety
Lock, Wire) ....A

SNAPS (Con.)

N. J.—Newark
Jenkinson & Co., R. C.
(Halter, Harness) ..AA
Marson, Arthur (Jewelers')
F
Taylor, Wm. H. (Jewelers')
F
N. Y.—Kenwood
Oneida Community (Ltd.)
(Halter, Harness) ..AAA
Sargent & Co., 151 Leonard
(Halter, Harness) AAAA
N. Y.—West Troy
Covert Mfg. Co. (Halter,
Harness) ....A
N. Y.—Windsor
Coburn Whip Co. (Whip)
AAA
OHIO—Cleveland
Eberhard Mfg. Co. (Breech-
ing) ....AA

SNATHS

IND.—Anderson
Fisher, Thos. C. C
IND.—Seymour
Seymour Mfg. Co. ......B
IOWA—Fort Madison
Iowa Farming Tool Co. ..A
MICH.—Jackson
Withington & Cooley Mfg.
Co. ....AA
OHIO—Cleveland
American Fork & Hoe Co.
AAAA
OHIO—Columbus
Brown, Hinman & Hunting-
ton Co. ....A
VT.—Bellows Falls
Derby & Ball ....B

SNIPS

See also Shear; Scissors

CONN.—Bridgeport
Acme Shear Co. (Tinners')B
CONN.—Southington
Peck, Stow & Wilcox Co.
Tinners'; Cotton Bale)
AAAA
N. J.—Newark
Heinischs Sons Co., R.
(Tinners') ....A
Wiss & Sons, J. (Tinners')A
N. Y.—Buffalo
Buffalo Dental Mfg. Co.
(Dental) C
Niagara Mach. & Tool Wks.
(Tinners') ....AAA
West Mfg. Co. (Tinners') D
New York City
Peck, Stow & Wilcox Co.,
27 Murray (Cotton Bale)
AAAA
OHIO—Fremont
Clauss Shear Co. (Dental)
AAA
Herbrand Co. (Tinners') .B
PA.—Philadelphia
National Cutlery Co., 3rd &
Lehigh Av. (Dental) ...C

SNUFF

ALA.—Birmingham
McNamara-Lord Co. C
ILL.—Galesburg
Peterson, N. ....A
MD.—Baltimore
Starr & Co., R. C
MICH.—Detroit
Scotten-Dillon Co., Fort W.
&. Campan. ....AAAA
Williams-Davis-Brooks &
Hinchmans Sons, 26 Con-
gress E. ....AA
N. J.—Helmetta
Helme & Co., G. W., (Br.
Amer. Snuff Co.) .AAAA
N. J.—Jersey City
Goetze & Bro. Co., F. A. D
Laneland Co.. P. ....AAAA
N. J.—New Brunswick
Parsons, J. M. ....B
New York City
American Snuff Co., 111
5th Av. ....AAAA
American Tobacco Co., 509
W. 22nd ....AAAA
Scharlin & Son, S., 110
Division C

SNUFF (Con.)

Weyman & Bro., 11 Bway.
.... A
N. C.—Durham
Morris & Son, R. F. ......B
PA.—Philadelphia
Garrett & Sons, W. E. AAA
Weyman & Bro. ....AA
PA.—Pittsburg
Weyman & Bro., 1112 Park
Bldg. ....A
TENN.—Clarksville
Meriweather Snuff & Tobac-
co Co. ....A
Stewart Snuff Co. ......A
Standard Snuff Co. .....A
VA.—Petersburg
Venable & Co., W. L. ...A

SNUFFLES

CONN.—New Britain
North & Judd Mfg. Co. AA

SOAKERS: BOTTLE

See Machinery

SOAP

ALA.—Birmingham
Bremer, W. P...........AA
CAL.—Berkeley
Standard Soap Co. .....AA
CAL.—Los Angeles
Los Angeles Soap Co. ..AA
CAL.—Sacramento
Sacramento Soap Co. C
CAL.—San Francisco
Everding & Co. J., 48 Clay A
Fishbeck Soap Co., 214
Sacremento ....A
Horstman, John, 667 Bry-
ant (Wash Powder) ....B
Lucy & Co., 123 Calif ...A
Lukin & Co., O., 117
Diamond C
Mission Soap & Candle Co.,
16-1 ....B
Newell & Bros., 217 Davis B
N. E. Soap Co., 214 Sacra-
mento ....A
(Wash Compound) AAAA
Pioneer Soap Co., 220 Calif
(L.; T.) ....B
San Fran. Candle Co., 402
Front ....A
Seidel, F. E., 1779 San
Bruno Av. ....A
Standard Soap Co., 113 Sac-
ramento ....AA
CAL.—Stockton
Williams & Moore X
COLO.—Denver
Dunwoody Bros. Soap Co. B
Geyserite Soap Co. .....A
CONN.—Bridgeport
Fairchild & Shelton ...AA
CONN.—Clinton
Pratt Chemical Co.
(Toilet) ....A
CONN.—Glastonbery
Williams Co., J. B. (Toilet;
Landry; Shaving) ......A
CONN.—Middletown
Allison Bros. C
CONN.—New Britain
Taplin Mfg. Co. (Toilet) D
CONN.—New Haven
Elm City Mfg. Co., 379 State
C
Hemingway & Co., L. R. C
DEL.—Wilmington
Kelly & Co. .... B
D. C.—Washington
Weaver, Kengla & Co., 3244
K. N. W. ....B
FLA.—Jacksonville
Florida Soap Co. ....B
GA.—Atlanta
Carlton Co., Jas. ....B
Georgia Soap Co. C
Trepoline Mfg. Co. C
GA.—Mascon
McCaw Mfg. Co. ...AAA
GA.—Savannah
Juehter, J. C
ILL.—Aurora
Shedd, O. N. ....B
ILL.—Chicago
Armour Soap Works, 205

SOAP (Con.)

Lasalle (Toilet; Laundry)
AAAA
Atwood & Steele, 18 River
(Toilet) C
Babbitt, B. T., 37 N. State
Soap; Powder) ....AAAA
Burr & Co., David, 125
Indiana (Toilet) C
Colgate & Co., 56 5th Av.
AAA
Conkling Chemical Co., 96
Erie Av. ....AA
Cosmo Buttermilk Soap Co.,
315 Dearborn ....B
Crofts & Reed, 842 Austin
Av. C
Fairbanks Co., N. K. (Soap
Powder; Laundry; Wash
Compound) ...... AAAA
Fitzpatrick Co., J., 424 W.
Canal ....B
Geyserite Soap Co., 13 S.
Center Av. ....A
Globe Soap Co., 21 River
Br. Cinn O.) ....A
Graham Bros. & Co., 421
W. Lake (Toilet) ....A
Jergens & Co., A. 171
Randolph ...... AA
Kendall Mfg. Co., 260 W.
Van Buren (Soap Powder)
AAA
Kirk & Co., Jas. S., 360
W. Water (Laundry;
Toilet) .... AAA
Liberty Mfg. Co., Kingsbury
& Superior ....A
Nelson Mfg. Co., 12 State B
Pacific Coast Borax Co.,
Ashland Blk. ......AAAA
Schmidt & Co., G. A., 405
North Av. C
Strong & Co., C. H., 218
Washg (Arnica; Tooth) D
Swift & Co., Union Stock
Yards .... AAAA
Turner Co., C., 39th & Iron
B
Wrisley Co., A. B., 477 5th
Av. (Toilet; Laundry) ..A
ILL.—Monmouth
Maple City Soap Works ..B
ILL.—Pearia
Mexican Amole Soap Co. ..C
ILL.—Quincy
Flacks & Co. C
ILL.—Rock Island
Warnock & Ralston .....B
ILL.—Springfield
Zwicky's Sons, M. (Toilet;
Laundry) ....B
IND.—Evansville
Melzer Bros. (Toilet) ...A
IND.—Ft. Wayne
Berghoff, G. A. C
Summit City Soap Works C
IND.—Goshen
Cosmo Buttermilk Soap Co.
B
IND.—Indianapolis
Kingan & Co. (Laundry
Chip) .... AAAA
Williams, W. M., 448 S.
Meridian C
Williams & Hunt ....A
IND.—Lafayette
Schnaible, M. & J. ....B
IND.—Logansport
Heppe & Sons, W. C
Lynas & Sons, J. B. (Toilet)
C
IND.—Michigan City
Union Soap Works C
IND.—Wabash
Spricker & Rees Co. .... B
IOWA—Burlington
Iowa Soap Co. (Inc.)
(Toilet; Laundry) C
IOWA—Des Moines
Prouty Barber Soap Co. ..C
IOWA—Dubuque
Beach & Sons, Jas. (Laun-
dry:: Powder) .... A
IOWA—Iowa City
Nelson Mfg. Co. C
IOWA—Marshalltown
Marshall Vinegar Co. C
IOWA—Sioux City
Haskins Bros. & Co. .....A
KANS.—Kansas City
Morris, Butt & Muller ..AA
Peet Bros. Mfg. Co. ..AA

SOAP (Con.)
KANS.—Leavenworth
National Soap Co. ....B
KANS.—Ottawa
Sheldon, E. M. C
KANS.—Wichita
Wichita Soap Mfg. Co.
  (Laundry) C
KY.— Lexington
Allen & Thompson ...... A
KY.—Louisville
Globe Refg. Co. (Laundry;
  Scouring) .... A
Kentucky Refg. Co.
  (Scouring) .... AAAA
Louisville Soap Co. (Laun-
  dry) .... AA
LA.—New Orleans
Fairbank Co., N. K., 430
  Graiver (Br. Chicago, Ill)
  .... AAAA
Keeler's Soap Works, 528
  Graiver .... A
MD.—Baltimore
Armstrong Soap Co. ..... AA
Babbitt, B. T., 39 S.
  Holiday (Br. N. Y. City)
  .... AAAA
Fairbanks Co., N. K., 44
  South .... AAAA
Hoefner & Sons, 403 Exch.
  Place (Laundry; Toilet;
  Scouring; Castile; Powder)
  .... AA
Lipps Co., C., Hollins, near
  Calvert Rd. .... A
Proctor & Gamble Co., 406
  Exch. Pl. ....AAAA
Resinol Chemical Co.
  (Medicinal) ....B
MD.— Salisbury
Standard Chemical Co.
  (Scouring) .... B
MASS.—Boston
Davis & Son, J. G., 200 N.
  Beacon C
Fickin, G. E., 30 Broad B
Gregory & Co., F. W., 162
  High C
Hanson & Co., P., 218 State
  (Castile) C
Marsh & Co., G. E., 69 Com-
  merce .... A
Marse & Co., J. F., 66 Nor-
  folk Av. (Laundry) C
Nathan, Jo. J., 71 Prentiss B
Potter Drug & Chemical
  Corpn. (Medicinal) ...A
Reardon & Sons, J. (Corpn.)
  24 Commerce .... A
Schulz & Co., 69 Broad
  (Laundry) ....AAAA
Speare's Sons Co., Alden
  (Laundry) .... AA
Whitney, E. W., 59 Long
  Wharf (Powder Castile) C
Wing, Mitchell Co., 111
  Broad C
MASS.—Cambridge
Davis & Sons, Jas. C. C
Dow & Co., J. C. C
E. Cambridge Mfg. Co. ..A
Kemp & Son. L C
Reardon & Sons, John ..A
Savina Mfg. Co. (Soap
  Powder) .... B
MASS.—Haverhill
Beach Soap Co. .... B
MASS.—Holyoke
Abbott, W. H. C
MASS.—Lawrence
Beach Soap Co. C
Glennie & Co., J. C
MASS.—Lowell
Lowell Rendering Co. C
MASS.—Lynn
Marsh & Co G. E. ....A
MASS.—Walden
Robinson Bros & Co. ....AA
Robinson, Willard C
MASS.—New Bedford
Herson & Co.. Thos. .... B
Robinson & Co., W. A.
  (Whale Oil) ....B
MASS.—Somerville
Norton, G. W. C
MASS.—Springfield
Bartlett & Holmes C
Castle, W. A. .... B
Fisk Mfg. Co. (Laundry;
  Mill) .... B
MASS.—Worcester
Albertson, W. R. (Harness)
  .... A

SOAP (Con.)
MICH.—Detroit
Babbitt, B. T., 83 Shelby
  .... AAAA
Detroit Soap Co., Foot
  Leib (Laundry) ....A
Parke, Davis & Co.
  (Medicinal) ...... AAAA
Schuete Soap Co., 945
  River (Laundry) .....B
Sylvan Toilet Co., Foot W.
  & Trumbull Av ....E
MICH.—Grand Rapids
Challenge Soap Co. ...... B
MICH.—Houghton
Lake Superior Soap Co. C
MICH.—Jackson
Central City Soap Co. ...A
MICH.—Saginaw
Passolt, Henry .... B
MINN.—Duluth
Elliot & Co.. H. R. C
MINN.—Minneapolis
Armour Soap Works, 219 N.
  5th .... AAAA
Kleansall Soap Co. ....A
Minnesota Soap Co., Bk. of
  Commerce Blg. ....A
Northwestern Soap Co.
  (Laundry; Toilet) ....D
MINN.—St. Paul
Minnesota Soap Co. ......A
Proctor & Gamble Co. AAAA
MO.—Kansas City
Clark & Co., H. H. ....A
Cudahy Packing Co. ..AAAA
Morris, Butt & Miller ..AA
Peet Bros. Mfg. Co. (Toilet)
  .... AA
MO.—Poplar Bluff
Arbor Oil Chemical Co. ..C
MO.—St. Louis
Bell Mfg. Co., 943 N. 2nd
  (Scouring) .... B
Fairbank Co., 3rd & Convent
  .... AAAA
Haas Soap Co.. J. J., 5020
  Benedict Av. ....A
Hygienic Chemical Co., 518
  N. Main .... A
Schaeffer Bros. & Powell
  Mfg. Co., 325 N. 2nd
  (Toilet) .... A
Tripolium Soap Co., 411
  Olive .... B
Waltke & Co., W. H., 2nd
  near E. Grand Av. ....AA
NEBR.—Omaha
Cudahy Packing Co. AAAA
Haskins Bros. & Co. ....A
Proctor & Gamble Co.
  .... AAAA
NEBR.—So. Omaha
Cudahy Packing Co. AAAA
N. H.—Dover
Beach Soap Co. .... B
N. H.—Manchester
Holt & Co., J. S. C
N. H.—Portsmouth
Freeman. H. J. C
N. J.—Camden
Baxter's Sons, J. C
Camden & Phila. Soap Co.
  .... A
Dobbins Soap Mfg. Co. AA
N. J.—Gloucester
Baxter's Sons, J. C
N. J.—Hoboken
Stenken & Sons, A. ......A
N. Y.—Jersey City
Colgate & Co. ....AAA
Oakley Soap & Perfy. Co. C
N. Y.—Newark
Babbitt, B. T., 667 Broad
  .... AAAA
Brown & Co., D. S., 100
  Bank ....AAA
Peters Harness & Saddlery
  Co. (Harness) C
N. Y.—Albany
Mendleson & Sons, A
  (Powdered) ....A
N. Y. Brooklyn
Baar Bros., 102 Rilhardson
  (Laundry) C
Babbitt, B. T., 699 Bway
  (Laundry) ....AAAA
Brown & Co., D. S., 33
  Thornton ....AAA
Chesebrough Mfg. Co.,
  Delevan & Dwight ..AAA
Columbia Chemical Works
  (Ammonia Laundry) ...B
Gill Soap Co., 711 Kent Av.

948

SOAP (Con.)

(Borax) .... B
Kirkman & Son, 227 Water
  (Laundry) ....AA
Rutherford & Barnes, 400
  Driggs Av. (Laundry)..B
N. Y.—Buffalo
Baker & Co., H. H. .....B
Erie Preserving Co., 941 N.
  Ferry .... AA
Faxon, Williams & Faxon,
  399 Main ....A
Gowans & Sons, 213 Chicago
  .... AA
Harris Jabesh Mfg. Co., 5
  Stetson ....B
Hoefner Sons, A. ....A
Larkin Soap Mfg. Co. AA
Lantz Bros. & Co. ..AAA
N. Y.—Cohoes
Amer. Soap & Washholme
  Co. ....B
N. Y.—Elmira
White, J. Frank ....B
N. Y.—Newburgh
Belknap, W. C. ....B
Granite City Soap Co.
  (Laundry; Toilet) C
New York City
Amer. Cotton Oil Co. (Cotton Seed Oil) ....AAAA
Amer. Soap Co., 73 Murray
  .... AA
Archibald & Lewis (Castile)
  C
Atlas Soap C o.,81 Beach C
Babbitt, B. T., 82 Washn
  .... AAAA
Bon Ami Co., 10 Battery
  Place .... A
Brown & Co., D. C., W. 51st
  .... AAA
Carbolic Soap Co., 230
  Pearl (Launry; Medicinal;
  Toilet; Dog; Animal; Disinfecting) C
Caswell, Massey & Co.
  (Tar X
Colgate & Co., 55 John
  (Toilet; Laundry) ..AAA
Condon & Co., T. F., 220
  Bway C
Daggitt, W. H., 383 W. 12th
  C
Fairbank Co., N. K. Prod.
  Exch. ....AAAA
Fay Bros., 92 Monroe ..AA
Gaunt & Janvier, 365 Canal
  .... B
Gross & Co., A., 75 Murray
  .... AA
Holbrook Mfg. Co., 470
  Washn. (Toilet) .....B
Jergens & Co., A., 365 Bway.
  .... AA
Jones Chemical Co., 51 Jay
  .... B
Manhattan Soap Co., 550 W.
  56th .... A
Miller Co., Frank (Harness)
  .... A
Moore Co., 288 Greenwich C
Morgan's Sons, E., 439 West
  .... AA
N. Y. Soap Works, 6 Desbrosses (Castile Chips) B
Nordlinger, J. D., 77
  Chambers .... AA
Pacific Coast Borax Co., 100
  William .... B
Packer Mfg. Co., 81 Fulton
  (Toilet) ....B
Palmer Solon (Toilet) ....D
Pinner, W. H., 521 W. 30th
  (Medical) .... B
Pyle & Sons, Jas., 436
  Greenwich (Pealine) ..A
Recamier Mfg. Co. (Toilet)
  .... D
Reichhend & Sons, 539 W
  43rd C
Ricksecker Co., Theo. (Animal; Shaving; Toilet) C
Rohe & Bro., Produce Exchange .... AAA
Rosenblatt & Co., 6
  Desbrosses C
Schultz & Co., 105 Hudson
  .... AAAA
Seabury & Johnson
  (Medicinal) ....AA
Smith, Chas. W. (Est.) 119
  Elizabeth .... AA
Stanley, J. T., 650 W. 30th
  .... AA

SOAP (Con.)

Starace, Achille, 76 Pearl
  .... B
Tomson & Co., P. C., 114
  5th Av. (Laundry) AAAA
Troy Laundry Mich Co., 33
  Warren .... AA
N. Y.—Poughkeepsie
Scott & Co., W. E. ......B
N. Y.—Rochester
Rochester Chemical Co. ..B
N. Y.—Rome
Rome Soap Mfg. Co. ....B
N. Y.—Syracuse
Finn's Sons, G. ....B
N. Y.—Troy
Troy Laundry Machy. Co.
  .... AA
OHIO—Canton
Biechele Soap Co., Jas.
  (Laundry; Toilet; Castile)
  .... A
OHIO—Cincinnatti
Babbit, B. T., 804 Race
  .... AAAA
Colgate & Co., Neave Bldg.
  .... AAA
Eureka Soap Wks., 2261 Sp.
  Grove .... A
Globe Soap Co., 121 E.
  Water .... A
Hall Capsule Co. (Toilet)
  .... D
Hunnewell H. G. 1606
  Plumb (Powd.) ....B
Jergens & Co., A., Sp. Garden & Alfred ....AA
Lease Soap Co., 41 Race A
Long, J. M., Co., 309 E. 2nd
  C
Proctor & Gamble Co.,
  United Bk. Bldg. AAAA
Remmers Soap Co., 1456
  Harrison Av. C
Themann Anton, 113 N.
  Canal .... B
Waters Laundry Supply Mfg.
  Co. .... B
Werk Co.. M., 411 Poplan
  .... AA
OHIO—Cleveland
Buchan Soap Co., Leonard
  & Hume C
OHIO—Columbus
Janton & Co., Fred......B
Janton & Sons, G........B
Ross, Thos. C
OHIO—Dayton
Beaver Soap Co. ....AAAA
Brown Soap Co. C
Davies, J. P. ....B
Hewett Bros. Soap Co. ..B
OHIO—Findlay
Happer & Co., C.H. .....B
OHIO—Ironton
Wiehl Soap Co. C
OHIO—Newark
Styron Briggs & Co. ....A
OHIO—Toledo
Bell & Co., L. W. C
OHIO—Washn. C. H.
Ludlow Soap Mfg. Co. ....B
OHIO—Zanesville
Schultz & Co. ....AAAA
OREGON—Oregon City
Oregon City Soap Wks...AA
OREGON—Portland
Luckel King & Cake Soap
  Co. .... B
Portland Soap & Chemical
  Co. C
PA.—Allegheny
Hasley & Sons, Geo. ....A
Walker, W. & H. .....AAAA
PA.—Bethlehem
De Journo Bros. Co. (Silk) E
PA.—Chester
Rocver Co., Hy..........A
PA.—Darby
Thayer-Harvey Soap Co.
  (Naptha) ....B
PA.—Lancaster
Penns. Soap Co. ....AA
PA.—McKeesport
Patterson, Warren & Co. C
PA.—Philadelphia
Babbitt, B. T., Co. 9th &
  Jeff ....AAAA
Champion & Co., J. W.
  (Toilet) .... D
Colgate & Co., 700 Arch
  .... AAA
Day & Frick, 1760 N. Howard ....B

SOAP (Con.)

Dobbins Soap Mfg. Co., 119 S. 4th (Laudry) ......AA
Eavenson & Sons, J., 320 N. 20th ....A
Ecker & Co., 2111 E. Susq. Av. ....B
Elkinton, J. S. & T., 121 So. 3rd ....A
Fels & Co., 73rd & Woodland (Toilet; Laundry) A
Hamilton & Son, R., 709 Tasker C
Kendall Mfg. Co., 1207 Fairmount Av. ....AAA
Kirk & Co., J. S., 207 S. Front ....AAA
Kranskopf, L., 430 N. 3rd B
Lantz Bros. & Co., 13 S. Front (Laundry) ......AAA
Leberman & Son, A. 2229 No. 12th ....B
Lever Bros., 2314 Wood ....AAA
Mason Chemical Co., 515 Arch (Animal) ....B
Miller, C. F., 45 N. Front (Toilet) ....B
Parker, Oliver 1095 G'town Av. ....B
Reiner & Rees, 1631 North B
Schultz & Co., 2 S. Front (Laundry) .... AAAA
Taylor Milne Co., 23 S. Front ....B
Thayer & Co., P. W., 23 S. Front ....B
Tomson & Co., P. C. 25.... Wash Av. ....AAAA
Tully, James, 179 Washn. A
Vail Bros. (Toilet) C
Warren Soap Mfg. Co., 113 Chestnut .... B
Wrigley Mfg. Co., 4478 Green .... B
Young & Co., C. W., 1251 N. 26th ....B
PA.—Pittsburg
Babbitt, B. T., 414 Liberty Av. .... AAAA
Fairbank, N. K. Co., McCance Blk. ...... AAAA
Pittsburg Soap Co., 23rd & Josephine ....AAAA
Stunz & Son, S., 716 Bingham C
Walker, W. & H. (Laundry) AAAA
Wilson & Gorman, 543 4th Av. ....A
PA.—Reading
Leaman, W. K. C
PA.—Stony Greek Mills
Hunter & Co., No. D. (Laundry; Castile) ....A
PA.—Titusville
Natl. Soap Works ....B
Rice Soap Co. C
PA.—Warren
Warren Specialty Co. ....B
PA.—Wilkesbarre
Ahlborn Bros. ....B
Bauer, Frank C
PA.—Williamsport
Thrall & Co., F. R. ......B
PA.—York
Rupp, D. ....B
R. I.—Pawtucket
Draper & Co., J. O. ......B
Perry Oil Co. (Harness) ..C
R. I.—Providence
Kendall Mfg. Co. (Powder) AAA
Place Mfg. Co. W. H. B
Union Oil Co. (Cotton Seed (Oil) ....AAA
Woodley Soap Mfg. Co. ..C
S. C.—Charleston
Palmetto Soap Mfg. Co. ..C
Storen, W. J. C
S. C.—Chattanooga
Scholze Bros. & Co. ......A
Steward Mfg. Co., D. M. B
S. C.—Nashville
Cassetly Oil Co. ....B
Enterprise Soap Works ..A
UTAH—Stalt Lake City
Utah Soap Co. C
VT.—Bennington
Adams Co., E. C
VA.—Richmond
Crew & Co., P. J. C
WASH.—Seattle
Seattle Soap Co. C

SOAP (Con.)

W. VA.—Parkersburg
Upson Oil & Soap Co. (Laundry; Toilet) ......B
WIS.—Green Bay
Green Bay Soap Co. C
WIS.—Kenoska
Charles, J. H. C
WIS.—Marinette
Marinette Soap Co. C
WIS.—Milwaukee
Crystal Soap Co., 56 5th Av. C
Delaney Oil & Lubricant Co. (Laundry) X
Johnson Soap Co., 4th & Fowler ....A
Sercomb Mfg. Co., C. A., 52 3rd ....AA
Trenkamp & Co., F., 209 Mich. C
Wadhams Oil & Grease Co., 211 National Av. ......B
WIS.—Sheboygan
Aladdin Soapp Co. C

SOAPSTONE

ILL.—Chicago
Barrett & Co., M. L., 219 Lake ....A
MASS.—Boston
Bowker Torrey & Co. ..AA
Troy Bros. & Co., 91 Haverhill C
Union Soapstone Co., 14 Marshall C
New York City
Alberene Soapstone Co., 393 Pearl ....B
Hammell & Gillespie, 240 Front ....A
Pettit Chemical Co. ....B
N. Y.—Marietta
Fairfax Soapstone Co. ....F
PA.— Easton
Williams & Co., C. R. ..A
PA.—Philadelphia
Wetherill Co., S. P., 925 Chestnut ....B
PA. Pittsburg
McCormick Co., J. S. ...B
VT.—Chester Depot
Amer. Soapstone Finish Co. (Concrete Dressing) ....F
VT.—Ludlow
Francestown Soapstone Finish Co. ....E
VT.—Pittsfield
New England Talc Co. ...D
VA.—Schuyler
Virginia Soapstone Co. Kitchen Sinks; Laundry Tubs; Slabs; Hearths, etc.) ....B

SOCKETS

See also **Hardware; Carriage**

CONN.—Bridgeport
Bryant Electric Co. (Electric Lamp) ......B
Hubbell, Harvey (Incandescent Lamp) ......B
Perkins Electric Switch Mfg. Co. (Electric Lamp) ....B
CONN.—Danielsonville
Scott, E. W. (Whip) C
CONN.—Hartford
Billings & Spencer Co. (Drill) .... A
CONN.—Mount Carmel
Woodruff & Sons, Walter W. (Pole) ....A
CONN.—New Britain
Corbin, P. & Y. (Sash) AAAA
CONN.—New Haven
Cowles & Co. (Inc.) (Canopy; Whip) .....A
Fitch Co., W. E. & T. (Whip) ....AA
Hoggson & Pelks Mfg. Co. A
Seward & Son, M. (Canopy) A
CONN.—Stamford
Yale & Towne Mfg. Co. (Sash) ....AAAA
CONN.—Worcester
Fowler & Co. (Curtain Rod) B
ILL.—Chicago
Burdett-Rowntree Mfg. Co., 85 W. Jackson Boul'd (Incadescent Lamp Ball) .C

SOCKETS (Con.)

IND.—Indianapolis
Automatic Grip Neck Yoke
Co. (Spoke) .... B
IND.—Peoria ..
Peoria Electric Mfg. Co.
(Electric Lamp) ......A
IWOA—Sioux City
Electrical Supply Co. (In-
candescent Lamp) .....E
MASS.—Boston
Bernstein Elect. Mfg. Co.
286 Roxbury (Electric
(Lamp) ....B
MASS.—New Bedford
Moorse Twist Drill & Mach.
Co. (Drill) .... AAA
MASS.—South Boston
Gilmore Electric Co. (In-
candescent Lamp) ....A
MASS.—Taunton
New Process Twist Drill Co.
(Drill) ....E
MASS.—West Somerville
New England Elec. Mfg. Co.
(Incandescent Lamp) E
MO.—St. Louis
Leschen & Sons, Rope Co.
(Wire Rope) ....AA
N. J.—Newark
Searless Mfg. Co. (Whip) .B
N. Y.—Auburn
Clapp Mfg. Co., E. D.
(Canopy) ....A
N. Y.—Binghamton
Crandal Stone & Co. (Bow;
Canopy) ....A
N. Y.—Brooklyn
Williams & Co., J. H.
(Wire Rope) ....AA
N. Y.—Buffalo
Keystone Mfg. Co. (Drill;
Wire Rope) C
Pratt & Letchworth (Whip)
AA
New York City
Estes & Sons, E. B., 45
John (Whip) .... AA
Etna Mfg. Co., 253 Bway.
(Drill) ....D
Johns-Manville Co., H. W.
(Electric Lamp) ..AAAA
Judd & Co., H. L. (Carpet
Pins; Pole; Window Rod)
X
Kinsman Electric & Railway
Supply Co., 91 Liberty
(Electric Lamp) C
Metal Stamping Co. (Bow;
Whip) .... B
Peck, Stow & Wilcox Co.,
27 Murray (Whip) AAAA
Tiebout, N. & J., 118 Cham-
bers (Hay Pole) ......B
N. Y.—Niagara Falls
Oneida Community (Ltd.)
(Drill) ....AAA
N. Y.—Rochester
Crescent Elect. Mfg. Co.
(Waterproof Incandescent
Lamp) ....F
N. Y.—Schenectady
General Electric Co. (In-
canndescent Lamp) AAAA
N. Y.—Syracuse
Crouse-Hinds Elec. Co.
(Waterproof Incandescent
Lamp) .... A
Pass & Seymour (Electric
Lamp; Porcelain Incan-
descent Lamp) ....A
OHIO—Cincinnati
Cincinnati Screw & Tap Co.
(Drill) ....B
OHIO—Cleveland
Cleveland Hdw. Co.
(Canopy) .... A
Cleveland Twist Drill Co.
(Drill) .... A
Standard Tool Co., 1260
Central Av. (Drill) AAA
Tonliff Mfg. Co. (Bow) AA
OHIO—East Liverpool
Brunt, G. F. (Incandescent
Lamp) .... B
OHIO—Elyria
Topliff & Ely Co. (Bow) A
OHIO—Toledo
Yost Electric Mfg. Co.
(Electric Lamp) .....D
PA.—Allegheny
Sawyer-Man Electric Co.
(Electric Lamp) X

SOCKETS (Con.)

PA.—Mechanicsburg
Wilcox Mfg. Co., D.
(Canopy) ....B
PA.—Philadelphia
Paiste & Co., H. T., 3101
Ludlow (Electric Lamp) B
Pringle, W. T. (Regulating;
Incandescent Lamp) ....D
Stow Flexible Shaft Co.,
26th & Callowhil (Drill)
B.
VT.—Barre
Trow & Holden (Wire Rope)
B
WIS.—Racine
Imperial Bit & Snap Co.
(Drill) ....B
Racine Malleable & Wrought
Iron Co. (Whip) X

SODA

See also next Heading

COLO.—Denver
Hutchinson & Son, Wm. H.
(Sal) .... A
MD.— Baltimore
Baltimore Chrome Wks
(Bichromate) ....AA
Thomsen Chemical Co.
(Phosophate; Sulphate;
Sal; Hypophosphite Caus-
tic; Bi-Carbonated ....B
MASS.—Boston
Cochrane Chemical Co.
(Acetate; Bi-Sulphite; Hy-
po-Sulphite; Sulphate) AA
Linder & Meyer (Caustic) A
Merrimac Chemical (Ace-
tate; Bi-Sulphite; Hypo-
Sulphate; Sulphate) ..AA
MICH.—Bay City
North American Chemical
Co. (Chlorate) ....A
MCH.—Wyandotte
Ford Co., J. B. (Washing)
A
Michigan Alkali Co.
(Caustic) ....AAAA
MO.—St. Louis
Mallinckrodt Chemical Co.
(Caustic) ....AAAA
N. Y.—Buffalo
Schoelkopf, Hartford &
Hanna (Chlorate) AAAA
New York City
Battele & Renwick
(Nitrate) .... AA
Beggs & Co., E. J., 101
Beekman (Dry Bi-Sul-
phite) .... D
Church & Dwight Co. (Sal)
(Bicarbonate) ....AAAA
Colgate & Co. (Sal) ..AAA
Fries Bros., 92 Reade
(Salicylate) .... A
Fuerst Bros. & Co. (Chlor-
ate; Caustic) ....D
General Chemical Co.
(Acetate; Bi-Sulphate;
Sulphate; Caustic) AAAA
Heller, Hirsh & Co.
(Nitrate) .... AA
Heyden Chem. Wks., 40
Pine (Salicylate; Ben-
zoate) ....A
Hill's Sons Co., Edw (Bi-
Carbonate; Caustic) ..AA
Jones Chemical Co., Enos F.,
51 Jay C
Klipstein & Co., A (Hypo-
Sulphite; Chlorate; Caus-
tic) .... AA
Kuttroff, Pickhardt & Co.
(Bi-Sulphite; Chlorate;
Hypo-Sulphite) ....A
Lee & Co., James (Caustic;
Sal; Hypo-Phosphate)..A
Pyle & Sons, James .....A
Riker, J. S. & D. S.
(Chlorate) ....A
Roessler & Hasslacher Chem.
Co. (Acetate; Benzoate;
Caustic; Chlorate) ..AA
Selling Co. (The) (Acetate;
Bi-Sulphite; Hypo-Sul-
phite) C
Sholes Co., C. E. (Sal) X
Williamson & Co., D. D.
14 Dey (Bi-Carbonate) B
Wing & Evans (Ash; Caus-
tic; Sal) ....AAA

SODA (*Con.*)

N. Y.—Niagra Falls
Acker Process Co. (Caustic)
.............................D

N. Y.—Syracuse
Solvay Process Co. C(austic;
Ash) ....AAAA

OHIO—Cincinnati
Amer. Chemical Co. (Bi-
carbonate; Caustic Sal) F
Berghausen Chem. Co., The
E. (Benzoate) ....B
Winkler & Co., Isaac
(Caustic) ....A

OHIO—Cleveland
Clark Co., Fred G.
(Caustic) C
Grasselli Chemical Co.
(Acetate, Bi-Sulphite; Sal;
Hypo-Sulphite; Silicate)
.............................AAAA
Harshaw, Fuller & Good-
win Co. (Acetate) ....AA

PA.—Philadelphia
Elkinton's Sons, L. M.
(Sal) ....D
Harrison Bros. & Co.
(Cyanide; Nitrate) AAAA
Keller, Robt. (Bi-Sulphatte)
.............................D
Hempstead & Sons, O. G.
(Borate) ....A
Hollingsworth & Peterson
(Caustic; Sal) ....B
Kalion Chemical Co.
(Bichromate) ....AA
Phila. Quartz Co.
(Silicate) ....AA
Pennsylvania Salt Mfg. Co.
(Caustic; Sal Ash; Bi-
Carb) ....AAAA
Powers - Weightman-Rosen-
garten Co. (Bicarbonate;
Bi-Sulphate; Sulphate)
.............................AAAA

PA.—Pittsburg
Columbia Chemical Co.
(Caustic) ....AAAA

PA.—Finkelt
Hachmeister Chemical Co.
(Caustic) ....D

R. I.—Providence
Arnold, Hoffman & Co.
(Caustic) ....AA

WIS.—Milwaukee
Diamond Soda Wks. (Bi-
Carb.; Cal) ....AAA

SODA & SALERATUS

CAL.—San Francisco
Griswold & Co., E., 16th &
R. I. ....B
Hortsman. J., 667 Bryant B
Kittle & Co., 202 Calif.AAA
Stauffer Chemical Co., 318
Front ....AA
Schilling & Co., A., 2nd &
Folsom ....AAA

GA.—Savannah
Moorhouse Mfg. Co. C

ILL.—Chicago
Atwood & Steele, 18 River
.............................C
Barrett & Co., M. L., 219
Lake ....A
Church & Dwight Co., 67
Wabash Av. ......AAAA
Grant Hygienic Baking
Powder Co., 25 So., Desp.
.............................B
Puhl-Webb Co., 119 W.
Randolph C

ILL.—Wabash
Wabash Baking Powder Co.
.............................B

MASS.—Boston
Slade Co., D. & L., 13
India ....A

MICH.—Wyandotte
Ford Co., J. B. ....AAA
Mich. Alkali Co. ....AAAA

MO.—St. Louis
Hygienic Chemical Co. ..A
Waltke & Co., W., 2nd nr.
E. Grand ....AA

NEBR.—South Omaha
Cudahy Packing Co. AAAA

New York City
Archibald & Lewis, 193
Front C

SODA & SALERATUS

Babbitt, B. T., 82 Washn.
.............................AAAA
Church & Dwight Co., 63
Wall ....AAAA
Condon & Co., T. F., 220
Bway. C
Fuerst Bros. & Co., 2
Stone ....B
Taylor Chemical Co., J. M.,
29 Cortlandt ....A
Williamson & Co., D. D., 14
Dey ....B

N. Y.—Syracuse
Church & Dwight Co.
.............................AAAA

OHIO—Cleveland
Frasch Process Soda Co. .B

OHIO—Newark
Styron, Beggs & Co. .....A

PA.—Philadelphia
Elkinton, J. S. & T., 532 N.
American ....A
Penn Chemical Works
.............................AAAA
Tomson & Co., P. C., 25
Wash. Av. ....AAA

TENN.—Nashville
Southern Soda Works ....A

WIS.—Milwaukee
Wadhams Oil & Grease Co.,
211 Natl. Av. ....B

SODIUM

MD.—Baltimore
Thomsen Chemical Co. (Am-
monium Phosphate) ....B

MO.—St. Louis
Herf & Frerichs Chemical
Co. (Salicvate) ....A

New York City
Roessler & Hasslacher
Chem. Co. (Metallic) AA
Williamson & Co., D. D., 14
Dey ....B

PA.—Easton
Baker & Adamson Chemical
Co. (Metallic) ....A

SOFAS

See also Furniture

ILL.—Chicago
Revell & Co., Alex. H.
(Inc.) ....AA

MASS.—Boston
Davenport, Albert H. ..AA

MASS.—Gardner
Heywood Bros. & Wakefield
Co. (Rattan) ......AAAA

New York City
Aimone Mfg. Co. (Bamboo)
.............................B
Fuldner, Henry ....B
Schwarzwaelder & Co., Wm.
(Office) X

WIS.—Milwaukee
Kipp Co., B. A. ....B

SOFTNERS

MASS.—Boston
Thayer & Co., E. M., 106
Broad (Cotton).........C

New York City
Arabol Mfg. Co., 155
William (Cotton) ......A

PA.—Philadelphia
Loos & Dilworth, 44 N. Delaware Av. (Cotton) ....B

SOLDER

CAL.—San Francisco
Pacific Metal Works .....B
Selby Smelting & Lead Co.
(Bar; Strip; Drop; Wire)
.............................AAA

COLO.—Denver
Creswell Mfg. Co., Joseph,
1624 Blake ....A

CONN.—Bridgeport
Bridgeport Brass Co.
(Braziers) ....AAA
Rowell & Co., W. G. ....D

CONN.—Hartford
Nev & Co., J. M. (Gold) C

CONN.—New Haven
Graham & Co., Jas. ....A

CONN.—Waterbury

SOLDER (Con.)

Scovill Mfg. Co. (Braziers')
............AAAA
ILL.—Chicago
Besly & Co., Chas. H., 15
Clinton ....AA
Blatchford & Co., E. W., 70
N. Clinton ....AA
Great Western Smelting &
Refining Co., 173 W. Kin-
zie ....A
Illinois Smelting & Refin-
ing Co., Kinzie & Peoria
A
Kramer & Son, H., 401 S.
Canal ....E
Krembs & Co., 55 Waldo Pl.
(Flux) C
Lausten Lead Works (Br.
Am. Shot & Lead Co.) 78
Pratt ....AAAA
Raymond Lead Co., 59 W.
Lake ....AAAA
MAINE—Portland
Lang Co., E. M. (Wire;
Drop; Stick; Gold) C
MD.—Baltimore
Balt. Chemical Co., 13 P.
O. Av. (Flux) ....B
Shultz & Co., A., 1016 E.
Balto. (Wire; Drop, etc.)
A

MASS.—Boston
Chadwick-Boston Lead Co.,
162 Congress ....AA
Richards & Co. (Inc.) 60
Union ....B
Star Refining Co., 170 Sum-
mer ....B
MICH.—Detroit
Detroit Lead Pipe & Sheet
Lead Works, 57 2d ....A
MINN.—South Minneapolis
National Brass & Metal Co.,
256 3d Av. C
MO.—St. Louis
Hiertz & Son, Theo. .....D
Moore-Jones Brass & Metal
Co., 3138 Bway ....A
Rumsey Mfg. Co., L. M.,
806 N. 2d ....AAA
N. J.—Jersey City
Brady Brass Co., 204 10th
B
Williams & Son, E. A., 107
Plymouth (Silver) ..AAA
N. Y.—Brooklyn
McLaughlin's Sons, P., 230
N. 12th C
N. Y.—Buffalo
Shepard & Co., Sidney, 145
Seneca ....AAAA
New York City
American Metal Co., 52
Bway ....AAA
Ansonia Brass & Copper Co.,
99 John (Braziers')
AAAA
Druce & Cook, 186 Water
AA
Columbia Smelting & Re-
fining Works, 307 Water
AA
Colwell Lead Co., 63 Centre
AA
Grasselli Chemical Co.
(Flux) ....AAAA
Green & Co., W., 6 Maiden
Lane (Gold; Silver) ..C
Hendricks Bros., 49 Cliff
(Plumbers'; Braziers')
AAAA
Hungerford Brass & Copper
Co., U. T. (Coppersmiths')
AA
Kahn Bros., 525 E. 19th AA
Lissberger & Co., B., 738 E.
14th (for all purposes) ..B
Lissberger & Son, Marks,
397 W. 12th ....B
Nassau Smelting & Refin-
ing Works, ft. W. 28th
AA
National Lead Co., 100
William ....AAAA
Sanborn, John, 217 Water D
N. Y.—Rochester
Clum & Co., P. A., 18 Fay C
Rochester Lead Works, 382
Exchange ....B
N. Y.—Syracuse
Empire Metal Co. (Alumi-
num; Silver) ....A

SOLDER (Con.)

Pierce, Butler & Pierce
Mfg. Co. ....AAA
Syracuse Smelting Wks. X
N. Y.—Utica
Millar & Son Co., Charles
AA
OHIO—Canton
Berger Mfg. Co. (Tin Plate)
AA
OHIO—Cincinnati
Crane-Hawley Co., Court &
Sycamore ....A
Huenefeld, E. H., 225 E.
9th ....A
OHIO—Cleveland
Garry Iron & Steel Co. ...A
PA.—Philadelphia
Delaware Metal Refinery,
18th & Washn. Av. ...X
Disston & Sons, Hy. (Bra-
ziers') ....AAAA
Janney-Steinmetz & Co.,
Drexel Bldg. (Aluminum)
D
Koch & Fox, 22d & Glen-
wood Av. ....D
Lewis & Bro. Co., Jno. T.,
231 So. Front ....AAAA
Merchant & Co. (Inc.) 517
Arch (Braziers') .....AA
North American Smelting
Co., 9th & Thompson AA
Woodfall Bros., 1105 Fair-
mount Av. ....D
PA.—Pittsburg
Anderson, Du Puy & Co.
(Silver) ....AAAA
R. I.—Pawtucket
Fuller & Son, Geo. H.
(Gold; Silver) ....A
R. I.—Providence
Briggs & Sons Co., J.
(Gold; Silver) ....A
Hough Co., W. S. Jr.
(Gold) C
United Wire & Supply Co.
(Gold) ....AA
WIS.—Milwaukee
Windsor Mfg. Co., 570 Clin-
ton ....A

SOLES

CONN.—Hartford
Wiley & Son, Wm. H.
(Woolen) ....A
ILL.—Chicago
Wilder & Co., 212 Lake
(Cut) ....AA
MASS.—Boston
Boston Belting Co. (Rub-
ber) ....AAAA
Breed & Badger, 131 Sum-
mer (Cut) ....B
Thayer Co., N. F. (Shoe) C
MASS.—Lynn
Hilliard & Merrill (Cut
Leather) ....A
Houghten & Sons, James
(Woolen) X
MASS.—New Bedford
Hersom & Co., Thos. (Cut) C
MASS.—Worcester
Graton & Knight Mfg. Co.
(Cut) ....AAAA
N. Y.—Buffalo
Buffalo Last Works (Clog;
Wooden) ....B
Schoellkopfs Sons, J. F.
(Cut Leather) ....A
New York City
Frank & Co., S. H., 8
Jacobs (Cut Leather) AAA
Gutta Percha & Rubber
Mfg. Co., 126 Duane
(Rubber) ....AAAA
Keck, Mosser & Co., 21
Park Pl. (Cut Leather)
AAA
Krieg & Co., J. K. (Cut) B
N. Y. Counter Co. (Cut
Leather) ....AAA
OHIO—Canton
Canton Brass & Aluminum
Co. (Aluminum) .....D
OHIO—Cincinnati
Amer. Oak Lea. Co. (Cut
Leather) ....AAAA
PA.—Noxen
Mosser Tanning Co. (Cut
Leather) ....A

SOLES (Con.)

WIS.—Milwaukee
Kalt-Zimmers Mfg. Co.
(Cut Leather) C
Pfister & Vogel Leather
Co. (Cut Leather) AAAA

SOLING

MASS.—Boston
Boston Belting Co. (Rubber)
AAAA
Boston Woven Hose & Rubber Co. (Rubber) ..AAAA
N. J.—Jersey City
New Jersey Car Spring &
Rubber Co. (Rubber) AA
N. J.—Trenton
Home Rubber Co. (Rubber)
AA
Trenton Rubber Co. (Rubber) .... A
New York City
Goodyear's India Rubber
Glove Mfg. Co., 503
Bway.. (Rubber) ..AAAA
Gutta Percha & Rubber Mfg.
Co. (Rubber) ....AAAA
New York Belting & Packing Co. (Rubber) ..AAA
OHIO, Akron
Akron Rubber Works (Rubber .... AAAA

SOLUTIONS

ILL.—Chicago
Hazlitt & Co., Geo. K.
(Gold & Silver Plating).D
MO.—St. Louis
Hammer Dry Plate Co.
(Photographic; Developing) ....A
N. J.—Newark
Eureka Cement Co. (Rubber) ....D
PA.—Philadelphia
Powers - Weightman - Rosengarten Co. (Chemical)
AAAA

SOLVENTS

See Removers

SOMNOES

See Furniture

SORTERS

COLO.—Denver
Denver Iron & Wire Wks.
Co. (Screens; Potato) .D
IOWA—Prairie City
Dowden Mfg. Co. (Potato)
B
MICH.—Jackson
Aspinwall Mfg. Co. (Potato) ....B
MICH.—Pontiac
Bacon Mfg. Co. (Bacon) ..X
MICH.—Rochester
Miller Bros. (Picker; Potato) X
OHIO—Avery
Hoover, Prout & Co. (Potato) ....A
PA.—York
Hench & Dromgold Co.
(Peach; Potato) ......B
WIS.—Racine
Johnson & Field Mfg. Co.
(Bean) ....F

SOUNDERS

PA.—Philadelphia
Riggs & Bro., 310 Market
(Marine) ....B

SOUPS

CAL.—San Francisco
Van Camp Packing Co., 307
Sansome ....A
COLO.—Longmont
Empson Packing Co. .....A
FLA.—Key West
Granday & Co.. A. (Turtle)
C
ILL.—Chicago
Armour Packing Co. .AAAA
Canepa Bros., 101 Indiana

SOUPS (Con.)

(Italian) ....B
Libby, McNeill & Libby
AAAA
Polk Co., J. T., 46 River
(Br. Greenwood, Ind.).AA
Van Camp Packing Co., 42
River ....A
IND.—Greenwood
Polk Co., J. T. ....AA
IND.—Indiaapolis
Columbia Conserve Co. ...A
Huffman Packing Co., 24
Dunlap C
Van Camp Packing Co...AA
MAINE—Portland
Portland Packing Co. ..AA
MASS.—Boston
Huckins & Co., J. H., 60
Commercial C
MASS.—Cambridge
Alghieri Soup Co. C
MICH.—East Tawas
National Milling & Evaporating Co. C
N. J.—Camden
Campbell Pres. Co., Jos..AA
N. J.—Jersey City
Franco-American Food Co.
A
N. J.—Passaic
American Compressed Food
Co. C
N. Y.—Buffalo
Erie Preserving Co. .AAAA
N. J.—Kenwood
Oneida Community (Ltd.)
AAAA
New York City
Burnham Co., ℭ. S., 61
Gansevoort ....B
Columbia Conserve Co., 247
W. B'way ....B
Curtice Bros. Co., 138
Franklin ....AA
Eastman's Co. ....AAA
Heinz Co.. H. J., 216
Spring (Br. Pittsburg)
AAAA
Oneida Community. 413
B'way ....AAAA
Snider Pres. Co., A., 105
Hudson ....A
N. Y.—Rochester
Curtice Bros. Co. ......AA
OHIO—Cincinnati
Loudon, Chas. F., Court &
Sycamore C
National Pure Food Co., 920
Sycamore C
Snider Pres. Co. 209 Sycamore ....A
PA.—Philadelphia
Ritter Conserve Co.. P. J.,
2156 E. Dauphin ......A

SOUVENIRS

See also Jewelry

ILL.—Chicago
Crow Metal Mfg. Co., 71
W. Jackson Boul. ......E
MASS.—Springfield
Fletcher Aluminum Novelty
Corp. (Aluminum) X
R. I.—Providence
Childs Novelty Co.. D. R.
(Aluminum) ....F

SOWERS

See Seeders

SPADES

See also Shovels

ILL.—Streator
Iwan Bros. (Drain) .....D
IND.—Anderson
Wright Shovel Co. (Iron
Hand) ....B
IND.—Vincennes
Star Shovel & Range Co.
(Drain) ....B
MASS.—Boston
Ames Shovel & Tool Co.
AAAA
MASS.—Greenfield
Nichols Bros. (Butter)....C
MASS.—Shelburne Falls
Lamson & Goodnow Mfg.
Co. (Butter) ....A

SPADES (Con.)

N. H.—Antrim
Gordell Co. (Butter) ....A
OHIO—Canton
Ney Mfg. Co. (Drain)...B
OHIO—Cleveland
American Fork & Hoe Co.
(Drain) ....AAAA
Avery Stamping Co. (Drain)
..............A
PA.—Mt. Pleasant
Mt. Pleasant Tool Co.
(Drain) ....B
PA.—Philadelphia
Griffiths Co., George, 515
Locust (Iron Hand)....A
Pfeifer & Co., John (Iron
Hand) ....A
PA.—Pittsburg
Hussey-Binns Co., 541 Wood
(Iron Hand) ....AA
Klein, Logan & Co. (Iron
Hand) ....A
Russell Shovel Co., J. C.
(Iron Hand) ....B
PA.—Wyoming
Wyoming Shovel Co. (Iron
Hand) ....A
W. VA.—Wheeling
Laughlin Nail Co. (Iron
Hand) ....AA
WIS.—Oshkosh
Jones, J. R. (Iron Hand).H

SPAGHETTI

See Macaroni

SPANGLES

See also Jewelry

New York City
Hirsch's Sons, G., 653
B'way ....B
Siegman & Weil, 110 Greene
A

SPANNERS

N. Y.—Brooklyn
Williams & Co., J. H. (Carriage) ....AA

SPARS

See also Masts

N. Y.—Ogdensburg
Spaulding St. Lawrence
Boat Co. C
N. Y.—Roslyn
Clapham, Thomas ....F

SPATULAS

ILL.—Chicago
American Cutlery Co. ..AA
MASS.—Northampton
Clement Mfg. Co. ......B
MASS.—Shelburne Falls
Lamson & Goodnow Mfg.
Co. ....A
MICH.—Detroit
Moore & Son, E. C. (Wax)
F

SPEARS

CONN.—Collinsville
Collins & Co. (Fish) .AAAA
ILL.—Freeport
Arcade Mfg. Co. (Fish)..A
MASS.—Boston
Dame, Stoddard & Co.
(Fish) ....A
PA.—Mars
Sheridan & Co., J. J.
(Side) ....D

SPECTACLES

See Optical Goods

SPECULUMS

New York City
Goodyear's India Rubber
Glove Mfg. Co. (Rubber)
AAAA

SPEEDERS

MASS.—Lowell
Lowell Machine Shop.AAAA
MASS.—Newton Upper Falls
Saco & Pettee Machine

SPEEDERS (Con.)

Shops ....AAA
MASS.—Taunton
Mason Machine Wks. .AAA
R. I.—Providence
Providence Machine Co.AAA

SPELTER

ILL.—Chicago
Blatchford & Co., E. W.,
70 N. Clinton .....AA
Illinois Smelting & Refin-
ing Co., Peoria & Kinzie
A
Mineral Point Zinc Co., 204
Dearborn ....AA
Raymond Lead Co., 51 W.
Lake ....AAAA
Sandoval Zinc Co., 122 N.
Peoria ....B
ILL.—La Salle
Matthiessen & Hegeler Zinc
Co. ....AAAA
ILL.—Peru
Illinois Zinc Co. ......AAA
IND.—Marion
Latourette, James .....B
KANS.—Cherryvale
Edgar Zinc Co. ....AAA
MASS.—Boston
Butter & Co., Samuel, 549
Atlantic Av. C
MASS.—Plymouth
Edes Mfg. Co. C
MICH.—Detroit
Detroit White Lead Works
AAA
MO.—St. Louis
Edgar, S. C. X
Granby Mining & Smelting
Co. ....AAA
Hiertz & Son, Theo. .....D
New York City
American Metal Co. (Ltd.),
52 B'way ....AAA
Ansonia Brass & Copper Co.
AAAA
Behr & Steiner, 81 Fulton
A
Bertha Mineral Co. ......A
Davol & Sons, John, 100
John ....AA
Hendricks Bros., 49 Cliff
AAAA
New Jersey Zinc Co., 11
B'way ....AA
Phelps, Dodge & Co...AAAA
Trench & Co., C. S., 81
Fulton ....AA
Wilson & Co., R. T..AAAA
OHIO—Toledo
National Cement & Rubber
Mfg. Co. (Brazing) C
PA.—Carbondale
Hendrick Mfg. Co. ....AA
PA.—Easton
Baker & Adamson Chemical
Co. ....A
PA.—Philadelphia
Delaware Metal Refinery.X
Trotter & Co., Nathan, 36
N. Front ....AA
United States Smelting
Wks. (Brazing) ....B
VA.—Austinville
Wythe Lead & Zinc Mine
Co. ....AA

SPERMACETI

MASS.—New Bedford
Robinson & Co., W. A...B

SPICES

See Tea; Coffee, etc.

SPIDERS

See also Holloware; Car-
riages

N. Y.—Brooklyn
New York Stamping Co.,
N. 11th & Berry (Steel)
A
N. Y.—Cortland
Cortland Wagon Co. (Car-
riage) ....AA
OHIO—Cleveland
Avery Stamping Co. (Steel)
B
OHIO—Columbus

SPIDERS (Con.)

Buckeye Buggy Co. (Vehicle) ....AAA
Kilbourne & Jacobs Mfg. Co. ....AAAA
PA.—Erie
Griswold Mfg. Co. ......A

SPIEGELEISEN

ALA.—Birmingham
Tennessee Coal, Iron & Railroad Co. ....AAAA
COLO.—Denver
Colorado Fuel & Iron Co. ....AAAA
N. J.—Newark
Coe & Co., Jas. A.......A
New York City
Crocker Bros., 99 John (German) ....AAA
Dana & Co., 32 B'way (English; German) ......AA
Leavitt & Co., C. W., 15 Cortlandt (English; German) ....D
New Jersey Zinc Co. ..AA
PA.—Johnstown
Cambria Steel Co. ..AAAA
PA.—Philadelphia
Penn Steel Co. ......AAAA
Samuel, Frank (Firm of), 1502 Market ....A
PA.—Pittsburg
Carnegie Steel Co. ..AAAA

SPIKES

ALA.—Sheffield
Sheffield Rolling Mill Co. (Boat; Railroad Track; Ship; Wharf) ....A
CAL.—San Francisco
Judson Mfg. Co. (Boat; Railroad Track; Ship; Wharf) ....AA
COLO.—Denver
Colorado Fuel & Iron Co. (Boat; Railroad Track; Ship; Wharf) ..AAAA
CONN.—Bridgeport
Knapp & Cowles Mfg. Co. (Marlin) C
CONN.—Middletown
Wilcox, Crittendon & Co. (Marlin) ....A
CONN.—New Britain
Corbin, P. & F. (Railroad) AAAA
CONN.—New Haven
National Steel & Wire Co. (Wire) ....AAAA
DEL.—Wilmington
Diamond State Steel Co. (Boat; Countersink; Railroad Track; Ship; Wharf) AAA
ILL.—Chicago
American Steel & Wire Co., The Rookery (Boat; Ship; Wharf; Wire) ....AAAA
Illinois Steel Co., The Rookery (Railroad Track) AAAA
Morgan & Wright, 333 W. Lake (Rubber) ......AA
Republic Iron & Steel Co., Stock Exchange Bldg. (Boat; Railroad Track; Dock; Ship; Wharf) AAAA
Sellers Mfg. Co., 27 W. Chicago Av. (Railroad Track) ....B
IND.—Kokomo
Kokomo Steel & Wire Co. (Wire) ....AAA
KY.—Ashland
Norton Iron Works (Inc.) (Cut) ....AA
MAINE—Bath
Allen & Co., J. H. (Railroad) ....A
MAINE—Rockland
Torrey & Son, J. G. (Ship; Wharf) ....E
MD.—Baltimore
Baltimore Galvanizing & Spike Works, 207 Hughes Av. X
MASS.—Boston
Sylvester & Co., 8 Oliver (Boat; Ship; Wharf; Railroad Track) ....D

SPIKES (Con.)

MICH.—Detroit
Michigan Bolt & Nut Wks. (Boat; Ship; Wharf)...A
MICH.—Saginaw
Morley Bros. (Hand) ..AA
MO.—Kansas City
Kansas City Bolt & Nut Co. (Boat; Railroad Track).A
MO.—St. Louis
Handlan-Buck Mfg. Co. (Railroad) ....AA
N. J.—Jersey City
Ames & Co., W., 312 Wash. (Boat; Railroad Track; Ship; Wharf) ....A
N. Y.—Brooklyn
Kohlmann's Sons, Peter, 483 Lorimer (Ship; Wharf; Hand Made & Galvanized) E
New York City
Hall's Sons, Samuel, 229 W. 10th (Dock; Wharf) A
Lefferts' Galvanized Works (Galvanized) ....D
New Jersey Fdy. & Machine Co., 9 Murray (Boat; Dock; Wharf)...D
New York Boat Oar Co. (Boat) ....A
Salem Nail Co., 279 Pearl (Cut; Ship; Wharf) ..B
Tiebout, W. & J., 118 Chambers (Marlin; Picker) ....B
OHIO—Cleveland
H. P. Nail Co. (Boat; Railroad) X
OHIO—Ironton
Kelly Nail & Iron Co. (Cut) AA
OHIO—Steubenville
La Belle Iron Works (Boat; Cut; Ship; Wharf; Steel; Railroad) ....AAAA
PA.—Allentown
Allentown Rolling Mills (Railroad Track) ..AAA
PA.—Birdsboro
Brooke Iron Co., E. & G. (Cut) ....AAA
PA.—Hollidaysburg
Hollidaysburg Iron & Nail Co. (Cut) ....A
PA.—Lancaster
Penn Iron Co. (Boat; Railroad Track; Ship; Wharf) A
PA.—Lebanon
American Iron & Steel Mfg. Co. (Boat; Railroad Track; Dock; Ship; Wharf) ....AAAA
PA.—Milton
Godcharles Co., F. A. (Cut) AA
PA.—Northumberland
Van Alen & Co. ....A
PA.—Philadelphia
Davis Bros., 29th n. Bristol (Boat; Ship; Wharf; Railroad Track) ....A
Duncannon Iron Co., 122 Race (Cut) ....AA
Hoopes & Townsend Co., 1330 Buttonwood (Boat) AAA
PA.—Pittsburg
Dilworth, Porter & Co. (Boat; Marlin; Railroad Track; Ship; Wharf).AA
Jones & Laughlin Steel Co. (Boat; Railroad Track; Dock; Ship; Wharf) AAAA
Lanz & Sons, Matthew, 101 S. 29th (Boat; Countersink; Dock; Ship; Wharf) B
Pittsburg Mfg. Co. (Dock; Wharf) ....A
Severance, Samuel, Murtland Bldg. (Boat; Cut; Railroad Track; Ship; Wharf) ....A
PA.—Pottsdown
Pottsdown Iron Co. (Cut; Steel) ....A
PA.—Reading
National Bolt, Nut & Rivet Wks. (Boat; Railroad).B

956

SPIKES (Con.)

PA.—Scranton
Green Ridge Iron Wks....X
Scranton Bolt & Nut Co.
(Boat; Railroad Track).A
PA.—Steelton
Pennsylvania Steel Co.
(Railroad) ....AAAA
VA.—Richmond
Old Dominion Iron & Nail
Wks. Co. (Ship; Wharf;
Railroad; Cut) ....A
Richmond Standard Spike &
Iron Co. (Railroad; Cut)
..................X
Tredegar Co. (Boat; Railroad Track; Ship; Wharf)
..................AAA
W. VA.—Wheeling
Laughlin Nail Co. (Steel
Cut) ....AA
Wheeling Steel & Iron Co.
(Cut) ....AAAA

SPILES

MAINE—Portland
Portland Cooperage Co. ..C
MASS.—Lowell
Bachelder & Co.; A......E
N. J.—Newark
Sommers' Sons, John ...A

SPINDLES

See also Woodwork; Carriage

CONN.—Collinsville
Hartigan, Wm. R. (Carriage; Wagon; Electric
Car Seat) ....H
CONN.—New Haven
Dann Bros. & Co. ......B
CONN.—North Windham
Hartson Co., L. M. (Wood)
..................X
IND.—South Bend
Stephenson Mfg. Co. (Chair)
..................B
KY.—Covington
Ohio Scroll & Lumber Co.
(Carriage; Carved) ....D
MAINE—Ellsworth
Ellsworth Hardwood Co.
(Wood of all Varieties)
..................E
MASS.—Boston
Leigh, Evan Arthur .....B
MASS.—Charlemont
Frary Mfg. Co. (Chair)..E
MASS.—Hopedale
Draper Co. ....AAAA
Westcott. A. W. ....F
MICH.—Detroit
Detroit Shipbuilding Co.
(Brass Dept.-Lathe)
..................AAAA
MICH.—Holland
Michigan Toy & Novelty
Co. (Wood) ....E
N. H.—Hampton
Marston & True ....E
N. J.—Elmer
Ward & Vandegrift .....D
N. J.—Paterson
Buckley's Son, B. ....E
OHIO—Columbus
Nelson & Co., C. T......D
PA.—Philadelphia
Diamond Textile Machine
Works, 2d & Diamond
(Spooler) ....E
PA.—Pittsburg
Shelby Steel Tube Co.,
Frick Bldg. (Lathe)
..................AAAA
R. I.—Bridgeton
Hopkins Machine Wks....X
R. I.—Pascoag
Bamford & Smith X
R. I.—Pawtucket
Easton & Burnham Machine
Co. ....A
Payne & Co.. Geo. W.
(Dresser; Reel; Ring;
Spooler) ....D
R. I.—Providence
Chase & Co.. F. A......B
Providence Machine Co..AA

SPINNERS

See Spools

SPINNING

CONN.—Naugatuck
Naugatuck Mfg. Co. (Metal) ....E
CONN.—Winsted
Goodwin & Kintz Co. (Metal) ....D
ILL.—Chicago
Acorn Brass Mfg. Co., 206
Fulton (Metal) ....B
IOWA—Council Bluffs
Specialty Mfg. Co. (Brass)
..................X
MICH.—Holland
Holland Stamping Works
(Brass) ....D
OHIO—Cleveland
Gas Fixture & Brass Co.
(Brass) ....B
LA.—New Orleans
Louisiana Distillery Co.
(Cologne) ....AA
MD.—Baltimore
Webb & Sons, A. L. (Cologne) ....B

SPIRITS

See also Alcohol

MICH.—Detroit
Berry Bros. (Ltd.) (Colonial) ....AAAA
MO.—St. Louis
Herf & Frerichs Chemical
Co. (Ammonia; Nitre)..A
Mallinckrodt Chemical Wks.
(Ammonia; Nitre) .AAAA
New York City
American Distilling Co. (Cologne) ....A
American Spirits Mfg. Co.,
29 William (Liquor)....X
Cook & Bernheimer (Cologne) ....AAA
Webb & Son. Jas. A. (Cologne) ....B
PA.—Philadelphia
Powers - Weightman - Rosengarten Co. (Ammonia;
Nitre) ....AAAA

SPITTOONS

See Cuspidores

SPLICERS

CONN.—Bridgeport
Belknap Mfg. Co. (Hose).C
ILL.—Downer's Grove
Dicke Tool Co. (Wire)....C
New York City
Smith & Hemenway Co.,
296 B'way (Wire) .....D
N. Y.—Utica
Utica Drop Forge & Tool
Co. (Wire) ....B
OHIO—Cincinnati
Kisinger-Ison Co. (Trolley
Wire) ....D

SPLINTS

ILL.—Chicago
Ambulatory Pneumatic
Splint Mfg. Co. ....F
New York City
Seabury & Johnson .....AA
PA.—Conshohocken
Lee Co., J. Elwood (Metallic) ....AA
PA.—Philadelphia
Kolbe & Son, D. W.......X

SPLITS

See Leather

SPLITTERS

See also Mach'y

ALA.—Selma
Peacock's Iron Works
(Wood) C
MASS.—Adams
Allen Iron Wks. (Warp).D
MASS.—Greenfield
Nichols Bros. (Beef) ....D
MASS.—Harvard
Hildreth Bros. (Wood)...B

SPLITTERS (Con.)

N. J.—Lebanon
Sovereign Fdy. & Mfg. Co. (Kindling Wood) ......D

N. Y.—Albany
Dederick's Sons, P. K. (Kindling Wood) ......A

N. Y.—Sandy Hill
Sandy Hill Iron & Brass Wks. (Kindling Wood; Wood) ....A

PA.—Philadelphia
Nittinger, August (Beef) .A

PA.—York
Spangler Mfg. Co. (Wood)
......................C

TENN.—Chattanooga
Chattanooga Machinery Co. (Kindling Wood) C

VT.—Bennington
Scott, Olin (Wood) ......A

WIS.—Appleton
Valley Iron Works Mfg. Co. (Wood) C

WIS.—Manitowoc
Smalley Mfg. Co. (Wood) .B

SPOKES

See also Woodwork; Carriage

CONN.—Torrington
Excelsior Needle Co. (Automobile; Bicycle) ..AAAA

CONN.—Waterbury
Manville Mach. Co., E. J. (Bicycle) C

ILL.—Chicago
American Steel & Wire Co. (Bicycle) ....AAAA

MASS.—Worcester
Wire Goods Co. (Automobile; Bicycle; Sulky) ...A

OHIO—Cleveland
Federal Mfg. Co. (Bicycle)
......................AAAA

PA.—Norristown
Reading Screw Co. (Bicycle) ....A

SPOKESHAVES

See Shavers

SPONGES

CAL.—San Francisco
American Sponge Co., 150 New Montgomery C

CONN.—Plainville
Clark & Son, A. N. (Ear)
......................B

MO.—St. Louis
Ettman Sponge Co., 1112 Pine C

N. J.—Newark
Celluloid Co. (Ear) ......B

New York City
Collman Sponge Co., 522 B'way ....A
Davis & Sons, D., 148 William ....D
Heineman, J., 108 Fulton.F
Huneke Sponge Co., 259 Pearl ....F
Isaacs & Co., A., 58 Beekman ....A
National Sponge & Chamois Co., 160 William ......B
Seabury & Johnson (Surgical) ....AA
Van Amringe, T., 97 Beekman ....B
Vollman Sponge Co., 518 B'way ....A
Wrightington & Jackson, 90 Maiden Lane C

OHIO—Akron
Faultless Rubber Co. (Rubber) ....AA
Goodrich Co., B. F. (Rubber) ....AAAA

PA.—Philadelphia
Burk & Co., 534 Arch ....A
Haehnlen & Co., E. G., 700 Arch ....B
Louden & Hill, 623 Arch ..B
Murray, Barnes & Murray Co., 9th & Ontario ....D

SPOOLERS

MASS.—Boston

SPOOLERS (Con.)
Stoddard, Haserick, Richards & Co., 152 Congress (Cotton) ....AAA

MASS.—Hopedale
Draper Co. (Cotton) .AAAA

MASS.—Lowell
Lowell Machine Shop (Cotton) ....AAAA

MASS.—Newton Upper Falls
Saco & Pettee Machine Shops (Cotton) ......AAA

MASS.—Westfield
Foster Machine Co. (Cotton; Dresser; Wool; Yarn)
......................A

MASS.—Whitinsville
Whitin Machine Works (Cotton) ....AAAA

MASS.—Worcester
American Card Clothing Co. (Wool) ....AAA
Cleveland Machine Works (Wool; Worsted) X

PA.—Philadelphia
Altemus, Jacob K., 2816 N. 4th (Cotton; Dresser; Wool; Yarn) ....D
Diamond Textile Machine Works, 2d & Diamond (Cotton; Dresser; Wool; Worsted; Yarn) ......F
Furbush & Son Machine Co., M. A. (Cotton; Presser)
......................A
Klein, Chas. C., 2850 N. Marshall (Cotton) .....D
Lever, Oswald, Lehigh Av. & Mascher (Dresser; Yarn) ....D
Schaum & Uhlinger (Cotton) ....AA
Smith Woolen Machinery Co., Jas. (Cotton; Wool; Worsted) ....A

R. I.—Pawtucket
Easton & Burnham Machine Co. (Cotton; Wool)....B
Payne & Co., Geo. W. (Doubling) ....A

SPOOLS

CONN.—Rayville
Arnold, O. S. .... .E

CONN.—Mystic
Allen Spool Printing Co...B

GA.—Macon
Georgia Spool & Bobbin Mfg. Co. C

KY.—Maysville
Ohio Valley Pulley Works
......................B

MAINE—Albany
Elliott & Bartlet ....D

MAINE—Dixfield
Stowell & Co., N. S. (Silk Thread) ....F

MAINE—Locke's Mills
Tebbets & Co., E. L.......C

MASS.—Adams
Adams Bobbin & Spool Co.
......................D

MASS.—Fall River
Fall River Bobbin & Shuttle Co., 821 Cambridge
......................AAAA
Fall River Fdy. & Machine Co. ....F

MASS.—Lawrence
Hale, T. J. ....AAAA
Union Shuttle Co. ....D
Weld Bobbin & Spool Co., 42 Island ....D

MASS.—Lowell
New England Shuttle Co., 64 Leverett ....D

MASS.—New Bedford
Greene & Wood ....B

MASS.—Winchendon
Winchendon Spool & Bobbin Co. ....A

MICH.—Alpena
Kline, Lewis T. (Thread).D

N. H.—Manchester
Baldwin Co., James ..AAAA

N. H.—Nashua
Murray, Charles O. X

N. J.—Paterson
Atkinson & Co., J........E
Van Riper Mfg. Co.......B

N. Y.—Utica
Williams Co., J. H.......A

SPOOLS (Con.)

N. C.—Greensboro
Sherwood Bobbin & Mfg. Co. ....D
PA.—Carbondale
Clover Leaf Mfg. Co. (Dogwood Spinners'; Maple Winder) ....D
PA.—Philadelphia
Bradford Woodworking Co., 2154 N. 3d ....F
R. I.—Pawtucket
Atwood-Crawford Co. (Silk Thread) ....B
Payne & Co., Geo. W. (Silk Thread; Warp) ....D
Weatherhead, Thompson & Co. ....A
R. I.—Providence
American Supply Co. ...AA
Brown Bros. Co. ....B
United States Bobbin & Shuttle Co. ......AAAA
R. I.—Woonsocket
Colburn, Fred. S., 243 Main X
S. C.—Charleston
Woodstock Hardwood & Spool Mfg. Co. ....E
VT.—Essex Junction
Vermont Spool & Bobbin Co. C

SPOONS

See also Silverware; Tinware

CAL.—San Francisco
Doble Co., Abner (Post Hole) ....A
CONN.—Bridgeport
Acme Shear Co. (Steel; Iron) ....B
CONN.—Meriden
International Silver Co. (Aztec Coin Metal; Mexican Silver) ......AAAA
Parker Co., Charles (Steel; Iron; Metal) ......AAA
Rogers & Bros., C. (Tinned) AAAA
CONN.—New Haven
Atlas Mfg. Co. (Tinned)..G
CONN.—Stamford
Yale Mfg. Co., C. I. (Iron) X
CONN.—Unionville
Humphreys, H. W. (Tin; Basting) ....D
CONN.—Wallingford
Wallace & Sons Mfg. Co., R. (Tin; Basting; Iron) AAAA
MD.—Baltimore
Sinclair-Scott Co. (Peach Pitting) ....E
MASS.—Attleboro
Robbins Co., Chas. M. (Souvenir) C
MASS.—North Attleboro
Codding & Heilborn Co. (Souvenir) ....A
MICH.—Bellaire
Richardi & Bechtold (Wooden) ....B
MICH.—Kalkaska
Freeman Mfg. Co. (Wooden) ....B
MO.—St. Louis
St. Louis Shovel Co. (Post Hole) ....B
St. Louis Stamping Co. (Basting) ....AAAA
N. Y.—Buffalo
Shepard & Co., Sidney (Iron) ....AAAA
N. Y.—East Syracuse
Benedict Mfg. Co., M. S. (Souvenir) ....AA
New York City
Estes & Sons. E. B., 45 John (Mustard) ......AA
International Silver Co. (Silver; Silver Plated; Soda Water) ......AAAA
Lalance & Grosjean Mfg. Co. (Basting) ...AAAA
National Enameling & Stamping Co., 81 Fulton (Enameled Iron) .AAAA
Thurnauer & Bro., G. M., 35 Park Pl. (Egg) X

SPOONS (Con.)

N. Y.—Niagara Falls
Oneida Community (Ltd.) (Silver; Silver Plated; Soda Water) ......AAA
OHIO—Piqua
Piqua Handle & Mfg. Co. (Mustard) ....A
OHIO—Sidney
Wagner Mfg. Co. (Aluminum) ....A
PA.—Beaver Falls
Myers Co., H. M. (Telegraph, &c.; Digging)..A
PA.—Erie
Erie Specialty Co. (Soda Water) ....B
PA.—Philadelphia
Nittinger, August (Lard).A
PA.—Pittsburg
Hubbard & Co., Murtland Bldg. (Digging) .....AA
Pittsburg Shovel Co., Frick Bldg. (Digging) ......B
WIS.—Oshkosh
Oshkosh Logging Tool Co. (Digging) ....F

SPORTING GOODS

COLO.—Denver
Mason & Co., Geo. (Club Room Supplies) C
CONN.—Bridgeport
Bridgeport Gun Implement Co. (Golf) ....AA
CONN.—New Haven
Dann Bros. & Co. (Polo).B
ILL.—Chicago
Chicago Sporting Goods Mfg. Co., 126 S. Jefferson ....B
Diamond Whip Co., 85 W. North (Leather) ......E
Kernan Mfg. Co., 192 Van Buren ....E
MASS.—Brockton
Stall & Dean Mfg. Co.....C
MASS.—Boston
Wright & Ditson (Tennis; Archery) ....AA
MASS.—Springfield
Victor Sporting Goods Co. B
MICH.—Grand Rapids ..
Rodemaker & Sons, H. (Polo) ....E
New York City
Empire Sporting Goods Co., 16 Thames ....F
Schoverling, Daly & Gales, 302 B'way ....A
Spaulding & Bros., A. G. (Golf; Polo; Baseball; Tennis, &c.) .....AAAA
Treinis Bros., 498 B'way..F
United States Rubber Co., 9 Murray ....AAAA
PA.—Philadelphia
Reach Co., A. J. (Baseball) AA
R. I.—Pawtucket
Bliss Mfg. Co., R. (Archery) ....AAAA

SPOTS

CONN.—Waterbury
American Ring Co. (Harness) ....A
MASS.—Boston
Standard Rivet Co. (Harness) ....B
N. J.—Newark
Greacen & Co., Walter (Harness) ....E
Reynolds & Zahn (Harness) B
OHIO—Akron
Enterprise Mfg. Co. (Harness) ....A

SPOUTINGS

PA.—Philadelphia
Gara, McGinley & Co. (Metallic) ....B

SPOUTS

ILL.—Chicago

SPOUTS (Con.)

Caldwell & Son Co., H. W.
Western Av. & 17th
(Grain) ....A

Thornburgh-Creel Company
(Grain) ....F

Weller Mfg. Co., 118 North
Av. (Car Loading; Dock;
Elevator) ....A

Wilson & Co., F. C. (Bung)
..............................B

ILL.—Sterling

Novelty Iron Wks. (Iron
Pump) X

MD.—Baltimore

Poole & Son Co., Robert
(Grain) ....A

MO.—St. Louis

Kay-Pim Mfg. Co. (Distributing) X

New York City

Stoutenborough, X. (Sap).D

N. Y.—Utica

Millar & Son, Chas. (Sap)
.............................AA

OHIO—Cleveland

Taylor & Boggis Fdy. Co.
(Iron Pump) ....AA

SPRAYERS

ILL.—Paxton

Paxton Hardware Mfg. Co.
(Garden; Orchard).....X

IND.—Elkhart

Buescher Mfg. Co. (Insect
Exterminator) C

IND.—Indianapolis

Everitt, J. A. (Insect Exterminator) ....B

MICH.—Jackson

Aspinwall Mfg. Co. (As-
paragus; Cotton) .....B

N. J.—Grenloch

Bateman Mfg. Co. ......A

N. J.—Hightstown

Shangle, Sering & Son (Potato) C

New York City

Mattson Rubber Co. (Insect
Exterminator) ....B

N. Y.—Rome

Rome Mfg. Co. (Insect)..B

N. Y.—Utica

Utica Sprayer Co. ....B

OHIO—Canton

Hurst Mfg. Co., H. L. (Orchard) ....F

O.—Toledo

Hickox, Mull & Hill Co.
(Automatic) ....A

Yost Electric Mfg. Co.
(Lawn) ....D

SPREADERS

See also Agr. Imps

CONN.—Derby

Birmingham Iron Foundry
(Rubber) ....AA

MASS.—Boston

American Tool & Machine
Co. (Rubber) ....AA

MASS.—Worcester

Richardson Mfg. Co. (Ma-
nure) ....AA

N. Y.—Newark Valley

Kemp Mfg. Co., J. S.
(Lime) ....A

N. Y.—Syracuse

Kemp & Burpee Mfg. Co.,
119 W. Fayette (Manure;
Agricultural) ....B

OHIO—Akron

Akron-Selle Co. (Horse
Power) ....A

OHIO—Cincinnati

Francis & Bros., Chas. E.
(Glue) ....B

PA.—York

Spangler Mfg. Co. (Lime;
Horse Power) ....D

WIS.—Racine

Foster & Williams Mfg. Co.
(Lime) ....B

SPREADS

See also Bedding

CONN.—Middletown

Palmer, I. E. (Hammock)
AAA

SPREADS (Con.)

GA.—Columbus

Swift Mfg. Co. (Bed)...AA

IND.—South Bend

South Bend Toy Mfg. Co.
(Hammock) ....A

IOWA—Cedar Rapids

Adams Mfg. Co., A. L.
(Hammock) ....E

N. H.—Claremont

Monadnock Mills (Bed).AA

N. C.—McAdenville

McAden Mills (Bed) ...AA

PA.—Philadelphia

Rumpf Bros. & Witty (Bed)
AA

WIS.—Menasha

Menasha Woodenware Co.
(Hammock) ....AA

SPRIGS

MASS.—Taunton

Atlas Tack Corpn. ..AAAA

PA.—Philadelphia

Duncannon Iron Co. ....AA

SPRING BEDS

See Furniture

SPRINGS

**See .also Hardware; Car-
riage; Furniture**

CAL.—San Francisco

Betts Spring Co. (Car;
Coach; Steel) ....D

CONN.—Bridgeport

American Tube & Stamping
Co. (Shuttle) ....AAAA

Bridgeport Chain Co. (Ag-
ricultural Implements;
Bed; Car Seat; Extension;
Compression; Furniture;
Helical; Bird Cage; Wire;
Upholstery; Governor;
Electrical Equipment;
Machine; Door; Oil Tem-
pered; Rocker; Sash;
Trolley; Wagon Pole;
Wringer) ....A

Burns, Silver & Co. (Car)
A

Canfield, H. O. (Rubber).D

Farist Steel Co. (Car; Coil
or Spiral; Elliptic; Car
Steel; Locomotive; Spiral)
AA

Gaynor & Mitchell Mfg. Co.
(Spiral Wire; Spiral
Brass) ....D

CONN.—Bridgeport

Miller Wire Spring Co.
(Car Seat; Furniture;
Steel; Bed) ....D

Spring Perch Co. (Carriage;
Wagon; Coach) ....B

CONN.—Bristol

Barnes, Wallace Co. (Ma-
chinery; Window; Wire;
Furniture; Steel; Oil
Tempered; Truss; Door;
Burglar Alarm; Clock;
Car Seat; Organ; Piano;
Bicycle; Electrical Equip-
ment; Governor; Motor;
Pump Valve; Sash; Type-
writer) C

Dunbar Bros. (Small Sheet
Steel; Machinery; Wire;
Oil Tempered; Window;
Governor; Snap; Sweat
Pad; Organ; Coil; Clock)
D

Warner, Hobart A. (Hair)
D

CONN.—Forestville

Mauros, F. N. (Clock; Mu-
sic Box, &c.; Clock;
Hair) ....G

CONN.—Hartford

Connecticut Rubber Co.
(Wagon; Rubber) .....F

Hartford Woven Wire Mat-
tress Co. (Bed; Car Seat)
A

CONN.—New Britain

Russell & Erwin Mfg. Co.
(Door; Check) ....AAAA

Stanley Works (Window)
AAA

Union Mfg. Co. (Door;
Door Coil) ....AA
CONN.—New Haven
Fitch Co., W. & E. T.
(Carriage; Wagon)...AA
New Haven Clock Co.
(Door; Burglar Alarm;
Window; Burglar Alarm)
AA
New Haven Spring Co. (Car-
riage; Wagon) ....H
New Haven Wire Mfg. Co.
(Lock) C
CONN.—Plainville
Clark & Son, A. M. (Watch
Case) C
Clark & Cowles (Oil Tem-
pered; Snap) ....B
CONN.—Southington
Peck, Stow & Wilcox Co.
(Door; Window) .AAAA
CONN.—Thomaston
Thomas Clock Co., Seth
(Clock) ....AAA
CONN.—Waterbury
American Pin Co. (Car
Seat) ....A
DEL.—Wilmington
Diamond State Car Spring
Co. (Car; Coil or Spiral;
Elliptic; Machinery; Lo-
comotive Elliptic; Trol-
ley; Locomotive Spiral;
Locomotive Truck) ....B
Harlan & Hollingsworth Co.
(Car Seat) ....AAAA
ILL.—Chicago
American Steel & Wire Co.,
The Rookery (Air Brake;
Agricultural Implements;
Car; Bicycle; Coil or Spi-
ral Door; Machinery;
Trolley Wire) ....AAAA
Chicago Spring Butt Co.,
491 Carroll Av. (Door).B
Gibson Co., Wm. D., 25 N.
Clinton (Air Brake; Car
Seat; Trolley; Carriage;
Wagon; Coil; Elliptic;
Machinery; Oil Tempered;
Agricultural Implements;
Bed; Door; Gun; Bicycle;
Governor; Furniture; Up-
holstery; Electrical
Equipment; Loom; Motor;
Organ; Piano Rocker;
Squaring Shear; Steel;
Typewriter; Valve; Wire;
Wringer) ....B
Haggard & Marcusson Co.
(Bed) ....B
McGuire Mfg. Co., 122 N.
Sangamon (Car Coil or
Spiral; Car; Steel) ....A
Morgan & Wright, 333 W.
Lake (Car; Wagon, &c.;
Rubber Channeler for
Quarrying Machinery).AA
Rocker Spring Co. (Tilting
Chair) C
Tuthill Spring Co., 315 S.
Clinton (Carriage; Wa-
gon) C
Weber Wagon Co. (Wagon)
AA
ILL.—Freeport
Arcade Mfg. Co. (Door)..B
ILL.—West Pullman
Whitman & Barnes Mfg. Co.
(Rubber) ....AAAA
IND.—Connersville
Ansted Spring Co., E. W.
(Carriage; Wagon) ....A
IND.—Hammond
Simplex Railway Appliance
Co. (Coil; Elliptic Car;
Locomotive) ....A
IND.—Indianapolis
Laycock Mfg. Co., T. B.
(Bed; Furniture; Spiral)
B
Over, Ewald (Wagon)....D
IND.—Lafayette
Haggard Wagon Spring Co.
(Wagon) X
IND.—South Bend
Studebaker Bros. Mfg. Co.
(Wagon; Bolster) .AAAA
MASS.—Andover
Tyer Rubber Co. (Door;
Rubber) ....AA
MASS.—Boston

Ashton Valve Co. (Valve).A
Boston Belting Co. (Wagon;
Rubber; Car Rubber)
AAAA
Boston Gear Wks. (Clock)
B
Boston Woven Hose & Rub-
ber Co. (Car; Rubber)
AAAA
Palmer, Jos., 261 Ruther-
ford (Carriage; Wagon)
H
MASS.—Brockton
Tuck Mfg. Co. (Bicycle;
Wire; Tempered; Steel;
Typewriter) ....E
MASS.—Cambridge
Duff Spring Co. (Carriage;
Wagon) ....D
MASS.—Clinton
Clinton Wire Cloth Co.
(Bed) ....AAA
MASS.—Lowell
Austin, Chas. E. (Organ).D
MASS.—North Easton
New England Specialty Co.
(Picker Rod; Shuttle;
Steel) ....F
MASS.—Springfield
Bemis Car Box Co. (Car;
Car Steel) ....D
MASS.—Worcester
Eagan, Thos. F. (Window)
H
Morgan Spring Co. (Agricul-
tural Implements; Air
Brake; Bicycle; Brush
Holder; Car Steel; Car
Seat; Carriage; Wagon;
Coil; Door; Door Rod;
Elliptic; Engine House
Door; Machinery; Pipe
Bending; Trolley; Win-
dow; Wire; Bed; Special;
Automobile; Bird Cage;
Gun; Bobbin Ring; Drill;
Buggy Boot; Check; Cut-
ter Bar; Electrical Equip-
ment; Furniture; Friction
Washer; Upholstery; Gov-
ernor; Hinge; Lever;
Loader Teeth; Loom; Mo-
tor; Oil Tempered; Or-
gan; Piano; Plow; Pump
Valve; Rocker; Sash;
Sheaf Carrier; Steel;
Valve; Tedder Fork;
Typewriter; Wringer;
Wagon Pole; Windmill;
Shuttle) ....B
Parker Wire Goods Co.
(Bird Cage; Door) ....E
Wire Goods Co., 20 Union
(Agricultural Implements;
Wire; Bird Cage; Door;
Furniture; Upholstery;
Steel; Wringer) ......B
Wright Wire Co. (Bed).AA
MICH.—Detroit
Wilson Carriage Co., C. R.
& J. (Carriage) ......F
MICH.—Flint
Armstrong Mfg. Co., J. B.
(Carriage; Wagon) ....A
MICH.—Jackson
Lewis Spring & Axle Co.
(Carriage; Wagon) C
MICH.—Kalamazoo
Harrow Spring Co. (Agri-
cultural Implements; Car;
Bicycle; Coil; Machinery;
Car Seat; Railroad Track
Scraper) ....B
Kalamazoo Spring & Axle
Co. (Carriage; Wagon;
Coil or Spiral; Elliptic).B
MICH.—Pontiac
Pontiac Spring & Wagon
Wks. (Bolster; Carriage;
Wagon) ... .A
Vehicle & Implement Spring
Co. (Carriage; Wagon;
Agricultural Implements)
B
MO.—Kansas City
Lloyd, J. H. (Bed) ......D
MO.—St. Louis
Ludlow-Saylor Wire Co.,
4th & Elm (Coil; Wire)
AA

SPRINGS (*Con.*)

Rice Coil Spring Co. (Coil or Spiral) ....D

Smith & Davis Mfg. Co. (Bed) ....A

N. H.—Concord

Abbot-Downing Co. (Wagon) X

N. H.—Tilton

Lord Bros. Mfg. Co. (Coil or Spiral; Wire) ......B

N. J.—Carlstadt

Gross, Carl (Watch Case).E

N. J.—Jersey City

New Jersey Car Spring & Rubber Co. (Rubber; Wagon; Rubber Car) ...AA

N. J.—Newark

Delaney & Son, D. (Carriage; Wagon; Elliptic) A

Jenkinson & Co., R. C. (Steel; Wire) ....A

Myer Co., Benj., 470 Broad (Engine House Door)...C

Pryor Hardware Mfg. Co., W. W. (Door) ....E

Tomlinson Spring Co., 233 N. J. R. R. Av. (Carriage; Wagon) ....A

N. J.—Trenton

Consolidated Rubber Co. (Rubber) ....B

Empire Rubber Mfg. Co. (Rubber; Wagon) ..AA

Home Rubber Co. (Rubber) AA

Mercer Rubber Co. (Car; Rubber) ....A

Stokes Rubber Co., Joseph (Rubber) ....A

Trenton Rubber Mfg. Co. (Rubber; Car) ....A

United Rubber Co. (Rubber; Car) ....E

United & Globe Rubber Mfg. Co. (Rubber Wagon; Rubber Car; Rubber).AAA

Whitehead Bros. Rubber Co. (Rubber) ....A

N. Y.—Amsterdam

Shuler & Son. D. W. (Coil or Spiral; Elliptic; Coach) A

N. Y.—Auburn

Meyer & Co. (Bolster; Car Seat; Coil or Spiral)...B

N. Y.—Brooklyn

Miller & Van Winkle, 18 Bridge (Air Brake; Bicycle; Car Steel; Coil; Door; Wire; Machinery; Trolley; Bird Cage; Agricultural Implements; Bed; Carriage; Wagon; Furniture; Upholstery; Governor; Check; Electrical Equipment; Rocker; Oil Tempered; Organ; Piano; Pump Valve; Sash; Typewriter; Seat; Wagon Pole; Windmill; Window; Wringer) ....A

Wurster & Co., Fred W., 375 Kent Av. (Carriage; Wagon) ....AA

N. Y.—Buffalo

King Spring Co. 1410 Niagara (Carriage; Wagon).C

Western Wire Goods Co. (Bird Cage) ....D

N. Y.—Dunkirk

Mulholland Spring Co. (Carriage; Wagon) ....B

N. Y.—Homer

Phoenix Hardware Mfg. Co. (Coil Door) ....D

N. Y.—Leonardsville

Babcock Mfg. Co. (Agricultural Implement) ....D

New York City

Cary Spring Works, 240 W. 29th (Clock; Machinery; Coil; Trolley; Wire; Agricultural Implements; Steel; Flat Wire; Music Box; Air Brake; Electrical Equipment; Governor; Automobile; Motor; Oil Tempered; Pump Valve; Typewriter; Valve; Window; Wagon Pole;

SPRINGS (*Con.*)

Watch) ....D

Chatillon & Sons, Jno., 85 Cliff (Cast Steel; Spiral; Door; Oil Tempered; Wire Coil) ....A

Cook Spring Co., 255 Centre (Coil or Spiral) ....E

Edwards & Co. (Door; Window) C

Eureka Spring Co., 465 Greenwich (Machinery; Trolley; Coil or Spiral).D

New York City

Goodyear Rubber Co. (Car; Rubber; Door) ....AAAA

Goodyear's India Rubber Glove Mfg. Co. (Rubber) AAAA

Gutta Percha & Rubber Mfg. Co. (Wagon; Rubber; Car; Door Rubber; Roller Skate) ....AAAA

Hodgman Rubber Co. (Car; Wagon; Rubber) ....AA

Manhattan Rubber Mfg. Co., 18 Vesey (Rubber) AA

Mechanical Rubber Co., 22 Murray (Wagon; Rubber; Car) ....AAAA

Merrill Spring Co., E. R., 530 W. 28th (Automobile; Carriage; Wagon; Elliptic; Trolley; Coach) ....B

Metal Stamping Co. (Furniture) ....B

New York Belting & Packing Co., 25 Park Place (Rubber; Wagon; Car) AAA

New York Rubber Co., 84 Reade (Rubber) ......AA

Ostrander & Co., W. R., 22 Dey (Check) ....B

Peckham Truck Co. (Car) A

New York City

Railway Steel Spring Co., 71 B'way (Air Brake; Brush Holder; Carriage; Wagon; Car; Coil; Elliptic; Helical; Oil Tempered; Trolley; Wire; Bird Cage; Governor; Door; Electrical Equipment; Sash; Steel; Window) ....AAAA

Sargent & Co., 151 Leonard (Check; Door; Window) AAAA

Schneider's Sons & Co., Peter (Furniture) .....A

Stephenson Co., John (Ltd.) (Car) ....A

Vose Spring Co., 115 B'way (Car; Coil or Spiral; Elliptic; Machinery; Trolley; Steel Graduated; Car Steel) ....D

Wardlow, S. & C., 95 John (Steel) ....AA

N. Y.—Oneida

Ideal Mfg. Co. (Steel)...D

N. Y.—Rochester

Caldwell Mfg. Co., 12 Jones (Door) ....E

Pullman Mfg. Co. (Door; Coil; Wire) C

N. Y.—Syracuse

Sweets Mfg. Co. (Carriage) A

N. Y.—Troy

Hayes, Edward J. (Coach) F

Taylor Electric Truck Co. (Coil or Spiral; Elliptic) B

N. Y.—Utica

Foster Bros. Mfg. Co. (Carriage; Wagon; Furniture; Bed) ....A

OHIO—Akron

Akron Rubber Works (Car; Rubber) ....AAAA

Diamond Rubber Co. (Rubber) ....AAAA

Goodrich Co., B. F. (Rubber) ....AAAA

OHIO—Canton

Cleveland-Canton Spring Co. (Automobile; Elliptic; Carriage; Wagon) .....B

962

OHIO—Carthage
Hess Spring & Axle Co.
(Carriage; Wagon; Elliptic) ....A
OHIO—Cincinnati
Haven Co., Jas. L. (Door) B

OHIO—Cleveland
Cleveland Wire Spring Co.,
Wason & Hamilton (Agricultural Implements; Air
Brake; Bolster; Door;
Coil; Carriage; Wagon;
Machinery; Pipe Bending;
Trolley; Wire; Furniture;
Automobile; Bed; Bicycle;
Check; Upholstery; Electrical Equipment; Hinge;
Governor; Oil Tempered;
Motor; Organ; Piano;
Pump Valve; Sash; Seat
Steel; Typewriter; Valve
Wagon Pole; Windmill
Wringer) C
Columbia Hardware Co.,
Cox & Hamilton (Door) AA
Cooper & Co., Geo., Western
Reserve Bldg. (Carriage;
Wagon; Elliptic) ......A
Upson Nut Co. (Check) AAA
Van Dorn & Dutton Co.
(Car) C
OHIO—Columbus
Simpson Iron Co. (Door).D
OHIO—Hamilton
Meyers Mfg. Co., Fred. J.
(Door) ....B
OHIO—Mt. Gilead
Murray, William (Coil or
Spiral) ....H
OHIO—Toledo
Heartley Mach. Variety Iron
& Tool Works (Children's
Carriage; etc.) ....D
OHIO—Youngstown
Republic Rubber Co. (Rubber) ....AA
PA.—Allegheny
Iron City Spring Co. (Car;
Oil Tempered; Carriage;
Wagon; Coil or Spiral;
Oil Tempered; Elliptic).F
PA.—Allentown
Allentown Platform Co.
(Wagon) ....B
PA.—Corry
Raymond Mfg. Co. (Ltd.)
(Air Brake; Bicycle; Carriage; Wagon; Coil; Machinery; Pipe Bending;
Agricultural Implement;
Automobile; Buggy; Boot
Check; Door; Exerciser;
Electrical Equipment; Governor; Gun; Hinge;
Lever; Loader Teeth Oil
Tempered; Organ; Piano;
Pump Valve; Rocker
Squaring Shear; Steel;
Valve Tedder Fork; Trolley
Wagon Pole; Windmill;
Wire Wagon Brake;
Wringer) C
PA.—Monongahela
Liggett Spring & Axle Co.
(Carriage; Wagon) ...AA
PA.—Philadelphia
Brill Co., J. G., 62d &
Woodland Av. (Car).AAA
Cambria Steel Co., Arcade
Bldg. (Agricultural Implement; Car; Steel)
.................AAAA
Insull, Thos., 1429 Hutchinson (Coil or Spiral; Elliptic) C
Latrobe Steel Co., Girard
Bldg. (Elliptic; Car)
.................AAAA
Lehigh Valley Spring Wks.
Bullitt Bldg. (Car; Coil
or Spiral) ....D
Rowland, William & Harvey (Carriage; Elliptic;
Coach; Wagon; Steel; Car
Steel) ....A
Weston & Wells Mfg. Co.
(Carriage; Torsion Braided Wire; Dining Chairs;
Theatre Seats) C

PA.—Pittsburg
American Spiral Spring &
Mfg. Co. (Spiral; Car;
Car Seat; Door) ......E
Crescent Steel Co. (Coil;
Steel; Car) ......AAAA
Crucible Steel Co. of America (Machinery) ...AAAA
French Spring Co., A.
(Ltd.) (Coil; Wagon;
Tempered; Elliptic; Locomotive) ....AAAA
Independent Steel & Wire
Co. (Carriage; Hat; Coil;
Couch; Rocker; Railway)
C
Pittsburg Spring & Steel
Co., Farmers' Bank Bldg.
(Trolley; Agricultural Implement; Air Brake; Car;
Elliptic; Coil or Spiral;
Machinery Wire .....AA
Simonds Mfg. Co. (Brush
Holder for Electric Railways) C
Union Spring & Mfg. Co.,
Frick Bldg. (Coil & Elliptic Car; Machinery; Locomotive Equipment; Railway Equipment; Coil or
Spiral) ....B
PA.—Reading
Reading Hardware Co.
(Check; Window)..AAAA
PA.—Wilkesbarre
Sheldon Axle Co. (Carriage;
Wagon; Coil or Spiral;
Elliptic) ....AAA
R. I.—Pawtucket
Haskell Mfg. Co., Wm. H.
(Clearer) ....A
R. I.—Phillipsdale
Washburn Wire Co. (Clock;
etc.; Wire) ....AAAA
R. I.—Providence
Davol Rubber Co. (Door;
Rubber) ....AA
VT.—Montpelier
Sabin Mach. Co. (Agricultural Implement; Bicycle;
Coil; Door; Machinery;
Wire; Oil Tempered; Organ; Piano; Governor;
Piano Player; Steel) ...E
WIS.—Milwaukee
Hirsch Bros. (Bolster; Carriage; Wagon) ....D
WIS.—Racine
Adams & Son, E. B.
(Wagon) C
Higgins Spring & Axle Co.
(Carriage; Wagon) ....B
Racine General Mfg. Co.
(Carriage) ....E
Racine Malleable &
Wrought Iron Co.
(Wagon) ....B
Racine Pole & Spring Co.
(Bolster; Carriage;
Wagon) X

SPRINKLERS

CONN.—Bridgeport
Belknap Mfg. Co. (Hose).C
CONN.—New Britain
Union Mfg. Co. (Garden;
Lawn) ....AA
CONN.—New Haven
Foskett & Bishop Co. (Automatic Fire) ....B
Hotchkiss & Co., E. M.
(Lawn) ....F
Peck Bros. & Co. (Garden
Hose; Lawn Hose) ....A
ILL.—Aurora
Wilcox Mfg. Co. (Lawn).B
ILL.—Chicago
Clow & Sons, Jas. B., 342
Franklin (Park; Arm Revolving Spray; etc.) ...A
Illinois Malleable Iron Co.,
30 W. Monroe (Fire)
.................AAAA
Independent Fire Sprinkler
Co., 30 W. Monroe (Automatic Fire) ....E
ILL.—Harvey
Austin Mfg. Co., F. C.
(Street) ....AA
ILL.—Moline
Moline Pump Co. Lawn).A

SPRINKLERS (*Con.*)

IOWA—Des Moines
Chemical Fire Engine Co.
  (Automatic Fire) ......H
IOWA—Ottumwa
Johnston & Sharp Mfg. Co.
  (Lawn) ....D
KY.—Louisville
Caldwell Co., W. E. (Auto-
  matic Fire; Complete
  Plants Erected) ......A
MASS.—Boston
Braman, Dow & Co., 239
  Causeway (Automatic
  Fire) ....A
Hersey Mfg. Co., 314 W. 2d
  (Hose) ....AA
Jones & Co., M. D., 71 Port-
  land (Lawn) ....F
Wolworth Mfg. Co., 132
  Federal (Automatic Fire;
  Lawn) ....AAAA
MASS.—Haydenville
Haydenville Co. (Lawn;
  Hose) ....B
MASS.—South Boston
Hersey Mfg. Co. (Garden
  Hose; Lawn Hose) ..AA
MASS.—Springfield
Blair Mfg. Co. (Lawn) ..C
Stebbins Mfg. Co., E.
  (Lawn) ....B
MASS.—Taunton
Taunton Locomotive Mfg.
  Co. (Street) ....AA
MASS.—Worcester
Hamblin & Russell Mfg. Co.
  (Wire Clothes) ......B
MICH.—Detroit
Buckley-Hart Mfg. Co., 527
  Franklin (Lawn) ....D
Detroit Lead Pipe & Sheet
  Lead Works (Lawn)...A
Standard Sanitary Mfg. Co.
  of Michigan, 942 Cham-
  plain (Lawn) X
MICH.—Jackson
Aspinwall Mfg. Co. (Pota-
  to) ....A
MICH.—Traverse City
Potato Implement Co. (Po-
  tato) ....E
MO.—St. Louis
Kupferle, Jno. C., 2d &
  Mound (Lawn) ......A
Pleuger & Henger Mfg. Co.
  11th & Hebert (Lawn).A
N. H.—Concord
Abbott-Downing Co.
  (Street) X
N. H.—Laconia
Esty Sprinkler Co., N. Mill
  (Automatic Fire) ....A
N. J.—Hightstown
Peppler, Thomas (Two
  Row Potato) ....D
Shangle, John R. (Potato)
  C
New York City
Empire Rubber Mfg. Co.
  (Garden; Lawn) ....AA
Haydenville Co. (Hose)..A
McNab & Harlin Mfg. Co.,
  56 John (Lawn) ....AA
Manufacturers' Sprinkler
  Sprinkler, 56 Liberty (Au-
  tomatic Fire) ......A
Mattson Rubber Co. (Gar-
  den; Lawn) ....D
Mott Iron Wks., J. L., 88
  Beekman (Lawn) ..AA
Simmons Co., John, 106
  Centre (Automatic Fire)
  AA
Westervelt, A. B. & W. T.,
  102 Chambers (Lawn).B
N. Y.—Rochester
Pullman Mfg. Co. (Lawn)
  C
OHIO—Akron
Goodrich Co., B. F. (Gar-
  den; Lawn) ......AAAA
OHIO—Canton
Kohler & Co., F. E. (Lawn)
  C
OHIO—Cincinnati
McGowan, Co., John H.
  (Lawn) ....A
OHIO—Cleveland
Cleveland Lock Co., Wason
  & Hamilton (Lawn)....D
Cleveland Stamping & Tool
  Co., Hamilton near Col.

SPRINKLERS (*Con.*)
  (Adjustable Lawn).....C
OHIO—Hamilton
Meyers Mfg. Co., Fred
  (Lawn) ....B
OHIO—Mansfield
Humphreys Mfg. Co.
  (Lawn) ....A
OHIO—Salem
Deming Co. (Potato; Lawn)
  A
OHIO—Toledo
Yost Electric Mfg. Co.
  (Lawn) ....D
PA.—Erie
Hays Mfg. Co. (Lawn)..B
PA.—Macungie
Neumeyer H. F. (Lawn).E
PA.—Philadelphia
Boekel & Co., Wm., 518
  Vine (Hose; Bath; Cock;
  &c.) ....A
Enterprise Mfg. Co., 3rd
  & Dauphin (Lawn)AAAA
Francis Bros. & Jellett
  (Inc.) 245 N. Broad (Au-
  tomatic Fire) ....F
International Sprinkler Co.,
  517 Arch (Automatic Fire;
  Wet; Dry Pipe Systems)
  A
Philadelphia Lawn Mower
  Co., 3107 Chestnut(Lawn)
  B
R. I.—Pawtucket
Collyer Machine Co. (Auto-
  matic Fire) C
R. I.—Providencee
Davol Rubber Co. (Rubber;
  Plant; Shampoo) ....AA
General Fire Extinguisher
  Co. (Automatic Fire)
  AAAA
S. C.—Spartansburg
Morgan Iron Wks. (Auto-
  matic Fire) C

SPROCKETS

MASS.—Boston
Boston Gear Wks., Pur-
  chase & Pearl (Mchy.).B
N. Y.—Buffalo
Keim, John R. (Bicycle)
  AA
PA.—Mechanicsburg
Wilcox Mfg. Co., D. (Bicy-
  cle) ....B

SPRUCE

See Lumber

SPRUES

CONN.—Clinton
Kelsey Horatio (Moulders')
  E

SPUDS

MICH.—Jackson
Withington & Cooley Mfg.
  Co. (Tobacco, Dandelion)
  AA
N. Y.—Buffalo
White Co., L. & I. J.
  (Bark) ....A
OHIO—Canton
Buckeye Mfg. Co. (Elec-
  tric) ....D
OHIO—Cincinnati
Bishop & Co., Geo. H.
  (Tobacco; Dandelion)..A
OHIO—Cleveland
American Fork & Hoe Co.
  (Tobacco; Dandelion)
  AAAA
OHIO—Clyde
Clyde Cutlery C. (Tobacco)
  D
PA.—Eldred
Prouty & Co., C. (Bark).B
PA.—Honesdale
White Axe Co., G........D
PA.—Warren
Warren Axe & Tool Co.
  (Bark) ....B
WIS.—Oshkosh
Sanford Logging Tool Co.
  (Bark) ....D

SPURS

CONN.—New Britain
North & Judd Mfg. Co.
(Malleable Iron; Solid
Brass) ....AA
CONN.—New Haven
North & Co., O. B. ....AA
N. J.—Newark
Baldwin & Co., Jos......D
Buermann, August .....B
Mehlbach Saddle Co.
(Riding) C
Peters Harness & Saddlery
Co. C
OHIO—Canton
Elbel & Co.............B
TENN.—Chattanooga
Southern Saddlery Co.....A

SQUARES

CONN.—Hartford
Billings & Spencer Co.
(Caliper) ....A
CONN.—New Britain
Russell & Erwin Mfg. Co.
(Iron; Steel) ....AAAA
Stanley Rule & Level Co.
(Iron; Steel; Try; Mitre)
.............AA
CONN.—New Haven
Hoggson & Pettes Mfg. Co.
(Machinists) ....A
CONN.—Southington
Peck, Stow & Wilcox Co.
(Iron; Steel; Plate Glass;
Machinists) ......AAAA
Southington Cutlery Co.
(Iron; Steel) ......AA
CONN.—Thomsonville
Hartford Carpet Corpn.
(Ingrain) ......AAAA
ILL.—Chicago
Dietzgen Co., Eugene, 181
Monroe ("T") ....A
IND.—Indianapolis
Atkins & Co., E. C. (Fry;
Mitre) ....AAA
IOWA—Ottumwa
Nicholls Mfg. Co. (Iron;
Steel; Framing) .....D
MASS.—Athol
Athol Machine Co. (Bevel;
Combination; Iron; Steel;
Machinists; Center Try;
Mitre; Adjustable)....B
Standard Tool Co. (Center;
Combination; Steel; Steel
Hardened; Try) X
Starrett Co., L. S. (Bevel;
Caliper; Combination Iron;
Steel; Machinists Try;
Mitre; "T"; Double Ton-
gue) ....A
MASS.—Boston
Welch & Co., T. F., 65
Sudbury ("T") ......D
Wyke & Co., J., 50 Saratoga
("T") ....D
MASS.—Chicopee Falls
Stevens Arms & Tool Co.,
J. (Machinists) ......A
MASS.—Fitchburg
Sawyer Tool Mfg. Co. (Com-
bination; Iron; Steel;
Machinists; Try; Mitre;
Adjustable; Steel Hard-
ened; "T") C
MASS.—Greenfield
Goodell-Pratt Co. (Carpen-
ters' Combination; Ma-
chinists) ....B
MASS.—Reading
Pierce Organ Pipe Co
(Organ) C
MASS.—Shelburne Falls
Mayhew & Co., H. H....C
MASS.—Springfield
Bemis & Call Hardwarde &
Tool Co. (Iron; Steel
Pocket) ....B
N. J.—Irvington
Belcher Bros. & Co. (Dress-
makers; Taylors; Plate
Glass) X
New York City
Hammacher, Schlemmer &
Co., 209 Bowery (Caliper;
Machinists; "T"; Try;
Mitre) ....AAA
Keuffel & Esser Co., 127

SQUARES (Con.)
Fulton (Iron; Steel; Try;
Mitre; "T") ......AA
Sargent & Co., 151 Leonard
(Iron; Steel; Machinists)
.............AAAA
Soltmann, E. G., 125 E. 42d
("T"; Triangles) .....B
N. Y.—Rochester
American Drafting Furni-
ture Co., 223 Mill (Mov-
able "T") ....E
PA.—Bristol
Leedom & Co., Thos. L.
(Ingrain) ....AAA
PA.—Philadelphia
Bromley Bros. (Ingrain) .A
Bromley, Jas. & Geo. D.
(Ingrain) ....B
Dobson, John & Jas. (In-
grain) ....AAAA
Holmes & Sons, Henry (In-
grain) ....A
Ivins, Dietz & Magee (In-
grain) ....AAAA
PA.—Pittsburg
Kopp & Co., Geo. L., 538
T. Smithfield ("TT")..D
Stieven Co., Wm. E., 644
Smithfield ("T") .....D
PA.—Tacony
Disston & Sons (Inc.) Henry
(Bevel; Combination; Iron
Steel; Machinists; "T";
Try; Mitre) ......AAAA
R. I.—Providence
Brown & Sharpe Mfg. Co.
(Caliper; Combination;
Machinists; Iron; Steel;
Try) ....AAAA

SQUASH

See Canned Goods

SQUEEZERS

Hotchkiss, Edward S.
(Lemon) ....A
Knapp & Cowles Mfg. Co.
(Lemon) C
CONN.—Meriden
Manning, Bowman & Co.
(Lemon) ....AAAA
Parker Co., Chas. (Lemon)
.............AAA
CONN.—New Britain
Landers, Frary & Clark
(Lemon) ....AAA
ILL.—Chicago
Bartlett & Son, M. J., 196 S.
Clark (Lemon) ....H
Nicol & Co. (Lemon) .....D
ILL.—Freeport
Arcade Mfg. Co. (Lemon), A
IND.—Indianapolis
Tucker & Dorsey Mfg. Co.
(Wooden; Lemon) ......A
MASS.—Somerville
Birch Bros. ....D
MASS.—Springfield
Springfield Machine Screw
Co. (Lemon) ....D
MO.—St. Louis
Pleuger & Henger Mfg. Co.
(Lemon) ....A
N. J.—Newark
Sommer's Son, John (Lemon)
.............B
N. J.—Paterson
Watson Machine Co. ......A
N. Y.—Brooklyn
Bliss Co., E. W. .....AAAA
Union Porcelain Works
(Lemon) ....B
N. Y.—Buffalo
Shepard & Co., Sidney
(Lemon) ....AAAA
West Mfg. Co. ....D
New York City
Ioewenstein, Max (Lemon;
Glass) X
Silver & Co. (Inc.) (Lemon;
Glass) X
OHIO—Ravenna
Williams, A. C. (Lemon), A
PA.—Danville
Curry & Vannan (Puddle
Ball) ....A
PA.—Erie
Erie Specialty Co. (Lemon)
.............B
Reed Mfg. Co. (Lemon) ...B

SQUEEZERS (Con.)

PA.—New Brighton
Logan & Strobridge Iron Co.
(Lemon) ....B
PA.—Philadelphia
Philadelphia Roll & Machine
Co., 23d & Wash. Av.
(Puddle Ball) ....A
PA.—Pittsburg
Garrison Foundry Co., A.,
9th & Bingham (Rotary
Puddle Ball) ....AAA
PA.—Pittsburg
Hogg Iron & Steel Foundry
Co., G. A. (Puddle Ball)
...........................A
Lewis Foundry & Machine
Co., 1001 Bingham (Ro-
tary) ....A
Mesta Machine Co. (Puddle
Ball). ....AAA
United Engineering & Foun-
dry, 54th & A. V. Ry.
(Rotary) ....AAAA
PA.—Reading
Penn Hardware Co. (Lemon)
.............................AA
R. I.—Providence
Textile Finishing Machinery
Co., 17 Exchange Pl.
.........................AAAA

SQUIBS

PA.—Plymouth
Powell, J. R. (Miners) ...D
PA.—St. Claire
Miners Supply Co. (Miners)
...........................B
PA.—Wilkesbarre
Luzerne Cap Co. (Miners) H

SQUILGEES

ILL.—Chicago
Bosley Co., D. W. (Rubber)
...........................B
Haisler Bros. Co., 3 So.
Franklin (Rubber Floor) E
MO.—St. Louis
Nevins Mfg. Co. (Double
Rubber) ....F
New York City
Goodyear Rubber Co. (Rub-
ber) ....AAAA
Gutta Percha & Rubber Mfg.
Co. (Rubber) ......AAAA

STACKERS

See also Agr. Imps

STACKS

GA.—Augusta
Lombard Iron Works & Sup-
ply Co. (Smoke) ....A
ILL.—Chicago
Stirling Co. (Steel; Self-Sup-
porting Smoke) ....AAAA
IOWA—Burlington
Murray Iron Works Co.
(Smoke) ....A
LA.—New Orleans
New Orleans Roof & Metal
Works (Smoke) ....B
MAINE—Portland
Portland Co. (Smoke) ...AA
MASS.—Boston
Hodge & Co., E. (Smoke), A
MASS.—Waltham
Davis & Farnum Mfg. Co.
(Steel Plate; Smoke) ...B
MINN.—Minneapolis
Howell & Co., R. R.
(Smoke) ....B
MISS.—Meridian
Soule Steam Feed Works
(for Lumber) C
MO.—St. Louis
Wangler Boiler & Sheet Iron
Works Co., J. F. (Smoke)
...........................A
N. Y.—Brooklyn
Clonbrock Steam Boiler Co.
(Smoke; Steel; Self-Sup-
porting Smoke) ....D
Logan & Son, Farrell
(Smoke) ....B
New York City
Fenton Metallic Mfg. Co.,
346 Bway. (Book) .....A
Hazleton Boiler Co. (Smoke)
...........................A
OHIO—Columbus
Rarig Engineering Co. (Steel

STACKS (Con.)

Plate; Smoke) ....A
OHIO—Marietta
Marietta Boiler Works
(Steel; Self - Supporting
Smoke) ....A
OHIO—Youngstown
Pollock & Co., Wm. B.
(Smoke) ....AA
PA.—Allegheny
Carlin's Sons, Thos. (Smoke)
...........................A
PA.—Harrisburg
Harrisburg Mfg. & Boiler Co.
(Smoke) ....B
PA.—Pittsburg
Munrie & Son, R. (Smoke)
.............................AA
Ritter-Conly Co. (Smoke)
.............................AA
PA.—Warren
Struthers, Wells & Co.
(Smoke) ....AA
PA.—Waynesboro
Frick Co. (Smoke) ....AAA
PA.—Wilkesbarre
Vulcan Iron Works (Smoke)
.........................AAAA
PA.—York
York Mfg. Co. (Smoke).AA
VT.—Fair Haven
Dalrymple Iron Works
(Smoke) ....F
WIS.—Racine
Freeman & Sons Mfg. Co., S.
(Smoke) ....A

STAFFS

ILL.—Chicago
Dietzgen Co., Eugene (Ar-
tists' Umbrella) ....A
ILL.—Freeport
Stover Mfg. Co. (Flag), AA
KANS.—Leavenworth
Great Western Mfg. Co.
(Grist Mill; Proof). ..AA
MASS.—Boston
Boston Regalia Co., 7 Tem-
ple Place (Banner) .....F
MO.—St. Louis
Nelson Mfg. Co., N. O. (Iron
Flag) ....AAA
N. Y.—Buffalo
Noye Mfg. Co., John T.
(Grist Mill; Proof) .....D
New York City
Goldberg, Samuel (Artists
Umbrella). ....E

STAGES

See also Carriages & Wagons

CONN.—New Haven
Goodrich & Co., J. F.....AA
ILL.—Chicago
Sherman, I. N. W........A
PA.—Philadelphia
Fulton & Walker Co., 35 N.
20th ....AA

STAIN

See also Paints

COLO.—Denver
Hallock Paint, Oil & Glass
Co. (Wood) ....A
CONN.—New Milford
Bridgeport Wood Finishing
Co. (Wood) ....AA
ILL.—Chicago
Adams Etting Co. (Wood) A
Chicago Wood Finishing Co.
(Wood) ....A
Heath & Milligan Mfg. Co.
(Water) ....AAA
Rubber Paint Co. (Varnish)
...........................A
Wadsworth-Howland Co., In-
diana Av. & 18th (Shingle;
Wood) ....A
IND.—Terre Haute
American Asbestos Co.
(Shingle; Wood) ....D
LA.—New Orleans
McWilliams. R. (Ltd.)
(Varnish; Water; Wood)
...........................X
MASS.—Boston
Baker & Co., Charles F.
(Shoe) ....A
MASS.—Lynn
Crooker, John W. & McKen-

STAIN (Con.)
zie Mfg. Co. (Shoe) C
Kent & Smith (Shoe) .....D
MICH.—Detroit
Acme White Lead Works
(Varnish) ....AAA
MO.— St. Louis
Mound City Paint & Color
Co. (Varnish; Wood) ..AA
N. J.—Jersey City
Woolsey Paint & Color Co.,
C. A. (Varnish; Wood), A
N. Y.—Brooklyn
Moore & Co., Benjamin
(Wood) ....AA
Wiarda & Co., John C.
(Pink) ....AA
New York City
F. W. Devoe & C. T. Rey-
nolds Co., Fulton & Wil-
liam (Wood; Shingle)
AAAA
Gerstendorfer Bros. (Var-
nish) ....B
Johns Mfg. Co., H. W.
(Wood) X
Longman & Martinez
(Wood) ....AAA
Pierce Co., F. O. (Varnish;
Wood). ....B
Pratt & Lambert (Inc.)
(Wood) ....B
Zinsser & Co., W. (Wood) A
N. Y.—Troy
Conners Paint Mfg. Co.,
Wm. (Shingle; Wood) ..A
OHIO—Cleveland
Billings-Chapin Co. (Var-
nish; Wood) ....A
PA.—Philadelphia
Harkinson & Co., Robert
(Shoe) ....D
Lucas & Co., John (Water;
Wood; Shingle) ....B
Nice, Eugene E., 272 So. 2d
(Shinle; Wood) ....A
PA.—Pittsburg
Lawrence & Co., W. W.
(Varnish) ....AA
R. I.—Providence
United States Gutta Percha
Paint Co. (Varnish) ....A
S. C.—Summerville
Summerville Fernoline
Works (Wood) X

STAIRCASES

KANS.—Emporia
Jones & Sons. Jos. (Iron), D
MO.—St. Louis
Christopher & Simpson Arch
Iron & Fdy. Co. (Orna-
mental Iron) ....AA
N. Y.—Baldwinsville
Morris Machine Works (Iron
Spiral) ....A
N. Y.—Brooklyn
Hecla Iron Works (Iron
Spiral) ....AA
New York City
Fiske, J. W. (Iron Spiral) A
Atis Elevator Co., 71 Bway.
(Moving) ....AAAA
Reno Inclined Elevator Co.,
551 W. 35th (Moving) ..E
OHIO—Springfield
Rogers Iron Works (Iron) B
PA.—Mechanicsburg
Potts Mfg. Co. (Iron) ....E
PA.—Philadelphia
Link Belt Engineering Co.
(Moving) ....AA
S. C.—Spartanburg
Morgan Iron Works (Iron
Spiral). C

STAIRS

ILL.—Chicago
True & True Co., 810 W.
19th (Wood) ....A
MICH.—Detroit
Kotcher, Chas. W. (Wood)
AA
MINN.—Minneapolis
Flour City Ornamental Iron
Works (Bronze) ....B
MO.—Kansas City
Kansas City Wire & Iron
Works (Iron) ....B
Ludlow-Saylor Wire Co.
(Iron; Steel) ....AA
N. J.—Boonton
Lincoln Iron Works (Iron) B

STAIRS (Con.)
N. Y.—Brooklyn
Hecla Iron Works (Iron) AA
N. Y.—Kingston
Palen's Sons, H. W. (Wood)
A
New York City
Cornell, J. B. & J. M. (Iron)
AA
OHIO—Cincinnati
Stewart Iron Works (Iron;
Steel) ....A
OHIO—Columbus
Forest City Steel & Iron Co.
(Iron; Steel) ....A
Van Dorn Iron Works Co.
(Iron; Steel) ....AA
OHIO—Hamilton
Meyers Mfg. Co., Fred. J.
(Iron; Steel) ....B
OHIO—Kenton
Champion Iron Co. (Iron)
AA
OHIO—Springfield
Rogers Iron Co. (Iron) C
OHIO—Toledo
Donovan Wire & Iron Co.
(Iron; Steel) C
PA.—Ellwood City
Glen Mfg. Co. (Iron; Steel)
D
PA.—Nazareth
Nazareth Foundry & Machine
Co. (Iron; Steel) ....B
PA.—Philadelphia
Shannon Mfg. Co. (Iron) ..C
PA.—Pittsburg
Kratzer & Co., W. N. (Iron;
Steel) ....D
PA.—Rochester
Miller & Sons, Wm. (Wood)
A
PA.—So. Bethlehem
Bethlehem Foundry & Ma-
chine Co. (Iron; Steel) ..C
PA.—York
Variety Iron Works (Iron) A
TENN.—Memphis
Chicasaw Iron Works (Iron)
A
WIS.—Malwaukee
Bagley & Sons Co., Wm.
(Iron; Steel) ....A
Willer Mfg. Co. (Wood) ..A

STAKES

CONN.—Southington
Peck, Stow & Wilcox Co.
(Tinners') ....AAAA
MINN.—Minneapolis
Kilgore Machine Co. (Log-
ging Car) X
N. Y.—Buffalo
Niagara Machine & Tool
Works (Tinners'; Cornice
Makers') ....AAA
West Mfg. Co. (Tinners'), D
PA.—Easton
Bangor Excelsior Slate Co.
(Slaters') ....A
PA.—Philadelphia
Plumb, Fayette R. (Cornice
Makers') ....AA

STALKS

New York City
Estes & Sons. E. B., 45 John
(Whip) ....AA

STALLS

ILL.—Edwardsville
Illinois Marble Co. (Slate) C
MASS.—Cambridge
Hall & Co., Chas. E. (Mar-
ble) ....A
MO.—St. Louis
Nelson Mfg. Co., N. O.
(Marble Urinal) .....AAA
PA.—Lynnport
New York Standard Slate
Works (Slate Urinal) ..D
VT.—Fairhaven
Fairhaven Marble & Marble-
ized Slate Co. (Closet Uri-
nal) ....B
VT.—Poultney
Fleming Slate Co. (Slate
Urinal) C

STAMPED WARE

See Tinware

STAMPING

See also Hardware; Carriage

CONN.—Bristol
Smith, Ira B. (Sheet Metal) .....E

CONN.—Plainville
Clark & Son, A. N. (Bicycle) C

CONN.—Waterbury
Waterbury Brass Co. (Sheet Metal) ....AAAA

CONN.—Winsted
Goodwin & Kintz Co. (Sheet Metal) ....B

ILL.—Chicago
Acorn Brass Mfg. Co., 206 Fulton (Sheet Metal) ...B

MASS.—Attleboro
Mossberg Co., Frank (Sheet Metal) ....B

MASS.—Worcester
Bay State Stamping Co. (Sheet Metal) ....E
Wilson & Smith (Sheet Metal) ....D

N. J.—Newark
Jenkinson & Co., R. C. (Sheet Metal) ....A

N. Y.—Brooklyn
Adriance Machine Works (Sheet Metal) ....A
Leffler & Co., Charles (Sheet Metal) ....D

N. Y.—Buffalo
Crosby Co. (Sheet Metal) ..A
Diamond Saw & Stamping Works (Sheet Metal) ..:D

N. Y.—Niagara Falls
Metal Stamping Co. (Sheet Metal) ....B

OHIO—Cleveland
Avery Stamping Co. (Heavy Metal; Steel) ....A
Cleveland Stamping & Tool Co. (Sheet Metal) C
Federal Mfg. Co. (Sheet Metal) ....AAAA
Globe Machine & Stamping Co. (Sheet Metal) .....E
Konigslow Stamping & Tool Works, E. (Sheet Metal) ....E

OHIO—Salem
Clarke Co., W. J. (Sheet Metal) ....B

PA.—Philadelphia
Standard Pressed Steel Co., 20th & Clearfield (Sheet Metal) C

PA.—Pittsburg
Scaife & Sons Co., Wm. B. (Sheet Metal) ......AAA

R. I.—Central Falls
Mossberg Wrench Co. (Sheet Metal) C

WIS.—Milwaukee
Wrought Washer Mfg. Co. (Sheet Metal) ....A

STAMPS

See also Mills; Machinery

COLO.—Denver
Denver Novelty Work & Mfg. Co. (Rubber) .....E

CONN.—Bridgeport
Hatheway Mfg. Co. (Steel) ....E
Schwerdtle Stamp Co. (Steel; Rubber; Brass; Embossing) ....G
Smith & Egge Mfg. Co. (Pencil; Self-Inking) ...A

CONN.—Bristol
Smith, Ira B. (Steel) .....E

CONN.—New Haven
Hoggson & Pettis Mfg. Co. (Steel; Dating; Hand; Railroad; Rubber; Self-Inking) ....A

CONN.—Waterbury
Blake & Johnson (Steel) ..A

DEL.—Wilmington
Hilles & Jones Co. (Steel) ....AA

STAMPS (Con.)

ILL.—Chicago
Baird Mfg. Co., 23 Mich (Dating; Time) C
Consolidated Press & Tool Co., 92 No. Clinton (Steel) ....D
Hanson, C. H. (Boot; Shoe) ....B
Perry Time Stamping Co., 80 So. Canal (Time) ......D
Swisher Mfg. Co., R. D. (Rubber) ....D
Wood & Co., Charles H. (Ribbon) ....F

IND.—Evansville
Ellert, C. H. (Rubber) ....F

MD.—Baltimore
Dorman Co., J. F. W. (Steel; Rubber) ....F

MASS.—Boston
Automatic Time Stamp Co., 160½ Congress (Time), E
Becker Name Plate Co. (Steel) ....B
Harvey, H. H. (Steel) ....B
Powers & Co., J. H. (Boot; Shoe; Dating) ....E
Webster & Co., F. S. (Ribbon) ....AA
Woodman Mfg. & Supply Co., R. (Perforating; Dating Railroad Ticket) ...F

MASS.—Brockton
Snell & Atherton (Boot) ..B
Tuck Mfg. Co. (Boot) ....E

MASS.—Springfield
Morgan, Crossman & Co. (Dating) ....D
Smith Mfg. Co., R. H., 293 Main (Air Cushion; Dating; Rubber; Metal Self-Inking; Time; Hand; Numbering; Pencil; Pocket; Perforating; Post Office; Railroad; Ribbon) C

MASS.—Westfield
Smith Mfg. Co., H. B. (Time) ....AA

MASS.—Worcester
Wilson & Smith (Steel) ...D

MICH.—Detroit
Anderson & Sons, Wm. H. (Steel) C
Detroit Rubber Stamp Co., 99 Griswold (Steel; Ribbon; Post Office Rubber) H
Michigan Printing & Stamp Co. (Railroad) X

MINN.—St. Paul
North Western Stamp Wks. (Log) ....E

MO.—St. Louis
Barnard Stamp Co. (Dating; Rubber) ....E

N. Y.—Brooklyn
Adriance Machine Works, 254 Van Brunt (Steel) ..A
Bliss Co., E. W. (Steel) ....AAAA
Leffler & Co., Charles (Steel) ....D

N. Y.—Buffalo
Howard Iron Works (Steel) ....AA
Niagara Machine & Tool Works (Steel) ....AAA

New York City
American Bank Note Co. (Postage) ....AAA
American Railway Supply Co. (Dating) ....B
Brooks & Co., E. J. (Post Office) ....B
Buck Mfg. Co., T. S., 211 Canal (Rubber) C
Butler, A. G., 248 Pearl (Steel) ....F
Carragan, Geo. (Steel; Rubber) ....D
Cushman & Dennison Mfg. Co., 240 W. 23d (Dating; Numbering) C
Everson & Reed (Rubber) F
Force & Co., Wm. A. (Hand Rubber) ....B
Imhauser & Co., E. 206 Bway. (Automatic Time) C
Ingersoll & Bro., Robt. H., 51 Maiden Lane (Dating) ....A
Loyd Co., Jno., 558 Water (Steel) ....B

STAMPS (Con.)

Nanz & Co., C., 12½ Duane (Time) ....F
New York City
Ness, Jr., Geo. M., 61 Fulton (Rubber; Steel; Brass Metal) ....G
New York Stencil Works (Steel; Dating; Hand; Numbering; Pencil; Pocket; Perforating; Railroad Ribbon; Rubber; Self-Inking) ....D
Stafford, Nelson (Steel; Rubber) ....F
Stimpson & Son, E. B. (Boot) ....A

N. Y.—Niagara Falls
Metal Stamping Co., (Steel) ....B

N. Y.—Syracuse
Franklin Mfg. Co., H. H. (Dating Railroad Ticket) C

OHIO—Cincinnati
Cressler, Wm. T. (Steel; Hand) C

OHIO—Cleveland
Globe Machine & Stamping Co. (Steel) ....E
Konigslow Stamping & Tool Works, E., 184 Champlain (Steel) ....E

PA.—Bloomsburg
Richard Mfg. Co. (Ltd.) (Steel) C

PA.—Harrisburg
Hickok Mfg. Co., W. O. (Hand) ....AA

PA.—Philadelphia
Hill Mfg. Co., B. B. (Dating; Numbering; Perforating; Railroad Ticket; Rubber) ....B
Quint & Sons, S. H. (Steel; Brass; Hosiery) ....B
Riggs & Bro., 310 Market (Time) ....B

WIS.—Milwaukee
Schwaab Stamp & Seal Co. (Metal; Rubber; Steel) X

STANCHIONS

CONN.—Forestville
Barnard & Co., S. M. (Cattle) ....F

MASS.—Boston
Edson Mfg. Co. (Hand Rope) E
Prescott, Edwin (Cattle), E

MICH.—Monroe
Wilder-Strong Implement Co. (Cattle) ....E
New York City
Tiebout, W. & J ., 118 Chambers (Hand Rope), B

N. Y.—Rochester
Rochester Steel Stanchion Co. (Steel; Cattle) X

N. Y.—Warsaw
Warsaw Elevator Co. (Cattle) ....B

STANDARDS

CONN.—Meriden
Bradley & Hubbard Mfg. Co. (Lamp) ....AAAA
Miller & Co., Edward (Lamp) ....AAA

CONN.—New Haven
Cowles & Co., C. (Inc.) (Canopy) ....A
Seward & Son, M. (Canopy) A

N. J.—Newark
Weston Electrical Inst. Co. (Laboratory) ....A

N. Y.—Auburn
Clapp Mfg. Co., E. D. (Canopy) ....A

N. Y.—Binghampton
Crandal, Stone & Co. (Canopy) ....A
New York City
Frink, I. P. (Lamp) ....AA

N. Y.—Troy
Rensselaer Mfg. Co. (Floor Indicator) ....A

OHIO—Cleveland
Cleveland Hardware Co. (Canopy) ....A

PA.—Mechanicsburg
Wilcox Mfg. Co., D.

STANDARDS (Con.)
(Canopy) ....B

STANDPIPES
See Pipes

STANDS
See also Jardinerres; Furniture

ALA.—Huntsville
Huntsville Foundry & Machine Works (Nolan & Jones Props.) (Emery Wheel) ....B

CONN.—Bridgeport
Bridgeport Gun Implement Co. (Bicycle; Folding), A

CONN.—Cromwell
Stevens Co., J. & E. (Sad Iron; Toy) ....A

CONN.—Deep River
Williams & Marvin (Water Color) ....D

CONN.—Georgetown
Gilbert & Bennett Mfg. Co. (Umbrella; Wire; Flower Pot) ....AA

CONN.—Meriden
Bradley & Hubbard Mfg. Co. (Music; Brass; Blower; Umbrella; Brass; Toilet, Complete) ....AAAA
Manning, Bowman & Co. (Tea; Coffee Pot; Tile Table) ....AAAA
Meriden Britannia Co. (Flower) ....AAAA

CONN.—New Britain
Landers, Frary & Clark (Water Color; Sad Iron) AAA

CONN.—New Haven
Burgess, E. A. (Estate of) (Bicycle Folding) ......E

CONN.—Norwich
Norwich Nickel & Brass Co. (Umbrella; Brass; Draping; Show Case; Umbrella Show; Window Display) B

CONN.—Torrington
Turner & Seymour Mfg. Co. (Banner, also Rods) ....A

CONN.—Waterbury
American Pin Co. (Banner) A

CONN.—Winsted
Goodwin & Kintz Co. (Umbrella) ....D

ILL.—Carpentersville
Illinois Iron & Bolt Co. (Copying Press) ......AA

ILL.—Chicago
Ajax Forge Co. (Switch) AA
Anderson, Jonas A. (Camera) ....D
Barbel Wire & Iron Works (Flower; Fruit; Plant; Tea Coffee Pot; Soap; Umbrella; Wire; Draping; Sad Iron) ....B
Braumoeller & Son, Henry (Show Case) ....B
Caldwell & Son Co., H. W., Western Av. & 17th (Floor; Mule Pulley) ...A
Chicago Wheel & Mfg. Co., 39 W. Randolph (Polishing; Emery Wheel) ....D
Illinois Malleable Iron Co. (Boiler) ....AAAA
Leger & Sons, Edward (Display; Shoe) ....F
McGuire Mfg. Co. (Switch) A
Morden Frog & Crossing Works (Switch) ....A
Nicol & Co. (Light Tea; Coffee Pot; Sad Iron; Toy) D
Olbrich & Golbeck (Shaving) B
Warren Mfg. Co., J. D. (Axe; Scythe) ....B

ILL.—Decatur
Faries Mfg. Co. (Window Display) ....A

ILL.—East St. Louis
Elliott Frog & Switch Co. (Switch) ....A

ILL.—Freeport
Stover Mfg. Co. (Tea; Coffee Pot; Flower Pot; Sad Iron) ....B

STANDS (Con.)

ILL.—Harvey
Buda Foundry & Mfg. Co. (Switch) ....A

ILL.—Quincy
Modern Iron Works (Range Boiler) ....A

ILL.—Rockford
East Rockford Mantle Co. (Jardiniere) ....A

IND.—Indianapolis
Udell Works (Ironing) ...A

IND.—Mishawaka
Dodge Mfg. Co. (Floor) AAA

IND.—South Bend
Bowsher Co., N. P. (Banner)
..................................B

IOWA—Cedar Rapids
Adams Mfg. Co., A. L. (Hammock) ....F

KY.—Louisville
Louisville Bridge & Iron Co. (Switch) ....A

MD.—Baltimore
Poole Engineering & Machine Co. (Guide Pulley)
..................................AA

MASS.—Boston
Boston & Lockport Block Co. Warren (Range Boiler), X
Davenport, Albert H. (Hall; Shaving) ....AA
Derby Desk Co. (Copying Press) ....AA
Empire Laundry Machinery Co. (Sad Iron).........E

MASS.—Boston
Jones & Co., Melville D. (Flower Pot) ....F
Paine Furniture Co. (Shaving) ....A

MASS.—Chelsea
Low Art Tile Co. (Tile; Table; Window Display) ..F

MASS.—Gardner
Heywood Bros. & Wakefield Co. (Music; Rattan Work; Rattan) ....AAAA

MASS.—Lowell
Woods, Sherwood & Co. (Dish Wire; Tea; Coffee Pot; Banner; Sad Iron), C

MASS.—North Cambridge
Hews & Co., A. H. (Flower Pot) ....A

MASS.—Springfield
Hawkins Iron Works, R. F. (Switch) C
Morgan Envelope Co. (Mucilage) ....AAAA
Wason Mfg. Co. (Switch)
..................................AA

MASS.—Worcester
National Mfg. Co. (Tea; Coffee Pot) ....B
Wire Goods Co. (Bicycle) .A
Wright Wire Co. (Flower Pot) ....AA
Michigan Detri..,.. .. rao

MICH.—Detroit
Barnum, E. T. (Flower Pot)
..................................B
Northwestern Foundry & Supply Co., Orleans & Grand Boul. (Range Boiler) ....D

MICH.—Fenton
Phillips & Co., A. J. (Bicycle; Folding Tub) ......A

MICH.—Galien
Montross Richard W. (Hammock) X

MICH.—Grand Rapids
Berkey & Gay Furniture Co. (Hall) ....AA

MICH.—Port Huron
Crosby & Poole Co. (Store Display) X

MO.—St. Louis
Kupferle, Jno. C. (Range Boiler) ....A
Ludlow-Saylor Wire Co. Flower Pot; Umbrella)
..................................AA
St. Louis Stamping Co. (Sugar; Flour)..........AAA
Scarritt-Comstock Furniture Co. (Work) ....A

N. H.—Nashua
Fletcher & Webster Furniture Co. (Umbrella; Hall)
..................................C
Maine Mfg. Co. (Flower Pot)
..................................A

STANDS (Con.)

N. J.—Burlington
Stewart & Peterson Co. (Retort) ....A

N. J.—Hoboken
New York Switch & Crossing Co. (Switch) ....A

N. J.—Newark
Bless & Drake (Sad Iron)
..................................B
Gould's Son Co., M. (Banner) ....A
Hemmer Bros. (Copying Press) ....B

N. J.—Smithville
Smith Machine Co., H. B. (Emery Wheel) ....A

N. J.—Trenton
Maddock & Sons, Thos. (Umbrella) ....AA

N. Y.—Albany
Troy Nickel Works (Stove)
..................................C

N. Y.—Brooklyn
Brooklyn Furniture Co. (Hall) ....A
Cooper & McKee (Flour) .A
Gregory, Thos., 65 Frost (Galvanized Range Boiler)
..................................E
Miller & Van Winkle (Bicycle) ....A
New York Stamping Co. (Ginger Ale) ....A
Simpson, J. S. & G. F., 30 Rodney (Emery Wheel)
Sweeney Mfg. Co., W. H. (Water Color) ....B
Worn & Co., Wm. F. (Hall)
..................................D

N. Y.—Buffalo
Aldrich & Ray Mfg. Co. (Umbrella; Brass) .....A
Buffalo Wire Works Co. (Flower Pot; Umbrella)
..................................A
Jewett Mfg. Co., John C. (Water Color Umbrella; Iron) ....AA

N. Y.—Cataraugus
Oakes & Burgher (Toilet; Complete) ....B

N. Y.—Herkimer
Horrocks Desk Co. (Copying Press) ....B

N. Y.—Hillburn
Ramapo Iron Works (Switch) ....AA

New York City
Conover Fire Place Mfg. Co. (Music; Brass) X
Cordley & Hayes (Umbrella)
..................................A
Crandall & Godley Co. (Window Display) ....AA
Estey Wire Works Co., 65 Fulton (Flower Pot; Umbrella) ....E
Fiske, J. W. (Flower; Music; Blower; Umbrella Iron; Toilet; Complete; Show Case) ....A
Folmer & Schwing Mfg. Co. (Camera) ....B
Gennert, G. (Camera) ...B
Gould-Mersereau Co. (Banner; Umbrella; Brass)..C
Hoe & Co., R. (Copying Press) ....AAAA
Howard & Morse (Flour Pot)
..................................D
Iron Clad Mfg. Co., 4 Cliff (Range Boiler) ....AAAA
Judd & Co., H. L. (Blower; Fire Iron; Umbrella Brass)
..................................AA
Koven & Bro., L. O., 50 Cliff (Galvanized Range Boiler)
..................................A
Krieg & Co., J. K. (Ironing)
..................................B
Lalance & Grosjean Mfg. Co. (Umbrella; Iron Toilet Complete) ....AAAA
Lamb, J. & R. (Banner) ..D
Mace & Co., L. H. (Butler's; Flower; Umbrella)
..................................B
Mohr & Co., Fred (Hall) ..A
Neppert, Francis Jr. (Music) X
Palmenberg's Sons, J. R. (Umbrella; Draping;

STANDS (Con.)
Wire) ....B
Peck, Stow & Wilcox Co., 27
Murray (Blower; Coffee
Pot; Sad Iron; Umbrella)
AAAA
Russell & Erwin Mfg. Co.,
43 Chambers (Umbrella)
AAAA
Sargent & Co., Geo. F.
(Reading) X
Sargent & Co., 151 Leonard
(Blower; Coffee Pot; Sad
Iron; Umbrella; Shovel;
Tong) ....AAAA
Slotkin & Praglin, 210 Canal
(Emery Wheel) C
Sperling Bros. (Work; Rat-
tan) ....F
Swain & Son, H. C. (Inc.)
(Hall) ....D
Vogel & Co., F. (Hall) ..X
N. Y.—Poughkeepsie
Lane Bros. Co. (Bicycle)
A
N. Y.—Rochester
Castle, Wilmot & Co. (Um-
brella) ....B
Copeland & Durgin Co.
(Shaving) ....B
Rochester Optical Co. (Cam-
era) X
Streeter & Co., N. R. (Mir-
ror Cheval) ....B
N. Y.—Seneca Falls
Westcott-Jewell Co. (Bicy-
cle Folding) ....D
N. Y.—Syracuse
Stearns & Co., E. C. (Bicy-
cle Folding) ....AA
N, Y.—Troy
McMurray, Clarence F.
(Guide Pulley) ......A
N. C.—Hickory
Martin, W. N. (Axe; Dis-
play) X
OHIO—Ashland
Meyers & Bro., F. C. (Bicy-
cle Folding) ....AAAA
OHIO—Bucyrus
Campbell Frog Works
(Switch) ....A
Geiger & Bush (Kettle).D
OHIO—Cincinnati
Bromwell Brush & Wire
Goods Co. (Flower; Um-
brella; Wire Flower Pot)
A
Dormette & Bros., J.
(Copying Press) ....A
Haven Co., Jas. L. (Sad
Iron) ....B
Kelsall Co., Thos. (Copy-
ing Press) ....B
Kruse & Co., H. (Show
Case) ....B
Mitchell Furniture Co., Rob-
ert (Work) .....AAAA
Rookwood Pottery Co. (Um-
brella Pottery) ....B
Tatum Co., Samuel C. (Copy-
ing Press; Typewriter;
Sewing Machine) .....B
Weir Frog Co. (Switch) ..A
Wiggers & Sons Furniture
Co., H. H. (Bracket) ..B
OHIO—Cleveland
Bowler & Co. (Switch) ..B
Van Dorn Iron Works Co.
(Umbrella; Iron) .....AA
OHIO—Columbus
Case Mfg. Co. (Floor Mule
Pulley) ....A
OHIO—Cuyahoga Falls
Holloway Co. (Reading) ..E
OHIO—Dayton
City Forge & Iron Works
(Bicycle; Folding) ....A
Stillwell-Bierce & Smith-
Vaile Co. (Guide Pulley)
AAAA
OHIO—Hamilton
Krauth & Benninghofen
(Music; Brass) ....A
Meyers Mfg. Co., F. J.
(Tea & Coffee Pot; Wash
Umbrella; Wire; Show
Case; Flower Pot; Sad
Iron; Display; Garment)
B
OHIO—Lorain
Lorain Steel Co. (Switch)
AAA
OHIO—Miamisburg
Allen & Co., D. H. (Collap-

STANDS (Con.)
sible; Flower) C
OHIO—Salem
Clark Co., W. J. (Umbrella;
Brass) ....B
PA.—Allegheny City
Pitts Lamp & Brass Co.
(Umbrella; Brass; Screen;
Window Display) ..AAAA
PA.—Allentown
Allentown Rolling Mills
(Switch) ....AAA
PA.—Easton
Standard Emery & Supply
Co. (Emery Wheel) ...X
PA.—New Brighton
Pittsburg Clay Mfg. Co.
(Umbrella; Pottery)
AAAA
PA.—Philadelphia
Cresson Co., Geo. V.
(Guide Pulley; Floor)
AA
Darby & Sons, Edw., 233
Arch (Flower Pot Umbrel-
la) ....A
Fairmont Machine Co.
(Guide Pulley) ......A
Fleck Bros. Co., 44 N. 5th
(Range Boiler) ......A
Harrison's Sons, W. H.
(Fire; Iron) ....F
Hawthorne & Sheble (Phono-
graph Horn) ....B
Pennsylvania Steel Co.
(Switch) ....AAAA
Strauss, Wm. (Draping) ..F
Sutterley & Co., Gilbert T.
(Umbrella; Brass) C
Wall Mfg. Co., R. C.
(Brazing; Wheel Trueing)
E
Wiler, Wm. (Banner; Um-
brella Brass) ....D
PA.—Pittsburg
Jones & Laughlins (Guide
Pulley; Floor) ...AAAA
Scaife & Sons Co., Wm. B.,
221 1st Av. (Galvanized
Iron Range Boiler) ..A
Standard Mfg. Co. (Boiler)
AA
PA.—Royersford
Royersford Foundry & Ma-
chine Co. (Polishing
Emery Wheel) C
PA.—So. Bethlehem
Bethlehem Foundry & Ma-
chine Co. (Umbrella) ..C
PA.—Swissvale
Union Swich & Signal Co.
AAAA
PA.—Union City
Novelty Wood Works
(Umbrella) ....B
PA.—Williamsport
Otto Furniture Co. (Toilet
Complete) ....D
PA.—Wrightsville
Wrightsville Hardware Co.
(Tea; Coffee Pot Calen-
der) C
R. I.—Providence
Diamond Machine Co.
(Emery Wheel) ....A
New England Butt Co. (Sad
Iron) ....A
R. I.—Woonsocket
Woonsocket Machine & Press
Co. (Guide Pulley) ..AA
VT.—Montpelier
Lane Mfg. Co. (Guide Pul-
ley) ....A
VT.—North Bennington
Cushman Mfg. Co., Henry T.
(Music; Umbrella) C
WIS.—Milwaukee
Meinecke & Son, A. (Brack-
et; Enamelled & Gilt;
Work) ....AA

STANHOPES
See also Carriages

IND.—Richmond
Wescott Carriage Co. ....A
IND.—South Bend
Studebaker-Baker Mfg. Co.
AAAA
MASS.—Amesbury
Dennett & Co., C. N. X
Hassett & Hodge ....A

STANHOPES (Con.)

MASS.—Merrimac
Pease & Son, S. C. C

MICH.—Flint
Durant-Dort Carriage Co.
..................AAAA

MICH.—Pontiac
Pontiac Buggy Co. ......A

MO.—St. Louis
Union Carriage Co. ......B

OHIO—Columbus
Buckeys Buggy Co. ..AAA

STAPLERS

N. Y.—New York City
Hurd & Co., 576 W. B'way
(Pin) ....D

STAPLES

CONN.—Bridgeport
Gaynor & Mitchell Mfg. Co.
(Wire) ....D

CONN.—Georgetown
Gilbert & Bennett Mfg. Co.
(Fence; Wire) ....AA

CONN.—New Britain
Humason & Beckley Mfg.
Co. (Wrought) ....A
North & Judd Mfg. Co.
(Hame) ....AA
Stanley Works (Fence;
Wrought) ....AAA

CONN.—New Haven
Sargent & Co. (Wagon Bow;
Wire) ....AAAA

ILL.—Belleville
Stanley Co., Geo. W. (Barbed; Blind; Hoops) ....F

ILL.—Chicago
American Steel & Wire Co.,
Rookery Bldg. (Wire)
..................AAAA
Chicago Tack Co., 7800
Woodlawn Av. ......B
Grand Crossing Tack Co.
(Wire; Fence; Furniture)
....................A
Gibson Co., Wm. D., 23 N.
Clinton (Wire) ....B
Pratt Mfg. Co., Wm. E.,
91 Lake (Barbed; Blind
Netting; &c.) ....B
Vaughan & Bushnell Mfg.
Co., 877 Carroll Av. ...B

ILL.—Sterling
Dillon-Griswold Wire Co.
(Wire) ....A
Lawrence Bros. (Wrought
Iron) ....AA

IND.—Crawfordsville
Crawfordsville Wire & Nail
Co. (Wire) ....B

IND.—Kokomo
Kokomo Steel & Wire Co.
(Fence; &c.) ......AAAA

IND.—Madison
Tower Mfg. Co. (Wire
C l a m p Electricians';
Broom; Hoop; Harness;
Fence; &c.) C

IND.—Muncie
Indiana Steel & Wire Co.
(Wire; Fence; &c.) ..A

KY.—Ashland
Norton Iron Works (Inc.)
(Polished; Galvanizel
Wire) ....AA

KY.—Louisville
Avery & Sons, B. F. (Inc.)
(Wire) ....AAA

MASS.—Boston
Austin & Eddy, 117 Broad
(Blind) C

MASS.—Clinton
Clinton Wire Cloth Co.
(Wire) ....AAA

MASS.—Fairhaven
Atlas Tack Co. (Wire)
..................AAAA

MASS.—Plymouth
Cobb & Drew (Wire) ....AA
Plymouth Mills (Wire) ..B

MASS.—Winchendon
Townsend, G. G. (Barrel;
Key Hoop) X

MASS.—Worcester
Morgan Spring Co. (Wire)
....................A
Parker Wire Goods Co.
(Wire) ....E
Spencer Wire Co. (Wire) .A
Wire Goods Co. (Blind;

STAPLES (Con.)
Fence; Wrought; Wire)
....................A
Wright Wire Co. (Fence;
Wire) ....AAA

MO.—St. Louis
Ludlow-Saylor Wire Co.
(Fence) ....AA
St. Louis Wire & Iron Co.,
520 Chouteau Av. .....D

N. Y.—Binghamton
Titchener & Co., E. H.
(Blind; Wire) ....B

N. Y.—Buffalo
Pratt & Letchworth (Tail
Board) ....AA
Western Wire Goods Co.
(Wire) ....D

N. Y.—Cortlandt
Wickwire Bros. (Wire)
....................AA

N. Y.—Elmira
Cronk & Carrier Mfg. Co.
....................B

N. Y.—New York City
Howard & Morse (Fence)
....................D

N. Y.—Penn Yan
Superior Tack & Nail Co.
(Coppered Casket; Han-
dles; Hoop; Galvanized
Poultry Netting; &c.)..B

N. Y.—Syracuse
Central City Bolt Co. (Nutted) C

OHIO—Canton
Ney Mfg. Co. ....B

OHIO—Cincinnati
Cincinnati Mfg. Co., 512
Main (Wire) C
Globe Rolling Mill Iron &
Steel Co. (Fence) .....B
Globe-Wernecke Co. (Copy-
ing Press) ....AAAA

OHIO—Cleveland
Cleveland Hardware Co.
(Wagon Box) ....A
H. P. Nail Co. X
Upson Nut Co. (Nutted)
..................AAA

OHIO—Cuyahoga Falls
Cuyahoga Steel & Wire Co.
(Wire) X

PA.—Erie
Griffin Mfg. Co. ....A

PA.—Norristown
Reading Screw Co. (Wire;
all kinds) ....B

PA.—Philadelphia
Darby & Sons, Edw. (Wire)
....................A

PA.—Pittsburg
Pittsburg Steel Co., Peoples
Saving Bank Bldg. (Wire)
..................AAAA

PA.—Reading
Reading Hdw. Co. (Wrought
Son) ....AAAA

PA.—Sharon Hill
Pickering, Ridgeway S. ..F

PA.—Williamsport
Williamsport Staple Co. ..B

W. VA.—Wheeling
Wheeling Hinge Co. (Steel;
Wrought) ....AA

WIS.—Milwaukee
Milwaukee Tack Co. (Wire;
Fence) C

WIS.—Racine
Racine General Mfg. Co.
....................E

STARCH

CAL.—San Francisco
Everding & Co., J., 48 Clay
....................A
Newell Bros., 217 Davis ..B

CONN.—Bridgeport
Fairchild & Shelton .....AA

CONN.—New Haven
Hubinger Bros. Co. ..AAAA

CONN.—Westport
Atlantic Starch Wrks. Co.
....................B

FLA.—De Land
Seminole Mfg. Co. ......B

FLA.—Lake Mary
Planters Mfg. Co. ....A

ILL.—Chicago
Archer Starch Co., Rialto
Bldg. ....AA
Atwood & Steele, 18 River
....................C
Corn Products Co. ....AAAA
Natl. Starch Co., The Rook-

STARCH (Con.)
ery ....AAAA
Oswego Starch Factory, 83
Michigan Av. ....AA
Puhl-Webb Co., 119 W.
Randolph C
Stein, Hirsh & Co., 2597
Archer Av. (Corn; Laun-
dry) ....AA
ILL.—Franklin Park
Archer Starch Co. ......AA
ILL.—Hammond
Western Starch Association
AA
IND.—Aurora
Steele-Rudell Starch Co. ..C
IND.—Indianapolis
Natl. Starch Co., 601 W.
Morris ....AAAA
IND.—Wabash
Wabash Baking Powder Co.
B
IOWA—Cedar Rapids
Douglass & Co. ....A
IOWA—Davenport
Glucose Sugar Refg. Co.
AAAA
IOWA—Des Moines
Natl. Starch Co. ....AAAA
IOWA—Keokuk
Hubinger Bros Co., J. C.
AAAA
IOWA—Sioux City
Natl. Starch Co. ....AAAA
KY.—Covington
Natl. Starch Co. ....AAAA
MAINE—Ashland
Hayward, G. B. C
MAINE—Cary
Cleveland & Ludwig ......B
MAINE—Easton
Phair, T. H. ....B
MAINE—Houlton
Cleveland & Ludwig ......B
Watson Co., John ....A
MAINE—Patten
Patten Starch Factory ....A
MAINE—Prisque Isle
Phair, Thos. H. ....B
MAINE—Sherman
Phair, Thos. H. ....B
MAINE—Smyrna Mills
Watson, J. C
MAINE—Van Buren
Martin & Lon, Jos. C
MD.—Baltimore
Read & Co., T. (Corn) ..C
MASS.—Boston
Barker & Co., H., Chamber
of Commerce ....A
Coburn & Co., H. B., 69
Broad ....B
Crystal Springs Paste Co.,
70 Kilby ....B
Cummings, David, 19 High
(Corn; Laundry) X
Electric Lustre Starch Co.,
26 Central C
Eustis, Pennock & Co., 63
Kilby (Dextrine; Gums)
AA
Gregory & Co., F. W. (Inc.)
162 High ....AA
Kehew & Bradley Co., 24
Purchase ....B
Marble & Co., J. H., 124
High ....AA
Sherman Mfg. Co., R. I., 290
State C
Spear's Sons Co., Alden, 369
Atlantic Av. (Laundry)
AA
Whitney, E. W., 59 Long
Wharf (Laundry) C
Wing-Mitchell Co., 111
Broad C
MASS.—Harwich
Harwich Starch Co. ..AAA
MASS.—Lexington
Sherman Mfg. Co., R. I.
(Laundry) C
MASS.—Lowell
Coburn & Co., H. B ..C
MASS.—Watertown
Barker & Co., Hiram ....A
MICH.—Harbor Beach
Huron Milling Co. ......AA

MICH.—Jackson
Pacific Starch Co. ....B
MICH.—Traverse City
Michigan Starch Co........A
MICH.—Wyandote
Ford Co., J. B. ......AAA

STARCH (Con.)
MINN.—Monticello
Nickerson Starch Co. ....B
MO.—Kansas City
Eclipse Starch Co., 829 S.
Western Boul. C
Faultless Starch Co., 9th &
Santa Fe ....A
Natl. Starch Co., 211 N. 7th
AAAA
MO.—St. Louis
Eddy & Eddy, 500 Main
(Corn; Laundry) .....A
Natl. Molasses Co., 204 S.
Main ....A
Oswego Starch Factory, 510
Pine ....AA
NEBR.—Nebraska City
Natl. Starch Co. ....AAAA
N. J.—Camden
Camden & Phila. Soap Co.
(Laundry) ....A
N. Y.—Brushton
Sargent, J. H. (P) C
N. Y.—Buffalo
Natl. Starch Co. ....AAAA
N. Y.—Ellenburg
Carter, L. S. & J. L. ....B
N. Y. Fairport
Monroe Co., Chemical Co.
(Corn) ....B
N. Y.—Malone
Hale, G. W. ....A
New York City
Anthony Co., H. M., 48 W.
B'way ....B
Arabol Mfg. Co., 100 Wil-
liam ....B
Celluloid Starch Co., 3
Waverly Pl. ....AA
Hoyt, A. S., 90 W. B'way
(Wheat Cooking; Laun-
dry)) ....B
Kingsford's Oswego Starch
Depot, 22 Harrison
AAAA
Klipstein & Co., 123
Pearl (Potato) ......AA
Kohnstamm & Co., 87 Park
Place ....AA
National Starch Co., 25
Broad ....AAAA
Speare's Sons Co., A., 100
William ....A
Troy Laundry Mach. Co., 33
Warren (Laundry) ..AA
N. Y. Oswego
Kingsford's Oswego Starch
Factory ....AAAA
Oswego Corn Product Co.
(Laundry) ....AAAA
N. Y.—Schuylers Falls
Turner, C. ....B
N. Y.—Troy
Troy Laundry Machine Co.,
(Laundry; Corn) .....AA
N. Y. Ushers
Anthony, Joshua (Corn)..A
OHIO—Cincinnati
Natl. Starch Co., 120 E. 2d
AAAA
OHIO—Columbus
Keever Starch Mfg. Co...A
OHIO—Lockland
Fox, Geo. (Sr. Nat. Starch
Mfg. Co.) ....AAAA
PA.—Knowlton
Barnet, Wm. ....B
PA.—Letitz
Wellington Mfg. Co. (Corn;
Textile) ....A
PA.—Philadelphia
Barnett, Wm., 730 S. Broad
B
Celluloid Starch Co., 715
Vine ....A
National Starch Co., 104 S.
Water ....AAAA
WASH.—Tacoma
Pacific Starch Co. ......A
WIS.—Black River Falls
Black River Falls Starch
Co. ....B
WIS.—Waupaca
Waupaca Starch & Potato
Co., ...C

STARCHERS

See also Machy

ILL.—Chicago
Sinclair Laundry Machinery
Co., 54 N. Clinton (Shirt)
C

STARCHERS (Con.)

MASS.—Boston
Empire Laundry Machinery Co. (Collars; Cuff) .....E

N. Y.—Troy
Troy Laundry Machinery Co. (Ltd.) (Collars; Cuff) ....AA

OHIO—Cincinnati
American Laundry Machinery Co. (Collars; Cuff) ..A
Watkins Laundry Machinery Co. (Collar; Cuff) .....B
Watkins Co., Frank M. (Collars; Cuff) C

PA.—Columbia
Wilson Laundry Machinery Co. (Collars; Cuff) ....B

PA.—Columbia
Wilson Laundry Machinery Co. (Collars; Cuff) ....B

STARTERS

CONN.—Torrington
Union Hardware Co. (Bung) ....AA

ILL.—Belleville
Richardi & Bechtold (Wood Bung) ....B

ILL.—Chicago
Redlich Mfg. Co. (Bung) .B
Wilson & Co., F. Cortez (Bung) ....B

MASS.—Boston
Boston & Lockport Block Co. (Bung) ....A

MICH.—Kalkaska
Freeman Mfg. Co. (Wood Bung) ....B

N. J.—Newark
Sommer's Son, John (Bung) ....B

N. Y.—Brownville
Ward-Leonard Electric Co. (Motor) ....A

OHIO—Piqua
Piqua Handle & Mfg. Co. (Bung) ....A

OHIO—Sandusky
Sandusky Tool Co. (Bung) ....A

PA.—Pittsburg
Westinghouse Elect. Mfg. Co. (Motor) ....AAAA

WIS.—Milwaukee
Cutler, Hammer Mfg. Co. (Motor) ....A

STATIONS

MICH.—Three Rivers
Sheffield Car Co. (Coaling) ....AA

N. Y.—New York City
Hunt Co., C. W. (Locomotive Coaling) ....AA

OHIO—Canton
Aultman Co. Locomotive Coaling) ....AAAA

OHIO—Cleveland
Garry Iron & Steel Co. (Locomotive Coaling) .....A

PA.—Philadelphia
Link Belt Engineering Co. Locomotive Coaling) .AA

PA.—Steelton
Pennsylvania Steel Co. (Railway Iron) ....AAAA

STATUARY
See also Marble

CONN.—Bridgeport
Monumental Bronze Co. (White Bronze) ....A

ILL.—Carpentersville
Illinois Iron & Bolt Co. (Lawn) ....AA

ILL.—Chicago
Amer. Bronze Fdry Co., 73d & Woodlawn Av. (Bronze) ....D
American Terra Cotta & Ceramic Co. (Terra Cotta) ....A
Friedley & Voshardt, 196 Mather (Sheet Metal) ..C
Nicols & Co. ....D
Winslow Bros. Co., 368 Carroll Av. (Bronze) ....AA

MASS.—Boston
Jones & Co., Melville D...F

STATUARY (Con.)

MASS.—Chicopee
Ames Foundries (Bronze)..F
Masman, M. H. C

MASS.—Quincy
Merry ount Granite Co. ..C

MO.—St. Louis
Mesker Bros., 421 S. 6th (Sheet Metal) ....AA

N. J.—Perth Amboy
Perth Amboy Terra Cotta Co. (Terra Cotta) ....AA

N. Y.—Brooklyn
Miller & Doing, 83 Wash'n (Sheet Metal) ....H
Seelig & Co., M. J., 115 Maujer (Zinc; Sheet)..E
White Co., James, 446 Adelphia (Sheet Metal) ....D

N. Y.—New York City
Cabaret & Co., Paul E., 342 W. 14th (Bronze) ....D
Fiske, J. W. (Lawn) ....A
Gorham Mfg. Co., 19th & B'way (Bronze) .AAAA
Henry-Bonnard Bronze Co., 430 W. 16th (Bronze) ..C
Hergert, Theo. E., 382 2d Av. (Sheet Metal) .....D
Lamb, J, & R. ....D
Moore Bronze & Plate Co., M. E. 546 W. 23d C
Mott Iron Works, J. L. (Lawn) ....AA
Stolzenberg Co., 51 Barclay C
Westerbelt, A. B. & W. T. (Lawn) ....B

OHIO—Cincinnati
Edwards Mfg. Co. (Sheet Metal) ....D

OHIO—Kenton
Champion Iron Co. (Lawn) ....AA

OHIO—Salem
Mullins, W. H. (Sheet Metal; Lawn) ....A

OHIO—Zanesville
Townsend, Wm. C. ....AA

PA.—Philadelphia
Bureau Bros., 21st & Allegheny Av. (Bronze) ....D
Cassel, Jacob C. (Terra Cotta) ....D
Galloway, Wm., 3216 Walnut ....A
Harvey, Moland & Co. ...X
Tacony Iron & Metal Co. (Bronze) ....A

VT.—Bellows Falls
Bellows Falls Machine Co. C

WIS.—Milwaukee
Hennecke Co. C. ....A

STATUETTES

CONN.—Meriden
Bradley & Hubbard Mfg. Co. ....AAAA

STAVES
See Cooperage

STAYBOLTS
See also Bolts

MO.—St. Louis
Thompson, Chas. A., 516 N. 3d. (Flexible) C

OHIO—Cuyahoga Falls
Falls-Hollow-Staybolt Co. ....AA

PA.—Philadelphia
Hooper & Townsend Co., 1330 Buttonwood ....AAA

STAYS

CONN.—Bridgeport
Taylor, Thos. P. (Dress)..A
Warner Bros. Co. (Dress) ....AAAA

CONN.—Bristol
Sessions & Son, J. H. (Trunk Lid) ....AA

CONN.—Hartford
Pope Mfg. Co. (Bicycle) ....AAAA

CONN.—New Haven
Peck Bros. Co. (Chain) ..AA

CONN.—Waterbury

STAYS (Con.)
Waterbury Mfg. Co. (Chain)
............................AAAA
ILL.—Chicago
Clow & Sons, Jas. B., 342
  Franklin (Chain) ..AAA
Street & Kent Mfg. Co., 41
  Fulton (Chain) ....B
Wolff Mfg. Co., L., 117 W.
  Lake (Chain) .....AAAA
IND.—Peru
B. B. Fence Co. (Wire
  Fencing) X
IOWA—Dubuque
McDonald, A. Y. & Morrison Mfg. Co. (Chain) ..AA
MD.—Baltimore
McShane Mfg. Co., Hy
............................AAAA
MASS.—Haydenville
Haydenville Co. (Chain) ..B
MICH.—Detroit
Detroit Sanitary Supply Co.
  (Chain) ....D
Diamond Stamped Wire Co.
  (Chain) ....A
MICH.—Ypsilanti
Rubber Tipped Dress Stay
  Co. (Dress, Rubber) ....B
MICH.—Three Oaks
Warren Featherbone Co.
  (Dress) ....AA
MO.—St. Louis
International Steel Post Co.
  (Wire Fencing) ......B
Nelson Mfg. Co., N. O., 8th
  & St. Charles (Chain)AAA
N. J.—Newark
Bernz, Otto, 13th & Orange
  (Chain) ....B
Bowers & Co., Jas. (Dress)
............................AAA
Jenkinson, & Co., R. C.,
  (Trunk Lid) ....AA
N. Y.—Brooklyn
Reid Brass Mfg. Co., 272
  Kent Av. (Chain) ......F
N. Y.—Delevan
Globe Fence Co. (Fence) ..F
N. Y.—Elmira
Cronk & Carrier Mfg. Co.
  (Roller) ....B
New York City
Cohn & Co., M. (Dress;
  Corset) ....E
Du Bois & Co., N. F., 245
  9th Av. (Chain) ....AAA
Mott Iron Works, J. L., 88
  Beekman (Chain) ....AA
Peck, Stow & Wilcox Co., 7
  Murray (Roller) ..AAAA
Sargent & Co., 151 Leonard
  (Roller) ....AAAA
Warner Bros. Co. (Dress)
............................AAAA
Yale & Towne Mfg. Co., 9
  Murray (Transom) AAAA
N. Y.—Poughkeepsie
Lane Bros. Co. (Roller) A
N. Y.—Weedsport
Weedsport Skirt & Waist Co.
  (Dress) ....B
OHIO—Canton
Ney Mfg. Co. (Roller) ..B
OHIO—Cincinnati
Gholson Fence Co., W. C.,
  1746 Reading Rd. (Steel
  Fence) ....H
OHIO—Cleveland
Sanitary Co., 335 Huron
  (Chain) C
OHIO—Columbus
Columbus Brass Co. (Chain)
............................B
OHIO—Covington
Crescent Metallic Fence
  Stay Co. (Fence) ......F
PA.—Allegheny
McKinney Mfg. Co. (Roller)
............................AA
PA.—Philadelphia
Haines Jones & Cadbury Co.,
  1237 Ridge Av. (Chain)AA
PA.—Pittsburg
Scaife & Sons Co., Wm. B.
  (Roller) ....AAA
Standard Sanitary Mfg. Co.,
  Arrott Bldg. (Chain)
............................AAAA
PA.—Reading
Reading Hardware Co.
  (Roller) ....AAAA
W. VA.—Wheeling
Wheeling Hinge Co. (Hand
  Rail; Stair Rail) ....AA

STAYS (Con.)
WIS.—Milwaukee
Hoffman & Billings Mfg. Co.
  (Chain) ....AA
WIS.—Racine
Racine Tank Lug Co.
  (Wire Fencing) X
WIS.—South Milwaukee
Stowell Mfg. & Foundry Co.
  (Roller) ....A

STEAMBOATS
See also Ships

STEAMERS
CONN.—Meriden
Manning, Bowman & Co.
............................AAAA
ILL.—Chicago
Henion & Hubbell (Feed) B
White Mfg. Co., 93 Mich.
  Av. (Thawing) ....D
ILL.—Paxton
Paxton Hdw. Mfg. Co. (for
  Cooking Purposes) X
IND.—Indianapolis
Nordyke & Marmon Co.
  (Feed) ....AAA
IOWA—Waterloo
Kelley & Taneyhill (Feed)G
Litchfield Mfg. Co. (Feed)A
IOWA—Webster City
Litchfield Mfg. Co. (Feed)A
MD.—Baltimore
Hutchinson Bros., 116 N.
  Howard (Vegetable) ...D
MASS.—Boston
McDowell Oven Co. (Brown
  Bread) ....H
MINN.—Minneapolis
Howell & Co., R. (Feed) B
N. Y.—Buffalo
Shepard & Co., Sidney
............................AAAA
N. Y.—Cortland
Lewis, L. R. (Feed) X
New York City
Lalance & Grosjean Mfg. Co.
............................AAAA
Gorton & Lidgerwood Co.
  (Feed) ....B
N. Y.—Troy
Troy Stamping Wks. J. M.
  Warren & Co.)....AAAA
OHIO—Bucyrus
American Clay Working
  Mach. Co. (Clay) .....B
OHIO—New Philadelphia
Spicer Mfg. Co. (Clay)....D

STEAMSHIPS
See Ships; Boats

STEARINE
ILL.—Chicago
Morris & Co., Nelson AAAA
Swift & Co. ....AAAA
IOWA—Cedar Rapids
Sinclair & Co., S. M. AAA
MASS.—Boston
Reardon & Sons, J. J. X
MO.—Kansas City
Armour Packing Co. AAAA
N. Y.—Brooklyn
Davis Oil Co., 95 Ninth ...C
New York City
Donahue & Son, P., 652 W.
  29th ....A
Habermann, Joseph, 625 W.
  40th ....B
Manhattan Oil Wks. .....D
Welch, Holme & Clark Co.,
  381 West ....A
OHIO—Cincinnati
Amer. Cotton Oil Co. of
  Ohio ....AA
Emery Candle Co. ......AA
R. I.—Providence
Union Oil Co. ....AAA

STEEL
See Iron & Steel

STEELS
CONN.—Ansonia
Union Fabric Co. (Corset)D
CONN.—Bridgeport
Connecticut Clasp Co.

STEELS (Con.)
(Corset) ....D
CONN.—New Britain
Landers, Frary & Clark
(Butcher) ....AAA
ILL.—Chicago
American Cutlery Co.
(Butcher) ....A
Chicago Wheel & Mfg. Co.,
39 W. Rand (Butcher)..D
MASS.—Brockton
Tuck Mfg. Co. (Buffer;
Scraper) ....E
N. H.—Antrim
Goodell Co. (Butcher) ....A
New York City
Chatillon & Sons, Jno.
(Butcher) ....A
PA.—Philadelphia
Hoffman, C. A. (Butcher) B
R. I.—Providence
Nicholson File Co.
(Butcher) ....AA

STEEPERS
ILL.—Clyde
Coonley Mfg. Co. (Tea)..B
MO.—St. Louis
St. Louis Stamping Co.
(Tea) ....AAAA
N. Y.—Buffalo
Shepard & Co., Sidney (Tea)
AAAA

STEINS
New York City
Levy & Co., L. W., 194
Bway. (Beer, etc.) ....B
OHIO—Zebring
Zebring Pottery Co. (Beer,
etc.) ....AA

STEINWARE
IND.—Marion
Canton Glass Co. ....B
PA.—Beaver Falls
Co-operative Flint Glass Co.
A
PA.—Philadelphia
Gillinder & Sons ....A
PA.—Pittsburg
McKee & Bros. X
U. S. Glass Co. ....AA
PA.—Tarentum
Tarentum Glass Co. ......A
PA.—Washington
Duncan's Sons & Co., Geo. A
W. VA.—Moundsville
Fostoria Glass Co. ....AAA
W. VA.—Wellsburg
Riverside Glass Wks. C
W. VA.—Wheeling
Central Glass Wks. ......A

STEMMERS
OHIO—Sandusky
Klotz Machine Co. (Grape)C
VA.—Richmond
Richmond Cedar Wks.
(Cedar; Kraut) ....AAAA

STENCILS
COLO.—Denver
Denver Novelty Work Mfg.
Co. ....D
CONN.—Bridgeport
Schwerdtle Stamp Co. ....F
CONN.—New Haven
Hoggson & Pettis Mfg. Co.
A
CONN.—Unionville
Monce, S. G. (Interchange-
able Lock) ....D
IND.—Evansville
Elbert. C. H. ....F
MD.—Baltimore
Dorman Co., J. F. W. ...F
MASS.—Boston
Power & Co., J. H. ....G
MASS.—Springfield
Smith Mfg. Co., R. H. ...C
MO.—St. Louis
Barnard Stamp Co. ......E
N. Y.—Albany
Lang, Jacob S. X
New York City
Carragan, Geo. ....
Devoe. F. W. & C. T. Ray-
nolds Co. ....AAAA
Force & Co., Wm. A., 50
Beekman ....B

STENCILS (Con.)
Majert, Emil, 26 Elm ....D
Ness Jr., Geo. M. ....H
New York Stencil Wks...D
Reilly Bros. (Fresco) .....D
Stafford Co., Nelson, 66
Fulton ....F
N. Y.—Utica
Balch Bros. & West Co. ..D
OHIO—Cambridge
Crescent Seal Stamp Co. H
OHIO—Cincinnati
Cressler, Wm. T. C
OHIO—Dayton
Howard, Wm. H. ....E
PA.—Philadelphia
Quint & Son, S. H., 15 So.
4th C
Weber & Co., W. (Fresco)
A
WIS.—Milwaukee
Schwaab Stamp & Stencil
Co. C

STEP LADDERS
See Ladders

STEPS
See Stairs; Hardware; Carriage

CONN.—Hartford
Hartford Machine Screw Co.
(Bicycle) ....AAAA
CONN.—Plantsville
Atwater Mfg. Co. (Car-
riage) ....A
Blakeslee Forging Co.
(Carriage; Wagon) ....B
Smith & Co., H. D. (Car-
riage) ....AA
DEL.—Wilmington
Diamond State Steel Co.
(Pole) ....AAA
ILL.—Chicago
American Steel & Wire Co.
Rookery Bldg (Pole)
AAAA
Barbee Wire & Iron Wks.
(Carriage) ....B
Cutter Co. Geo., 100 Lake
(Removable Pole) C
Railway Appliance Co., Old
Colony Bldg. (Car)....A
Republic Iron & Steel Co.
(Pole) ....AAAA
MASS.—Boston
Boston Bolt Co., 33 Pur-
chase (Pole) ....B
MICH.—Detroit
Anderson & Sons, W. H.
(Pole; Sewer Manhole)C
Co-operative Fdry. (Sewer
Manhole) X
Michigan Bolt & Nut Wks.
(Pole) ....A
MO.—Kansas City
Kansas City Bolt & Nut Co.
(Pole) ....A
MO.—St. Louis
Moran Bolt & Nut Mfg. Co.
(Pole) ....A
N. H.—Exeter
Rubber Step Mfg. Co. (Car-
riage) ....D
N. J.—Newark
Maher & Flockhart, 62 Polk
(Sewer Manhole) ......A
Strieby & Foot Co. (Car-
riage & Wagon) ......B
N. Y.—Auburn
Clapp Mfg. Co., E. D. (Car-
riage) ....B
N. Y.—Brooklyn
Cooper & McKee (Library;
Pantry) ....A
N. Y.—Buffalo
Pratt & Letchworth (Car-
riage) ....AA
New York City
American Steel & Wire Co.,
71 B'way (Hole)..AAAA
Mace & Co., L. H. (Library;
Pantry) ....B
Mason & Co., J. W. (Li-
brary) ....D
N. Y.—Oxford
Clark Blue Stone Co., F. C.
(Stone) ....A
OHIO—Cleveland
Cleveland Hdw. Co.......A

STEPS (Con.)

OHIO—Mansfield
Ohio Brass Co. (Pole)....B
PA.—Lebanon
American Iron & Steel Mfg.
Co. (Pole) ....AAAA
PA.—Mechanicsburg
Wilcox Mfg. Co., D. (Car-
riage) ....B
PA.—Philadeelphia
Hoopes & Townsend Co.,
1330 Buttonwood (Pole)
AAA
PA.—Pittsburg
Lanz & Sons, Mathew, 101
S. 29th (Pole) ....B
Oliver Iron & Steel Co.
(Pole) ....AAAA
R. I.—Providence
Safety Electric Switch Co.
(Detachable Pole) X
VA.—Richmond
Old Dominion Iron & Nail
Wks. Co. (Pole) ......A
W. VA.—Wheeling
Wheeling Hinge Co. (Pole)
AA

STEREOGRAPH-
OSCOPES

ILL.—Chicago
Geneva Optical Co......B
VT.—North Bennington
White Co., H. C.........B

STEREOPTI-
CONS

ILL.—Chicago
Martin Co., Edw. P......C
MASS.—Boston
Tompson & Co., A. T., 26
Bromfield X
New York City
Colt Co., J. B., 21 Barclay
B
McAllister, T. H., 49 Nas-
sua ....B
PA.—Philadelphia
Queen & Co., 1010 Chestnut
AA
Williams, Brown & Earle
A

STEREO-
SCOPES

PA.—Philadelphia
McIntire, Magee & Brown
A
VT.—North Bennington
White Co., H. C........B

STERILIZERS

ILL.—Chicago
Barber Mfg. Co., A. H.
(Milk) ....B
IND.—Indianapolis
Armstrong & Co., Wm. H.
(Eye Ointment) .....B
MASS.—Boston
Empire Laundry Machy Co.
(Laundry) ....E
N. J.—Haddonfield
Star Milk Cooler Co. (Milk)
C
N. Y.—Brooklyn
Wallace Co., Jno. B., 400 S.
2d (Brass; Copper).....B
New York City
Hospital Supply Co. (In-
strument; Steam; Dress-
ing, etc.) ....A
N. Y.—Rochester
Castle & Co., Wilmot
(Milk; Steam) ....B
OHIO—Cincinnati
Amer. Laundry Mchy. Co.
(Laundry; Steam) .....A
Watkins Mfg. Co., F. M.
(Steam) ....B
OHIO—Sandusky
Warren Electric Mfg. Co.
(Laundry) ....A
OHIO—Toledo
Toledo Cooker Co.
(Steam) C
PA.—Philadelphia
Bockel & Co., Wm., 578

STERILIZERS (Con.)
Vine (Steam) ....A
Forbes Co., 1234 Callowhill
(Water) C

STETHO-
SCOPES

New York City
Tiemann & Co., Geo., 107
Park Row ....A
Tutschek, F., 209 Centre..G
VT.—North Bennington
White Co., H. C.........B

STICKS

**See also Clubs; also Wood-
work; Carriage**

CONN.—Central Village
Torrey Bros. Co. (Polo)...E
CONN.—Danielson
Jacobs Mfg. Co., E. H.
(Picker) ....B
CONN.—West Thompson
Tatem & Son, J. B.
(Picker) ....B
ILL.—Chicago
Kester Elect. Mfg. Co., 251
S. Jeff. (Soldering) ...D
Spinks & Co., W. A., 93
Erie (Billiard) C
ILL.—Freeport
Arcade Mfg. Co. (Mop)..A
Stover Mfg. Co. (Hop).AA
IND.—Indianapolis
Leedy Mfg. Co. (Drum)..E
MASS.—Boston
Golding & Co. (Shooting).C
MASS.—Charlemont
Frary Mfg. Co. (Flag) ...E
MASS.—Lowell
New England Shuttle Co.
(Picker) X
MASS.—Worcester
Crompton & Knowles Loom
Wks. (Picker) ....AAAA
MICH.—Ludington
Tubbs Mfg. Co. (Printers'
Cutting; Printers' Galley)
B
N. H.—Horn's Mills
Horn, James (Picker)....X
N. H.—Rumney
Loveland, Jr., L. H.
(Picker) ....G
N. J.—Cedar Brook
Bailey, Frank (Dye) ....B
N. J.—Irvington
Belcher Bros. & Co. (Size)
X
N. J.—Jersey City
Winter & Ball Mfg. Co.
(Umbrella) X
N. Y.—Auburn
James Mfg. Co. (Mop)...F
N. Y.—Middletown
Morgan & Wilcox Mfg. Co.
(Composing; Shooting).D
New York City
Bresnan Type Foundry Co.,
P. H. (Side; Foot) ....B
Estes & Sons, E. B.
(Clapper) ....AA
Goldberg & Weber (Um-
brella) C
Harvey & Watts Co.
(Umbrella) ....F
Hoe & Co., R. (Shooting;
Composing) ....AAAA
Liberty Machine Co.
(Composing) ....E
N. C.—Greensboro
Southern Bobbin Co. (Hick-
ory Picker) ....D
OHIO—Cleveland
Chandler & Price Co.
(Composing; Shooting)..A
OHIO—Piqua
Piqua Handle & Mfg. Co.
(Gambrel) ....A
OHIO—Toledo
Toledo Billiard Ball Co.
(Billiard) ....D
PA.—New Brighton
Logan & Strobridge Iron
Co. (Mop) ....B
R. I.—Providence
Amer. Emery Wheel Wks.
(Emery; Corundum) C

STICKS (Con.)

VA.—Petersburg
South Side Mfg. Co.
(Shooting) C
WIS.—Two Rivers
Hamilton Mfg. Co. (Cutting for Paper Cutters)..
AA

STIFFENERS

CONN.—Danbury
Morlock & Husk (Roll)...E
N. J.—Newark
Sacks Iron Fdry., Louis
(Heel) ....A
WIS.—South Milwaukee
Stowell Mfg. & Fdry. Co.
(Heel) ....A

STILLS

ALA.—Birmingham
Dimmick Pipe Co. (Oil;
Tar) ....A
CAL.—Los Angeles
Lacy Mfg. Co. (Refinery)
AA
ILL.—Chicago
Harris & Bro., Geo. P., 64
W. Lake (Distillery)...B
Royal Distillery Co.
(Water) ....E
LA.—New Orleans
Connell Iron Wks. Co., J.
D. (Turpentine) ......B
MD.—Baltimore
Baltimore Cooperage Co.
(Distillery) ....B
MICH.—Detroit
Colton, Arthur (Pharmaceutical) C
MICH.—Saginaw
Morley Bros. ....AA
N. Y.—Brooklyn
Clowbrock Steel Boiler Co.
(Tar) ....D
N. Y.—Buffalo
Case & Son, W. A.
(Whiskey) ....AA
New York City
Bailey Mfg. Co., A. R.
(Water) ....D
Eimer & Amend ....AA
Heipershausen Bros. (Oil)
D
Trageser Steam Copper
Wks., 447 W. 26th (Alcohol Plant) ....B
OHIO—Cincinnati
American Copper & Brass
Wks. (Whiskey) ......A
Blymyer Iron Wks. Co.
(Whiskey) ....B
Day & Co., H. (Druggists')
A
Hauser, Bremer & Fath Co.
B
Tudor Boiler Mfg. Co.
(Oil; Tar) ....B
OHIO—Marietta
Marietta Boiler Wks. ....A
OHIO—Youngstown
Pollock & Co., Wm. P.
(Oil; Tar) ....AA
PA.—Pittsburg
Carroll-Porter Boiler &
Tank Co. (Oil) ....B
Riter-Conley Mfg. Co. (Oil;
Tar) ....AA
PA.—Warren
Struthers, Wells & Co.
(Oil; Tar) ....AA

STILTS

MICH.—Fenton
Phillips Co., A. J.
(Boys') ....A
MO.—St. Louis
Benjamin Air Rifle Co.
(Boys') ....E
OHIO—East Liverpool
Burgess & Co. (Potters')
B

STIRRUPS

CONN.—New Haven
North & Co., O. B........AA
IND.—Indianapolis
Holliday & Wyon ....A
N. J.—Newark
Baldwin & Co., Jos. (Steel)
D

STIRRUPS (Con.)

Buerman, August ......B
Peters' Harness & Saddlery
Co. (Leather; Steel;
Wood) C
N. Y.—Buffalo
Pratt & Letchworth ...AA
OHIO—Canton
Elbel & Co. (Steel) .....B
OHIO—Sandusky
Knight, H. H. (Wooden).D
PA.—Wrightsville
Wrightsville Hdw. Co.
(Harness) C
R. I.—Bristol
Dixon Lubricating Saddle
Co. ....B
R. I.—Pawtucket
Haskell Mfg. Co. (Steel for
Cotton Machinery) ...AA
TENN.—Chattanooga
Southern Saddlery Co.
(Wooden) ....A
TEXAS—Dallas
Speer, Steinmann Co. X

STITCHERS

See also Machy

CONN.—Hartford
Smyth Mfg. Co. (Thread)
AA
CONN.—New Haven
Brown & Co., R. H. (Wire)
B
Hoggson & Pettis Co. (Rubber Hand) ....A
Thompson & Sons, H. G.
(Wire) ....B
ILL.—Chicago
Latham Mchry. Co. (Wire)
C
MASS.—Lynn
Cilley & Co., W. W. (Shoe)
F
Coffin & Shines (Shoe)...X
MASS.—Medford
Wellman Sole Cutting Mach.
Co. (Thread) ....D
New York City
Morrison Co., J. L. (Wire)
D
Sheridan, T. W. & C. B.
(Wire) ....A
PA.—Harrisburg
Hickok Mfg. Co., W. O.
(Thread) ....AA
PA.—Philadelphia
Shoemaker & Co., J. L.
(Wire) ....D

STOCK: GEAR; WHEEL, ETC.

See Woodwork; Carriage, etc.

STOCK: PAPER

See Rags

STOCKINGS

See Hosiery

STOKERS

ILL.—Chicago
Green Engineering Co., 138
Jackson Boul. (Mechanical) ....D
Hawley Down Draft Furnace Co. (Mechanical)..A
Little Giant Stoker Co.,
3906 S. Halsted (Mechanical) ....B
Under Feed Stoker Co., 204
Dearborn (Under Feed
Mechanical) ....B
MICH.—Detroit
Detroit Automatic Stoker
Co. (Mechanical) ......D
MINN.—Duluth
Duluth Stoker Co. (Mechanical) ....B
New York City
Babcock & Wilcox Co., 85
Liberty (Mechanical)....
AAAA
Ross & Co., 95 Liberty
(Mechanical) X

STOKERS (Con.)

Westinghouse, Church, Kerr
& Co., 8 Bridge (Mechan-
ical) ....A

OHIO—Cincinnati
Day-Kincaid Stoker Co.
(Locomotive) ....B

OHIO—Cleveland
Brightman Furnace Co., 648
B'way (Mechanical) ...D

PA.—Bridgeport
Wilkinson Mfg. Co. (Me-
chanical) C

PA.—Philadelphia
Box & Co., Alfred (Cechan-
ical) ....D
Sellers & Co., Wm. (Me-
chanical) ....AAAA

PA.—Pittsburg
Cahill Sales Department
(Mechanical) ....A
Westinghouse Machine Co.
(Mechanical) .....AAAA

STONE

**See also Bluestone; Lime-
stone; Pumice; Sand-
stone; Granite; Soap-
stone.**

CAL.—Los Angeles
California Portland Cement
Co. (Crushed Limestone)
B

CONN.—Bridgeport
Pierce Mfg. Co. (Artificial)
E

CONN.—Cromwell
New England Brown Stone
Co. (Brown; Foundation;
Rubble) ....AA

CONN.—Meriden
Conn. Trap Rock Quarries
(Crushed) ....A

CONN.—Middletown
Haddam Granite Co. (Crush-
ed; Granite) ....B
Caldwell, Chas. B.
(Crushed) ....B

CONN.—New Haven
Blakeslee & Sons, C. W.
(Crushed) ....AA
Connecticut Concrete Co.
(Crushed) ....A
Connecticut Trap Rock
Quarries (Trap Rock;
Crushed) ....A

CONN.—New London
Scott, Thos. A. (Crushed).A

D.C.—Washington
Palmer Hollow Concrete
Building Co., H. S. (Arti-
fical Building) ....D

ILL.—Chicago
Artesian Stone & Lime Wks
Co. (Crushed) ....B
Brownell Improvement Co.
(Limestone; also Concrete
Crushed) ....A
Chicago Crushed Stone Co.,
108 La Salle (Crushed).B
Chicago Union Lime Works
Co., W. 19th (Crushed).B
Doles & Shepherd Co., 184
La Salle (Crushed; Gra-
nite) ....B
Lake Shore Sand & Gravel
Co. (Crushed) ....B
Portage Entry Quarries Co.
(Sand; Red) ....B
Sherman & Flavin (Marble)
B
Stearns Lime & Stone Co.,
165 E. Randolph (Lime-
stone Crushed) ......AA
Western Consolidated Gra-
nite Co., Chamber of Com.
Bldg (Granite Crushed).B
Western Stone Co., Chamber
of Com. Bldg. (Crushed)
AAA

ILL.—Naperville
Dolese & Shepard Co.
(Crushed) ....B

IND.—Evansville
Bedford & Nugent
(Crushed) ....B

IOWA—Marshalltown
Le Grand Quarry Co.
(Lime; Marble) ......A

KANS.—Wichita
Wichita Hydraulic Stone &
Brick Co. (Artifical

STONE (Con.)

Building) ....E

KY.—Dayton
Trapp, John (Crushed)...B

KY.—Louisville
Caron Stone Co. (Litho-
graphic) ....D

MAINE—Frankfort
Mount Waldo Granite Wks.
(Granite; Rough) .....A

MAINE—Hallowell
Hallowell Granite Co. (Gra-
nite Dressed; Granite
Rough) ....AA

MAINE—Red Beach
Maine Red Granite Co.
(Foundation; Granite
Red; Granite Rough) ..B

MD.—Dickersons
Standard Lime & Stone Co.
(Crushed) ....A

MD.—Port Deposit
McClenahan & Bro. Granite
Co. (Granite) ....A

MASS.—Boston
Bowker, Torrey & Co.
(Soap) ....AA
Gilbreth Seam Face Granite
Co. (Seam Face Granite)
D
Rockport Granite Co., 31
State (Granite Crushed)
A

MASS.—Pigeon Cove
Pigeon Hill Granite Co.
(Crushed) ....A

MASS.—Rockport
Rockport Granite Co. (Granite; Crushed) ....A

MICH.—Detroit
Griffin, M. J., 104 Lafferty
Pl. (Crushed) ....B
Little Co., C. H., Penna.
Bank Bldg. (Crushed)..B

MICH.—Manistique
White Marble Lime Co.
(Crushed) ....B

MICH.—Monroe
Monroe Stone Co. (Crushed)
B

MO.—St. Louis
Eyermann Jr. & Bro., G.,
Hickory (Crushed) ....B
Nelson Mfg. Co., N. O.
(Marble; Plumbers').AAA
Schneider Granite Co., Ful-
lerton Bldg. (Granite;
Crushed) ....A

N. H.—Pike Station
Pike Mfg. Co. (Gold Test-
ing) ....A

N. H.—West Lebanon
Pigeon Hill Granite Co.
(Granite; Crushed) ....A

N. J.—Jersey City
Shanley Co., B. M. & J. F.
(Crushed) ....AA

N. J.—Paterson
McKiernan & Bergin
(Crushed) ....A
Sharpe, Joseph (Artificial)
D

N. Y.—Albany
Callahan Road Improvement
Co., 51 State (Limestone;
Crushed) ....B
Dumary, Henry T., 40 State
(Crushed) ....B

N. Y.—Brooklyn
Wiarda & Co., John C.
(Ground Cliff; Ground
Cornwall; Rotten) ...AA

N. Y.—Buffalo
Buffalo Cement Co., 110
Franklin (Crushed; Build-
ing; Cut) ....AAAA
German Rock Asphalt &
Cement Co., Morgan Bldg.
(Crushed) ....A

New York City
Behr & Co., Herman, 75
Beekman (Pumice) ...AA
Dunn, Thos. J. (Blue)....D
Hammill & Gillespie, 240
Front (Pumice) ......A
(Brown) ....B
Henry & Co., M. C.
(Brown) X
Klaber, Adolph (Marble).B
O'Brien Bros., 54 South
(Crushed) ....A
Phoenix Towing & Trans-
portation Co., 17 State
(Crushed or Broken)....B

979

STONE (*Con.*)
Pettit Chemical Co. (Soap) ....B

Taintor Mfg. Co., H. F. (Ground Cliff) ....B
Tomkins & Calvin, 120 Liberty (Crushed Blue) ....B
Van Amringe, Theo., 97 Liberty (Pumice) ......B
Waddell & Co., R. J., 52 Beekman (Pumice) ..AA
N. Y.—Oxford
Clarke Blue Store Co., F. G. (Building; Blue; Planed; Sawed; Flagging; Curbing) ....A
N. Y.—Potsdam
Potsdam Red Sandstone Co. ...D
N. Y.—Schenectady
Shear & Co., A. (Crushed) ....B
N. Y.—Tompkins Cove
Tompkins Cove Stone Co. (Crushed) ....A
N. Y.—Warsaw
Warsaw Blue Stone Co...B
OHIO—Cincinnati
Hummel Building Co. (Free) ....AA
Obermayer Co., S. (Pumice) ....AA
OHIO—Cleveland
Cleveland Concrete & Building Blk. Co. (Artificial Building Blocks) ......A
Cleveland Stone Co. (Building; Curbing; Flagging) .....AAAA
Malone Stone Co. (Blue; Face; Lime) ....A
Spence Bros., 2923 Euclid Av. (Crushed) ....A
OHIO—Columbus
Casparis Stone Co. (Crushed) ....B
Columbus Stone Co., 319 Dublin Av. (Crushed)..B
OHIO—East Liverpool
Knowles, Taylor & Knowles Co. (Granite; White) .....AAAA
OHIO—Lowellville
Carbon Limestone Co. (Crushed; Concrete a Specialty) ....A
OHIO—Marion
Evans Stone & Lime Co., Jno. (Crushed) ....A
OHIO—Springfield
Mills Bros. (Crushed)....B
OHIO—Youngstown
Bessemer Limestone Co. (Crushed) ....A
OHIO—Zanesville
Townsend, Wm. C. (Granite; Marble) ....AA
PA.—Easton
Easton Lime Co. (Crushed) .....A
Williams & Co., C K. (Pumice; Pulverized Pumice & Soap) ....A
PA.—Norristown
Block & Tile Paving Co. (Limestone; Crushed) .B
Dyer Quarry Co., Jno. L. (Crushed) ....AA
PA.—Philadelphia
Cedar Hollow Lime Co., Land Title Bldg. (Crushed) ....A
Dyer Quarry Co., Jno. T., 12 So. 15th (Crushed)...A
Holmesburg Granite Co., Fidelity Bldg. Seam Face Granite) ....B
Krause & Son, Wm. (Artificial) ....A
McIlvaine Bros. (Pumice)B
Pennsylvania Salt Mfg Co. (Blue) ....AAAA
Sharpless & Watts (Marble) ....A
Warner Co.. Charles, Land Title Bldg. (Limestone; Crushed) ....AA
PA.—Pittsburg
Booth & Flinn (Ligonier Granite) ....AAAA
Consolidated Stone & Mining Co.. Hamilton Bldg. (Limestone: Crushed)..B
McCormick Co., J. S.

STONE (*Con.*)
(Soap) ....B
Minsinger Bros. & Co., 562 2d Av. (Crushed) ......B
Pope Cement & Brick Co., 421 Wood (Crushed)....B
Winfield Mineral Co., 421 Wood (Crushed) ......A
PA.—South Bethlehem
General Crushed Stone Co. (Crushed) ....A
PA.—Tyrone
Amer. Lime & Stone Co. (Limestone; Crushed) .....AAAA
PA.—Waltonville
Hummelstown Brown Stone Co. ....A
R. I.—Westerly
Smith Granite Co. (Granite Rough) ....D
TEXAS—El Paso
El Paso Ice & Refrigerator Co. (Crushed) ....B
VT.—Proctor
Vermont Marble Co. (Marble Sawed; Finished) .....AAAA
WIS.—Green Bay
Flatley Bros. & Co. (Artificial Building) ....B
WIS.—Racine
O'Laughlin Stone Co., Jno. (Crushed) ....B
Racine Cement & Pipe Co. (Artificial) X

STONERS

MD.—Baltimore
Sinclair-Scott Co. (Cherry) .....E
N. H.—Antrim
Goodell Co. (Cherry).....A
N. Y.—Buffalo
Buffalo Specialty Mfg. Co. (Cherry) ....B
New York City
Graham & Co., Jno. H., 113 Chambers (Cherry) ..AA
PA.—New Brighton
Logan & Strobridge Iron Co. (Cherry) ....B
PA.—Mount Joy
Rollman Mfg. Co. (Cherry; Peach) ....G
PA.—Philadelphia
Enterprise Mfg. Co. of Pa. (Cherry) ....AAAA

STONES

See also Grindstones; Tables; Millstones

CONN.—Bridgeport
Bridgeport Safety Emery Wheel Co. (Emery) ....F
CONN.—Higganum
Cutaway Harrow Co. (Scythe) X
ILL.—Chicago
Chicago Wheel & Mfg. Co., 39 W. Rand (Axe; Emery; Oil; Water; Razor; Rubbing; Scythe) ......D
Kaestner & Co. (Burr)...A
MASS.—Boston
Harvey, H. H. (Jack)....B
MASS.—Leeds:
Northhampton Emery Wheel Co. (Dry Rubbing; Sharpening; Emery; Oil; Rub) ...A
MASS.—Waltham
Waltham Emery Wheel Co. (Emery; Oil; Rub) C
MASS.—Westfield
Vitrified Wheel Co. (Emery; Oil; Water) ......B
MASS.—Worcester
Morton Emery Wheel Co. (Dry Rubbing; Sharpening; Emery; Oil; Rub; Water; Scythe) ....AAA
MICH.—Detroit
Strelinger Co., Charles (Emery; Oil; Rub) ....A
N. H.—Keene
Wilkins Toy Co. (Jack)..X
N. H.—Pike Station
Pike Mfg. Co. (Oil; Tool Sharpening; Scythe; Wood Pulp; Axe; Curriers;' Tanners'; Emery;

STOOLS (Con.)

OHIO—Columbus
Holtzman & Sons, Henry
(Organ; Piano) ....A
OHIO—Dayton
Stomps-Burhardt Co. (Type-
writers') ....AA
OHIO—Hamilton
Meyers Mfg. Co., Fred J.
(Store) ....B
PA.—South Bethlehem
Bethlehem Fdy & Machine
Co. (Store) C
PA.—Union City
Novelty Wood Wks. (Foot)
B
TENN.—Knoxville
Knoxville Coffin Co.
(Coffin) ....D
VT.—Readsboro
Readsboro Chair Mfg Co.
(Foot) ....B
WIS.—Milwaukee
Kipp Co., B. A. (Foot;
Piano; Store) ....B
Meinecke & Son, A. (Foot)
AA
WIS.—Racine
Gold Medal Camp Furniture
& Novelty Co. (Store;
Camp) ....B
WIS.—Sheboygan
Crocker Chair Co. (Office;
Store) ....AAA

STOOPS

New York City
Cornell, J. B. & J. M.
(Iron) ....AA
Dimond, Thomas (Iron)...A

STOPPERS

CONN.—Bridgeport
Canfield, H. O. (Bottle).D
CONN.—Meriden
Manning, Bowman & Co.
(Bottle) ....AA
CONN.—New Britain
Taplin Mfg. Co. (Bottle).D
Traut & Hine Mfg. Co.
(Bottle) ....AA
CONN.—Oakville
Baird Machine Co.
(Bottle) ....F
ILL.—Chicago
Bartlett & Son, N. J., 196
. Clark (Bottle)......F
Hutchinson & Son, W. H.
(Bottle) ....A
Perfection Bottle Stopper
Co. (Bottle) ....F
ILL.—Paxton
Paxton Hdw. Mfg. Co.
(Flue) X
ILL.—Rockford
Clark Hardware Co., J. L.
(Flue) ....D
MD.—Baltimore
Crown Cork & Seal Co.
(Beer Bottle) ......AAA
N. J.—Newark
Williams Wire Novelty Co.,
C. L. (Bottle) ....B
N. Y.—Brooklyn
Sweeney Mfg. Co., W. H.
(Flue) ....A
N. Y.—Buffalo
Shepard & Co., Sidney
(Flue) ....AAAA
New York City
Ansonia Brass & Copper Co.
(Flue) ....AAAA
Deverall Mfg. Co. (Bottle)
G
Gutmann, Ferdinand & Co.
(Beer Bottle) ....A
Hutter, Karl (Bottle)....A
Phoenix Cork Co. (Beer
Bottle) C
Putnam, Henry W. (Bottle)
B
Wittemann Bros. (Beer
Bottle) ....A
OHIO—Cincinnati
Cramer, Jos. (Beer Bottle)
X
PA.—Philadelphia
Fox & Sons, H. C. (Bottle)
AA
Hero Fruit Jar Co.
(Bottle) ....AA
Seidel, R. B., 1334 Callow-
hill (Ladle) ....A

STOPPERS (Con.)

Twitchell Co., S. (Bottle).A
Wirtz, A. H., (Bottle)....A
PA.—Pittsburg
McCullough-Dalzell Crucible
Co. (Plumbago) ....A
R. I.—Providence
Amer. Ship Windlass Co.
(Chain; Hawser; Pipe,
etc.) ....AA
W. VA.—Wheeling
Wheeling Hinge Co. (Bot-
tle) ....AA

STOPPLES

CONN.—New Haven
Seamless Rubber Co.
(Rubber) ....AA
MASS.—Andover
Tyer Rubber Co. (Rubber)
AA
MASS.—Boston
Boston Belting Co. (Rub-
ber) ....AAAA
N. J.—Trenton
Union Rubber Co. (Rubber)
E
New York City
Goodyear Rubber Co.
(Rubber) ....AAAA
Goodyear's India Rubber
Glove Mfg. Co. (Rubber)
AAAA
Gutta Percha & Rubber
Mfg Co. (Rubber)AAAA
Hodgman Rubber Co....AA
India Rubber Comb Co.
(Rubber) X
Mattson Rubber Co. (Rub-
ber) ....B
N. Y. Belting & Packing
Co. (Rubber) ......AAA
Parker, Stearns & Sutton
(Rubber) ....B
OHIO—Akron
Akron Rubber Wks.
(Rubber) ....AAAA
Goodrich Co., B. F.
(Rubber) ....AAAA
R. I.—Providence
Davol Rubber Co. (Rubber)
AA

STOPS

CONN.—Bridgeport
Knapp & Cowles Mfg. Co.
(Door) C
CONN.—Bristol
Sessions & Son, J. H.
(Rubber Tip Door)..AAA
CONN.—Deep River
Denison Bros. (Organ)...D
CONN.—New Britain
Judd, Oliver S. (Door)....A
Russell & Erwin Mfg. Co.
(Door; Bead) .....AAAA
CONN.—New Haven
Hoggson & Peltes Mfg. Co.
(Organ) ....A
Mallory, Wheeler Co.
(Door) ....AA
Peck Bros. & Co. (Corpora-
tion) ....A
CONN.—Pine Meadow
Chapen-Stephens Co. (Door;
Plane) ....A
CONN.—South Norwalk
Norwalk Lock Co. (Door).A
CONN.—Torrington
Union Hdw. Co. (Door)..A
ILL.—Aurora
Wilcox Mfg. Co. (Door &
Bench) ....B
ILL.—Chicago
Crane Co. (Corporation;
Water Works) ....AAAA
Hine-Watt Mfg. Co. (Door)
D
ILL.—Decatur
Mueller Mfg. Co., H. (Cor-
poration; Water Works)A
ILL.—Freeport
Arcade Mfg. Co. (Door)..B
Stover Mfg. Co. (Bench)..A
MASS.—Boston
Blount Mfg. Co. (Door)..F
MASS.—Brightwood
Stebbings Mfg. Co., E.
(Corporation; Water
Works; Rough) ....B
MASS.—Fitchburg
Novelty Turning Co.
(Organ) ....E

MASS.—North Adams
Hunter Machine Co., Jas.
(Elevator; Safety) ....A
MASS.—Salem
Locke Regulator Co. (Auto-
matic Engine; Speed Lim-
it) ....A
MASS.—Springfield
Whipple & Co., R. P. (Com-
bination Bench) ....H
MICH.—Detroit
Detroit Ship Building Co.
(Door) ....AAAA
MICH.—Fenton
Phillips Co., A. J. (Door)A
MICH.—Kalamazoo
Hill & Co., W. E. (Log)..D
MO.—St. Louis
Bleha Patent Door Stop Co.,
2117 Bismark (Door)..X
N. J.—Newark
Williams Wire Novelty Co.,
C. T. (Door) ....B
N. Y.—Buffalo
Pratt & Letchworth (Plow;
Hooks) ....AA
N. Y.—Elmira
Cronk & Carrier Mfg. Co.
(Door) ....B
New York City
Bardsley, Joseph, 147 Bax-
ter (Door) ....B
Consolidated Engine Stop
Co., 98 B'way (Engine;
Speed Limit) ....D
Millers Falls Co., 28 War-
ren (Bench) ....AA
Morrill Co., Chas., 277
B'way (Bench) ....D
Peck, Stow & Wilcox Co.,
27 Murray (Bench)AAAA
Sargent & Co., 15 Leonard
(Bench; Door) ....AAAA
Yale & Towne Mfg. Co.
(Door) ....AAAA
N. Y.—Poughkeepsie
Lane Bros. Co. (Door)..A
N. Y.—Rochester
Caldwell Mfg. Co., 8 Jones
(Door) ....E
Pullman Mfg. Co. (Door).C
Yawman & Erbe Mfg. Co.
(Elevator Lock) .....AA
OHIO—Cincinnati
Miller, L. J., 1233 Harrison
(Elevator) X
OHIO—Norwood
Cincinnati Tool Co. (Bench).
A
OHIO—Piqua
Piqua Handle & Mfg. Co.
(Door) ....A
PA.—Philadelpia
Brohard Co., 1624 N. 9th
(Door) ....B
Shaw, Thos. (Siding)....A
PA.—Reading
Reading Hardware Co.
(Door) ....AAAA
VT.—Montpelier
Lane Mfg. Co. (Log)....A
WIS.—Milwaukee
Filer & Stowell Co. (Log)
AAA
WIS.—Racine
Freeman & Sons Mfg. Co.,
S. (Electric Engine)....A

STOUT

N. J.—Newark
Ballantine & Sons, P.....A
Feigenspan, Christian
AAAA
N. Y.—Brooklyn
New York & Brooklyn
Brewing Co...........A
N. Y.—Hudson
Evans & Sons, C. H.....AA
New York City
Beadleston & Woerz......A
N. Y.—Syracuse
Greenway Brewing Co...B
PA.—Philadelphia
Bergner & Engle Brewing
Co. ....AAAA

STOVES

CAL.—San Francisco
Us & Co., Jno. G., 814 Kear-
ney (Steel Ranges) C
CONN.—Cromwell
Stevens & Co., J. & E.

(Toy) ....A
CONN.—New Haven
Yale Gas Stove Co. (Gas
Ranges) ....F
CONN.—South Norwalk
Challenge Mfg. Co. (Gas
Ranges) X
CONN.—Stamford
Stamford Gas Stove Co.
(Gas Ranges) C
CONN.—Waterbury
Plume & Atwood Mfg. Co...
(Oil Lamp) ....AAA
ILL.—Batavia
Sperry & Co., D. R. (Laun-
dry) C
ILL.—Belleville
Belleville Stove Wks.
(Laundry; Wood) ......B
ILL.—Chicago
Adams & Westlake Co.
(Gas; Oil; Vapor) ..AAA
Amer. Stove Co., 72 Lake
(Gas; Oil; Gasoline Ran-
ges) ....AAAA
Barler Mfg. Co., 104 Lake
(Oil) C
Bramhall Range Co., 81
Market (Steel Ranges) B
Chicago Stove Works
(Parlor) ....A
Clark & Co., Geo. M. (Gas;
Gasoline; Oil; Vapor)
AAAA
Cribben & Sexton Co., 52
Erie (Vapor; Wood; Steel
Ranges) ....AAAA
Illinois Malleable Iron Co.,
30 W. Monroe (Laundry;
Heater; Taylors') AAAA
McGuire Mfg. Co., 122 N.
Saginaw (Car) ....A
M. & D. Range Co., 100
Lake Av. (Steel Ranges)B
Nicol & Co. (Oil Lamp) ...D
Rubel & Co. (Gas; Steel
Ranges) ....B
Smith Co., Charles, 123 Lake
(Laundry) ....B
Stearnes' Steel Range Co.,
31 Market (Steel Ranges)
F
Wilson & Co., F. Cortez
(Cooking) ....B
ILL.—Harvey
Buda Foundry & Mfg. Co.
(Railway) ....B
ILL.—Marengo
Collins & Burgie Stove Co.
(Gas) ....B
ILL.—Peoria
Culter & Procter Stove Co.
(Parlor) ....A
ILL.—Quincy
Comstock-Castle Stove Co.
(Steel Ranges) ......AA
ILL.—Rockford
Eclipse Gas Stove Co. (Gas
Ranges) ....B
IND.—Evansville
Indiana Stove Works (Dairy;
Farmers'; Wood) ......A
IND.—Indianapolis
Home Stove Co. (Steel
Ranges) ....A
IND.—Kokomo
Globe Stove & Range Co.
(Steel Ranges) ....A
IDD.—South Bend
Malleable Steel Range Mfg.
Co. (Steel Ranges; Laun-
dry) ....B
IND.—Vincennes
Star Shovel & Range Co.
(Wood; Coal) ....B
KANS.—Leavenworth
Great Western Stove Co.
(Cooking) ....AA
KY.—Louisville
Bridgeford & Co. (Steel
Ranges) ....A
MD.—Baltimore
Bryan Mfg. Co. (Gas) ...H
Hutchinson Bros., 116 N.
Howard (Steel Ranges) D
Schulz & Co., A. S. (Gas)G
Weiskittel & Son, A. (Gas;
Oil; Gas Ranges) ......A
MASS.—Boston
Highland Foundry Co.
(Parlor) ....B
Howes Co.. S. M. (Gas; Gas-
oline; Oil; Coal; Wood) C'
Magee Furnace Co. (Laun-

STOVES (Con.)

dry; Parlor; Wood) ..AA
Walker & Pratt Mfg. Co., 31 Union (Laundry; Steel Ranges) ....AA
White & Co., Chas.H., 22 Bowker (Confectioners') F
MASS.—Chelsea
Low Art Tile Co. (Tile) .F
MASS.—Gardner
Central Oil & Gas Stove Co. (Gas; Wickless Oil) ...C
MASS.—Springfield
Gilbert & Barker Mfg. Co. (Vapor) ....A
MASS.—Taunton
Weir Stove Co. (Parlor; Wood) ....A
MICH.—Big Rapids
Michigan Heater Co. (Steel Ranges) C
MICH.—Chelsea
Glazier Stove Co. (Oil) ...A
MICH.—Detroit
Detroit Heating & Lighting Co., 335 Wight (Gas Ranges) ....B
Detroit Stove Wks. (Dairy; Hot Blast; Laundry; Open Grate Parlor; Street Car; Wood; Gas Ranges) AAA
Ideal Mfg. Co., 546 Franklin (Gas Ranges) ......A
Peninsular Stove Co. (Steel Ranges; Parlor; Car; Wood Stoves) ....AA
Sun Vapor Stove Mfg. Co. (Gasoline) ....A
MICH.—Dowagiac
Beckwith, Philo D. (Parlor) AAA
MICH.—Grand Rapids
Michigan Hdw. Mfg. Co. (Oil) ....F
MICH.—Jackson
Electric Oil Stove Co. (Oil) B
Novelty Mfg. Co. (Oil; Gas; Gasoline; Ranges) .....A
MICH.—Kalamazoo
Economy Gas Stove Co. (Gas Ranges) ....D
MINN.—St. Paul
Wolterstorff & Haskell Mfg. Co., 186 E. 6th (Hotel; Family; Steel Ranges) E
MO.—Kansas City
Kansas City Steel Range Mfg. Co., 610 Bway. C
MO.—St. Louis
Majestic Mfg. Co., 2014 Morgan (Steel Ranges) ...A
Meyrose Lamp Mfg. Co. (Oil) X
Ringer Stove Co. (Vapor) A
NEBR.—Lincoln
Buckstaff Bros. Mfg. Co. Steel Ranges) ....A
Hall Bros. Co. (Steel Ranges) ....D
N. Y.—Albany
Albany Foundry Co. (Gas; Oil) C
Littlefield Stove Co. (Parlor; Wood) ....A
Rathbone, Sard & Co. (Dairy; Farmers'; Parlor; Vapor; Wood) AAA
N. Y.—Brooklyn
Eagle Iron Works, 1850 De Kalb Av. (Plasterers') C
Hauck & Son, Chas. J., 36 Stagg (Pocket Alcohol) B
Vogel & Bros., Wm. (Oil) AA
New York City
Abendroth Bros. Corp., 109 Beekman (Gas Ranges) A
Abercrombie & Fitch, 314 Bway. (Folding Camp) C
Amer. Gas Furnace Co. (Gas) ....A
Bramhall, Deane Co., 264 Water (Steel Ranges) ..D
Cosmopolitan Range Co., 26 Sullivan (Steel Ranges) X
Crane Co., W. M., 1133 Bway. (Gas; Laundry; Tailors'; Ranges) .....A
Criterion Gas Stove Mfg. Co., 445 Greenwich (Gas Ranges) ....A
Dietz Co., R. E. (Oil) ....A
Dunarquet, Hnot & Moneuse, 43 Wooster (Steel Ranges) AA

STOVES (Con.)

Houchin Co., Thos. W. (Pocket Alcohol) ......D
Munsell & Co., Eugene (Gas; Laundry; Oil; Parlor; Vapor; Wood) ....B
Nichthauser & Levy, 96 Beekman (Oil) C
Richardson & Boynton Co. (Parlor) ....AA
Union Stove Wks. (Laundry; Oil; Parlor) ....A
Walsh Co., Owen, 19 Roosevelt (Pocket Alcohol) ..D
Wellington Mfg. Co. (Oil Lamp; Vapor) ....D
N. Y.—Troy
Burdett, Smith & Co. (Parlor) ....A
Fales, A. B. (Wood) ......D
Fuller & Warren Co. (Dairy; Laundry; Open Grate; Parlor; Wood) ....AA
Mahoney, Michael (Laundry; Vapor) ....B
OHIO—Akron
Taplin, Rice & Co., (Steel Ranges) ....A
OHIO—Cincinnati
Fischer Mfg. Co., Wm. G., 19 Church Pl. (Laundry; Steel Range) ....H
Lawson Co., F. H. (Wood) A
Lotze's Sons & Co., A., 527 Walnut (Steel Ranges) B
Miller Range & Furnace Co., W., 127 E. 5th (Portable Steel Ranges) ....A
Obermayer Co., S. (Brass Founders') ....A
Resor & Co., Wm. (Steel Ranges) ....AA
Van Range Co., Jno., 419 Elm (Laundry; Steel Ranges for Families, Hotels & Institutions) ....A
OHIO—Cleveland
Born Steel Range Co. (Steel Ranges) ....AA
Cleveland Co-operative Co. (Wood) ....AA
Cleveland Foundry Co. (Cooking; Heating; Oil Gas; Gas Ranges) ....A
Dangler Stove Mfg. Co. (Gasoline; Gas; Oil) AAAA
Fanner Mfg. Co. (Oil Lamp) A
Federal Mfg. Co. (Oil Lamp) ....AAAA
National Stove & Illuminating Co., New England Bldg. (Acetylene) ......D
Schneider & Trenkamp Co., 479 Case Av. (Gas; Gasolene; Oil; Coal; Laundry; Tailors' Gas; Ranges) AAA
Standard Lighting Co. (Gas; Oil; Vapor) ......AAAA
Taylor & Boggis Foundry Co. (Oil; Vapor; Gas; Gasolene) ....AA
Tyler, E. W. (Pocket Alcohol) X
OHIO—Columbus
Peerless Stove & Range Co. (Gas Ranges) ....D
OHIO—Crestline
Schell Bros. Co. (Steel Ranges) ....A
OHIO—Dayton
Kinsey Mfg. Co. (Gasoline) B
OHIO—Freeport
National Light & Heating Co. (Gas Ranges) ......B
OHIO—Hamilton
Kahn & Bros., F. L. (Gas; Laundry; Wood) ......A
OHIO—Hillsboro
Bell & Co., C. S. (Caboose; Heavy Heating) ......A
OHIO—Mansfield
Eclipse Stove Co. (Laundry; Steel Ranges) ....A
Monarch Stove & Mfg. Co. (Gasolene; Gas; Oil) ..B
New Process Stove Co. (Natural Gas; Heating; Cooking Ranges) ....B
OHIO—Massillon
Hess, Snyder Co. (Laundry; Wood; Coal) ....AA

984

STOVES *(Con.)*

OHIO—Newburgh
Franke Steel Range Co., H.,
1911 Harvard (Steel Ran-
ges) ....A

OHIO—Pisua
Favorite Stove & Range Co.
(Parlor; Wood) ......AA

OHIO—Portsmouth
Portsmouth Stove & Range
Co. (Steel Ranges) ....B

OHIO—Springfield
Progress Furnace & Stove
Co. (Gas Ranges) ......B

OHIO—Warren
Warren Hardware Co.
(Steel Ranges) ....B

OHIO—Youngstown
Pollock & Co., W. B. (Hot
Blast) ....AA

PA.—Allegheny
Carlin's Sons, Thos.
(Plasterers') ....A
Stevenson Mfg. Co. (Laun-
dry; Gas; Ranges) ....E

PA.—Erie
Griswold Mfg. Co. (Gas) A
Hollands Mfg. Co. (Gas;
Gasolene; Oil) C
Odin Stove Mfg. Co. (Gas
Ranges) ....B

PA.—Harrisburg
Hickok Mfg. Co., W. O.
(Gas; Gasolene) ....:.AA

PA.—Lebanon
Lebanon Stove Works (Cooking) ....D

PA.—Philadelphia
Clad & Sons, V., 239 S. 12th
(Steel Ranges) ....B
Cox Stove Co., Abram (Hot
Blast; Laundry; Oil; Open
Grate; Wood) ....AA
Phila Engineering Wks.
(Hot Blast) ....A
Sheppard & Co., Isaac A.
(Laundry; Wood) ..AAA

PA.—Pittsburg
Bartlett, J. O., 632 Liberty
Av. (Coal; Gas Steel Ran-
ges) ....B
McClure Son & Co., G. W.
(Fire Brick) ....D
Riter-Conley Co. (Hot
Blast) ....AA

PA.—Pittston
Pittston Stove Co. (Parlor) A

PA.—Reading
Mount Penn Stove Works
(Laundry; Parlor; Confec-
tioners') ....A
Reading Stove Works (Laun-
dry; Parlor; Wood) ..AA

PA.—South Bethlehem
Bethlehem Foundry & Ma-
chine Co. (Drying for
Lump Sugar)..........C

PA.—Uniontown
Johnson Machine Co. (Gas
Ranges) ....E

TENN.—Chattanooga
Chattanooga Car & Foundry
Co. (Coal; Wood) .....A
Chattanooga Roofing Foun-
dry Co. (Coal; Wood) ..B

WIS.—Neenah
Bergstrom Bros. & Co.
(Cooking; Wood) .....AA

STRAIGHT-
ENERS

ILL.—Freeport
Hoefer Mfg. Co. (Wire) ..C

IND.—Elkhart
Elkhart Frog & Crossing
Wks. (Angle) C

MASS.—Greenfield
Wells Bros. Co. (Axle) ...A

PA.—Pittsburg
Lewis Fdy. & Machine Co.
(Angle) ....A

STRAINERS

CONN.—East Hadden
Boardman & Son, L. (Bowl)
AA

CONN.—Meriden
Meriden Britannia Co.
(Tea; Coffee) ....AAAA

CONN.—Southport
Jelliff & Co.. C. O. (Wire) C

STRAINERS *(Con.)*

CONN.—Wallingford
Wallace & Sons Mfg. Co., R.
(Tea; Coffee; Toddy) AAA

ILL.—Batavia
U. S. Wind Engine & Pump
Co. (Pump) ....A

ILL.—Belleville
Belleville Pump & Skein
Wks. (Pump) ....A

ILL.—Chicago
American Spiral Pipe Works,
1173 S. Paulina (Pipe) B
Barbee Wire & Iron Wks.
(Conductor) ....B
Dietzgen Co., Eugene
(Artists') ....A
Illinois Malleable Iron Co.
(Well; Sink) ......AAAA
Jewell Filter Co., O. H.
(Faucet) X

ILL.—Peoria
Clark, Quien & Morse (Conductor Pipe) ....A

ILL.—Rockford
Clark Hardware Co., J. L.
(Dredge; Sifter) ....D

IND.—Lawrenceburg
Cook, A. D. (Tube Well) B

MASS.—Boston
Edson Mfg. Co. (Suction;
Globe) ....E

MASS.—Lowell
Woods, Sherwood & Co.
(Faucet; Tea; Coffee;
Wire) C

MASS.—Worcester
National Mfg. Co. (Cup;
Faucet; Gravy; Tea; Cof-
fee; Toddy; Wire; Bowl) B
Parker Wire Goods Co. (Con-
ductor Pipe; Sink) ....E
Wire Goods Co. (Conductor
Pipe; Sink) ....A
Wright Wire Co. (Conductor
Pipe) ....AA

MICH.—Battle Creek
Sigrist Martin Co. (Coffee;
Tea Pot) ....G

MO.—St. Louis
Ludlow-Saylor Wire Co.
(Conductor Pipe) ....AA

N. J.—Haddonfield
Star Milk Cooler Co. (Milk) C

N. J.—Newark
Bernz, Otto (Gutter) ....B

N. Y.—Brooklyn
Sweeny Mfg. Co., W. H.
(Tea; Coffee) ....A

N. Y.—Buffalo
Shepard & Co., Sidney
(Milk) ....AAAA
Western Wire Goods Co.
(Conductor Pipe; Sink) D

N. Y.—Cortland
Wickwire Bros. (Bowl)
AAAA

New York City
Caws Pen & Ink Co.
(Artists') ....D
Eaton, Cole & Burnham Co.
(Pump) ....AAAA
Fredericks, E. H. (Artists')
A
Gilbert & Bennett Mfg. Co.,
277 Bway. (Conductor
Pipe) ....AAA
International Silver Co., 9
Maiden Lane (Silver Pla-
ted Tea) ....AAAA
Iron Clad Mfg. Co. (Milk)
AAA
Lalance & Grosjean Mfg. Co.
(Cup; Tea; Coffee; Tod-
dy) ....AAAA
Reilley Bros. (Kalsomine
Paint) ....D
Stoutenborough, X. (Tea;
Coffee) ....D
Sweet & Co., L. W. 39
Maiden Lane (Tea; Cof-
fee) C
Worthington Pumping En-
gine Co. (Pump) ..AAAA

N. Y.—Seneca Falls
Rumsey & Co. (Ltd.)
(Pump) ....A

N. Y.—Troy
Ludlow Valve Mfg. Co.
(Pump) ....AAA
Parks & Parks (Milk) ....D

OHIO—Ashtabula
Barber Mfg. Co. (Sink) ...C

STRAINERS (Con.)

OHIO—Canton
Berger Mfg. Co. (Conductor
Pipe) ....AA
Canton Steel Roofing Co.
(Conductor Pipe) ......A
OHIO—Cincinnati
Bromwell Brush & Wire
Goods Co. (Wire) ......A
OHIO—Cleveland
Garry Iron & Steel Co.
(Conductor Pipe) ......A
OHIO—Hamilton
Meyers Mfg. Co., Fred. J.
(Tea; Coffee; Conductor
Pipe) ....B
PA.—Philadelphia
Berger Bros. Co., 231 Arch
(Conductor Pipe) ......A
Darby & Sons, Edw., 233
Arch (Conductor Pipe) A
WIS.—Kenosha
Frost Mfg. Co. (Basin) ..B
WIS.—Milwaukee
Wallman Mfg. Co. (Calci-
mine) ....E

STRAPS

CONN.—Bridgeport
Hotchkiss, Edward S.
(Shawl) ....A
Smith & Egge Mfg. Co.
(Single; Double Pipe) ..A
CONN.—Danielson
Jacobs Mfg. Co., E. H.
(Harness; Loom) .....B
CONN.—Easthampton
Bevins Bros. Mfg. Co.
(Sleighbell) ....
CONN.—Torrington
Union Hardware Co. (Skate;
Car Bell) ....AA
CONN.—Waterbury
American Pin Co. (Brass
Pipe; Shawl) ....AA
Steele & Johnson Mfg. Co.
(Pipe) ....A
DEL.—Wilmington
Rhoads & Sons, J. E. (Street
Car) ....A
ILL.—Chicago
Acme Flexible Clasp Co.
(Box; Embossed Flat
Wire; Barbed; Crate) ..A
Chicago Raw Hide Mfg. Co.,
75 Ohio (Harness; Raw
Hide Luggage) ....A
Continental Bolt & Iron
Works (Pole) ....A
Fitzgerald Trunk Co.
(Shawl; Shoulder) ....A
Haskell Bros. (Shawl;
Trunk) ....A
Illinois Malleable Iron Co.,
34 W. Monroe (Pipe)
...................AAAA
Pick Mfg. Co., 10 5th Av.
(Baby Carriage) C
Western Leather Mfg. Co.
(Shawl; Tourists'; Trunk)
.....................D
Wilt, Chas. T. (Shawl;
Tourists') ....B
Wolff Mfg. Co., L., 117 W.
Lake (Pipe) ......AAAA
IND.—Anderson
Buckeye Mfg. Co. (Shaft;
Pole) ....AA
IOWA—Dubuque
Dubuque Harness & Saddlery
Co. (Hame; Harness) ..X
KY.—Newport
Higgin Mfg. Co. (Back
Stay) ....A
MD.—Baltimore
National Supply Co., 7 W.
Lombard (Timber) ....B
MASS.—Boston
Boston Belting Co., 456 Dev-
onshire (Deckle for Foun-
drinier Paper Machines)
...................AAAA
Boston Bolt Co., 33 Purchase
(Pipe) C
Boston Brass Co., 36 Oliver
(Pipe) C
Boston Woven Hose & Rub-
ber Co. (Deckle) ..AAAA
Revere Rubber Co. (Deckle)
...................AAAA
Walworth Mfg. Co., 132
Federal (Pipe) ....AAAA
MASS.—Dedham
Abbott Mfg. Co., J. V.

STRAPS (Con.)
(Loom) ....D
MASS.—Fall River
Union Belt Co. (Loom) ..B
MASS.—Franklin
Milliken & Son, L. W.
(Lug.) ....D
MASS.—Holyoke
Holyoke Belting Co. (Trunk)
.....................C
MASS.—Lowell
Gates & Sons, Josiah (Loom)
.....................X
MASS.—South Attleboro
Coupe & Co., Wm. (Harness)
.....................X
MASS.—Worcester
Warren Co., J. J. (Book;
Handy; Shawl; Tourists';
Trunk; Fish Basket;
Slings; Baggage Check;
Children's Carriage;
Skate; Street Car) ....B
MICH.—Detroit
Anderson & Sons, W. H.
(Pipe; Pole) C
Diamond Stamped Ware Co.
(Pipe) ....NA
MO.—Kansas City
Kansas City Bolt & Nut Co.
(Timber; Bridge) ......A
N. H.—Concord
Page' Belting Co. (Loom;
Hame; Skate; Strapping)
....................AA
N. J.—Harrison
Headley & Farmer Co.
(Shoulder; Tourists';
Trunk) ....A
N. J.—Newark
Caille Co. (Shoulder) ....D
Hager & Co. (Shoulder;
Tourists') ....H
Peddie & Co., T. B. (Shawl;
Shoulder; Tourists';
Trunk) ....AA
Peters Harness & Saddlery
Co. (Hame) C
Sterling-Meeker Co., 420 Og-
den (Hand Hold for Cars)
.....................D
N. Y.—Binghamton
Crandal, Stone & Co. (Cur-
tain) ....A
N. Y.—Brooklyn
De Haven Mfg. Co., 50
Columbia Hts. (Box) ..A
N. Y.—Buffalo
Buffalo Weaving Co.
(Shawl; Trunk; Web Tel-
escope) ....A
McKinnon Dash Co. (Cur-
tain) ....AA
N. Y.—Interlaken
Covert's Saddlery Wks.
(Hame) C
New York City
American Box Strap Co.,
501 W. Bway. (Box) ..D
American Railway Supply
Co., 24 Park Pl. (Baggage
Check) X
Cary Mfg. Co. 19 Roosevelt
(Box; Soft Steel) .....B
Evory Mfg. Co., 102 John
(Pipe) ....E
Fee & Mason, 66 Beekman
(Pipe) ....F
Goodyear's India Rubber
Glove Mfg. Co. (Trousers)
....
Gutta Percha & Rubber Mfg.
Co. (Deckle; Hose)AAAA
Hahn & Co., A. (Shawl) .B
Haydenville Mfg. Co. (Hose)
.....................A
Lalance & Grosjean Mfg.
Co., 19 Cliff (Wrought
Steel; Gas, etc.) ..AAAA
Standard Metal Strap Co.,
336 E. 38th (Box) .....F
Twisted Wire Box Strap Co.,
451 Gwich. (Box) ......D
Wintjen, John G. (Cane;
Umbrella) ....E
N. Y.—Unadilla
Tie Co. (Shawl) ....D
N. Y.—Watervliet
Covert Mfg. Co. (Hame) A
OHIO—Canton
Elbel & Co. (Hame) .....A
OHIO—Cleveland
Cleveland Hardware Co.
(Box) ....AA
Likly & Rockett (Shawl) B

986

STRAPS (Con.)

OHIO—Columbus
Peters & Herron Dash Co.
(Roll Up) C
OHIO—Hamilton
Black & Clawson Co.
(Deckle) ....AAA
PA.—Philadelphia
Berger Bros. Co., 237 Arch
(Gas Pipe) ....A
Devlin & Co., Thos., 3d &
Lehigh Av. (Malleable
Iron) ....AA
Horstman Co., Wm. H.
(Shoulder) ......AAAA
Houghton Co., E. F., 240 W.
Somerset (Mill) ......AA
Rhoads & Son, J. E. ......A
R. I.—Pawtucket
Weatherhead, Thompson &
Co. (Loom) ....A
R. I.—Providence
American Supply Co. (Loom)
AA
Brown Bros. Co. (Loom) B
Burgess & Son, A. (Harness;
Loom) X
WIS.—Racine
Racine Malleable & Wrought
Iron Co. (Hammer) ....A
Seor Trunk Co., M. M.
(Shawl) ....A

STRAW GOODS

MASS.—Amherst
Hills & Co. ....B
MASS.—Boston
Broderson & Day, 287 Devon-
shire ....B
New York City
Blum & Koch, 90 5th Av...A
Carroll-Hixon-Jones Co., 585
Bway. C
Comey & Co., 584 Bway...C
Hirsh & Park, 593 Bway. AA
Knowlton & Sons, Wm., 564
Bway. ....AAAA
Lewis, Hirsh & Co., 593
Bway. C
Sawyer & Co., H. F., 43
Bleecker ....B
Searle, Dailey & Co., 602
Bway. ....AA
Shumway & Son, Albert, 633
Bway. ....D
OHIO—Cleveland
Comey & Johnson ....B
PA.—Philadelphia
Muller & Co., G. P., 113 N.
7th ....D
Potter & Son, Jos, 261 Arch
D
Rosenau Bros., 305 N. 8th A
WIS.—Milwaukee
Slocum Straw Wks. C

STRAWS

D. C.—Washington
Stone, Marvin C. (Paper) A
N. J.—Camden
Sayford Paper Goods Co.
(Paper) C
New York City
Coe Mfg. Co., 50 Warren
(Soda) ....F
Tharnauer & Bro., G. M., 37
Park Row (Julep; Lemon-
ade) X
OHIO—Lisbon
Union Mfg. Co. (Soda)....D

STRETCHERS

CONN.—Ansonia
Farrell Fdry. & Machine
Co. (Rubber Belt).AAAA
CONN.—Bridgeport
Knapp, Geo. S. (Carpet;
Shoe) ....E
Knapp & Cowles Mfg. Co.
(Carpet; Wire) C
CONN.—Chester
Brooks & Sons, M. S.
(Trousers) ....B
CONN.—Georgetown
Gilbert & Bennett Mfg. Co.
(Wire) ....AAA
CONN.—New Haven
National Steel & Wire Co.
(Wire) ....AAAA

STRETCHERS (Con.)

CONN.—Oakville
Smith & Son, Seymour
(Carpet) ....D
CONN.—Plainville
Hill, Edwin (Carpet) ...A
ILL.—Aurora
Wilcox Mfg. Co. (Fence;
Wire) ....B
ILL.—Chicago
Amer. Steel & Wire Co.,
Rookery Bldg. (Wire)...
AAAA
Chicago Curtain Stretcher
Co., 100 W. Lincoln
(Curtain) ....D
Chicago Woodenware Co.
(Curtain) ....D
Dietzgen Co., Eugene
(Artists') ....A
Holliday Mfg. & Eng. Co.,
160 Bunker (Carpet;
Fence; Wire) ....D
Janesville Hay Tool Co., 122
Lake (Wire) C
National Hoist & Machine
Co., 463 W. 22nd (Wire;
Cable) ....G
Whipple Mfg. Co., Royal
Ins. Bldg. (Curtain) ..E
ILL.—De Kalb
De Kalb Fence Co. (Wire;
Fence) ....AA
ILL.—Freeport
Arcade Mfg. Co. (Fence;
Wire; Carpet) ....A
ILL.—Harvard
Hunt. Helm, Ferris & Co.
(Wire) ....AA
ILL.—Peoria
Keystone Fence Co. (Wire)
AA
ILL.—St. Charles
Leader Fence Machine Mfg.
Co. (Wire) C
ILL.—Sterling
Novelty Iron Wks. (Wire)
E
IND.—Anderson
Dwiggins Wire Fence Co.
(Wire) ....B
IND.—Indianapolis
Enterprise Fdry. & Fence
Co. (Wire) ....B
IND.—Richmond
Elliott & Reid Co. (Wire;
Fence) ....D
IOWA—Lyons
Buell Mfg. Co., W. E.
(Shoe) ....E
MASS.—Boston
Chandler & Farquhar Co..
36 Federal (Wire) .....B
Power & Co., J. H. (Shoe)
X
MASS.—Holyoke
Holyoke Machine Co.
(Cloth) ....AA
MASS.—Stoughton
Belcher, Geo. C. (Shoe)...C
MASS.—Worcester
Cleveland Machine Wks.
(Cloth) ....A
Curtis & Marble Machine
Co. (Cloth) ....A
Wire Goods Co. (Trousers)
A
MICH.—Detroit
Majestic Wire Fence Co.
(Fence; Wire) ....F
MICH.—Galion
Montross, R. W. (Carpet)
B
MICH.—Grand Rapids
Baldwin, Tuthill & Bolton
B
MICH.—Muskegon
Sargent Mfg. Co. (Hospi-
tal) ....B
MO.—St. Louis
Ludlow-Saylor Wire Co.
(Wire; Fence) ......AA
N. J.—Montclair
Heller & Co., W. C.
(Wire; Fence) ....F
N. J.—Newark
Celluloid Co. (Glove) ....B
Kraeuter & Co. (Carpet)..X
Osborne & Co., C. S.
(Carpet) ....B
Sayre & Co., L. A. (Car-
pet) ....B
Wiemer & Co. (Carpet)...C

STRETCHERS (*Con.*)

N. Y.—Albion
Malloy, C. M. (Carpet)..F
N. Y.—Buffalo
Buffalo Last Wks. (Shoe)
           B
Gilroy Stretcher Co. (Carpet; Curtain) ....D
Hard Mfg. Co. (Invalid)..B
N. Y.—Canandaigua
Standard Wire Fence Co.
  (Wire) ....D
New York City
Cary Mfg. Co., 19 Roosevelt
  (Box Strap) ....B
Cuming, Mari A. (Hat)..F
Friedrichs, E. H. (Artists')
           A
Grote & Co., F., E. 14th
  (Glove) ....F
Peck, Stow & Wilcox Co.,
  27 Murray (Carpet) ....
          AAAA
Sargent & Co., 151 Leonard
  (Carpet) ....AAAA
Silver & Co. (Inc.)
  (Trousers) ....E
Smith & Hemenway Co.,
  296 B'way (Fence; Wire)
           D
Stokes & Co., Wm. A., 30
  Warren (Curtain) ....D
Tower & Lyon (Carpet)..B
N. Y.—Painted Post
Townsend, F. J. (Wire)..D
N. Y. —Rochester
Pullman Mfg. Co. (Fence;
  Wire) ....B
N. Y.—Troy
Trojan Button Fastener Co.
  (Inc.) (Shoe) ....B
N. Y.—Watervliet
Covert Mfg. Co. (Trousers)
           A
OHIO—Canton
Ney Mfg. Co. (Wire;
  Fence) ....AA
OHIO—Cincinnati
Schriver & Co., O. P., 208
  Elm (Wire) ....B
OHIO—Cleveland
Burr Mfg. Co., 131 Viaduct (Fence; Wire) ...X
OHIO—Columbus
International Fence &
  Wire Proofing Co., Buttles Av. (Fence; Wire).A
OHIO—Leesburg
Mason Fence Co., W. H.
  (Wire) ....D
OHIO—Sunbury
Matthews & Miller
  (Wire) ....F
OHIO—Toledo
McClusky Wire Fence Co.
  (Wire) X
OHIO—Warren
Denison Mfg. Co. (Carpet)
           F
OHIO—West Farmington
Never Slip Wire Stretching & Novelty Co. (Wire)
PA.—Atglen
Chalfant Hardware Mfg.
  Co. (Carpet) X
PA.—North East
Eureka Tempered Copper
  Works (Electric; Barbed
  Wire) ....A
PA.—Philadelphia
Butterworth & Sons Co., H.
  W. (Cloth) ....A
R. I.—Pawtucket
Luther & Co., C. A. (Cloth)
           C
R. I.—Providence
Textile Finishing Machinery Co., 17 Exch. Pl.
  (Cloth) ....AAA
WIS.—Racine
Racine Malleable &
  Wrought Iron Co. (Wire)
           A
WIS.—South Milwaukee
Stowell Mfg. & Fdry. Co.
  (Fence; Wire) ....A

STRINGERS

ILL.—Chicago
Vaughan & Bushnell Mfg.
  Co. (Ham) ....A

STRINGERS (*Con.*)

N. J.—Newark
Osborne & Co., C. S. (Ham)
           B
N. Y.—Buffalo
White Co., L. & I. J.
  (Ham) ....A
N. Y.—Kenwood
Oneida Community (Ltd.)
  (Fish) ....AAA
OHIO—Akron
Enterprise Mfg. Co.
  (Fish) ....A

STRINGS

ILL.—Chicago
Chicago Rawhide Mfg. Co.
  (Hame) ....A
MASS.—Boston
Lockhart, Wm. J. (Musical)
           F
MASS.—Everett
Faxton Co., Geo. H.
  (Piano) ....D
MO.—Washington
Schwarzer, Franz (Instrument) ....E
N. H.—Concord
Page Belting Co. (Hame)..
           AA
N. J.—Belleville
Gibson Musical String Co.
  (Musical) X
N. J.—New Brunswick
National Musical String Co.
  (Harp; Piano; Violin;
  Banjo) ....A
New York City
Ditson & Co., Chas. H., 867
  B'way (Musical Instrument) ....B
Doll & Sons, Jacob (Piano;
  Wire Covered) ......AA
Koch, R. C., 306 2nd Av.
  (Covered Piano) ......D
Mapes, S. S., 511 E. 137th
  (Covered Piano) ......D
New York Co-operative
  Piano String Co. (Harp)
           X
Ramaciotti, Francis (Est.)
  (Piano; Covered Wire).D
Tonk & Bro., Wm., 452 10th
  Av. (Musical Instrument)
           C
OHIO—Middletown
Fouts, C. C. (Sealing Wax)
           E
PA.—Philadelphia
Albert, Charles F. (Wire;
  Covered) ....D

STRIPPERS

MASS.—Boston
Seelye Mfg. Co. (Power)
           C
MASS.—Worcester
Howard Bros. Mfg. Co.
  (Hand) ....A
New York City
Sheriden Co., T. W. & C.
  B. (Power) ....A
OHIO—Alliance
Morgan Engineering Co.
  (Ingot) ....AAAA
PA.—Philadelphia
Chambers Bros. Co.
  (Power) ....AA

STRIPS

See also Iron & Steel; Woodwork; Carriage

CONN.—Middletown
Russell Mfg. Co. (Weather)
          AAAA
CONN.—New Haven
Reeves Mfg. Co. (Automatic Weather) C
ILL.—Chicago
Bosley Co., D. W., 303 Fulton (Weather Felt; Metallic; Rubber) ....A
Dunfee & Co., J., 104
  Franklin (Weather)....X
Harsha Mfg. Co., 793 Carroll Av. (Weather; Rubber) ....B
Oakley, Charles (Weather)
           A

STRIPS (Con.)
Pfleger Mfg. Co., 958 N.
Spaulding (Weather; Rubber) ....A
IOWA—Cedar Falls
Wagner Mfg. Co. (Metallic
Door) ....E
MASS.—Boston
Mann, E., 11 Province
(Weather) ....G
May & Freeman, 178 Devonshire (Invisible Weather) ....E
Osgood & Co., H. H., 4
Charlestown (Weather).F
Prince, W. O., 26 Edinboro
(Weather) ....E
MASS.—West Hanover
Church & Co., E. I. (Axle;
All Steel Weather) ....H
MICH.—Detroit
Chamberlin Metal Weather
Strip Co., 37 W. Congress
(Metallic Weather) C
Teakle & Golden (Metallic
Weather) ....B
MO.—St. Louis
Roehrig & Jacoby Wall
Paper Co. (Weather) ..B
N. J.—Jersey City
New Jersey Car Spring &
Rubber Co. (Weather)..
AA
N. Y.—Albany
Valentine & Son, W. T.
(Weather; Rubber) ....B
New York City
Amer. Weather Strip Co.,
70 Warren (Weather)...X
Gage, John S. (Weather;
Rubber) ....E
Goodyear Rubber Co.
(Weather; Rubber) ...:
AAAA
Gutta Percha & Rubber
Mfg. Co. (Weather; Rubber) ....AAAA
Mechanical Rubber Co.
(Weather; Rubber) AAAA
Mineralized Rubber Co., 18
Cliff (Weather) ....A
Patent Metallic Weather
Strip Co., 133 W. 23rd
(Weather; Metallic; Rubber) ....E
Protective Ventilator Co.,
129 Fulton (Weather;
Rubber) ....B
Roebuck Weather Strip &
Wire Screen Co., 172 Fulton (Weather; Metallic;
Rubber) ....D
OHIO—Canton
Novelty Iron Co. (Weather)
A
PA.—Allegheny
National Metal Weather
Strip Co. (Weather) ...F
PA.—Philadelphia
Heaton & Wood (Weather)
G

STROPPERS

PA.—Philadelphia
McCullough-Dalzell Crucible
Co. (Ladle) ....A

STROPPING

N. H.—Concord
Page Belting Co. (Mill).AA

STROPS

ILL.—Chicago
Frost & Co., Peter F.
(Razor) ....G
MASS.—Boston
Howard Mfg. Co. (Razor)
B
MASS.—Plymouth
Badge Strop Co., F. B.
(Razor) ....B
MASS.—Worcester
Torrey Razor Co., J. R.
(Razor) C
N. H.—Pike
Pike Mfg. Co. (Razor)...A
New York City
Silberstein, A. L., 459
B'way (Razor) ....A
Smith & Hemenway Co.,
296 B'way (Razor) ....D

STROPS (Con.)
PA.—Philadelphia
Shull, W. A. (Razor) ...F

STRYCHINE

MO.—St. Louis
Herf & Frericks Chemical
Co. ....A
Mallinckrodt Chemical Wks.
AAAA
New York City
Merck & Co. ....AAA
N. Y. Quinine & Chemical
Wks. ....A
Pfizer & Co. Chas...AAAA
PA.—Philadelphia
Powers - Weightman - Rosengarten Co.......AAAA

STUBS

New York City
Peck, Stow & Wilcox Co.,
27 Murray (Store Shutter)
AAAA
Russell & Edwin Mfg. Co.,
45 Chambers (Store Shutters) ....AAAA
Sargent & Co., 151 Leonard
(Store Shutter) ...AAAA
PA.—Reading
Reading Hardware Co.
(Store Shutter)....AAAA

STUDS

**See Hardware; Carriage;
Jewelry**

CONN.—Bridgeport
Bridgeport Brass Co.
(Brass) ....AAAA
CONN.—Chester
Brooks & Sons, M. S.
(Harness) ....B
CONN.—Hartford
Hartford Machine Screw Co.
(Bicycle Chain) ..AAAA
CONN.—New Britain
Landers, Frary & Clark
(Harness) ....AAA
CONN.—New Haven
North & Co., O. B.
(Harness) ....AA
CONN.—Torrington
Progressive Mfg. Co.
(Milled Iron; also Steel;
Brass, etc.) ....A
CONN.—Waterbury
Blake & Johnson (Milled
Iron; Brass) ....A
ILL.—Chicago
Standard Screw Co., 2 N.
Canal (Milled Iron; Machine) ....AAA
Walker & Ehrman Mfg. Co.,
127 Washington (Brass;
Iron) ....A
MAINE—Portland
Cox & Son, A. F. (Shop)..A
MASS.—Attleboro
Daggett & Clapp Co. (Gold)
A
Horton, Angell & Co.
(Separable) ....:.A
MASS.—Attleboro Falls
Mason, Ruggles C. X
MASS.—Boston
Ripley-Howland Mfg. Co.
(Gold) ....A
Tubular Rivet & Stud Co.
(Lacing; Shop) ...AAA
MASS.—Chartley
Freeman, Daughaday & Co.
(Gold) C
MASS.—Greenfield
Automatic Machine Co.
(Brass; Iron) C
MASS.—Hopedale
Draper Co. (Iron)...AAAA
MASS.—Lowell
Hope & Co., Wm. H.
(Milled Iron) X
MASS.—North Attleboro
Bugbee & Niles Co.
(Rolled Gold) ....B
Franklin & Co., E. I.
(Gold) C
MASS.—Reading
Pierce Organ Pipe Co.,
Samuel (Organ) C

STUDS (*Con.*)

MASS.—Worcester
Reed & Curtis Machine
  Screw Co. (Milled Iron)
  ....D
Wire Goods Co. (Harness)
  ....A
Worcester Machine Screw
  Co. (Milled Iron; Engine)
  ....AAA

MICH.—Detroit
Detroit Screw Works, 343
  Franklin (Milled Iron)..
  ....AAA

N. J.—Jersey City
Mack Mfg. Co., Thos. A.
  (Brass; Iron) X

N. J.—Newark
Block & Bergfeld (Gold)..B
Durand & Co. (Inc.) (Gold)
  ....AA
Hedges & Co., A. J. (Gold)
  ....A
Jenkinson Co., R. C. (Dog
  Collar; Bag; Harness)..
  ....AA

N. Y.—Buffalo
Buffalo Specialty Mfg. Co.
  (Belt) ....B
Niagara Screw Co. (Brass;
  Milled Iron) X

New York City
Alling & Co. (Gold) ....AA
Cottle Co., S. (Gold) ....E
Day, Clark & Co. (Gold)..B
Fogel & Co., R. R. (Rolled
  Gold) ....A
Larter & Sons (Gold) ....A
Richards & Co., E. Ira
  (Gold; Rolled Gold; Sepa-
  rable) ....AAA
Sloan & Co. (Inc.) (Gold)
  ....B

OHIO—Cincinnati
Cincinnati Screw & Tap Co.,
  2442 Beekman (Milled
  Iron) ....A

PA.—Lebanon
American Iron & Steel Co.
  (Brass; Milled Iron).....
  ....AAAA

PA.—Pittsburg
Pittsburg Screw & Bolt Co.
  (Brass; Milled Iron) ...A

R. I.—Pawtucket
Haskell Mfg. Co., Wm. H.
  (Brass; Milled Iron)..AA
Pawtucket Mfg. Co.
  (Milled Iron) ....A

R. I.—Providence
Ballou & Co., B. A. (Gold)
  ....AA
Barker Mfg. Co. (White
  Stone) X
Devereux & Co., O. C.
  (Rolled Gold) ....D
Hancock Co., Chas. E.
  (Gold) ....B
Luther & Son, Wm. H.
  (Gold) ....B
Moorhead & Co., R. L.
  (Gold; Rolled Gold;
  White Stone) ....B
New England Pearl Co...F
Potter & Buffington Co.
  (Gold) ....A
Rhode Island Tool Co. (Ma-
  chine) ....AAA
Schofield, Battey & Co.
  (Gold) C
Snow & Westcott (Gold).A
Tockwotton Co. ....F
Vose Mfg. Co. (Rolled
  Gold) ....B
Waite-Thresher Co. (Gold)
  ....A

STUFFS: DYE

See Dyestuffs

STUFFERS

CONN.—Southington
Peck, Stow, Wilcox Co.
  (Sausage) ....AAAA

IOWA—Burlington
Murray Iron Wks. Co.
  (Sausage) ....A

MASS.—Boston
Ames Plow Co. (Sausage)
  ....AAAA

N. Y.—Buffalo
Smith's Sons Co., Jno. E.

STUFFERS (*Con.*)

  (Sausage) ....B

New York City
Sargent & Co., 151 Leonard
  (Sausage) ....AAAA
Stanbach, B. (Sausage)...A

OHIO—Salem
Silver Mfg. Co. (Sausage)
  ....AA

PA.—Atglen
Chalmant Hardware Mfg.
  Co. (Sausage) X

PA.—Philadelphia
Enterprise Mfg. Co. of Pa.
  (Sausage) ....AAAA
Mittinger, August (Sau-
  sage) ....A

SUBSTITUTE

CAL.—Oakland
Condensed Coffee Co.
  (Coffee) ....F

CAL.—San Jose
A. & C. Prime Coffee Co.
  (Coffee) ....B
Figprune Cereal Co. (Cof-
  fee) ....B
  ....B

CONN.—Stamford
Stamford Rubber Supply
  Co. (Rubber) ....F

D. C.—Washington
Standard Material Co.
  (Hard Rubber) ....D

ILL.—Chicago
Dickinson Co., Albert (Coffee; Rye) ....AA

ILL.—Peoria
Central City Cereal Coffee
  Co. (Coffee) ....A

IND.—South Bend
Schreyer, J. C. (Coffee)..D

MASS.—Boston
Ayer & Co., M. S. (Coffee;
  Cereal) ....AA
Bonner Mfg. Co. (Rubber)
  ....D

MASS.—Orange
Whitman Grocery Co. (Cof-
  fee) C

MICH.—Battle Creek
Postum Cereal Co. (Coffee)
  ....AAA

MICH.—Benton Harbor
Lindon Cereal Co. (Ltd.)
  (Coffee) ....B

MICH.—Charlotte
Middletown Cereal Co.
  (Coffee) ....F

MICH.—Grand Rapids
Grand Rapids Cereal Co.
  (Coffee) ....A
Royal Blend Beverage Co.
  (Coffee) ....AA

MICH.—Kalamazoo
Kalamazoo Pure Food Co.
  (Coffee) C
Michigan Pure Food Co.
  (Coffee) ....D

N. J.—Jersey City
American Ferment Co.
  (Cofee) ....D

N. J.—Newark
Listers Agricultural Chem-
  ical Wks. (Asphalt).....
  ....AAAA

N. Y.—Buffalo
Bachert, Philip (Coffee).A

N. Y.—Flushing
Francke, Sohne & Co.
  (Coffee) ....A

N. Y.—Le Roy
Genesee Pure Food Co.
  (Coffee) ....A

N. Y.—Mount Morris
Bauer Co., J. F. (Coffee).E

New York City
Blume, F. E. (Coffee)....C
Pantasote Leather Co., 11
  B'way (Leather) ....AA

N. Y.—Niagara Falls
Natural Food Co. (Coffee)
  ....AAAA

N. Y.—Oxford
New York Food Co.
  (Coffee) ....F

N. Y.—Warsaw
Roka Food Co. (Coffee)...E

OHIO—Toledo
Hygienic Cereal Co. (Cof-
  fee) ....A

SUBSTITUTE (Con.)
PA.—Bradford
Emery, Jr., & Co., L.
(Linseed Oil) .....AAAA
PA.—Philadelphia
Magoffin, Wm. H. (Lin-
seed Oil) ....B
Weikel & Smith Spice Co.
(Coffee) ....A
R. I.—Providence
Rumford Chem. Works
(Cream Tarter) ...AAAA
WIS.—Manitowoc
Kneipp Malt Food Co.
(Coffee Malt) ....B
WIS.—Milwaukee
Delaney Oil & Lubricant
Co. (Linseed Oil) X
WIS.—Plymouth
Schneider Bros. (Coffee
Malt) ....F

SUBSTRUCT-
URES

IND.—Kendallville
Flint & Walling Mfg. Co.
(Angle; Steel; Wood).AA
MICH.—Kalamazoo
Phelps & Bigelow Windmill
Co. (Iron) ....B

SUCCATASH

See Canned Goods

SUGAR: BEET;
CANE, ETC.

**See also following Headings
for other Sugars**

CAL.—Alvarado
Alameda Sugar Co. (Beet)
A
CAL.—Chino
Amer. Beet Sugar Co.
AAAA
CAL.—Crockett
Calif. Beet Sugar Ref'g Co.
AAAA
CAL.—Los Alamitos
Los Alamitos Sugar Co.
(Beet) ....AAAA
CAL.—Oxnard
Amer. Beet Sugar Co.,
AAAA
CAL.—San Francisco
Alameda Sugar Co., 132
Market (Beet) ....A
Alexander & Balwind, 308
Market (Importers) .AA
Amer. Beet Sugar Co. 123
California ....AAAA
Brandenstein & Co., M. J.,
AAAA
Hawaiian Com'l & Sugar
Co., 308 Market ..AAAA
Hutchinson Sugar Planta-
tion Co., 327 Market
AAAA
Parrott & Co., 306 Califor-
nia (Importers) ....A
Spreckels Sugar Co.,AAAA
Union Sugar Co., 132 Mar-
ket ....AAA
CAL.—Santa Maria
Union Sugar Co ....A
CAL.—Spreckels
Spreckels Sugar Co. (Br.
San. Fran.) ......AAAA
COLO.—Eaton
Eaton Sugar Co......AAAA
COLO.—Grand Junction
Colo. Sugar Mfg. Co......A
COLO.—Greeley
Greeley Sugar Co........A
COLO.—Longmont
Longmont Sugar Co.......A
COLO.—Loveland
Great Western Sugar Co.
AAAA
COLO.—Rocky Ford
Amer. Beet Sugar Co.
AAAA
IDAHO—IDAHO FALLS
Idaho Sugar Co. (Beet)
AAA
ILL.—Chicago
Amer. Sugar Ref'g Co., 31
Lake ....AAAA
Corn Products Co. .AAAA

SUGAR: BEET &c. Con.
Glucose Sugar Ref'g Co.,
Rookery Bldg. ....AAAA
Illinois Sugar Ref'g Co.,
Rookery Bldg......AAAA
Rockwood Bros. & Co., N.
State & Ohio (Powdered)
A
ILL.—Pekin
Ill. Sugar Ref'g Co..AAAA
ILL.—Rockford
Glucose Sugar Ref'g Co.
AAAA
ILL.—Waukegan
U. S. Sugar Refg. Co.
AAAA
IND.—Terre Haute
Southern Sugar Co...AAAA
LA.—Adeline
Adeline Sugar Factory Co.
AA
LA.—Baldwin
Berg, Joe ....A
LA.—Baton Rouge
Baton Rouge Sugar Co....A
Goyer & Co., R. L.....AA
LA.—Cinclaire
Cinclaire Central Factory
AAAA
LA.—Darcyville
Soniat, L. M............A
LA.—Donaldsonville
Lemann & Bro., B.
(Planters) ....AAAA
LA.—Gheens
Golden Ranch, Sugar &
Cattle Co. ....A
LA.—Grammercy
Grammercy Co. (Ltd.)
(Ref.) ....AA
LA.—Houma
Caillouet & Maginnis.....A
Minor, H. C............A
LA.—Jeannette
Phar & Bussy..........AA
LA.—Jeanerette
Prevost, J. A...........A
LA.—Louisa
Burgueres, J. M........AA
LA.—Monroe
Monroe Sugar & Molasses
Co. ....A
LA.—Montegut
Lower Terrebonne Refg. &
Mfg. Co. ....A
LA.—Napoleonville
Godchaux Co., L. (Ref.)
AAAA
LA.—New Orleans
Abraham & Son, H., 218
Baronne ....AA
Alexander Co., M. H., 319
Decatur ....A
Amer. Sugar Refg. Co., 132
N. Peters ....A
Barkley & Co., J., 219 N.
Peters ....A
Bodenhemier & Bro., 209 N.
Peters ....A
Delgado & Co., 203 N.
Peters ....AA
Ellington Planting Co.,
(Ltd.), 219 N. Peters...A
Ermann & Cahn, 233 N.
Peters ....AA
Godchaux Co., Leon (Plant-
ers) ....AAAA
Grammercy Sugar Co. 107
Camp (Ref.) ......AAAA
Henderson, W., 239 N.
Peters (Ref.) ....AA
Hobart & Co., H. L., 307 N.
Front ....A
La Molasses Co., 414 St.
Jos. (Ref.) ....A
Laws & Co., H. L.AAAA
Lehman, Stern & Co., Ltd.,
839 Gravier ....A
McDerott, Thos., 225 N.
Peters ....A
Miles Plant'g Mfg. Co., 217
N. Peters ....AA
LA.—Placuemine
LeBlanc & Danos........A
MD.—Baltimore
Taylor & Levering, 109
Commerce ....A
MASS.—Boston
Amer. Sugar Refg. Co. 24
Broad ....AAAA
Revere Sugar Refinery, 23
Broad ....AAAA
MICH.—Alma
Alma Sugar Co. (Beet)...A

SUGAR : BEET &c. Con.

MICH.—Battle Creek
Post Sugar Co. (Ltd.)..AA
MICH.—Bay City
Bay City Sugar Co. (Beet)
            AA
Mich. Sugar Co. (Beet).AA
MICH.—Caro
Peninsular Sugar Refg. Co.
  (Beet) ....A
MICH.—Charlevoix
Charlevoit Sugar Co. (Beet)
            AA
MICH.—Crosswell
Sanilac Sugar Refg. Co.
  (Beet) ....AAA
MICH.—Detroit
Peninsular Sugar Refg. Co.
            A
Sanilac Sugar Refg. Co., S.
  Griswold ....AAA
MICH.—Holland
Holland Sugar Co. (Beet)
            A
MICH.—Owosso
Owosso Sugar Co. (Beet)
            AAAA
MICH.—Rochester
Detroit Sugar Co. (Beet).A
MICH.—Saginaw
Saginaw Sugar Co.......AA
Valley Sugar Co (Beet)
            AAA
MISS.—Natchez
Natchez Molasses & Vine-
  gar Co. ....AA
MO.—St. Louis
Lakeside Sugar Refg. Co.,
  706 Chestnut ....A
NEBR.—Ames
Standard Beet Sugar Co.
            AAA
NEBR.—Grand Island
Amer. Beet Sugar Co.....
            AAAA
Oxnard Beet Sugar Co....A
NEBR.—Leavitt
Standard Beet Sugar Co....
            AAA
NEBR.—Norfolk
Amer. Beet Sugar Co.....
            AAAA
N. J.—Jersey City
Amer. Sugar Refg. Co.....
            AAAA
N. Y.—Brooklyn
Amer. Sugar Refg. Co.,
  Kent Av. & S. 4th.AAAA
Dryden & Palmer, Bedford
  Av. & N. 12th (Pulvd.;
  Powd.) ....F
Mollenhauer Sugar Refg.
  Co., Kent Av. & S. 11th
            AAAA
N. Y.—Lyons
Empire State Sugar Co.
  (Beet) ....A
New York City
Adams. Jr., H., 18 Wall
  (Raw) ....A
Amer. Beet Sugar Co., 32
  Nassau ....AAAA
Amer. Sugar Refg. Co., 117
  Wall ....AAAA
Arbuckle Bros., 71 Water
            AAAA
Brandenstein & Co., M. J.,
  96 Wall ....AAAA
Crooks & Co., R., 136 Front
  (Imps.) ....AA
Czarnikow, McDougal & Co.,
  112 Wall (Imp. Raw)..A
Davis. A.. 90 Wall ......A
Federal Sugar Refg. Co.,
  138 Front ....AAAA
Hales. John. 138 Front ..A
Howell Son & Co., B. H.,
  109 Wall ....AAAA
Natl. Sugar Refg. Co., 109
  Wall .... AAAA
N. Y.—Yongers
Federal Sugar Refg. Co.
            AAAA
Natl. Sugar Refg. Co.,
            AAAA
OHIO—Cincinnatti
Continental Sugar Co., 25
  Frankfort .... AA
OHIO—Tremont
Contenetal Sugar Co. ..AAA
PA.—Philadelphia
Francisco Sugar Co., 143 S.
  Front ....AA
Franklin Sugar Refg. Co.,

SUGAR : BEET &c. Con.

  Stock Ex. Place ..AAAA
Heyl Bros., 147 S. Front
            AA
McCahan Sugar Refg. Co.,
  147 Front ....AAAA
Rogers Holloway & Co., 131
  S. 4th ....A
Speckles Sugar Refg. Co.
            AAAA
TENN.—Memphis
Goyer & Co., W. 185th Tenn.
            AA
TEXAS—Lakeside
Lakeside Sugar Refg. Co. A
UTAH—Lehi City
Utah Sugar Co. (Beet)
            AAAA
UTAH—Ogden
Ogden Sugar Co.........AA
UTAH—Salt Lake City
Utah Sugar Co. (Beet) AAA
Western Sugar Refg. Co.
            AAAA
WASH.—Spokane
Washington State Sugar Co.
            A
WASH.—Waverly
Washington State Sugar Co.
            A

SUGAR: (MISC.)

ILL.—Chicago
Barrett & Co., M. L.
  (Burnt) ....A
Glucose Sugar Refining Co.
  (Grape) .... AAAA
ILL.—Marengo
Marengo Creamery & Sugar
  of Milk Co. ....D
MO.—St. Louis
Donnell Mfg. Co.
  (Lemon) ....B
New York City
Bush & Co., W. J. (Burnt)
            AA
Schwenker, W. M.
  (Anhydrous) ....B
Williamson & Co., D. D.
  (Burnt) ....B
OHIO—Kinsman
Kinsman Refining Co.
  (Milk) ....E

SUGAR & SYR-UP: MAPLE

ILL.—Chicago
Berry Maybrun Co., 59
  Larabee C
Bradshaw, J. H., 190 C. H.
  Place ....A
Manierre-Yoe Syrup Co.,
  30 River ....B
IOWA—Davenport
Davenport Vinegar & Pickle
  Co. ....D
IOWA—Elgin
Maple Grove Sugar & Syrup
  Co. ....D
KY.—Louisville
Goodwin Pres. Co., 407
  9th ....A
Price & Lucas, Cider &
  Vinegar Co. ....A
MAINE—Portland
Pettengill Co.. E. D. ....B
MASS.—Boston
Geer & Son., D. H., 448
  Southampton ....A
BOSTON—Holliston
Maple Syrup Co. ....D
MASS.—Somerville
Lamb, W. J. C
MASS.—Springfiel
Vermont Farmers (The ..D
MICH.—Detroit
Charbonnean & Co., E. A.,
  603 Fort W............D
MICH.—Shelby
Mikersell & Co.. J. ....B
MINN.—St. Paul
St. Paul Syrup Refg. Co.
            AAA
MO.—Kansas City
Bliss Syrup Refg. Co. ...B
N. J.—West Hoboken
Palisade Mfg. Co. ....D
N. Y.—Brooklyn
Barker & Co., J. H., 89
  Bedford Av. ....A
Leslie. Dunham & Co., 281
  Greene Av. ....D

SUGAR & SYRUP (Con.)
Rigney Co., 348 Park Av. D
N. Y.—Buffalo
Brennisen & Son., F., 156
Michigan ....B
Gleason & Lansing, 150
Michigan .... A
N. Y.—Lowville
Richardson & Co., R. J. C
New York City
Ams, Max, 372 Gwich. AA
Falcon Packing Co., 158
Franklin C
Hildreth & Segelken, 265
Gwich. C
Isreal & Bro., C., 490 Canal
B
N. Y.—Norwich
Norwich Pro. Co. ....A
OHIO—Bellefontaine
Johnson Co., F. N. ....A
OHIO—Chagrin Falls
Phillips & Co., C. F. ....D
OHIO Cincinaatti
Spencer & Son., W. M., 324
E. 2nd ....D
OHIO—Garrettsville
Crane & Co., A. E. ......B
OHIO—Warren
Crane, C. A. ....D
OHIO—Liberty
Henkle, Alf. H...........X
PA.—Braford
Boyle & Williams C
R. I.—Providence
Huntington Maple Syrup &
Sugar Co. ....D
VT.—Brattleboro
Brattleboro Jelly Co. ....B
VT.—Burlington
Welch Bros. Maple Co. C
VT.—Morrisville
Maplewood Sugar & Syrup
Co. ....D
VT.—St. Johnsbury
Cary Co., Geo. C. C

SUITINGS

See Woolen Goods

SUITS:

BATHING

For other Suits, see Clothing: Men's & Women's;
also Underwear

MASS.—Millbury
Kotedsilk Underwear Co. D
N. Y.—Brooklyn
Am. Knit Goods Mfg. Co.
AAA
Sheindelman, Samuel C
Simon, Julius C
New York City
Crescent Co. C
Levy-Stiefel Co. C
N. Y.—Utica
Olympian Knit Goods Co.
C
Weavers, Van R. ....D
PA.—Philadelphia
Geneva Knitting Mills....C
Noon & Sons, Edw. ......D
Osborne, Wm. .... D

SULKIES

See Carriages & Wagons

SULPHUR

ILL.—Chicago
Rhodes & Co., James H.,
117 Kinzie ....B
MD.—Baltimore
Thomsen Chem. Co.
(Crude) ....B
MASS.—Boston
Billings-Clapp Co. ......B
Linder & Meyer ....A
MO.—St. Louis
Herf & Frerick's Chemical
Co. ....A
Mallinckrodt Chemical
Wks. ....AAAA
New York City
Battelle & Renwick, 163
Front (Flour) ....AA
Beggs, E. J., 118 Beekman
(Nassau Sulphur Wks) D
Cooper & Co., Chas. ....AA
General Chemical Co., 25

SULPHUR (Con.)
Broad ....AAAA
White Co., L. & S. C., 28
Burling Slip ....B
N. Y.—Niagara Falls
Archer Process Co.
(Chloride) ....D
OHIO—Cleveland
Graselle Chemical Co.
AAAA
PA.—Philadelphia
Dreding Bros. Co. ......AA

SUMAC

KY.—Ashland
Great Diamond Sumac Co.
X
New York City
Hoople & Androvette, 218
Fulton ....A
Leber & Meyer, 5 William B
Phelps Bros. & Co., 31
Bway. ....AA
VA.—Fredericksburg
Hurkamp Co., John G. ..B
Knox & Bros., Robert T. D
VA.—Hallsboro
Baker, W. W. C
VA.—Manchester
Shotwell & Co., A. D. ..B
VA.—Petersburg
Jones, Vaughn & Co. ....B
VA.—Richmond
Moore, Warner & Co. ..AA
VA.—Winchester
Smith German ....B
W. VA.—Charleston
Tanners & Dyers Extract Co.

SUNBONNETS

See Millinery

SUPER-
HEATERS

New York City
Babcock & Wilcox Co., 85
Liberty (Steam) ..AAAA
Potter Separator Co., 43
Cortlandt (Steam) ....F
Power Specialty Co., 126
Liberty (Steam) ...... E
PA.—Pittsburg
Westinghouse Machine Co.
(Steam) .... AAAA

SUPPLIES

PA.—Philadelphia
White Dental Mfg. Co., S.
S., 12th & Chest. Branch-
es at New York, Boston,
& Atlanta (Tooth Pastes
& Powders for Druggists;
Oxygen for Physicians,
Chemists, etc. ..AAAA

SUPPORTERS

See Bandages; Suspenders

SUPPORTS

See Hardware; Carriage, etc.

CONN.—Bridgeport
Smith & Egge Mfg. Co.
(Sash) .... A
CONN.—East River
Munger & Son. (Blackboard)
H
CONN.—Middletown
Palmer, J. E. (Hammock)
A
ILL.—Chicago
Barbee Wire & Iron Works
(Counter) .... B
Tuthill Spring Co.
(Tongue) .... B
Weber Wagon Co. (Tongue)
AA
ILL.—Downer's Grove
Dickle Tool Co. (Pole) ..C
ILL.—Plano
Earl Mfg. Co., T. H.
(Clothes Line) C
IND.—Lafayette
Haggard Wagon Spring
Co. (Tonue) X
MASS.—Springfield
Barney & Berry (Ankle
(Skate ....G

SUPPORTS (Con.)

MICH.—Detroit
Bolles Iron & Wire Wks (Counter) X

MICH.—Grand Rapids
Grand Rapids Brass Co. (Brass Desk) C
Hardware Supply Co. (Desk Lid) X

MO.—St. Louis
Kupferle, John C. (Foot Rail Forch) ....AA
Plenger & Henger Mfg. Co. (Porch) .... A

N. Y.—Brooklyn
Brooklyn Wire Forming Co. (Incand. Mantle) ......G
New York Silicate Book Slate Co. (Blackboard) F
Sargent & Co., 151 Leonard (Table Leaf) ....AAAA

N. Y.—Seneca Falls
Westcott Jewell Co. (Book-keeper's Book) ....D

OHIO—Cincinnatti
Schreiber & Sons Co., L. ,(Cask & Vat.) ....AA

OHIO—Hamilton
Meyers Mfg. Co., Fred J. (Counter) .... B

OHIO—Ravenna
Williams, A. C. (Porch) A

OHIO—Salem
Clark Co., W. J. (Screen Door) C

PA.—Columbia
Columbia Grey Iron Co. (Porch) .... D

PA.—Philadelphia
Horn & Bro., W. H. (Abdominal) ....B

PA.—Reading
Reading Hardware Co. (Porch) ....AAAA

PA.—South Bethlehem
Bethlehem Fdy. & Mach. Co. (Counter) C

PA.—Wrightsville
Susqehanna Casting Co. (Porch) .... B
Wrightsville Hardware Co. (Porch) .... B

SUPPOSITO-RIES

ILL.—Chicago....
Baker & Co., Chas. S. ..C

MD.—Baltimore
Sharp & Dohme ......AAA

MICH.—Detroit
Parke, Davis & Co. ....AAA
Stearns & Co., Frederick AAA

New York City
Fougera & Co., E., 30 N. William .... A
Schieffel'n & Co. ......AA

PA.—Philadelphia
Blair, Henry C. ....B
Wyeth & Bros., John AAAA

SURAHS

See Silk Goods

SURCINGLES

See also Harness & Saddlery

CONN.—Middletown
Russell Mfg. Co. ....AAAA

N. J.—Newark
Peters Harness & Saddlery Co. C

N. Y.—Buffalo
Buffalo Weaving & Belting Co. C

N. Y.—Watervliet
Covert Mfg. Co. .... A

SURFACERS

See also Machy.

CONN.—Bridgeport
Springfield Mfg. Co. (Emery) .... B

CONN.—Norwich
Rogers & Co., C. B. ..AAAA

ILL.—Chicago
Fischer Machine Works B

MASS.—Boston

SURFACERS (Con.)
Woods Machine Co., S. A. AA

N. J.—Smithville
Smith Machine Co., H. B. A

N. Y.—Buffalo
Holmes Machinery Co., E. & B. ....B

New York City
American Wood Working Machinery Co. .....AAAA

OHIO—Cincinnatti
J. A. Fay & Egan Co. AAAA

OHIO—Toledo
Baker Bros. ....A

PA.—Philadelphia
Power & Co., L. C

PA. Stroudsburg
Tanite Co. (Emery) C

R. I.—Providence
Diamond Machine Co. (Emery) .... B

VT.—Montpelier
Lane Mfg. Co. (Wood) ..A

WIS.—Beloit
Berlin Machine Works AAAA

SURGICAL GOODS

CAL.—Los Angeles
Sweeney Co., W. W., 421 S. B'way (Elastic Knit) C

MASS.—Highlandville
Gorse Co., F. W. (Knit) E
Gorse & Co., Wm. (Knit) X

MO.—St. Louis
Willbrandt Surg. Mfg. Co. B

New York City
Lawson, A. M., 2611 Bway. (Knit) ....D

N. Y.—Lockport
Empire Mfg. Co. (Elastic) .... B

SURREYS

See Carriages & Wagons

SUSPENDERS . GARTERS, ETC.

CAL.—Los Angeles
Cohn, Goldwater & Co. (Suspenders) ....B

CAL.—San Francisco
Carson Glove Co. (Suspenders) C
Heineman, H. M. (Suspenders) .... B
Heyneman & Co. ....A
Zekind, S. (Suspenders & Hose Supporters) ......E

CONN.—Bridgeport
Armstrong Mfg. Co. (Hose & Sleeve Supporters) ..A
Canfield Rubber Co. (Stocking Supporters) .....AA
Taylor, Thos P. (Hose Supporters) .... A
Warner Bros. Co. (Hose Supporters, Etc.) ..AAAA

CONN.—Middletown
Russell Mfg. Co. (Suspenders) ....AAA

CONN.—New Haven
Hickok Co. (Hose Supporters, Etc.) ....E

CONN.—New Britain
White, C. J. & Co. (Men's Garters & Armbands) ..D

CONN.—Waterbury
Waterbury Buckle Co. (Hose Supporters) ....A

GA.—Atlanta
Robinson Neckwear Co. (Suspenders) ....D

ILL.—Arthur
Rigney & Haney (Suspenders) ....D

ILL.—Aurora
American Suspender Co. (Suspenders) ....D

ILL.—Chicago
Black Cat Garter Co. (Hose Supporters) ....D
Bunker Saddle & Specialty

Co. (Leather) ....F
Common Sense Truss Co. (Abdominal Supporters) D
Field & Co., Marshall (Suspenders) ......AAAA
Hackner Bros. & Bruski (Suspenders) ....D
Haussmann & Dunn (Abdominal Supporters) C
Hoyt, G. W. & Co. (Hose Supporters) ....B
Illinois Suspender Co. (Suspenders) C
Riordan, T. G. Mfg. Co. (Suspenders) C
Stein, A. & Co. (Garters; Stocking Supporters) ..B
Wilson Bros (Suspenders) AAAA
Worms & Loeb (Suspenders) D

ILL.—Mattoon
Buck, Geo. N. Mfg. Co. (Hose Supporters) .... B
Kern, Frank (Hose Supporters) C
ILL.—Urbana
Urbana Suspender Co. (Suspenders) ....D
ILL.—Mishawaka
Mishawaka Pad & Harness Co. (Leather Suspenders) C
ILL.—Peru
Peru Bagging Co. (Suspenders) ....B
IND.— Indianapolis
Stevenson, Chas. N. & Co. (Suspenders) ....E
Union Mfg. Co. (Suspenders; Hose Supporters; Armbands) ....D
IOWA—Des Moines
Des Moines Skirt & Skirt Corset Mfg. Co. (Hose Supporters) ....
Northwestern Suspender Co. (Suspenders; Hose & Sleeve Supporters) C
IOWA—Sioux City
Kalish Bros. (Suspenders) D
KANS.—Lawrence
Victor Suspender Mfg. Co. (Suspenders; Armbands; Hose Supporters) ....D
KY.—Louisville
Martin, R. M. Co. (formerly Monarch Mfg. Co.) (Suspenders) ....D
LA.—New Orleans
Nick, H. L. & Co. (Suspenders) C
MD.—Baltimore
Silberman, Abraham (Standard Suspender Co.) (Suspenders; Garters) .... D
MASS.—Boston
Boston Suspender Mfg. Co. (Hose Supporters) ....D
Chester Suspender Co., Roxbury ....A
Clark Mfg. Co. (Women's Hose Supporters; Men's Garters) ....E
Frost, Geo. G. (Hose; Abdominal; Skirt Sleeve; Stocking Supporters) .. A
Hewes & Potter (Suspenders) ....A
Hub Gore Makers (Sleeve Supporters) ....
New England Novelty Mfg. Co. (Skirt) ....A
Trafton, H. O. (Hose Supporters) ....E
Ziegler, A. & Son. (Chester Suspender Co.,) (Garters) B

MASS.—Chicopee Falls
Taylor-Bramley Co., (Abdominal Supporters) ....B
MASS.—Easthampton
Dible & Warner (Suspenders; Stocking Supporters) B
Nashwannuck Mfg. Co. (Suspenders; Garters) AA
MASS.—Holyoke
Bullard, W. H. & Co. (Garters; Hose Supporters) ....D
MASS.—Shirley
Edgarton, C. A. Mfg. Co. (Suspenders) ....B

MICH.—Ann Arbor
Crescent Works (Hose Supporters) ....D
MICH.—Jackson
Reliance Corset Co. (Hose Supporters) C
MASS.—Kalamazoo
Kalamazoo Corset Co. (Hose Supporters) ...... AA
Puritan Corset Co. (Hose Supporters) ....B
MINN.—Albert Lea
Case Corset Co. (Hose Supporters) ....E
MINN.—Minneapolis
North Star Suspender Co. (Suspenders) ....D
MISS.—Enterprise
Enterprise Knitting Mills (Suspenders) ....E
MO.—St. Louis
Ferguson, McKinney Dry Goods Co. (Suspenders) AAAA
Hurst, Zucker Neckwear Co. (Suspenders) ....D
Marks, M. (Garters; Armbands; Hose Supporters) E
St. Louis Corset Co. (Shoulder Braces) ......B
St. Louis Suspender Co. (Suspenders) ....E
N. J.—Jersey City
Consolidated Manhattan Suspender Co. (Suspenders) B
N. J.—Newark
Delsarte Mfg. & Supply Co. (Shoulder Braces) .... D
N. Y.—Adams
Rice, Dr. W. S. (Hose Supporters) C
N. Y.—Brooklyn
Goodman & Mandel (Suspenders) C
N. Y.—Buffalo
Adam, J. N. & Co. (Suspenders) ....AAAA
N. Y.—Lockport
Empire Mfg. Co. (Abdominal Supporters) ....A
N. Y.—McGraw
McGraw Corset Co., A. P. (Hose Supporters) C
New York City
Braum, L & Co. (Lion Suspender Co.) (Suspenders) D
Blaver, Isador (Suspenders) E
Blechman & Son (Suspenders) ....E
Bloomberg, C. & Co. (Crown Suspender Co.) (Suspenders) C
Cohen, M. (Monarch Suspender Co.) (Suspenders) D
Eder, Saul & Bros. (Garters) .... E
Elk Mfg. Co. (Garters) ..D
Ferris Bros. Co. (Abdominal; Stocking Supporters ....A
Fisk, Clark & Flagg (Stocking Supporters; Braces) A
Glickman, I. M. (Equitable Suspender Co.) (Suspenders) ....D
Gotham Garter & Novelty Co. (J. N. Cohen & Co.) (Hose Supporters; Garters) C
Habeeb, E. & Bros. (Suspenders) ....E
Haley, C. J. & Co. (Hose Supporters) C
Harris Suspender Co. (Suspenders; Garters; Braces) A
Hilpoltsteiner, Samuel (Suspenders) C
Hirsh & Smith (Royal Suspender Co.) (Suspenders) C
Keys, Collier & Tillard (Shoulder Diaper Suspenders) ....D
Kleinert Rubber Co., I. B. (Hose Supporters) ....A
Knothe Bros. (Suspenders) C
Lublintz, Adolph (Knickerbocker Suspender Co.) (Suspenders) C

SUSPENSORIES

See Bandages

SWABS

SWAGES

SWAGES (Con.)
Forge Co., Arrott Bldg.
(Tie Plate) .... D
WIS.—Eau Claire
Phoenix Mfg. Co. (Saw) A
WIS.—South Milwaukee
Filer & Stowell Co. (Saw) A

SWEATERS

CONN.—Hartford
Plaisted & Co., C. C. ....F
ILL.—Chicago
Dornbaum, Albert ....F
Empire Knitting Mills, 147
W. Van Buren ....F
Fettig, Theodore, 1865
Ogden Av. ....E
Lorenz, Rich, 241 Clybourn
Av. ....D
Royal Knitting Mills ....E
MASS.—Boston
Kingston Knitting Co. ...C
Sterling Knit Goods Co. ..E
MASS.—Chicopee Falls
Taylor-Bramley Co. ....B
MASS.—Highlandville
Wye & Co., Geo. E. ......E
Wye, Wm. H. ....E
MASS.—Millbury
Kotedsilk Underwear Co. D
MASS.—Needham
Brooks Co., Jno. F. C
MICH.—Detroit
Angora Knitting Co. ....E
Ryan Bros. Knitting Co. C
MICH.—Lansing
Michigan Knitting Co. ...D
MINN.—Duluth
Neilson Bros. C
MINN.—Northfield
Northfield Knitting Co. ..F
N. H.—Canterbury
Shaker Knitting Co. C
N. J.—Woodbine
Quaker City Knitting Mills
(Boys'; Infants') ......A
N. Y.—Amsterdam
Waldron & Cassidy ......D
N. Y.—Augusta
Cunningham & Son, Jas..D
N. Y.—Brooklyn
Amer. Knit Goods Mfg. Co.
AAA
Barnard & Co., Geo. .....B
Central Knitting Co. ....D
Plate & Clark ....D
Sheindelman, Samuel ...C
Siegel, N. ....E
Standard Knitting Mills ..D
N. Y.—Cohoes
Barnet & Aufsesser Knit
Co. ....B
N. Y.—Herkimer
Brooks Mfg. Co., W. W. D
N. Y.—Ilion
Sterling Mills C
N. Y.—Little Falls
Rockton Knitting Mills
(Cotton; Wool) ....A
Swanson Knitting Co. ....D
New York City
Crescent Co. C
Levy-Stiefel Co. C
Lippman, Israel ....D
Reichman, Wm., 98 Fkln. B
Robertson & Bruhn (Mfrs.
Agts) ....B
Rosenfeld & Co., 87 Warren
D
Stokes Cromie & Co. (Com.)
B
Wertheimer & Hollander,
159 Greene ....B
N. Y.—Oriskany Falls
Hatheway & Reynolds ..A
N. Y.—Philmont
Aken Knitting Co. ....AA
N. Y.—Prospect
Hoag, C. F. ....B
N. Y.—Utica
Albin Knit Goods Co. ....D
Athletic Knitting Co. ....B
Mohawk Valley Cap Factory
B
Olympian Knit Goods Co. C
Weaver, Van R. ....D
PA.—Hawley
U. S. Knitting Mills Co. D
PA.—Honesdale
Amer. Knitting Co. .....D
Maple City Knitting Mills D

SWEATERS (Con.)
PA.—Philadelphia
Feld & Co. C
Geneva Knitting Mills C
Greaves, Thomas ....B
Gutsche, R. C
Koch, Justus ....B
Leicester & Continental
Mills Co. ....AA
Osborne, Wm. ....D
Pebesdy & Sons, Geo. ....B

SWEATS

CONN.—Bethel
Shepard & Son Co., Geo. A.
(Hat) ....F
N. J.—Newark
Riordan Leather Co. (Hat)
X
New York City
Bracher Mfg. Co., Geo. L.,
22 W. 3d (Hat) ......B
Mast Co., J. B. (Hat) ...X
Wintjen, John G. (Hat) ..E

SWEEPERS

CONN.—Deep River
Rogers Brush Works
(Carpet) ....F
ILL.—Aurora
Wilcox Mfg. Co. (Carpet) B
ILL.—Chicago
Austin Mfg. Co. (Street)
AAA
IND.—Marion
National Sweeper Co.
(Carpet) ....AAAA
IND.—Richmond
F. N. Lawn Mower Co.
(Lawn) ....A
IND.—South Bend
Knoblock-Heideman Mfg.
Co. (Street) ....D
Studebaker Bros. Mfg. Co.
(Street) ....AAAA
MASS.—Boston
Edson Mfg. Co. 132 Com-
mercial (Street) C
MASS.—Taunton
Taunton Locomotive Mfg.
Co. (Street; Railroad) .C
MICH.—Grand Rapids
Bissell Carpet Sweeper Co.
(Carpet; Toy Carpet) AA
Goshen Sweeper Co. (Car-
pet) ....D
Sweeperette Co. (Carpet)
AAA
N. Y.—Brooklyn
American Car Seat Co., 18
Guernsey (Rattan) ....D
OHIO—Milford
Milford Mfg. Co. (Carpet) X
OHIO—Springfield
Green Mfg. Co. (Hand
Lawn; Hand Street) ..F
PA.—Philadelphia
Philadelphia Lawn Mower
Co. (Lawn) ....B
R. I.—Pawtucket
Thayer's Sons, Ellis (Car-
pet) X

SWEEPS

ILL.—Bradley
Bradley Mfg. Co., David
(Cotton) ....A
KY.—Louisville
Avery & Sons, B. F.
(Cotton) ....A
VA.—Norfolk
Whitehurst & Co., R. W.
(Cotton) ....B

SWEETENERS
Saccharine, etc.

MO.—St. Louis
Monsanto Chemical Wks.,
1818 S. 2d ....D
New York City
Heyden Chem. Wks., 40
Pine (Artificial) .....A
Klipstein & Co., A., 123
Pearl (Saccharin) ....AA
Kuttroff, Pichardt & Co.
(Artificial) ....A
Lieber & Co., H. C
Merck & Co. ....AAAA

997

SWEETENERS (Con.)
OHIO—Cincinnati
Berghausen Chemical Co.,
The E. (Artificial) ..B

SWINGS
ILL.—Batavia
Batavia Wind Mill Co.
(Steel Lawn) ....B
Challenge Wind Mill & Feed
Mill Co. (Lawn) ....AAA
Snow Mfg. Co. (Street
Lawn) ....E
ILL.—Chicago
Bristol & Gale Co., 110 W.
Washn. (Lawn) ....D
ILL.—De Kalb
Haish Wire & Implement
Co. (Lawn) ....B
ILL.—Galva
Hayes Pump & Planter Co.
(Lawn) ....A
ILL.—Moline
Sechler Carriage Co., D. M.
(Lawn) ....AA
ILL.—Plano
Earl Mfg. Co., F. H.
(Lawn) C
Sears Co., Albert H.
(Lawn) ....A
IND.—Bluffton
Bluffton Folding Chair Co.
(Lawn) C
IND.—Butler
Butler Co. (Lawn) .....B
IND.—Goshen
Goshen Mfg. Co. (Lawn) B
IND.—Laporte
Michael Mfg. Co., Chas. H.
(Lawn) C
IND.—Muncie
Glascock Bros. Mfg. Co.
(Lawn) ....D
IND.—Richmond
Fry Bros. (Lawn) ......F
Wayne Wks. (Lawn) ....A
IND.—Vernon
Reed & Rogers Mfg. Co.
(Lawn) ....E
IOWA—Cedar Rapids
Adams, A. L. (Lawn) ....E
IOWA—Des Moines
Purington Mfg. Co. (Lawn)
G
IOWA—Iowa City
Kelly Western Mfg. Co., O.
S. (Lawn) ....B
IOWA—Prairie City
Dowden Mfg. Co. (Lawn) B
MAINE—Brunswick
Fairfield Lawn Swing Co.
(Automatic; Lawn) ....E
IOWA—South Paris
Paris Mfg. Co. (Lawn) ..A
MASS.—Orange
Leavitt Machine Co. (Bar-
rel) ....F
MICH.—Jackson
Aspinwall Mfg. Co.
(Lawn) ....B
MICH.—Rochester
Miller Bros. (Lawn) X
MINN.—Sauk Center
Keller Mfg. Co. (Lawn) .D
MO.—Carrollton
Farm Tool Mfg. Co.
(Lawn) ....B
MO.—Huntsville
Fleming & Sons Mfg. Co.
(Lawn) ....B
N. J.—Trenton
Rogers. C. C. (Automatic)G
New York City
Sargent & Co., 151 Leonard
(Barrel) ....AAAA
N. Y.—Tonawnda
Gillie Engine & Machine Co.
(Steam) C
OHIO—Ashland
Myers & Bro., F. E. (Lawn)
AAAA
OHIO—Dayton
Ohio Rake Co. (Lawn) AA
OHIO—Norwalk
Gregory, Giles R. (Lawn) F
Greene Mfg. Co. (Lawn) F
OHIO—Tippecanoe City
Tippecanoe Building & Mfg.
Co. (Lawn) ....B
PA.—Bausman
Bausman, D. H. (Steel;
Lawn) C

SWINGS (Con.)
PA.—Elizabethtown
Buchs Sons Co., A. (Lawn)
A
PA.—Titusville
Specialty Mfg. Co.
(Lawn) ....B
PA.—York
Keystone Farm Machinery
Co. (Lawn) ....B
VT.—Readsboro
Readsboro Chair Mfg. Co.
(Lawn) ....B
WIS.—Sheboygan
Garton Toy Mfg. Co.
(Parlor) ....A

SWITCH-BOARDS
ILL.—Chicago
Amer. Electric Telephone
Co. ....B
Western Electric Co. (Tele-
graph; Telephone) AAAA
Western Electric Mfg. Co.
(Telephone) ....B
IND.—Fort Wayne
Fort Wayne Electric Works
AAA
IND.—Indianapolis
Jenney Elect. Mfg. Co. C
IND.—Kokomo
Kokomo Telephone & Elect.
Mfg. Co. ....F
MD.—Baltimore
Maryland Telephone & Tele-
graph Co. ....B
Viaduct Mfg. Co. X
MASS.—Peabody
Helios-Upton Co. ....D
MO.—St. Louis
Emerson Elect. Mfg. Co. C
N. Y.—Newburgh
Hewitt & Warden ....D
New York City
Bunnell & Co., J. H., 20
Park Pl. (Telegraph) B
Electric Co., O. & C. ..AA
Zucker & Levett & Loeb Co.,
526 W. 25th ....A
N. Y.—Schenectady
General Electric Co. AAAA
N. Y.—Troy
Bernard Co., E. G. .....D
OHIO—Cincinnati
Bullock Elec. Mfg. Co. AA
OHIO—Mansfield
Mansfield Tempered Copper
Co. ....B
PA.—Philadelphia
Keystone Electrical Instru-
ment Co. (Telephone) ..B
Partrick, Carter & Wilkins
(Telegraph) ....B
Pringle, William T. ....D
Quaker City Electric Co
(Power) ....D
United Elect. Importing Co.
A
PA.—Pittsburg
McKenna Bros. Brass Co.
A
Westinghouse Electric &
Mfg. Co. ....AAAA
VA.—Richmond
Richmond Electric Co. ..AA

SWITCHES
See also Frogs

COLO.—Denver
Davis Iron Works Co., F.
M. (Mine) ....AA
Flint-Lomax Electric Mfg.
Co., 1937 Curtis (Flush;
Snap; Push) ....B
Mine & Smelter Supply Co.
(Mine) ....AAAA
Sechrist Mfg. Co., Albert,
1033 16th (Automatic) B
CONN.—Bridgeport
Bryant Electric Co. (Snap;
Knife) ....A
Perkins Electric Switch
Mfg. Co. (Snap; Ordinary;
Knife) ....A
CONN.—Hartford
Hart Mfg. Co. (Push; Snap;
Ordinary) ....A
Hart & Hegeman Mfg. Co.

SWITCHES (*Con.*)

(Push; Snap; Ordinary)B

CONN.—Plainville
Trumbull Electric Co.
  (Knife; Baby Knife) ..C

GA.—Atlanta
May & Spalding (Railroad)
  ....D
Wotten Electric & Mfg. Co.
  (Knife) ....B

ILL.—Chicago
Austin & Co., M. B., 56 W.
  Van Buren (Flush; Snap;
  Push) X
Borden & Selleck Co., 48
  Lake (Industrial Rail-
  way) ....B
Clark & Burris Mfg. Co., 63
  S. Canal (Knife) .....B
Klute-Berthold Elect. Co.,
  126 35th (Knife) .....B
Lang Electric Co., 44 Mich-
  igan (Knife) ....D
Morden Frog & Crossing
  Works (Split) C
Sterion, Brass, Copper &
  Bronze Co. 67 N. Ashland
  (Knife) ...AAAA
Western Electric Co., 259 S.
  Clinton (Knife) ...AAAA

ILL.—East St. Louis
Elliott Frog & Switch Co.
  (Split) ....AA

IND.—Fort Wayne
Fort Wayne Electric Wks.
  (High Voltage; Knife)
  AAA

IND.—Peru
Peru Electric Mfg. Co.
  (Knife) C

MASS.—Boston
Anderson Mfg. Co., 289 A.
  (Knife) C
Boston Electric Co., 29 Har-
  rison Av. (Knife) .....B
Condit Jr., & Co., S. B., 63
  Oliver (Pneumatic Oil
  Break) ....B
Lundin Electric & Machine
  Co., 176 Federal (Knife)E
Marshall Electric Mfg. Co.,
  301 Congress (Snap; Push;
  Knife, etc.) ....B

MASS.—Cambridge
Barbour-Stockwell Co.
  (Railroad) ....A

MASS.—New Bedford
Hill Electric Co., W. S.
  (Knife) X

MASS.—Springfield
Davis Electric Mfg. Co.
  (Knife) ....D
Springfield Elect. Mfg. Co.
  (Knife) ....E

MASS.—Worcester
Linton & Southwick (Knife)
  X
Worcester Electric Mfg. Co.
  (Knife; Oil Break) ...H

MICH.—Birmingham
Wilson-Railway Gate Co.
  (Derailing) ....F

MICH.—Detroit
Proctor-Raymond Mfg. Co.
  (Knife) ....B
Russell Wheel & Foundry
  Co. (Indus) X

MICH.—Three Rivers
Sheffield Car Co. (Automatic Railroad; Cut Out)..B

MINN.—Minneapolis
Peteler Portable Railway
  Mfg. Co. (Contractors'
  Portable) C

MO.—St. Louis
Adam Electric Co., Frank,
  914 Pine (Knife) C
Wagner Elect. Mfg. Co.,
  2017 Locust (Knife) AA

N. J.—Hoboken
New York Switch & Cross-
  ing Co. (Automatic Railroad; Derailing) .....B

N. Y.—Brooklyn
Columbia Mch. Wks., 167
  Chestnut (Canopy; Power
  House) ....A
Krantz Mfg. Co., H., 160
  7th (Knife) ....B
White Mfg. Co., J. H., 127
  N. 10th (Knife) ......B

N. Y.—Buffalo
McCarthy Bros. & Ford, 45

SWITCHES (*Con.*)

N. Division (Knife) C

N. Y.—Hillburn
Ramapo Iron Works (Auto-
  matic Railroad; Split;
  Cut Out; Interlocking;
  Mine Track; Contractors'
  Portable) ....A

N. Y.—Long Island City
Steubner, G. L. (Industrial
  Railway; Mine) ....B

N. Y.—Newburgh
Hyer-Sheehan Elect. Motor
  Co. (Knife) C
Apex Equipment Co., 11
  Bway. (Industrial Rail-
  way) ....D

New York City
Automatic Switch Co., 143
  Liberty (Automatic) ..D
Bunnell & Co., J. H., 20
  Park Pl. (Electric) ..B
Edwards & Co., 417 E. 144th
  (Snap & Push; Snap. Or-
  dinary) ....D
Fox Bros. & Co., 24 Vesey
  (Industrial Railway) ..A
General Incandescent Arc
  Light Co., 572 1st Av.
  (Flush; Snap & Push;
  High Voltage; Knife; Oil
  Break) ....A
Hunt Co., C. W., 45 Bway.
  (Industrial Railway;
  Mine) ....AA
Koppel, Arthur, 68 Broad
  (Industrial Railway; Nar-
  row Gauge; Mine) .....A
La Roche Co., F. A., 656
  Hudson (Knife) ....A
Leavitt & Co., C. W., 15
  Cortlandt (Industrial
  Railway) ....D
Manhattan Electrical Supply
  Co., 32 Cortlandt (Knife)
  AA

N. Y.—Rochester
Bradley & Co., E. C. (Telephone) ....H
General Electric Co. (Flush;
  Snap & Push; High Volt-
  age; Knife; Snap Ordi-
  nary; Trolley) ....AAAA

N. Y.—Syracuse
Crouse-Hinds Electric Co.
  (High Voltage; Knife) A
Pass & Seymour (Snap &
  Push; Snap, Ordinary) A

N. Y.—Troy
Bernard Co., E. G. (Elec-
  tric) ....D

N. Y.—Utica
Bossert Elect. Construction
  Co. (Knife) ....B
Johnson & Morton, 44
  Whitesboro (Flush; Snap
  & Push; Knife) C

N. C.—Statesville
Steele & Son, J. C. (Industrial Railway) ....B

OHIO—Akron
Akron Electric Mfg. Co.
  (Snap Ordinary) .....D

OHIO—Cincinnati
Creaghead Engineering Co.,
  313 Walnut (Trolley) ..D
Weir Frog Co. (Split) ...A

OHIO—Cleveland
Atlas Bolt & Screw Co. (In-
  dustrial Railway) ...AA
Cleveland Frog & Crossing
  Co., 116 Bessemer Av.
  (Split) ....B
Cleveland Switchboard &
  Elect. Mfg. Co., 54 Mich-
  igan (Knife) ....E
Electric Controller & Supply
  Co. (Knife) ....A
Erner Electric Co., 62
  Public Sq. (Knife) ...D
Fulton Foundry Co.)Throw
  Over) C
Leonard & Bundy Electrical
  Co., 156 Champlain
  (Knife) ....G

OHIO—Cleveland
Barkelou Elect. Mfg. Co.
  (Knife) ....F

OHIO—Salem
Davis & Son, M. (Knife) A

OHIO—Youngstown
Banner Electric Co. (Knife)
  B

999

SWITCHES (Con.)

PA.—Allentown
Allentown Rolling Mills (Derailing; Interlocking; Signalling) ....AAA
PA.—Chester
Johnston R. R. Frog & Switch Co. (Derailing) B
PA.—Erie
Keystone Electric Co. (Reversing Elevator) ......B
PA.—North East
Eureka Tempered Copper Co. (High Voltage; Knife) A
PA.—Philadelphia
Heinemann & Co., Geo. M., 737 Girard Av. (Knife) F
Helios Mfg. Co., 1231 Callowhill (Knife) ....D
Levis & Co., Hy., 26 S. 15th (Railroad) ....B
Novelty Electric Co., 54 N. 4th (Knife) ....AA
Paiste Co., H. T., 310 Ludlow (Snap, Knife; Snap, Ordinary) ....B
Parke & Co., John Y., 728 Cherry (Knife) ......D
Partrick, Carter & Wilkins (Electric) ....B
Penna Steel Co., Girard Bldg. (Automatic Railroad; Mine Track; Contractors', Portable, Signalling; Split) ....AAAA
Pringle, Wm. T. (Electric; Knife) ....D
Weston & Co., W. H., 1303 Buttonwood (Knife) ...X
Wharton Jr. & Co., Wm. (Automatic Railroad; Industrial Railway) ..AAA
White Co., H. P. (Knife)F
PA.—Pittsburg
Carlin's Sons, Thos. (Railroad) ....A
Crescent Elect. & Mfg. Co. (Knife) ....E
McKenna Bros. Brass Co. (Knife) ....A
Pittsburg Trolley Pole Co., 115 Water (Knife) X
Schoenman Electric & Mfg. Co. (Knife) ....D
Westinghouse Elect. & Mfg. Co.(Canopy; High Voltage; Knife) ......AAAA
PA.—Reading
Reading Crane & Hoist Wks. (Overhead Track) A
PA.—Swissvale
Union Switch & Signal Co. (Interlocking; Signalling) ....AAAA
PA.—Wilkesbarre
Vulcan Iron Works (Cut Out; Mine Track) AAAA
PA.—York
York Electric & Machine Co. (Knife) ....F
R. I.—Providence
Safety Electric Switch Co. (Instantaneous Make & Break Safety Knife) ..X
VA.—Richmond
Electric Construction Co. of Va. (Knife) ....D
Richmond Electric Co. (Electric) ....AA
Tower-Bimford Elect. & Mfg. Co. (Knife) C
W. VA.—Wheeling
Mutual Electric & Machine Co. (Knife) C

SWIVELS

CONN.—Bridgeport
Bridgeport Chain Co. (Chain) ....A
Smith & Egge Mfg. Co. (Brass) C
CONN.—Chester
Brooks & Sons, M. S. (Solid Flat; Nickel; Brass or Steel) ....D
CONN.—New Britain
North & Judd Mfg. Co. (Harness; Lariat) ....AA
CONN.—New Haven
North & Co., O. B. ......B
ILL.—Chicago
Nicol & Co. (Iron) ......D

SWIVELS (Con.)

MD.—Baltimore
National Supply Co., 7 W. Lombard ....D
MASS.—Attleboro Falls
Fisher & Co., W. N. ...B
MASS.—Worcester
Wire Goods Co. (Chain) ..A
MICH.—Detroit
Michigan Bolt & Nut Wks., ft. Meldrum Av. ....AA
MICH.—Lansing
Lansing Wheelbarrow Co. (Iron) ....A
MO.—St. Louis
Leschen & Sons Co., A. (Rope) ....AA
N. J.—Newark
Taylor, Thos. H. (Jewelry) F
N. Y.—Buffalo
Pratt & Letchworth Co. (Lariat; Chain; Rope) AAA
N. Y.—Kenwood
Oneida Community (Ltd.) (Chain) ....AAA
New York City
Tiebout, W. & J., 118 Chambers (Rope) ....B
OHIO—Dayton
Dayton Malleable Iron Co. A
PA.—Chester
Keystone Drop Forge Works (Open Arm; Iron; Chain) B
PA.—Lebanon
Amer. Iron & Steel Mfg. Co. AAAA
PA.—Philadelphia
Bradlee & Co. (Chain) ...B
Hoopes & Townsend Co., Buttonwood (Closed or Pipe Open or Arm) AAA
R. I.—Pawtucket
Fuller & Son, Geo. H. ..A
R. I.—Providence
Hamilton & Hamilton Jr. A
Rhode Island Tool Co. AAA
Waite, Mathewson & Co. B
Wall & Co., A. T. C
WIS.—Racine
Racine Malleable & Wrought Iron Co. (Iron)A

SWORDS

MASS.—Chicopee
Ames Sword Co. ....B
New York City
Koehler & Co., A., 54 Union Sq. (Theatrical) C
OHIO—Cincinnati
Pettibone Bros. Mfg. Co. A
OHIO—Columbus
Lilley & Co., M. C. AAAA
PA.—Philadelphia
Schoenhut & Co., A. (Toy)A

SYNCHRONIZERS

New York City
Prentiss Clock Improvement Co. (for Clocks) ......D

SYPHONS

ILL.—Chicago
Illinois Malleable Iron Co., 30 W. Monroe ....AAAA
Marsh & Co., Jas. P. (Soda Water) ....B
ILL.—Fort Wayne
Bowser & Co., L. F. .....A
ILL.—Kewanee
Western Tube Co. (Steam Gauge) ....AAA
IND.—Fort Wayne
Bowser & Co., S. F. .....A
MASS.—Andover
Tyer Rubber Co. (for Bottling Liquors, etc.) .AA
MASS.—Boston
American Soda Fountain Co. ....AAAA
Crosby Steam Gauge & Valve Co. ....AA
MICH.—Detroit
American Injector Co. ....D
N. Y.—Brooklyn
Deverall Perfection Mfg.

SYPHONS (*Con.*)
Co., Johnson Pl. (Can) D
New York City
Bishop Gutta Percha Co.,
420 E. 25th (Gutta Per-
cha) ....B
Matthews, John (Firm of)
(Soda Water) ....AA
N. Y.—Stapleton
Walters & Son, Chas. ...B
OHIO—Cincinnati
Vanduzen Co., E. W. ....B
PA.—Philadelphia
Eynon-Evans Mfg. Co., 1519
Clearfield (Lead Lined
Acid) ....A

SYRINGES .

CONN.—New Haven
Seamless Rubber Co. (Foun-
tain; Rubber) ....AA
ILL.—Chicago
Haussman & Dunn (Hypo-
dermic) C
IND.—Indianapolis
Armstrong & Co., Wm. H.
(Rubber; Hypodermic) B
MD.—Baltimore
Chesapeake Glass Co., 424
W. Conway (Glass) ...D
MASS.—Andover
Tyer Rubber Co. (Eye; Ear;
Fountain; Rubber) ..AA
MASS.—Boston
Codman & Shurtleff (Inc.)
(Hypodermic) C
Davidson Rubber Co. (Rub-
ber) ....A
Leach & Greene (Hypoder-
mic) ....F
MASS.—Cambridge
McElroy, P. J. (Glass) E
MICH.—Detroit
Parke, Davis & Co. (Hypo-
dermic) ....AAAA
MO.—St. Louis
Bobe, Peter F. (Glass) ...C
Leslie Medicine Co., Chas.
(Fountain) ....D
N. J.—New Brunswick
Johnson & Johnson (Hypo-
dermic) ....AAAA
N. Y.—Buffalo
Buffalo Dental Mfg. Co.
(Dental) ....B
New York City
Becton, Dickinson & Co.,
160 Duane (Hypodermic)
A
Consolidated Dental Mfg.
Co. (Dental) ....F
Ellis & Goltermann (Rub-
ber) C
Goodyear Rubber Co. (Rub-
ber) ....AAAA
Goodyear's India Rubber
Glove Mfg. Co. (Rubber)
AAAA
Hodgman Rubber Co. (Rub-
ber) ....AA
Hoehn Co., R., 80 Chambers
(Hypodermic) ....B
Hussey & Co., E. J., 80
John (Rubber) ....F
Maris & Co., John M., 219
Fulton (Glass) ....B
Parker, Stearns & Sutton
(Eye; Ear; Fountain; Hy-
podermic; Rubber; Si-
phon) ....B
Weinhagen, Henry, 22 No.
William (Hypodermic) B
N. Y.—Senaca Falls
Rumsey & Co. (Inc.)
(Garden) ....A
OHIO—Akron
Goodrich Co., B. F. (Foun-
tain; Rubber) .....AAAA
PA.—Philadelphia
Boekel & Co., Wm., 578
Vine (Veterinary Injec-
tion) ....A
Johnson & Lund (Dental)
AA
Ware Co., Walter F. (Foun-
tain; Rubber) ....B
Whital, Tatum & Co. (Hy-
podermic; Glass) ..AAAA
White Dental Mfg. Co., S.
S. (Hypodermic; Dental)
AAAA

SYRINGES (*Con.*)
R. I.—Providence
Davol Rubber Co. (Rubber)
AA

SYRUP

**See also Molasses; also
Sugar & Syrups: Maple**

CAL.—San Francisco
California Fig Syrup Co.
(Fig) ....AA
ILL.—Chicago
Glucose Sugar Refining Co.
(Glucose) ....AAAA
Scully Syrup Co., D. B.
(Glucose) ....AA
LA.—New Orleans
Dunbar's Sons, G. W.
(Fruit) ....AA
McCann & Co. (Glucose) D
MO.—St. Louis
St. Louis Syrup & Preserv-
ing Co. (Glucose) ..AAA
NEBR.—Omaha
Farrell & Co. (Glucose) ..A
New York City
Cohen & Co., Wm. H.
(Fruit) X
Matthews, John (Fruit) AA
OHIO—Cincinnati
Alexander Co. (Glucose) A
OHIO—Unionville
Cleveland Cider Co. (Cider)
D
PA.—Philadelphia
Hance Bros. & White
(Fruit) ....AA
Whitman & Son, S. F.
(Chocolate) ....A

SYRUPS

ILL.—Chicago
Baker & Co., Chas. S.
(Medicinal) C
IND.—Indianapolis
Lilly & Co., Eli (Medicinal)
AA
LA.—New Orleans
Jungua Co., (Ltd.) J. B.
(Fruit) ....D
MASS.—Cambridge
Thayer & Co., Henry
(Medicinal) ....A
MICH.—Detroit
Parke, Davis & Co.
(Medicinal) ....AAAA
Stearns & Co., Fred
(Medicinal) ....AAA
MICH.—Kalamazoo
Upjohn Co. (Medicinal) AA
MO.—St. Louis
West India Mfg. Co.
(Bottlers') ....B
New York City
McKesson & Robbins
(Medicinal) ....AA
Schieffelin & Co., W. H.
(Medicinal) ....AA
Taussig & Co., N. W.
(Bottlers') ....A
PA.—Philadelphia
Hance Bros. & White
(Medicinal) ....AA
TENN.—Nashville
Spurlock, Neal & Co.
(Medicinal) ....A

SYSTEMS

IND.—Fort Wayne
Fort Wayne Electric Wks.
Alternating Current; Arc
Light; Incandescent Elec-
tric Lighting) ......AAA
IOWA—Burlington
Murray Iron Wks. Co.
(Electric Lighting) ...A
MO.—St. Louis
St Louis Car Co. (Electric
Railway) ....AAAA
N. Y.—Long Island City
Daimler Mfg. Co. (Portable
Lighting Complete) ...D
New York City
C & C Electric Co. (Electric
Lighting) ....B
Sprague Electric Co. (Elec-
tric Railway) ....AAAA
N. Y.—Schenectady
General Electric Co. (Arc

SYSTEMS (Con.)

Light; Incandescent and Continuous Current; Electric Lighting; also Electric Railway) ....AAAA

OHIO—Alliance

McCaskey Account Register Co. (Short Account) ...D

OHIO—Cincinnati

Triumph Electric Co. (Arc Light; Incandescent Electric Lighting) ....A

PA.—Erie

Keystone Electric Co. (Arc Light; Incandescent Electric Lighting) ....B

PA.—Philadelphia

Dallett Co., Thos. H. (Continuous Current; Electric Lighting) ....B

Fell Mfg. Co., E. C., 1112 Sansom (Short Account) D

PA.—Pittsburg

Westinghouse Elec. Mfg. Co. (Alternating Current; Arc Light; Incandescent Electric Lighting) .AAAA

TABLES

See also Furniture

COLO.—Denver

Colorado Iron Wks. Co., 721 17th (Concentrating) AA

CONN.—Meriden

Bradley & Hubbard Mfg. Co. (Brass; Card; Bronze) AAAA

CONN.—New Haven

Atwood First Aid Veterinary Co., Dr. F. G. (Veterinary) ....F

CONN.—Norwich

Rogers & Co., C. B. (Cut-Off; Metal Saw; Slitting Saw; Swing Cut Off; Edging) ....AAAA

CONN.—South Norwalk

McKibbin Mfg. Co. (Bronze) B

CONN.—Waterbury

Holmes, Booth & Haydens (Inc.) (Onyx) ....AAAA

Matthews & Willard Mfg. Co. (Onyx) ...... AAAA

Waterbury Farrel Foundry & Machine Co. (Metal Saw) ....AA

DEL.—Wilmington

Hilles & Jones Co. (Spacing) ....AAAA

ILL.—Batavia

Challenge Wind Mill & Feed Mill Co. (Saw) ......AA

U. S. Wind Engine & Pump Co. (Saw) ....AA

ILL.—Chicago

Akam Billiard Mfg. Co., 390 Wabash Av. (Billiard) D

Allis-Chalmers Co. (Concentrating) ....AAAA

American Bronze Fdy. Co. (Bronze) ....D

Borden & Selleck Co., 48 Lake (Picking) ....B

Chicago Ornamental Iron Co. (Bronze) C

Clark & Co., A. C. (Physicians') ....A

Dietzgen Co., Eugene (Draughting) ....A

Link Belt Machinery Co. (Picking) ....AAA

Merle & Heaney Mfg. Co., 185 Washn. (Billiard) AA

Niemann & Weinhardt Table Co. (Card; Checker) ....A

Passon & Sons, Chas., 706 Centre Av. (Billiard) .AA

Peterson & Co., Leonard, 51 Institute Pl. (Draughting) F

Post Co., Frederick, 218 S. Clark (Draughting) ....D

Smith Wire & Iron Wks., F. P. (Bronze) ....B

Winslow Bros. Co., 368 Carroll Av. (Bronze) ....AA

IND.—Indianapolis

Allison Co., W. D. (Gynaecological; Surgical; Physicians') ....B

Atkins & Co., E. C. (Brazing

TABLES (Con.)

Iron Saw Leveling) AAAA

Chandler & Taylor Co. (Edging; Slitting) ....AA

Clark & Roberts (Physicians') ....B

Perfection Chair Co. (Physicians') ....D

Udell Works (Card; Dressing; Work; Folding; Sewing Machine) ....A

IND.—Kendallville

Baker Sons & Co., J. R. (Bedside) C

IND.—Richmond

Robinson & Co., Inc. (Slitting Saw) ......AA

MAINE—Brunswick

Fairfield Lawn Swing Co. (Folding) ....E

MAINE—Fairfield

Fairfield Furniture Co. (Folding; Lap) ....D

MAINE—South Paris

Paris Mfg. Co. (Children's; Folding) ....A

MASS.—Boston

Davenport Co., A. H. (Card; Coffee; Dressing) ....AA

Golding & Co. (Imposing).B

McCafferty & Co., J. H., 436 Harrison Av. (Bronze) C

McGann, Thos. F., 104 Portland (Bronze) ....E

Murdock Corporation, 156 Boylsten (Bronze) ....B

Shreve Crump & Low Co., 14 Randolph (Bronze) ..AA

MASS.—Brockton

Kimball Bros. & Sprague (Saw) ....B

MASS.—Gardner

Derby & Co., P. (Brass) AA

Heywood Bros. & Wakefield Co. (Rattan) .....AAAA

MASS.—Taunton

Reed & Barton Corporation (Restaurant Steam) AAA

MASS.—Worcester

Hill Dryer Co. (Ironing).D

Kidder, R. E., 2 Hermon (Draughting) ....G

MICH.—Bay City

Industrial Wks. (Transfer) AA

MICH.—Belding

Belding-Hall Mfg. Co. (Folding) ....AA

MICH.—Benton Harbor

Spencer & Barnes Co. (Dressing) ....A

MICH.—Detroit

Amos & Co., Chas., 94 W. Larned (Bronze) ......E

Buckley-Hart Mfg. Co., 527 Franklin (Bronze) .....D

Schulenberg Mfg. Co. (Billiard) C

Vulcan Co. (Bronze) .....F

MICH.—Grand Rapids

Alexander Mfg. Co., J. G. (Draughtsmen') ......F

Backe Mfg. Co. (Billiard; Pool) X

Berkey Furniture Co., Wm. A. (Centre Extension) .A

Durfee Embalming Fluid Co. (Embalming ....B

Fox Machine Co. (Saw) ..A

Hetterscheid Mfg. Wks. (Draughting) ....H

MICH.—Muskegon

Rodgers Iron Mfg. Co. (Swing Cut Off; Edging) A

MINN.—Stillwater

Stillwater Mfg. Co. (Billiard) ....A

MO.—St. Louis

Progress Press Brick & Machine Co. (Brick Cutting) ....B

Whitman Agricultural Co. (Saw) ....AA

N. H.—Lebanon

Baxter Machine Co. (Saw) C

N. H.—Nashua

Maine Mfg. Co. (Folding) A

N. J.—Hoboken

New York Switch & Crossing Co. (Transfer) ....A

(Lunch Bar) C
PA.—Union City ..
Novelty Wood Works Co.
(Folding; Library) ....B
VT.—Montpelier
Lane Mfg. Co. (Swing Cut-
Off; Edging) ....A
VT.—Putney
Stowell Co. (Folding) ....D
VT.—Readsboro
Readsboro Chair Mfg. Co.
(Folding) .... B
WIS.—Cudahy
Power & Mining Machinery
Co. (Concentrating) AAA
WIS.—Milwaukee
Meinecke & Son, A. (Toy;
Toy Folding) ....AA
WIS.—Racine
Gold Medal Camp Turn
Mfg. Co. (Camp Folding)
B
WIS.—Sheboygan
Mattoon Mfg. Co. (Centre;
Extension; Fancy; Kit-
chen; Lap; Library; Pil-
lar) .... A
Winter Lumber Co., M.
(Folding) .... B

TABLETS

See also Pad & Tablet Mfrs.

IND.—Indianapolis
Lilly Co., Eli (Medical;
Compressed; Hypodermic)
AA
MD.—Baltimore
Burrough Bros. Mfg. Co.
(Medicinal) X
Foutz Co., David E. (Med-
ical) ....D
Sharpe & Dohme (Medical;
Compressed Hypodermic)
AAA
MASS.—Cambridge
Thayer & Co., Hy. (Med-
ical; Compressed) ......A
MICH.—Detroit
Nelson, Baker & Co. (Med-
icinal) .... AA
Parke, Davis & Co. (Med-
ical;; Compressed; Hy-
podermic) ....AAAA
Stearns Co., Fdk. (Medical;
Compressed) ....AAA
MICH.—Kalamazoo
Upjohn Pill & Granule Co.
(Medicinal) ....AA
MO.—St. Louis
Anti Kamnia Chemical Co.
(Medicinal) ....B
N. Y.—Little Falls
Hansen's Laboratory, Chris.
(Junket; Medicinal) ....B
New York City
Boericke & Tafel (Medi-
cinal; Compressed) ....F
Caswell Massey & Co. (Med-
icinal; Compressed) ....B
Edison Chemical Co., Thos.
A., Jr., 14 Stone (Ink;
Perfume) X
Fairchild Bros. & Foster
(Medical; Compressed)
AA
Fraser Tablet Co. (Medi-
cinal; Compressed; Hy-
podermic) ....AA
Lyon & Sons, I. W., 520
W. 27th (Medicinal) ..C
McKesson & Robbins (Med-
icinal) .... AAAA
Requa Mfg. Co., 131 Wil-
liam (Charcoal) ...... D
Schieffelin & Co., W. H.
(Medicinal) .... AA
Seabury & Johnson, Inc.
(Medicinal; Compressed)
AA
N. Y.—Norwich
Norwich Pharmacal Co.
(Medicinal) ....A
N. Y.—Rochester
Dunn Co., T. B. (Medi-
cinal) .... B
OHIO—Cincinnati
Altenheim Medical Dis-
pensary (Medicinal) ...A
Merrell Chem. Co., Wm. S.
(Hypodermic; Dispensary;
Compressed) ....AAA

PA.—Ambler
Keasby & Mattison Co.
(Medicinal; Compressed)
AAAA
PA.—Philadelphia
Hance Bros. & White
(Medicinal; Compressed)
AA
Handy Table Co., 1021 N.
Front (Medicinal) X
Mason Chemical Co., 515
Arch (Medicinal) .... B
Mulford Co., H. K. (Medi-
cinal; Compressed) AAA
Warner & Co., Wm. R.
(Lithia Water) .....AAA
Wyeth & Bros., Jno (Inc.)
(Medicinal; Compressed)
AAAA

TABOURETS

ILL.—Rockford
East Rockford Mantel Co.
A
MASS.—Gardner
Haywood Bros. & Wakefield
Co. .... AAAA
PA.—Union City
Novelty Wood Works Co. B
WIS.—Milwaukee
Meinecke & Son, A. ....AA

TACHOM-ETERS

CONN.—Hartford
Veeder Mfg. Co. ....A
N. Y.—Brooklyn
Schaffer & Budenberg Mfg.
Co., 10 Division ......D
New York City
Keuffel & Esser Co., 120
Fulton ....AA
N. Y.—Troy
Gurley, W. & L. E. (Inc.)
A
PA.—Philadelphia
Queen & Co. (Inc.), 1010
Chestnut .... AA

TACKLE

See Blocks: Fishing Tackle

New York City
Hunt Co., C. W. (Chain
Hoisting) ....AA
PA.—Harrisburg
Jackson Mfg. Co. (Chain
Hoisting) .... B
PA.—Philadelphia
Harrington Son. & Co.
E. (Inc.) (Chain Hoist-
ing) ....AA
WIS.—Milwaukee
Chain Belt Co. (Chain
Hoisting) .... B

TACKS

See also Hardware; Carriage

CAL.—San Francisco
Judson Mfg. Co. ....AA
CONN.—Bridgeport
Canfield, H. O. (Rubber
Head) ....B
CONN.—Bristol
Horton Mfg. Co., (Thumb
for Blotters) ....B
CONN.—Derby
Shelton Co. (Cut; Trimmers;
Upholstery) ....A
CONN.—New Britain
Stanley Wks. (Swedish
Iron; Looking Glass) AAA
CONN.—New Haven
Cowles & Co., C. (Inc.)
(Carriage) .... A
English & Mersick Co.
(Carriage; Rubber Head)
B
ILL.—Belleville
Stanley Co., Geo. W.
(Double Pointed) ......F
ILL.—Chicago
Amer. Steel Wire Co.
(Double Pointed) AAAA
Chicago Tackle (Bill Poster;
Carpet; Galvanized;
Leather Carpet; Steel; Up-

holstery) .... B
Gibson Co., Wm. tD., 23
N. Clinton (Double Point-
ed) .... B
Grand Crossing Tack Co.
(Double Pointed; Bill
Posters; Carpet Carriage;
Galvanized; Leather Car-
pet; Upholstery; Zinc;
Box; Basket; Trimmers)A
ILL.—Rockford
Rockford Nail & Tack Co.
C
IND.—Madison
Tower Mfg. Co. (Steel;
Iron; Copper; Double
Pointed) C
MD.—Baltimore
Holland Mfg. Co. ....D
MASS.—Boston
Baker & Co., Chas. F.
(Shoe) .... A
Elastic Tip Co. (Rubber
Head) .... B
MASS.—Bridgewater
Miller's Sons, H. J.
(Shank; Machine; Shoe)
D
MASS.—East Walpole
Bird & Son., F. W.
(Double Pointed) ....AA
MASS.—Fairhaven
Atlas Tack Co. (Cut; Wire;
Bill Posters; Carpet; Car-
riage; Copper; Covered;
Crimping; G alvnized;
Leather Carpet; Looking
Glass; Miners; Shoe;
Steel; Swede; Iron; Up-
holstery; Wire ....AAAA
MASS.—Hanover
Salmon & Son, Saml.
(Carpet) .... AA
Waterman, R. C. (Carpet)
D
MASS.—Lakeville
Osborn & Co., W. ....D
MASS.—Lynn
Churchill & Allen (Shoe) F
MASS.—Plymouth
Cobb & Drew (Double
Pointed; Galvanized;
Leather; Shoe; Carpet;
Zinc; Upholstery) ....AA
Plymouth Mills (Double
Pointed; Box; Basted
Trimmers; Upholstery) B
Ripley & Bartlett (Miners;
Shoe; Upholstery) .... B
MASS.—Raynham
Diamond Tack & Nail
Works C
MASS.—Rockland
Anderson Tack Co. .....F
MASS.—South Braintree
Stevens & Willis Co. ....B
MASS.—South Hanover
Phillips & Sons, Ezra
(Double Pointed; Bill
Posters; Carpet; Galvan-
ized; Miners; Shoe;
Tinned; Upholstery; Zinc;
Box; Basket Trimmers) A
MASS.—Taunton
Glove Mfg. Co. (Bill Pos-
ters; Railroad; Box;
Basket; Upholstery) ..E
Taunton Wire Nail Co.
(Wire; Carpet; Bill
Poster, Etc; Double
Pointed) .... D
MASS.—Whitman
Gurney, David B. ...... A
MASS.—Worcester
Morgan Spring Co. ......A
Parker Wire Goods Co.
(Double Pointed) .... D
Reed & Prince Mfg. Co. ..B
Wire Goods Co. (Double
Pointed; Wire) ......A
Wright Wire Co. (Double
Pointed) .... AA
N. H.—East Jaffrey
Granite State Tack Co.
(Shoe) C
N. H.—Keene
Fuller, G. E. & A. J. ..E
N. J.—Newark
Williamson Novelty Co.
(Thumb) .... B
N. Y.—Binghampton
Binghamton Tack Co.
(Carpet; Shoe; Uphol-

stery; Trimmers; Etc.) B
Crandal Stone & Co. (Inc.)
(Carpet) .... A
Tetchener & Co., E. H.
(Inc.) (Double Pointed) B
N. Y.—Buffalo
McKinnon Dash Co. (Phos-
phor Bronze) .... AA
Western Wire Goods Co.
(Double Pointed) ......D
New York City
American Book Co.
(Thumb) ....AAAA
Ansonia Brass & Copper
Co. (Copper) .....AAAA
Faber, Eberhard, 545 Pearl
(Thumb) ....AAA
Hungerford Brass & Copper
Co., U. T. (Copper) AA
Judd & Co., H. L. (Double
Pointed) ....AA
Keuffel & Esser Co., 127
Fulton (Thumb) ....AA
Metal Stamping Co.
(Galvanized) ....A
New York Button Wks.
(Inc.) (Covered) .....B
Russell & Erwin Mfg. Co.,
43 Chambers ......AAAA
Sargent & Co., 151 Leonard
(Double Pointed) ..AAAA
N. Y.—Pen Yan
Superior Tack & Nail Co.
(Double Pointed) C
N. Y.—Rome
Rome Brass & Copper Co.
(Brass; Copper) ..AAAA
OHIO—Cleveland
Cleveland Tack Co., Hamil-
ton cor. Kirtland ...AAA
H. C. Tack Co., C. & P. Ry.
N. Euclid Av. ....B
Kirk-Latty Mfg. Co. (Cut)A
National Screw & Tack Co.
(Carpet; Galvanized) AA
PA.—Norristown
Penn Tack Co. (Double
Pointed) C
Redding Screw Co. (Double
Pointed) ....A
PA.—Philadelphia
Phosphor Bronze Smelting
Co. (Ltd.) (Phosphor
Bronze) ....A
PA.—Pittsburg
Anchor Nail & Tack Wks.,
So. 19th & Merrimac ..B
Union Steel Casting Co.
Carnegie Bldg. (Wire)
AAA
PA.—Sharon Hill
Pickering. R. S. (Double
Pointed) ....E
PA.—York
York Tack & Nail Wks.
(Thumb; Carpet; Car-
riage; Crimping; Looking
Glass; Steel) ....A
WIS.—Milwaukee
Milwaukee Tack Co., Wahl
& 27th & Av. L. P.
(Double Pointed; Car-
riage; Crimping; Looking
Glass; Swedes Iron; Wire)
X

TAFFETAS

See Silk Goods

TAGS

CONN.—Waterbury
Waterbury Brass Co.
(Brass) ....AAAA
ILL.—Chicago
Crowe Metal Mfg. Co., 71
West Jack. Boul. (Brass)
E
Kersten. C. 464 No. Paul-
ina Av. (Laundry) X
IND.—South Bend
Folding Paper Box Co.
(Linen Shipping) ......B
MASS.—Boston
Dennison Mfg. Co. (Hook;
Merchandise; Jewelers)
AAAA
MASS.—North Attleboro
Gilbert F. S. (Bag) .....D
MASS.—Worcester
Warren Leather Goods Co.

TAGS (Con.)

(Bag) ....B
MICH.—Battle Creek
American Mfg. Co. (Shipping; Coupon; Shop; Duplicate Copying) ......F
Keyes-Davis Co. (Ltd.) (Overall) ....H
NEBR.—Exeter
Smith, Chas. C. (Ledger Indexing) ....D
N. J.—Newark
Headley & Farmer Co. (Bag) ....A
N. Y.—Brooklyn
Gair Co., Robert, Washn. (Shipping) ....A
New York City
American Tag Co., 186 Wooster (Shipping) ...B
Dennison Mfg. Co., 15 John (Shipping, etc.) ..AAAA
Medford Fancy Goods Co. (Dog Collar Licence) ..E
OHIO—Cincinnati
Murdock Jr., Jas. (Tin) ..C
Robinson Mfg. Co., J. M. (Tin) C
OHIO—Dayton
Howard, Wm. H. (Dog) E
PA.—Hanover
Hanover Tag Co. (Shipping) X
PA.—Philadelphia
Grayson, R. H., 1801 Berks (Laundry) ....D
Philadelphia Tag Co. (Hook) ....F
PA.—West Chester
Denny Tag Co. (Shipping) C
W. VA.—Wheeling
Wheeling Metal & Mfg. Co. (Zinc; Tin) ....D

TALC

N. J.—Lincoln
Atlas Mineral & Machine Co. ....D
N. Y.—Gouverneur
Union Talc Co. X
United States Talc Co. (Inc.) ....A
New York City
Pettit Chemical Co. ......B
Solomon & Bro., L. A., 216 Pearl (Powdered) ....AA
Whittaker, W. H., 245 Front (Powdered) .....E
OHIO—Cincinnati
Garlick & Co., H. ....B
N. C.—Hewitt
North Carolina Talc & Mining Co. (Powdered) ..B
Obermayer Co., S. ......AA
PA.—Easton
Williams & Co., C. K. (Powdered) ....A
PA.—Philadelphia
Nevins Co., Samuel, 109 S. 2nd (French; Powdered)D
TENN.—Chattanooga
Crescent Novelty Mfg. Co. (Flour; Scrap) ....E
Steward Mfg. Co., D. M. (Powdered) ....B

TALLIES

WIS.—Milwaukee
Durant, W. N. (Flour) ..E

TALLOW

ILL.—Chicago
Bierce, Wm. W. ....A
Darling & Co. ....A
Fairbank Co., N. K. AAAA
Fitzpatrick Co., Jno. ....B
Hately Bros. ....A
Libby, McNeill & Libby (Inc.) ....AAAA
Morris & Co., Nelson AAAA
Swift & Co. ....AAAA
IND.—Hammond
Hammond Co., G. H. AAAA
MASS.—Boston
American Glue Co. AAAA
Dow & Co., John C. ...,..C
MASS.—Cambridge
Reardon & Sons Corpn., John X

TALLOW (Con.)

Squire & Co. (Inc.) Jno. P. AAAA
MASS.—New Bedford
Hersom & Co., Thos. C
MINN.—Minneapolis
McMillan Fur & Wool Co. X
MO.—Kansas City
Armour Packing Co. AAAA
MO.—St. Louis
St. Louis Hide & Tallow Co. C
N. Y.—Brooklyn
Davis Oil Co., 95 9th C
New York City
Colgate & Co. ......AAAA
Donahue & Son, P., 652 W. 39th ....A
Habermann, Joseph, 625 W. 40th ....B
Manhattan Oil Co., 51 Front D
Swan & Fench Co. ......A
Welch, Holme & Clark Co. A
N. Y.—Palmyra
Knowles, H. P. C
OHIO—Cincinnati
Whites Golden Lubricator Co. ....B
OHIO—Defiance
Miller Co., H. P. C
OHIO—Marietta
Streeker Bros. ....A
OHIO—Norwalk
Richardson & Co., J. W. C
PA.—Philadelphia
Douredoure Bros., 103 Walnut ....B
VT.—Hyde Park
Page, Carroll S. ....A

TAMPERS

ILL.—Quincy
Modern Iron Wks. (Iron Handle Dirt; Sod) ...B
IOWA—Ottumwa
Hardsocg Mfg. Co. (Coal Miners) ....B
N. Y.—Medina
Swett Iron Wks., A. L. (Dirt; Sod) ....A

TAMBOURINES

See Musical Insts.

TANKS

ALA.—Montgomery
Hartley's Boiler Wks. (Iron; Steel) C
CAL.—Los Angeles
Gregory, Wm. (Windmill)C
Lang Mfg. Co., 4 Baker Blk. (Oil, etc.; Iron; Steel) ....AA
Los Angeles Cooperage Co. (Wood) ....A
Thompson & Boyle Co. (Cyanide; Iron; Steel) ....B
CAL.—San Francisco
Excelsior Redwood Co., Channel & 4th (Wood) A
Hooper Co., C. A., 4th & Channel (Wood) ..AAAA
Korbel & Bros., F. (Wood) AA
Pacific Tank Co., 35 Beale (Cyanide; Iron; Steel; Cedar; Pine for Water, Oil; Mining) ....A
Woodin & Little (Windmill) ....A
CAL.—Santa Clara
Pacific Mfg. Co. (Redwood) ....AA
COLO.—Denver
Mine & Smelter Supply Co. (Cyanide) ....AAAA
Weigele Steel Pipe Wks., Wm. A., 2949 Larimer AAA
CONN.—New London
Hopson & Chapin Mfg. Co. (Cast Iron Automatic Feed Expansion) ......B
DEL.—Wilmington
Edge Moor Iron Co. (Iron; Steel) ....AAA
Pusey & Jones Co. (Iron; Steel) ....AAA

TANKS (Con.)

Remington Machine Co.
(Iron) ....A

FLA.—Apalachicola
Cypress Lumber Co.
(Cistern) ....AA

FLA.—Palatka
Selden Cypress Door Co.
(Cypress Wood) ....A

GA.—Atlanta
Van Winkle Gin & Machine
Wks., E. (Windmill)
AAA

GA.—Newnan
Cole Mfg. Co., R. D.
(Water) ....B

GA.—Savannah
Kehoe & Sons, Wm. (Iron;
Steel) ....A

ILL.—Aurora
Amer. Well Wks. (Wind-
mill) ....AA

ILL.—Batavia
Challenge Windmill & Feed-
mill Co. (Galvanized
Steel; Windmill; Wooden)
AAA

United States Wind Engine
& Pump Co. (Wood; Wa-
ter; Cedar; Iron & Steel;
Windmill Dairy) .....AA

ILL.—Chicago
Aermotor Co., W. 12th &
Rockwell (Steel; Wood)
AAA

Allis-Chalmers Co., Home
Ins Bldg. (Cyanide; Pres-
sure) .... AAAA

American Radiator Co. (Automatic Expansion; Black;
Galvanized Steel; Hot Wa-
ter Storage).......AAAA

Chicago Bridge & Iron Co.,
105th & Throop (Steel for
Railroads, etc.; Water)
AAA

Fairbanks, Morse & Co.,
Franklin & Monroe (Gal-
vanized; Steel or Iron;
Railroad Water; Wood;
Water; Windmill; Wine;
Cistern; Dairy) ...AAAA

Hamler Boiler & Tank Co.,
3906 So. Halstead (Iron;
Steel) ....B

Headen, Frank, 120 Indiana
(Wood) ....A

Keastner & Co. ....A

Pacific Flush Tank Co., 84
La Salle (Automatic Si-
phon for Flushing Pipe
Sewers) C

Pfeiffer Boiler Co., Chris.,
70 Michigan (Iron; Steel)
B

Ryerson & Son, Jos. T., 18
Milwaukee Av. (Gas; Air;
Soda Water) ......AAAA

Thaler Bros. Cooperage
Wks. ....B

Wendnagel & Co., W. 22d &
So. Jefferson (Wood) ..A

Wilson & Co., F. Cortez, 239
Lake (Galvanized Steel or
Iron; Wood; Oil) ......B

Wolf Co., Fred. W. (Brine;
Ice; Iron; Water; Dairy)
AAA

Wolf Mfg. Co. L., 117 W.
Lake (Expansion)..AAAA

ILL.—Edwardsville
Illinois Marble Co. (Slate) C

ILL.—Elgin
Elgin Wind Power & Pump
Co. (Windmill) ....B

ILL.—Freeport
Stover Mfg. Co. (Wood; Wa-
ter; Windmill; Dairy;
Stock) ....AA

Woodmans Mfg. Co. (Wind-
mill) ....A

ILL.—Galesburg
Frost Mfg. Co. (Expansion)
A

May Bros. (Iron; Windmill)
B

ILL.—Galva
Hayes Pump & Planter Co.
(Wood) ....A

ILL.—Kewanee
Kewanee Boiler Co. (Expansion). ....AA

ILL.—Marseilles
Marseilles Mfg. Co. (Wood;

TANKS (Con.)

Water) ....A

ILL.—Moline
Moline Pump Co. (Water)
A

ILL.—Peoria
Avery Mfg. Co. (Windmill)
AAA

Cody & Sons, Jos. (Expan-
sion) ....B

ILL.—Quincy
Michelman Boiler Co. (Ex-
pansion) ....B

ILL.—Sandwich
Sandwich Mfg. Co. (Wind-
mill) ....AA

ILL.—Springfield
Drake, Wm. (Expansion)..B

Springfield Boiler Mfg. Co.
(Expansion; Iron; Steel)
A

IND.—Auburn
Zimmermann Mfg. Co.
(Windmill) ....B

IND.—Butler
Butler Co. (Wood; Water)
B

IND.—Fort Wayne
Bowser & Co., S. F. (Inc.)
(Gasoline Storage; Oil;
Self-Measuring Tank; Var-
nish) ....A

Kear, Murray Mfg. Co.
(Iron; Steel) ....A

IND.—Goshen
Kelley Foundry & Machine
Co. (Galvanized Steel or
Iron) ....A

IND.—Indianapolis
Sinker-Davis Co. (Galvan-
ized Steel; Grain; Oil;
Steam; Refrigerator) ..B

IND.—Kendallville
Flint & Walling Mfg. Co.
(Stock; Cedar; Windmill;
Steel; Wood; Water;
Cypress; Galvanized Steel;
Cistern) ....AA

IND.—Mishawaka
Perkins Wind Mill Co.
(Windmill) ....A

IOWA—Burlington
Murray Iron Works Co. (Expansion; Steam Render-
ing) ....A

IOWA—Des Moines
Dempster Mfg. Co. (Water)
B

IOWA.—Waterloo
Tallerday Steel Pipe & Tank
Co. (Stock; Storage;
Creamery; Galvanized
Steel or Iron Water
Mounted on Wheels)....C

KANS.—Junction City
Muenzermayer, J. J. & W.
F. (Galvanized Iron
Stock). ....B

KY.—Louisville
Caldwell Co., W. E., Brandeis Av. & Brook (Cya-
nide; Galvanized Steel or
Iron; Wood; Water; Fac-
tory; Stock; Windmill)
AA

Sengel, Philip ....A

Vogt Machine Co., Henry
(Iron; Steel) ....AA

LA.—New Iberia
Tranor's Son, O. J. (Wood)
B

LA.—Patterson
Cypress Tank & Mfg. Co.
(Wood) ....B

MAINE—Portland
Portland Co., 58 Fore (Iron;
Steel) ....AA

MD.—Baltimore
Baltimore Cooperage Co.
(Wood) ....B

MASS.—Boston
Atlantic Works, 70 Borden
(Iron; Steel; Marine), AA

Cypress Lumber Co., 153
Milk (Cypress Wood Wa-
ter). ....AA

Hodge Boiler Wks., Sumner
near No. Ferry (Iron;
Steel) ....A

Stearns Lumber Co., A. T.
(Wood; Water) ......AA

MASS.—Cambridge
Kendall & Sons, Edw. (Iron;
Steel) ....AA

Roberts Iron Wks. Co.
(Iron; Steel) ....B

MASS.—Lawrence

Horne & Sons Co., J. H.
(Filtering) ....A

MASS.—Lowell

Cragin, F. W. & Co. (Wood)
...........................F

Eastern Oil Tank Co. (Self-
Measuring Oil) X

MASS.—Waltham

Davis & Farnum Mfg .Co.
(Galvanized Steel) .....A

MASS.—Worcester

Warren Leather Goods Co.
(Bag) ....B

MICH.—Battle Creek

Nichols & Shepard Co.
(Wood; Water; Mounted
on Wheels) ......AAAA

MICH.—Detroit

Detroit Range Boiler Co.,
619 24th (Expansion) ..B
Ideal Mfg. Co., 546 Franklin (Expansion) ....A
United States Heater Co.,
251 Campbell (Expansion)
...........................A

MICH.—Kalamazoo

Kalamazoo Railway Supply
Co. (Railroad; Water), B
Phelps & Bigelow Wind
Mill Co. (Wind Mill;
Wooden) C

MICH.—Lansing

Maud Windmill & Pump
Co., S. (Water) ....B

MICH.—Port Huron

Port Huron Engine &
Thresher Co. (Steel; Wa-
ter) ....AAA

MICH.—Saginaw

National Engineering Co.
(Wood). C
Wickes Bros. (Factory;
Gas; Air; Soda Water;
Steel; Wagon) ......AAA

MINN.—Anoka

Reed- & Sherwood Co.
(Wood) C

MINN.—Minneapolis

Howell & Co., R. R. (Grain;
Wooden) ....B
Minneapolis Steel & Machry.
Co. (Cyanide; Steel; Iron;
Water) ....AAA
Northwestern Wind Engine
Co., 110 3d Av. (Wood)
.........................AA
Puffer-Hubbard Mfg. Co.,
26th and 32nd Avs.
(Wood) C

MO.—Harville

Mangold Stave & Cooperage
Co. (Beer; Wine) ......B

MO.—St. Louis

Harry Steel Works, O. K.
(Iron; Storage; Water), B
O'Brien Boiler Wks. Co.,
Jno. (Oil) ....AA
Stecher Cooperage Wks.,
2907 So. 7th (Wood), AA
Wanger Boiler & Sheet Iron
Co., Jos. F., 1547 No. 9th
(Iron; Steel; Brine; Oil;
Water) ....A

N. J.—Jersey Citty

Smith & Sons Co., Theo., ft.
of Essex (Pressure) ...A

N. J.—Phillipsburg

Tippett & Wood (Inc.)
(Iron; Steel; Water) ...B

N. Y.—Brooklyn

Bliss Co., E. W., 17 Adams
(Pressure) ....AAAA
Iron Clad Mfg. Co. (Steel;
Soda Water) ....AA
Logan Iron Wks. (Inc.)
(Oil; Water) ....B
Ronalds & Johnson Co., 51
Boerum Pl. (Expansion)
.........................AA

N. Y.—Buffalo

Fedders Mfg. Co. (Automa-
tic; Oil) ....D

N. Y.—Frankfort

Acme Road Machry. Co.
(Streel Sprinkler Wagon;
Water, Mounted on
Wheels) ....B

N. Y.—Little Falls

Hansens Laboratory, Chr.
(Rennet) ....B

New York City

American Bridge Co., 100
Bway. (Water) ....A
Bartlett Hayward & Co., 100
Bway. (Iron; Steel; Oil;
Water) ....B
Corcoran, Andrew J., 11
John (Wood) ....B
Deeley & Co., R. (Inc.) AA
Griffing Iron Co., A. A.
(Expansion) ....AA
Kelley & Son, Benj., 91 Lib-
erty (Factory) ....B
Koven & Bros., L. O., 50
Cliff (Expansion; Galvan-
ized Steel; Iron; Gas En-
gine; Mixing; Pressure;
Water; Anti-Expansion;
Factory; Oil) ....A
Mott Iron Wks., J. L., 88
Beekman (Expansion), AA
Schwartzwalder & Sons, J.,
629 W. 51st (Wood)
......................AAAA
Staubach, B. (Slaughter
House) ....A
Trageser's Steam Cooper
Wks., Jno. (Inc.), 477 W.
26th (Expansion; Gaso-
line; Hot Water; Beer
Pump; Air; Braziers Gaso-
line) ....B
Zucker & Levett & Loeb
Co., 526 W. 25th (Chemi-
cal Proof) ....A

N. Y.—North Tonawanda

Niagara Radiator Co. (Ex-
pansion). ....A

N. Y.—Oswego

Fitzgibbons Boiler Co.
(Iron; Steel) ....B

N. Y.—Rochester

Yawman & Erbe Mfg. Co.
(Bottle Saoking; Steam-
ing) ....AA

N. Y.—Rome

Rome Mfg. Co.. (Copper;
Stove) ....B

N. Y.—Syracuse

Pierce, Butler & Pierce
Mfg. Co. (Inc.) (Expan-
sion) ....AAA

OHIO—Alliance

Reeves Bros. Co. (Iron;
Steel) ....A

OHIO—Cincinnati

Cincinnati Cooperage Co.
......................AAA
Hauser, Brenner & Fath Co.,
McLean Av. & Bank
(Wood Brewers Steep), B
Littleford Bros., 453 E.
Pearl (Galvanized Steel or
Iron; Oil; Water; Steel;
Iron Street Sprinkler
Wagon) ....B
Schott & Sons, J. M. C
Schreiber & Sons Co., L.
(Water) ....AA
Stacey Mfg. Co., 239 Mill
(Gas) ....AA
Tudor Boiler Mfg. Co. (Iron;
Gas; Air; Soda Water), B

OHIO—Cleveland

Avery Stamping Co. (Gal-
vanized Steel Gas; Air;
Soda Water) ....B
Norcross Co. (Acid) ......A
Variety Iron Wks. Co.
(Iron; Steel) ....B

OHIO—Columbiana

Columbiana Boiler Co.
(Iron; Steel) C

OHIO—Dayton

Gem City Boiler Co. (Iron;
Steel) ....B

OHIO—Delphos

Delphos Can Co. (Factory;
Dispensing) ....B

OHIO—Forest

Dickelman Mfg. Co. (Gal-
vanized Steel; Iron) ....A

OHIO—Lowellville

Meehan Boiler & Construc-
tion Co. (Iron; Steel; Factory; Gas; Air; Soda Wa-
ter) ....B

OHIO—Mansfield

Aultman & Taylor Mchry.
Co. (Iron) ....AAAA

OHIO—Marion

Huber Mfg. Co. (Water;

TANKS (Con.)
Mounted on Wheels) AAA
Marion Mfg. Co., of Ohio
(Water Mounted on
Wheels) .... AA

OHIO—Niles
Ohio Galvanizing & Mfg .Co.
(Steel) ....B

OHIO—Salem
Clarke Co., W. J. (Steel
Water Tight; Factory), A
Michel Bros. Cooperage Co.
(Wood) ....A

OHIO—Warren
Warren City Boiler Wks.
(Iron; Steel; Water) ...A

OHIO—Youngstown
Enterprise Boiler Co. (Iron;
Steel) ....B
Pollock Co., Wm. B. (Wa-
ter; Factory; Gas; Air;
Soda Water; Oil; Iron;
Steel) ....AA

PA.—Allegheny
Porter Fdry. & Machine Co.
(Iron; Steel) ....B

PA.—Allentown
Allentown Boiler Wks., Col-
lins & Knouse Props.
(Iron; Steel) C
Heilman Boiler Wks. (Iron;
Steel) ....AA

PA.—Bausman
Bausman, D. H. (Wind
Mill) C

PA.—Carbondale
Hendricks Mfg. Co. (Oil;
Water) ....AA

PA.—Chester
Wetherhill & Co., R. (Iron)
AAAA

PA.—Coatsville
Coatsville Boiler Wks. (Iron
Coatsville Boiler Wks.
(Iron; Steel). ....AA

PA.—Conshohocken
Wood Mfg. Co., Jno. (Elec-
tric Welded; Seamless;
Expansion) ....B

PA.—Du Bois
Du Bois Iron Wks. (Iron;
Steel) ....AAAA

PA.—Elizabeth
Buchs Sons Co., A. (Inc.)
(Steel Stock; Steel Wind-
mill) ....A

PA.—Erie
Pennsylvania Boiler Works
(Iron; Steel) ....AA
Stearns Mfg. Co. (Iron;
Steel) ....B

PA.—Harrisburg
Harrisburg Fdry. & Mach.
Wks. (Iron; Steel; Oil)
AA
Harrisburg Mfg. & Boiler
Co. (Water) ....A

PA.—Lebanon
Union Boiler & Mfg. Co.
(Iron; Steel) ....B

PA.—Marietta
Marietta Hollowware &
Enameling Co. (Refriger-
ator) ....B

PA.—Meadville
Phoenix Iron Wks. Co.
(Iron; Steel) ....A

PA.—Middletown
Amer. Tube & Iron Co.
(Ammonia; Acid)..AAAA

PA.—Newcastle
Pennsylvania Engineering
Wks. (Gas; Air; Soda Wa-
ter; Oil) ....AA

PA.—Norristown
Newbold & Son Co., R. S.
(Inc.) (Iron; Steel) ....A

PA.—Oil City
Oil City Boiler Wks. (Inc.)
(Iron; Steel) ....AA

PA.—Philadelphia
Belmont Iron Wks., 22d &
Wash. (Water) .....AA
Hall, Son & Co., Amos H.,
2915 N. 2d (Cedar, etc.;
Wood; Water) C
Hilbs, E. I., 212 Quarry
(Expansion; Oil; Drip;
Blow-off; Storage; Iron;
Steel) ....B
Green & Son, Robert M.
(Steel; Soda) ....AA
Kensington Engine Works
(Ltd.), 245 N. Broad

TANKS (Con.)
(Iron; Steel) ....A
Moore & White Co. (Iron)
AA
North Penn Iron Co. (Iron;
Steel) ....B
Penn. Range Boiler Co.,
10th Cor. Norris (Expan-
sion) ....B
Sheppard & Co., Isaac A.,
1810 N. 4th (Expansion)
AAA
Smith & Sons, Jno. M., 1429
Cedar) ....B
Spring Garden (Wood;
Underwood & Co., H. B.,
1025 Hamilton (Pressure)
B
Wood & Co., R. D. (Gas
Works) ....AAAA
Woolford Wood Tank Mfg.
Co., Geo., Real Estate
Trust Bldg. (Cedar; Cy-
press; Wood; Brewers
Steep) ....B

PA.—Pittsburg
Carroll-Porter Boiler & Tank
Co., Empire Bldg. (Iron;
Steel; Water; Oil) ....B
Lappan Mfg. Co., Jas., 20th
& Pike (Iron; Steel) ..A
McNeil Bros. Co., Jas., 29th
& A. V. Ry. (Iron; Steel;
Water) ....A
Munroe & Son, R., 23d &
Smallman (Iron; Steel;
Grain; Oil; Water) ...AA
Riter-Conley Mfg. Co. (Gas
Tanks; Air; Soda Water;
Oil) ....B
Scaife & Sons Co., Wm. B.,
221 1st Av. (Air; Calcium
Light; Car Lighting; Car-
Wheel Annealing; Com-
pressed Air; Cyanide; Ex-
pansion; Galvanized Steel
or Iron; Gas Engine; High
Pressure; Hydrogent; Oxy-
gen; Muffle; Oil; Pres-
sure; Steel Dipping; Anti-
Expansion; Soda Water;
Grain; Stock; Windmill;
Stove; Steel Wagon; Fac-
tory; Hot Water) ...AAA
Standard Mfg. Co. (Ammo-
nia; Acid) ....AA

PA.—Pottstown
Sotter Bros. (Inc.) (Iron;
Steel) ....B

PA.—South Bethlehem
Betlehem Fdry. & Machine
Co. (Factory) C

PA.—Steelton
Pennsylvania Steel Co.
(Steel) ....AAAA

PA.—Warren
Struthers-Wells Co. (Iron;
Steel; Storage; Factory;
Oil; Stock; Windmill)
AA

PA.—Washington
Petroleum Iron Wks. Co.
(Steel; Acid; Cyanide;
Galvanized Steel or Iron;
High Pressure; Gas; Oil
or Water Iron;Steel,also
Molasses) ....A

PA.—Waynesboro
Frick Co. (Iron; Water; Refrigerator) ....AAAA

PA.—Wilkesbarre
Vulcan Iron Works (Iron;
Water) ....AAAA

PA.—Williamsport
Keeler Co., E. (Iron; Steel;
Factory; Gas; Air; Soda
Water; Oil; Stock; Wind-
mill) ....A

PA.—York
Motter & Sons, Geo. F.
(Iron; Water; Steam Ren-
dering; Steam; Refriger-
ator) C
York Mfg. Co. (Iron; Oil;
Water). ....AAA

R. I.—Providence
Textile Finishing Mchry.
Co., 17 Exchange Place
(Dipping) ....AAA

TENN.—Chattanooga
Casey & Hedges Mfg. Co.
(Iron). ....A
Lookout Boiler & Mfg. Co.

TANKS (Con.)
(Iron; Steel; Railroad
Water) ....B
TENN.—Jackson
Southern Engine & Boiler
Wks. (Factory; Steel;
Stock; Steel Windmill)AA
TEXAS—San Antonio
Collins Mfg. Co., F. F.
(Wooden) ....AA
UTAH—Salt Lake City
Silver Bros. Iron Wks. Co.
(Cyanide) ....A
VT.—Bellows Falls
Vermont Farm Machine Co.
(Dairy) C
VA.—Norfolk
Whitehurst Co., R. W. (Water; Stock; Wood; Windmill Wood) ....B
WASH.—Cosmopolis
Gray's Harbor Commercial
Co. (Fir Wood) .....AAA
WIS.—Cudahy
Power & Mining Machinery
Co. (Air; Automobile;
Compressed Air; Cyanide;
Galvanized Steel; Iron;
Muffle; Water Mounted
on Wheels) ....AAA
WIS.—Evansville
Baker Mfg. Co. (Iron;
Steel; Windmill; Wooden)
AA
WIS.—Fort Atkinson
Cornish, Curtis & Green
Mfg. Co. (Dairy; Refrigerator) ....A
WIS.—Jefferson
Fernholz Lumber Co.
(Wood) C
WIS.—Milwaukee
Allis-Chalmers Co. (Mining;
Pressure) ....AAAA

Ketter, Fred., 584 4th
(Wood) ....B
Milwaukee Boiler Co., 220
Ogden (Iron; Steel) ...A
Pressed Steel Tank Co.
(Seamless Steel; Air; Car
Lighting; Expansion; Gas
Engine; High Pressure;
Hydrogen; Oxygen; Seamless Steel Cylinder; Gas)B
Vilter Mfg. Co. (Factory;
Steel Stock; Steel Windmill) ....AA
WIS.—Racine
Case Threshing Mach. Co., J.
J. (Steel; Water mounted
on Wheels)........AAAA
Freeman & Sons Mfg. Co. S.
(Iron; Steel, also Wood;
Water; Grain; Oil; Windmill; Mining) Steam Rendering; Refrigerator) ..A
WIS.—Superior
Duplex Mfg. Co. (Water;
Windmill) ....AA
WIS.—Waupun
Athaus-Wheeler Co. (Water) ....A

TANNIN

MASS.—Boston
Billings, Clapp & Co.....B
MO.—St. Louis
Mallinckrodt Chemical Wks.
AAAA
New York City
Matheson & Co., Wm. J...A
PA.—Philadelphia
Drueding Bros. ....AA
Powers-Weightman-Rosengarten Co. ....AAAA

TAPERS

New York City
Columbia Wax Works, 85
Crosby (Wax) X
Houchin Co., Thos. W.
(Wax; Wax Floating)..D
Smith & Nicols (Wax)...A
N. Y.—Syracuse
Cathedral Candle Co.
(Wax) ....B
Mack Miller Candle Co.
(Wax) X
Will & Baumer Co.
(Wax) ....AA

TAPERS (Con.)
R. I.—Providence
United Wire & Supply Co.
(Copper; Gold; Nickle)
AA

TAPES

See also Measures

CONN.—Ansonia
Ansonia O. & C. Co.
(Cotton) ....A
CONN.—Hamden
New Haven Web Co.
(Cotton) ....A
CONN.—Hartford
Hartford Rubber Wks. Co.
(Electrical Friction) .AA
CONN.—Middletown
Russell Mfg. Co. (Skirt)
AAAA
Wilcox, Crittenden & Co.
(Tape Lines, etc.; Measuring) ....A
CONN.—Wallingford
New York Insulated Wire
Co. (Cotton Insulating).B
CONN.—Waterbury
Waterbury Brass Co.
(Measuring) ......AAAA
CONN.—Westport
Lees Mfg. Co. ....A
ILL.—Chicago
Chicago Steel Tape Co.,
Temple Court Bldg.
(Measuring) X
Dietzger Co., Eugene, 181
Monroe (Measuring) ..A
Electric Appliance Co., 94
W. Van Buren (Insulating) ....B
Morgan & Wright, (Inc.),
33 W. Lake (Insulating)
AA
Post Co., Fred'k, 218 Clark
(Measuring) ....D
Seelig, R., 122 So. Clark
(Measuring) ....G
MASS.—Boston
Boston Belting Co., 256
Devonshire (Electrical
Friction) ....AAAA
Boston Rubber Shoe Co.
(Insulating) .....AAAA
Simplex Electrical Co.
(Insulating) ......AAA
MASS.—Cambridgeport
Boston Woolen Hose & Rubber Co. (Rubber; Electric Insulating) ..AAAA
MASS.—Springfield
Hutchins Narrow Fabric Co.
(Spool) C
MASS.—Worcester
Thayer Mfg. Co., L. D.
(Cotton) C
Whitter & Co., H. M.
(Cotton) ....B
MICH.—Detroit
Thorpe Mfg. Co., 50 Woodward Av. (Car Wheel
Measuring) X
MICH.—Saginaw
Lufkin Rule Co. (Steel;
Linen Measuring; Cotton)
AA
MO.—St. Louis
Missouri Tent & Awning
Co. (Insulating) ......B
N. J.—Trenton
Home Rubber Co. (Electric
Friction) ....AA
N. Y.—Brooklyn
Eddy & Co., Geo. M., 345
Classon Av. (Measuring;
Linen; Cotton; Spring
Pocket; Steel) ....A
New York City
Brixey, W. R., 203 Bway.
(Insulating) ....B
Conover Co., C. E.
(Common) ....D
Dresser & Olmstead (Common) C
Johns-Manville Co., H. W.,
100 William (Insulating;
Asbestos Rubber) .AAAA
Keuffel & Esser Co., 127
Fulton (Steel; Metallic &
Linen Measuring) ....AA
Mechanical Rubber Co. 22
Murray (Insulating)
AAAA

TAPES (Con.)

Mica Insulator Co., 218 Water (Insulating; Oiled) ....B

New York Insulated Wire Co., 114 Liberty (Insulating; Water Proof Electric Friction) ....B

Okonite Co., (Ltd.), 253 B'way (Insulating Manson Protecting; Water Proof) ....AA

Reis & Bro., G. 640 B'way (Advertising) ....D

Sills-Eddy Mica Co. (Varnish Cloth; Insulating).X

Snedeker & Co. (Common)C

Standard Paint Co., 100 William (Insulating) ..A

Wicks Co., Wm. (Silk)...X

Wright & Graham (Common; Silk) ....B

N. Y.—Patchogue

Roe & Sons, Justus (Steel Measuring) ....D

N. Y.—Troy

Gurley, W. & L. E. (Measuring) C

OHIO—Akron

Diamond Rubber Co. (Electrical Friction; Insulating) ....AAAA

Goodrich Co., B. F. (Electrical Friction; Insulating) ....AAAA

OHIO—Cleveland

Ulmer & Co., J. C., 225 Champlain (Chain Measuring) ....H

PA.—Philadelphia

Hoffman Mfg. Co. .... AA

Hooper Sons Mfg. Co. ..B

Kroute & File Mfg. Co...B

Queen & Co. (Inc.), 1010 Chestnut (Measuring) .B

Sidebotham, John (Cotton) ....

Sullivan & Sons Mfg. Co., J. (Cotton; Silk) ...... AA

Weber & Co., F., 1125 Chestnut (Measuring) ..... A

Wilson & Sons, Jas. (Cotton) ....B

R. I.—Bristol

National India Rubber Co. (Insulating) ......AAAA

R. I.—Pawtucket

Kenyon Mfg. Co., John J. (Cotton) ....B

New England Thread Co. (Cotton) ....A

Pawtucket Tape Co. (Cotton) ....A

R. I.—Providence

Hope Webbing Co. (Insulating; for Dynamos).AAA

TAPIOCA

CAL.—San Francisco

Brandenstein & Co., M. J. ....AAAA

FLA.—Lake Mary

Planters Mfg. Co ....A

ILL.—Chicago

Lenfesty Milling Co., 27 Michigan Av. C

MASS.—Boston

Slade Co., D. & L., 13 India ....A

MASS.—Orange

Whitman Grocery Co.....C

New York City

Archibald & Lewis, 193 Front ....

Brandenstein & Co., M. J., 96 Wall ....AAAA

Fuerst Bros. & Co., 2 Stone ....D

Jones Chemical Co., E. F., 51 Jay C

Leggett & Co., F. H. AAAA

OREGON—Portland

Oriental-American Co. (Impts.) C

PA.—Philadelphia

Ceylon Spice Co., 244 N. Front ....D

Thayer & Co., P. W., 23 S. Front ....B

TAPPERS

MASS.—Worcester

TAPPERS (Con.)

Reed Co., Francis (Nut)..E

N. Y.—Buffalo

Howard Iron Works (Nut) ....A

OHIO—Cincinnati

Kinsey & Co., E. A. (Nut) ....A

OHIO—Tiffin

National Machinery Co. (Turnbuckle) ....AA

TAPS

See also Plates

CONN.—Bridgeport

Armstrong Mfg. Co......A

Curtis & Curtis Co......A

CONN.—Hartford

Billings & Spencer Co. (Blacksmiths'; Machinists' Hand) ....

Pratt & Whitney Co. (Bit Brace; Boiler; Machinists' Hand; Die; Machine Nut; Machine Screw; Pulley; Stay Bolt; Pipe)..AAAA

CONN.—New Britain

Corbin, P. & F. (Machine Nut; Machine Screw; Machinists' Hand; Pulley) ....AAAA

Landers, Frary & Clark (Champagne) ......AAA

CONN.—New Haven

Geometric Drill Co. (Collapsing; Adjustable) ...C

Peck Bros. & Co. (Champagne; Ale; Cider).....A

Reynolds & Co., 321 East (Machine Nut; Machine Screw; Machinists' Hand) ....A

ILL.—Chicago

Besly & Co., Chas. H.. 15 Clinton (Machine Nut; Machine Screw) ......AA

Chicago Scale Co., 292 Jack. Boul. ....B

Chicago Screw Co., 98 W. Washington (Machine Nut; Machine Screw; Machinists' Hand; Pulley) ....AA

Crane Co. ....AAAA

Standard Screw Co., 2 N. Canal (Machine Nut; Machine Screw; Machinists' Hand; Pulley) ....AAAA

ILL.—Decatur

Mueller Mfg. Co., H. (Combined Drill & Reamer; Pipe) ....A

MAINE—Portland

Portland Cooperage Co. (Ale; Cider) C

MASS.—Boston

Dalton-Ingersoll Co., 175 High (Collapsing) .....A

Thayer Co., N. F. (Shoe) C

Walworth Mfg. Co..AAAA

MASS.—Greenfield

Amer. Tap & Die Co. (Stove; Bolt) ....E

Automatic Machine Co. (Nut) C

Goodell-Pratt Co.......B

Reese & Co., E. F. (Die; Machine Screw; Machinists' Hand; Patch Bolt; Pulley) ....D

Wells & Son, F. E.......E

Wells Bros. Co. (Bit Brace; Blacksmith; Boiler; Machine Screw; Machine Nut; Machinists' Hand; Pulley; Stay Bolt; Pipe) ....A

Wiley & Russell Mfg. Co. (Bit Brace; Blacksmiths'; Boiler; Machine Nut; Machine Screw; Pulley; Stay Bolt; Pipe) .....AA

MASS.—Lynn

Houghton & Sons, James (Shoe) X

MASS.—Mansfield

Card Mfg. Co.. S. W. (Bit Brace; Machine Nut; Pulley; Pipe) ....B

MASS.—New Bedford

Morse Twist Drill & Machine Co. (Blacksmiths'; Boiler Combined Drill & Reamer; Die; Hob; Machine Nut; Machine Screw; Machinists' Hand; Patch Bolt; Pulley; Stay Bolt; Stove Bolt; Tapper; Pipe) ....AAA

MASS.—Wrentham
Winter Bros. Co. (Blacksmiths'; Hob; Machine Screw; Machinists' Hand; Pulley; Stay Bolt; Stove Bolt; Tapper) X

MICH.—Detroit
American Tap Bush Co. (Beer) C

MICH.—Lansing
Western Tool Co. (Machine Screw; Machinists' Hand) ....F

MO.—St. Louis
St. Louis Screw Co., 3017 N. 13th (Bit Brace; Blacksmiths'; Boiler; Die; Machine Nut; Machine Screw; Machinists' Hand; Patch Bolt; Pulley; Stay Bolt; Stove Bolt) ......A

N. J.—Newark
Sommers' Sons, John (Ale; Cider) ....B
Williamson Wire Novelty Co., C. T. (Champagne) ....B

N. J.—Paterson
McNab & Horlin Mfg. Co. (Pipe) X

N. Y.—Brooklyn
U. S. Bung Mfg. Co. (Ale; Cider) ....A

New York City
Fairbanks Co. (Pipe) ....AAAA
Golden Gate Mfg. Co. (Beer) X
Hall's Sons, Sam'l, 229 W. 10th ....A
Haydenville Mfg. Co. (Champagne) ....B
Krieg & Co., J. K. (Shoe) ....B
Niles-Bement-Pond Co., 136 Liberty ....AAAA
Ricksecker Co., Theo. (Champagne) C

N. Y.—Oswego
Oswego Tool Co. (Patch Bolt; Stay Bolt) C

N. Y.—Utica
Utica Drop Forge & Tool Co. (Champagne) C

N. Y.—Waterford
Holroyd & Co. (Bit Brace; Blacksmiths' Combined Drill & Reamer; Hob; Machine Nut; Machine Screw; Machinists' Hand; Patch Bolt; Pulley; Stay Bolt; Tapper; Pipe; Bicycle) ....A
King & Co., J. M. (Machine Nut; Machine Screw; Machinists' Hand; Pipe)...A

N. Y.—Yonkers
Saunders' Sons, D. ......A

OHIO—Akron
Whitman & Barnes Mfg. Co. (Bit Brace; Blacksmiths'; Boiler; Die; Machine Nut; Machine Screw; Machinists' Hand; Patch Bolt; Pulley; Stay Bolt) ....AAAA

OHIO—Cincinnati
Cincinnati Screw & Tap Co., 2442 Beekman (Blacksmiths'; Boiler ; Die; Machine Nut; Machine Screw; Machinists' Hand; Patch Bolt; Pulley; Stay Bolt) ....B

OHIO—Cleveland
Acme Machinery Co.....AA
Bishop & Babcock (Beer) ....AAA
Cleveland Faucet Co. (Beer) ....AAA
Cleveland Twist Drill Co. (Boiler; Machine Nut; Machinists' Hand; Pulley; Stay Bolt) ....A

Hart Mfg. Co., Wood & St. Clair (Machinists' Hand) ....B
National Screw & Tack Co. (Machine Screw) ....AA
Reliance Machine & Tool Co. C
Standard Tool Co. (Bit Brace; Boiler; Hob; Machine Nut; Machine Screw; Machinists' Hand; Pulley; Pipe) ......AAA

PA.—Ellwood City
Standard Engineering Co. ....AA

PA.—Erie
Hollands Mfg. Co.......C
Jarecki Mfg. Co......AAAA

PA.—Lancaster
Champion Blower & Forge Co (Blacksmiths') .....B

PA.—Lebanon
Amer. Iron & Steel Co. (Machine Nut) ....AAAA

PA.—Millersburg
Polk & Son, A. J. (Taper, etc.; Blacksmiths'; Combined Drill & Reamer; Hob; Machine Nut; Machine Screw; Machinists' Hand; Patch Bolt; Pulley; Stay Bolt; Stove Bolt; Tapper) ....D

PA.—Philadelphia
Hoopes & Townsend Co., 1330 Buttonwood (Machine Nut; Machinists' Hand) ....AAA

R. I.—Pawtucket
Carpenter Tap & Die Co., J. M. (Bit Brace; Blacksmiths'; Boiler; Die; Machine Nut; Machine Screw; Machinists' Hand; Patch Bolt; Pulley; Stay Bolt;; Stove Bolt; Tapper) C
Haskell Mfg. Co., W. H. (Machine Nut; Machinists' Hand) ....A
Pawtucket Mfg. Co. (Blacksmiths'; Machine Nut; Machine Screw; Machinists' Hand; Patch Bolt; Pulley; Stay Bolt; Stove Bolt) ....A

R. I.—Providence
American Screw Co. (Machine Nut; Machine Screw) ....AAAA

VT.—Derby Line
Butterfield & Co. (Machine Nut; Machine Screw; Machinists' Hand; Pulley; Spindle Stay Bolt; Stay Bolt; Bicycle, etc.; Tapper) ....B

VT.—Springfield
Superior Tap Co. (Hob; Machine Nut; Machine Screw; Machinists' Hand; Patch Bolt; Pulley; Stay Bolt; Tapper) ....F

WIS.—Milwaukee
Pfisker & Vogel Leather Co. (Shoe) ....AAAA

TAR

GA.—Savannah
Shotter Co., S. P. (Marine) ....AAAA

New York City
Barett Mfg. Co. (Coal) ....AAAA
Hayne, H. J., 142 Front (Coal) ....D
Longman & Martinez, 207 Pearl (Vegetable) ..AAA
Sealy, Thomas, 142 Front (Coal; Vegetable) C
Warren Chemical & Mfg. Co., 17 Battery Pl. (Coal) ....A

N. Y.—Syracuse
Solway Process Co. (Coal) ....AAAA

OHIO—Cincinnati
Emery Candle Co. (Candle) ....AA

PA.—Bradford
Smith Chemical Co., A. B. (Vegetable) ....B

TAR (Con.)

PA.—Erie
Watson Co., H. F. (Coal)
........................AAA

PA.—Philadelphia
Crew-Levick Co., 113 Arch
(Coal) ....AAA
Garrett & Sons, C. S. (Coal)
........................AA

PA.—Pittsburg
McClintock & Irvine (Coal)
........................B

VA.—Richmond
Armitage Mfg. Co. (Coal).B

TARGETS

ILL.—Freeport
Arcade Mfg. Co. (Shooting)
........................A

MASS.—Boston
Dennison Mfg. Co....AAAA
MO.—St. Louis
Kufferle, John C. (Cast
Iron) ....AA
N. Y.—Herkimer
Quackenbush, H. M. (Fly-
ing; Clay; Steel).......A

TARLATANS ..

N. Y.—Valley Falls
Thompson & Co., Jas...AA

TARPAULINS ..

CAL.—San Francisco
Nelville & Co.............A
GA.—Dalton
Smith, M. D. & H. L....D
ILL.—Chicago
Cook & Bro., E. C........A
Iroquois Bag & Oil Co...X
MO.—St. Louis
Missouri Tent & Awning Co.
........................B
Morrison Tent & Awning
Co. C
Zeltlosen Mfg. Co. .....B
New York City
Abercrombie & Litch, 314
B'way C
Boyle & Co., John, 112
Duane ....AA
McHugh, Jno. F..........C
Rehm & Co., 141 Fulton..D
Skelton, Fred ....D
Standard Oiled Clothing Co.
........................E
OHIO—Cincinnati
Patton Co., R. J.........B
OHIO—Cleveland
Wagner Mfg. Co..........C

TARTAR:
CREAM

CAL.—Fresno
California Products Co...X
CAL.—San Francisco
Amer. Cream of Tartar Co.
........................A
Horstman Co., Jno.......B
Tyler & Son, S. H.......C
ILL.—Chicago
Thompson & Taylor Spice
Co. ....AA
IND.—South Bend
Russ Co. (The)..........C
MASS—Boston
Slade Co., D. & L., (The)
........................A
Slickney & Poor Spice Co.
........................AA
N. J.—Jersey City
Tartar Chem. Co......AAA
N. Y.—Brooklyn
Amer. Tartar Co.......AA
New York City
Archibald & Lewis.......C
Condon & Co., T. F......C
Gillies & Co., E. J......AA
Havens, Jno. R..........A
Jones Chem. Wks., Enos. F.
........................B
Wood & Selick (Inc.)....A
N. Y.—Utica
Hinman, F. C............F

TASSELS:
SILK, ETC.

See Trimmings: Upholstery

TEAS, COFFEES
& SPICES

CAL.—San Francisco
Blanchard & Page, 623 San-
some (Bkrs. T.).......B
Bloom Bros., Hayward
Bldg. (Imp. C.)......AA
Brandenstein & Co., M. J.,
118 Mkt. (Imp. T., C., &
S.) ....AAAA
Burr & Co., C. C., 2111
Stockton (M., S.).......A
Castle Bros., 463 Mission
(Whol. T. & Coffee)..AA
Dieckmann & Co., 421 Mkt.
(Imp. C.) ....A
Huddleston & Co., H., 52
Mkt. (Imp. T.).......AA
Jones, Paddock & Co., 26
Tremont (T., C. & S.)
........................AAA
Leege & Haskins, 3 Front
(C., T. Mills).........A
McCarthy Bros., 113 Front
(T., C., S. Mills).......A
Macondray & Co., 116 Cal.
(Imp. T.) ....B
Mau Sadler & Co., 38
Steuart (Imp.) ....A
Mitchalitschke Bros. & Co.,
410 Mkt. (Imp. C.)..AA
Montealegre & Co., 230 Cal.
(Imp. C.) ....B
Moore & Co., Geo. A., 208
Cal. (Imp. C.).........B
Otis, McAllister & Co., 109
Cal. (Imp. C.).........A
Parrott & Co., 306 Cal.
(Com. C.)............A
Schilling & Co., A., 2d &
Folsom (Whol. T., C. &
S.) ....AAA
Schwartz Bros., 421 Mkt.
(Imp. Whol. C.).....AAA
Sherwood & Sherwood, 212
Mkt. (Imp. T., C., & S.)
........................AAA
Siegfried & Co., Jno. C., 202
Mkt. (Whol. T.).......A
Urloste & Co., 202 Mkt.
(Whol. C.)...........AA
COLO.—Denver
Morey Mills, 16th & Wyn-
koop (T., C., S.)....AAA
GA.—Atlanta
South Coffee & Spice Mills
........................D
A. I. C. Coffee Co., 21
River (Imp. & Job. C.)
........................A
Atwood & Steele, 18 River
(C. & S.)............C
Bell & Co., 62 Mich. Av.
(Whol. C.)...........A
Cafetal Co., Carlota, 21
Monroe (Whol. C.).....A
Coward & Co., J. H., 3
Lake Whol. T., C., S.)
........................A
Doane & Co., 25 Wabash
Av., (Br. N. Y. City)
(Imp. C., T.).........X
Fisher, Hart C., 20 Mich.
Av. (T.) ....A
Gottlieb & Co., M., 34
Wabash Av. (Imp. T.).C
Hayes & Co., J. E., 57 So.
Water (Imp. Job & Roast
C.) C
Hellyer & Co., 19 Wabash
Av. (Imp. T.).......AA
Hunt & Co., 34 Wabash Av.
(Imp. T.) ....A
Irwin McBride & Co., 47
Mich. Av. (Imp. T.)..AA
Jaques, Tea Co., Frank F.,
41 River (Imp. & Job.)B
McLaughlin & Co., W. F.
82 S. Water (Phg. C. &
S.) ....AAAA
Marshall & Co., F. C., 217
Kinzie (Whol. & Imp. C.)
........................C
Martin & Co., N., 46 S.
Water (Whol. T., S.)AA
Millar & Co., E. B. 45 Mich.
Av. (Whol. T. C. S.)...A
Morrell & Co.. C. A., 87
Mich. Av. (Whol. T.)AA
Murray & Nickell Mfg. Co..
147-155 W. Polk (S.
Mills) ....B

Quinn & Co. J. T., 40
Dearborn (Whol. T.)...B
Sherer Bros. Co., 33 River
(W. C. & T. & Millers S.)
Sherman Bros. & Co., 22 S.
Water (Whol. C., T., S.)
............................A
Siegfried & Co., Jno. C.,
5 Lake (Imp.) ....A
Sprague, Warner & Co.,
Rand & Mich. Avs. (Job,
C., T., S.) ....AAAA
Thomson & Taylor Spice
Co., 66 Mich. Av. (Whol.
T., C., S.) ....AAA
Wallace & Co., 39 River
(T.) ....B
Wichert Co., H., 1205 St.
Paulina (S.) C
KY.—Louisville
Dinkelspiek Sons, S. (Ginseng Sp.) ....AA
Louisville Spice Mills, 148
5th ....F
Southern Coffee Co., 207 W.
Main (C. Roast).......A
Southern Molasses & Coffee
Co., 110 3d............D
LA.—New Orleans
Aron & Co., J., 416 Poydras
(Imp.) .... A
Cage, Drew & Co., 419 S.
Front (Whol. C.).....B
Dittmann, C., 628 Gravier
(Com. C.) C
Hard & Rand (Br.), 300
Magazine (mp. & Job C.)
.....................AAAA
Israel Leon, 417 Poydras
(C.) ....B
Merchants Coffee Co. of N.
O., 211 S. Peters (Whol.
C.) ....B
New Orleans Coffee Co.,
(Ltd.), 206 Fulton (Job,
Imp. & C. Roast).......A
Reily, Taylor & Co., 413 S.
Peters (Roast C. & Imp.
T.) C
Schmidt & Ziegler (Imp. C.)
.....................AAA
Smith Bros. & Co., (Ltd)
(Job & C. Roast)...AAA
Westfeldt Bros. 621 Gravier (Imp. & Com. Co.).A
MD.—Baltimore
Enterprise Coffee Co., 421
Exch. Pl. (Impts. & C.
Roast) ....A
Gillett, Martin & Co., 308
Exch. Pl. (Imp. T.)....A
Hoffman, Lee & Co., Donnell Bldg. (Imp. C.)...B
Hook & Co., 612 Forrest
(Whol. T., C. Roast)...B
Levering & Co., E., 102
Com. (Impts. & C. Roast)
.....................AAA
Levering Bros., 107 Com.
(W. Coffee) C
Lurman & Co., Theo. G.,
100 S. Gay (Imp. C.).AA
McCormick & Co., 44 S.
Chas (Imp. & Gdrs. Sp.)
.....................C
Merchants Coffee Co., 513
E. Lombard (Job. & C.
Roast) ....B
Parrish Bros., 115-117 E.
Lombard (Impts. T. &
Spice Grinding) ......B
Read & Co., at 113 S. Fk'd
(Whol. T., C., S.)....C
Rollins, T., 421 Exch. Pl.
(Imp. C.) ....A
Sanders & George, 26 E.
Lombard (Whol. T.) ..A
Taylor & Levering, 109
Com. (Imp. C.)........A
MASS.—Boston
Brayton & Co., L., 217
State (Whol. T. & C.)..A
Chase & Sanborn, 87 Brood
(Imp. & Pkg. T. & C.)
.....................AAAA
Clark, Coggin & Johnson
Co., 202 State (Imp. &
Roast C.) C
Dwinnill Wright & Co., 45
Battery March (Imps. C.,
S.) ....AAA
Fay. T. R., 70 Kilby (Imp.

T.) ....B
Goodridge & Co., 34 S. Mkt.
(T. & C.) ....B
Matherson, S., Jr., 32 Brood
(Bkr. C.) ....A
Montgomery & Aull, 34
Brood (Whol. T.).....B
Nash & Hopkins, 32 Brood
(Impt. T.) ....B
National Coffee Co., 498
Commercial (C.) ......B
Quimby Co., W. S., 69 S.
Mkt. (Imp. & Job. T. C.)
.....................B
Robinson & Woodworth, 28
Brood (Whol. C., T.)...B
Shapleigh Cofftt Co., 36
Brood (Job. C.).......B
Slade Co., D. & L., 13 India
(Imp. & Mfrs. S.).....A
Spurr Coffee Co., H. W., 23
Commercial ....AA
Stickney & Poor Spice Co.,
184 State (S.) ....AA
Swain, Eearle & Co., 36
Com'l (Whol. T., C.)AA
Tenney & Co., Wm. P., 161
Milk ....B
Williams & Hall, 30 Broad
(T.) ....A
Winslow, Rand & Watson,
199 State (Whol. C., T.)
.....................A

MICH.—Detroit
Farrand, Williams & Clark,
11 Larned ....AAA
Gehlert Coffee Co., 59 Jefferson Av. C
Lafer Bros., 9 Cadillac Av.
(T. & C.) C
Soudan Mills, 138 Larned
(C. & S.) ....A
MINN.—Minneapolis
Baker & Co., 214 N. 2d
(Imp. & Roast C.).....B
Strait & Co., H. B., 106 2d
Av. N. (Whol. T., C. & S.)
.....................B
MINN—St. Paul
McCormick, Behnke & Co.,
233 E. 4th (Whol. T., C.,
S.) ....A
MO.—Kansas City
Merrill & Merrill, 335 New
Ridge Bldg. (Whol. C. &
T.) ....A
Murdock Mfg. Co., C. A.,
1225 Union Av. (Whol. T.
& S.) ....A
Pope, J. Wm., New Ridge
Bld. (Impt. T. & C.)..C
MO.—St. Louis
Blanke Tea & Coffee Co.,
P. F., Clarke Av. & 7th
.....................AA
Forbes Bros. & Co., 509 N.
2d (T., C. S.).........A
Forbes, J. H., 112 Locust
(Whol. T., C., S.)....A
Gregg Tea & Coffee Co., C.
D., 7th & Elm (Whol. T.,
C., S.) C
Hanley & Kinsella Coffee
& Spice Co., 713 Spruce
(T., C., S.) ....AA
Menown & Gregory, 414 N.
2d (Whol. T., C., S.)..C
Meyer Bros. Coffee & Spice
Co., 21 W. Main (Whol.
T., C., S.)...........C
Nash-Smith Tea & Coffee
Co., 916 N. 6th (Whol. T.,
C., S.) ....A
Roth, Homeyer Coffee Co.,
517 N. 2d (Whol. T., C.,
S.) ....B
St. Louis Coffee & Spice
Mills, 407 N. Main....D
Steinwender-Stoffregan Coffee Co., 12 S. 7th (Imp.
T., C.) ....AAA
Weston Tea & Spice Co.,
Edw., 1000 Clark Av...A
N. Y.—Brooklyn
Amer. Coffee Co., ft.
Metropolitan Av. .....A
Bohn & Co., A. W., 50
Wash'n Av (Whol. T., C.,
S.) ....A
James & Bro., D. R., 89
Furman ....AA
N. Y.—Buffalo
Cumpson-Prentiss Coffee

Co., 98 Mich..........B
Witkop & Holmes, 274
Genesee (T. & C.) C
New York City
Aborn & Cushman, 103
Front (Bkr. C.)........C
Acton, Angell & Co., 171
Front (Whol. T., C. &
S.) ....A
Amer. Coffee Co., 117 Wall
(Whol. C.) ....A
Arib & Co., E. J., 53 E.
9th (Imps. C.).........B
Arbuckle Bros., 71 Water
(Imp. & Pkgs. C.).AAAA
Archibald & Lewis, 193
Front (Imps. S.).....C
Armstrong, J. E., 197 Cham-
bers (Whol. T., C., S.)
B
Arnold, Dorr & Co., 109
Front (Bkrs. C.)......B
Arnold & Aborn, 39 Old
Slip (Whol. T., C.)....A
Baker & Co., H. M., 100
Front (Whol. & Imptrs.
C.) ....B
Banks & Parsons, 93 Front
(C.) ....B
Banks & Co., H. W., 103
Front (Whol. T., C.)..A
Bayne & Davison, 97 Front
(Imp. & Job. C.).....AA
Bayne & Co., W., 95 Front
(Impts. & Job. C.).....A
Beard & Co., S. S., 180
Duane (Impts. C. T. S.)
A
Bennett, Sloane & Co., 101
Wall (Whol. T., C.)..AA
Berry-Hall Co., 104 Water
(T., C. & S.) ....B
Blanke Tea & Coffee Co., C.
F., 44 Hudson (Whol. C.
T.) ....A
Bloom & Co., David, 66
Beaver (Imp. C.) ...AA
Bloom Bros., 66 Beaver
(Imp. C.) ....AA
Brandenstein & Co., M. J.,
96 Wall (Roast & Ground
Coffee & Imp. T.).AAAA
Brown & Co., Jno. B., 142
Front (Imp. C.)......B
Browning & Baines, 81 No.
Moore (Imp. C.).......B
Burchard & Co., 265 Wash.
(Whol. C. T. & S.)...B
Buttfield, W. J., 90 Wall
(W. & Impt. T.).......A
Buttlar & Co., R., 623 Hud-
son (Whol. C., T., S.).B
Carter, Macey & Co., 106
Water (Impt. T.)..AAA
Central Amer. Trading Co.,
(Ltd.), 109 Front (Imp.
C.) ....B
Champion & Standinger, 124
Pearl (Whol. C., T., S.)
A
China & Japan Trading Co.,
32 Burling Slip (Imp. T.)
AAA
Clarke, John, 126 Front
(Bkr. S.) C
Consumers Coffee Co., 169
Reade ....B
Creighton & Ashland, 87
Wall (Imp. C.)........B
Crooks & Co., R., 136
Front (Imp. C., S.)..AA
Crossman & Bro., W. H., 77
Broad (Impts. C.).AAAA
Cruikshank & Co., D. P., 7
Front (Imp. S.).......A
Dean & Son, W. G., 361
Wash'n (Mfg. S.).....A
Dixon, F. J., 458 G'wich
(Whol. T. & C.)......B
Doane & Co., J. W., 87
Front (Whol. & Imp. C.,
T., S.) ....AAAA
Dooley, Smith & Co., 135
Front (Imp. C.).......B
Duryee & Barwise, 107
Water (Bkr. T.)......C
Durkee & Co., E. R., 534
Wash'n ....A
Elmenhorst & Co., 94 Wall
(Com. C. & S.) ....A
Emmans & Co., John, 93
Water (Whol. T.)......B

Eppens, Smith Wiemans
Co., 271 Wash (Whol. C.
T.) ....AA
Ertheiler & Son, M., 172
Water (Bkr.)..........B
Farrington Co., G. B., 141
Front (Impts. T.).....A
Fischer & Co., B., 395
G'wich (Whol. T., C. &
S.) ....AAAA
Fitzpatrick & Co., A. C.,
156 Chambers (C., T., S.
Mills ....A
Formosa Trdg. Co., 96
Front, (T.) ....AA
Fuerst Bros. & Co., 2 Stone
(Cassia) ....D
German & Co., L., 136 Wat-
er (Imp. & Bkr's S.)..A
Gillies & Co., E. J., 245
Wash'n (C. Roast, T., S.)
AA
Gillies Coffee Co., (Whol.
& C. Roast) ....A
Glynn & Co., M. J., 76
Front (Whol. C. T.)....A
Gordon, F. P., 99 Wall
(Bkr. C.) ....B
Green & Son, Volney, 112
Front (C. Bkrs.).......B
Gunning & Holmes, 398
G'wich (Whol. T.)....C
Hard & Rand, 107 Wall
(Imp. C.) ....AAAA
Harris Coffee Co., 260 Front
(Imp. C.) ....AAAA
Harris, L. A., 136 Front
(Imp. & Job. T. & C.)..C
Hewlett & Lee, 101 Wall
(Com. & Impts. T.)....A
Hill, R., Jr., 39 Old Slip
(T.) ....B
Hilliers Son Co., R., 100
William (Bkr. S.)......A
Hills Bros. Co., 99 Wall
(Bkr. C.) ....AA
Hunt & Co., 138 Front
(Whol. T.) C
International Coffee Co.,
269 Front (Roast).AAAA
Irving & Co., Gugy, A. E.,
90 Front (Imp. T.)....C
Irwin, McBride & Co. (T)
90 Wall ....AAA
Israel, Leon (C.) 113 Wall
C
Jahn & Co., G. A. (Imps.
C.) 98 Wall ....B
James & Bro., D. R. (S.)
123 Maiden Lane......AA
Japan Tea Exptg. Co., 96
Front ....AA
Johnson Coffee Co. (Wh. T.
& C.) 83 Water ....B
Labaree & Co., J. H. (Wh.
C.) 125 Front ....A
Lane & Co., G. W. (Wh.
Imp. T.) 93 Front.....A
Lewisohn Bros. (C.) 92
Front ....AAAA
Lipton, T. J. (Imp.) 39
Pearl ....AAAA
Littlejohn & Co., L. (Imp.
S.) 136 Front ....B
London & Johnson (Wh. C.
T.) 181 Chambers......A
Marquardt & Co., H. (Com.
C.) 35 S. Williams.....A
Materne & Hess (Bkrs. S.)
165 Duane ....B
Mead & Co., F. (Imp. T.)
104 Water ....AAAA
Meehan & Co., P. C. (Bkr.
C.) 96 Front ....B
Mitchell Bros. (Wh. C.) 110
Water ....A
Montanye & Co., W. H.
(Mills C. T. S.) 64 Bar-
clay ....A
Montgomery Auction & Com.
Co. (T.) (Auctions) 132
Front ....B
Montgomery & Co., J. & J.
R. (Bkr. T.) 127 Water
A
Montgomery & Aull (Wh.
C. T.) 102 Front ......A
Morrison, Cornelius (Bkr.
C.) 89 Wall ....A
Morss, Opdyke & Co. (Wh.
C. T.) 339 Greenwich..A
Nordlinger & Co., H. (C.

S.) 81 Front ....A
O'Donohue Coffee Co. (Imp.
C.) 104 Wall ....B
O'Donohue's Sons, J. (Imp.
C.) 88 Front ....AAAA
O'Donohue Sons, J. J. (Imp.
C.) 101 Front ....AAAA
Osborn & Co., E. M. (Imp.
T.) 104 Front ....B
Palmer & Co., H. H. (Bkrs.
C. T.) 43 Harrison....A
Paterson Boardman Co. (S.)
& Bridge ....AAA
Peck, E. H. & W. J.
(Imptrs. C.) 28 Old Slip
AA
Phipps & Co., J. L. (Imptrs.
C.) 82 Wall ....A
Phyfe & Co., J. W. (Imp.
C. S.) 121 Front.....AA
Pustan & Co., C. W. (S.)
90 Wall ....A
Recknagel & Son, J. H.
(Bkrs. S.) 90 Wall....A
Robertson, A. R. (Imp.
Ceylon T.) 138 Front...C
Roloff & Lappin (Roast C.)
188 Duane ....B
Russell & Co. (Imp. T.) 94
Front ....A
Scotts Son & Co., Wm. (C.
Bkrs.) 107 Front .....A
Schramm, Arnold (C. Bkr.)
87 Front ....B
Seggerman Bros. (C. Bkr.)
108 Front ....B
Shaw & Co., D. A. (S.) 69
Pine ....B
Smith, Baker & Co. (Imptrs.
Agts.) Water & Pearl
AA
Smith & Schipper (Bkrs. T.
& C.) 138 Front C
Smith & Walbridge (Imp.
C.) 111 Front ....A
Somervilles' Sons, Wm.
(Imp. C.) 188 John....B
Steinwender, Stoffregen &
Co. (Imp. C.) 87 Wall
AAAA
Stumpp, A. (W. C.) 90
Wall ....B
Taylor & Co., J. H. (Imp.
C.) 107 Front ....A
Tetley & Co., Jos. (T) 13
White ....AAAA
Thomas & Turner (Imp. C.)
181 Duane ....B
Thorn, H. C. (Bkr. T) 97
Wall ....A
Tropic Tea & Coffee Co.
(Imp. P. & C.) 103 Water
B
Turnbull & Co., J. G. (Wh.
C. T.) 296 Pearl ......B
Turner Bros. (Bkrs. T.)
120 Front ....B
Upham Bros. (Imp. C.) 197
Chambers ....B
Van Loan, Maguire & Gaff-
ney (C. S. Roast &
Grinders) 64 N. Moore..A
Vickers Sons, P. (T.) 132
Water ....A
Weir & Co., R. W. (Imp.
T. C.) 60 Front ......AA
Wells Bros. (Imp. C.) 131
Front ....A
Weyl & Co., G. C. (Bkrs.
C.) 99 Front ....B
Whittall & Co. (Wh. T.)
138 Front ....A
Wilde Sons Co., Sam'l, 13
Dutch ....A
Willard & Co., E. A. (Bkr.
T.) 24 State C
Williams, Russell & Co.
(Bkrs. C.) 101 Front..AA
N. Y.—Rochester
French & Co., R. T. (S.)..A
OHIO—Cincinnati
Bour Co., J. M. (C. T. S.)
204 Main ....B
Droste & Co., H. R. (Mills
C. T. S.) 328 E. 2nd....A
Frank Tea & Spice Co., 20
W. 2nd ....A
Harrison & Co., W. H. (C.
S.) 17 E. 2nd C
Heekin & Co., Jas. (C. T.
S.) Walnut & Water....A
Heekin Spice Co. (C. S.)

65 Main C
Hinz, F. W. (C. T. S.) 30
W. 2nd ....B
Kenton Bak. Prod. Co.
(Mills C. T. S.) 326 E.
3rd ....A
Koenig & Co., J. Hy. (C. T.
S.) 215 Vine C
Ullman, Drefus & Co. (Wh.
T.) 230 E. 5th ....B
Von der Hoya & Co., F.
(T.) 1103 Walnut ......B
OHIO—Cleveland
Bennett-Sloan-Gage Co., 147
Sheriff ....AA
Smith & Co., S. C. (Wh. T.
C. S.) 192 Bank .....AA
Widlar & Co., Francis (Wh.
C. T. S.).............AA
OHIO—Columbus
Andrus, Scofield & Co. (T.
C. & S.) 42 W. State....C
Ohio Coffee & Spice Co....C
OHIO—Dayton
Canby, Arch & Canby (C.
S.) 508 E. 3rd.....AAAA
Dayton Spice Mills Co. (C.
S.) ....A
Ware Coffee Co., C. F. (Wh.
C. & S.)..............A
OHIO—Toledo
Bour Co., J. M. (T. C. & S.)
113 Ontario ....B
Woolson Spice Co. (C. S.
Pkg. & Roast).....AA A
PA.—Philadelphia
Aull & Co., James A. (Wh.
C. T.) 9 S. Front .....A
Carter, Macy & Co. (Br.)
(Imp. T.) 37 S. Front
AAAA
Clawson Co. (Spices) 45 S.
2nd C
Colburn Co., A. (Spices) 110
N. 2nd ....AA
Divnie & Co., Clemens M.
(Wh. T. & C.) 26 So.
Front ....B
Heraty Co., E. J. (Wh. T.)
121 S. Front ....A
Hill & Sons, Wm. (Imp. &
Job.) 210 Dickinson....B
Irwin, McBride & Co. (Imp.
T.) 50 So. Front......AA
Knight, Coane & Churchill
(Ltd.) (Imp. C.) 36 So.
Front C
Middleton Co. (C. Roast;
Wh. T.) 19 S. 2nd.....A
Parke & Co., L. H. (Wh.
C. T. S.) 232 Market...A
Roberts & Co., Thomas
(Imp. Roast Co.) 116 S.
Front ....AAA
Rodgers Sons, P. (Whol. C.)
43 So. Front ....A
Rulon & Sons, J. W. (S.)
32 No. Front ....A
Sower, McEvoy & Co. (C.
Imp.) 118 So. Front..AA
Sutton & Vansant (C. Job.
Imp.) 120 So. Front..AA
Thayer & Co., P. W. (T.)
23 So. Front ....B
Weikel & Smith Spice Co.
(C. S.) 129 N. Front..A
PA.—Pittsburg
New York & Pittsburg Cof-
fee Co., 941 Liberty Av.
E
Young, Mahood & Co. (Wh.
C. T. S.) 935 Liberty Av.
A
TENN.—Chattanooga
Stagmaier & Fletcher
(Roast Mills; C. P.)....A
TENN.—Nashville
Nashville Coffee Roasting
& Imp. Co. (Wh. C.)...B
Thomas & Son, J. W. (W.
C. T. S.) ....B
W. VA.—Wheeling
Wheeling Coffee & Spice
Co. ....D
WIS.—Milwaukee
Grossman & Co., Wm. (Job.
T. C. & S.) 274 E. Water
C
Jewett & Sherman Co. (Wh.
C. T.) 289 B'way......A

TEDDERS: HAY

See Agr. Imps

TEES

See also Angles & Iron & Steel

ILL.—Chicago
Illinois Malleable Iron Co. (Suchon) ....AAAA
N. J.—Newark
McIntire Co., C. (for underground construction).D
OHIO—Dayton
Dayton Malleable Iron Co. (Chain) ....AA
PA.—Harrisburg
Harrisburg Pipe Bending Co. (Ltd.) (Suction) AA
PA.—New Castle
New Castle Forge & Bolt Co. (Chain) ....A
PA.—Philadelphia
Watson & McDaniels (Suction) C

TEETH

CAL.—San Jose
Christian, Jno. (Thresher)
.............................D
CONN.—Derby
Shelton Co. (Cider Mill)..A
ILL.—Canton
Parlin & Orendorff Co. (Harrow; Cultivator)
.........................AAAA
ILL.—Chicago
Gibson Co., Wm. D., 23 N. Clinton (Hay Loader) ..B
Inland Steel Co., 204 Dearborn (Harrow; Steel)
.........................AAAA
Republic Iron & Steel Co. (Harrow) ....AAAA
ILL.—Peoria
Avery Mfg. Co. (Thresher)
..............................A
Herschel Mfg. Co., R. (Harrow) ....A
MASS.—Millville
Holman, Isaac T. (Picker)
..............................G
MASS.—Worcester
Morgan Spring Co. (Hay Loader) ....B
MICH.—Kalamazoo
Harrow Spring Co. (Harrow; Cultivator; Hay Loader; Hay Rake; Rake; Bundle Carrier; Hay Tedder) ....B
MICH.—Lansing
Bement & Sons, E. (Cultivator) ....AAAA
MICH.—Port Huron
Port Huron Engine & Thresher Co. (Thresher)
.........................AAAA
MICH.—St. Johns
Mason & Co., F. C. (Spring Spike Harrow) C
MINN.—Minneapolis
Howell & Co., R. R. (Thresher) ....B
N. J.—Grenloch
Bateman Mfg. Co. (Cultivator) ....A
N. J.—Newark
Crabb & Co., Wm. (Picker)
..............................B
N. Y.—Leonardsville
Babcock Mfg. Co. (Harrow) ....D
N. Y.—Mt. Morris
Genesee Valley Mfg. Co. (Harrow) ....B
N. Y.—Munnsville
Munnsville Plow Co. (Harrow) C
New York City
Consolidated Dental Mfg. Co., 115 W. 42d (Artificial) ....B
N. Y.—Tonawanda
Buffalo Steel Co. (Harrow)
..............................AA
OHIO—Akron
Akron Machine Co. (Thresher) ....A
Whitman & Barnes Mfg. Co. (Harrow; Cultivator;

TEETH (Con.)
Hay Loader; Thresher)
.........................AAAA
OHIO—Alliance
Transue & Williams Co. (Drop Forged Thresher)
..............................A
PA.—Chester
Keystone Drop Forge Wks. (for Crusher Rolls; Picker; Coal Breaker; Threshing Machine) ....A
PA.—Johnstown
Cambria Steel Co. (Harrow; Cultivator; Rake) .....B
PA.—Philadelphia
Allen & Co., S. L., 1017 Market (Cultivator) ..AA
Johnson & Lund (Artificial)
..............................AA
Justi & Sons, H. D. (Artificial) ....AA
Kusel, Hy. F., 248 S. 11th (Artificial) ....F
Penna. Dental Mfg. Co. (Artificial) ....D
Sibley, Gideon (Artificial)
..............................AA
White Dental Mfg. Co. S. S. (Artificial) ....AAAA
PA.—Pittsburg
Lanz & Sons, M., 101 S. 29th (Harrow) ....B
PA.—Scranton
Scranton Forging Co. (for Boal or Salt Crusher Rolls) ....A
PA.—York
Farquhar Co. (Ltd.), A. B. (Cultivator) ....AAA
Hench & Drongold Co. (Harrow; Cultivator) .....A
R. I.—Providence
Rhode Island Tool Co. (Thresher) ....AAA
VA.—Norfolk
White & Bro., S. R. (Harrow) ....A
VA.—Richmond
Old Dominion Iron & Nail Works Co. (Harrow)...A
WIS.—Madison
Fuller & Johnson Mfg. Co. (Harrow) ....AA
WIS.—Racine
Case Threshing Machine Co., J. J. (Thresher)..AAAA
Herrick, H. F. (Thresher)
..............................D

TELEPHONES

CONN.—Meriden
Connecticut Telephone & Electric Co. C
CONN.—New Haven
Burgess, E. A., 67 Court..E
DEL.—Wilmington
Garrett, Miller & Co., 4th & Orange ....D
GA.—Atlanta
Wotton Electric & Mfg. Co., 52 Greenwood Av. .....B
ILL.—Chicago
Ackerman & Co., Chas. N., 287 Elm (Inter-Communicating) ....E
Acme Electric Co., 194 S. Clinton (Interior) .....H
Altman & Co., 69 Dearborn (Interior; Automatic Inter-Communicating)
..............................X
American Electric Telephone Co., 36 W. Jackson Boul. (Electric) ....B
Automatic Electric Co., Morgan & Van Buren
.........................AAAA
Cook, Frank B. ....B
Electric Appliance Co., 92 Van Buren ....B
Farr Telephone & Construction Supply Co., 118 W. Jackson Boul. ....D
Globe Automatic Telephone Co., 153 W. Jackson Boul.
..............................X
International Telephone Mfg. Co., Harrison & Clinton X
Kellogg Switchboard Supply Co., Green & Congress.AA

TELEPHONES (Con.)

Monarch Telephone Mfg. Co., 14 S. Clinton .....D

Stromberg-Carlson Telephone Mfg. Co., 72 W. Jackson Boul. ....AAAA

Swedish - American Telephone Co., 76 W. Jackson Boul. ....A

Western Telephone Mfg. Co., Fisher Bldg. ......B

IND.—Elkhart
Chicago Telephone Supply Co. ....A

IND.—Indianapolis
Elliott, Larkin V., 520 Mass. Av. ....F
McQuat, Robt. L. X

IND.—Kokomo
Kokomo Telephone & Electric Mfg. Co. ....F

IND.—Lafayette
Sterling Electric Co. ....AA

IOWA—Burlington
Modern Electric Co. ......E

IOWA—Sioux City
Electric Supply Co. .....E

MD.—Baltimore
Viaduct Mfg. Co., 10 S. Howard X

MASS.—Boston
Couch Co., S. H., 156 Pearl ....E
Couch & Seeley Co., 26 Binford C
Electric Gas Lighting Co., 195 Devonshire ....A
Tucker & Co., Frank S., 1 Hartford ....H

MASS.—Brookline
Holtzer-Cabot Electric Co. ....A

MICH.—Caro
Moore Telephone Mfg. Co. ....D

MICH.—Monroe
Stoddard Telephone Construction Co. X

MINN.—South Minneapolis
Minnesota Electric Co., 309 2d Av. ....D

MO.—Kansas City
Hodge-Walsh Electric Engineering Co., 701 Delaware Av. C

MO.—St. Louis
Central Telephone & Electric Co., 909 Market....D
Commercial Electrical Supply Co., 1007 Market....B
Kusel, David A., 1119 Pine ....E

N. J.—Weehawken
Schmidt Telephone Mfg. Co. 325 B'way (Exterior: Long Distance) X

N. Y.—Buffalo
Century Telephone Construction Co., Elliott Bldg...A
Wilhelm Telephone Mfg. Co., 45 N. Division X

N. Y.—Mt. Vernon
West Electric Co. ....H

New York City
American Watchman's Time Detector Co., 234 B'way (Interior) X
Bunnell & Co., J. H., 20 Park Pl. ....B
De Veau Telephone Mfg. Co., 27 Rose (Automatic Switchless) ....B
Ericsson Telephone Co., 296 B'way (Ericsson System Interior) ....D
Kinsman Electric & Railway Supply Co., 91 Liberty ....E
Manhattan Electrical Supply Co., 32 Cortlandt (Interior) ....AA
New York Telephone Co., 18 Cortlandt (Interior) ....AAAA
Pattengell, Son & Co., C. E., 51 Cliff X
Pettes & Randall, 150 Nassau ....F
Spencer Electrical Co., 163 Greenwich ....D

N. Y.—Utica
Utica Fire Alarm Telegraph Co. ....B

TELEPHONES (Con.)

OHIO—Akron
Garl Electric Co. (Interior; Inter - Communcating Long Distance; Inter-Communicating; Desk; Hotel; Factory; Store; Portable Street Railway, &c.) ....F

OHIO—Cincinnati
Electrical Appliance Co., 132 Opera Pl. ....E
Fitzsimmons Telephone Mfg. Co., 5th & Sycamore...F
Simplex Interior Telephone Co., 19 E. 3d ....
Standard Electric Co., 113 W. 3d ....B

OHIO—Cleveland
North Electric Co., 149 St. Clair ....A
Ohio Electric Works ....D
Williams - Abbott Electric Co ....B

OHIO—Elyria
American Construction & Trading Co. ....AA
Rawson Electric Co. ....B

OHIO—Piqua
American Mach. Telephone Co. X

PA.—Allegheny
Hipwell Mfg. Co., 831 North Av. ....D

PA.—Philadelphia
Atwater-Kent Mfg. Works, 49 N. 6th ....F
Novelty Electric Co., 52 N. 4th C
Pullen Electric Co., Leon H., 618 Chestnut .....F

PA.—Pittsburg
Keystone Electric Telephone Co., 565 Diamond Av....B

PA.—West Chester
Eastern Telephone Mfg. Co. ....A

R. I.—Pawtucket
Bliss Mfg. Co., R. (Toy) ....AAA

R. I.—Providence
Clark Automatic Telephone Switchboard Co. (Automatic Interior) ....D
Rhode Island Telephone & Electric Co. ....D

S. C.—Sumter
Sumter Telephone Mfg. Co. ....A

WIS.—La Crosse
Vought-Berger Co. (Interior) C

WIS.—Milwaukee
Andrae & Sons Co., Julius, 225 W. Water ....B
Green Telephone & Electric Mfg. Co., 204 Grand Av. ....F
Signalphone Co. ....D

TELESCOPES

MASS.—Cambridge
Clark & Sons, Alvan .....F

MASS.—Chicopee Falls
Stevens Arms & Tool Co., J. (Rifle) ....AAA

New York City
Spencer Optical Mfg. Co., 15 Maiden Lane C

N. Y.—Rochester
Bausch & Lomb Optical Co. ....AAA
Gundlach Manhattan Optical Co. ....A

OHIO—Cleveland
Warner & Swasey ......A

TELLURIANS

ILL.—Chicago
Andrews Co., A. H.....AA

New York City
Schedler, Herman ....E

TEMPLATES

ILL.—Kewanee
Western Tube Co. (for Drilling Flanges) ..AAA

TEMPLES:
LOOM
MASS.—Boston
Stoddard, Haserick & Richards Co., 152 Congress .... AAA
MASS.—Worcester
Crompton & Knowles Loom Works .... AAAA
Roy & Son, B. S. .... B
R. I.—Pawtucket
Draper & Co., J. O. ...... B

TEMPLETS
N. J.—Newark
National Saw Co. ..AAAA

TENDERS:
FARM ENGINE
OHIO—Canton
Aultman Co. .... A
WIS.—Racine
Case Threshing Machine Co., J. J. .... AAAA

TENNIS
See Sporting Goods

TENONERS
See Machy

TEN PINS
See Pins

TENTS
See Awnings

TEREBENE
New York City
McKesson & Robbins, 91 Fulton .... AAAA
Schieffelin & Co., W. H., 170 William .... AA

TERMINALS
ILL.—Chicago
American Electric Telephone Co., 38 W. Jackson Boul. (Telephone Cable) .... B
Harvard Electric Co., 224 S. Clinton (Telephone Cable) .... D
Moon Mfg. Co., 49 S. Canal (Fuse; Telephone Cable) .... E
IND.—Lafayette
Sterling Electric Co. (Fuse; Telephone Cable) ..... AA
MO.—St. Louis
Central Telephone & Electric Co., 909 Market (Fuse) .... D
N. J.—Newark
McIntire Co., C., 13 Franklin (Electric Cable; Fuse) .... D
OHIO—Toledo
Bissell Co., F. (Telephone Cable) .... A
PA.—Pittsburg
Standard Underground Cable Co. (Electric Cable) .... AAAA
W. VA.—Wheeling
Mountain State Electrical Co. (Telephone Cable) ..D

TERNE PLATE
See Plate; Terne

TERRA ALBA
New York City
King & Co., J. B., 1 B'way .... AAAA
Pettit Chemical Co. ...... B
PA.—Easton
Keystone Plaster Co. .... A
Williams & Co., C. K. ....A

TERRA ALBA (Con.)
PA.—Philadelphia
Nevins Co., Samuel, 109 S. 2d .... D

TERRA COTTA
CAL.—San Francisco
Clark & Sons, N., 17 Spear (Architectural) .... A
Gladding, McBean & Co., Rialto Bldg. (Architectural; Enameled) ...... AA
CAL.—San Jose
Steiger Sons, A. (Architectural) .... B
CONN.—Hartford
Hartford Faience Company (Glazed) .... B
GA.—Atlanta
Atlanta Terra Cotto Co., Austell Bldg. (Architectural; Glazed) .... B
Southern Terra Cotta Co. (Architectural) X
ILL.—Chicago
American Terra Cotta & Ceramic Co. (Architectural) .... A
North Western Terra Cotta Co. cor. Clybourn & Wrightwood Av. (Architectural; Glazed) ...AAA
ILL.—Streator
Streator Clay Mfg. Co. (Rustic) .... A
IND.—Brightwood
Indianapolis Terra Cotta Co. (Architectural) .... B
MD.—Baltimore
Burns, Russell & Co. (Architectural) .... B
MASS.—Boston
Boston Fire Brick Co. (Geo. M. Fiske, Mgr.), 164 Devonshire (Architectural; Glazed) .... A
Grueby Faience Co., 2A Park (Glazed) .... D
MO.—St. Louis
St. Louis Terra Cotta Co., 5815 Manchester Av. (Architectural) C
N. Y.—Corning
Brick Terra Cotta & Tile Co. (Architectural) ....B
New York City
Atlantic Terra Cotta Co., 287 4th Av. (Architectural; Glazed) .... A
Excelsior Terra Cotta Co., 287 4th Av. (Architectural) .... A
Kreischer Brick Mfg. Co., 119 E. 23d (Architectural) .... B
New Jersey Terra Cotta Co., 108 Fulton (Architectural) .... B
New York Architectural Terra Cotta Co. 1 Madison (Architectural) .... AA
Perth Amboy Terra Cotta Co., 160 5th Av. (Architectural; Glazed) .....AA
OHIO—Cincinnati
Cincinnati Sewer Pipe Co., cor. Elm & Water (Rustic) .... E
OHIO—Columbus
Union Brick & Supply Co., Ruggery Bldg. (Architectural) .... E
PA.—Philadelphia
Conkling-Armstrong Terra Cotta Co., 24 S. 7th (Architectural) .... A
PA.—Pittsburg
White, Scott A., 811 Lewis Blk. (Architectural) .'...B
PA.—Reading
Reading Terra Cotta & Stove Lining Wks. (Architectural) C
PA.—Wilkesbarre
American Clay Product Co. (Architectural) .... D
WASH.—Spokane
Washington Brick, Lime & Mfg. Co. (Architectural) .... A

TERRETS

CONN.—New Britain
North & Judd Mfg. Co...AA
CONN.—New Haven
North & Co., O. B....AA
N. J.—Newark
Grossner, F. W., 392 Bank
G
OHIO—Canton
Elbel & Co. ....B

TESTERS

CAL.—Petaluma
Petaluma Incubator Co.
(Egg) ....B
ILL.—Carpentersville
Illinois Iron & Bolt Co.
(Metal) ....AA
ILL.—Chicago
Creamery Package Mfg. Co.
(Creamery) ....AAA
Sharpless Co. (Creamery).C
ILL.—Quincy
Stahl, Geo. H. (Egg)....B
IND.—Indianapolis
Atkins & Co., E. C. (Flour)
AAAA
IND.—Lafayette
Polar Creamery Co. (Im-
proved Creamery) .....D
IND.—Peru
Zero Creamery Co. (Cream-
ery) ....D
MASS.—Athol
Starrett Co., L. S. (Center)
A
MASS.—Holyoke
Perkins & Son, B. F. (Pa-
per) ....A
MASS.—Worcester
Union Water Meter Co.
(Cement) ....B
MICH.—Detroit
Johnston Optical Co. (Eye)
A
N. J.—Salem
Ayars Machine Co. (Auto-
matic Can) ....B
New York City
Ashcroft Mfg. Co., 85 Lib-
erty (Oil) ....A
Kohlbusch, Herman (Hand
Grain) ....B
Spencer Optical Mfg. Co.
(Eye) C
N. Y.—Union Center
Edson, Wyman L. (Cream-
ery; Cream) ....H
N. Y.—Utica
Jones, Frank L. (Creamery)
C
PA.—Philadelphia
Dairymen's Supply Co.
(Cream) ....B
Olsen & Co., Tinius (Ce-
ment) ....A
Rue Mfg. Co., 228 Cherry
(Boiler) ....AAAA
Sellers & Co., Wm. (Inc.)
(Cement; Metal) ..AAAA
Shaw, Thomas (Gas) ....F
PA.—West Chester
Dairy Specialty Co. (Cream-
ery) ....G
R. I.—Providence
Slocomb & Co., J. T. (Cen-
ter) ....D
VT.—Bellows Falls
Vermont Farm Machine Co.
(Creamery; Cream) C
WIS.—Lake Mills
Fargo & Co., F. B. (Cream-
ery) ....B

TESTS

ILL.—Harvey
Whiting Fdy. Equipment
Co. (Drop) ....AA
New York City
Weinhagen, Henry (Coal
Fire) ....B
OHIO—Columbus
Case Mfg. Co. (Drop) ....A

TETHERS: ANIMAL

CONN.—Bridgeport
Bridgeport Chain Co. .....A

MASS.—Athol
Athol Machine Co. ....A

THERMOM-ETERS

CONN.—Meriden
Bradley & Hubbard Mfg.
Co. ....AAAA
CONN.—Pequabuck
Cooper, D. G. (Oven) ....F
CONN.—Waterbury
Bristol Co. (Recording, &c.)
D
Electrical Appliance Co.
(Oven) ....G
ILL.—Chicago
Hausmann & Dunn (Clini-
cal) C
Weiskopf, A. (Advertising;
Brewers'; Distillers'; Hot
Well; Metallic; Chemical)
E
??.—Boston
American Steam Gauge
Valve Mfg. Co., Bis-
marck & Boylston (Hot
Water; Steam; Hot Well)
F
Ashton Valve Co., 271
Franklin (Heating) ....A
Crosby Steam Gauge &
Valve Co., 97 Oliver (Hot
Water; Heating; Steam;
Steam Pipe) ....AA
Gurney Heater Mfg. Co., 74
Franklin (Heating) ....B
N. H.—Peterboro
Wilder, Chas. (Est. of)...C
N. J.—Jersey City
Griffing Iron Co., A. A.
(Hot Water) ....AA
N. Y.—Brooklyn
Green, Henry J. X
Schaffer & Budenberg (Dis-
tillers'; Heating; Brew-
ers') ....A
N. Y.—Buffalo
Buffalo Specialty Mfg. Co.,
375 Ellicott ....B
New York City
Abercrombie & Fitch, 314
B'way C
Ashcroft Mfg. Co. ....A
Bayer & Son, Adolph (Clini-
cal) ....F
Becton, Dickinson & Co.,
160 Duane (Clinical) ...A
Fairbanks Co. ....AAAA
Greiner, Emil ....E
Hoehn Co., R. (I. Mayer &
Co., Props.), 80 Chambers
B
Imhauser & Co., E., 206
B'way C
International Silver Co.,
9 Maiden Lane (Silver
Plated) ....AAAA
Tagliabue, Chas. J., 53 Ful-
ton (Clinical) ....A
Tagliabue, Guiseppe (Clini-
cal; Dairy) ....B
Tiemann & Co., Geo. (Clini-
cal) ....A
Wagner Glass Works, 965
E. 132d ....D
Weinhagen, Henry (Adver-
tising; Brewers'; Distil-
lers'; Clinical) ....B
N. Y.—Phelps
Bussey Bros. ....F
N. Y.—Rochester
Hohman & Maurer Mfg. Co.
(Heating; Brewers'; Dis-
tillers'; Hot Well; Sugar
Refinery; Varnish) ....D
Taylor Bros. Co., 29 Eliza-
beth (Heating) ......AA
N. Y.—Watertown
Watertown Thermometer
Co. C
N. Y.—Williamsburg
Large & Son, Jos. F......E
OHIO—Toledo
Beckman Co., L., 318
Adams (Chemical) ....D
PA.—Philadelphia
Helios-Upton Co., 1231 Cal-
lowhill (Heating; Maxi-
mum; Minimum; Oven;
Recording) ....D

THERMOMETERS
Queen & Co. (Inc.), 1010
Chestnut (Technical; Hot
Water; Heating) ....AA
Whitall, Tatum & Co.
(Chemical) ......AAAA
WIS.—Milwaukee
Johnson Service Co. (Hot
Water; High Pressure of
Air) ....AAA

THERMO-STATS

ILL.—Chicago
Weiskopf, A. ....E
MASS.—North Attleboro
Corey Mfg. Co. X
N. Y.—Brooklyn
Acton, Jno. ....D
New York City
Bunnell Co., J. H., 20 Park
Pl. ....B
Crane Co., Wm. M., 1131
B'way ....A
Edwards & Co., 144th &
4th Av. .... D
Kieley & Mueller, 7 W.
13th (for Hot Water;
Tanks, &c.) ....B
Ostrander & Co., W. R., 22
Dey ....A
Standard Steam Specialty
Co., 111 5th Av. (Boiler)
D
N. Y.—Rochester
Beers Bros. Thermostat Co.,
18 Elm ....D
PA.—Philadelphia
Partrick, Carter & Wilkins,
1231 Callowhill C
Queen & Co. ....AA

THIBETS

See Woolen Goods

THIMBLES

See also Jewelry

CONN.—Middletown
Wilcox, Crittenden & Co.
(Wire Rope) ....A
MAINE—Portland
Laughlin & Sons, Thomas
(Wire Rope) ....A
MASS.—Boston
Durable Wire Rope Co., 288
Congress (Wire Rope)...B
MASS.—North Attleboro
Whiting Co., F. M. (Gold;
Silver) ....A
MO.—St. Louis
Broderick & Bascom Rope
Co., 809 N. Main (Wire
Rope) ....AA
Leschen & Sons Rope Co.,
920 N. 1st ....AAA
N. J.—Newark
Durand & Co. (Inc.) (Gold)
AA
N. J.—Trenton
Trenton Iron Co. (Wire
Rope) ....AA
N. Y.—Buffalo
Contractors' Plant Mfg. Co.,
129 Erie (Wire Rope)..B
N. Y.—Lockport
Western Block Co. (Steel
Wire Rope) C
N. Y.—Manlius
Cheney & Son, S. (Stove
Pipe) ....A
New York City
Goodyear's India Rubber
Glove Mfg. Co. (Rubber)
AAAA
Goodyear Rubber Co. (Rubber) ....AAAA
Grote & Co., Fred. (Ivory)
D
Hodgman Rubber Co. (Rubber) ....AA
Ketcham & McDougall, 37
Maiden Lane (Gold; Silver) ....B
Macomber, Whyte, Moon
Co., 131 Worth (Wire
Rope) ....H
Sargent & Co., 151 Leonard
(Rope) ....AAAA

THIMBLES (Con.)
Sloan & Co. (Inc.) (Gold).B
Standard Steam Specialty
Co., 111 5th Av. (Wire
Rope) ....D
Stern Bros. & Co., 68 Nassau (Gold; Silver).AAAA
N. Y.—Syracuse
Stearns & Co., E. C. (Stove
Pipe) ....AA
N. Y.—Troy
Troy Stamping Wks. (Stove
Pipe) ....AAAA
N. Y.—West Troy
Covert Mfg. Co. (Rope)..X
OHIO—Dayton
City Forge & Iron Works
(Stove Pipe) ....D
OHIO—New Philadelphia
Ohio Stove Pipe & Mfg. Co.
(Stove Pipe) ....E
PA.—Harrisburg
Jackson Mfg. Co. (Wire
Rope; Bolt; Axle) ....B
PA.—Philadelphia
Muhr's Sons, H. (Gold; Silver) ....D
Simons Bros. & Co. (Gold;
Silver) ....A
PA.—Pittsburg
Lanz & Sons, Mathew, 101
S. 29th (Wire Rope; Guy)
B
PA.—Williamsport
Williamsport Wire Rope Co.
(Rope) ....A
R. I.—Providence
Waite-Thresher Co. (Gold;
Silver) ....A

THORIUM

New York City
Lieber & Co., H., 25 W.
B'way ....D
Pfaltz, Hy., 284 Pearl...X
Reno, Morris, 100 William
X
Roessler & Hasslacher
Chemical Co. ....AA

THREAD

CAL.—San Francisco
Carlson-Currier Co., 6 Sutter (Spool Silk; Twist;
Knitting Silk) ....B
Higginbotham & Co. (Silk,
Knitting) ....B
CONN.—East Hampton
Summit Thread Co. (Cotton)
A
CONN.—Mansfield
Macfarlane, Jos. S. (Sewing
Silk) ....D
CONN.—New Haven
Globe Silk Works (Marvin
& Pardee) (Sewing; Spun
Silk) ....B
CONN.—New London
Brainerd & Armstrong Co.
(Sewing Silk; Machine
Twist) ....AAA
CONN.—Norfolk
Aetna Silk Co. (Sewing
Silk; Twist) C
CONN.—Putnam
Hammond, Knowlton & Co.
(Machine Twist) .....B
Dady & Co., Jno. A. (Machine; Sewing Silk)....D
CONN.—Rockville
Belding Bros. & Co. (Sewing Silk; Twist) .AAAA
CONN.—South Manchester
Cheney Bros. (Spun Silk)
AAAA
CONN.—Warehouse Point
Warehouse Point Silk Co.
(Sewing Silk; Machine
Twist) ....A
CONN.—Watertown
Heminway & Bartlett Silk
Co. (Spool Silk; Twist;
Embroidery; Knitting
Silk) C
Heminway & Sons Silk Co.,
H. (Spool Silk; Twist)..B
CONN.—Willimantic
Holland Mfg. Co. (Machine
Twist; Sewing Silk)....A
Hall & Co., Gardiner Jr.
(Spool Cotton) ......AA

THREAD (*Con.*)

CONN.—Windsor Locks
Montgomery & Co., J. R. (Metal) ....AA

CONN.—Winsted
Winsted Silk Co. (Sewing Silk) ....A

GA.—Columbus
Eagle & Phoenix Mills (Cotton Ball) ....AAAA

ILL.—Chicago
Belding Bros. Co. (Silk Machine) ....AAAA
Linen Thread Co. (Boot; Shoe; Linen; Cotton)..B
Spool Cotton Co. (Boot; Shoe) ....A

LA.—New Orleans
Lane Mills of New Orleans (Cotton; Ball Sewing).AA

MASS.—Andover
Smith & Dove Mfg. Co. (Shoe; Flax, &c.)....AA

MASS.—Athol
Adams, D. E. (Silk, Sewing) ....B

MASS.—Becket
Becket Silk Mills (Silk)..F

MASS.—Boston
Boston Thread & Twine Co. (Saddlers') ....B

MASS.—Canton
Eureka Silk Mfg. Co. (Silk Sewing) ....A

MASS.—Florence
Nonotuck Silk Co. (Silk) AAA

MASS.—Grafton
Finlayson Flax Spinning Co. (Linen) ....B

MASS.—Holyoke
Cressy Thread Co. (Spool Cotton) ....D
Skinner Mfg. Co., Wm. (Silk) ....AA

MASS.—Leominster
U. S. Thread Co. (Spool Cotton) ....A

MASS.—Millbury
West End Thread Co. (Flax; Linen Shoe) ....E

MASS.—Northampton
Belding Bros. & Co. (Silk; Shoe) ....AAAA

MASS.—Pittsfield
Rice & Co., A. H. (Silk).A

MASS.—Southbridge
Central Mills Co. (Sewing) A

MASS.—Springfield
Bay State Thread Works (Cotton) ....B

MASS.—Westfield
Warren Thread Works, W. B

MASS.—Worcester
Cranska Thread Co. (Spool Cotton) ....B
Wachusett Thread Company (Spool Cotton) ....D
Worcester Thread Co. (Flax Shoe) ....B

MICH.—Belding
Belding Bros. & Co. (Spool Silk) ....AAAA
Richardson Silk Co. (Silk) A

N. J.—Florence
Florence Thread Co. (Soft; Glazed Cotton) C

N. J.—Jersey City
Chadwick & Bro., Jas. (Cotton) ....A

N. J.—Newark
Clark Thread Co. (Spool Cotton) ....AAAA

N. J.—Paterson
Barbour Flax Spinning Co. (Flax) ....AAAA
Caspers Silk Co. (Silk Sewing) ....D
White, Joseph (Sewing Silk) C

N. Y.—Greenwich
Dunbarton Flax Spinning Co. (Linen) ....B

N. Y.—Hornellsville
Steuben Silk Co. (Silk Sewing) ....B

N. Y.—Kenwood
Oneida Community (Silk Sewing; Twist) .....AAA

THREAD (*Con.*)

New York City
American Thread Co. (Boot; Shoe) ....AAAA
Boston Thread Co. (Shoe).E
Commercial Supply Co., 31 Union Sq. (Incand. Gas Mantle) X
Gudebrod Bros. Co. (Spool Silk) ....B
Hammond, Knowlton & Co. (Sewing Silk) ....B
Hart Co., A. H. (Shoe) AAA
Hemingway - Bartlett Silk Co. (Sewing) ....A
Hess, Goldsmith & Co. (Sewing Silk) ....A
Holland Mfg. Co. (Sewing Silk) ....A
Johns-Manville Co., H. W. (Asbestos) ....AAAA
Nonotuck Silk Co. (Sewing Silk) ....AAAA
Oneida Community (Ltd.) (Sewing Silk) ......AAAA
Richardson Silk Co. (Sewing Silk) ....A
Skinner Mfg. Co., Wm. (Sewing Silk) .....AAAA
Winne Co., D. P. (Com.) C
Winsted Silk Co. (Sewing Silk) ....A

N. Y.—Schaghticoke
Cable Flax Mills (Boot; Shoe) ....B

N. C.—Albemarle
Efird Mfg. Co. (Sewing Twine) ....A

N. C.—Jamestown
Oakdale Cotton Mills (Cotton Sewing) ....B

PA.—Bethlehem
Bethlehem Silk Co. (Silk) A

PA.—Philadelphia
Hackenburgh & Co., Wm. B. (Silk Sewing) .....B
Hughes Mfg. Co. (Soft; Glazed) C
Phila. Thread Co. (Spool Cotton) ....D

PA.—Pottstown
Champion Silk Co. (Sewing; Machine) C

R. I.—Lincoln
Samoset Co. (Cotton Sewing) ....A

R. I.—Pawtucket
Blodgett & Oswell Co. (Cotton) ....B
Coats, J. & P. (Spool Cotton) ....AAAA
Dexter Yarn Co. (Knitting Co.) ....A
Greene & Daniels Mfg. Co. (Spool Cotton; Shoe Thread) ....AA
Kenyon Mfg. Co., Jno. J. (Spool Cotton) ....B
Littlefield Mfg. Co. (Cotton) ....A
New England Thread Co. (Spool Cotton) ....A

R. I.—Warwick
Elizabeth Mill Co. (Cotton) AAAA

THREADERS

CONN.—Bridgeport
Armstrong Mfg. Co. (Pipe) A

CONN.—East Hampton
Brown & Co., H. B. (Bolt) E

CONN.—Hartford
Cook Co., Asa S. (Bolt; Lay Screw) ....B
Pratt & Whitney Co. (Bolt) AAAA

CONN.—New Haven
Geometric Drill Co. (Bicycle Spoke) C

CONN.—Waterbury
Blake & Johnson (Bicycle Spoke; Bolt) ....A
Manville Machine Co., E. J. (Bicycle Spoke; Bolt)..C

ILL.—Chicago
Crane Co. (Pipe) ....AAAA

THREADERS (Con.)

MD.—Baltimore
Detrick & Harvey Machine Co. (Bolt; Bicycle Spoke) ...AA

MASS.—Boston
Walworth Mfg. Co. (Pipe) ...AAAA

MASS.—Greenfield
Goodell-Pratt Co. (Bicycle Spoke) ....B
Wells Bros. & Co. (Bolt) .A
Wiley & Russell Mfg. Co. (Bolt) ....AA

MASS.—Lowell
Lahue & Co., M. M., 107 Cushing (Shuttle) ....F

MICH.—Marcellus
Chapman, H. L. (Bolt) ...F

New York City
Fairbanks Co., 416 Broome (Bolt) ....AAAA

N. Y.—Rochester
Rochester Pipe Tongs Co. (Pipe) ....F

N. Y.—Yonkers
Saunders' Sons, D. (Bolt) ...A

OHIO—Cleveland
Acme Machinery Co. (Bolt) ...AA
Hart Mfg. Co. (Bolt) ....B
Reliance Machine & Tool Co. (Bolt) C

OHIO—Hamilton
Niles Tool Works Co. (Bolt) ...AAAA

OHIO—Springfield
Webster & Perks Tool Co. (Bolt; Bicycle Spoke) ..D

OHIO—Tiffin
National Machinery Co. (Bolt) ....AA

OHIO—Toledo
Baker Bros. (Lag Screw) .A

PA.—Erie
Jarecki Mfg. Co. (Pipe) ...AAAA

PA.—Philadelphia
Morris, Tasker & Co. (Pipe) ...AAA

R. I.—Pawtucket
Pawtucket Mfg. Co. (Bolt) ...A

THRESHERS
See Agr. Imps.

THYMOL

New York City
Lehn & Fink ....AAA

TICKETS

CONN.—New Haven
Thompson & Son, H. G. (Pin) ....B

ILL.—Chicago
Rand, McNally & Co. (Inc.) (Railway) ....AAAA

MASS.—Boston
Dennison Mfg. Co., 26 Franklin (Pin; Price) ...AAAA
Forbes Litho. Mfg. Co. (Pin) ....AA
Rand-Avery Supply Co. (Duplicate Coupon Railway) ...AA

New York City
American Bank Note Co. (Railway) ....AAAA
Franklin-Lee Bank Note Co. (Railway) ....A
International Bank Note Co. (Railway) ....A
N. Y. Bank Note Co. (Railway) ....A

PA.—West Chester
Denny Tag Co. (Pin) C

R. I.—Providence
Salisbury Mfg. Co. (Pin) .A

VA.—Glen Allen
Cussons, May & Co. (Duplicate Coupon) ....B

TICKING
See Cotton Goods

TIES
See also Neckwear

ALA.—Carney
Carney Lumber Co. (Wooden) ....B

ALA.—Dothan
Wilson, W. S. (Wooden) ..C

ALA.—Sheffield
Sheffield Rolling Mill Co. (Cotton) ....A

ARK.—Paragould
Bertig Bros. (Wooden) ...A

ARK.—Texarkana
Red Water Lumber Co. (Wooden) ....B

CAL.—San Francisco
Albion Lumber Co. (Wooden) ....AA
Byxbee & Clark, 48 Market (Wooden) ....B
Caspar Lumber Co., Hayward Bldg. (Wooden) ...AAA
Gray & Co., Geo. D., 421 Market (Wooden) ......A
Hooper & Co., C. A., California & Front (Wooden) ...AAAA
Nelson & Co., Chas., 6 California (Wooden) .AAA
Pacific Lumber Co. (Inc.) Rialto Bldg. (Wooden) ..A
Pacific Pine Co., 237 California (Wooden) ......A
Richardson Co., 6 California (Wooden) ....A
White Lumber Co., L. E., 303 California (Wooden) ...AAA
Wood Lumber Co., E. K., 6 California (Wooden) ...AAAA

COLO.—Denver
Western Lumber & Pole Co., 1025 17th (Wooden) ....B

CONN.—Bridgeport
American Tube & Stamping Co. (Cotton) ......AAAA
Bridgeport Chain Company (Cattle) ....A

CONN.—Danbury
Irving, J. G. (Hat Bow) ..E
Tweedy, A. E. (Hat Bow) ...B

CONN.—New Haven
National Steel & Wire Co. (Bale) ....AAAA

FLA.—Jacksonville
Baxter & Co., G. S. (Wooden) ....B
Hunter, Dexter (Wooden) ...A

FLA.—Pensacola
Thornton, H. H. (Railroad) ...F

GA.—Atlanta
Atlanta Steel Hoop Co. (Bale) ....A

GA.—Brunswick
Aiken, Frank D. (Wooden) ...C
Cooney, Eckstein & Co. (Wooden) ....A
Emanuel & Co., N. (Wooden) ....AA
Hilton & Dodge Lumber Co. (Wooden) ....AAAA

GA.—Savannah
Cooney, Eckstein & Co. (Wooden) ....A
Dixon Lumber Co., 737 Wheaton (Wooden) ...A
Georgia Lumber Co., 2 Bay E. (Wooden) C
Hirsch & Co., C. S., 128 Bay, W. (Wooden R. R.) ...AA
Southern Pine Co., Provident Bldg. (Wooden) .AAA
Wylly, Gabbett, Provident Bldg. (Wooden) ....AAA

GA.—Thomasville
Watt Bros. & Co., James (Wooden) ....A

ILL.—Batavia
Newton Co., E. C. (Cattle) ...B

ILL.—Chicago
American Steel & Wire Co., The Rookery (Bale; Cotton) ....AAAA
Ayer & Lord Tie Co., Old

TIES (Con.)

Colony Bldg. (Wooden) ....AAA

Beidler & Co., Francis W., 22d & Loomis (Poles; Idaho Cedar; Michigan White Cedar, 40 ft. & up) ....AA

Gillis & Moulton, 204 Dearborn (Wooden) C

Grand Crossing Tack Co. (Bale) ....AAA

Holcomb - Lobb Co., 204 Dearborn (Cedar) .....B

Marsh & Bingham, Old Colony Bldg. (Wooden)....A

Monarch Lumber Co., 184 Lasalle (Wooden Bridge; Switch) C

Mueller & Co., M., Marquette Bldg. (Wooden).A

Naugle Tie Co., E. E., 159 La Salle (Wooden) ....A

Raber & Watson, Old Colony Bldg. (Cedar) ....A

Ripley & Son, Wm., 36 La Salle (Wooden) ......AA

Schultz Bros., Old Colony Bldg. (Ties) ....A

Stone, Frank B., 279 Dearborn (Wooden) ....A

Wallce Supply Co., 169 Jackson Boul. (Cedar)..C

ILL.—East St. Louis

New Process Steel & Wire Co. (Wire Bale) ....A

ILL.—Joliet

Joliet Bale & Tie Co. (Bale) ....E

ILL.—M'Leansboro

Wilson, John H. (Wooden) ....B

ILL.—Sterling

Dillon-Griswold Wire Co. (Steel Bale) X

IND.—Crawfordsville

Crawfordsville Wire & Nail Co. (Bale) ....AA

IND.—Evansville

Gray Tie & Lumber Co., B. H. A. Bldg. (Wooden).AA

IND.—Muncie

Indiana Steel & Wire Co. (Bale) ....A

IND.—Richmond

Johnson & Son, B. (Wooden R. R.) ....A

IOWA—Des Moines

Des Moines Bale Tie Co. (Bale) ....B

KY.—Burnside

Wheeler, Holden & Co. (Wooden R. R.) ....A

KY.—Jackson

Day, Flood (Wooden) ....A

LA.—Donner

Dibert, Stark & Brown Cypress Co. (Hewn; Sawn Wooden) ....AAA

LA.—Franklin

Hanson Lumber Co., Albert (Wooden) ....AA

LA.—Lake Charles

Bradley-Ramsay Lumber Co. (Railroad) ....AAAA

MD.—Baltimore

Hoskins Lumber Co., J. S. (Wooden) C

MD.—Brandywine

Robinson, A. T. (Wooden) C

MASS.—Springfield

Wagor Mfg. Co., P. R. (Wall) ....G

MASS.—Webster

Prescott & Son, J. B. (Veneer; Wall; Bends).....B

MASS.—Worcester

Hamblin & Russell Mfg. Co. (Perforated Steel Wall) ....B

MICH.—Ausable

Loud's Sons Co., H. M. (Wooden) ....AA

MICH.—Bay City

Michigan Pipe Co. (Creosoted Wooden) ....AA

MICH.—Bovee

Robinson & Freeman (Wooden R. R.) ....B

MICH.—Detroit

Anderson & Sons. W. H. (Pressed Brick) C

TIES (Con.)

Grace Harbor Lumber Co. (Wooden) ....B

Standard Tie Co., Chamber of Com. Bldg. (Wooden) ....A

MICH.—Escanaba

Erickson & Bissell (Cedar) ....A

MICH.—Escanaba

Mueller Co., Wm. (Wooden) ....A

Pittsburg & Lake Superior Iron Co. (Cedar) .....AA

MICH.—Grand Rapids

Union City Lumber Co. (Wooden) ....B

MICH.—Hardwood

Spies Lumber & Cedar Co., Augustus (Wooden) ....A

MICH.—Herrmansville

Wisconsin Land & Lumber Co. (Cedar) ......AAAA

MICH.—Honor

Guelph Patent Cask Co. (Wooden) ....B

MICH.—Ingalls

Carley, Ira (Wooden)....B

MICH.—Manistique

White Marble Lime Co. (Cedar R. R.) ....B

MICH.—Menominee

Lindsley Bros. Co. (Wooden) ....B

MICH.—Monroe

Sterling & Son, H. C. (Wooden) ....A

MICH.—Newhall

Pittsburg & Lake Superior Iron Co. (Cedar) .....

MICH.—Omer

Sterling & Son, W. C. (Wooden) ....A

MICH.—Rapid River

Madden Shingle Co., Jerry (Wooden) ....A

MICH.—Saginaw

Morse Cedar Co. (Cedar).C

MICH.—Spalding

Mueller & Co., Wm. (Wooden) ....A

MICH.—Vanderbilt

Sterling & Son, W. C. (Wooden) ....A

MINN.—Duluth

Duluth Log Co. (Wooden).C

Martin, L. R. (Wooden)..C

MINN.—Minneapolis

Bradley-Watkins Co. (White Cedar) ....AA

Coolidge Co., M. H., Guaranty Loan Bldg. (Wooden) ....B

Coolidge Fuel & Supply Co. (Railroad) ....B

Minneapolis Cedar & Lumber Co., Lumber Exchange (Wooden) C

Pillsbury - Watkins Co., Lumber Exch. (Wooden) ....B

MISS.—Meridian

Brownlee Lumber Company (Wooden Cross) ....B

MO.—Eldon

Harvey & Co., N. E. (Wooden) ....A

MO.—Kansas City

Badger Lumber Co. (Railroad) ....AAA

Missouri Timber & Tie Co. (Wooden) ....A

Sedgwick Tie Co., Beals Bldg. (Wooden) ....A

MO.—St. Louis

Abelers & Taussig Commercial Bldg. (Wooden) ....B

Bagnell Timber Co. (Wooden) ....AA

Berthold & Jennings (Wooden) ....A

Harry, Owen K., 2335 Papin (Bale) ....B

Moss. Tie Co., T. J., 319 W. 4th (Wooden) ....AA

New Process Mfg. Co., 2200 N. 2nd (Bale).......X

Western Tie & Timber Co., Century Bldg. (Wooden) ....AA

1024

TIGHTENERS BELT, ETC.

CAL.—San Francisco
Union Iron Wks., 222 Market ....AAAA
COLO.—Denver
Davis Iron Wks. Co., F. M. 8th & Larimer ....A
Midland Fdry. & Mach. Wks. Co. C
CONN.—Hartford
Billings & Spencer Co.....A
CONN.—New Haven
Hoggson & Pettis Mfg. Co. X
ILL.—Chicago
Allis-Chalmers Co., Home Ins. Bldg. .... AAAA
Link Belt Mchry. Co., W. 39th & Stewart Av.....A
Plamondson Mfg. Co., A., 57 So. Clinton ....A
ILL.—Marseilles
Marseilles Mfg. Co........A
ILL.—Moline
Barnard & Leas Mfg. Co. AA
IND.—Mishawaka
Dodge Mfg. Co........AAA
IND.—Richmond
Richmond City Mill Wks..A
IOWA—Dubuque
Adams Co. ....B
KANS.—Leavenworth
Great Western Mfg. Co..AA
MD.—Baltimore
Poole & Son Co., Robt., 233 E. German ....A
MASS.—Boston
Amer. Tool & Machine Co., 109 Beach ....AA
MASS.—Orange
Hunt, Rodney Machine Co. ....A
MO.—St. Louis
Medart-Patent Pulley Co., 3500 DeKalb ....AA
N. Y.—Buffalo
Noye Mfg. Co., John T....D
New York City
Brown Co., A. & F., 26 Cortlandt ....A
OHIO—Cincinnati
Lane & Bodley Co., John & Water ....A
OHIO—Cleveland
Hill-Clutch Co., ft. Waverly Av. ....D
OHIO—Cuyahoga Falls
Falls Rivet & Machine Co. ....A
PA.—Chambersburg
Wood Sons. T. B.........A
PA.—Nicetown
Link Belt Engineering Co. ....A
PA.—Philadelphia
Cresson Co., Geo. V., 18th & Allegheny Av......AA
Fairmount Machine Co.,22nd & Wood ....A
Sellers & Co. (Inc.) 1600 Hamilton ....AAAA
PA.—Pittsburg
Jones & Laughlins Steel Co. ....AAAA
PA.—Williamsport
U. S. Machine Co........B
VT.—Montpelier
Lane Mfg. Co. ....A
WIS.—Milwaukee
Filer & Stowell Co., Becker & Zeimer ....AAA

TILE

CAL.—Los Angeles
Pacific Clay Mfg. Co., 651 So. B'way (Drain).....A
Pacific Mfg. Co. (Locomotivee; Hollow Partition).AA
CAL.—San Francisco
Clarke & Sons, N., 17 Spear (Drain; Vetrifield; Roofing) ....A
Forderer Cornice Wks. (Galvnized Iron; Roofing)..D
Gladding, McBean & Co., Rialto Bldg. (Terra Cotta Roofing Drain) ......AA
Patent Brick Co. (Paving) AA

TILE (Con.)
CAL.—San Jose
Steiger, Geo. A. (Terra Cotta Roofing) X
COLO.—Denver
Denver Fire Clay Co., 1742 Champa (Locomotive).AA
CONN.—Elmwood
Goodwin Bros. Pottery Co. (Drain) ....B
CONN.—Hartford
Hartford Taience Co. (Terra Vitral) ....B
CONN.—New London
Burch & Co., H. O. (Drain) X
D. C.—Washington
National Terra Cotta Wks., Thos. Somerville & Sons, 316 13th N. W. (Drain) ....A
GA.—Macon
Stevens Sons Co., H. (Locomotive; Drain) ....A
ILL.—Carbon Cliff
Argillo Wks. (Drain).....A
ILL.—Chicago
Brown Bros. Mfg. Co., 22nd & Campbell Av. (Illuminating; Illuminating Sidewalk) ....B
Chicago Retrot Fire Brick Co., 45th & Clark (Locomotive) ....A
Chicago Sidewalk Light Co. (Illuminating) ....F
Dauchy Iron Wks., 88 Illinois (Illuminating)....B
Garden City Land Co., Security Bldg (Locomotive) ....A
Globe Iron Wks. (Paving) B
Ludowici Roofing Tile Co., 138 Washington (Terra Cotta Roofing) .... G
Pioneer Fire Proofing Co., 204 Dearborn (Bake Oven; Sidewalk) ....AA
Richards & Kelly Mfg. Co., 389 23rd (Illuminating) ....D
Sherman & Flavin (Marble) B
William Co., N. A., Chamber of Commerce Bldg. (Drain) ....B
ILL.—Hillsboro
Hillsboro Brick & Tile Co. (Drain) X
ILL.—Joliet
Joliet Mound Drain Tile Co. (Drain) ....B
ILL.—Lincoln
Lincoln Coal Co. (Drain) ....AA
ILL.—Lodi
Goodell, Adison Tile Wks. (Drain) ....A
ILL.—Momence
Tiffany Enameled Brick Co. (Enameled) ....A
ILL.—Monmouth
Monmouth Mining & Mfg. Co. (Drain) ....AA
ILL.—Springfield
Dawson Brick & Tile Co. (Drain) ....D
ILL.—Streator
Streator Clay Mfg. Co. (Drain) ....A
IND.—Evansville
Evansville Pressed Brick Co. (Paving) C
First Av. Brick & Tile Co. (Drain) C
IND.—Indianapolis
Clay Shingle Co. (Vetrified Roofing) ....D
United States Encaustic Tile Co. (Art; Decorative; Encaustic Floor; Mosaic Oramic Floor; Vitrious Floor) ....AA
IND.—Lapel
White, S. C. (Drain).....D
IOWA—Des Moines
Dale Brick Co. (Drain)...C
Iowa Pipe & Tile Co. (Drain) ....A
IOWA—Grand Junction
Goodwin Tile &   Co.

TILE (Con.)
(Drain) ....B
IOWA—Keota
Clarke & Leacock (Drain) F.
IOWA—Mason City
American Brick & Tile Co.
  (Drain) ....B
Mason City Brick & Tile
  Co. (Drain; Vetrified;
  Sidewalk) ....B
Mason City Clay Wks.
  (Drain) C
IOWA—Sheffield
Fox, E. P. (Drain) ......H
KY.—Covington
Cambridge Tile Mfg. Co.
  (Art; Decorative; Enam-
  elled; Encaustic Floor;
  Mosaic Ceramic Floor;
  Vitreous Floor) ....A
KY.—Newport
Alhambra Tile Co. (Vitreous
  Floor) ....D
MAINE—Bath
Monson Consolidated Slate
  Co. (Slate Floor) .....B
MD.—Baltimore
Baltimore Rubber Co. (In-
  terlocking Rubber) ....D
Baltimore Terra Cotta Wks.
  (Emma Puttenhouse,
  Propss.) Cor. Covington
  & Clement (Drain) ....B
Bennett Roofing Tile Wks.
  Edw., Eden & Alicemann
  (Terra Cotta Roofing)..A
MASS.—Boston
American Slate Co., Cor.
  Somerset & Beacon (Slate
  Floor) X
Boston Fire Brick Co., Geo.
  M. Fiske, Mgr., 164 De-
  vonshire, Mfrs. Agts.
  (Drain; Terra Cotta Roof-
  ing) ....A
Mathews Consolidated Slate
  Co., 199 Washington
  (Slate Floor) X
Monson Maine Slate Co., 113
  Devonshire (Slate Floor)
  X
Murdock Corporation, 156
  Boylston (Grate; Flooring
  Terra Vitrae) X
MASS.—Chelsea
Low Art Tile Co. (Paving)
  F
MASS.—Springfield
Hampden Brick Wks. (Pav-
  ing) ....A
MASS.—Taunton
Presbury Stove Lining Co.
  (Bake Oven) ....B
MASS.—Worcester
Algonquin Red Slate Co.,
  108 Worcester (Slate
  (Floor) ....B
Brownsville Maine Slate Co.
  (Slate Floor) ....B
MICH.—Benton Harbor
McCord & Muller Co.
  (Drain) ....E
MICH.—Detroit
Barnum Wire & Iron Wks.,
  E. T., 99-105 Shelby (Il-
  luminating) ....B
Christa & Sons, Philip, 504
  Lafayette Av. (Slate
  Floor) ....B
Russel Wheel & Fdy. Co.
  (Illuminating; Illuminat-
  ing Sidewalk) ....AA
MICH.—Jackson
Michigan Sewer Pipe Co.
  (Drain) ....AAAA
MINN.—St. Paul
Portland Stone Co. (Ce-
  ment) ....•D
MO.—Kansas City
Dickey Clay Mfg. Co., W.
  S. (Drain) ....A
MO.—St. Louis
Bruner Granitoid Co., P.
  M., 304 N. 8th (Illumin-
  ating) C
Evens & Howard Fire Brick
  Co., 920 Market (Locomo-
  tive; Drain) ......AAAA
Koken Iron Wks., Koken
  Bldg. (Illuminating)...B
Mound City Roofing Tile

TILE (Con.)
  Co. (Terra Cotta Roofing)
  B
Nelson Mfg. Co., N. O.
  AAA
St. Louis Terra Cotta Co.,
  5815 Manchester Av. (Ter-
  ra Cotta Roofing) C
St. Louis Vitrified & Fire
  Brick Co. (Locomotive)
  A
Union Iron & Fdry. Co.,
  1458 So. 2nd (Illuminat-
  ing) ....A
N. J.—Camden
Montrose Metal Shingle Co.
  (Copper; Galvanized Steel;
  Tin) ....D
N. J.—Jersey City
Gautier & Co., J. H. (Gas
  House) ....AA
N.J.—Matteawan
New Jersey Mosaic Tile Co.
  (Mosaic Cramic Floor)..C
N. J.—Newark
Gerhard, Frank J., 236 18th
  Av. (Drain) ....D
N. J.—Old Bridge
Old Bridge Enamelled Brick
  & Tile Co. (Art; Decora-
  tive) ....B
Pardee Works, C. (Art &
  Decorative) ....AAA
Perth Amboy Terra Cotta
  Co. (Paving) ....AA
N. J.—Sewaren
Boynton, C. W. (Roofing;
  Drain) ....A
N. J.—Trenton
Imperial Porcelain Wks.
  (Art; Decorating) ....AA
Providential Tile Wks., En-
  terprise Av. (Art Decor-
  ative) C
Superior Fire Lining Co.
  (Locomotive) ....D
Trenton Tile Co. (Art; Dec-
  orative; White; Colored;
  Vitreous Floor) ......AA
N. J.—Woodbridge
Valentine & Bro. Co., M.
  D. (Drain) ....AA
N. Y.—Albany
Jackson, Jno. H., 142 3rd
  Av. (Drain) ....B
N. Y.—Alfred
Alfred Clay Co. (Terra Cot-
  ta Roofing) ....E
N. Y.—Brooklyn
Cooper, Jno., 496 Oakland
  (Drain) C
Meurer Bros. Co. (Metallic;
  Spanish Shapes; Roofing)
  AA
New York Vitrified Tile Co.,
  79 4th (Encaustic Floor)
  E
N. Y.—East Bethany
Peck, Richard (Drain)...D
N. Y.—Dutchess Junction
Aldridge Bros. & Co. (Pav-
  ing) ....B
New York City
Buess, Wm. (Slate Floor)
  E
Celadon Roofing Tile Co.
  (Ltd.) 156 5th Av. (Con-
  osera Roofing; Glass Roof-
  ing; Promenade Roofing;
  Celadon Roofing; Terra
  Cotta Graduated Roofing)
  A
Cornell, J. B. & J. M., 26th
  & 11th Av. (Illuminating)
  AA
Duffy & Co., J. P., 440 E.
  138th (Drain) ....B
Graf, Frank H., 322 7th Av.
  (Mosaic) ....D
Gutta Percha & Rubber Mfg.
  Co., 126 Duane (Rubber)
  AAAA
Jackson & Co., Wm. H.
  (Paving) ....D
Kriescher & Sons, B. (Inc.)
  (Paving) ....B
Manhattan Glass Tile Co.,
  157 10th Av. (Opal Glass)
  D
Manhttan Rubber Mfg. Co.,
  18 Vesey (Rubber) ...AA
Mark, Jacob, 7 Worth (Il-

TILE (Con.)
House Bldg. (Locomotive)
B
White, Scott A., Lewis Blk.
(Mfrs. Agt.) (Terra Cotta
Roofing) ....B
PA.—Slatington
Slatington Slate Co. (Slate
Floor) ....B
Washington Slate Co.
(Slate Floor) C
PA.—Wind Gap
Pelican Slate Mfg. Co.
(Wind Gap) ....E
TENN.—Chattanooga
Montague & Co. (Drain;
Boiler) ....A
TEXAS.—San Antonio
Mackey Brick & Tile Mfg.
Co. (Paving) ....B
VT.—Fair Haven
Allens' Sons; S. (Slate
Floor) ....D
Coulman & Westcott (Slate
Floor) ....D
Eureka Slate Quarries (A.
Tuttle, Treas.) ....B
Fair Haven Marble & Mar-
bleized Slate Co. (Slate
Floor; Marble) ....B
VT.—Hydeville
Minogue Bros. & Quinn
(Slate Floor) ....D
VT.—Poutlney
Fleming Slate Co. (Slate
Floor) C
VT.—Rutland
Rutland Fire Clay Co. (Lo-
comotive) ....B
VA.—Arvonia
Williams Slate Co. (Slate
Floor) ....B
WASH.—Seattle
Denny Clay Co. (Drain; Lo-
comotive) ....A
WASH.—Spokane
Washington Brick, Lime &
Mfg. Co. (Locomotive) A
W. VA.—Huntington
Ohio Valley Clay Shingle
Co. (Vitrified Flat Terra
Cotta Roofing; Shingles)
E
W. VA.—Parkersburg
United States Roofing Tile
Co. (Terra Cotta Roofing)
B
WIS.—Boscobel
Ruka Bros. Mfg. Co.
(Paving) C
WIS.—Milwaukee
Bayley & Sons Co., Wm.,
782 Greenbush (Illumina-
ting) X

TILINGS

COLO.—Denver
Denver Fire Clay Co. (Fire
Clay) ....AA
CONN.—Bridgeport
American Tube & Stamping
Co. (Steel Floor) ..AAAA
New York City
N. Y. Belting & Packing Co.
(Interlocking Rubber)
AAA
Reconstructed Granite Co.,
14 Dey (Acid; Proof for
Chemical Works) ......D
OHIO—Cleveland
Dover Fire Brick Co. (Fire
Clay) ....B
OHIO—Wellsville
Vulcan Clay Co. (Fire Clay)
B
PA.—Dunbar
Dunbar Fire Brick Co. (Fire
Clay) ....B
PA.—Pen Argyl
Crown Slate Co. C
PA.—Philadelphia
Pfeifer & Co.. (Ltd.) ,Jno.,
224 Race (Slate) ......A

TILLS

ILL.—Chicago
Chicago Scale Co. (Alarm)
A
IND.—Indianapolis
Tucker & Dorsey Mfg. Co.
(Alarm) ....A

TILLS (Con.)
R. I.—Providence
Miles Alarm Till Mfg. Co.
(Alarm) C

TIMBER

See also Lumber

FLA.—Pensacola
Thornton, H. H. (Bridge) F
GA.—Savannah
Southern Pine Co., of Geor-
gia (Bridge) ....AAA
KANS.—Verdi
Verdi Mill Co. (Building;
Mining) ....D
LA.—Lake Charles
Bradley-Ramsey Lumber Co.
(Bridge) ....AAAA
MICH.—Bay City
Michigan Pipe Co. (Bridge;
Creosoted) ....AA
MINN.—Minneapolis
Coolidge Fuel & Supply Co.
(Bridge) ....E
TEXAS—Nona
Cameron & Co., Wm.
(Bridge) ....AAAA
VA.—Norfolk
Roper Lumber Co.. John L.
(White Cedar; Boat) AAA

TIN

See also Sheets: Iron &
Steel; also Tinplate

CAL.—San Francisco
Selby Smelting & Lead
Co. (Bar; Pig)......AAA
COLO.—Denver
Colorado Fuel & Iron Co.
(Plate) ....AAAA
DEL.—Marshallton
Marshallton Iron & Steel Co.
(Plate) ....D
DEL.—Newport
Marshall Iron Co. (Plate) B
ILL.—Chicago
Warrington & King Perfor-
ating Co., 224 Union (Per-
forated) ....A
Raymond Lead Co., 51 W.
Lake (Pig) ....AAAA
Ryan & Co., J. J., 68 W.
Monroe C
IND.—Atlanta
Atlantic Rolling Mill & Tin
Plate Co. (Plate) C
KY.—Covington
Licking Rolling Mill Co.
(Plate, also Black Plate)
B
MD.—Cumberland
Cumberland Steel & Tin
Plate Co. (Bright Sheet)
AA
MASS.—Boston
Brown-Wales Co. ....A
Chadwick - Boston Lead
Works (Bright Sheet) AA
Merrimac Chem. Co. (Crys-
tals) ....AA
Waite-Ranlet & Co. ......B
MO.—St. Louis
Hiertz Metal Co. Theo.
(Bar) ....D
St. Louis Stamping Co.
(Bright; Sheet) ..AAAA
N. J.—Jersey City
Williams & Son E. A. (Bar)
AAA
N. Y.—Brooklyn
Tin Plate Derorating Co.
(Decorated) C
Wiarda & Co. John C.
(Teathered) ....AA
New York City
American Metal Co. 52
Bway. (Bar; Pig) ..AAA
Behr & Steiner, 81 Fulton
(Pig) ....A
Davol & Sons John, 100 John
(Bar; Pig) ....AA
Frankel, J., 81 Fulton (Pig)
B
Hendricks Bros., 49 Cliff
(Bar; Pig) ....AAAA
Lisberger & Co., B., 738 E.
14th (Bar; Pig).......B
Lissberger & Son, Mark, 397
W. 12th (Bar; Pig) ....B

TIN (Con.)

Mundt & Son, Chas., 441 Pearl (Perforated) ....B
Nassau Smelting & Refg. Co. (Bar) ....AAA
National Lead Co., 100 William (Pig) ....AAAA
Phelps, Dodge & Co., 99 John (Pig) ....AAAA
Rutter & Co., Arthur T., 256 Bway. ....F
French & Co., C. S., 81 Fulton (Pig). ....A
Vogelstein, L., 90 Wall (Pig) X
Vulcan Detinning Co., 157 Cedar (Pig) ....A

N. Y.—Niagara Falls

Archer Process Co. (Bichloride; Oxide) ....D

N. Y.—Syracuse

Empire Metal Co. (Phosphor) ....A
Syracuse Smelting Works (Pig) X

OHIO—Canton

Carnahan Tin Plate & Sheet Co. (Plate; Black Sheets for Tin Plate).........AA

OHIO—Cincinnati

American Galvanized & Tin Plate Co. (Roofing) ....E

OHIO—Cleveland

Bassett-Pressley Co. ....AA
Garry Iron & Steel Co. ...A
Grasselli Chem. Co. (Bichloride; Crystals) ....AAAA

OHIO—Lisbon

Beaver Tin Plate Co. (Br. American Tin Plate Co., N. Y. C.) (Roofing; Bright Sheet) ....AAAA

OHIO—Zanesville

Muskingum Valley Steel Co. (Plate) ....A

PA.—Canansburg

Canonsburg Iron & Steel Co. (Plate; Roofing; Bright Sheet) ....A
Standard Tin Plate Co. (Plate) ....B

PA.—Philadelphia

American Tin & Terne Plate Co. (Plate) ....A
Gummey, McFarland & Co. (Bright Sheet) ....A
McClure & Co., 115 N. 7th (Plate) ;...........AAA
Marshall Bros. & Co. (Roofing) ....AA
Merchant & Co. .....,....A
Taylor Co., N. & J. (Plate; Roofing; Bright Sheet) ....AAAA
Trotter & Co., Nathan, 36 N. Front (Pig) ....AA

PA.—Pittsburg

Alcania Co., Murtland Bldg. (Plate) ....B
American Sheet & Tin Plate Co. (Continuous Roofing Taggers) .AAAA
American Tin Plate Co., Carnegie Bldg. (Br. N. Y. C.) (Plate) ......AAAA C
Duquesne Co. (Bright Sheet) C
Ferguson Tin Plate Co. (Ltd.) (Terne Plates) ..D
Follansbee Bros. Co. (Plate) ....AA
Pope Tin Plate Co., 421 Wood (Plate) ....A

PA.—Washington

Griffiths Charcoal Iron Mills (Plate) ....B
Washington Charcoal Iron Tin Mills (Plate) ......A

PA.—Waynesburg

Griffiths Co., W. H. (Plate) ....A
Waynesburg Forge Sheet & Tin Mill (Plate) ......A

VA.—Richmond

Old Dominion Iron & Nail Works Co. (Plate; Roofing).................A

W. VA.—Clarksburg

Jackson Iron & Tin Plate Co. (Plate) X

W. VA.—Parkersburg

Parkersburg Iron & Steel Co. (Plate) ....AA

TIN (Con.)

W. VA.—Wheeling

Wheeling Corrugating Co. (Plate; Roofing; Bright Sheet) ....A

WIS.—Waukesha

Waukesha Sheet Steel Co. (Plate) C

TINCTURES

ILL.—Chicago

Baker & Co., Chas. S. C

IND.—Indianapolis

Lilly & Co., Eli ....AA

MD.—Baltimore

Sharpe & Dohme ......AAA
New York City
Fairchild Bros. & Foster AA
Keith & Co., B. ....F
McKesson & Robbins AAAA
Schieffelin & Co., W. H. AA

PA.—Philadelphia

Hance Bros. & White ..AA

TENN.—Nashville

Spurlock, Neal & Co. ....A

TINFOIL

See also Foil

ILL.—Chicago

Crooke Co., J. J. (Br. N. Y. C.), 88 ILL. ....AA
Hutchinson & Son, W. H., 196 Desplaines ....A

MASS.—Boston

Cabot, Edwin S., 83 Sudburg B
Rosenfeld Co., M. C., 16 Portland ....E

MO.—St. Louis

Johnston Tinfoil & Metal Co., 6016 S. Bway. .....A

N. Y.—Brooklyn

Witeman Bros., Walcott & Ferris ....A

N. Y.—Kingston

Republic Tinfoil & Bottle Cap Co. ....D
New York City
Budde & Westerman, 50 Vesey ....B
Conley Tin Foil Co., 539 W. 25th, ...AAA
Crooke Co., J. J., 155 Av. D. AA
Lehmaier. Schwartz & Co., 207 E. 22d.............AA

PA.—Philadelphia

Patent Metal Co., 609 N. 24th (for Tob. Confec.; Perfumery) ....AA

TINPLATE

See also Tin

DEL.—Newport

Marshall Iron Co. ....A

ILL.—Chicago

Sturgis & Burn Mfg. Co. (Harrison & Greene) ..A

KY.—Louisville

Todd-Donegan Iron Co., 817 W. Main ....A

MD.—Cumberland

Maryland Tinplate Co. .AA

MICH.—Detroit

Buhl Stamping Co. .....AA

MO.—St. Louis

Souther Iron Co., E. E. ..A

N. Y.—Brooklyn

Meurer Bros.. 569 Flushing Av. ....A

N. Y.—New York Ctiy

Dickerson. Van Dusen & Co.. 27 Cliff ....AA

OHIO—Canton

Carnahan Tinplate & Sheet Co. ....AA

OHIO—Cincinnati

Lawson Co., F. H., 440 Maine ....A

OHIO—Cleveland

Garry Iron & Steel Co. ..A

OHIO—Zanesville

Muskingum Valley Steel Co. A

PA.—Philadelphia

Hall & Carpenter, 518 Race AA

TINPLATE (Con.)
McClure & Co., 301 Forest .... AAA
Merchant & Co., 517 Arch .... AA
Taylor & Co., N. & G., Marine & Merchant Bldg .... AAA
PA.—Pittsburg
American Sheet & Tin Plate Co., Frick Bldg. ..AAAA
Dilworth, Porter & Co. ..A
Follansbee Bros. Co. ..AAA
Hellman & Son, J. H. ..A
Pope Tin Plate Co., 421 Wood ....A
PA.—Washington
Griffiths Charcoal Iron Mills .... A
PA.—Waynesburg
Griffiths Co., W. H. ....A
Waynesburg Forge Sheet & Tin Mlls ....A
VA.—Richmond
Old Dominion Iron & Nail Works Co. ....AA

TINS

See also Tinware

ILL.—Chicago
Acme Flexible Clasp Co., 17th & Clark (Bung; for Barrels) ....B
MICH—Lowell
Lowell Specialty Co. (Cake) .... F
N. Y.—Bath
Richardson Mfg. Co. (Cake) .... E
N. Y.—Brooklyn
Silver & Co., 304 Hewes (Egg) C
N. Y.—Buffalo
Shepard & Co., Sidney (Pie; Cake) ....AAAA
N. Y.—Rochester
Rochester Stamping Co. (Pie) ....AAA
PA.—Pittsburg
Forster, J. C., 101 Water (Cake; Cracker) ......F

TINWARE

CONN.—Meriden
Manning, Bowman & Co. .... AA
CONN.—Middletown
Smith Mfg. Co., J. O. (Stationers) X
ILL.—Chicago
Adams & Westlake Co. (Japanned) ....AAA
Norton Bros. (Inc.) (Japanned; Druggists') ....AAA
Sturgis & Burn Mfg. Co. (Pieced; Stamped) ....A
Wilson & Co., F. C. (Druggists'; Painters') ......B
ILL.—Peoria
Stuber & Kuck ....B
IND.—Indianapolis
Cooney & Geiger ....B
MAINE—Bangor
Wood & Bishop Co. ......A
MD.—Baltimore
Matthi. Ingram & Co. (Anti Rustling; Heavy; Japanned; Ornamented; Pieced; Stamped) ....F
MASS.—Boston
Gray & Sons, Peter, 88 Union C
MASS.—Holyoke
Holyoke Machine Co. (Decorated) ....AA
MO.—Kansas City
Gille Mfg. Co. ....A
MO.—St. Louis
Geisel Mfg. Co., A. ....A
Handlan-Buck Mfg. Co. (Railroad) ....AA
St. Louis Stamping Co. (Japanned) ....AAAA
Standard Stamping Co. .... AAA
N. Y.—Albany
Hoy & Co. (Japanned; Stamped) ....A
N. Y.—Brooklyn
Bliss Co., E. W. (Ornamental) ....AAAA

TINWARE (Con.)
Somers Bros. (Amer. Can Co.) (Ornamental) .... AAAA
Sweeney Mfg. Co., W. H., 66 Water ....B
Vogel & Bro., Wm. (Druggists) ....AA
Wallace Co., John, 400 So. 2d ....B
N. Y.—Buffalo
Shepard & Co., Sidney (Japanned; Pieced; Stamped; Druggists'; Grocers'; Spice Dealers') ....AAAA
N. Y.—Canandaigua
Lisk Mfg. Co. (Ltd.) .... AAA
N. Y.—Cattaraugus
Oakes & Burger (Cheese Factory; Creamery) ..B
New York City
Block, Jacob (Japanned; Stamped) ....D
Central Stamping Co., 24 Cliff (Stamped) ....AA
H. & H. Mfg. Co., 554 W. 25th (Nickel Silver Cooking) ....A
Haberman Mfg. Co. (Japanned; Stamped) X
Iron Clad Mfg. Co. (Japanned) ....AAA
Lalance & Grosjean Mfg. Co., 19 Cliff (Japanned) .... AAAA
Morgan & Cornell (Grocers) X
National Enamelling & Stamping Co. ....AAAA
Reilley Bros. (Shop; Painters') ....D
Schlesinger & Co., Leo, 372 South ....A
Sternan & Co., S., 204 Churc (Cooking; Etc.) .... A
Stoutenborough, X (Anti-Rusting; Grocers') .....D
N. Y.—Syracuse
Fisk, C. H. C
N. Y.—Troy
Troy Stamping Works (Japanned; Ornamented; Stamped) ....AAAA
OHIO—Cincinnati
Cincinnati Stamping Co. (Stamped; Japanned) ..B
Cincinnati Tin & Japan Co. .... B
OHIO—Cleveland
Hunt Stamping Works, H. B. (Amer. Can Co., N. Y. C.) ....AAAA
Osborn Mfg. Co. (Pieced; Stamped) ....A
PA.—Allegheny
Wall Mfg. Supply Co., P. .... B
PA.—Parsons
Trethaway Bros. .... A
PA.—Philadelphia
Ellis & Sons Co., Geo. D. (Curriers') C
Haslet, Flanagan & Co. 16k 2d (Japanned) ....B
Hilley & McAleer, Grand & 5th ....A
PA.—Wilkesbarre
Bertel's Son & Co., W. B. .... A
R. I.—Providence
Hill Mfg. Co., Jas. ....B
TENN.—Memphis
Wetter Mfg. Co. (Japanned; Pieced; Stamped) ....AA
TENN.—Nashville
Phillips & Buttorf Mfg. Co. .... AAA
WIS.—Milwaukee
Kieckhefer Bros. Co. (Br. Nat'l Enamel & Stamp Co., N. Y. C.) ....AAAA

TIPPERS

See Machy: Laundry

TIPPLES

ILL.—Chicago
Allis-Chalmers Co., Home Ins. Bldg. (Mine) AAAA

TIPPLES (Con.)

MINN.—Minneapolis
Minneapolis Steel & Mchry.
Co. (Mine) ....A

OHIO—Akron
Webster, Camp & Lane
Mach. Co. (Mine; Steel)
................A

OHIO—Cleveland
Brown Hoisting Machry Co.
(Coal) ....AAAA
Garry Iron & Steel Co.
(Coal) ....A

OHIO—Columbus
Jeffrey Mfg. Co. (Coal)
................AA

OHIO—Nelsonville
Nelsonville Foundry & Ma-
chine Co. (Mine; Steel)
................B

PA.—Claysville
South Pittsburg Iron Wrks.
(Coal) ....B

PA.—Monongahela
Monongahela Mfg. Co.
(Mine; Steel; Wood)..C

PA.—Pittsburg
Heyl & Patterson (Coal;
Mine; Steel) ....A
Scaife & Sons Co., Wm. B.
(Coal; Mine; Steel) AAA

PA.—Shamokin
Mullen & Son, John (Coal
(Mine) ....A

W. VA.—Fairmont
Helmick Foundry Machine
Co. (Mine) ....D

WIS.—Cudahy
Power & Mining Mchy. Co.
(Mine) ....AAA

TIPS

See also Hardware; Carriage

CONN.—Bridgeport
Canfield, H. O. (Rubber)
................B
Gaynor & Mitchell Mfg. Co.
(Acorn) C

CONN.—Middletown
Rogers & Hubbard Co.
(Syringe) ....A

CONN.—Mount Carmel
Woodruff & Sons, Walter
W. (Shaft; Hame; Neck
Yoke; Pole; Whiffletree)
................A

CONN.—New Haven
Cowles & Co., C. (Shaft;
Neck Yoke) ....A

ILL.—Chicago
Morgan & Wright (Inc.), 333
W. Lake (Rubber for
Chairs; Canes; Crutches;
Etc.) ....AA
Spinks & Co., Wm. A., 3
N. Clark (Billiard Cue)
................C

IND.—Elkhart
Buescher Mfg. Co. (Shaft)
................X

IND.—Indianapolis
Automatic Crip Neck Yoke
Co. (Shaft; Neck Yoke)
................B

MAINE—Portland
Cox & Son, A. F. (Shoe)
................F

MASS.—Andover
Tyer Rubber Co. (Rubber
Chair; Crutch) ......AA

MASS.—Boston
Amer. Shoe Tip Co. (Shoe)
................B
Bailey & Co., C. J. (Crutch)
................A
Chase & Co., L. C. (Horse;
Ear) ....AAA
Elastic Tip Co. (Chair;
Crutch; Screw) ......B

MASS.—Lynn
Cochey, Joseph H. (Shoe)
................D
Houghton & Sons, Jas.
(Shoe) X

MICH.—Detroit
Schulenburg Mfg. Co. (Cue)
................C

N. J.—Newark
Dawson & Co., I. W. (Shoe)
................X
Searles Mfg. Co. (Shaft) B
Smith Co., Hugh (Inc.)

TIPS (Con.)

(Shoe) ....A

N. Y.—Binghampton
Crandal, Stone & Co.
(Shaft) ....A

N. Y.—Buffalo
Pratt & Letchworth (Neck
Yoke) ....AAA

N. Y.—Dobbs Ferry
Clough, Theo. (Gas Burner)
................D

New York City
Grote & Co., F. (Cue) ..D
Kelsey, Albert (Horse;
Ear) ....B
Kirchberger & Co., M., 50
Warren (Imptrs-Lava Gas
Burner) C
Marks, A. A., 70 B'way
(Rubber; Chair; Crutch)
................AA
Metal Stamping Co. (Shaft)
................A
New York Belting & Pack-
ing Co. (Rubber; Chair;
Crutch) ....AAA
Parker, Stearns & Sutton
(Pencil) ....B
Rubber Goods Mfg. Co., 253
B'way (Rubber Chair;
Crutch) ....AAAA
Smith, Worthington & Co.
(Horse; Ear) ....B
Thurnauer & Bro., G. M.,
35 Park Place (Imptrs.
Lava Gas Burner) X

OHIO—Akron
Goodrich Co., B. F.
(Crutch) ....AAAA

OHIO—Cleveland
Cleveland Hardware Co.
(Shaft) ....AA

TENN.—Chattanooga
State Line Mfg. Co. (Lava
Gas Burner) C
Steward Mfg. Co., D. M.
(Lava Gas Burner) ....B

WIS.—Racine
Racine General Mfg. Co.
(Shaft) ....E
Racine Malleable &
Wrought Iron Co. (Shaft)
................A

TIRES

See also Hardware; Carriage

CONN.—Hartford
Hartford Rubber Wrks. Co.
(Pneumatic; Carriage;
Rubber) ....AAAA

ILL.—Chicago
Bunker Saddle Co. (Car-
riage; Pneumatic) .....F
Illinois Steel Co., The Rook-
ery) (Steel) ......AAAA
Morgan & Wright (Pneu-
matic) ....AA
Republic Iron & Steel Co.
Half Oval Steel) ..AAAA

IND.—Indianapolis
G. & J. Tire Co. (Pneumat-
ic) ....B
Indianapolis Rubber Co.
(Pneumatic) ....A

MASS.—Boston
Bailey & Co., C. J. (Bicy-
cle) ....B
Boston Belting Co. (Bicycle;
Carriage; Rubber)
................AAAA
Boston Woven Hose & Rub-
ber Co. (Bicycle) ..AAAA

MICH.—Three Rivers
Sheffield Car Co. (Steel)
................AA

N. J.—Trenton
Crescent Belting & Packing
Co. (Bicycle) ....A
Empire Rubber Mfg. Co.
(Bicycle) ....AA
Home Rubber Co. (Bicycle)
................AA
Stokes Rubber Co., Joseph
Pneumatic) C
Trenton Rubber Co. (Bicy-
cle) ....A

N. Y.—Batavia
Sweet Tire & Rubber Co.
(Pneumatic) C

New York City
Hodgman Rubber Co. (Bicy-
cle) ....AA
New York Belting & Pack-

TIRES (con.)

ing Co. (Bycicle) ..AAA
Prosser & Co., Thos., 15
Gold (Steel) ....A
N. Y.—Watertown
Union Carriage & Gear Co.
(Carriage; Pneumatic)
.......................B
OHIO—Akron
Diamond Rubber Co. (Pneu-
matic; Carriage; Rubber)
.....................AAAA
Goodrich Co., B. F. (Akron
Rubber Wrks.) (Pneumat-
ic; Bicycle; Carriage;
Rubber) ....AAAA
Goodyear Tire & Rubber Co.
(Pneumatic; Carriage;
Rubber) ....B
Whitman & Barnes Mfg. Co.
(Bicycle; Carriage; Rub-
ber) ....AAAA
OHIO—Cincinnati
Mowry Car Wheel Wrks.,
2401 Eastern Av. (Steel;
Steel Car Wheel) ......B
OHIO—Dayton
Meeker Mfg. Co. (Carriage
Rubber; Carriage Pneu-
matic) ....D
OHIO—Springfield
Victor Rubber Tire Co.
(Carriage; Rubber) ....B
PA.—Burnham
Logan Iron & Steel Co.
(Carriage; Wagon) .... B
PA.—Chester
Chester Steel Castings Co.
(Steel) ....AA
PA.—Philadelphia
Latrobe Steel Co. (Car; Lo-
comotive Steel) ...AAAA
Midvale Steel Co. (Car;
Locomotive; Steel) AAAA
Standard Steel Wrks., 1502
Market (Car; Locomotive
Steel) ....AAAA
PA.—Pittsburg
Amer. Steel Hoop Co., Car-
negie Bldg. (Steel) X
Crucible Steel Co. of Amer-
ica, Frick Bldg. (Steel)
.....................AAAA

TISSUE

See Paper

TOASTERS

ILL.—Rockford
Clark Hardware Co., J. L.
.......................D
MASS.—Worcester
National Mfg. Co. (Wire
Bread) ....A
Parker Wire Goods Co.
.......................E
N. J.—Newark
Williamson Wire Novelty
Co. ....B
N. Y.—Brooklyn
New York Stamping Co.
(Chafing Wood) ....A
N. Y.—Buffalo
Western Wire Goods Co...D
N. Y.—Rochester
Streeter & Co., N. R.
(Wire) ....A
OHIO—Cleveland
Dangler Stove Mfg. Co.
.....................AAAA
Schneider & Trenkamp
.....................AAAA
OHIO—Toledo
Ohio Steam Cooker Co.
(Wire) ....E

TOBACCO

ARIZ.—Tucson
Steinfield, A. (Smoking)
.....................AAA
ILL.—Chicago
Heegaard & Co., W. H.,
Lake & State ....B
Spaulding & Merrick, 9
Rush ....AAAA
KY.—Georgetown
Stone-Kinzea..... ......A
KY.—Greenville
Martin & Co., H. N.
(Plug) ....A

TOBACCO (con.)

KY.—Henderson
Robards Tobacco Co. (Plug)
.......................A
KY.—Louisville
Amer. Tobacco Co. ..AAAA
Currie Tobacco Co. (Smok-
ing) ....A
Finzer & Bros., J. (Inc.)
.....................AAAA
Martin & Co., H. N. ....A
Mathews & Sons, W. S.
.....................AAA
Nat'l Tobacco Wrks.
.....................AAAA
Strater Bros. Tobacco Co.
(Inc.) ....AA
KY.—Paducah
Smith & Scott ....A
KY.—Princeton
Orr & Co., J. G. ....B
MD.—Baltimore
Gail, G. W. & A. (Br.
Am. Tob. Co.) E Barre
.....................AAAA
Marburg Bros. (Br. Am.
Tob. Co.) 423 S. Charles
.....................AAAA
Neudicker, L. H., 701 E.
Lombard ....A
Vorke, Class & Co., 218 So.
Charles ....A
MASS.—Boston
Kaffenbaugh & Son, I., 40
Broad ....A
McGreenery & Manning, 24
Fulton ....A
Scott & Co., L. W., 133
Broad ....A
MICH.—Detroit
Bagleg & Co., J. J., 48
Bates ....AA
Banner Cigar Mfg. Co. ..B
Globe Tobacco Co., 25 Fort
E. ....A
Kuttnauer Co., L. ......B
Moebs & Co., W. D., 92
Woodward Av. ....A
Peters & Co., L. ......AA
Rothschild & Bro. ...AAA
Scotten-Dillion Co., Fort W
& Campan ....AAAA
Woodouse & Co., J. T. ..B
MINN.—Minneapolis
Winecke & Doerr, 27 Wash.
Av. S. ....AA
MO.—Boonville
Gott & Son, J. M....B
MO.—Carrollton
Martin & Rea ....AA
MO.—Kansas City
Lederman, I. W. ....B
Switzer Cigar Co., H., 603
Main ....A
MO.—Louisiana
Addison-Tinsley Tobacco Co.
.......................B
MO.—St. Louis
Amer. Tobacco Co., 1224
Chestnut ....AAAA
Continental Tobacco Co.
.....................AAAA
Peper, Chas., 721 N. Main
.....................AAA
Weisent Bros. Tobacco Co.,
1314 Merchant ....A
Weisent Tobacco Co., 120
So. Main ....A
N. J.—Caldwell
Lane & Lockward ......A
N. J.—Jersey City
Lorillard Co., P., 111 1st
.....................AAAA
N. Y.—New Brunswick
Parsons, J. M. ....B
N. J.—Trenton
Bowers Snuff & Tobacco Co.
.......................B
Grumbacher, J. ....B
N. Y.—Albany
Levy & Bro., I. ....B
Shilds, F. ....AA
Van Slyke & Horton ....A
N. Y.—Baldwinsville
Upson, J. W. ....B
N. Y.—Binghamton
Hummell & Co. ....A
N. Y.—Brooklyn
Berbert, H., 267 Bushwick
Av. ....B
N. Y.—Buffalo
Wagner & Son, Matt. ....B

1083

TOBACCO (Con.)

PA.—Schoeneck
Weist, S. S. ....B
PA.—Scranton
Clark & Snover Co. .....AA
PA.—Womelsdorf
Fidler & Co., H. F. ......B
PA.—York
Frysinger, C. ....B
Myers, Adams & Co. ....A
Stollman, C. H. ....B
S. C.—Charlston
Follin Bros. ....B
TENN.—Bristol
Reynolds Tobacco Co.
  (Plug; Smoking) ......A
TENN.—Buchanan
Gatlin, Z. T. ....B
TENN.—Chatanooga
Kelly, J. W. ....A
Peeples & Pitner Bros. ..B
Trotter Bros ....A
TENN.—Clarksville
Meriwether Snuff & Tobacco
  Co. (Plug; Smoking) ..A
Morrow & Bro., C. E. ....B
Wood & Smith ....B
TENN.—Greensville
Greenville Tobacco Mfg. Co.
  (Plug; Smoking) ....AA
TENN.—New Providence
Gold & Peters ....B
TENN.—Paris
Porter, Hudson & Co. ....A
TENN.—Springfield
Bell & Sons, C. C. ......B
TENN.—Willard
Williard Tobacco Co. ....B
TEXAS—Dallas
Philipson, L. ....B
TEXAS—El Paso
Kohlberg Bros. ....B
VT.—Burlington
Reed & Co., J. G. ......B
Taylor & Co., O. C. .....B
VA.—Bedford City
Clark & Co. ....B
VA.—Brosville
Burton & Bro., J. W. ....B
VA.—Chatham
Riddle & Hargrave ......A
VA.—Danville
American Tobacco Co.
  ....AAAA
Arnett & Overing Co. ...A
Barton & Co., F. X. ....AA
Carlton & Co., E. S. ...B
Coles & Co., R. J. ...B
Dibbelb Bros. ....B
Dixon & Co. ....B
Henderson & Co., J. A.
  (Smoking) ....B
Hickey, C. H. ....B
Hickey & Cousins ....B
Hubbard & Co., R. M. ..B
Hughes, J. E. Jr. & Co. ..B
Jordan & Co., M. P. ....B
Mosely & Co., E. G. .....B
Pemberton & Penn ......AA
Penn, Sons & Co., G. ...B
Penn & Ryan ....B
Schoolfield & Watson
  (Plug) ....A
Schoolfield, Boatwright &
  Co. ....A
Swain & Wyllie ....A
Taylor, Spencer & Co. ...A
Watson & Co., W. D. ...A
Wemple, Ellerson & Co. ..A
Wemple & Co. ....A
Wyllie & Co., J. W. ....A
VA.—Farmville
Dunnington, W. G. .....A
Gilliam & Co., W. P. ..A
Paulett & Son ....B
VA.—Leatherwood
Granely & Sons, B. F. ..A
VA.—Lynchburg
Adams, Chambers & Co. ..B
Bowman & Co., N. R. ..AA
Carroll, J. W. ....A
De Witt, C. ....B
Ford & Co., W. A. .....A
Gilliam & Co., W. P. ....A
Hancock Bros. & Co. ....A
Hancock, Moorman Tobacco
  Co. ....B
Katz, Jr., J. ....B
Stallings, Hancock & Co.
  ....B
West & Co., J. W. ......A
West Tobacco Co., Winfree
  ....B

TOBACCO (Con.)

VA.—Petersburg
Bland Tobacco Co. ......B
Cameron & Bro., W. ..AAA
Dunlap, D. ....AAAA
Roper & Son, L. ....AA
Venable Tobacco Co., S. W.
  ....AA
Watson & McGill ....AA
VA.—Richmond
Cameron & Co., Alex ..AAA
Cameron & Cameron ..AAA
Cullingworth, Joseph N. ..A
Hancock, W. T. ....A
Larus & Bro. ....B
Mayo & Bro., P. H.
  ....AAAA
Pace Tobacco Co., J. B. ..A
Patterson Tobacco Co., R.
  A. ....A
Spicer, Son & Co. ....A
Williams Co., T. C. ....AAA
Yarbrough & Sons, W. J.
  ....B
VA.—South Boston
Edmonson, Son & Co. ....B
Sheperd & Noblin Tobacco
  Co. ....B
VA.—Spencer
Spencer & Son, D. H. ..A
WASH.—Seattle
Levy & Co., M. ....B
Schwabacher Bros. & Co.
  (Inc.) ....AA
WASH.—Spokane
Grinsfelder & Co., W. S.
  ....B
W. VA.—Wheeling
Bloch Bros. Tobacco Co.
  ....AAAA
West Va. Tobacco Co. ..B
WIS.—Edgerton
Child, H. W. ....A
WIS.—Evansville
Brand & Co., J. ......AAA
Rumrill. G. H. ....A
WIS.—Janesville
Carle & Son, L. B. ....A
Green, M. F. ....A
Rumrill, G. H. ....A
WIS.—Milwaukee
Adams Tobacco Co., 90 W.
  Water ....AA
Leidersdorf & Co., B. ....A

TOBOGGANS

MAINE South Paris
Paris Mfg. Co. ....A
N. Y.—Canton
Rushton, J. H. ....F
VT.—Burlington
Champlain Mfg. Co. ....B
WIS.—Milwaukee
Meinecke & Son, A. ....AA

TOKENS

N. Y.—New York City
Amer. Railway Supply Co.,
  24 Park Place ....B

TOMATOES

See Canned Goods

TOLANITE

PA.—Philadelphia
Philadelphia Clay Mfg. Co.
  ....B

TOMAHAWKS

PA.—Glassport
American Axe & Tool Co.
  ....AAAA

TONGS

CAL.—San Francisco
Doble Co.. Abner, 200 Tre-
  mont (Rail) ....B
CONN.—Branchville
Branchville Ice Tool Wks.
  (Ice) ....F
CONN.—Bridgeport
Knapp & Cowles Mfg. Co.
  (Ice) C
CONN.—Hartford
Billings & Spencer Co. (Car-
  bon; Pipe) ....A

TONGS (Con.)

CONN.—Meriden
Bradley & Hubbard Mfg. Co. (Coal) ......AAAA
CONN.—New Haven
Barnes Tool Co. (Pipe) ....A
Kilborn & Bishop Co. (Pipe) C
CONN.—Shelton
Clark & Co., D. N. (Sugar) C
CONN.—Southington
Peck, Stow & Wilcox Co. (Coal; Roofing Shutter) AAAA
ILL.—Chicago
Crane & Co., 10 N. Jefferson (Pipe) ......AAAA
Illinois Malleable Iron Co., 30 Monroe (Pipe) .. .. AAAA
Nicol & Co. (Fishing; Handling) ....D
Pratt Mfg. Co., Wm. E., 91 Lake (Hog) .... B
Solid Steel Tool Co., 11 So. Jefferson (Blacksmiths'; Girder; Ice; Rail; Rivet) E
Union Drop Forge Co., 66 E. Ohio (Pipe; Parts only; Rail) ....A
Vaughn & Bushnell Mfg. Co., 875 Carroll Av. (Blacksmiths'; Ice) . .B
ILL.—Downer's Grove
Dicke Tool Co. (Bent; Crucible; Machinists'; Straight Lip) C
ILL.—Evanston
Mark Mfg. Co. (Blacksmiths') ....B
ILL.—Harvey
Whiting Foundry Equipment (Crucible) ....AA
IND.—Evansville
Evansville Tool Wrks. (Blacksmiths'; Rail) ..A
IND.—Indianapolis
Atkins & Co., E. C. (Brazing) ....AAA
IOWA—Fairfield
Louden Machinery Co. (Ice) D
MAINE—Clinton
Spaulding & Davis (Clothes) F
MASS.—Arlington
Wood & Co., Wm. T. (Ice) A
MASS.—Boston
Harvey, H. H., 608 Atlantic Av. (Pipe; Rail; Stone) ....B
Knapp, Jas. M., 12 Bowker (Pipe) ....E
Walworth Mfg. Co. (Pipe) AAAA
MASS.—Lowell
Woods, Sherwood & Co. (Candy) C
MASS.—Roxbury
Tremont Mfg. Co. (Pipe) D
MASS.—Winthrop
Winthrop Wire Goods Co. (Olive) X
MICH.—Detroit
Anderson & Sons, W. H. (Blacksmiths'; Coal; Crucible; Foundry; Log Skidding; Rail; Pipe) C
Byram & Co., 435 Guion (Crucible; Rail) ......D
Northern Engineering Works (Crucible) .... A
MICH.—Kalkaska
Freeman Mfg. Co. (Fish) B
MICH.—Saginaw
Morley Bros. (Skidding) AA
MINN.—Minneapolis
Howell & Co., R. R. (Chain) ....B
N. J.—Newark
Atha Tool Co. (Blacksmiths'; Rail) ....A
Heller Bros. Co. (Blacksmiths') ....AA
Johnson, Wm. (Curling) ..D
Osborne & Co., C. S., 96 Mechanic (Pipe; Curling) B
N. Y.—Albany
Troy Nickel Wrks. (Stove;

TONGS (Con.)

Coal) C
N. Y.—Brooklyn
Brass Goods Mfg. Co., 92 3d (Candy) ....B
Hay-Budden Mfg. Co. (Blacksmiths; Ice) ....B
Williams & Co., J. H. (Pipe) ....AAAA
N. Y.—Buffalo
Case & Son, W. A., 31 Main (Pipe) ....A
Niagara Machine & Tool Wks. (Roofing) ....A
West Mfg. Co., 374 7th (Roofing) ....D
White, L. & I. J. (Ice)..A
N. Y.—Groton
Morton, D. B. (Ice) C
New York City
Ashcroft Mfg. Co., 87 Liberty (Pipe) ....A
Graf, Frank H., 322 7th Av. (Fireplace) ......D
Lalance & Grosjean Mfg. Co. (Coal) ....AAAA
Peck, Stow & Wilcox Co., 27 Murray (Coal) AAAA
Russell & Erwin Mfg. Co., 43 Chambers (Coal) AAAA
Sargent & Co., 151 Leonard (Blacksmiths' Coal) .... AAAA
N. Y.—Syracuse
Stearns & Co., E. C. (Blacksmiths) ...... AA
N. Y.—Yonkers
Saunders' Sons, D. (Pipe) A
N. C.—Wilmington
Whitlock, Chas. M. (Logging) ....E
OHIO—Cincinnati
Cincinnati Tool Co. (Coal) .. X
Haven & Co., Jas. L. (Coal) B
Keene & Co., Geo. C., 502 E. Front (Roofing) ....F
Morris Fdy. Co., Jno. B. (Fire Place) ....A
Obermayer Co., S., 647 Evans (Crucible) ......A
OHIO—Cleveland
Federal Mfg. Co., Amer. Trust Bldg. (Ice) AAAA
Fanner Mfg. Co. (Coal; Ice) ....A
Garry Iron & Steel Co. (Pipe Hanger; Roofing) A
Gerlach Co., Peter (Skidding) ....B
Smith Foundry Supply Co., J. D., 40 S. Water (Crucible) ....D
OHIO—Toledo
Stevens. Banj. A. (Ice) A
PA.—Erie
Hollands Mfg. Co. (Pipe) C
Jarecki Mfg. Co. (Pipe) AAAA
PA.—Philadelphia
Berger Bros. Co., 231 Arch (Pipe Hanger) ....A
Plumb, Fayette R. (Inc.) Frankford (Blacksmiths) AA
Stortz & Son, Jno., 210 Vine (Ice; Pipe; Roofing) F
PA.—Pittsburg
Hubbard & Co., Murtland Bldg. (Rail) ....A
Iron City Tool Wks. (Rail) B
Oliver Iron & Steel Co. (Rail) ....AAAA
Pittsburg Tool & Drop Forge Co., Arrott Bldg. (Cross Tie; Rail) ....E
PA.—Reading
Reading Hardware Co. (Coal) ....AAAA
PA.—Verona
Verona Tool Wks. (Rail) A
PA.—Wilkesbarre
Nicholson & Co., W. H. (Chain) C
PA.—Williamsport
Darling Pump & Mfg. Co. (Pipe) ....B
VT.—Barre
Trow & Holden (Granite

TONGS (Con.)
W. VA.—Wheeling
Wheeling Hinge Co. (Coal)
AA
WIS.—Oshkosh
Oshkosh Logging Tool Co.
(Joist or Timber, for
Hoisting Timber, Etc., in-
to High Buildings) C

TONGUES

MAINE—Portland
Cox & Son, A. F. (Shoe) A
MASS.—Boston
Windram & Son, W. J.
(Shoe) .... B
MASS.—Lynn
Houghton & Sons, Jas.
(Shoe) X
N. J.—Newark
Brooklyn Gas Fixture Co.
(Buckle) .... H
N. J.—Palmyra
Palmyra Tongue Co. (Shoe)
C
R. I.—Pawtucket
Cobb & Co., W. R. (Pin) B
Fuller & Son., Geo. H.
(Pin) .... A
R. I.—Providence
Wall & Co., A. T. (Pin) C

TOOLS

See also Mills; Machy; also
look for Specific Name of
Tool Desired.

ALA.—Mobile
Barney-Cavanagh Hdw. Co.
(Turpentine) .... A
CONN.—Bethel
Gilbert Bros. (Hatters) E
CONN.—Branchville
Gruman, Geo. B. (Ice) ..F
CONN.—Bridgeport
Bridgeport Gun Implement
Co. (Gun Cleaning; Re-
loading) .... A
Knapp & Cowles Mfg. Co.
(Ice; Garden; Floral) C
CONN.—Collinsville
Collins Co. (Coopers';
Miners') ....AAAA
CONN.—Danbury
Reid, Chas. H. (Hatters')
B
CONN.—Georgetown
Gilbert & Bennett Mfg. Co.
(Barbed Wire Fence), AA
CONN.—Hamden
Hamden Mfg. Co. (Wood
Boring) C
CONN.—Hartford
Billings & Spencer (Lathe;
Thread Cutting Calkers';
Cutting-Off; Machinist'
Jewelers'; Toolmakers') A
Dwight Slate Machine Co.
(Lathe; Lathe Cut-Off;
Machine) C
Pratt & Whitney Co. (Mill-
ing Machine; Planer;
Screw Machine; Thread
Cutting; Cutting-Off;
Lathe; Machinists'; Brass-
working) ....AAAA
Tucker, W. W. & C. F.,
302 Asylum (Thread Cut-
ting) .... F
CONN.,Meriden
Meriden Machine Tool Co.
(Lathe; Forming Lathe)
D
Parker Bros. (Gun Cleaning;
Reloading) ...... AAAA
CONN.—Middleton
Wilcox Crittenden & Co.,
(Calking) .... A
CONN.—Milldale
Ellis & Son, F. L. (Special)
F
CONN.—New Britain
Bennett Tempering Co.
(Hand Forged Lathe;
Hand Forged Planer) ..E
Landers, Frary & Clark
Ice) ....AAA
Skinner Chuck Co. (Cutting-
Off) .... B
CONN.—New Haven
Barnes Tool Co. (Plumbers')
B

TOOLS (Con.)
Belden Machine Co.
(Slaters') .... D
Ideal Mfg. Co. (Reloading)
C
Kilkorn & Bishop Co. (Saw)
A
Martin Fire Arms Co. (Re-
loading) .... A
New Haven Mfg. Co. (Ma-
chinists') .... AA
Schollhorn Co., Wm.
(Cigarmakers') ..... B
Spargo, Edward, 68 Com-
merce (Granite; Stone-
cutters) .... F
Winchester Repeating Arms
Co. (Reloading) ..AAAA
CONN.—Pine Meadow
Chapin-Stephens Co. (Coop-
ers'; Carriagemakers) A
CONN.—Plainville
Clark & Son, A. N.
(Watch) C
Norton & Jones Mach.
Tool Wks. (Machine) F
CONN.—Saugatuck
Doscher Plane & Tool Co.
(Plasters' Floats; Darbys;
Plumb Rules & Mortar
Hocks) ....E
CONN.—Seymour
Swan Co., James (Coopers')
A
CONN.—Southington
Peck, Stow & Wilcox Co.
(Boring; Slaters' Pavers';
Garden; Tinroofing Tin-
smiths') .... AAAA
CONN.—South Norwalk
Wheeler, W. A. (Hatters')
F
CONN.—Torrington
Hendey Machine Co.
(Planer; Machine) ....A
Union Hdw. Co. (Gun
Cleaning; Reloading) ..A
CONN.—Waterbury
Blake & Johnson (Brass
Working) .... A
Manville Machine Co., E.
J. (Brass Working) ..C
Waterbury Brass Co. (Re-
loading .... AAAA
CONN.—Westport
Bradley's Sons, C. W.
(Turpentine) .... D
CONN.—Westville
Geometric Drill Co. (P. O.
New Haven) (Adjustable
Hollow Milling Machine;
Special; Geometric Bor-
ing; Turning; Thread
Cutting) C
DEL.—Wilmington
Betts' Machine Co. (Ma-
chine; Machinists') ....A
Hilles & Jones (Boiler-
makers'; Bridge Build-
ers'; Machine) ......AA
Slocomb & Co., F. F.
(Pneumatic Punches;
Riveters') C
GA.—Lithonia
Southern Granite Co.
(Granite; Stonecutters')
A
ILL.—Alton
Beall Bros. (Miners') ....A
ILL.—Aurora
Amer. Well Wks. (Artesian
Well; Oil Well) ....AA
Aurora Auto. Machinery Co.
(Pneumatic) .... A
ILL.—Batavia
U. S. Wind Engine &
Pump Co. (Hay) ......A
ILL.—Cairo
Reed, Joseph B. (Ma-
chinists') .... B
ILL.—Carpentersville
Illinois Iron & Bolt Co.
(Blacksmiths') ......AA
ILL.—Chicago
Armstrong Bros. Tool Co.,
617 Austin Av. (Boring;
Lathe; Planer; Thread
Cutting; Slotting; Gang;
Shaper) C
Austin Mfg. Co., Manhat-
tan Bldg. (Contractors')
AAA
Barbee Wire & Iron Wks.
(Ice) ....B

TOOLS (*Con.*)

Carpenter & Co., Geo. B., 202 S. Water (Contractors') ....AA

Channon Co., H., Market &Randolph (Contractors') ....AA

Chicago Pneumatic Tool Co., Fisher Bldg. (Pneumatic Granite; Stoncutters; Pneumatic Stone Carving; Pneumatic Stone Dressing) .... AAAA

Chicago Scale Co. (Blacksmith) ....A

Chicago Wheel & Mfg. Co., 39 Randolph (Diamond Pointed) ....\.A

Clow & Sons (Inc.), James B. (Boilermakers) ....A

Contractors' Supply & Equipment Co., 232 5th Av. (Contractors) C

Crane Co. (Thread Cutting Lathe) .... AAAA

Crosby & Co., G. A. (Tinsmiths') X

Eureka Digger Co. (Drainage) ....F

Fairbanks, Morse & Co., Franklin & Monroe (Railroad Track) ......AAAA

Hardinge Bros., 1036 Lincohn Av. (Watchmakers' Jewelers') .... B

Henion & Hubbell, 63 N. Jeffn. (Contractors').. B

Hiles & Co., C. H., 336 Carroll Av. (Ice) ..... D

Janeville Hay Rake Co., Ashland Blk. (Haying) E

Klein & Son, Mathias, 87 W. Van Buren (Linemen's) .... A

Lyman, W. C., 49 Michigan (Paving) ....D

McCrea & Co., James, 67 W. Washn. (Boring).. F

McDonnell Odometer Co. (Special) X

Macomber & Whyte Rope Co., 19 S. Canal (Contractors') .... A

Monighan's Machine Wks., 813-823 Carrol Av. (Contractors'; Hoisting Engines) C

Olmsted & Co. (Artesian Well) .... A

Orr & Lockett Hdw. Co., 71 Randolph (Paving) ..A

Parkhurst & Wilkinson Co., 143 Kinzie (Contractors') ....AA

Railway Appliance Co., Old Colony Bldg. (Peumatic) ....A

Shaw, Willis, 506 N. Y. Life Bldg. (Contractors') ....D

Solid Steel Tool Co., 11 S. Jeffn. (Railroad Track) ....F

Steel Roll Mangle Co., 142 Washn. Boulv. (Pneumatic) ....E

Union Drop Forge Co., 66 E. Ohio (Railroad Track) ....A

Vaughn & Bushnell Mfg. Co., 877 Carroll Av. (Coopers'; Farriers'; Blacksmiths'; Tinsmiths'; Ice) ....B

Vulcan Iron Wks., 63 Milwaukee Av. (Contractors') ....AA

Watson Co., Geo. E., 38 Randolph (Paperhangers') ....B

Western Electric Co. (Telegraph Construction) AAAA

ILL.—Decatur

Fairies Mfg. Co. (Gun Cleaning) .... A

Mueller .Mfg. Co., H., (Plumbers'; Tinners')..A

ILL.—Downer's Grove

Dicke Tool Co. (Linemen's; Cabinetmakers'; Lathe; Machinists'; Thread Cutting; Tack Pointing; Telegraph Construction; Wire) C

TOOLS (*Con.*)

ILL.—Elgin

Moseley Lathe Co. (Watchmakers') ....D

ILL.—Evanston

Sheldon & Co., E. H. (Cement Sidewalk) ....D

ILL.—Freeport

Stover Mfg. Co. (Ice).. A

ILL.—Harvard

Hunt, Helm, Ferris Co. (Haying) .... B

ILL.—Harvey

Austin Mfg. Co., F. C. (Artesian Well; Oil Well) ....AA

Whiting Fdry. Equipment Co. (Moulders') ......AA

ILL.—Moline

Deere & Mansur Co. (Hand Farming; Garden) ..AA

ILL.—Ottawa

Porter Co., J. E. (Haying) ....A

ILL.—Peoria

Diamond Meter Co. (Meter Sealing) C

Herchel Mfg. Co., R. (Haying) .... A

ILL.—Quincy

Quincy Valve & Mfg. Co. (Valve Refacing Machine) ....E

ILL.—Rockford

Barnes Co., W. F. & John (Machine) .... AA

ILL.—Sterling

Keystone Mfg. Co. (Hay) ....AA

ILL.—Streator

Iwan Bros. (Drainage; Miners') ....D

ILL.—Waterloo

Oldendorph, Jacob (Blacksmiths') ....E

IND.—Anderson

Globe Mfg. Co. (Coopers') F

IND.—Cambridge City

Bertsch & Co. (Tinsmiths') ....D

IND.—Columbus

Reeves & Co. (Inc.) (Lumbering) ....AA

IND.—Elkhart

Elkart Frog & Crossing Wks. (Railroad Track) C

IND.—Evansville

Evansville Tool Wks. (Coopers'; Farriers'; Pitching; Rock Drill Sharpening; Turpentine) ....A

IND.—Indianapolis

Atkins & Co., E. C. (Coopers'; Circular Saw Lumbering) .... AAA

Barry Saw & Supply Co., W. B. (Circular Saw) D

Over, Ewald (Barbed Wire Fence) .... D

IND.—Muncie

Muncie Gas Engine & Supply Co. (Drilling; Fishing; Oil Well) ....B

IOWA—Dubuque

Novelty Iron Wks. (Oil Well) .... H

IOWA—Fairfield

Louden Mchry. Co. (Haying) ....D

IOWA—Ft. Madison

Iowa Farming Tool Co. (Haying; Walk Cleaning; Hand Farming) ....A

KANS.—Ft. Scott

Ft. Scott Fdry. & Macn. Co. (Artesian; Oil Well; Miners') .... H

Penneman & Son, A. C. (Contractors') .... D

KANS.—Topeka

Baird Portable Mach. Co. (Pneumatic) .... B

KY.—Henderson

Blackwell & Co., P. A. (Contractors') .... A

KY.—Louisville

Belknap Hdw. Mfg. Co. (Inc.) (Contractors') ....AAAA

Todd-Donegan Iron Co. (Contractors') .... A

TOOLS (Con.)

MAINE—Belfast

Kelly & Co., Benj.
(Granite; Stonecutters') D

MAINE—Portland

Edwards & Walker Co.
(Contractors') .... A

Lang Co., E. M. (Can-
makers') C

MAINE—Rockland

Livingston Mfg. Co.
(Granite; Stonecutters') D

MD.—Baltimore

Brown, F. S. & G. L.
(Tinsmiths') .... D

Meyer, Henry H., 110 S.
Howard (All kinds Con-
tractors) .... E

Ryan-McDonald Mfg. Co.,
44 South (Contractors') A

MASS.—Arlington

Wood & Co., W. T.
(Granite; Stonecutters;
Ice) .... B

MASS.—Athol

Athol Machine Co. (Me-
chanics' Fine) .... B

Starrett& Co., L. S.
(Mechanics' Fine; Ma-
chinists') .... A

MASS.—Boston

Amer. Tool & Machine Co.
(Brassworkers') .....AA

Ames Plow Co., Quincy Hall
(Contractors'; Paving)
AA

Bond & Co., Harold, cor.
Pearl & Purchase (Con-
tractors') .... E

Boston & Lockport Block
Co. (Lumbering) ...... B

Brown-Wales Co. (Slaters)
A

Carson Trench Machine Co.
(Contractors') .... B

Chandler & Farquhar
(Dowell) .... A

Contractors' Plant Co.,
37 Pittsburg (Portable;
Gravity Concrete Mixers.
Etc.; Contractors') ....D

Dame, Staddard & Co.
(Parting; Wood Engravg.)

Dodge, Daley & Co., 218
High (Contractors') AA

Faneuil Watch Tool Co.
(Thread Cutting; Watch-
makers'; Jewelers';
Watch Staking) C

Ferdinand & Co., L. W.,
152 Federal (Contractors')
X

Fitts Mfg. & Supply Co.,
Frank E., 88 Purchase
(Contractors') .... D

Flintoff, Wm., 121 Haver-
hill (Contractors') ....H

Golding & Co., 177 Fort
Hill Sq. (Printers') ..B

Harrington, Robinson & Co.,
272 Franklin (Contrac-
tors') .... D

Harvey, H. H., 608 Atlantic
Av. (Calking; Contrac-
tors'; Granite; Stonecut-
ters'; Marble; Brown-
stone; Blacksmiths';
Brickmakers'; Ice; Pav-
ers'; Mechanics'; Miners';
Sandstone) .... B

Isele & Son, A. W.:, 51
Pitts (Granite; Stonecut-
ters'; Railroad Track;
Slaters' Hammers; Cut-
ters'; Stakes; Scratching
Bars, Etc.) .... G

McDowell Oven Co. (Con-
fectioners') ....H

Perrin, Seamans & Co., 57
Oliver (Contracors') ....D

Sampson, Geo. H., 15 Pearl
(Contractors) .... E

United States Steel Co.,
145 Oliver (Cast Steel
Granite; Stonecutters') D

Walworth Mfg. Co.. 132
Federal (Thread Cutting)
AAAA

MASS.—Brockton

Snell & Atherton (Boot &
Shaves; Edge Planes) C

Tuck Mfg. Co. (Burnising;
Parting) .... E

TOOLS (Con.)

MASS.—Cambridge

Standard Turning Wks.
(Plumbers') C

MASS.—Canton

Kinsley Iron & Mach. Co.
(Blacksmiths') ..... AA

MASS.—Chicopee Falls

Stevens Arms & Tool Co.,
J., (Thread Cutting; Re-
loading Cartridge) .... A

MASS.—Fitchburg

Fichburg Machine Wks.
(Planer; Machine; Ma-
chinists') .... A

Putnam Machine Co. (Cog
Shaping; Special; Ma-
chine; Machinists') ..AA

Simonds Mfg. Co. (Logging;
Lumber; Sawmakers')
AAA

MASS.—Greenfield

Goodell Mfg. Co. (Cutting-
Off) .... B

Noyes & Co., B. B. (Floral)
E

Wells Bros Co. (Farriers';
Blacksmiths') .... B

Wiley & Russel Mfg. Co.
(Blacksmiths'; Thread
Cutting Lathe) .... AA

MASS.—Kingston

Drew & Co., C. (Calking;
Coopers'; Machinists) C

MASS.—Lowell

Dennis & Co., Jno. (Roll
Covers) .... E

MASS.—Lynn

Bullock, W. F. (Boot;
Shoe) .... F

MASS.—Mansfield

Card Mfg. Co., S. W. (Boot;
Shoe) .... B

MASS.—Millbury

Buck Bros. (Carving) ....A

Buck, Chas. (Carving) B

MASS.—Millers Falls

Miller's Falls Co. (Boring;
Carving) ....AA

MASS.—New Bedford

Morse Twist Drill & Ma-
chine Co. (Lathe; Thread
Cutting; Blacksmiths Spe-
cial; Machinists') ..AAA

MASS.—North Easton

New England Specialty Co.
(Toy) .... F

MASS.—North Hadley

Howe, Jno. C. (Broom-
makers') ....D

MASS.—Quincy

Clark & Co., Alex. (Granite;
Stonecutters') .... G

Drummond, D. T. (Granite;
Stonecutters') .... H

Kemp, J. F. (Granite;
Stonecutters') .... G

Pinel Bros. (Granite; Stonecutters') X

Martin & Collins (Granite;
Stonecutters') .... H

Willbas, Gustof (Granite;
Stonecutters') X

MASS.—Shelburne Falls

Mayhew Co., H. H. (Bor-
ing) C

MASS.—Southbridge

Harrington, T. J. (Boot;
Shoe) .... D

Harrington Cutlery Co.
(Boot; Shoe) C

Hyde Mfg. Co. (Boot;
Shoe) ....D

Richard Stephen Co. (Boot;
Shoe) .... E

MASS.—Springfield

Bemis & Call Hdw. & Tool
Co. (Plumbers'; Tinners';
Mechanics') .... A

Bullock & Co., O. W. (En-
gravers'; Watch) ......A

Potwin, Henry, 98 Tyler
(Granite; Stonecutters') F

Smith Mfg. Co., R. H.
(Rubber Stamp Making) C

Waltham Watch Tool Co.
of Springfield (Watch) B

MASS.—Taunton

New Process Twist Drill
Co. (Machinists') .... E

MASS.—Waltham

Amer. Watch Tool Co.
(Watch) .... AAAA

TOOLS (Con.)
Stark Tool Co. (Jewelers') B

Waltham Emery Wheel Co. (Diamond Turning; Lathe) C
Waltham Machine Works (Watch) .... E
MASS.—Worcester
Blaisdell & Co., P. (Lathe; Machine; Brassworking) A
Brown, W. H. (Carders') E
Draper Machine Tool Co. (Machine) .... A
National Mfg. Co. (Boring) B
Prentice Bros. (Machinists') A
Reed Co., Francis (Lathe; Machine) .... D
Roy, B. S. (Carders') ....B
Whitcomb Mfg. Co. (Planer; Machine; Machinists') A
Young Mfg. Co., W. C. (Lathe) .... D
MASS.—Wrentham
Winter Bros. Co. (Thread Cutting; Lathe) ......E
MICH.—Detroit
Anderson & Sons, W. H. (Asphalt Paving; Calking Carving; Contractors'; Granite; Stonecutters'; Ice; Logging; Lumbermans'; Paving; Pitching; Railroad Track; Slaters'; Plumbers'; Planer; Lathe) C
Burr's Damascus Tool Wks., 66 Fort, E. (Moulders') D
Lauer, Jno., 112 St. Antoine (Pneumatic) C
Mitshkun Co., M., Chamb. of Com. Bldg. (Contractors') C
Strellinger Co., Chas. A., 98 Betts (Slaters) .... A
MICH.—Evart
Champion Tool & Handle Wks. (Logging; Lumbermans') .... A
MICH.—Galien
Montrose, Richard W. (Hand Farming) X
MICH.—Jackson
Withington & Cooley Mfg. Co. (Haying; Combination Garden; Miners') ....AA
MICH.—Kalamazoo
Kalamazoo Railway Supply Co. (Contractors') .... B
MICH.—Lansing
Bement & Sons, E. (Hand Farming; Garden).. AAA
MICH.—Manton
Meyer Hdw. Co. (Contractors') C
MICH.—Port Huron
Draper Mfg. Co. (Valve Facing) .... D
Port Huron Air Tool Co. (Pneumatic) .... F
MICH.—Saginaw
Morley Bros. (Inc.) (Logging; Lumber) ...... AA
Saginaw Hdw. Co. (Lumbering) .... A
Stocker Bros. & Co. (Logging; Lumbermans') ..G
MICH.—Three Rivers
Sheffield Car Co. (Railroad Track) .... AA
MINN.—Duluth
Clyde Iron Wks. (Inc.) (Logging; Lumbermans') A
Marshall-Wells Hdw. Co. (Contractors') ....AAAA
Northwestern Mfg. Co. (Logging; Lumberman's) F
MINN.—Merriam Park
Law Mfg. Co. (Haying) F
MINN.—Minneapolis
Morrison & Co., W. K., 249 Nicollet Av (Contractors') .... A
Therien Tool Wks., 116 1st Av. (Granite; Stonecutters') .... E
MINN.—St. Paul
Amer. Hoist & Derrick Co. (Contractors') .... A
Helwig Mfg. Co. (Pneu-

TOOLS (Con.)
matic) .... F
MISS.—Meridian
Soule Steam Feed Wks. (Lumber) C
MO.—Browning
Jenkins Hay Rake Staker Co. (Haying) .... A
MO.—Kansas City
Amer. Frog & Mfg. Co., New England Bldg. (Railroad Track) .... E
Hauck & Son, Jno., 20th & Southwest Boul. (Granite; Stonecutters; Concrede, Etc.; Paving) ...... G
Smith & Sons Mfg. Co. (Plows; Grades; Ditches, Etc.; Contractors') ..AA
Vogl, Geo., 1910 Walnut (Granite; Stonecutters) E
MO.—St. Joseph
Hochenauer, Jno. (Granite; Stonecutters') .... G
MO.—St. Louis
Brecht Butchers' Supply Co., Gus. V. (Butchers') AAA
Broderick & Bascom Rope Co., 809 N. Main (Contractors') .... AA
Cahill, Swift Mfg. Co., 20 S. 12th (Contractors') A
Crescent Novelty Mfg. Co., 703 S. Bway. (Coopers'; Granitoid Sidewalk Paving; Pitching) .... D
Davis Expansion Boring Tool Co. (Expansion Boring, for Boring Mills, Lathers or Drill Presses) A
Handlan-Buck Mfg. Co., 210 N. 3rd (Contractors'; Railroad Track) .... AA
Hirsch &Sons Iron & Rail Co., Cal., 212 Clark Av. (Contractors') ....AA
Leschen & Sons Rope Co., A., 920 N. 1st (Contractors') .... AAA
Mound Tool & Scraper Co., 710 Howard (Packing; Scraping) X
Rumsey Mfg. Co., L. M., 806 N. 2nd (Contractors') AAA
St. Louis Pneumatic Tool Co., 319 N. 4th (Pneumatic) .... B
St. Louis Shovel Co. (Br. Amer. Shovel & Tool Co., Boston, Mass.) (Drainage) .... AAAA
St. Louis Well Mach. & Tool Co. (Oil Well) ..C
Schueddig & Son. F., 525 S. Jeffn. (Granite; Stonecutters') .... E
Standard Railway Equipment Co., Union Trust Bldg. (Pneumatic) ....D
Swaine Co., Fred J., (Tinsmiths') C
Waycott Supply Co., 527 N. 2nd (Contractors') ....F
Zelnicker Supply Co., Walter A., (Railroad Track) C
NEBR.—Omaha
Baum Iron Co., 1210 Harney (Contractors') ...... AA
Lee-Glass-Andreesen Hdw. Co., 9th & Harney (Contractors') .... A
Lehmer, Joseph R., 1212 Farnham (Contractors') D
Martin-Anderson Co. (Haying) .... A
Morton & Son Co., James, 1511 Dodge (Contractors') B
N. H.—Concord
Nutling & Hayden (Granite; Stonecutters') .... F
N. H.—Lebanon
Kendrick & Davis (Watchmakers') .... A
N. H.—Nashua
Flather & Co. (Machinists') A
N. J.—Bayonne
Nagengast & Co., Joseph (Coopers') .... F

1040

N. J.—Bridgeton
Ferracute Machine Co.
(Canmakers'; Tinsmiths)
............................A

N. J.—Elizabeth
Braunsdorf - Mueller Co.
(Bell Centering; Piano-
makers' Plasterers';
Wood Turners') ....D
Elizabeth Hdw. Co., 202
Broad (Contractors') ..B

N. J.—Gloucester City
Rogers Boat Gauge & Drill
Wks., Jno. M. (Thread
Cutting) .... B

N. J.—Grenlock
Bateman Mfg. Co. (Garden)
............................A

N. J.—Newark
Atha Tool Co. (Calking;
Coopers'; Drill Sharpen-
ing; Farriers'; Lathe;
Pitching; Railroad Track;
Blacksmiths') .... A
Currier & Son, Cyrus (En-
gravers') .... AA
Gould & Eberhardt (Thread
Cutting; Cut-Off; Lath) A
Heller Bros. Co. (Farriers';
Blacksmiths') ...... AA
Hewes & Phillips Iron Wks.
(Machinists') .... A
Johnson, Wm., 249 Plane
(Plumbers'; Tinners') D
Kraeuter Co. (Piano;
Plumbers') ....E
National Saw Co. (Circular
Saw; Molders') ....AAAA
Osborne & Co., C. S. (Calk-
ing; Plumbers'; Saddlers')
............................B
Osborne Co., H. F. (Sad-
dlers') ....E
Roe & Conover, 200 Market
(Contractors') .... A
Sargent Mfg. Co. (Sad-
dlers') .... A
Winkler, Fred (Saddlers')
............................F

N. J.—New Brunswick
Lea, Thos. (Boring) ....H

N. J.—New Orange
Wright Co., The Chas. E.
(for Band Saw Machines)
............................B

N. J.—Plainfield
Pond Machine Tool Co.
(Br. Niles-Bement-Pond
Co., N. Y. City, N. Y.)
(Machinists') .... AAAA

N. J.—Salem
Ayars Machine Co. (Can-
makers') .... B

N. J.—Smithville
Smith Machine Co., H. B.
(Machinists') .... A

N. Y.—Albany
Albany Steam Trap Co.
(Boilermakers') ...... D

N. Y.—Athens
Dernell & Co., H. F. (Ice)
............................E

N. Y.—Binghamton
G. & E. Electric Co. (Bor-
ing) .... E
Star Electric Co. (Boring)
............................D

N. Y.—Brooklyn
Adams & Co., J. J. (Sash)
............................A
Bliss Co., E. W. (Can-
makers'; Brassworking)
............................AAAA
Brown, James H., 139 3rd
Av. (Granite; Stonecut-
ters') .... F
Evans, F. H. (Gas Works;
Roofers'; Pavers') C
Pioneer Iron Wks., 151
William (Asphalt Paving)
............................A
Pollard, Joseph G., 141
Raymond (Calking; Pav-
ing) ....F
Williams & Co., J. H., 9
Richards (Railroad Track)
............................AAA

N. Y.—Buffalo
Beals & Co., 44 Terrace
(Contractors') ..... B
Diamond Saw & Stamping
Co. (Saw) ....D
Iroquois Iron Wks., 178

Walden Av. (Asphalt
Paving) .... A
Niagara Machine & Tool
Wks. (Plumbers'; Tin-
ners'; Slaters'; Can-
makers'; Tinroofing) AAA
Oliver Mfg. Co., W. W.,
1483 Niagara (Watch-
makers'; Jewelers') C
Osgood, J. L., (Diamond
Pointed; Diamond Shap-
ing) C
Shepard & Co., Sidney (Ice)
............................AAAA
Union Mfg. & Plating Co.
(Rubber Tire Repair) D
Walbridge & Co., 392 Main
(Contractors') .... A
West Mfg. Co. (Canmakers';
Tinroofing; Tinsmiths') D
White Co., L. & I. J.
(Calking; Coopers'; Ice;
Butchers'; Slaters'; Ship
Carpenters') .... A

N. Y.—Canastota
Dobson, Wm. (Moulders) F

N. Y.—Frankfort
Acme Road Mchry. Co.
(Contractors') C
Continental Tool Co. (Walk
Cleaning) .... A

N. Y.—Ilion
Remington Arms Co. (See
N. Y. City) (Reloading)
............................AAAA

N. Y.—Ithaca
Williams Bros. (Artesian;
Oil Well) .... AA

N. Y.—Lansingburg
Empire Forge Co., 464 4th
Av. (Ice) .... F
Cheney Hammer Co., Henry
(Farriers'; Blacksmiths')
............................L

N. Y.—Lockport
Trevor Mfg. Co. (Coopers')
............................B

N. Y.—Marathon
Climax Road Machine Co.
(Contractors') .... B

N. Y.—Montour Falls
General Pneumatic Tool Co.
(Pneumatic Marble; Stone-
cutters') C

New York City
Amer. Axe & Tool Co., 253
Bway. (Coopers'; Edge)
............................AAAA
Amer. Gas Furnace Co.
(Machinists') .... A
Amer. Steel & Wire Co. (U.
S. Steel Corpn.) (Barbed
Wire Fence) ....AAAA
Ashcroft Mfg. Co. (Boiler-
makers') .... A
Bacon Earle C., Havemeyer
Bldg. (Contractors') ..D
Baldwin, Frank, 33 South
(Contractors') .... E
Beggs & Co., James, 9 Dey
(Mfrs. Agts.) (Contrac-
tors') .... B
Brodie & Co., Wm. H., 45
Vesey (Contractors') ..F
Clayton Air Compressor
Wks. (Pneumatic) ....B
Davies, Frank, 68 Broad
(Contractors') X
Dickinson, Jno. (Est. of)
64 Nassau (Diamond Op-
ticians) .... B
Dickinson, Thomas L.
(Diamond Turning Lathe)
............................H
Dienst & Co., A. P., 3rd
Av. & 140th (Contrac-
tors') C
Dudgeon, Richard (Boiler-
makers') ....A
Eaton, Cole & Burnham Co.
(Plumbers') ...... AAA
Eyeless Tool Co., 26 Cort-
landt (Contractors' Hand;
Railroad Track) ...... A
Fairbanks Co., 186 Elm
(Contractors'; Black-
smiths'; Machinists')
............................AAAA
Force & Co., Wm. A. (Rub-
ber Stamp Making) ..E
Fox Bros. & Co., 24 Vesey
(Contractors') .... D
Frasse Co. (Bicylce Repair;

TOOLS (Con.)

Kinsey Co., E. A., 331 W. 4th (Contractors'; Railroad Track) ....B

Lodge & Shipley Machine Tool Co. (Machine; Machinists') ....A

Obermayer Co., S., 647 Evans (Moulders') ....A

Robinson & Co., J. M. (Tinsmiths') ....B

Rogan, Wm., 262 W. McMicken (Granite; Stonecutters') X

Sebastian Lathe Co. (Br. Covington, Ky.) (Machinists') C

Tatum Co., Samuel (Mechanics') ....B

OHIO—Cleveland

Amer. Fork & Hoe Co. (Floral) ....AAAA

Bardons & Oliver (Special) A

Cleveland Pneumatic Tool Co., 74 Frankfort (Pneumatic) ....A

Crescent Mfg. Co. (Boilermakers') X

Gerlach & Co., Peter, 28 Columbus (Ice; Logging; Lumber) ....B

Hart Mfg. Co., 22 Wood (Thread Cutting) .....B

Reliance Machine & Tool Co. (Thread Cutting Lathe) C

Smith Fdry. Supply Co., J. D., 40 S. Water (Moulders') ....D

Standard Tool Co. (Special; Combination Handy) AAA

Strong, Carslisle & Hammond Co., 61 Frankfort (Contractors') ....A

Warner & Swasey (Brassworkers'; Machine) ...A

OHIO—Columbus

Brown, Hinman & Huntington Co. (Hand; Farm; Garden) ....A

Columbus Machine Co. (Machinists') ....A

Columbus Pneumatic Tool Co. (Pneumatic) .....D

Ohio Tool Co. (Coopers'; Mechanics') ....A

OHIO—Dayton

Amer. Bolt & Seven Case Co. (Bicycle Repair) ..D

Dayton Malleable Iron Co. (Miners') ....AA

Trimbach, Geo. (Granite; Stonecutters') ....F

OHIO—Geneva

Geneva Tool Co. (Hand; Farming) ....AA

OHIO—Hamilton

Advance Mfg. Co. (Hand; Farming) ....D

Niles Tool Wks. (Machine; Machinists') ......AAAA

OHIO—Lima

Ackerman & Castle (Drilling; Fishing; Oil Well) E

Sinclair & Morrison Co. (Drilling; Fishing; Oil Well) ....A

OHIO—Mansfield

Ohio Brass Co. (Ice) ....B

OHIO—Marietta

Leidecker Tool Co. (Drilling; Fishing; Oil Well) .A

OHIO—Piqua

Piqua Handle & Mfg. Co. (Coopers') ....A

OHIO—Ravenna

Byers Machine Co., Jno. F. (Contractors') ....B

OHIO—Salem

Clark Co., N. J. (Garden) B

OHIO—Sandusky

Sandusky Tool Co. (Hand; Farming; Coopers') ....A

OHIO—Springfield

Foos Mfg. Co. (Hand, Farming; Blacksmiths') ...A

Ridgely, Chas. T. (Paperhangers') C

Webster & Peerks Tool Co. (Machinists'; Paperhangers'; Brickmakers') ...D

Western Mfg. Co. (Lathe; Side; Planer) ....E

TOOLS (Con.)

OHIO—Toledo

Heartley Machine Variety Iron & Tool Wks. (Stonecutters'; Granite; Ice) D

Toledo Machine & Tool Co. (Range Builders) ....A

Union Mfg. Co. (Toy) X

OREGON—Portland

Avery & Co. (Logging; Lumberman's) C

PA.—Allegheny

Carlin Mchry. & Supply Co., 103 Lacock (Contractors'; Rolling Mill) ....A

Heathcote, Thos., 829 Penna Av. (Granite; Stonecutters') ....G

PA.—Allentown

Grammes & Sons, L. F. (Brush Nailing Mchry.)B

PA.—Altoona

Wolf Hdw. Co., S. J., 1414 11th Av. (Contractors') D

PA.—Athens

Imperial Pneumatic Tool Co. (Pneumatic) ....A

PA.—Bangor

Flory Mfg. Co., S. (Slaters) A

PA.—Beaver Falls

Emerson, Smith & Co. (Ltd.) (Coopers') ....AA

Keystone Driller Co. (Drilling; Fishing; Oil Well) B

Myers Co., H. M. (Drainage) ....AAAA

PA.—Bradford

Bovaird & Seyfang Mfg. Co. (Drilling; Fishing; Oil Well) ....A

Robertson, D. W. (Drilling; Fishing; Oil Well) ...B

PA.—Butler

Kesselman & Co. (Drilling; Fishing; Oil Well) ....B

Larkin & Co. (Drilling; Fishing; Oil Well) ....B

PA.—Cadwallader

Herbertson's Sons, J. (Oil Well) C

PA.—Chester

Black & Co., H. B. (Butchers') ....A

PA.—Danielsville

Hower, J. K. (Slaters'; Supplies) ....B

PA.—Duke Centre

Irvine, A. T. (Oil Well) X

PA.—Eldred

Prouty & Co., C. (Logging; Lumberman's) ....A

PA.—Erie

Erie Pump & Engine Co. (Contractors'; Pumps) C

Erie Specialty Co. (Ice) B

PA.—Frankford

Plumb, Fayette R. (Drill Sharpening; Pitching; Railroad Track; Blacksmiths'; Miners') ....AA

PA.—Harrisburg

Hickok Mfg. Co. (Bookbinders') ....A

PA.—Hazleton

Hazleton Mchry. & Supply Co. (Contractors') ....AA

PA.—Jamestown

Columbia Tool Co. (Farriers') X

PA.—Kittanning

Kittanning Drilling Tool Co. (Drilling; Fishing; Oil Well) ....G

PA.—Lancaster

Hubley Mfg. Co. (Jewelers'; Toolmakers') ....A

Reisner & Co., L. C. (Jewelers') ....B

Stehman & Coho Mfg. Co. (Jewelers') ....B

PA.—Mars

Sheridan & Co., James J. (Drilling; Fishing; Oil Well) ....D

PA.—Ogontz

Hammond & Son, C. (Farriers'; Blacksmiths') ...A

PA.—Philadelphia

Bement, Niles & Co. (Br. Niles-Bement-Pond Co., N. Y. City) (Planer; Machine; Machinists') AAAA

TOOLS (Con.)

Bickerton, T. B., 23 N. 6th (Contractors') ....F
Calvert & Holloway (Tinsmiths') ....B
Contractors' Tool Co., 118 S. 6th (Asphalt Paving; Pitching) ....F
Dallett & Co., Thos. H., 2303 York (Pneumatic; Marble; Stonecutters'; Boilermakers') ....A
Economy Tool Mfg. Co., 11th & Wood (Pneumatic) X
Ellis & Sons Co., Geo. D. (Tanners'; Curriers') ..C
Griffiths Co., Geo. (Drainage) ....A
Harper & Sons, Smith (Hand; Farming) .....A
Harrington Son & Co., E. (Machine; Machinists') AA
Horn & Co., Wm. H. (Boot; Shoe; Curriers'; Tanners') B
Johnson, Jr. & Co., I. H. (Machine) ....A
Kueny, Nicholas M. (Brickmakers') X
McFadden Co. (Lathe) ...X
Mills & Bro., Thomas (Confectioners') ....A
Mitton, Job. G., S. 30th & Locust (Granite; Stonecutters') ....H
Model Mfg. Co. (Combination Handy) ....F
Newton Machine Tool Wks. (Machine) ....A
Nittinger, August (Butchers') ....A
Noble, Henry A. (Artificial Stone; Finishers') .....E
Paxson Co., J. W., 1021 N. Del. Av. (Moulders') ..AA
Pedrick & Ayer Co., 1001 Hamilton (Pneumatic; Blacksmiths'; Machinists') ....A
Philadelphia Novelty Mfg. Co. (Combination Garden) B
Phila. Pneumatic Tool Co., 21st & Allegheny Av. (Pneumatic Stone Carving; Pneumatic Stone Dressing) C
Phosphor Bronze Smelting Co. (Ltd.) (Powder Mills) A
Sellers & Co., (Inc.) Wm. (Machine; Machinists') AAAA
Shannon & Co., J. Jacob, 1744 Market (Contractors') ....A
Standard Supply & Equipment Co., 1710 Market (Contractors') ....D
Stortz & Son, Jno., 210 Vine (Ice; Lathe; Linemen's; Oysterman's; Paperhangers'; Pitching; Plumbers'; Tinners'; Slaters' Hammers; Rippers; Stalkes. etc.; Tinroofing) .....F
Thompson & Campbell (Curriers') X
U. S. Smelting Wks. (Bicycle Repair) ....B
Williamson & Cassedy, 526 Market (Contractors') A

PA.—Pittsburg

Anderson, Du Puy & Co. (Crucible Steel Co. of Amer.) (Miners'; Blacksmiths'; Railroad) AAAA
Bailey-Farrel Mfg. Co. (Plumbers') ....AA
Baker Mfg. Co., James H., Park Bldg. (Railroad Track) ....A
Carlin Co., W. J., 25th & A. V. Ry. (Contractors') A
Carron & Co., A. M., 108 Market (Pneumatic Tool Lubricators) ....D
Frick & Lindsay Co., 109 Wood (Contractors') ...C
Gloekler, Bernard (Butchers') ....A
Hubbard & Co., Murtland

TOOLS (Con.)

-Bldg. (Railroad Track) A
Iron City Tool Wks. (Railroad Track; Blacksmiths') B
Jones & Laughlin Steel Co. (Ltd.) (Railroad Track) AAAA
Kirk & Son, Arthur, 910 Duquesne Way (Contractors') X
Klein-Logan Co., S. 13th & Breed (Stonecutters'; Pitching; Railroad Track) A
Logan-Gregg Hdw. Co., 125 7th (Contractors') ....A
McIlwain & Co., J. D., 208 3d Av. (Contractors' Mchry.; Supplies) X
O'Halloran & Jacobs, 335 5th Av. (Slaters'; Supplies) ....D
Oil Well Supply Co. (Oil Well) ....AAAA
Oliver Iron & Steel Co. (Railroad Track) AAAA
Pittsburg Gauge & Supply Co., 309 Water (Contractors') ....AA
Somers, Fitler & Todd Co., 327 Water (Contractors') A
Standard Scale & Supply Co., 211 Woods (Contractors') ....B
Tretheway & Co., (Ltd.) Saml., 47th nr. Butler (Roll Turning; Rolling Mill) ....F
Wickes Bros., 45th & A. V. R. R. (Br. Saginaw, Mich.) (Contractors') AA
Yagle & Co., (Ltd.) Wm., 400 32nd (Contractors' Blake; Rock; Ore Crushers) C

PA.—Reading

Reading Mach. & Tool Co. (Wire Fence) ....B
Reading Standard Cycle Mfg. Co. (W. F. Remppis. Prop.) (Lathe Boring) ....B

PA.—Sharon Hill

Rose & Bros., Wm. (Brickmakers') ....D

PA.—Slatington

McKenna, David (Slaters'; Supplies) ....E

PA.—Stroudsburg

Tanite Co. (Diamond Turning; Lathe) ....A

PA.—Tacony

Disston & Sons (Inc.) Henry (Moulders'; Saw) .AAAA

PA.—Verona

Verona Tool Co. (Railroad Track; Miners') ....A

PA.—Warren

Best, Jno. (Drilling; Fishing; Oil Well) ....F
Warren Axe & Tool Co. (Turpentine) ....B

PA.—Waynesboro

Landis Tool Co. (Machine) B

PA.—Wilkesbarre

Penna. Supply Co. (Contractors') ....A

PA.—Wrightsville

Wrightsville Hdw. Co. (Toy) C

R. I.—Pawtucket

Carpenter Tap & Die Co., J. M. (Machinists') C
Thayers' Son, Ellis (Sash) X

R. I.—Providence

Amer. Emery Wheel Wks. (Diamond Pointed) ...C
Amer. Supply Co. (Roll Coverers') ....AA
Beaman & Smith (Machine) B
Brown & Sharpe Mfg. Co. (Milling; Machine; Screw Machine; Special; Machinists') ....AAAA
Coleman & Sons, Walter, 300 S. Water (Contractors') C
Congdon & Carpenter Co.

TOOLS (Con.)

(Contractors') ......AA
Diamond Machine Co.
(Lathe; Diamond Turning, Lathe) ....A
McWilliams Mfg. Co. (Jewelers'; Watchmakers') .D
Mann, Chas. A. (Watchmakers'; Jewelers') ....E
Nicholson File Co. (Filers'; Jewelers'; Toolmakers')
AAAA
Standard Mchry. Co. (Jewelers'; Toolmakers') ...A
Thomas & Lowe Mchry. Co.
(Repoussé) C
Thurston Mfg. Co. (Watchmakers'; Jewelers') C
R. I.—Westerly
Rhode Island Granite Tool
Co. (Granite; Stonecutters') ....E
Weseterly Granite Tool Co.
(Stonecutters') X
TENN.—Chattanooga
James & Co., 101 W. 8th
(Contractors') ....B
TENN.—Knoxville
Luttrell & Co., S. B. (Contractors') ....AA
McClung & Co., C. M. (Contractors') ....AA
TENN.—Memphis
Livermore Fdry. & Machine
Co. (Contractors') .....A
TEXAS—Fort Worth
Ft. Worth Iron Wks. (Artesian; Oil Well) ....A
VT.—Barre
Ahern, James (Granite; Stonecutters') ....F
Trow & Holden (Granite; Stonecutters'; Paving Cutters') ....D
VT.—Bellows Falls
Derbey & Ball (Garden) ..B
VT.—Brookfield
Peck, Clark & Co. (Hand; Farming) ....D
VT.—Derby Line
Butterfield & Co. (Haying; Blacksmiths') ....B
VT.—East Highgate
Rixford, Oscar S. (Hand; Farming) ....B
VT.—Hartford
French; Watson & Co.
(Hand; Farming) .....D
VT.—Springfield
Jones & Lamson Machine
Co. (Machine) ....AA
Superior Tap Co. (Thread Cutting Lathe) ....F
VA.—Richmond
McGraw, James, 1440 E.
Main (Contractors') ...B
Smith-Courtney Co. (Contractors') ....B
WASH.—Hoquiam
Grays Harbor Iron Wks.
(Logging; Lumberman's)F
WASH.—Kelso
Remick, A. R. (Logging; Lumberman's) ....G
WASH.—Seattle
Adair & Son, Geo. B. (Contractors') ....D
Loggers Supply Co. (Logging; Lumberman's) ...B
W. VA.—Sistersville
Finlayson, Jno. (Drilling; Fishing; Oil Well) ....F
West Virginia Tool Co.
(Drilling; Fishing; Oil Well) ....D
W. VA.—Wheeling
Wheeling Hinge Co. (Blacksmiths'; Machinists')AAA
WIS.—Janesville
Rock River Machine Co.
(Haying) ....B
WIS.—Milwaukee
Filer & Stowell Co. (Ltd.)
(Band Saw; Circular Saw; Lumbering) ...AAA
Milwaukee Hay Tool Co.
(Haying) ....A
WIS.—Oshkosh
Oshkosh Logging Tool Co.
(Haying; Logging; Lumberman) C
Sanford Logging Tool Co.

TOOLS (Con.)

(Logging; Lumbermans')
D
WIS.—Racine
Racine Malleable & Wrought Iron Co. (Blacksmiths') ....B
WIS.—Sheboygan
Spratt & Co., Geo. (Hand; Farming) ....D

TOOTHPICKS

CONN.—Chester
Bates, C. J. (Alaska Ivory)
D
MAINE—Deering
Scammon Mfg. Co. ......E
MAINE—Dixfield
Forster, Chas. (Est. of) ..D
MAINE—Mechanics Falls
Hallett Toothpick Co. (Br. Prov. R. I.) X
MASS.—Boston
Cutter-Power Co., 234 Devonshire (Wooden) .....B
MICH.—Clayton
Perfection Mfg. Co. .....B
MICH.—Detroit
Natl. Toothpick Co. ....F
Perfection Mfg. Co. .....D
MICH.—River Rouge
Perfection Mfg. Co. .....D
MICH.—Saginaw
Berst Mfg. Co. ....D
New York City
Aikin, Lambert & Co., 19
Maiden Lane (Gold) ..C
Estes & Sons, E. B., 45
John (Wooden) ......AA
Grote & Co., E. 14th ....D
Johnson & Co., E. S. (Gold)
D
Knapp Co., John H., 23
John (Gold) ....D
Mabie, Todd & Bard, 130
Fulton (Gold) ....A
PA.—Bradford
Union Dish Co. (Wooden) D
R. I.—Providence
Hallett Toothpick Co. X
Pearce & Co., F. T. (Gold) C

TOPAZ

See Jewelry

TOPS

CAL.—Los Angeles
Pacific Clay Mfg. Co.
(Chimney) ....A
CAL.—San Francisco
Clark & Sons, N., 17 Speer
(Chimney) ....A
Clawson & Co., L. E., 1340
Market (Chimney) .....E
Gladding, McBean & Co.,
Rialto Bldg. (Chimney)
AA
CONN.—Meriden
Hall, Wilbur B. (Salt; Pepper Box) ....D
CONN.—New London
Burch & Co., H. O.
(Chimney) X
CONN.—Newtown
Beers & Co., D. G. (Canopy, also Trimmings, Wagon, Carriage) ....E
CONN.—Wallingford
Wallce & Sons Mfg. Co., R.
(Salt; Pepper Box) AAAA
GA.—Atlanta
Southern Terra Cotta Wks.
(Chimney) X
GA.—Macon
Stevens Sons Co., H. (Chimney) ....A
ILL.—Chicago
Adams & Westlake Co., Ontario & N. Franklin (Pole)
AAA
Chicago Top & Cushion Co.
(Wagon) X
Cutter Co., Geo., Union & Fulton (Pole) C
Davidson Bros. Marble Co.
(Marble, Raditor) .....B
Dee, Wm. E., 169 Jackson
Bould. (Chimney) .....B
Hutchinson & Son, W. H.
(Inc.) (Bottle) ....A

TOPS (*Con.*)

Northwestern Terra Cotta
Co. (Chimney) ......AAA
Redlich Mfg. Co. (Bottle) E
Sherman & Flavin (Marble,
Furniture; Marble, Radiator) ....B
Sprague, Smith Co. (Mantel)
C

ILL.—Macomb
Macomb Sewer Pipe Co.
(Chimney) ....B
ILL.—Monmouth
Monmouth Mining & Mfg.
Co. (Chimney) ......AA
ILL.—Peoria
Clark, Quien & Morse
(Chimney, Revolving) ..A
ILL.—Sterling
Lawrence Bros. (Chimney,
Revolving) ....AAA
ILL.—Streator
Iwan Bros. (Chimney, Revolving) C
Powers Bros. (Chimney, Revolving) ....B
Streator Clay Mfg. Co.
(Chimney) ....A
IND.—Anderson
Buckeye Mfg. Co. (Canopy,
also Trimmings) C
IND.—La Porte
La Porte Carriage Co.
(Carriage) ....A
MD.—Baltimore
Baltimore Terra Cotta Wks.
(Chimney) ....D
MASS.—Boston
Anderson Mfg. Co., Albert
& J. M. (Pole) ....A
Boston Fire Brick Co., 164
Devonshire (Chimney) ..A
MASS.—Westfield
Smith Co., H. B. (Marble,
Radiator) ....AA
MICH.—Detroit
Anderson & Sons, W. H.
(Pole) C
MINN.—Minneapolis
Therien Tool Wks., 116 First
Av., N. (Pole) ....E
MO.—Kansas City
Dickey Clay Mfg. Co., W.
S., N. Y. Life Ins. Bldg.
(Chimney) ....A
MO.—St. Louis
Evens & Howard Fire Brick
Co., 920 Market (Chimney) ....AAAA
Laclede Fire Brick Mfg. Co.,
105 N. 7th (Chimney) AAA
Missouri Tent & Awning Co.
(Carriage) ....B
St. Louis Basket & Box Co.
(Trunk) ....A
Schoenlan & Kukkuk Trunk
Top & Veneer Co. (Trunk)
B
N. J.—Hoboken
Woodman, Joel H. (Carriage) ....A
N. J.—New Brunswick
New Jersey Lamp & Bronze
Wks. (Clock) .....AAAA
N. Y.—Brooklyn
Vogel & Bros., Wm.
(Fruit Jar) ....AA
N. Y.—Elmira
Elmira Sewer Pipe & Fire
Brick Co. (Chimney) ..X
N. Y.—Munnesville
Munnesville Plow Co.
(Chimney) ....B
New York City
Consolidated Fruit Jar Co.
(Fruit Jar) ....AA
Estes & Sons, E. B. (Cork)
AA
Giffing Iron Co., A. A.
(Marble, Radiator) ..AA
Klaber, A. (Marble, Furniture) ....B
Sargent & Co., 151 Leonard
(Hitching Post) .AAAA
Stimpson & Son, E. B.
(Boot) ....B
Wittemann Bros. (Bottle) A
N. Y.—Oneida
Halliday, C. A. (Carriage) F
OHIO—Akron
Robinson Clay Product Co.
(Chimney) ....AAAA

TOPS (*Con.*)

OHIO—Canton
Berger Mfg. Co. (Chimney,
Revolving) ....AA
Gibbs Mfg. Co. (Toy) ....A
Kohler & Co., F. E. (Malleable D. Handle) ....B
OHIO—Cincinnati
Cincinnati Sewer Pipe Co.
(Chimney) ....E
Electric Railway Equipment
Co. (Pole) ....A
Warner Pole & Top Co. (Carriage) C
OHIO—Cleveland
Avery Stamping Co. (Malleable D. Handles) ......B
Garry Iron & Steel Co.
(Chimney, Revolving) .A
Osborn Mfg. Co. (Chimney,
Revolving) ....B
OHIO—Columbus
Wassall Fire Clay Co.
(Chimney) ....D
OHIO—Haydenville
Haydenville Mining & Mfg.
Co. (Chimney) ....A
OHIO—Logan
Hocking Clay Mfg. Co.
(Chimney) ....B
OHIO—Massillon
Hess, Snyder & Co., (Chimney; Revolving Chimney)
AA
OHIO—Piqua
Piqua Handle & Mfg. Co.
(Malleable D. Handles) A
OHIO—Tiffin
Ohio Lantern Co. (Fruit
Jar; Molasses Can; Tin;
Jar Tin; Salt; Pepper
Box) ....B
OHIO—Toledo
Kroh Co., C. Z. (Carriage) E
OHIO—Toronto
Francy's Sons & Co., Jno.
(Chimney) ....AAAA
OHIO—Ulrichsville
Buckeye Fire Clay Co.
(Chimney) ....B
OHIO—Zanesville
Townsend & Co., Wm. C.
(Marble, Furniture) ..AA
PA.—New Brighton
Pittsburg Clay Mfg. Co.
(Chimney) ....AAAA
PA.—Philadelphia
Grundy & Co., Wm. H.
(Toy) ....B
Hero Fruit Jar Co. (Fruit
Jar) ....AA
Keystone Silk Weaving Co.
(Silk, Shoe) ....D
Mason Fruit Jar Co. (Fruit
Jar) X
PA.—Pittsburg
Amer. Sewer Pipe Co., 2nd
Natl. Bank Bldg. (Chimney) ....AAAA
R. I.—Pawtucket
Luther & Co., C. A. (Bottle)
C
TENN.—Chattanooga
Montague & Co. (Chimney)
A
VT.—Fair Haven
Fair Hven Marble & Marbleized Slate Co. (Marble,
Furniture) ....B
WASH.—Little Falls
Little Falls Fire Clay Co.
(Chimney) ....B
W. VA.—Wheeling
Wheeling Hinge Co.
(Ointment Pot) ......AA
Wheeling Metal Co. (Jar,
Tin) ....D
Wheeling Stamping Co.
(Fruit Jar) ....A

TORCHES

CONN.—Bridgeport
Bridgeport Brass Co. (Gasoline etc.; Gasoline Blow;
Oil) ....AA
CONN.—New Haven
Henn & Co., A. S. (Gas
Lighting) ....F
ILL.—Chicago
Acorn Brass Wks., 193 Fulton (Gasoline Blow) ..B
Glogau Mfg. Co. (Alcohol) C

TORCHES (Con.)

Holland, Wm., 54 So. Clinton (Alcohol; Gasoline Blow) ....E
Turner Brass Wks., 69 N. Franklin (Alcohol; Hand Gasoline etc.; Gasoline Blow; Oil) ....B
White Mfg. Co., 192 Michigan (Alcohol; Wall Gasoline, etc.; Brazing; Gasoline Blow; Oil) ......D
Wilson & Co., F. Cortez, 239 Lake (Factory Acetylene) ....B

IND.—Kendallville
Kaker & Sons Co., J. R. (Gasoline) C
MD.—Baltimore
Hull Mfg. Co., J. S., 125 E. Falls (Gasoline Blow) ..D
I.—Detroit
Clayton & Lambert Mfg. Co. (Alcohol; Factory; Mine; Gasoline, etc.; Gasoline Blow) ....B
Globe Brass Wks., 13 Macomb (Gasoline Blow)...F
Union Heater Supply Co. (Gasoline Blow) ......G
MICH.—Northville
Phillips & Harmon (Gasoline, etc.) ....F
MO.—St. Louis
Amer. Stove Co. (Gasoline Blow) ....AAAA
N. J.—Newark
Bernz, Otto, So. 13th cor. So. Orange Av. (Gasoline, etc.; Gasoline Blow)....B
Osborne & Co., C. S. (Alcohol) ....B
N. Y.—Brooklyn
Deverall Perfection Mfg. Co., 36 Bridge (Factory; Mine; Shop; Engine) ..D
Vogel & Bros., Wm. (Oil) ....AA
N. Y.—Buffalo
Shepard & Co., Sidney (Campaign) ....AAAA
New York City
Bogert, A. L., 123 Liberty (Electric; Electric Gas Lighting) ....F
Electric Contract Co., 202 Centre (Portable Electric for Plumbers)..........D
Gleason Mfg. Co., E. P., 20 W. Houston (Gasoline Blow) ....A
Houchin Co., Thos. W. (Gas Lighting) ....D
Hydro-Carbon Burner Co., 197 Fulton (Gasoline, etc.; Gasoline Blow) X
Knapp Mfg. Co., 22 Frankfort (Alcohol; Gasoline Blow) ....E
Mitchell-Vance Co. (Alcohol; Taper) ....AA
Munsell & Co., Eugene (Gas Lighting) ....B
Stoutenborough, X. (Campaign; Oil; Portable) ...D
Wellington Mfg. Co., 470 Cherry (Alcohol; Gasoline Blow; Oil; Portable) ...D
N. Y.—Troy
Troy Stamping Wks. (Tin) ....AAAA
OHIO—Akron
Akron Mfg. Co. (Gasoline, etc.) C
OHIO—Canton
Berger Mfg. Co. (Brazing; Gasoline; Oil) ....AA
Best Street Light Co. (Gasoline. etc.; Gasoline Blow; Brazing) ....B
Sun Vapor Street Light Co. (Gasoline Blow) ....A
OHIO—Cincinnati
Macleod & Co., Walter, 463 E. Front (Factory Oil or Gasoline; Gasoline Blow)A
OHIO—Cleveland
Dangler Stove & Mfg. Co., (Amer. Stove Co.) 365 Perkins Av. (Gasoline; Oil) ....AAAA
Hull Co., M. L., 24 Bway. (Gasoline Blow; Electric;

TORCHES (Con.)

Gas Lighting; Wall) ..H
Reserve Foundry & Mfg. Co., 1302 Euclid Av. (Gasoline Blow) X
Schneider & Trenkamp Co. (Amer. Stove Co., St. Louis, Mo.) (Gasoline, etc.; Gasoline Blow; Oil) ....AAAA
Standard Lighting Co. (Amer. Stove Co., St. Louis, Mo.) (Gasoline, etc.; Oil) ....AAAA
OHIO—Dayton
Dayton Malleable Iron Co. (Shop; Engine, made entirely of Malleable Iron) ....AA
OHIO—Toledo
National Cement & Rubber Mfg. Co. (Gasoline) C
PA.—Allegheny
Sands Mfg. Co., Market & Bayard (Steel Brazed Shop; Engine) ....H
Wall Mfg. Co., P. (Brazed Steel Factory; Mine) ..G
PA.—Erie
Hollands Mfg. Co. (Gasoline; Oil) C
PA.—Philadelphia
Boekel & Co., Wm., 518 Vine (Gasoline Blow) ..A
Gefrorer & Son, C., 248 N. 8th (Gasoline Blow) ....F
Paxson Co., J. W., 1021 N. Delaware Av. (Foundry) ....AA
Roberts Electric Supply Co., H. C., 831 Arch (Gasoline Blow) ....E
Wiler, Wm. (Alcohol) ....D
PA.—Pittsburg
Gem Mfg. Co. (Factory; Mine; Steel Shop; Engine; Gasoline; Oil) .....A
Kirk & Son, Arthur (Iron)X

TORPEDOES

CONN.—Wallingford
Backes Sons, Michael (Toy) ....D
DEL.—Wilmington
Hercules Torpedo Co. (Oil Well; Navel) ....B
ILL.—Peoria
Acme Railway Signal & Mfg. Co. (Railway Signal) ....E
MASS.—Weymouth
Hunt & Sons, Edmund S. (Toy) C
N. Y.—Brooklyn
Bliss & Co., E. W. (Navel) ....AAAA
New York City
Consolidated Fireworks Co. (Track) ....A
Detwiller & Street Fireworks Mfg. Co. (Track) A
OHIO—Berea
Crescent Appliance Co. (Railway Signal) X
OHIO—Bucyrus
Columbia Fire Cracker Co. (Railway Signal) ......D
OHIO—Fostoria
Western Railway Signal Co. (Railway Signal) ......B
Wood Mfg. Co. (Railway Signal) ....G
PA.—Allegheny
Granite Railway Signal Co. (Railway Signal) ......B
PA.—Philadelphia
Jackson's Sons, Samuel, 1129 S. 15th (Railway Signal) C

TORTOISE SHELL GOODS

MASS.—Attleboro
Allen, Smith & Thurston Co. X
N. J.—Newark
Beppart, Griscom & Osborn ....B
Krementz & Co........AAA
Newark Tortoise Shell Novelty Co. ....D

TORTOISE SHELL
New York City
Day, Clark & Co., 21 Maiden
Lane ....B
Dietsch Bros., 14 E. 19th
AA
Kapp Sons Ivory Co., A.
Joseph, 255 4th Av......F
Krementz & Co., 170 B'way
AAA
Rice & Hochster, 485 B'way
A
Taylor, Thos. J., 404 B'way
D
Trenkmann, A., 403 Broome
AAA
Wagner Mfg. Co., 41 Union
Sq. ....B

TOW

See Flax; Hemp

TOWELS ..

GA.—Columbia
Muscogee Mfg. Co. (Cotton)
A
GA.—Griffin
Kincaid Mfg. Co. (Cotton)
AA
GA.—La Fayette
Union Cotton Mills (Cotton)
A
MAINE—Lewiston
Avon Mfg. Co. ....B
MD.—Ilchester
Thistle Mills Co. (Cotton).A
MD.—Millington
Unicorn Mills (Woolen)...A
MASS.—Great Barrington
Riverdale Mills (Cotton)..C
MASS.—Lowell
Lowell Textile Co. (Linen)
C
MASS.—Millbury
Holbrook Mfg. Co. (Crash)
C
MASS.—Webster
Stevens Linen Wks. (Linen
Crash) ....AAA
MASS.—Worcester
Wachusetts Mills (Bath)..C
N. H.—Meredith
Atlas Linen Co. (Linen)...C
N. J.—Mt. Holly
Standard Hicks Hammock
Co. C
N. J.—Sussex
Sussex Mills (Turkish) ..D
N. Y.—Jamestown
Chautauqua Towel Mills
(Linen Union & Turkish)
C
Falconer Towel Co. ......B
New York City
Boland Commission Co.
(Com.) ....F
Burgess & Co., W. H. (Com-
mission) ....AAA
Converse, Stanton & Co.
(Com.) ....AAA
Gardner & Co., 268 Church
(Cotton) X
Greer & Hutton (Manufac-
turers' Agents) ....D
Warner, M. J. (Turkish
Com.) ....D
Whiteside, Jos. S. (Turkish
Com.) ....D
Whitman & Phelps (Com.)
AAA
N. C.—Charlotte
Crowley Mfg. Co. (Honey-
comb; Crash) C
PA.—Chester
Chester Mfg. Co. (Turkish)
A
PA.—Philadelphia
Boyleston Turkish Towel Co.
(Turkish; Plain) C
Schadewald & Sons, Hy...B
Star & Crescent Mills Co.
(Turkish) ....A
Thorpe, Richard ....B
S. C.—Greenville
Huguenot Mills (Cotton)..B

TOWERS

GA.—Augusta
Lombard Iron Works & Sup-
ply Co. (Water) ....A

TOWERS (Con.)
ILL.—Batavia
Challenge Windmill & Feed-
mill Co. (Tank; Steel
Tank; Windmill) ...AAA
United States Wind Engine
& Pump Co. (Bell) ...AA
ILL.—Chicago
Aermotor Co., 12th & Camp-
bell Av. (Bell) ......AAA
ILL.—Freeport
Stover Mfg. Co. (Tank).AA
ILL.—Galesburg
May Bros. (Windmill) ....B
ILL.—Moline
Moline Pump Co. (Wind-
mill) ....A
IND.—Kendallville
Flint & Walling Mfg. Co.
(Steel; Tank) ....AA
KY.—Louisville
Caldwell Co., W. E. (Tire
Bell; Tank) ....A
MICH.—Kalamazoo
Phelps & Bigelow Windmill
Co. (Steel) ....B
Williams Mfg. Co. (Steel).B
MINN.—Minneapolis
Gillette-Herzog Mfg. Co.
(Water) X
MO.—St. Louis
Ruemmeli-Dawley Mfg. Co.,
3900 Choteau Av. (Water
Cooling) ....B
New York City
Alberger Condenser Co., 95
Liberty (Water Cooling)
A
Hayward & Co., S. F. (Wa-
ter) ....AA
Wheeler Condenser & Engi-
neering Co., 120 Liberty
(Water Cooling) ....A
OHIO—Cleveland
Forest City Steel & Iron Co.
(Tank) ....A
Garry Iron & Steel Co.
(Tank) ....A
OHIO—Salem
Denning Co. (Spraying)..A
PA.—Pittsburg
Riter - Conley Mfg. Co.
(Hoist; Tank) ......AAA
Scaife & Sons, Wm. B.
(Tank) ....AAA
PA.—South Bethlehem
Bethlehem Steel Co. (Con-
ing) ....AAAA
PA.—Warren
Struthers, Wells & Co. (Wa-
ter; Tank) ....AA
WIS.—Evansville
Baker Mfg. Co. (Steel;
Windmill) ....A
WIS.—Racine
Freeman & Sons Mfg. Co.,
S. (Windmill) ....A

TOXINS

MICH.—Detroit
Parke, Davis & Co.
(Biological) ....AAAA

TOYS

See also Novelties

CAL.—San Francisco
California Notion & Toy Co.
A
CONN.—Bridgeport
Ives Mfg. Corpn. (Iron; Me-
chanical; Steam; Bridges;
Signals; Stations; Tun-
nels; Switches; Engines;
Cars; Locomotives) ....D
CONN.—Cromwell
Stevens Co., J. & E. (Iron
Beds; Banks) ....AAAA
CONN.—Derby
Gilbert & Sons, A. (Wood)
E
CONN.—Easthampton
Bevin Bros. Mfg. Co. (Bell)
B
Gong Bell Mfg. Co. (Bell)
B
Hill Brass Co., N. N. (Bells)
A
CONN.—Middletown
Kirby Mfg. Co. (Bell)....B

TOYS *(Con.)*

CONN.—New Haven
Elm City Mfg. Co. C
New Haven Toy & Game Co. ....D

CONN.—Stamford
Murphy Mfg. Co. (all kinds) ....E

CONN.—Waterbury
Novelty Mfg. Co. (Bell)...A

ILL.—Chicago
Hofner & Co., W. F., 19 S. Clinton ....E
Nicol & Co. (Banks) .....D

ILL.—Freeport
Arcade Mfg. Co. (Beds; Coffee Mills; Hatchets; Jack-Stones; Lawn Mowers; Pumps; Sad Irons; Savings Banks; Scales; Iron; Steel; Stoves; Tools)...A

IND.—Indianapolis
Kindergarten Toy Co. ....F

IND.—South Bend
South Bend Toy Mfg. Co. (Horses) ....A

IOWA—Ft. Madison
Iowa Farming Tool Co. (Rakes) ....A

MD.—Baltimore
Carriage & Toy Co. (Furniture) ....D

MASS.—Greenfield
Wells Bros. & Co. (All Kinds) ....A

MASS.—Leominster
Union Toy Co. ....F
Whitney Reed Chair Co. (All Kinds) ......AAAA

MASS.—New Bedford
Weeden Mfg. Co. (Banks; Steam) ....D

MASS.—North Cambridge
Hews & Co., A. H. (Banks) ....A

MASS.—North Easton
New England Specialty Co. (Chisels; Plane Irons)..F

MASS.—Springfield
Bradley, Milton Co. ......A

MASS.—Westfield
Hampden Toy Co. ....D

MASS.—Winchendon
Converse & Co., M. E. ....A

MICH.—Holland
Michigan Toy & Novelty Co. (Wood) ....E

MICH.—Jackson
Withington & Cooley Mfg. Co. (Iron) ....AA

MO.—St. Louis
National Candy Co. (Christmas Sugar) ......AAAA
Pleuger & Henger Mfg. Co. (Sad Irons) ....A

N. H.—Manchester
Osgood Toy Co., M. F. (Dancing) ....F

N. H.—Nashua
Nashua Novelty Works....B

N. H.—West Ridge
Butler, Otis P. (Wood)...F

N. J.—Dumont
Scheler, George (Horses)..F

N. Y.—Brooklyn
Schulze Sons, Thos., 370 Cleveland (Tin) X
Teichmann, Richard, 85 Water (Tin; Bell) ....D

N. Y.—Castile
Eliesac Mfg. Co. (Wood)..D

N. Y.—Dunkirk
Armstrong & Fleischman (Chinaware) ....D

N. Y.—Hogansburg
Silkworth & Langtry Co. (Baskets) ....B

New York City
American Doll & Toy Mfg. Co., 55 Great Jones X
Baker & Bigler, 79 Bleecker (Mfrs. Agts.) ....E
Borgfeldt & Co., Geo., 48 W. 4th (Rubber) ..AAAA
Estes & Sons, E. B., 45 John (Wooden) ......AA
Horsman, E. I., 354 B'way C
Ingersoll & Bro., Robert H., 51 Maiden Lane (All Kinds) ....A
Judd & Co., H. L. (Bell; Banks) ....AA

TOYS *(Con.)*

Knapp Electric & Novelty Co., 511 W. 51st (Electric) ....D
Mace & Co., L. H., 111 E. Houston ....B
National Novelty Corpn., 826 B'way ....AAAA
N. Y. Rubber Co., 84 Reade (Rubber) ....AA
Pidget Novelty Co., 265 B'way ....D
Schlesinger & Co., Leo., 372 South (Steam; Tin) ....A
Travers, G. W., 146 Chambers (Mechanical) .....B

N. Y.—Sidney
Sidney Novelty Co. (Horses) ....B

OHIO—Akron
Goodrich Co., B. F. (Rubber) ....AAAA

OHIO—Cleveland
Tanner Mfg. Co. (Cap Pistols; Stoves) ....A
Globe Mach. & Stamping Co. (Stoves) ....E

OHIO—Dayton
Clark & Co., D. P.........C
Dayton Pattern & Model Works (W. S. Hawker, Prop.) (Cannons) .....F

OHIO—Ravenna
Williams, A. C. (Wheelbarrows; Coffee Mills; Coal Hods; Hatchets; Locomotives; Sad Irons; Iron Safes; Savings Banks; Iron; Steel; Stoves; Tools; Trucks) ....A

OHIO—Toledo
American Metal Wheel & Toy Co. ....B
Harris Toy Co. (All Kinds) ....B
Toledo Carriage Woodwork Co. (Wooden) ....A

PA.—Columbia
Columbia Grey Iron Co. (Engines; Carts; Carriages; Wagons; Cars; Hammers; Hatchets; Jack-Stones; Rakes; Sad Irons; Savings Banks; Shovels; Spades; Iron; Steel; Tools; Stoves) C

PA.—Freemansburg
Jones & Bixler Mfg. Co. (Iron) ....D
Shiriner, Son & Co., W. M. (Animals; Iron) ......B

PA.—Lancaster
Hubley Mfg. Co. (Iron; Mechanical; Carts; Wagons; Carriages; Coffee Mills; Engines; Cars; Fire Apparatus; Steel; Savings Banks; Locomotives) ..A

PA.—Monroeton
Booth & Rockwell (Penny) ....F

PA.—Mt. Joy
Rollman Mfg. Co. (Meat Choppers; Iron; Steel)..G

PA.—Mt. Pleasant
Mt. Pleasant Tool Co. (Shovels; Spades) ....B

PA.—Philadelphia
Hammond & Son, J. T., 4534 Hedge ....B

PA.—Reading
Reading Hdw. Co. (Savings Banks) ....AAAA

PA.—Wrightsville
Wrightsville Hardware Co. (Iron; Hammers; Jack-Stones; Hatchets; Pincers; Sad Irons; Shovels; Spades; Steel; Tools....B

VT.—Putney
Stowel Mfg. Co. (Wooden Furniture) ....E

VA.—Richmond
Richmond Cedar Works (Tubs) ....AAAA

WIS.—Milwaukee
Instructive Toy Co. ......D
Meinecke & Son, A. (Furniture; Wooden) ....AA

WIS.—Sheboygan
Garton Toy Co. (Sleds; Wagons, etc.) ....B

TRAGACANTH
See Gum

TRACKERS
MASS.—Reading
Pierce Organ Pipe Co., Sam
(Organ) C

TRACKS
See also Rails
ILL.—Aurora
Wilcox Mfg. Co. (Overhead
Carrying) ....B
ILL.—Chicago
Atlas Railway Supply Co.
(Trolley) ....D
Paige Iron Works (Trolley)
C
ILL.—Ottawa
Porter Co., J. E. (Overhead
Carrying) ....A
IND.—Goshen
Goshen Mfg. Co. (Hay Car-
rier) ....B
IOWA—Fairfield
Louden Machinery Co. (Over-
head Carrying) ....D
MASS.—Boston
Harrington, Robinson & Co.
(Trolley) ....D
MASS.—Cambridge
Barbour, Stockwell Co.
(Trolley) ....A
MASS.—Holyoke
Coburn Trolley Track Mfg.
Co. (Trolley) ....B
MICH.—Detroit
Northern Engineering Co.
(Overhead Carrying) ...A
MICH.—St. Johns
Mason & Co., F. C. (Hay
Carrier) C
MO.—St. Louis
Brecht Butchers' Supply Co.,
G. V., 1201 Cass Av.
(Overhead) ....AAA
Leschen & Sons Rope Co.
(Overhead Carrying) ..AA
N. J.—Hoboken
New York Switch & Cross-
ing Co. (Trolley) ......A
New York City
Carey, Geo. H. (Trolley)..D
Koppel, Arthur, 66 Broad
(Industrial) ....AA
McCabe Hanger Mfg. Co.,
425 W. 25th (Overhead
Carrying) C
New Jersey Fdy. & Mach.
Co., 9 Murray (Industrial;
Overhead Carrying; Port-
able) ....D
Niles-Bement-Pond Co., 111
B'way (Overhead Carry-
ing) ....AAAA
Steel Rail Supply Co. (Trol-
ley) ....A
Weber Railway Joint Mfg.
Co. (Trolley) ....B
N. Y.—West New Brighton
Hunt Co., C. W. (Indus-
trial) ....AA
OHIO—Ashland
Myers & Bro., F. E. (Over-
head Carrying) ...AAA
OHIO—Cambridge
Cambridge Rolling Mill Co.
(Bessemer Steel Hay Car-
rier) ....A
OHIO—Canton
Ney Mfg. Co. (Overhead
Carrying) ....B
OHIO—Cincinnati
Weir Frog Co. (Trolley)..A
OHIO—Cleveland
Atlas Car & Mfg. Co. (Over-
head Carrying) ....A
OHIO—Columbus
Case Mfg. Co. (Overhead
Carrying) ....A
Cleveland Frog & Crossing
Co. (Trolley) ....B
PA.—Philadelphia
Harrington & Son Co., E.
(Overhead Carrying)..AA
Penn Steel Co. (Trolley)
AAAA
Wharton & Co., Wm. Jr.
(Trolley) ....AAA

TRACKS (Con.)
PA.—Reading
Speidel, J. G. (Overhead
Carrying) ....D
PA.—South Bethlehem
Bethlehem Fdy. & Machine
Co. (Industrial) C

TRAINERS
ILL.—Chicago
Barbee Wire & Iron Works
(Vine; Wire) ....B
OHIO—Ashland
Myers & Bro., F. E. (Home;
Bicycle) ....AA
R. I.—Providence
Narragansett Machine Co.
(Bicycle) ....A

TRAMMELS
CONN.—New Britain
Stanley Rule & Level Co.
AAA
MASS.—Athol
Athol Machine Co. ......A
Starrett Co., L. S........A
MASS.—Fitchburg
Sawyer Tool Mfg. Co......C
New York City
Keuffel & Esser Co., 127
Fulton ....AA
Tower & Lyon Co., 95 Cham-
bers ....B
PA.—Philadelphia
Diston & Sons, Henry.AAAA
Paxson Co., J. W., 45 N.
Del. Av. ....AA

TRAMWAYS
CAL.—San Francisco
Vulcan Iron Works (Wire
Rope) ....A
COLO.—Denver
Colorado Iron Works Co.
(Wire Rope) ....AA
Dillen Iron Works Co.
(Aerial; Gravity) .....F
ILL.—Chicago
Allis-Chalmers Co. (Wire
Rope) ....AAAA
Macomber & Whyte Rope
Co. (Wire Rope)......AA
Webster Mfg. Co. (Wire
Rope) ....AA
ILL.—Harvey
Whiting Foundry Equipment
Co. (Overhead) ......AA
MASS.—Holyoke
Coburn Trolley Track Mfg.
Co. (Overhead) ....B
MO.—St. Louis
Broderick & Bascom Rope
Co. (Wire Rope) ...AA
Leschen & Sons Rope Co.,
A. (Wire Rope) .....AAA
N. J.—Newark
Mundy, J. F., 22 Prospect
(Wire Rope) ....A
New York City
Lidgerwood Mfg. Co., 96
Liberty (Wire Rope) .AAA
McCoy Co., Jos. F., 26 War-
ren (Overhead) ....B
Niles-Bement-Pond Co., 111
B'way (Overhead).AAAA
Trenton Iron Co. (Wire
Rope) ....AA
OHIO—Columbus
Jeffrey Mfg. Co. (Overhead)
AAAA
OREGON—Portland
Hammond Mfg. Co. (Wire
Rope) X
PA.—Bangor
Flory Mfg. Co., S. (Wire
Rope) ....A
PA.—Philadelphia
Harrington, Son & Co.,
Edwin (Inc.) (Overhead)
AA
PA.—Pittsburg
Westinghouse Electric &
Mfg. Co. (Electric).AAAA
PA.—Reading
Reading Crane & Hoist
Works (Overhead) C

TRANSFERS
LA.—Lecompte

TRAPS (Con.)
Steam; Sewer; Stench)
           AAAA
Klipfel & Thomas Co., 74
  W. Lake (Steam) X
Lausten Lead Wks, 78 Pratt
  (Bi-Metallic Plated)
           AAAA
McCrea & Co., Jas. (Inc.),
  67 Washn. (Steam)....E
Marsh & Co., Jas. P. (Auto-
  matic Steam) ....B
Monash-Younker Co., 203 S.
  Canal (Steam) ....B
Pearce Construction Co., 269
  Dearborn (Steam) .....F
Raymond Lead Co., 51 W.
  Lake (& Lead Bends; Fer-
  rules) ....AA
Western Valve Co., 43 W.
  Randolph (Steam) .....B
Wolff Mfg. Co., L., 117 W.
  Lake (Sewer Gas).AAAA
ILL.—Dixon
Reynolds Wire Co. (Fly).B
ILL.—Edwardsville
Edwardsville Brass Co.
  (Brass Bell) ....B
ILL.—Kewanee
Western Tube Co. (Steam)
           AAA
ILL.—St. Charles
Glenn Mfg. Co. (Steam) ..D
IOWA—Marshalltown
Dunham & Co., C. A. (Drain
  Valve; Steam) ....E
IOWA—Muscatine
Barry Mfg. Co. (& Bends;
  Ferrules; Lead; Sewer
  Gas) ....A
MD.—Baltimore
Robertson Mfg. Co., James,
  30 Hanover (& Bends;
  Ferrules; Lead; Sewer
  Gas) ....A
MASS.—Boston
Boston Brass Co., 36 Oliver
  (Sewer Gas) C
Boston Specialty Co.,
  168 Congress (Steam)...D
Bourdon Co., 7 Pearl
  (Steam) X
Brainerd Steam Trap Co.,
  Chamber of Com. Bldg.
  (Steam) ....H
Burditt & Williams Co.
  (Rat; Mouse) ....B
Dececo Co., 146 High (Sew-
  er Gas) ....D
D'Este Co., Julian, 24 Ca-
  nal (Steam; Balance
  Valve Steam) ....B
Mason Regulator Company
  (Steam) ....A
Sanitas Mfg. Co., 48 Union
  (Sewer Gas) ....AA
Sturtevant Co., B. F.
  (Steam) ....AAA
Walworth Mfg. Co., 132
  Federal (Steam)..AAAA
Watts Regulator Company
  (Steam) X
MASS.—Peabody
Helios Mfg. Co. (Steam).D
MASS.—Salem
Locke Regulator Company
  (Steam) ....:.A
MASS.—Worcester
National Mfg. Co. (Fly;
  Rat; Mouse) ....A
Parker Wire Goods Co. (Fly;
  Rat; Mouse) ....D
Wire Goods Co. (Fly; Rat;
  Mouse) ....A
MICH.—Detroit
American Blower Company
  (Steam) ....AA
Decoy Fly Paper Co. (Ltd.)
  (Fly; Roach) ....B
Detroit Sanitary Supply Co.,
  27 Jefferson (& Bends;
  Ferrules; Lead Sewer Gas)
           D
Ideal Mfg. Co., 546 Frank-
  lin (Sewer Gas) ....A
Northwestern Fdy. & Supply
  Co. (Cast Iron Sewer Gas)
           B
Park & McKay Co., 55 Bag-
  ley (Sewer Gas) C
Wright Mfg. Co., 99 W.
  Woodbridge (Low Pres-

TRAPS (Con.)
  sure Steam) ....B
MICH.—Grand Rapids
Sproul & McGurrin, 37 S.
  Division (Sewer Gas)...D
MINN.—Minneapolis
Minnesota Beekeepers Sup-
  ply Mfg. Co. (Queen;
  Drone) ....G
MO.—St. Louis
Collier Shot Tower Works,
  319 N. 4th (Bi-Metallic
  Plated) ....AAAA
Kupferle Co., John (Stench)
           AA
Ludlow-Saylor Wire Co.
  (Rat; Mouse) ....AA
Pleuger & Henger Mfg. Co.,
  11th & Herbert (Steam;
  Stench) ....AA
N. H.—Concord
Concord Fdy. & Mach. Co.
  (Sewer) ....B
N. H.—Exeter
Exeter Machine Works
  (Steam) ....B
N. J.—Hasbrouck Heights
Olmsted, L. H. (Mole)....B
N. J.—Jersey City
Griffing Iron Co., 449 Com-
  munipaw Av. (Steam).AA
N. Y.—Albany
Albany Brass & Iron Co.
  (Sewer Gas) ....D
Albany Steam Trap Co., 60
  Church (Steam; Return
  Steam) ....D
N. Y.—Brooklyn
Acton, Jno., 118 John
  (Steam) ....A
Brooklyn Metal Wks. (Inc.)
  cor. 4th Av. & Degraw
  (& Bends; Ferrules; Lead)
           D
Clarke, Robert, 98 Scher-
  merhorn (Sewer Gas)...F
Ronalds & Johnson Co., 51
  Boerum Pl. (Sewer Gas;
  Bends; Ferrules; Lead)
           AA
Schaffer & Budenberg Mfg.
  Co., 10 Division (Steam)
           D
N. Y.—Buffalo
Buffalo Forge Co. (Steam)
           AAA
Buffalo Wire Works (Rat;
  Mouse) ....D
Shepard & Co., Sidney (Fly)
           AAAA
N. Y.—Kenwood
Oneida Community (Ltd.)
  (Bear; Game; Rat; Steel;
  Mouse) ....AAA
N. Y.—Lockport
American District Steam Co.
  (Steam) ....AAA
New York City
Aller, A., 47 Dey (Steam)
           D
Ashcroft Mfg. Co. (The), 85
  Liberty (Steam) ......A
Bushnell Co., John S., 126
  Liberty (Steam) ......E
Cabble Excelsior Wire Mfg.
  Co., Wm. (Rat; Mouse).B
Chasse. R. (Mouse) X
Du Bois & Co., F. N., 247
  9th Av. (& Bends; Fer-
  rules; Lead; also Anti-
  Syphon Trap Vent; Sewer
  Gas) ....A
Estey Wire Works Co., 59
  Fulton (Rat; Mouse)...D
Fairbanks Co., 186 Elm
  (Steam) ....AAA
Ford Co., Thos. P. 81 Cen-
  tre (Compound Steam)..D
Gould's Mfg. Co., 16 Mur-
  ray (Sewer Gas) ....AAA
Haydenville Co. (Sewer Gas)
           A
Hussey & Son, Wm., 37 Dey
  (Steam) ....B
Jenkins Bros., 71 John
  (Steam) ....A
Kieley & Mueller, 7 W.
  13th (Steam) ....B
Libby Mfg. Co., 75 Water
  (Steam) ....E
McNab & Harlin Mfg. Co.,
  56 John (Steam) ....AAA

TRAPS (Con.)

Meyer-Sniffen Co. (Ltd.) (Sewer Gas) ....A
Mott Iron Works, J. L., 88 Beekman (Sewer Gas).AA
Nason Mfg. Co., 71 Beekman (Steam) ....B
National Lead Co., 100 William (& Bends; Ferrules; Lead) ....AAAA
Roberts & Bro., Geo. I. (Inc.), 471 4th Av. (Steam) ....A
Rutzler Co., E. (Steam)...A
Sargent & Co., 151 Leonard (Game) ....AAAA
Standard Steam Specialty Co., 542 W. B'way (Steam) ....D
Thorpe, Platt & Co., 97 Cedar (Steam) ....F
Victor Excelsior Brass Wks., 42 Mott (Sewer Gas)...A
N. Y.—Niagara Falls
Oneida Community (Steel; Game) ....AAA
N. Y.—Oswego
Kitts Mfg. Co. (Steam)...D
N. Y.—Rochester
Streeter & Co., N. R. (Rat; Mouse) ....A
N. Y.—Seneca Falls
Climax Specialty Co. (Sewer Gas) ....B
Rumsey & Co., Ltd. (Inc.) (Sewer Gas) ....A
N. Y.—Syracuse
Direct Separator Company (Steam) C
N. Y.—Watervliet
King Mfg. Co. (Sewer Gas; Bends; Ferrules; Lead).D
N. Y.—Yonkers
Van Auken-Clevauc Company (Steam) ....E
N. C.—Charlotte
Tompkins Co., D. A. (Steam) ....AA
OHIO—Ashtabula
Barber Mfg. Co. (Bell)...C
OHIO—Cincinnati
Bromwell Brush & Wire Goods Co. (Fly) ......AA
Lunkenheimer Co., Beekman & Waverly (Steam)...AA
Sportsman's Shot Works (& Bends; Ferrules; Drawn Lead) ....AAAA
OHIO—Cleveland
Anderson Co., V. D. (Steam) ....B
Chamberlain Cartridge & Target Co. (Pigeon)....A
Cudell, F. E. (Sewer Gas) ....B
Ohio Brass & Iron Mfg. Co. (Sewer Gas) ....B
Reliance Gauge Column Co., 74 E. Prospect (Steam).D
OHIO—Columbus
Sun Mfg. Co. (Rat) .....A
OHIO—Greenfield
Waddell Woodenware Works (Rat; Mouse) ....E
OHIO—Hamilton
Meyers Mfg. Co., Fred J. (Fish; Fly; Rat; Mouse; Roach) ....B
OHIO—Mansfield
Barnes Mfg. Co. (Sewer Gas) ....A
Humphreys Mfg. Co. (Sewer Gas) ....B
PA.—Erie
Advance Mfg. Co. (Sewer Gas) ....H
Erie City Iron Works (Sewer Gas) ....AAAA
Lovell Mfg. Co. (Ltd.) (Rat; Mouse) ....AA
PA.—North East
Fernald Mfg. Co. (Mouse; Rat; Game) ....D
PA.—Philadelphia
Belfield & Co., H., 435 N. Broad (Steam) ......AA
Bickel, Fred L., 1348 Palmer (Float; Thermostatic Steam) ....D
Darby & Sons, Edw., 233 Arch (Rat; Mouse) ....A
Enterprise Mfg. Co. of Pa

TRAPS (Con.)

(Mole) ....AAAA
Eynon-Evans Mfg. Co., 1519 Clearfield (Steam) ....A
Glover Bros. (Jno. Glover) (Steam) ....B
Haines Co., Wm. S., 136 S. 4th (Steam) X
Harrison Safety Boiler Wks. (Steam) ....A
Houghton & Co., E. F., 240 W. Somerset (Steam; also Railway Taps) ......AA
Hydraulic Specialty Co., 427 Walnut (Sewer Gas)...D
Lewis & Bros. Co., Jno. T. (Inc.), 231 S. Front (& Bends; Ferrules; Lead) ....AAAA
Lonergan & Co., J. E. (Steam) ....AA
McCambridge & Co. (Ltd.), 527 Cherry (Sewer Gas).B
Watson & McDaniel Co., 146 N. 7th (Steam) C
PA.—Pittsburg
Bailey-Farrell Mfg. Co. (Sewer Gas) ....AA
Bonar & Co., Jas. (Inc.), Carnegie Bldg. (Steam).B
Kelly & Jones Co., 135 Water (Steam) ....AA
Standard Mfg. Co. (Sewer Gas) ....AA
Standard Sanitary Mfg. Co. (Sewer Gas) ......AAAA
PA.—South Bethlehem
Bethlehem Foundry & Mach. Co. (Sewer) C
R. I.—Providence
General Fire Extinguisher Co. (Steam) ......AAAA
Providence Steam Trap Co. (Brass; Lead; Sewer Gas; Steam) ....D
WIS.—Milwaukee
Bayley & Sons Co., Wm., 732 Greenbush (Steam)..X
National Blower Wks. (Inc.) (Steam; Balance Valve) ....A
Windsor Mfg. Co., 570 Clinton (& Bends; Ferrules; Lead) ....B

TRAM
See Silk Goods

TRAVELERS

CONN.—North Windham
Hartson Co., L. M. (Ring) X
MASS.—New Bedford
Reliance Mfg. Co. (Ring).F
Standard Ring Traveler Co. (Ring) ....B
MINN.—St. Cloud
St. Cloud Iron Wks. (Overhead) ....B
N. Y.—Brooklyn
De Haven Mfg. Co., 50 Columbia Hghts. (Ring)..A
New York City
Tiebout, W. & J., 118 Chambers (Boom; Deck) ....B
R. I.—Pawtucket
Jenckes Mfg. Co. (Ring)..A
R. I.—Providence
Chase & Co., F. A. (Ring) ....B
National Ring Traveler Co., 257 W. Exchange (Ring) ....AA
Shaw Ring Traveler Co., Victor (Ring) ....D

TRAVERSERS

OHIO—Akron
Taplin, Rice & Co. .....B
Webster Camp & Lane Mach. Co. (Clay)...AAAA

TRAYS
See also Sinks

CONN.—Meriden
Bradley & Hubbard Mfg. Co. (Ash) ....AAAA

TREES

CONN.—New Haven
North & Co., O. B. (Saddle)
........................AA
GA.—Demorest
Flor, Edw. (Cart) ....B
IND.—South Bend
Studebaker Bros. Mfg. Co.
(Saddle) ....AAAA
MASS.—Brockton
Brockton Last Co. (Boot;
Shoe) ....B
Miller, O. A. (Boot; Shoe)
........................B
MASS.—Stoughton
Belcher Last Co., Geo. E.
(Boot; Shoe) C
MASS.—Worcester
Howe & Littlefield (Boot;
Shoe) ....F
MICH.—Battle Creek
Johnson Fdy. & Machine
Wks. (Cloak) ....D
MO.—Jefferson City
Sullivan Saddle Tree Co.,
J. S. (Saddle) ....E
N. J.—Newark
Bevan, Joseph (Saddle)..F
Morrell & Abbott (Shoe)
........................X
Osborne & Co., C. S. (Inc.)
(Gig) ....B
Peters Harness & Saddlery
Co. (Express; Gig; Sad-
dle) C
Rubber & Celluloid Harness
Trimming Co. (Express;
Gig) ....AA
N. Y.—Buffalo
Buffalo Last Wks. (Boot;
Shoe) ....B
Pratt & Letchworth Co.
(Saddle) ....AAA
New York City
Olden & Son, Geoffry J.
(Boot; Shoe) ....E
OHIO—New Berlin
Hoover, W. H. (Saddle)..A

TRELLISES

CONN.—Georgetown
Gilbert & Bennett Mfg. Co.
(Wire) ....AAA
ILL.—Chicago
Barbee Wire & Iron Wks.
(Wire) ....B
MASS.—Springfield
Bigelow-Cheney Wire Wks.
(Wire) ....A
MASS.—Worcester
National Mfg. Co. (Wire).A
MO.—Kansas City
Kansas City Wire & Iron
Wks. (Wire) ....A
MO.—St. Louis
Ludlow-Saylor Wire Co.
(Wire) ....AA
N. Y.—Buffalo
Buffalo Wire Works Co.
(Wire) ....D
New York City
Estey Wire Wks. Co., 59
Fulton (Wire) ....B
Howard & Morse (Wire)..D
OHIO—Cleveland
Forrest City Steel & Iron
Co. (Wire) ....A
Tyler Co., W. S. (Wire)
.....................AAAA
OHIO—Columbus
International Fence & Fire-
proofing Co. (Vine)....A
OHIO—Hamilton
Meyers Mfg. Co., Fred J.
(Wire) ....B
PA.—Philadelphia
Darby & Sons, Edw., 233
Arch (Wire) ....A

TRESSELS

IND.—Indianapolis
Udell Works (Painters';
Plasterers') ....A
N. Y.—Rochester
Pease, F. B. (Painters')
........................D
N. Y.—Watervliet
Tilley, J. S. (Painters';
Plasterers') ....E

TRIANGLES

MASS.—Westfield
Crane Bros. (Pool) ....AAA
New York City
Keuffel & Esser Co., 127
Fulton (Steel) ....AA
PA.—Philadelphia
Disston & Sons, Henry
(Draughtsman's Steel)
......................AAAA
R. I.—Providence
Brown & Sharpe Mfg. Co.
(Draughtsman's Steel)
......................AAAA

TRICKS

New York City
Eureka Trick & Novelty Co.
........................F

TRICOTS

See Woolen Goods

TRICYCLES

ILL.—Chicago
Chicago Chair & Wheel Co.
........................A
MD.—Baltimore
Carriage & Toy Co. of Balti-
more, 220 W. Fayette ..C
MASS.—Boston
Pope Mfg. Co. ....AAAA
MASS.—Chicopee
Ames Sword Co. ....B
MASS.—Springfield
Taber-Prang Art Co....AA
MASS.—Waltham
Waltham Mfg. Co. (Gaso-
line) ....A
N. Y.—Buffalo
Pierce Co., Geo. N. (Chil-
drens') ....AA
New York City
Horsman, E. I. (Childrens')
........................C
Mace & Co. L. H. (Chil-
drens') ....B
Pope Mfg. Co., 21 Park Pl.
......................AAAA
Spalding & Bros., 126
Nassau (Childrens')
......................AAAA
OHIO—Elyria
Worthington Mfg. Co. (Chil-
drens'; Invalids) .....B
OHIO—Laura
Cassel Bros. (Invalids')..H
OHIO—Toledo
Gendron Wheel Co. (Chil-
drens') ....AA
Toledo Metal Wheel Co..AA
VT.—Brattleboro
Smith & Co., S. A. (Chil-
drens') ....AA

TRIERS

CONN.—New Britain
Humason & Beckley Mfg.
Co. (Butter; Cheese) ...A
Sargent & Co. (Butter;
Cheese) ....AAAA
ILL.—Chicago
American Cutlery Co. (But-
ter; Cheese) ....AA
Creamery Package Mfg. Co.
(Butter; Cheese) ..AAAA
Vaughan & Bushnell Mfg.
Co (Ham) ....A
MASS.—Boston
Dame, Stoddard & Co. (But-
ter; Cheese) ....A
N. J.—Newark
Johnson, Wm. (Ham) ....D
N. Y.—Buffalo
White Co., L. & I. J. (Ham)
........................A
N. Y.—Little Falls
Burrell & Co., D. H. (But-
ter; Cheese) ......AAAA
New York City
Peck, Stow & Wilcox Co.,
27 Murray (Butter;
Cheese) ....AAAA
VT.—Bellows Falls
Vermont Farm Machine Co.
(Butter; Cheese) C

TRIGS

IND.—La Porte
Lonn & Sons Co. (Hame)..A

TRIMMERS

See also Machy

CONN.—Bridgeport
Acme Shear Co. (Lamp)..B
Bridgeport Brass Company
(Lamp) ....AAA
CONN.—New Haven
Ives Co., H. B. (Lamp)...A
CONN.—Unionville
Monce, S. G. (Photograph)
D
GA.—Atlanta
De Loach Mill Mfg. Co.
(Lumber) ....B
ILL.—Chicago
Allis-Chalmers Co., Home
Ins. Bldg. (Lumber)
AAAA
Klein & Son, Mathias, 87
W. Van Buren.........B
Latham Machinery Co.
(Book) C
Link Belt Machinery Co.,
39th & Stuart Av. (Lumber) ....AAA
ILL.—Waukegan
Underwood, H. M. (Wall
Paper) X
MAINE—Bangor
Union Iron Works (Lumber) ....A
MAINE—North Wayne
North Wayne Tool Co.
(Hedge) C
MASS.—Boston
United Shoe Machinery Co.
(Boot; Shoe; Edge).AAAA
MASS.—Brockton
Snell & Atherton (Welt).C
MASS.—Kingston
Drew & Co., C. (Bricklayers') C
MASS.—Worcester
Barr, H. G. (Leather) ...B
MICH.—Bay City
Garland Co., M. (Two-Saw
Lumber) C
MICH.—Detroit
Strelinger Co., Chas. A.
(Universal) ....A
MICH.—Grand Rapids
American Machinery Co.
(Lumber; Wood) X
Fox Machine Co. (Ltd.)
(Wood) ....A
MICH.—Greenville
Gordon Hollow Blast Grate
Co. (Lumber) ....B
MICH.—Kalamazoo
Hill & Co., Wm. E. (Lath)
B
MICH.—Muskegon
Rodgers Iron Mfg. Co. (Box
Board) ....B
MICH.—Saginaw
Wickes Bros. (Lumber)
AAA
MINN.—Minneapolis
Howell & Co., R. R. (Lumber) ....B
MO.—St. Louis
Curtis & Co. Mfg. Co., 2201
Washn. Av. (Lumber)..A
N. Y.—Belmont
Clark Bros. Co. (Lumber)
A
N. Y.—Buffalo
Holmes Machinery Co., E.
& B. (Two Saw) .....D
Howard Iron Works (Book)
A
N. Y.—Newburgh
Coldwell Lawn Mower Co.
(Brush) ....A
New York City
Cottrell & Sons Co., C. B.
(Electrotype) ....AAA
Jennings Co., C. E., 42 Murray (Spoke) C
Lovejoy Co. (Electrotype).B
Millers Falls Co., 28 Warren (Spoke) ....AA
Reilley Bros. (Wall Paper)
D
Sheridan Co., T. W. & C. B.
(Book) ....A

TRIMMERS (Con.)
OHIO—Akron
Reading Mfg. Co. (Wall Paper) ....D
OHIO—Cincinnati
Lane & Bodley Co. (Two
Saw; Wood) ....B
Randall & Co. (Strap;
Trace) ....B
Smith, Myers & Schnier Co.,
621 W. Front (Lumber).B
OHIO—Dayton
Seybold Machine Co. (Book)
A
OHIO—Springfield
Ridgley Trimmer Co. (Wall
Paper) ....B
Webster & Perks Tool Co.
(Wall Paper) C
OHIO—Tiffin
National Machinary Co.
(Bolt Head) ......AA
PA.—Atglen
Chalfant Hardware Mfg. Co.
(Lamp) X
PA.—Erie
Standard Sawmill Machinery
Co. (Lumber) ......B
Stearns Mfg. Co.
(Lumber) ....B
PA.—Harrisburg
Hickok Mfg. Co., W. O.
(Book) ....AA
PA.—Williamsport
Moltz, Jacob J.:
(Lumber) C
United States Machine Co.
(Lumber) ....D
TENN.—Chatanooga
Wheeland Machine Wks.
(Lumber) ....A
TENN.—Jackson
Southern Engine & Boiler
Wks. (Lumber) ......AA
VT.—Montpelier
Lane Mfg. Co. (Lumber;
Lath) ....A
WIS.—Eau Claire
Phoenix Mfg. Co. (Lath;
Lumber) ....A
Shaw Lumber Co., Daniel
(Lumber) ....AA
WIS.—Milwaukee
Allis-Chalmers Co.
(Lumber) ....AAAA
Filer & Stowell Co.
(Lumber) ....AAA
WIS.—Oshkosh
Chaloner Co.
(Box Board) ......A
WIS.—Stevens Point
Cook, R. A. (Lumber) ..B
WIS.—Wausau
Murray Mfg. Co., D. J.
(Lumber) ....A

TRIMMINGS

See also Hardware; Carriage; also see Next Headings.

CONN.—Bridgeport
Amer. Tube & Stamping
C. (Nickel Plated Steel
Stove Edge) ......AAAA
Bridgeport Brass Co. (Lantern; Oil Lamp) .....AAAA
Bridgeport Coach Lace Co.
(Carriage) C
Burns, Silver & Co.
(Furniture) ....A
Hubbell, Harvey (Stove)
C
Knapp & Cowles Mfg. Co.
(Tin; Iron) C
CONN. Bristol
Sessions & Son, J. H.
(Trunk) ....AA
CONN.—Hartford
Howard & Co., Jas. L.
(Railway Car) ....A
CONN.—Meriden
Bradley & Hubbard Mfg. Co.
(Oil Lamp) ......AAAA
Meriden Britannia Co.
(Coffin) ....AAAA
Miller & Co., Edward
(Tin; Iron, Lantern Oil
Lamp) ....AAAA
Rogers & Bros., C. (Coffin)
AAAA

CONN.—Middletown
Palmer, J. E. (Canopy; Tops) .... AAA
CONN.—Milldale
Ellis & Son, F. L. (Furniture) .... E
CONN.—Mount Carmel
Woodruff & Sons, Walter W. (Carriage) .... A
CONN.—New Britain
North & Judd Mfg. Co. (Halter; Harness) ....AA
Stanley Wks. (Blind) AAA
CONN.—New Haven
Cowles & Co., C. (Pole; Shaft) .... A
English & Mersick Co. (Pole; Shaft) .... B
Mallory, Wheeler Co. (Door Knob) .... AA
North & Co., O. B. (Halter; Harness) ..AA
Sargent & Co. (Coffin) .... AAAA
CONN.—Norwich
Ossawan Mills Co. (Copper Brush) .... B
CONN.—Plainville
Clark & Son, A. N. (Clock) .... B
CONN.—Plantsville
Atwater Mfg. Co. (Pole; Shaft) .... A
CONN.—Stamford
Yale & Towne Mfg. Co. (Hardware) .... AAAA
CONN.—Torrington
Turner & Seymour Mfg. Co. (Curtain Pole) .... A
CONN.—Waterbury
Amer. Ring Co. (Brass; Iron Bedstead; Curtain Pole; Furniture) ...... A
Matthews & Willard Mfg. Co. (Brass; Iron Bedstead) .... AAAA
Novelty Mfg. Co. (Table Cutlery; Brass & Iron Bedstead; Furniture; Dog Collar; Fancy Box; Metal) .... A
Plume & Atwood Mfg. Co. (Tin & Iron; Furniture; Curtain Pole; Harness) AAA
Waterbury Buckle Co. (Suspender & Hose Supporter) AA
Waterbury Mfg. Co. (Curtain Pole) .... AAAA
CONN.—West Haven
Amer. Buckle Co. (Suspender) .... D
West Haven Buckle Co. (Suspender) C
CONN. Winsted
Strong Mfg. Co. (Coffin) A
ILL.—Chicago
Adams & Westlake Co., Ontario & N. Franklin (Car, Metal Coach Railway; Street Car) AAAA
Curtain Supply Co. (Car) AA
Illonois Malleable Iron Co. (Urinal) .... AAAA
Opaque Shade Cloth Co. (Shade) .... AA
Wallace Supply Co., 169 Jakson Boul. (Car)....D
ILL.—Edwardsville
Edwardsville Brass Co. (Lavatory) .... B
ILL.—Freeport
Arcade Mfg. Co. (Stove) A
ILL.—Sterling
Novelty Iron Wks. (Wooden Pump; Iron) .... E
Rock Falls Mfg. Co. (Coffin) .... A
IND.—Anderson
Buckeye Mfg. Co. (Canopy; Tops) .... AA
IND.—Elkhart
Buescher Mfg. Co. (Car) X
IND.—Fort Wayne
City Carriage Wks. (Carriage) C
IND.—La Porte
La Porte Carriage Co. (Carriage) .... A
MAINE—Portland

Cox & Co., A. F. (Shoe) A
Laughling Co., Thos. (Ship) .... A
Maine Red Granite Co.)Stone) .... B
MD.—Baltimore
Duer & Sons, John (Furniture) .... A
MASS.—Amesbury
Atwood Mfg. Co. (Pole; Shaft) C
MASS.—Attleboro
Wilmarth & Co., W. D. (Coffin) .... D
MASS.—Boston
Austin & Eddy (Blind) C
Crosby Steam Gage & Valve Co. (Steam Engine; Boiler) .... AA
Page Bros. Co., 347 Cambridge (Car) .... B
Sherburne & Co., 53 Olive (Car) .... B
Standard Rivet Co. (Dog Collar) .... B
MASS.—Haydenville
Haydenville Co. (Steam Engine) .... A
MASS.—Lynn
Houghton Heel & Leather Co. (Shoe) X
Parker Bros. Mfg. Co. (Shoe) .... E
Smith Co., A. F. (Shoe) B
MASS.—New Bedford
Pairpoint Corporation (Coffin) .... AA
MASS.—North Attleboro
Webster Co. (Sterling Silver) .... A
MASS.—Taunton
Dary & Son, Edwin A. (Stove) .... D
Reed & Barton Corporation (Coffin) .... AAA
MASS.—Worcester
Matthews Mfg. Co. (Stove) .... D
Spencer Wire Co. (Overall) .... A
Warren Leather Goods Co. (Horse Blanket) .... E
Worcester Terrul: & Mfg. Co. (Brass; Steel; Stove) C
MICH.—Detroit
Ireland & Matthews Mfg. Co. (Stove, in all metals) A
Park & McKay Co. (Lavatory) C
MICH.—Grand Rapids
Grand Rapids Brass Co. (Furniture; Metal Furniture) .... A
Waddell Mfg. Co. (Furniture) .... B
MO.—St. Louis
Central Union Brass Co., 811 N. 2nd (Car) ......E
Pleuger & Henger Mfg. Co. (Car; Brass) ....A
N. H.—Manchester
Campbell, John (Harness) H
N. J.—Newark
Goulds Son & Co., M. (Trunk) .... A
Jenkinson & Co., R. C. (Bag; Box; Trunk) AA
Lockwood Mfg. Co. (Carriage; Pole; Shaft) ....B
Rubber & Celluloid Harness Trimming Co. (Harness) AA
Sargeant Mfg. Co. (Harness) .... A
N. Y.—Albany
Burdick & Son (Stove; Specialties) .... B
N. Y.—Binghamton
Crandal, Stone & Co. (Harness; Vehicle Top) ....A
N. Y.—Brooklyn
Columbia Machine Wks. & Malleable Iron Co., 169 Chestnut (Car Electric) A
Gretsch, Fred (Musical Instrument) C
Union Porcelain Wks. (Porcelain; Hardware) D

TRIMMINGS (Con.)

Vogel & Bros, Wm. (Tin; Iron) .... D

N. Y.—Buffalo

McKinnon Dash Co. (Shaft Leather) .... AA

Pratt & Letchworth Co. (Halter; Pole; Shaft) AAA

Shepard & Co., Sidney (Tin; Iron) .... AAAA

New York City

Amer. Flag Co. (Flag; Banner) .... A

Boyle & Co., John (Flag; Banner) .... A

Creamer & Co.. W. G.. 96 John (Car; Railway Car) B

Gould-Merserean Co. (Picture Rod) .... B

Judd & Co., H. L. (Curtain Pole; Picture Rod) AA

Lalance & Grosjean Mfg. Co. (Tin; Iron) ..AAAA

Lamb, J. & R. (Flag; Banner) .... D

McKenna & Bros., Jas. J. (Railway Car) .... A

Metal Stamping Co. (Carriage) .... A

Meyer-Sniffen Co. (Ltd.) (Urinal) .... A

Nason Mfg. Co. (Radiator) B

N. Y. Nickel Plating & Mfg. Co., 73 Watts (Stove) .... D

Russell & Erwin Mfg. Co. (Hardware) ...... AAAA

Salomon & Phillips (Furniture) .... AA

Simpson Co., Thomas I. (Yacht) .... F

N. Y.—Oxford

Clarke Blue Stone Co., F. G. (Stone) .... A

N. Y.—Rochester

National Casket Co. (Coffin) .... AAAA

N. Y.—Troy

Kilbourne Mfg. Co. (Stove) C

N. Y.—Waterliet

Covert Mfg. Co. (Halter) A

OHIO—Akron

Baker-McMillan Co. (Tin; Iron) .... B

OHIO—Canton

Elbel Co. (Halter; Harness) A

OHIO—Cincinnati

Cinn. Coffin Co. (Coffin) AA

Crane & Breed Mfg. Co. (Coffin) .... AA

Electric Railway Equipment Co. (Street Car) .....B

Lunkenheimer Co. (Steam Engine) .... AA

McKowan Co.. Jno. H., (Tin; Iron; Steam Engine; Boiler) .... A

Peck-Williamson Htg. & Ventg. Co. (Urinal) ....B

OHIO—Cleveland

Cleveland Hdw. Co. (Pole; Shaft) .... AA

Fanner Mfg. Co. (Stove) A

Ohio Brass & Iron Mfg. Co. (Urinal) .... B

OHIO—Columbus

Columbus Bolt Wks. (Pole; Shaft) .... AA

OHIO—Dayton

Dayton Mfg. Co. (Car; Refrigerator; Railway; Vestibule Car) ...... A

OHIO—Mansfield

Ohio Brass Co. (Railway; Street Car) .... AA

OHIO—Springfield

Springfield Brass Co. (Steam Engine) ...... E

OHIO—Toledo

Kroh Co., C. Z. (Carriage) E

PA.—Mechanicsburg

Wilcox Mfg. Co., D. (Carriage) .... A

TRIMMINGS (Con.)

PA.—New Castle

Amer. Car & Ship Hdw. Mfg. Co. (Car; Brass; Bronze) .... D

PA.—Philadelphia

Adamson & Co., James (Suspender) .... A

Berger Bros. Co. (Tin; Iron) .... A

Brill Co., J. G. (Railway Car) .... AAAA

Devlin Mfg. Co., Thos.. (Tin; Iron) .... AA

Gaumer Co., Jno. L. (Railway Car) C

Green & Co., Henry W. (Shade) .... A

Halstead & Co., 1129 Cherry (Car) C

Horstmann Co., Wm. H. (Railroad Uniform; Carriage; Blind) .. AAAA

Lane's Sons, D. M. (Pole; Shaft) .... D

Loeb, Lipper & Co. (Bullion) A

McCambridge & Co. (Ltd.) (Bath Tub) .... B

Maurer & Sons. F. W. (Shade; Blind) ...... B

Miller Lock Co. (Railway Car) .... B

Porter & Co.. C. B. (Tin; Iron) .... B

Thorn Co., J. S. (Iron; Building) .... B

PA.—Pittsburg

Canonsburg Iron & Steel Co. (Tin; Iron) ...... B

Standard Mfg. Co. (Urinal) ....AA

PA.—Williamsport

Valley Iron Wks. (Pole; Shaft) .... A

PA.—Wrightsville

Wrightsville Hdw. Co. (Tin; Iron) .... B

R. I.—Pawtucket

Cobb & Co., W. R. (Jewelers' Chain) ... B

Fuller & Son, Co., Geo. H. (Jewelers' Chain) .... A

R. I.—Providence

Ballou & Co.. B. A. (Jewelers' Chain) ...AA

Dover Co., Geo. W. (Jewelers' Chain) .. B

Hamilton & Hamilton, Jr. (Jewelers' Chain) .. A

Heimberger & Pearson (Jewelers' Chain) .... F

Lederer Co.. S. & B. (Jewelers' Chain) C

Lind Co.; Thos. W. (Jewelers' Chain) .. A

New England Butt Co. (Door Knob) .... AA

Vose Mfg. Co., Geo. L. (Jewelers' Chain) .. B

Waite, Mathewson & Co. (Jewelers' Chain) .. B

VT.—Post Mills

Chubb Rod Co.. T. H. (Fishing Rod) ...... A

W. VA.—Wheeling

Wheeling Metal & Mfg. Co. (Tin; Metal; Jar; Metal for Glass Jars) ...... D

WIS.—Milwaukee

Loeffelholz & Co.. 170 Clinton (Car) .... A

WIS.—Oshkosh

Schmidt Bros. Trunk Co. (Trunk) .... A

WIS.—Racine

Racine General Mfg. Co. (Wagon; Harness) .... E

TRIMMINGS: CARRIAGE

N. Y.—Rochester

Schaefer & Klien (Silk Carr.) C

Schlegel Mfg. Co. (Silk Carriage) C

Vogt Mfg. & Coach Lace Co. (Silk Hearse, etc.) .....A

OHIO—Cincinnati

Albrecht & Co., Chas. (Silk

TRIMMINGS (Con.)
Carriage Fringes) ......B
PA.—Philadelphia
Horstmann & Co., Wm. H.
(Silk) ....AAA

TRIMMINGS: DRESS

See also Silk Goods

ILL.—Chicago
Fiedler & Sons, A. B.
(Fringes; Gimpes, etc.)A
...........................A
ILL.—Highland
Highland Embroidery Wks.
............................B
MASS.—Boston
Boston Braid Mfg. Co.
(Cloak; Dress) ....F
Weinz Trimming Co. (Silk)
............................E
Ziegler & Sons, A. (Silk;
Worsted) ....B
N. J.—Hoboken
Arnold & Co., A. (Silk Mil-
linery; Dress) ....D
N. Y.—Brooklyn
Castle Braid Co. (Silk
Dress; Cloak) ....AA
Jennings Lace Wks. (Silk)
..........................AAAA
New York City
Bernstein & Co. (Silk Cloak;
Dress). ....D
Buschmann, Chas. H. (Silk
Fringes; Cords, etc.) ...D
Fisher, M. (Silk) ....D
Hertlein, Chr. E. (Silk) ..A
Jung & Turnbull (Silk) ...D
Levue & Fimpel (Silk) ...D
Muller, J. (Silk) ....D
Neudorfer & Hochbaum
(Silk) ....D
Oehle & Brocker (Silk) ...C
Opper & Bro., H. L. (Silk)
............................C
Prosnitz & Greenebaum
(Silk) ....D
Sundheimer Bros. (Silk) ..B
Wolf & Newman (Silk)...D
N. Y.—Rochester
Schlegel Mfg. Co. (Silk
Skirt) C
PA.—Philadelphia
Bernstein, Kaufman & Co.
(Silk) ....A
Binns Patent Band Co.
(Silk) ....D
Goodman, Loeb & Co. (Silk)
............................A
Hensel-Colladay Co. (Silk) A
Horstmann & Co., Wm. H.
(Silk) ....AAA
Loeb, Lipper & Co. (Silk
Gimp, etc.) ....A
Rosenau & Co., S. (Silk)..A

TRIMMINGS: LAMP

ILL.—Chicago
Bennett, I. A., Monadnock
Block (Mfrs. Agent)....D
Block Light Co., 26 Lake, A
PA.—Philadelphia
Hensel Silk Mfg. Co. (Silk)
............................C

TRIMMINGS: MILITARY

CONN.—Waterbury
Waterbury Button Co. ....A
New York City
Eicke, Edward, 157 Canal
(Silk) ....E
Siegman & Weil, 77 Wooster
............................A
PA.—Philadelphia
Horstmann & Co., Wm. H.
............................AAA

TRIMMINGS: MILLINERY

See also Millinery

New York City
Brandt & Bros., Joseph

TRIMMINGS (Con.)
(Silk) ....D
Metzger & Co., Louis (Silk)
............................A
Prosnitz & Greenebaum
(Silk) ....D
Ungar, M. (Silk) C
Wolf & Newman (Silk)...D
PA.—Philadelphia
Bernstein, Kaufman & Co.
(Silk) ....A
Binns Patent Band Co.
(Silk) ....D
Goodman, Loeb & Co. (Silk)
............................A
Hensel-Colladay Co. (Silk) A
Loeb, Lipper & Co. (Silk), A
Rosenau & Co., S. (Silk), A

TRIMMINGS: SHADE

PA.—Philadelphia
Maurer & Sons, F. W., 528
Cherry (Silk) ....B

TRIMMINGS: UNDERTAKERS

New York City
Fisher, M., 61 Worth (Silk)
............................C
Frank & Lambert, 47 Greene
............................A
N. Y.—Rochester
Schaefer & Klein C
Schlegel Mfg. Co. ....B
PA.—Philadelphia
Schrack & Sherwood (Silk)
............................B
Wright & Co., S. D., 1017
N. Front. ....D

TRIMMINGS: UPHOLSTERY DRAPERY, ETC

ILL.—Chicago
Chicago Fringe & Embroid-
ery Co., Wash. and Mar-
ket ....D
Mackie-Lovejoy Mfg. Co.
(Brass; Furniture) C
Mansure Co., E. L., 75 Mich.
Av. (Upholstery) ......A
Peters Trimming Co., 229
Fulton ....B
Phoenix Trimming Co., of
Chicago C
New York City
Filer & Co., J. A. (Silk
Cords; Tassels, etc.) ...F
Grau & Lehman (Silk Up-
holstery) ....D
Hepner & Horwitz (Silk
Cords; Gimps; Tassels) C
Hofman & Ellrodt (Silk Up-
holstery Cords; Tassels) C
Leiter, I. H. (Silk Furn.
Guimps) ....F
Meyer & Co., Martin (Silk
Upholstery) C
Reshower & Co., Joseph
(Silk Fringes; Tassels;
Cords). ....B
Union Upholstery Trimming
Co., 603 W. 36th (Uphols-
tery) C
Waterman, Felix (Silk), D
Weinberg Co., C. (Silk) ..D
William's Sons, P. H.
(Silk) ....D
N. Y.—Valatie
Adhesive Guimp Mfg. Co.
(Furniture Gimps; Cords;
Headings for Fringe) ..D
OHIO—Cincinnati
Hoffmeister Co., Alb. F.
(Gimps; Fringes).......C
PA.—Emaus
Keystone Silk Mills (Silk
Draperies) ....AAA
PA.—Philadelphia
Eastlake Mfg. Co. (Furn.
Gimp, etc.) ....B
Hensel Silk Mfg. Co. (Silk)
............................C
Horstmann & Co., Wm. H.
)Silk) ....AAA
Maurer & Sons, F. W. (Silk)

TRIMMINGS (Con.)

Oehrle Bros. & Co. (Silk)...C
Schrack & Sherwood (Silk)
........................B
Siedmann & Sons Mfg. Co.,
David (Silk Fringes;
Cords Tassels; Curtain
Loops, etc.) ....B

TRIPODS

N. J.—Jersey City
Bauer, Max ....G
New York City
Anthony & Scovill Co., 122
5th Av. ....D
Folmer & Schwing Mfg. Co.,
407 Broome C
N. Y.—Rochester
Eastman Kodak Co., AAAA
OHIO—Cleveland
Cleveland Metal Stamping
Co. ....E
WIS.—Burlington
Multiscope & Film Co. ...D

TRIPOLI

GA.—Spring Place
Cohutta Talc Co. ....E
N. J.—Newark
Hansen & Van Winkle Co.
........................AA
N. Y.—Rochester
Eastman Kodak Co...AAAA

TRIPPERS

ILL.—Chicago
Weller Mfg. Co., 118 North
Av. (Belt) ....A

TRIPS

MICH.—Bay City
Garland Co., M. (Steam;
Cart) C
MICH.—Kalamazoo
Hill & Co., Wm. E. (Steam;
Cart) ....B
PA.—Chester
Berry Engineering Co.
(Steam) ....E
WIS.—Milwaukee
Filer & Stowell Co. (Ltd.)
(Steam; Cart)......AAA

TRITURATES

IND.—Indianapolis
Lilly & Co., Eli (Tablet)
........................AA
MICH.—Detroit
Parke, Davis & Co. (Tablet)
........................AAAA
New York City
Fraser Tablet Triturate
Mfg. Co. (Tablet) ....AA
OHIO—Cincinnati
Merrell Chemical Co., Wm.
S. ....AAA

TRITURATORS

CAL.—Los Angeles
Acme Triturator Co.......X
N. Y.—Newburgh
Coldwell-Wilcox Co. ......B

TROLLEYS

ALA.—New Decatur
North Alabama Engineering
Co. (Overhead) ...:.....D
ILL.—Aurora
Wilcox Mfg. Co. (Overhead)
........................B
ILL.—Chicago
Perrin & Co., W. R. (Beef;
Hog) ....A
MICH.—Detroit
Northern Engineering Wks.
(Pneumatic) ....A

New York City
Hunt Co., C. W. (Over-
head) ....AA
Ner Jersey Fdry. & Mach.
Co., 9 Murray (I. Beam)
........................D
Yale & Towne Mfg. Co., 9
Murray (I. Beam) AAAA

TROLLEYS (Con.)

OHIO—Cleveland
Atlas Car & Mfg. Co.
(Street Railway).....AA
Garry Iron & Steel Co.
(Pneumatic) ....A
PA.—South Bethlehem
Bethlehem Fdry. & Machine
Co. (Street Railway) ...C
PA.—Pittsburg
Nuttall Co., R. D. (Street
Railway) ....A
PA.—Reading
Reading Crane & Hoist Wks.
(Overhead) ....A

TROMMELS

WIS.—Milwaukee
Allis-Chalmers Co. ..AAAA
2056 TROUGHS

TROUGHS

ILL.—Chicago
Barbee Wire & Iron Wks.
(Watering) ....B
Caldwell & Son Co., H. W.
Western Av. & 17th (Con-
veyor) ....AA
MD.—Baltimore
Baltimore Cooperage Co.
(Bakers') ....B
MASS.—Boston
Johnson & Co., H. A. (Ba-
kers') ....A
N. J.—Paterson
Paterson Heater Co. (Eaves)
........................H
N. J.—Plainfield
Pond Machine Tool Co.
(Grindstone) ....AAAA
N. Y.—Cato
Dutton & Co., E. Q. (Cast
Iron, Hog) ....E
N. Y.—Manlius
Cheney & Son, S. (Pig) ..A
New York City
Fiske Iron Wks., J. W.
(Watering) ....B
N. Y.—Troy
West Side Fdry. Co. (Cat-
tle) ..::.............A
OHIO—Cleveland
Avery Stamping Co. (Cattle)
........................B
OHIO—Columbus
Kilbourne & Jacobs Mfg. Co.
(Seamless Steel) ..AAAA
OHIO—Salem
Clark Co., W. J (Seamless
Steel) ....A
OHIO—Tremont
Lehr Agr'l Co. (Hog) ....B
PA.—Bausman
Bausman, D. H. (Poultry;
Steel; Stock) C
PA.—East Bangor
East Bangor Consolidated
Slate Co. (Slate Feed) AA
East Bangor Mfg. Co. (Cast
Hog) ...::............X
PA.—Elizabethtown
Bucks Sons Co., A. (Poul-
try; Watering; Cattle;
Pump) ....A
PA.—Nazareth
Nazareth Fdry. & Mach. Co.
(Cattle) .::..........B
PA.—Philadelphia
Link Belt Engineering Co.
(Conveyor). ....AA
PA.—Tatamy
Messinger Mfg. Co. (Water-
ing) ....B
R. I.—Providence
Browne & Sharpe Mfg. Co.
(Grindstone).:...AAAA

TROUSERS

See Clothing: Men's

TROWELS

CONN.—Bridgeport
Knapp & Cowles Mfg. Co.
(Plastering; Pointing; La-
dies' Floral; Garden) ...C
CONN.—New Britain
Landers, Frary & Clark
(Garden) ....AAA
CONN.—Southington

TROWELS (Con.)

Peck, Stow & &Wilcox Co.
(Garden) ....AAAA
CONN.—Unionville
Humphrey, H. W. (Garden)
D
IND.—Indianapolis
Atkins & Co., E. C. (Brick;
Plastering) ....AAAA
IND.—Lawrenceburg
Bishof & Co., Geo. H.
(Plastering; Brick) ....A
MASS.—Sharon
Lathrop & Co., H. A. (Plast-
ing; Garden) X
N. J.—Newark
Johnson, Wm. (Brick; Plast-
ering; Garden) ....D
National Saw Co. (Brick;
Plastering) ....B
N. Y.—Brooklyn
New York Stamping Co.
(Garden) ....A
N. Y.—Buffalo
Shepard & Co., Sidney
AAAA
New York City
Sargent & Co., 151 Leonard
(Garden) ....AAAA
Wiebusch & Helger, 9 Mur-
ray (Brick; Plastering) A
OHIO—Canton
Gibbs Mfg. Co. (Garden) .A
Kohler & Co., F. E. (Gar-
den) ....B
OHIO—Cleveland
Avery Stamping Co. (Gar-
den) ....B
OHIO—Salem
Clarke Co., W. J. (Garden)
A
PA.—Philadelphia
Disston & Sons, Henry
(Brick; Plastering; Coke;
Garden) ....AAAA
Stortz & Sons, Jno., 210
Vine (Brick; Plastering)
E

TRUCKS

**See also Carriages & Wag-
ons; Wheels**

ALA.—New Decatur
North Alabama Enigneering
Co. (Logging; Lumber), D
ALA.—Selma
Peacock's Iron Wks. (Ball
Bearing, for Industrial
Cars; Logging; Lumber;
Steel; Dry Kiln; Cotton)
X
Union Iron Wks. Co. (Steel;
Dry Kiln) ....B
ARK.—Jonesboro
Hiett Wagon Co. (Stave;
Heading) ....E
CAL.—San Francisco
Hammond & Co. (Inc.), J.
(Car; Electric Railway) B
CONN.—New Haven
Mersick & Co., C. S., 286
State (Baggage; Stove) A
CONN.—Windsor Locks
Clark Co., Geo. P. (Bag
Barrel; Baggage; Store;
Warehouse; Factory; Rub-
ber Roll) C
DEL.—Elsmere
Diamond State Fibre Co.
(Mill) ....B
DEL.—Wilmington
Amer. Vulcanized Fibre Co.,
1017 Market (Mill) AAAA
ILL.—Chicago
Chicago Scale Co., 151 Jeff'n
(Baggage; Store; Ware-
house; Factory; Bacon;
Ham; Hog; Platform;
Barrel) ....A
International Harvester Co.
(Binder) ....AAAA
Fairbanks, Morse & Co.,
Franklin & Monroe
(Store; Warehouse; Fac-
tory) ....AAAA
Kindl Car Truck Co., 135
Adams (Steam Car) ....B
McGuire, Cumming Mfg.
Co., 122 N. Sangamon
(Electric,etc.) ....AA
McMullin Motor Power &
Construction Co. (Motor)
B

TRUCKS (Con.)

Nicol & Co. (Toy) ....D
Standard Car Truck Co., Old
Colony Bldg. (Roller Bear-
ing Passenger Electric;
Freight Car Locomotive
Tender) ....B
ILL.—Freeport
Arcade Mfg. Co. (Stove;
Warehouse Factory;
Store) ....A
ILL.—Harvey
Whiting Fdry Equipment
Co. (Fdry.; Ingot; Rolling
Mill) ....AA
ILL.—Joliet
Bates Machine Co. (Wire
Mill) ....B
ILL.—Marseilles
Marseilles Mfg. Co. (Binder)
A
ILL.—Moline
Moline Wagon Co. (Header)
AAAA
ILL.—Mt. Vernon
Mt. Vernon Car Mfg. Co.
(Logging; Lumber), AAA
IND.—Elkhart
Foster Novelty Co., C. A.
(Carriage; Crate) .....F
IND.—Evansville
Smith, I. L. (Store; Ware-
house; Factory) ....F
IND.—Indianapolis
Atkins & Co., E. C. (Lum-
ber; Timber) .....AAAA
Dietz Co., Fred., 1102 Madi-
son Av. (Store; Ware-
house; Factory) C
Nordyke, Marmon Co. (Bag;
Barrel) ....AAA
Over, Ewald (Binder) C
Potts Co. (Inc.), C. A.
(Brick; Tile) ....B
Tucker & Dorsey Mfg. Co.
(Barrel; Store; Ware-
house; Factory; Stove;
Bag) ....A
IND.—Logansport
Dorner Truck & Fdry Co.
(Electric Motor) X
IND.—Richmond
Richmond City Mill Wks.
(Bag; Barrel) ....B
IND.—South Bend
Bowsher Co., N. P. (Bag) B
IOWA—Clinton
Fish Bros. Mfg. Co. (Bind-
er; Header) ....A
IOWA—Dubuque
Adams Co. (Barrel; Bag;
Iron; Stove) ....A
MAINE—Kennebunk
Leatheroid Mfg. Co. (Store;
Warehouse; Factory) ...A
MASS.—Boston
Ames Plow Co. (Baggage;
Block; Platform; Ware-
house) ....AAAA
Boston Belting Co. (Rubber
Roll) ....AAAA
Boston & Lockport Block
Co. 160 Commercial (Bag;
Baggage; Box; Foundry;
Rolling Mill; Store; Ware-
house; Factory; Barrel;
Bacon; Ham; Block;
Book; Cotton; Dry Goods;
Platform; Brick; Store;
Stove; Timber) ....A
Sturtevant Co., B. F. (Lum-
ber; Dry Kiln Foundry)
AAA
MASS.—Chicopee Falls
Belcher & Taylor Agr'l Tool
Co. (Bag; Barrel; Store;
Warehouse; Factory) ...A
MASS.—Lawrence
Perkins Co., C. N. (Hook;
Ladder) ....D
MASS.—Springfield
Bemis Car Truck Co. (Elec-
tric, etc.) X
Wason Mfg. Co. (Steam;
Electric) ....AA
MD.—Baltimore
Balto. Car Wheel Co., Pat-
terson Av. & Payson (Elec-
tric) ....B
MASS.—Westfield
Crane Bros. (Warehouse)
AAA

TRUCKS (*Con.*)

MICH.—Battle Creek
Hart, R. A. (Printers Form)
................................E

MICH.—Detroit
Amer. Blower Co. (Steel;
Dry Kiln) ....AA
Byram & Co. (Inc.) (Foun-
dry). ....D
Northern Engineering Wks.
(Foundry; Ingot; Rolling
Mill) ....A
Russel Wheel & Fdry. Co.
(Car; Steam; Electric)
..........................AA

MICH.—Grand Rapids
Grand Rapids Hand Screw
Co. (Store; Warehouse;
Factory) ....B

MICH.—Holly
Michigan Mfg. & Lumber
Co. (Store; Warehouse;
Factory) ....B

MICH.—Jackson
Withington & Cooley Mfg.
Co. (Store; Warehouse)
..........................AA

MICH.—Kalamazoo
Kalamazoo Railway Supply
Co. (Baggage)............B

MICH.—Lansing
Lansing Wheelbarrow Co.
(Bag; Barrel; Baggage;
Box; Foundry; Rolling
Mill; Store; Warehouse;
Factory; Bacon; Ham;
Carpet; Cotton; Dry
Goods; Iron;Platform;
Post-Office; Printers';
Stevedores'; Stove; Wag-
on; Bottle Drawing) AAA

MICH.—Morenci
Michigan Brick & Tile
Mach. Co. (Brick)......D

MICH.—Northville
Dubuar Mfg. Co., J. A.
(Barrel) X

MICH.—Saginaw
Farmers' Handy Wagon Co.
(Logging; Lumber) ....B
Michigan Wheelbarrow &
Truck Co. (Logging; Lum-
ber; Store; Warehouse;
Factory) ....B
Morley Bros. (Inc.) (Tim-
ber) ....AA
Wickes Bros. (Inc.) (Dry
Kiln). ....AAA

MICH.—Three Rivers
Sheffield Car Co. (Electric
Motor; Logging; Lumber;
Foundry; Store; Ware-
house; Street Car) ...AA

MINN.—Faribault
Nutting Truck Co. (2, 3, 4
& 6 Wheeled Bag; Bar-
rel; Baggage; Basket;
Box; Store; Warehouse;
Factory; Dry Goods;
Platform) C

MINN.—Minneapolis
Puffer-Hubbard Mfg. Co.
(Store; Warehouse; Fac-
tory) C

MINN.—Winona
Winona Wagon Co.
(Header) ....AA

MO.—St. Charles
St. Charles Car Co. (Warehouse) ....AAAA

MO.—St. Louis
Amer. Car Co. (Steam; Elec-
tric) ....AAA
Amer. Car & Fdry. Co. 706
Chestnut (Car; Steam;
Electric) ....AAAA
Amer. Steel Fdry. Co., 509
Olive (Steel Car; Steam;
Electric) ....AAAA
Brownell Co., 2300 N. Bway.
(Car; Steam; Electric)
..........................AAA
Commonwealth Steel Co.,
B'k of Commerce Bldg.
(Cast Steel Car; Steam;
Electric) ....AAA
Cooney Mfg. Co., P. J., 900
Cass Av. (Hook & Ladder)
..........................C
Fernholtz Brick Mach. Co.,
Boyle & Manchester Av.
(Brick) ....D
St. Louis Car Co., 8000 N.
Bway. (Car; Steam; Elec-

TRUCKS (*Con.*)

tric; Street) .....AAAA
Whitman Agr'l Co., 6900 S.
Bway. (Baggage; Brick;
Store; Warehouse; Fac-
tory) ....AA

N. H.—Laconia
Laconia Car Co. Wks. (Electric) ....AA

N. H.—Manchester
Campbell, Jno. (Stove) ...H

N. J.—Elizabeth
Stephenson Co., Jno. (Electric; Street) ....B

N. J.—Grenloch
Bateman Mfg. Co. (Barrel)
..........................A

N. J.—Paterson
Bogert-Carlough Co. (Steel;
Store; Warehouse; Fac-
tory) ....F

N. Y.—Albany
Dederick Son, P. K. (Brick;
Tile) ....A

N. Y.—Betavia
Johnson Harvester Co.
(Binder) ....AAAA

N. Y.—Brooklyn
Phillips, Doup & Co., 56
Pearl (Baggage; Iron
Freight) C

N. Y.—Buffalo
Buffalo Forge Co. (Timber)
..........................AAA
Buffalo Scale Co. (Bag;
Barrel; Baggage; Store;
Warehouse; Factory; Plat-
form) ....AA

N. Y.—Elmira
Amer. La France Fire En-
gine Co. (Hook & Ladder)
Extension; Hook & Lad-
der) ....B

N. Y.—Homer
Phoenix Hdw. Mfg. Co.
(Barrel) ....D

N. Y.—Hoosick Falls
Wood Mowing & Reaping
Mach. Co., W. A. (Bind-
er) ....AAAA

New York City
Fairbanks Co., 186 Elm
(Bag; Baggage; Box;
Pipe; Rolling Mill; Store;
Warehouse; Factory; Wire
Mill; Barrel; Bakers';
Basket; Beam; Brick; Bul-
lion; Car; Coal; Dry Kiln;
Foundry; Garbage; Laun-
dry; Office; Paper Roll;
Printers' Forms; Stove;
Street Car; Tannery; Tim-
ber; Tip; Window Glass;
Wire) ....AAAA
Hayward & Co., S. F. (Hook
& Ladder Extension;
Hook & Ladder) ......D
Koppel, Arthur, 66 Broad
(Foundry) ....A
Peckham Mfg. Co., 26 Cort-
landt (Steam; Electric). B

N. Y.—Poughkeepsie
Adriance, Platt & Co.
(Binder) ....AAAA

N. Y.—Rochester
Stewart, A. E. & S. C.
(Hook & Ladder) ....E
Yawman & Erbe Mfg. Co.,
(Bottlers') ....AA

N. Y.—Seneca Falls
Rumsey & Co. (Ltd.) (Hook
& Ladder) ....A

N. Y.—Syracuse
Syracuse Chilled Plow Co.
(Barrel; Store; Ware-
house; Factory; Bag). AA

N. Y.—Troy
Taylor Truck Co. (Electric)
..........................B

N. Y.—Warsaw
Warsaw Elevator Co. (Bag;
Baggage; Basket; Box;
Foundry; Pipe; Store;
Warehouse; Factory; Bar-
rel; Brick; Dry Kiln;
Stove; Timber) .....B

N. C.—Statesville
Steele & Sons, J. C. (Brick;
Tile) ....B

OHIO—Barons
Amer. Clay Working Mchry.
Co. (Brick; Tile; Box)..X

OHIO—Cincinnati
Day & Co., J. H. (Store;

TRUCKS (Con.)

Warehouse; Factory) ..A
Fay, J. A. & Egan Co.
(Machinery) ......AAAA
Lane & Bodley Co. (Log;
Timber).............AA
Obermayer Co., S. (Stove)
AA
Tatum Co., Samuel C. (Bag;
Barrel; Dry Goods) ...B
Towsley Mfg. Co., Jno. T.
Evans N. of Gest (Log-
ging; Lumber; Store;
Warehouse; Factory) ...B
Zering Mfg. Co., H., 218
Charles (Store; Ware-
house; Factory) .....E

OHIO—Cleveland

Atlas Bolt & Screw Co.
(Brick; Logging; Lumber;
Rolling Mill; Store; Ware-
house; Factory; Wire Mill;
Barrel; Dry Kiln; Foun-
dry)................AA
Van Dorn & Dutton Co.,
1796 E. Madison Av.
(Electric) ....B

OHIO—Columbus

Case Mfg. Co. (Bag; Barrel)
A
Kilbourne & Jacobs Mfg. Co.
(Bag; Box; Foundry; Roll-
ing Mill; Store; Ware-
house; Factory; Coal; Ba-
con; Ham; Baggage;
Book; Bottlers'; Carpet;
Cotton; Dry Goods; Dye
House; Iron; Lumber;
Post Office; Printers';
Stevedores'; Stove; Wag-
on; Brick; Tile; Barrel;
Basket; Office) ...AAAA

OHIO—Cuyahoga Falls

Turner, Vaughn & Taylor
Co. (Brick; Wire Mill;
Store Warehouse) ......B

OHIO—Dayton

Barney & Smith Car Co.
(Steam; Electric)..AAAA
City Forge & Iron Wks.
(Dry Goods; Warehouse;
Box) ....D
Raymond Co., C. W. (Brick;
Tile) ....A

OHIO—Defiance

Defiance Box Co. (Store;
Warehouse; Foundry), AA

OHIO—Tremont

Lehr Agr'l Co. (Bag; Barrel)
B

OHIO—Hamilton

Black-Clawson Co. (Stuff
Box) ....AAA

OHIO—Mansfield

Barnes Mfg. Co. (Stove), A

OHIO—New London

Arnold-Creager Co. (Brick;
Tile) ....B

OHIO—New Philadelphia

Spicer Mfg. Co. (Rolling
Mill; Store; Warehouse;
Factory) C

OHIO—Sidney

Sidney Steel Scraper Co.
(Store; Warehouse; Fac-
tory; Baggage) ....A

OHIO—Springfield

Foss Mfg. Co. (Bag; Barrel)
A

OHIO—Wellington

Wellington Machine Co.
(Brick) ....B

PA.—Allegheny

Carlin's Sons, Thos. (Block;
Log; Lumber)..........A
McKinney Mfg. Co. (Store;
Warehouse; Factory; Bar-
rel) ....AAA

PA.—Elizabethtown

Buch's Sons Co., A. (Bag) A

PA.—Erie

Standard Saw Mill Mchry.
Co. (Logging; Lumber) B

PA.—Johnstown

Lorain Steel Co. (Car; Electric; Steam) ......AAAA

PA.—Lancaster

Martin Brick Mach. Mfg.
Co., Henry (Brick; Tile;
Bag) ....B

PA.—Lebanon

Weimer Machine Wks. Co.
(Foundry; Ingot; Rolling
Mill) ....AA

TRUCKS (Con.)

PA.—Mechanicsburg

Comstock, Geo. S. (Bag)..C

PA.—Muncy

Sprout, Waldron & Co.
(Bag) ....A

PA.—Oil City

Kramer Wagon Co. (Log-
ging; Lumber) ....A

PA.—Philadelphia

Brill Co., J. G., 62d &
Woodland Av. (Steam;
Electric) ....AAAA
Butterworth & Sons H. W.
(Dye House) ....A
Enterprise Mfg. Co. (Bar-
rel) ....AAAA
Paxson Co., J. W., 1021 N.
Del. Av. (Foundry) ...AA
Riehle Bros. Testing Ma-
chine Co. (Bag; Barrel;
Cotton; Baggage; Plat-
form) ....B
Sterlingworth Railway Sup-
ply Co. North Amer. Bldg.
(Rolled Steel, for Steam
Cars). ....B

PA.—Pittsburg

Jones & Laughlin Steel Co.
(Ltd.) (Foundry; Ingot;
Rolling Mill; Iron) AAAA
Pressed Steel Car Co. (Car;
Steam; Electric) ..AAAA
Standard Steel Car Co.,Frick
Bldg. (Steel Frames; Steel
Underframes for Wooden
Cars) ....B

PA.—Tatamy .

Messinger Mfg. Co. (Bag;
Barrel; Store; Warehouse;
Factory) ....B

PA.—Wrightsville

Wrightsville Hdw. Co.
(Bag) ....AAAA

PA.—York

Farquhar Co. (Ltd.) A. B.
(Bag; Barrel; Baggage;
Box; Store; Warehouse;
Factory; Dry Goods; Plat-
form) ....AAA
Keystone Farm Mach. Co.
(Ltd.) (Barrel) ....B

TENN.—Jackson

Southern Engine & Boiler
Wks. (Inc.) (Logging;
Lumber) ....AA

TENN.—Knoxville

Scotts Patent Brick Car Co.
(Brick)...............B

TENN.—Memphis

Chickasaw Iron Wks., 98 2d
(Logging; Lumber) ....A

VT.—Rutland

Howe Scale Co. (Bag; Bar-
rel; Baggage; Box; Store;
Warehouse; Factory; Car-
pet; Dry Goods) ......A

VT.—St. Albans

St. Albans Fdry. & Imple-
ment Co. (Bag) ....D

VA.—Danville

Horner Wagon Mfg. Co., W.
P. (Warehouse) ....D
Westbrooks Fdry. & Mach.
Co., J. B. (Store; Ware-
house; Factory) ....F

VA.—Norfolk

Whitehurst Co., R. W.
(Barrel; Store; Ware-
house; Factory; Bag; Bag-
gage; Stevedores'; Bas-
ket; Foundry; Stove) ..B

W. VA.—New Cumberland

Davis-Price Fdry & Machine
Co. (Brick) C

WIS.—Kenosha

Bain Wagon Co. (Logging;
Lumber) ....AAA

WIS.—Milwaukee

Bayley & Sons Co., Wm.,
732 Greenbush (Brick;
Logging; Lumber) X
Kieckhefer Elevator Co., A.
(Bacon; Ham; Bag; Bag-
gage; Barrel; Box; Car-
pet; Dry Goods; Factory;
Hog; Iron Freight; Iron;
Platform; Rubber Roll;
Stove; Warehouse) C
Meinecke & Son, A. (Wil-
low; Laundry; Toy) ..AA

WIS.—Racine

Fish Bros. Wagon Co. (Log-

TRUCKS (*Con.*)
ging; Lumber) ......AA
WIS.—Two Rivers
Hamilton Mfg. Co. (Printers') ....AA
WIS.—Wausau
Murray Mfg. Co., D. J. (Store; Warehouse; Factory)................ A

TRUERS

OHIO—Dayton
Dayton Globe Iron Wrks. Co. (Stone) ....B

TRUING

MICH.—Detroit
Wheel Truing Brake Shoe Co. (Brake Shoe Wheel)
D
N. Y.—Buffalo
Car Wheel Truing Brake Shoe Co. (Brake Shoe Wheel) X

TRUMPETS

CONN.—Meriden
Meriden Britannia Co. (Fire) ....AAAA
ILL.—Chicago
Haussmann & Dunn (Inc.) (Ear) C
MASS.—Boston
Bailey & Co., C. J. (Rubber; Toy) ....B
Leach & Greene (Ear) ..F
N. Y.—New York City
Braxmar Co., C. G. (Fire) B
Cairns & Bro. (Fire) ....D
International Silver Co., 9 Maiden Lane (Fire)
AAAA
Mechanical Rubber Co. (Fire) ....AAAA

TRUNKS

DEL.—Wilmington
Deleware Hard Fibre Co. (Vulcanized; Fibre) ....A
Vulcanized Fibre Co. (Vulcanized; Fibre) ..AAAA
ILL.—Chicago
Fitzgerald Trunk Co. (Sample; Sole Leather) ....A
Hartmann Trunk Co., 198 Jack. Boul. ....A
Haskell Bros. (Sample) ..A
Western Leather Mfg. Co. (Sample) ....D
Wilt, Chas. T. (Sample; Shoe Leather) ....B
MAINE—Kennebunk
Leatheroid Mfg. Co. (Sample) ....A
MASS.—Boston
Cummings' Son & Co., Josiah (Rawhide; Vulcanized Fibre; Steel) C
MASS.—Westfield
Crane Bros. (Linenoid)AAA
N. J.—Harrison
Headley & Farmer Co. (Sole (Leather) ....A
N. J.—Newark
Caille Co., P. (Sole Leather) ....D
Goldsmith & Son, L. ..AA
Hager & Co. (Sole Leather)
H
Peddie & Co. (Inc.) T. B. (Sample; Sole Leather; Toy) ....AA
N. Y.—Buffalo
Buffalo Trunk Mfg. Co. ..B
New York City
Boyle & Co., John, 112 Duane ....AA
Crouch & Fitzgerald (Sample; Sole Leather) .....A
Drucker & Co., N........A
Headley & Farmer Co., 14 Astor Pl. ....A
Lissa & Co., Henry (Sample; Sole Leather) ....B
Peddie & Co., T. B., 368 B'way ....AA
N. Y.—Rochester
Likly & Co., Henry (Sample) ....A

TRUNKS (*Con.*)
OHIO—Cincinnati
Drucker & Co. (Sample) ..A
Mendel & Co. ....B
OHIO—Columbus
Lilly Co., M. C. ....AAAA
Stallman, F. A. (Dresser)
C
PA.—Philadelphia
Twitchell S. (Carboy) ..A
VA.—Richmond
Rountree & Bro., H. W. .A
WIS.—Milwaukee
Abel & Bach Co. (Sole Leather) ....AA
Burroughs & Sons, Geo. ..B
Meincke & Son, A. (Toy)
AA
Romadka Bros. & Co. ..AA

TRUSSES

CAL.—San Francisco
Hatterotht W. ....B
ILL.—Chicago
Bowles, F. A. ....D
Common Sense Truss Co. (Surgical) ....D
Haussman & Dunn (Surgical) ....E
Wolfertz, Robt. ....E
IND.—Indianapolis
Armstrong & Co., Wm. K. (Surgical) ....B
KANS.—Lawrence
Victor Suspender Mfg. Co.
D
KANS.—Topeka
Smith Co. (Surgical) ....B
KY.—Covington
Ohio Scroll & Lumber Co. (Twisted; Piano) ......D
LA.—New Orleans
McDermott Surgical Instrument Co. (Surgical)....D
MASS.—Boston
Codman & Shurtleff (Surgical) C
Phelps & Co., W. H. ....D
White & Co., C. W. ....A
MINN.—St. Paul
Noyes Bros. & Cutler
AAAA
NEBR.—Omaha
Paxton & Vierling Iron Wrks. (Roof) ....AA
N. Y.—Adams
Rice W. L. (Dr.) C
N. Y.—Lockport
Empire Mfg. Co. (Surgical; Elastic) ....A
New York City
Pall Mall Electric Assn., 870 B'way (Electric) ..F
Pomeroy Co. (Surgical) ..A
N. Y.—Rochester
Fuller Co., Geo. R. (Surgical) ....E
OHIO—Cincinnati
Ohio Truss Co. C
OHIO—Cleveland
Hessler Truss Co., E. M.
D
King, Bridge Co. (Roof)
AAAA
Werum Bros. (Surgical)
H
PA.—Philadelphia
Ellis & Sons Co., Geo. D. (Surgical) C
Flavell & Bro., G. W. (Surgical) ....A
Hastings & McIntosh Truss Co. (Surgical; Elastic; Hard Rubber; Leather Covered) ....B
Horn & Bro., Wm. H. (Surgical; Hard Rubber; Leather Covered; Surgical Elastic) ....B
Phila. Truss & Bandage Co. (Surgical; Hard Rubber; Leather Covered) X
Phoenix Bridge Co. (Roof)
A
Seeley, Isaac B. (Elastic)
F
PA.—Pittsburg
Feick Bros. Co. (Surgical)
D

TRUSSES (Con.)
PA.—Steelton
Penna. Steel Co. (Roof)
..............AAAA
TENN.—Memphis
Chickasaw Iron Wrks.
(Roof) ....A
WIS.—Milwaukee
International Truss & Arti-
ficial Limb Co. ....E
Sauer, J. W. ....D

TRYERS

See Triers

TUBES

See also Tubing

CONN.—Ansonia
Ansonia Brass & Copper Co.
(Seamless Brass; Seam-
less Copper; Bronze)
..............AAAA
CONN.—Bridgeport
Bridgeport Deoxidized
Bronze & Metal Co.
(Bronze) ....B
Bridgeport Brass Co.
(Brass; Locked Seam;
Seamless Brass; Copper;
Seamless Copper) ..AAA
CONN.—Hartford
Pope Mfg. Co. (Boiler)
..............AAAA
CONN.—New Haven
English & Mersick Co.
(Speaking) ....B
CONN.—New London
New England Collapsible
Tube Co. (Collapsible)
..............A
CONN.—Seymour
Seymour Mfg. Co. (Brass;
Copper) ....AAAA
CONN.—Torrington
Coe Brass Mfg. Co. (Ger-
man Silver) ......AAAA
CONN.—Waterbury
Benedict & Burnham Mfg.
Co. (Brass; Seamless
Brass; Copper; Seamless
Copper) ....AAAA
Holmes, Booth & Haydens
(Inc.) (Brass; Seamless
Brass; Copper) ....AAAA
Plume & Atwood Mfg. Co.
Brass; Bronze; Copper)
..............AAA
Randolph & Clowes Co.
(Brass; Bronze; Copper;
Seamless Copper) ..AAA
Scovill Mfg. Co. (Brass)
..............AAAA
Waterbury Brass Co.
(Brass; Copper) ...AAAA
ILL.—Chicago
Besly & Co., Chas. H. (Boil-
er) ....A
Birtman Co., C. F. (X Ray;
accessories) C
Bostedo Pneumatic Tube
Co., 159 La Salle (Pneu-
matic) ....B
Chicago Paper Tube & Can
Co., 20 N. May (Paper;
for Mailing; Electrical
Purposes, &c.) X
Joseph, Jesse, 40 Dearborn
(Mailing) ....J
Ritchie & Co. W. C. (Paper;
Mailing) ....A
Western Box Co. (Mailing)
..............E
Whitman & Barnes Mfg. Co.
(Rubber Grain Drill)
..............AAAA
IND.—Alexandria
Lippincott Glass Co. (Glass)
..............A
MASS.—Boston
Amer. Tube Wrks. (Brass;
Seamless Brass; Copper;
Seamless Copper) ..AAA
Ashton Valve Co. (Glass)
..............A
Boston Belting Co., 256 De-
vonshire (Grain Drill)
..............AAAA
Eyelet Tool Co. (Punch)..X
Lamson Cons. Store Service
Co. (Pneumatic Cash)
..............AAAA

TUBES (Con.)
National Tube Wks. Co.
(Locomotive Boiler)
..............AAAA
Star Brass Mfg. Co. (Glass;
Water Gauge) ....A
Swett & Lewis Co. (X-Ray;
Accessories) ....E
U. S. Mailing Case Co.
(Wooden; Mailing) ....F
Walworth Mfg. Co. (Boiler)
..............AAAA
MASS.—Cambridge
Lamb & Ritchie (Speaking)
..............AA
McElroy, P. J. (Sick-Feed-
ing; Glass) ....E
MASS.—New Bedford
Pairpoint Corp'n. (Mailing;
&c.; Paper Cap) .....AA
MASS.—North Dighton
Lincoln & Co., L. (Paper
Mailing) ....D
MASS.—Westfield
Crane Bros. (Fibre) ..AAA
MICH.—Detroit
Detroit Copper & Brass
Rolling Mills (Brass; Cop-
per) ....AAAA
Detroit Paper Tube & Can
Co. (Mailing; Tin End
Cans; &c.) ....F
MO.—St. Louis
Bobe, P., 2711 Lemp Av.
(Test Inhaling) C
NEBR.—Omaha
Crane Co. (Boiler) ......A
N. J.—Paterson
Buckley's Son, Benj. (Spin-
ning) ....E
McNab & Harlin Mfg. Co.
(Brass; Copper) ....AAA
N. Y.—Brooklyn
Gair Co., R., Washn. (Pa-
per Mailing) ....A
Thompson & Norris Co.
(Mailing) ....AA
New York City
Amer. Tube & Stamping
Co., 20 Gold (Pnematic)
..............AAAA
Ashcroft Mfg. Co. (Glass;
Water Gauge) ....A
Bunnell & Co., J. H., 20
Park Pl. (Speaking) ..B
Consolidated Fruit Jar Co.,
290 B'way (Collapsible)
..............AA
Edison Phonograph Agency
(X-Ray; Accessories) ..D
Ford, T. P. (Mailing) ...D
Goodyear Rubber Co. (Exer-
cising) ....AAAA
Goodyear's Ind. Rubber
Glove Mfg. Co. (Exercis-
ing) ....AAAA
Hungerford Brass & Copper
Co., U. T., Boiler; Seam-
less Brass; Seamless Cop-
per) ....AA
Imp't'g Mailing Case Co.
(Mailing) ....F
Johns-Manville Mfg. Co., H.
W. (Asbestos) ....AAAA
Leng's Son & Co., John S.,
4 Fletcher (Hydraulic
Seamless Steel) ......B
Manhattan Brass Co.
(Brass) ....A
Manhattan Electrical Supply
Co., 32 Cortlandt (Speak-
ing) ....AA
Miles Pneumatic Tube Co.,
1123 B'way (Pneumatic)
..............D
N. Y. Belting & Packing
Co. (Grain Drill) ..AAA
Ostrander & Co., W. R., 22
Dey (Speaking) ....A
Pearsall Pneumatic Tube &
Power Co., 52 B'way
(Pneumatic) ....D
Plume & Atwood Mfg. Co.,
29 Murray (German Sil-
ver) ....AAA
Reilly Repair Supply Co.,
Jas., 229 West (Pneumat-
ic) ....AA
Remington Arms Co. (Gun)
..............A
Seabury & Johnson (Antisep-
tic) ....AA
Soltman, E. G., 125 E. 42d

TUBES (Con.)
(for Mailing; Drawing; Pasteboard) ....B
Stoutenborough, X. (Speaking) ....B
Union Paper Co., 844 Washington (Mailing; also Cans; Boxes; &c.) ...B
U. S. Mailing Tube Co., 122 Centre (Mailing) ......B
Van Wagoner & Linn Construction Co., 27 W. 24th (Speaking) ....D
Walsh Mfg. Co., Owen, 19 Roosevelt (Speaking)...D
Ware R. F., 108 Park Row (Paper Mailing) ......D
Western Electric Co., 57 Bethune (Speaking)
............AAAA
N. Y.—Rome
Rome Brass & Copper Co. (Brass) ....AAAA
N. Y.—Syracuse
Pass & Seymour (Porcelain)
..............A
N. Y.—Utica
Jones, Frank L. (Milking)
..............C
OHIO—Akron
Akron Machine Co. (Grain Drill) X
OHIO—Canton
Berger Mfg. Co. (Speaking)
..............F
Canton Steel Roofing Co. (Speaking) ....A
OHIO—Cleveland
Cleveland Wire Spring Co. (Grain Drill Wire) ....A
OHIO—East Liverpool
Thomas & Sons Co., R. (Porcelain; Electrical)..C
OHIO—Steubenville
La Belle Iron Wrks. (Boiler) ....AAAA
OHIO—Youngstown
Pollock Co., Wm. B. (Boiler) ....AA
PA.—Coatesville
Coatesville Rolling Mill Co. (Boiler) ....AAA
Worth Bros. Co. (Boiler)
..............A
PA.—Erie
Erie City Iron Wrks. (Boiler) ....AAAA
PA.—Malvern
Bishop & Co., J. (Platinum) ....D
PA.—Middletown
Amer. Tube & Iron Co. (Boiler; Butt Welded Boiler; Locomotive Boiler; ....AAAA
PA.—Philadelphia
Berger Bros. Co., 237 Arch Speaking) ....A
Brown, Jr., James (Paper; Worsted Mailing Tubes; Cones) ....F
Elliott & Co., A. G., 607 Chestnut (Mailing; &c.)
..............A
Ivins, Elwood (Seamless Speaking; Brass; Copper)
..............F
Noll & Co., E. P., 9 N. 6th (Mailing; &c.) ....D
Pilling & Son, Geo. P. (Milking) C
Wirz, A. H. (Collapsible)
..............A
PA.—Pittsburg
Byers & Co., A. M. (Boiler)
..............B
Monongahela Tube Co., Ferguson Blk. (Boiler) ....A
National Tube Co., Frick Bldg. (Boiler; Hydraulic Seamless Steel) ..AAAA
Pittsburg Tube Co. (Boiler)
..............B
Pittsburg Reduction Co. (Aluminum) .....AAAA
Shelby Steel Tube Co. Hydraulic Seamless Steel)
..............AAAA
PA.—Reading
Reading Iron Co. (Boiler; Lap Welded; Boiler)
..............AAAA
PA.—Washington
Tyler Tube & Pipe Co.

TUBES (Con.)
(Boiler) ....A
VT.—Fair Haven
Dalrymple, Geo. (Draft)..E

TUBING

See also Tubes

CONN.—Ansonia
Ansonia Brass & Copper Co. (Brass; Copper; Bronze; German Silver; Iron Lined) ....AAAA
CONN.—Bridgeport
Amer. Tube & Stamping Co. (Bicycle; Brass Lined; Seamless Steel; Brass; Copper) ....AAAA
Bridgeport Brass Co. (Brass; Copper; German Silver; Zinc) ......AAA
Canfield Co., H. O. (Rubber) ....B
CONN.—Bristol
Bristol Brass Co. (Brass Brazed; German Silver)
..............AAA
Edgerton, M. D. (Cotton Knit) C
CONN.—Derby
Birmingham Brass Co. (Brass; Copper) ......A
CONN.—Hartford
Hartford Rubber Wrks. Co. (Rubber) ....AAAA
Pope Mfg. Co. (Steel)
..............AAAA
CONN.—New Britain
Union Mfg. Co. (Wooden)
..............AA
CONN.—New Haven
Seamless Rubber Co. 356 Congress Av. (Rubber)
..............AA
CONN.—Seymour
Seymour Mfg. Co. (Brass; Copper; German Silver)
..............AAA
CONN.—Torrington
Coe Brass Mfg. Co. (Brass; Copper; Bronze; German Silver; Iron Lined)
..............AAAA
CONN.—Waterbury
Benedict & Burnham Mfg. Co. (Brass; Copper; Brass, Copper, Nickel Condenser; Plumbers' Seamless; in Brass; Copper; Nickel Silver; Zinc; German Silver) ....AAAA
Holmes, Booth & Haydens Co. (Brass; Copper; German Silver; Zinc)..AAAA
Plume & Atwood Mfg. Co. (Brass; Copper; German Silver; Zinc) ......AAA
Randolph-Clowes Co. (Brass; Copper; Bronze; Silver; German Silver; Zinc)
..............AAA
Scovill Mfg. Co. (Aluminum; Brass; Copper; Bronze; German Silver; Zinc) ....AAAA
Waterbury Brass Co. (Brass; Copper; German Silver; Zinc; Bronze)
..............AAAA
Wells & Co., A. H. (Brass; Copper) ....B
DEL.—Elsmere
Diamond State Fibre Co. (Hard Fibre) ....B
DEL.—Wilmington
Am. Vulcanized Fibre Co. (Hard Fibre) ....AAAA
GA.—Macon
Stevens's Sons Co. H. (Well) ....A
ILL.—Chicago
Braun, J. G., 322 S. Paulina (Square; Seamless Steel) ....A
Crane Co. (Well) ....AAAA
Mechanical Rubber Co. (Rubber) ....AAAA
Marsh & Co. James P. (Steel) ....B
Morgan & Wright (Inc.) 333 W. Lake (Hard Rubber)
..............AA

TUBING (Con.)

ILL.—Kewanee
Western Tube Co. (Square; also Restangular) ..AAA

IOWA—Des Moines
Iowa Pipe & Tile Co. (Well) ....A

MASS.—Andover
Tyer Rubber Co. (Rubber) ....AA

MASS.—Attleboro
Makepeace & Co., D. E. (Jewelers') ....A

MASS.—Boston
Amer. Tube Wrks., 137 Milk (Brass; Copper; Plumbers' Seamless; in Brass; Copper; Nickel Silver) ....AAA
Boston Belting Co. (Rubber; Beer; Cloth Insertion; Soda) ....AAAA
Davidson Rubber Co. (Rubber) ....A
National Tube Co. (Oil Well) ....AAAA
Revere Rubber Co., 63 Franklin (Rubber) AAAA

MASS.—Malden
Niedner, Chas. H. (Cotton; Electric) ....D

MASS.—New Bedford
Pairpoint Corp'n. (Glass; for Electrical Use) ...AA

MASS.—Westfield
Crane Bros. (Linenoid) ....AAA

MICH.—Bay City
Michigan Pipe Co. (Wooden; Pump) ....AA

MICH.—Detroit
Detroit Copper & Brass Rolling Mill Co. (Brass; Copper) ....AAAA

MO.—St. Joseph
St. Joseph Pump & Mfg. Co. (Steel Pump; Wood Pump) ....B

MO.—St. Louis
Flower & Co., Walter L., 721 Oliver (Flexible; Flexible Metallic) .....E

N. J.—Harrison
New Jersey Tube Co. (Brass; Copper; Steel) ....A

N. J.—Jersey City
N. J. Car Spring & Rubber Co. (Rubber) ....AA
Voorhees Rubber Mfg. Co., 18 Bostwick Av. (Rubber) ....B

N. J.—Trenton
Consolidated Rubber Co. (Rubber) ....B
Crescent Belting & Packing Co. (Corrugated; Plain Rubber) ....A
Empire Rubber Mfg. Co. (Rubber; Cloth Insertion) ....AA
Hamilton Rubber Mfg. Co. (Rubber) ....B
Home Rubber Co. (Rubber; Beer; Rubber; Gas; Soda) ....AA
Mercer Rubber Co. (Rubber) ....A
Stokes Rubber Co., Joseph (Rubber) ....A
Trenton Rubber Mfg. Co. (Rubber; Beer; Soda)..A
United & Globe Rubber Mfg. Co., of Ironton (Rubber) ....AAA
Whitehead Bros. Rubber Co. (Rubber) ....A

N. Y.—Brooklyn
Almond Mfg. Co., T. R., 83 Washington (Flexible Steel) C

N. Y.—Buffalo
Buffalo Weaving & Belting Co. (Cotton; for Carrying Electric Wires Under Heat) ....A

N. Y.—Croton-on-Hudson
Croton Mfg. Co. (Brass)..D

N. Y.—Elmira
Wyckoff & Son Co., A. (Wooden) ....B

N. Y.—Lockport
Empire Mfg. Co. (Cotton; Electric) ....A

TUBING (Con.)

New York City
Amer. Hard Rubber Co., 9 Mercer (Rubber) ..AAAA
Eagle Tube Co., 41 Dey (Steel) ....B
Goodyear Rubber Co. (Rubber) ....AA
Goodyears' Ind. Rub. Glove Mfg. Co. (Rubber) ....AAAA
Gutta Percha & Rubber Mfg. Co. (Rubber; Beer; Cloth Insertion; Hard Rubber; Soda) ..AAAA
Hungerford Brass & Copper Co., U. T., 479 Pearl (Seamless Brass; Copper; Brass Plain; Tinned Condenser; Zinc) ....AA
International Automobile & Vehicle Co., 346 B'way (Rubber) ....B
Johns-Manville Mfg. Co., H. W. (Flexible) ....AAAA
Leng's Son & Co., John S., 4 Fletcher (Bicycle; Seamless Steel) ....A
Manhattan Brass Co., 338 E. 28th (Brass; Copper; Bronze; Iron Lined; Zinc) ....A
Manhattan Rubber Mfg. Co., 18 Vesey (Rubber) ..AA
New York Belting & Packing Co. (Ltd.) 25 Park Place (Rubber) ..AAA
New York Gas Tubing Co., 97 Bank (Flexible) ....D
New York Rubber Co., 48 Reade (Rubber; Cloth Insertion) ....AA
Parker, Stearns & Sutton (Rubber) ....B
Peerless Rubber Mfg. Co., 16 Warren (Rubber) ..AA
Traun Rubber Co., 335 B'way (Rubber) ....E
Vulcanized Rubber Co., 568 B'way (Hard Rubber)..A

N. Y.—Rome
Rome Brass & Copper Co. (Brass; Copper) ..AAAA
Rome Tube Co. (Seamless; Brazed) ....B

N. C.—Pomona
Pomona Terra Cotta Co. (Well) ....B

OHIO—Akron
Goodrich Co., B. F. (Rubber; Hard Rubber; Flexible) ....AAAA
Whitman & Barnes Mfg. Co. (Rubber) ....AAAA

OHIO—Cleveland
Cleveland Galvanizing Wrks. (Steel Pump; Well) C
Federal Mfg. Co., Amer. Trust. Bldg. (Steel) ....AAAA
Standard Welding Co. (Automobile; Seamless Steel) ....AA
Strong, Carlisle & Hammond Co., 61 Frankfort Brass; Copper) ....A

OHIO—Mansfield
Mansfield Machine Wrks. (Steel) ....A

OHIO—Steubenville
La Belle Iron Wrks. (Steel Pump) ....AAAA

OHIO—Toledo
Standard Steel Tube Co. (Steel) C

OHIO—Youngstown
Republic Rubber Co. (Rubber) ....AA
Youngstown Iron Sheet & Tube Co. (Bedstead Iron or Steel; Seamless Steel) ....AAAA

PA.—Auburn
Delaware Seamless Tube Co. (Rubber) ....A

PA.—Beaver
Pittsburg Seamless Tube Co. (Seamless Steel) X

PA.—Danville
Danville Structural Tubing Co. (Structural) ......A

PA.—Ellwood City
Standard Seamless Tube Co. (Seamless Steel) ......B

TUBING (Con.)

PA.—Erie
Continental Rubber Wrks.
(Rubber) ....A
PA.—Jeannette
Penna. Rubber Co. (Rubber) ....H
PA.—Malvern
Bishop & Co., J. (Platinum) ....D
PA.—Middletown
Amer. Tube & Iron Co.
(Well; Oil Well; Pump)
AAAA
PA.—Philadelphia
Ivins, Elwood (Seamless
Aluminum; Brass; Copper; Platinum; Seamless
Steel Tool; Seamless Silver; Steel Pump; Aluminum; Steel; Atomizer; Bicycle; Cold Drawn Square;
German Silver; Gold;
High; Low; Carbon Steel;
Hypodermic Needle; Nickel; Seamless Bronze;
Seamless Lead; Tin;
Steel; Silver) ....F
Janney, Steinmetz & Co.
Drexel Bldg. (Cold Drawn
Steel) ....D
Justice & Co., Philip S., 14
N. 5th (Imported Seamless Steel) ....D
Merchant & Co. (Inc.) 517
Arch (Brass; Copper).AA
Rudolf & Summerill Tubing
Co., 302 N. Broad (Copper; Aluminum)........E
PA.—Pittsburg
National Tube Co. (Bicycle;
Seamless Steel; Well)
AAAA
National Supply Co.
(Wrought Iron) ..AAAA
Shelby Steel Tube Co.,
Frick Bldg. (Bedstead;
Bicycle; Automobile; Iron
Steel; Cold Drawn
Square; Seamless Steel)
AAAA
Spang, Chalfant & Co.
(Oil Well) ....AAAA
PA.—Reading
Reading Iron Co. (Well;
Oil Well) X
R. I.—Providence
Amer. Electrical Wrks.
(Flexible Gas) ....AAAA
Atlantic Tubing Co. (Flexible; Gas) X
Davol Rubber Co., 69 Paint
(Rubber) ....AA
Holt Co., A. (Jewelers')..E
VT.—Johnson
Stearns & Son, O. W.
(Wooden) C
WIS.—Kenosha
Chicago Brass Co. (Brazed
Brass) ....AA

TUBS

See also Woodenware;
Baths

CAL.—San Francisco
Gladding, McBean & Co.
(Glazed Fire Clay Laundry) ....AA
CONN.—New Haven
Peck Bros. & Co. (Bath;
Copper Bath; Laundry)
AA
ILL.—Chicago
Allis-Chalmers Co., Home
Ins. Bldg. (Hoisting;
Dumping Steel Hoisting;
Self-Filling) ......AAAA
Chicago Slate & Mantel Co.,
232 S. Clinton (Slate
Laundry) X
Clow & Sons, Jas. B., 342
Franklin (Slate Laundry;
Soapstone) ....AAA
Creamery Package Mfg. Co.
(Butter) ....AAA
Cribben & Sexton Co.
(Enamelled; Bath; Iron
Bath; Enamelled Iron;
Laundry) ....AA
Hardin, Jno., 4543 Cottage
Grove Av. (Artificial
Stone Laundry) ....A

TUBS (Con.)

Sherman & Flavin, 2515
State (Soapstone Laundry) ....B
Wolff Mfg. Co., L., 117 W.
Lake (Slate Laundry;
Soapstone; Porcelain;
Bath) ....AAAA
ILL.—Edwardsville
Illinois Marble Co. (Slate
Laundry; Soapstone) ...C
ILL.—Elgin
Elgin Butter Tub Co. (Butter) ....A
IOWA—Burlington
Murray Iron Wrks. Co.
(Scalding) ....A
ILL.—Keokuk
McElroy Iron Wrks. Co.
(Scalding) ....F
MAINE—Bath
Monson Consolidated Slate
Co. (Slate Laundry) ..X
MD.—Baltimore
Weiskittle & Son, A.
(Enamelled; Bath) ....A
MASS.—Boston
Amer. Slate Co. (Inc.) cor.
Somerset & Beacon (Slate
Laundry) X
Mathews Consolidated Slate
Co., 199 Wash'n Slate
Laundry) X
Monson Maine Slate Co., 113
Devonshire (Slate Laundry) X
Strater & Sons, Herman
(Brewers' Mash) ......A
Troy Bros. & Co., 91 Havenhill (Soapstone Laundry) C
Union Soapstone Co., 14
Marshall (Slate Laundry;
Soapstone) C
MASS.—Lawrence
Horne Sons Co., J. H.
(Bleaching) ....A
MASS.—Lowell
Entwistle Co., T. C. (Dye)
B
Lowell Slate Co. (Slate)
X
MASS.—Westfield
Crane Bros. (Linenoid;
Bath) ....AAA
MICH.—Detroit
Day Metallic Mfg. Co.
(Bath) ....E
MINN.—Minneapolis
Bonsfield Woodenware Co.
(Wash; Woodenware) ..A
MINN.—St. Paul
Amer. Hoist & Derrick Co.
(Hoisting ; Dumping)
AAA
MO.—St. Louis
Cahill-Swift Mfg. Co. (Copper; Bath) ....B
Evens & Howard Fire Brick
Co., 920 Market (Glazed
Fire Clay Laundry)
AAAA
Nelson Mfg. Co., N. O.
(Bath) ....AAA
N. H.—Keene
Beaver Mills (Wash; Wooden) ....A
N. J.—Burlington
Stewart & Peterson Co.
(Porcelain; Bath) .....A
N. J.—Hoboken
Union Iron Wrks (Hoisting;
Dumping) C
N. J.—Trenton
Maddock Sons Co., Thos.,
(Stoneware Laundry)
AA
Trenton Potteries Co. (Porcelain; Bath; Solid White
Crockery; Laundry)
AAA
N. Y.—Albany
Dedrick's Sons, P. K.
(Hoisting; Dumping; Self-Dumping) ....A
N. Y.—Brooklyn
Phillips, Doup & Co., 56
Pearl (Hoisting; Dumping) C
Robinson Stoneware Co., 244
Greenpoint Av. (Artificial
Stone Laundry; Soapstone) ....D

TUBS (Con.)

N. Y.—Buffalo
Shepard & Co., Sidney (Galvanized; Wash) ..AAAA

N. Y.—Kingston
Adams, E. G. (Artificial Stone Laundry) ......F

N. Y.—Long Island City
Stulbner, G. L. (Hoisting; Dumping; Steel Hoisting Self-Dumping) ....B

New York City
Alberene Stone Co., 393 Pearl (Soapstone Laundry) ....B
Biesecker, J. S. (Butter) C
Cordley & Hayes (Fibre; Fibre Wash) ....A
Fairbanks Co., 416 Broome (Hoisting) ....AAAA
Hunt Co., C. W., 45 B'way (Hoisting; Dumping; Self-Filling) ....AA
Irwin R. M. C., 103 Chambers (Folding Bath) ...X
Koppel, Arthur, 68 Broad (Hoisting; Dumping) ..A
Koven & Bros. L. O., 50 Cliff (Hoisting) ..... A
Leavitt & Co., C. W., 15 Cortlandt (Hoisting; Dumping) ....B
Mead & Co. Jno. A., 11 Bway. (Hoisting; Dumping) ....AA
Meyer-Sniffin Co. (Ltd.) (Wash; Bath) .... A
Mott Iron Wks., J. L., (Bath; Enamelled; Iron; Porcelain) ....AA
N. J. Fdry. & Machine Co., 13 Murray (Hoisting; Dumping) .... D
New York Slate Wks., 493 E. 138th (Slate Laundry) ....D
Ronalds & Johnson Co. (Bath; Copper Bath) AA
Steeger, Henry (Cooper; Bath) .... A
Stoutenborough, X. (Bath) ....D
Trageser Steam Copper Wks. Jno. (Copper; Bath; Enamelled; Steel Bath; Copper Lined) .... A

N. Y.—Niagara Falls
Dobbie Fdry. & Machine Co. (Hoisting; Dumping) ..B

N. Y.—Oswego
Cowmeadow Mfg. Co., John (Indurated Fibre Bath; Steel Bath) .... D

OHIO—Cincinnati
Gibson Co., Thos. (Porcelain; Bath) .... D
Hauser, Bremer & Fath Co. (Brewers' Fermenting; Wash) .... B
Littleford Bros., 453 E. Pearl (Hoisting; Dumping) .... B
Tatum Co., Samuel C. (Wash) .... B

OHIO—Cleveland
Brown Hoisting Mchry. Co., 1345 St. Clair (Hoisting; Dumping) .... AAAA
Norcross Co., 269 W. River (Euclid Stone Laundry) A

OHIO—Columbus
Jeffrey Mfg. Co. (Hoisting; Dumping) .... AAAA

OHIO—Dayton
Marbleithic Co. (Artificial Stone Laundry) X

OHIO—Mansfield
Humphreys Mfg. Co. (Crockery; Laundry) .... B

OHIO—Miamisburg
Acme Folding Boat Co. (Folding; Bath) ...... B

OHIO—Nelsonville
Nelsonville Fdry. & Mach. Co. (Self-Dumping) ....B

OHIO—Salem
Clark Co., W. J. (Hoisting; Dumping; Steel Hoisting; Self-Dumping; Metallic Factory) .... A

OHIO—Warren
Day-Ward Co. (Bath; Copper Bath; Enamelled

TUBS (Con.)

Bath) .... B

PA.—Bangor
Bangor Crescent Slate Co. (Slate Laundry) ..... B
Bangor Slate Co. (Slate Laundry) .... D
Flory Mfg. Co., S. (Hoisting; Dumping) ...... A

PA.—Coatesville
Coatesville Boiler Wks. (Hoisting; Dumping) .AA

PA.—Delta
Peerles Slate Co. (Slate Laundry) .... B

PA.—East Bangor
East Bangor Consolidated Slate Co. (Slate Laundry) .... AA

PA.—Easton
Penna Structural Slate Co. (Slate Laundry) ..... B

PA.—Lynnport
Ontalaunee Slate Mfg. Co. (Slate Laundry) C

PA.—Philadelphia
McCambridge & Co. (Ltd.) (Wash; Copper; Enamelled Bath) ...... B
Middleton, Edw. H., 4527 Hedge (Hoisting; Dumping) X
Miller & Co. Joseph S. (Laundry) .... E
Mills & Bros., Thos. (Ice Cream) .... A
Stambach & Love, 50 N. 7th (Soapstone Laundry) A
Woolford Wood Tank Mfg. Co., Geo. (Wooden Brewers' Mash; Wooden Acid; Wooden Dye) .... B

PA.—Pittsburg
Riter-Conly Co. (Brewers' Mash) .... AAA
Pittsburg Reduction Co., Smith Bldg. (Seamless Aluminum) ...... AAAA
Standard Mfg. Co. (Enamelled; Bath; Iron Bath; Laundry; Enamelled Iron; Laundry) .... AA

PA.—Pottstown
Pelican Slate Mfg. Co. (Slate Lundry) ...... E

PA.—Sharon
Sharon Boiler Wks. (Hoisting; Dumping; Self-Dumping) .... A

PA.—Slatington
McKenna, David (Slate Laundry) .... E
Provident Slate Co. (Slate Laundry) .... B
Slatington Slate Co. (Slate Laundry) .... B
Washington Slate Co. (Slate Laundry) C

PA.—Walnutport
Hahn, Granville (Slate Laundry) ....E

R. I.—Bridgeton
Hopkins Mach. Wks. (Dye) X

VT.—Fair Haven
Allens' Sons, S. (Slate Laundry) .... D
Fair Haven Marble & Marbleized Slate Co. (Slate Laundry) ....B
Pelkey, W. H. (Slate Laundry) .... E

VT.—Poultney
Fleming Slate Co. (Slate Laundry) C

VA.—Arvonia
Williams Slate Co. (Slate Laundry) .... B

VA.—Richmond
Richmond Cedar Wks. (Ltd.) (Cedar; Wash) .... AAAA

WIS.—Menasha
Menasha Woodenware Co. (Wash; Wooden) .... AA

WIS.—Racine
Gold Medal Camp Furniture & Novelty Co. (Folding Bath) .... B

WIS.—Sheboygan
Kohler Son Co., J. N. (Enamelled Bath) .... A

TUCKINGS

See Millinery

TUGS

See also Boats; Ships

IND.—Lafayette
Dienhart Harness Co.
(Hame) .... E
IND.—La Porte
Lonn & Sons Co., Jno.
(Hame) .... A
N. J.—Newark
Peters' Harness & Saddlery
Co. (Hame) C
OHIO—Canton
Elbel Co. (Hame) ....A

TUMBLERS

See also Barrels; Machy;
Glassware

ILL.—Harvey
Whiting Fdry. & Equipment
Co. (Foundry) ...... AA
IND.—Marion
Cauton Glass Co. (Glass) B
MD.—Cumberland
Maryland Glass Etching
Wks. (Glass; Jelly) C
OHIO—Newark
Heisey & Co., A. H.
(Glass) .... A
PA.—Beaver Falls
Co-operative Flint Glass Co.
(Glass) .... A
PA.—Coraopolis
Consolidated Lamp & Glass
Co. (Glass) .... A
PA.—Philadelphia
Gillinder & Sons (Glass) A
PA.—Pittsburg
McKee Glass Co. (Glass), B
National Glass Co. (Glass;
(Jelly) X
U. S. Glass Co. (Glass)
AAAA
PA.—Washington
Duncans & Miller Glass Co.
(Glass) .... A
W. Va.—Moundsville
Fostoria Glass Co. (Glass)
AAA
W. VA.—Wellsburg
Eagle Glass & Mfg. Co.
(Glass) .... A
W. VA.—Wheeling
Central Glass Wks. (Glass)
A

TURBINES

See also Engines; Wheels

CAL.—San Francisco
Hendy Machine Wks.,
Joshua (Water Wheel)
AA
COLO.—Denver
Mine & Smelter Supply Co.
(Water Wheel) ..AAAA
CONN.—West Stafford
Bradway Mach. Wks., C.
P. (Water Wheel) .... F
GA.—Atlanta
De Loach Mill Mfg. Co.
(Water Wheels) ...... B
GA.—Rome
Davis Fdry. & Machine
Wks. (Water Wheel) ..X
ILL.—Chicago
Sullivan Machinery Co., 135
Adams (Water Wheel)
AAAA
IND.—Logansport
Dowling & Co., Wm.
(Water Wheel) ....A
IOWA—Dubuque
Dubuque Turbine & Roller
Mill Co. (Water Wheel)
B
MD.—Baltimore
Poole Engineering & Ma-
chine Co. (Water Wheel)
AA
MASS.—Fitchburg
Putnam Machine Co.
(Water Wheel .... A
MASS.—Holyoke
Holyoke Machine Co.
(Water Wheel) .... AA
Jolly, J. & W. (Water

TURBINES (Con.)
(Wheel) ....A
MASS.—Lowell
Nichols, Albert F., 157
Willie (Water Wheel) D
MASS.—Orange
Chase Turbine Mfg. Co.
(Water Wheel) ...... A
Hunt, Rodney Machine Co.
(Water Wheel) ...... A
MASS.—Pittsfield
Jones & Sons Co., E. D.
(Water Wheel) ...... B
N. H.—Brentwood
Robinson, A. J. (Water
Wheel) .... D
N. H.—Keene
Humphrey Machine Co.
(Water Wheel) C
N. J.—Bartley
Bartley & Sons, Wm.,
(Water Wheel) ...... D
New York City
De Laval Steam Turbine
Co. 76 Cortlandt (Steam)
AA
Westinghouse, Church, Kerr
& Co., 8 Bridge (Steam)
A
N. Y.—Oswego
Kingsford Fdry. & Machine
Wks. (Water Wheel
AAAA
N. Y.—Schenectady
General Electric Co.
(Steam) .... AAAA
N. Y.—Syracuse
Dunning, W. D., 329 W.
Water (Water Wheel)
AA
N. C.—Greensboro
Glascock & Sons, G. T.
(Water Wheel) ...... D
Sergeant Mfg. Co. (Water
Wheel) .... D
N. C.—Winston Salem
Salem Iron Wks. (Water
Wheel) .... A
OHIO—Dayton
Dayton Globe Iron Wks.
Co. (Water Wheel) ....B
OHIO—Springfield
Leffel & Co., James
(Water Wheel) ......AA
Trump Mfg. Co. (Water
Wheel) .... A
PA.—Allentown
Allentown Fdry. & Ma-
chine Wks. (Inc.) (Water
Wheel) .... A
PA.—Christiana
Cristiana Machine Co.
(Water Wheel) ...... B
PA.—Glen Rock
Norrish, Burnham & Co.
(Water Wheel) ...... B
PA.—Philadelphia
Wood & Co., R. D., 400
Chestnut (Water Wheel)
AAAA
PA.—Pittsburg
Westinghouse Machine Co.
(Steam) .... AAAA
PA.—Reading
Reading Fdry. Co. (Water
Wheel) X
PA.—York
Smith Co., S. Morgan
(Water Wheel) .... AAA
R. I.—Pawtucket
Fales & Jenks Machine Co.
(Water Wheel) .... AAA
VT.—Montpelier
Lane Mfg. Co. (Water
Wheel) .... A
WIS.—Appelton
Valley Iron Wks. Co.
(Water Wheel) C

TUREENS

CONN.—Meriden
Manning, Bowman & Co.
(Soup) ....AA
CONN.—Walingford
Wallace & Sons Mfg. Co.,
R. (Soup) ....AAAA
MO.—St. Louis
St. Louis Stamping Co.
(Soup) .... AAAA
New York City
International Silver Co. 9
Maiden Lane (Silver
Plated) .... AAAA

TUREENS (Con.)
Lalance & Grosjean Mfg.
Co. (Soup) ...... AAAA

TURMERIC

ILL.—Chicago
Fuller & Fuller (Ground)
AA

TURNBUCKLES

CAL.—San Francisco
Payne's Bolt Wks., 121
Howard (Wrought Iron)
A
CONN.—Hartford
Stirling Blower & Pipe
Mfg. Co. ....A
CONN.—New Britain
Corbin, P. & F. ....AAAA
CONN.—Unionville
Upson Nut Co. (Wrought
Iron) .... AAAA
DEL.—Wilmington
Diamond Slate Steel Co.
(Wrought Iron) X
ILL.—Chicago
Continental Bolt & Iron
Wks., 22nd & Union
(Wrought Iron) ...... A
Kropp & Co., A., 52 Law
(Wrought Iron) ...... E
Republic Iron & Steel Co.,
Stock Exch. Bldg.
(Wrought Iron) ..AAAA
MD.—Baltimore
National Supply Co., 7 W.
Lombard (Wrought Iron)
C
MASS.—Boston
Boston Bolt Co., 31 Pur-
chase (Wrought Iron) C
New England Bolt & Nut
Co., 253 Atlantic Av.
(Wrought Iron) ...... B
MICH.—Detroit
Michigan Bolt & Nut Wks.
(Wrought Iron) .... AA
MO.—Kansas City
Kansas Bolt & Nut Co.
(Wrought Iron) ...... A
MO.—St. Louis
Leschen & Sons Rope Co.,
A., 920 N. 1st (Wrought
Iron) .... AA
Moran Bolt & Nut Mfg.
Co. (Wrought Iron) .. A
N. J.—Newark
Strieby & Foote Co .. B
N. Y.—Brooklyn
Merrill Bros., 465 Kent Av.
(Wrought Iron) ...... A
New York City
Halls' Sons, Saml., 229 W.
10th (Wrought Iron) A
Sargent & Co., 151 Leonard
AAAA
Tiebout, W. & J., 118 Cham-
bers .... B
N. Y.—Portchester
Russell, Burdsall & Ward
Bolt & Nut Co. (Wrought
Iron) .... AAAA
N. Y.—Syracuse
Central City Bolt Co.
(Wrought Iron) C
OHIO—Cincinnati
Cinn. Railway Supply Co.,
13 E. 2nd (Wrought Iron)
A
Cinn. Screw & Tap Co. A
OHIO—Cleveland
Cleveland City Forge &
Iron Co., 67 Case Av.
(Wrought Iron) .... AA
Columbus Bolt Wks.
(Wrought Iron) ...... B
PA.—Atglen
Chalfant Hdw. Mfg. Co. X
PA.—Lebanon
Amer. Iron & Steel Mfg. Co.
(Wrought Iron) .. AAAA
PA.—Philadelphia
Berger Bros. Co., 231 Arch
A
Hoopes & Townsend
Co., 1330 Buttonwood
(Wrought Iron) ....AAA
PA.—Pittsburg
Jones & Laughlin Steel Co.
(Ltd.) (Wrought Iron)
AAAA

TURNBUCKLES (Con.)
Lanz & Sons, M. ...... AA
Pittsburg Mfg. Co., 28th
& R. R. (Wrought Iron)
A
PA.—Williamsport
Williamsport Wire Rope Co.
A
R. I.—Pawtucket
Haskell Mfg. Co., Wm. H.
(Wrought Iron) .... AA
Pawtucket Mfg. Co. (Drop
Forged; Wrought Iron) A
R. I.—Providence
Rhode Island Tool Co. AAA

TURNERS

CONN.—Bridgeport
Knapp & Cowles Mfg. Co.
(Cake) C
CONN.—Unionville
Humphreys, H. W. (Cake)
D
CONN.—Wallingford
Wallace & Sons Mfg. Co.,
R. (Cake) ...... AAAA
ILL.—Chicago
Barbee Wire & Iron Wks.
(Pie) .... B
ILL.—Freeport
Arcade Mfg. Co. (Cake)..A
IND.—Columbus
Reeves & Co. (Log) AAAA
IND.—Indianapolis
Chandler & Taylor Co. (Log)
AA
IOWA—Cedar Falls
Wagner Mfg. Co. (Cake) E
MASS.—Boston
New England Novelty Mfg.
Co. (Pie) .... H
MICH.—Kalamazoo
Hill & Co., Wm. E.
(Steam; Log) ...... B
MICH.—Ludington
Handy Things Co. (Cake) C
N. Y.—Buffalo
Shepard & Co., Sidney
(Cake) .... AAAA
New York City
Dickinson, Jno. (Est of)
64 Nassau (Paper Cal-
ender Roll) .... B
Lalance & Grosjean Mfg.
Co. (Cake) .... AAAA
Pond Machine Tool Co.
(Grindstone) ...... AAAA
Sargent & Co., 151 Leonard
(Cake) .... AAAA
OHIO—Ravenna
Williams, A. C. (Cake) A
OHIO—Warren
Trumbull Mfg. Co. (Log) C
PA.—Philadelphia
Stow Flexible Shaft Co.
(Crank Pin) .... B
R. I.—Providence
Brown & Sharpe Mfg. Co.
(Grindstone) .... AAAA
TENN.—Jackson
Southern Engine & Boiler
Wks. (Log) .... AA
VT.—Montpelier
Lane Mfg. Co. (Log) .. A
WIS.—Milwaukee
Allis-Chalmers Co. (Steam
Log) ....AAAA
Filer & Stowell Co., Ltd.
(Log; Steam Log) ..AAA

TURNINGS

CONN.—Clinton
Kelsey, Horatio (Ship) ..E
ILL.—Chicago
Boynton & Co., 67 W.
Washn. (Automatic Wood)
B
Ehnborn & Co., C., 214 S.
Clinton (Electrical Wood)
G
IOWA—Cedar Falls
Harris & Cole Bros. (Auto-
matic Wood; Electrical
Wood) .... AA
KY.—Covington
Ohio Scroll & Lumber Co.
(Electrical Wood) ....D
N. H.—Milford
Pierce & Co., W. E. (Auto-

TURNINGS (Con.)

matic Wood) .... D

New York City

New York Carved Moulding
Co., 771 1st. Av. (Auto-
matic Wood; Electrical
Wood) .... D

PA.—Corry

Mahle & Son (Ltd.) C.
A. (Variety Automatic
Wood) .... F

R. I.—Providence

Amer. Enamel Co. (Auto-
matic Wood; Artistic
Novelty Small Turned;
Electrical Wood) .... B

Union Hdw. & Electric Supply Co. (Electrical Wood,
of all kinds) .... A

TURNS

MICH.—Grand Rapids

Hdw. Supply Co. (Cup-
board) X

New York City

Peck, Stow & Wilcox Co.
(Cupboard) ...... AAAA

Russell & Erwin Mfg. Co.,
43 Chambers (Bell; Cup-
board) .... AAAA

Sargent & Co., 151 Leonard
(Bell; Cupboard) AAAA

OHIO—Cleveland

Taylor & Boggis Fdy. Co.
(Cupboard) .... AA

PA.—Reading

Reading Hdw. Co. (Bell;
Cupboard) ...... AAAA

TURNSTILES

New York City

Amer. Passementerie Fact-
ory (H. Chajes, Prop.),
85 Worth .... F

Fiske Iron Wks., J. W.,
39 Park Place .... B

OHIO—Cleveland

Bright, H. V., 66 Clark-
wood Av. C

TURNTABLES

ALA.—Selma

Peacocks Iron Wks. X

DEL.—Wilmington

Edgemoor Iron Co. (Iron;
Steel) .... AAA

Lobdell Car Wheel Co.
(Sharp) .... AAAA

ILL.—Harvey

Buda Fdry. & Mfg. Co. B

Whiting Fdry. Equipment
Co. (Bridge; Railroad)
AA

KANS.—Leavenworth

Missouri Valley Bridge &
Iron Co. .... B

KY.—Louisville

Louisville Bridge & Iron
Co. .... A

MASS.—Boston

Boston Bridge Wks.
(Bridge; Railroad) ..AA

Sturtvant Co., B. F.
(Shop) .... AAA

MICH.—Bay City

Industrial Wks. ....AA

MICH.—Detroit

Bryam & Co. (Shop) ....D

Northern Engineering Wks.
(Mine; Shop) .... A

MINN.—Minneapolis

Peteler Portable Railway
Mfg. Co. (Portable) .. C

N. J.—Hoboken

N. J. Switch & Crossing
Co. .... A

N. J.—Paterson

Passaic Steel Co. (Bridge;
Railroad) .... A

New York City

Amer. Bridge Co. of N. Y.,
100 Bway. (Bridge; Rail-
road) .... A

Koppel, Arthur, 66 Broad
(Narrow Gauge; Bridge;
Railroad; Mine; Shop) A

N. Y.—West New Brighton

Hunt Co., C. W. (Shop) AA

OHIO—Bucyrus

TURNTABLES (Con.)

Amer. Clay Working Co. X

OHIO—Canton

Canton Fdry. & Mach. Co.
(Bridge; Mine; Railroad)
B

OHIO—Cleveland

Atlas Bolt & Screw Co.
(Overhead; Bridge Rail-
road) ....AA

Bowler Fdry. Co. ...... B

King Bridge Co. (Iron;
Steel) .... AAAA

OHIO—Columbus

Kilbourne & Jacobs Mfg.
Co. (Bridge; Railroad)
AAAA

OHIO—Massillon

Massillon Bridge Co. .... A

PA.—Allegheny

Carbins' Sons, Thos. (Narrow Gauge; Bridge Rail-
road) .... A

PA.—Allentown

Allentown Rolling Mills
AAA

PA.—Beaver Falls

Penn. Bridge Co. ... AA

PA.—Lancaster

Martin Brick Mach. Mfg.
Co., Henry .... B

PA.—Nazareth

Nazareth Fdry. & Mach. Co.
(Shop) .... B

PA.—Philadelphia

Brill Co., J. G. (Street Car)
AAAA

Harrington Son & Co., Edw.,
1511 Penna. Av. (Over-
head) .... AA

Link Belt Engineering Co.
(Bridge; Railroad).. AA

Phoenix Bridge Co. (Iron;
Steel; Portable; Street
Car) .... A

Roberts Co., A. & P. (Iron;
Steel) .... AAAA

Sellers & Co. (Inc.), Wm.,
16th & Hamilton (Pivot;
Bridge; Portable; Shop;
Street Car; Railroad;
Mine) .... AAAA

Wharton, Jr. & Co. (Inc.),
Wm. .... AAA

PA.—Pittsburg

Carnegie Steel Co. (Ltd.)
AAAA

PA.—Reading

Reading Crane & Hoist
Wks. (Overhead) .... A

PA.—South Bethlehem

Bethlehem Fdry. & Mach.
Co. (Shop) C

TURPENTINE

ALA.—Coffee Springs

Sellers & Co., W. B. .... B

ALA.—Dothan

Carmichael, D. ....B

ALA.—Elba

Duval, M. W. .... D

ALA.—Rutledge

Frot, Watson & Co. .... D

ALA.—Sellersville

Sellers, Bullard & Co. .. B

ALA.—Wager

Lewis, D. R. & W. P. ..D

FLA.—Albion

Medlin & Co., J. L. .... AA

FLA.—Belleview

Hall & Pope .... B

FLA.—Bonifay

Alford Bros. ....B

FLA.—Bristol

Covington & Co., A. D. AA

FLA.—Carters

Carter, W. J. .... A

FLA.—Caryville

Godwin & Co., E. M. .. B

FLA.—Cleveland

Heckman, Gear & Co. .. B

FLA.—Dade City

Braydon, McWhite & Co. C

FLA.—Dunnellon

Wiggs & Co., W. H. ..AA

FLA.—Fairfield

Wade, McNair & Co. .. A

FLA.—Gretna

Riley & Co., W. G. C

FLA.—Montbrook

Flynn & Co., D. M. .... AA

TURPENTINE (Con.)

FLA.—Port Richeey
Sessoms, Johnson & Co. AA
FLA.—Rock Bluff
Daisy Co. .... AA
FLA.—Tallahassee
Lutherloh, R. B. ....B
FLA.—Woodville
Williams & Co. ....A
FLA.—York
Horne, Lewis & Co. C
GA.—Ailey
Riddle, J. A. .... D
GA.—Allajaha
Baker, J. H. C
GA.—Autryville
Autry, D. A. C
GA.—Bainbridge
Callahan, J. W. .... A
GA.—Bickley
Hinson & Co. .... B
GA.—Bingham
Kirkland & Gaskins .... D
GA.—Bladen
Ward, J. A. C
GA.—Egypt
Foy Mfg. Co., E. E. .. A
GA.—Evergreen
Dorminey, Warren & Co. B
GA.—Fales
Tanner, B. H. .... B
GA.—Fargo
Georgia Pine Turpentine Co. D
GA.—Gomez
Moody & Co., Daniel .... D
GA.—Hartsfield
Spiney & Co., J. F. .. C
GA.—Hilton Station
McLauren & Co., J. A...A
GA.—Homerville
Reagler, H. J. C
GA.—Irwinville
Barber Bros .... A
GA.—Laff
Gray & Co., Geo. T. C
GA.—Lexsy
Youmans & Co., J. C. ..D
GA.—Lollie
Pritchett & Co., Geo. E...A
GA.—Lothair
Pritchett. W. .... A
GA.—Meigs
Carter, J. N. C
GA.—Millen
Parker, H. W. .... D
GA.—Moultrie
Barber, Sessions & Co. ....B
Barber & Co., W. H. ....B
Holmes & Co. .... B
Smith & Co., W. H. ....A
Spivey, J. F. C
Vereen, W. C. .... A
Vereen & Smith .... A
GA.—Mystic
Drew & McNeill .... B
GA.—Nashville
Brown, E. G. .... B
GA.—Nelwood
Robertson & Jones ......D
GA.—Nielly
Smith, T. J. ....D
GA.—Ocilla
Powell-Bullard & Co. ....A
GA.—Olympia
West Yellow Pine Co. ...C
GA.—Pfeiffer
Pfeiffer, C. B. (Est of) B
GA.—Philips Mill
Talum & Holland ...... D
GA.—Reynolds
Barber & Rawl C
GA.—Rochelle
Walker, Johnathan .... D
GA.—Rothersay
Watson & Co., A. M. ...C
GA.—Shepherd
Lott, J. S. C
GA.—Thomasville
Watson & Gibson ....B
GA.—Vienna
Peacock & Kelley C
GA.—White Oak
McKimnon, L. F. & G. S...C
GA.—Willacoochee
O'Berry Sons & Co., J. E. B
GA.—Willingham
Alford, C. A. .... A
LA.—Covington
Jones & Pickett..........D

TURPENTINE (Con.)

LA.—Independence
Holliday & Co. .... AA
N. C.—Angier
Williams, J. C. & B. F...D
N. C.—Newbern
Ellis, Mrs. E. B. ...... D
N. C.—Wilmington
Spiritine Chemical Co.
 (Wood Spirit) C
S. C.—Conway
Burroughs & Collins Co. AA

TURQUOISE
See Jewelry

TURRETS

CONN.—Bridgeport
Bullard Mach. Tool Wks.
 (Screw Machine) .... AA
CONN.—Winsted
Carter & Hakes Machine
 Co. .... D
OHIO—Cleveland
Warner & Swasey Co.
 (Screw Machine) ......A
VT.—Springfield
Jones & Lamson Mach. Co.
 (Screw Machine) .... AA

TWEEDS
See Woolen Goods

TWEEZERS

CONN.—Plainville
Clark & Son, A. N. .... B
MASS.—Attleboro
Blake Co., James E. ....A
MASS.—Springfield
Bullock Mfg. Co. ....A
Parker, E. M. (Printers') F
N. H.—Lebanon
Kendrick & Davis ...... A
N. J.—Newark
Celluloid Co. .... B
N. Y.—Brooklyn
Wesel Mfg. Co., F. X
New York City
Hoe & Co., R. .... AAAA
Walbridge Co., J. H., 337
 Bway. .... B
R. I.—Providence
Bens Co., Wm. C

TWILLS
See Cotton Goods

TWINE
See Cordage

TWIST
See also Silk

CONN.—Mansfield Center
Hanks, P. G. (Machine)..B
CONN.—New London
Brainerd & Armstrong Co.
 (Machine) ....AAAA
CONN.—Norfolk
Aetna Silk Co. (Machine), B
CONN.—Putnam
Hammond, Knowlton & Co.
 (Machine) .... A
CONN.—Turnersville
Turner & Co., P. W.
 (Machine) X
CONN.—Willimantic
Holland Mfg. Co. (Ma-
 chine) .... AA
CONN.—Winsted
Salter Silk Co. (Machine) B
Winsted Silk Co. (Machine) A
MASS.—Boston
Eureka Silk Mfg. Co.
 (Machine) .... A
MASS.—Florence
Nonotuck Silk Co. (Ma-
 chine) .... AAAA
MASS.—Holyoke
Skinner Mfg. Co., Wm.
 (Machine) .... AA
MICH.—Belding
Belding Bros. & Co. (Inc.)

TWIST (Con.)
(Tram; Machine)..AAAA
Richardson Silk Co. (Machine) .... AA
N. Y.—Kenwood
Oneida Community (Ltd.)
(Machine) .... AAA
PA.—Philadelphia
Hackenburg & Co., W. B.
(Machine)............. B
Hooley & Son, B. (Tram) B

TWISTERS

CONN.—Stonington
Atwood-Morrison Co. (Silk)
AA
MASS.—Boston
Riley & Co., C. E., 65
Franklin (Cotton; Wool
Yarn) ....A
Stoddard, Haserick, Richards & Co., 152 Congress
(Cotton) ....B
MASS.—Hopedale
Draper Co. (Cotton).AAAA
MASS.—Lowell
Lowell Machine Shop (Cotton; Wool) ....AAAA
MASS.—Newton Upper Falls
Saco & Pettee Machine
Shops (Cotton)......AAA
MASS.—Whitinsville
Whitin Machine Wks (Cotton) ....AAAA
Whitinsville Spinning Ring
Co. (Cotton) ....AA
MASS.—Worcester
American Card Clothing Co.
(Wool) ....AAA
Brownell, Geo. L. (Cordage;
Cotton; Silk; Wool)....D
Cleveland Machine Wks.
(Wool) ....A
N. J.—Passaic
Lyall, J. & W. (Cordage).A
N. J.—Paterson
Royle & Sons, Jno. (Silk)
A
OHIO—Cincinnati
Obermayer Co., S. (Straw
Rope) ....A
PA.—Philadelphia
Diamond Textile Machine
Wks., 2d & Diamond
(Cotton) ....E
Smith Woolen Machinery
Co., James, 411 Race
.(Wool) ....AA
R. I.—Pawtucket
Fales & Jencks Machine Co.
(Wool) ....AAA
Howard & Bullough American Machine Co. (Ltd.)
(Cotton) ....AAA
Pawtucket Spinning Ring
Co. (Cotton) ....D
R. I.—Providence
Franklin Machine Co. (Cotton) ....A
Providence Machine Co.
(Cotton) ....AA

TYPE

ILL.—Chicago
Barnhart Bros. & Spindler,
187 Monroe (Body; Metal)
AA
Inland Type Foundry.....A
Superior Rubber Type Co.
(Rubber) C
MD.—Baltimore
Dorman Co., J. F. W. (Rubber) ....F
MASS.—Boston
Hansen, H. C. (Metal)....B
MASS.—Springfield
Smith Mfg. Co., R. H., 293
Main (Rubber; Rubber
Metal Bodied) C
MICH.—Ludington
Tubbs Mfg. Co. (Wooden)
B
N. Y.—Middletown
Hamilton Mfg. Co. (Wooden) ....AA
Morgan & Wilcox Mfg. Co.
(Wooden) C
New York City
Bruce Type Foundry
(Metal) ....A
Force & Co., Wm. A., 50

TYPE (Con.)
Beekman (Rubber) ....B
Ingersoll & Bro., Robert H.
51 Maiden Lane (Rubber)
A
Ness, Jr., Geo. M. (Brass;
Steel) ....H
New York Stencil Wks
(Steel) ....D
Stewart & Holihan (Rubber; Metal Bodied) ....D
OHIO—Cambridge
Crescent Seal & Stamp Co.
(Rubber) ....H
PA.—Philadelphia
Hill Mfg. Co., B. B., 1020
New Market (Rubber)..B
WIS.—Milwaukee
Schwaab Stamp & Lead Co.
(Steel) C
WIS.—Two Rivers
Hamilton Mfg. Co. (Brass;
Wooden) ....AA

TYPERS

OHIO—Springfield
Downey & Co., W. C.
(Fodder) C

TYPEWRITERS

See also Machy

CONN.—Derby
Williams Typewriter Co...B
CONN.—Hartford
Underwood Typewriter Co.
AAA
CONN.—Stamford
Blickensderfer Mfg. Co.
AA
ILL.—Chicago
Fay-Sholes Co. ....AA
Oliver Typewriter Co., 107
Lake ....AA
IOWA—Des Moines
Jewett Typewriter Co. ..A
MICH.—Grand Rapids
Fox Machine Co. ....A
N. Y.—Ithaca
Ithaca Gun Co. ....B
New York City
American Typewriter Co. of
Va., 265 B'way ....D
American Writing Machine
Co., 343 B'way .....AA
Columbia Typewriter Mfg.
Cc., 56 Reade ......AA
Densmore Typewriter Co.,
309 B'way ....B
Elliot-Fisher Co. (Book)..A
Franklin Typewriter Co.,
812 Greenwich ....D
Hammond Typewriter Co.,
165 B'way ....D
Lambert Typewriter Co.,
1274 B'way ....D
R. & G. Typewriter Co.,
229 B'way ....E
Remington Typewriter Co.,
327 B'way ....A
Simplex Typewriter Co.,
644 1st Av. ....D
Sun Typewriter Co., 229
B'way C
N. Y.—Syracuse
Smith Premier Typewriter
Co. ....AAAA
PA.—Pittsburg
Pittsburg Writing Machine
Co., 208 Wood ....D

ULSTERS

See Clothing: Men's

ULTRA-MARINE

New York City
Ansbacher & Co., A. B.
AAA
Heller & Merz Co. .....AA
International Ultramarine
Wks. (Ltd.) 71 Duane..A
Tiemann & Co., D. F.....A

UMBRELLAS

MD.—Baltimore
Gans Bros. (& Parasols) A

UMBRELLAS (Con.)

MASS.—Boston
Moxey, Gill & Howlett...B
MASS.—Springfield
Burgin Bros. (Wagon)...F
MICH.—Detroit
Newland, Henry A. Co...B
MO.—St. Louis
Dougherty Bros. Tent &
  Awning Co. (Wagon)..C
Zittlosen Mfg. Co. (Wagon)
  ....B

New York City
Arnold, Schiff & Co., 54
  White (Cotton; Silk;
  Parasols) ....B
Schloss Bros. (& Parasols)
  ....B
Shields & Co., J. S., 596
  B'way ....B
OHIO—Cincinnati
Kuhn, E. C. (& Parasols) B
OHIO—Dayton
Cappel, A. (& Parasols), B
OHIO—Fremont
Lehr Argricultural (Wagon)
  ....B
OHIO—Norwalk
Sprague Umbrella Co. (Ad-
  vertising; Campaign; So-
  ciety) ....B
OHIO—Plain City
Moulton Wireless Umbrella
  Co. ....B
OHIO—Toledo
Hettrick Bros. Co. (Wagon)
 C
OHIO—Troy
Troy Carriage Sunshade Co.
  (& Parasols) ....B
PA.—Lancaster
Foller Clogg & Co. (& Para-
  sols) ....AAA
Rose Bros. & Co. ....B
PA.—Philadelphia
Fretz, S. S., Mfg. Co. (&
  Parasols, all grades) AAA
Hirsh & Bro. (& Parasols)
  ....A
Moxey, Howlett & Co. (&
  Parasols). ....B

UNDERSKIRTS

See Clothing: Laides'

UNDERWEAR

ALA.—Huntsville
Rowe Knitting Co., W. H.
  (Men's & Boy's Fleece
  Lined) ....B
CAL.—Los Angeles
Coulter Dry Goods Co.
  (Muslin) ....A
Cohn, Goldwater & Co.
  (Canton Flannell Draw-
  ers) ....B
CAL.—Oakland
Eagleson & Co. (Flannel)
  ....A
Keller Co., M. J........B
CAL.—San Francisco
Friedlander & Sons, E.
  (Women) C
Hirsch, Leopold (Flannel)
  ....B
Magnin & Co., I. (Ladies,
  Childrens; Infants Mus-
  lin) ....B
Newbauer Bros. (Ladies
  Muslin) ....D
Pfister Knitting Co., J. J.,
  60 Geary (Knit Silk; Cot-
  ton; Merino; Wool) ..B
Rothschild & Co., A
  (Ladies) ....B
CONN.—Bristol
Birge Sons Co., N. L. (Cot-
  ton; Wool; Merino; Cam-
  els Hair; Drawers, &c.)
  ....B
Bristol Mfg. Co. (Cotton;
  Wool) ....B
CONN.—Glastonbury
Glastonbury Knitting Co.
  (Men's Knit; Wool Shirts;
  Drawers) ....A
CONN.—Naugatuck
Dunham Hosiery Co. (La-
  dies Childrens; Camels
  Hair; Wool; Worsted;
  Silk) ....A

UNDERWEAR (Con.)

CONN.—New Britain
American Hosiery Co. (Cot-
  ton; Wool; Merino; Silk)
  ....AAAA
New Britain Knitting Co.
  (Wool; Cotton Shirts;
  Drawers) ....A
CONN.—Norwalk
Hutchinson, Pierce & Co.
  (Ladies; Boys) ....AAA
CONN.—Shelton
Radcliffe Bros. ....A
CONN.—Waterville
Welch Hosiery Co. (Ribbed;
  Flat) ....A
CONN.—Winsted
New England Knitting Co.
  (Men's Wool; Merino)..A
Winsted Hosiery Co. (Full
  Regular Made) ....A
D. C.—Washington
Hall, Philip T. C
GA.—Atlanta
Atlanta Knitting Mills,
  (Womens Knit Cotton).D
Wolf, H. (Men's Drawers)
 C
GA.—Barnesville
Georgia Underwear Co...D
Oxford Knitting Mills
  (Womens Knit) ....D
GA.—Cedartown
Josephine Mills (Light;
  Heavy Bleached Cotton)
  ....A
GA.—Dalton
Smith, M. D. & H. L.
  (Men's Drawers) .....D
GA.—Griffin
Griffin Knitting Mills
  (Men's Elastic Ribbed).D
GA.—Hampton
Henderson Mfg. Co. (Wo-
  mens Cotton) C
GA.—Macon
Scofield Mfg. Co. (Men's)
 C
GA.—Savannah
American Mfg. Co. (Men's
  Drawers) ....B
GA.—Union Point
Union Mfg. Co. (Fleeced).D
ILL.—Chicago
Lewis, Geo. (Womens Mus-
  lin) C
Parkside Mfg. Co. (Ladies)
 C
Phylli's Knitting Co. (Knit)
 C
Strauss-Cahn Knitting Co.
  (Worsted; Cotton; Silk;
  Merino) C
Vassar Swiss Underwear Co.
  (Knit Union Suits; Tights)
 C
IND.—Fort Wayne
Paragon Mfg. Co. (Ladies)
 C
IND.—Lafayette
Lafayette Underwear Co.
  (Men's Cotton; Silk! Mer-
  cerized) C
IND.—Muncie
Muncie Underwear Co.
  (Men's Cotton Knit)...D
IND.—New Albany
Robinson, Norton & Co.
  (Ladies Muslin) ....AAA
IND.—So. Bend
Stanley Mfg Co., A. C.
  (Men's Knit) ....B
LA.—New Orleans
Heidenheim, Levy & Co.
  (Drawers) ....A
Katz & Co., S. & J.
  (Drawers) ....A
Kaufman & Co., Chas. A.
  ....A
Kory & Sons, A. ....A
Perry, S. R. C
Schwartz & Isaacs Co.
  (Muslin) ....A
Weiss Mfg. Co. (Shirts;
  Drawers) C
MAINE—Portland
Chenery Mfg. Co. (Wo-
  men's) ....B
Russ Eveleth & Ingalls
  (Ladies'& Children's Mus-
  lin) ....A
MAINE—Waterville
Hathaway & Co., C. F.

(Women's Muslin) ....B
MD.—Baltimore
Bentley & Melvin ....D
Erlanger Bros. (Men's
  Drawers) ....AA
Kiehne & Co., E. A. ....D
Lauer, Lewis & Co. C
Morris & Co. (Men's Jeans
  & Nainsook Drawers) ..B
Myer. Henry & Co. C
North Bros. & Strauss ....A
Pheonix Mfg. Co. (Men's
  Drawers) .... AAA
Rosenfeld & Co., E.
  (Men's) ....A
Schenthal & Sons. Jos. ..C
Standard Overall Co. (Men's
  Drawers) ....D
Stratton & Son., T. S. ..C
Strauss Bros. (Men's
  Drawers) ....AAA
Stuart & Keith ....B
Towles Mfg. Co., Wm. H.
  (Drawers) C
Witz Bros. & Co. (Men's
  Drawers) ....B
MD.—Hagerstown
Roulett & Co., J. C.
  (Ladies' Cotton Fine
  Jersey Ribbed) ....B
MASS.—Boston
Austin & Co., H. A. (Belts;
  Silk Dress Shields) C
Sterling Knit Goods Co. E
MASS.—Chicopee Falls
Taylor Bramley Co. (Knit)
  B
MASS.—Everett
Bailey & Co., Oscar L.
  (Jersey Ribbed) C
Puritan Knitting Mills
  (Women's; Children's) C
MASS.—Florence
Nonotuck Silk Co. (Silk)
  AAA
MASS.—Highlandville
Moseley & Co. (Women's;
  Children's) ....D
MASS.—Lowell
Criterion Knitting Co.
  (Knit) ....D
Lawrence Mfg. Co. (Knit
  Cotton) ....AAAA
Whithall Mfg. Co. (Inc.)
  (Muslin; Cambric) ..C
MASS.—Millbury
Kotedsilk Underwear Co.
  D
MASS.—Natick
Natick Underwear Co.
  (Women's; Children's
  Muslin) C
Randall Bros. (Ladies';
  Children's Cotton) C
MASS.—Needham
Brooks Co., Jno. F. (Infant's) C
Carter Co., Wm. (Cotton,
  Merino; Wool; Silkateen)
  B
MASS.—Pittsfield
Collins & Co., D. M.
  (Knit) ....AA
Musgrove Knitting Co.
  (Ribbed) ....D
MASS.—Springfield
Medlicott Morgan Co. (Cotton Knit) ....D
Springfield Knitting Co.
  (Jersey Ribbed) ......A
MASS.—Stoughton
Stretton & Sons, Chas.
  (Knit) ....A
MASS.—Wakefield
Winship Boit & Co. (Wool;
  Cotton; Silk) C
MASS.—Waltham
Amer. Knitting Co. (Infant's; Children's Knit) E
MASS.—Watertown
Dalby Co.. Thos (Cotton;
  Merino; Silk) C
MASS.—Worcester
Burns Co.. Wm. H. (Women's; Children's Muslin
  & Flannellette) ......B
Green & Green (Muslin) ..C
MICH.—Adrian
Adrian Knitting Co. (Children's Cotton Ribbed) C

MICH.—Centerville
Michigan Central Woolen
  Co. (Men's Knit) C
MICH.—Grand Rapids
Globe Knitting Wks. (Women's; Children's Ribbed
  Cotton) ....D
Standard Mfg. Co. (Ladies'
  Muslin & Flannellette) B
Star Knitting Co. (Men's;
  Women's; Misses'; Children's Combination Suits)
  C
MICH.—Lansing
Michigan Knitting Co.
  (Knit Comb Suits) .....D
MICH.—Muskegon
Amazon Knitting Co. (Knit)
  A
Muskegon Knitting Mills
  (Men's; Women's; Infants'; Children's Woolen
  Silk) ....F
MICH.—Pontiac
Pontiac Knitting Co. (Knit)
  C
MICH.—Ypsilanti
Hay & Todd Mfg. Co.
  (Comb. Suits) C
MINN.—Duluth
Neilson Bros. (Knit) C
MINN.—Minneapolis
Belden & Evans ....D
Northwestern Knitting Co.
  (Worsted; Lisle Thread)A
MINN.—Northfield
Northfield Knitting Co.
  (Knit) ....F
MO.—Jefferson
Star Clothing Co. (Men's
  Drawers) C
MO.—St. Louis
Ely & Walker Dry Goods Co.
  AAAA
Ferguson McKinney Dry
  Goods Co. (Ladies' Muslin) ....AAAA
Gilbert Bros. C
Grabinsky & Co., S. (Women's Muslin) C
Lipshitz & Co., M. (Men's)C
Prince, Evans & Co. (Women's Muslin) ....B
N. H.—Hillsborough Bridge
Contoocook Mills Co. (Wool;
  Merino) ....A
N. H.—Lebanon
Everett Knitting Wks.
  (Ribbed) ....B
N. H.—Manchester
Elliott Mfg. Co. (Knit Wool;
  Silk) ....A
N. H.—Newport
Peerless Mfg. Co. (Women's; Children's Muslin) A
N. J.—Dover
Swiss Knitting Co. (Silk;
  Wool; Mixed; Lisle) C
N. J.—Hoboken
Wrights Health Underwear
  Co. ....B
N. J.—Newark
Cogswell & Boulter Co.
  (Women's Muslin) .....A
Delsarte Mfg. & Supply Co.
  D
N. Y.—Albany
Field & Hatch Knitting Co.
  (Jersey Ribbed) ..AAAA
Hubbard & Co., G. A.
  (Ladies' Muslin) .....D
N. Y.—Amsterdam
Atlas Knitting Co. (Fancy
  Knit) ....B
Dean & Co., L. L. (Men's
  All Wool) ....B
Gardiner-Warring Co.
  (Ladies'; Men's) ......B
Greene Knitting Co. .....D
Harrower. L. E. (Fleece
  Lined Knit) ....AAA
McFarlan & Co. (Fleeced)B
Morris & Sons, A. V. AAAA
Rowe Knitting Co., W. H.
  (Cotton; Wool) ......AA
Sovereign Knitting Co. (Fancy Balbriggan; Ladies'
  Jersey) C
Stewart, J. K. (Knit Cotton;
  Wool) ....AA
Van Brocklin & Stover Co.

UNDERWEAR (Con.)
(Men's Fleece Lined) ..B
Yunds, Kennedy & Yunds
(Knit Cotton; Wool) .B
N. Y.—Anderson
Blood Knitting Co. (Ribbed)
B
N. Y.—Arcade
Sanford, Jno. C. (Swiss
Ribbed) C
N. Y.—Athens
Athens Knitting Co. (Cotton; Wool Fleece Lined) C
N. Y.—Averill Park
Faith Knitting Co. (Cotton;
Wool Knit) ....D
N. Y.—Baldwinsville
Allen, Alexander (Women's
Ribbed) ....D
N. Y.—Broadalbin
Broadalbin Knitting Co.
(Cotton; Wool; Fleece
Lined) ....D
N. Y.—Brooklyn
Am. Knit Goods Mfg. Co.
(Knit) ....AAA
Standard Knitting Mills Co.
(Women's; Children's Ribbed) ....D
Wiley Mfg. Co. (Knit) ..A
Windsor Knitting Mills
(Infants' Ribbed) ....D
N. Y.—Camden
Camden Knitting Co. (Combination Suits) ......AA
N. Y.—Catskill
Malcolm Knitting Co.
(Plain; Fancy Cotton;
Wool Fleeced) ....B
N. Y.—Cohoes
Barnet & Aufsesser Knit Co.
(Ribbed) ....B
Cascade Mills (White; Nat.
Wool) ....B
Clark & Holsapple Mfg. Co.
B
Clifton Co., S. E. (Ladies'
Cotton Ribbed) ......D
Davitt, A. W. (Natural
Wool; Camels Hair) ...C
Empire Knitting Mills
(Fleece Lined) ....B
Himes Underwear Co. (Novelty; Fleece Lined) ..B
Hope Knitting Co. (Nat.
Wool; Camels Hair) ...A
Johnston, David S. (Balbriggan; Lisle Thread) ..D
Kavanaugh Mfg. Co., F. W.
(Cotton; Wool; Fleece
Lined Goods) C
Moore Knitting Co., Wm.
(White; Gray; Camels
Hair) ....B
Murphy Mfg. Co., Jno. H.
(Jersey Ribbed) ......B
Parsons Mfg. Co. ....B
Quinn, Jno. F. (Jersey
Knit) ....B
Riverside Knitting Mill
(Fleeced; Ribbed; Plain)D
Root Mfg. Co. ....A
Victor Knitting Mills Co.
(Nat. Wool; Black; Red;
Camels Hair) ....A
N. Y.—Elmira
Elmira Knitting Mills
(Men's Cotton) ....A
Queen City Knitting Mills
(Women's; Children's Cotton Ribbed) ....D
N. Y.—Ft. Plain
Bailey Knitting Mills
(Men's; Boys') ....B
N. Y.—Greenwich
Pleasant Vale Mills (Men's;
Boys' Fleece Lined) ...C
Van Zile Knitting Co.
(Women's; Misses' Ribbed)C
N. Y.—Herkimer
Mark Mfg. Co. (Men's;
Women's; Children's
Knit) ....D
Royal Gem Mills Co. (Cotton; Wool; Silk) ......A
N. Y.—Hoosick Falls
Superior Mfg. Co. (Men's;
Women's; Children's Cotton; Worsted; Silk Ribbed) ....D
N. Y.—Hornellsville
Underwear Mfg. Co. (Wom-

UNDERWEAR (Con.)
en's Muslin) ....A
N. Y.—Hudson
Union Mills (Wool; Fleece
Lined) ....A
N. Y.—Jamestown
Logan, R. T. ....D
N. Y.—Johnstown
Diana Knitting Co. (Women's Medium High Grade;
Men's Babbriggan) ....D
Johnstown Knitting Co.
(Men's; Boys'; Women's
Fleeced; Jersey Ribbed) B
N. Y.—Little Falls
Adams Mfg. Co., Victor
(Fine Jersey Ribbed) ..C
Gilbert Knitting Co. (Ribbed; Fleece) ....AA
Mackinnon & Co., Robt.
(Children's Cotton; Wool
Knit) ....AA
Rockton Knitting Mills
(Knit) ....A
Sheard Co., Titus (Red;
Nat. Wool) ....A
Walrath, R. (Knit) C
N. Y.—Mechanicville
Mechanicville Knitting Co.
(Men's Wool; Fleece
Lined) ....B
N. Y.—Milton
Bells' Sons Co., Hy. H. ..B
N. Y.—Mohawk
Mohawk Valley Knitting
Mills (Nat. Wool; Camels Hair) ....B
Paragon Knitting Co. (Nat.
Wool; Camels Hair) ...B
New York City
Acme Underwear Co. (Misses'; Children's Muslin;
Cambric; Canton Flannel)
C
Aitkin, Son & Co. ....AAAA
Alvis Co., Isaac ....B
Bacon & Co. (Com.) ..AAA
Ballin & Sons, M. (Men's)D
Bamberger, Gilbert C
Bamberger & Son (Infants';
Children's Flannel)....B
Birkenfeld, Strauss & Co.
(Muslin; Flannellete) .B
Boessneck Broesel & Co.
(Com.) ....B
Burgess & Co., W. H. (Knit;
Com.) ....AAA
Caeser & Co., H. A. (Com.)
AAA
Citron & Co., S. ....B
Claflin Co., H. B. (Muslin)
AAAA
Critten, Clift & Co. (Knit
Com.) ....B
Danenbaum Bros. (Women's
Muslin) ....A
Diamond, Wm. J. (Women's
Muslin) C
Dubinsky, Louis (Men's) D
Farber & Co., Fred. M.
(Ribbed, Com.) C
Farber, Drewrʳ & Co., H. J.
(Com.) C
Frankenthal Bros. & Co.
(Ladies') ....B
Guiterman & Co., Carl
(Com.) ....A
Hardt, Von Bernuth & Co.
(Com.) ....AAAA
Harris, Geo. (Ladies' Muslin) ....D
Herzig & Co., L. (Knit) ..C
Hess & Nelson (Women's
Muslin; Flannellette) ...C
Hirsch & Son Co., Isaac
(Ladies' Muslin) ......A
Iselin & Co., Wm. (Com.)
AAAA
Juilliard & Co., A. D.
(Com.) ....AAAA
Keep Shirt Co., H. V. ...D
Knitting Mills Trading Co.
(Com.) ....B
Ladyware Co. C
Lamson, Roger & Co. (Com.)
A
Lay & Way Co. (Infts';
Boys'; Girls' Underwaists)
C
Lewis & Bro., Henry (Ladies' Muslin) ....B

1077

UNDERWEAR (Con.)

Libman, B. Mrs. (Infants'
  Slips) C
Martin & Co., M. (Ladies';
  Misses') ....AA
Oelbermann, Dommerich &
  Co. (Com.) ....AAAA
Piddian & Wormser (Boys')
 C
Platzek. Wm. W. C
Porter Bros. & Co. (Com.) A
Robertson & Bruhn (Mfrs.
  Agts.) ....B
Roggen & Eisenstein
  (Ladies') C
Rosenberg, D. (Ladies' Mus-
  lin) C
Rosenstock & Cohn (Wom-
  ens') C
Rowe & Son, W. H. (Com.
  Knit) ....AA
Schefer, Schramm & Vogel
  (Knit Com.) ......AAAA
Schwed & Co., R. (Infants')
 C
Scriven Co., J. A. ....B
Sicher & Co., D. E. (Ladies'
  Muslin) ....AA
Sigel Bros. (Muslin) ..AAA
Spielmann & Co. (Com.)AAA
Steiner & Son (Night
  Shirts) ....A
Stearns, Simon & Co. (Wom-
  en's; Children's) ....AA
Talcott, James (Knit, Com.)
  ....AAAA
Verdier & Hardy (Com.) A
Vietor & Achelis, Fred.
  (Com.) ....AAAA
Watson, Porter, Giles & Co.
  (Com.) ....A
White & Co., Jas. F. (Com.)
  ....AAAA
Wilmerding & Bisset (Com.)
  ....AA
Wolbach. J. (Ladies') ...C
N. Y.—Oneonta
Buckley Bros. Co. (To Meas-
  ure) C
N. Y.—Oswego
Conde. Frederic (Cotton;
  Wool Knit) ....D
Oswego Knitting Co. (Bal-
  briggan) ....A
N. Y.—Oriskany Falls
Utica Knitting Co. (Wom-
  ens'; Children's Ribbed)
  ....AAA
N. Y.—Peekskill
Baker Underwear Co. (Wom-
  en's; Children's Muslin;
  Cambric) ....B
N. Y.—Perry
Perry Knitting Co. (Men's;
  Children's Knit) .....A
N. Y.—Philmont
Aken Knitting Co. (Fleece
  Lined) ....AA
Hayes & Co., Jno. (Fleece
  Lined) C
High Rock Knitting Co.
  (Men's Fleece Lined;
  Wool Mixed) ....A
N. Y.—Rexleigh
Brockway. Geo. E. (Wool;
  Camels Hair) ....D
N. Y.—Richmondville
Waiontha Knitting Co.
  (Jersey Ribbed) ......B
N. Y.—Rome
Columbia Knitting Mills
  (Men's Fine Balbriggan)B
Fort Stanwix Knitting Co.
  (Men's Plain; Fancy) ..D
Rome. Textile Co. (Cotton
  Ribbed) ....D
Williams Bros. Mfg. Co.
  (Cotton; Silk; Lisle; Wor-
  sted) ....B
N. Y.—St. Johnsville
Lion Mfg. Co. (Cotton Knit)
 C
Royal Gem Mills Co. (Wom-
  en's Cotton Ribbed) ....B
Union Knitting Co.
  (Fleeced) C
N. Y.—Sand Lake
McLaren. J. & R. (Men's;
  Boys' Knit) ....D
N. Y.—Sanquoit
Lewis Knitting Co. (Chil-
  dren's Ribbed) C

UNDERWEAR (Con.)

N. Y.—Schenectady
Alpha Knitting Co. (Wool)C
N. Y.—Sherburne
Canasawacta Knitting Co.
  (Men's Cotton) ....D
N. Y.—Stillville
Hackett & Atwood (Cotton
  Knit) ....B
N. Y.—Stillwater
Newland Denison & Co.
  (Knit) ....A
N. Y.—Stockport
Hoover, Jas. A. (Men's Fine
  Fleeced) ....A
N. Y.—Syracuse
Clinton Knitting Co. (Wom-
  en's Jersey Ribbed) ..AA
Oak Knitting Co. (Children's
  Cotton Knit) ....A
West Bros. (Cotton Fancy
  Ribbed) ....B
N. Y.—Troy
Commercial Knitting Mills
  Co. (All Wool; Cotton;
  Silk) ....A
Troy Knitting Co. (Ladies';
  Gents' Knit Wool) .....A
United Shirt & Collar Co.
  (Ladies' Chemisettes)
  ....AAAA
Wrights Health Underwear
  Co. ....A
N. Y.—Utica
Avalon Knitwear Co. (Wom-
  en's Cotton; Worsted) ..C
Capron Knitting Co. (Men's
  Fleeced Lined Balbriggan;
  Ribbed) C
Fisher Knit Goods Co.
  (Fleece Lined) C
Fort Schuyler Knitting Co.
  (Women's; Misses' Swiss
  Ribbed) ....D
Kendall Knitting Co. (La-
  dies'; Children's Ribbed)C
La Tosca Knitting Co.
  (Women's Ribbed) ....A
Oneita Knitting Mills (Knit)
  ....A
Regal Textile Co. (Wom-
  en's Fleece Lined) C
Richelieu Knitting Co.
  (Women's; Misses' Swiss
  Ribbed) ....D
Seal Back Underwear Co.
  (Children's Ribbed) ....E
Utica Knitting Co. (Knit)
  ....AAA
N. Y.—Waterford
Clover Knitting Co. (Men's;
  Women's; Children's) ..C
Ford Mfg. Co. (Knit) ....B
Kavanaugh Knitting Co.
  (Balbriggan) ....B
Novelty Knit Underwear Co.
  (Ribbed) ....A
Orinsby Textile Co. (Knit) B
Waterford Knitting Co. (La-
  dies'; Gents' Knit) ....A
N. Y.—Whitesboro
Ablett. Robert (Men's;
  Boys'; Children's Fleece
  Lined; Balbriggan) ..AA
N. C.—Raleigh
Melrose Knitting Mill Co.
  (Men's Knit) ....D
N. C.—Scotland Neck
Scotland Neck Cotton Mills
  (Knit Cotton) ....B
N. C.—Weldon
Roanoke Mills Co. (Knit)A
N. C.—Winston-Salem
Maline Mills Co. (Cotton
  Ribbed) C
OHIO—Cincinnati
Dormer Bros. Co. (Infants')
 C
Fairmount Woolen Mills
  (Knit) ....A
Reins & Meiss (Misses') ..B
Shillito Co. John ....AAAA
OHIO—Cleveland
Central Knitting Co. (Knit)
  ....B
Root & McBride Co. (Mus-
  lin) ....AAAA
Taylor, Son & Co., Wm.
  (Muslin) ....AAA
OHIO—Hamilton
Miami Valley Knitting
  Mills (Cotton Knit) ....B

UNDERWEAR (Con.)
Pioneer Knitting Mills Co.
(Cotton Knit ; Union
Suits) C
OHIO—Mentor
Mentor Knitting Mills
(Women's; Children's Cot-
ton Knit) C
OHIO—Piqua
Atlas Underwear Co.
(Union Suits) ....D
Piqua Hosiery Co. (Men's;
Women's; Children's
Knit) ....D
PA.—Allentown
Allentown Knitting Co.
(Knit Ribbed) ....B
Southdown Knitting Co.
(Women's Ribbed Cotton;
Lisle; Silk) C
Swartz, C. (Cotton Knit) D
PA.—Ashley
Ashley Knitting Mills ....B
PA.—Auburn
Diefenderfer & Co., W. H.
(Women's) ....D
PA.—Avon
Lebanon Textile Co. (Wom-
en's Cotton; Lisle; Mer-
cerized) ....D
PA.—Bridgeport
Kaufman Mfg. Co. (Ribbed)
A
PA.—Centreport
Centreport Knitting Co.
(Cotton Knit) ....D
PA.—Chicamauga
Chicamauga Knitting Mills
(Women's Ribbed) C
PA.—Hamburg
Hamburg Knitting Mills
(Cotton Ribbed) ....D
PA.—Hawley
U. S. Knitting Mills (Knit)B
PA.—Hazleton
Hazle Knitting Mill Co.
(Knit) ....D
Wilde & Co. (Knit) C
PA.—Kutztown
King Knitting Mills (Cot-
ton Ribbed) ....D
PA.—Lititz
Keystone Underwear Mills
(Men's Ribbed) C
PA.—Mohrsville
Wagner & Co., Jas. H.
(Women's Ribbed). ....D
PA.—Newville
Newville Knitting Co. (Cot-
ton; Lisle Knit) C
PA.—Norristown
Keystone Knitting Mills Co.
(Knit Cotton) ....D
Penn Knitting Co. (Knit) D
PA.—Philadelphia
Barrows & Son, David (La-
dies'; Children's Fancy
Knit) C
Behal, Jos. L. (Womens'
Ribbed) ....D
Blood & Bro., Jno. (Ribbed)
A
Brubaker & Son, E. (Men's
Drawers) ....D
Elk Knitting Mills Co. (Cot-
ton; Lisle; Silk; Woolen)C
Excelsior Underwear Co.
(Knit) ....E
Flavell Bros. (Men's; Wom-
en's) ....B
Florence Knitting Mills
(Eiderdown) C
Geneva Knitting Mills (Ei-
derdown) C
Godshalk Co., E. H. (Ei-
derdown) ....AA
Hagedorn, Merz Co. ......A
Hygienic Fleeced Under-
wear Co. (Fleeced) ...A
Iroquois Knitting Mills
(Ribbed) ....D
Kaufman & Rubin (Wom-
en's) C
Kremer & Co., Theo. E.
(Knit) ....B
Lamson & Co., Roger (Com.)
A
Lanark Knitting Co. (Cot-
ton Ribbed) ....AA
Lang & Co., H. A. (Muslin)
C
Pilling Mfg. Co. (Jersey

UNDERWEAR (Con.)
Ribbed) ....B
Querns Bros. (Cotton; Wor-
sted Ribbed) ....A
Rosenblatt, A. (Infants';
Children's; Women's) ..C
Rothchild & Co., S. (In-
fants'; Children's) C
Roxford Knitting Co.
(Balbriggan) ....A
Shenkin Bros. (Muslin) ...C
Stokes, Cromie & Co. (Com.)
B
Thompson, Foust & Co.
(Com.) C
Thurman, H. W. C
Townsend & Co., E. M.
(Com.) ....A
Underdown, A. R. C
Woodcock Bros. C
PA.—Phoenixville
Byrne, Thos. F. (Knit
Ribbed) ....AA
Parsons & Baker (Women's
Knit) ....A
Perseverance Knitting Co.
(Fine Ribbed) ....D
PA.—Pittston
Alpine Knitting Co.
(Ribbed) ....B
PA.—Pottsville
Phillips & Son, M. (Flexible
Seam Drawers) ....A
Luzerne Knitting Mills
(Flat; Ribbed Knit) ..B
PA.—Reading
Ammon, E. S. (Cotton;
Jersey Ribbed) ....D
Mt. Penn Knitting Co.
(Women's Fleeced) ..D
Reading Underwear Co.
(Knit) ....D
PA.—Riegelsville
Clymer, Lee S. (Knit) ..C
PA.—Royersford
Century Knitting Co. (Cot-
ton; Lisle, etc.) ....D
Chester Knitting Co. (Cot-
ton Knit) ....D
Emmers & Co., E. (Ladies'
Knit) ....AA
Nat. Underwear Co. (Knit
Cotton) C
PA.—Schuylkill Haven
Berger & Son, H. (Cotton
Knit) ....D
Kline, A. H. (Knit Ribbed)
D
Reed & Leminger (Women's
Knit) C
Sharadin, Daniel (Jersey
Cotton) ....D
Thomas Knitting Mills
(Knit) ....D
Lackawanna Mills (Knit) A
Shamokin Underwear Mill
(Knit) ....A
PA.—Shoemakersville
Wolf & Son, Wm. (Cotton
Knit) ....D
PA.—Wilkesbarre
Galland Bros. ....B
R. I.—Pawtucket
Lebanon Mill Co. (Knit)..B
U. S. Knitting Co. (Cotton
Knit) ....A
R. I.—Providence
Vista Knitting Mills (Cot-
ton; Woolen Knit) ...AA
S. C.—Bowling Green
Bowling Green Knitting
Mills (Women's Cotton
Knit) ....D
S. C.—Charleston
Wilbur & Son, T. A.
(Drawers) ....A
TENN.—Nashville
Fish & Weil C
Frank & Co. C
TEXAS—Dallas
Rose Mfg. Co. ....B
Sanger Bros. ....AAAA
TEXAS—Galveston
Pierson, A. L. (Drawers) C
VT.—Bennington
Bradford & Co., H. E.
(Knit Woolen) ....A
Rockwood & Co., Geo.
(Knit Woolen) ....A
Tiffany Bros. (Knit Woolen)
B

UNDERWEAR (Con.)

VT.—Pownal
Wrights' Health Underwear Co. (Fleeced Woolen Knit) ....B

VA.—Berkley
Chesapeake Knitting Mills (Cotton Knit) ....AA

VA.—Norfolk
Hatch & Dean ....D
Norfolk Knitting Mills (Knit) ....B
Steels' Union Overall Co. (Men's Drawers) .....D

VA.—Richmond
Cohen, Son & Co., M. (Men's Drawers) ....A

WIS.—Janesville
Lewis Knitting Co. (Full Fashioned Knit in Combination & Separate) ..B

WIS.—Kenosha
Cooper Underwear Co. (Men's Knit Wool; Cotton; Mercerized) ....B

WIS.—Milwaukee
Van Dyke Knitting Co. (General Line Knit) ...B

UNIFORMS

See also Clothing

OHIO—Columbus
Lilly & Co., M. O. (Military; Society) ....AAAA

UNIONS

CONN.—Bridgeport
Belknap Mfg. Co. C

ILL.—Chicago
Blatchford & Co., E. W., 70 N. Clinton (Soldering) ....AAAA
Crane Co. (Pipe) ...AAAA
Illinois Malleable Iron Co., 30 W. Monroe (Pipe) ....AAAA

ILL.—Decatur
Mueller Mfg. Co., H. (Soldering) ....AAA

ILL.—Edwardsville
Edwardsville Brass Co. (Soldering) ....B

ILL.—Kewanee
Western Tube Co. (Brass; Malleable Iron Soldering) ....AAA

MASS.—Boston
Walworth Mfg. Co. (Pipe) ....AAAA

MASS.—Lexington
Jefferson Mfg. Co. (for High & Low Pressure, Soldering) X

MO.—St. Louis
Pleuger & Henger Mfg. Co., 11th & Hebert ....A

N. J.—Belleville
Eastwood Wire Mfg. Co. ..A

N. J.—Paterson
McNab & Harlin Mfg. Co. ....AAA

N. Y.—Brooklyn
Williams & Co., J. H. (Forged) ....AA

N. Y.—Monroe
Newbury Mfg. Co. (Gray Iron) ....D

New York City
Mullaney's Son, Jas., 25th & Lex. Av. ....D

OHIO—Cincinnati
Lunkenheimer Co., Beekman & Waverly ....AA
Powell Co., Wm. (Brass) C
Queen City Brass & Iron Works (Brass; Soldering, etc.) ....B

OHIO—Cleveland
Cleveland Bronze & Brass Works (Brass Soldering)C
Glauber Brass Mfg. Co., 88 River (Soldering) ...AA
Sanitary Co., 335 Huron (Soldering) ....B

OHIO—Mansfield
Ohio Brass Co. ....AA

OHIO—Springfield
Nolte Brass Co. (Brass, Soldering, Pipe) ......D

UNIONS (Con.)

PA.—Erie
Campbell Brass Works, J. B. (Soldering) ....A

PA.—Philadelphia
Belfield & Co., H. ......AA
Flagg & Co., Stanley G., 19th & Penna. Av. (Soft Metal Seat) ....AAA
Haines, Jones & Cadbury Co., 1136 Ridge Av. (Soldering) ....AA
Pancoast & Co., Henry B., 243 So. 3d ....B
Savill, Thos., 11th & Wood (Soldering) C

PA.—Williamsport
Darling Pump & Mfg. Co. B

R. I.—Providence
Dart Mfg. Co., E. M., 136 Clifford (Pipe) ....B

UNLOADERS

ILL.—Chicago
Fairbanks, Morse & Co., Franklin & Monroe (Ballast) ....AAAA
Shaw, Willis, N. Y. Life Bldg. (Ballast) ....D

MICH.—Bay City
Industrial Works (Ballast) ....AAA

MO.—St. Louis
Broderick & Bascom Rope Co. (Ballast) ....AA
Leschens & Sons Rope Co., A., 920 N. 1st (Ballast) ....AAA

New York City
Lidgerwood Mfg. Co., 96 Liberty (Ballast) ...AAA

OHIO—Marion
Marion Steam Shovel Co. (Ballast) ....AA

OHIO—Toledo
Vulcan Iron Works (Ballast) ....A

UPHOLSTERY GOODS

See also Trimmings

MASS.—Boston
Schoenfuss, F. J. (Silk, Cords, Fringes, etc.)..F
Weinz Trimming Co. (Silk Trimmings) ....E

N. J.—Jersey City
Schaefer, L. B. (Silk) ....D

N. J.—Paterson
Ryer Son & Co., J. B. (Silk) ....AA

New York City
Empire Fringe Co. (Silk) D
Oelbermann, Dommerick & Co. (Com.) ....AAAA
Union Upholstery Trimming Co. (Silk) ....B
White & Co., Jas. F. (Com.) ....AAAA

PA.—Eden
Rumpf's Sons, Fred'k. ..B

PA.—Philadelphia
Barber & Co., J. W. (Covers) C
Barlow, Noah (Tapestry) D
Binder & Ellis C
Brooks Son Co., Geo. ...B
Davies Textile Co. (Tapestry) C
Derk & Co., Joseph (Tapestry) ....D
Eastlake Mfg. Co. (Furn. Guimp, etc.) ....B
Hewett, C. G. C
Hoyle, Harrison & Kaye ....AAA
Moss Rose Mfg. Co. (Silk)B
New York Tapestry Mills (Tapestry) ....D
Oldham Mills ....AAAA
Orinoka Mills ....A
Regar & Oughton C
Ritchie Co., Robt. J. & R. (Tapestry) ....D
Rosenheim Bros. & Co. (Tapestry) ....D
Schwehm & Sons, J. M. AA
Smith & Son, W. T. ....AA
Stead, Miller & Co. ....AA

UPHOLSTERY GOODS
Vigilant Mills (Silk Tapestry) C

UPPERS

MAINE—Portland
Cox & Son, A. F. (Shoe)..A
MINN.—St. Paul
Hardenbergh & Co., P. R. L. (Shoe) ....A
Scheffer & Rossum (Shoe; Boot) ....A
MO.—St. Louis
Scannell Leather Co., Alfred (Shoe) ....A

UPSETS

MICH.—Grand Rapids
Baldwin, Tuthill & Bolton B

UPSETTERS

ILL.—Carpentsville
Illinois Iron & Bolt Co. (Tire) ....AA
ILL.—Moline
Williams-White & Co. (Tire) ....AA
ILL.—Rockford
Weyburn Co. (Tire) C
MASS.—Greenfield
Wells Bros. Co. (Tire)....A
Wiley & Russell Mfg. Co. (Tire) ....AA
MASS.—Worcester
Boynton & Plummer (Tire) B
MICH.—Detroit
National-Fulton Brass Mfg. Co. (Tire; Bolt) ......AA
N. Y.—Buffalo
Buffalo Forge Co. (Tire) AAA
OHIO—Cleveland
Acme Machinery Co. (Bolt) AA
OHIO—Tiffin
National Machinery Co. (Bolt) ....AA
PA.—Mechanicsburg
Comstock, Geo. S. (Tire).C
R. I.—Pawtucket
Pawtucket Mfg. Co. (Bolt) A

URINALS

ILL.—Chicago
Illinois Malleable Iron Co., 30 W. Munroe ....AAAA
Wolff Mfg. Co., L. ..AAAA
MASS.—Andover
Tyer Rubber Co. (Rubber) AA
MASS.—Boston
Davidson Rubber Co. (Rubber) ....A
MASS.—Lowell
Lowell Slate Co. (Slate) .X
N. J.—Trenton
Maddock & Sons Co., Thos. A^a
Trenton Potteries Co. .AAA
New York City
Fiske Iron Works, J. W...B
Goodyear's India Rubber Glove Mfg. Co. (Rubber) AAAA
Haydenville Co. ....A
Hodgman Rubber Co. (Rubber) ....AA
Maris & Co., John M., 219 Fulton (Rubber) .....B
Meyer-Sniffen Co. (Ltd.).A
OHIO—Akron
Faultless Rubber Co. (Rubber) ....AA
Goodrich Co., B. F. (Rubber) ....AAAA
PA.—Danielsville
Hower, J. K. (Slate) ....B
PA.—East Bangor
East Bangor Consolidated Slate Co. (Slate) .....AA
PA.—Pittsburg
Standard Mfg. Co. .....AA
PA.—Slatington
Slatington Bangor Slate Syndicate (Slate) ......D
PA.—Wind Gap
Phoenix Slate Co. (Slate).D

URINALS (Con.)
R. I.—Providence
Davol Rubber Co. (Rubber) AA
WIS.—Milwaukee
Rundle Mfg. Co. (Enameled Iron) C
WIS.—Sheboygan
Kohler Sons Co., J. M. ..A

URNS

CAL.—San Francisco
Boesch Lamp Co. (Bar; Coffee) C
CONN.—Meriden
Manning, Bowman & Co. (Barbers'; Copper; Enamelled; Restaurant; Steam; Stove; Tea; Coffee) ....AA
ILL.—Chicago
Adams & Westlake Co., Ontario & N. Franklin (Buffet for Cars, etc.) AAAA
MASS.—Boston
Dallinger & Co., Frank W. (Coffee) ....E
Strater & Sons, Herman (Copper) ....A
MICH.—Detroit
Ireland & Matthews (Stove) A
MO.—St. Louis
Wrought Iron Range Co. (Tea; Coffee) ....AAAA
N. Y.—Brooklyn
Sweeney Mfg. Co., W. H. (Barbers'; Restaurant; Copper) ....A
N. Y.—Buffalo
Aldrich Mfg. Co. (Barbers'; Copper; Tea; Coffee) ..A
New York City
Bramhall-Deane Co. (Tea; Coffee) ....B
Crandall & Godley Co. (Tea; Coffee) ....AA
Lalance & Grosjean Mfg. Co (Barbers'; Enamelled) AAAA
Stoutenborough, X. (Copper; Restaurant; Steam Stove) D
N. Y.—Rochester
Castle & Co., Wilmot (Steam; Tea; Coffee)..B
OHIO—Cincinnati
Fischer Mfg. Co., Wm. G. (Tea; Coffee) X
Van Range Co., John (Tea; Coffee) ....A

UTENSILS

CONN.—Cromwell
Stevens Co., J. & E. (Toy; Cooking) ....AAAA
CONN.—Meriden
Manning, Bowman & Co. (Oil Stove) ....AA
ILL.—Lemont
Illinois Pure Aluminum Co. (Aluminum; Cooking) ..A
IND.—Fort Wayne
Boss Roaster Mfg. Co. (Oil Stove) ....E
MD.—Baltimore
Jones Hollow Ware Co. (Cooking) ....D
Maag Aug., 105 Hanover (Bakers'; Confectioners') D
MASS.—Boston
McDowell Oven Co. (Confectioners') ....E
MASS.—Somerville
Hillson & Co., H. M. (Oil Stove) ....D
MICH.—Ann Arbor
Harkin & Willis (Oil Stove) E
N. Y.—Brooklyn
New York Stamping Co. (Brass Cooking) ......A
N. Y.—Buffalo
Aldrich Mfg. Co. (Copper Household) ....A
Shepard & Co., Sidney (Aluminum Cooking) (AAAA
New York City
Bramhall-Deane Co. (Copper

UTENSILS (*Con.*)
Household) ....B
Hart William (Confectioners) ....A
Kny-Scheerer Co., 225 4th Av. C
Steeger Henry (Copper; Household) ....A
OHIO—Cincinnati
Huenefeld, E. H. (Oil Stove) ....A
OHIO—Cleveland
Avery Stamping Co. (Steel; Cooking) ....B
OHIO—Sidney
Wagner Mfg. Co. (Aluminum: Cooking) ....A
PA.—Clinton
Moseley & Pritchard Mfg. Co. (Creamery) ......D
PA.—Erie
Griswold Mfg. Co. (Aluminum; Cooking) ....A
PA.—Philadelphia
Anderson & Co., J. P. (Confectioners) X
Endriss George (Confectioners) ....B
PA.—Pittsburg
Knorr, W. L., 1108 Penn. Av. (Bakers') ....A
Standard Mfg. Co. (Toy; Cooking) ....AA
R. I.—Providence
Wall & Co., A. T. (Aluminum; Cooking) C
VT.—Bellows Falls
Vermont Farm Machine Co. (Butter Working) C

VACCINE

MASS.—Boston
Codmann & Shurtleff (Virus) C
PA.—Philadelphia
Mulford Co., H. K. (Virus) AAA
PA.—Swiftwater
Pocomo Laboratories (Virus) D

VALENTINES

MASS.—Springfield
Taber-Prang Art Co. ...AA
MASS.—Worcester
Whitney Co., Geo. C. ....A
New York City
McLoughlin Bros, 890 Bway AAA

VALISES

See Leather Goods

GA.—Atlanta
Lieberman. L. C
KY.—Louisville
Chilton Trunk & Bag Co., Guthrie C
MASS. Worcester
Warren Leather Goods Co. B
N. J. Harrison
Headley & Farmer Co. ..A
N. J.—Newark
Caille Co., P. ....D
Goldsmith & Son L. ....AA
Hager & Co. ....H
Peddie & Co., T. B. (Inc.) AA
New York City
Crouch & Fitzgerald, 680 B'way ....A
Lissa & Co. Henry .....B
OHIO—Cincinnati
Drucker & Co.. N. ....A
PA.—Philadelphia
Bains & Sons, G. B.. 412 Market ....A
Miller & Strockbine, 514 Market X
WIS.—Milwaukee
Abel & Bach Co. ....AA
Carpeles Co. ....A
Romadka Bros. Co. .....AA
WIS.—Oshkosh
Schmidt Bros. Trunk Co..A

VALLEYS

See also Cornices

MO.—Nevada

VALLEYS (*Con.*)
Norman & Co., W. F. (Galvanized) ....D
New York City
Wheeling Corrugating Co. (Tin) ....AAAA
OHIO—Canton
Berger Mfg. Co.........AA
OHIO—Cleveland
Garry Iron & Steel Co.....A

VALVES

See also Gates

CAL.—San Francisco
American Balance Slide Valve Co., 509 Howard (High Pressure Balance Piston) ....D
Dow Pumping Engine Co., Geo. E., 179 1st (Balance) AA
Garratt & Co. W. T. (Inc.) (Gas; Globe; Water) AA
CONN.—Bridgeport
Belknap Mfg. Co.; (Air Back Pressure; Check Globe; Angle; Balanced; Brass Butterfly; Cross; Iron; Radiator Tank & Whistle; Safety) C
Canfield Co., H. O. (Rubber) ....AA
Consolidated Safety Valve Co. (Locomotive; Pop Safety; Water Relief; Check; Spring Loaded Pop) ....B
CONN.—Hartford
Johns- Pratt Co. (Rubber) A
Pratt & Cady Co. (Asbestos Packed; Gate; Stop; Back Pressure; Check; Globe) .... AAA
CONN.—New Haven
Peck Bros. & Co. (Angle; Check; Gate; Globe; Brass Water Closet) AA
CONN.—Waterbury
Scovill Mfg. Co. (Bicycle) AAAA
DEL.—Elsmere
Diamond State Fibre Co. (Fibre) ....B
DEL.—Wilmington
American Vulcanized Fibre Co. (Fibre) ...... AAAA
Delaware Hard Fibre Co. (Fibre) ....A
ILL.—Aurora
American Well Works (Windmill Float) ....AA
ILL.—Batavia
Challenge Windmill & Feedmill Co. (Windmill Float) AAA
U. S. Wind Engine & Pump Co. (Lever; Water Windmill Float Tank) AA
ILL.—Chicago
American Radiator Co., Lake & Dearborn (Automatic: Air; Radiator; Radiator Hot Water) Water) .... AAAA
Chicago Air & Water Valve Co., 31 S. Canal (Air) F
Clow & Sons, Jas. B. (Float) ....AAA
Crane Co.. 10 N. Jefferson (Air; Asbestos; Packed; Balance Back Pressure; Blast & Gas; Check; Foot Gas Main; Globe & Angle Greenhouse; Hydraulic; Indicator Locomotive; Pop Safety; Radiator; Radiator Corner; Relief; Removable Seat; Steam Air; Safety Stop; Tank Whistle Throttle; Tubular Well; Blow Off Reducing; Snifting; Brass) AAAA
Croslen Mfg. Co., 119 La Salle (Automatic Pressure Reducing) X
Davis Co., Jno., 22nd & Halsted (Back Pressure Blow Off;; Pressure Re-

VALVES (Con.)
ducing Safety) ......AA
Davis Regulator Co., Geo.
M., 145 Milwaukee Av.
(Radiator Air; Back Pres-
sure Steam; Air &
Water Balance; Check;
Pressure Reducing; Open
Air Relief; Stop; Alson
Semi-Balanced Seated;
Water Relief, also Semi-
Balanced Seated) C
Excelsior Steel Furnace Co.,
40 W. Monroe (Radiator)
...............................A
Fairbanks, Morse & Co.
(Railroad; Flush; Float
Tank) ....AAAA
Federal Co., 63 Market
(Flushing) ....A
Glenn Valve Manufactory,
115 Tremont (Balance
Check; Globe & Angle;
Throttle) ....G
Illinois Malleable Iron Co.,
30 W. Monroe (Air; Back
Pressure; Check Foot;
Gate; Globe & Angle
Safety Fire Sprinkler
Flush) ....AAAA
Klipfel & Thomas Co., 74
Lake (Back Pressure
Balance; Relief; Vacuum;
Automatic Air) X
Mark Mfg. Co. (Tubular
Well) ....AA
Marsh & Co., James P., 224
Washn. (Steam Air;
Themostatic) X
Monash-Younker Co., 203
S. Canal (Air Back Pres-
sure; Globe & Angle
Steam Pressure Reducing
Radiator Vacuum; Auto-
matic Air) ....B
Morgan & Co., 40 Dearborn
(Air for Hot Water Rad-
iator) X
Morgan & Wright, 331 W.
Lake (Marine; Pump
Rubber) ....AA
Norwall Mfg. Co., 40 Dear-
born (Non-Adjustable
Air) ....E
Scott Valve Co., 32 W.
Randolph (Automatic Air;
Back Pressure; Balance
Check Chronometer; Gas
Main; Gate; Globe &
Angle; Pop Safety; Pre-
sure Reducing; Renewable
Seat; Stop; Throttle;
Water Relief; Whistle) D
Street & Kent Mfg. Co.,
109 S. Jefferson (Flush-
ing) ....B
Western Valve Co., 43 W.
Randolph (Blow Off As-
bestos .Packed; Check
Back Pressure; Radiator
Gate; Globe & Angle;
Safety Stop ....B
Wolf Co., Fred W., 139
Rees (Ammonia; Tank)
...................AAA

ILL.—Decatur
Mueller Mfg. Co. H. (Re-
ducing; Water Closet)
...................AAA

ILL.—Edwardsville
Edwardsville Brass Co.
(Back Pressure; Flushing
Hopper Tank) ....B

ILL.—Galva
Hayes Pump & Planter Co.
(Float) ....A

ILL.—Kankakee
Beaumont, Richard (Gas
Main, Gate for Water
Mains) ....D

ILL.—Kewanee
Western Tube Co. (Air;
Back Pressure; Check;
Foot Brass & Iron Gate;
Globe & Angle; Radiator;
Safety Working Barrel;
Radiator Hot Water)
...................AAA

ILL.—Peoria
Kinsey & Mahler Co.
(Check; Globe; Angle) A

ILL.—Quincy
Gardner Governor Co.
(Balance; Globe & Angle

VALVES (Con.)
Stop) .... AA
ILL.—St. Charles
Glenn Mfg. Co. (Globe
Greenhouse) ....D

ILL.—Sandwich
Sandwich Mfg. Co. (Wind-
mill Float) ....AA

ILL.—Waukegon
Thomas Brass & Iron Co.
(Back Pressure; Check;
Globe & Angle Pop
Safety; Whistle) .... A

IND.—Auburn
Zimmerman Mfg. Co.
(Windmill Float) .... B

IND.—Butler
Butler Co. (Float) ......B

IND.—Connersville
Connersville Blower Co.
(Blast & Gas) ....A
Root Co. P. H. & F. M.
(Blast & Gas) ......AA

IND.—Fort Wayne
Kerr, Murray Mfg. Co.
(Gas Main) ....A
Knott-Van Arnam Mfg. Co.
(Flushing) ....B
Kunkle & Co., E. B. (Lo-
comotive; Pop Safety
Pressure Reducing) ....A

IND.—Indianapolis
Monarch Governor & Ma-
chine Co. (Angle; Globe
Throttle) ....B
Nethery Hydraulic Valve
Co. (Flushing) ....B
Pioneer Brass Works, 212
S. Penn (Globe & Angle)
...................C

IND.—Kendallville
Flint & Walling Mfg. Co.
(Windmill Float Tank)
...................AA

IND.—Richmond
Meerhoff, Herman H.
(Vault for Outdoor Closets
with sewer Connections)
...................D

IOWA.—Dubuque
McDonald & Morrison Mfg.
Co., A. G. (Check Flush-
ing; Globe & Angle
Float) ....AA

IOWA.—Marshalltown
Fisher Governor Co. (Pre-
sure Reducing) ......D

KY.—Louisville
Caldwell Co., W. E.,
Brandus Av. & Brook
(Gas Float; Air; Water;
Steam) ....AA
Howe Mfg. Co. (Globe &
Angle Radiator) ......A
Vogt Machine Co. Henry
(Ammonia) ....AA

MD.—Baltimore
Coale Brass Mfg. Co.,
Fidelity Bldg. (Muffler
Locomotive; Pop Safety)
...................B
Register's Sons Co., J., 49
W. Holliday (Check;
Globe & Angle Radiator;
Brass) ....A
Robertson Mfg. Co. Jas.,
30 Hanover (Acid) ....A

MASS.—Boston
Amer. Steam Gauge Valve
Mfg. Co. (Air; Tank;
Pop Safety; Safety; Un-
derwriters'; Water Re-
lief; Portable Engine;
Gas; Steam; Snifting;
Hydraulic; Plain Muffled
Locomotive; Radiator) A
Ashton Valve Co., 271
Franklin (Acid & Am-
monia; Air; Asbestos
Packed; Gas; Blow Off;
Check; Gas & Gate; Hy-
draulic & Relief; Loco-
motive; Marine Pop
Safety; Steam; Snifting)
...................A
Boston Belting Co., 256
Devonshire (Ball; Rubber;
Tank) ....A
Boston Brass Co., 36 Oliver
(Flushing; Tank) C
Coffin Valve Co. (Air; Bal-
anced; Check; Foot; Gas;
Stop; Strain; Water) ..D
Crosby Steam Gauge &

VALVES (Con.)

Valve Co., 95 Oliver (Acid; Ammonia; Brass; Blow Off; Check; Heavy Pressure; Radiator; Locomotive; Globe & Angle; Pop Safety; Underwriters'; Water Relief; Whistle; Air; Rubber Iron; Steam; Portable Engine; Steam Engine & Throttle; Gas) ......AA

Dalton-Ingersoll Co., 169 High (Flushing) X

Dececo Co., 146 High (Flushing) ....D

D'Este Co., Julian, 24 Canal (Pressure Reducing; Water Relief) .... B

Exeter Machine Wks., 32 Oliver (Air; Gate; Radiator; Hot Water Radiator) .... B

Gurney Heater Mfg. Co., 74 Franklin (Air; Radiator) .... B

Mason Regulator Co., 158 Sumner (Balanced; By-Pass Lever; Pressure Reducing; Relief; Steam; Vacuum) .... A

Revere Rubber Co., 63 Franklin (Rubber) AAAA

Star Brass Mfg. Co. (Steam) .... A

Sturtevant Co., B. F. (Air) .... AAA

Walworth Mfg. Co., 132 Federal (Air; Blow-Off Check; Fire Extinguisher; Gas Main; Gate; Gate for Water Mains; Globe & Angel; Pop Safety; Radiator; Reducing; Water Relief; Steam)....AAAA

Waters Governor Co., 34 Oliver (Pressure Reducing) C

MASS.—Cambridge

Boston Woven Hose & Rubber Co. (Rubber) ..AAAA

MASS.—Haydenville

Haydenville Co. (Brass; Flushing; Gas; Iron; Oil; Radiator; Steam; Water; Water Closet) .... A

MASS.—Holyoke

Holyoke Valve & Hydrant Co. ....B

MASS.—Indian Orchard

Chapman Valve Mfg. Co. (Acid; Air; Ammonia; Blast & Gas; Blow-Off; Check; Fire Extinguisher; Gas Main; Gate; Gate for Water Mains; Globe & Angle; Hydraulic; Radiator; Radiator Corner; Radiator Hot Water; Removable Heat; Steam Air; Stop; Throttle; Water Relief; Exhaust; Whistle; Asbestos Packed; Bibb; Cross; Cyanide; Drip; Heavy Pressure; Hose; Indicator; Lever; Oil; Natural Gas; Quick Opening; Waste & Water; Service; Steamship; Electric Motor Operated) AAA

MASS.—Lawrence

Lawrence Machine Co. (Water) X

MASS.—New Bedford

New Bedford Boiler & Mach. Co. (Float; Foot; Globe & Angle; Pressure Reducing; Radiator; Stop, also Automatic Stop; Throttle). ....B

MASS.—Salem

Locke Regulator Co. (Balance; Check; Globe & Angle; Pressure Reducing; Radiator; Relief; Safety; Back Pressure) A

MASS.—Springfield

Bigelow, Cheney Wire Wks. (Lock) .... A

Emory Mfg. Co., P. P. (Lock for Rag Engines) C

MASS.—Worcester

Union Water Meter Co., 31

VALVES (Con.)

Herman (Chronometer; Steam) ....B

MICH.—Bay City

Garland Co., M. (Steam) C

MICH.—Detroit

Detroit Heating & Lighting Co. 335 Wight (Air; Radiator) .... B

Detroit Lubricator Co. Hodges Bldg. (Globe & Angle; Quick Opening & Interlocking Steam Radiator; Radiator; Hot Water; Throttle; Balanced; Corner; Heavy Pressure; Oil; Steam; Water) .... AA

Galvin Brass & Mach. Shop (Gate) X

Harvey's Sons Mfg. Co., A., 22 1st (Gate) .... A

Ideal Mfg. Co., 546 Franklin (Check; Flushing) ..A

McRae & Roberts Co. (Air) A

Michigan Lubricator Co. (Throttle) .... A

Park & McKay Co., 55 Bagley Av. (Flushing) C

Penberthy Injector Co., 346 Holden (Globe; Angle) .A

Stephens-Roe Mfg. Co., 1072 McKinley Av. (Back Pressure; Balance; Check; Gas Main; High Pressure Gate; Globe & Angle; Pop Safety; Pressure Reducing; Radiator; Radiator Corner; Hot Water Radiator; Steam Air; Stop; Throttle; Water Relief; Corner; Marine Pop Safety) ....A

United States Heater Co. (Radiator) ....A

MICH.—Muskegon

Heap & Son, Wm. (Syphon Flushing) ....D

MICH.—Port Huron

Draper Mfg. Co. (Ball Check) ....D

Lee Injector Mfg. Co. (Check; Foot) ....B

MICH.—Saginaw

Wickes Bros. (Blow-off) AAA

MICH.—Three Rivers

Sheffield Car Co. (Automatic Relief; Hydraulic) AA

MINN.—St. Paul

South Park Fdry. & Mach. Co. (Gate; for Water Mains) .... B

MO.—Kansas City

Crampton-Farley Brass Co. (Hopper) ....E

MO.—St. Louis

Cahill, Swift Mfg. Co. (Check; Gate) ....B

Nelson Mfg. Co., N. O., 8th & St. Charles (Check; Flushing) ....AAA

Pleuger & Henger Mfg. Co., 11th & Hebert (Globe & Angle; Air; Water; Gas; Steam) ....A

N. H.—Concord

Page Belting Co. (Leather, all Kinds) ....AA

N. H.—Exeter

Exeter Brass Wks. (Tank) C

N. J.—Belleville

Eastwood Wire Mfg. Co. (Gate; Pressure Reducing; Radiator; Radiator, Hot Water) ....A

N. J.—Camden

Fullmer & Co., A. J. (Check) ....A

N. J.—Jersey City

Griffling Iron Co., A. A. (Air; Radiator; Angle; Corner; Gate; Globe; Hydraulic Quick Opening; Steam) ....AA

New Jersey Car Spring & Rubber Co. (Rubber) .AA

Voorhees Rubber Mfg. Co., 18 Bostwick Av. (Rubber) A

VALVES (Con.)

N. J.—Newark

Fostor Engineering Co., 107 Monroe (Automatic Air; Back Pressure; Balance; Check; Float; Non-Return & Emergency Stop; Reducing; Safety) ....A

Isbell-Porter Co. (Gas) ...D

Smith Mfg. Co., A. P. (Gate for Water Mains) .....B

N. J.—Paterson

Royle & Sons, Jno. (Flushing; Waste) ....A

N. J.—Trenton

Consolidated Rubber Co. (Rubber) ....B

Crescent Belting & Pack'g Co. (Rubber) ....A

Empire Rubber Mfg. Co. (Rubber; Pump) .....AA

Hamilton Rubber Co. (Rubber) ....A

Home Rubber Co. (Rubber) AA

Mercer Rubber Co. (Rubber) ....A

Stokes Rubber Co., Joseph (Rubber) ....A

Trenton Rubber Mfg. Co. (Rubber; Rubber Ball) ..A

United & Globe Rubber Mfg. Co. (Rubber) ......AAA

Whitehead Bros. Rubber Co. (Rubber) ....A

N. Y.—Albany

Albany Brass & Iron Co. (Flushing) ....D

Albany Steam Trap Co. (Check; Gate; Radiator; Renewable Seat; Stop; Globe; Steam) ....D

N. Y.—Brooklyn

Acton, Jno., 118 John (Back Pressure; Balance; Pop Safety; Pressure Reducing; Atmospheric Relief Safety Stop; Water Relief) ....D

Continental Iron Wks. (Gas Works) ....A

N. Y.—Buffalo

Sherwood Mfg. Co., 34 Washington (Pop Safety; Whistle) ....B

Trout & Hickok, 226 Ohio (Safety) ....B

N. Y.—Coxsackie

Amer. Valve Co. (Ammonia; Check; Globe & Angle; Radiator) ....D

N. Y.—Elmira

Swift Lubricator Co. (Pop Safety) ....B

N. Y.—Frankfort

Utica Steam Gauge Co. (Radiator) X

N. Y.—Lockport

Amer. District Steam Co. (Back Pressure; Packless Iron; Brass Body Gate) ....AAA

N. Y.—Newburgh

Coldwell-Wilcox Co. (Back Pressure; Check; Gate, for Water Mains; Globe & Angle; Greenhouse; Stop) ....B

New York City

Aller, A., 109 Liberty (Mfrs' Agent - Back Pressure) .D

Ashcroft Mfg. Co. (Safety) A

Barr Co., Edward (Brass) X

Bushnell & Co., Jno. S., 120 Liberty (Pressure Reducing) ....E

Creamer Steam Specialties Co., 123 Liberty (Balance) ....B

Drummond & Co., M. J., 192 B'way (Gate, for Water Mains) ....A

Eaton, Cole & Burnham Co., 253 B'way (Back Pressure; Check; Gas Main; Gate; Radiator; Safety; Brass; Disk; Globe; Steam; Steam Engine; Throttle) ....AAAA

Fairbanks Co., 416 Broome

VALVES (Con.)

(Asbestos Packed; Back Pressure; Check; Gate; Globe & Angle; Radiator; Stop; Ammonia; Brass; Iron; Reducing; Air; Water; Gas; Steam; Balanced; Blow off; Exhaust; Fire Sprinkler; Float; Lever; Relief; Safety; Snifting; Vacuum) AAAA

Ford Co., Thomas P., 81 Centre (Back Pressure; Tank Balance; Balance Ball Cock High Pressure; Steam & Water Pressure Reducing; Balanced Tank) ....D

Gold Car Heating & Lighting Co., 6 N. Y. & Brooklyn Bridge (Air; Radiator) ....B

Goodyear Rubber Co. (Rubber; Ball) ....AAAA

Goodyears' Ind. Rubber Glove Mfg. Co. (Rubber; Ball) ....AAAA

Gutta Percha & Rubber Mfg Co., 126 Duane (Rubber; Rubber Ball) .....AAAA

Harlem Mfg. Co., 42 W 67th (Automatic Air; Pressure Reducing) ....F

Hunt Co., C. W. (Coal) .AA

Hussey & Son, Wm. H., 37 Dey (Back Pressure) ..B

Jenkins Bros., 71 John (Automatic Air; Back Pressure; Blow-Off; Check; Gate; Brass & Iron Body Globe & Angle; Radiator; Rubber; Safety; Water; Acid; Corner; Cross; Gas; Quick Opening; Oil; Ammonia; Lever Reducing; Relief) ....A

Jones, T. W., 18 Fletcher (Weather) ....E

Kennedy Valve Mfg. Co., 59 Beekman (Check; Gate; Globe & Angle; Indicator; Radiator; Acid; Ammonia; Brass; Corner; Gas; Hydraulic; Iron; Lever; Natural Gas; Oil; Quick Opening; Steam; Tank; Waste; Water; Windmill Float; Air; Balanced; Safety) ... A

Kenny Mfg. Co., 72 Trinity Place (Flushing) .... D

Kieley & Mueller, 7 W. 13th (Back Pressure; Pressure Reducing) ....B

Libby Mfg. Co., 75 Watts (Gate; Globe & Angle) E

McNab & Harlin Mfg. Co., 56 John (Check; Gas Main; Gate; Globe & Angle; Radiator; Safety; Throttle; Steam; Water; Air; Relief) ...... AAA

Manhattan Rubber Mfg. 18 Vesey (Rubber) ..AA

Mott Iron Wrks., J. L., 88 Beekman (Flushing) AA

Nason Mfg. Co., 81 Beekman (Pressure Reducing; Ammonia; Elevator; Quick Opening; Radiator) B

Nelson, Chas., 439 E. 10th (Check) ....D

New York Belting & Packing Co. (Ltd.) 25 Park Place (Rubber; Rubber Ball) ....AAA

N. Y. Rubber Co., 84 Reade (Rubber; Rubber Ball) AA

Peerless Rubber Mfg. Co., 16 Warren (Rubber) AA

Power Specialty Co., 126 Liberty (Rubber; Armored Pump) ...... E

Smith Co., H. B., 137 Centre (Air; Radiator) AA

Standard Steam Specialty Co., 111 5th Av. (Back Pressure; Pressure Reducing) ....D

Stein, Henry, 48 Cliff (Gate; Globe & Angle;

VALVES (Con.)
Main) ....A

PA.—Erie
Campbell Brass Wks., J. B. (Lock Shield Gas Main)A
Continental Rubber Wks. (Rubber) ....A
Jarecki Mfg. Co. (Air; Check; Gate; Globe & Angle; Radiator; Rubber; Safety; Throttle; Gas; Brass; Water; Steam; Ammonia; Relief) AAAA
Keystone Brass Co. (Globe & Angle) ....D

PA.—Homestead
Homestead Valve Mfg. Co. (Blow-Off; Straightway; Hydraulic; Blow-Off Locomotive) C

PA.—Jeannette
Penna. Rubber Co. (Rubber) ....AA

PA.—Lebanon
Weimer Machine Wks. Co. (Blast; Gas) ....AA

PA.—Nazareth
Nazareth Fdry. & Mach. Co. (Relief) ....B

PA.—New Castle
Penna. Engineering Wks. (Gate) ....AA

PA.—Philadelphia
Belfield & Co., H., 435 N. Broad (Air; Ammonia; Back Pressure; Balance; Blow-Off; Check; Foot; Gate; Globe & Angle; Hydraulic; Cylinder Locomotive; Radiator; Brass or Iron Safety; Stop; Throttle; Vacuum; Automatic Air; Iron, Reducing) ....AA
Berger Bros. Co. (Pump; Boat) ....A
Cooper Brass Wks., Wm. S., 437 N. 12th (Flushing) B
Eynon-Evans Mfg. Co., 1519 Clearfield (Blow-Off; Extra Heavy Check; Globe & Angle; Air; Water; Gas; Steam; Exhaust) ......A
Haines, Jones & Cadbury Co., 1136 Ridge Av. (Flushing; Steam; Water) ....AA
Homer Brass Wks. (Inc.), 231 Race (Check; Flushing; Globe & Angle)....C
Lonergan & Co., J. E., 211 Race (Check; Pressure Reducing; Spring Loaded Safety; Relief; Marine Pop Safety; Pop Safety; Water Relief) ....AA
McCambridge & Co. (Ltd.), 527 Cherry (Flushing; Brass) ....B
Pancoast & Co., H. B., 243 S. 13th (Foot)........B
Penn Engineering Co., 312 Cherry (Radiator; Radiator Hot Water)........E
Penna. Light Supply Co. (Gas Saving) X
Perkes, Chas., 627 Arch (Globe & Angle)......AA
Philadelphia Roll & Machine Co., 23rd & Washington Av. (Air; Water; Gas; Steam) ....A
Savill, Thos., 11th & Wood (Hopper) C
Sayen & Schultz, 13th & Commerce (Rubber) ...C
Schutte & Koering Co., 1251 N. 12th (Back Pressure; Balance; Check; Globe & Angle; Hydraulic; Locomotive; Radiator; Relief; Stop; Throttle) ....A
Thompson & Co., J., Cor. Van Horn & Sophia (Poppet Air; Check; Foot; Gas Main; Gate, for Water Mains; Stop) ...A
Watson & McDaniel Co., 416 N. 7th (Blow-Off; Balance Rotating Hydraulic; Pressure Reducing for Steam; Water & Air; Water Relief) C

VALVES (Con.)
Wood & Co., R. D., 400 Chestnut (Gate, for Water Mains; Air; Iron; Gas Works; Steam; Water) AAAA

PA.—Pittsburg
Amer. Furnace & Mach. Co. (Air; Water; Gas; Steam) ....D
Best Mfg. Co., 25th & A. V. Ry. (Back Pressure; Blow Off; Check; Foot; Gate; Globe & Angle; Gulland Tank; Pressure Reducing; Butterfly; Hydraulic Relief; Safety; Throttle) AA
Bonar & Co., Jas., Carnegie Bldg. (Pop Safety)....B
Cadman Mfg. Co., A. W., 63 Water (High Pressure Blow-Off; Brass) C
Chaplin-Fulton Mfg. Co. (Inc.) (Natural Gas; Reducing; Steam) ....A
Kelly & Jones Co., 135 Water (Compression & Lock Shield Air; Air for Coal Mines; Back Pressure; Blow-Off; Check; Chronometer; Iron Foot; Brass & Iron Gate; Brass & Iron Globe & Angle; Radiator; Radiator, Hot Water; Safety; Steam Air; Whistle) ....AA
Pittsburg Brass Mfg. Co., 107 Wood (Thermostat)D
Pittsburg Valve F'dry & Construction Co., 5th & Duquesne Way (Critchlow; Gas Main; Gate; Iron & Brass Globe & Angle; Hydraulic; Mud) AAA
Standard Sanitary Mfg. Co., Arrott Bldg. (Flushing) AAAA
Sterrit Fdy Co., Thos. (Gas) B
Trethewe & Co. (Ltd.), Sam'l, 47th & Butler (Piston) ....F
Velte Fdry & Machine Co., Home & A. V. R. R. (Gas; Siemen; Air; Water; Steam; Air Furnace) A
Wilson, Snyder Mfg. Co. (Steam) ....AA

PA.—Reading
Reading F'dry Co. (Gate, for Water Mains; Stop) X

PA.—Sayre
Cayuta Mfg. Co. (Gate for Steam, Gas, & Oil; Gate for Water Mains) .....B

PA.—Towanda
Loetzer Valve & Mfg. Co. (Air, for Water Mains; Check; Gas Main; Globe & Angle; Plug; Vacuum Automatic Air, for Water Mains) X

PA.—Warren
Bashlin Co. (Globe & Angle) ....B

PA.—Williamsport
Darling Pump & Mfg. Co. (Ltd.) (Air; Ammonia; Blow-Off; Check; Foot; Gas Main; Gate, for Water Main; Hydraulic; Radiator; Rubber; Leather) B

PA.—Waynesboro
Frick Co. (Ammonia)AAAA

PA.—Wyndmoor
Nelson Valve Co. of N. J. (Gate; Globe & Angle)..D

PA.—York
Burrows Mfg. Co. (Back Pressure) ....E
York Mfg. Co. (Ammonia) AAA

R. I.—Pawtucket
Fales & Jenks Machine Co. (Gate) ....AAA

R. I.—Providence
General Fire Extinguisher Co. (Brass; Iron; Fire Alarm) ....AAAA

VALVES (Con.)

Providence Steam Trap Co. (Iron) ....D
TENN.—Chattanooga
Gustafson Mfg. Co. (Globe & Angle) C
VA.—Lynchburg
Glamorgan Pipe & F'dry Co. (Gate) ....AA
WIS.—Milwaukee
Allis-Chalmers Co. (Ammonia) ....AAAA
Hoffmann Mfg. Co., B., 257 6th (Air; Back Pressure; Blow-Off; Check; Foot; Gas Main; Gate; Safety; Stop; Throttle) ....A
Hoffman & Billings Mfg. Co., 96 2nd (Air; Back Pressure; B l o w-O f f; Check; Gas Main; Gate; Safety; Stop; Throttle; Foot) ....AA
Johnson Service Co. (Steam, Water, Air & Gas Pressure Reducing) ....AAA
Milwaukee Brass Mfg. Co. (Hose, for Fire Escape Pipes) C
Pressed Steel Tank Co., 718 Hanover (Air Discharge; Pressed Steel) ....B

VANES

ILL.—Chicago
Barbee Wire & Iron Wks., 44 Dearborn (Weather).B
Booth, Jno., 114 E. Lake (Weather) ....B
Smith Wire & Iron Wks., F. P., 100 Lake (Weather) ....AA
MASS.—Boston
Jones & Co., M. D., 71 Portland (Weather) ...G
Snow & Co., W. A., 19 Portland (Copper Weather) C
MICH.—Detroit
Amos & Co., Chas., 94 W. Larned (Weather) ....F
Barnum Wire & Iron Wks., E. T., 103 Shelby (Weather) ....B
MO.—Kansas City
Kansas City Wire & Iron Wks. (Weather) ......A
New York City
Dorendorf, Dederick, 44 Centre (Weather) ....H
Fiske Iron Works, J. W., 39 Park Pl. (Weather) ....B
Washbourne & Co., Edw. G. (Weather) ......F
Westervelt, A. B. & W. T., 102 Chambers (Weather) ....B
OHIO—Canton
Canton Steel Roofing Co. (Weather) ....A
OHIO—Cleveland
Van Dorn Iron Wks. Co., 1793 E. Madison Av. (Weather) ....AA
OHIO—Hamilton
Meyers Mfg. Co., Fred J. (Weather) ....B
OHIO—Kenton
Champion Iron Co. (Weather) ....AA
OHIO—Salem
Mullins, W. H. (Weather) ....A
PA.—Philadelphia
Goodwin, Frederick O., 53d & Wyalusing (Weather) ....D
Henis, Wm. G., 1347 Ridge Av. (Weather) ....B
Jackson & Cook, 318 Market (Weather) ....B
Thorn Co., J. S., 1227 Callowhill (Weather) ....A
PA.—Pittsburg
Hum & Leatherman (Weather) ....B
Taylor & Dern, 205 Market (Weather) ......B

VANILLIN

New York City
Bischoff & Co., C. ......B
Dodge & Olcott ....AAA
Fries Bros., 92 Reade....A
Heyden Chemical Wks....A
Klipstein & Co., A......AA
Magnus & Lauer C
Warner Chemical Co...AAA
PA.—Philadelphia
Grow & Co., Howard....X

VANS

See Carriages & Wagons

VAPORIZERS

DEL.—Wilmington
Heinel Co., H. S........D
MICH.—Kalamazoo
National Vaporizer Co....F
New York City
Vapo-Cresoline Co., 180 Fulton C
N. Y.—Westfield
Burns Vaporizer Co.......C
PA.—Philadelphia
Physicians Supply Co., 125 N. Broad ....E

VARIATORS

See also Machy

N. Y.—Lockport
American District Steam Co. (Single & Double Expansion) ....AAA

VARNISHES

See also Paints

CAL.—San Francisco
Hueter, E. L. ....AA
CONN.—Bridgeport
Crockett Co., D. B., 24 P. O. Arcade ....B
Parrott Varnish Co., 453 N. Washn. Av. ....A
ILL.—Chicago
American Varnish Co.....A
Chicago Varnish Co., Dearborn Av. & Kinzie ..AA
Chicago Wood Finishing Co., 259 Elston Av. ....A
De Gollyer-Watts Co., 377 Illinois ....A
Eimendorf, Wm. A., 33 Larrabee C
Grace Varnish Co., 125 Larrabee ....D
Henderson Varnish Co., 1088 N. Wood ....D
Moller & Schuman, 319 S. Canal (Black; Carriage; Floor; House; Marine; Mixing; Shellac) ..AA
Nubian Paint & Varnish Co., N. 51st Av. ....D
Rubber Paint Co., 154 W. Van Buren ....AA
Stewart, Mowry & Co., 3218 Shields Av. C
Surrey Varnish Co., 926 Ainslie ....D
Thurston & Co., F. W., 29 River ....A
Vilas Bros., 227 5th Av...B
Washbourne, Thos. F., 14 Lester Av. C
Watson Co., Geo. E., 108 Lake ....B
IND.—Indianapolis
Ind. Varnish Co. ....B
Lilly Varnish Co. ......B
IND.—South Bend
O'Brien Varnish Co.......A
KY.—Louisville
Louisville Varnish Co., 14th & Maple ....A
LA.—New Orleans
Barrett Mfg. Co., Hennen Bldg. ....AAAA
McWilliams, R. H., 342 Camp C
Riggs & Bro., A. ......D
MAINE—Portland
Fuller Co., A. P.........C
MD.—Baltimore
Baltimore Dry Paint Works

VARNISHES (Con.)

Ostend & Stockholm (Asphaltum) ....E
Chesapeake Oil Co., Ostend & Stockholm ....D
Foy & Co., E. L., 16 W. Camden (Black) ....E
Macneal & Co., Jas. B., 34 S. Calvert ....A
Poppelein, G. & N., 220 North ....B

MASS.—Boston
Babcock & Co., John, 104 Water ....B
Babcock Varnish Co., 10 Oliver C
Burbank & Ryder, 62 Alford ....A
Gould & Cutler, 75 Union C
Mass. Chemical Co., 200 Summer ....A
Nash, Winslow & Co., 90 Pearl ....A
Stickney & Co., J. W., 79 Milk ....B
Wiley & Co., L. H., 92 Sudbury ....B

MASS.—Lowell
Kittredge & Co., A. L..C

MASS.—Springfield
Hampden Paint & Chemical Co. ....B

MICH.—Detroit
Acme Lead & Color Co., St. Aubin Av. & M. C. R. R. ....AAA
Acme White Lead & Color Wks., St. Aubin Av....A
Berry Bros., Ltd. ..AAAA
Boydell Bros. & White Lead & Color Co., 18 E. Congress ....AA
Buckeye Paint & Varnish Co., 715 Gratiot ......D
Continental Paint & Varnish Co., Clay & St. Aubin Avs. ....D
Detroit Varnish Co., 552 Milwaukee ....AA
Detroit White Lead Works, 532 Milwaukee ....AA
McNamara, Michael, Clark Av. ....B
Peninsula Paint & Varnish Co., St. Aubin Av. & M. C. R. R. ....A

MINN.—St. Paul
Twin City Varnish Co., 521 Cleveland Av. ....B

MO.—Kansas City
Continental Varnish & Color Co., 1315 W. 8th.....D
Hawkins Mfg. Co., 11 E. Levee ....D

MO.—St. Louis
Gregg Varnish Co., 811 N. 6th C
Hoffman Mfg. Co., L., 2720 De Kalb C
Vane-Calvert Paint Co., 823 Locust ....B
Wellpott, C. H. W., 3220 N. B'way ....D

N. J.—Hoboken
Hotopp Varnish Co. ...B

N. J.—Jersey City
Gillespie & Sons, Chas. H., Marion ....B

N. J.—Montclair
Hastings & Winslow C

N. J.—Newark
Anglo - American Varnish Co., 53 Johnson .....B
Beckwith-Chandler Co., 193 Emmett ....AA
Bigelow Varnish Co., 356 Mulberry (Black; Carriage; Floor; House; Marine; Mixing; Railroad; Shellac; Cabinet) ....B
Bolen-Bond Varnish Co., 352 Mulberry (Cabinet; Floor; Railway) X
Brooks & Co., Clarence, 249 Chestnut ....A
Fitzgerald Co., 365 Mulberry C
Flood & Conklin Co., 136 Chestnut ....A
Laute & Dax, 92 Vesey ..B
Murphy Varnish Co., 238 McWhorter ......AAAA

VARNISHES (Con.)

Newark Varnish Wks., 97 Delancey ....B
Palmer-Price-Bolen Co., 270 Chestnut ....D
Wheeler & Mitchell, 317 N. J. R. R. Av. (Black; House; Mixing; Shellac) D

N. J.—Rahway
Egyptian Lacquer Mfg. Co. D

N. Y.—Binghamton
Collier, W. C. C

N. Y.—Brooklyn
Bartels & Slitgenbauer, Stewart Av. ....B
Bohners Sons, Jos., 1093 Met. Av. ....B
Bungart, Peter, 295 Greenpoint Av. ....D
King Paint Mfg. Co., 23 Durham Pl. (Floor; Marine; House; Mixing; Shellac) ....B
Lizka, G. C., 215 Varet..B
Marx & Rawolle ......AA
Masury & Son, Jno. W., 50 Jay ....AAAA

N. Y.—Buffalo
Buffalo Enamel & Stain Co., Ellicott Sq. .....D
Buffalo Oil, Paint & Varnish Co., 1317 Elk ..AA
Chase, Roberts & Co....B
Denther & Beck, 50 Niagara ....B
Farr Mfg. Co., Marion & Fulton (Insulating) ...E
McDougall White Lead Co., 1317 Elk ....AA
McLennan Paint Co., 205 Rano (Black; Carriage; Floor; House; Marine; Mixing) ....A

N. Y.—L. I. City
Colman & Co., Emil....AA
Pratt & Lambert ....A
Queens Co. Varnish Wks. (Black; Carriage; Floor; House; Marine; Mixing; Shellac) ....E
Thibaut & Co., E. A.....A

New York City
Billings, King & Co., 438 Pearl ....A
Celluloid Zapon Co., 12 E. 18th ....B
De Bono Co., F. S., 46 Cliff C
Devoe, F. W. & C. T. Reynolds Co., 103 Fulton AAAA
Dunham, Thos. C., 68 Murray ....D
Excelsior Varnish Works, 381 Pearl ....A
Graves & Co., N. Z., 296 Pearl ....AAA
Harland & Son, Wm., 4 Gold ....AA
Hasenbalg & Co., F., 714 E. 166th ....D
Hildreth Varnish Co., 32 B'way ....A
Longman & Martinez, 207 Pearl ....AAA
Maver & Lowenstein, 164 Water ....AAA
Newcomb, Jas. G., 26 B'way (Black; Floor; House; Mixing; Shellac) AAAA
Pierce Co., F. O., 170 Fulton ....A
Pomeroy & Fisher, 28 Frankfort ....A
Schlegel, Oscar, 182 Grand D
Slee, J. Noah, 141 B'way D
Smith & Co., Edw., 45 B'way ....A
Standard Varnish Wks., 29 B'way ....AA
Stoeckel, Randolph E. ..D
Valentine & Co., 257 B'way ....AAA
Zinsser & Co., Wm., 197 William ....AA

N. Y.—Utica
Central N. Y. Varnish Co. B

VARNISHES (Con.)

OHIO—Akron
Akron Varnish Co. (Black; House; Marine) ......A

OHIO—Cincinnati
Becker & Co., R. A., 1337 Harrison Av. C
Bird Varnish Co., 246 Main B
Cincinnati Varnish Co., 218 E. Court ....A
U. S. Varnish Co., 2616 Colerain Av. ....D
Wolf & Co., Herman, 214 W. Liberty C

OHIO—Cleveland
Billings-Chapin Co., 37 Case Av. ....A
Cleveland Varnish Co., 14 Rockland Av. ....A
Colonial Paint & Varnish Co., Marquette & St. Clair ....B
Forest City Paint & Varnish Co., Hamilton & Kirkland ....B
Glenmore Color Works..A
Glidden Varnish Co., C. & P. R. R. ....AA
National Paint & Varnish Co., 37 St. Clair C
Ohio Varnish Co., Rockland Av. ....D
Patterson-Sargent Co., Wason & Hamilton ......AA
Sherwin-Williams Co., 100 Canal ....AAA
Star Varnish Co. (Black) D

OHIO—Columbus
Columbus Varnish Co., 257 Cozzens ....B

OHIO—Dayton
Threshen Varnish Co....AA
Tower Varnish & Dryer Co. D

OHIO—Lockland
Carey Mfg. Co., Ph. (Black) A

OHIO—Toledo
Buckeye Paint & Varnish Co., 719 S. 15th ......B

PA.—Allegheny
Eagle Paint & Varnish Wks., 225 Grant Av....B
Globe Varnish Mfg. Co., 1035 S. Canal C
Nevin Co. T. H., Preble & Island Avs. ....A

PA.—Jamestown
Jamestown Paint & Varnish Co. (Asphalt) ....B

PA.—Philadelphia
Barrett-Lindeman Co., 1400 Fk'd. Av. ....B
Evans & Son, Wm., 56 N. Front ....B
Felton, Sibley & Co., 140 N. 4th ....AA
French & Co., Saml. H., 4th & Callowhill ...AAA
Harrison Bros. & Co., 35th & Grays Ferry Rd. AAAA
Howell & Co., C. H., 212 Race ....A
Lucas & Co., John, 322 Race (Asphaltum) .AAA
McClusky & Co., L. J., 30th & Locust ....A
Nassau, James, Kens. & Erie Avs. ....B
Nice, Eugene E., 272 S. 2d ....B
Phoenix Paint & Varnish Co., 124 Market ......D
Rambo, Theo. G., 1134 Beach ....D
Rau, Conrad F. J., 4th & Bristol ....D
Schrack & Co., C., 152 N. 4th ....A
Shoemaker & Co., Robert, 201 N. 4th ....AA
Shrak & Co., C., 152 N. 4th ....A
Thompson Wood Finishing Co., 115 N. 4th C
Waterall & Co., Wm., 4th & Race ....A
Waterall & Co., Wm., 200 N. 4th ....A
Wocher & Son, Herman M...

VARNISHES (Con.)

1218 W. College Av. (Carriage; Black; Floor; Marine; House; Mixing; Shellac) C
Woodhouse, S. F., Unity & Franklin Fk'd.) (House; Shellac) ....D

PA.—Pittsburg
Iron City Oil & Varnish Co., Inwood & Frankstown Av. ....B
Lawrence & Co., W. W., Water & Penn Av.....A
McClintock & Irvine Co., Neville & P. R. R.....B
Sterling Varnish Co. .....A
Suydam Co., M. B., 61st & Butler ....B

PA.—Reading
Reading Paint Mills....AA
Ruth & Co., B. F., 216 S. 8th ....AA
Wilhelm Co., 217 Poplar..A

R. I.—Providence
Johnson & Co., Oliver, 31 Exch. ....B
Johnson, Oliver & Co., 3 Exch. ....AA
Starkweather & Williams Co., 47 Exch. Pl. C
U. S. Gutta Percha Paint Co., 34 Mathewson ....A

VA.—Richmond
Atlanta Varnish Works, 2829 Lester ....B
Worthington Co., 1424 E. Main ....B

VASELINE

See also Petrolatum

New York City
Cheesebrough Mfg. Co., 17 State ....AAAA

VASES

See also Furniture; Pottery, etc.

CONN.—Bridgeport
Pierce Mfg. Co. (Garden) E

CONN.—Meriden
Bradley & Hubbard Mfg. Co. (Brass) ......AAAA

CONN.—Winsted
Goodwin & Kintz Co. (Decorated Metal) ....B

ILL.—Chicago
Barbee Wire & Iron Wks. (Garden; Cemetery; Iron) B

ILL.—Sterling
Novelty Iron Works (Garden) ....E

IND.—Indianapolis
Enterprise Foundry & Fence Co. (Lawn) ....B
Over, Ewald (Garden; Flower) C

MASS.—Boston
Jones & Co., Melville D. (Garden) ....G

MASS.—Cambridge
Hews & Co., A. H. (Garden) ....A

MICH.—Detroit
Barnum Wire & Iron Wks., E. T. (Iron) ....B

MO.—St. Louis
International Steel Post Co. (Lawn) ....A
Ludlow-Saylor Wire Co. (Lawn) ....AA

N. J.—New Brunswick
New Jersey Lamp & Bronze Wks. (Bronze) ..AAAA

N. Y.—Brooklyn
Hecla Iron Wks. (Garden) AA

N. Y.—Buffalo
Shepard & Co., Sidney (Coal) ....AAAA

N. Y.—Manlius
Cheney & Son, S. (Lawn) A

New York City
Abendroth Bros. (Garden) A

VASES (Con.)

Ansonia Clock Co. (Bronze) .... AAAA

Cordley & Hayes (Garden; Flower) ....A

Fiske Iron Wks., J. W. (Garden) ....B

International Silver Co., 9 Maiden Lane (Silver Plated) ....AAAA

Judd & Co., H. L. (Brass) ....AA

Lamb, J. & R. (Brass)..D

N. Y.—Peekskill

Naylor Bros. (Flower)...A

OHIO—Cincinnati

Stewart Iron Wks. (Lawn) ....A

OHIO—Cleveland

Van Dorn Iron Wks. Co. (Garden Lawn) .....AA

OHIO—Findlay

Bell Pottery Co. (Earthenware) ....A

OHIO—Hamilton

Meyers Mfg. Co., F. J. (Lawn) ....B

OHIO—Kenton

Champion Iron Co. (Flower) ....AA

OHIO—Springfield

Rogers Iron Wks. (Iron) ....B

OHIO—Toledo

Donovan Wire & Iron Co. (Lawn) C

OHIO—Walkers

American Sewer Pipe Co. (Garden) ....AAAA

PA.—New Brighton

Pittsburg Clay Mfg. Co. (Garden) ....AAAA

PA.—Philadelphia

Harvey, Moland & Co. (Garden) X

TENN.—Chattanooga

Ornamental Iron Wks. Co. (Iron) X

WIS.—Sheboygan

Kohler Sons' Co., J. M. (Iron) ....A

VATS

See also Tanks

CAL.—Petaluma

Petaluma Incubator Co. (Cheese) ....B

DEL.—Wilmington

Pusey & Jones Co. (Iron Screw) ....AAA

ILL.—Batavia

United States Wind Engine & Pump Co. (Cedar)..AA

MAINE—Mechanic Falls

Penney & Sons Co., J. W. (Iron Screw) ....B

MASS.—Boston

Cypress Lumber Co., 153 Milk (Cypress) ......AA

MASS.—Holyoke

Holyoke Machine Co. (Iron Screw) ....AA

MASS.—Lowell

Lowell Machine Shop (Iron Screw) ....AAAA

MASS.—Pittsfield

Jones & Sons Co., E. D. (Iron Screw) ....B

MASS.—South Lawrence

Horne & Sons Co., J. H. (Drainer; Iron Screw).A

MASS.—Worcester

Rice, Barton & Fales Machine & Iron Co. (Iron Screw) ....AA

MICH.—Flint

Flint Cabinet Creamery Co. (Dairy Cooling) ......E

N. J.—Burlington

Birch, James H. ......AA

N. J.—Newark

Currier & Sons, Cyrus (Iron Screw) ....AA

N. Y.—Cattaraugus

Oakes & Burger (Cheese) ....B

N. Y.—Little Falls

Burrell & Co., D. H. (Cheese) ....AAAA

N. Y.—Syracuse

Gowing, D. H. (Dairy Cool-

VATS (Con.)

ing) C

N. Y.—Utica

Jones, Frank L. (Cheese; Dairy Cooling) C

Millar Son Co., Charles (Cheese) ....AA

OHIO—Cincinnati

Cincinnati Cooperage Co. (Brewers' Stock) ...AAA

Hauser, Brenner & Fath Co. (Brewers' Stock) ......B

OHIO—Hamilton

Black & Clawson Co. (Iron Screw) ....AAA

PA.—Philadelphia

Hall, Son & Co., Amos H. (Brewers' Stock; Cedar) C

Reid Creamery & Dairy Supply Co., A. H. (Dairy Cooling) ....A

Smith & Sons, John M. (Cedar) ....A

Woolford Wood Tank Mfg. Co., George (Cedar; Brewers' Stock) ......B

R. I.—Bridgeton

Hopkins Machine Works (Cedar) X

VT.—Bellows Falls

Vermont Farm Machine Co. (Cheese; Dairy Cooling; Milk Receiving; Milk Tempering) C

WIS.—Beloit

Beloit Iron Works (Iron Screw) ....A

WIS.—Fort Atkinson

Cornish, Curtis & Greene Mfg. Co. (Cheese; Dairy Cooling) ....A

WIS.—Racine

Winship Mfg. Co. (Cedar) ....E

VAULTS

See also Safes; also Cases; Burial

CAL.—San Francisco

Bay City Iron Works (Bank) ....F

Dyer Bros., 382 2d (Bank) ....D

Herring-Hall-Marvin Co., 400 B'way (Bank).....A

Western Iron Works, 123 Beale (Bank) ....B

Waltz Safe & Lock Co., 111 Market (Bank) ....H

ILL.—Chicago

Trumbull Safe & Vault Co., 117 Lake (Bank) .....D

ILL.—Peoria

Lucas & Sons, A., Cedar & Washn. (Bank) C

MASS.—Boston

Ham & Co., L. M., 152 Portland (Bank) ......B

Morris-Ireland Safe Co., 64 Sudbury (Bank) ......E

N. Y.—Brooklyn

Chrome Steel Wks. (Bank) ....AAA

N. Y.—Buffalo

Cary Safe Co., Chicago & Scott (Bank) ....A

New York City

Cornell Co., J. B. & J. M., 239 11th Av. (Fireproof; Burglar Proof) ......AA

Hibbard, Rodman & Ely Safe Co., 253 B'way (Bank) C

Jackson Co., Wm. H., 29 E. 17th (Bank) C

Pitt Composite Iron Wks., Wm. R., 111 5th Av. (Bank) ....D

Remington & Sherman Co., 23 Park Pl. (Bank)....A

OHIO—Canton

Diebold Safe & Lock Co. (Bank) ....AAA

OHIO—Cincinnati

Victor Safe & Lock Co., 9th & B'way (Bank) .....A

OHIO—Cleveland

National Safe & Lock Co. (Bank) ....D

Van Dorn Iron Wks. Co. (Fire Proof; Burglar

VAULTS (Con.)
Proof) ....AA
OHIO—Hamilton
Macneale & Urban Co.
(Bank) ....B
Mosler Safe Co. (Bank)
AAA
OHIO—Toledo
Donovan Wire & Iron Co.
(Fire Proof; Burglar
Proof) C
OREGON—Portland
Phoenix Iron Wks. (Bank)
E
PA.—Pittsburg
Barnes Safe & Lock Co.
325 3d Av. (Bank).....F
PA.—York
York Safe & Lock Co.
(Bank) ....B
WIS.—Milwaukee
Meyer Co., L. A. 448 E.
Water (Bank) ....E

VEALS

See Leather

WIS.—Milwaukee
Zohriant Leather Co., Herman (Yellow) ....AA

VEGETABLES: CANNED

See Canned Goods

VEILINGS

**See also Silk Goods; Mil-
linery Goods**

N. J.—Jersey City
Hall, H. S. (Silk) .....D
N. J.—Paterson
Caspers Silk Co. (Silk)..D
Enterprise Silk Co. (Silk)
B
N. Y.—Brooklyn
Jennings Lace Wks. (Silk)
AAAA
N. Y.—Hornellsville
Steuben Silk Co. (Silk)..B
N. Y.—Tarrytown
Husted, A. P. (Silk) ....B

VELOCIPEDES

ILL.—Harvey
Buda Fdy. & Mfg. Co.
(Railway) ....AA
MICH.—Kalamazoo
Kalamazoo Railway Supply
Co. (Railway) ....B
MICH.—Three Rivers
Sheffield Car Co. (Rail-
way; Motor Railway).AA
N. H.—Keene
Wilkins Toy Co. (Chil-
drens') ....AAA
N. Y.—Binghamton
Wilkinson Mfg. Co. (Chil-
drens') ....A
New York City
Crandall Carriage Co. (Chil-
dren) X
Mace & Co., L. H. (Chil-
drens') ....B
Spalding & Bros., A. G.
(Inc.) (Childrens')
AAAA
OHIO—Cleveland
Metal Goods Mfg. Co.
(Childrens') X
OHIO—Toledo
Gendron Wheel Co. (Chil-
drens') ....AA
Harris Toy Co. (Childrens')
B
Toledo Metal Wheel Co.
(Childrens') ....AA
VT.—Brattleboro
Smith & Co., S. A. (Chil-
drens') ....AAA

VELVETEENS

R. I.—Warwick
Crompton Co. ....AAA

VELVETS

See also Plushes; Silk Goods

VENEERS

GA.—Rome
King Mfg. Co., C. L.....D
IND.—Indianapolis
Indiana Lumber & Veneer
Co. ....B
Williamson Veneer Co. ...D
IND.—Jasper
Jasper Veneer Mills ....D
KY.—Louisville
Louisville Veneer Mills...A
MASS.—Boston
Palmer, Parker & Co....A
MICH.—Grand Rapids
Grand Rapids Veneer Wks.
AA
MO.—St. Louis
Schoeneau & Kukkuk
Trunk Co. ....B
N. Y.—Buffalo
Elias & Bro. Co........AA
N. Y.—Cattaraugus
Oakes & Burger ....B
N. Y.—Jamestown
Jamestown Panel & Veneer
Co. ....F
N. Y.—Long Island City
Astoria Veneer Mills (Inc.)
B
New York City
Uptegrove & Bros., W. E.
AA
N. C.—High Point
High Point Veneer Co....E
OHIO—Cincinnati
Albro Co., E. D........X
OHIO—Portsmouth
Portsmouth Veneer & Panel
Co. ....B
TENN.—Johnson City
Standard Oak Veneer Co.
B
TENN.—Memphis
Anderson-Tully Co.....AAA
VA.—Petersburg
South Side Mfg. Co......C
WIS.—Sheboygan
Frosts' Veneer Seating Co.
(Opera Chair) ....B

VENETIANS

See Woolen Goods

VENTILATORS

CONN.—Bridgeport
Drouve Co. ....B
ILL.—Chicago
Harrington & King Perfo-
rating Co., 224 N. Union
(Railroad Car) ....A
Redlick Mfg. Co. (Beer)..B
ILL.—Streator
Iwan Bros. (Chimney) ...C
MASS.—Boston
Edson Mfg. Co. (Hood)..B
MASS.—Greenfield
Wiley & Russell Mfg. Co.
AA
MASS.—Lowell
Mack & Co., W. A.......C
MICH.—Detroit
Scully Ventilator Co., W. J.
(Closet) ....B
MO.—St. Louis
Pleuger & Henger Mfg. Co.
A
N. J.—Jersey City
National Sheet Metal Roof-
ing Co. (Building) ...C
N. Y.—Buffalo
Buffalo Forge Co. (Gas
Jet) ....AAA
N. Y.—Manlius
Cheney & Son, S. ....A
N. Y.—Newburgh
Chadborn Mfg. Co. (Auto-
matic Ventilator & Heat
Control; Car) X
New York City
Creamer & Co., W. G., 96
John (Car) ....A
Howard & Morse (Mechani-
cal Building) ....D
Mettes & Son, E. (Hat).D
Protective Ventilator Co.

VENTILATORS (Con.)
(Window) ....B
Roebuck Weather Strip & Wire Screen Co. (Window) ....D
Tuttle & Bailey Mfg. Co., 83 Beekman (Brick Wall; Window) ....AA
N. Y.—Troy
Globe Ventilator Co. (Car; Building; Chimney; Skylight) C
OHIO—Canton
Berger Mfg. Co. (Building; Flue) ....AA
Canton Steel Roofing Co. A
OHIO—Cleveland
Columbian Hdw. Co. ..AA
Garry Iron & Steel Co. (Building) ....A
Osborn Mfg. Co. ....B
OHIO—Hamilton
Myers Mfg. Co., Fred J. (Car) ....B
OHIO—Massillon
Hess, Snyder Co. (Chimney) ....AA
PA.—Philadelphia
Berger Bros. Co., 231 Arch A
Fields' Sons, Chas. J., 633 Market (Window) ....B
Merchant & Co. (Inc.). 517 Arch (Car; Building; Flue) ....AA
Spear Stove & Heating Co., James (Car) ....A
Taylor Co., N. & G. (Car) AAA
PA.—York
Pullman Automatic Ventilator Co. (Car; also for Depots, Offices, &c.; Window for Lower Sash Rail) ....B
R. I.—Providence
Clason Architectural Metal Co. (Building) C
TEXAS—Ft. Worth
Fort Worth Iron & Steel Mfg. Co. (Gas Jet)...A
WIS.—South Milwaukee
Stowell Mfg. & Fdy. Co. (Flue) ....A

VENTS

ILL.—Chicago
Marsh & Co., Jas. P. (Radiator Air) ....B
MASS.—Boston
Cutter-Tower Co. (Ink)..B
N. J.—Newark
Sommer's Sons, John (Air) A

VERMICELLI

See Macaroni.

VERMIFUGE

MD.—Baltimore
Foutz Co., David E......D
McCormick & Co. ....D
MO.—St. Louis
Stobie Cereal Mills .....B
PA.—Pittsburg
Farnestock Drug Co., B. S. F

VERMILION

MICH.—Detroit
Acme White Lead & Color Works ....AAA
OHIO—Cincinnati
Moser Co., Charles .....AA
N. Y.—Buffalo
Century Mfg. Co., 2720 Genesee ....D
New York City
Pfeiffer Co., 92 William..A
Tiemann & Co.. D. F., 46 Duane ....A

VESSELS

MAINE—Bath
Kelly-Spear Co. (Sailing) A
Morse Bros. (Sailing)....F
New England Co. (Sailing) D

VESSELS (Con.)
MAINE—Rockport
Carleton, Norwood & Co. (Sailing) ....B
MD.—Baltimore
Skinner & Sons, Wm. (Sailing) ....B
MASS.—Boston
Boston Belting Co. (Acid) AAAA
N. J.—Camden
Dialogue & Son, John H. (Sailing) ....AA
New York City
Bishop Gutta Percha Mfg. Co., 422 E. 25th (Acid) A
Goodyear Rubber Co., 787 B'way (Acid) ....AAAA
Gutta Percha & Rubber Mfg. Co., 126 Duane (Acid) ....AAAA
Jochum, Andrew (Copper) E
Trageser Steam Copper Wks., John (Copper; Copper Air) ....B
N. Y.—Northport
Carll, Jesse (Sailing).....B
N. Y.—Port Jefferson
Bayles & Sons, James M. (Sailing) ....D
PA.—Philadelphia
Fields' Sons, Chas. J., 633 Market (Acid) ....B
R. I.—Providence
Feeley Co., W. J. (Altar) B

VESTIBULES

New York City
Gould Coupler Co., 20 W. 34th (Car) ....AAAA
Sjoberg & Co., J. P., 533 W. 32d (Car) ....D
PA.—Pittsburg
McConway & Torley Co., 48th & A. V. Ry. (Car) A

VESTMENTS

New York City
Lamb, J. & R. (Church)..C

VESTS

See Clothing: Men's & Boys; also Clothing: Ladies'

ILL.—Chicago
Bauer & Black (Chamois) A
N. J.—Jersey City
Zimmerman & Son Co., (Golf) ....D
N. Y.—Baldwinsville
Allen, Alexander (Nursing) D

VIADUCTS

DEL.—Wilmington
Edge Moor Iron Co. (Iron; Steel) ....AAA
N. J.—Trenton
Trenton Iron Co. (Iron; Steel) ....A
PA.—Beaver Falls
Penn Bridge Co. (Iron; Steel) ....AA
PA.—Philadelphia
Phoenix Bridge Co. (Iron; Steel) ....A
Roberts Co., A. & P. (Iron; Steel) ....AAAA
PA.—Pittsburg
Carnegie Steel Co. (Ltd.) (Iron; Steel) ....AAAA

VIALS

See also Bottles

MD.—Baltimore
Chesapeake Glass Company (Homeopathic) ....D
N. J.—Glassboro
Whiting Glass Works (Glass) ....AAA
N. J.—Millville
Wheaton Co., T. C. (Homeopathic) ....B
N. J.—Newark
Transparent Cellulose Prod-

VIALS (Con.)
ucts Co. ....D
New York City
Demuth Glass Mfg. Co.
(Glass) X
Steinbuch Bros. & Co., 275
Pearl (Homeopathic) ..D
PA.—Bradford
Penn Glass Tube Co.
(Homeopathic) ....D
PA.—Royersford
Diamond Glass Co. ....A

VIBRATORS

MICH.—Battle Creek
Globe Mfg. Co. (Com-
pressed Air) ....D
OHIO—Cleveland
Cleveland Faucet Co. (Mas-
sage) ....AAA

VICTORIAS

MASS.—Boston
French & Co., Ferd. F...D
Kimball Bros. & Co......B
Thomas & Co., Chauncey.C
MASS.—New Bedford
Brownell, Geo. L. (Est. of)
B
N. J.—Newark
Quimby & Co., J. M.....A
N. Y.—Albany
Goold Co., James ......B
New York City
Brewster & Co., J. B.
(Inc.) ....B
Demarest & Co., A. T.....A
Goodrich & Co., J. F...AA
Stivers, R. M. ....B
N. Y.—Troy
Troy Carriage Works ....B
N. Y.—Watertown
Babcock Co., H. H.....AA
N. C.—Carthage
Tyson & Jones Buggy Co.
B
OHIO—Columbus
Buckeye Buggy Co. ..AAA

VICUNAS

See also Woolen Goods

VINEGAR

See Cider; Vinegar, etc.

VINES

CONN.—New Canaan
Hoyt's Sons Co., Stephen
(Grape) ....B
N. Y.—Fredonia
Hubbard Co., T. S. (Grape)
B
Josselyn, Geo. S. (Grape)
A
Roesch, Lewis (Grape)...C
N. Y.—Rochester
Brown Bros. Co. (Grape).A
Ellwanger & Barry (Grape)
A
OHIO—Toledo
Lenk Wine Co. (Grape).AA
PA.—Carnegie
Beistle & Co., M. L. (Arti-
ficial Autumn) ....F

VIOLINS

See Mus. Insts.

VIRUS

See Vaccine

VISCOSI-
METERS

PA.—Philadelphia
Olsen & Co., Tinius ......A

VISES

CAL.—San Francisco
Richmond Fdy. & Mfg. Co.,
517 Market (Bench) ...X
CONN.—Bridgeport
Armstrong Mfg. Co. (Pipe;
Bench; Blacksmiths')..A

VISES (Con.)
Curtis & Curtis Co. (Pipe)
AA
Fray & Co., John S. (Hand)
A
CONN.—Hartford
Billings & Spencer Co. (Ma-
chinists' Hand; Line-
mens'; Amateur; Combi-
nation Bench) .....AA
Pratt & Whitney Co. (Mill-
ing Machine Planer)
AAAA
Vanderbeck Tool Works
(Milling Machine; Planer;
Machinists') ....B
Whitney Mfg. Co. (Milling
Machine) ....A
CONN.—Meriden
Parker Co., Chas. (Coach-
makers'; Woodworkers';
Parallel; Pipe; Saw; Die
Sinkers) ....AAA
CONN.—New Britain
New Britain Machine Co.
(Saw. for Filing Band
Saws) ....A
CONN.—New London
New London Vise Works
(Solid Box) ....E
CONN.—Pine Meadow
Chapins-Stephens Co. (Car-
riage Makers) ....A
CONN.—Rockfall
Smith, Otis A. (Hand)...B
CONN.—Rocky Hill
Billing Mfg. Co., C. E.
(Hand) ....D
CONN.—Stamford
Yale & Towne Mfg. Co.
(Pipe) ....AAAA
CONN.—Tolland
Clough, R. M. (Milling
Machine) ....D
CONN.—Torrington
Hendey Machine Co. (Mill-
ing Machine; Planer).AA
CONN.—Waterbury
Blake & Johnson (Horse-
shoers') ....A
CONN.—Willimantic
Vandeman Plumbing &
Heating Co., Wm. (Com-
bination; Self-Locking
Pipe) C
CONN.—Winsted
Carter & Hakes Machine
Co. (Milling Machine)..D
DEL.—Wilmington
Henderer Sons. A. L. (An-
vil; Pipe; Drill) ......E
ILL.—Carpentersville
Illinois Iron & Bolt Co.
(Machinists' Bench; Cab-
inet Makers; Coach Mak-
ers'; Hand; Steel Faced;
Parallel; Solid Box; Par-
allel Foot; Horse Shoers')
AA
ILL.—Chicago
Crane Co. (Bench; Pipe)
AAAA
Hanna Engineering Works,
550 N. Halsted (Auto-
matic; Quick Acting
Bench) ....B
Mark Mfg. Co. (Pipe) ..AA
Massey Vise Co., 30 S. Ca-
nal (Bicycle; Coachmak-
ers'; Milling Machine;
Parallel; Planer; Light-
ning Grip; Cabinet; Drill
Press; Pipe) ....F
Sears, Roebuck & Co.
(Bench) ....AAAA
Toles & Co., W. C. (Bench;
Coachmakers') ....B
ILL.—Downer's Grove
Decke Tool Co. (Linemens';
Carpet) C
ILL.—Edwardsville
Bignall & Keeler Mfg. Co.
(Parallel; Combination
Bench; Pipe) ....B
ILL.—Evanston
Sheldon & Co., C. H.
(Rapid Acting) ....D
ILL.—Ottawa
Porter Co., J. E. (Pipe)..A
ILL.—Rockford
Marsh, H. C. C

VISES (Con.)

ILL.—Sandwich
Enterprise Windmill Co.
(Pipe) ....D
IND.—Butler
Butler Co. (Pipe) ....B
IND.—Indianapolis
Atkins & Co., E. C. (Saw)
AAAA
IOWA—Dubuque
Adams Co. (Drill; Machin-
ists'; Parallel; Pipe; An-
vil; Hand) ....A
MD.—Baltimore
Kemp Mfg. Co., C. M.
(Pipe) ....B
MASS.—Athol
Athol Machine Co. (Bench;
Coachmakers'; Farmers';
Wood Workers'; Hand;
Parallel; Amateur; Rapid
Transit; Swivel; Heavy
Clipping; Oval Side)....B
MASS.—Boston
Burke, P. F., Dorr & Dor-
chester Av. (Horseshoers'
Foot) C
Butts & Ordway Co., 190
High (Horseshoers')...C
Walworth Mfg. Co., 132
Federal (Bench; Pipe)
AAAA
MASS.—Cambridge
Barbour-Stockwell Co. (Cab-
inet; Screw Bench; Wood-
workers') ....A
MASS.—Fairhaven
Fairhaven Iron Foundry Co.
(Horseshoers') ....D
MASS.—Fitchburg
Simonds Mfg. Co. (Saw)
AAA
MASS.—Greenfield
Goodell-Pratt Co. (Hand).B
Wells Bros. Co. (Horse-
shoers' Foot) ....A
Wiley & Russell Mfg. Co.
(Horseshoers') ......AA
MASS.—Hyde Park
Becker-Brainard Milling
Machine Co. (Horse-
shoers') ....AA
MASS.—Millers Falls
Millers Falls Co. (Parallel
Anvil; Drill; Hand)..AA
MASS.—Salem
Spencer Regulator Company
(Pipe) C
MASS.—Springfield
Bullock Mfg. Co. (Jewel-
ers' Watch; Pin) .....A
Hopkinson Machine Works
(Drill) ....F
MASS.—Westfield
Smith Co., H. B. (Amateur;
Bench; Blacksmiths').AA
MASS.—Worcester
Wyman & Gordon (Quick
Action; Coachmakers';
Woodworkers'; Bench;
Cabinet; Self-Adjusting
Jaw; Rapid Transit) ..A
ICH.—Detroit
Strelinger Co., Chas. A.,
98 Bates (Machinists').A
MICH.—Grand Rapids
Fox Machine Co. (Milling
Machine; Planer) .....A
MINN.—St. Paul
Helwig Mfg. Co. (Parallel)
D
MO.—St. Louis
Kupferle, Jno. C., 2d &
Mound (Saw) ....AA
Nixdorf-Krein Mfg. Co.
(Blacksmiths') ......AA
N. H.—Exeter
Exeter Machine Works
(Pipe) ....B
N. J.—Bound Brook
Timmis & Cissold (Coach-
makers'; Woodworkers')
X
N. J.—Elizabeth
Braunsdorf-Muller Company
(Hand) ....D
N. J.—Newark
Gould & Eberhardt (Planer;
Milling Machine) ......A
Kraeuter Co. (Carpet)....X
N. J.—Plainfield
Pond Machine Tool Co.

VISES (Con.)
(Milling Machine).AAAA
N. J.—Salem
Ayars Machine Co. (Ma-
chinists') ....B
N. J.—Smithville
Smith Mfg. Co., H. B.
(Bench) ....A
N. J.—Trenton
Fisher & Norris (Parallel;
Solid Box) ....B
N. Y.—Belmont
Clark Bros. Co. (Pipe)...A
N. Y.—Brooklyn
Merrill Bros., 465 Kent Av.
(Parallel; Swivel) ....A
N. Y.—Buffalo
Howard Iron Works (Pipe;
Fixed; Swivel; Parallel;
Bench; Farmers'; Black-
smiths'; Heavy Clipping;
Coachmakers'; Hand) .A
N. Y.—Homer
Phoenix Hardware Mfg. Co.
(Bench; Farmers'; Pipe;
Hand; Coachmakers';
Woodworkers'; Saw) ..D
New York City
Eaton, Cole & Burnham Co.,
253 B'way (Pipe) .AAAA
Fairbanks Co., 186 Elm
(Pipe; Drill; Combination;
Anvil; Hand; Milling Ma-
chine; Planer) ....AAAA
Garvin Machine Co. (Saw;
Silent; Milling Machine)
AA
Hammacher, Schlemmer &
Co. (Coachmakers'; Saw;
Woodworkers'; Parallel;
Solid Box) ....AAA
Jennings & Co., C. E., 101
Reade (Saw) ....B
Lewis Tool Co., 44 Barclay
(Coachmakers'; Wood-
workers'; Pipe; Bicycle;
Bench; Self-Adjustable
Jaw; Quick Acting Ma-
chinists'; Solid Jaw; Par-
allel) ....D
Nason Mfg. Co., 71 Beek-
man (Pipe) ....AA
Niles-Bement-Pond Co., 111
Bway. (Planer; Milling
Machine) ....AAAA
Peck, Stow & Wilcox Co.,
27 Murray (Parallel)
AAAA
Prentiss Vise Co., 44 Bar-
clay (Bench; Bicycle;
For Heavy Clipping;
Clamp; Coachmakers';
Woodworkers'; Drill; Le-
ver; Machinists'; Pipe;
Parallel; Solid Box; An-
vil; Amateur; Black-
smiths'; Offset Jaw;
Rapid Transit; Swivel;
Self-Adjusting Jaw) ...C
Sargent & Co., 151 Leonard
(Parallel; Saw) ..AAAA
Simmons Co., Jno., 110
Centre (Pipe) ....AA
Tower & Lyon Co., 95
Chambers (Bench; Jewel-
ers'; Leg Quick Acting
Parallel; Pipe; Cabinet;
Solid Box) ....B
N. Y.—Oswego
Oswego Tool Co. (Pipe)..B
N. Y.—Seneca Falls
Seneca Falls Mfg. Co.
(Saw) ....B
N. Y.—Syracuse
Stearns & Co., E. C. (Saw;
Bench; Silent Saw) ..AA
N. Y.—Utica
Utica Drop Forge & Tool
Co. (Hand; Linemens').B
N. Y.—Yonkers
Saunders' Sons, D. (Pipe;
Combination) ....A
OHIO—Cincinnati
Cincinnati Milling Machine
Co. (Milling Machine).AA
Cincinnati Tool Co. (Saw)
B
OHIO—Cleveland
Columbian Hardware Co.,
Coe & Hamilton (Bench;
Coachmakers'; Hand; Far-
mers'; Woodworkers';

VISES (Con.)
Horseshoers'; Parallel;
Solid Box) ....AA
OHIO—Columbus
Columbus Forge & Iron Co.
(Blacksmiths'; Solid Box)
A
OHIO—Dayton
Joyce-Cridland Co. (Bench)
B
Patterson Tool & Supply
Co. (Drill) ....A
OHIO—Mansfield
Humphreys Mfg. Co. (Pipe)
B
OHIO—Warren
Denison Mfg. Co. (Planer)
F
PA.—Erie
Erie Mfg. & Supply Co.
(Sectional Jaw Pipe) .B
Hollands Mfg. Co. (Bicycle;
Blacksmiths'; Pipe; Par-
allel; Cabinet; Carpen-
ters'; Wooden; Coachmak-
ers'; Planer; Drill Press;
Horseshoers'; Milling Ma-
chine; Woodworkers';
Polished Tubing) ......B
Jarecki Mfg. Co. (Pipe)
AAAA
Reed Mfg. Co. (Bench;
Combination; Pipe; Ma-
chinists'; Improved Com-
bination Pipe) ....A
PA.—Meadville
Meadville Vise Co. (Bench;
Bicycle; Cabinet Makers';
Coachmakers'; Woodwork-
ers'; Combination Pipe;
Farmers'; Heavy Clip-
ping; Offset Jaw; Paral-
lel; Swivel) ....A
PA.—Philadelphia
Atlantic Works (Inc.), 23d
& Arch (Saw) ....B
Bonney Vise & Tool Works,
3015 Chestnut (Coachmak-
ers; Woodworkers'; Drill;
Hand; Machinists'; Par-
allel; Pipe; Saw; Heavy
Clipping) C
Cox & Sons Co., 215 Race
(Pipe) ....B
Disston & Sons, Henry
(Saw) ....AAAA
PA.—Philadelphia
Pedrick & Ayer Co. (Bench)
A
PA.—Pittsburg
Hickman-Melhorn Co., 200
Liberty Av. (Pipe).....A
Iron City Tool Wks. (Ltd.)
(Solid Box; Heavy Clip-
ping; Blacksmiths') ..A
Jones & Laughlin Steel Co.
(Ltd.) (Bench; Coach-
makers'; Woodworkers';
Parallel) ....AAAA
PA.—Warren
Jacobson Machine Mfg. Co.
(Bench; Drill) C
PA.—Waynesboro
Emmert Mfg. Co. (Bench;
Machinists') C
R. I.—Pawtucket
Bliss Mfg. Co., R. (Car-
penters' Wooden) ..AAAA
R. I.—Providence
Brown & Sharpe Mfg. Co.
(Milling Machine; Plan-
er) ....AAAA
VT.—Derby Line
Butterfield & Co. (Pipe).A

VITRIOL

**See also Acids; Coper Sul-
phate**

OHIO—Cleveland
Grasselli Chemical Co.
(Blue) ....AAAA
PA.—Philadelphia
Fergusson Bros. (Blue)..A
Jordan, Jr., W. H. & F.
(Powdered Blue) ...AA

VOLTMETERS

See Meters; Ammeters

VULCABESTON

CONN.—Hartford
Johns-Pratt Co. (Insulat-
ing) ....A
New York City ..
Fairbanks Co. (Packing)
AAAA
Johns-Manville Co., H. W.,
100 William .....AAAA

VULCANIZERS

CONN.—Ansonia
Farrell Fdy. & Machine Co.
(Rubber) ....AAAA
MASS.—Springfield
Smith Mfg. Co., R. H....C
ILL.—Chicago
Elmes Engineering Works,
Chas. F. (Rubber) ....A
MD.—Baltimore
Dorman Co., J. F. W. (Rub-
ber) ....F
N. J.—Paterson
Smith & Son Co., Samuel..B
N. Y.—Buffalo
Buffalo Dental Mfg. Co...B
New York City
Rubber Goods Mfg. Co., 253
B'way (Rubber) ..AAAA
OHIO—Akron
Biggs Boiler Works Co.
(Rubber) C
OHIO—Cleveland
Cleveland Dental Mfg. Co.
(Cam Lock) ....B
United States Dental Mfg.
Co. (Dental) ....D
OHIO—Toledo
National Cement & Rubber
Mfg. Co. C
PA.—Philadelphia
Johnson & Lund ....AA
Wall Mfg. Co., R. C.....F
White Dental Mfg. Co., S.
S. ....AAAA

WADDING

IND.—Indianapolis
Merritt & Co., Geo. (Tail-
ors') ....A
MASS.—Medfield
Ray & Wilson (Clothiers')
C
MASS.—Winchester
Eastern Felt Co. (Wool)..C
N. Y.—Lockport
Evans & Co. (Wool).....C
Norman & Evans (Woolen)
C
OHIO—Cincinnati
Stearns & Foster Co. (Cot-
ton) ....AAA
OHIO—Lockland
Stearns & Foster Co. (Cot-
ton) ....AAA
R. I.—Pawtucket
Union Wadding Co. (Cot-
ton) ....AAAA
WIS.—Janesville
Rock River Cotton Co. (Cot-
ton) ....A

WADS

CONN.—Bridgeport
Union Metallic Cartridge
Co. (Gun) ....AAA
CONN.—New Haven
Winchester Repeating Arms
Co. (Gun) ....AAAA
CONN.—Waterbury
Waterbury Brass Co. (Gun)
AAAA
OHIO—Cincinnati
Peters Cartridge Co. (Gun)
AAAA

WAGONS

See also Carriages & Wagons

ALA.—Florence
Florence Wagon Works
(Farm; Log) ....A
ARK.—Little Rock
Roesh Fred (Logging) ....D
CAL.—Benicia
Benicia Iron Works (Ex-
press; Farm; Spring;
Truck; Road; Spring), AA

WAGONS (Con.)

CAL.—San Leandro
Best Mfg. Co. (Crude Oil
Motor) ....AA
CONN.—New Haven
Goodrich & Co., J. F. (Delivery; Beach; Concord Depot; Road; Spring)....AA
GA.—Atlanta
White Hickory Wagon Mfg.
Co. Farm; Turpentine;
Log) ....A
ILL.—Aurora
Frazier & Co., W. S. (Skeleton; Road; Speed) .....A
Western Wheeled Scraper
Co. (Dumping)........AA
ILL.—Batavia
Newton Wagon Co. (Farm;
Spring) ....AA
ILL.—Chicago
Kimball & Co., C. P. (Speed)
AA
National Drill & Mfg. Co.,
Pullman Bldg. (Dumping)
B
Schuttler & Holtz, 45 W.
Monroe (Dumping; Farm;
Spring) ....AAAA
Shaw, Willis, N. Y. Life
Bldg. (Dumping) ....E
Sherman I. N. W. (Army;
Bakers; Butchers; Brewers; Business; Coal; Delivery; Express Freight;
Furniture; Grocers; Ice;
Laundry; Mail; Market;
Milk; Spring Truck; Ambulance; Depot; Mountain;
Patrol; Spring) ....A
Weber Wagon Co. (Logging;
Farm; Spring) ....AA
ILL.—Dallas City
Burg Carriage Co., L.(Park;
Road; Spring) ....B
ILL.—Freeport
Henney Buggy Co. (Spring)
A
ILL.—Geneseo
Sargent & Son, D. F.
(Spring) ....B
ILL.—Harvey
Austin Mfg .Co. (Automatic
Dumping; Garbage), AAA
Buda Foundry & Mfg. Co.
(Baggage) ....AA
ILL.—Moline
Moline Wagon Co.;(Delivery; Farm; Freight;
Spring) ....AAAA
Sechler Carriage Co., D. M.
(Spring) ....AA
ILL.—Ottawa
King & Hamilton Co.
(Farm) ....AA
ILL.—Pekin
Smith & Co., T. & H. (Inc.)
(Farm; Spring) ....A
ILL.—Quincy
Electric Wheel Co. (Steel) A
Knapheide Wagon Co.
(Freight; Teaming, etc.)C
Koenig & Luhrs Wagon Co.
(Laundry) ....B
ILL.—Rock Falls
Eureka Co. (Spring) ......B
ILL.—Sterling
Rock Falls Mfg. Co. (Undertakers; Ambulance) ...A
IND.—Anderson
American Bridge & Scraper
Co. (Garbage) ....D
IND.—Connersville
McFarlan Carriage Co.
(Road; Speed; Spring) AA
IND.—Elkhart
Elkhart Carriage & Harness
Mfg. Co. (Spring) ......A
IND.—Fort Wayne
Olds. Wagon Works (Farm)
X
IND.—Goshen
Walker-Lewis Carriage Co.
(Road) ....B
IND.—Indianapolis
Parry Mfg. Co. (Road;
Speed) ....AAAA
IND.—Richmond
Wayne Works (Delivery;
Spring) ....A
IND.—South Bend
Birdsell Mfg. Co. (Delivery;
Farm; Lumber; Spring
Truck; Spring) ....AA

WAGONS (Con.)

Colfax Mfg. Co. (Spring), C
Coquillard Wagon Works
(Farm; Spring Truck;
Spring) ....A
South Bend Toy Mfg. Co.
(Asphalt; Dump Freight;
Teaming, etc.; Garbage;
Ice; Logging; Ore; Coal;
Mining; Live Stock;
Truck; Spring) ...AAAA
IOWA—Burlington
Burg Wagon Co. (Bakers;
Butchers; Farm; Freight;
Grocers; Mountain Milk;
Lumber; Spring) ......A
IOWA—Davenport
Bettendorf Axle Co. (Steel;
Gear Coal; Farm, etc.)AA
IOWA—Dubuque
Connelly, Tom (Est. of)
(Road) ....A
Cooper Wagon & Buggy Co.,
A. A. (Farm; Freight;
Grain; Lumber; Market;
Milk) ....A
IOWA—Grinnell
Spaulding Mfg. Co. (Spring)
AAA
KY.—Louisville
Kentucky Wagon Mfg. Co.
(Army; Dumping; Farm;
Freight; Grocers; Log;
Lumber; Truck Spring;
Turpentine) ......AAAA
KY.—Owensboro
Ames Co., F. A. (Road) ..A
Owensboro Wagon Co.
(Farm; Freight) ......AA
LA.—New Orleans
Schwartz Co. (Ltd.), Jos.
(Logging) ....A
MAINE—South Paris
Paris Mfg. Co. (Pony; Toy;
Childrens; Dog; Goat), A
MD.—Baltimore
Leonhardt Wagon Mfg. Co.,
412 E. Saratoga (Trolley)
C
MASS.—Amesbury
Bailey & Co., S. R. (Road)
A
Biddle & Smart Co. (Spring)
B
Briggs Carriage Co. (Trolley
Delivery; Farm) ....D
Dennett & Co., C. N. (Business; Beach; Depot;
Spring) X
Feltch & Co., E. S. (Road;
Spring) ....B
Hassett & Hodge (Depot), A
MASS.—Boston
Ames Plow Co. (Farm)
AAAA
French & Co., Fred F. (Ltd.)
(Delivery) ....D
MASS.—Leominster
Whitney Carriage Co., F. A.
(Toy) ....A
Whitney Reed Chair Co.
(Toy) ....AAAA
MASS.—New Bedford
Brownell, Geo. L. (Est. of)
(Undertakers; Spring) ..B
MICH.—Charlotte
Benton Mfg. Co. (Toy Express) ....
MICH.—Detroit
Anderson Sons, W. H. (Pole
Rising Trolley) C
MICH.—Flint
Durant-Dort Carriage Co.
(Delivery; Road; Spring)
AAAA
Flint Wagon Works (Farm;
Road; Spring) ....AA
MICH.—Grand Rapids
Belknap Wagon Co. (Express; Farm) C
Harrison Wagon Co. (Farm;
Freight) ....AA
MICH.—Jackson
Austin, Tomlinson & Webster Mfg. Co. (Farm;
Freight; Plantation; Lumber; Log) X
Fuller Buggy Co. (Road;
Spring) ....A
National Wheel Co. (Truck;
Spring) X
MICH.—Kalamazoo
American Carriage Co.

WAGONS (Con.)

OHIO—Defiance
Turnbull Wagon Co. (Farm) AA

OHIO—Elmwood Place
Highland Buggy Co. (Spring) X

OHIO—Marion
McMurray Sulky Co. (Skeleton; Spring)............B

OHIO—Miamisburg
Enterprise Carriage Mfg. Co. (Road; Spring) ..A
Kauffman Buggy Co. (Road) B

OHIO—Springfield
Mast & Co., P. P. (Dumping; Automatic; Spring) AAAA

OHIO—Toledo
Gendron Wheel Co. (Toy; Toy Spring; Express), AA
Milburn Wagon Co. (Dumping; Trolley; Bakers; Business; Butchers; Coal; Delivery; Express; Farm; Grain; Furniture; Grocers; Ice; Laundry; Lumber; Market; Milk; Truck; Spring) ....AAA

OHIO—Westerville
Bennett & Co., H. L. (Dumping; Farm) ....E

OHIO—Youngstown
Youngstown Carriage & Wagon Co. (Road; Spring) A

OHIO—Zanesville
Brown Mfg. Co. (Farm) AA

PA.—Allegheny
Beckert, Wm., 1001 Ohio (Dumping) ....B

PA.—Columbia
Columbia Wagon Co. (Dumping; Contractors; Army; Farm; Milk) ....A

PA.—Emigsville
Acme Wagon Co. (Dumping) B

PA.—Erie
Thayer Co., H. N. (Express; Toy) ....A

PA.—Harrisburg
Jackson Mfg. Co. (Steel; Ore; Coal; Mining; Mill; Coke) ....B

PA.—Philadelphia
Fulton & Walker Co. (Business; Delivery; Express; Freight; Furniture; Garbage; Grain; Grocers; Laundry; Mail; Truck; Undertakers; Milk; Ambulance; Patrol) ....AA
Morris, Henry G. (Sugar), B

PA.—Pittsburg
Duquesne Vehicle Co., 400 Duquesne Way (Dumping) X
Marshall Bros. (Farm) ..AA
Phillips Mine & Mill Supply Co. (Larry Coke) .....AA

PA.—Reading
Keystone Wagon Works (Bakers; Butchers; Delivery; Dumping; Express; Laundry; Ice; Market; Milk; Spring) ....A

PA.—Waynesboro
Frick Co. (Water; Fuel) AAAA

PA.—York
Hoover Wagon Co. (Bakers; Butchers; Delivery; Express; Grocers; Laundry; Milk) C
York Carriage Co. (Express) AA

TENN.—Memphis
Bodley Wagon Co. (Freight; Teaming, etc., up to 30 Tons; Logging; Army; Cane; Coal; Dumping; Farm; Lumber; Truck; Turpentine; Mountain; Plantation) ....A

VT.—Brattleboro
Smith Co., S. A. (Toy; Childrens; Dog Goat; Toy Express) ....AAA

VA.—Danville
Horner Wagon Mfg. Co., W. P. (Delivery; Grocers;

WAGONS (Con.)
Farm; Freight; Park), D

VA.—Norfolk
Wrenn & Son, A. (Farm; Spring) ....AA

W. VA.—Martinsburg
Auburn Wagon Co. (Freight; Teaming, etc.) ....B

WIS.—Boscobel
Buka Bros. Mfg. Co. (Ltd.) (Farm; Spring) C

WIS.—Fond-du-Lac
Sweet Co., B. F. & H. L. (Farm; Truck; Spring; Spring Truck) ....A

WIS.—Fort Atkinson
North Western Mfg. Co. (Farm; Spring) ......AA

WIS.—Jefferson
Vaughn Mfg Co., O. C. (Farm; Spring) ....D

WIS.—Kenosha
Bain Wagon Co. (Freight Farm; Ore; Spring) ..AAA
Kenosha Crib Co. (Childrens) ....B

WIS.—Madison
Fuller & Johnson Mfg. Co. (Farm; Road) ....AAA

WIS.—Milwaukee
Meinecke & Son A. (Toy Express; Toy) ....AA

WIS.—Oshkosh
Sanford Logging Tool Co., A. (Logging) ....D

WIS.—Racine
Case Threshing Machy. Co., J. I. (Water; Fuel) AAAA
Fish Bros. Wagon Co. (Freight; Teaming, etc.; Logging; Dumping; Express; Farm; Grain; Grocers; Ore; Lumber; Market; Overland; Milk; Truck; Mountain Plantation; Road; Spring) ..AA
Mitchell & Lewis Co. (Ltd.) (Bakers; Business; Delivery; Express; Farm; Freight; Grain; Grocers; Laundry; Log; Lumber; Market; Milk; Skeleton Truck; Spring Truck; Beach; Concord; Depot; Mountain; Park; Plantation; Pony Road), AAAA
Winship Mfg. Co. (Street Sprinkling) ....E

WIS.—Sheboygan
Garton Toy Co. ....A

WIS.—Stoughton
Stoughton Wagon Co. (Farm; Spring) ......AA

WAINSCOATING

MINN.—Minneapolis
Tennant. G. H. (Basswood) D

N. Y.—Binghamton
Roberson & Son. A. .....AA

N. Y.—Brooklyn
Brooklyn Metal Ceiling Co., 283 Greene St. C
Hecla Iron Works, 11th & Berry (Iron; Electro; Bronze Plated) ......AA

PA.—East Bangor
East Bangor Consolidated Slate Co. (Marbelized Slate) ....AA

VT.—Fair Haven
Fair Haven Marble & Marbleized Slate Co. (Marbleized Slate) ....B

WAISTS

See Clothing: Ladies'

WAITERS

N. J.—Newark
Storm Mfg. Co. (Dumb) AA

New York City
International Silver Co., 9 Maiden Lane (Silver Plated) ....AAAA

N. Y.—Warsaw
Warsaw Elevator Co.

WAITERS (Con.)
  (Dumb) ....B
OHIO—Cincinnati
Warner Elevator Mfg. Co.
  (Dumb) ....AA
PA.—Philadelphia
Energy Elevator Co. (Dumb)
                        D
Morse, Williams & Co.
  (Dumb) ....AA
PA.—Pittsburg
Marshall Bros. (Dumb), AA
PA.—Reading
Speidel, J. G. (Dumb) ....B
WIS.—Milwaukee
Kieckhefer Elevator Co., A.
  (Dumb) C

WAITER'S CLOTHING

See Clothing: Men's

WALKERS

ILL.—Chicago
Tothill, W. S., 128 W. Webster Av. (Baby) ....F
IND.—Kendallville
Baker & Sons Co., J. R.
  (Baby) C
IND.—Muncie
Glasscock Bros. Mfg. Co.
  (Baby) ....B
MO.—Breckenridge
Ward & Son, Frank (Baby)
                      D

WALLETS

See Leather Goods

WALLPAPER

See Paper: Wall

WALLS

N. Y.—Brooklyn
Brooklyn Metal Ceiling Co.,
  283 Greene Av. (Embossed) C
New York City
New York Metal Ceiling Co.
  (Steel) ....B

WALNUT

See Lumber

WALNUTS

See Nuts: Edible

WANDS

OHIO—Piqua
Piqua Handle & Mfg. Co.
  (Calesthenic) ....A

WARDROBES

See Furniture

WARE: CHINA

See Chinaware

WARE: EARTHEN

See Earthenware; Pottery

WARE: ENAMELED; AGATE, ETC.

See Enameled Ware

WARE: STONE

See Stoneware; Pottery

WARMERS

CONN.—Meriden
Manning, Bowman & Co.
  (Tumbler) ....AA
IND.—La Grange
La Grange Robe & Tanning
  Co. (Wrist) ....H

WARMERS (Con.)
MD.—Baltimore
Hutchinson Bros., 116 No.
  Howard (Dish) ....D
MICH.—Detroit
American Electrical Heater
  Co. (Foot) ....B
N. H.—Pike Station
Pike Mfg. Co. (Soapstone
  Tool) ....A
N. Y.—Brooklyn
Sweeney Mfg. Co., W. H.
  (Tumbler) ....B
N. Y.—Buffalo
Aldrich Mfg. Co. (Bed;
  Foot) ....A
Jewett Mfg. Co., John C.
  (Foot; Tumbler; Bed) AA
New York City
Hadaway Electric Heating &
  Engineering Co., 136 Liberty (Plate) ....D
Lalance & Grosjean Mfg. Co.
  19 Cliff (Foot; Bed)
                   AAAA
N. Y.—Dansville
Dick, W. H. (Foot) ......E
New York City
Lalance & Grosjean Mfg. Co.
  (Foot; Tumbler). ..AAAA
Stoutenborough, X. (Tumbler) ....D
Sudbury & Co., E. B.
  (Wrist) ....B
VT.—Bennington
Cooper, Chas. (Wrist) ....B

WARPERS

CONN.—Stonington
Atwood-Morrison Co. ...AA
MASS.—Boston
Riley & Co., C. E., 45 Franklin ....A
MASS.—Hopedale
Draper Co. ....AAAA
MASS.—Lowell
Entwistle Co., T. C. ...·.B
Lowell Machine Shop (Leese;
  Slasher) ....AAAA
MASS.—Whitinsville
Whitin Machine Works
                   AAAA
MASS.—Worcester
Crompton & Knowles Loom
  Works ....AAAA
N. J.—Paterson
Atherton Machine Co. ....B
Eastwood Co., Benj. (Horizontal; Swiss) ....A
Paterson Machine Works, 46
  Warren (Horizontal;
  Swiss) ....F
Royle & Sons, Jno. (Ribbon)
                    A
N. Y.—Cohoes
Cohoes Iron Foundry & Machine Co. ....A
PA.—Philadelphia
Altemus, Jacob K., 282 N.
  4th ....D
Butterworth & Sons Co., H.
  W., 2415 E. York ......A
Fairmount Machine Co., 2106
  Wood ....A
Globe Machine Works, 2009
  Oxford (Ball; Chain) ...X
R. I.—Pawtucket
H. & B. American Machine
  Co. (Ltd.) ....AA

WARPS

ALA.—Tallassee
Tallassee Falls Mfg. Co.
  (Cotton) X
CONN.—Norwich
Ossawan Mills Co. (Carpet)
                    B
CONN.—Vernon
Ravine Mills Co. (Cotton) X
CONN.—Windsor Locks
Montgomery Co., J. R. (Colored; Fancy Cotton) ..AA
GA.—Augusta
Riverside Mills (Carpet) AA
GA.—Macon
Bibb Mfg. Co. (Carpet; Cotton) ....AAAA
GA.—Roswell
Roswell Mfg. Co. (Cotton) A
KY.—Maysville
January & Wood Co. (Cotton) ....A

WARPS (Con.)

LA.—New Orleans
Lane Cotton Mills (Carpet)
AAA

MAINE—Westbrook
Dana Warp Mills ....A
MAINE—Winthrop
Winthrop Mills Co. Coton)
A

MD.—Alberton
Alberton Cotton Mills (Cotton) ....AAAA
MD.—Baltimore
Ashland Mfg. Co. (Cotton)
AA

MASS.—Adams
Plunkett & Sons, W. C.
(Cotton) ....AAA
Renfrew Mfg. Co. (Coton)
AAA
MASS.—Fall River
Westport Mfg. Co. (Cotton)
AA
MASS.—Fitchburg
Grant Yarn Co. ....A
MASS.—Holyoke
Lyman Mills (Cotton)
AAAA
MASS.—Housatonic
Monument Mills (Cotton)
AAA
MASS.—Indian Orchard
Indian Orchard Co. .....AA
MASS.—Lawrence
Atlantic Cotton Mills (Cotton) ....AAA
MASS.—New Bedford
City Mfg. Corporation (Cotton; Chain) ....AAA
Wamsutta Mills (Cotton)
AAAA
MASS.—North Oxford
Bartlett, Edwin (Satinet) B
MASS.—Pittsfield
Peck Mfg. Co., Jabez L. &
T. D. (Satinet) ....AA
MASS.—Southbridge
Central Mills Co. (Cotton)
A
New York City
Hoffman-Carr Mfg. Co., 107
Duane ....AA
Kelley & Co., Henry C. ..B
Sternberg & Co., F., 530
Bway. ....E
N. C.—Belmont
Stowersville Cotton Mill
(Cotton) X
N. C.—Bynums
Odell Mfg. Co. J. M. (Cotton). ....B
N. C.—Chapel Hill
Lloyd, Thos. F. (Cotton), B
N. C.—Charlotte
Atherton Mills (Cotton)..A
Charlotte Cotton Mills (Cotton) ....A
Cleveland Mills
Cleveland Cotton Mills
(Carpet) ....B
N. C.—Concord
Cannon Mfg. Co. (Cotton)
AA
N. C.—Dallas
Dallas Cotton Mills (Cotton)
B
N. C.—Double Shoal
Double Shoal Cotton Mills
(Cotton) ....D
N. C.—Franklinton
Sterling Cotton Mills (Cotton ....A
N. C.—Franklinville
Franklinville Mfg. Co. (Cotton) ....B
N. C.—Gastonia
Avon Mills (Cotton) ......A
N. C.—Granite Falls
Granite Falls Mfg. Co.
(Coton; Carpet) ....B
N. C.—Hillsboro
Eno Cotton Mills (Cotton) B
N. C.—Jamestown
Oakdale Cotton Mills (Inc.)
(Cotton) ....A
N. C.—Lawndale
Dickson Cotton Mill (Cotton)
B
N. C.—Lincolnton
Elm Grove Cotton Mills
(Cotton) ....B
Laboratory Cotton Mills
(Cotton) ....A

WARPS (Con.)

N. C.—Lowell
Lowell Cotton Mills (Cotton)
B
N. C.—McAdensville
McAden Mills (Cotton) ..AA
N. C.—Meriden
Providence Cotton Mills
(Cotton) ....B
Union Cotton Mills (Cotton)
B
N. C.—Mount Holly
Tuckaseege Mfg. Co. (Cotton) ....A
N. C.—Paterson
Gwyn-Harper Mfg. Co. (Carpet; Cotton) ....B
N. C.—Rockingham
Pee Dee Mfg. Co. (Cotton)
A
Roberdel Mfg. Co. (Cotton)
A
N. C.—Rockymount
Rockymount Mills (Cotton)
AA
N. C.—Salem
Arista Mills (Cotton) ...AA
N. C.—Salisbury
Vance Cotton Mills (Cotton)
B
N. C.—Wilson
Wilson Cotton Mills (Cotton) ....B
PA.—Philadelphia
Saffarlen & Co., Jos. A.
(Rag Carpet) ....B
R. I.—North Kingston
Rodman Mfg. Co. (White;
Colored Cotton) ....AAA
R. I.—Pawtucket
Greene & Daniels Mfg. Co.
(Cotton) ....AA
Jenkes Spinning Co.. ..AAA
Slater Cotton Co. (Cotton)
AA
R. I.—Woonsocket
Ray Cotton Co. (Cotton) ..X
S. C.—Orangeburg
Cornelson, Geo. H. (Cotton
Carpet) ....A
S. C.—Pelham
Pelham Mills (Cotton) ...A
TENN.—Englewood
Brient Bros. (Carpet) ....B
TENN.—Lawrenceburg
Dustin, W. H. (Carpet) ..D
TENN.—Nashville
Nashville Woolen Mill Co.
(Carpet) ....A
Tennessee Mfg. Co. (Carpet)
X
TENN.—Paris
Currier & Co., John T. (Carpet) X
TENN.—Rockford
Rockford Cotton Mills (Carpet) ....G

WASH

ILL.—Chicago
Stuart & Co., D. A. (Inc.)
(Cattle) C
N. J.—Jersey City
Dixon Crucible Co., Jos.
(Core) ....AAA
New York City
Caswell, Massey & Co.
(Mouth) X
Colgate & Co. (Mouth) AAA
OHIO—Cincinnati
Obermayer Co., S. (Core)
AA
OHIO—Cleveland
Smith Fdry. & Supply Co.,
J. D. (Founders') ......D
PA.—Philadelphia
Johnson & Lund (Mouth) AA
Paxson Co., J. W. (Core)
AA
White Dental Mfg. Co. S. S.
(Mouth) ....AAAA

WASHBOARDS

See also Woodenware

IND.—Easton
Standard Washboard Co. ..C

WASHBOARDS (Con.)
IND.—Fort Wayne
Bowser Co., S. F. ....B
MICH.—Saginaw
Saginaw Mfg. Co. ......AA
MINN.—Minneapolis
Lloyd Mfg. Co. ....A
MO.—St. Louis
Mississippi Glass Co....AA
New York City
Mace & Co., L. H. ......B
OHIO—Cleveland
American Washboard Co.,
1747 E. Mad. ....AA
Lapham, Owen T. ....B
OHIO—Salem
Clark Co., W. J. ....A
OHIO—Toledo
Union Mfg. Co. X
TEXAS—Farmersville
Farmersville Mfg. Co. ....B

WASHERS

**See also Burrs; Machinery;
Hardware; Carriage**

CAL.—San Francisco
Payne's Bolt Works (Cast
Iron; Wrought Iron;
Steel) ....A
Selby Smelting & Lead Co.
(Lead) ....AAA
CONN.—Bridgeport
Bridgeport Brass Company
(Brass; Copper) ....AA
Canfield, H. O. (Rubber)
D
Gaynor & Mitchell Mfg. Co.
(Brass; Copper) ......D
CONN.—Bristol
Sessions & Son, J. H.
(Wrought) ....AAA
CONN.—Derby
Birmingham Iron Foundry
(Cloth) ....A
Shelton Co. (Wrought)..A
CONN.—Hartford
Hartford Rubber Works Co.
(Rubber) ....AAAA
CONN.—Middletown
Douglas, W. & B. (Street)
A
Wilcox, Crittenden & Co.
(Iron; Steel) ....A
CONN.—Milldale
Clark Bros. & Co. (Iron;
Steel; Wrought) ......A
CONN.—Mt. Carmel
Mt. Carmel Bolt Co. (Iron;
Steel) ....B
CONN.—New Britain
Corbin, P. & F. (Iron;
Steel) ....AAAA
Stanley Works (Wrought;
Steel; Brass) ....AAA
CONN.—New Haven
Cowles & Co., C. (Iron)..A
Peck Bros. & Co. (Bottle)
A
Reynolds & Co. (Brass;
Copper; Iron; Steel)..B
CONN.—Plainville
Clark & Cowles (Iron;
Steel). ....B
CONN.—Southington
Aetna Nut. Co. (Iron;
Steel) ....A
CONN.—Unionville ..
Humphrey, H. W. (Brass;
Iron; Steel; Tin)......E
Union Nut & Bolt Co.
(Iron; Steel) ....A
Upson Nut Co. (Brass;
Copper; Iron; Steel;
Cast; Wrought) ....AAA
CONN.—Waterbury
Benedict & Burnham Mfg.
Co. (Brass; Copper)
AAAA
Plume & Atwood Mfg. Co.
(Brass; Copper) ..AAA
Steel & Johnson Mfg. Co.
(Brass; Copper) ......A
Waterbury Brass Co.
(Brass; Copper) ..AAA
CONN.—Winsted
Moore, Franklin Co. (Iron;
Steel) .. ..A
Richards Hardware Co., T
C. (Iron; Steel) ......A
DEL.—Wilmington
American Vulcanized Fibre

WASHERS (Con.)
Co. (Fibre; Axle; Insu-
lating) ....AAAA
Delaware Hard Fibre Co.
(Fibre; Axle; Insulating)
B
Diamond State Steel Co.
(Cast Iron; Fibre; Insu-
lating; Iron; Steel).AAA
Wilmington Malleable Iron
Co. (Malleable Iron)..A
ILL.—Chicago
Chicago Rawhide Mfg. Co.
(Carriage Axle) ......A
Continental Bolt & Iron
Wks., 22d & Union (Iron;
Steel) ....B
Gates Iron Wks. (Ore)
AAAA
Goodsell Packing Co.. 33
So. Canal (Leather)..B
Grand Crossing Tack Co.
(Wrought) ....A
Illinois Malleable Iron Co.
(Street) ....AAAA
King & Andrews Co.. 37
N. State (Cast Iron)..A
Morgan & Wright, 331 W.
Lake (Rubber) ....AA
Republic Iron & Steel Co.,
Stock Exch. Bldg. (Iron;
Steel; Cast; Wrought)
AAAA
Sills Mica Co., W. H.. 64
Michigan (Insulating).X
ILL.—Freeport
Stover Mfg. Co. (Cast Iron;
Steel) ....A
ILL.—Rockford
Sovereign Co., C. E.
(Leather) C
ILL.—Sterling
Lawrence Bros. (Wrought)
AA
IND.—Kendallville
Flint & Walling Mfg. Co.
(Street) ....AA
IND.—Madison
Tower Mfg. Co. (Basket)
C
IND.—Wabash
Launder, Harter & Harsh
Mfg. Co. (Leather Axle)
C
KANS.—Wichita
Wichita Mfg. Co. (Cast
Iron) C
MAINE—Kennebunk
Leatheroid Mfg. Co.
(Fibre; Insulating)....A
MD.—Baltimore
Bartlett, Hayward & Co.
(Gas House) ......AAA
Dietrich Bros., 344 North
(Iron; Steel) ....E
Levering Bros. (Cast)..C
National Supply Co., 7 W.
Lombard (Iron; Steel)..B
Ryan-McDonald Mfg. Co.,
44 South (Cast Iron)..A
MASS.—Boston
Bay State Axle Washer Co.
(Leather Axle) X
Boston Belting Co. (Air
Brake; Rubber; Hose)
AAAA
Boston Belt Co., 33 Pur-
chase (Cast Iron; Steel)
B
Empire Laundry Machinery
Co. (Hand; Clothes)..E
Marston & Co., I. G.
(Leather; Carriage Axle;
Rubber) ....D
New England Bolt & Nut
Co., 253 Atlantic Av.
(Iron; Steel) C
Revere Rubber Co.. 63
Franklin (Rubber) AAAA
Stoddard, Haserick. Rich-
ards & Co., 152 Congress
(Wool) ....AAA
MASS.—Lowell
American Bolt Co. (Iron;
Steel) ....B
MASS.—Lynn
Hoyt Bros. & Co. (Bottle)
A
MASS.—North Adams
Hunter Machine Co., Jas.
(Cloth; Wool) ....A
MASS.—Orange
Hunt, Rodney Machine Co.

WASHERS (Con.)
(Cloth) ....A
MASS.—Plymouth
Cobb & Drew (Iron; Steel;
Wrought) ....AA
Plymouth Mills (Small
Iron; Steel) ....B
MASS.—Somerville
Birch Bros. (Cloth) ....D
MASS.—Springfield
Springfield Machine Screw
Co (Nickel Plated)....D
MASS.—Taunton
Taunton Rivet Co. (Steel)
E
MASS.—Westfield
American Whip Co.
(Leather Axle) ...AAA
Planet Mfg. Co. (Spiral
Leather Axle) ....D
MASS.—Westford
Sargent's Sons, C. G.
(Wool) ....A
MASS.—Worcester
Reed & Prince Mfg. Co.
(Iron; Steel) ....B
Smith & Co., Thomas
(Iron; Steel) ....D
Wilson & Smith, 40 Vine
(Brass; Cast Iron; Cop-
per; Wrought; Lead)..D
MICH.—Battle Creek
Sherman Mfg. Co., H. B.
(Leather) ....B
MICH.—Detroit
Detroit Leather Specialty
Co., 271 Beecher Av.
(Leather) ....E
Michigan Bolt & Nut Wks.
(Iron; Steel) ....A
MICH.—Jackson
McKeel & Co., Geo. A.
B
MO.—Kansas City
Kansas City Bolt & Nut
Co. (Iron; Steel) ....A
MO.—St. Louis
Hager & Sons Mfg. Co.,
2427 De Kalb (Iron;
Steel) ....A
Kupferle, Jno. C., 2d &
Mound (Cast Iron) ....A
Moran Bolt & Nut Mfg. Co.
(Cast Iron; Steel) ....A
Nelson Mfg. Co., N. O.
(Street) ....AAA
Pleuger & Henger Mfg.
Co., Hebert & 11th (Cast
Iron; Street; Hydrant)
A
St. Louis Malleable Cast-
ings Co. (Malleable Iron;
Cast) ....A
Western Foundry & Sash
Weight Co., 2d & Miller
(Cast Iron) ....D
N. H.—Concord
Page Belting Co. (Leath-
er, all kinds) ....A
N. J.—Bound Brook
Graphite Lubricating Co.
(Insulating) ....A
N. J.—Jersey City
Maslin & Son, J. (Bottle)
D
New Jersey Car Spring &
Rubber Co. (Air Brake;
Rubber) ....AA
Voorhees Rubber Mfg. Co.,
18 Bostwick Av. (Rub-
ber) ....A
N. J.—Milltown
International Automobile
& Vehicle Tire Co. (Rub-
ber) ....B
N. J.—Newark
Bell, Andrew, 371 Market
(Leather) ....G
Jenkinson & Co., R. C.
(Wrought) ....A
National Lock Washer Co.,
65 Johnson (Lock) ....A
Newark Leather Washer
Mfg. Co. (Leather)....E
N. J.—Paterson
Watson Machine Co.
(Cloth; Wool) ....A
N. J.—Raritan
Kenyon & Son, D. R.
(Cloth; Wool) ....A
N. J.—Trenton
Consolidated Rubber Co.
(Rubber) ....B
Crescent Belting & Pack-

WASHERS (Con.)
ing Co. (Rubber) ....A
Empire Rubber Mfg. Co.
(Rubber) ....A
Hamilton Rubber Co. (Rub-
ber) ....A
Home Rubber Co. (Hose;
Rubber; Glass).......AA
Stokes Rubber Co., Jos.
(Rubber) ....A
Trenton Rubber Mfg. Co.
(Rubber; Hose) ......A
United & Globe Rubber
Mfg. Co. (Rubber)..AAA
Whitehead Bros. Rubber
Co. (Rubber) ....A
N. Y.—Auburn
Leather & Brass Mfg. Co.
(Leather; Asbestos; Felt
Paper; Bicycle Felt; Rub-
ber) ....E
Meyer & Co. (Iron; Steel)
B
N. Y.—Buffalo
Hoffeld & Co., R. (Car-
riage Axle) ....AA
McKinnon Dash Co. (Leath-
er Prop Block) .....AA
Squier Mfg. Co., George L.
(Coffee) ....A
N. Y.—Clifton Springs
Judd & Leland Mfg. Co.
(Leather) C
N. Y.—Manlius
Cheney & Son, S (Cast
Iron) ....A
New York City
Brass Goods Mfg. Co., 7
Warren (Brass; Copper)
B
Brooks & Co., E. J. (Lead)
B
Cahn & Co., Hugo (Cork)
A
Floyd's Sons, James R.
(Gas House) ....A
Glauber, Samuel S., 1395
3d Av. (Leather) .....E
Glauber & Co., M. 317 E.
58th (Leather) ......B
Goodyear Rubber Co., 787
B'way (Rubber)..AAAA
Grenlie, Wyatt & Co., 499
Water (Iron; Steel) ...B
Gutta Percha Rubber &
Mfg. Co., 126 Duane
(Rubber; Hose)...AAAA
Hall's Sons, Sam'l, 229 W.
10th (Iron; Steel).....A
Haydenville Mfg. Co.
(Street) ....A
Hungerford Brass & Cop-
per Co., U. T. (Mfrs.
Agts.) (Brass; Copper)
A
Jenkins Bros., 71 John
(Leather; Wrought)..AA
Johns-Manville Co., H. W.,
100 William (Insulating)
AAAA
Manhattan Rubber Mfg.
Co., 126 Duane (Rubber)
AA
Metal Stamping Co. (Car-
riage Axle) ....B
Mica Insulator Co., 218
Water (Insulating)....B
New York Belting & Pack-
ing Co. (Ltd.) 25 Park
Place (Rubber) ....AAA
New York Rubber Co.
(Rubber) ....AA
New York Washer Wks.
78 Barrow (Leather)...D
Ogden & Co., C. S., 674 E.
159th (Leather) ......D
Sargent & Co., 151 Leonard
(Wrought) ....AAAA
Schoonmaker, Adrain O.,
221 Fulton (Insulating)
D
Union Nut & Bolt Co., 107
Chambers (Wrought
Iron) ....A
Witteman Bros. (Bottle)
A
N. Y.—Portchester
Russell, Burdsall & Ward
Bolt & Nut Co. (Iron;
Steel) ....AAAA
N. Y.—Rochester
Yawman & Erbe Mfg. Co.
(Bottle; Tumbler)....AA

WASHERS (Con.)

N. Y.—Rome
Rome Brass & Copper Co.
(Brass; Copper) ..AAAA

N. Y.—Schenectady
General Electric Co. (Insulating) ....AAAA

N. Y.—Seneca Falls
Climax Specialty Co.
(Leather) ....B
Rumsey & Co. (Ltd.)
(Street) ....AAAA

N. Y.—Syracuse
Kendrick Valve & Washer
Co. (Leather) C
New Process Raw Hide Co.
(Leather; Rawhide)...C

N. Y.—Troy
Ludlow Valve Mfg. Co.
(Street) ....AAA
Troy Laundry Machine Co.
(Ltd.) (Hand; Clothes)
AA
Troy Stamping Wks. (Tin
Roofing) ....AAAA

N. C.—Charlotte
Mecklenburg Iron Wks.
(Ore) X

N. C.—Winston-Salem
Salem Iron Wks. (Coffee)
B

OHIO—Akron
Goodrich Co., B. F. (Rubber) ....AAAA
Whitman & Barnes Mfg.
Co. (Rubber) ....AAAA

OHIO—Canton
Whiteman Mfg. Co. (Tumbler) C

OHIO—Cincinnati
Blymer Iron Wks. Co.
(Coffee) ....D
Cincinnati Screw & Tap
Co., 2442 Beekman (Iron;
Steel; Wrought) .....B
Day & Co., J. H. (Bottle)
C
Evans Steel & Iron Co., C.
W., 22 W. 2d (Iron; Steel)
B
Littleford Bros. 453 E.
Pearl (Lead) ....D
Monarch Carriage Goods
Co. (Carriage; Prop
Block) ....B
Murdock & Co., J. G., 428
Plum (Street; Hydraut)
A
Norwood Machine & Mfg.
Co., 67 Plum (Finished
Steel) ....A
Robertson Steel & Iron Co.,
Front (Iron; Steel)....A
Van John Range Co.
(Steam Dish) ....A

OHIO—Cleveland
Avery Stamping Co.
(Wrought Steel; Iron;
Steel) ....A
Bettcher Mfg. Co. (Iron;
Steel) ....D
Browne & Knowles Mfg.
Co., 68 Main (Iron;
Steel) ....A
Chicholm Steel Shovel Wks.
(Steel) ....AAA
Lake Erie Iron Co., 155
St. Clair (Iron; Steel)
AAAA
Mechanical Rubber Co.
(Rubber) ....AAAA
Osborn Mfg. Co. (Railroad
Car) ....A
Topliff Mfg. Co., I. N.
(Steel) ....AA

OHIO—Columbiana
Columbiana Pump & Machine Co. (Street).....C

OHIO—Columbus
Columbus Bolt Wks. (Iron;
Steel) ....A
Lanman Co., E. B.
(Wrought Iron; Steel).X
Ohio Pump & Brass Co.,
18th & Oak (Nickel; Slab
Closet; &c. Plumber's).B

OHIO—Coshocton
Keagy & Lear Machine Co.
(Cast Iron) C

OHIO—Dayton
City Forge & Iron Wks.
(Malleable Iron) ......D

WASHERS (Con.)

OHIO—Mansfield
Barnes Mfg. Co. (Leather)
B

OHIO—Salem
Clark Co., W. J. (Iron;
Steel; Wrought; Leather)
B
Deming Co. (Street) ....A

OHIO—Youngstown
Republic Rubber Co. (Rubber) ....AA

PA.—Allegheny
Graham Nut Co., 755 Rebecca (Iron; Steel) ...C
McKinney Mfg. Co. (Steel;
Wrought) ....AA

PA.—Columbia
Wilson Laundry Machinery
Co. (Hand; Clothes) ..B

PA.—Corry
Raymond Mfg. Co. (Leather; Wire) C
Whittlesey & Sons. H. E.
(Leather) C

PA.—Erie
Continental Rubber Wks.
(Rubber) ....A
Griffin Mfg. Co. (Wrought
Iron; Steel) ....A
Lovell Mfg. Co. (Ltd.)
(Hand; Clothes) ....AA

PA.—Lancaster
Armstrong Cork Co. (Cork)
AAAA
Penn. Iron Co. (Car, &c.;
Iron; Steel) ....A

PA.—Lebanon
American Iron & Steel Mfg.
Co. (Brass; Cast Iron
Steel; Copper; Wrought)
AAAA

PA.—Mechanicsburg
Comstock, Geo. S. (Ore),D

PA.—Millersburg
Millersburg Fifth Wheel
Co. (Wrought) ....B

PA.—Milton
Milton Mfg. Co. (Iron;
Steel) ....A

PA.—New Castle
New Castle Forge & Bolt
Co. (Wrought Iron;
Steel) ....A

PA.—Philadelphia
Allison Mfg. Co., 32d &
Chestnut (Iron; Steel)
AAAA
Bancroft & Co., Drexel
Bldg. (Cast) X
Hoopes & Townsend Co.,
1330 Buttonwood (Cast
Iron; Steel) ....AAA
Houghton & Co., E. F. 240
W. Somerset (Leather).B
Nicetown Plate Washer Co.
(Brass; Lead; Wrought)
B
Phosphor Bronze Smelting
Co., 2200 Washington Av.
(Phosphor Bronze) ....A
Smith Woolen Machinery
Co., James, 411 Race
(Wool) ....A
Twitchell Co., S. (Bottle)
A

PA.—Phoenixville
Logan Mfg. Co. (Cast)...B

PA.—Pittsburg
American Steel Hoop Co.
(Wrought) ....AAAA
Baker Mfg. Co., Jas. H.
Park Av. (Steel) ......A
Hubbard & Co., Murtland
Bldg. (Iron; Steel)....A
Lanz & Sons, Mathew, 101
So. 29th (Square; Round;
Iron; Steel Cast;
Wrought) ....B
Marland Neely & Co. (Ltd.)
So. 22d & P. R. R. (Iron;
Steel) ....A
Oliver Iron & Steel Co.
(Iron; Steel) .....AAAA
Pittsburg Mfg. Co., 28th &
Railroad (Iron) ......A
Pittsburg Screw & Bolt
Co., Liberty Av. & 25th
(Iron; Steel) ....B
Westinghouse Electric Mfg.
Co. (Insulating)..AAAA

PA.—Scranton
Scranton Bolt & Nut Co.

WASHERS (Con.)
(Iron; Steel) ....A
PA.—So. Bethlehem
Bethlehem Foundry & Machine Co. (Cast) C
PA.—West Chester
Rapp, Barnet R. (Milk Can) ....H
PA.—Williamsport
Darling Pump & Mfg. Co. (Leather) ....B
R. I.—Bridgeton
Hopkins Machine Wks. (Cloth) C
R. I.—Bristol
National India Rubber Co. (Insulating) ....AAA
R. I.—East Providence
Eastern Bolt & Nut Co. (Cast; Wrought) .....A
R. I.—Pawtucket
Haskell Mfg. Co., Wm. H. (Brass; Cast Iron; Steel; Copper; Wrought) .....A
Pawtucket Mfg. Co. (Iron; Steel) ....A
R. I.—Providence
Rhode Island Tool Co. (Brass; Copper) ....AAA
Textile Finishing Machinery Co., 17 Exch. Place (Cloth; Warp; Yarn) AAAA
TENN.—So. Pittsburg
Blacklock Foundry (Cast) D
VA.—Richmond
Old Dominion Iron & Nail Wks. Co. (Iron; Steel) A
W. VA.—Wheeling
Wheeling Corrugating Co. (Lead) ....A
Wheeling Hinge Co. (Iron; Steel) ....AA
WIS.—Milwaukee
Allis-Chalmers Co. (Ore) AAAA
Vilter Mfg. Co. (Milk Bottle) ....AA
Wrought Washer Mfg. Co. (Iron; Steel) ....A
WIS.—Racine
Racine Jewelry Mfg. Co. (Spectacle) X
Winship Mfg. Co. (Hand; Clothes) C

WASHSTANDS
See also Furniture

ILL.—Chicago
Adams & Westlake Co., Ontario, Cor. N. Franklin (Car) ....AAAA
ILL.—Rockford
Forest City Furniture Co. (Desk; Reservoir; Table) A
IND.—Fort Wayne
Indiana Furniture Co. (Desk; Reservoir) C
OHIO—Hamilton
Meyers Mfg. Co., Fred J. (Reservoir) ....B

WASHTUBS
See also Tubs; Woodenware

WASTE
CONN.—Hazardville
Gordon Bros. Co. (Wool; Cotton) ....A
GA.—Augusta
Riverside Mills (Cotton; Wool; Spinning; Batting) AA
GA.—Marietta
Mariette Paper Mills (Cotton) ....A
ILL.—Chicago
Carpenter & Co., Geo. B., 1 5th Av. (Cotton)...AA
Gallagher Mfg. Co., J. D. (Cotton) C
MD.—Baltimore
Baltimore Waste Co. (Cotton; Woolen) ....A

WASTE (Con.)
MASS.—Boston
Bishop, Robt. (Est. of.) (Nat. Carpet Lining Co.) 175 W. 6th (Cotton Packing; Wiping) ....A
MASS.—Chicopee
Olmstead & Tuttle Co. (Cotton) ....A
MASS.—Fall River
Estes & Son, John H. (Cotton) ....A
Massasoit Mfg. Co. (Cotton) ....A
MASS.—Lowell
Lowell Waste Co. .....B
MASS.—Springfield
Lillie & Co., Dexter P. (Cotton) ....A
Springfield Waste Co. (Cotton) ....B
MO.—St. Louis
Broderick & Bascom Rope Co. (Cotton) ....AA
Leschen & Sons Rope Co. (Cotton) ....AA
N. Y.—Cohoes
United Waste Mfg. Co. (Cotton) ....B
N. Y.—Utica
Allison & Co., G. F. (Machine Wiping) ....B
OHIO—Cincinnati
Railway Supply & Mfg. Co. (Cotton; Wool) ......B
OHIO—Cleveland
Nat. Woolen Co. (Wool) AA
PA.—Philadelphia
Blakeley & Son, Jno. (Cotton; Wool) ....B
Dixon & Son, Wm. F. (Cotton; Woolen) C
Hall & Co. (Cotton; Woolen) ....B
Johnson, Wm. J. (Wool)..B
Sykes, David (Cotton; Wool) ....B
Wallace & Bro., Jno. H. (Fine Garnetted).....B
R. I.—Pawtucket
Briggs & Co., H. A. (Cotton) ....A
Union Wadding Co...AAAA
TENN.—Memphis
Livermore Fdry & Machine Co. (Cotton; Wool) ...A

WATCHES
CONN.—New Haven
New Haven Clock (Complete) ....AAA
CONN.—Thomaston
Thomas Clock Co., Seth. (Movements only) ..AAA
CONN.—Waterbury
New England Watch Co. (Mfrs. Complete) ..AAA
ILL.—Chicago
Schwab, Adolph, 131 Wabash Av. (Importer) ....A
Western Watch Case Mfg. Co., 103 State (Gold Cases only) C
ILL.—Elgin
Elgin National Watch Co. (Movements only) AAAA
Illinois Watch Case Co. (Cases only) ....AA
Star Watch Case Co. (Cases only) ....D
ILL.—Rockford
Rockford Watch Co. (Movements only) ....A
ILL.—Springfield
Illinois Watch Co. (Movements only) ....A
IND.—South Bend
South Bend Watch Co. (Movements only) ....AA
KY.—Dayton
Wadsworth Watch Case Co. (Filled Cases only) ....A
MASS.—Boston
Howard Watch & Clock Co., E. ....A
Margot, Eugene F., 3265 Washington (Gold Cases) E
MASS.—Waltham
American Waltham Watch

WATCHES (Con.)
Co. (Movements only)
..................AAAA
United States Watch Co.
(Movements only) ....AA
N. J.—Jersey City
International Watch Co.
(Complete) ....AAA
New York Standard Watch
Co. (Complete) ....AAA
N. J.—Riverside
Philadelphia Watch Case Co.
(Cases only) ....A
N. J.—Trenton
Trenton Watch Co. (Manu-
facturers; Complete) ..B
N. Y.—New York City
Alexander, Adolph, 12 John
(Importer) ....B
Ansonia Clock Co., 99 John
(Complete) ....AAAA
Bachrach, A. M., 51 Maiden
Lane (Cases only) C
Brooklyn Watch Case Co.,
(Joseph Fahys & Co.,
Props.) ....AAA
Courvoisier, Wilcox Mfg.
Co., 21 Maiden Lane
(Gold; Filled Cases only)
..................AA
Crescent Watch Case Co., 21
Maiden Lane (Filled; Sil-
ver Cases only).....AAA
Cross & Begueleu, 17 Maiden
Lane (Importers) .....AA
Didisheim & Bros., Hipp,
54 Maiden Lane (Import-
ers) ....A
Doll Mfg. Co., W. F. (Sou-
venir) ....D
Dubois Watch Case Co.,
21 Maiden Lane (Gold
Cases only) ....A
Fahys & Co., Jos., 54 Maid-
en Lane (Gold Cases only)
..................AAA
Hirsh, Leon, 37 Maiden
Lane (Importer) ......A
Ingersoll & Bros., R. H., 51
Maiden Lane (Mfs.; Com-
plete) ....AA
Keller & Untermeyer Mfg.
Co. ....AA
Levy, Manesseh & Co., 182
B'way (Importer) .....B
Mathey Bros., Mathez & Co.,
21 Maiden Lane (Import-
ers) ....B
Patek, Phillippe & Co., 68
Nassau (Importers) ....B
Racine & Co., Jules, 37
Maiden Lane (Importers)
....................B
Robert, Edmund E., 3 Maid-
en Lane (Importer) ....B
Roy Watch Case Co., 21
Maiden Lane (Gold Cases
only) C
Solidarity Watch Case Co.,
3 Maiden Lane (Gold Cases
only) ....B
Strassburger & Co., Byron
L., 17 Maiden Lane (Im-
porter) ....B
Wittnauer Co., Alb., 9
Maiden Lane (Importer)
....................AA
OHIO.—Canton
Dueber Watch Case Mfg. Co.
(Gold; Silver; Filled Cases
only) ....AAAA
Hampden Watch Co. (Move-
ments only) ....AA
OHIO.—Cincinnati
Gruen, Sons & Co., D. (Im-
porters) .... B
OHIO.—Cleveland
Ball Watch Co., Webb. C.
(Movements only) .....A
OHIO.—Mansfield
North American Watch Co.
(Cases only) ....A
PA.—Lancaster
Hamilton Watch Co. (Move-
ments only) ....AA
PA.—Philadelphia
Keystone Watch Case Co.
(Gold Filled; Silver Cases
only) ....AAAA
Riggs & Bro., 310 Market
....................B

WATER

ILL.—Quincy

WATER (Con.)
Flynn & Co., J. J. (Soda)
....................A
N. H.—Nashua
Londonderry Lithia Spring
Water Co. (Mineral) ..A
N. Y.—Ballston Spa
Artesian Lithia Spring Co.
(Table) ....D
N. Y.—New York City
Bear Lithia Springs Co.
(Mineral) ....D
Bolen & Byrne Mfg. Co.
(Mineral, Soda) X
Cooper & Co., Charles (Dis-
tilled) ....AA
Hygeia Sparkling Distilled
Water Co. (Table) ....B
Lanman & Kemp (Florida)
..................AAA
Matthews, John (Firm of)
(Soda) ....AA
Rubino Healing Spring Co.
(Mineral) ....D
Schultz, Carl H. (Table;
Mineral) ....B
Spencer Optical Co. (Eye)
....................C
Wetmore Co., S. H. (Flori-
da) ....D
N. Y.—Saratoga Sprigs
Champion Natural Carbonic
Acid Gas Co. (Mineral).X
Excelsior Spring Co. (Min-
eral) ....B
Geyser Spring Co. (Mineral)
....................D
Hathorn & Co. (Mineral)..A
Patterson Mineral Spring
(Mineral) X
Saratoga Carlsbad Spring
Co. (Table Mineral)....X
Saratoga Vichy Spring Co.
(Table; Mineral) .....B
Saratoga Victoria Spring
(Table; Mineral) .....D
OHIO.—Cincinnati
Arctic Ice Co. (Distilled)
....................B
TEXAS—El Paso
Houck & Dieter Co. (Soda)
....................A
VA.—Buffalo Lithia Springs
Goode, Thos. F. (Table)
..................AAA
WIS.—Milwaukee
Zwietusch, Otto (Soda) ...A
WIS.—Waukesha
Bethesda Mineral Spring Co.
(Mineral) ....A

WATERERS

ILL.—Chicago
Chicago Wheel & Mfg. Co.
(Stock) C
ILL.—Freeport
Stover Mfg. Co. (Stock)
..................AA
IOWA—Des Moines
Carter Windmill & Tank Co.
(Hog) ....F
N. Y.—New York City
Koven & Bro., L. O., 50
Cliff (Stock) ....A
OHIO—Dayton
Central Basket Wks. (Hog)
....................G

WATTMETERS

See also Meters

CONN.—Waterbury
Bristol Co. (Recording) ..D
ILL.—Chicago
Electric Appliance Co., 94
W. Van Buren (Interogat-
ing Alternating Current)
....................B
ILL.—Peoria
Diamond Meter Co. (Re-
cording) C
ILL.—Springfield
Sangamo Electric Co. (Al-
ternating Current) .....D
IND.—Fort Wayne
Fort Wayne Electric Works
(Alternating Current)
..................AAA
IND.—Lafayette
Duncan Electric Mfg. Co...B
MASS.—Great Barrington
Stanley Instrument Co. (Al-
ternating Current) ....AA

WATTMETERS (Con.)

MO.—St. Louis
Wagner Electric Mfg. Co., 2015 Locust ....AA

N. H.—Penacook
Whitney Electrical Instrument Co. ....D

N. J.—Waverly Park
Weston Electrical Instrument Co. ....A

N. Y.—New York City
Empire Electrical Instrument Co., 656 Hudson..E
General Inc. Arc. Light Co., 570 1st Av. ....A

N. Y.—Schenectady
General Electric Co. (Prepayment Recording)
.................AAAA

OHIO—Akron
Akron Electrical Mfg. Co. (Recording) ....D

PA.—Philadelphia
Keystone Electrical Instrument Co., 9th & Montgomery ....B

PA.—Pittsburg
Westinghouse Electrical Mfg. Co. (Alternating)
.................AAAA

WAX

See also Paraffine

CAL.—Hueneme
Levy, A. (Bees) ....A

CAL.—San Diego
Levi, Simon (Bees) ......B

CAL.—San Francisco
Guggenhime & Co., 118 Davis (Bees) ....A
Rosenberg Bros. & Co., 211 Calif. (Bees) ....A

ILL.—Chicago
Clark, F. C. (Paraffine)
.................D
Dennison Mfg. Co. (Sealing)
.................AAAA
Devoe & Raynolds Co., 176 Randolph (Floor) ..AAAA
Redlich Mfg. Co. (Sealing)
.................E
Sanford Mfg. Co. Sealing)
.................A

IND.—Columbia City
Pontius, Geo. A. (Sealing)
.................D

MASS.—Boston
Baker & Co., Charles F. (Burnishing) ....A
Bowdlear & Co., W. H. (Bees; Bleached; Sheet; White Sealing) ....B
Wiley Waxene Co., 92 Sudbury (Floor; Bayberry)
.................E

N. J.—Newark
Dovell Son Mfg. Co., R. B. (Sealing) ....D
Pomeroy Co., I. (Sealing)
.................F

N. J.—Rahway
Harrison Mfg. Co. (Sealing)
.................F

N. Y.—Albany
Holt Co., Jared (Leather) .E

N. Y.—Brooklyn
Wiarda & Co., John C. (Bees; White) ......AA

N. Y.—New York City
Brunn, A. W., 2 Stone (Ceresine; Carnauba) X
Columbia Wax Works, 85 Crosby (Bees) ....D
Cooper & Co., Charles (Bees; Bleached) ....AA
Davids Co., Thaddeus (Sealing) C
Dennison Mfg. Co. Sealing)
.................AAAA
Fuerst Bros. & Co., 2 Stone (Bees) ....B
Israel & Bro., 490 Canal (Bees) ....A
Loeb & Co., Herman (Paraffine) ....B
Marx & Rawalle Sealing)
.................AA
Miller Co., Frank (Shoemakers') ....A
Natl. Gum & Mica Co. ..A
Reed & Hewlett (Bees) ..B
Soloman & Bro., 216 Pearl (Bees) ....AA

WAX (Con.)

Smith & Nichols (Bees; Bleached; White; Parraffine) ....A
Standard Oil Co. (Paraffine)
.................AAA
Strohmeyer & Arpe Co. (Bees) ....A
Tidewater Oil Co. (Paraffine) ....AAAA
Zinsser & Co., W. (Sealing)
.................A

N. Y.—Syracuse
Will & Baumer Co. (Bees; Bleached; Ironing Thread; Sheet) ....AA

OHIO—Cincinnati
British-American Sealing Wax Co. (Sealing) ...D
Moore Oil Co., Chas. H. (Paraffine) ....A
Muth Co., F. W., Front & Walnut (Bees) ....D
Obermayer Co., S. (Bees)
.................AA
Wells & Co., S., 211 Vine (Bees) ....A

OHIO—Circleville
Circleville Sealing Wax Co. (Sealing) ....D

OHIO—Cleveland
Monitor Oil Co. (Paraffine)
.................C
Standard Oil Co. (Paraffine)
.................AAAA

OHIO—Dayton
Dicks & Wiggim (Sealing)
.................C

OHIO—Tarlton
Kelch, J. R. (Sealing) ...D

PA.—Allegheny
Chamberlin & Johnson (Bottle; Sealing) ....D

PA.—Chester
Manufacturers' Paraffine Co. (Paraffine) ....B

PA.—Easton
Baker & Adamson Chemical Co. (Paraffine) .....A

PA.—Freedom
Freedom Oil Works Co. (Paraffine) ....A

PA.—Petrolia
Petrolia Ref'g. Co. (Paraffine) ....H

PA.—Philadelphia
Continental Mfg. Co. (Sealing) ....D
Crew-Levick Co. (Paraffine)
.................AAA
Dennison Mfg. Co. (Sealing)
.................AAAA
Stevenson Bros. & Co. (Sealing) ....B

PA.—Pittsburg
Waverly Oil Wrks. (Paraffine) ....AA

PA.— Titusville
Penna. Paraffine Works (Paraffine) ....B

TENN.—McMinnville
Mead & Ritchey (Bees) ..D

WEANERS

CON.—New Britain
Landers, Frary & Clark (Calf.) ....AAA

ILL.—Chicago
Barbee Wire & Iron Works (Calf.) ....B
Pratt Mfg. Co., Wm. E., 91 Lake (Calf.) C

MASS.—Worcester
Hamblin & Russell Mfg. Co. (Wire Calf.) ....B

WEATHER-BOARDING

MO.—St. Louis
Harry Steel Works, O. K. (Steel) ....B

N. Y.—New York City
Wheeling Corrugating Co. (Iron) ....AAAA

TENN.—Loudon
Ward, A. W. ....D

WEBBING

CONN.—Ansonia
Ansonia O. & C. Co. (Cotton

WEBBING (Con.)
Elastic; Non-Elastic) ..A
CONN.—Bridgeport
Connecticut Web Co. (Cotton Suspender; Garter)..A
CONN.—Hamden
New Haven Web Co. (Cotton Suspender; Garter).A
CONN.—Middletown
Russell Mfg. Co. (Cotton Elastic Boot and Shoe)
AAA
CONN.—Waterbury
American Mills Co. (Elastic; Non-Elastic Boot & Shoe)
A
MD.—Baltimore
United States Cotton Duck Corp., Cont. Trust Bldg. (Black Band; &c.) X
MASS.—Boston
Boston Excelsior Co. (Furniture) ....A
Franklin Rubber Co. (Elastic) ....B
Hub Gore Makers Boot; Shoe; Garter; Elastic)
A
Ludlow Mfg. Associates (Upholsters' Jute)
AAAA
Ziegler & Sons, A. (Elastic)
A
MASS.—Chelsea
Boston Gore & Webb Mfg. Co. (Boot; Shoe; Suspender) ....D
Chadbourne & Moore (Shoe; Gaiter; Elastic) ....A
Martin & Bro. Mfg. Co. (Elastic; Non-Elastic Boot; Shoe; Rein; Truss; Silk) ....A
MASS.—E. Braintree
Hub Gore Makers (Corsets; Bandage; Elastic) ....A
MASS.—Easthampton
Colton, Geo. S. (Elastic Garter; Surgical) ....B
Easthampton Elastic Webb Co. Elastic Garter) ....E
Easthampton Rubber Thread Co. (Elastic) ....A
Glendale Elastic Fabrics Co. (Elastic) ....A
Nashawannuck Mfg. Co. (Elastic) ....AA
MASS.—Hudson
Taylor & Sons, Thos. (Elastic) ....F
MASS.—Littleton
Conant, Houghton & Co. (Elastic) ....B
MASS.—Lowell
Harriman Mfg. Co., 175 Hale (Elastic Suspender)
B
Perkins & Johnson (Elastic; Non-Elastic) ....E
MASS.—Milford
Lapworth & Sons, Wm. (Narrow Elastic) ......B
MASS.—No. Abington
Woodward, A. C. (Boot; Shoe) ....D
MASS.—Shirley
Edgarton Mfg. Co., C. A. (Suspender) ....B
MASS.—Springfield
Hutchins Narrow Fabric Co. (Elastic; Cotton; Non-Elastic) C
Springfield Webbing Co. (Non-Elastic Boot and Shoe) ....A
MASS.—Worcester
Thayer Mfg. Co., L. D. ..C
N. Y.—Buffalo
Buffalo Weaving & Belting Co. (Cotton; Belt; Elastic; Belting Cloth; Razor Strap) ....A
N. Y.—Lockport
Empire Mfg. Co. ....B
New York City
Canfield Rubber Co. (Elastic) X
Hoffman-Corr Mfg. Co., 107 Duane (Cotton) ......AA
Marks, A. A. (Deformity; Appliance; Elastic; Non-Elastic) ....AA

WEBBING (Con.)
OHIO—Mansfield
Mansfield Elastic Webb Co. (Suspender) ....B
PA.—No. Wales
Russell Mfg. Co. (Elastic Non-Elastic) ....AAA
PA.—Philadelphia
Adamson & Co., Joseph (Elastic; Non-Elastic)..A
Bilger Nicholas (Cotton; Worsted; Linen; Jute; Non-Elastic) C
Loeb, Lipper & Co. (Non-Elastic) ....A
Sidebotham, Jno. ....A
Sullivan & Sons Mfg. Co., J. (Non-Elastic) .....AA
R. I.—Hamilton
Hamilton Web Co. (Elastic; Non-Elastic; Boot; Shoe; Worsted) ....A
R. I.—Nooseneck Hill
Hamilton Webb Co. (Boot; Shoe; &c.) ....A
R. I.—Pawtucket
Hope Webbing Co. ......AA
Kenyon Mfg. Co., John J. (Boot; Shoe) ....B
Smith Webbing Co. (Narrow Elastic; Non-Elastic)
C
R.I.—Providence
Fletcher Mfg. Co. Cotton)
AAA
Hope Mfg. Co. (Elastic; Non-Elastic; Cotton Belt; Boot; Shoe) ....AAA
R. I.—Richmond
Columbia Narrow Fabric Co. (Silk; Cotton Elastic; Non-Elastic) C

WEBS

CONN.—Ansonia
Ansonia Co., O. & C. (Loom)
AA
CONN.—Bridgeport
Connecticut Web Co. (Loom)
A
IND.—Indianapolis
Atkins & Co., E. C. (Butcher! Billet Saw; Felly Twining) ....AAAA
Barry Saw Co. (Chair; Felly; Turning Saw) C
MASS.—Fitchburg
Simonds Mfg. Co. (Turning Felloe) ....AAA
N. J.—Newark
National SawCo. (Butcher; Billet; Saw Chair; Felly; Futtock Twining Saw)
B
N. Y.—New York City
Jennings Co., C. E., 42 Murray (Turning Felloe) ..B
Millers Falls Co., 28 Warren (Felloe; Turning)
AA
PA.—Philadelphia
Disston & Sons, Henry (Futtock; Turning) ...AAAA

WEDGES

CAL.—San Francisco
Doble Co., Abner (Steel; Coal; Woodchoppers'; Stone) ....A
CONN.—Collinsville
Collins Co. (Steel; Coal; Woodchoppers) ....AAAA
CONN.—Mt. Carmel
Woodruff & Sons Co., Walter W. (Axe; Steel) ...A
CONN.—New Haven
Dann Bros. & Co. (Wooden)
B
CONN.—Noank
Palmer & Son Ship Bldg & Marine Ry. Co., Robert (Treenail) X
ILL.—Chicago
Pratt Mfg. Co., 91 Lake (Axe) X
IND.—Evansville
Evansville Tool Works (Coal; Woodchoppers; Falling Stone; &c.; Steel)
A

WEIGHTS (Con.)
Window) ....F
IND.—Indianapolis
Over Ewald, 426 So. Penn.
(Round; Square Iron;
Lead Sash) C
IND.—South Bend
Sandage Steel Skein Co.
(Hitching) X
KY.—Owensboro
Guenther & Sons, W. A.
(Sash) ....A
MD.—Baltimore
Bates Sons, Jas. (Sash) ..B
Levering Bros. (Counter
Balance; Elevator; Sash)
.......................C
Robertson Mfg. Co., Jas.
(Lead Sash) C
MASS.—Boston
Austin & Eddy, 117 Broad
(Sash) C
Burditt & Williams Co., 18
Dock Square (Sash) ...B
Chadwick Boston Lead Co.
(Lead Sash) ....AAA
MASS.—Chelsea
Low Tile Co. (Paper) ....F
MASS.—Salem
Salem Elevator Works
(Counter Balance; Eleva-
tor) ....B
MASS.—Worcester
Wheeler Foundry Co. (Sash)
.......................D
MICH.—Detroit
Detroit Lead Pipe & Sheet
Lead Works (Sash) ....A
MO.—St. Louis
Kupferle, Jno. C. (Iron;
Lead Sash; Hitching)
.....................AAA
Pleuger & Henger Mfg. Co.
(Hitching) ....A
St. Louis Sash & Door Works
Dock & Maine (Sash) ..A
Western Foundry & Sash
Weight Co. (Hitching;
Cast Iron Sash).......D
NEBR.—Omaha
Paxton & Verling Iron
Works, 17th & U. P. Ry.
(Iron Sash) ....AA
N. H.—Lancaster
Thompson Mfg. Co. (Sash)
.......................B
N. H.—Manchester
Campbell, John (Hitching)
.......................H
N. J.—Jersey City
Williams & Son, E. A., 105
Plymouth (Lead Sash;
(Iron Sash) ....AA
N. Y.—Brooklyn
Kings County Iron Foundry,
N. 13th & Berry (Elevator;
Lead; &c.; Sash) ......D
N. Y.—Buffalo
Buffalo Scale Co. (Elevator
Scale) ....AA
N. Y.—Horseheads
Weller Hdw. & Foundry Co.
(Hitching) ....D
N. Y.—Manlius
Cheney & Son, S. (Hitching;
Cast Sash) ....A
N. Y.—New Rochelle
Becker, Christian (Scale)
.......................D
N. Y.—New York City
Benedict, Julius (Est. of)
548 W. 55th (Iron Sash)
.......................B
Colwell Lead Co. (Lead
Sash) ....AA
Fairbanks Co. (Scale; Test)
.....................AAAA
Judd & Co., H. L. Paper
......................AA
Kohlbusch, Herman (Scale)
.......................B
N. Y.—New York City
Leissberger & Son, Marks,
397 W. 12th (Lead Sash)
.......................B
National Lead Co., 100 Wil-
liam (Lead Sash) ..AAAA
Ross & Bro., W. A. (Coun-
ter Balance; Elevator
Sash) ....B
Sargent & Co., 151 Leonard
Paper) ....AAAA
United States Foundry &
Scales Co. (Iron; Lead

WEIGHTS (Con.)
Sash) ....F
N. Y.—Rochester
Rochester Lead Works, 382
Exchange (Lead Sash)..B
N. Y.—Watervliet
Coovert Mfg. Co. (Hitching)
.......................A
OHIO—Akron
Enterprise Mfg. Co. (Paper;
Hitching) ....A
OHIO—Ashtabula
Barber Mfg. Co. (Cast Iron
Sash) C
OHIO—Canton
Gibbs Mfg. Co. (Horses'
Toe) ....A
OHIO—Cincinnati
Knecht Co., Victor (Hitch-
ing) ....B
Tatum Co., Sam'l C. (Paper)
.......................B
OHIO—Cleveland
Gibson & Price Co., 375 St.
Clair (Lead Sash) ....A
OHIO—Columbus
Simpson Iron Co., West End,
Buttles Av. (Cast Iron
Sash) ....F
OHIO—Coshocton
Keagy & Lear Machine Co.
(Sash) C
PA.—Elizabethtown
Buchs Sons Co., A. (Hitch-
ing) ....A
PA.—Harrisburg
Hickok Mfg. Co., W. O.
(Cast Iron Sash)....AA
PA.—Philadelphia
Brown & Co., E. E., Mc
Keon & Meadow (Iron
Sash) ....D
Koch & Fox, 22d & Glen-
wood Av. (Elevator
Hitching Blocks; Lead,
etc., Sash) ....D
Lewis & Bros. Co., Jno.
T., 231 So. Front (Lead
Sash) ....AAAA
Philadelphia Novelty Mfg.
Co. (Paper) ....D
PA.—Pittsburg
Standard Scale & Supply
Co. (Ltd.) (Scale; Test)
.......................X
PA.—Wrightsville
Wrightsville Hardware Co.
(Paper) ....B
S. C.—Spartanburg
Morgan Wood & Iron Wks.
(Sash) ....D
TENN.—So. Pittsburg
Blacklock Foundry (Hitch-
ing) C
TEXAS—Fort Worth
Fort Worth Iron & Steel
Mfg. Co. (Sash) ......A
WIS.—Milwaukee
Kieckhefer Elevator Co., A.
(Elevator) C
Windsor Mfg. Co., 570
Clinton (Lead Sash)...B
WIS.—Racine
Racine Malleable &
Wrought Iron Co. (Sash)
.......................A

WELDERS & WELDING

ILL.—Moline
Williams, White & Co.
(Tire) ....A
MASS.—Lynn
Thomson Electric Welding
Co. (Electric) ....AA
MICH.—Detroit
Welded Steel Barrel Cor-
poration (Electric)AAAA
OHIO—Cleveland
Fix's Sons, S. Leonard &
Winter (Steam Flue) ..D
Standard Welding Co.
(Iron; Steel Pressed;
Electric) ....AA

WELTS

MAINE—Portland

Cox & Son, A. F. (Shoe)
.......................A

WELTS (*Con.*)
MASS.—Boston
Union Welting Co. (Shoe)
..........................F
MASS.—Lynn
Houghton Heel & Leather
Co. (Shoe) X
N. Y.—Rochester
Williams, Hoyt & Co.
(Shoe) ....A

WHALEBONE
New York City
Kaempfer, Max., 392 B'way
..........................A

WHEEL-BARROWS
See Barrows

WHEELS
**See Hardware; Carriage &
Woodwork; Carriage; also
Gears; Turbines.**
Kilby Locomotive & Machine Works (Logging
Car; Mine Car)........A
ALA.—Birmingham
Decatur Car Wheel & Mfg.
Co. (Car) ....AA
CAL.—San Francisco
Doeble Co., Abner, 200
Fremonht (Tangential Water) ....A
Hendy Machine Works, Joshua (Turbine Water).AA
Risdon Iron & Locomotive
Works (Car; Chilled Cast
Car Propeller) ....AAAA
Steiger & Kerr Stove &
Foundry Co. (Chilled Cast
Car) ....B
CAL.—Stockton
Holt Mfg. Co. (Carriage;
Sarven; Wagon Wooden
Hub) ....AA
CAL.—Sutter Creek
Knight & Co., (100 to 2500
h. p. Water) C
COLO.—Denver
Davis Iron Works Co., F.
M., 8th & Lorimer (Car
Self-Oiling) ....AA
Denver Engineering Works
Co., Blake & 30th (Self-Oiling) ....AA
Mine & Smelter Supply Co.
(Self-Oiling) ......AAAA
CONN.—Bridgeport
Bridgeport Safety Emery
Wheel Co. (Buffing; Emery Corundum; Polishing)
..........................F
Grant Mfg. & Machine Co.
(Counter & Register)...E
Rowell & Co., W. G.
(Bronze Trolley) ......D
Springfield Mfg. Co. (Buffing; Emery; Polishing)
..........................B
CONN.—Collinsville
Hartigan, W. R. (Wooden
Caster; Roller Skate)..H
CONN.—Deep River
Williams & Marvin Mfg.
Co. (Caster) ....D
CONN.—Hartford
Billings & Spencer Co.
(Sprocket Tracing) ..AA
CONN.—Killingly
Williamsville Mfg. Co.
(Polishing) ....A
CONN.—Lime Rock
Barnum-Richardson Co.
(Car; Hand & Push Car;
Mine Car) ....AAA
CONN.—New Haven
Barnes Tool Co. (Marine;
Steering) ....B
CONN.—Norwalk
Norwalk Brass Co.
(Propeller) ....D
CONN.—Southington
Peck, Stow & Wilcox Co.
(Well) ....AAAA
CONN.—South Windham
Radical Thread Buff Co.
(Buffing & Polishing)..X
CONN.—Torrington

WHEELS (*Con.*)
Union Hardware Co.
(Caster)............AA
CONN.—Waterbury
Holmes, Booth & Haydens
Co. (Trolley) .....AAAA
CONN.—Windsor Locks
Clark Co., Geo. P. (Rubber
Tired; Rubber Covered
Truck; Pneumatic Tired;
Carriage Iron Truck;
Truck & Stand) C
DEL.—Elsmere
Diamond State Fibre Co.
(Fly; Gear, Hard Fibre)
..........................B
DEL.—Wilmington
American Vulcanized Fibre
Co. (Gear, Hard Fibre)
.......................AAAA
Delaware Hard Fibre Co.
(Gear, Hard Fibre)....A
Harlan & Hollingsworth Co.
(Chilled Cast Car)....X
Kartavert Mfg. Co., Md.
Av. & Beach (Gear Hard
Fibre) X
Lobdell Car Wheel Co.
(Car; Chilled Bridge;
Hand & Push Car; Logging Car; Mine Car; Self-Oiling Street Car; Truck
& Stand Chilled Cast Car)
.......................AAAA
Pusey & Jones Co. (Propeller & Gearing) ..AAA
GA.—Atlanta
Atlanta Car Wheel & Mfg.
Co. (Chilled Car; Mine
Car; Chilled Street Car)
..........................A
DeLoath Mill Mfg. Co.
(Turbine Water) .....AA
ILL.—Aurora
American Well Works
(Bull) ....AA
Wilcox Mfg. Co. (Ball
Bearing) ....B
ILL.—Chicago
Allis-Chalmers Co., Home
Ins. Bldg. (Car; Fly;
Mine Car; Sectional Turbine Water) ....AAAA
American Engineering Specialty Co. (Mine Car)...B
American Steel & Wire Co.
of N. J., Rookery Bldg.
(Trolley) ....AAAA
Archer Iron Works, 34 Pl.
& Western Av. (Metal,
all kinds; Mine Car)...D
Austin Mfg. Co., F. C.,
Manhattan Building,
(Bull; Mine Car).......C
Besly & Co., Charles H., 15
Clinton (Polishing) ..AA
Borend & Selleck Co., 48
Lake (Sprocket) ......B
Caldwell & Son Co. H. W.,
17th & Western Av.
(Sprocket) ....AA
Cassady-Fairbank Mfg. Co.
(Tracing) C
Chicago Wheel & Mfg. Co.,
39 W. Randolph (Corundum Carborundum; Dental; Emery; Roll Grinding
Emery Razor; Polishing
& Buffing; Sewing Machine Grinding) C
Covel Mfg. Co. (Emery)..C
Ewart Mfg. Co. (Sprocket)
..........................A
Fairbanks, Morse & Co.
(Chilled Cast Car).AAAA
Gardner Sash Balance Co.,
164 Dearborn (Ball Bearing for all Purposes)....C
Griffin Wheel Co., 138 Jackson Boul. (Car; Mine Car;
Street Car; Chilled Cast
Car) ....AAAA
Hoisting & Conveying Machinery Co., 44 N. Elizabeth (Sprocket) ......E
Link Belt Machinery Co.,
39 & Stewart Av. (Fly;
Sprocket, for Ewart Link
Belting) ....AAA
Marine Iron Works
(Propeller) ....B
Porter & Berg, 309 Dear-

WHEELS (*Con.*)
born (Trolley & Supplies)
.........................D
Rosback, F. P. (Tracing).E
Skillin & Richards Mfg. Co.,
147 Fulton (Sprocket)..C
Sullivan Machinery Co., 135
Adams (Driving) .AAAA
Webster Mfg. Co., 1075 W.
15th (Sprocket) .....AA
Willard & Co., Charles P.
(Propeller) ....D
ILL.—Freeport
Arcade Mfg. Co.
(Tracing) ....A
ILL.—Galesburg
Frost Mfg. Co. (Sprocket)
....................A
ILL.—Harvey
Buda Foundry & Mfg. Co.
(Steel) ....AA
ILL.—Havana
Havana Metal Wheel Co.
(Metal) ....A
ILL.—Joliet
Bates Machine Co. (Fly)
....................AA
ILL.—Litchfield
Litchfield Foundry & Ma-
chine Co. (Mine Car)..A
ILL.—Marseilles
Marseilles Mfg. Co.
(Sprocket) ....A
ILL.—Mt. Vernon
Mt. Vernon Car Mfg. Co.
(Car) ....AAA
ILL.—Peru
Peru Plow & Wheel Co.
(Metal) ....AA
ILL.—Pullman
Union Foundry Works
(Chilled Cast Car)......A
ILL.—Quincy
Bush, Clement (Metal)..E
Electric Wheel Co. (Metal;
Steel) ....A

*Steel Wheels to fit any
wagon or cart; made any
size, with any width of
tires. We also make
Handy Wagons with low
wheels and wire tires;
wooden wagons with steel
wheels; or steel wagons
with steel wheels; log
wagons, and heavy truck
wagons of all kinds for
horses or traction engine
power; steel axles of any
size or shape.*

Empire Mfg. Co. (Metal)D
Little Metal Wheel Co., J.
R. (Metal) C
Quincy Corn Planter Co.
(Metal) ....D
ILL.—St. Charles
Moline Malleable Iron Co.
(Sprocket) ....A
IND.—Fort Wayne
Bass Foundry & Machine
Co. (Chilled Cast Car)..X
Olds Wagon Works
(Wagon) X
Rastetter & Son, Louis
(Wire) ....B
IND.—Indianapolis
Atkins & Co., E. C. (Edger)
....................AAAA
Indianapolis Drop Forging
Co. (Sprocket) X
Rockwood Mfg. Co. (Paper;
Buffing & Polishing)...A
IND.—Laporte
Niles & Scott Co. (Metal;
Steel Truck; Wagon; Ag-
ricultural Implement;
Barrow; Iron & Wooden;
Iron Hub) ....AA
IND.—Michigan City
Haskell & Barker Car Co.
(Chilled Cast Car) AAAA
IND.—Mishawaka
Dodge Mfg. Co. (Fly;
Sprocket) ....AAA
Studebaker Bros. Mfg. Co.
(Logging Car) ....AAAA
IND.—Terre Haute
Eagle Snow Works Co.
(Mine Car) C

WHEELS (*Con.*)
IOWA—Burlington
Murray Iron Works Co.
(Iron) ....A
IOWA—Davenport
Bettendorf Metal Wheel Co.
(Agricultural Implement
Metal; Wagon) ...AAAA
IOWA—Dubuque
Dubuque Turbine & Roller
Mill Co. (Turbine Water)
....................B
KANS.—Fort Scott
Fort Scott Foundry & Ma-
chine Co. (Chas. Eller,
Prop.) (Bull) ....H
KANS.—Leavenworth
Great Western Mfg. Co.
(Sprocket; Gear) ....AA
KANS.—Manhattan
Blue Valley Mfg. Co. (Iron;
Truck) ....F
KY.—Louisville
Louisville Car Wheel &
Railay Supply Co., 308
5th (Chilled Cast Car)..A
MAINE—Portland
Laughlin Co., Thos. (Ma-
rine; Steering) ....A
Portland Co. (Chilled Iron;
Driving; Gear) ....AA
MD.—Baltimore
Baltimore Car Wheel Co.,
Patterson Av. & Payson
(Car; Driving; Street Car
Chilled Cast Car; Steel
Tired Car; Interchange-
able Street Car; Steel
Truck) ....B
Maryland Car Wheel Works,
44 South (Car) ....A
Poole Engineer & Machine
Co. (Fly; Sprocket; Wa-
ter; Rope & Wire Rope
Turbine Water; Gear)AA
MASS.—Amesbury
Bailey & Co., S. R. (Pneu-
matic Tired; Carriage).A
MASS.—Boston
American Steam Gauge &
Valve Mfg. Co. (Reduc-
ing) ....A
Anderson Mfg. Co., Albert
& J. M., 287 A. (Trolley)
....................A
Boston Belting Co. (Rubber
Covered Truck) ..AAAA
Boston Gear Works
(Sprocket) ....B
Burnham & Duggin Railway
Appliance Co., 89 State
(Never Slip, Snow Plow)
....................X
Codman, F. L. & J. C.
(Polishing) ....A
Cutter, Wood & Stevens Co.
(Polishing) ....B
Dunning Co., Edw. L., 64
Federal (Trolley) .....F
Lockwood Mfg. Co. (Inc.),
85 Summer (Propeller)..X
Page Newall & Co., 139
Milk (Steel Tired Car;
Imp't'd) X
Sewing Machine Supplies
Co. (Tracing) ....B
Star Brass Mfg. Co., 103 E.
Dedham (Reducing Trol-
ley) ....A
MASS.—Brockton
Snell & Atherton (Stitch)
....................C
MASS.—Chester
Hamilton Emery & Corun-
dum Co. (Emery)......C
MASS.—Fall River
Kilburn, Lincoln & Co.,
(Inc.) (Turbine Water).A
MASS.—Fitchburg
Dean Machine Co., Herbert
C. (Reducing) ....E
Goodnow Foundry Co., L.
H. (Fly) C
MASS.—Greenfield
Wells Bros. Co. (Tire
Measuring) ....A
Wiley & Russell Mfg. Co
(Tire Measuring) .....AA
MASS.—Holyoke
Holyoke Machine Co.
(Turbine Water) .....AA
MASS.—Lawrence
Archibald Wheel Co. (Ball

WHEELS (Con.)
N. J.—Newark
Gould & Eberhardt (Gear) .... A
Hanson & Van Winkle Co., 219 Market (Buffing Polishing) .... AA
Jones & Co., Phineas (Carriage) .... A
Osborne & Co., C. S. (Tracing) .... B
Sommer's Son, John (Caster) .... A
Storm Mfg. Co. (Ice; Sleet Cutting Trolley) .... B
N. J.—Trenton
Home Rubber Co. (Brewers) .... AAAA
Thropp Sons Co., Jno. E. (Propeller) .... A
N. Y.—Albany
Thatcher & Co., Geo. H. (Car) .... AAA
N. Y.—Baldwinsville
Morris Machine Wks. (Propeller) .... AA
N. Y.—Brooklyn
Columbia Machine Wks. & Novelty Iron Co., 167 Chestnut (Trolley) .... A
Pioneer Iron Works, 153 William (Steel Truck) .... A
Schaffer & Budenberg Mfg. Co. (Reducing) .... D
N. Y.—Buffalo
Bickford & Francis Belting Co., 53 Exchange (Buffing; Polishing)...A
Brown Car Wheel Wks. Howard & Thomas (Car; Steel Truck; Chilled Cast Car) .... AA
Buffalo Forge Co. (Disk; Water) .... AAA
Griffin Machine Wks., P. H. (Car) .... A
Lumen Bearing Co., 1155 Sycamore (Trolley)....C
Magnus Metal Co., 830 Ellicott Sq. (Trolley)AAAA
Mey Chain & Belting Engineering Wks., 14 Perry (Chain Sprockets)......F
New York Car Wheel Co., Germain Ins. Bldg. (Car; Driving; Hand; Push Car; Mine Car; Street Car; Truck Chilled Cast Car; Iron Driving; Overhead Crane) .... AA
Noye Mfg. Co., John T. (Sprocket; Gear) X
Reading Car Wheel Co., Ellicott Sq. (Car) .... A
Squier Mfg. Co., Geo. L. (Turbine Water) .... AAA
Trout, H. G. (Propeller).B
N. Y.—Hillburn
Ramapo Iron Wks. (Car; Driving) .... AAA
N. Y.—Horseheads
Weller Hardwre & Fdry Co. (Well) .... D
N. Y.—Ithaca
Williams Bros. (Bull)..AA
N. Y.—Jamestown
Engineering & Power Co. (Reducing) .... E
N. Y.—Mount Morris
Genesee Valley Mfg. Co. (Turbine Water) .... B
New York City
Ashcroft Mfg. Co., 85 Liberty (Reducing) .... A
Best, Levi (Corundum; Emery) C
Bushnell Co., Jno. S., 126 Liberty (Reducing)....X
Estes & Sons, E. B. (Wooden Caster, Roller Skate; Seam Valve) .... AA
Garvin Machine Co. (Gear) .... AA
Gesswein Co., F. W., 39 John (Buffing; Polishing) .... A
N. Y.—New York City
Goodyear Rubber Co. (Rubber; Covered Truck) .... AAAA
Koppel, Arthur, 66 Broad

WHEELS (Con.)
(Car) .... A
McCabe Hanger Mfg. Co., 425 W. 25th (Ball Bearing) .... B
Mead Mfg. Co., Jno. A., 11 B'way (Sprocket) ....AA
Miles-Bement-Pond Co., 111 Bway. (Polishing)AAAA
New York Belting & Packing Co. (Emery) ....AAA
Peckham Mfg. Co., 26 Cortlandt (Car; Street Car Chilled Cast; Car Interchangeable; Street Car) .... B
Pelton Water Wheel Co., 143 Liberty (Water) ..AA
Pierce Well Engineering & Supply Co. (Bull) ....D
Prosser & Son, Thos., 15 Gold (Steel Tired Car; Steel Truck) .... A
Railway Steel Spring Co., 71 Broadway (Steel Tired Car; for Electric Railway; Steel Truck) .... A
Reichhelm & Co., E. P. (Jewelers' Felt) .... A
Robertson & Sons Co., Jas. L., 204 Fulton (Reducing) .... D
Sargent & Co., 151 Leonard (Well) .... AAAA
Sullivan, Jno. W., 385 South (Propeller) .... B
Thompson & Co., Richard, 126 Liberty (Reducing) .... F
Tingue, Brown & Co., 99 Chambers (Buffing; Polishing) .... D
Zucker & Levett & Loeb Co., 528 W. 25th (Buffing; Polishing) .... A
N. Y.—Niagara Falls
Carborundum Co., (Carborundum; Dental Emery Roll Grinding) .... A
N. Y.—Ramapo
Ramapo Foundry & Wheel Works (Chilled Cast Car; Driving; Car) X
N. Y.—Rome
Adams & Son. S. (Turbine Water) C
N. Y.—Schenectady
General Electric Co. Trolley) .... AAAA
N. Y.—Seneca Falls
Rumsey & Co. (Ltd.) (Well) .... A
N. Y.—Shortsville
Shortsville Wheel Co. (Hard Rubber Tired; Carriage; Wagon) .... B
N. Y.—Syracuse
Central City Brass & Mfg. Co., 120 Burnet Av. (Trolley) .... B
Franklin Mfg. Co., H. H. (Finished Casting Hand; Dental) .... A
Stearns & Co., E. C. (Bull) .... AA
N. Y.—Utica
Munson Bros. Co. (Turbine Water) .... A
Weston-Mott Co. (Steel Wire; Steel Rims; Wire; Agricultural Implements; Carriage Invalid Chair; Hand Car; Barrow; Pneumatic Tired Carriage) ..A
N. C.—Charlotte
Mecklenburg Iron Works (Turbine Water) X
N. C.—Greensboro
Sergeant Mfg. Co. (Turbine Water) .... D
OHIO—Akron
Whitman & Barnes Mfg. Co. (Sprocket) ....AAAA
OHIO—Barnesville
Watt Mining Car Wheel Co. (Car; Mine Car; Self-Oiling; Chilled Cast Car) ..A
OHIO—Bucyrus
American Clay Working Machine Co. (Clayworkers') X
OHIO—Canton
Aultman Co. (Sprocket, also

WHEELS (*Con.*)

with Crutch) ......AAAA

Timken Roller Bearing Axle
Co. (Ball or Roller Bear-
ing) ....A

OHIO—Cincinnati

Blymyer Iron Works Co.
(Overshot Water) .....B

Electric Railway Equip-
ment Co., 431 E. Front
(Trolley) ... .B

Greenwald Co., I. & E., 720
E. Pearl (Sprocket) ..A

Mowry Car Wheel Works
Co., 2401 Eastern Av.
(Chilled Cast Car) .....B

Royer Wheel Co. (Childrens'
Carriage; Sarven; Wagon)
X

OHIO—Cleveland

Atlas Bolt & Screw Co.
(Hand; Push Car; Mine
Car; Ball or Roller Bear-
ing Tracing; Truck) ..AA

Bartlett & Snow Co., C. O.,
French & Columbus
(Sprocket) ....A

Bowler Foundry Co. (Chilled Mine Car; Chilled Cast
Car) ....B

Federal Mfg. Co., American
Trust Bldg. (Tracing; Au-
tomoble Steering; Auto-
mobile Sprocket) ..AAAA

Fulton Foundry Co. (Chilled
Cast Car; Driving; Street
Car) C

Kirk, Latty Mfg. Co.
(Wire) ....A

Osborn Mfg. Co. (Polishing)
B

Otis Steel Co. (Ltd.) (Steel
Tired; Driving) ....A

Standard Car Wheel Co.,
Bessemer Av. & Todd
(Car. Chilled Street Car)
X

Van Dorn & Dutton Co.,
1796 E. Madison Av.
(Trolley) .... B

OHIO—Columbus

Case Mfg. Co. (Sprocket;
Traveling Crane) .... A

Jeffrey Mfg. Co. (Sprocket)
AAAA

Kilbourne & Jacobs Mfg.
Co. (Car; Steel Truck
Vehicle; Iron; Carriage
Rubber Covered Truck;
Wheel Scraper; Wagon
Barrow; Caster).. AAAA

Midgley Mfg. Co. (Tubular
Steel for Automobiles,
Vehicles. Etc.) ...... B

OHIO—Dayton

Barney & Smith Car Co.,
(Chilled Cast Car) AAAA

Dayton Globe Iron Works
Co. (Turbine Water) ..B

Dayton Malleable Iron Co.
(Fifth) .... AAA

Dayton Mfg. Co. (Trolley)
A

Meeker Mfg. Co. (Ball Bearing Carriage) .... D

Raymond Co., Charles W.
(Clay Workers) ...... A

OHIO—Defiance

Turnbull Wagon Co. (Ag-
ricultural Implement;
Wooden) .... AA

OHIO—Geneva

Geneva Metal Wheel Co.
(Metal) .... AA

OHIO—Lima

Coss & Stinebaugh (Bull) E

Lima Locomotive & Machine
Co. (Car; Chilled Cast
Car) .... AAA

OHIO—Mt. Vernon

Cooper Co., C. & G. (Fly)
AA

OHIO—Nelsonville

Nelsonville Foundry & Ma-
chine Co. (Capless Car;
Chilled Cast Car) ..... B

OHIO—New Lexington

Star Mfg. Co. (Mine Car) B

OHIO—New London

Arnold-Creager Co. (Barrow;
Clay Workers; Metal
Agil Implts. Wagon) ..B

WHEELS (*Con.*)

OHIO—Niles

Niles Mine & Mill Supply
Co. (Mine Car) .... B

OHIO—Piqua

Piqua Handle & Mfg. Co.
(Steam Valve) .... A

OHIO—Springfield

Leffel & Co., Jas. (Water;
Turbine & Sectional Tur-
bine Water; Impulse
Water; Mining Water) AA

Safety Emery Wheel Co.
(Emery) .... A

Trump Mfg. Co. (Turbine
Water; Mining & Twin
Water; Sectional Turbine
Water) .... A

Webster & Pergs Tool Co.
(Aluminum Reducing) C

OHIO—Swanton

Baker Co., A. D. (Metal) B

OHIO—Tiffin

Sterling Emery Wheel Mfg.
Co. (Emery; Corundum
Polishing) .... A

OHIO—Toledo

Gendron Wheel Co. (Iron;
Steel Wire) .... AA

Heartley, Geo. W.(Child-
ren's Carriage; Wheelbar-
row; Implements, Etc.) D

Toledo Metal Wheel Co.
(Wire; Metal) ...... AA

OREGON—Portland

Portland Iron Works
(Sproket) .... A

PA.—Allegheny

Carlin's Sons, Thos.
(Street Car) .... A

Penna. Car Wheel Co., 499
Preble (Chilled Cast Car)
AA

Porter Foundry & Machine
Co. (Fly).... ....A

PA.—Allentown

Allentown Foundry & Ma-
chine Works (Turbine
Water) .... A

Mosser & Son, Wm. F.
(Turbine Water) ......A

PA.—Bausman

Bausman, D. H. (Steel
Water) C

PA.—Bloomsburg

Bloomsburg Car Mfg. Co.
(Chilled Cast Car) ....A

PA.—Braddock

Braddock Machine & Mfg.
Co. (Mine Car & Supplies)
A

PA.—Chambersburg

Wolf Co. (Inc.) (Sprocket)
AA

PA.—Chester

American Steel Foundries
(Mine Car) ....AAAA

Chester Steel Castings Co.
(Car; Driving & Chilled
Cast Car; Propeller; Steel
Tired Car; Gear).....AA

Delaware River Iron Ship
Building & Engine Works
(Propeller) ....AAA

Seaboard Steel Casting Co.
(Propeller) .... AAA

PA.—Coatesville

Ridgway & Son Co., Craig
(Turbine Water) ..... A

PA.—Connellsville

Connellsville Machine & Car
Co. (Mine Car; Chilled
Cast Car) .... A

PA.—Corry

Trill, W. L. (Reducing) ..F

PA.—Erie

National Foundry Co.
(Car) .... A

Reed Mfg. Co. (Cutter) ..A

PA.—Fleetwood

Schaeffer-Wanner & Co.
(Turbine Water) ...... B

PA.—Fullerton

Lehigh Car Wheel & Axle
Works (Car; Drawing;
Mine Car; Self-Oiling
Steel Tired Car; Steel
Truck; Street Car) AAAA

PA.—Johnstown

Lorain Steel Co. (Trolley)
AAAA

PA.—Kutztown

Kutztown Foundry & Ma-

WHEELS (Con.)
chine Co. (Turbine Water)
A

PA.—Lancaster
Lancaster Peerless Emery
Wheel Co. (Emery) ....D
PA.—McKee's Rocks
Penna Malleable Co. (Car) A
PA.—Mechanicsburg
Wilcox Mfg. Co., D. M.
(Fifth) .... A
PA.—Muncy
Sprout; Waldron & Co.
(Water) .... A
PA.—Nazareth
Nazareth Foundry & Ma-
chine Co. (Sproket) ....B
PA.—North East
Eureka Tempered Copper
Works (Trolley) ...... A
PA.—Osceola Mills
Pie, Justin J. (Est. of)
(Mine Car) .... B
Stine & Son, S. B. (Mine
Car) .... B
PA.—Philadelphia
Abrasive Material Co.
(Corundum; Emery) ...A
Ajax Metal Co., 46 Rich-
mond (Trolley) ....AAA
Brill Co., J. G., 62nd &
Woodland Av. (Car; Street
Car; Chilled Cast Car)
AAAA
Cramp & Sons Ship & En-
gine Bldg. Co. William
(Propeller) ...... AAAA
Cresson Co., Geo. V., 18th
& Allegheny (Fly; Worm
Sproket) .... AA
Etting, Edw. J., Land Title
Bldg. (Car) .... B
Midvale Steel Co. (Chilled
Cast Car) .... AAAA
Pressed Steel Mfg. Co.,
Bridge Av. & Willow
(Ball) .... D
Southwark Foundry & Ma-
chine Co. (Fly) .... AAA
Standard Roller Bearing
Co., 15th & Girard Av.
(Ball & Roller Bearing)
AA
Standard Steel Works, 1502
Market (Steel Tired Car:
Metal; Chilled Cast Car)
Wharton & Co., Wm. Jr.
(Inc.) (Car) ...... AAA
White Dental Mfg. Co., S.
S. (Corundum) .... AAAA
Wood & Co., R. D. (Tur-
bine Water) ...... AAAA
PA.—Pittsburg
Armstrong Cork Co. (Buff-
ing; Polishing) .. AAAA
Central Car Wheel Co.,
Frick Bldg. (Chilled Iron
Car) .... B
Dixon Co., H. L. (Power
(Pottery) .... A
Jones & Laughlin Steel Co.
(Fly; Steel Truck Car)
AAAA
Milholland Co., J. & J. B.
(Sectional Turbine) ....A
Nuttal Co., R. D., Lafayette
& Garrison Place (Trolley)
A
Phillips Mine & Supply Co.
(Mine Car Self-Oiling) AA
Pittsburg Steel Foundry Co.
(Car) .... AA
Scaife Foundry & Machine
Co., 28th & Smallman
(Fly; Sprocket) ...... B
Simonds Mfg. Co., 25th
& Liberty (Trolley Worm
for Electric Railway,
Etc.) .... B
Westinghouse Electric &
Mfg. Co. (Trolley) AAAA
PA.—Reading
Penn. Hardware Co. (Well)
AA
Reading Hardware Co.
(Well) .... AAAA
PA.—Sayre
Cayuga Mfg. Co. (Chilled
Cast Car) .... B
PA.—Scranton
Scranton Forging Co. (Fifth)
A
Union Steam Specialty Co.

WHEELS (Con.)
(Reducing) .... A
PA.—South Bethlehem
Bethlehem Foundry & Ma-
chine Co. (Sprocket) ..C
PA.—Stroudsburg
Tanite Co. (Emery) .... A
PA.—Towanda
Frost's Sons, J. O. (Trolley)
B
PA.—Union City
Novelty Wood Work Co.
(Caster) .... B
PA.—Weissport
Lehigh Valley Emery Wheel
Co. (Emery; Corundum) E
PA.—Wilkesbarre
Vulcan Iron Works (Car;
Fly; Mine Car; Worm;
Bull; Friction; Gear)
AAAA
PA.—Wrightsville
Susquehanna Casting Co.
(Well) .... AA
Wrightsville Hardware Co.
(Well) ....B
PA.—York
Smith Co., S. Morgan
(Turbine Water) .. AAA
R. I.—Bristol
Herreshoff Mfg. Co.
(Bronze; Propeller) ....A
R. I. Pawtucket
Thayer's Son Ellis (Buff-
ing; Polishing) X
R. I.—Providence
American Emery Wheel
Works (Corundum; Emery
Roll Grinding) .... B
Builders Iron Foundry
((Buffing; Polishing) AA
Diamond Machine Co. (Buff-
ing; Wooden; Emery;
Household Emery; Polish-
ing) .... B
R. I.—Westerly
Stillman Wayland, F.
(Card Grinder) .... H
TENN.—Chattanooga
Chattenooga Car & Foundry
Co. (Street Car) ...... A
Wheland Machine Works
(Turbine Water) ...... A
TENN.—Memphis
Chickasaw Iron Works
(Steel Truck; Friction) A
TEXAS—Fort Worth
Davis Locomotive Wheel
Co. (Car) .... B
TEXAS—Houston
Dickson Car Wheel Co.
(Car) .... AA
TEXAS—Marshall
Marshall Car Wheel &
Foundry Co. (Car) .... A
VT.—Barre
Whitcomb Bros. (Wrought
Iron & Steel Granite Pol-
ishing) X
VT.—Bennington
Scott Olin (Turbine Water)
A
VT.—Brattleboro
Smith Co., S. A. (Children's
Carriage) .... AAA
VT.—Fair Haven
Dalrymple, Geo. (Turbine
Water) ....E
VT.—Montpelier
Lane Mfg. Co. (Turbine
Water; Mining Water
Gear) .... A
VT.—St. Albans
St. Albans Foundry & Implt.
Co. (Chilled Cast Car)..D
VA.—Norfolk
Whitehurst Co., R. W.
(Steel Truck) ....B
VA.—Petersburg
Petersburg Iron Works Co.
(Logging Car) .... D
VA.—Richmond
Tredegar Co. (Chilled Cast
Car) .... AAA
WASH.—Spokane
Union Iron Works (Inc.)
(Mine Car; Self-Oiling) B
W. VA.—Fairmont
Helmick Foundry & Machine
Co. (Self-Oiling) .... D
WIS.—Milwaukee
Bayley & Sons Co., Wm.
(Truck) X

WHEELS (Con.)

Chain Belt Co. (Sprocket) B
Falk Co., Ft. 30th (Drawing) .... AAA
Filer & Stowell Co. (Fly; Sproket) .... AAA
Kieckhefer Elevator Co., A. (Iron Truck) C
Meinecke & Son, A. (Spinning) .... AAA
Nordberg Mfg. Co., 476 Virginia (Fly) .... AAA
Sheriff's Mfg. Co., 124 Barclay (Propeller) ....B
WIS.—Racine
Winship Mfg. Co. (Tanners' Wash) .... E

WHETSTONES
See Stones

WHIFFLE-TREES
See Woodwork; Carriage

WHIPS
CONN.—Meriden
Manning, Bowman & Co., (Culinary) .... AA
CONN.—New Britain
Landers, Frary & Clark (Culinary) .... AAA
CONN.—Torrington
Turner & Seymour Mfg. Co. (Culinary) .... A
CONN.—Unionville
Humphrey, H. W. (Culinary) .... D
ILL.—Chicago
Chicago Rawhide Mfg. Co. (Farm; Rawhide) ......A
MD.—Baltimore
Day Son & Co., O. F. (Carriage) C
Millikin & Co., P. B. (Carriage; Coach; Farm; Rawhide; Riding) .... E
Sinclair-Scott Co., (Culinary) .... E
MASS.—Westfield
American Whip Co. (Carriage) .... AAA
Cargill, Cook & Co. (Carriage) .... B
Independent Whip Co. (Carriage) C
United States Whip Co. (Carriage; Riding; Wagon Coach; Drovers; Fancy Farm Rattan; Rawhide Whalebone Dog) ...AAA
MASS. Worcester
National Mfg. Co. (Culinary) .... A
Wire Goods Co. (Culinary) A
MO.—St. Louis
Loeblein Collar & Whip Co., B. (Carriage) ....B
Strauss Saddlery Co., Jacob (Drovers) .... A
Zelnicker Supply Co., W. A. (Ox) X
N. J.—Newark
Peters Harness & Saddlery Co. (Carriage; Riding) .C
N. Y.—Buffalo
Buffalo Glove & Whip Mfg. Co. (Carriage) .... A
N. Y.—Geneva
Chapman, C. A. (Egg) ..E
New York City
Follmer, Clogg & Co. (Riding) .... AAA
Silver & Co. (Inc.) (Culinary .... E
Smith, Worthington & Co. (Carriage) .... A
Lalance & Grosjean Mfg. Co. (Culinary) .... AAAA
Stoutenborough X (Culinary) .... D
N. Y.—Rochester
Woodbury Whip Co. (Carriage Coach; Rawhide Farm; Riding) ....A
N. Y.—Troy
Parks & Parks (Culinary) D
N. Y.—Windsor
Coburn Whip Co. (Carriage;

WHIPS (Con.)
Coach; Drovers; Farm; Fancy; Rattan; Rawhide; Riding Wagon; Whalebone) ....AAA
OHIO—Cincinnati
Day & Co., J. H. (Culinary) A
OHIO—Osborn
Ohio Whip Co. (Carriage) C
OHIO—Sandusky
Knight, H. H., 209 Monroe D

WHISKEY
See Liquors

WHISKS
See Brooms

WHISTLES
CAL.—San Francisco
Garratt & Co., W. T., 142 Fremont (Steam) .....AA
CONN.—Bridgeport
Belknap Mfg. Co. (Steam) C
Kinsley Mfg. Co., 20 South Av. (Chime Single Bell Chime; Steam) ....D
CONN.—Waterbury
Waterbury Brass Co. (Toy) AAAA
CONN.—Waterville
American Pin Co. (Toy) AA
ILL.—Chicago
Crane Co. (Steam; Alarm) AAAA
Scott Valve Co., 32 W. Randolph (Steam) ....D
ILL.—Waukegon
Thomas Brass & Iron Co. (Chime; Steam) ....A
MD.—Baltimore
Regester Sons Co., J., 49 W. Holliday (Steam) ......A
MASS.—Boston
American Steam Gauge & Valve Mfg. Co. (Chime; Steam) .... A
Ashton Valve Co., 271 Franklin (Steam) .....A
Crosby Steam Gauge & Valve Co., 95 Oliver (Chime; Steam; Locomotive; Gong) ....AA
Star Brass Mfg. Co., 103 E. Dedham (Chime) ......A
Walworth Mfg. Co., 132 Federal (Steam; Alarm) AAAA
Woodman Mfg. & Supply Co. R., 63 Oliver (Conductors; Starters) X
MASS.—Worcester
Union Water Meter Co. (Steam; Gong Steam) ..B
MICH.—Detroit
Detroit Shipbuilding Co. (Steam) ....AAAA
MICH.—Saginaw
Wickes Bros. (Steam) .AAA
MO.—St. Louis
Zelnicker Supply Co., W. A. (Steam) X
N. J.—Belleville
Eastwood Wire Mfg. Co. (Chime; Steam) ......A
N. J.—Camden
Fullmer & Co., A. J. (Steam) ....A
N. J.—Newark
Celluloid Co. (Toy) .....B
N. Y.—Brooklyn
Hauck & Son, Chas. J. (Toy) ....B
Schaffer & Budenberg Mfg. Co. (Chime; Steam) ..D
N. Y.—Buffalo
Sherwood Mfg. Co., 34 Wash'n (Steam) ......B
N. Y.—Elmira
Swift Lubricator Co. (Steam) ....B
N. Y.—Lynbrook
Sherman Bros. (Tin) .....E
New York City
Ashcroft Mfg. Co., 85 Liberty (Chime; Steam) A
Eaton, Cole & Burnham Co., 253 Bway (Chime; Steam) AAAA

WHISTLES (*Con.*)
Fairbanks Co., 416 Broome
 (Steam) ....AAAA
Gleason-Peters Air Pump Co.
 Mercer & Houston (Air)
 ....D
McNab & Harlin Mfg. Co.,
 56 John (Steam) ....AAA
Nelson, Charles, 439 E.
 10th (Steam) ....A
Ostrander & Co., W. R.
 (Carriage Pneumatic
 Alarm; Speaking Tube) A
OHIO—Canton
Berger Mfg. Co. (Speaking
 Tube) ....AA
OHIO—Cincinnati
Central Brass Works, 322
 W. Pearl (Steam) ....D
Fewlass Leen Brass & Iron
 Co., 456 E. 2d (Chime)..A
Lunkenheimer Co., Beek-
 man & Waverly (Chime;
 Steam Alarm) ....AA
Powell Co., Wm. (Chime;
 Steam) ....A
Queen City Brass & Iron
 Works (Single Bell Chime
 Steam) ....B
OHIO—Cleveland
Brightman Machine Co.
 (Steam) ....D
Chase Machine Co. (Fog) B
Farnan Brass Works Mrs.
 M. A., 25 Center (Steam)
 ....A
OHIO—Dayton
Buckeye Iron & Brass Works
 (Steam) ....AA
OHIO—Mansfield
Ohio Brass Co. (Steam) AA
OHIO—Springfield
Springfield Brass Co., 82 So.
 Limestone (Steam) ....E
PA.—Chester
Vulcan Works (Chime;
 Steam) ....B
PA.—Erie
Hays Mfg. Co. (Steam)..A
Jarecki Mfg. Co. (Steam)
 ....AAAA
PA.—Philadelphia
Belfield & Co., H., 435 N.
 Broad (Steam) ......AA
Horstman Co., Wm. H.
 (Carriage Pneumatic)
 ....AAAA
Lonergan Co., J. E., 211
 Race (Chime; Steam).AA
PA.—Pittsburg
Kelly & Jones Co., 135
 Water (Steam) ......AA
Mansfield Mfg. Co., 57 1st
 Av. (Steam) ....B
Pittsburg Brass Mfg. Co.,
 107 Wood (Steam) ....D
R. I.—Central Falls
Mossberg Wrench Co.
 (Alarm) C

WHITE
See also Zinc

New York City
Devoe, F. W. & C. T. Reyn-
 olds Co. (Paris) ...AAAA
Taintor Mfg. Co., H. F.
 (Paris) ....B

WHITING
MAINE—Hallowell
Fuller Sons, Geo. C
FLA.—Pensacola
Currie & Co., Chas. E. A
MD.—Baltimore
Thomas Paint Mfg. Co...X
MASS.—Boston
Briggs & Co., John .....D
Stickney & Co., J. W., 79
 Milk ....D
Stickney Tirrell & Co. ....B
N. Y.—Newburg
Higginson Mfg. Co. ......A
New York City
American Whiting & Putty
 Mfg. Co., 200 Water ..B
Dunham, Thos. C. 68 Murray
 ....D
Fox & Co., M. Ewing, 136th
 & Rider Av. ....D

WHITING (*Con.*)
Grote, Geo. W., 605 W. 39th
 ....D
Hammill & Gillespie, 240
 Front ....A
Knappmann & Co., Wm., 29
 Liberty C
Taintor Mfg. Co., H. F.,
 200 Water ....B
PA.—Philadelphia
Kelley Bros. & Spielman
 Inc. Swanson & Moore.B
Nevins Samme, 109 So. 2d.D
Southwark Mfg. Co., Mifflin
 & Swanson ....A

WICKER WORK
See Furniture

WICKETS
GA.—Atlanta
Atlanta Wire & Iron Wks.
 (Brass ....F
ILL.—Chicago
Barber Wire & Iron Works
 (Wire) ....B
N. Y.—Brooklyn
Forman, R. J., 127 Court
 (Wire) ....E
New York City
Gilbert & Bennett Mfg. Co.
 (Wire) ....AAA
N. Y.—Syracuse
Syracuse Wire Wks. (Brass;
 Bronze; Iron).........D
OHIO—Springfield
Rogers Iron Works (Desk)
 ....B

WICKS
CAL.—San Francisco
Doyle & Co., H. (Lamp)..C
CONN.—Ansonia
Ansonia, O & C. Co. (Lamp,
 etc.) ....AA
CONN.—Central Village
Collins, G. S. (Lamp; Stove
 Candle, etc.) X
CONN.—Westport
Lees Mfg. Co. (Candle;
 Lamp; Braided; Miners')
 ....A
IND.—Madison
Eagle Cotton Mills Co.
 (Cotton) ....AA
KY.—Maysville
January & Wood Co. (Cot-
 ton; Lamp; etc.) ......A
MD.—Baltimore
Green & Co., Amon (Cotton)
 ....AA
Hooper & Sons, Wm. E.
 (Lamp; Cotton; Ball
 Candle; etc.) ....AAAA
Unied States Cotton Duck
 Corp'n. (Lamp; Stove;
 etc.) X
MASS.—Boston
Fletcher Mfg. Co. (Lamp;
 Candle; Cotton; Cotton
 Ball; Miners) ......AAA
Pierce, F. H., 402 Boyl-
 ston (Felt Lamp) X
MASS.—Fall River
Estes & Son, John H.
 (Candle) ....A
MASS.—Westport
Westport Mfg. Co. (Cotton)
 ....AA
MO.—St. Louis
Leschen & Sons Rope Co.
 (Candle) ....AA
N. J.—Cedar Grove
Bowden, Anthony (Lamp;
 etc.) ....B
N. J.—Newark
New Jersey Wick Co.
 (Lamp; Stove, etc.) ..B
New York City
Cole & Co., G. W., 141
 Bway. (Incandescent Bi-
 cycle Lamp) ....D
Fletcher Mfg. Co., 72 Leon-
 ard (Lamp; Cotton Ball;
 Miners Stove; etc.) .AAA
Jonhs, H. W. Manville Co.
 (Asbestos) ......AAAA
Lees Co., W. Sherman, 320
 B'way (Lamp; Candle
 Miners; Cotton Ball; etc.)
 ....F

WICKS (Con.)

Massasoit Mfg. Co., 56 Leonard (Cotton Ball Lamp, etc.) ....AA
Standard Oil Co., (Lamp) ....AAAA
Travers & Son, J. P. (Candle; Cotton) ......D

N. C.—Cleveland Mills
Cleveland Cotton Mills (Inc.) (Lamp; etc.) .AA

OHIO—Cincinnati
Atkins & Pearce Mfg. Co., 5th & Eggleston (Lamp) ....D
Novelty Dye Works (Lamp) C

PA.—Erie
Watson Co., H. F. (Asbestos) ....AAA

PA.—Philadelphia
Hoffman-Corr Mfg. Co. (Lamp) ....A
Sidebotham, Jno. (Cotton)A

R. I.—Providence
Fletcher Mfg. Co. (Lamp; Cotton; Cotton Ball Miners; Candle) ......AAA

WIGS

ILL.—Chicago
Stre... Co., Wm. R., 34 Monroe (Theatrical) ......E

MASS.—Boston
Burgess & Son. B. H. ....F

New York City
Batchelor & Co., W. A. ..F
Conen, Robert, 116 3rd Av. G
Hepner, Wm., 1456 Bway. E
Lietz, Chas. L., 39 W. 28th D
Meyer, Chas. ....D

WILLOW WARE

See Furniture

WINCHES & WINDLASSES

CAL.—San Francisco
Kisdon Iron & Locomotive Works ....AAA

COLO.—Denver
Mine & Smelter Supply Co. AAA

CONN.—New Britain
Brady, T. H. (Windlasses; Arc Lamp) ......AAAA

ILL.—Chicago
Allis-Chalmers Co., Home Ins. Bldg. ....AAAA
Klemm, E. R., 103 Monroe E
Vulcan Iron Works, 59 Milwaukee Av. ......AA

IOWA—Waterloo
Kelly & Taneyhill ......G

MAINE—Bath
Hyde Windlass Co. ......B

MAINE—Portland
Laughlin, Thomas ......A

MD.—Baltimore
Ryan-McDonald Mfg. Co. 44 South (Derrick) ..A

MASS.—Boston
Edson Mfg. Co. (Chandelier) ....E
Harvey, H. H., 608 Atlantic Av. (for Quarries) B

MASS.—Newburyport
Russell & Sons, Albert ..C

MICH.—Grand Haven
Dake Engine Co. (Steam; Windlasses) ....A

MINN.—St. Paul
American Hoist & Derrick Co. ....A

MISS.—Meridian
Soule Steam Feed Works C

MO.—St. Louis
Brecht Butchers' Supply Co., G. V. 1201 Cass Av. (Slaughterhouse) ..AAA

N. Y.—Buffalo
Contractors Plant Mfg. Co. 129 Erie ....E

N. Y.—Frankfort
Acme Road Machinery Co. C

WINCHES (Con.)

New York City
Lidgerwood Mfg. Co., 96 Liberty ....AAA
Marine Mfg. & Supply Co., 158 South ....D
Pollock, Alexandra, 203 West ....AA

N. Y.—Niagara Falls
Dobbie Foundry & Machine Co. ....B

N. Y.—Orangeburg
Empire Engine & Motor Co. (Pneumatic) ....B

N. Y.—Schenectady
General Electric Co. (Electric Deck) ....AAAA

OHIO—Cincinnati
Creaghead Engineering Co. (Arc Lamp Windlasses)D

OHIO—Cleveland
Brown Hoisting Machinery Co., 1345 St. Clair (Winches) ....AAAA
Chase Machine Co., 111 Elm B
Globe Iron Works (American Ship Building Co.) AAA
Round & Son, D. 2287 Bway. C

OHIO—Columbus
Case Mfg. Co. (Winches) AA

PA.—Allegheny
Carlin's Sons, Thos. (Boat Lowering; Tanners') ..A

PA.—Pittsburg
Scaife Foundry & Machine Co., 28th & Smallman..B

PA.—South Bethlehem
Bethlehem Foundry & Machine Co. C

PA.—Warren
Textile Finishing Machinery Co. X

R. I.—Providence
American Ship Windlass Co. (Barge Winches; Boat Lowering; Yacht; Centerboard; Gypsey) ......A
Providence Steam Trap Co. D

WINDERS

See also Spools; also Machy

CONN.—Meriden
Meriden Machine Tool Co. D

CONN.—South Windham
Smith & Winchester Co. A

CONN.—Stonington
Atwood-Morrison Co. ..AA

CONN.—Waterbury
Waterbury Machine Co. (Sheet Metal; Trolley Wire) ....B

MASS.—Boston
Stoddard, Haserick, Richards & Co., 152 Congress AAA
Universal Winding Co., 95 South (Cone; Hosiery).A

MASS.—Lowell
Lowell Machine ShopAAAA

MASS.—Westfield
Foster Machine Co. (Cone Skein) ....A

MASS.—Whitinsville
Whitin Machine Works AAAA

MASS.—Worcester
American Card Clothing Co. (Bobbin) ....AAA
Cleveland Machine Wks., (Jas. H. Whittle) (Bobbin) ....A

N. J.—Paterson
Atherton Machine Co. ....B
Eastwood Co., Benjamin..A
Paterson Machine Works, 46 Warrent ....F
Royle & Sons. John (Cop)A
Sipp Electric & Machine Co., 1 Mill ....E
Watson Machine Co. ....A
Wrigley, John X

N. Y.—Cohoes
Campbell & Clute ....A
Kennedy, Thomas ....E

WINDMILLS (Con.)

MICH.—Weston
Vail & Smith ....E

MINN.—Albert Lea
Sharp Mfg. Co. C

MINN.—Faribault
Winter & Co., F. W. ....E

MINN.—Minneapolis
Northwestern Wind Engine
  Co., 110 3rd Av. ....AA

MO.—Kansas City
U. S. Water & Steam Sup-
  ply Co. ....A

NEBR.—Beatrice
Dempster Mill Mfg. Co. ..A

NEBR.—Fairbury
Fairbury Windmill Co. ..D

NEBR.—Nebraska City
Kregel, G. F. ....F

NEBR.—Omaha
U. S. Supply Co. ....B

N. Y.—Buffalo
Bagley Co., Elliott Sq...C
Squier Mfg. Co., Geo. L.,
  420 Niagara ....A

N. Y.—East Williston
Schmidt, Geo. ....G

N. Y.—Holland
Tanner, D. F. ....E

New York City
Corcoran, A. J., 11 John B
Phillips & Worthington, 136
  Liberty ....E
Pierce Well Engineering &
  Supply Co., 136 Liberty
 C

OHIO—Canton
McLain Co., Jas. H. ..AA

OHIO—Genoa
Genoa Mfg. Co. ....D

OHIO—Greenville
Ross Supply Co. C

OHIO—Massillon
Hess Snyder Co. ......AA

OHIO—Napoleon
Heller, Aller & Co.......A

OHIO—Springfield
Mast, Foos & Co. (Iron
  Turbine) ....AA
Springfield Machine Tool
  Co. ....B

TEXAS—Dallas
Southern Rock Island
  Plow Co. ....B

TEXAS—San Antonio
Collins Co., F. F. ......A

VA.—Richmond
Sydnor Pump & Well Co. D

WIS.—Burlington
Banks & Son, T. ....D

WIS.—Evansville
Baker Mfg. Co. (Steel) ..A

WIS.—Fort Atkinson
Cornish, Curtis & Greene
  Mfg. Co. ....A

WIS.—Janesville
New Doty Mfg. Co. .....B

WIS.—Racine
Freeman & Sons Mfg. Co.,
  S. (Iron; Steel) ......A
Winship Mfg. Co. C

WIS.—Sheboygan
Stehn Mfg Co. ....D

WIS.—South Superior
Duplex Mfg. Co. ....A

WIS.—Waupun
Althouse, Wheeler & Co. A

WINDOWS

CAL.—San Francisco
Butterworth, Thos. C., 15
  Polk (Memorial) X
Excelsior Redwood Co. ..A

CAL.—Jacksonville
Richardson & Co., H. H.
  (Memorial) ....H

ILL.—Chicago
Eberhardt & Co., Hugo,
  1148 W. 12th (Memorial)
  ....E
Flanagan & Biedenwey Co.,
  57-63 Illinois (Memorial)
  ....A
Ford Bros., 151 5th Av.
Knisely Bros., 28th & 5th
  Av. (Fire-proof; Wired
  Glass; Sheet Metal for
  Fire-proof Construction)A
McCully & Miles Co., 76
  Wabash Av. (Memorial)
 X
M'Farland & Co., J. C.,

WINDOWS (Con.)
27th & 5th Av. (Fire-
  proof; Wired Glass; Sheet
  Metal for Fire-proof Con-
  struction) ....B
Miller & Bro., Jas. A., 129
  So. Clinton (Wired Glass;
  Sheet Metal for Fire-proof
  Construction) ....A
Schuler & Mueller, Canal &
  Madison (Memorial) ..D
Voightmann & Co., 123 On-
  tario (Automatic Closing;
  Patent Fire-proof; Wired
  Glass; Sheet Metal for
  Fire-proof Construction)C
Western Sand Blast Co., S.
  Clinton Av. & West Jack-
  son Boul. (Memorial) C

IND.—Goshen
I. X. L. & Goshen Pump
  Co. (Screen) ....B

IOWA—Dubuque
Farley & Loetscher Mfg.
  Co. ....AA

KY.—Louisville
Blum Art Glass Co., 308
  7th (Memorial) X

MASS.—Athol
Tyler, Arthur F. (Glazed)C

MASS.—Boston
Badger & Sons, E. B., 65
  Pitt (Fire-proof; Wired
  Glass; Sheet Metal for
  Fire-proof Construction)B
Flagg & Co., L. G., Sud
  bury Bldg. (Memorial)
  ....AA
Hicks & Son, S. D., 9 Bow-
  ker (Sheet Metal for Fire-
  proof Construction) ....B
Redding, Baird & Co., 83
  Franklin (Memorial)..B
Smith-Warren Co., 93 Fed-
  eral (Fire-proof; Wired
  Glass; Sheet Metal for
  Automatic Fire-proof Con-
  struction) ....D
Spence, Moakler & Bell, 90
  Canal (Memorial) ....E

MICH.—Detroit
Friedrichs & Wolfrum, 107
  Gratiot Av. (Memorial)E

MINN.—St. Paul
St. Paul Roofing, Cornice &
  Ornament Co. (Fire-proof;
  Wired Glass; Sheet Metal
  for Fire-proof Construc-
  tion) ....B

MO.—St. Louis
Hafner Lothman Mfg. Co.
  (Glazed) ....A
Huttig Sash & Door Co.
  (Glazed) ....A
Kerwin Ornamental Glass
  Co., E. F., 925 N. 6th
  (Memorial) ....B
Wallis, A. H., 2000 &
  2002 Locust (Memorial)D

N. J.—Camden
Metallic Mfg. Co., 110 Erie
  (Sheet Metal for Fire-
  proof Construction) ....F

N. J.—Newark
O'Halloran & Sons, Thos.,
  73 Chambers (Memorial)
  ....D
Tabor Sash Co., 69 Polk
  (Sheet Metal for Fire-
  proof Construction) ....D

N. J.—Paterson
Payne, Geo. Hardy, 247
  Market (Memorial) ....F

N. Y.—Binghamton
Roberson & Son, A.
  (Glazed) ....AA

N. Y.—Brooklyn
Hecla Iron Works, N. 11th
  & Berry (Sheet Metal for
  Fire-proof Construction)
  ....AA
Heilmann, R., 177 Pacific
  (Memorial) ....E
Morgan Bros., 707 Gates
  Av. (Memorial) ....D
Summers & Lamb, cor. Jay
  & Johnson (Memorial) F

New York City
Benziger Bros., 38 Barclay
  (Memorial) ....A
Church Art Work Co., 253
  4th Av. (Memorial) ...B
Decorative Stained Glass

WINDOWS *(Con.)*
Co., 46 Wash. Sq. (Memorial) ....F
Doughtery. James, 435 W. Bway. (Memorial) ....F
Grimm, A. C., 43 E. 19th (Memorial) ....F
Haynes Co., Geo., 71 8th Av. (Fire-proof; Wired Glass; Sheet Metal for Fire-proof Construction)B
Heinigke & Bowen, 24 E. 13th (Memorial) ......B
Maginn, Charles, 17 E. 14th (Memorial) ....G
Morgan & Son, John, 32 E. 9th (Memorial) C
Rae & Co., G. 436 W. Bway. (Memorial) ....G
Righter & Kolb, 156 5th Av. (Memorial) ....E
Sellers, Benj., 80 Bible House (Memorial ....
Spiers, Richard N., 859 6th Av. (Memorial) ......E
Stottzenberg Co., 51 Barclay (Memorial) .....B
Tiffany Studios, 333 4th Av. (Memorial) ....AA

N. Y.—Syracuse
Wood Glass Co., 226 N. Salem (Memorial) C

OHIO—Canton
Berger Mfg. Co. (Sheet Metal for Fire-proof Construction) ....AA

OHIO—Cincinnati
Riodan & Co., G. C., 133 E. 5th (Memorial) ......D
Witt & Brown, 215 W. 3rd (Fire-proof; Wired Glass) A
Witt Cornice Co., Bway. & 8th (Sheet Metal for Fire-proof Construction) ....B

OHIO—Cleveland
Shakleton Co., 171 Prospect (Fire-proof; Wired Glass) F

OHIO—Dayton
Stevens Art Glass Co., 28 S. St. Claire (Memorial) H

PA.—Philadelphia
Century Stained Glass Co., 200 So. 11th (Memorial)E
Dukes Glass Works, Henry, 2129 Market (Memorial)D
Luptons Sons, David, Allegheny Av. & Tulip (Fireproof; Wired Glass; Sheet Metal for Fireproof Construction) ..AA
Meade Roofing & Cornice Co., 3717 Filbert (Sheet Metal for Fire-proof Construction) C
Quaker City Stained Glass Works, 504 Arch (Memorial) ....F
Reith, Wm., 134 N. 7th (Memorial) C
Thorn Co., J. S., 1227 Callowhill (Sheet Metal for Fire-proof Construction)A

PA.—Pittsburg
Kim & Co., Geo. A., 318 1st Av. (Memorial) ....B

R. I.—Providence
Clason Architectural Metal Co. (Fire-proof) C

WIS.—Milwaukee
Phenix Mfg. Co. (Reversible) ....F
Van Horn, Daniel (Memorial) ....H

WINES

See Liquors

WIPERS

N. J.—Bridgeton
Cox Bros. & Co. (Can)...E
N. Y.—Buffalo
West Mfg. Co. (Can) ....D
N. Y.—Syracuse
Hemingway Mfg. Co. (Can) A
Merrell-Soule Co. (Inc.) (Can) ....AA
PA.—Philadelphia
American Silk Mfg. Co., 312

WIPERS *(Con.)*
Walnut (Bicycle; Machinery) ....F

WIRE

See also Wires; Wire, Electric

ALA.—Birmingham
Alabama Steel & Wire Co. (Steel) ....AAAA
CAL.—Los Angeles
Pacific Electrical Works (Insulated) ....A
CAL.—San Francisco
California Wire Wks. (Barbed) X
CONN.—Ansonia
Ansonia Brass & Copper Co. (Br. N. Y. City) (Annunciator; Brass & Copper; Insulated; Magnet Trolley; Weather-proof; Spooling; Spring; Electric House Light; Leading; Connecting; Telegraph; Brass Pinion; Pin)AAAA
Ansonia Co., O. & C. (Corset) ....A
Ansonia Electrical Co. (Annunciator or Office Magnet; Weather-proof; Copper; Magnet; Cotton Covered; Electric House; Electric Light) ......A
Connecticut Insulating Wire Co. (Annunciator or Office; Insulated; Magnet) F

CONN.—Bridgeport
Bridgeport Brass Co. (Annunciator; Brass; Copper; German Silver; Weatherproof; Electric House; Electric Light; Insulated; Leading & Connecting; Magnet; Telegraph; Special; Bronze) ......AA
Bridgeport Deoxidized Bronze & Metal Co. (Copper) ....B
Taylor, Thomas P. (Dress Stay) ....B
CONN.—Bristol
Barnes, Wallace Co. (Brass) ....
Bristol Brass & Block Co. (Brass; German Silver) AAA
CONN.—Derby
Howe Mfg. Co. (Bent; Shaped; Pointed) .....A
CONN.—Georgetown
Gilbert & Bennett Mfg. Co. (Fence; Galvanized Iron; Hair; Iron; Tinned; Twist) ....AA
CONN.—Meriden
Todd, Henry B. (Threaded) X
CONN.—New Haven
McCluskey & Sons, H. & F. (Brass; Copper) ......F
National Steel & Wire Co. (Broom; Brush; Cable; Chain; Coppered; Gun Wrapping; Machinery; Market; Resistance; Rivet; Staple; Screw, etc.; Screen; Steel; Spooling) AAAA
National Wire Corporation (All Kinds) ....AA
New Haven Wire Mfg. Co. (All Kinds) C
CONN.—Norwich
Ossawan Mills Co. (Picture; Artificial Flower; Hair; Spool) ....B
Turner Mfg. Co. E. P. (Spooled) X
CONN.—Seymour
Seymour Mfg. Co. (Brass; Copper; German Silver; Resistance) ....AA
CONN.—Torrington
Coe Brass Mfg. Co. (Br. American Brass Co., Waterbury) (Brass; Copper; German Silver; Resistance; Trolley; Weatherproof; Spooling) ..AAAA

WIRE (Con.)
Progressive Mfg. Co.
  (Threaded) ....A
CONN.—Waterbury
American Brass Co.
  (Brass; Copper) ..AAAA
Benedict & Burnham Mfg.
  Co. (Brass; Copper; Ger-
  man Silver; Insulated;
  Electric Light; Leading;
  Connecting Magnet)AAAA
Blake & Johnson (Thread-
  ed) ....A
Chase Rolling Mill Co.
  (Brass; Copper) ....AAA
Hartley, Geo. (Cast Steel;
  Watch; Clock, etc.;
  Spring) ....D
Holmes, Booth & Haydens
  Co. (Brass; Copper; Ger-
  man Silver; Insulated;
  Magnet; Resistance; Trol-
  ley; Weather-proof; Elec-
  tric House; Electric
  Light; Leading; Connect-
  ing; Magnet; Telegraph)
                      AAA
Plume & Atwood Mfg. Co.
  (Brass; Copper; German
  Silver; Electric House)
Randolph Clowes Co.
  (Brass; Copper) ....AAA
Scovil Mfg. Co. (Alumi-
  num; Brass; Copper; Ger-
  man Silver; Resistance;
  Spring) ....AAAA
Waterbury Brass Co.
  (Brass; Bronze; Screw;
  Copper; German Silver;
  Resistance) ....?
DEL.—Marshallton
Marshallton Iron & Steel
  Co. (Corrugated; Black;
  Painted) ....D
ILL.—Chicago
American Steel & Wire Co.
  (Am. Steel Corp., N. Y.
  C.) (All Kinds) ..AAAA
Barbee Wire & Iron Works
  (Fence) ....B
Besley Co., Chas. H.
  (Bronze) ....AA
Chicago Insulated Wire Co.,
  152 Lake (Annunciator;
  Insulated; Magnet; Re-
  sistance; Weather-proof)
                        B
Grand Crossing Tack Co.,
  S. Chicago Av. & 79th
  (Baling; Barbed; Iron;
  Steel; Market; Fence) A
Illinois Steel Co. (Br. Fed-
  eral Steel Co., N. Y. C.)
  (Baling) ....AAAA
Illinois Wire Co., Monad-
  nock (Steel) ....B
Kellogg Switchboard &
  Supply Co., Green & Con-
  gress (Magnet) .....AA
McDermid Mfg., 118 W.
  Jackson Boul. (Magnet)C
Macomber & Whyte Rope
  Co. (Brass; Copper; Mar-
  ket; Iron; Steel Fence)E
Western Electric Co., 259
  So. Clinton (Insulated;
  Weather-proof; Electric
  Light; Trading; Connect-
  ing; Magnet; Telegraph)
                     AAAA
ILL.—Decatur
Chambers-Bering-Kuinlan
  Co. (Check Rower) ....A
Fairies Mfg. Co. (Check
  Rower) ....A
ILL.—DeKalb
Haish Mfg. Co. (Barbed)
                        A
Union Fence Co. (Fence)B
ILL.—East St. Louis
New Process Steel & Wire
  Co. (Barbed) ....A
ILL.—Joliet
Adam, W. J. (Fence) ....B
Bates Machine Co. (Barb-
  ing Machine) ....A
ILL.—Sandwich
Sandwich Mfg. Co.
  (Barbed) ....AA
ILL.—Sterling
Dillon-Griswold Wire Co.
  (Barbed; Annealed; Gal-
  vanized; Bright; Market;

WIRE (Con.)
  Steel) ....A
Northwestern Barb Wire
  Co. (Barbed) ....A
IND.—Anderson
Spring Steel Fence & Wire
  Co. (Music; Needle; Rope;
  Round Tempered) .....B
IND.—Crawfordsville
Crawfordsville Wire & Nail
  Co. (Steel; Barbed; Gal-
  vanized Market; Iron;
  Fence; Bond; Spring; Tel-
  egraph; Telephone) ....B
IND.—Fort Wayne
Fort Wayne Electrical Cor-
  poration (Electric Light;
  Magnet) ....AA
IND.—Jonesboro
Indiana Rubber & Insula-
  ted Wire Co. (Aerial; In-
  sulated; Rubber Covered)
                       AA
IND.—Kokomo
Kokomo Fence Machine Co.
  (Fence) ....AA
Kokomo Steel & Wire Co.
  (Barbed; Cable; Coiled
  Spring; Doubled Crimped
  Steel; Hercules made
  from four wires; Market;
  Braided; Steel) ......AAA
IND.—Marion
Marion Insulated Wire &
  Rubber Co. (Insulated)A
IND.—Muncie
Kitselman Bros. (Steel)..A
IND.—South Bend
Miller Knoblock Elec. Mfg.
  Co. (Insulated; Magnet)B
KY.—Ashland
Norton Iron Works (Inc.)
  (Market) ....AA
MASS.—Attleboro
Williams & Co., H. M.
  (Silver) ....D
MASS.—Boston
Boston Gear Works (Brass
  Pinion) ....B
Chadwick Lead Works
  (Lead) ....AA
Eastern Electric Cable Co.,
  61 Hampshire (Insulated;
  Rubber Covered) ......A
Simplex Electrical Co., 75
  Cornhill (Insulated; Wea-
  ther-proof; Leading; Con-
  necting) ....A
MASS.—Charlton
Prouty Wire Co. (Card;
  Iron) ....D
MASS.—Holyoke
Brown & Sellers Co., 21
  Ely (Fourdrinier) ....H
Buchanan & Bolt Wire Co.
  (Fourdrinier) ....B
Prentiss & Co., Geo. W.
  (All Kinds) ....AA
MASS.—New Bedford
Taunton-New Bedford Cop-
  per Co. (Copper) ....AAA
MASS.—Plymouth
Bradford, Kyle & Co. (An-
  nunciator or Office; In-
  sulated; Magnet; Resist-
  ance) ....B
MASS.—Taunton
Atlas Tack Corporation
  (Pointed) ....AAAA
MASS.—Worcester
Morgan Spring Co. (All
  Kinds) ....B
Parker Wire Goods Co.
  (Spooled) ....E
Spencer Wire Co. (All
  Kinds) ....A
Wire Gods Co. (Spooling;
  Pointed; Cast Steel; Flor-
  ists'; Iron; Steel; Market;
  Fence; Picture) ......B
Worcester Wire Co. (All
  Kinds) ....A
Wright Wire Co. ......AA
MICH.—Detroit
Detroit Copper & Brass
  Rolling Mills (Brass; Cop-
  per; German Silver)
                     AAAA
MO.—St. Louis
Broderick & Bascom Rope
  Co., 809 Main (Strand)
                       AA
Leschen & Sons Rope Co.,

WIRE (Con.)

A., 920 N. 1st (Strand) ....AAA

Ludlow Saylor Wire Co. (Barbed; Fence) ....AA

New Process Mfg. Co. (Annealed; Plain; Market; Steel) X

St. Louis Electrical Supply Co., 118 Pine (Weatherproof) C

St. Louis Wire & Iron Co. (Barbed) ....D

N. H.—Lisbon

New England Electric Works (Insulated; Magnet; Resistance) C

N. J.—Belleville

Eastwood Wire Mfg. Co. (Brass; Copper; Steel)

N. J.—Elizabethport

Waclark Wire Co. (Br. N. Y. C.) (Copper) ......A

N. J.—Harrison

Dziver-Harris Wire Co. (Brass; Copper; Insulated; Piano; Market; Resistance; Fine Wire Steel) ....B

N. J.—Jersey City

Williams & Son, E. A. (Fuse Lead Encased) AAA

N. J.—Newark

Baker & Co. (Platinum) AA

Bowers & Co., Jas. (Crinoline) ....A

Crabb & Co.. W. (Steel) B

Croselmire. C. F. (Platinum) ....B

Jenkinson & Co., R. C. (Threaded) ....A

N. J.—Riverside

Riverside Metal Co. (Resistance; Electric) .....A

N. J.—Trenton

Crescent Belting & Packing Co. (Insulated) ......A

Crescent Insulated Wire & Cable Co. (Annunciator or Office; Insulated; Magnet; Resistance; Weatherproof) ....A

Roebling's Sons Co., John A. (All Kinds) ...AAAA

Trenton Iron Co. (Br. N. Y. City) (Coppered; Market; Piano; Music; Steel; Steel Spring; Steel. Telephone; Telegraph; Tinned; Trolley; Fence; Galvanized Iron; Iron. Weaving, Music) ....AA

N. Y.—Brooklyn

Broklyn Brass & Copper Co., Pearl & Front (Br. N. Y. C.) (Brass; Copper) ..A

Igoe Bros. (Market; Steel; Iron; Tinned) C

Miller & Van Winkle (Cast Steel; Flat; Round Tempered) ....A

N. Y.—Cortland

Wickwire Bros. (Coppered; Bright; Galvanized; Steel; Tin; Iron; Fence; Market) ....AA

N. Y.—Hornellsville

Hollow Cable Mfg. Co. (Fence Braided) ......B

New York City

Bassett Co.. Robert N. (Corset. Covered) ....AA

Bishop Gutta Percha Co., 422 E. 25th (Annunciator; Feeder; Gas Fixture; Insulated. All Kinds; Magnet; Solid; Flexible Rubber Covered; Electric House; Light; Leading; Connecting; Telegraph) B

Herman Boker & Co. (Nickel; Steel; Nickel Covered) ....AAA

Brixey. W. R., 203 Bway. (Aerial; Insulated; Kerite) ....B

Cabble Excelsior Wire Mfg. Co.. Wm. (Brass; Bronze; Copper; Broom; Brush; Iron; Steel) ....B

Carey Spring Works, 240 W. 29th (Flat; Round Tempered; Brass; Steel; Steel

WIRE (Con.)

Music; Tempered; Clock Spring; Spring) ....B

Creccent Steel Co. (Steel) ....AAAA

Dewitt Wire Cloth Co. (Brass; Copper) ......A

Hammacher Schlemmer & Co., 209 Bowery (Piano or Music) ....AAA

Hartman Mfg. Co. (Barbed) X

Hazard Mfg. Co., 50 Dey (Barbed; Insulated; Fence; Market; Telegraph; Brass; Copper) ....AAAA

Hendricks Bros., 49 Cliff (Copper; Trolley)..AAAA

Hobson, Houghton & Co., 98 John (Ltd.) (Needle) ..B

Hungerford Brass & Copper Co., 497 Pearl (Brass; Copper; Bottling; German Silver) ....AA

India Rubber & Gutta Percha Insulating Co., 15 Cortlandt (Aerial; Insulated; Rubber Covered) ..B

Kemp, H. W., 165 Spring (Aluminum) ....B

Lewisohn Bros. (Inc.) (Copper) ....AAAA

Manhattan Brass Co., 338 E. 28th (Brass; Copper; Bronze) ....A

Montauk Fire Detecting Wire Co., 100 Bway. F(ire Detecting; Insulating), D

Morrison, J. L. (Bookbinders) ....D

National Conduit & Cable Co.. 41 Park Row (Insulated) ....AAAA

New York Insulated Wire Co., 114 Liberty (Insulated) ....B

Okonite Co. (Ltd.), 253 Bway. (Aerial; Insulated; Weatherproof) ......AA

Safety Insulated & Cable Wire Co.. 114 Liberty (Feeder; Insulated; Electric House; Rubber Covered) ....AAA

N. Y.—Rome

Rome Brass & Copper Co. (Brass; Copper; Spooling) ....AAAA

Spargo Wire Co., Jas. A., (Copper) C

N. Y.—Schenectady

General Electric Co. (Copper; Insulated all Kinds; Magnet; Waterproof; Weatherproof; Electric Light; Leading & Connecting; Telegraph) ....AAAA

N. Y.—Syracuse

Sanderson Bros Steel Co. (Br. Crucible Steel Co. Pittsburg, Pa.) (Needle) ....AAAA

OHIO—Cincinnati

Globe Rolling Mill Iron & Steel Co. (Coppered; Copper; Fence; Iron; Steel) ....B

OHIO—Cleveland

Cleveland Wire & Spring Co. (Heddle; Spring; Cast Steel Tempered C

Frost Wire Fence Co. (Boiled Spring; Iron; Sttel. Market; Fence) .E

Malin & Co.. 34 Long (Cast Steel; Piano or Music; Epooling; Brass; Copper; Florists; Hair; Spool; Steel; Steel Music; Tinned) ....D

OHIO—Columbus

nternational Fence & Fire Proofing Co. (Boiled Spiral Spring; Iron Steel; Market; Fence) ....A

Saurbrey. Geo. J., 259 E. Livingston Av. (Twisted in 1000 ft Boils and cut to Lengths) ....H

OHIO—Cuyahoga Falls

Cuyahoga Steel & Wire Co.,

1124

WIRE (Con.)

(Brush and Broom; Coppered; Fence, etc.; Market; Steel; Tinned; Spooling) X

PA.—Braddock
Braddock Machine & Mfg. Co. (Barbing Machines) B
Griswold Wire Co. (Annealed Market; Steel)..B

PA.—Easton
Stewart Wire Co. (Coppered; MMarket; Rivet; Staple Screw, etc.; Tinned) ....B

PA.—Johnstown
Cambria Steel Co. (Barbed; Baling; Nail; Needle; Tedder) ....AAAA

PA.—McKees Rocks
Kidd Bros & Burgher Steel Wire Co. (Polished Pinion:: Steel; Polished Steel Needle; Awl; Dental; Gimlet; Screw; Special; Watch; Wood Bit; Screw Driver) ....B

PA.—Malvern
Bishop & Co., J. (Platinum)
D

PA.—Monaco
Pittsburg Tool Steel Co. (Awl Cast Steel; Gimlet; Knurled; Needle; Pin; Screw; Screw Drived; S p e c i a l; Tempered; Watch; Wood Bit) C

PA.—New Brighton
Townsend C. C. & E. P. (Steel; Iron; Market; Fence) ....AA

PA.—Norristown
Reading Screw Co. (Coppered; Gunwrapping: Market: Rivet; Staple Screw, etc.; Cast Steel; Iron; Steel; Fence) ....A

PA.—Philadelphia
Hamilton's Sons. Thos. 1352 Vienna (Steel) ...B
Moore, Alfred F., 200 N. 3rd Annunciator (Office: Gas Fixture: Insulated: All Kinds; Magnet; Resistance: Solid and Flexible Rubber; Covered: Weatherproof; also Slow Burning; Electric House: Electric Light; Leading and Connecting Telegraph)
AAAA
Philips Townsend & Co. ..E
Phosphor Bronze Smelting Co., 2200 Wash'n (Phosphor. Bronze: Telegraph; Cord: Flat: Soft; Coppered: Annealed; Spring)..A
Tatham & Bros. (Lead Encased) ....AAA
White Dental Mfg. Co. S. S., (Gold; Gun Screw: Platinum; Silver) AAAA

PA.—Pittsburg
Crucible Steel Co. of America, Frick B'ld'g (Steel)
AAAA
Hussey & Co., C. G. (Brass: Copper) ....AAA
National Cable & Wire Co. Westinghouse B'ld'g (Insulated: Rubber Covered)
A
Oliver Wire Co. (Barbed: Coppered: Galvanized; Iron: Market; Tinned)
AAAA
Pittsburg Electrical & Machine Works (Electric: House) ....E
Pittsburg Reduction Co.. Smith B'ld'g (Bare & Insulated: Aluminum: Aluminum Bronze: Cable)
AAA
Pittsburg Steel Co.. Peoples' Sav. Bank B'ld'g (Barbed: Cable: Market: Steel: Tinned) ....AAAA
Standard Underground Cable Co. (All Kinds) ....AAA
United States Wire & Nail Co.. Lewis B. (Plain Steel) ....A

WIRE (Con.)
PA.—Reading
Carpenter Steel Co., (Br. N. Y. City) (Piano or Music; High Grade Steel) ....AA

PA.—Sharpsburg
Globe Wire Co. (Steel)..A

R. I.—Bristol
National India Rubber Co. (Insulated Weatherproof)
AAAA

R. I.—Pawtucket
Collyer Insulated Wire Co. (Annunciator; Insulated; Weatherproof) ....A
Fuller & Son, Geo. H. (Gold; Jewellers; Silver) ......A
Phillips Insulated Wire Co. (Insulated; Electric House; Electric- Light).A
Rhode Island Electric Wks. (Insulated; Magnet) ...B

R. I.—Phillipsdale
Washburn Wire Co. (All Kinds) ....AAAA

R. I.—Providence
American Electrical Works (All Kinds) .....AAAA
American Screw Co. (Pointed) ....AAAA
American Seamless Wire Co. (Jewelry) ....B
Bourn Rubber Co. (Insulated) ....A
Briggs & Sons Co., J. (Jewelers) ....A
Improved Seamless Wire Co. (Jewelers') ....B
Linton Co., P. & A. (Jewelers') ....B
Morgan Jewelry Co. (Jewelers') ....F
United Wire & Supply Co. (Jewelers') ....AA
Wall & Co., A. T. (All Kinds) C

WIS.—Janesville
Janesville Barb Wire Co. (Barbed) ....B

WIRE:
ELECTRIC

CONN.—Ansonia
Ansonia Elec. Co., The (Insulated) .... A
CONN.—Wallinford
New York Insulated Wire Co. (Insulated & Cables) B
CONN.—Waterbury
Holmes Booth & Hayden Co. (Cotton Insulated) .. AAAA
N, J.—Passaic
Okonite Co. (Insulated Electric) .... A
N. J.—Trenton
Roebling's Sons. Co., Jno., A. (Insulated) ....AAAA
N. H.—Lisbon
New England Elec. Wks. (Magnet & Resistance) C
New York City
Berlin & Trosky (Bonnet) B
Martin & Co., Thos. (Bonnet) ....D
N. Y.—Yonkers
India Rubber & Gutta Percha Insulating Co. ..B
PA.—Philadelphia
Moore. Alf. F. (Insulated Electrical) ....AAAA
PA.—Wilkesbarre
Hazard Mfg. Co. (Insulated Electric) .... AAA
R. I.—Pawtucket
Collyer Insulated Wire Co. (Insulated Electric) ....B
Phillips Insulated Wire Co. (Insulated Electric) ....A
R. I. Electrical Wks. (Magnet) C
R. I.—Providence
Am. Electrical Wks. (Insulated Electric) AAAA

WIRES

CONN.—Bethel
Shepard & Son, Geo., A. (Hat) ....F
CONN.—Chester
Brooks & Sons, M. S.

WIRE (*Con.*)
(Drop; Guide) ...... B
CONN.—New Haven
McCluskey & Sons, H. & T.
(Cylinders; Fourdrinier
Washer) ....F
New Haven Wire Mfg. Co.
(Hat) C
CONN.—New Windham
Hartson Co., L. M.
(Drop) ....E
IND.—Crawfordsville
Crawfordsville Wire & Nail
Co. (Bond; Galvanized) B
MASS.—Attleboro
Williams & Co., H. M.
(Ear) ....D
MASS.—Fitchburg
Davis & &Son, Ezekiel
(Fourdrinier) X
MASS.—Hopedale
Draper Co. (Guide) ..AAAA
MASS.—Lawrence
Hall, F. A. & P. (Drop) P
MASS.—Springfield
Bigelow Cheney Wire Works
(Fourdinier) ....A
MASS.—Worcester
Wire Goods Co., 20 Union
(Guide) ....B
New York City
De Witt Wire Cloth Co.
(Fourdinier) ....A
R. I.—Pawtucket
Blackstone Reed & Harness
Co. (Drop Guide) .... G
Fuller & Son, Geo. H.
(Ear) ....A
Jencks Mfg. Co., E.
(Guide) ....AA
R. I.—Providence
American Supply Co.
(Guide) ....AA
Heimberger & Lind (Ear) F

WITCHHAZEL

CONN.—Clinton
Pratt Chem. Co. ....A
Strickland, W. G. C
CONN.—Durham
Dickinson & Co., E. E. ..A
CONN.—Essex
Dickinson, Jr., P. M. ..D
Dickinson & Co., E. E. ..A
Lenifect Co. ....A
CONN.—Norwich
Johnson & Co. ....A
ILL.—Chicago
Atwood & Steele, 18 River
C
Puhl-Webb Co., 119 W.
Randolph C
MD.—Baltimore
McCormick & Co. ....D
MASS.—Malden
Gould & Bro., S. W......B
MO.—St. Louis
Tilden Co., 1718 Olive....A
N. H.—Hubbard
Gould & Bros., S. W......B
N. J.—Newark
Hallock, Denton & Co.....B
N. Y.—New Lebanon
Tilden Co. ....A
New York City
Burton & Co., W., 75 Bar-
clay ....B
Colonial Chem. Co., 4 War-
ren ....A
Condon & Co., Thos. F., 220
B'way C
Leggett & Co., Francis H.
AAAA
N. Y.—Utica
Sheehan Fruit Syrup Co...D
OHIO—Newark
Styron. Beggs & Co......A
PA.—Easton
World Refg. Co..........D

WOOD

For Ground Wood, see Pulp
& Fibre

CONN.—Bridgeport
Wheel & Wood Bending Co.
(Bent) ....B
CONN.—New Haven
Dann Bros. & Co. (Bent to
Order) ....B
IND.—Bremen
Wright, John J. (Bent)...B

WOOD (*Con.*)
New York City
Estes & Sons, E. B., 45
John (Bail) ....AA
OHIO—Akron
Bakes-McMillian Co. (Pail;
Bail) ....B

WOODEN-WARE

ALA.—Bridgeport
Bridgeport Woodenware
Mfg. Co. ....B
ALA.—Mobile
Partin Malcolm ....D
CAL.—San Francisco
Cupples Woodenware Co., S.
(Br.), 116 Cal...AAAA
Pacific Woodenware &
Cooperage Co., 122 Davis
B
Unna Co. of San Francisco,
Harry, 113 Battery.....A
COLO.—Denver
Craffey M. C
Post & Co., H. H........C
CONN.—New Haven
Elm City Mfg. Co., 379
State C
Bronson & Townsend Co...D
GA.—Atlanta
Atlanta Woodenware Co..B
ILL.—Chicago
Chicago Woodenware Co..E
Creamery Pack. Mfg. Co.
(Butter Tubs & Boxes)
AAAA
Cupples Woodenware Co.,
Sam'l, 55 So. Water
AAAA
Escanaba Woodenware Co.
(Wood Dishes, etc.)....A
Higbie, F. K., 35 So. Wa-
ter (Mfr's Agts. Pails,
etc.) ....D
King & Co., C. L., 13 La
Salle ....A
Mann Bros., 6 Wabash Av.
AA
Menasha Woodenware Co.,
25 W. Erie ....AA
Schmitt., Bromann & Co.,
80 W. Randolph........B
Sefton Mfg. Co., J. W.
241 S. Jeff. (Oyster
Pails) ....AA
ILL.—Elgin
Elgin Butter Tub Co.
(B. Tubs) ....B
ILL.—Moline
Dimock, Gould & Co...AA
ILL.—Peoria
National Cooperage &
Woodenware Co.........B
ILL.—Rockford
Palmer Co., H. H.
(Churns) ....D
IND.—Anderson
Sefton Mfg. Co., J. W.
(Pails) ....AA
IND.—Eaton
Standard Washboard Co..C
IND.—Indianapolis
Tucker & Dorsey Mfg. Co.,
State Av. & Bates...A
Udell Wks., 28 1-2 Barnes
A
IND.—Martinsville
Davis Cooperage Co. (Kegs;
Tubs; Half Barrels)..B
IOWA—Clinton
Clinton Paper Co........B
IOWA—Davenport
Brammer Mfg. Co., H. F
B
IOWA—Dubuque
Dubuque Woodenware &
Lumber Co. ....A
KY.—Louisville
Gould & Co., C. L., 145 E.
Jeff. (Mfrs. & Mfrs.
Agts.) ....D
MAINE—Biddeford
Biddeford & Natick Mfg.
Co. ....D
MAINE—Portland
Kendall & Whitney......B
MAINE—West Baldwin
Harding, F. D..........D
MAINE—West Paris
Mann, Lewis M. (Pails).C

WOODENWARE (Con.)

MD.—Baltimore

Southern Veneer Package
Co. C
Wysham Co., 16 W. Lombard ....D

MASS.—Ashley

Flint, L. E. (Tubs).....D

MASS.—Baldwinsville

Holman & Hanis (Pails;
Tubs, etc.) ....D

MASS.—Boston

Haskell, W. A., 37 John.D
Shepard, Clark & Co., 83
Com'l C

MASS.—Lowell

Clark, John A...........D

MASS.—West Acton

Hall Bros. (Pails)......B

MASS.—Winchendon

Clark, Wilder P. (Candy;
Lard; Fish & Jelly Pails;
Oyster Tubs)..........A
Murdock & Co., E........B
Woodcock Mills (Candy;
Lard; Fish & Jelly Pails;
Oyster Tubs) ....A

MICH.—Bay City

Bousfeld & Co. ....A

MICH.—Bellaire

Richardi & Bechtold....B
Richardi, H. ....B

MICH.—Cadillac

Cummer Mfg. Co......D

MICH.—Copemish

Chapman & Sargent Co. .
(Bowls) ....D

MICH.—Crystal Falls

Crystal Falls Woodenware
Co. C

MICH.—Decatur

Hinkley & Co., Robt.
(Measures) ....D

MICH.—Escanaba

Escanaba Woodenware Co.
(Clothes Pins; Broom
Handles; Dishes, etc.)A
Nat'l Cooperage & Woodenware Co. ....AA

MICH.—Frankfort

East Shore Woodenware
Co. ....B

MICH.—Grand Haven .

Kilbourn & Co., Silas (Fish
& Syr. Pk'gs) ....AA

MICH.—Grand Rapids

Mich. Barrel Co. (Measures) ....A

MICH.—Kalkaska

Freeman Mfg. Co........C

MICH.—Ludington

Ludington Woodenware Co.
C

MICH.—Petoskey

Lovelace & Birkett......A

MICH.—Saginaw

Palmerton Woodenware
Co., F. G.............AA
Saginaw Mfg. Co.......A

MICH.—St. Joseph

Colby Hinckley Co. (Br.)
(Fr. Pack.) ....B
Ward Kent Co. (Br.)
(Fr. Boxes) ....A

MICH.—South Haven

Pierce-Williams Co. (Fr.
Pkgs.) C

MICH.—Traverse City

Oval Wood Dish Co.
(Dishes) ....B
Wells-Higman Co. (Br.)
(Fr. Pkgs.) ....A

MICH.—West Bay City

Beutal Cooperage & Woodenware Co. ....B

MINN.—Minneapolis

Bousfeld Woodenware Co. A
A
Donaldson Co., Wm., Nicollet Av., S. E. Cor. 6th
AA
McVoy Tub, Pail & Package Co., 11th Av. & Water, N. E. (Mfrs. Tubs;
Pails, etc.) C

MO.—Chillicothe

Jackson Woodenware Co.,
T. E. ....D

MO.—Kansas City

Jackson Woodenware Co.,
T. E., Bd. Trade Bldg.
D

WOODENWARE (Con.)

MO.—St. Louis

Crunden-Martin Woodenware Co., 309 So. Main
A
Cupples Woodenware Co.,
S. ....AAAA
St. Louis Woodenware
Wks., Ft. St. George AA

N. H.—East Jaffrey

Annett Mfg. Co........C

N. H.—Enfield

Bradford, J. (Agt.)......C
Wilson, Wm. ....D

N. H.—Keene

Beaver Mills (Pails; Tubs;
Pkgs.) ....A
Griffin & Dana (Pails)...D

N. H.—Marlboro Depot

Fuller, L. A............D

N. H.—Milford

Peirce & Co., W. E.....D

N. H.—Nashua

Nashua Novelty Wks....B

N. H.—Rindge

Wellington, E. ....D

N. H.—Troy

Butterick & Co., E.
(Pails) ....D
Farrar, C. D...........D

N. H.—Westport

Marsh, J. ....D

N. H.—West Swanzey

Whitcomb Mfg. Co.......B

N. Y.—Albany

Doran, J. J............D

N. Y.—Brooklyn

Cooper & McKee........A
Lins & Sons, H., 4 Wash.
Av. Wallabout Mkt....A

N. Y.—Buffalo

Kirkholder & Rausch, 165
Mich. C

N. Y.—Conklingville

Sumner, A. A..........AA

N. Y.—Cuba

Bates Mfg. Co., W. A.
(Pails; Dairy) C

N. Y.—French Mountain

Reed & Co., J..........D

N. Y.—Harrisville

Universal Woodenware Co.
D

N. Y.—Newark

Arcadia Mfg. Co........D

New York City

Barron & Co., J. S., 202
W. B'way ....A
Cavanagh Bros. & Knapp,
111 Reade C
Cordley & Hayes, 172
Duane ....AAA
Cupples Woodenware Co.,
Sam'l, 359 G'wich.AAAA
Earley's Sons Co., J., 127
Reade ....A
Fink, D., 676 Hudson ..B
Goldberg, C. H. & E. S.,
114 Reade ....B
Jansen, Edward ....A
Kornahrens, H., 111
Murray ....B
Lane, L., 41 Harrison...B
Lovell Mfg. Co., 54 Warren ....AA
Mace & Co., L. H., 111 E.
Houston ....B
Saginaw Mfg. Co., (Br.)
44 Dey (Mfrs.).......A
Stokes & Co., Wm., A., 30
Warren C

N. Y.—Potsdam

Thatcher & Co., H. D.
(Lard Pails & Butter
Pkgs.) ....A

N. Y.—Saratoga Springs

Guiltenan, M. C

N. Y.—Sidney

Sidney Novelty Co......B

N. Y.—Syracuse

Thurwachter & Sons, L. L.
C

N. Y.—Troy

Warren & Co., J. M.AAAA

N. Y.—Waverly

Amer. Basket & Mfg. Co.
A

N. C.—Fayetteville

Fayetteville Woodenware
Co. C

OHIO—Chagrin Falls

Bullard & March........A

OHIO—Cincinnati

1127

WOODENWARE (Con.)

Ault Woodenware Co., 6tn & Carr (Mops) ......A
Curry Woodenware Co., 22 E. 2nd ....B
OHIO—Cleveland
Am. Washboard Co., 1747 E. Mad. ....AA
Arnold Woodenware Co., 138 Water ....B
OHIO—Columbus
Columbus Mdse Co. ....B
Tracy-Welks Co. ....A
OHIO—Conneaut
Record Mfg. Co. (Butter Tubs) ....B
OHIO—Delta
Oval Wood Dish Co. ....AA
OHIO—Mantua Station
Hine & Cook (Pails) ....A
OHIO—Marysville
Lentz & Sons, C. F. (B. Tubs) ....D
OHIO—Perryburg
Chapman & Sargent Co. ..B
OHIO—Sidney
Anderson & Carothers (Churns) C
CHIO—Toledo
Amer. Woodenware Mfg. Co. ....D
OHIO—Wapakoneta
Brown & Co., M. (Churns) ....A
Standard Churn Co. (Churn Mfrs.) ....A
ORE.—Portland
Zan Bros. ....B
PA.—Allentown
Grimley, J. M. ....B
Yeager & Co., L. H. ..AA
Ziegler & Co., A. J. ....B
PA.—Altoona
Prutzman & Co., H. S. ..B
PA—Bellaire
Mickley, S. K. (Forks; Rakes) ....D
PA.—Bradford
Union Dish Co. (Dishes; Toothpicks) ....D
PA.—Bristol
Morgan & Co., A. (Washboards) ....D
PA.—Clearfield
Clearfield Woodenware Co. ....D
PA.—Erie
Erie Pail Factory (Ltd.) (Pails) ....B
PA.—Norristown
Scheetz, Remandus ......A
PA.—Philadelphia
Hammond & Son, J. T. ..B
Landis & Co., 420 Market ....A
Needl & Co., W., 609 Market C
PA.—Pittsburg
Knorr, W. L., 1108 Penn. Av. ....B
PA.—Port Allegheny
Lav & Balcom Mfg. Co. (Butter Dishes) ....D
PA.—Scranton
Brown, F. P. ....D
R. I.—Providence
Morse, F. W. ....D
TENN.—Chattanooga
Trotter Bros. ....A
TENN.—Nashville
Weil Bros. ....D
VT.—Brandon
Newton & Thompson Mfg. Co. ....B
VA.—Richmond
Richmond Wood Wrkg Co. ....B
Richmond Cedar Works ....AAA
WASH.—Seattle
Cooper & Levy ....B
Schwabacher Bros. & Co. (Inc.) ....AA
Seller & Co., M. ....B
WASH.—Spokane
Meese & Co., G. ....D
WIS.—Berlin
Luther & Co., H. ....D
WIS.—Dundas
Dundas Woodenware Co. ....D
WIS.—Fond-du-Lac
Bowen Mfg. Co. ....B

WOODENWARE (Con.)

WIS.—Kiel
Kiel Woodenware Co. C
WIS.—Menasha
Menasha Woodenware Co. ....AA
WIS.—Milwaukee
Hoch & Loeber Co., 121 Clybourn ....B
WIS.—Sheboygan
Dillingham Mfg. Co. ...A
WIS.—Two Rivers
Two Rivers Mfg. Co. ....AA

WOODWORK: BUILDERS

ALA.—Birmingham
Brewer, W. P. (Door; Window Frames; Outside Blinds) ....A
Warrior Mfg. Co. (Sashes; Doors; Blinds) ....A
ALA.—Florence
Florence Wagon Wrks. (Porch Columns) ......A
ARK.—Appleton
Yow, R. F. (Casings) ....D
ARK.—Brinkley
Brinkley Car Wks. & Mfg. Co. (Outside Blinds) D
ARK.—Lester
Lester Mill Wrks. (Caseings) ....A
ARK.—Little Rock
Abeles & Co., C. T. (Sashes; Doors; Blinds) ....A
ARK.—Marianna
L'Anguille Lumber Co. (Sashes; Doors; Blinds) ....A
ARK.—Pine Bluff
Bluff City Lumber Co. (Sashes; Doors; Blinds) ....AAA
CAL.—Los Angeles
Kerchoff-Cuzner Mill & Lumber Co. (Sashes; Doors; Blinds) ....AAA
Raphael Co., H. (Sashes; Doors; Blinds) ....AA
Smith, Jno. A. (Venetian Blinds) ....H
CAL.—Sacramento
Friend & Terry Lumber Co. (Sashes ;Doors; Blinds) ....A
CAL.—San Francisco
California Door Co., 18 Drumm (Sashes; Doors; Blinds) ....AA
Hammond Lumber Co., Hayward Bldg. (Sashes; Doors; Blinds) ....A
Hinds & Co., Edw. B., 328 Howard (Inside Sliding; Venetian Blinds) ......B
Scott & Van Arsdale Lumber Co. (Sashes; Doors; Blinds) ....AAAA
Sierra Lumber Co., 320 Sansome (Sashes; Doors; Blinds) ....A
Wilson & Bro., 22 Drumm (Sashes; Doors; Blinds) ....AA
CAL.—San Jose
Chase Lumber Co., S. H. (Sashes; Doors; Blinds ....A
Santa Clara Valley Mill & Lumber Co. (Sashes; Doors; Blinds) ....AA
CAL.—Santa Clara
Pacific Mfg. Co. (Sashes; Doors; Blinds) ......AA
COLO.—Delta
Stockham & Hillman Co. (Sashes; Doors; Blinds) ....A
COLO.—Denver
Bingham & Co., H. W. (Sashes; Doors; Blinds) ....A
English Lumber Co., R. W. (Sashes; Doors; Blinds) ....A
Hallack & Howard Lumber Co. (Sashes; Doors; Blinds) ....A
McPhee & McGinnity (Sashes; Doors; Blinds)

WOODWORK *(Con.)*

Sayre-Newton Lumber Co.
(Sashes; Doors; Blinds)
AAAA

COLO.—Pueblo
Newton Lumber Co. (Outside Blinds) ....AAAA

CONN.—Bridgeport
Miller Lumber Co. (Sashes; Doors; Blinds) ....AAA

CONN.—New Britain
Rogers & Co., D. N. (Hardwood; Veneered Doors)
A

CONN.—Torrington
Hotchkiss Bros. Co. (Sashes; Doors; Blinds) ..AA

CONN.—Waterbury
Waterbury Lumber & Coal Co. (Sashes; Doors; Blinds) ....D

DEL.—Wilmington
Simmons & Bro., S. G. (Sashes; Doors; Blinds)
A

FLA.—Apalachicola
Cypress Lumber Co. (Sashes; Doors; Blinds) ..AA

FLA.—Palatka
Selden Cypress Door Co. (Sashes; Doors; Blinds)
A

GA.—Augusta
Augusta Lumber Co. (Sashes; Doors; Blinds) ....A
Perkins Mfg. Co. (Sashes; Doors; Blinds) ....A

GA.—Dalton
Farrar Lumber Co. (Sashes; Doors; Blinds) ....A

GA.—Gainsville
Queen City Planing Mill Co. (Sashes; Doors; Blinds) A

GA.—Macon
Willingham Sash & Door Co. (Sashes; Doors; Blinds)

GA.—Savannah
Bacon & Sons, A. S. (Sashes; Doors; Blinds) ....A
Southern Pine Co. (Sashes; Doors; Blinds) ......AAA

GA.—Washington
Washington Mfg. Co. (Sashes; Doors; Blinds) A

IDAHO—Boise City
Shaw Lumber Co. (Sashes; Doors; Blinds) ....A

ILL.—Belleville
Reis, M. & H. (Sashes; Doors; Blinds) ....A

ILL.—Bloomington
Harwood & Bro., W. S. (Sashes; Doors; Blinds)
A

ILL.—Blue Island
Schmitt Bros. (Sashes; Doors; Blinds) ....A

ILL.—Chicago
California Mfg. Co., 922 S. Troy (Porch Columns) ..B
Chicago Sash, Door & Blind Mfg. Co., 48 W. North
A
Chicago Veneered Door Co., Chamber of Com. (Hardwood; Veneered Doors)
D
Dodge & Co., H. B., 108 La Salle (Inside Sliding; Venetian Blinds) ....H
Foster, Munger & Co., 20th & S. Sangamon (Inside Folding; Venetian Blinds; Porch Columns) ......A
Gauger & Co., John A., 22d & Lafflin (Sashes; Doors; Blinds; Porch Columns)
AA
Means & Co., Chas. H., 1113 Belmont Av. (Sashes; Doors; Blinds) ......AA
Morgan Sash & Door Co., So. Union & W. 22d (Sashes; Doors; Blinds)
A
Nollau & Wolff Mfg. Co., 45 Fullerton (Sashes; Doors; Blinds) ....A
Palmer, Fuller & Co., 2244 Lumber (Sashes; Doors; Inside; Outside Folding

WOODWORK *(Con.)*
Blinds; Porch Columns) B

Radford Sash & Door Co., 192 W. 22d (Sashes; Doors; Inside Folding Blinds) ....A
Roberts & Co., E. L., W. 22d & Union Pl. (Sashes; Doors; Inside; Outside Folding Blinds; Door; Window Frames; Porch Columns) ....A
Schroth & Ahrens, 635 S. Halsted (Sashes; Doors; Blinds) ....A
South Side Lumber Co., 22d & Ashland Av. (Sashes; Doors; Blinds) ....A
True & True Co., Blue Island & Lincoln Avs. (Sashes; Doors; Blinds)
A

ILL.—East St. Louis
Goedde & Co., B. (Sashes; Doors; Blinds) ....A

ILL.—Galena
Hoskins & Co., Wm. (Sashes; Doors; Blinds) ....A

ILL.—Jacksonville
Andrews & Sons, R. P. (Sashes; Doors; Blinds)
AA

ILL.—Lagrange
Lord Lumber Co. (Hardwood; Veneered Doors)
B

ILL.—Mattoon
Andrews Bros. (Sashes; Doors; Blinds) ....AA

ILL.—Moline
Dimock, Gould & Co. (Sashes; Doors; Blinds)
AA

ILL.—Peoria
Cutright & Russell (Sashes; Doors; Blinds) ....A

ILL.—Peru
Zimmerman & Co., C. (Sashes; Doors; Blinds)
A

ILL.—Rock Island
Rock Island Lumber & Mfg. Co. (Outside Blinds)
AA
Rock Island Sash & Door Wks. (Sashes; Doors; Blinds) ....AA

ILL.—Springfield
Vredenburgh Lumber Co. (Sashes; Doors; Blinds)
A

IND.—Cicero
Cicero Lumber Co. (Sashes; Doors; Blinds) ....A

IND.—Fort Wayne
Gilmartin, Edw. (Sashes; Doors; Blinds) ....A

IND.—Goshen
Goshen Sash & Door Co. (Sashes; Doors; Blinds)
A
I. X. L. & Goshen Pump Co. (Blinds, Hardwood; Veneered Doors) ....B

IND.—Indianapolis
Eldridge Lumber Co., E. H. (Hardwood; Veneered Doors) C
Greer-Wilkinson Lumber Co. (Sashes; Doors; Blinds)
AA
Indianapolis Mfrs. & Carpenters Union (Sashes; Doors; Blinds) ....A
Michigan Lumber Co. (Sashes; Doors; Blinds) ..AA

IND.—Kokomo
Armstrong-Landon Co. (Sashes; Blinds; Hardwood; Veneered Doors)
... A

IND.—Lafayette
Biggs Pump Co., L. F. (Porch Columns) ......A
Taylor Lumber Co., Hy. (Sashes; Doors; Blinds)
A

IND.—Seymour
Carter-Travis Co. (Hardwood; Veneered Doors)
D

IOWA—Burlington
Gilbert-Hedge Lumber Co.

WOODWORK (Con.)
(Sashes; Doors; Blinds)

IOWA—Carroll A

Joyce Co., W. T. (Sashes; Doors; Blinds) ....A

IOWA——Cedar Rapids

Harris & Cole Bros. (Porch Columns) ....AA

Williams & Hunting Co. (Outside Blinds) ......B

IOWA—Clinton

Curtis Bros. & Co. (Inside Sliding Blinds; Sashes; Doors; Columns) ....AA

IOWA—Council Bluffs

Hoagland, Geo. A. (Sashes; Doors; Blinds) ......AA

IOWA—Davenport

McClelland Co. (Sashes; Doors; Blinds) ....A

Roberts Co., U. N. (Sashes; Doors; Blinds) ....AA

IOWA—Dubuque

Carr, Ryder & Adams Co. (Sashes; Doors; Blinds) AA

Farley & Loetcher Mfg. Co. (Outside Blinds; Hardwood; Veneered Doors; Sashes) ....AA

IOWA—Fort Madison

Atlee, S. & J. C. (Sashes; Blinds; Doors) ......AAA

OHIO—Independence

Independence Lumber Co. (Sashes; Doors; Blinds) A

IOWA—Lyons

Disbrow & Co., M. A. (Sashes; Hardwood; Veneered Doors; Blinds) ..A

IOWA—Muscatine

Huttig Mfg. Co. (Sashes; Hardwood; Veneered Doors; Outside Blinds) AA

Roach & Musser Sash & Door Co. (Sashes Hardwood; Veneered Doors; Blinds) ....AAA

IOWA—Sioux City

Queal & Co., J. H. (Sashes; Doors; Blinds) .....AAA

IOWA—Spencer

Floete Lumber Co. (Sashes; Doors; Blinds) ....A

IOWA—Waterloo

Nauman Co. (Sashes; Doors; Blinds) ....A

KANS.—Atchison

Carlisle-Pennel Lumber Co. (Sashes; Doors; Blinds)

KANS.—Independence

Rock Island Lumber & Mfg. Co. (Sashes; Doors; Blinds) ....AA

KANS.—Kansas City

Badger Lumber Co. (Sashes; Doors; Blinds) ....AAA

Byrne Lumber Co., John M. (Sashes; Doors; Blinds) A

KANS.—McPherson

Lake Superior Lumber Co. (Sashes; Doors; Blinds) A

KANS.—Parsons

Clark & Bates Lumber Co. (Sashes; Doors; Blinds) A

KANS.—Wichita

United Sash & Door Co. (Sashes; Doors; Blinds) AA

KY.—Louisville

Bell & Coggeshall Co. (Sashes; Doors; Blinds) A

Lortz & Frey Planing Mill Co. (Hardwood; Veneered Doors) ....B

KY.—Paducah

Langstaff-Orm Mfg. Co. (Sashes; Doors; Blinds) AA

LA.—Franklin

Hanson Lumber Co., Albert (Sashes; Doors; Blinds) AA

LA.—Lutcher

Lutcher & Moore Cypress Lumber Co. (Sashes;

WOODWORK (Con.)
Hardwood; Veneered Doors; Blinds) ....AAAA

LA.—New Iberia

Iberia Cypress Co. (Sashes; Doors; Blinds) .....AA

LA.—New Orleans

Berwick Lumber Co. (Sashes; Doors; Blinds) ....AA

Lambow & Noel Lumber Co. (Sashes; Doors; Blinds) A

L'hote Lumber Mfg. Co. (Sashes; Doors; Blinds) AA

LA.—Patterson

Cypress Tank & Mfg. Co. (Hardwood; Veneered Doors; Porch Columns) B

Trellue Cypress Lumber Co. (Sashes; Doors; Blinds) AA

LA.—Ramos

Ramos Lumber & Mfg. Co. (Ltd.) (Outside Blinds; Door; Window Frames) AA

LA.—Shreveport

Victoria Lumber Co. (Sashes; Doors; Blinds) ....A

MAINE—Augusta

Lawrence, Newhall & Page Co. (Sashes; Doors; Blinds; Porch Columns) AA

MAINE—Bangor

Morse & Co. (Sashes; Doors; Blinds) ....A

MAINE—Belfast

Matthews Bros. (Blinds).B

MAINE—Portland

Berlin Mills Co. (Sashes; Doors; Blinds) .. AAAA

Burrows Co., E. T. (Car; Train Blinds) ....AA

MD.—Baltimore

Baltimore Blind Co., 18 W. Camden (Outside Venetian Blinds) ....F

Baltimore Sash & Door Co., (Sashes; Doors; Blinds) A

Duker & Co., Otto (Sashes; Doors; Blinds) ......AA

Hiss Co., Philip (Inside Blinds) X

Sloan & Bro., Geo. F. (Sashes; Doors; Blinds)

MD.—Havre de Grave

Dubois, John E. (Sashes; Doors; Blinds) ...AAAA

MASS.—Athol

Tyler, Arthur F. (Outside; Inside; Venetian Blinds; Door; Window Frames) C

MASS.—Boston

Carlisle, E. A. & Pope Co., 2 Sudbury (Sashes; Doors; Blinds) ....A

Cypress Lumber Co., 153 Milk (Sashes; Hardwood; Veneered Doors; Blinds) AA

Hastings & Co., A. W., 142 Friend (Sashes; Doors; Blinds) ....A

Stearns Lumber Co., A. T., 166 Devonshire (Sashes; Hardwood; Veneered Doors; Blinds; Capitals; Porch Columns) .....AA

MASS.—Fall River

Borden Cook & Co. (Sashes; Doors; Blinds) ....A

MASS.—Holyoke

Merrick Lumber Co. (Sashes; Doors; Blinds) A

MASS.—Lawrence

Briggs & Allyn Mfg. Co. (Sashes; Doors; Blinds)

Lawrence Lumber Co. (Sashes; Doors; Blinds) A

MASS.—Lynn

Brockway - Smith Corp. (Sashes; Doors; Blinds) A

MASS.—So. Hadley

Howard, Gaylord & Co.

WOODWORK (Con.)
(Sashes; Doors; Blinds)
A

MASS.—Springfield
Walker & Co., T. M. (Sashes; Doors; Blinds) ...AA
MASS.—Taunton
Taunton Lumber Co. (Sashes; Doors; Blinds) ..AA
Williams & Co., A. G. (Sashes; Doors; Blinds) A
MASS.—Worcester
Rice & Griffin Mfg. Co. (Hardwood; Veneered Doors) C
MICH.—Bay City
Lamont, Matthew (Hardwood Veneered Doors)..B
MICH.—Calumet
Armstrong-Thielman Lumber Co. (Sashes; Doors; Blinds) ....A
MICH.—Detroit
Heubner Mfg. Co. (Hardwood; Veneered Doors) D
Kotcher, C. W. (Sashes; Doors; Blinds) ......AA
Sibley Lumber Co., F. M. (Sashes; Doors; Blinds) A
Vinton Co. (Sashes; Doors; Blinds) ....A
Weber & Co., J. F. (Sashes; Doors; Blinds) ......AA
MICH.—Grand Rapids
Fuller & Rice Lumber & Mfg. Co. (Sashes; Doors; Blinds) ....AA
Ocker & Ford Mfg. Co. (Hardwood; Veneered Doors) .... B
MICH.—Kalamazoo
Dewing & Sons (Sashes; Doors; Blinds; Porch Columns) ....AAA
Kalamazoo Interior Finish Co. (Hardwood; Veneered Doors) C
MICH.—Lansing
Rikered Lumber Co. (Hardwood; Veneered Doors) D
MICH.—Lapeer
Tuttle & Burritt (Hardwood; Veneered Doors) F
MICH.—Manistique
Western Lumber Co. (Sashes; Doors; Blinds) ..AA
MICH.—Marquette
Read & Co., F. W. (Sashes; Doors; Blinds) ....AA
MICH.—Marysville
Mills, N. & B. (Sashes; Doors; Blinds) ....A
MICH.—Muskegon
Gray Mfg. Co. (Hardwood; Veneered Doors) C
McGraft & Son (Sashes; Doors; Blinds) ....A
Mann-Watson Co. (Porch Columns) ....AAA
MICH.—Newaygo
Kennicott, Edw. (Moulded Base Boards; Porch Balusters) ....D
MICH.—Saginaw
Avery & Co. (Sashes; Doors; Blinds) .....AAA
Bliss & Van Auken (Sashes; Doors; Blinds) ......AAA
Booth & Boyd Lumber Co. (Sashes; Doors; Blinds) A
Mershon Co., Wm. B. (Sashes; Doors; Blinds) A
Schuette & Co., Wm. (Sashes; Doors; Blinds) ...AA
MICH.—St. Joseph
Compound Door Co. (Hardwood; Veneered) ......B
MINN.—Cloquet
Northern Lumber Co. (Sashes; Doors; Blinds) AAAA
MINN.—Duluth
Scott-Graff Lumber Co. (Sashes; Doors; Blinds) AA
MINN.—Minneapolis
Bardwell-Robinson Co.

WOODWORK (Con.)
(Sashes; Doors; Outside Blinds) ....AA
Curtis & Yale Co. (Sashes; Doors; Blinds) ......AA
Fulton & Libbey Co. (Sashes; Doors; Blinds) ...AA
Nelson-Tuthill Lumber Co. (Sashes; Doors; Blinds) AA
Smith & Wyman (Sashes; Doors; Outside Blinds; Door; Window Frames) AA
Wabash Screen Door Co. (Sashes; Doors; Blinds) AA
MINN.—St. Paul
Brooks Bros. (Sashes; Doors; Blinds) ....AAAA
McGraft & Son (Porch Columns) ....A
Osgood & Blodgett (Sashes; Doors; Blinds) ....A
St. Croix Lumber Co. (Sashes; Doors; Blinds) AAA
MINN.—Stillwater
Stillwater Mfg. Co. (Sashes; Doors; Blinds) ......A
MINN.—Thief River Falls
Thief River Falls Lumber Co. (Sashes; Doors; Blinds) ....AAA
MINN.—Winona
Empire Lumber Co. (Sashes; Blinds; Doors) .....A
Laird-Norton Co. (Sashes; Doors; Outside Blinds) AAAA
Schrott & Ahrens Co. (Sashes; Doors; Blinds) ....A
Winona Lumber Co. (Sashes; Doors; Blinds) ..AA
MISS.—Jackson
Enoch's Lumber & Mfg. Co. (Sashes; Doors; Blinds) A
MO.—Kansas City
Roach & Kienzie Sash & Door Co. (Sashes; Doors; Blinds) ....A
Western Sash & Door Co. (Sashes; Doors; Blinds) A
Mo.—St. Joseph
Huttig-Moss Mfg. Co. (Sashes; Hardwood; Veneered Doors; Blinds) AA
MO.—St. Louis
Crescent Planing Mills Co. (Sashes; Doors; Blinds) A
Fox Bros. Mfg. Co. (Sashes; Doors; Blinds) ....A
Frye Mfg. Co., Wm. T. (Sashes; Doors; Blinds) AA
Ganahl Lumber Co., J. J. (Sashes; Doors; Blinds) A
Gaus & Sons Mfg. Co., Hy. (Sashes; Doors; Blinds) A
Hafner Mfg. Co. (Sashes; Doors; Inside; Outside Blinds) ....A
Huttig Sash & Door Co. (Sashes; Doors; Outside Blinds) ....A
Mechanics Planing Mill Co. (Sashes; Hardwood; Veneered Doors; Blinds) ..A
Phoenix Planing Mill Co. (Sashes; Blinds; Columns; Doors) ....A
Riddle, Rehbein Mfg. Co. (Sashes; Doors; Blinds) A
St. Louis Sash & Door Wks. (Sashes; Doors; Blinds) A
MONT.—Butte
Anaconda Copper Mining Co. (Sashes; Doors; Blinds) AAAA
Big Black Foot Milling Co. (Sashes; Doors; Blinds) AAA
Carroll Lumber Co., J. T. (Sashes; Doors; Blinds) A
Western Lumber Co. (Sashes; Doors; Blinds) AAA
NEBR.—Lincoln
Curtis & Bartlett Co. (Sashes; Doors; Blinds; Porch Columns) ....A

WOODWORK (Con.)

Searle & Chapin Lumber Co. (Sashes; Doors; Blinds) A
NEBR.—Omaha
Bullard Hoagland & Benedict (Sashes; Doors; Blinds) ....AA
Cady Lumber Co. (Sashes; Doors; Blinds) ....A
Chicago Lumber Co. (Sashes; Doors; Blinds) AAa
Dietz Lumber Co., C. N. (Sashes; Doors; Blinds) A
Disbrow & Co., Inc., M. A. (Outside Blinds) ....A
Hampton Lumber Co. (Sashes; Doors; Blinds) AA
Watkins & Co., J. B., South Omaha (Sashes; Doors; Blinds) ....AA
NEV.—Verdi
Verdi Lumber Co. (Sashes; Doors; Blinds) ....AA
N. H.—Manchester
Head & Dowst Co. (Sashes; Doors; Blinds) ....A
N. H.—Nashua
Roby & Swart Mfg. Co. (Sashes; Doors; Blinds) A
Tolles & Co., J. H. (Sashes; Doors; Blinds) ....A
N. J.—Asbury Park
Buchanan & Smock Lumber Co. (Sashes; Doors; Blinds) ....A
N. J.—Atlantic City
Somers Lumber Co. (Sashes; Doors; Blinds) ....A
N. J.—Bayonne
Booth & Bro., A. W. (Sashes; Doors; Blinds) A
N. J.—Camden
Coles & Co., C. B. (Sashes; Doors; Blinds) ....A
N. J.—Elizabeth
Heidritter, F. L. & A. (Sashes; Doors; Blinds) AA
N. J.—Newark
Hedden & Sons, V. J. (Sashes; Doors; Blinds) AA
Schrafft, A. (Blinds; Door; Window Frames) C
N. J.—Paterson
New Jersey Blind Co. (Inside Sliding; Venetian Blinds) ....D
N. J.—Trenton
Leuckel & Co., A. K. (Sashes; Blinds; Doors) A
N. J.—Woodbury
Woodbury Mill & Lumber Co. (Hardware; Veneered Doors) C
N. Y.—Addison
Park, Winton & True (Sashes; Doors; Outside Blinds) ....A
N. Y.—Albany
Burton Co., Wm. H. (Hardwood; Veneered Doors), D
N. Y.—Binghamton
Bartlett & Co. (Sashes; Doors; Blinds) ......AA
Hobson & Son, A. (Hardwood; Veneered Doors) AA
Roberson & Son, A. (Inside; Outside; Sliding Blinds; Doors; Window Frames) AA
N. Y.—Brooklyn
Bossert & Son, Louis (Inside Sliding Blinds; Hardwood; Veneered Doors) ..AAAA
Cropsey & Mitchell, Cropsey Av. & Bay 35th (Sashes; Doors; Blinds) ....AA
Girard, Son & Co., G. H., 257 Greenpoint Av. (Sashes; Doors; Blinds) A
Hardy, Voorhees & Co., Met. Av. & Newton Creek (Sashes; Doors; Blinds) AA
Loomis Co., John S., Baltic & Nevins (Sashes; Doors; Blinds) ....A

WOODWORK (Con.)

Meisel, Danowitz & Co., 55 Eckford (Sashes; Doors; Blinds) ....A
Orr & Co., J. C., 45 Java (Sashes; Doors; Blinds) AAAA
White, Potter & Paige Mfg. Co., 415 Willoughby Av. (Sashes; Doors; Blinds) A
N. Y.—Buffalo
Boller & Sons, Chas. (Sashes; Doors; Outside Blinds) ....A
Churchyard, Jos. J. (Blinds) X
Dohn, Fisher & Beyer (Sashes; Doors; Blinds) AA
Elias & Bro., G. (Sashes; Doors; Blinds) ......AA
Hager & Sons Co., E. M. (Sashes; Doors; Blinds) A
Henrichs Sons, Wm. (Sashes; Doors; Blinds) A
Montgomery Bro. & Co. (Hardwood; Veneered Doors) ....AA
N. Y.—Cazenovia
Thayer Co., T. W. (Sashes; Doors; Blinds) ....A
N. Y.—Cohoes
Griffin, A. J. (Inside; Outside Blinds)..............A
N. Y.—Corning
Drake & Co. (Sashes; Doors; Blinds) ....AA
N. Y.—Cornwall Landing
Mead & Taft (Sashes; Doors; Blinds) ....A
N. Y.—Elmira
Doane & Jones Lumber Co. (Sashes; Doors; Blinds; Porch Columns) ....A
Spaulding & Co. (Sashes; Doors; Blinds) ......AA
N. Y.—Gloversville
Burr Bros. (Sashes; Doors; Blinds) ....A
N. Y.—Hornellsville
McConnell Mfg. Co. (Sashes; Hardwood; Veneered Doors; Inside; Outside Sliding Blinds; Window Frames) ....AA
N. Y.—Hudson
Traver & Son, W. H. (Sashes; Doors; Blinds) A
N. Y.—Jamestown
Watson Mfg. Co. (Inside Folding; Inside Sliding; Venetian Blinds) ....D
N. Y.—Kingston
Palens Sons, Hy. W. (Sashes; Doors; Blinds) A
N. Y.—Mechanicsville
Orcutt & Co., J. B. (Sashes; Doors; Blinds) ....A
N. Y.—Middleport
Rowley & Eddy (Sashes; Doors; Blinds) ....A
N. Y.—Mt. Vernon
Hartmann Bros. Mfg. Co. (Exterior Columns) ....B
N. Y.—New Rochelle
Mahlstedt Lumber & Coal Co., J. A. (Sashes; Doors; Blinds) ....A
New York City
Carl, Jno. H., 510 1st Av. (Hardwood; Veneered Doors). ....D
Currier Co., E. Bradley, 119 W. 23d (Inside Folding; Inside Sliding Blinds; Hardwood; Veneered Doors) C
Kertscher & Co., 13 Lawrence (Hardwood; Veneered Doors).........A
Morstatt & Son, 227 W. 29th (Inside Folding; Inside Sliding Blinds) ....A
Nesbit Co., D. M., 116 Nassau (Sashes; Doors; Blinds) ....A
Tide Water Bldg. Co., 517 W. 30th (Sashes; Doors;

WOODWORK (Con.)

Blinds) ....A
Wilson Mfg. Co., Jas. G., 3
W. 29th (Sashes; Doors;
Venetian Blinds) ....A

N. Y.—North Tonawanda
Charlton, J. & F. (Sashes;
Doors; Blinds).........AA
Thompson, Hubman & Fisher (Sashes; Doors; Blinds)
A

N. Y.—Patchogue
Bailey & Sons, E. (Sashes;
Doors; Blinds) ......AAA

N. Y.—Poughkeepsie
Lumb & Son, Geo. W.
(Sashes; Doors; Blinds)
AA

N. Y.—Rochester
Ocorr & Rugg Co. (Sashes;
Doors; Blinds) ......AA

N. Y.—Roslyn
Hicks & Co., Jno. D.
(Sashes; Doors; Blinds)
AA

N. Y.—Sandy Hill
Griffin Lumber Co. (Sashes;
Doors; Blinds) ....A

N. Y.—Schenectady
Peckham. Wolf & Co.
(Sashes; Doors; Blinds)
A

N. Y.—Syracuse
Merriam Mfg. Co. (Sashes;
Doors; Blinds) ....A

N. Y.—Utica
Kellogg & Sons Co., Chas.
C. (Sashes; Doors; Blinds)
AA

N. Y.—Whitesboro
Denton & Waterbury
(Sashes; Doors; Blinds)A

N. C.—Charlotte
Withers. B, F. (Sashes;
Doors; Blinds) ....A

N. C.—Gilkes
Warlick Lumber Co. (Inside
Moulded) ....D

N. C.—High Point
Snow Lumber Co. (Sashes;
Doors; Blinds) ....A

N. C.—Wilmington
Fore & Foster Planing Mill
& Sash Blind Mfg. Co.
(Sashes; Doors; Blinds)
A

N. DAK.—Wahpeton
McCulloch Lumber Co.
(Sashes; Doors; Blinds) A

OHIO—Akron
Akron Lumber Co. (Sashes;
Doors; Blinds) ....A

OHIO—Alliance
Weybrecht's Sons, J. F.
(Hardwood; Veneered
Doors; Porch Columns), B

OHIO—Bellaire
Dubois & McCoy (Sashes;
Doors, Blinds) ....A

OHIO—Bellefontaine
Leonard & Sons. A. (Sashes;
Doors; Blinds) ....A

OHIO—Bridgeport
Scott Lumber Co. (Sashes;
Doors; Blinds) ....A

OHIO—Cadiz
Long & Sons, E. M. (Sashes;
Doors; Blinds) ....A

OHIO—Cincinnati
Boskin & Brechelt, 3408
Warsaw Av. (Sashes;
Doors; Blinds) ....A
Griffith & Son, Jas., Reading Rd. (Sashes; Doors;
Blinds) ....A
Pease Co., Fredonia Av.
(Sashes; Hardwood; Veneered Doors; Venetian
Blinds) ....A

OHIO—Cleveland
Nahius. John, 181 Lake Av.
(Sashes; Doors; Blinds) A
National Box Co., 105 Jeff
(Porch Columns) ......B
Nicola Bros. Co., New England Bldg. (Sashes;
Doors; Blinds) ......AA
Potter, Teare & Co., 7 Carter (Sashes; Doors;
Blinds) ....AA
Saginaw Bay Co., 714 Seneca (Sashes; Doors;
Blinds) ....AAA
Standard Door & Sash Co..

WOODWORK (Con.)

200 Euclid Av. (Sashes;
Doors; Blinds) ......AAA
Teachout Co., A., 42 Mich
(Sashes; Doors; Blinds) A

OHIO—Columbus
Hildreth & Martin Lumber
Co. (Sashes; Doors;
Blinds) ....A

OHIO—Dayton
Dayton Lumber & Mfg. Co.
(Sashes; Doors; Blinds) A
Requarth Co., F. A.
(Blinds; Porch Columns)
B
Rouzer Co., John, 73 S.
Wyandot (Sashes; Doors;
Blinds) ....A

OHIO—Fostoria
Eureka Planing & Lumber
Co. (Sashes; Doors;
Blinds) ....A

OHIO—Hamilton
Bender Bros. & Co., J. F.
(Sashes; Doors; Blinds) A

OHIO—Hillsboro
Enterprise Planing Mill Co.
(Hardwood; Veneered
Doors) ....B

OHIO—Ironton
Ironton Wood Mantel Co.
(Hardwood; Veneered
Doors) ....E

OHIO—Kenton
Callam Co., John (Sashes;
Doors; Blinds) ....A

OHIO—Mansfield
Ford & Co., S. N. (Sashes;
Doors; Blinds) ....A

OHIO—Marietta
Becker Mill Co. (Porch Columns) ....A

OHIO—Massillon
Brown Lumber Co. (Sashes;
Doors; Blinds) ....A

OHIO—Middletown
Caldwell & Iseminger
(Hardwood; Veneered
Doors). ....B

OHIO—Norwalk
Bostwick-Goodell Co. (Venetian Blinds) C

OHIO—Sandusky
Schoepffe Mfg. & Lumber
Co. (Sashes; Doors;
Blinds) ....A

OHIO—Toledo
Maclaren, Sprague Lumber
Co. (Sashes; Doors;
Blinds) ....A
Spangler Co., Frank (Capitals; Columns) ....D

OHIO—Youngstown
Heller Bros. Co., 346 S.
Phelps (Sashes; Doors;
Blinds) ....A

OHIO—Zanesville
Herdman Door & Lumber
Co. (Sashes; Doors;
Blinds) ....A

OKLA. TER.—Oklahoma
Oklahoma Sash & Door Co.
(Sashes; Doors; Blinds) A

ORE.—Mansfield
Dean Lumber Co. (Sashes;
Doors; Blinds) ....AA

PA.—Beaver Falls
Commercial Sash & Door Co.
(Sashes; Doors; Blinds)
AA

PA.—Bradford
Tuna Mfg. Co. (Sashes;
Doors; Blinds) ....A

PA.—Brookville
Van Leer Bros. (Hardwood;
Veneered Doors) ....B

PA.—Butler
Purvis & Co., S. G. (Sashes;
Doors; Blinds) ....A

PA.—Darby
Gotshall & Morgan (Sashes;
Doors; Blinds) ....A

PA.—Erie
Carroll & Bro., Geo., ft.
French (Sashes; Doors;
Blinds) ....A
Constable Bros. Co., 5th &
Sassafras (Sashes; Doors;
Blind) ....A
Schlosser & Sons, David
(Sashes; Doors; Blinds)
AA
Shenk Co., Henry, 12th &
Sassafras (Sashes; Doors;

WOODWORK (Con.)
Blinds) ....AA
PA.—Johnstown
Rose & Sons, W. J. (Sashes;
Doors; Blinds) ....A
PA.—Kane
Kane Sliding Blind Co. (In-
side Sliding; Venetian
Blinds) ....E
PA.—Kittanning
Heilman Bros. (Sashes;
Doors; Blinds) ....A
PA.—Knoxville
Edgecomb's Sons, I. M.
(Sashes; Doors; Blinds) A
PA.—Lancaster
Wohlsens & Son, Wm.
(Sashes; Doors; Blinds) A
PA.—Lewisburg
Nesbit Co., D. M. (Sashes;
Hardwood; Veneered
Doors; Blinds) ....A
PA.—Marietta
Cassal & Son, A. N. (Sashes;
Doors; Blinds) ....A
PA.—New Bethlehem
Andrew's Lumber Co., C. E.
(Sashes; Blinds; Doors) A
PA.—New Brighton
Martsolf Bros. (Sashes;
Doors; Blinds) ....A
PA.—Pen Argyl
Fitzgerald, Speer & Co.
(Sashes; Doors; Blinds) A
PA.—Philadelphia
Alcott-Ross Co., 2917 N.
Broad (Sashes; Hardwood;
Veneered Doors; Blinds)
A
Blatchley, Chas., Swanson &
Meadow (Porch Col-
umns) ....B
Hall Bros. & Wood, Lancas-
ter Av. & 54th (Sashes;
Doors; Blinds) ....B
Haney-White Co., 2730 N.
Broad (Sashes; Doors;
Blinds) ....A
Keeley & Sons, S. S., Myk.
(Sashes; Doors; Blinds) A
PA.—Pittsburg
Commercial Sash & Door
(Sashes Doors Blinds)
AA
Miller & Sons, Wm. (Hard-
wood; Veneered Doors) A
Penna Door & Sash Co., 906
2d Av. (Sashes; Doors;
Blinds) ....A
Schuette & Co,, Wm., Fer-
guson Blk. (Sashes;
Doors; Blinds) ....A
PA.—Pittston
Dershiner & Griffin (Sashes;
Doors; Blinds) ....A
Patterson & Co., J. E.
(Sashes; Doors; Blinds) A
PA.—Ridgeway
Hyde Murphy & Co.
(Sashes; Doors; Blinds;
Hardwood; Veneered
Doors) ....A
PA.—Rochester
Miller & Sons Co., Wm.
(Sashes; Doors; Blinds) A
PA.—Scranton
Peck Lumber Mfg. Co., 101
E. Mkt. (Sashes; Doors;
Blinds) ....A
Washburn, Williams & Co.
(Sashes; Doors; Blinds) A
PA.—Sharon
Wallis & Carley (Sashes;
Doors; Blinds) ....A
PA.—Wilkesbarre
Shepherd & Sons, W. H.
(Sashes; Doors; Blinds) A
PA.—Williamsport
Brown, Clark & Co. (Sashes;
Doors; Blinds) ......AAA
Williamsport Planing Mill
Co. (Sashes; Blinds; Porch
Columns; Hardwood; Ve-
neered Doors) ....A
PA.—York
Moss & Sons, Herman
(Sashes; Doors; Blinds) A
S. C.—Greenville
Mallard Lumber Co. (Cas-
ings) C
S. C.—Spartanburg
Morgan Iron Wks. (Blinds)
D

WOODWORK (Con.)
TENN.—Chattanooga
Central Mfg. Co. (Sashes;
Doors; Blinds) ....A
Loomis & Hart Mfg. Co.,
719 E. 9th (Sashes;
Doors; Blinds) ......AA
TENN.—Cookeville
Dow, D. L. (Porch; Stair
Balusters) ....E
TENN.—Knoxville
Rose & Co., D. M. (Sashes;
Doors; Blinds) ....A
TENN.—Memphis
Cole Mfg. Co., 27 Hernando
(Sashes; Doors; Blinds)
AA
Moore & McFerren, Henry &
Wolf River (Sashes;
Doors; Blinds) .....AAAA
Williams & Co., 371 2d
(Sashes; Doors; Blinds) A
TENN.—Nashville
Davidson-Benedict Co.
(Sashes; Doors; Blinds)
AA
TEXAS—Albany
Rockwell Bros. & Co.
(Sashes; Doors; Blinds) A
TEXAS—Austin
Malle & Co., 609 E. 6th
(Sashes; Doors; Blinds)
AA
TEXAS—Cleburne
Conway-Leeper Co. (Sashes;
Doors; Blinds) ....A
TEXAS—Colorado
Burton-Lingo Co. (Sashes;
Doors; Blinds) ......AA
Roe, A. J. (Sashes; Doors;
Blinds) ....A
TEXAS—Corpus Christi
Sidbury, E. D. (Sashes;
Doors; Blinds) ....A
TEXAS—El Paso
Bassett & Co., O. T.
(Sashes; Doors; Blinds) A
TEXAS—Ft. Worth
Ripy & Irwin (Sashes;
Doors; Blinds) ....A
Waples-Painter Co. (Sashes;
Doors; Blinds) ....A
TEXAS—Galveston
Moore & Goodman, 2827 Me-
chanic (Sashes; Doors;
Blinds) ....A
Smith & Bro., J. F., 2315
Strand (Sashes; Doors;
Blinds) ....A
TEXAS—Hallettsville
Hill & Son, S. A. (Sashes;
Doors; Blinds) ....A
TEXAS—Houston ...
Bering Mfg. Co. (Sashes;
Doors; Blinds) ....AA
House, Henry (Sashes;
Doors; Blinds) ......AA
TEXAS—Orange
Miller, L. (Sashes; Doors;
Blinds) ....AA
TEXAS—San Antonio
Steves & Son, Ed. (Sashes;
Doors; Blinds) ....A
TEXAS—Taylor
Thompson, J. A. (Sashes;
Doors; Blinds) ....A
TEXAS—Waco
Brazleton & Johnson
(Sashes; Doors; Blinds) A
Cameron & Co., Wm.
(Sashes; Doors; Blinds)
AAAA
UTAH—Salt Lake City
Morrison, Merrill & Co.
(Sashes; Doors; Blinds) A
VT.—Burlington
Booth, J. R. (Sashes;
Doors; Blinds) ....AAAA
Burlington Venetian Blind
Co. (Inside Sliding; Vene-
tian Blinds) ....B
Champlain Mfg. Co.
(Blinds) ....B
Mason & Co. (Hardwood &
Veneered Doors) ....B
VT.—Poultney
Ripley Lumber Co. (Hard-
wood; Veneered Doors), C
VA.—Lynchburg
Adams-Monroe Mfg. Co.
(Victoria Venetian
Blinds) C
VA.—Norfolk
Nash & Sons, C. A. (Sashes;

WOODWORK (Con.)

Doors; Blinds) ....A
VA.—Richmond
Montague Mfg. Co., 400 S. 9th (Sashes; Doors; Blinds) ....A
Sittering-Carmel-Davis Co., 8 E. Broad (Sashes; Doors; Blinds) ....A
Stagg, Thos. E., 1444 E. Main (Sashes; Doors; Blinds) ....B
Whitehurst, W. J. (Outside Blinds) ....B
Woodward & Son, 330 S. 9th (Sashes; Doors; Blinds) ....A
WASH.—Bellingham
Whatcomb Falls Mill Co. (Red Cedar Doors) ....B
Wollaeger Mfg. Co. (Hardwood; Veneered Doors), A
WASH.—Everett
Wheelahan - Weidauer Co. (Porch Columns) ......B
WASH.—Seattle
Stetson & Post Mill Co. (Sashes; Doors; Blinds) A
WASH.—South Bend
Kleeb Lumber Co. (Porch Columns) ....B
WASH.—Spokane
Washington Mill Co. (Sashes; Doors; Blinds) A
WASH.—Tacoma
Wheeler-Osgood Co., Tide Flags (Sashes; Red Cedar Doors; Blinds) ......AA
W. VA.—Berkeley Springs
Crossfield, Wm. D. (Stair Balusters) ....D
W. VA.—Clarksburg
Williams & Davidson Co. (Sashes; Doors; Blinds) A
W. VA.—Morgantown
Morgantown Planing Mill Co. (Sashes; Doors; Blinds) ....A
W. VA.—Wheeling
Chapman & Sons, W. H. (Sashes; Doors; Blinds) ....A
Wilson & Sons, W. A. (Sashes; Doors; Blinds) ....AA
WIS.—Eau Claire
Shaw Lumber Co., Daniel (Sashes; Doors; Blinds) ....AA
WIS.—Fond-du-Lac
Moore & Galloway Lumber Co. (Sashes; Doors; Blinds) ....AA
WIS.—Hayward
North Wisconsin Lumber & Mfg. Co. (Sashes; Doors; Blinds) ......AA
WIS.—La Crosse
Colman Lumber Co., C. L. (Sashes; Doors; Blinds) ....AAAA
Segelke & Kohlhaus Mfg. Co. (Sashes; Doors; Blinds) ....AA
Trow & Co., A. S. (Sashes; Doors; Blinds) ......AA
WIS.—Lake Geneva
Wilbur Lumber Co. (Sashes; Doors; Blinds) ......AA
WIS.—Madison
Brittingham & Hixon Lumber Co. (Sashes; Doors; Blinds) ....AA
WIS.—Manauwa
Little Wolf River Lumber Co. (Sashes; Doors; Blinds) ....A
WIS.—Merrill
Wright Lumber Co., H. W. (Sashes; Doors; Blinds) ....AA
WIS.—Milwaukee
Cream City Sash & Door Wrks., 7th Av. & Park (Sashes; Doors; Blinds; Porch Columns) ......AA
Poppert Mfg. Co. Geo. (Sashes; Doors; Blinds)
Rockwell Mfg. Co., Park & 6th Av. (Sashes; Doors; Blinds; Porch Columns) ....AA
Wilbur Lumber Co., Pabst

WOODWORK (Con.)

Bldg. (Sashes; Doors; Blinds) ....AA
Willer Mfg. Co., 313 Cedar (Inside Folding; Inside Sliding; Venetian Blinds) ....B
WIS.—New Richmond
Willow River Lumber Co. (Sashes; Doors; Blinds) ....A
WIS.—Oshkosh
Foster, Lothman Mills (Sashes; Doors; Blinds) ....AA
Gould Mfg. Co. (Sashes; Doors; Outside Blinds) ....A
McMillen Co., R. (Sashes; Doors; Blinds; Hardwood Stair Ballusters) ......A
Morgan Co. (Sashes; Doors; Inside Folding Blinds; Porch Columns) ......AA
Paine Lumber Co. (Sashes; Doors; Inside Folding; Outside Blinds; Porch Columns) ......AAAA
Radford Bros. & Co. (Sashes; Doors; Outside Blinds) ....B
Williamson & Libbey Lumber Co. (Sashes; Doors; Blinds) ....A
WIS.—Wausau
Curtis & Yale Co. (Sashes; Doors; Inside Sliding; Venetian Blinds; Woodwork; Carriage, etc.) ....A

WOODWORK: CARRIAGE, WAGON, ETC.

ALA.—Troy
Henderson & Minchener (Spokes) ....A
ARK.—Bradford
Lee, W. J. Jr. (Hubs)...D
ARK.—Clarendon
Galloway, J. B. ....D
ARK.—Fayetteville
Fayetteville Wagon, Wood & Lumber Co. ......B
Pitkin, Mayes & Co. C
ARK.—Marianna
Marianna Spoke & Novelty Wks. (Spokes) ....D
ARK.—Marvel
McDonald Bros. & Co. (Spokes) ....D
ARK.—Minturn
Shirey, A. W. (Spokes)..B
ARK.—Red Star
Red Star Spoke & Hub Co. ....D
CAL.—Sacramento
Waterhouse & Lester (Wagon Bodies; Spokes; Hubs; Wheels) .....AA
CAL.—San Francisco
Holt Bros. Co., 30 Main (Bodies; Gears) ......A
CAL.—Stockton
Holt Mfg. Co. (Bodies; Wheels) ....A
CONN.—Bridgeport
Wheel & Wood Bending Co. (Wheels; Spokes; Hubs; Bows; Shafts)..B
CONN.—Central Village
Torrey Bros. Co. (Sleigh Runners; Wheel Rims).D
CONN.—Clinton
Kelsey, Horatio (Spokes).E
CONN.—Hartford
Premier Mfg. Co. ....B
CONN.—Mt. Carmel
Woodruff & Sons Co., Walter W. (Neck Yokes)..A
CONN.—South Coventry
Armstrong & Sons, Henry (Spokes; Hubs) ......E
CONN.—Stafford Springs
Preble & Sons (Spokes)..E
GA.—Beach Hill
Ivey, H. J. (Carriage Rim Strips) ....E
GA.—Rome
Towers & Sullivan Mfg. Co. (Doubletrees) ....B

WOODWORK (Con.)
trees) ....B
IND.—Warsaw
Lesh Mfg. Co., G. B.
(Wagon) ....D
IOWA—Burlington
Buffington Wheel Company
(Wheels) C
IOWA—Glenwood
Glenwood Mfg. Co. (Neck
Yokes) ....E
IOWA—Keokuk
Mills, Ellsworth Co. (Poles;
Shafts) C
IOWA—Sioux City
Sioux City Iron Co. (Wa-
gon) ....A
KANS.—Coffeyville
Zeigler Neck Yoke Co.
(Neck Yokes) ....E
KANS.—Covington
Ohio Scroll & Lumber Co.
(Body; Panels; Spindles)
D
KANS.—Dayton
Bellevue Planing Mill Co.
(Bodies; Seats) ......D
KANS.—Hawesville
Hawesville Hub & Mfg. Co.
(Wagon) ....E
KANS.—Hickman
Hickman Wagon Company
(Spokes) ....A
KANS.—Hodgensville
Hodgensville Spoke Mfg.
Co. (Spokes) ....E
KANS.—Kuttama
Suwanee Spoke & Lumber
Co. (Spokes; Singletrees;
Neck Yokes) ....D
KANS.—Lebanon
Royer Wheel Co. (Spokes;
Wheels; Singletrees) ..A
KY.—Louisville
Fulton, Conway & Co.
(Hubs; Spokes) ......A
Louisville Spoke & Bending
Co. (Spokes; Shafts;
Rims; Poles) C
Turner, Day & Woolworth
Mfg. Co. (Neck Yokes;
Whiffletrees) ......AA
Von Behrens, Russell Co.
(Poles; Whiffletrees) .D
KY.—Madisonville
Buckeye Spoke Co. (Rims;
Spokes) ....B
KY.—Nicholasville
Standard Wheel Co. (Wa-
gon) X
KY.—Owensboro
Owensboro Wagon Co. (Hub
Spokes; Rims) ....A
Owensboro Wheel Company
(Wheels) ....B
KY.—Paducah
Bell, E. E. (Spokes) ...E
Lack Singletree Co. (Neck
Yokes; Spokes; Single-
trees) C
Little, J. W. (Spokes)...C
KY.—Scottsville
Allen, J. W. (Spokes)....C
KY.—Seven Hills
Vollman Buggy Body Co.
(Bodies) ....E
KY.—Somerset
Longworth Co., S. R.
(Spokes) ....E
Royer Wheel Co. (Spokes;
Wheels; Singletrees) ..A
KY.—Winchester
Scobel-Williams Spoke Co.
(Wagons) ....E
MAINE—Foxcroft
Ranger & Ayer Mfg. Co.
(Sleigh Panels; Dashes)
E
MAINE—Houlton
Watson Co., John (Whiffle-
trees) ....B
MAINE—Newport
Cooper Bros. (Basswood
Panels) ....D
MAINE—Portland
Bailey Carriage Co. (Bod-
ies) ....A
Stevans & Co., A. E.
(Hubs; Wheels, &c.)...C
MAINE—W. Falmouth
West Falmouth Mfg. Co.
(Wheel Stock) ....D

WOODWORK (Con.)
MD.—Baltimore
Baltimore Hub Factory, 322
N. Holliday (Wheels;
Hubs; All Supplies) ..C
Stinson Mfg. Co., 327 North
(Wheels; Wheel Stock).B
MD.—Frederick
Frederick Wheel & Bend-
ing Works (Wheels)....D
MD.—Hagerstown
Hagerstown Spoke & Bend-
ing Co. (Spokes; Rims).C
Pomeroy Bros. & Co.
(Spokes) ....B
MD.—Henderson
Casho, W. H. (Rims) ...E
MD.—Wheel
Hollingsworth Wheel Co.,
J. C. (Wheels) ....E
MASS.—Amesbury
Bailey & Co., S. R. (Poles)
A
Biddle & Smart Co. (Bod-
ies; Gears) C
Briggs Carriage Co. (Bod-
ies) C
Carr, Prescott & Company
(Wheels) ....D
Carrier-Cameron Co. (Bod-
ies; Gears; Shafts; Poles)
C
Lane, John A. (Bodies)...E
Lane, T. W. (Bodies)....E
Leitch, J. N. (Bodies;
Gears) ....D
Lunt, Smith & Co. (Bodies;
Gears) ....E
Merrill, F. S. (Wheels)..C
Miller Bros. (Bodies)....E
MASS.—Ayer
K. & C. Mfg. Co. (Rims).E
MASS.—Boston
Gillett & Sons, E. A., 230
Rutherford Av. (Bent
Stuff) ....A
Heywood Bros. & Wakefield
Co., 174 Portland (Rat-
tan Mouldings) ....AAAA
Reed Wheel Co., C. G., 90
Utica (Wagon) C
Wood Co., A. M., 51 Bev-
erly (Wagon) C
MASS.—Charlemont
Payne, W. L. (Poles; Rims)
E
MASS.—Lawrence
Archibald Wheel Company
(Wheels) ....B
MASS.—Lynn
Perkins, I. W. (Bodies).E
MASS.—Merrimac
Carriage Wheel & Gear Co.
(Wagon) ....D
MASS.—Newburyport
Sargent, L. W. (Bows)..E
MASS.—Rowley
Daniels, G. E. (Heavy
Wheels) ....E
MASS.—S. Framingham
Eames & Co., A. M.
(Wheels) ....E
MASS.—Wakefield
Heywood Bros. & Wakefield
Co. (Rattan Mouldings)
AAAA
MICH.—Detroit
Michigan Auto. & Carriage
Body Co. (Bodies) ....G
Wheeler Mfg. Co. (Rattan
Seats) ....E
Wilson Body Co., C. R.
(Bodies; Gears) ......**E**
MICH.—Flint
Flint Wagon Wks. (Wheels)
A
Imperial Wheel Co. C
Stewart Co., W. T. ......B
MICH.—Freeport
Freeport Cutter Co. (Bod-
ies) ....E
MICH.—Grand Rapids
Grand Rapids Veneer Wks.
(Carriage; Cutter Panels)
A
Mack, John (Bodies) X
Waddell Mfg. Co. (Carv-
ings; Mouldings) C
MICH.—Jackson
Imperial Wheel Co. (Wa-
gon) ....D
Jackson Body Co. (Bodies)
D

OHIO—Dayton
Brown & Co., S. N. (Bows)
Finnes & Daniels Co. (Hubs;
Spokes; Wheels) X
Zwick & Greenmald Wheel
Co. (Hubs; Spokes; Fel-
lors; Wheels; Wheel
Stock) ....A
OHIO—Defiance
Turnbull W a g o n Co.
(Spokes; Rims; Wheels)
AA
OHIO—Delphos
Ohio Wheel Co. (Hubs;
Hub Clocks; Spokes;
Rims) ....E
OHIO—Erhart
Haury. Jno. F. (Spokes;
Rims) ....E
OHIO—Ft. Recovery
Reuter & Wilson (Hubs;
Spokes) ....D
OHIO—Fostoria
Cunningham Mfg. Co.
Spokes; Bentwork)....B
OHIO—Fremont
West Wood Turning Co.
(Neck Yokes; Single-
trees) ....E
OHIO—Galion
Flickinger Wheel Co.
(Wheels) ....A
Weaver Bending Co. (Rims;
Spokes) ....D
OHIO—Geneva
Geneva Metal Wheel Co.
(Gears) ....B
OHIO—Hagerman
Burns & Co., D. (Hubs;
Spokes) X
OHIO—Hamilton
Donges & Co.. J. (Hubs;
Spokes; Felloes; Bows)
C
Hamilton Spoke & Hub Co.
(Spokes; Hubs) ......D
OHIO—Haverhill
Folding Wagon Box Co..F
OHIO—Ironton
Deidcrick, F. E. (Wheel
Stock) X
Eilert Bros. (Hubs;
Wheels) ....E
OHIO—Logan
Plenk & White (Wheels;
Spokes) X
Snider-Miller Mfg. Co.
(Bent Work) C
OHIO—Loramie
Wise, August (Spokes)..D
OHIO—Madison
Madison Wheel Co.
(Wheels) ....D
OHIO—Mansfield
Union Fdry & Mach. Wks.
(Wood Axles; Thimble;
Skein Fitter) ....D
OHIO—Medina
Medina Bending Wks. ...E
OHIO—Miamisburg
Bookwalker Wheel Co.
(Wheels) ....A
Mitchell Wheel Co.
(Wheels) ....A
OHIO—Monroeville
Yingling Bros. Co........B
OHIO—Mt. Vernon
Standard Gear Wood Co.
D
OHIO—Newton Falls
Newton Falls Mfg. Co.
(Spokes; Neck Yokes).E
OHIO—Petersburg
Miller & Tailor (Spokes;
Rims) ....E
OHIO—Piqua
Pioneer Pole & Shaft Co.
(Poles; Shafts; Rims)
AAAA
OHIO—Portsmouth
Portsmouth Rim & Spoke
Co. C
OHIO—St Marys
St. Marys Wheel & Spoke
Co. (Hubs; Spokes; Rims;
Wheels) ....A
OHIO—Sandusky
Woolsey Wheel Co.
(Wheels) ....AA

OHIO—Shanesville
Shanesville Woodworking
Mfg. Co. (Neck Yokes;
Whippletrees; Spokes).F
OHIO—Sidney
Pioneer Pole & Shaft Co.
AAAA
OHIO—South Zanesville
Kohlerd. F. F. (Spokes;
Rims; Bent Hounds)..E
OHIO—Struthers
Cooper, Co., J. A. & D. P.
(Gear Wood; Singletrees)
D
OHIO—Tippecanoe City
Ford & Co. (Wheels)....B
OHIO—Toledo
Skinner Bending Co. J. M.
(Bent Folloes; Hardwood
Lumber, &c.) ....B
Toledo Bending Co. (Shafts;
Wheel Stock) ....B
Toledo Carriage Woodwork
Co. (Shafts; Wheel Stock)
B
OHIO—Troy
Pioneer Pole & Shaft Co.
(Shafts; Poles; Rims)
AAAA
OHIO—Wapakoneta
Wapakoneta Bending Co.
(ubs; Spokes) X
Wapakoneta Wheel Co.
(Wheels) C
OHIO—Waverly
Waverly Bent Wood Co...D
OHIO—Wellingtton
Pioneer Pole & Shaft Co.
(Shafts; Poles; Rims)
AAAA
OHIO—West Liberty
Dodson, E. (Wheel Stock)
E
OHIO—Wilmington
Chancellor Bros. (Spokes;
Rims) ....E
OHIO—Winchester
Winchester Lumber Co.
(Spokes; Rims) ......D
OHIO—Zanesville
Kimble. H. J. (Rims;
Hounds) ....D
PA.—Allentown
Allentown Platform Co.
(Wagon Gears) ......B
PA.—Boyertown
Hartman, F. H. (Bodies;
Gears) ....E
PA.—Bradford
American Wood Rim Co.
(Rims for Auto Wheels)
A
Bradford Body Co. (Bodies)
X
Brown-Ensor Mfg. Co.
(Bodies) ....E
PA.—Carlisle
Carlsisle Body & Gear
Wks. ....D
PA.—Carverton
Heft & Bro., M. J.
(Wagon Stock) ......D
PA.—Cogan Station
Bovee. Sm'l B. (Hubs)...E
PA.—Coopersburg
Coopersburg Bending Wks.
(Rims; Bows) ....E
PA.—Doylestown
Worstall & Carl Spoke &
Wheel Co. ....D
PA.—Effort
Shupp. Simon (Spokes)...E
PA.—Elimsport
Bailey & Co., C. (Hubs;
Spokes) ....E
PA.—Erie
Erie Steam Bending Wks.
D
Reno Mfg. Co. (Neck
Yokes) ....E
PA.—Hanover
Hanover B e n d i n g Co.
(Bows; Rims; Reaches)
D
PA.—Jordan
Rausch. Handwerk & Co.
(Wheels & Wheel Stock)
D
PA.—Kauffman
Fuss, J. C. (Spokes).....F
PA.—Lancaster
Downey Bros. Spoke &

WOODWORK (*Con.*)

Bending Co. (Wheels; Wheel Stock; Poles; Shafts; Gear Stock, &c.) C

Lebzelber & Son, P. (Wheels; Wheel Stock; Poles; Shafts; Whippletrees; Neck Yokes)....A

PA.—Marienville
Bell, I. Scott (Hubs)....D

PA.—Mechanicsburg
Eberly & Orris (Wheels; Wheel Stock) C
Koller & Co., J. B. (Spokes; Rims; Hubs).C
Seidle, F. (Wheels; Wheel Stock) C

PA.—Milford
Klaer, Jacob (Spokes; Hubs) ....D

PA.—Millville
Eves & Co., J. (Hubs; Bending) C

PA.—Muddy Creek Farks
Fulton, C. S. M. (Spokes) C

PA.—Newville
Derrick & Hursh (Spokes; Wheel) ....E

PA.—North Water Gap
Hill & Piper (Spokes)....X

PA.—Oil City
Eagle Spoke Wks........D

PA.—Ottowa
Ott & Sons (Spokes).....D

PA.—Perkasie
Moyer, Jos. G. (Felloes).D

PA.—Philadelphia
Buckley, Hub, Spoke & Wheel Co. ....D
Scott & Co., Chas. (Wheels) ....AA
Schwartz Patent Wheel Co. X

PA.—Picture Rocks
Little & Co., J. P. (Bent Wood) ....E

PA.—Quakertown
Landis & Bro., S. H. (Hubs; Spokes) ....E

PA.—Reading
Keystone Wagon Wks. (Bodies; Wagon Gears).B
Leippe's Sons, J. A. (Shafts; Rims) ....B

PA.—Souderton
Souder, Wm. (Spokes; Rims, &c.) C

PA.—Tidionte
Martin, Joseph (Hubs)...E

PA.—Titusville
Titusville Handle Co. (Whippletrees; Neck Yokes) ....A

PA.—Warren
Peterson, Samuel (Spokes; Neck Yokes; Whippletrees) ....A

PA.—West Chester
Hoopes Bro. & Darlington (Inc.) (Wheels; Hubs; Spokes; Rims) ....B

PA.—York
Eberly Wheel Wks. (Wheels; Hubs) C
Eureka Bending & Wheel Wks. (Rims; Spokes; Wheels) ....D
Ness Bros. & Co. (Wheels) X
Smith, Erwin & Co. (Rims; Spokes) ....D
York Wagon Gear Co. (Bodies; Gear) ....D

R. I.—Providence
Kilner, Geo. T. (Hubs)..E

S. C.—Darlington
Carolina Spoke & Bending Co. (Spokes) X

TENN.—Algood
Pennock & Walters Mfg. Co. (Spokes) ....E

TENN.—Barnville
Garrett, J. W. (Hubs)...X

TENN.—Bristol
Beveridge & Taylor (Spokes) C

TENN.—Brownsville
Chattanooga Washing Machine & Mfg. Co. (Single; Doubletrees) .....B

WOODWORK (*Con.*)

Hatchie Mfg. Co. (Spokes) ....E

TENN.—Dresden
Dresden Spoke Co. (Spokes) ....D

TENN.—Dyersburg
Imperial Wheel Co. (Wheel Stock) ....AA
Tennessee Spoke Co. (Spokes) C
Wernier Spoke Co. (Spokes; Neck Yokes; Singletrees) ....E

TENN.—Gallatin
Gallatin Spoke Wks......E

TENN.—Greenfield
Ward & Brasfield (Spokes) ....E

TENN.—Humboldt
Foltz, Frank (Spokes)...F

TENN.—Jackson
Weis & Lesh Mfg. Co. (Spokes) ....AAA

TENN.—Manchester
Manchester Mfg. Co. (Spokes; Rims) ......B

TENN.—McMinnville
Burroughs-Ross-Colville Co. (Spokes; Yokes; Cross Bars, &c.) C
Elkins, McClarty & Co. (Spokes) ....D

TENN.—Memphis
Memphis Rim & Bow Co. (Bows; Rims; Hounds) ....A
Pioneer Pole & Shaft Co. (Shafts; Poles; Rims) ....AAAA
Standard Wheel Co. (Wheels) ....AAA
Weis-Lesh Mfg. Co. (Spokes) ....AAA
Weis & Sons Co., Jacob (Spokes; Rims) ......D

TENN.—Murfreesboro
Boch, Adam (Gears).....D

TENN.—Nashville
Goodwin-Clark Wagon Stock Co. ....D
Nashville Spoke & Handle Co. (Spokes) C
Parker & Co., G. S. (Club; Spokes) ....B

TENN.—Newbern
Inman Bros. Mfg. Co. (Club Spokes) C

TENN.—Retro
Rock, Creeks Lumber & Mining Co. (Hubs; Spokes) ....?

TENN.—Shelbyville
Rarsom & Son, G. W. (Spokes) ....E

TENN.—Sparta
Sparta Spoke Factory (Spokes) ....D

TENN.—Spring City
Blanchard, N. C. (Spokes) X

TENN.—Tullahoma
Campbell, M. R. (Hubs; Spokes; Neck Yokes; Singletrees) C
Campbell & Darm Mfg. Co. (Shafts; Rims; Bows; Poles) ....B

TENN.—Woodville
Wilson, W. J. (Spokes)..D

TEXAS—Longview
Northcut, W. G. (Spokes) ....D

VA.—Attoway
Atkins Bros. (Hubs; Spokes) ....D

VA.—Farmville
Farmville Mfg. Co. (Spokes) ....D

VA.—Fredericksburg
Fredericksburg Spoke Wks. (Spokes) ....D

VA.—Front Royal
Rudacell, L. (Spokes)....E

VA.—Gays
Hardenburgh, Chas. (Felloes) ....F

VA.—Manasses
Prescott & Co., J. W. (Spokes) ....F

VA.—Marion
Atkins Bros. (Hubs; Spokes) X

WOODWORK (Con.)

Look, Lincoln (All Kinds)A

VA.—Martinsville

Martinsville Spoke Co.
(Spokes; Rims) ....E

VA.—Parkersburg

Parkersburg Bending Co.
(Spokes; Neck; Yokes
Poles; Whippletrees)...C

VA.—Pembroke

Peek & Co., J. P. (Spokes)
X

VA.—Petersburg

Petersburg Rim & Veneer
Co. (Rims) C

VA.—Radford

Morgan & Pratt Co.
(Wagon Stock) ......E

VA.—Red Oak

Adams Spoke Co. ....E
Fowler & Son, A. J.
(Spokes) X

VA.—Richmond

Va. & No. Car. Wheel Co.
(Spokes; Rims) ......A

WIS.—Algonia

Ahnapee Veneer & Seating
Co. (Veneers) C

WIS.—Antigo

Kellogg Lumber & Mfg. Co.
(Hubs; Spokes; Neck
Yokes) ....B

WIS.—Boscohel

Ruka Bros. Mfg. Co. (Bent
Wood) ....B

WIS.—Cadott

Cadott Mfg. Co. (Hubs;
Spokes) ....E

WIS.—Grand Rapids

Mackinnon Mfg. (All Kinds)
B

WIS.—La Crosse

La Crosse Wagon Stock
Mfg. Co. (Wheel Stock;
Whippletrees) X

WIS.—Lomira

Wolf, P. (Felloes) C

WIS.—Madison

Wiedenbeck, Doblin & Co.
(All Kinds) C
Wisconsin Wagon Co.
(Bodies) ....E

WIS—Mayking

Wunderlich, C. (Spokes).D

WIS.—Milwaukee

Milwaukee Spoke & Bend-
ing Co. X
Milwaukee Wagon Iron
Wks. (Whippletrees Neck
Yokes, &c.) ....A

WIS.—Neillsville

Johnson Mfg. Co. (Hubs;
Spokes) ....A

WIS.—Oshkosh

Clark Carriage Wks.
(Gears; Bodies, &c.)..B
Thompson Carriage Co.
(Gears; Bodies, &c.)...C

WIS.—Racine

Adams & Son, E. B. (Neck
Yokes) ....B
Racine General Mfg. Co.
(Doubletrees) ....E
Racine Mall & Wrought
Iron Co. (Whippletrees;
Eveners; Yokes) ......A
Racine Pole & Spring Co.
(Poles; Neck Yokes)..E

WIS.—Spring Valley

Spring Valley Spoke, Stave
& Heading Co. (Spokes)
D

WIS.—West Bend

Schmidt & Stony (Hubs;
Spokes) ....E

WOODWORK:
MISC.

CAL.—San Francisco

Budde, Jos., 577 Mission
(Plumbers) X

CONN.—Bridgeport

Sewing Machine Cabinet
Co. (Electrical) ......A

CONN.—Essex

Essex Wood Turning Co.
(Twist) X

CONN.—Torrington

Union Hardwarde Co.
(Electrical) ....AA

WOODWORK: MISC.

ILL.—Chicago

Akam Mfg. Co., C. G.
(Sewing Machine) ....F
Clow & Sons, Jas. B., 344
Franklin (Plumbers)
AAA
Furdiesen & Kropf Mfg.
Co., 21st Pl. & Rockwell
(Plumbers) ....A
Humane Tug Post Co. (Pa-
tent Stiff Bar Pole)....E
Lever Mfg. Co., 19 No.
Jefferson (Electrical)..D
Light Mfg. Co., Geo. W.
(Ornamental) ....E
Noblett Co., E. J., 898 5th
(Electrical; Battery; Bell
Boxes; Switch) C
Wolff Mfg. Co., L. 117 W.
Lake (Plumbers)..AAAA

ILL.—Edwardsville

Leclaire Mfg. Co. (Plumb-
ers) ....B

IND.—Bremen

Wright, John J. (Bent)..B

IND.—Evansville

Von Behren Mfg. Co.
(Bent) X

IND.—Fort Wayne

Knott & Van Arnam Mfg.
Co. (Plumbers) ......B

IND.—Lafayette

Taylor Lumber Co., Henry
(Plumbers) ....A

IND.—Vincennes

Hartwell Bros. (Wagon).B

IND.—Wabash

Wabash Cabinet Co. (Elec-
trical; Special of all
Kinds) ....A

KY.—Louisville

Ahrens & Ott Mfg. Co.
(Plumbers) ......AAAA

LA.—New Orleans

Schwartz Co., Joseph
(Ltd.) (Bent) ....A

MASS.—Boston

Davenport, A. H. (Archi-
tectural) ....AA

MASS.—Fitchburg

Novelty Turning Co. (Electrical) ....E

MICH.—Ann Arbor

Peninsular Mfg. Co. (Plumbers' Low Tanks; Seats,
&c.) C

MICH.—Detroit

Hygienic Steel Co. (Plumbers) ....D
Ideal Mfg. Co., 546 Franklin (Plumbers) ....A
Park & McKay Co. (Plumb-
ers) C
Standard Sanitary Mfg. Co.
of Michigan (Plumbers)
AAAA

MICH.—Grand Rapids

Ferguson Marcellus Co.
(Plumbers) C
Waddell Mfg. Co. (Orna-
mental) ....A

MICH.—Kalamazoo

Smith & Pomeroy (Plumb-
ers) ....B

MICH.—Muskegon

Heap, William (Plumber)
D

MICH.—Northville

Globe Furniture Co.
(Plumbers) ....D

MICH.—Port Huron

Crosby & Poole Co. (Ltd.)
(Plumbers) X

MICH.—Romulus

Serstedt Bros. Mfg. Co.
(Plumbers) X

MICH.—Sturgis

Miller, Hubbard Mfg. Co.
(Plumbers) ....B

MO.—St Louis

Nelson Mfg. Co., N. O. 424
N. 8th (Plumbers) .AAA

N. H.—Milford

Pierce & Co., W. E.
(Plumbers) ....D

N. Y.—Brooklyn

Cross Austin & Ireland
Lumber Co. (Ornamental)
AA

N. Y.—Buffalo

Cutting, Henry (Interior)
D

WOODWORK: MISC.

N. Y.—Geneva
Catchpole, E. A. & L. G.
(Bent) C

N. Y.—Jamestown
Jamestown Mantel Co.
(Plumbers) X

New York City
Burrows Mfg. Co., Wm.,
72 Cliff (Plumbers)....F
Emery, W. S., 94 Beekman
(Plumber) ....B
Huber Co., Henry, 244 5th
Av. (Plumber) ....D
Lamb, J. & R. (Architect-
ural: Ornamental).....B
Schwabb Bros. Co., 42 Cliff
(Plumbers) ....E
Siebrecht & Son, 409 5th
Av. (Rustic) X

N. Y.—Oswego
Cowmeadow Mfg. Co.
(Plumbers) ....D

N. Y.—Rome
Rome Sanitary Wks.
(Plumbers) ....B

OHIO—Cincinnati
Douglas Co., Jno., 900
Poplar (Plumbers)....A
Lipp Co., Louis (Plumber)
A
Japan Mfg. Co., 536 Read-
ing Rd. (Plumbers) ...B

OHIO—Columbus
Ascher Fox Mfg. Co.
(Plumbers) ....B
Columbus Brass Co.
(Plumbers) ....A

OHIO—Delphos
Ohio Wheel Co. (Bent)...B

OHIO—Hamilton
Sanitary Mfg. Co. (Plumb-
ers) ....B

OHIO—Portsmouth
Portsmouth Veneer Wks.
(Bent) ....B

OHIO—Toledo
Toledo Bending Co. (Bent)
A
Toledo Carriage Woodwork
Co. (Bent) ....A

PA.—Philadelphia
Blessing, C. A., 516 Mont-
gomery Av. (Plumbers)
AA
Hale & Kilburn Mfg. Co.,
18 N. 6th (Plumbers)
AAAA
Hall & Garrison (Orna-
mental) X
Swain Mfg. Co., 7 &
Morris (Plumbers).....F

PA.—Pittsburg
Standard Sanitary Mfg. Co.
Arrott Bldg. (Plumbers)
AAAA

R. I.—Providence
American Enamel Co. (En-
ameled Turning Electri-
cal) ....B

TENN.—Chattanooga
Dewess Mfg. Co., S. T.
(Plumbers) ....D

VT.—Burlington
Burlington Venetian Blind
Co. (Plumbers) ....A

VA.—Grottoes
American Hardwood Mfg.
Co. (Electrical) C

VT.—Petersburg
South Side Mfg. Co. (Thin
Sawed) C

WIS.—Boscobel
Ruka Bros. Mfg. Co. (Ltd.)
(Bent Carriage) C

WIS.—Oshkosh
Paine Lumber Co. (Plumb-
ers) ....AAAA

WOOL
DEALERS

ALA.—Mobile
Piser & Co., Henry, 109 N.
Commerce ....B

ARK.—Ft. Smith
Arkansas Hide & Fur Co.
B

CAL.—Los Angeles
Los Angeles Soap Co.....B

WOOL DEALERS (Con.)

CAL.—Napa
Sawyer Tanning Co. (Pul-
lers) ....A

CAL.—San Francisco
Allen, Hy. F. (Com.) 202
California ....AA
Bissinger & Co., 215 Clay
(Pullers) ....A
Bloom & Sons, Sam'l, 344
Clay (Pullers) ....B
Catton, Bell & Co., 436
Townsend (Also Scour-
ing) ....A
Denigan Son & Co., Thos.,
132 Market ....A
Koshland & Co., S., 222
California ....AAAA
Moore, Furguson & Co., 310
Columbia (Com.)......A
Norton Tanning Co., 312
Clay (Pullers) ....B
Sawyer Tanning Co., 312
Clay (Pullers) ....A
Summer & Co., W. B., 415
Front (Com.) ....A

CAL.—Stockton
Wagner Leather Co......A

COLO.—Denver
McLean & Co., E. J......B

CONN.—Hartford
Beach & Co., 209 State
(Imp.) ....AAAA
Judd & Root, H. C., Cor.
High & Allyn. (Com.)
AA

CONN.—Norwich
Brewster & Son, M., 35
Shetauket (Com.)....AA
Hall Bros., 29 Commerce
AA

D. C.—Washington
Hopfenmaier, Lewis......B

GA.—Blackshear
Brantley Co., A B........A

ILL.—Chicago
Armour & Co. (Pullers)
AAAA
Bach, Becker & Co., 107
Michigan (Also Com.)..A
Boller & Rogers, 142
Kinzie ....B
Dreyfus, J., 212 Michigan
B
Miller & Co., John, 121
Michigan ....A
Silberman Bros., 122 Michi-
gan ....AA
Swift & Co., Stock Yards
(Pullers) ....AAAA
Thompson & Co., H. T., 201
Michigan (Scourers)...A
Union Feather & Wool Co.
F
Weil & Eisendrath, 413 N.
Halstead (Pullers) ....B

IND.—Albion
Straus, Ackerman & Co.
(Buyers) ....AA

IND.—Fort Wayne
Weil Bros. & Co.........A

IND.—Indianapolis
Merritt & Co., Geo. (Inc.)
B

IND.—Kendallville
Campbell & Co. ....B

IND.—Ligonier
Straus Wool Co..........A

KY.—Louisville
Rosenbaum & Sons, Isaac,
321 E. Market ....A
Sabel & Sons, M., 233 E.
Market ....A

LA.—New Orleans
McShane, Andrew J., 630
Commerce ....B

MAINE—Bangor
Maxfield Co., S. A. (Pul-
lers) ....AAAA

MD.—Baltimore
Baer & Co., Lewis, 206
Light ....A
Marcus & Son, Hy., 30 So.
Calvert ....A
Rosenburg, Happ & Siegel
(Pullers) ....A

MD.—Cumberland
Hirsch Bros. (& Pullers).B

MASS.—Boston
Brown & Adams, 274 Sum-
mer (Com.) ....AA
Cordingly & Son, W. S.

WOOL DEALERS (Con.)

559 Atlantic Av........B
Crimmius & Peirce, 127
 Federal ....A
Demsy, Rice & Benedict,
 610 Atlantic Av.......A
Dewey, Gould & Co., 600
 Atlantic Av. (Com.)..AA
Eisemann Bros. ....A
Follett Wool Co., 214 Sum-
 mer ....A
Goohue & Studley, 556 At-
 lantic Av. ....B
Hollowell & Co., Donald
 252 Summer (Com.)..AA
Harding & Caverly, 286
 Summer (Com.) ......A
Harrington, Geo., 212 Sum-
 mer ....B
Hartley, H., 620 Atlantic
 Av. (Also Foreign)....B
Hecht, Liebmann & Co.
 (Com.) ....AA
Hobbs, Taft & Co., 18
 Matthews ....A
Keenan, P. J., 56 Fulton
 (Also Wool Stock).....A
Koshland & Co., J., 268
 Summer (Com.) ...AAAA
Lewis, E. Frank, 293 Con-
 gress (Scourer) ......A
Lodge & Co., John T., 555
 Atlantic Av. (Waste)..B
Luce & Manning, 138 Fed-
 eral (Com.) ....AAA
National Woolen Co., 170
 Summer (Shoddy) ...AA
New England Dressed Meat
 & Wool Co., 20 North
 (Pullers) ....AAA
Nichols, Dupee & Co., 262
 Summer ....A
Parsons Bros., 560 Atlan-
 tic Av. ....B
Peabody & Co., Hy. W.
 (Mason Bros.) (Imp.)AA
Purdy & Co., O. N., 290
 Summer ....B
Remick & Co., T., 489 At-
 lantic ....A
Smith & Co., A. W., 125
 Federal ....A
Stoddard, Haserick, Rich-
 ards & Co., 152 Congress
 AA
Stone, Timlow & Co., 237
 Congress (Com.) .....A
Swift & Co., 620 Atlantic
 Av. ....AAAA
Thacher & Co., T. C. 16
 Pearl ....A
Union Carpet Lining Co.
 179 Devonshire (Imp.).A
Wheelock & Co., J. H., 620
 Atlantic Av. (Foreign)
 (Com.) ....B
Whitman, Farnsworth &
 Thayer, 118 Federal.AAA
Wilcox & Cordingly, 246
 Summer ....A
Willett & Co., Geo. T. 248
 Summer (Inc.) ....A
Willey & Co., Francis, 556
 Atlantic Av. ......AAAA
Williams & Co., Jeremiah,
 300 Summer ....AAAA
Wright, John G., 620 At-
 lantic Av. ....AAA
Wyman, Franklin A. 101
 High ....B
MASS.—No. Chelmsford
Moore, Geo. C. (Scourer)
 AAA
MASS.—Peabody
Thomas Co., J. B. (Pullers)
 A
MASS.—Springfield
Mayo & Co., A. N., 156
 Lyman (Waste) ......A
MICH.—Detroit
Schmidt, Carl E., 54 Ma-
 comb (& Puller) ......A
Schmidt & Sons. Traugott,
 138 Monroe Av. (Pullers)
 AA
Sloman & Co., M., Majestic
 Bldg. ....B
MICH.—Eaton Rapids
Vaughn & Son, W.   B
MICH.—Grand Rapids
Cappon-Bertsch Leather Co.
 (Pullers) ....A

WOOL DEALERS (Con.)

MICH.—Saginaw
Carlisle & Co., F. W.....A
 ....1.—Stockbridge
Dupuy Co., C. E.........B
MINN.—Minneapolis
McMillan Fur & Wool Co.
 200 First Av. (Pullers)
 B
MO.—Kansas City
Biggs & Hoch ....B
Lyon & Co., M. (Com.)..A
MO.—St. Louis
Byrne & Co., Jos., 222 No.
 Main ....B
Crowdus & Co., J. C., 104
 N. Main (Com.) ......A
Donzelot & Son, Eugene, 16
 S. Main (Com.).......B
Funsten Bros. & Co., 109
 N. Main (Com.).......A
Harris & Co., B., 22 S.
 Second ....A
Landau & Co., A., 720 N.
 Main ....A
Marx & Co., Hy., 208 N.
 Main ....B
Sachs, I. & S., 100 N.
 Main ....B
N. H.—Manchester
Gerrish Wool & Leather
 Co. ....A
N. J.—Newark
Newark Beef Co. (Pullers)
 AAAA
N. J.—Paterson
Muhs Co., Hy. River
 (Pullers) ....A
N. MEX.—Albuquerque
Ilfeld Bros. ....B
Rosewald Bros. ....B
N. MEX.—East Las Vegas
Friedman & Bro., Myer..A
Ilfeld, Chas...........AA
N. Y.—Albany
Glavin & Son, John (Pul-
 lers) ....A
Newman & Co., Chas., 457
 B'way ....A
N. Y.—Batavia
Page, Geo. A. & R. I....B
N. Y.—Binghamton
Conklin & Son, E. W.....A
N. Y.—Buffalo
Kraus & Co., A ....B
Schoellkopf & Co.......AA
N. Y.—Columbus
Rosenthal Bros. & Basch
 (Pullers) ....B
N. Y.—Holley
Kennedy & Co. ....B
New York City
Bach, Becker & Co., 104
 Greene ....A
Denby, Isaac, Wool Ex-
 change ....A
Follett Wool Co., Wool Ex-
 change Bldg. ....B
Lobsitz, Samuel, 260
 Church ....A
McMurtry, John E., 2
 Walker ....A
Rawitser & Co., S., Cor.
 Canal & Bway (Waste,
 &c.) ....AA
Swift & Co., Wool Ex-
 change ....AAAA
Thompson's Nephew & Co.,
 Sam'l, 142 Duane....AA
Wallace, Mueller & Co.
 (Ltd.) (Imp.) ....B
Willett & Co., Geo. F.
 Wool Exchange ....A
Harrington & Co., J. J.,
 770 1st Av. (Pullers)..A
Schwarzschill & Sulzberger
 Co., 45th & 1st Av. (Pul-
 lers) ....AAAA
Shea, John, 648 W. 39th
 (Puller) ....B
Simon & Kaufman (Pul-
 lers) ....B
N. Y.—Syracuse
Falker, August (Puller) ..B
Marshall & Son, Jacob
 (Pullers) ....B
N. Y.—York
Stewart, Chas. N. (& Grow-
 er) ....B
N. DAK.—Fargo
Balles & Rogers ....A
OHIO—Cincinnati
Wise & Bros., L., 36 Main

OHIO—Georgetown B
Boon & Bevington Co. ...B
OHIO—Mantua
Crafts, Wm. H. ....A
OHIO—Toledo
Mack, J. ....B
OREGON—Portland
Allen & Lewis (Com.)...A
Bissinger & Co. (Com.) ..A
PA.—Kittanning
Gault & Co., J. A........B
PA.—Philadelphia
Adams & Co., Jas. M. Main
  & Myk (Scourers) .....A
Allen & Co., Wm. F., 132
  Front ....AA
Coats Bros., 127 Market
  (Com.) ....AAA
Cooper. H. L. ....B
DeLong & Coffin, 11 N.
  Front ....B
Erben. Harding & Co., 25th
  & Spring Garden (Scour-
  ers) ....AAAA
Gregg Bros., 18 S. Front
  (Com.) ....AAA
Grubnau. Carl, 30 N. Front
  ....A
Hoffman, G. E., 248 Chest-
  nut (Waste) ....A
Jagode & Co., Phillip, 14
  Letitia ....A
Justice. Bateman & Co., 122
  S. Front (Com) ....AAA
Kay. John J., 132 Allen
  (Waste) ....B
Kenworthy & Bro., T., 111
  Church ....AA
Kenworthy's Sons, Thos.,
  130 Arch ....A
Kitchen & Co., James G.,
  55 N. Front ....AA
Lee & Co., Thomas, 11
  Letitia ....A
McCloskey. J. J., 34 N.
  Front (Waste) ....A
McCullough & Co., Jas. A.,
  71 N. Front ....B
O'Neil. Chas., 57 N. Front
  (Waste) ....AA
O'Neil Bros., Columbia Av.
  & Howard (Waste) ....A
Reifsnyder Son & Co., I.,
  110 S. Front ....A
Reineke & Co., Hy. G., 1632
  N. 5th (Pullers) .....B
Smith & Bro., Bradford, 111
  Chestnut ....B
Stephenson & Craft, 107
  Church (Waste) ......B
Swift & Co., 107 Chest-
  nut ....AAAA
Tilden, W. T., 254 N. Front
  ....B
Toland & Hance, 124 S.
  Front ....B
Wallace & Bro., John J.,
  1620 Lombard (Waste).B
Wallworth & Sons. J., 221
  Chestnut (Waste) ....B
Webb & Co., Chas. J., 116
  Chestnut ....AAAA
Weil Bros., 216 Chestnut
  ....AA
Willey, J. H., 235 N. Water
  ....B
Willey & Co., Francis. 32
  Strawberry ......AAAA
Wood Bros. & Co., 27 N.
  Front ....AAAA
Woolston & Moore, 110
  Chestnut (Waste) ....B
Yewdall & Jones Co., 54th
  & Poplar (Scourers) ...A
PA.—Potersville .
Humphrey & Sons, Wm. ..B
R. I.—Providence
Peck & Co., Asa, Atwells
  & Harris Av. (Waste;
  Noils) ....AA
Slade Co., Walter F., 75
  Exchange Pl. (Shoddy;
  Noils) ....B
Smith & Co., Albert W., 20
  Davis ....A
TENN.—Nashville
Lefkovitz & Co., J. ......B
TEXAS—Houston
Finnegan Co., John ......A
TEXAS—Lampasas
Stokes Bros. ....B

TEXAS—Laredo
Bruni & Bro., A. M. .....A
TEXAS—San Antonio
Halff & Bro., M. (Com.) A
Hugo-Schmeltzer Co. (Com.)
  ....A
UTAH—Ogden City
Kuhn & Bro., A. ....A
WASH.—Seattle
Bissinger & Co. ....A
W. VA.—Wheeling
Hockheimer Bros. ......AA
WIS.—Edgerton
Child, H. W. ....B
WIS.—Madison
Cook Bros. C
WIS.—Milwaukee
Rosenberg & Liberman, 104
  W. Water ....B
WIS.—Reedsburg
Harris & Hostler ....B
WIS.—Viroqua
Eckhardt. Fred. ....A
WYO.—Rawlins
Hugus & Co., J. W. (sell
  for others) ....A

WOOL:
MINERAL

ILL.—Chicago
Chicago Fire Proof Covering
  Co. ....E
MINN.—Winona
Union Fibre Co. ....B
MO.—St. Louis
Amer. Insulating Material
  Mfg. Co., 213 N. 3rd ...B
New York City
United States Mineral Wool
  Co.. 143 Liberty ......D
PA.—Easton
Baker & Adamson Chemical
  Co. ....A
PA.—Pittsburg
McConnell & Co., John A.
 X

WOOLEN
GOODS

ARK.—Centre Point
Centre Point Woolen Mills
  (Tweeds; Lindseys, etc.)C
CAL.—Napa
Napa Woolen Mills (Flan-
  nels; Lap Robes) C
CAL.—San Francisco
Golden Gate Woolen Mfg.
  Co. (Tweeds; Cassimere;
  Flannels; Ladies Suitings)
  ....A
CAL.—Stockton
Stockton Woolen Mills
  (Blankets; Flannels; Che-
  viots; Tweeds; Cassi-
  meres) C
CONN.—Broad Brook
Broad Brook Co. (Fine Fan-
  cy Cassimere; Worsted
  Suitings; Coverts; Coat-
  ings) ....AA
CONN.—Buckland
Hilliard Co., E. E. (Fan-
  cy & Union Cassimere;
  Kerseys. etc.) ....AA
CONN.—Danielson
Danielson Worsted Co.
  (Men's Wear) ....A
CONN.—East Lynne
Niantic Mfg. Co. (Cassi-
  meres; Cheviots; Fancy
  Dress Gds.) ....B
CONN.—Killingly
Elmville Mills (Cheviots;
  Overcoatings) ....AAAA
CONN.—Meriden
Meriden Woolen Mills (Ra-
  wister & Bro.) (Cloak
  ings; Cassimeres; Wor-
  steds) ....AA
CONN.—Norwich
Thames Valley Mills (Hall
  Bros.) (Dress Goods;
  Cloakings; Cassimeres)A
CONN.—Poquetanuck
Lucas & Co., B. (Dress;
  Carriage Linings) .....A
CONN.—Preston
Hall Bros. (Dress Goods;

Cloakings; Cassimeres)AA

CONN.—Rockville
Amer. Mills Co., The (Cassimeres; Fancy Worsteds;
Meltons; Kerseys) ....B
Hockanuh Co. (Fancy Cassimeres; Worsted Gds.)A
New England Co. (Cassimeres; Worsteds) .....A
Springville Mfg. Co. (Fancy
Cassimeres; Worsteds) A

CONN.—Seymour
Tingue Mfg. Co. (Worsted
Suitings; Mohair; Plushes; Mohair & Worsted
Genapped) ....A

CONN.—Somersville
Somersville Mfg. Co. (Men's
Wear) ....A

CONN.—Stafford
Central Woolen Co. (Fancy
Cassimeres; Fancy Black
Coverts; Venetians)...A
Phoenix Woolen Co. (Kerseys; Overcoatings) ...A
Riverside Woolen Co.
(Overcoating) ....A

CONN.—Stafford Springs
Warren Woolen Co. (Cassimeres; Coverts; Overcoatings; Worsteds) ....A

CONN.—Torrington
Warrenton Woolen Co.
(Uniform Goods & Kerseys; Doeskin; Broad)..A

CONN.—Vernon
Vernon Woolen Co. (Union
Cassimeres; Satinets)..B

CONN.—Yantic
Yantic Woolen Co. (Flannels; Dress) ....A

GA.—Atlanta
Atlanta Woolen Mills (Cassimere;; Jeans) ....A

GA.—Columbus
Eagle & Phoenix Mills
(Jeans; Doeskins; Kerseys; Cassimeres; Satinets; Twills) ......AAAA

GA.—Pickajack
Concord Woolen Mills (Cassimeres) ....B

ILL.—Chicago
Converse, Stanton & Co.
(Com. Cassimeres; Flannels; Cloakings) ..AAA
Faulkner, Page & Co. (Com.
Cassimeres; Flannels)
..................AAA
Foster & Co., F. A. (Com.)
..................AA
Shaw & Co., T. A. (Com.)
..................AAA

ILL.—Hanover
Hanover Woolen Mfg. Co.
(Fancy Cassimeres) ...A

ILL.—Jacksonville
Capps & Sons, J. (Cassimeres; Worsteds) .....A

ILL.—Springfield
Springfield Woolen Mills .
(Cassimeres) ....A

IND.—Evansville
Evansville Woolen Mills Co.
(Fancy Cassimeres; Dress
Goods) ....B

IND.—La Porte
Fox's Sons. Saml. (Women's Dress Goods) ....A

IND.—Madison
Schofield & Son, Jno.
(Jeans; Flannels) C

IND.—New Albany
New Albany Woolen Mill
Co. (Jeans; Flannels; Cassimeres) ....B

IND.—Seymour
Seymour Woolen Fcty. Co.
(Flannels) ....B

IOWA—Amana
Amana Society Woolen Mill;
(Jeans; Sackings; Cheviots; Cassimeres)AAAA

IOWA—Bonaparte
Meek Bros. Co. (Cassimeres; Meltons) ....B

IOWA—Davenport
Davenport Woolen Mills Co.
(Flannels; Cassimeres) B

IOWA—Des Moines
Capital City Woolen Mills
(Flannels; Cassimeres) A

IOWA—Farmington
Sterling Woolen Mills Co.
(Flannels; Cassimeres) C

KANS.—Topeka
Topeka Woolen Mill Co.
(Cassimeres) ....B

KY.—Henderson
Henderson Woolen Mills
(Jeans; Cassimeres)....B

KY.—Louisville
Eclipse Woolen Mills (Cassimeres; Jeans) ......B
Falls City Woolen Mills
(Cassimeres; Meltons;
Kty. Jeans) ....A
Louisville Woolen Mills
(Kty. Jeans) ....AA

MAINE—Bridgton
Pondicherry Co. (Cheviots;
Cloakings; Cassimeres) B

MAINE—Dexter
Abbott. Co., Amos (Fancy
Cassimeres; Dress Goods)
...................A

MAINE—Fairfield
Mayo & Son (Tricots; Dress
Goods; Cloakings) ...;B

MAINE—Guilford
Piscataquis Woolen Co.
(Sackings; Dress Goods;
Overcoatings; Cassimeres)
...................A

MAINE—Hartland
Linn Woolen Co. (Cloakings; Cassimeres; Dress
Goods) ....A

MAINE—Lewiston
Cowan Woolen Co. (Fancy
Cassimeres; Dress Goods)
...................B
Libbey & Dingley (Cloakings; Cheviots) ......A

MAINE—Lisbon
Farnsworth Co. (Dress
Goods; Flannels) ......B

MAINE—Madison
Indian Spring Woolen Co.
(Cassimeres; Dress
oGods) ....B
Madison Woolen Co. (Dress
Goods; Kerseys; Beavers)
...................B

MAINE—Pittsfield
Dobson & Co.. Robt....AA

MAINE—Sanford
Sanford Mills ......AAAA

MAINE—Waterville
Riverview Worsted Mills
(Worsteds) ....A

MD.—Baltimore
Dickey & Sons, W. J.
(Com.) ....AAA
Maryland Woolen Co. (Kerseys; Cheviots) ......A
Woodward, Baldwin & Co.
(Com.) ....AAAA

MD.—Haight
Oakland Mfg. Co. (Kerseys) ....A

MD.—Oella
Dickey & Sons (Oella Mills)
(Kerseys; Cassimeres)
...................AAA

MASS.—Agawam
Agawam Co. (Flannels;
Dress Goods) ....B

MASS.—Andover
Ballardvale Mills (Fine
White Flannels) ..AAA
Stevens & Sons Co., M. T.
(Flannels; Dress Goods)
....................AAA

MASS.—Bellingham
Charles River Woolen Co.
(Meltons; Cassimeres; Satinets) .;..........A
Taft, Murdock & Co. (Cassimeres; Satinets) ....A

MASS.—Billerica
Faulkner Mfg. Co. (Twill
Flannels; Dress Goods)B
Talbot Mills (Flannels;
Dress Goods; Cheviots)AA

MASS.—Boston
Amer. Woolen Co. (All
Kinds) ....AAAA
Battelle, Hurd & Co. (Com.
Cassimeres; Suitings;
Dress Goods) ....A
Blake & Stearns (Com.) A
Converse, Stanton & Co.
(Com. Cassimeres; Flan-

nels; Cloakings) ...AAA
Deering, Milliken & Co.
(Com. Flannels; Cassimeres; Cloakings) AAAA
Faulkner, Page & Co. (Com.
Flannels) ....AAA
Foster & Co., F. A. (Com.)
AA
Greeley & Cushman & Record (Com. Cassimeres;
Beavers; Suitings) AAA
Harding, Whitman & Co.
(Com. Dress Goods; Worsteds) ....AAAA
Joy, Langdon & Co. (Com.
Dress Goods; Cassimeres;
Worsteds) ....AAAA
Mackintosh, Tafts &
McKenney (Com.) ....A
Parker, Wilder & Co. (Com.
Flannels; Cassimeres)
AAAA
Smith, Hogg & Co. (Com.
Flannels) ....AAAA
Wendell, Fay & Co. (Com.
Cloth; Flannel) ....A
MASS.—Brookfield
Mann & Stevens Woolen Co.
(Satinets) ....D
MASS.—Clinton
Clinton Worsted Co. (Suitings; Trouserings) ....B
MASS.—Dedham
Merchants Woolen Mills
(Friezes; Cheviots; Meltons; Kerseys) ....AA
MASS.—Douglass
Haywood & Co., W. E.
(Cassimeres; Suitings) B
MASS.—Dudley
Merrimack Woolen Co.
(Cloakings; Dress Goods)
A
MASS.—Franklin
Haywood, Harry T. (Flannels; Satinets) ....A
Singleton Worsted Co.
(Fancy Worsteds) ...B
MASS.—Groveland
Groveland Mills (Dress
Goods; Flannels) .....A
MASS.—Hinsdale
Hinsdale Woolen Co. (Cassimeres; Kerseys; Suitings) ....B
MASS.—Holden
Eagle Lake Woolen Co.
(Cassimeres; Black Cheviots; Satinets) ......A
Jefferson Mfg. Co. (Cassimeres; Cheviots) .....A
Wood & Co., C. G. (Satinets) ....A
MASS.—Holyoke
Beebe-Webber Co. (Cassimeres; Fancy Worsteds;
Kerseys; Meltons) .....B
Farr Alpaca Co. (Worsteds)
AAA
Germania Mills (Overcoatings; Kerseys; Beavers;
Cloakings) ....B
MASS.—Hyde Park
Bleakie Co., Robt. (Cassimeres) ....A
MASS.—Lawrence
Arlington Mills (Worsted
Dress) ....AAA
Brown & Whittier (Fine
Worsted Dress Goods) B
Kunhardt, Geo. E. (Worsteds for Men's Wear)
AAAA
MASS.—Leicester
Carlton & Sons, E. G.
(White; Colored Flannels)
B
Rochdale Mills (Opera Flannels; Dress Goods; Suitings; Broadcloth) .....B
Valley Woolen Mills
(Dress Goods) ....B
MASS.—Lowell
Belvidere Woolen Mfg. Co.
(Flannels; Dress Goods) A
Middlesex Co. (Beavers;
Kerseys; Meltons; Meltons; Thibets; Uniform
Cloth; Venetians)...AAA
Stirling Mills (Flannels;
Cheviots; Dress Goods) A
U. S. Bunting Co. (Worsted

Dress Goods) ....AA
MASS.—Millbury
Mayo Woolen Co. (Men's;
Women's Wear) ....B
MASS.—Monson
Ellis & Son, D. W. (Kerseys; Dress Goods) AA
MASS.—New Bedford
Oneko Woolen Mills ..AA
MASS.—North Adams
North Adams Mfg. Co.
(Fancy Cassimeres; Cheviots) ....A
Strong, Hewat & Co. (Fancy Cassimeres; Scotch
Cheviots; Overcoating)B
MASS.—North Andover
Stevens Mills (Flannels;
Dress Goods) .....AAA
MASS.—Northbridge
Riverdale Woolen Co.
(Shoddies) ....B
MASS.—North Dana
Success Worsted Co. (Fancy Worsteds; Clay's;
Serges) ....AAA
MASS.—Oxford
Howarth & Son, Andrew
(White Flannels) ...AA
MASS.—Pittsfield
Peck Mfg. Co., J. L. & T.
D. (Flannels) ....A
Pontoosuc Woolen Mfg. Co.
(Suitings; Cloths) ....A
Russell Mfg. Co., S. N. &
C. (Kerseys) ....B
Tillotson Mfg. Co. ....AA
MASS.—Plymouth
Standish Worsted Co. (Fine
Worsted) ....A
MASS.—Saugus
Scott & Son, F. (Fancy
Dress Goods) ......B
MASS.—Stoughton
French & Ward (Flannels;
Dress Goods) ....A
MASS.—Uxbridge
Calumet Woolen Co. (Cassimeres) ....A
MASS.—Ware
Gilbert Mfg. Co., Geo. H.
(Worsteds) ....AAA
Stevens & Co., C. A. (Flannels; Dress Goods) ...A
MASS.—Warren
Sayles & Jenks Mfg. Co.
(Worsted; Cassimeres;
Overcoatings) ....A
MASS.—Watertown
Aetna Mills (Worsteds; Kerseys; Ladies' Dress Gds.)
A
Bemis Mills (Serges; Dress
Goods) ....B
MASS.—Webster
Slater Woolen Co. (Doeskins; Flannels; Broadcloth; Cheviots; Beavers)
AAAA
MASS.—Worcester
Curtis Mfg. Co. (Satinets;
Flannels) ....B
Thayer, E. D. Jr. (Cheviots;
Dress Goods) ....AA
MICH.—Clinton
Clinton Woolen Mfg. Co.
(All Wool Cassimeres) A
MICH.—Yale
Andrae & Sons, Chas. (Cassimeres) C
MINN.—Faribault
Klemer & Sons, C. H. (Cassimeres) C
MINN.—Minneapolis
No. Star Woolen Mill Co.
(Flannels) ....AA
MINN.—Rushford
Webster & Co., Jonathan
(Flannels) C
MO.—California
California Woolen Mill Co.
(Flannel) C
MO.—St. Joseph
Buell Mfg. Co. (Flannels) A
MO.—Sedalia
Lamy Mfg. Co., J. A.
(Cassimeres) ....B
N. H.—Bristol
Dodge-Davis Mfg. Co. (Fine
Flannels) ....B
N. H.—Concord
Dustin Island Woolen Mills

WOOOLEN GOODS

(Flannels; Dress Goods)B

N. H.—Hillsborough Bridge
Hillsborough Woolen Mill
Co. (Suitings; Kerseys)A

N. H.—Hinsdale
Amidon & Son, Chas. J
(Meltons; Cheviots) B
Haile & Frost Mfg. Co.
(Kerseys; Cassimeres;
Flannels) ....B

N. H.—Lebanon
Carter & Rogers ...... B

N. H.—Manchester
Devonshire Mills (Cassimeres; Cloakings; Dress
Goods) ....B

N. H.—Newport
Richards & Sons, Dexter
(Twilled Flannels; Suitings) ....AAA

N. H.—Rochester
Cocheco Woolen Mfg. Co.
(Cheviots; Outings; Suitings; Broadcloths; Cassimeres) ....A
Gonic Mfg. Co. (Flannels;
Dress Goods; Suitings) A

N. H.—Tilton
Tilton Mills (Tweeds; Meltons) .... A

N. J.—Bloomfield
Oakes & Co., Thomas
(Cloths) ....AAA

N. J.—Bound Brook
Bound Brook Woolen Mills
(Overcoatings; Cloakings)
AA

N. J.—Passaic
Algonquin Co. (Cotton
Warp) ....AA
Botany Worsted Mills
(Dress Goods) ....AAAA
Dundee Woolen Co. (Fancy
Cassimeres) C
Gera Mills (Dress Goods) A
Passaic Woolen Co.
(Cassimeres) ....B
Robertsford Worsted Mills
(Serges; Dress Goods) B

N. J.—Raritan
Raritan Woolen Mills
(Chinchillas; Beavers;
Kerseys; Meltons) .... A
Somerset Mfg. Co. (Cassimeres; Overcatings) A

N. J.—Somerville
Somerville Woolen Mills
(Worsteds; Cassimeres) A

N. J.—Trenton
Colonial Woolen Co.
(Cassimeres) ....B
Williams Mfg. Co., Jno.
(Flannels; Cassimeres;
Dress Goods) .... A

N. J.—Auburn
Auburn Woolen Co. .... B
Brooks & Sons, Jas. (Flannels) .... D

N. Y.—Fulton
Fulton Worsted Mills
(Clays; Serges; Diagonals) ....AAAA

N. Y.—Honeoye Falls
Hunt, A. H. (Flannels) D

N. Y.—Jamestown
Broadhead & Sons, Wm.
(Worsted; Dress Goods;
Suitings) ....AAAA
Empire Worsted Mills
(Worsted Dress) .....A
Jamestown Woolen Mills
(Flannels; Cassimeres)
AAAA
Jamestown Worsted Mills
(Dress Goods; Suitings)
AAAA
Meadow Brook Mills
(Dress Goods) ....AAAA

N. Y.—Madrid
Madrid Woolen Mills
(Pant Cloth) C

N. Y.—Malone
Ballard & Co., J. O.
(Cassimeres) C
Lawrence Webster Co.
(Cassimeres) .... B

N. Y.—Marcellus
Crown Mills (Fancy) ....A
New York City
Abegg & Rusch (Com.
Serges; Cloakings; Dress
Goods) ....AAAA
Abrahams & Schwarz

WOOOLEN GOODS

(Imprt.) ....A
Armstaedt & Co. (Imp.) AA
Auffmordt & Co., C. A.
(Com. Cloakings; Dress
Goods; Etc.; Also Imp.)
AAAA
Bachmann, Emmerich & Co.
(Com.) .... B
Bacon & Co. (Com.) AAA
Bairendahl & Co., H.
(Imp.) .... A
Battelle, Hurd & Co.
(Com.) .... A
Boessneck, Broesel & Co.
(Com. Worsted; Dress
Goods; Cloakings) AAAA
Brigg & Sons, Jno. F.
(Com. Worsteds; Also
Imp.) ....AAA
Brooke & Co., J. (Import.)
A
Brown Sons & Co., M.
(Com. Flannels) .... B
Butterfield & Co., Frank
(Impt.) ....AAAA
Caeser & Co., H. A. (Com.
Dress Goods) ...... AAA
Cohn, Salo. (Com. Dress
Goods) .... A
Converse, Stanton & Co.
(Com. Cassimeres; Worsteds; Cloakings; Overcoatings; Dress Goods)..AAA
Cooke & Co., Jas. W.
(Com.) .... ?
Curtis & Warren (Com.) B
Deering, Milliken & Co.
Com.) ....AAAA
Derby & Co., W. E.
(Com.) .... A
Dickey & Sons, W. J.
(Com.) ....AAA
Downing, Clark & Co.
Import.) .... A
Ellison & Sons, Jno. B.
(Imp.) ....AAAA
Farish-Stafford Co. (Com.)
B
Faulkner, Page & Co.
(Com. Dress Good, Etc.)
AAA
Fisher Sons & Co., M.
(Import) ....AAAA
Fithian & Co., J. H.
Com.) .... A
Fleitmann & Co. (Com.,
Also Com. Dress Goods)
AAAA
Floyd Bros. (Com.) ....AA
Fornes & Co., C. V. (Imp.)
AA
Forstman & Co. (Imp.) AAA
Foster & Co., F. A. (Com.)
A
Galey & Lord (Com.) ....A
Gittermann & Co., Hy.
(Import) .... B
Greely, Cushman & Record
(Com. Cassimeres; Beavers; Suitings) ...... AAA
Harding, Whitman & Co.
(Com. Worsteds; Dress
Goods) ....AAAA
Hardt, Von Bernuth & Co.
(Com. Worsteds) ..AAAA
Hayes & Co., O. H. (Com.)
AA
Iselin & Co., Wm. (Com.
Worsteds; Dress Goods)
AAAA
Joy, Langdon & Co. (Com.
Cassimeres; Dress Goods)
AAAA
Julliard & Co., A. D. (Com.
Worsteds; Cassimeres;
Dress Goods) .....AAAA
King Beals & Co. (Mfgs.
Agts. Dress Goods) AAAA
Kirnhardt & Stockton (Com.
Worsteds; Dress Goods;
Cloakings) .... AA
Lamb, Finlay & Co. (Com.)
AA
Langley & Co., W. H.
(Com.) ....AAAA
Lawrie, Mann & Drowne
(Com. Worsteds) .... A
Leonard, Wm. B.
(Import) .... A
Libby & Co., H. J. (Com.
Cloakings, Etc.) .... A
McEvoy, Jno. F. (Import)
B

Mackintosh, Taft & McKenney (Com.) ....A

Mali & Co., Hy. W. T. (Com.; Also Import) AA

Mason & Hanson (Import) ....AA

Masters & Co., Francis R. (Com. Flannels) ..... B

Metclaf Bros. & Co. (Com. Worsteds; Cloakings; Coatings; Meltons; Cassimeres) ....AAA

Miller, Doull & Co. (Com. Dress Goods) ....A

Minot Hooper & Co. (Com. Worsteds) ....AAAA

Neuss, Hesselin & Co. (Import) ....B

Oelbermann, Dommerich & Co. (Com. Flannels) ....AAAA

Ogden & Brook (Import) ....AAA

Oright & Co., A. (Import) ....AAA

Parker, Wilder & Co. (Com. Flannels; Ladies' Suitings; Sackings) ..AAAA

Patterson & Greenough (Com. Broadcloth) .... B

Pippey Co., B. Y. (Com.) B

Reynols & Co., E. B. (Import.) ....B

Rockfellow & Co., W. H. (Com.) ....A

Rothschild & Co., V. Henry (Com.) ....B

Rubenstein, Louis (Import.) ....B

Sawyer & Blake (Com. Cloakings; Dress Goods) ....AA

Schefer, Schramm & Vogel (Com. Dress Goods)AAAA

Schnabel Bros. (Woolens; Worsteds; Cassimeres) Also Import.) ...... AAA

Shreve & Adams (Com.) A

Siebert, Stolte & Co. (Import.) ....B

Slater & Sons, S. (Com.) ....AAAA

Smith, Hogg & Co. (Com.) ....AAAA

Stein & Co., S. (Import) ....AAA

Stern & Co., Jas (Com. Dress Goods) ....A

Stevens & Co., J. P. (Com) ....A

Stevens, Sanford & Handy (Com. Worsteds) ....AA

Stieglitz & Son, M. L. (Import) ....A

Stoney & Son, W. (Com.) B

Stursburg, Schell & Co., W. (Import) ....A

Sullivan Vail & Co. (Com. Worsteds, Cassimeres, Cloakings; also Import) ....AAA

Talcott, James (Com. Kerseys; Cassimers; Worsteds) ....AAAA

Townsend & Co., E. M. (Com.) ....A

Treat & Converse (Com.) ....AAA

Uhlige & Co. (Import) ..B

Van Ingen & Co., E. H. (Import) ....AAAA

Victor & Achelis, Fred (Com.) .... AAAA

Wallach, Hoexter & Co. (Import.) ....A

Watson, Porter, Giles & Co. (Com.) ....A

Weed & Bro. (Com.) ..AAA

Wellington, W. L. (Com. Dress Goods) ....A

Wendel Fay & Co. (Com. Cassimeres, Suitings; Overcoats; Flannels; Uniform Cloth) ....A

Whitman & Phelps (Com. Worsteds) ....AAA

Willis & Co., W. P. (Import.) ....B

Wilmerding & Bisset (Com.) ....AA

Wilson & Bradbury (Com.) ....AAA

Woods, Lowry & Co. (Im-

port) .... A

N. Y.—Rochester
Allen Woolen Mills (Dress Goods) .... B

N. Y.—Rockwells Mills
Rockwell & Co., C. W. (Cassimeres) .... B

N. Y.—Sandusky
Hayden, Theodore (Flannel Shirting) C

N. Y.—Seneca Falls
Seneca Woolen Mills (Suitings; Overcoatings; Cloakings) .... B

N. Y.—Skaneateles Falls
Glenside Woolen Mills (Unions; Meltons) .... A

N. Y.—Stottville
Stott Woolen Co. (Flannels; Dress Goods; Cloakings) .... B

Warrensburg Woolen Co. (Cassimeres) .... A

N. Y.—Waterloo
Waterloo Woolen Mfg. Co. (Indigo Uniform Cloths; Overcoatings) .... A

N. C.—Elkin
Clatham Mfg. Co. (Jeans, Flannels; Cassimeres) B

N. C.—Patterson
Gwyn-Harper Mfg. Co. (Cassimeres; Jeans) ..B

N. C.—Spray
Leakesville Woolen Mills A

OHIO—Ashtabula
Ashtabula Worsted Mills (Women's Dress Goods) B

OHIO—Cincinnati
Putnam Hooker & Co. (Com.) .... A

OHIO—Cleveland
Beckman Co., The (Cheviots; Clays) .... A

OHIO—Columbus
Columbus Woolen Mill Co. (Skirtings) .... B

OHIO—Dresden
Muskigum Valley Woolen Mfg. Co. (Plain & Fancy Cassimeres) .... B

OHIO—Napoleon
Napoleon Woolen Mills (Flannels) C

OREGON—Eugene
Willamette Valley Woolen Mfg. Co. (Flannels; Cassimeres) C

OREGON—Oregon City
Oregon City Mfg. Co. (Cassimeres; Flannels) A

OREGON—Portland
Portland Woolen Mills (Fancy) ... .B

PA.—Aston Mills
Rhodes Bros. (Jeans; Doeskins; Kerseys) ...... B

PA.—Bloomsburg
Caswell & Co., C. E. (Cassimeres) .... B

PA.—Bridgeport
Smith, Isaac W. (Cassimeres) .... B

PA.—Bristol
Steel & Co., Edw. T. (Men's Worsteds) AAAA

PA.—Brookville
Brookville Woolen Mills (Dress Goods) .... B

OHIO—Canton
Cardington Mills (Cassimeres) .... A

PA.—Chambersburg
Chambersburg Woolen Co. (Cheviots; Cassimeres; Cloakings) .... B

PA.—Chester
Aberfoyle Mfg. Co. (Dress Goods; Shirtings; Cheviots)) .... AAA

Hetzel Co., Geo. C. (Worsted Suitings; Coatings) A

Irving & Son, Jas (Cassimeres) .... B

PA.—Clifton Heights
Kent Mfg. Co., Thomas (Flannels; Kerseys) AA

PA.—Conshohocken
Conshohocken Woolen Co. (Kerseys; Diagonals; Suitings; Overcoating) A

PA.—Darby

Verlenden Bros. (Jeans, Etc.) .... B

PA.—Honesdale
Birdsall Bros. (Cassimeres; Flannels) .... B

PA.—Norristown
Norristown Woolen Co. (Cassimeres; Blouse Flannels; Government Kerseys) ....B
Watt & Son, Wm. (Cheviots; Cassimeres) B
Woodstock Mills Co. (Cassimeres; Cloakings; Chinchillas) ....B

PA.—Philadelphia
Bochmann & Co., Francis (Worsted Dress) ...... A
Brown & Co., C. M. **(Cassimeres)** .... B
Carruth & Co., Jno. G. Men's; Women's Worsteds) .... AAA
Connelly & Sons, Jas. **(Checks; Cheviots)** ...A
Culbertson & Sons, Jno. (Dress Goods) .... B
Dobson, Jno. (Overcoatings; **Cloakings)** .... B
Farnum & Co., Jno. (Com.) AAAA
Greer, Benj. W. (Worsteds) B
Griffen Co. (Plain & Fancy Dress) .... B
Imperial Woolen Co. (Overcoatings; Kerseys) AA
Keim & Co., J. R. (Worsteds; Suitings; Trouserings) .... AAA
Long Bros. Co. (Worsted (Dress) .... A
Porter & Son, Chas. (Worsteds; Dress Goods) AAA
Southwark Mills Co. (Cloakings; Dress Goods; Suitings) .... AA
Sullivan & Co., Wm. (Men's Worsted Wear) B
Vogler, Jno. G. (Worsted **Dress)** .... B
Williams Mfg. Co., Jno. (Dress Goods; Flannels; Cassimeres) .... A
Wilson, Thomas H. (Dress Goods) .... B
Wilson & Bradbury (Com.) AAA
Wood & Co., Wm. (Worsted Suitings; Woolen; Cassimeres; Flannels; Cloakings) .... AAAA

PA.—Reading
Brumbach, Alb. J. (Cassimeres) .... AA
Leinbach & Co., J. G. (Cassimeres) ....A

PA.—Stony Creek Mills
Kraemer & Co., Louis (Cassimeres) .... A

PA.—Woolrich
Rich & Bros., Jno. (Flannels) .... A

PA.—Worthington
Graff & Co., Peter(Flannels) .... A

R. I.—Burrillville
Oakland Worsted Co. (Worsted Sackings) A
Glendale Woolen Mill (Fancy Cassimeres; Worsteds) .... B
Sayles & Sons, A. L. (Fancy Cassimeres; Worsteds) A
Sayles Co., Fred L. (Suitings; Worsteds) ..... B

R. I.—Hopkinton
Ashaway Woolen Co. (Cassimeres; Suitings) .... B

R. I.—No-Kingston
Belleville Woolen Mills (Cassimeres; Kerseys; Vicunas) .... B
Oak Hill Mill (Unions; Worsteds) .... AAA
Rodman Mfg. Co. (Doeskins; Jeans; Suitings) AAA
Wickford Worsted Mills (Worsteds) .... AA

R. I.—No-Providence
Lymansville Co. (Worsted

Suitings) .... AAA

R. I.—Pascoag
Farwell Worsted Mills (Worsted Suitings; Trouserings) .... AA

R. I.—Pawtucket
Lorraine Mfg. Co. (Worsted; Cotton Dress; Shirtings) .... AAAA

R. I.—Potter Hill
Atlantic Mills ...... AAAA

R. I.—Providence
Earnscliffe Worsted Mills (Fancy Worsteds) ..B

R. I.—Richmond
Carolina Mills Co. (Fancy Cassimeres; Worsteds) A
Kenyon & Son, E. (Fancy Cassimeres; Overcoatings) A

R. I.—South Kingston
Peace-Dale Mfg. Co. (Cassimeres; Chevits; Overcoatings; Serges) AAAA

R. I.—Warwick
Kent Mfg. Co. (Cassimeres; Worsteds) ....A

R. I.—Westerly
Westerly Woolen Co. (Cassimeres; Worsteds) ....A

R. I.—Woonsocket
Lippitt Woolen Co. (Fancy Cassimeres; Worsteds) AA
Perserverance Worsted Co. (Men's Fancy Worted) B

S. C.—Knoxville
Knoxville Woolen Mills (All Wool Cassimeres) AAA

TENN.—Jefferson City
Jefferson City Woolen Mills (Cassimeres) .... B

TENN.—Pine Wood
Pine Wood Cotton Mills (Sheetings) .... A

TENN.—Sweetwater
Sweetwater Woolen Mills (Jeans; Doeskins; Mixed Fabrics) .... A

TENN.—Waco
Slayden-Kirksey Woolen Mills (Cassimeres; Worsteds; Jeans) .... AA

UTAH—Ogden
Ogden Woolen Mills Co. (Flannels; Batts; Etc.) B

UTAH.—Provo City
Provo Woolen Mills Co. (Cassimeres; Worsteds; Dress Goods; Linseys) B

VT.—Bennington
Holden & Co., Leonard (Dress Goods; Cloakings; Overcoatings) ...... AA

VT.—Bridgewater
Mackenzie, F. S. (Suitings) A

VT.—Ludlow
Black River Woolen Co. (Overcoatings; Cloakins) .... B

VT.—North Hartland
Ottauquechee Woolen Co. (Meltons; Kerseys; Beavers) .... A

VT.—Springfield
Slack & Bro., W. H. H. (Shoddy; Flocks) .... A

VA.—Charlottesville
Charlottesville Woolen Mills (Cadet Greys; Sky & Dark Blue) .... A

VA.—Mouth of Wilson
Fields & Hash Mfg. Co. (Cassimeres) .... B

W. VA.—Martinsburg
Crawford Woolen Co. ....B

WIS.—Beaver Dam
Beaver Dam Woolen Mills (All Wool Cassimeres; Dress Goods) ....A

W. VA.—Menasha
Hewitt & Co., W. P. (Flannels; Skirtings; Dress Goods) ....AA

WORK

For Bent Carriage Work, etc., See Woodwork; Carriage; For Fretwork, see Grilles; For Ironwork, see Iron, etc.

WORK (Con.)

GA.—Dawson
Variety Works Co. (Ornamental Turned) ....D

ILL.—Chicago
Amer. Terra Cotta Ceramic Co., 204 Dearborn (Terra Cotta) ....A
Light Mfg. Co., Geo. W. (Fret) ....E

MD.—Baltimore
Burns, Russell & Co. (Terra Cotta) ....B

MASS.—Springfield
Cheney-Bigelow Wire Works (Elevator Wire) ......A

MICH.—E. Saginaw
Mershon & Co., Wm. B. Inc. (Fret) ....A

MO.—St. Louis
Mesker & Bro. (Ornamental Zinc) ....AA

N. J.—Perth Amboy
Perth Amboy Terra Cotta Co. (Terra Cotta) ....AA

N. Y.—Binghamton
Roberson & Son, A. (Fret) AA

N. Y.—Brooklyn
Cross, Austin & Ireland Lumber Co. (Fret) ...AA

New York City
Excelsior Terra Cotta Co., 287 4th Av. (Terra Cotta) A
Fiske, J. W. (Art Iron)..B
Howard & Morse (Elevator Wire) ....D
Jackson Architectural Iron Wrks. (Art Iron) X
Westervelt, A. B. & W. T. (Ornamental Zinc) ....B

N. Y.—Syracuse
Will & Baumer Co. (Wax) AA

OHIO—Cincinnati
Cinn. Sewer Pipe Co. (Terra Cotta) ....E

OHIO—Hamilton
Meyers Mfg. Co., Fred J. (Elevator Wire) ......B

PA.—Philadelphia
Cassel, Jacob C., 709 Arch St. (Terra Cotta) ......D
Hall & Garrison (Fret) ..X

PA.—Reading
Reading Terra Cotta & Stove Lining Works (Terra Cotta) C

WORKERS

ILL.—Chicago
Creamery Package Mfg. Co. (Butter) ....AAAA

ILL.—Elgin
Barclay, D. F. (Butter) ..A

ILL.—Rockford
Palmer Co., H. H. (Butter) D

IOWA—Clinton
Moseley & Pritchard Mfg. Co. (Butter) ....D

MICH.—Flint
Flint Cabinet Creamery Co. (Butter) ....E

N. Y.—Flemington
Mallory Mfg. Co. (Shutter) E

N. Y.—Cattaraugus
Oakes & Burger (Butter) B

N. Y.——Little Falls
Burrell & Co., D. H. (Butter) ....AAAA

N. Y.—Potsdam
Thatcher Mfg. Co. (Butter) A

N. Y.—Syracuse
Gowing, D. H. (Butter) C

N. Y.—Utica
Jones, Frank L. (Butter) C

PA.—Philadelphia
Reid, A. H. (Butter) ..A

VT.—Bellows Falls
Vermont Farm Machine Co. (Butter) C

WIS.—Fort Atkinson
Cornish, Curtis & Greene Mfg. Co (Butter) ....A
2182 WORKS.

MD.—Baltimore

WORKERS (Con.)
Poole & Son Co., Robt. (Gearing) ....A

N. Y.—New York City
Jochum, Andrew (Boiling) D

PA.—Philadelphia
Bilgram, Hugo (Gearing) A

PA.—Wilkesbarre
Vulcan Iron Works (Gearing) ....AAAA

WORKS: FIRE

See Fire Works

WORSTEDS

See Woolen Goods

WRAPPERS: BOTTLE

See also Clothing: Ladies', for Wrappers

ILL.—Chicago
Sefton Mfg. Co., J. W., 241 S. Jeff. ....AA

MO.—St. Louis
Yocum & Kacer Mfg. Co., 2008 S. 8th ....E

N. J.—Hoboken
Excelsior Wrapper Co. ..C

N. Y.—Brooklyn
Thompson & Norris Co. AA

New York City
Hinde & Dauch Paper Co. A

OHIO—Dayton
Nixon & Costello Co. C

OHIO—Sandusky
Sandusky Wrapper Co. (Straw) ....D

WREATHS

N. Y.—New York City
Neumann, A. A., 24 E. 4th (Bridal; Communion) ..C

WRENCHES

CAL.—San Francisco
Atlas Pipe Wrench Co. Flood Bldg. (Pipe)....B
Doble Co., Abner (Railroad Track) ....A

CONN.—Bridgeport
Armstrong Mfg. Co. (Pipe Reamer) ....A
Bridgeport Gun Implement Co., 219 Elm (Bicycle; Pocket) ....A
Hotchkiss, Edward S., Wrenches (S) ....A
Hurwood Mfg. Co. (Carriage Wagon) ....B
Knapp & Cowles Mfg. Co. (Pocket) C
Smith & Egge Mfg. Co (Adjustable Socket; Bicycle; Pocket; Screw; Mechanics; Agricultural) ...A

CONN.—Bristol
Turner & Deegan (Bicycle; Pocket) ....E

CONN.—Easthampton
Bevin Bros. Mfg. Co. (Nipple) ....B

CONN.—Forestville
Andrews, C. E. (Bicycle; Pocket) ....A

CONN.—Hartford
Billings & Spencer Co. (all Kinds) ....A
Pratt & Whitney Co. (Adjustable Top; Engineers'; Machinists'; Tap; Reamer) ....AAAA

CONN.—Mount Carmel
Woodruff & Sons, Walter W. (Carriage; Wagon) A

CONN.—New Haven
Barnes Tool Co. (Bicycle; Pipe Pocket) ....B
Bolden Machine Co. (Brass; Nickle Pipe) ....D

WRENCHES (Con.)

Brown & Co., R. H. (Drop
Forge) ....B
Killborn & Bishop Co.
(Drop Forged Pipe) C
CONN.—Rockfall
Smith, Otis A. ....B
CONN.—Southington
Peck, Stow & Wilcox Co.
(Bicycle; Engineers' Ma-
chinists'; Pipe; Screw;
Pocket; Mechanics' Agri-
cultural) ....AAAA
CONN.—South Norwalk
Le Count, Wm. G. (Steel
Dog; Screw) ....A
CONN.—Torrington
Union Hardware Co. (Pipe)
A
ILL.—Carpentersville
Star Mfg. Co. (Adjustable;
Alligator; Pipe-Jaw; Bi-
cycle; Pocket; Screw;
Mechanics; Agricultural)
A
ILL.—Chicago
Beckley-Ralston Co., 178
Lake (Bicycle; Pocket;
Screw) C
Besly & Co., Chas. H., 10
N. Canal (Reamer; Tap)
AA
Crane Co. (Adjustable
Steam Pipe) ......AAAA
Duffy, J. F., 125 Indiana
(Bicycle; Pocket) ...X
Harris & Co., Samuel, 23
So. Clinton (Socket) ...B

Illinois Malleable Iron Co.
30 W. Monroe (Pipe)
AAAA
Klein & Son, Mathias, 87 W.
Van Buren (Lag Screw;
Splicing) ....A
Lovejoy, T. H., 90 Ohio
(Ratchet) ....G
Mark Mfg. Co. (Adjustable)
B
Monash Younker Co., 201 S.
Canal (Pipe) ....B
Parmelee Wrench Co., 1058
W. Monroe (Gridle Pipe)
E
Railroad Supply Co., Bed-
ford Bldg. (Ratchet)...A
Sheffy Mfg. Co., 184 La Sal-
le (Pipe) ....D
Solid Steel Tool Co., 11 So.
Jeffin (Drop Forged; Off
Set; Track) ....F
Sturges & Burn M'f'g Co.
Bicycle Pocket ......A
Union Drop Forge Co., 66 E.
Ohio (Track) ....A
Vaughan & Bushnell Mfg.
Co. (Pipe) ....B
Whitman & Barnes Mfg. Co.
(Alligator; Bit; Combina-
tion; Engineers' and Ma-
chinists' Pipe) ....AAAA
ILL.—Downers' Grove
Dicke Tool Co. (Lag Screw;
Splicing) C
ILL.—Kewanee
Western Tube Co. (Steam &
Gas Stock) ....AAA
IND.—Evansville
Evansville Tool Works
(Track) ....A
IND.—Indianapolis
Indianapolis Drop Forging
Co. (Drop Forged) .....B
IND.—Shelbyville
Vandergrift Mfg. Co. (Agri-
cultural; Combination;
Pipe) ....F
IND.—South Bend
Sandage Steel Skein Co.
(Wagon Skein) ....B
IOWA.—Marshalltown
Hawkeye Wrench Co. (Com-
bination; Pipe) ....B
MD.—Baltimore
Kemp Mfg. Co., C. M., 1501
Guilford Av. (Ratchet) C
MASS.—Athol
Athol Machine Co. (Screw)
A
MASS.—Attleboro
Mossberg Co., Frank
(Forged Steel Pipe; Bi-
cycle; Pocket; Screw;

WRENCHES (Con.)
Mechanics Agricultural)
B
MASS.—Boston
Harvey, H. H., 608 Atlantic
Av. (Track) ....B
Walworth Mfg. Co. (Engi-
neers; Machinists; Pipe;
Tap; Reamer; Trap)
AAAA
Welch & Co., T. F., 65
Sudbury (Adjustable;
Tap) ....D
MASS.—Chicopee Falls
Stevens Arms & Tool Co., J.
(Tap; Reamer) ....A
MASS.—Fitchburg
Johnson-Iver Arms & Cycle
Works (Pipe) ....A
Sawyer Tool Mfg. Co. (Tap
Reamer) C
MASS.—Greenfield
Reece Co., E. F. (Tap;
Reamer) ....E
Wells Bros. Co. (Tap; Car-
riage; Wagon; Reamer;
Ratchet) ....A
Wiley & Russell Mfg. Co.
(Tap; Brace; Reamer) AA
MASS.—Mansfield
Card Mfg. Co., S. D. (Engi-
neers'; Machinists'; Tap;
Reamer) ....B
MASS.—Millers Falls
Millers Falls Co. (Carriage
Wagon) ....AA
MASS.—New Bedford
Morse Twist Drill & Ma-
chine Co. (Tap; Reamer)
AAA
MASS.—Pittsfield
Robbins, Gamwell & Co.
(Chain Pipe) ....A
MASS.—Roxbury
Trimont Mfg. Co. (Chain;
Combination; Drop
Forged; Pipe) ....D
MASS.—Springfield
Bemis & Call Hdw. & Tool
Co. (Adjustable; Combina-
tion; Pipe; Screw; Me-
chanics; Agricultural)..A
MASS.—Worcester
Coes Wrench Co. (Agricul-
tural; Engineers'; Ma-
chinists'; Knife Handle;
Metal Handle; Nut;
Screw; Mechanics) .....A
Smith & Co., Thomas (Bi-
cycle Pocket) ....D
Wakefield, Jno. E. (Pipe;
Bicycle; Pocket; Combina-
tion) ....B
Wilson & Smith (Drop
Forged)
MASS.—Wrentham
Winter Bros. Co. (Socket;
Tap; Reamer) ....E
MICH.—Battle Creek
La Gripper Wrench Co.
(Drop Forged; Pipe) ...D
MICH.—Detroit
Anderson & Sons, W. H.
(Track) C
MICH.—Kalamazoo
Kalamazoo Railway Supply
Co. (Track) ....B
MICH.—Menominee
Dudley Mfg. Co., A. (Bi-
cycle Pocket Combination;
Pipe, Nut Combined) ...F
MINN.—Owatonna
Washington Tool Co. (Steel
Alligator) ....D
MINN.—St. Paul
Helwig Mfg. Co. (Screw;
Mechanics; Agricultural)
F
MISS.—St. Louis
Handlan-Buck Mfg. Co. 212
N. 3rd (Engineers'; Ma-
chinists'; Pipe) ....AA
N. H.—Antrim
Goodell Co. (Carriage; Wa-
gon) ....A
N. J.—Elizabeth
Braunsdorf-Mueller Co. (Ad-
justable; Brace; Tap;
Reamer; Socket) ......D
N. J.—Garwood
Brock Wrench Mfg. Co.
(Chain; Drop Forged;
Flange; Pipe; Spanner).E

WRENCHES (Con.)
PA.—Pittsburg
Hubbard & Co., Murtland
Bldg. (Track) ....A
Iron City Tool Wks. (Ltd.).
32d & Smallman (Track)
................B
Jones & Laughlins Steel Co.
(Engineers' & Machinists')
AAAA
Klein-Logan Co., So. 13th &
Breed (Track) ....A
Oliver Iron & Steel Co.
(Track) ....AAAA
Pittsburg Tool & DropForge
Co., Arrott Bldg. (Track)
E
PA.—Reading
Reading Machine & Tool Co
(Pipe) ....B
PA.—Verona
Verona Tool Wks. (Straight
and "T" Track) ......A
PA.—Wilkesbarre
Nicholson & Co., W. H.
(Pipe) C
PA.—Williamsport
Darling Pump Mfg. Co.
(Ltd.) (Pipe) ....B
R. I.—Central Falls
Mossberg Wrench Co. (Adjustable; Pocket; Bicycle;
Screw) C
R. I.—Pawtucket
Carpenter Tap & Die Co.
(Tap; Reamer) C
Pawtucket Mfg. Co. (Tap;
Reamer) ....A
R. I.—Providence
Rhode Island Tool Co. (Drop
Forged; Machine) ..AAA
VT.—Derby Line
Butterfield & Co. (Tap;
Reamer) ....B

WRINGERS

See also Machy

IND.—Anderson
Anderson Pole & Shaft Co.
(Mop) ....E
IND.—Indianapolis
Tucker & Dorsey Mfg. Co.,
State Av. & Bates (Mop;
Bucket) ....A
IND.—Marion
National Sweeper Co.
(Clothes) ....AAAA
MICH.—Grand Rapids
Goshen Sweeper Co.
(Clothes) ....D
MO.—St. Louis
Williard, Wm. G. (Clothes)
A
New York City
American Wringer Co.
(Clothes) ....AAAA
Oakley & Keating (Clothes)
B
N. Y.—Troy
Troy Laundry Machinery Co.
(Ltd.) (Clothes) .....AA
OHIO—Cincinnati
American Laundry Machinery Co. (Clothes) ....A
OHIO—Circleville
Eagle Cooperage Works
(Wringer; Mop; Bucket)G
OHIO—Springfield
Ohio Wringer & Lawn
Mower Co. (Clothes) ..D
PA.—Columbia
Wilson Laundry Machinery
Co. (Clothes) ....B
PA.—Erie
Lovell Mfg. Co. (Ltd)
(Clothes) ....AA
PA.—Philadelphia
North Bros., Mfg. Co.
(Clothes) ....A
VA.—Richmond
Richmond Cedar Wks.
(Mop Pail) ....AAAA

YACHTS

See also Boats

CAL.—San Francisco
Risdon Iron & Locomotive
Works (Steam) ..AAAA

YACHTS (Con.)
CONN.—Noank
Palmer & Son Ship Bldg. &
Marine Ry. Co., R ..X
DEL.—Wilmington
Harlan & Hollingsworth Co.
(Iron; Steel; Steam) X
Pusey & Jones Co. (Iron;
Steel) ....AAA
ILL.—Chicago
Cuthbert, A. G. ....E
Willard & Co., Chas P.
(Steam) ....D
MAINE—Bath
Harrington, Chas B. ....H
New England Co. (Iron;
Steel; Steam) ....A
MAINE—Portland
Stickney, Henry R. (Steam)
D
MD.—Baltimore
Nilson Yacht Building Co.
(Steam) ....D
Thomas & Son, Jos. ....D
MASS.—East Boston
Atlantic Works (Steam) AA
Clark, Edward S. (Steam)
X
Lawley & Son, Geo. (Inc.)
A
Sheldon Co., Orin (Steam)
D
MASS.—Wollaston
Stuart & Co., John X
MICH.—St. Joseph
Truscott Boat Mfg. Co.
(Steam) ....A
N. Y.—Brooklyn
Wallin & Gorman X
N. Y.—Long Island City
Daimler Mfg. Co. ....D
N. Y.—Morris Heights
Gas Engineering & Power
Co., (C. L. Seabury &
Co.) (Steam) ......AAA
N. Y. Yacht Launch & Engine Co. (Iron; Steel;
Steam) ....B
N. Y.—Newburgh
Marsel & Co., T. S.
(Iron; Steel) ....B
N. Y.—New Rochelle
Huntington Mfg. Co. ....D
New York City
N. Y. Safety Steam Power
Co. (Steam) ....B
N. Y. Nyack
Smith Co., John P. ....E
N. Y.—Ogdensburg
Spaulding St. Lawrence
Boat Co. C
N. Y.—Port Jefferson
Bayles & Sons, James M.
B
N. Y.—Port Richmond
Burlee Dry Dock Co.
(Iron; Steel; Steam) A
N. Y. Tottenville
Ellis & Son, Jacob T. ..D
N. Y.—Upper Nyack
Ayers & Sons, Samuel ..C
N. Y.—Yonkers
Fearon. Thos. .... H
PA.—Chester
Delaware Iron Ship Building & Engine Works
(Iron; Steel) ......AAA
PA.—Philadelphia
Cramp & Sons Ship & Eng.
Bldg. Co., Wm. (Iron;
Steel; Steam) ....AAAA
R. I.—Bristol
Herreshoff Mfg. Co.
(Steam; Steel) ...... A

YARDS

CONN.—Southington
Peck. Stow & Wilcox Co.
(Steel) ....AAAA
ILL.—Chicago
Fairbanks, Morse & Co.
(Steel) .... AAAA
MASS.—Springfield
Bemis & Call Hdw. & Tool
Co. (Steel) .... A
New York City
Fairbanks Co. (Steel)
AAAA

YARDSTICKS

CONN.—New Britain

YARN (*Con.*)
(Fancy Warps; Hosiery;
Weaving Cotton) ....AA
McCord & Wright, 715 W.
Main (Dlrs. Twines, Etc.)
........................B
Robinson-Hughes Co.
(Dlrs. Cotton Warps) A
KY.—Maysville
January & Wood Co. (Car-
pet; Mop Cotton; Hosiery)
..........................A
LA.—New Orleans
Maginnis Cotton Mills (Cot-
ton) .... AAA
MAINE—Lewiston
Continental Mills (Coarse &
Fine Cotton) .... AAAA
Libbey & Dingley Co. (Cot-
ton) .... A
MD.—Alberton
Gary & Son, Jas. S.
(Cotton) .... AAAA
MD.—Baltimore
Ashland Mfg. Co. (Cotton)
........................AAA
Green & Co., Amon (Dlrs.
Cotton; Also Com.) ....B
Hooper & Sons, Wm. E.
(Cotton) .... AAAA
MASS.—Andover
Smith & Dove Mfg. Co.
(Flax Carpet) ...... AA
MASS.—Ashburnham
Ashburnham Sheeting Mills
(Cotton) .... AA
MASS.—Boston
Catlin Co., 67 Chauncey
(Dlrs. Cotton) ....AAAA
Cushing & Bliss (Dlrs.
Worsted; Mohair) ....A
Fearing, Whiton & Co., 91
Commercial (Dlrs.) ....B
Harding, Whitman & Co.
(Dlrs. Cotton; Mercerized
Worsted; Tops; Also Com.
Worsted) .... AAAA
Ludlow Mfg. Associates
(Jute Carpet) .. AAAA
Meyer & Co., John C., 80
Kingston (Dlrs. Thread) B
Mitchell & Co., James E.
(Dlrs.) .... AAA
Murphy & Co., Chas. F.,
26 Chauncy (Dlrs.) ....A
Putnam, Hooker & Co.
(Dlrs. Cotton; Woolen;
Worsted) .... A
Riley & Co., C. C. (Dlrs.
Cotton) .... A
Saxonville Mills (Woolen;
Worsted) .... AAAA
Spool Cotton Co., The, Cor.
Adams & Market (Dlrs)
........................A
Stoddard, Haserick, Rich-
ards & Co. (Foreign) AA
Wellington, Sears & Co., 202
Devonshire (Dlrs. Cotton)
........................AAAA
MASS.—Colerain
Massameet Mills (Cotton) B
MASS.—Conway
Tucker & Cook Mfg. Co.
(Cotton) .... D
MASS.—Easthampton
West Boylston Mfg. Co. ..A
MASS.—Fall River
Estes & Sons, J. H. (Cot-
ton) .... B
Kerr Thread Co. (Cotton)
........................AAAA
Massasoit Mfg. Co.
(Wick.) A
MASS.—Fitchburg
Grant Yarn Co. (Cotton) A
Oswell Mills (Cotton) ..AA
Star Worsted Co. (Woolen)
........................A
MASS.—Florence
Nonotuck Silk Co. (Silk)
........................AAAA
MASS.—Great Barrington
Monument Mills (Cotton)
........................AAA
MASS.—Lawrence
Arlington Mills (Fine Cot-
ton) ....AAA
Atlantic Cotton Mills (Cot-
ton; Hosiery) ......AAA
Crescent Worsted Co.
(Worsted) C
MASS.—Lowell
Appleton Co. (Cotton) AA

YARN (*Con.*)
Hamilton Mfg. Co.
(Hosiery) ....AAAA
Lawrence Mfg. Co. (Cotton
Hosiery) ....AAAA
Tremont & Suffolk Mills
(Hosiery) ....AAAA
Walsh, Wm. E. (Worsted)
........................D
MASS.—New Bedford
City Mfg. Corp. (Cotton)
........................AAA
Grinnell Mfg. Corpn. (Cot-
ton) ....AAAA
New England Cotton Yarn
Co. (Cotton) .....AAAA
Wamsutta Mills (Cotton)
........................AAAA
MASS.—North Chelmsford
Moore, Geo. C. (Worsted)
........................AAA
MASS.—Oxford
Bartlett, Edwin (Satinet)B
MASS.—Springfield
Indian Orchard Co. (Cotton
Weaving) ....AA
Wilcox, Calder & Co., L.
M., Phoenix Bldg. (Dlrs.
Cotton) ....B
MASS.—Taunton
Canoe River Mills (Combed
Cotton) ....B
Winthrop Cotton Yarn Co.
(Combed Cotton) .....A
MASS.—Westfield
Warren Thread Wks., W.
(Lisle Thread) ......A
MASS.—Westford
Abbott Worsted Co. (Car-
pet; Woolen) .....AAA
MASS.—Worcester
Queensbury Mills (Worsted)
........................B
Whittall & Thomas (Wor-
sted Carpet) ......AAAA
MICH.—Eaton Rapids
Horner Bros. (Wool Merino
& Knitting) C
MINN.—Rushford
Webster & Co., Jonathan
(Hosiery) C
MISS.—Stonewall
Stonewall Cotton Mills
(Hosiery) ....AA
MISS.—Wesson
Mississippi Mills (Cotton)
........................AAA
MO.—St. Louis
Putnam, Hooker & Co.
(Dlrs. Cotton; Woolen;
Worsted) ....A
St. Louis Cordage Co.
(Lath) ....AA
N. H.—Concord
N. H. Spinning Mills (Sea
Island; Egyptian Skeins)
........................A
N. H.—Manchester
Stark Mills (Cotton
Hosiery) ....AAAA
N. H.—Wilton
Hillsboro Mills (Carpet)..D
N. J.—Bordentown
Springfield Worsted Mills
(Worsted) ....AAAA
N. J.—Camden
Croft Sons & Co., H.
(Worsted) ....AAA
Highland Worsted Mills
(Worsted) ....B
Linden Worsted Mills
(Worsted) ....AAAA
N. J.—Gloucester
Argo Mills Co. (Comb. &
Carded White; Egyptian
Cotton) ....AA
N. J.—Jersey City
Chaddick & Bro., Jas. (Cot-
ton) ....A
N. J.—Kearney
Marshall & Co. (Carpet;
Linen) ....AA
N. J.—Passaic
Botany Worsted Mills
(Worsted) ....AAAA
Brighton Mills (Combed
Sea Island) ....A
Pitkin-Holdworth Worsted
Co. (Worsted) C
N. J.—Paterson
Barbour Flax Spinning Co.
(Carpet Hemp; Linen)
........................AAAA

1156

YARN (Con.)

Dolphin Jute Mills (Jute) ....AAA

Sutherland & EdwardsCo. (Jute) ....A

N. Y.—Amsterdam

McFarlan & Co. (White; Colored Cotton) ....B

Morris & Sons, A. V. (Cotton Underwear) ...AAAA

Quilhot & Son, S. (Dlrs. Cotton) ....B

N. Y.—Auburn

Columbia Cordage Co. (Lath) ....AA

N. Y.—Brooklyn

Barthels Mfg. Co. (Glazed Turkey Red) ....A

Perkins Co., J. T. (Worsted) ....AA

Planet Mills Mfg. Co. (Jute) ....AAA

N. Y.—Firthcliffe

Firth Carpet Co. (Worsted) AAA

N. Y.—Greenwich

Dunbarton Flax Spinning Co. (Linen) ....B

N. Y.—Jamestown

Chautauqua Worsted Mills (Worsted) ....B

Falconer Worsted Mill (Worsted) ....B

Meadow Brook Mills (Worsted) ....AAAA

N. Y.—Montgomery

Crabtree & Sons, Wm. (Worsted) ....B

New York City

Abegg & Rusch (Dlrs. Cotton; Mohair; Worsted; Tussah; Spun Silk)AAAA

American Mfg. Co. (Lath) AAAA

Buckingham, Paulson & Co. (Com. also Dlrs. Cotton) A

Catlin & Co. (Dlrs. Cotton; also Com.) ....AAAA

Chelsea Jute Mills (Carpet Jute) ....A

Cone Export & Com. Co. (Com. Cotton) ....AAA

Frankenberg Co., H. E. (Dlrs. Cotton; Woolen) .A

Haines & Bishop (Dlrs. Cotton) ....A

Harding, Whitman & Co. (Com.; Dlrs. Cotton; Mercerized Worsted; Tops) ....AAAA

Hardt Von Bermuth & Co. (Silk; Dlrs. Cotton; Silk; also Com.) ....AAAA

Hart Co., A. H. (Carpet; Upholstery) ....AAA

Holland & Webb (Dlrs. Cotton; Worsted; Spun Silk; Tussah) ....A

Johns-Manville Co., H. W. (Asbestos) ....AAAA

Kelly & Co., Henry C. (Dlrs. Carpet Warps, etc.) ..B

Lane & Co., J. H. (Dlrs. Cotton; Mercerized) AAA

Linen Thread Co. (Dlrs. Flax) ....A

Moeller & Littauer (Dlrs. Cotton; Worsted; Silk; Woolen; Mercerized) ...A

Oelbermann, Dommerich & Co. (Dlrs. Worsted; Spun Silk) ....AAAA

Osborne & Wilson (Dlrs. Twine) ....B

Poor & Co., J. Harper (Dlrs. Cotton) ....A

Reynolds & Co., James E. (Dlrs. Cotton; also Com.) A

Robinson-Hughes Co. (Dlrs. Cotton Warp, etc.) .....A

Skerry & Co., A. T. (Dlrs. Worsted; Mohair; Silk; Noils; Fancies) ....A

Spool Cotton Co. (Dlrs.) A

Standard Rope & Twine Co. (Fodder) ....AAAA

Strauss & Co., F. A. (Dlrs. Cotton; Worsted; Silk) AAA

Turner Co., J. Spencer (Dlrs. Cotton; Woolen) ...AAA

YARN (Con.)

Union Selling Co. (Fodder; Lath) ....AAA

Ulmann & Co., Bernhard (Dlrs. Cotton; Wool Knitting) ....AAAA

Vietor, Frederick & Achelis (Dlrs. Cotton; Woolen; Worsted) ....AAAA

Warner & Co., M. (Dlrs.) A

White & Co., Jas. F. (Com.; Dlrs. Cotton; Woolen) AAAA

N. Y.—New York Mills

New York Mills (Hosiery) AAAA

Walcott & Campbell Spinning Co. (White; Mercerized; Colored Hosiery) A

N. Y.—Oswego

Standard Spinning Co. (Hosiery) ....AA

N. Y.—Schaghticoke

Cable Flax Mills (Carpet, Linen) ....A

N. Y.—Utica

Globe Woolen Co. (Woolen; Worsted) ....AAA

Skenandoah Cotton Co. (Hosiery; Cotton) ....AA

Utica Steam & Mohawk Valley Cotton Mills (Cotton) AAA

N. Y.—Whitehall

Champlain Silk Mills (Silk) A

N. C.—Albermarle

Efird Mfg. Co. (Hosiery) A

N. C.—Alula

Wiscassett Mills Co. (Cotton) ....A

N. C.—Burlington

Carolina Cotton Mills (Cotton) ....B

N. C.—Charlotte

Charlotte Cotton Mills (Cotton) ....A

Elizabeth Mills (Combed Egyptian; Peelers) ....B

N. C.—Cherryville

Cherryville Mfg. Co. (Cotton) ....A

Gaston Mfg. Co. (Cotton) A

N. C.—Concord

Cannon Mfg. Co. (Cotton; Hosiery) ....AA

N. C.—Cumberland

Cumberland Cotton Mills Co. (Cotton Warp; Skein) B

N. C.—Durham

Commonwealth Cotton Mfg. Co. (Cotton Hosiery; Underwear) ....A

N. C.—Edenton

Edenton Cotton Mills (Cotton) ....B

N. C.—Elkin

Chatham Mfg. Co. (Woolen) B

N. C.—Fayetteville

Holt-Williamson Mfg. Co. (Cotton) ....B

Toler, Hart & Holt Mills (Cotton) ....B

N. C.—Gastonia

Arlington Cotton Mills (Cotton) ....A

Avon Mills (Cotton) .....A

Mena Cotton Mills (Cotton) ....A

Ozark Cotton Mills (Cotton Combed) ....A

N. C.—Goldsboro

Borden Mfg. Co. (Cotton)A

N. C.—Graham

Holt, L. B. (Cotton) AAA

N. C.—Henderson

Harriet Cotton Mills (Hosiery) ....B

Henderson Cotton Mills (Cotton) ....B

Henrietta Mills (Cotton)AA

N. C.—Hope Mills

Hope Mills Mfg. Co. (Cotton) ....AA

N. C.—Jamestown

Oakdale Cotton Mills (Cotton) ....B

N. C.—Kings Mountain

Bonnie Cotton Mills Co. (Cotton) ....B

Cora Cotton Mills (Cotton)B

Kings Mountain Mfg. Co.

YARN (Con.)

(Cotton) ....B
Lula Mfg. Co. (Cotton
Hosiery) ....B
N. C.—Kinston
Kinston Cotton Mills
(Hosiery) ....A
N. C.—Landis
Linn Mills Co. (Cotton) B
N. C.—Laurel Hill
Ida Yarn Mill (Cotton)...B
Richmond Cotton Mills
(Cotton) ....B
Springfield Cotton Mill (Cotton Knitting; Weaving) B
N. C.—Laurinburg
Scotland Cotton Mills
(Hosiery) ....B
N. C.—Lenoir
Lenoir Cotton Mills (Cotton) ....B
N. C.—Lincolnton
Daniel Mfg. Co. (Combed
Sea Island) ....B
Laboratory Cotton Mills
(Cotton) ....A
N. C.—Long Shoals
Long Shoals Cotton Mills
(Cotton) ....B
Lumberton Cotton Mills
(Hosiery) ....B
N. C.—McAdenville
McAden Mills (Cotton) AA
N. C.—Mayodan
Avalon Mills (Hosiery) ..A
Mayo Mills (Hosiery; Underwear) ....A
N. C.—Monbo
Monbo Mfg. Co. (Cotton) B
N. C.—Monroe
Monroe Cotton Mills
(Hosiery Cotton) ......A
N. C.—Mt. Holly
Tuckaseege Mfg. Co. (Cotton) ....A
N. C.—Northville
Newton Cotton Mills (Cotton) ....B
N. C.—Norwood
Norwood Cotton Mills (Cotton) ....B
Oxford Cotton Mills (Cotton) ....B
N. C.—Patterson
Gwyn-Harper Mfg. Co. (Cotton) ....B
N. C.—Raleigh
Raleigh Cotton Mills
(Hosiery) ....A
N. C.—Rocky Mount
Rocky Mount Mills (Cotton) ....AA
N. C.—Salisbury
Kisler Mfg. Co. (Cotton) B
Vance Cotton Mills (Cotton)
B
N. C.—Saxapahaw
White, Williamson & Co.
(Cotton) ....A
N. C.—Shelby
Belmont Mills (Cotton) ..B
N. C.—Smithfield
Smithfield Cotton Mills ..B
N. C.—Spray
Leakesville Woolen Mills
(Woolen) ....A
Spray Cotton Mills (Cotton) ....B
N. C.—Statesville
Statesville Cotton Mills
(Cotton) ....A
N. C.—Tarboro
Tarboro Cotton Factory
(Cotton) ....B
N. C.—Wadesboro
Wadesboro Cotton Mills
Co. (Cotton) ....B
N. C.—Waxhaw
Rodman-Heath Cotton Mill
(Cotton) ....B
N. C.—Wilson
Wilson Cotton Mills (Cotton) ....B
N. C.—Winston-Salem
South Side Mfg. Co. (Cotton) ....A
OHIO—Cincinnati
Goodlin, Weaver, Ried &
Co. (Dlrs.) ....B
Jacobs Cordage Co. (Fodder) ....B
Overman & Schrader Cordage Co. (Fodder) ....A

YARN (Con.)

Putnam, Hooker & Co.
(Dlrs. Cotton; Woolen;
Worsted; Com.) ......A
OHIO—Hamilton
Shuler & Benninghofen AA
OHIO—New Richmond
Clasgens Co., J. H. (Wool;
Merino) C
OHIO—Xenia
Kelly Co., R. A. (Fodder) A
OREGON—Oregon City
Oregon City Mfg. Co.
(Woolen) ....AA
PA.—Allentown
Allentown Spinning Co.
(Jute; Carpet; Rug) ..A
PA.—Bethlehem
Sanquoit Silk Mfg. Co.
(Silk) ....AAAA
PA.—Bridgeport
Lees & Sons Co., Jas.
(Weaving; Knitting Woolen; Worsted) ....B
PA.—Bristol
Grundy & Co., Wm. (Worsted Knitting; Weaving)
A
PA.—Chester
Grove Worsted Mills (Worsted Weaving; Knitting)
AAA
Irvin & Leiper Mfg. Co.
(Underwear) ....B
Lincoln Mfg. Co. (Weaving)
B
Standard Spinning Co.
(Hosiery) C
PA.—Conshohocken
Merion Worsted Mills (Fine
Worsted) ....A
PA.—Darby
Griswold Worsted Co. (Worsted) ....A
PA.—Philadelphia
Adams & Co., Jos M.
(Backing; Woolen Carpet)
A
Allen & Son, Wm. (Woolen
Carpet) ....A
Asbestos Fibre Spinning Co.
(Asbestos) ....B
Bailey C. (Fodder) ...AA
Ball, Thos. H. (Dlrs. Worsted; Woolen) ....B
Ball & Co., H. C. (Worsted)
A
Beatty & Co., Robt. (Cotton; Combed; Hosiery;
Knitting) ....B
Beswick, Saml. (Merino) C
Blythe, Richard A. (Dlrs.
Cotton) ....A
Buckingham, Paulson & Co.
(Dlrs. Cotton) ....A
Cameron & Co., A. J. (Woolen; Worsted; Dlrs. Woolen; Worsted) ....AA
Cameron Worsted Co., A. J.
(Worsted; Weaving; Hosiery; Knitting) .....AA
Catlin & Co., (Dlrs. Woolen;
Worsted) ....AAAA
Crow, Alex. Jr. (Woolen;
Worsted) ....A
Davies Textile Co. (Car
Box Waste) ....B
D'Olier & Co., Wm. (Dlrs.
Cotton) ....A
Dearnley, Jno. H. (Worsted; Woolen) ....A
Doak & Co., Jas. Jr. (Worsted) ....A
Dobson, John & Jas. (Worsted) ....AAAA
Emsley & Bro., Wm. (Cotton; Merino; Woolen; Hosiery; Weaving) .....B
Erben-Harding Co. (Worsted; Wool; Merino)
AAA
Fitler Co., Edwin H. (Fodder) ....AAAA
Flanagan & Bro., A. (Wool
Carpet) ....B
Fleisher, S. B. & B. W.
(Woolen; Worsted) AAA
Flings Sons, Jos. (Merino) B
Ford, W. & R. (Woolen
Carpet) ....B
Germantown Spinning Co.
(Cotton; Hosiery; Weaving) ....A

YARN (Con.)

Grundy & Co., Wm. H.
(Worsted) ....AA
Hamill & Co. (Merino) ..X
Henry & Sons, Thos.
(Hosiery) ....AAA
Hey & Son, Richard
(Mohair) ....AA
Hoffman-Corr Co. (Dlrs.
Cotton) ....AA
Holland & Webb (Dlrs. Cot-
ton: Worsted; Silk) ...A
Hyde, Edward S. (Dlrs.
Cotton) ....B
Imperial Woolen Co.
(Worsteds) ....AA
Kenworthy & Bros., I.
(Woolen; Worsted; Car-
pet; Also Dlrs. Woolen
Worsted; Carpet) ....AA
Keystone Spinning Mills Co.
(Woolen; Carpet) Rug)
A
Lane & Co., J. H. (Dlrs.
Cotton; Also Com.) AAA
Leicester & Continental
Mills Co. (Woolen; Mer-
ino) ....AAA
Lodge, Jno. F. (Cotton;
Woolen Carpet) ......A
McClosky, J. J. (Dlrs
Carpet) ....A
Malcolm Mills Co. (Fancy
Worsted; Novelty) ....B
Manningham Worsted Co.
(Worsted) ....A
Mays Landing Water Power
Co. (Cotton) ....AA
Mitchell & Co., James E.
(Dlrs. Cotton) .... AAA
Moore & Co., C. (Dlrs. Cot-
ton) ....B
O'Neil, Chas. (Dlrs. Wool
Spun) ....AA
Ontario Spinning Co. (Cot-
ton Hosiery) ....B
Platt & Son. A. (Cotton;
Hosiery; Woolen) ...B
Randall & Bro., Jos.
(Merino) ....B
Read, Wm. F. (Dlrs.) AA
Ring & Son, Jonathan
(Wool; Marino; Hosiery)
B
Roosevelt Worsted Mills
(Worsted) ......AAAA
Schell, Taylor & Long-
streth (Dlrs. Cotton) B
Scatchards Sons, Jos. (Wool;
Merino; Hosiery) .... A
Schlichter Jute Cordage Co.
(Jute) ....AA
Schofield, Mason & Co.
(Woolen; Worsted) ....A
Scholes & Son, Wm.
(Woolen) ....AA
Seffarlen, Jos. A. (Dlrs.
Cotton) ....B
Sharples, W. H. & F. W.
(Dlrs. Cotton) ......AA
Southwark Mills Co.
(Worsted) ....AA
Stafford & Co. (Carpet) B
Stead, Miller & Co. (Silk)
AA
Steel & Co. Edw. T.
(Woolen; Worsted) AAAA
Stephenson & Co. (Dlrs.
Worsted Woolen; Mohair)
A
Sykes Bros. (Woolen; Jute
Carpet) ....B
Thomas & Sons, Hy. (Cot-
ton; Carpet) ....B
Thornton, Wm. (Cotton;
Woolen Carpet) ......B
Tracy Worsted Mills
(Worsted; Knitting;
Weaving) ....A
Turner Co., J. Spencer
(Dlrs. Cotton) ....AAA
Webb & Co., Chas J.
(Dlrs. Cotton) ....AAAA
Whitaker & Sons, Wm.
(Woolen) ....A
White & Co., Jas. F., 233
Chestnut (Dlrs. Cotton;
Worsted; Woolen) AAAA
Wilde & Bros., Jno.
(Woolen Carpet) .... B
Wilde's Son, Robt.
(Woolen Carpet) .... B
Willey, J. H. (Dlrs. Worst-
ed; Mohair) ....B

YARN (Con.)

Wilson & Bradbury (Dlrs.
Cotton) ....AAA
Wolstenholme & Clarke
(Worsted; Marino) ....B
Wolstenholme Sons & Co.,
Thos. (Worsted) ....AAA
Yewdall & Jones Co.
(Worsted) ....A
PA.—Reading
Jackson & Son, T.
(Fodder) ....AA
Reading Cotton Mill (Cot-
ton) ....AAAA
PA.—Wallingford
Columbia Worsted Co.
(Worsted) ....B
R. I.—Bristol
Cranston Worsted Mills
(Mohair; Worsted) ....A
PA.—Burrillville
Laurel Hill Yarn Co.
(Woolen; Merino) .... A
R. I.—Hamilton
Hamilton Web Co. (Cotton)
A
R. I.—Hillsgrove
Elizabeth Mills (Cotton)
AA
R. I.—North Kingston
Rodman Mfg. Co. (White;
Colored) ....AAA
R. I.—North Providence
Centredale Worsted Mills
(Woolen) ....B
R. I.—Pascoag
Sayles Co., F. L. (Cotton)
AA
R. I.—Pawtucket
Blodgett & Oswell Co.
(Glazed) ....B
Dexter Yarn Co. (Cotton)
A
Goff & Sons, D. (Mohair;
Worsted) ....AAA
Greene & Daniels Mfg. Co.
(Cotton) ....AA
Jenckes Spinning Co.
(White; Colored Cotton)
B
Littlefield Mfg. Co. (Cot-
ton) ....A
Slater Cotton Co. (Cotton)
AA
Stafford Mfg. Co. (Cotton)
A
R. I.—Providence
Brown, Peter (Dlr.) AAAA
Fletcher Mfg. Co. (Cotton)
AAA
Joslin Mfg. Co. (Cotton) B
Phœnix Spinning Co.
(Wool; Merino) ...... B
Steere Worsted Mill (Worst-
ed) ....A
Tillinghast Co., Stiles,
Industrial Bldg. (Single
& Double; White & Col-
ored; Also Dlrs. Cotton;
Worsted) ....B
Wilcox, Colder & Co., L.
M. (Dlrs. Cotton) .... B
R. I.—Thornton
Pocasset Worsted Co.
(Worsted) ....AAAA
R. I.—Warren
Cutler Mfg. Co. (Cotton) A
Warren Mfg. Co. (Combed;
Carded Cotton) ..AAAA
R. I.—Warwick
Elizabeth Mill Co. (Fine
Combed Cotton) ..AAAA
Warwick ills (Cotton) AAA
R. I.—Woonsocket
Guerm Spinning Co.
(Merino) ....A
Lafayette Worsted Co.
(Worsted) ....A
Lawton Spinning Co. (Fine
Cotton) ....A
River Spinning Co. (Woolen;
Merino) ....AA
Woonsocket Worsted Mills
(Worsted) ....B
S. C.—Anderson
Riverside Mfg. Co. (Cotton)
B
S. C.—Autun
Pendleton Mfg. Co. (A. J.
Sifton) (Cotton) ......B
S. C.—Bamberg
Bamberg Cotton Mills
(Cotton) ....A

YARN (Con.)

S. C.—Bath
Aiken Mfg. Co. (Cotton) A

S. C.—Chester
Eureka Cotton Mills (Cotton; Soft Hosiery; Knitting) ....B
Wylie Mills (Cotton) ....B

S. C.—Columbia
Columbia Mills Co. (Cotton)
AAAA

S. C.—Dillon
Dillon Cotton Mills (Cotton; Hosiery) .... A

S. C.—Edgefield
Edgefield Mfg. Co. (Cotton)
B

S. C.—Gaffney
Gaffney Mfg. Co. (Cotton Twisted) .... AAAA
Limestone Mills (Cotton) A

S. C.—Greenville
Amer. Spinning Co. (Cotton) .... AA

S. C.—Knoxville
Knoxville Woolen Mills (Woolen; Cotton) ..AAA

S. C.—Lancaster
Lancaster Cotton Mills (Cotton) .... AAA

S. C.—McColl
Iceman Mills (Cotton; Combed Egyptian) C
McColl Mfg. Co. (Cotton Knitting) .... A
Marie Mills (Cotton Hosiery) .... B

S. C.—Marion
Ashby Cotton Mills (Cotton) .... A

S. C.—Pelham
Pelham Mills (Cotton) ..A

S. C.—Piedmont
Riedmout Mfg. Co. (Cotton)
AAAA

S. C.—Rock Hill
Manchester Cotton Mill Co. (Cotton Brown) ...... A

S. C.—Spartanburg
Arcadia Mills (Cotton) ..A
Beamont Mfg. Co. (Cotton)
B
Saxton Mills (Cotton) ..A

S. C.—Yorkville
Tavora Cotton Mills (Cotton Hosiery) C
York Cotton Mills (Cotton) .... A

TENN.—Chattanooga
Richmond Spinning Co. (Cotton) .... B

TENN.—Knoxville
Knoxville Cotton Mills (Cotton Hosiery) ...... A

TENN.—Strathmore
Laurel Hill Mill (Cotton Mop) .... D

TEXAS—Waco
Hayden-Kirksey Woolen Mills (Woolen) ...... AA

UTAH—Ogden
Ogden Woolen Mills Co. (Woolen) .... B

UTAH—Provo City
Provo Woolen Mills Co. (Woolen) .... B

VA.—Mouth of Wilson
Fields & Hash Mfg. Co. (Woolen) .... B

VA.—Norfolk
Cotton Oil & Fibre Co. (Cotton) ....AA

VA.—South Boston
Century Cotton Mills (Cotton) .... B

WIS.—Cedarburg
Cedarburg Woolen Mills (Woolen; Worsted) (Bradford System) .... B

WIS.—Milwaukee
Milwaukee Worsted Mills (Worsted) .... A

WIS.—Portage
Porfage Hosiery Co. (Hosiery) .... A

YAWLS

See also Boats, Yachts

MASS.—Fall River
Read Bros. .... D

YEAST

CAL.—Los Angeles
Golden Gate Comp. Yeast Co., 348 Sutter C

CAL.—San Francisco
Golden Gate Distilling Co., 160 New Montgomery ..B

COLO.—Denver
Fleischmann & Co. ..AAAA

D. C.—Washington
Fleischmann & Co. ..AAAA

ILL.—Chicago
Bunge Co., Wm. H., 71 N. Aun .... A
Callahan & Co., A. P., 2407 La Salle .... AA
Gillett, E. W. (Cake) ....B
Queen City Eureka Yeast Co., 533 W. Chic. Av. ..B
Riverside Yeast Co., 148 Superior C
Seidel & Sons, A., 123 Garfield Av. C
Spielman Bros. Co. (Comp.), 93 North Av. .... A

ILL.—Freeport
Burrell Bros. .... B

LA.—New Orleans
Dennery, Theo., 524 Magazine C

MD.—Baltimore
Elmer & Sons, Lewis, 104 South .... A

MICH.—Detroit
Fleischmann & Co. ..AAAA

MINN.—Minneapolis
Fleischmann & Co., 15 S. 7th .... AAAA

MINN.—St. Paul
Nat'l Distillery Co., 73 W. 3rd .... AA

MO.—Kansas City
Riverside Yeast Co. C

NEB.—Omaha
On Time Yeast Co. C

N. Y.—Brooklyn
Schlegel, J., 132 22nd ....B

N. Y.—Buffalo
Buffalo Vinegar & Preserving Co., 642 Mich. ....B
Fleischmann & Co. ..AAAA

New York City
Alart & McGuire, 70 Mad. A
Fleischmann & Co., 699 Washn. .... AAAA
Vienna Pressed Yeast Co., 141 E. 25th (Cake) ....D

N. Y.—Tonawanda
Niagara Cider & Vinegar Wks. .... A

OHIO—Cincinnati
Fleischmann & Co., Perry & Plum (Compressed) AAAA
Queen City Eureka Yeast Co., 1317 Central Av. B

OHIO—Marysville
Marysville Candy Co. (Foam) C

OHIO—West Carrollton
Shaw Yeast Co. ...... AA

OREGON—Portland
Fleischmann & Co. ..AAAA

PA.—Philadelphia
Alart & McGuire, 126 Cuthbert .... A
Fleischmann & Co., 1221 Race .... AAAA

R. I.—Providence
Rumford Chem. Works
AAA

S. C.—Charleston
Margenhoff, O. G. C

WIS.—Manitowoc
Richter & Sons, A. M. (Comp.) C

WIS.—Milwaukee
Milwaukee Vinegar Co., 456 Virginia ...... AAA
Red Star Yeast Co., 456 Virginia .... AAA

N. Y.—Brooklyn
Wiarda & Co., Jno. S. (Naples) .... AA

YOKES

See also Woodwork: Carriage

CONN.—Mt. Carmel
Woodruff & Sons, Walter W. (Horses Neck) ....A

ZINC & ZINCS

Zinc White, see Paints & White

ZETROPES

ZYMOSI-METERS

BUTTER

CONN.—Middletown
Cook & Brady...........A
ILL.—Elgin
Elgin Butter Co ....A
Newman Co., John.......A
Nolting Co., A...........A
Wood Butter Co., D. E....A
IND.—Cambridge City
Boyd & Drisoll...........A
IND.—Indianapolis
Jordan Co., Arthur......AA
IOWA—Clarinda
Clarinda Poultry, Butter &
Egg Co. ....AA
IOWA—Deep River
Hatter & Baird ....A
IOWA—Jesup
Jesup Hand Separator
Creamery Co. ....A
IOWA—Waterloo
Fowler Co. ....AA
KANS.—Topeka
Continental Creamery Co.
AA
MASS.—Cambridge
Brigham Co., C..........A
MASS.—Lowell
Dexter, S. K.............A
MICH.—Alma
Wright & Co., A. W.
AAAA
MICH.—Mt. Clemens
Detroit Creamery Co......A
MICH.—Owosso
Dudley, Eben F..........A
MICH.—Sebewaing
Liken & Co., Jno. C......A
MINN.—Dodge Centre
Dodge Centre Creamery Co.
A
MO.—Herculaneum
Bonne Terre Farming &
Cattle Co. ....AAA
N. Y.—Middletown
Pound & Jordan..........A
N. Y.—Utica
Grant, Wm. D...........A
PA.—Bernville
Ahrens & Rihardson......A
PA.—Darling
Darlington, J. J..........A
PA.—Hanover
Hanover Creamery ....A
PA.—Leboeuf
Wheeler, C. M...........A
PA.—Lititz
Garber, Reist & Co.......A
PA.—Mt. Joy
Reist, Nissley & Co.......A
PA.—Transfer
Frampton, D. A.........AA
VT.—Randolph
Brigham Co., C..........A
VA.—Norfolk
Fentress & Co., C. W...AA
WIS.—Big Bend
McCanna & Frazer Co.....A
WIS.—Elkhorn
Wisconsin Butter & Cheese
Co. ....A
WIS.—Fond-Du-Lac
Muir, David & White.....A
WIS.—Kewaskum
Rosenheimer, M. & A....A
WIS.—South Wayne
Wood & Co., D ....A
WIS.—Waukau
Rush Lake Creamery Co..A
WIS.—Waukesha
Wisconsin Butter & Cheese
Co. ....A

CHEESE

CAL.—San Francisco
Wieland Bros., 121 Clay..A
ILL.—Chicago
Diederichs, Otto (Swiss;
Limberger; American) .B
ILL.—Elgin
Cornell Bros............B
Newman Co., John........A
Nolting, A. ....A
Sherwin, W. W...........A
Wood Butter Co., D. E....A
IND.—Cambridge City
Boyd & Driscoll..........A
IND.—Indianapolis
Jordan Co., Arthur......AA

CHEESE (Con.)

IOWA—Cedar Rapids
Shaver Cheese Co., I. H...A
IOWA—Charles City
Ford, W. A. ....B
White & Co..............B
IOWA—Waterloo
Fowler Co. ....AA
MASS.—Boston
Cochrane, Geo. A., 88 So.
Market (Imp.) ....D
MASS.—Cambridge
Brigham Co., C..........A
MICH.—Carleton
Carleton Cheese Co.......B
MICH.—Columbiaville
Peter, Wm. (Est.).....AAA
MICH.—Farmington
Warner, F. M............B
MICH.—Fruit Ridge
Horton, Geo. B............B
MICH.—Houghton
Lake Superior Produce &
Cold Storage Co....AAAA
MICH.—Northville
Power, A. D. & Son.......A
MICH.—Novi
Warner, F. M............B
MINN.—St. Paul
Crescent Creamery Co....B
N. Y.—Antwerp
Baumert & Co., F. X....B
N. Y.—Buffalo
Hasselbeck Cheese Co.
(Swiss; Limberger; Brick)
B
N. Y.—Chester
Lawrence & Son, W. A...B
N. Y.—East Aurora
Richardson-Beebe Co. ....B
N. Y.—Elton
Lewis, J. B...............B
N. Y.—Fairfield
Old Fairfield Cheese Fac-
tory Co. ....B
N. Y.—Little Falls
Zoller, J. ....AAA
N. Y.—Massena
Simpson, McIntire & Co...A
N. Y.—Philadelphia
Gebler, M. ....B
N. Y.—Richfield
Brockway, H. C..........B
N. Y.—Rochester
Hasselbeck, M. ....B
N. Y.—Rodman
Dry Hill Cheese Factory..B
N. Y.—Sandusky
Lewis, J. B.............B
N. Y.—Syracuse
Surbeck, John C..........A
N. Y.—Utica
Brown's Sons, J. P. .....B
Grant, W. D.............A
N. Y.—Warren
Young & Son, L. D. .....B
OHIO—Columbus
Lang, Shenck & Co.......B
OHIO—Willington
Willington Cheese Co. ..B
PA.—Bulger
Hermes & Son, P.........A
PA.—Carnegie
Bisi, E. (Imp'rs).........A
PA.—Edinboro
Marsh, William ....B
PA.—Mansfield
Zimmer & Clark ....B
PA.—Philadelphia
Hildman & Co., A., 105
Pine (Imptr's) ....F
PA.—Seeleyville
Smith & Son, G. (Mfrs;
Impts) ....B
PA.—Souderton
Holly Bros. ....B
VT.—St. Albans
Franklin County Creamery
Ass'n ....A
WIS.—Bangor
Bangor Swiss Cheese Mfg.
Co. ....B
WIS.—Dover
McCanna & Frazer Co.....A
WIS.—East Farmington
Koch, Wm. F. ....B
WIS.—Fond-Du-Lac
Fond-Du-Lac Cheese &
Butter Co. ....B
Muir, David & White.....A

CHEESE (Con.)

WIS.—Ft. Atkinson
Hoard Creamery Co.......B
WIS.—Manitowoc
Schuette Bros. Co. ....A
WIS.—Monroe
Wenger & Co., Jno. C.
(Swiss; Limb.) ....B
WIS.—Sheboygan
Udell & Co., C. E........A
WIS.—Troy Centre
Wisconsin Butter & Cheese
Co. ....A

CORN MEAL

ALA.—Lincoln
Schmidt & Co., G. L......C
CAL.—Colton
Colton Grain & Milling Co.
B
CAL.—Los Angeles
Los Angeles Farming &
Milling Co. ......AAAA
CAL.—Sacramento
Phoenix Milling Co., 13th &
J. ....A
CAL.—San Francisco
Stockton Milling Co.....AA
D. C.—Washington
Cissel Co., G. W.........B
GA.—Camilla
Mitchell County Fertilizer
Co. ....B
GA.—Macon
Carstarphen Warehouse Co.,
T. J. ....B
ILL.—Brighton
Hilliard, G. W...........B
I. T.—Chickasha
Chickasha Milling Co.....B
IOWA—Burlington
Derby Mill & Elevator Co.
B
KANS.—Arkansas City
New Era Milling Co....B
KANS.—Clyde
Clyde Milling & Elevator
Co. ....B
KANS.—Junction City
Tyler & Co. ....A
KANS.—Newton

CORN MEAL (Con.)

Eagle Milling Co. ......B
KANS.—Pleasanton
Blaker Milling Co.......B
KANS.—Salina
Western Star Milling Co.
B
KANS.—Stafford
Larabee Flour Mills Co....A
MICH.—Flint
Genesee Flouring Mills...B
MICH.—Holland
Walsch-DeRoo Milling &
Cereal Co. ....B
MICH.—Lowell
King Milling Co..........B
MICH.—Tecumseh
Hayden Milling Co., Wm. B
MINN.—Edgerton
Edgerton Flouring Mill Co.
B
MO.—Independence .
Waggoner-Gates Milling Co.
A
MO.—Marionville .
Marionville Roller Mill Co.
B
NEBR.—Crete
Crete Mills ....B
NEBR.—Kearney
Kearney Flour Mills......A
NEBR.—Oakdale
Gallaway Flour Mill & Ele-
vator Co. ....B
KANS.—Schuyler
Wells-Abbott-Nieman Co.
AA
N. Y.—Troy
Boutwell Milling & Grain
Co. ....A
N. C.—Lexington
Grimes Bros. ....A
N. C.—Washington
Havens, J. ....B
N. C.—Tellico Junction . .
Tellico Junction Mills....B
WASH.—North Yakima . .
North Yakima Milling Co.
B
WASH.—Seattle ..
Seattle Cereal Co.......B
WIS.—Appleton
Willy & Co............B

INDEX

1388, 1498, 1616, 1665.
BOLTING—879, 1484; (*Drug & Chemical*), 1506.
BOOKBINDERS'—53, 76, 193, 194, 384, 541, 871, 885, 900, 989, 1000, 1066, 1080, 1327, 1462, 1494.
BOOT & SHOE—245, 427, 442, 443, 458, 470, 474, 475, 476, 479, 480, 483, 484, 486, 495, 496, 504, 533, 534, 551, 552, 553, 554, 569, 650, 841, 1034, 1125, 1243, 1647.
BORDER (*Shirt*), 1704.
BORES (*Metal Gang*), 274.
BORING—22, 80, 179, 772, 898, 1198, 1481½, 1522, 1671; (*Automatic*), 1307; (*Axle Bearing*), 410; (*Bench*), 834, 959, 1217, 1466, 1570; (*Car*), 179, 959, 1217, 1570; (*Car Box*), 410, 1060; (*Car Wheel*), 100, 524, 632, 1060, 1202, 1417, 1577; (*Chord*), 1337; (*Crank*), 1060, 1561; (*Cylinder*), 166, 187, 632, 1060, 1202, 1385, 1391, 1478, 1554, 1561, 1577, 1671; (*Cylinder Metal*), 1478; (*Double*), 80, 1217, 1337; (*Elect. Wiring*), 200, 853, 856; (*Electric; Portable; Horizontal*), 1517; (*Floor*), 1577; (*Gang*), 80, 275; (*Horizontal*), 51, 100, 281, 410, 523, 524, 612, 620, 860, 1044, 1060, 1198, 1218, 1290, 1307, 1754; (*Horizontal Metal*), 523, 524, 612, 620, 860, 1060, 1290; (*Hub*), 80, 1156, 1217, 1328, 1368; (*Metal*), 73, 338, 523, 524, 612, 620, 632, 668, 857, 1009, 1048, 1060, 1198, 1202, 1290, 1307, 1391, 1393, 1534, 1554, 1561, 1577, 1583, 1671; (*Metal, Vertical*), 982; (*Multiple*), 173; (*Multiple, Veneer*), 170; (*Multiple Spindle, Wood*), 221, 1199; (*Pinhole*), 80, 857, 959; (*Pneumatic, Wood*), 153, 757, 1566; (*Portable*), 151, 857, 959, 1217, 1583; (*Portable, Cylinder*), 1583, 1590; (*Portable, Radial*), 1217; (*Post*), 668, 771, 834, 1211, 1212, 1494; (*Pulley*), 187, 631; (*Shaft*), 51; (*Turret*), 1337; (*Universal*), 1337; (*Universal, Multiple, Wood*), 1751; (*Vertical*), 73, 80, 100, 520, 898, 959, 1217, 1328, 1337, 1498, 1554, 1570; (*Vertical, Metal*), 632, 775, 1198; (*Wood*), 179, 500, 522, 523, 545, 566, 678, 771, 808, 834, 899, 931, 959, 967, 1009, 1091, 1195, 1211, 1212, 1258, 1328, 1333, 1494, 1570.
BOTTLERS'—435, 439, 450, 736, 859, 970, 1109, 1113, 1213, 1287, 1516, 1753.
BOTTLING—227, 259, 450, 1213, 1589; (*Drug & Chemical*), 188.
BOX—555, 575, 1471; (*Cheese*), 914, 916, 936; (*Cigar*), 1122, 1217, 1419, 1427; (*Dovetail*), 719; (*Lock Corner*), 1217; (*Match*), 1394; (*Paper*), 541, 625, 1134, 1497; (*Wooden*), 1419.
BOXING—191, 834, 1217, 1368.
BOXMAKERS'—500, 597, 629, 688, 699, 774, 834, 899, 931, 959, 1135, 1211, 1217, 1570.
BOX-TOE (*Shoe*), 505.
BRACKET (*Telephone*), 938, 1696.
BRAIDING—1633, 1684, 1686.
BRANDING (*Brewers'*), 1280; (*Cigar*), 1002, 1236.
BRASS WORKING—1234, 1498, 1714.
BRAZING—310, 618, 666, 907, 959, 1742.
BREAKER—526.
BREAKING—477; (*Hard Waste*), 619.
BREWERS'—348, 351, 585, 658, 725, 736, 905, 1220, 1747, 1757.
BRICK (*See also Pressing*), 69, 116, 143, 149, 155, 266, 289, 294, 296, 308, 324, 325, 340, 342, 352, 355, 377, 639, 640, 658, 689, 734, 740, 749, 750, 813, 840, 917, 924, 1084, 1121, 1143, 1187, 1191, 1261, 1293, 1326, 1331, 1351, 1356, 1357, 1360, 1362, 1386, 1390, 1403, 1404, 1444, 1468, 1507, 1646, 1723, 1775.
BRIDGE WORK—100, 1337, 1498, 1650.
BRIQUETTING—155, 1613.
BROACHING—862.
BRONZING—1001.
BROOM—265.
BRUSH—320, 416, 475, 672, 1149.
BRUSHING (*Cloth*), 40, 615, 619, 1322, 1428, 1505, 1539, 1667, 1690, 1715.
BUCKLE—75, 92.
BUCKRAM—1471.
BUCKWHEAT—320, 374, 905.
BUFFING—21, 31, 458, 543, 608, 661, 796, 870, 906, 1009, 1060, 1072, 1102, 1114, 1198, 1204, 1380, 1384, 1389, 1524, 1583, 1640, 1673, 1674.
BULLDOZING—1258.
BUNCHING (*Cigar*), 1236.
BUNDLING (*Wood*), 867.
BURRING—558, 602, 619, 782, 962, 1011, 1568, 1580.
BUTCHERS'—728, 1006, 1086, 1397.
BUTTING—1221, 1706.
BUTTON—280, 364, 848, 1078.
BUTTONHOLE—445, 469, 476.
CABINETMAKERS'—80, 899, 959, 1217, 1706.
CABLING (*Wire*), 93, 1684.

835; (*Portable*), 699, 1480, 1577; (*Portable Hydraulic*), 699; (*Power*), 103; (*Screw*), 91; (*Spoke*), 275; (*Steam*), 105, 1060, 1184, 1577, 1639.
ROAD—119, 267, 321, 1464.
ROAD BUILDING—321.
ROAD MAKING (*Asphalt*), 878.
ROASTING (*Cocoa Bean*), 193; (*Coffee*), 193, 279; (*Malt*), 188; (*Peanut*), 193, 279.
ROD—522, 603.
ROD, PIN & DOWEL—834, 899, 936, 938, 959, 1211, 1217, 1391, 1494.
ROLL (*Paint*), 1227, 1242.
ROLLING (*See also Mill*), 40, 456, 479, 984; (*Braid*), 1686; (*Carpet*), 619, 1490; (*Cloth*), 615, 619, 967, 1505, 1690; (*Keg*), 188, 1747, 1748; (*Lead*), 524; (*Mill*), 16, 40, 93, 351; (*Paper Tube*), 152, 1134; (*Screw Thread*), 90, 92, 93, 874; (*Taper*), 23, 275; (*Thread, Screw*), 92, 93.
ROOFING—46, 414, 883, 904; (*Tin*), 84, 1227.
ROPE—517.
ROUNDING—1217.
ROUTING—823, 834, 1211; (*Stair*), 232.
ROVING—570.
RUBBER—823, 836, 416.
RUBBING (*Seam*), 487, 496; (*Wood*), 714.
RUFFLING—1104.
RUG (*Carpet*), 1396.
RULING—592, 875, 1677; (*Cycloidal*), 823; (*Paper*), 1462, 1541.
SALT WORKS—371, 986, 1097, 1650.
SAMPLING—133.
SANDER (*Molding*), 432, 761.
SANDING—619, 1715; (*Brick*), 1360; (*Brick Mold*), 1403; (*Curtain Pole & Finishing*), 221.
SAND MIXING—1300, 1301; (*Incorporator*), 1299.
SANDPAPER—456.
SANDPAPERING—179, 479, 714, 771, 834, 1195, 1211, 1217, 1494, 1765; (*Pneumatic*), 153.
SANITARY (*Can Makers'*), 858.
SASH—6, 31, 80.
SASH, DOOR & BLIND—179, 808, 834, 898, 899, 959, 1217, 1482, 1570, 1706, 1727, 1730.
SATURATING (*Roofing Paper*), 1546.
SAVING (*Gold*), 1080, 1462.
SAWING (*See also Mill*), 80, 194, 340, 459, 823, 834, 959, 1080, 1193, 1217, 1462, 1483, 1509, 1706, 1761, 1771, 1773; (*Band*), 310, 500, 618, 664, 666, 697, 699, 738, 761, 815, 834, 907, 959, 1127, 1129, 1217, 1221, 1239, 1328, 1368, 1512, 1540, 1570, 1730, 1731, 1742; (*Band, Conveying*), 299; (*Band, Double*), 1328; (*Band, Elevating*), 299; (*Band, Metal*), 1554; (*Band, (Self-Feeding)*), 645; (*Barrel*), 603; (*Box Board*), 1653; (*Brass*), 70; (*Chair*), 61; (*Churn, etc.*), 603; (*Circular, Wood*), 62-471, 643, 1217, 1494, 1520, 1657; (*Cold Metal*), 51, 862, 1060, 1554, 1622; (*Conveying Band*), 299; (*Crosscut*), 80, 500, 834, 899, 959, 1211, 1217, 1221, 1570, 1706; (*Cutoff*), 80, 471, 500, 575, 834, 898, 899, 959, 1177, 1211, 1217, 1554, 1705, 1706; (*Double Band*), 1328; (*Drag*), 575; (*Edging*), 326, 390, 699, 899, 904, 959, 1009, 1148, 1177, 1217, 1706, 1742; (*Elevating Band*), 299; (*Hand Power*), 62, 1520; (*Hot*), 1273, 1567, 1607, 1622, 1626; (*Hydraulic, Iron Shop*), 646; (*Iron*), 500; (*Iron Shop*), 1060, 1273, 1554; (*Iron Shop, Hydraulic*), 646; (*Iron Shop, Portable*), 222; (*Iron Shop, Power*), 222; (*Metal*), 223, 473, 1128, 1133, 1522, 1538, 1639; (*Metal Band*), 1554; (*Metal, Hand Power*), 189; (*Pipe*), 959; (*Rip*), 80, 281, 326, 471, 500, 645, 898, 899, 959, 967, 1211, 1212, 1217, 1318, 1419, 1494, 1570; (*Stave*), 603, 604; (*Stave, Barrel*), 1314; (*Rail*), 223, 1554; (*Self-Feeding Band*), 645; (*Shingle*), 357, 730, 938, 1283; (*Slap Band*), 1653; (*Stone Gang*), 333; (*Variety*), 1211, 1221; (*Wood*), 3, 272, 292, 357, 500, 532, 556, 614, 628, 695, 923, 1333, 1419, 1643, 1655, 1698, 1729.
SCALDING (*Tomato*), 851.
SCALE (*Testing*), 892.
SCALLOPING—1087.
SCARFING (*Plate*), 410.
SCOURING—320; (*& Cutting*), 1134; (*Leather*), 465; (*Yarn*), 1493, 1565, 1568; (*Wool*), 477, 571, 619, 845, 1505, 1580.
SCOURING, POLISHING & SEPARATING, COMBINED—273, 1149.
SCRAPING (*Hog*), 372; (*Metal*), 93.
SCRATCHING—90.
SCREENING—490, 1465.
SCREW—74, 620, 780, 1009, 1117, 1198, 1215, 1303, 1307, 1538, 1665, 1687, 1714; (*Automatic*), 20, 47, 54, 528, 1060, 1269, 1678, 1716; (*Multiple Spindle, Automatic*), 1292; (*Wood*), 44.

MACHINERY

APPENDIX—Machinery (2-43)

ALA.—Birmingham
2—White-Blakeslee Mfg. Co. (Veneer Cutting)....A

ALA.—Huntsville
3—Huntsville Fdry & Mach. Wks. (Woodsawing & Splitting) ....B

CAL.—San Francisco
4—Doble Co., Abner (Hydraulic)................A
5—Garrett Co., W. T. (Air-Moving & Refrigerating) AA
6—Hendy Mach. Wks., Joshua (Sash Door & Blind Slotting) ....AA
7—Henshaw, Bulkley & Co., Fremont & Mission (Conveying; all kinds for all purposes)...............AA
8.—Meese & Gottfried Co., 167 Fremont (Ice & Refrigerating) ....A
9—Pacific Acetylene Gas Co., 115 Montgomery (Acetylene Gas) ....G
10—Risdon Iron & Locomotive Wks. (Refrigerating) AAAA
11—San Francisco Tool Wks. (Water Wks., Pumping) A

CAL.—San Leandro
12—Best Mfg. Co. (Grain Cleaning)..............AA

COLO.—Denver
13—Hendrick & Bolthoff Mfg. & Supply Co. (Mining Timber Framing) ....AA
14—Hingley Laundry Specialty Co. (Steam Laundry Dampeners) X
15—Stearns-Rogers Mfg. Co. (Chlorinating, Cyaniding, Hoisting) ....A

CONN.—Ansonia
16—Farrell Fdry. & Mach. Co. (Rubber; Veneer Cutting; Rolling Mill) ....AAAA

CONN.—Bridgeport
17—Adams, A. L., cor. Water & South Av. (Corset).F
18—Amer. Tube & Stamping Co. (Straightening; Cutting Strip Metal; Swaging)..................AAAA
19—Armstrong Mfg. Co. (Pipe Cutting; Threading).A
20—Automatic Mach. Co. (Automatic Screw; Wire Straightening; Cutting) ....B
21—Bridgeport Safety Emery Wheel Co. (Buffing; Polishing) ....F
22—Bullard Mach. Tool Wks. (Brass Working; Boring; Drilling; Vertical Metal Boring; Turning; Railroad Shop) ....AA
23—Coulter & McKenzie Mach. Co. (Car Spring; Bending; Forming; Spring Coiling; Taper Rolling; Wire Forming) ....D
24—Curtis & Curtis Co. (Pipe; Pipe Cutting; Threading) ....AA
25—Hubbell, Harvey (Riveting; Screw Slotting; Tapping) C
26—Model Mach. Co. (Sewing) ....D
27—Nilson Mach. Co., A. H. (Wire Straightening; Cutting) ....E
28—Pacific Iron Wks. (Hoisting; Steam Power)....A
29—Smith & Egge Mfg. Co. (Automatic Hand Sewing) ....A
30—Special Machy. Co. (Automatic Buckle Wire; Automatic Paper Clip; Fastener; Special Automatic Staple) ....F
31—Springfield Mfg. Co. (Buffing; Grinding; Polishing; Brick Surfacing; Sash; Door; Stropping).....B
32—Union Metallic Cartridge Co. (Cartridge)...AAA
33—Wheeler & Wilson Mfg. Co. (Buttonhole; Cloth Room Sewing; Corset; Cylinder; Double Needle; Fancy Stitch; Boot; Shoe Sewing; Glove Pointing; Glove Stitching; Hand Sewing; Hat Binding; Hat Sweat Stitching; Hem Stitch Sewing; Leather Stitching; Lock Stitch Sewing; Overseaming; Serging; Spoke Stitch; Vamping) ....AAAA

CONN.—Bristol
35—Root, C. J. (Counting) ....B
36—Smith, Ira R. (Adjustable Stamping for Stamping Name on Spoons & Metal) ....E

CONN.—Danbury
38—Hull Bros. & Co. (Acetylene Gas)............C
39—New Mach. Co. (Hat) ....F

CONN.—Derby
40—Birmingham Iron Fdry. (Axe; Rolling Mill; Rubber Friction Calendering; Cloth Brushing; Pick Rolling; Soling; Upper; Tubing) ....AA

CONN.—East Hampton
41—Brown Co., H. B., The (Bolt; Nut; Heading Tapping Threading) C

CONN.—Hartford
42—Billings & Spencer Co. (Cold Metal Cutting-Off; Forging) ....AA
43—Colt's Patent Fire Arms Mfg. Co. (Rifling) AAAA

1179

44—Cook Co., Asa F. (Bolt Heading for Stove & Fire Bolts, etc.; Bolt Threading for Stove & Fire Bolts, etc.; Die Sinking, Milling; Wood Screw) ....B

45—Dart Marking Machine Co., P. O. Box 82 (Dart Marking; Addressing Shipping Cases) X

46—Dwight Slate Mach. Co. (Metal Cutting-Off; Double Seaming; Gear Cutting; Marking; Plain Milling; Rack Cutting; Roofing; Screw Slotting; Sheet Metal Workers; Tools; Thread Tool Grinding) ....B

47—Hartford Machine Screw Co. (Die Chamfering; Forming; Bending; Small Bench Milling; Automatic Screw; Screw Slotting; Slotting; Tapping) AAAA

48—Merrow Machine Co. (Crocheting; Crochet; Bed Blanket; Knit Goods Finishing; Overseaming; Sewing; Blanket Finishing; Horse Blanket Whipping) B

49—Phoenix Iron Wks. Corp'n (Bleaching) ......B

50—Pope Mfg. Co. (Automobile; Bicycle) ....AAAA

51—Pratt & Whitney Co .(Bolt; Nut; Bolt Pointing; Bolt Threading; Horizontal Boring; Drilling; Tapping; Centering; Chucking; Counting; Brass Working; Cold Metal Cutting-Off; Cold Metal Sawing; Cutting-Off Wood; Horizontal & Vertical Milling; Horizontal Tapping; Bench Milling; Automatic Shaping Screw; Die Sinking; Drilling & Tapping Combined; Flang Facing; Forging; Forging & Bending; Upright Gang Drilling; Hand Shearing; Marking; Involute & Epicycloidal Gear Cutting; Monitor (made only to order); Oil Testing; Profiling; Roll Grooving; Screw Shaving; Screw Slotting; Shaft Boring; Shafting; Slotting; Spring Coiling; Thread Cutting; Automatic Weighing for Granular Materials; Wheel-Rim Turning; Cartridge Varnishing; Rifling; Gun Barrel Drilling) ....AAAA

52—Quint, A. D., 31 Wells (Milling; Tapping) ....D

53—Smyth Mfg. Co. (Bookbinders'; Book Sewing; Book Case) ....AAA

54—Spencer Automatic Mach. Screw Co. (Automatic Screw) X

55—Whitney Mfg. Co. (Bench Hand Milling; Plain Milling) ....A

CONN.—Meriden

56—Kelsey Press Co. (Presss; Hand Printing) ....A

57—Merriman, A. H. (Forging).................C

CONN.—Middletown

58—Douglas, W. & B. (Hydraulic)........... ...A

59—Palmer, I. E. (Cloth Finishing; Cotton Finishing; Sheer Finishing) ....AAA

CONN.—Mystic

60—Standard Machry. Co. (Paper Cutting) ....A

CONN.—New Britain

61—New Britain Mach. Co. (Saw Setting; Chair Saw; Wood Mortising) ....A

CONN.—New Haven

62—Barnes Tool Co. (Circular Saw; Hand Power; Match; Match Box) ....B

63—Belden Mach. Co. (Wire Straightening; Cutting) D

64—Bishop, Walter S., Atwater Blk. (Electro-Plating) E

65—Brooks, Chas. J., 27 Artizan (Nut Tapping) ....E

66—Brown & Co., R. H. (Pamphlet Stitching; Type Setting; Type Distributing; Wire Stitching).......E

67—Burgess, E. A. (Est. of) (Boxmakers' Nailing; Trimming, &c.) ....E

69—Eastern Machinery Co. (Brick; Supplies; Hoisting; Steam Power) ....B

70—Griswold, Geo. M. (Brass Sawing; Milling; Watch Case; Match) ....D

71—Harrison, Leonard D. (Flour Mill) ....H

72—Herrick & Cowell (Match; Toothpick)..........C

73—New Haven Mfg. Co. (Metal Boring; Shaft Straightening; Shafting; Slotting; Boring; Turning; Vertical) ....AA

74—Reynolds & Co. (Sand Molding; Wood Molding; Screw) ....B

75—Shuster Co., F. B. (Automatic Buckle Tongue; Butt Drilling; Milling; Automatic Cold Roll Pointing; Countersinking; Drilling; Drilling Multiple Spindle; Drilling Rivet; Double Head; Double End Milling; Automatic Ring Forming; Tubular Rivet; Elastic Rotary Blow, &c.; Riveting; Shear; Barbed Point; Automatic Staple; Automatic Wire Straightening; Cutting; Sheet Metal Straightening; Tack Cutting; Wire Cutting; Wire Forming)....................X

76—Thompson & Son Co., Henry G., 6 Elm (Bookbinders') ....B

CONN.—New London

77—Whiton Machine Co., D. E. (Centering; Gear Cutting) ....AA

CONN.—Norwich

78—Barber, M. A. (Bicycle Chain Testing; Cork Cutting) X

79—Lester & Wasley (Envelope)................C

80—Rogers & Co., C. B. (Bench; Boring; Cabinet Makers'; Car Cut-Off; Gaining; Car Mortising; Car Tenoning; Combination Saw; Dado; Chair; Cross-Cut Saw; Cut-Off Saw; Double Boring; Floring; Gang Boring; Hub Boring; Hub Mortising; Moulding; Boring Pinhole; Sawing; Sash; Door; Blind; Handle; Spoke; Tenoning; Tonguing; Grooving; Vertical Boring) ....AAAA

CONN.—Oakville

81—Baird Machine Co. (Bottle Stopper; Pin, &c.)...E

CONN.—Plainville

82—Norton & Jones Machine Tool Wks. (Drilling; Slitting; Special) ....H

CONN.—Seymour

83—Swan Co., Jas. (Spoke) ....A

CONN.—Southington

84—Peck, Stow & Wilcox Co. (Corrugating; Crimping; Beading; Double Seaming; Sheet Metal Forming; Bending; Notching; Sheet Metal Workers'; Tools; Cornice; Tin Roofing; Tinsmiths'; Tobacco Cutting; Turning; Wiring) ....AAAA

CONN.—Stonington

85—Atwood-Morrison Co. (Cotton Thread; Silk)..AA

CONN.—Thompsonville

86—Bushnell Press Co., Geo. H. (Oil Mill; Hydraulic) A

CONN.—Tolland

87—Clough, R. M. (Vertical Milling) ....D

CONN.—Torrington

88—Excelsior Needle Co. (Rod; Tube Pointing; Swaging) ....AAAA

89—Hendey Machine Co. (Horizontal; Plain; Universal, &c.; Milling) ....AA

CONN.—Waterbury

90—Cross & Speirs Mach. Co. (Jack Pump, &c.; Chain Making; Buffing; Polishing; Perforating; Double Blow Riveting; Scratching; Overhauling for Removing Bad Spots from Brass Plate, &c.; Screw Thread Rolling; Gang, &c., Slitting; Automatic Wire Straightening; Cutting) X

91—Draher, Jno. (Riveting; Screw) ....F

92—Manville Machine Co., E. J. (Buckle; Cartridge; Eyelet; Pin Pointing; Screw Heading; Screw Slotting; Screw Thread Rolling; Tapping; Wire Straightening; Cutting) C

93—Waterbury Farrell Fdry. & Mach. Co. (Automatic Cold Bolt Heading; Buffing; Polishing; Die Sinking; Nut Blanking; Screw Thread Rolling; Slitting; Swaging; Wire Straightening; Cutting; Metal Scraping; Metal Straightening; Rivet; Threading; Wire Cabling; Bolt; Nut; Hinge; Rolling Mill; Cartridge)......AA

CONN.—Willimantic

94—Vanderman Plumbing & Heating Co. (Smoke Test) C

95—Willimantic Machine Co. (Thread; Silk) .....B

CONN.—Windsor Locks

96—Clark Co., Geo. P. (Sizing) C

97—Windsor Locks Machine Co.. (Carpet; Paper Making) ....E

CONN.—Winsted

98—Carter & Hakes Machine Co. (Milling).......D

DEL..—Wilmington

99—Baker & Co., Geo. W. (Leather Working)......B

100—Betts Machine Co. (Bridge Working; Boring; Turning Vertical; Horizontal Boring; Drilling; Car Wheel Boring; Planing; Slotting from 2 to 8 inch Stroke) ....AA

101—Delaware Mach. Wks. (Leather Working) ....D

102—Henderer's Sons, A. L. (Punching Hydraulic; Steel Punching; Screw) ....E

103—Hilles & Jones Co. (Milling; I Beam Punching; Multiple Punching; Power Riveting).........AAAA

104—Poole Co., J. M. (Leveling for Sheets).......AA

105—Pusey & Jones (Cocoa-Nut Oil; Cylinder; Steam Riveting; Paper; Pulp; Sugar) ....AAA

106—Remington Machine Co. (Cane-Seat Chair; Canning; Ice; Refrigerating) ....A

107—Slocomb & Co., F. F. (Pneumatic Riveting; Leather Working) C

108—Walker & Elliott (Cement Grinders; Mixers; Conveying; Fertilzer Factory; Phosphate Mill).......B

D. C.—Washington

109—Acetylene Lighting Co. (Acetylene Gas) X

110—Morrison Paper Co., E. (Paper Testing).......B

GA.—Atlanta

111—Atlanta Machine Wks. (Ice; Refrigerating)....B

112—De Loach Mill Mfg. Co. (Coppers; Flour Mill; Saw Mill; Wood Moulding) ....B

113—Van Winkle Gin & Mach. Wks. (Fertilizer Factory) ....AAA

GA.—Columbus

114—Columbus Iron Wks. (Ice; Refrigerating).....AA

115—Golden's Fdry. & Mach. Co. (Ice; Refrigerating) .... A

GA.—Rome
116—Morrison, Trammel Brick Co. (Brick; Supplies) . D

GA.—Savannah
117—Kehoe & Co., Wm. (Phosphate; Rice; Saw Milling) .... A

ILL.—Aurora
118—Amer. Well Wks. (Compressed Air; Pumping; Artesian Well; Oil Well; Horse Power; Pumping; Traction Drilling; Well Sinking) .... AA
119—Western Wheeled Scraper Co. (Ditching; Railroad Ditching; Street Sweeping; Road) .... AA

ILL.—Batavia
120—Appleton Mfg. Co. (Horse Power Pumping) .... A
121—Challenge Wind Mill & Feed Mill Co. (Horse Power Pumping) .... AAA
122—U. S. Wind Engine & Pump Co. (Ensilage; Irrigating) .... AA

ILL.—Belleville
123—Belleville Pump & Skein Wks. (Coal; Coal Cutting) .... AA
124—Harrison Mach. Wks. (Threshing) .... AA

ILL.—Belvedere
125—National Sewing Mach. Co. (Sewing) .... AAA

ILL.—Cairo
126—Reed, Jos. B. (Tripple Gear, &c.; Shaping) .... B

ILL.—Carpentersville
127—Illinois Iron & Bolt Co. (Paper Testing) ..... AA
128—Star Mfg. Co. (Threshing) .... A

ILL.—Chicago
129—Acetylene Apparatus Mfg. Co., 157 Michigan Av. (Acetylene Gas) .... A
130—Acorn Brass Mfg. Co., 15 So. Jefferson (Paint Spraying) .... D
131—Addressograph Co., 173 So. Canal (Addressing) . A
132—Advance Mach. Co., 194 S. Clinton (Incand. Gas Mantle) .... F
133—Allis-Chalmers Co., Home Ins. Bldg. (Cement; Coal Mining; Coal Washing; Copper Converting; Elevating; Conveying; Cyaniding; Mixing; Prospecting; Sampling; Hoisting; Steam Power) ...... AAAA
134—Amer. Can Co., 135 Adams (Notching; Spring Coiling) .... AAAA
135—Am. Fdry. & Machy. Co. (Soap; Fertilizer; Drying) .... AA
136—Anderson & Co., Carl (Horse Power Pumping) . . C
137—Austin Mfg. Co., F. C. Manhattan Bldg. (Elevating; Conveying; Tile Ditching; Earth Moving; Street Cleaning) .... AAA
138—Barber Creamery Supply Co., A. H., 229 So. Water (Ice; Refrigerating; Portable Ice; Tinners' Grooving) .... B
139—Benedict, Louis, 128 So. Clinton (Tin Can Testing; Seaming) .... D
140—Birtman Co., C. F., 35 Randolph (Static Electric; X-Ray) C
141—Blickensderfer Mfg. Co. (Typewriting) ...... AA
142—Borden & Selleck Co., 48 Lake (Coal; Ore Handling; Elevating; Conveying) .... B
143—Boland Machy. Co., 209 S. Clinton (Brick; Supplies) .... F
144—Bottlers' Special Machy. Co., 110 E. Indiana (Automatic Bottle Filling; Labeling; Washing) .... D
145—Brewers' & Bottlers' Machy. Wks. (Bottle Washing) .... G
146—Brown Specialty Machy. Co., Jackson Boul. & Clinton ("Hammer" Core Making) .... E
147—Caldwell & Son Co., H. W., 17th & Western Av. (Elevating; Conveying; Lead; Soap; Oil Mill; Power Transmitting) .... AA
148—Challenge Machy. Co. (Printers') .... A
149—Chicago Brick Machy. Co., 225 Dearborn (Brick; Supplies) .... E
150—Chicago Clothes Dryer Wks., 346 Wabash Av. (Clothes Drying) .... D
151—Chicago Flexible Shaft Co., La Salle Av. & Ontario (Portable Boring; Horse Clipping; Sheep Shearing; Portable Tapping; Reaming) .... B
152—Chicago Paper Tube & Can Co., 20 N. May (Paper Tube Rolling; Cutting) X
153—Chicago Pneumatic Tool Co., Fisher Bldg. (Pneumatic Paint Spraying; Pneumatic Riveting; Pneumatic Sand Papering; Pneumatic Wood Boring; Portable Pneumatic Riveting) .... AAAA
154—Chicago Sewing Mach. Co. (Sewing; Lock Stitch) .... A
155—Chisholm, Boyd & White Co., W. 56th. cor. Wallace (Brick; Supplies; Briquetting; Dry Brick Press) .... A
156—Clow & Sons, Jas. B., 344 Franklin (Portable Pipe Cutting; Threading) .... AAA
157—Clyde Mach. Wks., 22d & Shields Av. (Crank Pin

Turning) ....E
158—Consolidated Press & Tool Co., 98 N. Clinton
    (Sheet Metal Workers'; Tools)....................D
159—Cooper Sheep Shearing Mach. Co., 142 Illinois
    (Sheep Shearing) ....B
160—Covel Mfg. Co., 8 S. Canal (Saw Sharpening)...C
161—Crane Co. (Pipe Cutting; Threading)......AAAA
162—Creamery Package Mfg. Co., 182 E. Kinzie (Ice;
    Refrigerating; Creamery) ....AAAA
163—Cross Press & Sign Co., 57 Dayton (Wooden Box
    Printing) ....B
164—Cummings Co., B. F. (Check Cancelling)......C
165—Dreis & Krump, 3214 S. Halsted (Sheet Metal
    Workers'; Tools) ....E
166—Elmes Engineering Wks., Chas. F. (Cylinder Bor-
    ing) ....A
167—Fairbanks, Morse & Co., Franklin & Monroe
    (Portable Iron Shop Sawing; Water Works; Wine
    Pumping; Coal; Ore Handling; Hoisting; Conveying;
    Mining; Track) ....AAAA
168—Featherstone Fdry. & Mach. Co., 348 Halsted
    (Heavy Pneumatic Forging; Ice; Refrigerating)..AA
169—Felt & Tarrant Mfg. Co., 52 Illinois (Adding)..B
170—Fischer Mach. Wks., 345 So. Canal (Multiple Bor-
    ing; Veneer; Wooden Box Matching; Re-Sawing;
    Surfacing) ....B
171—Folding Sawing Mach. Co. (Saw; Folding)....D
172—Foley & Williams Mfg. Co., 46 E. Jackson Boul.
    (Sewing) ....A
173—Garden City Fan Co. (Multiple Boring) ....B
174—Garland Gas Machine & Supply Co., Geo. D.
    (Laundry; Gas) ....E
176—Goetz & Flodin Mfg. Co. (Brewers' Mashing)..A
177—Goldman & Co., E. (Bottle Soaking)..........A
178—Goodman Mfg. Co., Halsted & 48th Place (Elec-
    tric Coal Mining; Coal Cutting; Chain Mining)..AA
179—Greenlee Bros. & Co., 225 W. 12th (Car Boring;
    Panel Raising; Sand Papering; Boring; Mortising;
    Car Tenoner; Car Cut-Off; Gaining; Car Mortising;
    Furniture; Sash; Door; Blind; Boring all kinds).AA
180—Harvard Electric Co., 224 S. Clinton (Static Elec-
    tric) ....D
181—Healy Ice Mach. Co., 641 30th (Ice; Refrigerat-
    ing) ....F
182—Heimbuecher & Co., W. C., 36 La Salle (Acetylene
    Gas) ....D
183—Hoisting & Conveying Machy. Co., 44 N. Elizabeth
    (Coal; Ore Handling; Elevating; Conveying)......B
184—Hunter's Acetylene Gas Co. (Acetylene Gas)....B
185—Illinois Sewing Mach. Co., Wabash & Randolph
    (Sewing; Lock Stitch) ....AA
186—International Harvesting Mach. Co. (Threshing)
    ....AAAA
187—Jones Fdry. & Mach. Co., W. A., cor. North Av.
    & Noble (Cylinder Boring; Pulley Boring; Turning)
    ....A
188—Kaestner & Co. (Inc.), (Moved to So. Bend, Ind.)
    (Automatic Beer Racking; Barley; Malt Cleaning;
    Keg Rolling; Scrubbing; Brewers' Mashing; Pitching;
    Malt Roasting; Drug; Chemical Bottling; Soap; Lead;
    Putty; Oil; Cement) ....A
189—Kelley-Maus & Co., 184 Lake (Hand Power Metal
    Sawing) ....AA
190—Chicago Solder Co., 44 N. Union (Improved Auto-
    matic Tipping) ....D
191—Knapp Co., Fred H., 80 Wabash Av. (Bottle Label-
    ing; Can Labeling; Boxing; Riveting)............D
192—Kroeschell Bros. Co. (Ice; Refrigerating)......A
193—Lange, Henry G., 22 N. May (Bookbinders'; Con-
    fectioners'; Coffee; Peanut; Cocoa Bean Roasting;
    Glass Beveling; Polishing) ....E
194—Latham Machy. Co. (Bookbinders'; Numbering;
    Paging; Perforating; Wire Stitching; Back Forming;
    Backing; Sawing; Stabbing) C
195—Laubenheimer Co., Geo. H. (Brewers' Washing).D
196—Laun Bros. (Acetylene Gas) X
197—Link Belt Machy. Co., W. 39th & Stewart (Auto-
    matic Barrel Washing; Can Washing; Elevating; Con-
    veying; Ensilage; Coal Hoisting; &c.; Leather Belt-
    ing; Rubber Belting) ....AAA
198—Lovejoy, T. H., 90 Ohio (Cast; Forged Steel;
    Screw Punching) ....D
199—Liquid Carbonic Acid Mfg. Co., 76 Illinois (Bot-
    tlers'; Carbonating) ....AAAA
200—McCrea & Co., Jas., 67 W. Washn. (Boring for
    Electric Wiring; Drilling Bit Brace)............E
201—McDonnell Odometer Co. (Counting; Special)..X
202—McElliott, D. P., 37 State (Static Electric)....X
203—McGuire-Cummings Mfg. Co., 122 N. Sangamon
    (Street Railway Sweeping) ....AA
204—Macdonald Engineering Co., Monadnock Bldg.
    (Engineers'; Contractors' Coal; Ore Handling)....B
205—Magnus Sons Co., A., 244 E. Randolph (Bottle

Washing) ....B
206—Mateer & Co., F. W., 7 S. Jeff. (Laundry
Tumbling) ....E
207—Matthews Gas Mach. Co., 40 Dearborn (Gas)..B
208—Moore & Lorentz Co., 115 So. Clinton (Elevating;
Conveying) ....D
209—Morgan-Gardner Electric Co., 2640 Shields Av.
(Coal Mining; Electric Coal Mining; Electric Coal
Cutting; Electric Chain Mining) ....AAA
210—Municipal Engineering & Contracting Co., 315
Dearborn (Sewer; Trench Excavating; Tile Ditching)
A
211—Murphy & Co., Christopher, 204 Dearborn (Flue
Welding) ....B
213—National Mach. Wks., Sheffield & North Av.
(Pitching) C
214—Nelson & Kreuter Co. (Ironing; Laundry).....A
215—New England Mfg. Co., 59 Clark (Acetylene Gas)
B
216—Novelty Tufting Machine Co. (Upholstering;
Tufting) C
217—Oliver Typewriter Co. (Typewriting) ....AA
218—Olsen & Filgner (Barley; Malt Cleaning; Washing)
C
219—Pettibone, Mulliken & Co., 204 Dearborn (Roller
Rail Bending; Straightening) ....AAAA
220—Pridmore, Henry E., 19th & Rockwell (Car Wheel
Molding; Pulley Molding; Sand Molding)........A
221—Pringle & Brodie Machy. Co., 277 So. Canal (Curtain Pole Sanding; Finishing; Sanding; Buffing
Dowel; Rosette; Corner Block; Multiple Spindle
Wood Boring; Wood Ring; Valve Handle)........D
222—Railroad Supply Co., Bedford Bldg. (Power; Portable Iron Shop Sawing) ....B
223—Railway Appliances Co., Old Colony Bldg. (Metal
Cutting-Off; Metal Sawing; Pneumatic Riveting; Rail
Sawing) ....A
224—Rand Drill Co., 128 Monadnock Bldg. (Stone
Channelling; Tunnelling; General Mining)...AAAA
225—Raymond Bros. Impact Pulverizer Co., 143 Laflin
(Pulverizing; Separating) ....D
226—Rebsamen & Almeroth (Ice) ....E
227—Redlich Mfg. Co. (Bottling; Corking; Filling; Tinfoil Capping; Labeling; Washing)...............B
228—Rosback, F. B. (Stabbing) ....E
229—Schneider, Adolph (Bottle Filling)..........X
230—Schniedewend & Co., Paul (Paper Cutting; Electrotypers'; Stereotypers'; Photo Engravers')...X
231—Shaw, Willis, N. Y. Life Bldg. (Ditching; Stone
Channeling) ....E
232—Smith & Phillips Mfg. Co., 97 W. Adams (Pulley
Mortising; Sash Grooving; Stair Routing) ....D
233—Star Brass Wks., 675 Canal (Paint Spraying)..F
234—Stier Mfg. Co., Herman (Brewers' Mashing)...D
235—Stiles-Morse Co. (Auto. Tin Can) C
236—Streeter-Amet Weighing & Recording Co. (Automatic Weighing) ....B
237—Stoud & Co., E. H., 38 La Salle (Pulverizing;
Street Cleaning) ....D
238—Sullivan Machy. Co., 135 Adams (Coal Mining;
Cutting; Stone Channeling; Drilling; Quarrying)....
AAAA
239—Thexton Electric Envelope Sealer Co. (Envelope
Sealing) X
240—Thornburgh & Co., H. L., 245 Jefferson Av.
(Flour Mill; Grain Elevator) X
241—Trenkhorst, Frank (Brewers' Mashing).......F
242—Turner & Co., W. W., 38 La Salle (Acetylene
Gas) ....D
243—Twentieth Century Machy. Co. (Bottle Soaking).X
244—Union Carbide Co., 157 Michigan Av. (Acetylene
Gas) ....A
245—United Shoe Machy. Co., 40 La Salle (Boot;
Shoe) ....B
246—Wallace Supply Co., 169 Jackson Boul. (Hand
Power Bending; Paint Spraying) C
247—Webster Mfg. Co., 1075 W. 15th (Cement; Elevating; Conveying; also Cement; Oil; Fertilizer Mills)
AA
248—Western Electric Co. (Electricl) ....AAAA
249—Weller Mfg. Co., 118 E. North Av. (Elevating;
Conveying) ....A
250—Wells Steam Pump Co., F. C. (Water Works;
Pumping) ....AA
251—Whitcomb & Co., Geo. D., 86 Ohio (Coal Cutting)
B
252—Williams Lloyd Machy. Co. (Type High)......X
253—Wold, Torris & Co., 66 N. Jefferson (Can Makers';
Sheet Metal Workers'; Tools) C
254—Wolf Co., Fred W., 139 Rees (Beet Washing; Slicing; Ice; Refrigerating; Sugar)..............AAA
255—Wrigley Co., Thos., 300 Dearborn (Conduit Pipe

Bending; Silk Doubling) ....G

ILL.—Cobden

256—Cobden Mach. Wks. (Basket Stapling) ....D

ILL.—Decatur

257—Mueller Mfg .Co., H. (Drilling; Pipe Pressure; Tapping; Gas; Water Main Tapping; Pipe; Dry Pipe Tapping) ....AAA

ILL.—Downers Grove

259—Dicke Tool Co. (Bottling Capping; Corking; Filling; Supplies) C

ILL.—Du Quoin

260—Higgins, J. J. (Watch Cleaning) ....E

ILL.—Edwardsville

261—Bignall & Keeler Mfg. Co. (Pipe Cutting; Threading) ....B

ILL.—Freeport

262—Arcade Mfg. Co. (Slicing Bread; Fruit; Meat; Vegetables, &c) ....A

263—Hoefer Mfg. Co. (Automatic Furniture Spring Coiling; Spring Knotting; Staple; Wire Spooling; Wire Straightening; Cutting) C

264—Stover Mfg. Co. (Irrigating) ....AA

ILL.—Galesburg

265—Boyer Broom Co., A. (Broom).................X

ILL.—Harvey

266—Frost Mfg. Co. (Brick; Supplies).............A

267—Austin Mfg. Co., F. C. (Ditching; R. R. Ditching; Sewer; Trench Excavating; Steel Street Sweeping; Artesian Well; Oil Well; Road; Traction Drilling; Well Sinking) ....AA

268 Buda Fdry. & Mfg. Co. (Rail Bending; Straightening) ....AA

269—Whiting Fdry. Equipment Co. (Cart Wheel Testing; Moulding; Axle; Draw-Bar, &c., Testing; Hoisting) ....AA

ILL.—Hoopeston

270—Sprague Canning Machy. Co. (Can Testing; Canning) ....A

ILL.—Joliet

271—Bates Machine Co. (Die Plate Hammering, Automatic Numbering; Staple; Wire; Nails; Wire Nail Barbing; Wire Twisting) ....AA

ILL.—Marseilles

272—Marseilles Mfg. Co. (Wood Sawing; Splitting).A

ILL.—Moline

273—Barnard & Leas Mfg. Co. (Packing; Cement Packing; Grain Cleaning; Flour Milling; Rice Milling; Scouring; Polishing; Separating Combined)....AA

274—Moline Tool Co. (Metal Gang Bores)..........E

275—Williams, White & Co. (Bolt; Nut; Carriage Builders'; Coal; Ore Handling; Bending Tire; Banding; Forming; Forging; Bending; Gang Punching; Multiple Drilling; Punching; 6-10 Holes in Wood Gang Drilling; Riveting; Spoke Riveting; Swaging; Taper Rolling; Gang Boring; Tire Welding)....AA

ILL—Oswego

276—Edwards, J. H. (Acetylene Gas) ....F

ILL.—Ottawa

277—Amer. Hardware Mfg. Co. (Sheet Metal Workers') C

278—Knowles, W. H. (Brick Clay Pans, &c.)......D

ILL.—Peoria

279—Bartholomew Co. (Coffee; Pea Nut Roasting)..B

ILL.—Quincy

280—Central Iron Wks. (Button) ....B

ILL.—Rockford

281—Barnes Co., W. F. & John (Horizontal Boring; Drilling; Foot Power; Foot Power Wood Turning; Hand & Foot Power Wood Mortising; Moulding; Circular Saw; Cutting-Off Wood; Polishing Rip Saw) ....AA

282—Ingersoll Milling Mach. Co. (Heavy Horizontal; Vertical; Vertical Spindle Milling) ....D

283—Marsh, H. C. (Mitreing) C

284—Palmer Co., H. H. (Clothes Washing) ....D

ILL.—St. Charles

285—Leader Fence Mach. Mfg. Co. (Fence)........C

286—Moline Malleable Iron Co. (Elevating; Conveying) ....A

ILL.—Sandwich

287—Estep & Dolan (Hand Bending).............F

IND.—Anderson

288—Amer. Bridge & Scraper Co. (Street Sweeping) D

289—Anderson Fdry. & Mach. Wks. (Brick; Supplies; Tin Plate) ....B

290—Hill Tool Co. (Key Seating) ....E

291—Woolley Fdry. & Mach. Co. (Gas; Gasoline)...B

292—Sandwich Mfg. Co. (Wood Sawing).........AA

ILL.—Streator

293—Iwan Bros. (Digging; Ditching) C

ILL.—Vandalia

294—Craycroft, Benj. (Brick; Brick Press; Supplies).D

295—Aurora Tool Wks. (Drilling; Tapping; Plain; Universal Milling) ....B
296—Stedman Fdry. & Mach. Wks. (Brick; Supplies; Grinding) ....B

IND.—Bluffton
297—Bluffton Mfg. Co. (Clothes Washing).........C

IND.—Columbus
298—Reeves & Co. (Threshing) ....AAAA

IND.—Connersville
299—Roots Co., P. H. & F. M. (Band Sawing; Elevating; Conveying; Pneumatic) ....AA

IND.—Crawfordsville
300—Lyle & Reynolds (Fence) ....E

IND.—Dana
301—Draper Mfg. & Gas Co. (Acetylene Gas).......F

IND.—Elkhart
302—Elkhart Frog & Crossing Wks. (Rail Bending; Straightening) C

IND.—Evansville
303—Bernardin Bottle Cap Co. (Bottlers' Supplies)..B
304—Heilman Mach. Wks. (Threshing) ....A

IND.—Fort Wayne
305—Horton Mfg. Co. (Clothes Washing) ....B
306—Indiana Road Mach. Co. (Street Railway Sweeping) ....A
307—Wayne Mfg. Co., Anthony (Clothes Washing).X

IND.—Frankfort
308—Wallace Mfg. Co. (Brick; Brick Press; Supplies) C

IND.—Fountain City
309—Hampton, O. H. (Acetylene Gas).............G

IND.—Indianapolis
310—Atkins & Co., E. C. (Barrel; Keg; Stave; Heading; Brazing; Band Saw; Coopers') ....AAAA
311—Capitol Mach. Wks. (Veneer Cutting)........D
312—Castle Ice Mach. Co. (Ice; Refrigerating)....X
313—Chandler & Taylor Co. (Saw Mill)..........AA
314—Commercial Electric Co. (Dynamo; Electric)..A
315—Electro Therapeutic Mfg. Co. (Static Electric).X
316—Embossing Art Die & Mach. Co. (Embossing)...D
317—Hall, Albert B. (Tablet) X
318—Hensley, Jas. W. (Brick Press) ....D
319—Hetherington & Berner (Asphalt)............A
320—Nordyke & Marmon Co. (Distillery; Grain Cleaning; Buckwheat; Flour; Oat Meal; Rice Mill; Packing; Brush; Scouring; Polishing; Separating Combined; Smut) ....AAA
321—Over, Ewald (Road Building) C
322—Poindexter Mfg. Co. (Corn Splitting).......X
323—Potter Mfg. Co., 2018 Northwestern Av. (Elevating; Conveying; Sewer; Trench Excavating)..B
324—Potts & Co., C. & A., 814 W. Washn. (Brick; Supplies) ....B
325—Rockwood Mfg. Co. (Brick; Flower Pot) .....A
326—Sinker-Davis Co., 230 So. Missouri (Edging Saw; Lumber Mill) ....B
327—Union Embossing Mach. Co. (Automatic Embossing; Wood Embossing; Drop Carving).......B

IND.—Kendallville
328—Flint & Walling Mfg. Co. (Well Sinking) ..AA

IND.—Kokomo
329—Kokomo Fence Mach. Co. (Woven Wire; Wire Fence) ....AAA

IND.—La Porte
330—Rumely Co., M. (Threshing) ....AAA

IND.—Mishawaka
331—Dodge Mfg. Co. (Cement; Grain Elevator)..AAA

IND.—Muncie
332—Kitselman Bros. (Woven Wire; Woven Wire Fence) ....A

IND.—New Albany
333—New Albany Mfg. Co. (Glass Works; Quarry; Stone Cutting; Stone Gang Sawing; Stone Planing) C

IND.—Princeton
334—Maddocks & Herschell (Automatic Hand; Power Flue Welding) ....H

IND.—Richmond
335—Elliott & Reid Co. (Fence) ....D
336—Eureka Fence Mfg. Co. (Fence) ....F
337—Gaar, Scott & Co. (Picket; Threshing)....AAAA
338—Henley, M. C. (Metal Boring; General).......A
339—Richmond City Mill Wks. (Flour Dressing; Flour Mill) ....B
340—Richmond Mach. Wks. (Brick; Tile; Supplies; Saw Mill) ....D
341—Robinson & Co. (Threshing) ....AA

IND.—Rushville
342—Madden & Co. (Brick; Tile)................D

IND.—South Bend
343—Studebaker Bros. Mfg. Co. (Street Sweeping) AAA

IND.—Terre Haute
344—Prox & Brinkham Mfg. Co. (Coal Mining)....A
IND.—Waveland
345—Johnson Acetylene Gas Co. (Acetylene Gas)..H
IND.—Winchester
346—Winchester Mach. Wks. (D Handle) X
IOWA—Atlantic
347—Diamond Lighting & Heating Co. (Acetylene Gas) ....F
IOWA—Burlington
348—Murray Iron Wks. (Brewers'; Fertilizer Factory; Refrigerating; Ice; Portable Ice; Saw Mill)......A
IOWA—Cresco
349—Cavard, R. S. (Grubbing) ....E
IOWA—Davenport
350—Brammer Mfg. Co., H. F. (Clothes Washing)..A
351—Davenport Fdry. & Mach. Co. (Macaroni; Saw Mill; Sugar; Rolling Mill; Brewery)............B
IOWA—Des Moines
352—Des Moines Mfg. & Supply Co. (Brick; Supplies; Elevating; Conveying) ....A
353—Dodd & Struthers (Static Electric) ....A
354—Eagle Iron Works (Coal Mining) ....B
355—Globe Machy. & Supply Co., 418 W. Court Av. (Brick; Supplies) ....B
IOWA—Dubuque
356—Adams Co. (Automatic; Multiple Sand Molding) ....A
357—Davis, Geo. E. (Key Seating; Wood Sawing; Splitting; Power Hammer; Shingle Sawing; Punching; Shearing) ....E

Our entire time, energy and money are devoted to the manufacture of special machines—no job work. A Shingle Sawing Machine; capacity 50,000 per day, also machines of less capacity. A Blacksmith Trip Hammer, 25-lb. and 50-lb. sizes; the heavier one strikes a 300-lb. blow, fast or slow, or as light as may be required. at any speed. A Hand Power Punch for metal. A $10,-00 shear; cuts iron or soft steel ⅜-in. thick. A $100,-000 shear; cuts ONE INCH thick. A Key Seating Machine for pulleys, gears, sprockets, balance wheels, etc., price $100.00

IOWA—Kensett
358—Locke Mfg. Co., C. E. (Adding)..............B
IOWA—Keokuk
359—Scott Mfg. Co. (Brick Press)................D
IOWA—Lone Tree
360—Monarch Grubber Mfg. Co. (Harvesting)......B
IOWA—Marshalltown
361—Fisher Governor Co. (Cross Head; Pin Turning; Tapping; Gas; Water Mains) ....D
362—Lennox Machine Co. (Tapping for Tapping Water Mains under pressure) ....B
IOWA—Mason City
363—Mason City Bedding Co. (Mattress Stuffing)..C
IOWA—Muscatine
364—Barry Mfg. Co. (Pearl Button) ....A
IOWA—Ottumwa
365—Ottumwa Iron Wks. (Coal; Quarry; Stone Hoisting; Steam Power Hoisting)...................AA
IOWA—Prairie City
366—Jenks & Son (Acetylene Gas)................D
IOWA—Waterloo
367—Eppworth Gas Light & Heating Co. (Acetylene Gas) ....F
368—Kelley & Taneyhill Co. (Prospecting)..........C
369—Swem Gas Machine Co. (Gasoline)..........D
KANS.—Enterprise
370—Ehrsam & Sons Mach. Co., J. B. (Cement)....C
KANS.—Fort Scott
371—Fort Scott Fdry. & Mach. Co. (Artesian Well; Cane Cutting; Shredding; Coal Washing; Friction Hoisting; Horse Power Hoisting; Oil Well; Stone Planing; Well Sinking; Salt Well) ....H
KANS.—Kansas City
372—Riverside Iron Wks. (Can Stuffing; Can Sealing; Can Capping; Beef; Pork Slicing; Hog Scraping; Ice; Refrigerating) ....A
KANS.—Leavenworth
373—Fisher Mach. Wks. Co. (Portable Cylinder for Re-Boring) C
374—Great Western Mfg. Co. (Cement; Grain Elevator; Buckwheat; Flour Mill; Wine Pumping)..AA
KANS.—Manhattan
375—Blue Valley Mfg. Co. (Well Sinking).......F
KY.—Bowling Green
376—Bowling Green Machine Co. (Axe Handle)....C
KY.—Covington
377—Hollingsworth, W. T. (Brick; Supplies).......F
KY.—Louisville
378—Brennan & Co. (Drilling; Corn Shelling)..

379—Daylight Acetylene Gas Co. (Acetylene Gas)...F
380—Drummond Mfg. Co. (Moulding) ....A
381—Howe Mfg. Co. (Tin Foil Bottle Capping).....A
382—Kentucky Gear & Mach. Co. (Gear Cutting)...E
383—Vogt Machine Co., Henry, 10th & Ormsby Av. (Ice; Refrigerating) ....AA
KY.—Newport
384—Crawley Book Machy. Co. (Bookbinders')......B
LA.—New Orleans
385—Coleman, H. Dudley (Fumigating, &c.)......X
386—Kracke & Flanders, 640 Gravier (Acetylene Gas) B
387—Whitney Iron Wks. Co. (Rice Milling) ......A
MAINE—Auburn
388—Victoria Mfg. Co. (Acetylene Gas) ....D
MAINE—Bangor
389—Bangor Fdry. & Mach. Co. (Clapboard).......X
390—Union Iron Wks. (Clapboard; Coal; Ore Handling; Hoisting; Loading; Unloading; Conveying; Cutting-Off; Wood; Edging Saw) ....A
MAINE—Belfast
391—Duplex Roller Bushing Co. (Barrel; Keg; Stave; Heading) ....E
MAINE—Brunswick
392—Brunswick Acetylene Gas Co. (Acetylene Gas).D
MAINE—Dexter
393—Fay & Scott (Milling; Shaping) C
MAINE—Lewiston
395—Goss Co., A. L. & E. F. (Acetylene Gas)......C
MAINE—Old Town
396—Chapman & Son Co., T. M. (Barrel; Keg; Stave; Heading; also Box Edging).....................D
MAINE—Portland
397—Conant Co., R. O. (Canning) ....F
398—Lang Co., E. M. (Can Makers'; Canning; Capping Irons; Soldering; Dies; Presses; Forming; Bending) C
399—Maine Electric Co. (Electric Coal; Ore Handling) D
400—Southorth Bros. (Round Cornering)...........B
401—Stickney Machine Co. (Canning; Cond. Milk Can Filling) ....E
MAINE—South Paris
402—Paris Mfg. Co. (Clothes Washing)............A
MAINE—Waterville
403—Webber & Philbrick (Wood Barking)..........B
MD.—Baltimore
404—Adt, John B. (Tobacco Cutting; Tobacco Drying; Tobacco Packing; Tobacco Vibrating)............A
405—Bartlett, Hayward & Co. (Beet Washing; Slicing) B
407—Brown, F. S. & G. L., 20 E. Fort Av. (Sheet Metal Workers'; also Tools) ....E
408—Burt Machine Co., 226 N. Holliday (Labeling).B
409—Crown Cork & Seal Co., 1511 Guilford Av. (Bottlers' Stoppers, &c.) ....AAA
410—Detrick & Harvey Mach. Co., 508 E. Preston (Bolt; Nut; Bolt Pointing; Bolt Threading; Horizontal Boring; Drilling; Countersinking; Drilling; Nut Facing; Automatic Nut Tapping; also Multiple Spindle Nut Tapping; Pipe Cutting; Threading; Plate Scarfing; Saw Filing; Slitting; Axle Bearing Boring; Car Box Boring; Radial Countersinking; Saw Setting; Filing) ....AA
411—Ellicott Machine Co. (Dredging; Hydraulic)....A
412—Hooper, F. X. (Wood Printing) X
413—Kemp Mfg. Co., C. M., 1501 Guilford Av. (Gas; Acetylene Gas) ....B
414—Lyon, Conklin & Co., 13 Balderston (Roofing).B
415—Murray & Son, James, 102 E. York (Clay Tempering) ....B
416—Poole Engineering & Machine Co., Woodbury Station (Brush; Stone Hoisting; Handling; Grain Elevator; Rolling Mill; Cable Railroad; Coffee; Fertilizer Factory; Flour Mill; Hydraulic Dredging; Rubber; Stone; Marble Working; Tin Plate; White Lead Works; Cloth Measuring; Tripping)......AA
417—Rosenberg Co., A. (Air Compressing; Exhausting) H
418—Schultz & Co., A. (Wire Solder) ....A
419—Sinclair-Scott Co., cor. Wells & Patapsco (Cane Seat Chair; Canning; Fruit Paring; Pineapple Paring; Coring; Sizing Combined; Peach Pitting)....E
420—Sloan & Co., Frank B. (Pulley Mortising).....D
421—Starr & Co., B. F., 455 North (Cement; Buhr Stones) ....D
422—Vaduer Mfg. Co. (Magneto) X
MASS.—Arlington Heights
423—Arlington Machine Co. (Bleaching; Calico Printing; Drying; Finishing)........................D
MASS.—Athol
424—Gay & Ward (Gear Cutting).................A

425—Gerry & Son, Geo. (Cloth Measuring; Napping) X

MASS.—Barre
426—Allen & Co., G. (Clothes Washing)............D
MASS.—Beverly
427—Naumkeag Buffing Mach. Assn. (Boot; Shoe)..B
MASS.—Boston
428—Agnew Auto-Mailing Mach. Co., 156 Pearl (Addressing; Mailing) ....B
429—Amer. Moistening Co., Equitable Bldg. (Dampening) ....B
430—Amer. Tool & Mach. Co. (Leather Wkg.; Splitting; Belt Knife Leather Splitting; Valve Seat-Milling; Centrifugal) ....AA
431—Ames Plow Co. (Coopers') ....AA
432—Austin & Eddy, 177 Broad (Dado; Molding Sander; Pulley Mortising) C
434—Blake Mfg. Co., Geo. F. (Br. International Steam Pump Co., N. Y. City) (Water Works Pumping) ....AAAA
435—Blue Seal Supply Co., 12 Portland (Bottlers'; Supplies) C
436—Boston Bottle Wiring & Labeling Co., 404 Atlantic Av. (Bottle Labeling) ....E
437—Bottlers' Machinery Co. (Bottle Labeling).....D
438—Brooks & Co., E. D. (Leather Splitting)......A
439—Boston Bottle Wiring & Labeling Co., Franklin (Bottlers'; Supplies) ....E
440—Bradley Pulverizer Co., 92 State (Cement)....X
441—Brooks & Co., E. D. (Leather Working; Splitting) ....A
442—Buzzel & Co., Jno. G. (Boot; Shoe) ....E
443—Campbell-Bosworth Machy. Co. (Boot; Shoe)..A
444—Carson Trench Machine Co. (Hoisting; Conveying for Trench Work; Sewer; Trench Excavating) ....B

445—Champion Buttonhole Machine Co., 10 High (Buttonhole) X

Our Buttonhole Machine is fitly named the "Champion." It far outclasses every other Machine ever designed for this work.
The Champion makes a perfect Double-faced, Double-purl Buttonhole with Interlocking Stitch and Different Color on either side if desired, which looks better and wears longer than hand-made holes.
It is adapted to all classes of work, in woolen or cotton goods.
It makes a hole in any size from an eyelet to an inch and five-eighths.
It is adapted to steam, electricity or foot power.
Price $200 cash, without rental or royalty, F. O. B., Boston.

446—Chandler & Farquhar Co., 36 Federal (Wire Straightening; Cutting) ....B
447—Clark & Mills Electric Co., 543 Boylston (Abrading for Testing Road Making Materials; Cement Testing; also for Testing Stone; Road Materials; Automatic Sifting; for Separating Dust from Broken Stone; Sifting) ....D
448—Coffin Valve Co. (Drilling; Pipe; Facing Pipe) ....D
449—Duplesis Shoe Machy. Co. (Boot; Shoe Pegging) ....A

450—Edson Mfg. Co., 257 Atlantic Av. (Bottlers'; Supplies; Automatic Bottle Filling; Bottling; Corking; Filling) ....B
451—Elliott Add. Mach. Co., 98 Purchase (Addressing) C
452—Elliott Co., 100 Purchase (Card Index Mailing; Addressing) C
453—Empire Laundry Machinery Co. Clothes Washing; (Bleaching; Starching) C
454—Faneuil Watch Tool Co. (Toolmakers'; Bench Hand Milling) ....B
456—Fifield Shoe Machy. Co. (Sewing; Boot; Shoe; Heel; Edge Trimming; Rolling; Sandpaper; Shoe Moulding) ....D
457—Firth Co., Wm., 150 Devonshire (Yarn Testing) ....B
458—Globe Buffer Co. (Boot; Shoe; Buffing)....AA
459—Ham & Co., L. M. (Sawing) ....B
460—Hansen, H. C. (Curving. &c.) ....B
461—Hartford Bros. (Boot; Shoe Pattern) ....E
462—Harvey, H. H. (Pointing; Stone Carvers')....D
463—Hersey Mfg. Co. (Friction Hoisting; Soap; Sugar Malting) ....AAA
464—Hill, Clarke & Co., 156 Oliver (Key-Way; Stone Planing) ....A
465—Holmes Machine Co., Chas., 299 Marginal (Belt Stretching; Leather Scouring; Curriers').......D
467—Knott Apparatus Co.. L. E., 12 Ashburton Pl.

(Static Electric) C

468—Lapointe Machine & Tool Co., 36 Hartford (Key-Seating) ....D

469—Lufkin, Jno. W., 38 Chardon (Buttonhole; Iron-ing) ....A

470—Lufkin, R. H. (Boot; Shoe; Vamp Folding)....C

471—Marston & Co., J. M. (Foot Power; Rip Saw; Cut-Off Saw; Circular Saw Hand Power; Hand Cutting-Off Wood) ....D

472—Morley Button Sewing Mach. Co., 68 Essex (Button Sewing; Sewing; Automatic Thread Cut-Off for Bars; Tacks in Shoes; Clothing) ....A

473—Nutter-Barnes & Co. (Cold Metal Cutting-Off; Metal Sawing) ....D

474—Peerless Machy. Co. (Boot; Shoe) C

475—Puritan Mfg. Co. (Harness; Boot; Shoe; Sewing; Wax Thread; Stitching Horse Brush) ....D

476—Reece Button Hole Mach. Co. (Boot; Shoe; But-tonhole) ....AAA

477—Riley & Co., C. E., 65 Franklin (Balling; Break-ing Hard Water; Cotton Waste; Dyeing Skein; Engine Cleaning Waste; Wool Scouring; Wool Wil-lowing) ....A

478—Ringset Co., 8 Waltham (Ring-making; Jewelers') X

479—Seelye Mfg. Co., 118 South (Boot; Shoe; Sand Papering; Cloth Cutting; Leather Splitting; Rolling; Shoe Moulding; Shoe Splitting; Stripping).......C

480—Shawmut Machy. Co. (Boot; Shoe)..........E

481—Sherburne & Co. (Valve Setting; Locomotive).A

482—Spaulding Print Paper Co. (Continuous Blue Print) ....E

483—Spaulding Sons & Co. (Boot; Shoe)..........B

484—Standard Shoe Tying Machine Co. (Boot; Shoe Tying) ....E

485—Standard Rivet Co. (Spot Setting; Riveting; Stapling) ....A

486—Steam Heated Horn Co. (Boot; Shoe) ....E

487—Stanley Mfg. Co. (Shoe Sewing; Leather Split-ting; Seam Rubbing) ....B

488—Steel Cable Engineering Co., 92 State (Coal; Ore; Ash Handling; Elevating; Conveying) X

489—Stoddard, Haserick, Richards & Co., 152 Con-gress (Carpet; Tentering; Wool; Worsted Finishing) ....B

490—Sturtevant Mill Co., B. F., Harrison Sq. (Cement; Air Moving; Crushing; Grinding; Screening)....AA

491—Swett & Lewis Co., 657 Washn. (Static Electric) ....E

492—Tubular Rivet & Stud Co. (Hook Setting Rivet; Tubular) ....AAA

493—Turner Tannery Machy. Co. (Tanners')......AAA

494—Union Button Sewing Mach. Co., 164 High (Sew-ing; Strapping) ....E

495—Union Edge Setter Co. (Boot; Shoe) ....D

496—United Shoe Machy. Co. (Boot; Shoe; Seam Rubbing; Waukenphast Imitation)...............AAAA

497—Walworth Mfg. Co., 132 Federal (Gas; Pipe Cut-ting; Threading; Tapping; Gas; Water Mains) AAAA

498—Ward Sons, Edgar T., 23 Purchase (Sand Blast) ....B

499—Whitcher & Co., Frank W. (Leather Stitching).A

500—Woods Machine Co., S. A., South Boston Dist. (Boxmakers'; Clapboard; Cutting-Off Wood; Wood Boring; Car Builders'; Rip Saw; Wood Flooring; Sawing; Planing Mill; Band Sawing; Automatic Railway Cut-Off; Iron Sawing; Wood Moulding; Hollow Chisel Wood Mortising; Circular Re-Sawing; Cross-Cut Saw; Cut-Off Saw; Tenoning) ......AA

MASS.—Bridgewater

501—Miller, H. J .(Wire Nail) ....D

502—Miller's Sons, H. J. (Nail Barbing; Wire Nail Barbing) ....D

503—Perkins Co., Henry (Die Making) ....B

MASS.—Brockton

504—Burr & Smith (Boot; Shoe) ....F

505—Kimball Bros. & Sprague (Nail Mill; Wire Nail; Slitting; Shoe Box Toe; Tack; Last Turning)....B

506—Miller, O. A. (Treeing) X

507—Sweeteer, Wm. A. (Nail Mill; Wire Nail; Staple; Shoe Shank; Tack) X

MASS.—Cambridgeport

508—Barbour-Stockwell Co. (Confectioners')........A

MASS.—Cambridge

509—Rawson & Morrison Mfg. Co. (Coal; Ore Hand-ling; Elevating; Conveying) ....B

MASS.—Charlestown

510—Carson Trench Machine Co., 16 Dorrance (Ele-vating; Conveying) C

MASS.—Chelsea

511—Hecla Compressed Gas Co. (Carbonating).......E

512—Lovewell & Co., S. K. (Cordage) ....D

513—Lovewell-Herici Co. (Flooring) X

MASS.—Chicopee
514—Ames Foundries (Hand Milling) ....E
MASS.—Chicopee Falls
515—Belcher & Taylor Agrl. Tool Co. (Tobacco Hoeing) ....A
516—Lamb Knitting Machine Co. (Knitting Cardigan Jacket; Hosiery Knitting; Seaming) ....B
MASS.—East Boston
517—Lockwood Mfg. Co. (Inc.), 61 Sumner (Cordage; Binder wine; Rope) ....H
MASS.—East Bridgewater
518—Carver Cotton Gin Co. (Oil Mill) ....A
MASS.—Fall River
519—Kilburn, Lincoln & Co. (Inc.) (Cloth Calendaring) A
MASS.—Fiskdale
520—Snell Mfg. Co. (Vertical Boring) ....B
MASS.—Fitchburg
521—Brown Bag Filling Mach. Co. (Bag Filling) ..E
522—Cowdrey Machine Wks., C. H. (Rod; Pin; Dowel; Wood Boring) ....D
523—Fitchburg Machine Wks. (Boiler Shop; Metal Boring; Horizontal Metal Boring; Countersinking; Drilling; Metal Cutting-Off; Horizontal Boring; Drilling; Shaft, &c., Straightening; Shaping; Wood Boring; Railroad Shop) ....B
524—Putnam Machine Co. (Bolt Heading; Horizontal Boring; Drilling; Car Wheel Boring; Cold Metal Cutting-Off; Involute; Epicycloidal Gear Cutting; Metal Boring; Horizontal Metal Boring; Milling; Nut Tapping; Shaft Straightening; Shafting; Slotting; Lead Rolling; Link Drilling; Slotting; Paring)....A
525—Union Machine Co. (Cylinder) ....B
MASS.—Florence
526—Norwood Engineering Co. (Paper Finishing; Cutlery; Basket; Breaker; Friction; Web, &c.).......B
MASS.—Gardner
527—Bancroft, Frank H. (Wood Bending).........E
MASS.—Greenfield
528—Automatic Machine Co. (Automatic Screw)....C
529—Horton, James A. (Mailing) ....E
530—Wells Bros. Co. (Bolt; Nut; Grinding; Bolt Heading; Bolt Threading; Screw Cutting) ....A
531—Wiley & Russell Mfg. Co. (Bolt; Nut; Bending; Bolt Heading for Shoeing; Bolt Threading; Drilling; Screw Cutting; Horse Shoe) ....AA
MASS.—Harvard
532—Hildreth Bros. (Wood Sawing; Splitting)......B
MASS.—Haverhill
533—Allen Mach. Co. (Boot; Shoe) ....E
534—Bussfield, Jas. (Boot; Shoe) ....E
MASS.—Holyoke
535—Deane Steam Pump Co. (Br. International Steam Pump Co., N. Y. City) (Water Works; Wine Pumping) ....AAAA
536—Holyoke Machine Co. (Bleaching; Blacking; Dyeing; Breaker; Friction; Web. &c., Calendering; Cloth Finishing; Wood Barking; Wool; Worsted Finishing; Cotton Finishing; Cylinder) ....AA
537—Koegel & Son, Chas. (Coating Mill) ....E
538—Perkins & Son, B. F. (Power Testing)........A
MASS.—Hopedale
539—Draper & Co. (Cotton) ....AAAA
MASS.—Hyde Park
540—Becker-Brainard Milling Machine Co. (Automatic Gear Cutting; Horizontal; Plain; Vertical; Universal Milling) ....AA
541—Robinson & Co., Jno. T. (Bookbinders'; Card Cutting; Paper Box) ....B
MASS.—Lawrence
542—Horne & Sons Co., J. H. (Paper Making Cylinder) A
MASS.—Leeds
543—Northampton Emery Wheel Co. (Belt Strapping; Buffing; Polishing; Lapping) ....A
MASS.—Leominster
544—Cook & Co., F. H. (Comb) ....E
MASS.—Lowell
545—Carey, W. W. (Variety Molding; Wood Boring).B
546—Entwistle Co., T. C. (Balling; Card Grinding; Cotton Mill) ....B
547—Kitson Machine Co. (Blacking; Cotton; Wool Washing) ....AAAA
548—Lowell Machine Co. (Cotton) ....AAAA
549—Lowell Machine Shop (Card Cutting; Card Grinding; Cloth Folding; Cloth Stamping; Slubbing; Cloth Calendering; Threshing) ....AAAA
550—Turner, Jno. D. (Rail Bending; Straightening).D
MASS.—Lynn
551—Beaudry Edge Setting & Steel Burnishing Mach. Co. Boot; Shoe).................................E
552—Cole & Co., G. A. (Boot; Shoe) ....F
553—Embree & Co., W. F. (Boot; Shoe) ....E

554—Emerson & Co., Geo. W. (Boot; Shoe).........D
555—Glazier & Briggs (Box) ....D
556—Hemingway, Jno. (Boxmakers' Sizing, &c., Wood Sawing; Splitting) ....D
557—Hemingway Machy. Co., A. C. (Leather Working; Unhairing Machines) ....D
558—Hemingway Machine Co. (Burring)..........D
559—Hoyt Bros. & Co. (Bottle Washers, &c.).....A
560—Phinney, W. B. (Acetylene Gas) C
561—Stewart Bros. (Boot; Shoe Counter Moulding).E
562—Tripp Giant Leveler Co. (Boot; Shoe Leveling).C
563—Young, W. J. (Boot; Shoe Counter Moulding).E

MASS.—Malden
564—Greene, F. P. (Brick Press) ....E

MASS.—Medford
565—Wellman Sole Cutting Machine Co. (Boot; Shoe Rubber; Leather Staking; Wooden Last Trimming).C

MASS.—Miller's Falls
566—Miller's Falls Co. (Wood Boring) ....AA

MASS.—Neponset
567—Coffin Valve Co. (Hydraulic) ....B

MASS.—New Bedford
568—New England Acetylene Mfg. Co. (Acetylene Gas) X
569—Tripp, Frank S. (Boot; Shoe) ....F

MASS.—Newton Upper Falls
570—Saco & Pettee Machine Shops (Cotton; Slubbing Testing; Roving; Yarn) ....AAA

MASS.—North Adams
571—Hunter Machine Co., James (Crabbing; Steaming; Wool Scouring) ....A

MASS.—No. Andover Depot
572—Davis & Furber Machine Co. (Woolen) ......AA

MASS.—Northampton
573—Herick, Chas. E. (Gear Cutting)..............D

MASS.—North Andover
574—Davis & Furber Machine Co. (Napping)......AA

MASS.—Orange
575—Chase Turbine Mfg. Co. (Box; Drag Saw; Cut-Off Saw; Shingle) ....A
576—Hunt Machine Co., Rodney (Woolen; Soaping; Dyeing; Bleaching) ....A
577—Leavitt Machine Co. (Valve Re-Seating) ......D
578—New Home Sewing Machine Co. (Sewing; Sewing Fancy Stitch; Sewing Hand; Sewing Lock Stitch)
AAAA

MASS.—Peabody
579—Boyle Co., John (Leather Working).........F
580—Boyle Machine Co., Jno. (Glue Spreading)....D
581—Vaughn Machine Co. (Tanners').............A

MASS.—Salem
582—Broadley, J. S. (Tanners' Pebble Roll Cutter)..E
583—Dinsmore Mfg. Co. (Sewing) ....E

MASS.—Somerville
584—Birch Bros. (Bleaching; Cloth Finishing; Crabbing; Dampening; Mercerizing; Napping; Sewing; Soaping; Steaming; Tentering) C

MASS.—South Boston
585—Hersey Mfg. Co. (Hoisting; Brewers'; Malt House; Soap; Sugar) ....AA

MASS.—Southbridge
586—Amer. Optical Co. (Optical) ....AAAA

MASS.—South Sudbury
587—Hurlbut, Rogers Mach. Co. (Centering; Cold Metal Cutting-Off; Cutting-Off Wood) C
588—Baush Machine Tool Co. (Countersinking; Drilling; Drilling; Tapping Combined).................A

MASS.—Springfield
589—Bullock Mfg. Co. (Drilling Jewelers'; Moulding; Shaving) ....A
590—Ford, H., 964 Main (Brick Press; Supplies)....D
591—Hopkins Son Machine Wks., 123 Taylor (Envelope) ....F
592—Piper, E. J. (Ruling) ....D
593—Russell, Jno. W. (Button Sewing) ....D
594—Smith Mfg. Co., R. H., 293 Main (Automatic Numbering) C
595—Waltham Watch Tool Co. (Milling; Watch Case) B

MASS.—Taunton
596—Mason Machine Wks. (Cotton; Card Cutting; Card Grinding; Cotton Lap) ....AA
597—Strange's Machine Wks. (Barrel; Keg; Stave; Hoisting; Boxmakers') ....E
598—Taunton Locomotive Mfg. Co. (Street Railway Sweeping) ....A

MASS.—Walpole
599—Fales, L. F. (Sewing) ....E

MASS.—Waltham
600—Davis & Farnum Mfg. Co. (Inc.) (Hydraulic).B

MASS.—Westboro
601—Macker & Co., Geo. A. (Leather Splitting for Bag; Lint Case, &c., Mfrs.) X

MASS.—Westford

602—Sargents' Sons, C. G. (Burring; Wool Washing)
....A

MASS.—Winchendon

603—Goodspeed Machine Co. (Tub; Pail; Chair; Spool;
Bobbin; Barrel; Churn, &c., Stave Sawing; Keg; Rod;
Pin; Dowel; Heading; Coopers')................E

604—Whitney & Son, Baxter D. (Stave Sawing;
Chair; Coopers') ....AA

MASS.—Winchester

605—Whitney Machine Co. (Leather Working; Unhairing; Fleshing) ....D

MASS.—Whitinsville

606—Whitin Machine Wks. (Slubbing; Cotton).AAAA

MASS.—Williamstown

607—Amer. Napping Machine Co. (Napping)........X

MASS.—Woburn

608—Freeman && Co., J. T. (Leather Glazing; Leather
Polishing; Leather Whitening; Buffing; Leather Staking) ....D

609—Smith & Wallace (Electric Street Railway Sweeping) ....D

MASS.—Worcester

610—Amer. Card Clothing Co. (Woolen) ....AAA

611—Barr, H. G. (Automatic Pin for Straight; Shoulder
Pins) ....D

612—Blaisdell & Co., P. (Horizontal Boring; Drilling;
Gear Cutting; Metal Boring; Horizontal Metal Boring) ....A

613—Boynton & Plummer (Bolt Heading; Upright;
Horizontal Hand Power Self Feeding Drilling; Hand;
Power Shaping) ....B

614—Burlingame Co., A .(Wood Sawing; Splitting)..D

615—Cleveland Machine Wks. (Woolen; Whipping;
Banding; Card Cutting; Chinchilla; Cloth Brushing;
Cloth Finishing; Cloth Rolling; Cloth Winding;
Worm, &c., Milling; Napping; Tentering; Wool;
Worsted Finishing; Wool Willowing; Cotton Finishing;
Gigging) ....A

616—Coes & Co., Loring (Paper Making)..........A

617—Crompton & Knowles Loom Wks. (Carpet; Silk;
Carpet Finishing; Key Seating; Repeating; Wire
Weaving) ....AAAA

618—Cunningham, E. E. (Brazing; Band Saw; Saw
Filing; Slitting) ....H

619—Curtis & Marble Machine Co. (Carpet; Woolen;
Breaking Hard Waste; Burring; Carpet Finishing;
Carpet Rolling; Cloth Brushing; Cloth Finishing;
Cloth Inspecting; Cloth Measuring; Cloth Rolling;
Cloth Winding; Folding; Measuring; Napping; Sand-
ing; Railroad Sewing; Textile Shearing; Singeing;
Steaming; Wool; Worsted Finishing; Wool Scouring;
Cloth Calendering; Cotton Finishing; Gigging).....A

620—Draper Machine Tool Co. (Cotton; Boring; Drilling; Horizontal Boring; Drilling; Metal Boring; Horizontal Metal Boring; Screw) ....B

621—Economic Machy. Co. (Bottle Labeling) X

622—Elliott & Hall (Cloth Folding; Cloth Measuring;
Folding; Measuring; Silk Folding; Measuring)....C

623—Gessner, David (Cloth Finishing; Napping).....D

624—Heald Machine Co. (Crimping; Bending; Dado;
Sash Trimmer; Grinding) ....B

625—Hobbs Mfg. Co. (Paper Box) ....A

626—Jacques & Son, Jno. (Card Cutting)..........D

627—Johnson & Prentice (Metal Cutting-Off).......D

628—Kidder, R. E. (Hand Shearing; Wood Sawing;
Splitting; Wood Working) ....E

629—Luther & Co., B. G., 91 Forster (Wood Boxmakers'
Double Cutting-Off; Wood) ....E

630—Morgan Construction Co. (Galvanizing; Gas Plant;
Rod Mill; Rolling Mill; Steel; Wire Testing; Wire
Pointing) ....A

631—Pond Machine & Fdry. Co., L. W. (Metal Planer)
....X

632—Prentice Bros. Co. (Car Wheel Boring; Cylinder
Boring; Metal Boring; Vertical Metal Boring; Tapping) ....A

633—Reed Co. Francis (Hand; Power Drilling)......D

634—Rice, Barton & Fales Mach. & Iron Co. (Calendering; Cloth Printing; Paper) ....AA

635—Roy & Son, B. S. (Card Grinding)............B

636—Union Machine Co. (Glossing)...............X

637—Whitcomb Mfg. Co. (Rolling Mill; Rail Punching;
Metal Planing) ....B

638—Windle, J. E. (Cloth Finishing; Cloth Folding;
Cloth Measuring) ....E

MICH.—Adrian

639—Adrian Brick & Tile Mach. Co. (Brick; Supplies)
....C

640—Kells Fdry. & Mach. Co. (Brick; Tile Auger)..D

MICH.—Alpena

641—Kline, Lewis T. (Pail Handle) ....D

MICH.—Battle Creek
642—Advance Thresher Co. (Bagging; Threshing)..
AAAA
643—Amer. Steam Pump Co. (Circular Sawing Wood; Dovetailing; Rosette; Corner Block; Wood Carving; Wood Moulding) ....AAA
644—Nichols & Shepard Co. (Threshing) ......AAAA
MICH.—Bay City
645—Garland Co., M. (Self Feeding Band Sawing; Rip Saw; Lath; Barrel; Keg; Stave; Heading; Box Board; Coopers') C
646—Industrial Wks. (Rail Bending; Straightening; Hydraulic; Rail Cutting Hydraulic; Iron Shop Sawing; Hydraulic) ....AA
MICH.—Blissfield
647—Davenport, Harry (Metal Cutting-Off)........F
MICH.—Detroit
648—Amer. Blower Co. (Brick Dryers; Air Moving).
AA
649—Anderson & Sons, W. H. (Concrete Mixing; Cement; Rail Bending; Straightening) C
650—Behr Bros. (Boot; Shoe) ....D
651—Briscoe Mfg. Co., 1427 Woodward Av. (Acetylene Gas) ....A
652—Buhl Malleable Co., Wight & Adair (Coal; Ore; Elevating; Conveying) ....A
653—Clayton & Lambert Mfg. Co. (Acetylene Gas)..B
654—Colton, Arthur, 184 Brush (Capsule; Gelatine Coating; Granulating; Gelatine Pill Coating; Autotmatic Pill Making; Cold Compressed Suppository; Tablet) C
655—Detroit Auto. Sterilizer Co. (Bottle Soaking)..X
656—Detroit Heating & Lighting Co., 335 Wight (Gas)
B
657—Fulton Iron & Engine Wks. (Bending) X
658—Huetteman & Cramer Co., Mack Av. & M. C. R. R. Belt Line (Brick; Supplies; Ice; Refrigerating; Brewers'; Brewers' Mashing; Barley; Malt Cleaning; Pitching) ....B
659—Leland & Faulconer Mfg. Co., 480 Trombly Av. (Gear Cutting; Gear Generating; Wood Trimming)
A
660—Michels & Co., James (Barrel Hoop; Stave; Heading) ....E
661—Star Corundum Wheel Co. (Ltd.) (Buffing; Polishing; Grinding) C
662—Superior Fence Machine Co. (Fence) ....F
MICH.—Grand Haven
663—Challenge Machy. Co. (Paper Cutting) ....A
MICH.—Grand Rapids
664—Oliver Machy. Co. (Band Sawing; Bolt Heading; Bolt Threading; Bolt Upsetting; Forging; Nut Tapping; Wood Trimming; Upsetting) ....B
665—Austin & Son (Box Board; also Heading)......B
666—Baldwin, Tuthill & Bolton (Brazing; Band Saw; Saw Sharpening; Saw Fitting) ....B
667—Butterworth & Lowe (Clapboard; Lath; Shingle)
A
668—Fox Machine Co., 127 N. Front (Vertical Hand Milling; Metal Boring; Light Milling; Mitreing; Pipe Cutting; Post Boring; Shaping; Wood Trimming) ....A
669—Owens, Geo. F., 71 N. Market (Acetylene Gas)..E
670—Perkins & Co. (Shingle; Barrel; Heading; Box Board; Lumber Mill) ....A
671—Porter, C. O. & A. D. (Wood Shaping; Spindle Carving; Wood Carving) C
672—Vandeweld Mach. Wks. (Brush Mfrs.; Voting).H
MICH.—Hancock
673—Portage Lake Fdry. & Machy. Co. (Copper Working) ....B
MICH.—Holly
674—Cyclone Woven Wire Fence Co. (Chain Fence).C
MICH.—Hudson
675—Abbott Voting Machine Co. (Voting)..........B
676—Hook-Hardie Co. (Pneumatic Paint Spraying)..D
MICH.—Jackson
677—Coltrin Mfg. Co. (Cement Moulding).........D
678—Dennis Machine Co. (Wood Boring; Wood Surfacing) ....D
679—Walcott & Son, Geo. D. (Gear Cutting; Geared; Crank Shaping) C
MICH.—Kalamazoo
680—Hill & Co., Wm. E. (Lumber Mill) ....B
681—Kalamazoo Railway Supply Co. (Rail Bending; Straightening; Pumping) ....B
682—Kalamazoo Tubular Well Co. (Well Sinking)..D
MICH.—Lansing
683—Lansing Wheel Barrow Co. (Fence) ....AAA
MICH.—Manistee
684—Brady Cooperage Machy. Co. (Barrel Heading).X
685—Manistee Iron Wks. (Saw Mill) ....,....B

MICH.—Menominee
686—Henes & Keller Co. (Automatic Bottle Filling)..A
MICH.—Monroe
687—Monroe Fdry. & Furnace Co. (Acetylene Gas)..B
MICH.—Montague
688—Montague Iron Wks. Co. (Boxmakers')........B
MICH.—Morenci
689—Michigan Brick & Tile Mach. Co. (Brick; Supplies; Clay Working; Brick Repress; Tile; Hollow Block; Shingle) ....D
MICH.—Mt. Clemens
690—Charbeneau & Son, J. C. (Acetylene Gas)......D
MICH.—Northville
691—Phillips & Co., Wm. (Laundry) ....F
MICH.—Pontiac
692—Bacon Mfg. Co. (Green Pea Picking; Cranberry; Bean; Seed Sorting) ....F
693—Gem Wire Fence Co. (Fence) ....D
MICH.—Port Huron
694—Draper Mfg. Co. (Milling; Valve) ....D
695—Port Huron Engine & Thresher Co. (Wood Sawing; Splitting; Threshing) ....AAA
MICH.—Saginaw
696—Bartlett & Co., A. F. (Hoop; Barrel; Keg; Stave; Heading; Cement; Coal Mining) ....A
697—Mershon & Co., W. B. (Band Sawing).......A
698—Mitts & Merrill (Key-Seating; Lapping for Band Saws; Key-Seat Milling; Key Making)............B
699—Wickes Bros. (Bag Making; Barrel; Keg; Stave; Heading; Boxmakers'; Elevating; Conveying; Band Sawing; also Re-Sawing; Plate Bending; Cutting-Off Wood; Edging Saw; Heavy Milling; Boilermakers' Punching; Riveting; Portable Hydraulic Riveting; Portable Riveting) ....AA
MICH.—Rochester
700—Miller Bros. (Bean; Seed Sorting)............H
MICH.—St. Joseph
701—St. Joseph Iron Wks. (Veneer Lathes Cutting; Basket; Crate; Fruit Package) ....B
702—Saranac Machine Co. (Fruit Packing; Basket; Butter Dish Stapling) C
MICH.—Tecumseh
703—Brewer & Co., H. (Clay Working)............C
MICH.—Vicksburg
704—Dentler Bagger Co. (Bag Filling) ....E
MINN.—Albert Lea
705—Edwards, C. D. (Ditch) ....D
MINN—Minneapolis
706—Crown Iron Wks. Co. (Saw Sharpening).......B
707—Diamond Iron Wks. (Saw Mill; Grain Elevator; Coal Hoisting; Handling) ....B
708—Howell & Co., R. R. (Artesian Well; Threshing; Well Sinking) ....B
709—Kilgore-Peteler Co. (Ditching) ....A
710—Minneapolis Bedding Co. (Wire Weaving)......A
711—Minneapolis Electric & Construction Co. (Wire Measuring) ....F
712—Minneapolis Threshing Mach. Co. (Threshing) AAAA
713—Minneapolis Steel & Machy. Co. (Elevating; Conveying) ....A
714—Moore Carving Machine Co., 1919 Portland Av. (Carriage Builders'; Sandpapering; Wood Carving; Wood Rubbing) ....
715—Rapid Computer Co., Andrus Bldg. (Adding)..X
716—Willford Mfg. Co. (Flour Mill)...............C
MINN.—St. Cloud
717—St. Cloud Iron Wks. (Granite Column Cutting).B
MINN.—St. Paul
718—Brownson & Co., B. (Harness)...............B
719—Dovetail Box Mach. Co. (Dovetail Box) ......D
MISS.—Corinth
720—Adams Mach. Co., W. T. (Saw Mill; Cotton Gin; Cutting-Off Wood; Wood Trimming; Shingle)..AA
MO.—Kansas City
721—Mathews, Hugh (Portable Cylinder Boring; Bars) B
722—Smith & Sons Mfg. Co., Lydia & Guinotte Av. (Ditching) ....AA
MO.—St. Joseph
723—Missouri Anchor Fence Co. (Fence) ....D
724—St. Joseph Pump & Mfg. Co. (Pumping)......B
MO.—St. Louis
725—Barry-Wehmiller Machy. Co. (Bottle Soaking; Grain Elevator; Brewers'; Coffee; Malt House; Flour Mill; Pasturizing) C
726—Benbow-Brammer Mfg. Co. (Clothes Washing).B
727—Bradley Stencil Machine Co. (Stencil Cutting).B
728—Brecht Butchers' Supply Co., Gus V. (Butchers') A
729—Cahill, Swift Co. (Air Moving)...............A
730—Curtis & Co. Mfg. Co., 2201 Washn. Av. (Barrel; Keg; Stave; Heading; Carriage Builders'; Shingle Sawing; Saw Mill; Felly) ....A

731—Eagle Generator Co., 16th & Pine (Automatic Acetylene Gas) ....A

732—Elite Gas Generator Co., 8 N. 16th (Acetylene Gas) ....F

733—Ellison & Sons Mfg. Co., Wm. (Coal Mining)..B

734—Fernholtz Brick Machy. Co., Boyle & Old Mass. Avs. (Brick; Supplies; Brick Press)............B

735—Fritsch Fdry. & Mach. Co., Arthur (Glass Works) ....B

736—Fritz, Geo. J. (Brewers'; Bottlers'; Coopers')..C

737—Gohlke, Theo., 12th & Locust (Double Seaming; Sheet Metal Workers'; also Tools)................X

738—Hall & Brown Woodworking Machy. Co (Box Board Matching; Wood Surfacing; Band Sawing; Wood Flooring; Wood moulding) ....A

739—Ice & Cold Mach. Co., 912 N. Main (Ice; Refrigerating) ....AA

740—Illinois Supply & Construction Co., 311 N. 9th (Brick; Supplies) ....E

741—Inland Type Fdry. (Electrotypers'; Photo-Engravers'; Stereotypers') ....A

742—Kingsland-Hay-Cook Mfg. Co., B'way & 2nd (Elevating; Conveying) ....D

743—Kingsland Mfg. Co. (Threshing; Saw Mills)..B

744—Landis Mach. Co. (Leather Stitching) ......AA

745—Leschen & Sons Rope Co., A., 920 N. 1st (Coal Mining; Ditching Railroad; Coal; Ore Handling; Elevating; Conveying) ....AAA

746—Maynard, J. F., 320 S. 3d (Ice; Refrigerating; for Brewers; Packers; Confectioners; Dairies)..E

747—Model Bottling Machy. Co. (Bottlers' Pasteurizing; Soaking) ....E

748—Philper, H. H., 2620 S. 13th (Ice; Refrigerating) X

749—Progress Press Brick & Mach. Co., S. Kings Highway & Oak Hill R. R. (Brick; Supplies; Brick Grindering; Mitering; Brick Press)..............B

750—Ross-Keller Triple Pressure Brick Mach. Co., Fullerton Bldg. (Brick; Supplies; Dry; Semi-dry Brick Press) ....D

751—Ruemmell-Dawley Mfg. Co., 3900 Chouteau Av. (Ice; Refrigerating) ....AA

752—St. Louis Iron & Machine Co. (Water Works; Pumping; Glass Works) ....A

753—St. Louis Machine & Tool Co., 1114 S. 8th (Grinding; Emery Grinding; Drilling) X

754—St. Louis Well Machine & Tool Co. (Oil Well; Well Sinking) C

755—Scott Mfg. Co., Commonwealth Trust Bldg. (Brick Pulverizer; Molds, etc.) ....D

756—Standard Adding Mach. Co. (Adding) ....A

757—Standard Railway Equipment Co. (Pneumatic Riveting; Pneumatic Wood Boring) ....G

758—Swaine Co., F. T. (Can Makers'; Crimping; Beading; Double Seaming; Can Body Forming; Bending; Sheet Metal Workers'; Tools; Swaging)..B

759—Welch, Robert (Stave Jointer) ....D

760—Whitman Agricultural Co., 6900 S. B'way (Sawing Headers, etc.) ....AA

761—Yerkes Finan Wood Working Mach. Co. (Wood Printing; Band Sawing; Molding Sander; Wood Molding) ....B

762—Zelnicker Supply Co., Walter A., 408 N. 4th (Portable Key-Seating; Rail Bending; Straightening) X

NEBR.—Beatrice

763—Dempster Mill Mfg. Co. (Well Sinking) .....AA

NEBR.—Omaha

764—Monarch Gas Co., 1012 Farnam (Acetylene Gas) C

N. H.—Antrim

765—Goodell Co. (Paring Fruit; Seed Sowing) ....A

N. H. Claremont

766—Sullivan Machy Co. (Coal; Quarry) ......AAAA

N. H.—Concord

767—Abbott-Downing Co. (Street Cleaning; Street Sweeping) X

N. H.—Derry

768—Angell, E. R. (Acetylene Gas) X

N. H.—Dover

769—Flagg & Son, J. C. (Leather Splitting) ....F

770—Kidder Press Co. (Paper Slitting; Rotary Printing; Rewinding; Sheet Paper Cutting; Slitting) .....A

771—White Co., Jno. A. (Post Boring; Sandpapering; Wood Boring; Wood Molding) C

N. H.—Exeter

772—Exeter Machine Wks. (Boring; Drilling; Air Drying) ....B

N. H.—Franklin Falls

773—Mayo Knitting Mach. & Needle Co. (Hosiery Knitting) ....A

N. H.—Keene

774—Humphry Machine Co. (Shoe Peg; Box Makers';

Clothes Pin; Box Board) C

N. H.—Lakeport

775—Bickford & Co., H. (Vertical Metal Boring)....D
776—Cole Mfg. Co. (Bolt Heading) ....A
777—Pepper Mach. Wks. (Cuff Flat Ribbed) ......B

N. H.—Manchester

778—Leighton Machine Co. (Seamless Hosiery; Hosiery Knitting) ....B

N. H.—Nashua

779—Amer. Shearer Mfg. Co. (Sheep Shearing) ....B
780—Flather & Co. (Screw; Shaping) ....A

N. H.—Penacook

781—Concord Axle Co. (Marble; Granite Polishing)..A

N. H.—Belleville

782—Atlas Fdry. & Machine Co. (Balling; Burring)..D

N. J.—Bridgeton

783—Cox Bros. (Capping; Topping; Canning) .....E
784—Ferracute Machine Co. (Can Makers'; Cartridge; Coining; Punching for Light Metal; Paper, etc.; Sheet Metal Workers'; also Tools; Fibre; Soldering)
A,

N. J.—Camden.

785—Industrial Mfg. Co. (Overseaming; Sewing) ..B

N. J.—Elizabeth

786—Diehl Mfg. Co. (Dynamo Electric) ....A

N. J.—Gloucester City

787—Rogers Boat Gauge & Drill Wks., Jno. M. (Calipering; Measuring for Tool Room, etc.) ....A

N. J.—Jersey City

788—Smith & Sons Co., Theo., ft. of Essex, (Bridge Operating) ....A
789—Steele & Condict, 70 Pearl (Ice; Refrigerating)..B
790—Williams & Son, E. A. (Soap) ....AAA

N. J.—Newark

791—Arnold Sewing Machine Co., 216 High (Knit Goods; Finishing; Sewing) ....·......D
792—Atha Tool Co. (Enamelled Cloth) ....A
793—Crabb & Co., Wm. (Flax) ....B
794—Currier & Sons, Cyrus (Enamelled Cloth; Embossing Leather; Varnishing) ....AAA
795—Freeman, A W., 67 R. R. Av. (Hand Bending)
E

796—Gould & Eberhardt (Bolt; Nut; Metal Printing; Engraving; Wrench; Buffing; Polishing; Centering; Drilling; Tapping; Drilling and Tapping Combined; Gear Cutting; Milling; Shaping; Slotting; Foot Wood Mortising; Sifting)................................A
797—Hanson & Van Winkle Co. (Dynamo Electric; Polishing) ....AA
798—Hewes & Phillips Iron Wks. (Slotting) ....A
799—Isbell-Porter Co/ (Ice; Refrigerating) ....D
800—Lambert Hoisting Engine Co., 115-121 Poinier (Coal; Ore Handling; Hoisting) C
802—Mundy, J. S. (Friction Hoisting; Steam Power Hoisting) ....A
803—Noble & Hunt (Jewelers') ....E
804—Ohl & Co., Geo. A. (Cornice; Sheet Steel Lath)
B
805—Ohl Auto. Mach. Co. (Varnishing; Slat for Trunk Mfrs.) X
806—Osborne Co., H. F. (Fly Net) ....E
807—Osborne & Co., C. S. (Harness Loop; Leather Creasing; Leather Embossing) ....B
808—Seymour & Whitlock, 43 Lawrence (Sash; Door; Blind; Blind Wiring; Foot; Hand Power Mitering; Wood Boring; Wood Mortising; Wood Molding; Wood Surfacing; Brad Driving) ....B
809—Sloan & Chace Mfg. Co., Ltd. (Watch Case; Precision) X
810—Smith Mfg. Co., Anthony P. (Automatic Pipe Calking; Tapping Gas and Water Mains) ....B
811—Royal Machine Co. (Special of all kinds; Bag Making; Embossing) X
812—Traud Co., Alex. (Sulphur; Embossing; Bakers')
A

N. J.—New Brunswick

813—National Water Tube Boiler Co. (Crown Wheels; Wild Horses; Racks; Saddles, etc.; Brick; Grinding Mill) ....A
814—Waldron Co., Jno. (Wall Paper) ....B

N. J.—New Orange

815—Wright Co., Chas. E. (Band Sawing).........B

"Our twenty-five years' experience operating and designing special sawing machinery has developed many improvements in connection with these tools, which cannot fail to be appreciated. If interested you can surely make no mistake in getting our prices before placing order. We can show a guaranteed saving of 40 per cent. in time, labor, saws, etc., where our automatic filing, setting and brazing machines, and patent roller guides are adopted for general use. Our warranted band and circular saws are sold under absolute

guarantee. Send for catalogue *"B"* with article on *Secrets of Successful Band Sawing describing the art of cold metal cutting."*

N. J.—Paterson

816—Atherton Machine Co. (Silk; Silk Doublers; Quillers; Winders; Looms; Polishers; Warpers; Singeing, etc.) ....B

817—Eastwood Co., Benj. (Silk; Cloth Measuring; Silk Doubling; Power Transmission) ....A

818—Gerber, Eugene (silk) C

819—King-Quick-Gerber Co. (Silk) ....D

820—Knapp, C. H.,cor. Waite & Rye (Singeing) ....F

821—Paterson Machine Wks. (General) ....F

822—Rink-Quick-Gerber Co. (Silk Dyeing; Finishing) ....D

823—Royle & Sons, Jno. (Silk; Electrotypers'; Photo-Engravers Beveling; Rubber; Jacquard Card Cutting; Die Sinking; Electrotype Trimming; Piano; Routing; Repeating; Wire; Cable Insulating; Rubber Tubing; Insulating; Wire Weaving; Cycloidal Ruling; Sawing;) ....A

824—Sipp Electric & Mach. Co., 1 Mill (Cloth Testing; Silk Winders) ....D

825—Terhune Mach. Wks., J. I., 164 Ward (Cloth Finishing) ....E

826—Verdol-Jacquard Mach Co. (Silk) X

827—Walder, J. (Silk) ....A

828—Watson Machine Co., 77 R. R. Av. (Embossing; Pressure; Friction; Calendering; Padding; Cordage; Bleaching; Singeing; Soaping; Wool; Worsted; Calico Printers'; Silk; Dyeing; Finishing) ....A

829—Webendorfer Mach. Co. (Silk Lustreing) C

N. J.—Perth Amboy

830—Graecen-Derby Engineering Co. (Box Nailing)..E

N. J.—Raritan

831—Kenyon & Son, D. R. (Chinchilla; Soaping; Whipping; Tentering; Wool Willowing; Wool Washing)..B

N. J.—Riegelsville

832—Taylor, Stiles & Co. (Rag Cutting; Glue Stock Cutting) ....A

N. J.—Salem

833—Ayars Machine Co. (Can Makers' Canning; Sheet Metal Workers') ....B

N. J.—Smithville

Smith Machine Co., H. B., (Box Makers'; Sash; Blind Slat Crimping; Band Sawing; Door; Blind; Handle; Blind Wiring; Corner Block Carving; Curtain Pole; Cutting off Wood; Mitreing; Panel Raising; Post Boring; Rod; Pin; Dowel; Routing; Sandpapering; Wood Shaping; Wood Tenoning; Wood Boring; Wood Flooring; Wood Mortising; Wood Molding; Bench Boring; Boxing; Cross-cut Saw; Cut-off Saw; Picket; Picket Pointing; Sawing; Spoke)........AA

N. J.—Trenton

835—Crossley Mfg. Co. (Pottery; Tile; Electric Porcelain; Clay Washing) ....B

836—Mackenzie, Duncan (Potters'; Rubber)..........A

837—Morse & Walsh Co. (Adding) ....E

838—Thropp & Sons Co., Jno. E. (Cement) ....A

839—Trenton Iron Co. (Br. N. Y. City) (Elevating; Conveying) ....AA

840—Wilkes, Moses (Est. of) (Brick; Supplies) ....F

N. J.—Vineland

841—Keighley & Sons, Chas. (Boot; Shoe) ....A

N. Y.—Albany

842—Dederick's Sons, P. K. (Horse Power Hoisting) ....A

843—Osgood Dredge Co. (Drainage; Ditching; Hoisting Steam Power.) ....A

844—Townsend Furnace & Machine Shop Co. (Aniline Bridge Work) ....B

N. Y.— Amsterdam

845—Gilliland's Sons, Francis, 39 Bridge (Wool Scouring) ....B

846—Inman Mfg. Co. (Paper Cutting) ....A

847—Klauder-Weldon Dyeing Mach. Co. (Slubbing; Mercerizing) ....A

848—McCurdy- Burton Machy. Co. (Automatic Pearl Button) ....D

N. Y.—Auburn

849—Crane Fdry. & Machine Wks., W. W. (Die Sinking) ....D

850—New Birdsall Co. (Threshing) ....AA

N. Y. Baldwinsville

851—Fancher Mach. Co. (Tomato Scalding) ....G

N. Y.—Belmont

852—Clark Bros. (Saw Mill; Lumber Mill) ....A

N. Y.—Binghamton

853—G. & E. Electric & Construction Co. (Boring for Electric Wiring) ....D

854—Rex Acetylene Generator Co. (Acetylene Gas)..D

855—Shapley & Wells (Tanners' Hair Washers; Bark

Mills) ....A
856—Star Electric Co. (Boring for Electric Wiring)..D
857—Stow Mfg. Co. (Portable Boring; Drilling; Tapping; Metal Boring; Reaming; Portable Tapping; Reaming; Drilling Electric; Boring Pinhole) ......A
N. Y.—Brooklyn
858—Adriance Machine Wks., 254 Van Brunt (Can Makers'; Soldering; Sanitary; Sheet Metal Workers'; also Tools) ....A
859—Amer. Stopper Co., cor .Pearl & Water (Bottlers'; Supplies) ....D
860—Bliss Co., E. W., 19 Adams (Can Makers'; Bicycle Chain Making; Soap; Horizontal Boring & Drilling; Capping; Coining; Corrugating; Crimping; Bending; Double Seaming; Embossing; Can Body Forming & Bending; Horizontal Metal Boring; Armature Disk, etc.; Notching; Perforating; Polishing; Gang Punching; Sheet Metal Workers'; also Tools; Slitting; Swaging for Sheet Metal; Wire Handle; Wire Ring) ....AAAA
861—Brown & Patterson, 33 Marcy Av. (Candle; Soap) ....A
862—Burr & Sons, Jno T., 32 S. 6th (Broaching; Key-Seating; Cold Sawing) ....A
863—Carpenter, Thos. D., 93 Pearl (Veneer Cutting) ....B
864—Doane, Chas. R., 26 Meserole (Seidlitz Powder) C
865—Doig, Wm. S. (Est of), 54 Franklin (Wooden Box Nailing; Brad Driving) ....B
866—Foster Pump Wks. (Inc.), 36 Bridge (Pitching) ....B
867—Green Mfg. Co., 296 Oakland (Kindling Wood of all kinds) ....B
868—Guild & Garrison (Air Drying; Water Works Pumping; Pneumatic) ....B
869—Hayes Machine Co., 100 West (Box Board Printing; Veneer Slicing; Box Nailing; Dye Wood Chipping) ....E
870—Hibbard Mfg. Co., Wm. H., 79 Wash'n (Buffing; Polishing; Can Sleaning; Crimping; Beading; Double Seaming; Vertical Milling) C
871—Hoole Mach. & Engraving Wks., 29 Prospect (Bookbinders') ....D
872—Houchin & Huber, 39, 53d (Mixing; Candle; Bed Feather; Soap; Spring Bed; Wire Mattress) ....D
873—Hubbard's Sons, Norman, 265 Water (Veneer Cutting) ....D
874—Lefferts & Co., Chas. A., 63 Clymer (Briar Pipe; Can Makers'; Canning; Circular Folding used in Packing Baking Powder, Medicines, etc.; Crimping; Beading; Double Seaming; Can Forming; Bending, etc.; Bottle, Can & Package Labeling; Notching; also Bench Notching; Screw Thread Rolling; Sheet Metal Workers'; Tools; Slitting) ....D
875—McAdams & Sons, Jno. (Ruling) ....D
876—Milliken Bros., 79 Washington Av. (Box Nailing) X
877—Pioneer Iron Wks. William & King (Asphalt; Paper Tarring) ....A
878—Pioneer Machine Wks. (Jas. Hartley, Prop.) (Road Making Asphalt) ....B
879—Ross & Son Co., Chas., 148 Classon Av. (Bolting; Packing; Grinding; Mixing; Sifting) ....D
880—Taylor & Co .(Inc.) (Hydraulic; Oil Well; Ice; Hoisting Steam Power; Wrecking; White Lead Works) ....D
881—Unitype Co. (Typesetting; Type Distributing) AA
882—Wetter Mfg. Co., 331 Classon Av. (Ptg. Press Numbering) ....F
883—White Engineering Works, Robt., ft. Columbia (Roofing) ....D
N. Y.—Buffalo
884—Automatic Husker Co., 129 Erie (Green Corn Husking) X
885—Blackhall Mfg. Co., 10 Lock (Envelope; Bookbinders') ....D
886—Bryant & Sons & Co., O., 1453 Niagara (Sand Molding) ....F
887—Buffalo Engine Co. (Ice; Refrigerating).......X
888—Buffalo Forge Co. (Air Moving) ....AAA
889—Buffalo Last Wks. (Shoe Molding) ....B
890—Buffalo Pitts Co. (Threshing) ....AAAA
891—Buffalo Refrigerating Mach. Co. (Refrigerating) X
892—Buffalo Scales Co. (Testing; Testing Scale) ..AA
893—Burdict, O. C., White Bldg. (Bolt; Nut) X
894—Case Refrigerating Mach. Co., 31 Main (Ice; Refrigerating) ....A
895—Contractors' Plant Mfg. Co., 129 Erie (Earth Moving; Horse power Hoisting; Steam Power Hoisting) ....B
896—Dopp Co., H. W. (Candle; Confectioners'; Soap; Oil Mill; Drying) ....D

897—Double Truss Cornice Brake Co. (Cornice Makers'; Gutter Forming; Sheet Metal Workers'; Tools)........................C

898—Frank Machy. Co. (Cutting-Off Wood; Dowel; Cut-Off Saw; Mortising; Tonguing; Grooving; Rip Saw; Wood Shaping; Tenoning; Boring; Molding; Vertical Boring; Veneer Cutting; Sash; Door; Blind)........C

899—Holmes Machy. Co., 59 Chicago (Barrel; Keg; Stave & Heading; Box Makers'; Box Nailing; Cabinet Makers'; Coopers' Planing Mill; Sash, Door & Blind; Shingle; Cutting-Off Wood; Traction Ditching Tile; Edging Saw; Rip Saw; Rod Pin; Dowel; Two Saw Wood Trimming; Wood Bending; Wood Boring; Wood Flooring; Wood Molding; Box Dressing; Car Cut-Off; Gaining; Cross-Cut Saw; Cut-Off Saw; Knife Balancing; Crozing; Hoop Nailing)....B

900—Howard Iron Wks. (Automatic Bolt & Nut; Bookbinders'; Stabbing; Automatic Bolt Threading; Bookbinders' Backing; Bolt Heading for Square, Hex & Carriage Bolts; Bolt Pointing; Nut Tapping; Ice; Refrigerating) ....B

901—Iroquois Iron Wks., 178 Walden Av. (Asphalt)..A

902—Lobee Pump & Mfg. Co., (Soap; Lead; Oil Well; Fertilizer) ....G

903—Mey Chain Belting Engineering Wks., 14 Perry (Elevating; Conveying) ....F

904—Niagara Machine & Tool Wks. (Beveling; Blind Wiring; Can Testing; Corrugating; Crimping; Beading; Double Seaming; Edge Saw; Flanging, Sheet Metal Forming & Bending; Gutter Forming; Hand Bending; Notching; Can Makers'; Canning; Cornice Makers'; Conductor Pipe; Eave Trough; Roofing; Slitting; Straightening & Cutting Strip Metal; Nut Tapping; Perforating; Light Punching; Boiler Makers' Punching; Gang & Multiple Punching; Punching & Shearing; Riveting; Turning; Wiring) ....A

Manufacturers of Tools and Machines for working Sheet metals.

Presses for Power and Foot, Drop and Screw Presses.

Dies for Cutting, Forming and Stamping.

Outfits of machinery for making cans, sheet metal packages, and other articles of sheet metals.

Automatic Can Machinery.

Complete line of Tinsmiths' Tools and Machines.

Tools for Sheet Metal Roofing.

Squaring, Slitting and Circle Shears of various sizes and capacities.

Punches, Forming and Bending Rolls.

Dies and Special Machinery for Sheet Metal Work according to specifications, drawings or samples.

905—Noye Mfg. Co., Jno. T. (Brewers'; Malt House; Buckwheat; Flour Mill; Oat Meal; Rice Milling; Mixing; Sifting) X

906—Oliver Mfg. Co. W. W. (Buffing; Polishing) ..C

907—Rogers & Co. S. C., 10 Lock (Brazing; Band Saw; Saw Sharpening; Emery Wheel; Paper Bag) C

908—Ruger Mfg. Co., J. W. (Coopers'; Dry Fruit Cleaning; Bakers') ....B

909—Snow Steam Pump Wks. (Wine Pumping) X

910—Squier Mfg. Co., Geo. L. (Centrifugal; Coffee; Distillery; Rice Milling; Sugar) ....AAA

911—White Co., L. & I. J. (Coopers') ....A

N. Y.—Canandaigua

912—Rush Acetylene Generator Co. (Acetylene Gas).X

913—Standard Wire Fence Co. (Fence)...........D

N. Y.—Cattaraugus

914—Oakes & Burgher (Cheese Box; Dairy) ....B

N. Y.—Cohoes

915—McCreary, Edw. M. (Cloth Folding; Napping).E

N. Y.—Delavan

916—Goo & Hopkins (Cheese Box) ....H

N. Y.—Dunkirk

917—Hilton Mach. Co. (Brick; Supplies) X

N. Y.—Fishkill on Hudson

918—Dutchess Tool Co (Tenoning) ....D

N. Y.—Frankfort

919—Acme Road Machy. Co. (Street Sweeping) ....B

N. Y.—Fredonia

920—Barnum, W. P. (Valve Re-Seating) X

N. Y.—Fulton

921—Dilts Machine Wks. (Cylinder; Paper Making; Wood Pulp) ....B

N. Y.—Glens Falls

922—Dix Foundry Co., J. L. (Barrel; Keg; Stave; Heading) ....D

N. Y.—Gowanda

923—Gowanda Agricl. Wks. Co. (Wood Mill with Jack; Wood Sawing & Splitting) X

N. Y.—Grassy Point

924—Wiles Co., A. M. & W. H. (Brick Press; Brick;

Supplies; General) ....B

N. Y.—Greenwich
925—Eddy Plough Co., W. (Flax) ....B

N. Y.—Groton
926—Groton Bridge Co. (Threshing) ....B

N. Y.—Haverstraw
927—Waldron, Chas. (Brick Machine Moulds) ......G

N. Y.—Ilion
928—Remington Arms Co. (Typewriting; Sewing Hand) ....AAA

N. Y.—Ithaca
929—Williams Bros. (Artesian Well; Oil Well; Well Sinking; Glass Wks.) ....AA

N. Y.—Jamestown
930—American Mfg. Concern (Clothes Washing) ..A

N. Y.—Lestershire
931—Heath Machine Co., W. A. (Box Makers'; Curtain Pole; Panel Raising; Wood Shaping; Tenoning; Boring) ....D

N. Y.—Little Falls.
932—Burrell & Co., D. H. (Testing Milk; Cream Separating) ....AAAA
933—Snyder Mfg. Co., Homer P. (Rib Knitting) ..B
934—Stafford & Holt (Rib Knitting) ....B

N. Y.—Lockport
935—Holly Mfg. Co. (Water Wks.; Pumping) .....A
936—Merritt Mfg. Co. (Curtain Pole; Rod, Pin & Dowel; Rotary Veneer Cutting; Spoke; Barrel; Keg; Stave; Heading; Basket; Butter Dish; Cheese Box; Coopers'; Handle; Table Leg; Wood Turning) ....D
937—Richmond Mfg. Co. (Brush; Smut) ....A
938—Trevor Mfg. Co. (Headings; Staves, etc.; Coopers'; Handle; Shingle Sawing; Wrecking; Grate Slat Cutting; Rod, Pin & Dowel; Tumbling for Smoothing Handles; Veneer Cutting; Wood Barking; Sand Belt; Telephone Pin & Bracket; Veneer Clipping; Wood Pulp Splitting; Wood Pulp Wet) C

N. Y.—Long Island City
940—Stuebner, G. L., 162, 3d (Coal & Ore Handling) ....B

N. Y.—Malone
941—Hinds, Thos. (Stone & Marble Working) ....D

N. Y.—Middletown
942—Morgan & Wilcox Mfg. Co. (Mailing) C

N. Y.—Montour Falls
943—General Pneumatic Tool Co. (Compression Pneumatic Riveting) ....B

N. Y.—Mount Morris
944—Empire Machine Wks. (Spoke) ....E

N. Y.—New Brighton
945—Muralo Co. (Paint Spraying; Sanitary Wall Coating; Painting) ....A

N. Y.—Newburgh
946—Coldwell-Wilcox Co. (Asphalt) ....B
947—Newburgh Ice Machine & Engine Co. (Ice; Refrigerating; Water Cooling) ....A

N. Y.—New York City
948—Abbe Engineering Co. (Cement; Lead; Drying; Fertilizer) ....D
949—Acetylene Gas Illuminating Co., 105 Walker (Acetylene Gas) ....E
950—Allen, Jno. F., 370 Gerard Av. (Pneumatic Riveting; Pneumatic Riveting Portable) C
951—Alsing & Co., J. K. (Lead; Cement) X
952—Amer. Chocolate Machy. Co. 49 W. 66th (Confectioners) ....D
953—Amer. Linde Refrigeration Co., 45 B'way (Ice; Refrigerating) ....B
954—Amer. Mutascope Co. (Moving Pictures) X
955—Amer. Slicing Machine Co., 9 E. 14th (Dried Beef Slicing) X
956—Amer. Soda Fountain Co., 449, 1st Av. (Bottlers' Supplies) ....AAAA
957—Amer. Type Founders Co. (Wire Stitching) ....AAAA
958—Amer. Typewriter Co. (Typewriting) ....D
959—Amer. Wood Working Mchry. Co., 136 Liberty (Band Sawing; Blind Slat Crimping; Blind Wiring; Brazing; Car Boring; Corner Block Carving; Cutting-Off Wood; Edge Saw; Gang Drilling; Port Boring; Rip Saw; Rod Pin & Dowel; Sand Papering; Wood Shaping; Tenoning; Timber Graining; Wood Boring; Carving Flooring; Mortising; Boxmakers; Carriage Builders; Chair; Cabinet Makers; Sash Door & Blind; Planing Mill; Furniture; Wood Molding Wood Polishing; Wood Surfacing; Bench Boring; Combination Saw & Dado; Cross Cut Saw; Cut-Off Saw; Lath; Picket Heading; Sawing; Pinhole Boring; Pin Making & Pointing; Tonguing; Grooving; Vertical Boring) ....AAAA
960—Amer. Writing Machinery Co., 343 B'way (Typewriting) ....AA

In addition to manufacturing the New Century Typewriter and Invincible Typewriters Supplies, Ribbons, Carbon Paper, Oil, etc., we are wholesale dealers in remodeled and rebuilt typewriters of all makes. We are in position to supply dealers with typewriters in saleable condition or in the rough.

961—Ams Mach. Co., Max, 372 Greenwich (Can Making) ....AA

962—Arthur Co., 188 Front (Burring) ....A

963—Ashcroft Mfg. Co. (Oil Testing) ....A

964—Atwood-Morrison Co., 445 Broome (Double Seaming; Silk Doubling; Silk Reeling) ....AA

965—Bacon, Earle C., 26 Cortlandt Coal & Ore Handling; Elevating; Conveying) ....B

966—Bates Mfg. Co., 83 Chambers (Hand Numbering; Automatic Numbering) ....A

967—Berlin Machine Co., 149 B'way (Cloth Rolling; Rip Saw; Sandpapering; Timber Graining; Wood Boring; Mortising; Molding; Polishing; Lumber Mill; Picket Pointing; Tenoning; Spiral Molding) ....AAAA

968—Bracher Mfg. Co., Geo. S. (Hat Binding) .....B

969—Bradley, A. J., 99 Beekman (Stencil Making) X

970—Budde & Westermann, 50 Vesey (Bottlers; Supplies) ....A

971—Bunnell & Co., J. H. (Electro-Magnetic; Pocket) ....B

972—Burns & Sons, Jabez, 542 Greenwich (Coffee & Spice Mill; Sifting) ....B

973—Butler, A. G., 284 Pearl (Automatic Numbering) ....F

974—C. & C. Electric Co. (Dynamo; Electric) .....AA

975—Cameron Steam Pump Wks. A. S. (Wine Pumping) ....AAA

976—Campbell Printing Press & Mfg. Co. (Varnishing) ....B

977—Cavagnaro, John J. (Macaroni) ....B

978—Coin Counting Machine Co., 25 Broad (Coin Counting) ....F

979—Colt Co., J. B., 21 Barclay (Acetylene Gas)....B

980—Colwell, A. W. (Cane Cutting) ....B

981—Commercial Acetylene Co., 80 B'way (Acetylene Gas) ....D

982—Cornell Co., J. B. & J. M., 26th & 11th Av. (Beet Sugar; Cane Sugar; Vertical Metal Boring) ....AA

983—Cottrell & Sons Co., C. B. (Electrotypers'; Printing) ....AAA

984—Crandall & Godley Co., 157 Franklin (Confectioners'; Egg Beating; Mixing; Rolling) ....AA

985—Cushman & Denison Mfg. Co., 240 W. 23rd (Hand Numbering) ....B

986—Deely Co., Robert (Centrifugal; Salt Wks.; Sugar) ....AA

987—De La Vergne Mach. Co., ft. E. 138th (Ice & Refrigerating) ....AAAA

988—Densmore Typewriter Co. (Typewriting) ......B

989—Dexter Folder Co., 290 B'way (Bookbinders') AA

990—Dietsch Bros., 14 E. 17th (Jewelers' Die Cutting) ....AA

991—Domestic Sewing Mach. Co., (Double Needle Sewing; Fancy Stitch Sewing; Lock Stich Sewing; Hand Sewing) X

992—Dudgeon, Richard, 24 Columbia (Punching; Hydraulic) ....A

993—Dunlap Machinery Co. (Sewing; Boot; Shoe) F

994—Eaton, Cole & Burnham Co., 253 B'way (Pipe; Pipe Cutting; Threading) ....AAAA

995—Eaton & Glover Co. (Engraving; Jewelers') ..D

996—Eddy, Geo. B., 398 Madison (Cloth Inspecting) D

997—Edison Mfg. Co. (Drilling; Electric) ....A

998—Edison Phonograph Agency (X-Ray) ....D

999—Ewards & Co., Jos., 414 Water (Bridge Operating; Irrigating) ....B

1000—Egbert & Co., H. L., 21 New Chambers (Bookbinders') ....G

1001—Emmerich & Vonderlehr, 191 Worth (Printers Bronzing; Dusting) X

1002—Ermold, Edw., 664 Hudson (Automatic Bottle Filling & Labeling; Corking; Cork Cleaning; Cigar Branding) ....E

1003—Fabric Measuring & Packaging Co., 82 Centre (Cloth Folding; Measuring) ....B

1004—Fairbanks Co., 186 Elm (Cement Testing; Pipe Cutting & Threading; Automatic Rail Bending & Straightening) ....AAAA

1005—Federoll, Rudolph, 267 W. 35th (Acetylene Gas) ....E

1006—Forschner & Sons, Chas. (Butchers') X

1007—Fox Bros., 24 Vesey (Lever Rail Bending & Straightening) ....A

1008—Fraser Mfg. Co., 26 Cortlandt (Coffee & Spice

Mill) ....D

1009—Garvin Machine Co., 137 Varick (Buffing; Polishing; Chucking; Drilling; Tapping; Edging Saw; All Kinds Forming & Bending; Gear Cutting; Metal Boring; Plain, Vertical & Universal Milling; Profiling; Riveting; Screw; Screw Slotting; Shaping; Slotting; Spring Coiling; Tapping; Wood Boring; Lath; Chain Making; Bicycle; Handle) ......AA

1010—Gibbs-Brower Co., 150 Nassau (Addressing; Stencil Cutting) ....A

1011—Goubert Mfg. Co., 85 Liberty (Burring) ......B

1012—Greason Mfg. Co., 108 W. 99th (Acetylene Gas) D

1013—Haiss Mfg. Co., Geo., 141st & Rider Av. (Coal; Ore Handling) ....D

1014—Hammacher, Schlemmer & Co., 4th Av. & 13th (Hand & Power Glue Spreading) ....AAA

1015—Hammond Typewriter Co. (Typewriting) ....D

1016—Hayward Co., 97 Cedar (Ditching; Coal & Ore Handling) ....B

1017—Hepworth Co., S. S. (Sugar) ....D

1018—Hillyard Co., 75 Fulton (Confectioners') ....F

1019—Hoe & Co., R., 504 Grand (Mitreing; Mailing; Coopers') ....AAAA

1020—Howard & Morse (Ventilating; Air Moving) D

1021—Hunt Co., C. W. (Coal Hoisting & Handling; Hoisting; Steam Power; Elevating; Conveying) AA

1022—Hungerford Bros. & Co. (Macaroni) ....B

1023—Iden & Co., 40 University Pl. (Acetylene Gas) B

1024—Imperial Gas Machine Co., 32 Park Pl. (Gas).X

1025—Ingersoll-Sergeant Drill Co., 36 Cortlandt (Coal Cutting; Coal Mining; Quarry; Bar, Track & Undercutting Stone Channeling; Tunnelling) ...AAAA

1026—James, Emile, 44 Clinton Pl. (Boot; Shoe Sewing) C

1027—Jochum, Andrew, 148 E. 50th (Self-Acting Mashing) ....E

1028—Keller Mechanical Engineering Co., 570 W. B'way (Jewelers' Die Cutting) ....B

1029—Kent Mill Co., 170 B'way (Cement Pulverizers) A

1030—Knapp Mfg. Co., 22 Frankfort (Smoke Test) D

1031—Koppel, Arthur, 68 Broad (Coal & Ore Handling) ....A

1032—Koven & Bro., L. O., 50 Cliff (Acetylene Gas) A

1033—Krajewski-Pesant Co., 32 B'way (Sulphur; Sugar; Centrifugal; Fibre) ....AA

1034—Krieg & Co., J. K. (Embossing; Lacing Stud; Boot; Shoe) ....B

1035—Kruse Sewing Machine Co., 218 6th Av. (Sewing) ....D

1036—Kruse & Murphy Mfg. Co., 100 E. 130th (Sewing; Automatic Sewing; Chain Stitch Sewing; Double Needle Sewing) ....D

1037—Lalance & Grosjean Mfg. Co. (Kneading) AAAA

1038—Leavitt & Co., C. W., 15 Cortlandt (Coal & Ore Handling) ....D

1040—Lidgerwood Mfg. Co. (Hoisting; Handling; Hoisting Steam Power; Coal & Ore Handling; Elevating & Conveying; Logging) ....AAA

1041 Lightning Bottle Wiring Mach. Co. (Bottle Wiring) X

1042—Lovejoy Co. (Black Leading; Electrotypers' Woodworking; Moulding; Shaving) ....B

1043—McAllister, T. H., (Moving Picture) ......B

1044—McCabe, J. J., 15 Dey (Horizontal Boring & Drilling; Plain & Universal Milling) ....B

1045—McCoy Co., Joseph F., 157 Chambers (Rail Bending; Straightening) ....B

1046—McDougall & Potter Co., (Oil Well) ....D

1047—Machine Mantle Sewing Co., 630 E. 184th (Incand. Gas Mantle) X

1048—Manning, Maxwell & Moore, 85 Liberty (Buffing; Polishing; Gear Cutting; Metal Boring; Multiple Punching; Shaping; Wood Working) ......AA

1049—Marine Engine & Machine Co., 1123 B'way (Acetylene Gas; Ship) ....B

1050—Mason & Co., Marcus, 329 Produce Ex. (Coffee & Rice Plantation) ....B

1051—Mead Mfg. Co., Jno. A., 11 B'way (Coal & Ore Handling) ....AA

1052—Mergenthaler Linotype Co., 154 Nassau (Typesetting) ....AAAA

1053—Mergenthaler, Horton Basket Mach. Co., 253 B'way (Basket) X

1054—Morris & Cummings Dredging Co. (Drainage) X

1055—Morrison Co., J. L. (A. G. Mackay, Prop.) (Wire Stitching) ....D

1056—Ness Jr., Geo. M. (Soap) ....A

1057—Newell Mfg. Co., 149 B'way (Cement Mills) D

1058—N. J. Fdry. & Mach. Co., 9 Murray (Coal & Ore Handling; Elevating & Conveying) ....D

1059—N. Y. Labeling Mach. Co., 407A Broome (Bottle

Labeling) ....D
1060—Niles-Bement-Pond Co., 111 B'way (Bolt; Nut;
Punching; Hydraulic; Multiple; Bending; Hydraulic
Bending; Bolt Heading; Bolt Pointing; Bolt Thread-
ing; Bolt Upsetting; Bolt Drilling; Horizontal Bor-
ing & Drilling; Buffing; Polishing; Car Box Bor-
ing; Car Wheel Boring; Centering; Charging; Chuck-
ing; Crank Boring; Cutting-Off Metal; Cylinder
Boring; Horizontal Drilling; Drilling; Tapping;
Boiler Head, etc. Flanging; Forging; Forming; Bend-
ing; Gear Cutting; Hand Shearing; Key Seating;
Key-Way; Lapping; Metal Boring; Horizontal Metal
Boring; Vertical Metal Boring; Cold Metal Sawing;
Horizontal, Plain, Vertical & Universal Milling; Nut
Facing; Hand & Power Pipe Cutting & Threading; Pol-
ishing; Boilermakers' Punching; I Beam Punching;
Quartering; Rail Bending & Straightening; Rail Cut-
ting; Reaming; Riveting; Hydraulic Riveting; Steam
Riveting; Saw Sharpening; Automatic Screw; Shaft
Straightening; Shaping; Iron Shop Sawing; Crank,
Gear & Frame Slotting; Tapping; Upsetting; Valve
Seat Planing) ....AAAA

1061—Peck, Stow & Wilcox Co., 27 Murray (Cornice-
makers') ....AAAA
1062—Pels & Co., Henry, 68 Broad (Metal Cutting-Off;
Hand Shearing; I Beam Punching; Rail Cutting;
Rail Punching; Sheet Metal Workers'; Tools)....C
1063—Pierce Well Engineering & Supply Co. (Artesian
Well; Oil Well; Traction Drilling; Well Sinking;
Water Works Pumping) ....D
1064—Pond Machine Tool Co. (Hoisting; Steam Power)
AAAA
1065—Power Specialty Co., 126 Liberty (Acetylene
Gas) ....E
1066—Premier Machine & Engraving Wks. (Bookbinders') ....D
1067—Prosser & Son, Thos., 15 Gold (Cement)......A
1063—Pryibil, P. (Est. of), 512 W. 41st (Wood Working; Power Transmission) ....AA
1069—Rand Drill Co. (Quarry; Mining) ....AAAA
1070—Rapid Addressing Mach. Co., 290 B'way (Envelope Addressing) ....D
1071—Rauch & Son, Henry, 47 Centre (Pitching)..D
1072—Reichhelm & Co., E. P., 23 John (Buffing; Polishing) ....A
1073—Reilley Bros., 322 W. 41st (Wall Paper Pasting;
Wall Paper Trimming) ....D
1074—Reisinger, Hugo, 11 B'way (Pulp Washing)..AA
1075—Ringler Co., F. A. (Curving) ....A
1076—Robins Conveying Belt Co., 15 Park Row (Cement Belt Conveyors; Coal; Ore Handling; Belt Conveying) ....A
1077—Schock, G., 341 E. 59th (Barrel Washing) ...D
1078—Schott Bros., 346 B'way (Button Making; Lace
Tipping) ....D
1079—Schwenker, W. M. (Brewers' Keg Scrubbing;
Pitching) ....B
1080—Sheridan Co., T. W. & C. B., 56 Duane (Bookbinders', &c., Beveling; Book Covering; Bookbinders'
Embossing; Bookbinders' Eyelet; Folding Paper;
Numbering; Paging; Paper Cutting; Wire Stitching;
Back Forming; Backing; Gold Saving; Leather Embossing; Paper Feeding; Sawing; Stabbing)......A
1081—Simmons Co., Jno., 106 Centre (Pipe Cutting;
Threading) ....AA
1082—Simplex Typewriter Co. (Typewriting).......D
1083—Singer Mfg. Co., 149 B'way (Buttonhole; Jac-
quard Card Stitching; Cloth Room Sewing; Sewing;
Overseaming; Automatic Sewing; Belt Sewing; Boot;
Shoe Sewing; Carpet Mitreing; Serging; Carpet Sew-
ing; Chain Stitch Sewing; Corset Stitching; Cylinder
Sewing; Darning; Double Head Sewing; Double
Needle Sewing; Embroidering; Fancy Stitch Sewing;
Fur Sewing; Glove Stitching; Hand Sewing; Hat
Binding; Hat Sweat Stitching; Horse Boot Sewing;
Leather Stitching; Lock Stitch Sewing; Oscillating
Shuttle Sewing; Overseaming Sewing; Serging; Harness Sewing; Ruffling; Vamping) ....AAAA
1084—Smidth & Co., F. L., 80 William (Brick; Supplies; Cement) ....B
1085—Stafford Co., N., 66 Fulton (Automatic Number-
ing) ....F
1086—Staubach, B. (Fat Cutting; Butchers').......A
1087—Stimpson & Son, Edwin B., 14 Spruce (Cap;
Eyelet; Creasing for Leather, &c.; Embossing for
Leather; Cardboards; Gang Eyelet; Grommet; Pinking; Scalloping; Zinc; Copper Plates, &c.; Polishing;
Leather Riveting; Splitting for Leather, &c.; Stapling; Corset Steel Tipping; Eyelet Hook Setting;
Grommet Setting; Lace Tipping; Lace Stud; Leather
Punching; Shoe Splitting; Stay Folding; Suspender
Vamp Wrinkling; Toe Cap Carding) ....B

1088—Sunlight Gas Mach. Co., 261 B'way (Acetylene Gas) ....B
1089—Tennis, A. H. (Boot; Shoe Sewing; Cylinder Sewing; Double Head Sewing; Lock Stitch Sewing; Special) ....B
1090—Terril Gas Mach. Lighting Co. (Gas) X
1091—Terwillinger Mfg. Co., 3 W. 23d (Wood Boring) ....D
1092—Thomson, W. S., 418 W. 27th (Wood Moulding) ....F
1093—Thurnauer & Bro., G. M., 35 Park Place (Acetylene Gas) X
1094—Tirrill Gas Mach. Co., 441 B'way (Gas; Acetylene Gas) X
1095—Torchiani, H. (Brewers' Pitching) ....D
1096—Trageser Steam Copper Wks., John (Thawing) ....B
1097—Turl's Sons, Jno., 534 W. 28th (Forming; Bending; Centrifugal; Salt Works)..................D
1098—Union Special Mach. Co., 47 Leonard (Bag Sewing; Boot; Shoe Sewing; Chain Stitch Sewing; Double Needle Sewing; Fancy Stitch Sewing; Leather Stitching; Lock Stitch Sewing; Mail Bag Sewing; Special Sewing; Knit Goods Finishing)..........B
1099—Van Houten & Tenbroeck Co., 300 4th Av. (Static Electric; X-Ray) ....D
1100—Waite & Bartlett Mfg. Co., 217 E. 23d (Static Electric) ....D
1101—Watkins & Son, Jas Y., 10 Catherine (Bakers'; Confectioners') ....D
1102—Watson-Stillman Co., 210 E. 43d (Hydraulic Bending; Buffing; Polishing Lathes; Pipe Testing; I Beam Punching; Punching; Shearing Combined; Riveting; Hydraulic Rail Bending; Straightening; Hydraulic Riveting; Shaft Straightening; High Pressure Hydraulic; Hydraulic Punching; Tunnelling; Weighing; Shipyard) ....A
1103—Weiss & Co., H., 20 Cliff (Sheet Metal Workers'; Tools) ....F
1104—Weiss, Geo. W., 374 Canal (Plaiting; Pinking; Ruffling; Embroidering) X
1105—Wesel Mfg. Co., F., 82 Fulton (Printers' Mitreing; Stereotypers') ....A
1106—Westinghouse Machine Co. (Ice; Refrigerator) ....AAAA
1107—Williams Wire Hinging Mach. Co., 30 Greenwich Av. (Box Hinging) ....B
1108—Witteman Bros. (Beer Bottle Washing; Corking; Filling) ....A
1109—Witteman Co., 188 William (Bottlers' Specialties) ....A
1110—Wood & Nathan Co., 1 Madison Av. (Typesetting) X
1111—Worthington Pumping Engine Co., (Water Wks.; Wine Pumping) ....AAAA
1112—Yaryan Co., 41 Park Row (Bleaching; Evaporating) ....B
1113—Zoller & Co., Chas., 12 Water (Bottlers'; Supplies) ....B
1114—Zucker & Levett & Loeb Co., 528 W. 25th (Buffing; Polishing) ....A
N. Y.—Niagara Falls
1115—Niagara Falls Acetylene Gas Generator Co. (Acetylene Gas) X
N. Y.—North Tonawanda
1116—Buffalo Steam Pump Co. (Ice; Refrigerating).A
N. Y.—Oswego
1117—Oswego Tool Co. (Boilermakers' Steel Punching; Screw) ....D
1118—Oswego Mach. Wks, (Paper Cutting)..........B
N. Y.—Pearl River
1119—Dexter Folder Co. (Paper Folding; Folding; Enveloping) ....:...................AA
N. Y.—Peekskill
1120—Anderson, Homer (Winding) ....H
1121—Naylor Bros. (Brick; Supplies; Power Transmission) ....A
N. Y.—Phoenix
1122—Baker, E. B. (Cigar Box) ....H
N. Y.—Plattsburg
1123—Williams Mfg. Co. (Sewing; Typewriting)..AA
N. Y.—Rochester
1124—Amer. Drafting Furniture Co., 223 Mill (Electric Blue Print) ....E
1125—Booth Bros. (Boot; Shoe Folding; Beading).B
1126—Century Cement Mach. Co. (Artificial Stone Making) ....D
1127—Clement Co., Frank H. (Band Sawing)..AAAA
1128—Cochrane-Bly Co. (Filing for Sawing Out; Filing Blanking Dies; Metal Sawing) ....D
1129—Connell & Dengler Machine Co. (Band Sawing; Double Color Box Board Printing; Surfacing, &c.).B
1130—Davis Machine Co., W. P. (Cold Metal Cutting-

Off; Key-Seating; Key-Way) ....A
1131—Erdle & Schenck (Perforating; Punching for
Light Metal; Paper, &c.)....................B
1132—Gleason Works (Gear Cutting) ....A
1133—Huther Bros., 229 Mill (Core Box Cutting; Metal
Sawing) ....B
1134—Knowlton Co., M. D. (Cutting; Scouring; Bending Paper Box; Cornering Paper Box; Rolling Paper
Tube) ....AA
1135—Morgan Machine Co. (Box Board Matching;
Grinding; Setting-Up; Wooden Box Printing; Boxmakers'; Tonguing; Grooving; Box Nailing)....AA
1136—Rochester Barrel Machy. Co. (Slack Barrel; Keg;
Stave; Heading) C
1137—U. S. Standard Voting Machine Co. (Voting)..B
1138—Yawman & Erbe Mfg. Co. (Bottle Labeling; Filling; Soaking; Washing; Copying for Letters)....AA
N. Y.—Rome
1139—Adams & Son, S. (Lumber Mill; Shingle; Coopers') C
N. Y.—Rouse Point
1140—Perfect Gas Machine Co. (Acetylene Gas).....F
N. Y.—Sandy Hill
1141—Friction Pulley & Machine Wks. (Wet Paper
Mill) ....B
1142—Sandy Hill Iron & Brass Wks. (Wood Barking;
Cylinder; Pulp Mill; Paper Mill) ....A
N. Y.—Saugerties
1143—Canner & Co., P. (Brick; Supplies)..........C
N. Y.—Schenectady
1144—General Electric Co. (Electric Coal Cutting;
Mining; Electro-Magnetic Pocket)...........AAAA
1145—Westinghouse Co. (Threshing; Winnowing) AA
N. Y.—Seneca Falls
1146—Goulds Mfg. Co. (Horse Power Pumping; Wine
Pumping; Hydraulic) ....AAA
1147—Rumsey & Co. (Ltd.) (Horse Power Pumping).A
1148—Seneca Falls Mfg. Co. (Edging Saw; Roll Groov-
ing; Hand; Foot Power Wood Mortising; Hand;
Foot Power Wood Molding; Tonguing; Grooving)..B
N. Y.—Silver Creek
1149—Howes Co., S. (Green Pea Grading; Blending;
Sifting; Cement Packing; Valve Re-Seating; Brush;
Brush Separators Combined; Corn Mill; Scouring;
Polishing; Separating Combined)................A
1150—Huntley Mfg. Co. (Packing; Corn Mill; Canning)
....................................A
1151—Invincible Grain Cleaner Co. (Packing; Corn
Mill) ....A
N. Y.—Suspension Bridge
1152—Chisholm-Scott Co. (Pea Harvesting; Hulling;
Cleaning) ....A
N. Y.—Syracuse
1153—Kane & Roach, Niagara & Shonnard (Wood Tenoning; Rolling Mill) ....B
1154—Merrell-Soule Co. (Inc.) (Corn Cutting)....AA
1155—Moore, Thos. F. (Sewer; Trench Excavating)..C
1156—Moyer, H. A. (Hub Boring) ....A
1157—Smith Premier Typewriter Co. (Typewriting)..
AAAA
1158—Stearns & Co., E. C. (Spoke; Spoke Turning) AA
1159—Syracuse Malleable Iron Wks. (Economic; Roll-
ing-Over Sand Molding) ....A
N. Y.—Troy
1160—Adams Laundry Machy. Co. (Clothes Washing;
Dyeing; Clothes Ironing; Clothes Starching)......B
1161—Bernard Co., E. G. (Dynamo Electric)........D
1162—Brewer, Wm. W. (Candle; Soap) ....F
1163—Eclipse Machine Co., 677 River (Sheet Metal
Workers'; also Tools) ....G
1164—Empire Forge Co. (Pulley Mortising) ....F
1165—McDermott Ornamental Sewing Mach. Co. (Sewing) ....B
1166—Palmer Hdw. Mfg. Co. (Emery Wheel) ......D
1167—Tolhurst & Son, W. H. (Laundry)..........B
1168—Tompkins Bros. Co. (Clothes Washing; Knitting
Underwear) ....B
1169—Troy Laundry Mach. Co. (Ltd.) (Clothes Washing; Clothes Ironing; Clothes Starching)......AA
1170—Whelan, Dennis J. (Sheet Metal Workers';
Tools) ....A
N. Y.—Unadilla
1171—Unadilla Machine Wks. (Air Moving).......E
N. Y.—Utica
1172—International Heater Co. (Heating) ......AAA
N. Y.—Waterford
1173—Mohawk & Hudson Mfg. Co. (Axe; Hammer;
Hatchet) ....B
N. Y.—Watertown
1174—Bagley & Sewall Co. (Paper Making; Wood
Pulp) ....AA
N. Y.—Weedsport
1175—Burritt & Bros., O. W. (Sheet Metal Workers';

Tools) C

N. Y.—Yonkers

1176—Saunders Sons, D .(Bolt Threading; Pipe Cutting; Threading; Tapping; Gas; Water Mains; Nut; Pipe; Tapping; Drilling) ....A

N. C.—Charlotte

1177—Mecklenburg Iron Wks. (Cutting-Off Wood; Edging Saw; Cut-Off Saw) X

N. C.—Statesville

1178—Steele & Son, J. C. (Auger Brick; Brick Represses; Brick Automatic Cutting Tales; Dies; Crushers; Cars; Winding Drums, &c.) ....B

N. C.—Winston-Salem

1179—Salem Iron Wks. (Inc.) (Railroad Cross Tie; Coffee Hulling; Wood Working)...............B

1180—Winston Cigarette Machine Co. (Cigarette Making) C

OHIO—Akron

1181—Taplin, Rice & Co. (Brick Sewer Pipe; Presses; Dry; Wet Pans; Potters')....................A

1182—Webster, Camp & Lane Co. (Gravity Incline; Clay Tempering; Hoisting Steam Power; Coal; Ore Handling; Car Dumping; Oatmeal; Potters') ....A

OHIO—Alliance

1183—Alliance Machine Co. (Punching Horizontal; Punching Hydraulic; Punching Multiple; Hoisting) AA

1184—Morgan Engineering Co. (Blast Furnace; Hydraulic Bending; Rolling Mill; Charging for Billets; Blooms, &c.; Flanging; Forging; Hydraulic Forging; Riveting; Fire Door Riveting; Hydraulic Riveting; Steam Riveting; Steam Forge) ....AA

OHIO—Ashland

1185—Myers & Bro., F. E. (Horse Power Pumping) AAAA

OHIO—Ashtabula

1186—Barber Mfg. Co. (Screw Punching) C

OHIO—Bucyrus

1187—Amer Clay Working Machy. Co. (Dry; Semi-Dry Press; Re-Press Brick; Sizing; Brick Machines; Pug Mills Combined; Fire-Proofing; Hollow Block; Cement; Terra Cotta; Lumber; Tile; Brick; Supplies) ....B

1188—Pilling-Kruse Air Engine Wks. (Compressed Air Hoisting) ....A

OHIO—Canton

1189—Arctic Machine Co. (Ice; Refrigerating)......X

1190—Aultman Co. (Pig Iron Casting; Threshing; Elevating; Conveying) ....AAAA

1191—Bonnot Co. (Brick Press; Brick; Supplies; Cement) ....B

1192—Knight Mfg. Co. (Saw Mills) ....E

1193—McLain Co., Jas. H. (Sawing) ....AA

1194—Universal Machine Co. (See Canton Fdry. & Mach. Co.) (Conductor Pipe; Eave Trough).....B

OHIO—Chagrin Falls

1195—Ober Mfg. Co. (Wood Chucking; Sand Papering; Wood Shaping; Wood Boring)...............C

1196—Ober Lathe Co. (Handle) C

OHIO—Cincinnati

1197—Amer. Laundry Machy. Co. (Clothes Tumbling; Laundry; Clothes Washing; Clothes Ironing; Clothes Starching; Sterilizing; Sterilizing Washing)......A

1198—Amer. Tool Wks. Co., 6th & Eggleston Av. (Boring; Drilling; Horizontal Boring; Drilling; Buffing; Polishing; Chucking; Drilling; Tapping; Forming; Metal Boring; Vertical Metal Boring; Screw; Screw Shaving; Screw Slotting; Shaping) ....AA

1199—Andrew & Co., M. L., 77 Elm (Panel Raising; Whiting for Picture Frames; Multiple Spindle Wood Boring; Iron Drilling) C

1201—Barker & Co., Wm., cor. Pioneer & Culvert (Crank; Geared Shaping) ....B

1202—Bickford Drill & Tool Co., Front, cor .Pike (Car Wheel Boring; Cylinder Boring; Bicycle Drilling; Drilling; Tapping; Metal Boring) ....A

1203—Blymyer Iron Wks. Co., Spring Grove Av. & Township (Centrifugal; Coffee; Rice Plantation; Distillery) ....B

1204—Buchanan & Co., Thos., 216 Elm (Buffing; Polishing) ....E

1205—Bullock Electric Mfg. Co. (Dynamo; Electric) AAAA

1206—Canda Co., L. (Coin Actuated) ....E

1207—Cinn. Milling Machine Co. (Plain; Universal Milling) ....AA

1208—Cinn. Punch & Shear Co., 1416 Plum (Beam Coping; Multiple Punching; Shearing; Bending)..D

1209—Cinn. Shaper Co., Garrard Av., cor. Elam (Crank; Geared; Traversed Head Shaping))......A

1210—Coleman Gas Wks. Mfg. Co., 627 Main (Gas; Acetylene Gas) ....F

1211—Cordesman Mach. Co., 27 Butler (Blind Wiring;

Cutting-Off Wood; Post Boring; Rip Saw; Rod; Pin;
Dowel; Routing; Sand Papering; Wood Shaping;
Wood Tenoning; Variety Sawing; Wood Boring;
Wood Mortising; Wood Molding; Cross-Cut Saw;
Cut-Off Saw; Spiral Molding; Boxmakers'; Carriage
Builders'; Chair; Wheel).........................X

1212—Cordesman, Meyer & Co., 53 Central Av. (Cutting-Off Wood; Carriage Builders'; Panel Raising;
Post Boring; Rip Saw; Wood Shaping; Wood Tenoning; Wood Boring; Wood Mortising; Wood Molding;
Wood Surfacing) ....B

1213—Day & Co., J. H., 144 Harrison Av. (Pill Mak-
ing; Tablet; Bottling; Corking; Filling; Catsup; Dry
Fruit Cleaning; Egg Beating; Agitating for Liquids;
Mixing; Sifting; Bottlers'; Supplies; Bakers', &c.;
Paint; Perfumery; Pill) C

1214—Deters & Co., F., 906 Elm (Pop-Corn).......H

1215—Dreses Machine Tool Co. (Screw)..........AA

1216—Echert Co., P., 27 W. Court (Confectioners')
AAAA

1217—Fay & Egan Co., J. A., cor. John & Front (Band
Sawing; Blind Wiring; Car Boring; Corner Block
Carving; Circular Sawing; Wood; Cutting-Off Wood;
Dovetailing; Edging Saw; Wood Gang Drilling; Lock
Corner Box; Mitreing; Panel Raising; Port Boring;
Rip Saw; Rod; Pin; Dowel; Sand Papering; Wood
Shaping; Wood Tenoning; Timber Graining; Wood
Bending; Wood Carving; Wood Flooring; Wood Mor-
tising; Wood Molding; Wood Polishing; Wood Sur-
facing; Babbitting; Bench Boring; Box Dressing;
Boxing; Box Setting; Car Cut-Off; Gaining; Car
Mortising; Carriage; Car Tenoning; Circular Re-
Sawing; Cornering; Rounding; Cross-Cut Saw; Cut-
Off Saw; Double Boring; Edge Molding; Shaping;
Felly; Friezing; Shaping; Spoke; Gluing; Staining;
Hub Boring; Bub Mortising; Radil Boring Portable;
Sawing; Spiral Molding; Vertical Boring; Boxmak-
ers'; Carriage Builders'; Chair; Cabinet Makers'; Cigar
Box; Saw Mill; Sash; Door; Blind; Car Builders';
Felloe; Planing Mill; Furniture; Gluing; Handle;
Piano Factory; Ship Builders'; Wheel; Boxboard
Matching) ....AAAA

1218—Fosdick Machine Tool Co. (Horizontal Boring;
Drilling; Milling) ....B

1219—Francis & Bro., Chas. E., 425 E. 8th (Glue
Spreading; Gluing) ....B

1220—Fritsch Mfg. Co., Francis (Tanners'; Brewers';
Barley; Malt Cleaning; Mashing) C

1221—Greaves, Klusman & Co., Cook & Alfred (Band
Sawing; Variety Sawing; Butting; Cross-Cut Saw;
Lumber Mill) ....B

1222—Grever & Co., Edw. C., 71 Cent. Av. (Laundry)
F

1223—Heilman, Jno. C., 1652 Dorman (Confectioners')
H

1224—Hilbert-Freiberg Mach. Co., 20 W. Court (Confectioners') ....E

1225—Homan & Co., 214 E. 7th (Candle) ....AA

1226—International Harness Machy. Co. (Harness)..C

1227—Keene & Co., Geo. C., 502 E. Front (Corrugat-
ing; Crimping; Bending; Double Seaming; Flanging;
Paint Roll; Sheet Metal Workers'; Tools; Cornice;
Tin Roofing; Cornice Makers')................F

1228—Kingery Mfg. Co., 106 E. Pearl (Confectioners')
C

1229—King Mach. Tool Co. (Boilermakers' Punching)
C

1230—Kisinger-Ison Co., 466 Pioneer (Street Sweeping) ....D

1231—Laidlaw-Dunn-Gordon Co. (Br. Int. Steam Pump
Co., N. Y. City) (Water Works Pumping; Wine
Pumping) ....AAAA

1232—Lane & Bodley Co., cor. John & Water (Wood
Trimming; Lath; Mortising; Cable Railroad; Power
Transmission) ....A

1233—Le Blond Mach. Tool Co., R. K., 4609 Easton
Av. (Chucking; Lapping; Plain; Universal Milling;
Rack Cutting) ....A

1234—Lodge & Shipley Mach. Tool Co., 3055 Colerain
Av. (Chucking; Lathe; Brass Working)..........A

1235—McLeod, & Co., Walter, 463 E. Front (Acetylene Gas; Pneumatic Paint Spraying) ....B

1236—Miller Dubrul & Peters Mfg. Co. (Cigar Branding; Cigar Bunching; Cigarette Making; Tobacco).B

1237—Obermayer Co., S., 647 Evans (Core Making;
Sand Mixing; Sand Molding; Sand Sifting)......AA

1238—Oesterlein Machine Co., 2846 Spring Grove Av.
(Plain; Universal Milling) ....B

1239—Parks, L. F., Knowlton & C. H. & D. R. R.
(Band Sawing) ....F

1240—Pocock, Oliver, 1042 Harriet (Sheet Metal Forming; Bending; Sheet Metal Workers' Forming; Tools;
Broom) ....F

1241—Randall & Co., 802 W. 6th (Leather, &c., Embossing; Harness; Leather Creasing; Leather Folding; Leather Splitting; Leather Stitching; Skiving; Collar Stiffening Power; Stripping; Strap Slitting)......B

1242—Robinson Mfg. Co., J. M., 2d & Central Av. (Corrugating; Crimping; Beading; Double Seaming; Sheet Metal Forming; Bending; Paint Roll; Sheet Metal Workers'; Tools; Cornice Makers')........B

1243—Ross-Mayer Mfg. Co. (Leather Polishing; Harness; Boot; Shoe)....................................A

1244—Schriver & Co., O. P., 208 Elm (Wire Cloth Measuring) ....B

1245—Shepard Lathe Co., 129 W. 2d (Shaping) .....F

1246—Smith, Myers & Schnier Co. (Lath; Lumber Mill) B

1247—Smith & Mills (Crank; Geared; Shaping).....A

1248—Steptoe Shaper Co., Jno., 2949 Colerain Av. (Crank; Geared Shaping) ....A

1249—Streit Machine Co., A., 1108 Harrison Av. (Tapping) ....D

1250—Sunlight Gas Co., 539 Main (Acetylene Gas)..X

1251—Tatum Co., Saml. C., 414 W. Water (Punching for Light Metal; Paper Punching; Perforating Binders') ....B

1252—Towsley Mfg. Co., Jno. T., Evans near Gest. (Glue Spreading) ....B

1253—Triumph Ice Machine Co., 610 Baymiller (Ice; Refrigerating) ....A

1254—Triumph Electric & Ice Machine Co. (Refrigerating) ....A

1255—Union Light & Heat Co., 2321 W. 8th (Acetylene Gas) X

256—Watkins Laundry Machy. Co. (Ironing; Laundry) A

OHIO—Cleveland

1257—Acme Machy. Co. (Bolt Heading; Bolt Pointing; Bolt Upsetting; Forging; Nut Facing; Nut Finishing; Nut Tapping; Staybolt Threading; Taper Threading; Upsetting; Bolt Forging; Bolt; Nut) ....AA

1258—Ajax Mfg. Co., Lake & Wasson (Bending; Bulldozing; Bolt Heading; Bolt Pointing; Bolt Upsetting; Forging; Forming; Bending; Automatic Hot Forged; Hot Pressed Nut Tapping; Solid Die Hot Rivet; only Makers'; Upsetting; Wood Boring; Bolt; Nut)....AA

1259—Bardons & Oliver (Bicycle Hub) ....B

1260—Bartlett & Snow Co., C. O., French St. (Mixing; Barley; Carbon; Elevating; Conveying; Cement; Flour Mill; Drug; Fertilizer) ....B

1261—Battenfield Mfg. Co., Williamson Bldg. (Brick; Supplies) ....D

1262—Bishop & Babcock Co. (Bottle Filling) ......AA

1263—Brown Hoisting Machy. Co., 1345 St. Clair (Hoisting Steam Power; Coal; Ore Handling; Elevating; Conveying) ....AAAA

1264—Bultman & Co., F. H., 106 Canal (Gear Cutting) F

1265—Chandler & Price Co. (Printers; Paper Cutting) B

1266—Chase Machine Co., 111 Elm (Automatic Steam Towing) ....B

1267—Chisholm & Moore Mfg. Co., Lake, near Kirtland (Pneumatic Riveting) ....AA

1268—Chisholm & Sons, Wm., 358 Case Av. (Coal Hoisting; Handling; Ore Hoisting; Handling; Hoisting Steam Power) ....AAA

1269—Cleveland Automatic Machine Co., 131 2d Av. (Chucking; Automatic Screw; Worm Milling) AAA

1270—Cleveland Brewers' Supply Co., 317 Pearl (Barrel Washing) ....B

1271—Cleveland Elevator Bucket Co., 225 St. Clair (Elevating; Conveying) ....D

1272—Cleveland Laundry Mchy. Co., 124 Track (Carpet Cleaning) X

1273—Cleveland Punch & Shear Wks. Co., 156 Case Av. (Metal Cutting-Off; Hat Sewing; Pneumatic Riveting; Boilermakers' Punching; Gang Punching; Iron Shop Sawing) ....A

1274—Cummer & Son Co., F. D., The Arcade (Asphalt; Brick Dryers) ....A

1275—Drake Acetylene Burner & Supply Co., 37 Hathaway (Acetylene Gas) ....F

1276—Dyer & Co., E. H., New England Bldg. (Beet Washing; Slicing) ....AAA

1277—Dyer & Co., E. H., New England Bldg. (Beet Sugar) ....AAA

1278—Eilers Mfg. Co., H. P., 26½ S. Water (Bolt; Nut) X

1279—Engeln & Co., H. P., Rose Bldg. (Static Electric) ....D

1280—Eureka Machine Co. (Brewers' Branding; Keg Scrubbing; Pitching) ....D

1281—Francis, A. E., 780 Cedar Av. (Jewelers' Engraving) ....F

1283—Gerlach & Co., Peter, 28 Columbus (Barrel; Keg; Stave; Heading; Coopers'; Shingle Sawing) . . . . . . A

1284—Harris Mfg. Co., 51 Middle (Acetylene Gas) . . C

1285—Hart Mfg. Co., Wood, cor. St. Clair (Bolt Threading; Pipe Cutting; Threading) . . . . B

1286—Kaltenbach & Griess (Elevating; Conveying) . . B

1287—Loew Filter Co., 398 Erie (Bottlers'; Supplies) C

1288—Loew Supply & Mfg. Co. (Bottle Soaking; Washing) . . . . B

1289—Lord, Bowler & Co., 35 Centre (Stone Channeling) C

1290—Lucas Machine Tool Co., Belden & Mason (Horizontal Boring; Drilling; Metal Boring; Horizontal Metal Boring; Milling) X

1291—National Acetylene Gas Co., New England Bldg. (Acetylene Gas) X

1292—National Acme Mfg. Co. (Multiple Spindle Automatic Screw) . . . . AA

1293—Ohio Ceramic Engineering Co., 50 Fall (Dry; Repress Brick Press; Brick; Supplies) . . . . B

1294—Ohio Electric Wks. (Dynamo; Electric) . . . . . D

1295—Oram, Jno. S., 160 Coe (Barrel; Keg; Stave; Heading; Coopers') . . . . A

1296—Oster Mfg. Co., 85 E. Prospect (Pipe Cutting; Threading) . . . . B

1297—Reade Mchy. Co., Amer. Trust Bldg. (Countersinking; Drilling; Boilermakers' Throat Punch; I Beam Punching; Punching; Shearing Combined; Riveting) X

1298—Reliance Mach. & Tool Co., 31 W. Center (Nut Tapping; Bolt; Nut) C

1299—Sly Mfg. Co., W. W. (Incorporator; Sand Mixing) . . . . D

1300—Smith Fdry. Supply Co., J. D., 40 S. Water (Sand Mixing; Sand Molding) . . . . D

1301—Standard Sand & Mach. Co., 1434 Superior (Sand Mixing) C

1302—Standard Sewing Machine Co. (Buttonhole; Overseaming; Sewing; Sewing Double Needle; Sewing Fancy Stitch; Sewing Hand; Hat Sweat Stitching; Hem Stitch Sewing; Lock Stitch Sewing; Overseaming Sewing) . . . . AAA

1303—Strong, Carlisle & Hammond Co., 61 Frankfort (Milling; Screw; Wood Tenoning; Wood Mortising; Wood Surfacing) . . . . A

1304—Van Dorn & Dutton Co. (Street Railway Sweeping) X

1305—Walker Co. (Boiler Shop; Cable Railroad; Carbon; Hydraulic) X

1306—Walworth Run Fdry. Co., 883 Empress (Brick Cars) C

1307—Warner & Swasey Co., 57 E. Prospect (Horizontal Boring; Drilling; Automatic Boring; Tapping; Chucking; Metal Boring; Valve Milling; Screw; Tapping) . . . . A

1308—Wellman-Seaver-Morgan Engineering Co., New England Bldg. (Coal; Ore Handling) . . . . AAAA

1309—White Sewing Machine Co., Rose Bldg. (Sewing; Sewing Boot; Shoe; Sewing Hand; Sewing Lock Stitch) . . . . AAAA

OHIO—Collinwood

1310—Browning Engineering Co. (Coal; Ore Handling; Hoisting) X

OHIO—Columbiana

1311—Enterprise Mfg. Co. (Ditching) . . . . A

OHIO—Columbus

1312—Case Mfg. Co. (Electric; Hand Power Hoisting; Flour Mill; Rice Milling) . . . . AA

1313—Columbus Machine Co., 223 W. Broad (Hand; Power Pipe Cutting; Threading) . . . . A

1314—Gerlach & Co., Peter (Barrel Heading; Stave Sawing) . . . . A

1315—Jeffrey Mfg. Co. (Ditching Railroad; Coal Hoisting; Handling; Coal Washing; Coal Mining Electric; Fertilizer; Oil Mill; Drying; Electric Coal Mining; Ore Handling; Coke Crushing; Elevating; Conveying; Ash Handling; Pulverizing) . . . . AAAA

1316—Kilbourne & Jacobs Mfg. Co. (Ditching; Drainage; Earth Moving; Road Building) . . . . A

1317—Ohio Pump & Brass Co., Oak & 18th (Acetylene Gas) C

1318—Ohio Tool Co. (Combination Saw; Dado; Flooring) . . . . AA

OHIO—Cuyahoga Falls

1319—Turner, Vaughn & Taylor Co. (Double Acting Direct Steam Brick Press; Chain Testing; Wire Straightening; Cutting; Nail Mill; Chain Making) . B

OHIO—Dayton

1320—Buckeye Iron & Brass Wks. (Cutting Tobacco; Tobacco; Linseed; Cotton Seed Oil) . . . . AA

1321—Callahan & Co., W. P. (Ice; Refrigerating; Cotton Seed Oil) . . . . AA

1322—Davis Sewing Mach. Co. (Cloth Brushing; Sewing; Sewing Boot; Shoe; Sewing Hand; Sewing Lock Stitch), ...AAA

1323—Dayton Globe Iron Wks. Co. (Paper Making; Power Transmission) ....A

1324—National Labeling Mach. Co. (Kramer Bros., Props.) (Labeling) C

1325—Gordon Tank Pump Co. (Confectioners') ......E

1325½—Platt Iron Works Co. (Pumping; Abbatoir, &c.) ....AAAA

1326—Raymond Co., Chas. W. (Brick Press; Clay Tempering; Cement; Clay Washing; Brick; Supplies; Pottery) ....A

1327—Seybold Machine Co. (Paper Cutting; Bookbinders'; Backing) ....A

OHIO—Defiance

1328—Defiance Machine Wks. (Band Sawing; Hoop; Sand Papering; Wood Shaping; Wood Tenoning; Rim; Felloe, &c.; Wood Bending; Wood Boring; Wood Mortising; Wood Polishing, also Handle; Felloe, &c.; Box Dressing; Box Setting; Carriage; Double Band Sawing; Felly; Hub Boring; Hub Mortising; Knife Balancing; Lumber Mill; Pulley Balancing; Spoke; Vertical Boring; Wagon; Shaft; Wheel; Handle; Bobbin; Wooden Dish; Barrel Hoop; Carriage Builders'; Pole; Shaft; Coopers') ....AAA

OHIO—Elyria

1329—Western Automatic Mach. Screw Co. (Tapping) AA

OHIO—Freeport

1330—National Light & Heating Co. (Acetylene Gas) C

OHIO—Galion

1331—Freese & Co., E. M. (Brick Cutting; Brick Press; Brick; Supplies; Terra-Cotta; Tile) C

OHIO—Ghent

1332—Purdy Machine Co. (Cane-Seat Chair; also Wood Seat Chair) X

OHIO—Hamilton

1333—Bentel & Margedant Co. (Sand Drum; Sand Papering; Wood Shaping; Wood Tenoning; Wood Boring; Wood Mortising; Wood Sawing; Splitting; Spoke; Timber Gaining; Carriage Builders'; Planing Mill; Wheel) ....A

1334—Black-Clawson Co. (Calendering; Clyinder; Ink Grinding; Plating Paper) ....AAA

1335—Hooven, Owens & Reutschler Co. (Cable Railroad) ....AAAA

1336—Long & Allstatter Co. (Bending; Coping; Forming; Bending; Disc Armature Notching; I Beam Punching; Multiple Punching; Riveting; Slitting Fire Welding; Welding) ....AA

1337—Niles Tool Wks. Co. (Arch Bar Drilling; Chord Boring; Double Boring; Straightening Metal; Nut; Railroad Shop; Steam Forge; Switch; Frog Planing; Turret Boring; Universal Boring; Vertical Boring; Turning; Boiler Shop; Bridge Work; Car Builders'; Ship Yard) ....AAAA

1338—Salzman Mfg. Co. (Blending; Sifting) ......G

OHIO—Lima

1339—East Iron & Machine Co. (Gas) ....A

OHIO—Lindsay

1340—Johnson-Keyt Mfg. Co. (Butter Dish; Hoop Cutting; Pointing; Lapping) X

OHIO—Mansfield

1341—Aultman & Taylor Mach. Co. (Threshing) .AAAA

1342—Humphreys Mfg. Co. (Pneumatic Paint Spraying) ....B

1343—Phoenix Electric Mfg. Co. (Electro-Plating) ..B

OHIO—Marion

1344—Huber Mfg. Co. (Threshing) ....AAA

1345—Marion Mfg. Co. (Threshing) ....AA

1346—Marion Steam Shovel Co. (Dredging; Ditching; Drainage; Wrecking; Ditching Railroad) ......AAA

OHIO—Massillon

1347—Russell & Co. (Threshing) ....AAA

OHIO—Medina

1348—Root Co., A. I. (Honey Making) ....AA

OHIO—Mechanicsburg

1349—Packham-Crimper Co. (Sheet Metal Workers'; Tools) ....E

OHIO—Miamisburg

1350—Hoover & Gamble Co. (Twine; Cordage......B

OHIO—Middleport

1351—Ohio Machine Co. (Brick; Supplies; Nail Mill) .C

OHIO—Mt. Sterling

1352—Carter Wire Fence Machy. Co. (Fence) ......D

OHIO—Mount Vernon

1353—Cooper & Co., C. & G. (Threshing) ....AA

OHIO—Nelsonville

1354—Nelsonville Fdry. & Mach. Co. (Elevating; Conveying) ....B

OHIO—Newark
1355—Scheidler Mach. Wks. Co. (Threshing).......B
OHIO—New London
1356—Arnold, D. J. C. (Brick; Supplies).........X
1357—Arnold-Creager Co. (Brick; Supplies) C
OHIO—Norwalk
1358—Bowen Cable Stave Fence Co. (Fence)......F
OHIO—Painesville
1359—Coe Mfg. Co. (Veneer Cutting; Veneer Drying;
Clipping) ....A
1360—Horton Mfg. Co. (Brick Press; Brick Sanding;
Brick; Supplies) C
OHIO—Piqua
1361—Poorman Mfg. Co. (Conductor Pipe; Eave
Trough; Cornice Makers) ....E
OHIO—Plymouth
1362—Fate Co., J. D. (Brick Press; Brick; Supplies).B
1363—Root Bros. Co. (Hand Riveting)............B
OHIO—Port Clinton
1363½—Ohio Pump Co. (Pumping) X
OHIO—Portsmouth
1364—Simpson Bros. (Fire Brick Press; Brick Molds)
D
OHIO—Salem
1365—Buckeye Engine Co. (Gas Engine).......AAA
1366—Clark Co., W. J. (Coal Hoisting; Handling;
Conveying) ....B
1367—Deming Co. (Horse Power Pumping)......AA
1368—Silver Mfg. Co. (Band Sawing; Boxing; Hub
Boring; Spoke) ....AA
OHIO—Sandusky
1369—Klotz Machine Co. (Wood Shaping; Wood Tenoning; Wood Polishing; Carriage Builders')......C
1370—Sandusky Tool Co. (Coopers').............A
1371—Warren Electric Mfg. Co. (Laundry) ....A
OHIO—Shelby
1372—Brightman Mfg. Co. (Shaft Polishing; Shaft
Straightening) ....AA
OHIO—Sidney
1373—Sidney Steel Scraper Co. (Ditching).........B
OHIO—Springfield
1374—Foos Mfg. Co. (Grinding) ....F
1375—Green Mfg. Co. (Street Sweeping) ....F
1376—Kelly Co., O. S. (Pick-Up Street Sweeping;
Feed Milling) ....AA
1377—Owen Mach. Tool Co. (Plain; Universal Milling)
D
1378—Long, W. Z. (Pop-Corn) ....D
1379—Rogers Iron Co. (Cutting Tobacco) ....B
1380—Safety Emery Wheel Co. (Emery Wheel; Buffing; Polishing) ....D
1381—Shawver Co. (Wood Fluting; Wood Twisting;
Molding, &c.) ....D
1382—Springfield Mach. Tool Co. (Crank; Geared
Shaping) ....A
1383—Warder, Bushnell & Glessner Co. (Harvesting)
AAAA
1384—Webster & Perks Tool Co. (Bolt Threshing;
Grinding; Self-Oiling; Buffing; Polishing; Sand
Molding; Nut Tapping; Bicycle Threading)....C
1385—Western Mfg. Co. (Metal Cutting-Off; Cylinder
Boring) ....D
OHIO—Steubenville
1386—Means Foundry & Machine Co. (Brick Press;
Brick; Supplies) ....B
OHIO—Tiffin
1387—Loomis Machine Co. (Well Sinking) .....AA
1388—National Machinery Co. (Bolt Heading; Bolt
Pointing; Bolt Threading; Bolt Upsetting;
& Pin; Forming & Bending; Nut Blanking; Nut Fac-
ing; Nut Milling; Nut Tapping; Pipe Threaders;
Screw Slotting; Slitting; Upsetting; Washer Cut-
ting; Bolt Forging; Forging & Bending; Glass
Banding; Glass Cracking-off; Glass Grinding; Rivet;
Spike; Washer; Bolt & Nut; Wire Nail) ....AA
1389—Sterling Emery Wheel Mfg. Co. (Buffing;
Polishing ....A
1390—Tiffin Wagon Co. (Brick; Supplies) ....A
OHIO—Toledo
1391—Baker Bros. (Cylinder Boring; Drilling & Tapping; Key-Seating; Key-Way; Metal Boring; Rod;
Pin; Dowel; Tapping) ....A
1392—Haughton Elevator & Mach. Co., 116 S. Huron
(Elevating; Conveying) ....B
1393—Heartley, Geo. W. (Metal Boring; Riveting, for
Metal Wheels; Sheet Metal Workers' & Tools; Slitting; Tire Welding; Carriage Builders') ......D
1394—Kent Machine Co. (Match Box; Match).......B
1395—Merrill Mfg. Co. (Pipe Cutting; Threading; Pipe
Nipple) ....B
1396—Ross & Co., E. (Carpet Rug)................A
1397—Stevens Co.. B. A. (Butchers').............A
1398—Toledo Mach. & Tool Co. (Car Testing; Double

Seaming; Riveting; Sheet Metal Workers' & Tools; Shipping Tag; Slitting; Soldering; Wiring).......A

1399—Vulcan Iron Works (Ditching; Ice & Refrigerating; Coal Hoisting & Handling; Horse Power Hoisting; Steam Power Hoisting) ....A

OHIO—Upper Sandusky

1400—National Steam Pump Co. (Combination Bolt Clipper; Bolt Wrench; Fire Bolt Holder).......B

OHIO—Wapaconeta

1401—Brown & Co., M. F. (Dairy)..............A

OHIO—Warren

1402—Excelsior Hoisting Machinery Co. (**Coal;** Ore Handling) X

OHIO—Wellington

1403—Wellington Machine Co. (Brick Mold Sanding; Brick; Supplies; Brick Press)..............B

OHIO—Wellsville

1404—Stevenson Co. (Tin Plate; Brick; Supplies; Can Makers'; Rolling Mill).....................B

OHIO—Westerville

1405—Bennett & Co., H. L. (Tile Ditching)......E

OHIO—Willoughby

1406—American Machinery Co. (Bolt Heading; Threading; Hot Pressed Nut, &c.).....................X

OHIO—Wilmington

1407—Irwin Auger Bit Co. (Conveying)...........B

OHIO—Xenia

1408—Kelly Machine Co., R. A. (Crank Shaping; Crank Shafting; Cordage) ....A

OHIO—Youngstown

1409—Tod & Co., Wm. (Water Works; Pumping)..AA

1410—Youngstown Foundry & Mach. Co. (Rolling Mill) C

OREGON—Astoria

1411—Astoria Iron Works (Inc.) (Canning)........A

1412—Scow Bay Iron & Brass Works (Cane Seat Chair) X

PA.—Allegheny

1413—Albree Iron Works, Chester B., 1115 Market (Pneumatic Riveting) ....B

1414—Carlin Machinery & Supply Co., 103 Lacock (Elevating; Conveying; Hoisting) ....A

1415—Carlins' Sons Co., Thos. (Coal; Ore Handling).A

1416—Eagle Tool & Machine Co., 120 Sandusky (Gear Cutting; Special Tools; Machinery) ....F

1417—Pittsburg Machine Tool Co. (Car Wheel Boring) ....A

PA.—Allentown

1418—Allentown Foundry & Mach. Works (Water Works Pumping; Wine Pumping) ....A

1419—Grammes & Sons, L. F. (Cigar Box, &c.; Board Printing; Box Nailing; Card Cutting; Cutting-off; Wood; Embossing, for Wood, Paper, Cloth, Silk, &c.; Paper Cutting; Rip Saw; Sand Papering; Wood Sawing & Splitting; Wooden Box; Brush Nailing; Printers') ....B

1420—Mosser & Son, Wm. F. (Cement Rotary Crushers; Bark Mills) ....A

PA.—Ashland

1421—Goyne Steam Pump Works (Wine Pumping)..B

PA.—Bangor

1422—Flory Mfg. Co., S. (Elevating; Conveying)...A

PA.—Beaver

1423—Beaver Mfg. Co. (Acetylene Gas).............X

PA.—Beaver Falls

1424—Keystone Driller Co. (Artesian Well; Traction Drilling; Well Sinking; Mineral Prospecting)......A

The oldest manufacturers of portable drillers.
Water Well Machines. They embody the result of 30 years' experience in drilling and drill making. Traction and Non-traction styles, 100 to 1,000 foot capacity.
Oil Well Rigs, 1,000 to 3,000 feet. The simplest, strongest and speediest deep well drillers sold. Used throughout the Pennsylvania oil fields.
Mineral Prospecting Machines. Used in testing for Gold, Zinc, Coal, etc. Make 8-inch hole through anything. Bring everything to the surface. Sectionalized for transportation in rough country.
Contractors' Machine for making large Blast Holes, Air Holes for Shafts, Bridge Pier Soundings, etc.

PA.—Bellefonte

1425—Tenkins & Lingle (Axe Factory)..............D

PA.—Birdsboro

1426—Diamond Drill & Mach. Co. Belt Lacing; Well Sinking) ....A

PA.—Blue Ball

1427—Shirk, P. E. (Wrapper Cutting; Cigar Box)...D

PA.—Bristol

1428—Ardrey & Sons, S. B. (Cloth Brushing; Napping) ....F

PA.—Brownsville
1429—Herbertson's Sons, J. (Oil Well).............D
PA.—Carbondale
1430—Carbondale Machine Co. (Ice; Refrigerating).AA
1431—Hendrick Mfg. Co. (Ltd.) (Perforated Sheet Metal) ....AA
PA.—Chambersburg
1432—Chambersburg Engineering Co. (Riveting; Hydraulic Riveting) ....A
1433—Wolf Co. (Inc.) (Gear Cutting) ....AA
1434—Woods' Sons, T. B. (Pulley Molding; Wood Molding) ....A
PA.—Chester
1435—Chester Steel Casting Co., 407 Sansom (Br. Phila.) (Locomotive; Electric Machinery; Rolling & Sugar Mills; Castings) ....AAA
1436—Stevenson Co. (Ltd.) (Ice Recording) ......B
1437—Vulcan Works (Cement) ....B
PA.—Clearfield
1438—Clearfield Machine Shops (Ltd.) (Fire Brick; Press) ....D
1439—Gearhart & Son, Joseph E. (Family Knitting)..C
PA.—Coatesville
1440—Ridgway & Son Co., Craig (Hydraulic).......A
PA.—Columbia
1441—Smith, E. G. (Power Reaming).............D
1442—Wilson Laundry Mach. Co. (Tumbling; Laundry) ....A
PA.—Connellsville
1443—Boyts, Porter & Co. (Wine Pumping).......A
1444—Connellsville Mach. & Car Co. (Brick; Supplies; Coke Crushing) ....A
PA.—Downingtown
1445—Downingtown Mfg. Co. (Ltd.) (Paper Mill)..B
PA.—East Downingtown
1446—Downingtown Mfg. Co. (Ltd.) (Paper Making) B
PA.—Du Bois
1447—Du Bois Iron Works (Elevating; Conveying) AAAA
PA.—Lake Centre
1448—Irvine, A. T. (Oil Well).....................X
PA.—Ellwood City
1449—Standard Engineering Co. (Pipe Threading).AA
PA.—Erie
1450—Brown Folding Mach. Co. (Paper Folding)...B
1451—Chapman Separator Works, C. L. (Dairy)......D
1452—Erie City Iron Works (Dynamo; Electric).AAAA
1453—Erie Machine Shops (Asphalt).............B
1454—Erie Specialty Co. (Chill Shaking, for Milk Lemonade, &c.; Tobacco Cutting) ....B
1455—Jarecki Mfg. Co. (Pipe Cutting; Threading; Pipe; Screw Plate) ....AAAA
1456—Burke Electric Co. (Dynamo, Electric) ......A
1457—Stearns Mfg. Co. (Lath; Saw Mill).........AA
1458—Williams Tool Co. (Pipe Cutting; Threading)..B
PA.—Frankford
1459—Frankford Machine Works (Calico Printers').X
PA.—Hanover
1460—American Foundry & Machine Co. (Pulley Molding) X
PA.—Harrisburg
1461—Harrisburg Foundry & Mach. Works (Road Building) ....A
1462—Hickok Mfg. Co., W. O. (Bookbinders'; Backing; Case Binding; Gold Saving; Paper Ruling, Paging; Numbering; Backing; Perforating; Sawing; Eyeletting; Self-Feed; Stabbing; Striker; Lapper)..AA
PA.—Hollidaysburg
1463—McLanahan-Stone Machine Co. (Phosphate Washing; Coal; Ore Handling; Elevating; Conveying)..A
PA.—Kennett Square
1464—American Road Machine Co. (Ditching; Street Sweeping; Road; Elevating; Conveying).........AA
1465—Good Roads Machinery Co. (Crushing; Ditching; Screening; Street Sweeping; Elevating; Conveying) ....D
PA.—Lancaster
1466—Champion Blower & Forge Co. (Bench Boring) AA
1467—Martin, Wm. R. (Cement)...................B
1468—Martin Brick Mach. Mfg. Co., Henry (Brick Press; Brick; Supplies; Elevating; Conveying).....B
1469—Potts, David H. (Air Moving) ....D
PA.—Lebanon
1470—American Iron & Steel Mfg. Co. (Bolt Pointing) ....AAAA
PA.—Landsdowne
1471—Howard Foundry & Machine Works (Buckram; Carpet; Hoisting; Dyeing; Felt; Box; Hydraulic; Metal Printing; Engraving; Mint; Paper Making; Printers'; Road Building; Street Cleaning).......D

PA.—*Lansdale*
1472—Heebner & Sons (Threshing) ....A
PA.—*Lanesboro*
1473—Barnes Mfg. Co. (Quarry)..................B
PA.—*Lansdale*
1474—Heebner & Sons (Saw Mill)...............A
PA.—*Lebanon*
1475—Weimer Machine Tool Co. (Pig Iron Casting; Blast Furnace; Sugar) ....AA
PA.—*Lewisburg*
1476—Sober, C. K. (Acetylene Gas) ....B
PA.—*Mauch Chunk*
1477—Stroh, W. H. (Coal Washing)..............C
PA.—*Meadville*
1478—Meadville Vise Co. (Cylinder Boring; Cylinder Metal Boring) ....A
PA.—*Mechanicsburg*
1479—Comstock, Geo. S. (Coal Washing)..........C
PA.—*Media*
1480—Wood, Wm. H. (Forming; Bending; Hydraulic Riveting; Portable Riveting) ....D
PA.—*Milton*
1481—Shimer & Sons, Samuel J. (Spiral Molding)..A
PA.—*Monroeton*
1481 1-2—Booth & Co., O. N. (Boring; Pointing)....D
PA.—*Montgomery*
1482—Houston & Levi Co. (Br. Amer. Woodworking Mach. Co., N. Y. City) (Sash; Door; Blind).AAAA
PA.—*Montrose*
1483—Beach, H. W. (Mitreing; Sawing) ....B
PA.—*Muncy*
1484—Sprout, Waldron Co. (Bolting; Corn Mill; Flour Mill) ....A
PA.—*Norristown*
1485—Rittenhouse, Frank (Confectioners') ....F
1486—Rothe Mfg. & Supply Co., O. & P. (Bleaching) ....E

PA.—*Philadelphia*
1488—Acme Staple Co., 500 N. 12th (Staple)......X
1489—Allen & Co., S. L., 1017 Market (Tobacco Hoeing) ....AA
1490—Altemus, Jacob K., 2816 N. 4th (Carpet Rolling; Carpet) C
1491—Alteneder & Sons, Theo., 945 Ridge Av. (Graduating) ....D
1492—American Carbide Lamp Co., Phila. Bourse (Acetylene Gas) ....D
1493—American Drying Machinery Co., Westmoreland & P. & R. Ry. (Yarn Scouring) ....D
1494—Atlantic Works (Inc.), 23d & Arch (Circular Sawing, Wood; Cutting-off, Wood; Dado; Panel Raising; Post Boring; Rip Saw; Rod, Pin & Dowel; Sand Papering; Saw Sharpening; Wood Shaping; Wood Tenoning; Wood Boring; Wood Flooring; Wood Mortising; Wood Surfacing; Bookbinders')..B
1495—Barker, James (Card Grinding) ....A
1496—Barr Pumping Engine Co. (Water Works Pumping) ....A
1497—Beck Paper Co., Chas. (Paper Box) ....B
1498—Bement, Niles & Co. (Br. N. Y. City) (Arch Bar Drilling; Axle Finishing; Link Drilling; Nut; Railroad Shop; Steam Forge; Boring & Turning, Vertical; Boiler Shop; Bolt; Bridge Work; Brass Working; Car Builders'; Ship Yard) ....AAAA
1499—Berger Bros. Co., 237 Arch (Sheet Metal Workers') ....A
1500—Bilgram, Hugo, 12th & Noble (Internal Gear Cutting) ....A
1501—Borchers & Co., Richard C., 1708 G'tn. Av. (Napping) ....D
1502—Branson Mach. Co., 504 N. American (Incand. Gas Mantle; Hand Knitting; Automatic Knitting; Boot Knitting) ....A
1503—Brill Co., J. G., 62d & Woodland Av. (Street Railway Sweeping) ....AAAA
1504—Brinton & Co., H., 213 Race (Seamless Knitting) ....AA
1505—Butterworth & Sons Co., H. W., 2415 E. York (Blacking; Blueing; Calendering; Carpet Finishing; Cloth Brushing; Cloth Finishing; Cloth Rolling; Cloth Measuring; Crabbing; Band Cutting-off, Wood; Drying; Print Work; Padding; Textile Shearing; Singeing; Sizing; Tentering; Wool & Worsted Finishing; Wool Scouring; Wool Willowing; Cloth Calendering; Cotton Finishing; Drying; Lath; Worsted Finishing; Bleaching; Calico Printers'; Carpet; Dyeing) ....A.
1506—Campbell, P. F. (Drug & Chemical Bolting; Cement; Fertilizer; Putty; Lead) ....D
1507—Carnell, George (Est. of), 1819 N. 5th (Fire & Red Brick Press; Clay Tempering; Brick; Supplies).B
1508—Challenge Machine Co., 3223 Turner (Grinding) D

1509—Chambers Bros. Co., 52d, below Lancaster Av. (Brick Press; Paper Folding, for Printers, Bookbinders, &c.; Glossing; Varnishing; Pasting; Sawing) ....AA
1510—Champion Candy Mach. Co., 3257 Old York Rd. (Candy) ....B
1511—Champion Machine Co. (Crocheting) C
1512—Colladay, Joseph A., 624 Race (Band Sawing; Wood Shaping; Wood Molding) ....B
1513—Contractors' Tool Co., 118 S. 6th (Asphalt)...F
1514—Cox & Sons' Co., 215 Race (Pipe Cutting; Threading; Ice) ....B
1515—Cresson Co., Geo. V., 18th & Allegheny Av. (Cement) ....AA
1516—Cunningham Mfg. Co., 113 S. 7th (Bottlers' Supplies) ....B
1517—Dallett Co., Thos. H., York & Sedgley (Electric Portable; Horizontal Boring; Drilling; Centre Grinding; Electric Portable Shaft Key-Seating; Pneumatic Riveting; Stone Cutting; Pneumatic Stone Surfacing; Portable & Boiler Shell Drilling) ....B
1518—Diamond Textile Machine Works, 2d & Diamond (Carpet) ....F
1519—Dill Machine Co. (Inc.), T. C. (Slotting) ....F
1520—Disston & Sons (Inc.), Henry (Saw Sharpening; Circular Saw, Hand Power) ....AAAA
1521—Dodge Coal Storage Co., Nicetown (Coal & Ore Handling) ....A
1522—Espen-Lucas Machine Works, Broad & Noble (Cold Metal Cutting-off; Metal Sawing, &c.; Boring; Milling; Drilling, &c.) ....D
1523—Etting, Edw. J., Land Title Bldg. (Sand Molding) ....B
1524—Evans' Sons, Jno., 13th & Buttonwood (Car; Cariage Spring; Farmers'; Flashing; Slating; Striking-out; Buffing; Polishing; Light & Heavy Spring Coiling; Spring Testing) ....B
1525—Franklin Machine Works (Inc.) (Printers')....X
1526—Furbush & Son Mach. Co., M. A. (Carpet; Woolen) ....A
1527—Girard Mach. & Tool Co., 2616 Girard Av. (Cork Sticking; Dating; Labeling; Lidding; Packing; Snuff Packing in Bottles) C
1528—Gleason Spoke, Lathe & Machinery Co., 2d & Diamond (Wood Molding) X
1529—Gliem & Co., F. H., 1037 Ridge (Gear Cutting) ....D
1530—Globe Machine Works, Frankfort (Hammer; Hatchet) X
1531—Gordon, W. J., 235 Bread (Sheet Metal Workers'; Tools) ....D
1532—Griscom & McFeeley (Flour Mill) C
1533—Hatton's Sons, Thos. (Silk) ....A
1534—Harrington, Son & Co., Edwin, 1515 Penn Av. (Gear Cutting; Metal Boring) ....AA
1536—Horton, Pembroke D., 15th & Fairmount (Bakers') X
1537—Jefferson & Bro., Edw., 127 S. 2d (Carpet)...D
1538—Johnson, Jr. & Co., Israel H., 1424 Callowhill (Metal Sawing; Pipe Cutting; Threading; Screw)..A
1539—Jones, Lewis, 60 1-2 Media (Cloth Brushing; Napping) ....AA
1540—Kennedy, Ralph M., 117 N. 7th (Band Sawing) X
1541—Keystone Type Foundry Co. (Paper Ruling)..AA
1542—Klein, Chas. C., 2850 N. Marshall (Sizing)..D
1543—Liberman, Isadore, 223 S. 5th (Cigar).......F
1544—Link Belt Engineering Co., Nicetown (Coal & Ore Handling; Elevating; Conveying; Coal Hoisting) ....A
1545—Mills & Bro., Thos., 1301 N. 8th (Confectioners') ....A
1546—Moore & White Co., 15th & Lehigh Av. (Fourdrinier & Cylinder Paper; Linoleum & Floor Cloth Printing; Rolling Mill; Paper Making; Roofing Paper Saturating) ....AA
1547—Morris, Henry G., 333 Walnut (Cane Shredding; Sugar; Centrifugal) ....B
1548—Morris, P. Hollingsworth, Phila. Bourse (Pipe Cutting; Threading) C
1549—Morse, Williams & Co. (Bell Power Hoisting; Hand Power Hoisting; Horse Power Hoisting)..AA
1550—Mulford Co., H. K., 412 S. 13th (Granulating; Tablet; Capsule) ....AAA
1551—Moyer & Co., J. W., 1736 N. Howard (Elevating; Conveying) ....D
1552—National Automatic Knitter Co. (Automatic Knitting) ....B
1553—Nazel Machine Tool Works, 1042 Ridge Av. (Centering; Portable Key-Seating) ....E
1554—Newton Machine Tool Works (Inc.), 2343 Vine (Cold Saw Sharpening; Metal Cutting-off; Cylinder Boring; Die Sinking; Die Sinking & Milling,

Combined; Gear Cutting; Metal Boring; Cold Metal Sawing; Horizontal, Vertical & Universal Milling; Nut Facing; Nut Milling; Pulley Hub Drilling & Tapping; Rail Ending; Rail Sawing; Shaping; Iron Shop Sawing; Slotting; Tapping; Cutting-off Saw; Journal Box Shaping; Metal Band Sawing; Vertical Boring) ....AA

1555—Nittinger, August (Cutting, Fat) ....A

1556—Nye & Fredick Co., 606 Arch (Circular Rib Knitting) ....D

1557—North Bros. Mfg. Co., Lehigh Av. & American (Fluting; Tobacco Cutting) ....AA

1558—Olsen, Tinius & Co., 500 N. 12th (Cement Testing; Oil Testing; Hydraulic; Chain Testing; Marble Molding & Countersinking; Testing; Wire Testing; Impact Testing; Leather Testing; Paper Testing; Cloth Testing) ....B

1559—Ott, Geo. F., 209 Buttonwood (Ice; Refrigerating) ....A

1560—Paxson Co., J. W., 1021 N. Delaware Av. (Sand Blast, for Cleaning Steel & Castings; Sand Mixing; Sand Molding) ....AA

1561—Pedrick & Ayer Co., 1001 Hamilton (Crank Boring; Cylinder Boring; Metal Boring; Milling; Pneumatic Riveting) ....A

1562—Peerless Belt Lacing Mach. Co., cor. Swanson & Moore (Belt Lacing) ....E

1563—Penna. Globe Gaslight Co., Broad & Arch (Gas) ....A

1564—Penna. Iron Works Co., 50th & Lancaster Av. (Ice; Refrigerating; Hydraulic Riveting) .....AAA

1565—Phila. Drying Machinery Co., 6721 Germantown Av. (Yarn Scouring; Tobacco Drying) .....D

1566—Phila. Pneumatic Tool Co., 21st & Allegheny Av. (Pneumatic Riveting; Pneumatic Yoke Riveting; Pneumatic Wood Boring) ....B

1567—Phila. Roll & Mach. Co., 23d & Washn. Av. (Wire Nail; Rolling Mill; Hydraulic Riveting; Hot Sawing; Tin Plate; Straightening, Metal; Pipe)...A

1568—Phila. Textile Machinery Co., Hancock & Somerset (Burring; Garnett; Wool Willowing; Yarn Scouring; Drying, Tobacco) ....AA

1569—Pennsylvania Crusher Co., Stephen Girard Bldg. (Coal Crushers; Coke Crushers) X

1570—Power & Co., L., 20 S. 23d (Band Sawing; Car Boring; Cutting-off, Wood; Rip Saw; Wood Boring; Wood Mortising; Wood Molding; Bench Boring; Cross-Cut Saw; Tenoning; Vertical Boring; Boxmakers'; Sash; Door; Blind; Planing Mill; Furniture) ....AA

1571—Queen & Co. (Inc.), 1010 Chestnut (Static Electric) ....AA

1572—Reid Creamery & Dairy Supply Co., A. H. (Testing, Milk) ....A

1573—Riehle Bros. Testing Machine Co., 1424 N. 9th (Cement Testing; Marble Molding & Countersinking; Testing) ....B

1574—Rutschmann Bros. (Soap) C

1575—Schaum & Uhlinger (Piano; Jacquard; Silk; Card Stamping, Power; Repeating) ....AAA

1576—Scott & Williams, 2079 E. Cumberland (Knit Goods Finishing) ....A

1577—Sellers & Co. (Inc.), Wm., 1600 Hamilton (Bolt Screwing; Grinding; Car Wheel Boring; Cylinder Boring; Drill Pointing; Facing Machines; Forcing; Gear Cutting; Metal Boring; Milling; Pneumatic Riveting; Multiple Punching; Punching & Shearing, Combined; Quartering; Rail Bending & Straightening; Riveting; Hydraulic Riveting; Portable Riveting; Steam Riveting; Sand Mixing; Shaft Straightening; Shaping; Slabbing; Slotting; Hydraulic Testing; Traction Testing; Arch Bar Drilling; Floor Boring; Hoisting & Handling; Horizontal Milling; Plate Straightening; Mixing; Switch & Frog Planing) ....AAAA

1578—Sheip Mfg. Co., H. H., Col. Av. & Rand (Packing Box Stock Trimming) ....AA

1579—Smith, Drum & Co., 2503 Canal (Singeing) ...B

1580—Smith Woolen Machinery Co., James (Spinning; Garnett; Burring; Balling; Woolen; Card Grinding; Garnett & Card, Combined; Hank Winding; Napping; Wool Scouring; Wool Willowing; Cloth Cutting; Pickering; Wool Washing) ......AA

1581—Southwark Foundry & Mach. Co. (Rolling Mill; Wine Pumping; Hydraulic) ....AAA

1582—Stokes & Parrish Elevator Co. (Hoisting, Steam Power; Hydraulic) ....A

1583—Stow Flexible Shaft Co., N. 26th cor. Buttonwood (Portable Boring; Buffing & Polishing; Crank Pin Turning; Portable Cylinder Boring; Glass Polishing; Metal Boring; Portable, Wood & Metal Polishing; Portable Tapping & Reaming; Valve Seat Planing) ....B

1585—Taylor, James, 835 Arch (Hosiery Knitting; Yarn Raveling) C
1586—Teal, Chas. A., 1361 Ridge Av. (Elevating; Conveying) X
1587—Thompson & Campbell (Cement; Chocolate; Glue; Wheat Polishing; Flour Mill; White Lead Wks.)...X
1588—Tilghman, B. C. & R. A., 1126 S. 11th (Sand Blast) ....B
1589—Twitchell Co., S. (Bottling; Corking; Filling).A
1590—Underwood & Co., H. B., 1023 Hamilton (Crank Pin Turning; Portable Cylinder Boring; Portable Milling; Valve Seat Milling) ....B
1592—Walter's Sons, Wm. P., 1233 Market (Mitreing; Vise Combined) ....B
1593—Walton, P. M. (Chocolate) ....G
1594—Wenzell Machine Co., S. S., 443 N. 12th (Bottle Washing; Rinsing) C
1595—Wirz, A. H. (Hand Pill) ....A

PA.—Pittsburg

1597—Amer. Bedding & Machy. Co. (Filling Machines)
....X
1598—Bailey-Farrell Mfg. Co., 619 Smithfield (Smoke Test) ....AA
1599—Baird Machy. Co., U. (Iron; Wood Working)..A
1600—Carron & Co., A. M., 108 Market (Pneumatic Riveting) ....D
1601—Diescher Coupler Co., 41st & A. V. Ry. (Cork Cutting) ....D
1602—Fisher Fdry. & Machine Co. (Glass Works; Plate Glass) ....A
1603—Hand-Stitch Broom Sewing Mach. Co. (Broom Sewing) ....B
1604—Heyl & Patterson, 51 Water (Slag; Cinder for Blast Furnaces; Coal Washing; Elevating; Conveying for Mine; Steel Plants) ....A
1605—Hickman-Melborn Co., 200 Liberty (Screw Cutting; Vise Combined) ....A
1606—Hogg Iron & Steel Fdry. Co., Geo. A., 24th & R. R. (Furnace Charging for Annealing Furnaces).A
1607—Lewis Fdry. & Machine Co., 1001 Bingham (Corrugating; Hot Sawing) ....A
1608—McCormack Co., J. S., 25th & A. V. Ry. (Core Making; Automatic Sand Molding)...............B
1609—Mackintosh-Hemphill & Co. (Ltd.) (Rolling Mill)
....AAA
1610—Marshall Bros. (Hoisting; Steam Power)....AA
1611—Mesta Machine Co. (Rolling Mill; Tin Plate)..
....AAA
1612—Milholland, J. & J. B. (Hoisting; Steam Power)
....A
1613—Mould Co., Henry S., Empire Bldg. (Briquetting)
....B
1615—Oil Well Supply Co. (Oil Well; Well Sinking)..
....AAAA
1616—Phillips & McLaren, 24th & Smallman (Bolt; Nut) ....B
1617—Pittsburg Mfg. Co., 28th & R. R. (Bending; Straightening; Metal Straightening; Nut; Spike)...A
1618—Pittsburg Mfg. Co. (Bending; Nail Mill) ....A
1619—Pittsburg Tool & Drop Forge Co., Arrott Bldg. (Rail Bending; Straightening) ....D
1620—Rees & Sons Co., Jas. (Hoisting Steam Power; Ship Yard) ....AA
1621—Riter-Conly Mfg. Co. (Mixing)...........AAA
1622—Scaife Fdry. & Machine Co., 28th & Smallman (Hot Sawing; Cold Metal Sawing; Blast Furnace; Coal Mining; Coal Washing; Elevating; Conveying)
....B
1623—Simonds Mfg. Co., 25th & Liberty (Car Wheel Truing) ....D
1624—Sommerfeld Mach. & Mfg. Co., R. G., 224 3d Av. (Glass Blowing) ....B
1625—Tate, Jones & Co., Empire Bldg. (Link Belt Appliances) ....E
1626—United Engineering & Fdry. Co., 54th & A. V. Ry. (Corrugating; Hot Sawing; Pipe Cutting; Threading; Tapping for Tube Mills) ....AAAA
1627—Westinghouse Electric & Mfg. Co. (Electric Coal Mining, &c.) ....AAAA

PA.—Pittston
1628—Exeter Machine Wks. (Coal Mining; Coal; Ore Handling; Elevating; Conveying) ....AA
PA.—Pottstown
1629—Ellis Keystone Agrl. Wks. (Threshing).......B
PA.—Reading
1630—Boss Knitting Machine Wks. (Seamless Knitting; Automobile) ....B
1631—Penn. Hdw. Co. (Tobacco Cutting).........AA
1632—Reading Iron Co. (Refrigerating; Rolling Mill)
....AAAA
1633—Textile Machine Wks. (Braiding; for Insulating Electric Wires) C

1585—Taylor, James, 835 Arch (Hosiery Knitting; Yarn Raveling) C
1586—Teal, Chas. A., 1361 Ridge Av. (Elevating; Conveying) X
1587—Thompson & Campbell (Cement; Chocolate; Glue; Wheat Polishing; Flour Mill; White Lead Wks.)..X
1588—Tilghman, B. C. & R. A., 1126 S. 11th (Sand Blast) ....B
1589—Twitchell Co., S. (Bottling; Corking; Filling).A
1590—Underwood & Co., H. B., 1023 Hamilton (Crank Pin Turning; Portable Cylinder Boring; Portable Milling; Valve Seat Milling) ....B
1592—Walter's Sons, Wm. P., 1233 Market (Mitreing; Vise Combined) ....B
1593—Walton, P. M. (Chocolate) ....G
1594—Wenzell Machine Co., S. S., 443 N. 12th (Bottle Washing; Rinsing) C
1595—Wirz, A. H. (Hand Pill) ....A
P.A.—Pittsburg
1597—Amer. Bedding & Machy. Co. (Filling Machines) X
1598—Bailey-Farrell Mfg. Co., 619 Smithfield (Smoke Test) ....AA
1599—Baird Machy. Co., U. (Iron; Wood Working)..A
1600—Carron & Co., A. M., 108 Market (Pneumatic Riveting) ....D
1601—Diescher Coupler Co., 41st & A. V. Ry. (Cork Cutting) ....D
1602—Fisher Fdry. & Machine Co. (Glass Works; Plate Glass) ....A
1603—Hand-Stitch Broom Sewing Mach. Co. (Broom Sewing) ....B
1604—Heyl & Patterson, 51 Water (Slag; Cinder for Blast Furnaces; Coal Washing; Elevating; Conveying for Mine; Steel Plants) ....A
1605—Hickman-Melborn Co., 200 Liberty (Screw Cutting; Vise Combined) ....A
1606—Hogg Iron & Steel Fdry. Co., Geo. A., 24th & R. R. (Furnace Charging for Annealing Furnaces).A
1607—Lewis Fdry. & Machine Co., 1001 Bingham (Corrugating; Hot Sawing) ....A
1608—McCormack Co. J. S., 25th & A. V. Ry. (Core Making; Automatic Sand Molding)...............B
1609—Mackintosh-Hemphill & Co. (Ltd.) (Rolling Mill) AAA
1610—Marshall Bros. (Hoisting; Steam Power)....AA
1611—Mesta Machine Co. (Rolling Mill; Tin Plate)..AAA
1612—Milholland, J. & J. B. (Hoisting; Steam Power) A
1613—Mould Co., Henry S., Empire Bldg. (Briquetting) B
1615—Oil Well Supply Co. (Oil Well; Well Sinking).. AAAA
1616—Phillips & McLaren, 24th & Smallman (Bolt; Nut) ....B
1617—Pittsburg Mfg. Co., 28th & R. R. (Bending; Straightening; Metal Straightening; Nut; Spike)...A
1618—Pittsburg Mfg. Co. (Bending; Nail Mill)......A
1619—Pittsburg Tool & Drop Forge Co., Arrott Bldg. (Rail Bending; Straightening) ....D
1620—Rees & Sons Co., Jas. (Hoisting Steam Power; Ship Yard) ....AA
1621—Riter-Conly Mfg. Co. (Mixing)............AAA
1622—Scaife Fdry. & Machine Co., 28th & Smallman (Hot Sawing; Cold Metal Sawing; Blast Furnace; Coal Mining; Coal Washing; Elevating; Conveying) B
1623—Simonds Mfg. Co., 25th & Liberty (Car Wheel Truing) ....D
1624—Sommerfeld Mach. & Mfg. Co., R. G., 224 3d Av. (Glass Blowing) ....B
1625—Tate, Jones & Co., Empire Bldg. (Link Belt Appliances) ....E
1626—United Engineering & Fdry. Co., 54th & A. V. Ry. (Corrugating; Hot Sawing; Pipe Cutting; Threading; Tapping for Tube Mills) ....AAAA
1627—Westinghouse Electric & Mfg. Co. (Electric Coal Mining, &c.) ....AAAA
P.A.—Pittston
1628—Exeter Machine Wks. (Coal Mining; Coal; Ore Handling; Elevating; Conveying) ....AA
P.A.—Pottstown
1629—Ellis Keystone Agrl. Wks. (Threshing).......B
P.A.—Reading
1630—Boss Knitting Machine Wks. (Seamless Knitting; Automobile) ....B
1631—Penn. Hdw. Co. (Tobacco Cutting) ....AA
1632—Reading Iron Co. (Refrigerating; Rolling Mill) AAAA
1633—Textile Machine Wks. (Braiding; for Insulating Electric Wires) C

1717—Bonsack Machine Co. (Cigarette Making)......A
VA.—Petersburg
1718—Titus, Elmer E. (Automatic Power Quark Basket Stapling; Barrel; Basket; Butter Dish; Veneer Cutting) C
VA.—Richmond
1719—Cardwell Machine Co. (Cigarette Making; Tobacco Cutting; Drying; Packing; Steam Power Hoisting; Oil Extracting; Water Works; Pumping; Peanut) ....A
1720—Mayo, Hysore & Co. (Drying; Tobacco)......B
WASH.—Fair Haven
1721—Letson & Burpee (Canning) ....D
W. VA.—Fairmont
1722—Wagner-Palmros Mfg. Co. (Coal Mining)....A
W. VA.—Wheeling
1723—Centre Fdry. Co. (Brick; Supplies)...........C
WIS.—Appleton
1724—Valley Iron Wks. Co. (Wood Barking).......C
WIS.—Beaver Dam
1725—Roswell Mfg. Co., J. S. (Threshing)..........A
WIS.—Beloit
1726—Beloit Iron Wks. (Cylinder) ....A
1727—Berlin Machine Wks. (Sash Door; Blind)AAAA
1728—Fraser Mfg. Co. (Wood Trimming) X
1729—Thompson & Sons Mfg. Co., J. (Wood Sawing; Splitting) ....AA
WIS.—Eau Claire
1730—McDonough Mfg. Co. (Band Sawing; Lumber Mill; Sash; Door; Blind) ....A
1731—Phoenix Mfg. Co. (Band Sawing; Centering)..A
WIS.—Fort Atkinson
1732—Cornish, Curtis & Greene Mfg. Co. (Testing Milk) ....A
WIS.—Janesville
1733—New Doty Mfg. Co. (Boilermakers' Punching; Bolt Heading; I Beam Punching; Hand Shearing; Screw; Multiple Punching) ....D
WIS.—Kenosha
1734—Badger Brass Mfg. Co. (Acetylene Gas)......C
WIS.—La Crosse
1735—Smith Mfg. Co. (Grubbing) ....A
WIS.—Madison
1736—Fuller & Johnson Mfg. Co. (Tobacco Hoeing).. AAA
WIS.—Manitowoc
1737—Smalley Mfg. Co. (Ensilage) ....B
WIS.—Milwaukee
1738—Allis-Chalmers Co. (Cyaniding; Ice; Conveying; Flour Mill; Saw Mill; Refrigerating; Water Works; Wine Pumping) ....AAAA
1739—Brodesser Elevator Mfg. Co. (Angle Straightening) X
1740—Chain Belt Co. (Coal Hoisting; Conveying; Handling) ....B
1741—Durant, W. N., 234 22d (Counting)..........E
1742—Filer & Stowell Co. (Brazing; Band Saw; Edging Saw; Coal Hoisting; Handling; Picket; Coopers' Flour Mill; Shingle; Saw Mill) ....AAA
1743—Grotenrath, Fred., 111 Water (Elevating; Conveying) ....E
1744—Hide & Leather Wkg. Mach. Co. (Tanners')..B
1745—Kempsmith Mfg. Co., Linus & Woodward (Shaft Centering; Plain; Universal; Lincoln Pattern Milling) C
1746—Kieckhefer Elevator Co., A. (Hoisting; Steam Power) C
1747—Kiewert Co., Chas. L. (Brewers'; Bottle Machinery; Keg Rolling; Pitching)................A
1748—Koss & Bros. Co., Chas. (Brewers'; Bottle Washing; Keg Rolling; Pitching)...................A
1749—Milwaukee Cock Grinding Mach. Co. (Cock Grinding for Ground Key Work) X
1750—Milwaukee Harvester Co. (Int. Harvester Co.) (Harvesting) ....AAAA
1751—Nash, J. M. (Universal Multiple Wood Boring; Special Chair; Wood Polishing) ....D
1752—National Blower Wks. (Air Moving)..........B
1753—Nordberg Mfg. Co. (Bottlers'; Supplies)......AA
1754—Pawling & Harnischfeger (Horizontal Boring; Drilling; Dynamo; Electric; Brewers' Pitching).AAA
1755—Polachek & Bro., Chas., 429 Chestnut (Acetylene Gas) ....B
1756—Prinz & Rau Mfg. Co. (Cockle) ....A
1757—Vilter Mfg. Co., 854 Clinton (Bottle Soaking; Washing; Brewers' Mashing; Ice; Refrigerating).AA
WIS.—Oshkosh
1758—Hayes Machine Co., E. B. (Cutting-Off; Wood; Lumber Mill; Double End Wood Shaping; Double End Wood Tenoning) ....B
WIS.—Racine
1759—Belle City Mfg. Co. (Ensilage; Threshing) ....B

1717—Bonsack Machine Co. (Cigarette Making)......A
VA.—Petersburg
1718—Titus, Elmer E. (Automatic Power Quark Basket Stapling; Barrel; Basket; Butter Dish; Veneer Cutting) C
VA.—Richmond
1719—Cardwell Machine Co. (Cigarette Making; Tobacco Cutting; Drying; Packing; Steam Power Hoisting; Oil Extracting; Water Works; Pumping; Peanut) ....A
1720—Mayo, Hysore & Co. (Drying; Tobacco)......B
WASH.—Fair Haven
1721—Letson & Burpee (Canning) ....D
W. VA.—Fairmont
1722—Wagner-Palmros Mfg. Co. (Coal Mining)....A
W. VA.—Wheeling
1723—Centre Fdry. Co. (Brick; Supplies)...........C
WIS.—Appleton
1724—Valley Iron Wks. Co. (Wood Barking)........C
WIS.—Beaver Dam
1725—Roswell Mfg. Co., J. S. (Threshing)..........A
WIS.—Beloit
1726—Beloit Iron Wks. (Cylinder) ....A
1727—Berlin Machine Wks. (Sash Door; Blind)AAAA
1728—Fraser Mfg. Co. (Wood Trimming) X
1729—Thompson & Sons Mfg. Co., J. (Wood Sawing; Splitting) ....AA
WIS.—Eau Claire
1730—McDonough Mfg. Co. (Band Sawing; Lumber Mill; Sash; Door; Blind) ....A
1731—Phoenix Mfg. Co. (Band Sawing; Centering)..A
WIS.—Fort Atkinson
1732—Cornish, Curtis & Greene Mfg. Co. (Testing Milk) ....A
WIS.—Janesville
1733—New Doty Mfg. Co. (Boilermakers' Punching; Bolt Heading; I Beam Punching; Hand Shearing; Screw; Multiple Punching) ....D
WIS.—Kenosha
1734—Badger Brass Mfg. Co. (Acetylene Gas)......C
WIS.—La Crosse
1735—Smith Mfg. Co. (Grubbing) ....A
WIS.—Madison
1736—Fuller & Johnson Mfg. Co. (Tobacco Hoeing)..
AAA
WIS.—Manitowoc
1737—Smalley Mfg. Co. (Ensilage) ....B
WIS.—Milwaukee
1738—Allis-Chalmers Co. (Cyaniding; Ice; Conveying; Flour Mill; Saw Mill; Refrigerating; Water Works; Wine Pumping) ....AAAA
1739—Brodesser Elevator Mfg. Co. (Angle Straightening) X
1740—Chain Belt Co. (Coal Hoisting; Conveying; Handling) ....B
1741—Durant, W. N., 234 22d (Counting).........E
1742—Filer & Stowell Co. (Brazing; Band Saw; Edging Saw; Coal Hoisting; Handling; Picket; Coopers' Flour Mill; Shingle; Saw Mill) ....AAA
1743—Grotenrath, Fred., 111 Water (Elevating; Conveying) ....E
1744—Hide & Leather Wkg. Mach. Co. (Tanners')..B
1745—Kempsmith Mfg. Co., Linus & Woodward (Shaft Centering; Plain; Universal; Lincoln Pattern Milling) ....A
1746—Kieckhefer Elevator Co., A. (Hoisting; Steam Power) C
1747—Kiewert Co., Chas. L. (Brewers'; Bottle Machinery; Keg Rolling; Pitching)................A
1748—Koss & Bros. Co., Chas. (Brewers'; Bottle Washing; Keg Rolling; Pitching).......................A
1749—Milwaukee Cock Grinding Mach. Co. (Cock Grinding for Ground Key Work) X
1750—Milwaukee Harvester Co. (Int. Harvester Co.) (Harvesting) ....AAAA
1751—Nash, J. M. (Universal Multiple Wood Boring; Special Chair; Wood Polishing) ....D
1752—National Blower Wks. (Air Moving).........B
1753—Nordberg Mfg. Co. (Bottlers'; Supplies)......AA
1754—Pawling & Harnischfeger (Horizontal Boring; Drilling; Dynamo; Electric; Brewers' Pitching).AAA
1755—Polachek & Bro., Chas., 429 Chestnut (Acetylene Gas) ....B
1756—Prinz & Rau Mfg. Co. (Cockle) ....A
1757—Vilter Mfg. Co., 854 Clinton (Bottle Soaking; Washing; Brewers' Mashing; Ice; Refrigerating).AA
WIS.—Oshkosh
1758—Hayes Machine Co., E. B. (Cutting-Off; Wood; Lumber Mill; Double End Wood Shaping; Double End Wood Tenoning) ....B
WIS.—Racine
1759—Belle City Mfg. Co. (Ensilage; Threshing) ....B

APPENDIX—Machinery (1760-1775)

1760—Case Threshing Mach. Co., J. I. (Threshing)..
....AAAA
1761—Freeman & Sons Mfg. Co., S. (Sawing) ......A
1762—Gorton Machine Co., Geo. (Engraving)........B
1763—Johnson & Field Mfg. Co. (Chafting; Smut;
    Brush Combined; Grain Cleaning) ....F
1764—Racine Malleable & Wrought Iron Co. (Picket
    Pointing) ....A
1765—Winship Mfg. Co. (Sand Papering)...........E
WIS.—Sheboygan
1766—Jenkins Machine Co. (Chair) ....B
1767—Stehn Mfg. Co. (Sand Blast for Founders)....D
1768—Winter Lumber Co., M. (Slot) ....B
WIS.—South Milwaukee
1769—Bucyrus Co. (Ditching; Railroad).....:.....AAA
WIS.—Stevens Point
1770—Cook, R. A. (Barrel; Keg; Stave; Heading)..B
WIS—Superior
1771—Duplex Mfg. Co. (Sawing) ....AA
1772—Superior Iron Wks. (Wood Bending) ....F
WIS.—Waupun
1773—Althouse-Wheeler Co. (Sawing) ....A
WIS.—Wausau
1774—Murray Mfg. Co., D. J. (Box Board; Saw Mill
    Lever) ....A
CANADA—Ontario
ONT.—Park Hill
1775—Baird & Son, H. C. (Brick; Supplies)........B

MILLINERY GOODS

See also Hats; Flowers; ..Feathers; Plants; Trimmings, etc.

CAL.—San Francisco
Union Hat Co., 578 Mission (Goods) ....B
GA.—Atlanta
National Straw Hat Works (Straw Hats) C
ILL.—Chicago
Chicago Braiding & Embroidery Co., 120 Market (Braiding; Embroidery) ....A
Raike, Lippert & Co., 264 Wabash Av. (Goods)..B
Thompson & Co., T. N., 150 Michigan (Goods) C
MO.—St. Louis
Judge, S. C., 1825 Pine (Goods) ....B

New York City
Adelson & Bro. Philip, 625 B'way (Artificial Flowers; Ostrich & Fancy Feathers) ....B
Adelson & Son, L., 603 B'way (Goods) ....B
Ailand Bros., 661 B'way (Goods) ....B
Alpi & Co., 69 W. Houston (Artificial Flowers; Ostrich & Fancy Feathers)B
Apple & Co., 8 Astor Place (Goods) C
Bendel, Henri, 67 E. 9th (Pattern & Trimmed Hats) C
Berg Bros., 223 Wooster (Goods) ....AA
Berlin & Trosky, 133 Bleeker (Goods) ......A
Berlinger, Brown & Friedeman, 708 B'way (Artificial Flowers; Ostrich & Fancy Feathers) C
Bloom & Mayer, 577 Bway. (Goods) ....A
Comey & Co., 584 B'way (Goods) ....B
Dearberg Bros., 96 Prince (Goods) ......A
Donat & Co., John, 594 B'way (Goods) ....B
Edwards & Rierdan (Agts.) 565 B'way (Goods).....A
Eiseman & Co., E., 68 W. Houston (Ostrich Feathers) C
Fatton, Henry, 46 E. 8th (Ostrich Feathers) ....A
Friedlander, I., 636 B'way (Pattern & Trimmed Hats) ....B
Glanckoff, Oscar, 637 B'way (Pattern Hats)..B
Goldzier, Morris, 661 B'way (Artificial Flowers; Ostrich & Fancy Flowers) ....A
Goodman & Co., E. B., 711 B'way (Artificial Flowers; Ostrich & Fancy Feathers) ....A
Gotthold & Co., 580 B'way (Goods) ....A
Grove Straw Hat Mfg. Co., 100 Wooster (Straw Hats) ....A
Heimann & Lichter, 600 B'way (Goods) ......AA
Henry & Co., L., 723 B'way (Artificial Flowers; Ostrich & Fancy Feathers) AA
Hepner & Horwitz, 30 Howard (Goods) ......B
Herman, Max & Co., 618 B'way (Artificial Flowers; Ostrich & Fancy Feathers; also Materials) B
Hirsh & Co., A., 137 5th Av. (Artificial Flowers;

MILLINERY GOODS
Ostrich & Fancy Feathers) ....B
Hirsh & Park, 593 B'way (Goods) ....AA
Hochheimer, A., 719 B'way (Artificial Flowers; Ostrich & Fancy Feathers; also Pattern Hats) ....B
Isler & Guge, 111 Bleeker (Goods) ....A
Jennings Lace Works, 450 Broome (Goods) ......A
Kaufman, Aron & Warsahuser, 650 B'way (Goods) ....B
Kimmerle & Dawes, 629 B'way (Artificial Flowers; Ostrich & Fancy Feathers) ....B
Knowlton & Sons, Wm., 564 B'way (Goods) ....AAAA
Koch & Sons, 24 W. 23rd (Pattern Hats) ....A
Konemana & Co., 706 Bway. (Artf. Flowers; Ostr.; Fancy Feathers) C
Legg, Geo., 5 Wash. Pl. (Artf. Flow.; Ostr.; Fancy Feathers) ....AA
Lehman Bros., 10 Bond (Artificial Flowers; Ostrich & Fancy Feathers) B
Levin & Kupfer, 26-32 E. Houston (Goods) .... B
Lewis & Co., Alfred, 33 E. 10th (Ostrich Feathers) B
Lindheim & Son, R., 652 B'way (Artificial Flowers; Ostrich & Fancy Feathers) ....A
Love, Scott & Jaursch, 192 Greene (Goods) C
Metzger & Co., Louis, 637 B'way (Goods) ....A
Mindheim, Max, 67 Prince Av. (Goods) ....A
Phipps & Atchison, 141 5th Av. (Goods) ....B
Rosenberg, Max, 132 5th Av. (Goods) ....A
Rosenshine Bros., 57 E. 10th (Ostrich Feathers) AA
Reshower & Co., J., 565 B'way (Goods) ....B
Robinson & Co., Jonh J., 20 W. 18 (Goods) ....B
Sacks, G. M. L., 581 B'way (Goods) ....B
Sawyer & Co., H. F., 605 B'way (Goods) ....B
Schiff & Co., Samuel, 659 B'way (Goods) ....A
Schiller, S., 608 B'way (Pattern Hats) C
Schultz & Co., Jos., 593 B'way (Goods) ......B
Searle, Dailey & Co. (Matteawan Mfg. Co.) 602 B'way (Goods) ......AA
Siegman & Weil, 81 Wooster (Goods) ....A
Simon & Co., Alfred L., 706 B'way (Artificial Flowers; Ostrich & Fancy Feathers) ....B
Spero Co., David, 702 B'way (Artificial Flowers; Ostrich & Fancy Feathers) ....A
Spitka & Co., Chas., 706 B'way (Artificial Flowers; Ostrich & Fancy Feathers) C
Stadecker & Emsheimer, 583 B'way (Bonnet; Hat Frames) ....AA
Stein, J. A., 58 E. 9th (Ostrich Feathers) ....A
Stiehl & Co., C. H., 205 Greene St. (Goods) C
Tenney & Co., C. H., 8 Wash. Pl. (Goods)AAAA
Unger & Co., M., 31 Bond (Goods) C
Ury & Mendelson Bros., 696 B'way (Pattern Hats)..C
Veit Son & Co., 629 B'way

MILLINERY GOODS
(Goods) ....A
Veith, A. & H., 624 B'way
Warshauer & Rosemond, 608 B'way (Goods) ....B
Weisker & Co., Chas., 55 8th Oibrettes)) C
Williamson & Sleeper, 598 B'way (Goods) ....B
Wurzburger & Hecht, 5th Av. & 19th (Artificial Flowers; Fancy & Ostrich Feathers) ....AA
Zimmermann & Meyer, 142 Greene (Goods) ....B
Zimmermann Co., John, 129 Greene (Goods) ......AA
Zucker & Josephy, 17 B'way (Artificial Flowers; Ostrich & Fancy Feathers) ....A

OHIO.—Cleveland
Comey & Jonhson, 13 Academy (Goods) ....B

PA.—Philadelphia
Bernstein, Kaufman & Co., 1103 Race (Goods).....A
Eames, H. A., 1135 Arch (Goods) ....
Espen, Stewart & Loeb, 1239 Callowhilll (Goods) .....B
Goodman, Loeb & Co., 428 No. 13th (Goods)....AA
Henley's Sons, David, 831 Arch (Birds) ....A
Pine Tree Silk Mills Co., 806 Arch (Pattern Hats) .....B
Rosenan & Co., S., 449 N. Darien (Goods) ......AA
Rosenfield & Burak, 730 Cherry (Goods) ....B
Shaw & Ewing Co., 1009 Race (Goods) ....B

PA.—Reading
Alexander & Co., G. W. (Goods) ....A
Mohn & Co., John G., 916 Penn (Goods) ....AA

WIS.—Milwaukee
Blumenfeld, Locher & Brown Co., 374 B'way (Bonnet & Hat Frames) .....B
National Straw Co. (Goods) .....A
Northwestern Straw Wks., 623 Reed (Goods)......A
Slocum Straw Works, Reed Cor. So. Water (Goods) C

MUSICAL INSTRUMENTS

See also Pianos; Organs & other Specific Headings.

ILL.—Chicago
Bohmann, Joseph, 376 Madison C
Holton & Co., Frank, 70 E. Madison ....D
Lyon & Healy, Wabash & Adams (Guitars; Harps; Cymbals; Dulcimers; Banjos) ....AAAA
Maurer & Co., 33 Ind. Av. .....F

IND.—Elkhart
Buescher Mfg. Co. (Clarinets) ....AA
Conn, C. G. (Fifes; Enphoniums; Flutes; Guitars; Bugles; French Horns; Cymbals; Clarinets; Trumpets) .....AA

IND.—Indianapolis
Leedy Mfg. Co., 1063 E. Palmer (Bass Drums; Xylophones) ....E
Regal Mfg. Co. (Banjos; Guitars) X

LA.—New Orleans
Grunewald Rene (Mandolins) C

MD.—Baltimore
Holdapfell & Beitel (String) X

MUS. INSTRUMENTS
MASS.—Boston
Boston Musical Instrument Co., 51 Chardon (Band) .....F
Fairbanks Co., A. C. (Banjos; Guitars) X
Haynes & Co., Jonh C..AA
Phonoharp Co., 150 Liverpool C
Pierce Organ Pipe Co., S. (Clarinets) C
Vega Co., 62 Ludbury (Guitars; Mandolins; Banjos; Trombones) ...F

MASS.—Cambridge
Auto Mfg. Co. (Automatic Banjos) X

MASS.—Northampton
Hyde, Andrew (Violins)..D

PA.—Reading
Pierce Organ Pipe Co., 104 S. 4th (Trombones)....C

MICH.—Detroit
Bryant-Newell Co. (Band) .....F

MICH.—Kalamazoo
Gibson Mandolin & Guitar Mfg. Co. ....D

MICH.—Saginaw
Waldo Mfg. Co. (Guitars; Banjeaurines; Mandolins) .....D

MO.—Washington
Schwarzer, Franz (Guitars; Zithers; Mandolins) ..E

N. J.—Camden
Ernest & Son, G. A. (Guitars) ....E

N. J.—Jersey City
Schmidt, Oscar (Guitars; Mandolins; Banjos) ....A

N. Y.—Brooklyn
Cloos, George, 39 Stagg (Fifes; Clarinets; Flutes) .....E
Gretsch Mfg. Co., Fred, 104 S. 4th (Tambourines)..C
Houdlett, Alfred, 40 Melrose (Banjos; Drums)..C
Maryland, R. H., 351 Adams (Orchestra Bells) .....E

N. Y.—Mount Vernon
Aluminum Musical Instrument Co. (Guitars)....X
Anderberg, Erland (Banjos; Guitars) C

New York City
American Automatic Music Co., 53 B'way (Banjos) .....D
Bercioux, Eugene, 1106 Park Av. ....F
Bertling Co., Theo., 177 Bowery (Clarinets; Flutes; Oboes) X
Bruno & Son, C., 356 B'way (Banjos; Guitars) ...AA
Busch, Fred'k, 255 Bowery .....H
Carlucci & Ressa, 188 W. Houston (Guitars; Mandolins) ....F
Cohn, Adolph, 157 W. 23d .....E
Ditson & Co., Chas. C., 867 B'way (Fifes; Flutes; Guitars) ....B
Eisele, Hy, 211 Grand (Drums) ....F
Favilla Bros., 60 Centre (Guitars) ....F
Fischer, Carl, 50 Cooper Sq. W. ....A
Foote, J. Howard, 33 Maiden Lane (Fifes; Flutes; Guitars; Banjos) X
Friedrich & Bro. John, 360 4th Av. ....E
Gemunder & Son, Aug. (Cymbals; Basoons; Oboes) ....D
Gordon, H. S., 139 5th Av. (Banjos) ....D
Gratz Co., Wm. R., 11 E. 22d ....E
Hohner, M., 354 B'way (Harmonicas; Mouth Organs; Accordeons) X

APPENDIX

PRODUCE (*Con.*)
IOWA—Auduborn
Bilhorz & Son, E.
(Shippers Potatoes) ....A
IOWA—Avery
Avery Supply Co. ...... A
IOWA—Conrad
Stark & Marsh (Shippers'
Apples) ....B
IOWA—Gladbrook
Fedderson, Davenport & Co.
(Potato Shippers) ....B
IOWA—Le Mars
Kehrberg Co., C. H. (Shippers Potatoes; Eggs) ..B
IOWA—Macedonia
Dye Bros. Co. (Shippers Apples; Potatoes; Poultry;
Butter; Eggs) ....A
IOWA—Sioux City
Palmer & Co. (Wholesale
Shippers; Apples; Cabbage; Potatoes; Fruit;
Vegetables; Butter) ...A
KANS.—Arkansas City
Canal City Produce Co. ..A
KANS.—Clay Center
Swenson Bros. (Wholesale
Potatoes) ....B
KY.—Mer Rouge
Davenport, C. C. (Shippers
Potatoes) .../.......B
LA.—Shreveport
Highhouse Commission Co.,
A. M. (Wholesale Shippers Potatoes) ....D
Rose Merc. & Mfg. Co. Hy.
(Wholesale Shippers Potatoes) ....A
MAINE—Bar Harbor
Locke & Co., I. ....B
MAINE—Caribou
Edwards Co., H. A. (Shippers Potatoes) C
MAINE—Houlton
Cleveland Co., E. L. ...D
MAINE—Phillips
Wilbur & Co. (Cabbage)
C
MD.—Hagerstown
Holzapfel, H. ....B
MASS.—Lawrence
Murray Bros. Co. (Wholesale) C
MASS.—Lowell
Nichols, G. N. & E. ...C
MASS.—Lynn
Hyde, E. V. C
MICH.—Brighton
Hyne, Fred. T. ....B
MICH.—Carsonville
McCaren & Co. ....B
MICH.—Daggett
Perrigo Sons (Shippers Potatoes) C
MICH.—Dowagiac
Swindall & Rollins C
MICH.—Flint
Edwards Bros. (Shippers
Potatoes) ....B
MICH.—Flushing
Ottaway & Co., J. E. (Shippers Potatoes) ....D
MICH.—Greenville
Gibson & Co., C. H. (Shippers Potatoes) C
Miller & Miller C
MICH.—Howard City
Lovely, W. H. (Shippers
Potatoes) ....A
MICH.—Hudson
Pierce, Orrin R. ....B
MICH.—Ingalls
Dobeas, L. (Potato Shippers) ....
MICH.—Iron Mountain
Brauns & Vandenbraak
(Potatoe Shippers) ....B
MICH.—Ishpeming
Braastadt & Co., F. (Potato
Shippers) ....A
Larson & Co., W. (Potato
Shippers) ....A
MICH.—Jackson
McLaughlin, Ward & Co.
A
MICH.—Lansing
Schlee & Co., J. G. C
MICH.—Lowell
McCarty & Co., C. (Potato

PRODUCE (*Con.*)
Shippers) ....B
MICH.—Nadeau
Nadeau Bros. (Potato Shippers) ....B
MICH.—Oxford
Randall & Co., C. L. (Potato Shippers) ....A
MICH.—Plainwell
Harwood & Co., F. A.
(Fruit; Potatoes) ......D
MICH.—Williamston
Van Buren, F. P. ....B
MINN.—Adrian
Becker, A. M. (Potato Shippers) ....B
Jones & Co., J. R. (Potato
Shippers) ....A
MINN.—Albert Lea
Stacy Fruit & Produce Co.
A
MINN.—Elmore
Dustin, W. O. (Fruit) ..A
MINN.—Eyota
Blair & Son, C. R. (Potato
Shippers) C
MINN.—Harris
Wolf, F. H. (Shippers Butter; Eggs; Potatoes) ..C
MINN.—Luverne
Nelson Bros. Co. (Potato
Shippers) ....A
MINN.—Madelia
Olson, M. (Potato Shippers)
B
MINN.—Marshall
Schneider & Hollo (Potato
Shippers) ....B
MINN.—Mountain Lake
Woodruff, A. E. (Potato
Shippers) C
MINN.—New Ulm
Neumann, J. F. (Potato
Shippers) C
MINN.—Olivia
Olivia Produce Co. C
MINN.—Owatonna
Nelson, Hartvig & Co. (Potato Shippers) ....B
MINN.—Sleepy Eye
Christensen, P. (Potato
Shippers) ....A
MINN.—Waseca
Brown & Son, H. A. (Potato Shippers) ....B
MISS.—Cassville
Cassville Produce Co. ...A
MISS.—Odessa
La Fayette Produce Co...A
MISS.—Olden
Olden Fruit Co. (Fruit
Growers) ....AA
MISS.—Sedalia
Sedalia Egg Co. (Shippers
Butter; Eggs; Potatoes;
Poultry; Grapes; Fruit;
Cabbage) ....D
NEBR.—Auburn
Kirschbraun, L. & C. ....B
NEBR.—Crawford
Crawford Merc. Co. (Potato
Shippers) C
N. J.—Pedricton
Justice & Co., H. S. (Sweet
Potatoes) ....D
N. J.—Plainfield
Clifton & Campbell ......B
N. Y.—Albion
Morgan & Linson C
Rogers, L. A. (Apples; Cabbage; Potatoes) C
Tilden, M. W. C
N. Y.—Bergen
Miller Bros. & Co. C
N. Y.—Bombay
Reynolds, A. G. ....A
N. Y.—Brighton
Le Clarr, J. F. ....B
N. Y.—Brocton
Chautauqua & Erie Grape
Co. ....B
Ryckman & Son, G. E.
(Grapes) ....B
N. Y.—Dalton
Baker, A. D. (Potato Shipper) C
N. Y.—Dunkirk
Day. R. B. (Est. of)
(Grapes) ....A
N. Y.—Fairport
Becker, D. C. (Apples) ..C

1226

PRODUCE (*Con.*)

N. Y.—Fishers
Ford & Co., C. W. (Seed Potatoes) C
N. Y.—Geneseo
Belden & Co. C
N. Y.—Geneva
Dillman Bros. (Shippers Fruit; Veg.; Potatoes) ....B
Maxwell & Bros., T. C. (Fruit Growers) .....AA
N. Y.—Groveland Station
Ewart & Lake ....B
N. Y.—Hoosick Falls
Deming & Co., J. J. C
N. Y.—Kingston
McGill, Edw. T. ....B
N. Y.—Le Roy
Gleason Cold Storage Co. (Fruit Shippers) ......B
N. Y.—Lockport
Ferrin Bros. Co. ....B
N. Y.—Mount Vernon
Reynolds Co., J. L. (Potato Shippers) ....B
N. Y.—Naples
Hemenway, Geo. B. (Potatoes; Apples) C
N. Y.—Newark
Pierson & Co., E. V. ...B
N. Y.—Ossining
Chadeayne & Sons, J. ..B
N. Y.—Palmyra
Knowles & Co., H. P. ..B
N. Y.—Penn Yan
Hollowell & Wise (Grape Shippers) ....B
N. Y.—Perry
Tomlinson & Son, Geo. ..B
N. Y.—Ravena
Ward & Son, J. G. (Apples) A
N. Y.—Sherman
Sheldon, A. B. ....A
N. Y.—Sodus
Williams, A. B. (Apple Shipper) ....A
N. Y.—Victor
Loomis & Woodruff (Apples) ....A
N. Y.—Walworth
McCrea & Co., J. (Apple Shippers) C
N. Y.—Waverly
Walker & Sons, T. S. ...B
N. Y.—Williamson
Pearsall Co., G. A. (Apples) A

N. C.—Grand Forks
Grand Forks Fruit Co. ..B
N. C.—Newbern
Watson, C. T. C
N. C.—Southern Pines
Niagara Grape & Fruit Co. B
OHIO—Clyde
Comstock & Slessman ...B
OHIO—East Palestine
Rothwell & Co. (Fruit) ..B
OHIO—Lima
Thomas & Sons, M. .....B
OHIO—Wellington
Horr-Warner Co. ......AA
PA.—Bradford
Boyle & Williams C
PA.—Canton
Burk & Co., Thos. ......A
PA.—Hazelton
Moyer, Noah ....B
PA.—Masontown
Sterling, J. & E. W. (Fruit Growers) ....AA
PA.—Shippenburg
Rummel, Himes & Co. (Fruit) ....A
PA.—Vinemont
Shearer, S. (Fruit Growers) B
S. DAK.—Elkton
Meyer & Co., T. (Potatoes) B
S. DAK.—Huron
Truncbower & Co., B. F. (Potatoes) ....B
S. DAK.—Lake Preston
Lewis Bros. & Lindner (Potatoe Shippers) ....B
TENN.—Murfreesboro
Ransom Bros. & Co. ....B
TEXAS—Sherman

PRODUCE (*Con.*)

Hazard & McConville (Wholesale Shippers Potatoes) .... B
UTAH—Kaysville
Kaysville Co-Op. Merc. Inst. ....B
UTAH—Logan
Cache Valley Merc. Co. (Potato Shippers) ....B
UTAH—Salt Lake City
Bailey & Sons (Potato Shippers) ....B
WIS.—Amherst
Peterson, P. N. C
WIS.—Aniwa
Goldrick, G. H. C
WIS.—Arcadia
Masseure & Co., W. P. (Potato Shippers) ....B
WIS.—Argyle
Rossing, L. A. (Shipper Fruit; Butter; Eggs)..B
WIS.—Ashland
Cramer & Co., C. ......B
WIS.—Auburndale
Conner & Co., R. (Potatoes) AAA
WIS.—Bangor
Roberts, E. R. (Potato Shippers) ....B
WIS.—Berlin
Stedman & Sons, H. (Potato Shippers) C
WIS.—Birnamwood
Roepke, John F. (Potato Shippers) C
Van Doren & Anderson ..C
WIS.—Black River Falls
Werner, A. F. (Potato Shippers) ....B
WIS.—Campbellsport
McCollough Bros. (Potato Shippers) ....B
WIS.—Cato
Killen, W. N. (Potato Shipper) C
WIS.—Cecil
Zachon, W. S. (Potato Shipper) ....B
WIS.—Chippewa Falls
Clark, Robert B. (Potatoes) A
WIS.—Coloma Station
Follett, Vilas (Shipper Butter; Potatoes) ....B
WIS.—Cuba
Donohoo, Splinter & Co. (Potatoes Shippers) ...C
WIS.—De Pere
Jackson & Sons (Potato Shippers) ....B
WIS.—Elroy
Hart & Hart (Potato Shippers) ....B
Huntley & Co., C. S. (Potato Shippers) C
WIS.—Fairchild
Foster Lumber Co., N. C. (Potato Shippers) ...AAA
WIS.—Grantsburg
Peterson, P. E. (Potato Shipper) ....B
WIS.—Green Bay
Schilling, Frank C. (Wholesale Shipper Fruit, Vegetables Apples; Butter;

936 6:2 '5 543 Register 893 Potatoes) ....B
WIS.—Hartford
Dennison, Liver & Cooper (Potato Shipper) ......B
WIS.—Hixton
Van Gordon & Son, S. H. (Potato Shipper) ......B
WIS.—Jackson
Frank, J. G. & Froehlick Co. (Potatoes) C
WIS.—Jefferson
Puerner Son & Co., A. (Potato Shippers) ....B
WIS.—Juneau
Mansfield Co., G. C. ....A
WIS.—Kewaskum
Rosenheimer Malt & Grain Co., L. (Apples; Potatoes) ....A
WIS.—Kewaunee
Seyk & Co., W. (Potato Shippers) ....**B**

APPENDIX